YOUR
£10,000
OPPORTUNITY!

The Racing Post Yearling Bonus Scheme would like to thank all vendors and purchasers who have supported this scheme and wish all participants the best of luck in the bonus maidens during 2012

RACING POST
YEARLING BONUS
£10,000

For more information visit **www.yearlingbonus.com**

HORSES

IN TRAINING 2012

122nd YEAR OF PUBLICATION

Raceform

INDEX TO GENERAL CONTENTS

	Page
Amateur Riders, their riding weights and contact details	699
Apprentices, their Employers, riding weights and contact details	694
Champions on the flat and over jumps	682
Classic Winners	657
Conditionals, their Employers, riding weights and contact details	697
Dates of Principal Races	22
Derby Entries, 2012	579
Flat Jockeys, their riding weights and contact details	692
Flat Statistics 2011 and National Hunt Statistics 2010-2011	608
Free Handicap and Weight Classifications 2011	583
Grand National Winners	664
High Priced Yearlings of 2011 at Tattersalls, Goffs, Doncaster and Tattersalls Ireland	644
Horses in Training	46
Index to Horses	470
Index to Trainers	34
Jockeys' Agents	687
Jump Jockeys, their riding weights and contact details	696
Late Entries	558
Median Times for Courses	592
Property of H.M. The Queen	45
Racecourses of Great Britain	562
Raceform Champions 2011	590
Racing Fixtures and Principal Bloodstock Sale dates 2012	5
Record Times for Courses	596
Sire Statistics 2011 and Jump Sire Statistics 2010-2011	616
Winners of Great Races	665

Editor	Richard Lowther; Raceform Ltd., Compton, Newbury, RG20 6NL. Fax: 01635 578101 E-mail: richard.lowther@racingpost.com
Assistant Editor	Simon Turner
Production Editor	Adrian Gowling; Bloodstock Services, Weatherbys
Production Assistants	Lucy Brown, Kerry D'Elia, Michelle Dalley, Chris Hill, Lauren Roberts.
Typesetting	Maggie Elvie; Printing Services, Weatherbys, Sanders Road, Wellingborough, NN8 4BX.
Orders	Raceform Ltd., Sanders Road, Wellingborough, Northants NN8 4BX. Tel: 01933 304858 www.racingpost.com/bookshop Fax: 01933 270300 E-mail: Shop@racingpost.com
Advertisements	Julian Brown; Raceform Ltd., Compton, Newbury, RG20 6NL. Tel: 01635 577603 E-mail: julian.brown@racingpost.com
ISBN	978-1-906820-91-6

Printed and bound by CPI Group (UK) Ltd, Croydon, CR0 4YY.

INDEX TO ADVERTISERS

	Page		Page
Arkenfield	Colour ii	Racing Post Jobs	Colour vii/3/15
Equestrian Surfaces	Colour iii	Racing Welfare	9/702
Form Book Collection	Colour vi/19/629	Ransley, J & J	Colour i
Haygain	Inside Back Cover	ROA	12
Injured Jockey Fund	6/691	Twydil	Back Cover
London Thoroughbred Services Ltd.	44	Windsor Clive	Colour v
Martin Collins Enterprises	Inside Front Cover	Yearling Bonus	Colour iv/17/642
Monarch Equestrian	Colour viii		

2012

RACING FIXTURES

AND SALE DATES

(SUBJECT TO ALTERATION)

Flat fixtures are in **Black Type**; Jump in Light Type; Irish in *Italic;*
asterisk (☆) indicates an evening or Twilight meeting;
† indicates an All Weather meeting. Sale dates are at foot of fixtures

MARCH

Sun	Mon	Tues	Wed	Thur	Fri	Sat
				1 **Kempton**†☆ Ludlow **Southwell**†† Taunton *Thurles*	**2** Doncaster *Dundalk*☆ **Lingfield Park**† Newbury **Wolverhampton**†☆	**3** Doncaster Kelso **Lingfield Park**† *Navan* Newbury Doncaster Sale
4 Huntingdon *Leopardstown* Sedgefield	**5** Hereford **Lingfield Park**†	**6** Exeter Newcastle **Southwell**††	**7** Catterick Bridge *Downpatrick* Fontwell Park **Kempton Park**†☆ **Lingfield Park**†	**8** Carlisle *Clonmel* **Southwell**†† Wincanton **Wolverhampton**†☆	**9** Ayr *Dundalk*☆ Leicester Sandown Park Wincanton **Wolverhampton**†☆	**10** Ayr Chepstow *Gowran Park* Sandown Park **Wolverhampton**†
11 Market Rasen *Naas* Warwick	**12** Plumpton Stratford-on-Avon Taunton	**13** Cheltenham Sedgefield **Southwell**††	**14** Cheltenham Huntingdon **Kempton Park**†☆ **Southwell**††	**15** Cheltenham Hexham Towcester **Wolverhampton**†☆	**16** Cheltenham *Dundalk*☆ Fakenham **Lingfield Park**† **Wolverhampton**†☆	**17** *Down Royal* *Flos Las* Kempton Park Newcastle Uttoxeter *Wexford* **Wolverhampton**†☆
18 Carlisle *Limerick* *Naven* Newton Abbot	**19** **Kempton Park**† *Limerick* Southwell	**20** Exeter **Kempton Park**† **Southwell**††	**21** Haydock Park Hereford **Kempton Park**†☆ Warwick	**22** Carlisle Chepstow *Cork*☆ Fontwell Park **Kempton Park**†☆ **Wolverhampton**†	**23** *Dundalk*☆ **Lingfield Park**† Newbury Sedgefield **Wolverhampton**†☆	**24** Bangor-on-Dee *Gowran Park* Kelso **Lingfield Park**† Newbury Stratford-on-Avon
25 *Curragh* *Downpatrick* Hexham Wincanton	**26** **Lingfield Park**† Towcester Fasig-Tipton Sale	**27** Hereford Market Rasen **Southwell**††	**28** **Kempton Park**†☆ *Leopardstown*☆ **Lingfield Park**† Ludlow Taunton	**29** Flos Las **Kempton Park**†☆ Newcastle *Thurles* **Wolverhampton**†	**30** *Dundalk*☆ **Lingfield Park**† Newcastle Wetherby **Wolverhampton**†☆	**31** **Doncaster** **Kempton Park**† *Navan* Stratford-on-Avon Uttoxeter

APRIL

Sun	Mon	Tues	Wed	Thur	Fri	Sat
1 Ascot **Doncaster** *Limerick*	**2** Kelso **Redcar**	**3** Fontwell Park *Limerick*☆ Sedgefield **Southwell**† Goffs Sale	**4** *Dundalk*☆ Exeter Hereford **Lingfield Park**† **Wolverhampton**†☆ Fasig-Tipton Sale	**5** *Clonmel*☆ **Folkestone** Ludlow Wincanton Keeneland Sale	**6**	**7** Carlisle *Cork* Haydock Park **Kempton Park**† **Musselburgh** Newton Abbot
8 Cork *Fairyhouse* **Musselburgh** Plumpton Towcester	**9** Chepstow *Cork* *Fairyhouse* Fakenham Huntingdon Plumpton **Redcar** **Warwick** **Yarmouth** Keeneland Sale	**10** *Fairyhouse* **Pontefract** **Southwell**† **Yarmouth**	**11** **Catterick Bridge** *Dundalk*☆ **Kempton Park**†☆ **Lingfield Park**† **Nottingham**	**12** Aintree **Folkestone** *Gowran Park*☆ Taunton **Wolverhampton**†☆	**13** Aintree *Dundalk*†☆ **Leicester** Sedgefield **Wolverhampton**†☆	**14** Aintree Chepstow **Lingfield Park**† **Newcastle** *Tramore* **Wolverhampton**†☆
15 Ffos Las *Leopardstown* Market Rasen *Tramore*	**16** **Windsor** **Wolverhampton**†	**17** Exeter Kempton Park **Southwell**† Tattersalls Sale	**18** **Beverley** Cheltenham *Dundalk*☆ **Kempton Park**†☆ Newmarket Cheltenham Sale Tattersalls Sale	**19** Cheltenham **Newmarket** **Ripon** *Tipperary*☆ **Wolverhampton**†☆ Tattersalls Sale	**20** Ayr **Bath**☆ Fontwell Park **Newbury** Southwell☆ *Wexford*☆	**21** Ayr Bangor-On-Dee *Naas* **Newbury** **Nottingham**†☆ Thirsk **Wolverhampton**†☆
22 *Curragh* Stratford-on-Avon Wincanton Doncaster Sale Tattersalls (IRE) Sale	**23** *Cork*☆ *Ffos Las*☆ Hexham **Pontefract** **Windsor**☆ Doncaster Sale	**24** **Folkestone** **Newcastle**☆ Newton Abbot *Punchestown*☆ Towcester☆ **Wolverhampton**† Ascot Sale Doncaster Sale	**25** **Catterick Bridge** **Epsom Downs** Hereford☆ **Kempton Park**†☆ Perth *Punchestown*☆	**26** **Beverley** **Brighton**☆ Perth Uttoxeter☆ **Wolverhampton**† Goffs Sale	**27** Chepstow☆ **Doncaster** Perth Plumpton☆ *Punchestown*☆ **Sandown Park**	**28** **Doncaster**☆ **Haydock Park**☆ **Leicester** Market Rasen *Punchestown*☆ **Ripon** **Sandown (mixed)**
29 Ludlow *Navan* Wetherby	**30** **Kempton Park**† Towcester **Windsor**☆ **Wolverhampton**†☆					

MAY

Sun	Mon	Tues	Wed	Thur	Fri	Sat
		1	**2**	**3**	**4**	**5**
		Ballinrobe☆ Exeter **Kempton Park**☆ **Lingfield Park**☆ Sedgefield☆ **Yarmouth**	**Ascot** Cheltenham☆ *Dundalk*☆ Kelso☆ **Pontefract** Southwell	**Brighton**☆ **Folkestone** Hereford **Leicester**☆ **Musselburgh** *Tipperary*☆ Tattersalls Sale	Bangor-on-Dee☆ **Chepstow** *Dundalk*☆ Fontwell Park☆ *Kilbeggan*☆ **Musselburgh** **Wolverhampton**† Tattersalls Sale	**Doncaster**☆ **Goodwood** Hexham☆ Limerick **Newmarket** **Thirsk** Uttoxeter
6	**7**	**8**	**9**	**10**	**11**	**12**
Gowran Park **Hamilton Park** Newmarket Salisbury *Sligo*	**Bath** **Beverley** *Curragh* *Down Royal* **Kempton Park**† **Warwick** **Windsor**	**Catterick Bridge**☆ Exeter☆ Fakenham Newcastle	**Chester** Ffos Las☆ **Kempton Park**†☆ *Punchestown*☆ **Southwell**† Stratford-on-Avon	**Chester** *Clonmel*☆ **Goodwood** Kelso☆ Newton Abbot Wincanton☆ **Yarmouth**☆	**Ascot**☆ **Chester** *Cork*☆ *Downpatrick*☆ **Hamilton Park**☆ **Lingfield Park** Market Rasen **Nottingham**☆ **Ripon**☆ Arqana Sale	Ascot **Haydock (Mixed)** Hexham *Kilbeggan*☆ **Lingfield Park** Nottingham **Thirsk**☆ **Warwick**☆ Ascot Sale Arqana Sale
13	**14**	**15**	**16**	**17**	**18**	**19**
Killarney *Leopardstown* Plumpton Uttoxeter Worcester	*Killarney*☆ **Redcar** Towcester☆ **Windsor**☆ **Wolverhampton**†	**Beverley** Hereford **Kempton Park**†☆ *Killarney*☆ Southwell☆ Wincanton	**Bath**☆ Fontwell Park **Lingfield Park**† *Naas*☆ Perth☆ **York**	Folkestone☆ *Gowran Park*☆ Ludlow☆ **Newmarket**☆ Perth **Salisbury** **York**	Aintree☆ *Dundalk*☆ **Hamilton Park**☆ **Newbury** **Newcastle**☆ **Newmarket** **York** Baden-Baden Sale	Bangor-on-Dee☆ **Doncaster**☆ Newbury Newmarket **Thirsk** Uttoxeter☆ *Wexford*☆
20	**21**	**22**	**23**	**24**	**25**	**26**
Limerick Market Rasen *Navan* **Ripon** Stratford-on-Avon	**Leicester**☆ Newton Abbot **Redcar** *Roscommon*☆ **Windsor**☆ **Wolverhampton**† Fasig-Tipton Sale	**Brighton** **Kempton Park**†☆ **Nottingham** Towcester☆ Fasig-Tipton Sale	**Chepstow** **Lingfield Park** Sedgefield☆ *Sligo*☆ **Southwell**† Worcester☆	**Goodwood** **Haydock Park** **Salisbury**☆ **Sandown Park**☆ *Tipperary*☆ Wetherby Goresbridge Sale Cheltenham Sale	**Catterick Bridge**☆ *Cork*☆ **Goodwood** **Haydock Park** **Musselburgh**☆ Towcester☆ **Yarmouth** Goresbridge Sale	**Chester** *Curragh* **Goodwood** **Haydock Park** **Lingfield Park**☆ **Newbury**☆ **York**
27	**28**	**29**	**30**	**31**		
Curragh Fakenham Kelso	*Ballinrobe*☆ **Carlisle**☆ **Kempton Park**† **Leicester** **Windsor**☆	*Ballinrobe*☆ **Chepstow** Hexham☆ Huntingdon☆ **Lingfield Park**† **Ripon** Doncaster Sale	**Ayr** **Beverley**☆ **Folkestone**☆ Newton Abbot *Punchestown*☆ Sedgefield Doncaster Sale	**Ayr** **Brighton** *Clonmel*☆ Ffos Las **Newcastle**☆ **Sandown Park**☆ Wetherby☆ Doncaster Sale		

JUNE

Sun	Mon	Tues	Wed	Thur	Fri	Sat
					1	**2**
					Brighton *Down Royal*☆ **Epsom Downs** Haydock Park☆ Newcastle Pontefract☆ *Stratford-on-Avon*☆ *Tramore*☆	**Beverley** Cartmel☆ **Catterick Bridge** **Epsom Downs** **Haydock Park** **Musselburgh** Stratford-on-Avon☆ *Tramore*
3	**4**	**5**	**6**	**7**	**8**	**9**
Fontwell Park *Kilbeggan* *Listowel* **Nottingham** Uttoxeter	**Carlisle** Cartmel **Chepstow** **Leicester** *Listowel* *Naas* **Redcar** Towcester	*Downpatrick* Ffos Las **Leicester** **Redcar** **Yarmouth**	Cartmel *Fairyhouse*☆ Fontwell Park Kempton Park†☆ **Nottingham** **Ripon**☆	**Hamilton Park** **Lingfield Park** **Sandown Park**☆ *Tipperary*☆ Uttoxeter☆ Wetherby☆ **Wolverhampton**† Ascot Sale	**Bath**☆ **Catterick Bridge** **Doncaster** **Goodwood**☆ *Leopardstown*☆ Market Rasen **Newmarket**	**Chester** **Doncaster** Hexham *Navan* **Newcastle**☆ **Newmarket** **Windsor**☆ Worcester
10	**11**	**12**	**13**	**14**	**15**	**16**
Curragh Perth Worcester	Folkestone Newton Abbot **Pontefract**☆ *Roscommon*☆ **Windsor**☆	**Brighton**☆ **Lingfield Park** *Roscommon*☆ **Salisbury** Southwell☆	**Beverley** *Fairyhouse*☆ **Hamilton Park**☆ **Haydock Park** **Kempton Park**☆ **Yarmouth** Goffs Sale	**Haydock Park**☆ Hereford☆ *Leopardstown*☆ **Newbury** **Nottingham** Uttoxeter☆ **Yarmouth** Goffs Sale	Aintree☆ **Chepstow**☆ *Clonmel*☆ **Goodwood**☆ **Musselburgh** *Navan*☆ **Sandown Park**☆ **York**	**Bath** Hexham **Leicester**☆ *Limerick*☆ **Lingfield Park**☆ **Sandown Park** **York**
17	**18**	**19**	**20**	**21**	**22**	**23**
Cork **Doncaster** **Salisbury**	**Carlisle** **Warwick**☆ **Windsor**☆ **Wolverhampton**†	**Ascot** **Brighton**☆ Newton Abbot☆ *Sligo*☆ **Thirsk**	**Ascot** **Hamilton Park** **Kempton Park**☆ **Ripon**☆ *Wexford*☆ Worcester	**Ascot** Ffos Las☆ Fontwell Park☆ **Leicester**☆ *Leopardstown*☆ **Ripon** **Warwick**	**Ascot** **Ayr**☆ *Down Royal*☆ **Goodwood**☆ *Limerick*☆ Market Rasen **Newmarket**☆ **Redcar**	**Ascot** **Ayr** *Down Royal* **Haydock Park**☆ **Lingfield Park**☆ **Newmarket** **Redcar**
24	**25**	**26**	**27**	**28**	**29**	**30**
Gowran Park Hereford Hexham **Pontefract**	**Chepstow** *Kilbeggan*☆ **Thirsk**☆ **Windsor**☆ **Wolverhampton**†	*Ballinrobe*☆ **Beverley** **Brighton** **Newbury**☆ Newton Abbot☆	**Bath**☆ **Carlisle** Kempton Park†☆ *Naas*☆ **Salisbury** Worcester	**Hamilton Park**☆ **Leicester**☆ **Newcastle** *Tipperary*☆ **Warwick** **Yarmouth** Tattersalls (IRE) Sale	**Chester**☆ *Curragh*☆ **Doncaster** Folkestone **Musselburgh** **Newcastle**☆ **Newmarket**☆ Tattersalls (IRE) Sale	**Chester** *Curragh* **Doncaster**☆ **Lingfield Park**☆ **Newcastle** **Newmarket** **Windsor**

JULY

Sun	Mon	Tues	Wed	Thur	Fri	Sat
1 *Curragh* **Salisbury** *Uttoxeter* **Windsor**	**2** **Ffos Las**☆ **Pontefract** **Windsor**☆ **Wolverhampton**†	**3** **Brighton** *Gowran Park*☆ **Hamilton Park** **Kempton Park**☆ *Stratford-on-Avon*☆ Arqana Sale	**4** **Catterick Bridge** **Chepstow**☆ *Fairyhouse*☆ **Kempton Park**†☆ *Perth* *Worcester* Arqana Sale	**5** **Epsom Downs**☆ **Haydock Park** *Leopardstown*☆ **Newbury**☆ *Perth* **Yarmouth** Arqana Sale	**6** *Bellewstown*☆ **Beverley**☆ **Doncaster** **Haydock Park**☆ **Sandown Park** **Warwick** *Wexford*☆	**7** *Bellewstown*☆ **Beverley** *Carlisle*☆ **Haydock Park** **Leicester** **Nottingham**☆ **Sandown Park**
8 **Ayr** *Bellewstown* *Limerick* Market Rasen	**9** **Ayr** Newton Abbot **Ripon**☆ *Roscommon*☆ **Windsor**☆ Ascot Sale Tattersalls Sale Fasig-Tipton Sale	**10** **Pontefract** *Roscommon*☆ **Southwell**†☆ *Uttoxeter*☆ **Wolverhampton**† Tattersalls Sale Fasig-Tipton Sale	**11** **Catterick Bridge** **Kempton Park**†☆ **Lingfield Park** *Naas*☆ *Worcester*☆ **Yarmouth**	**12** **Doncaster** *Dundalk* **Epsom Downs**☆ **Folkestone**☆ *Leopardstown*☆ **Newmarket** **Warwick** Tattersalls Sale	**13** *Chestow*☆ **Chester**☆ *Cork*☆ *Downpatrick* **Hamilton Park**☆ **Newbury** **Newmarket**☆ Tattersalls Sale	**14** **Chester** **Hamilton Park**☆ **Newbury** **Newmarket** **Salisbury**☆ *Tipperary* **York**
15 *Fairyhouse* *Perth* *Sligo* Southwell Stratford-on-Avon	**16** **Ayr** *Killarney*☆ **Southwell**†☆ **Windsor**☆ **Wolverhampton**†☆	**17** **Beverley** **Ffos Las** *Killarney*☆ **Southwell**†☆ **Yarmouth**☆	**18** **Catterick Bridge** *Killarney*☆ **Lingfield Park** **Sandown Park**☆ *Uttoxeter* *Worcester* Gorresbridge Sale	**19** **Bath**☆ **Brighton** **Epsom Downs**☆ **Hamilton Park** *Killarney* **Leicester** *Leopardstown*☆ Goresbridge Sale	**20** **Ascot** **Haydock Park** *Kilbeggan*☆ **Newmarket**☆ **Nottingham** **Pontefract**☆	**21** **Ascot** *Cartmel* *Curragh* **Haydock Park**☆ **Lingfield Park**☆ Market Rasen **Newmarket** **Ripon**
22 **Ascot** *Curragh* Newton Abbot **Redcar** *Tipperary*	**23** **Ayr** *Ballinrobe*☆ **Beverley**☆ *Cartmel* **Windsor**☆	**24** *Ballinrobe*☆ Bangor-on-Dee☆ **Ffos Las**☆ **Musselburgh** **Yarmouth**	**25** **Catterick Bridge** **Leicester**☆ **Lingfield Park**† *Naas*☆ **Sandown Park**☆ *Worcester*	**26** **Bath** **Doncaster**☆ **Epsom Downs**☆ **Folkestone**☆ *Leopardstown*☆ *Limerick*☆ **Sandown Park** *Uttoxeter*	**27** **Ascot** **Chepstow**☆ *Down Royal*☆ **Newmarket**☆ Southwell **Thirsk** *Wexford*☆ **York**☆	**28** **Ascot** **Lingfield Park**☆ **Newcastle** **Newmarket** **Salisbury**☆ *Wexford* **York**
29 **Carlisle** **Pontefract** Stratford-on-Avon	**30** **Ayr** *Galway*☆ *Uttoxeter*☆ **Wolverhampton**†☆ **Yarmouth**	**31** **Beverley** *Galway*☆ **Goodwood** *Perth*☆ *Worcester*☆				

AUGUST

Sun	Mon	Tues	Wed	Thur	Fri	Sat
			1	**2**	**3**	**4**
			Galway☆	*Epsom Downs☆*	*Bangor-on-Dee*	**Doncaster**
			Goodwood	*Ffos Las☆*	*Bath☆*	*Galway*
			Leicester☆	*Galway*	*Galway☆*	**Goodwood**
			Perth☆	**Goodwood**	**Goodwood**	**Hamilton Park☆**
			Redcar	**Nottingham**	**Musselburgh☆**	**Lingfield Park☆**
				Stratford-on-Avon	**Newmarket☆**	**Newmarket**
					Thirsk	Newton Abbot
						Thirsk
5	**6**	**7**	**8**	**9**	**10**	**11**
Chester	**Carlisle☆**	**Bath**	**Brighton**	**Brighton**	**Brighton**	**Ascot**
Cork	*Cork*	**Catterick Bridge**	**Kempton Park†☆**	**Chepstow☆**	**Haydock Park☆**	**Ayr☆**
Galway	**Kempton Park†**	**Kempton Park☆**	**Newcastle**	**Haydock Park**	**Lingfield Park†**	**Haydock Park**
Market Rasen	*Naas*	**Ripon☆**	**Pontefract**	*Leopardstown☆*	**Musselburgh**	*Kilbeggan☆*
Newbury	**Ripon**	*Roscommon☆*	*Sligo☆*	**Sandown Park☆**	**Newmarket☆**	**Lingfield Park☆**
	Wolverhampton†☆		**Yarmouth☆**	*Sligo☆*	*Tipperary☆*	**Newmarket**
				Southwell†☆		**Redcar**
				Yarmouth		
		Doncaster Sale				
	Fasig-Tipton Sale	Fasig-Tipton Sale	Doncaster Sale	Tattersalls (IRE) Sale	Tattersalls (IRE) Sale	Fasig-Tipton Sale
12	**13**	**14**	**15**	**16**	**17**	**18**
Curragh	*Ballinrobe☆*	**Ayr**	**Beverley**	**Beverley**	**Catterick Bridge☆**	**Chester**
Downpatrick	**Ffos Las**	**Bath**	*Gowran Park☆*	**Chepstow☆**	**Kempton Park†☆**	**Doncaster**
Folkestone	**Kempton Park†**	**Nottingham☆**	**Kempton Park†☆**	*Fontwell Park☆*	**Newbury**	**Lingfield Park☆**
Leicester	**Thirsk☆**	**Yarmouth**	**Salisbury**	*Leopardstown☆*	**Newcastle**	Market Rasen☆
	Wolverhampton†☆		**Southwell†☆**	**Newmarket**	**Newmarket☆**	**Newbury**
				Salisbury	**Nottingham**	**Newmarket**
				Stratford-on-Avon☆	*Tramore☆*	Perth
				Tramore☆		**Ripon**
						Tramore☆
Fasig-Tipton Sale						
19	**20**	**21**	**22**	**23**	**24**	**25**
Dundalk	**Kempton Park†☆**	**Brighton**	*Bellewstown☆*	**Bath**	**Ffos Las (Mixed)**	Cartmel
Pontefract	*Roscommon☆*	*Sligo☆*	**Kempton Park†☆**	*Bellewstown☆*	**Goodwood☆**	*Curragh*
Southwell	**Thirsk**	**Warwick☆**	**Lingfield Park**	Cartmel☆	**Hamilton Park☆**	**Goodwood**
Tramore	**Windsor☆**	*Worcester☆*	Newton Abbot☆	Ffos Las	*Kilbeggan☆*	**Newmarket**
	Wolverhampton†	**Yarmouth**	**York**	**Folkestone**	**Newcastle☆**	**Redcar☆**
				Tipperary☆	**Newmarket**	**Windsor☆**
				York	*Wexford☆*	**York**
					York	
		Ascot Sale				
	Arqana Sale	Arqana Sale	Arqana Sale	Arqana Sale		
26	**27**	**28**	**29**	**30**	**31**	
Beverley	Bangor-on-Dee	*Ballinrobe☆*	**Carlisle**	*Fontwell Park☆*	Bangor-on-Dee	
Cork	Cartmel	**Epsom Downs**	**Catterick Bridge**	**Hamilton Park**	*Down Royal☆*	
Curragh	**Chepstow**	**Ripon**	**Kempton Park†☆**	Hereford☆	*Killarney☆*	
Goodwood	*Downpatrick*	Sedgefield☆	*Killarney☆*	**Kempton Park†☆**	**Salisbury☆**	
Yarmouth	**Epsom Downs**	**Southwell†☆**	**Wolverhampton†☆**	*Killarney☆*	**Sandown Park**	
	Huntingdon		Worcester	**Lingfield Park**	**Thirsk**	
	Newcastle			Stratford-on-Avon	**Wolverhampton†☆**	
	Ripon					
	Warwick					
		Fasig-Tipton Sale	Doncaster Sale	Doncaster Sale	Baden-Baden Sale	

SEPTEMBER

Sun	Mon	Tues	Wed	Thur	Fri	Sat
30 *Clonmel* *Curragh* **Epsom Downs** **Musselburgh**						**1** **Bath**☆ **Beverley** **Chester** *Killarney* Market Rasen☆ Newton Abbot **Sandown Park** Baden-Baden Sale
2 *Dundalk* **Folkestone** Newton Abbot	**3** **Ffos Las** **Hamilton Park** *Roscommon*☆ **Wolverhampton**†	**4** Goodwood **Leicester** **Musselburgh**	**5** **Bath** *Gowran Park*☆ Hereford **Kempton Park**†☆ **Lingfield Park**	**6** *Clonmel*☆ **Haydock Park** **Kempton Park**†☆ **Salisbury** Sedgefield	**7** **Brighton** **Chepstow** **Haydock Park** **Kempton Park**†☆ *Kilbeggan*☆	**8** **Ascot** **Haydock Park** **Kempton Park**† *Leopardstown* Stratford-on-Avon **Thirsk** **Wolverhampton**†☆
9 *Curragh* Fontwell Park *Galway* **York** Keeneland Sale	**10** **Bath** *Galway*☆ **Newcastle** Newton Abbot Keeneland Sale	**11** *Galway*☆ **Leicester** **Redcar** Worcester Keeneland Sale	**12** **Carlisle** **Doncaster** **Kempton Park**†☆ Uttoxeter Keeneland Sale	**13** **Chepstow** **Doncaster** **Epsom Downs** *Laytown*☆ **Wolverhampton**†☆ Doncaster Sale Keeneland Sale	**14** **Chester** **Doncaster** *Down Royal*☆ **Sandown Park** **Wolverhampton**†☆ Doncaster Sale Keeneland Sale	**15** **Bath** **Chester** *Curragh* **Doncaster** **Kempton Park**†☆ **Newcastle** Keeneland Sale
16 **Bath** **Ffos Las** *Gowran Park* Keeneland Sale	**17** **Brighton** *Fairyhouse*☆ *Listowel* **Musselburgh** **Wolverhampton**† Keeneland Sale	**18** **Folkestone** *Listowel* **Thirsk** Yarmouth Keeneland Sale	**19** **Beverley** **Kempton Park**†☆ *Listowel* **Sandown Park** Yarmouth Keeneland Sale	**20** **Ayr** **Kempton Park**†☆ *Listowel* **Pontefract** Yarmouth Keeneland Sale	**21** **Ayr** **Lingfield Park** *Listowel* **Newbury** **Wolverhampton**†☆ SGA Sale Keeneland Sale	**22** **Ayr** **Catterick Bridge** *Listowel* **Newbury** **Newmarket** **Wolverhampton**†☆ SGA Sale Keeneland Sale
23 **Hamilton Park** *Listowel* Plumpton Uttoxeter	**24** *Ballinrobe* **Hamilton Park** **Kempton Park**† **Leicester**	**25** **Beverley** **Folkestone** Newton Abbot Tattersalls (IRE) Sale	**26** *Downpatrick* **Goodwood** **Kempton Park**†☆ Perth **Redcar** Tattersalls (IRE) Sale	**27** **Newmarket** Perth **Pontefract** **Wolverhampton**†☆	**28** *Dundalk*☆ **Haydock Park** **Newmarket** **Wolverhampton**†☆ Worcester	**29** **Chester** **Haydock Park** Market Rasen *Navan* **Newmarket** **Ripon** **Wolverhampton**†☆

YOUR
£10,000
OPPORTUNITY!

The Racing Post Yearling Bonus Scheme would like to thank all vendors and purchasers who have supported this scheme and wish all participants the best of luck in the bonus maidens during 2012

RACING POST
YEARLING BONUS
£10,000

OCTOBER

Sun	Mon	Tues	Wed	Thur	Fri	Sat
	1 **Bath** **Hamilton Park** Newton Abbot *Roscommon*	**2** **Ayr** **Folkestone** Sedgefield	**3** **Kempton Park†☆** **Newcastle** **Nottingham** **Salisbury** *Sligo*	**4** Bangor-on-Dee **Southwell†** **Wolverhampton†☆**	**5** **Ascot** *Dundalk☆* Fontwell Park *Gowran Park* Hexham **Wolverhampton†☆**	**6** **Ascot** Fontwell Park *Gowran Park* **Newmarket** Redcar **Wolverhampton†☆**
		Goffs Sale Fasig-Tipton Sale	Goffs Sale Fasig-Tipton Sale	Goffs Sale		Arqana Sale
7 Huntingdon Kelso *Tipperary* Uttoxeter	**8** **Pontefract** **Windsor** **Wolverhampton†**	**9** **Brighton** **Catterick Bridge** **Leicester** *Tipperary*	**10** **Kempton Park†☆** Ludlow *Navan* **Nottingham** Towcester	**11** **Ayr** Exeter **Kempton Park†☆** *Tramore* Worcester	**12** Carlisle *Dundalk☆* Newton Abbot **Wolverhampton†☆** **York**	**13** Chepstow *Fairyhouse* Hexham **Newmarket** **Wolverhampton†☆** **York**
		Tattersalls Sale Ascot Sale	Tattersalls Sale	Tattersalls Sale	Tattersalls Sale	
14 *Curragh* *Ffos Las* **Goodwood** *Limerick*	**15** **Musselburgh** **Salisbury** **Windsor**	**16** Huntingdon **Leicester** **Newcastle**	**17** **Kempton Park†☆** **Lingfield Park†** **Nottingham** *Punchestown* Wetherby	**18** **Brighton** **Kempton Park†☆** *Punchestown* Uttoxeter Wincanton	**19** Cheltenham *Dundalk☆* **Haydock Park** Redcar **Wolverhampton†☆**	**20** **Ascot** **Catterick Bridge** Cheltenham *Cork* Kelso **Wolverhampton†☆**
	Tattersalls Sale	Goresbridge Sale Tattersalls Sale	Goresbridge Sale Tattersalls Sale	Baden-Baden Sale Tattersalls Sale	Baden-Baden Sale Tattersalls Sale	Baden-Baden Sale Ascot Sale
21 **Bath** *Cork* Kempton Park *Naas*	**22** Plumpton **Pontefract** **Windsor**	**23** Exeter **Lingfield Park†** **Yarmouth**	**24** Fontwell Park **Kempton Park†☆** *Navan* **Newmarket** Worcester	**25** Carlisle Ludlow **Southwell†** *Thurles* **Wolverhampton†☆**	**26** **Doncaster** *Dundalk☆* Fakenham **Newbury** **Wolverhampton†☆**	**27** Aintree Chepstow **Doncaster** *Leopardstown* **Newbury** Stratford-on-Avon *Wexford* **Wolverhampton†☆**
	Arqana Sale Fasig-Tipton Sale	Arqana Sale Fasig-Tipton Sale	Arqana Sale Fasig-Tipton Sale	Arqana Sale	SGA Sale	SGA Sale
28 Aintree *Galway* *Wexford* Wincanton	**29** Bangor-on-Dee *Galway* **Leicester** *Naas* **Redcar**	**30** **Catterick Bridge** Taunton **Yarmouth**	**31** Haydock Park **Kempton Park†☆** **Lingfield Park†** **Nottingham** *Punchestown*			
	Tattersalls Sale	Tattersalls Sale	Tattersalls Sale			

NOVEMBER

Sun	Mon	Tues	Wed	Thur	Fri	Sat
				1	**2**	**3**
				Clonmel Hereford **Kempton Park**☆ **Lingfield Park**† Stratford-on-Avon	*Down Royal* *Dundalk*☆ **Newmarket** Uttoxeter Wetherby **Wolverhampton**†☆	Ascot Ayr *Down Royal* **Newmarket** Wetherby
				Tattersalls Sale	*Goffs Sale* *Tattersalls Sale*	
4	**5**	**6**	**7**	**8**	**9**	**10**
Carlisle *Cork* Huntingdon *Leopardstown*	Kempton Park Plumpton **Wolverhampton**†	Exeter **Redcar** **Southwell**†	Chepstow *Fairyhouse* **Kempton Park**†☆ **Nottingham** Warwick	**Lingfield Park**† Musselburgh *Thurles* Towcester **Wolverhampton**†☆	*Dundalk*☆ Fontwell Park Hexham Musselburgh **Wolverhampton**†☆	**Doncaster** Kelso *Naas* Sandown Park Wincanton
	Keeneland Sale *Fasig-Tipton Sale*	*Ascot Sale* *Doncaster Sale* *Keeneland Sale*	*Doncaster Sale* *Keeneland Sale*	*Doncaster Sale* *Keeneland Sale*	*Cheltenham Sale* *Doncaster Sale* *Keeneland Sale*	*Keeneland Sale*
11	**12**	**13**	**14**	**15**	**16**	**17**
Ffos Las *Limerick* Market Rasen *Navan*	Carlisle *Limerick* Southwell	Huntingdon Lingfield Park Sedgefield	Bangor-on-Dee *Downpatrick* Exeter **Kempton Park**†☆ **Southwell Park**†	*Clonmel* **Kempton Park**†☆ Ludlow **Southwell**† Taunton	Cheltenham *Dundalk*☆ **Lingfield Park**† Newcastle **Wolverhampton**†☆	Cheltenham **Lingfield Park**† *Punchestown* Uttoxeter Wetherby **Wolverhampton**†☆
Tattersalls (IRE) Sale *Keeneland Sale*	*Tattersalls (IRE) Sale* *Arqana Sale* *Keeneland Sale*	*Tattersalls (IRE) Sale* *Arqana Sale* *Keeneland Sale*	*Tattersalls (IRE) Sale* *Keeneland Sale*	*Tattersalls (IRE) Sale* *Keeneland Sale*	*SGA Sale* *Tattersalls (IRE) Sale*	*SGA Sale* *Tattersalls (IRE) Sale*
18	**19**	**20**	**21**	**22**	**23**	**24**
Cheltenham *Cork* Fontwell Park *Punchestown*	Leicester Plumpton **Wolverhampton**†	Fakenham Folkestone **Southwell**† *Wexford*	*Fairyhouse* Hexham **Kempton Park**†☆ **Lingfield Park**† Warwick	Hereford **Kempton Park**†☆ Market Rasen *Thurles* Wincanton	Ascot *Dundalk*☆ *Ffos Las* Haydock Park **Wolverhampton**†☆	Ascot *Gowran Park* Haydock Park Huntingdon **Lingfield Park**† **Wolverhampton**†☆
Tattersalls (IRE) Sale		*Goffs Sale*	*Goffs Sale*	*Goffs Sale*	*Goffs Sale*	*Goffs Sale*
25	**26**	**27**	**28**	**29**	**30**	
Exeter *Navan* Towcester	Kempton Park Ludlow **Southwell**†	Lingfield Park Sedgefield **Southwell**†	Fontwell Park **Kempton Park**†☆ **Lingfield Park**† Wetherby	**Kempton Park**†☆ Newbury Taunton *Thurles* Uttoxeter	Doncaster *Dundalk*☆ Musselburgh Newbury **Wolverhampton**†☆	
Goffs Sale	*Tattersalls Sale*	*Tattersalls Sale*	*Tattersalls Sale*	*Tattersalls Sale*	*Tattersalls Sale*	

DECEMBER

Sun	Mon	Tues	Wed	Thur	Fri	Sat
30	**31**					**1**
Haydock Park **Lingfield Park**† Taunton	*Lingfield Park*† *Punchestown* *Tramore* Uttoxeter Warwick					Bangor-on-Dee *Fairyhouse* Newbury Newcastle Towcester **Wolverhampton**†☆ Doncaster Sale Tattersalls Sale
2	**3**	**4**	**5**	**6**	**7**	**8**
Carlisle *Fairyhouse* Leicester	**Kempton Park**† Plumpton **Wolverhampton**† Tattersalls Sale Fasig-Tipton Sale	Folkestone Southwell **Wolverhampton**† Tattersalls Sale	Catterick Bridge Hereford **Kempton Park**†☆ **Lingfield Park**† Tattersalls Sale	*Clonmel* Leicester Market Rasen Wincanton **Wolverhampton**†☆ Tattersalls Sale	*Dundalk*☆ Exeter **Lingfield Park**† Sandown Park **Wolverhampton**†☆ Cheltenham Sale Tattersalls Sale	Aintree Chepstow *Navan* Sandown Park Wetherby **Wolverhampton**†☆ Arqana Sale
9	**10**	**11**	**12**	**13**	**14**	**15**
Cork Kelso *Punchestown* Warwick Arqana Sale Fasig-Tipton Sale	Fakenham **Lingfield**† Musselburgh Arqana Sale	Fontwell Park Sedgefield **Southwell**† Ascot Sale Arqana Sale	*Dundalk*☆ Hexham **Kempton Park**†☆ Leicester **Lingfield Park**† Doncaster Sale	*Gowran Park* Huntingdon **Kempton Park**†☆ Ludlow Taunton	Bangor-on-Dee Cheltenham *Dundalk*☆ **Southwell**† **Wolverhampton**†☆	Cheltenham Doncaster *Fairyhouse* Lingfield Park **Southwell**† **Wolverhampton**†☆
16	**17**	**18**	**19**	**20**	**21**	**22**
Carlisle Hereford *Navan*	*Ffos Las* Plumpton **Wolverhampton**† Goffs Sale	Catterick Bridge Folkestone **Southwell**†	**Kempton Park**†☆ **Lingfield Park**† Ludlow Newbury	*Downpatrick* Exeter **Kempton Park**†☆ **Southwell**† Towcester	Ascot *Dundalk*☆ **Southwell**† Uttoxeter **Wolverhampton**†☆	Ascot Haydock Park **Lingfield Park**† *Navan* Newcastle
23	**24**	**25**	**26**	**27**	**28**	**29**
Thurles			*Down Royal* *Ffos Las* Fontwell Park Huntingdon Kempton Park *Leopardstown* *Limerick* Market Rasen Sedgefield Towcester	Chepstow Kempton Park *Leopardstown* *Limerick* **Southwell**† Wetherby **Wolverhampton**†☆ Wetherby Wincanton **Wolverhampton**†	Catterick Bridge Leicester *Leopardstown* *Limerick* **Lingfield Park**† **Wolverhampton**†☆	Doncaster Kelso *Leopardstown* *Limerick* Newbury **Southwell**†

DATES OF PRINCIPAL RACES
(SUBJECT TO ALTERATION)

JANUARY

Dipper Novices' Steeple Chase (Cheltenham)... 1st
victorchandler.com Steeple Chase (Handicap) (Cheltenham)... 1st
E.B.F. "High Sheriff of Gloucestershire's" "Junior" Standard Open National Hunt Flat Race (Cheltenham)..... 1st
Holden Plant Chase (Tramore)... 1st
32Red Novices' Hurdle Race (Registered as The Tolworth Hurdle Race) (Sandown Park)....................... 7th
32Red Anne Boleyn Mares' Hurdle Race (Sandown Park).. 7th
Phil Sweeney Chase (Thurles).. 7th
Slaney Novices' Hurdle (Naas)... 8th
William Hill Lanzarote Hurdle Race (Handicap) (Kempton Park)... 14th
Neptune Investment Management Leamington Novices' Hurdle Race (Warwick)...................................... 14th
Betfred Classic Steeple Chase (Handicap) (Warwick)... 14th
Betfred Goals Galore Bonus "Newcomers" Standard Open National Hunt Flat Race (Warwick)................ 14th
Juvenile Hurdle (Punchestown)... 14th
Foxrock Handicap Chase (Navan).. 15th
Kinloch Brae Chase (Thurles)... 19th
Coolmore EBF Mares Novices' Chase (Thurles)... 19th
25th Anniversary of the Victor Chandler Steeple Chase (Registered as The Clarence House Steeple Chase) (Ascot)........ 21st
1942 Was a Vintage Year Mares' Hurdle Race (Registered as The Warfield Mares' Hurdle Race) (Ascot)..... 21st
Bet with your mobile at victorchandler.com Holloway's Hurdle Race (A Limited Handicap) (Ascot)......... 21st
Rossington Main Novices' Hurdle Race (Haydock Park)... 21st
StanJames.com Champion Hurdle Trial (Haydock Park)... 21st
Altcar Novices' Steeple Chase (Haydock Park).. 21st
Peter Marsh Steeple Chase (A Limited Handicap) (Haydock Park).. 21st
Woodlands Novices' Chase (Naas).. 21st
Limestone Lad Hurdle (Naas)... 21st
Normans Grove Chase (Fairyhouse)... 22nd
Goffs Thyestes Handicap Chase (Gowran Park).. 26th
Galmoy Hurdle (Gowran Park).. 26th
Neptune Investment Management Novices' Hurdle Race (Registered as The Classic Novices' Hurdle Race) (Cheltenham).... 28th
Cleeve Hurdle Race (Cheltenham)... 28th
Argento Steeple Chase (Registered as The Cotswold Steeple Chase) (Cheltenham)............................. 28th
JCB Triumph Hurdle Trial (Registered as The Finesse Juvenile Hurdle Race) (Cheltenham).................... 28th
Murphy Group Steeple Chase (A Handicap) (Cheltenham)... 28th
Lightning Novices' Steeple Chase (Doncaster)... 28th
Albert Bartlett Novices' Hurdle Race (Registered as The River Don Novices' Hurdle Race) (Doncaster)..... 28th
Doncaster Mares' Hurdle Race (Doncaster).. 28th
Sky Bet Chase (A Handicap) (formerly The Great Yorkshire Chase) (Doncaster).................................... 28th
Killiney Novices' Chase (Leopardstown)... 28th
Leopardstown Chase (Leopardstown).. 28th
MCR Handicap Hurdle (Leopardstown).. 28th
Toshiba Irish Champion Hurdle (Leopardstown).. 29th
Frank Ward Solicitors Arkle Novices' Chase (Leopardstown)... 29th
Golden Cygnet Novices' Hurdle (Leopardstown)... 29th

FEBRUARY

Powerstown Novices' Hurdle (Clonmel).. 2nd
William Hill Welsh Champion Hurdle Race (Ffos Las).. 4th
Betfred Goals Galore Challengers Novices' Steeple Chase (Registered as The Scilly Isles Novices' Steeple Chase) (Sandown Park)........ 4th
Betfred and Levy Board Heroes Handicap Hurdle Race (Sandown Park).. 4th
Betfred "Double Delight" Contenders Hurdle Race (Sandown Park)... 4th
Betfred Masters Handicap Steeple Chase (Sandown Park).. 4th
totepool Towton Novices' Steeple Chase (Wetherby)... 4th
Grand National Trial Handicap Chase (Punchestown).. 5th
Tied Cottage Chase (Punchestown)... 5th
Moscow Flyer Novices' Hurdle (Punchestown).. 5th
Betfair Denman Steeple Chase (Newbury).. 11th
Betfair Super Saturday Steeple Chase (Registered as The Game Spirit Chase) (Newbury)...................... 11th
Betfair Winter Bumper (A Standard Open National Hunt Flat Race) (Newbury)...................................... 11th
Betfair Hurdle Race (Handicap) (Newbury)... 11th
Warwick Kingmaker Novices' Steeple Chase (Warwick)... 11th
Molson Coors Hurdle Race (Exeter).. 12th
Deloitte Novices' Hurdle (Leopardstown)... 12th
Dr PJ Moriarty Novices' Chase (Leopardstown).. 12th
Hennessy Gold Cup (Leopardstown).. 12th
Spring 4yo Hurdle (Leopardstown).. 12th
Betfair Ascot Steeple Chase (Ascot)... 18th
Sodexo Prestige Reynoldstown Novices' Steeple Chase (Ascot)... 18th

Albert Bartlett Novices' Hurdle Race (Registered as The Prestige Novices' Hurdle Race) (Haydock Park) 18th
Betfred Goals Galore Hurdle Race (Registered as The Rendlesham Hurdle Race) (Haydock Park) 18th
Betfred Grand National Trial (A Handicap Steeple Chase) (Haydock Park) 18th
Bathwick Tyres Kingwell Hurdle Race (Wincanton) 18th
Red Mills Trial Hurdle (Gowran Park) 18th
Red Mills Chase (Gowran Park) 18th
Ladbrokes Boyne Hurdle (Navan) 19th
Flyingbolt Novices' Chase (Navan) 19th
Ten Up Novices' Chase (Navan) 19th
williamhill.com Dovecote Novices' Hurdle Race (Kempton Park) 25th
Adonis Juvenile Hurdle Race (Kempton Park) 25th
Pendil Novices' Steeple Chase (Kempton Park) 25th
Kempton Park Steeple Chase (Handicap) (Kempton Park) 25th
Download the Blue Square iphone App Cleves Stakes (Lingfield Park) 25th
Winter Derby Trial Stakes (Lingfield Park) 25th
totesport.com Eider Steeple Chase (Newcastle) 25th
At The Races Bobbyjo Chase (Fairyhouse) 25th
Winning Fair Juvenile Hurdle (Fairyhouse) 25th
totesport.com National Spirit Hurdle Race (Fontwell Park) 26th
Paddy Power Newlands Chase (Naas) 26th
Paddy Power Johnstown Novices' Hurdle (Naas) 26th
Paddy Power Nas Na Riogh Novices' Chase (Naas) 26th

MARCH

Michael Purcell Novices' Hurdle (Thurles) 1st
Grimthorpe Chase (A Handicap Steeple Chase) (Doncaster) 3rd
totepool Premier Kelso Novices' Hurdle Race (Kelso) 3rd
Barbury International Supporting Greatwood Gold Cup Handicap Steeple Chase (Newbury) 3rd
DBS Spring Sales Bumper (A Standard Open National Hunt Flat Race) (Newbury) 3rd
Carrickmines Handicap Chase (Leopardstown) 4th
Paddy Power Imperial Cup Handicap Hurdle Race (Sandown Park) 10th
European Breeders' Fund paddypower.com 'National Hunt' Novices' Handicap Hurdle Race Final (Sandown Park) 10th
EBF/DBS Mares' Standard Open National Hunt Flat Race Final (Sandown Park) 10th
William Hill Lady Wulfruna Stakes (Wolverhampton) 10th
wolverhampton-racecourse.co.uk Lincoln Trial Handicap Stakes (Wolverhampton) 10th
Shamrock Handicap Chase (Gowran Park) 10th
Directors Plate Novice Chase (Naas) 11th
Lucan Racing Leinster National (Naas) 11th
William Hill Supreme Novices' Hurdle Race (Cheltenham) 13th
Racing Post Arkle Challenge Trophy Novices' Steeple Chase (Cheltenham) 13th
Stan James Champion Hurdle Challenge Trophy (Cheltenham) 13th
David Nicholson Mares' Hurdle Race (Cheltenham) 13th
Festival Handicap Steeple Chase (Cheltenham) 13th
Cheltenham Novices' Handicap Steeple Chase (Cheltenham) 13th
Glenfarclas Handicap Steeple Chase (A Cross Country Steeple Chase) (Cheltenham) 13th
Neptune Investment Management Novices' Hurdle Race (Registered as The Baring Bingham Novices' Hurdle Race) (Cheltenham) 14th
RSA Novices' Steeple Chase (Cheltenham) 14th
sportingbet.com Queen Mother Champion Steeple Chase (Cheltenham) 14th
Weatherbys Champion Bumper (A Standard Open National Hunt Flat Race) (Cheltenham) 14th
Fred Winter Juvenile Novices' Handicap Hurdle Race (Cheltenham) 14th
The Coral Cup (A Handicap Hurdle Race) (Cheltenham) 14th
Diamond Jubilee National Hunt Steeple Chase (Amateur Riders' Novices' Steeple Chase) (Cheltenham) 14th
Ladbrokes World Hurdle Race (Cheltenham) 15th
Ryanair Steeple Chase (Registered as The Festival Trophy Steeple Chase) (Cheltenham) 15th
Jewson Novices' Steeple Chase (Registered as The Golden Miller Novices' Steeple Chase) (Cheltenham) 15th
Byrne Group Plate (A Handicap Steeple Chase) (Cheltenham) 15th
Pertemps Final (A Handicap Hurdle Race) (Cheltenham) 15th
Fulke Walwyn Kim Muir Challenge Cup Handicap Steeple Chase (Amateur Riders) (Cheltenham) 15th
Albert Bartlett Novices' Hurdle Race (Registered as The Spa Novices' Hurdle Race) (Cheltenham) 16th
JCB Triumph Hurdle Race (Cheltenham) 16th
Betfred Cheltenham Gold Cup Steeple Chase (Cheltenham) 16th
Johnny Henderson Grand Annual Steeple Chase Challenge Cup (Handicap) (Cheltenham) 16th
Vincent O'Brien County Handicap Hurdle Race (Cheltenham) 16th
Christie's Foxhunter Steeple Chase Challenge Cup (Cheltenham) 16th
Martin Pipe Conditional Jockeys Handicap Hurdle Race (Cheltenham) 16th
Betfred Midlands Grand National Steeple Chase (A Handicap) (Uttoxeter) 17th
Dawn Run EBF Mares Novices' Chase (Limerick) 18th
Shannon Spray EBF Mares Novices' Hurdle (Limerick) 18th
EBF Novices' Final Handicap Chase (Navan) 18th
Sportingbet Supports Heros Winter Derby (Lingfield Park) 24th
Sportingbet Supports Heros Hever Sprint Stakes (Lingfield Park) 24th
Sportingbet Supports Heros Spring Cup (Lingfield Park) 24th
European Breeders' Fund/Thoroughbred Breeders' Association Mares' Novices' Steeple Chase Finale (A Handicap) (Newbury) .. 24th
European Breeders' Fund Mares' 'National Hunt' Novices' Hurdle Race (A Handicap) (Newbury) 24th
EBF Park Express Stakes (Curragh) 25th

William Hill Lincoln (Heritage Handicap) (Doncaster) ... 31st
williamhill.com Cammidge Trophy (Doncaster) ... 31st
William Hill Spring Mile (Handicap) (Doncaster) ... 31st
williamhill.com Magnolia Stakes (Kempton Park) ... 31st
An Uaimh Chase (Navan) ... 31st

APRIL

Fergusson Coal Doncaster Mile Stakes (Doncaster) ... 1st
Hugh McMahon Memorial Novices' Chase (Limerick) ... 1st
Kevin McManus Bumper (Limerick) ... 1st
William Hill Snowdrop Fillies' Stakes (Kempton Park) ... 7th
Cork Sprint Stakes (Cork) ... 7th
Imperial Call Chase (Cork) ... 7th
Easter Handicap Hurdle (Cork) ... 7th
Power Gold Cup (Cork) ... 7th
Rathbarry Novices' Hurdle (Cork) ... 7th
INHSO Final Novices' Handicap Hurdle (Cork) ... 7th
EBF Mares Novices' Hurdle Final (Cork) ... 7th
Ladbrokes Irish Grand National (Handicap Chase) (Fairyhouse) ... 9th
Arkle Bar Novices' Handicap Chase (Fairyhouse) ... 9th
John Fowler Memorial Mares Chase (Fairyhouse) ... 10th
Dan Moore Memorial Handicap Chase (Fairyhouse) ... 10th
Coolmore NH Sires Festival Novices' Hurdle (Fairyhouse) ... 10th
thetote.ie Handicap Hurdle (Fairyhouse) ... 10th
Weatherbys 4yo Hurdle (Fairyhouse) ... 10th
Free Grand National Bets with freebetting.co.uk International Trial Stakes (Lingfield Park) ... 11th
totesport.com 'Further Flight' Stakes (Nottingham) ... 11th
Matalan Anniversary 4-Y-O Juvenile Hurdle Race (Aintree) ... 12th
BGC Partners Liverpool Hurdle Race (Aintree) ... 12th
totesport Bowl Steeple Chase (Aintree) ... 12th
totepool Manifesto Novices' Steeple Chase (Aintree) ... 12th
matalan.co.uk Red Rum Handicap Steeple Chase (Aintree) ... 12th
John Smith's Fox Hunters' Steeple Chase (Aintree) ... 12th
Silver Cross Handicap Hurdle Race (Aintree) ... 12th
John Smith's Sefton Novices' Hurdle Race (Aintree) ... 13th
John Smith's Melling Steeple Chase (Aintree) ... 13th
John Smith's Mildmay Novices' Steeple Chase (Aintree) ... 13th
John Smith's Top Novices' Hurdle Race (Aintree) ... 13th
John Smith's Topham Steeple Chase (Handicap) (Aintree) ... 13th
John Smith's Cross Handicap Hurdle Race (Aintree) ... 13th
John Smith's Mares' Standard Open National Hunt Flat Race (Aintree) ... 13th
John Smith's Maghull Novices' Steeple Chase (Aintree) ... 14th
John Smith's Aintree Hurdle (Aintree) ... 14th
John Smith's Champion Standard Open National Hunt Flat Race (Aintree) ... 14th
John Smith's Mersey Novices' Hurdle Race (Aintree) ... 14th
John Smith's Grand National Steeple Chase (Handicap) (Aintree) ... 14th
John Smith's Handicap Steeple Chase (Aintree) ... 14th
John Smith's Handicap Hurdle Race (For Conditional Jockeys and Amateur Riders) (Aintree) ... 14th
1000 Guineas Trial (Leopardstown) ... 15th
2000 Guineas Trial (Leopardstown) ... 15th
Ballysax Stakes (Leopardstown) ... 15th
Heritage Stakes (Leopardstown) ... 15th
Masterson Holdings Silver Trophy Steeple Chase (A Handicap) (Cheltenham) ... 18th
Lanwades Stud Nell Gwyn Stakes (Newmarket) ... 18th
Bet at bluesq.com European Free Handicap (Newmarket) ... 18th
Blue Square Feilden Stakes (Newmarket) ... 18th
£150,000 Tattersalls Millions 3-Y-O Sprint (Newmarket) ... 18th
Thoroughbred Breeders' Association Mares' Novices' Hurdle Race (Cheltenham) ... 19th
Breeze Up Vendors Craven Stakes (Newmarket) ... 19th
Weatherbys Earl of Sefton Stakes (Newmarket) ... 19th
Connaught Access Flooring Abernant Stakes (Newmarket) ... 19th
£250,000 Tattersalls Millions 3-Y-O Trophy (Newmarket) ... 19th
European Breeders' Fund Lansdown Fillies' Stakes (Bath) ... 20th
Scottish Sun Future Champion Novices' Steeple Chase (Ayr) ... 21st
Isle of Skye Blended Whisky Scottish Champion Hurdle Race (A Limited Handicap) (Ayr) ... 21st
Coral Scottish Grand National Handicap Steeple Chase (Ayr) ... 21st
AON Greenham Stakes (Newbury) ... 21st
Dubai Duty Free Stakes (Registered as The Fred Darling Stakes) (Newbury) ... 21st
Dubai Duty Free Finest Surprise Stakes (Registered as The John Porter Stakes) (Newbury) ... 21st
Woodlands Stakes (Naas) ... 21st
Gladness Stakes (Curragh) ... 22nd
Alleged Stakes (Curragh) ... 22nd
Loughbrown Stakes (Curragh) ... 22nd
Boylesports Champion Chase (Punchestown) ... 24th
Evening Herald Champion Novices' Hurdle (Punchestown) ... 24th

Growise Novices' Chase (Punchestown) 24th
3' Handicap Hurdle (Punchestown) 24th
Investec City and Suburban Stakes (Handicap) (Epsom Downs) 25th
Punchestown Guinness Gold Cup (Punchestown) 25th
betchronicle Champion Bumper (Punchestown) 25th
Guinness Handicap Chase (Punchestown) 25th
War of Attrition Novice Hurdle (Punchestown) 25th
Ladbrokes World Series Hurdle (Punchestown) 26th
Ryanair Novices' Chase (Punchestown) 26th
bet365 Classic Trial (Sandown Park) 27th
Rabobank Punchestown Champion Hurdle (Punchestown) 27th
Cathal Ryan Memorial Champion Novices' Hurdle (Punchestown) 27th
Motivatechallenge Novices' Handicap Chase (Punchestown) 27th
totetentofollow.co.uk Leicestershire Stakes (Leicester) 28th
bet365 Mile (Sandown Park) 28th
bet365.com Celebration Steeple Chase (Sandown Park) 28th
bet365 Gold Cup Steeple Chase (Handicap) (Sandown Park) 28th
bet365 Gordon Richards Stakes (Sandown Park) 28th
Champion 4yo Hurdle (Punchestown) 28th
www.thetote.com Handicap Hurdle (Punchestown) 28th
Tulfarris Hotel Pat Taaffe Handicap Chase (Punchestown) 28th
ITBA Mares Hurdle (Punchestown) 28th
Salsabil Stakes (Navan) 29th
Vintage Crop Stakes (Navan) 29th
Prix Ganay (Longchamp) 29th

MAY

totepool Sagaro Stakes (Ascot) 2nd
Britain's Got Talent Paradise Stakes (Ascot) 2nd
Cleanevent Pavilion Stakes (Ascot) 2nd
totepool E.B.F. Conqueror Stakes (Goodwood) 5th
totesport.com E.B.F. Daisy Warwick Fillies' Stakes (Goodwood) 5th
Qipco 2000 Guineas Stakes (British Champions' Series) (Newmarket) 5th
Qipco Jockey Club Stakes (Newmarket) 5th
Pearl Bloodstock Palace House Stakes (Newmarket) 5th
Makfi Newmarket Stakes (Newmarket) 5th
Qipco 1000 Guineas Stakes (British Champions' Series) (Newmarket) 6th
Qatar Bloodstock Dahlia Stakes (Newmarket) 6th
Tweenhills Pretty Polly Stakes (Newmarket) 6th
Victor McCalmont Stakes (Gowran Park) 6th
Athasi Stakes (Curragh) 7th
Mooresbridge Stakes (Curragh) 7th
Tetrarch Stakes (Curragh) 7th
Weatherbys Bank Cheshire Oaks (Chester) 9th
totesport.com Chester Cup (Heritage Handicap) (Chester) 9th
MBNA Chester Vase (Chester) 10th
Betfair Huxley Stakes (for The Tradesman's Cup) (Chester) 10th
Addleshaw Goddard Dee Stakes (Chester) 11th
Boodles Diamond Ormonde Stakes (Chester) 11th
John Doyle Buckhounds Stakes (Ascot) 12th
totesport Victoria Cup (Heritage Handicap) (Ascot) 12th
toteplacepot Spring Trophy Stakes (Haydock Park) 12th
totescoop6 Swinton Handicap Hurdle Race (Haydock Park) 12th
totesport 0800 221 221 Chartwell Fillies' Stakes (Lingfield Park) 12th
totesport.com Derby Trial Stakes (Lingfield Park) 12th
totepool Oaks Trial Stakes (Lingfield Park) 12th
Weatherbys Bloodstock Insurance Kilvington Fillies' Stakes (Nottingham) 12th
Ladbrokes Handicap Hurdle (Killarney) 13th
Derrinstown Derby Trial (Leopardstown) 13th
Derrinstown 1000 Guineas Trial (Leopardstown) 13th
Amethyst Stakes (Leopardstown) 13th
Poule d'Essai des Poulains (Longchamp) 13th
Poule d'Essai des Pouliches (Longchamp) 13th
sportingbet.com Stakes (Registered as The Royal Windsor Stakes) (Windsor) 14th
Duke of York Blue Square Stakes (York) 16th
Tattersalls Musidora Stakes (York) 16th
Blue Wind Stakes (Naas) 16th
totesport Dante Stakes (York) 17th
totesport.com Middleton Stakes (York) 17th
totesport 0800 221 221 Hambleton Stakes (Handicap) (York) 17th
William Hill Braveheart Stakes (Handicap) (Hamilton Park) 18th
Swettenham Stud Fillies' Trial Stakes (Newbury) 18th
Whitman Howard Investment Bank Carnarvon Stakes (Newbury) 18th
Emirates Airline Yorkshire Cup (British Champions' Series) (York) 18th
sportingbet.com Fillies' Stakes (Registered as The Michael Seely Memorial Stakes) (York) 18th

Langleys Solicitors E.B.F. Shirocco Fillies' Stakes (Registered as The Marygate Fillies' Stakes) (York) 18th
JLT Lockinge Stakes (British Champions' Series) (Newbury) 19th
JLT Aston Park Stakes (Newbury) 19th
Stobart Group King Charles II Stakes (Newmarket) 19th
Novae Bloodstock Insurance Fairway Stakes (Newmarket) 19th
IBA Cocked Hat Stakes (Goodwood) 24th
Casco Height Of Fashion Stakes (Goodwood) 24th
ITWCP Festival Stakes (Goodwood) 26th
Southern Daily Echo Tapster Stakes (Goodwood) 26th
West Sussex County Times On The House Stakes (Goodwood) 26th
Betfred The Bonus King Stakes (Registered as The Cecil Frail Stakes) (Haydock Park) 26th
betfred.com Temple Stakes (British Champions' Series) (Haydock Park) 26th
Betfred Silver Bowl (Heritage Handicap) (Haydock Park) 26th
Stowe Family Law LLP Grand Cup (York) 26th
Abu Dhabi Irish 2000 Guineas (Curragh) 26th
TRI Equestrian Ridgewood Pearl Stakes (Curragh) 26th
Weatherbys Greenlands Stakes (Curragh) 26th
TP Waters Marble Hill Stakes (Curragh) 26th
Etihad Airways Irish 1000 Guineas (Curragh) 27th
Tattersalls Gold Cup (Curragh) 27th
Gallinule Stakes (Curragh) 27th
Prix d'Ispahan (Longchamp) 27th
Coolmore Prix Saint Alary (Longchamp) 27th
sportingbet.com Stakes (Registered as The Leisure Stakes) (Windsor) 28th
Hilary Needler Trophy (Beverley) 30th
Charles Heidsieck Champagne Heron Stakes (Sandown Park) 31st
Charles Heidsieck Champagne Henry II Stakes (Sandown Park) 31st
Piper Heidsieck Champagne Brigadier Gerard Stakes (Sandown Park) 31st
Piper Heidsieck Champagne National Stakes (Sandown Park) 31st

JUNE

Investec Coronation Cup (British Champions' Series) (Epsom Downs) 1st
Investec Oaks (British Champions' Series) (Epsom Downs) 1st
Investec Surrey Stakes (Epsom Downs) 1st
Investec Diomed Stakes (Epsom Downs) 1st
Princess Elizabeth Stakes (Sponsored by Investec) (Epsom Downs) 1st
Piper-Heidsieck Achilles Stakes (Haydock Park) 1st
W+S Recycling Stratford Foxhunters Champion Hunters' Steeple Chase (Stratford) 1st
Investec Derby (Epsom Downs) 2nd
Investec Entrepreneurial Class 'Dash' (Heritage Handicap) (Epsom Downs) 2nd
Investec Woodcote Stakes (Epsom Downs) 2nd
Timeform Jury Stakes (Registered as The John of Gaunt Stakes) (Haydock Park) 2nd
Blue Square Sandy Lane Stakes (Haydock Park) 2nd
E.B.F. New Approach Grosvenor Casinos Pinnacle Stakes (Haydock Park) 2nd
totesport.com Edinburgh Cup (Heritage Handicap) (Musselburgh) 2nd
Prix du Jockey Club (Chantilly) 3rd
Coolmore Stud Juvenile Fillies Stakes (Naas) 4th
Rochestown Stakes (Naas) 4th
Whitehead Memorial Stakes (Naas) 4th
Savel Beg Stakes (Leopardstown) 8th
Nijinsky Stakes (Leopardstown) 8th
Silver Stakes (Curragh) 10th
Lord Weinstock Memorial Stakes (Registered as The Ballymacoll Stud Stakes) (Newbury) 14th
Ballycorus Stakes (Leopardstown) 14th
Ballyogan Stakes (Leopardstown) 14th
totesport.com Scurry Stakes (Sandown Park) 16th
Bond Tyres Trophy (Heritage Handicap) (York) 16th
Bridget Swire's Palace Affair & Sakhee's Secret Cathedral Stakes (Salisbury) 17th
Kerry Group Noblesse Stakes (Cork) 17th
Midsummer Sprint Stakes (Cork) 17th
Prix de Diane Longines (Chantilly) 17th
Voute Sales Warwickshire Oaks Stakes (Warwick) 18th
King's Stand Stakes (British Champions' Series & Global Sprint Challenge) (Royal Ascot) 19th
Queen Anne Stakes (British Champions' Series) (Royal Ascot) 19th
St James's Palace Stakes (British Champions' Series) (Royal Ascot) 19th
Coventry Stakes (Royal Ascot) 19th
Windsor Castle Stakes (Royal Ascot) 19th
Ascot Stakes (Handicap) (Royal Ascot) 19th
Prince of Wales's Stakes (British Champions' Series) (Royal Ascot) 20th
Queen Mary Stakes (Royal Ascot) 20th
Sandringham Handicap Stakes (Royal Ascot) 20th
Windsor Forest Stakes (Royal Ascot) 20th
Jersey Stakes (Royal Ascot) 20th
Royal Hunt Cup (Heritage Handicap) (Royal Ascot) 20th
Gold Cup (British Champions' Series) (Royal Ascot) 21st

Norfolk Stakes (Royal Ascot) 21st
Ribblesdale Stakes (Royal Ascot) 21st
King George V Stakes (Handicap) (Royal Ascot) 21st
Britannia Stakes (Heritage Handicap) (Royal Ascot) 21st
Tercentenary Stakes (Formerly The Hampton Court Stakes) (Royal Ascot) 21st
Glencairn Stakes (Leopardstown) 21st
Coronation Stakes (British Champions' Series) (Royal Ascot) 22nd
King Edward VII Stakes (Royal Ascot) 22nd
Albany Stakes (Royal Ascot) 22nd
Queen's Vase (Royal Ascot) 22nd
Wolferton Handicap Stakes (Royal Ascot) 22nd
Buckingham Palace Stakes (Handicap) (Royal Ascot) 22nd
Martin Molony Stakes (Limerick) 22nd
Scottish News of the World E.B.F. "Major Cadeaux" Land O'Burns Fillies' Stakes (Ayr) 23rd
Diamond Jubilee Stakes (British Champions' Series & Global Sprint Challenge) (Royal Ascot) 23rd
Chesham Stakes (Royal Ascot) 23rd
Hardwicke Stakes (Royal Ascot) 23rd
Wokingham Stakes (Heritage Handicap) (Royal Ascot) 23rd
Queen Alexandra Stakes (Conditions Race) (Royal Ascot) 23rd
Duke of Edinburgh Stakes (Handicap) (Royal Ascot) 23rd
totepool Pontefract Castle Stakes (Pontefract) 24th
Grand Prix de Saint-Cloud (Saint-Cloud) 24th
Colliers International Rating Services Eternal Stakes (Warwick) 28th
E.B.F. 'Kheleyf' Hoppings Stakes (Newcastle) 29th
totesport.com Chipchase Stakes (Newcastle) 30th
John Smith's Northumberland Plate (Heritage Handicap) (Newcastle) 30th
John Sunley Memorial Criterion Stakes (Newmarket) 30th
Try timeform.betfair.com On Your Smartphone Fred Archer Stakes (Newmarket) 30th
totesport.com Empress Stakes (Newmarket) 30th
£150,000 Tattersalls Millions 3-Y-O Cup (Newmarket) 30th
Bet On The Irish Derby At totesport.com Stakes (Registered as The Midsummer Stakes) (Windsor) 30th
Dubai Duty Free Irish Derby (Curragh) 30th
Dubai Duty Free Railway Stakes (Curragh) 30th
Woodies Sapphire Stakes (Curragh) 30th
Dubai Duty Free Celebration Stakes (Curragh) 30th

JULY

Britannia English Summer National (A Handicap Steeple Chase) (Uttoxeter) 1st
Grangecon Stud Stakes (Registered as The Balanchine Stakes) (Curragh) 1st
Stobart Pretty Polly Stakes (Curragh) 1st
At The Races Curragh Cup (Curragh) 1st
International Stakes (Curragh) 1st
Abu Dhabi Sorouh Prix Jean Prat (Chantilly) 1st
Brownstown Stakes (Fairyhouse) 4th
Ambant Gala Stakes (Sandown Park) 6th
Bank Of New York Mellon Dragon Stakes (Sandown Park) 6th
bet365 Lancashire Oaks (Haydock Park) 7th
bet365 Old Newton Cup (Heritage Handicap) (Haydock Park) 7th
Coral-Eclipse (British Champions' Series) (Sandown Park) 7th
Coral Charge (Registered as The Sprint Stakes) (Sandown Park) 7th
Coral Challenge (Heritage Handicap) (Sandown Park) 7th
Coral Distaff (Sandown Park) 7th
Coral Marathon (Sandown Park) 7th
Lenebane Stakes (Roscommon) 9th
Weatherbys Bloodstock Insurance Pipalong Stakes (Pontefract) 10th
Princess of Wales's sportingbet.com Stakes (Newmarket) 12th
TNT July Stakes (Newmarket) 12th
Bahrain Trophy (Newmarket) 12th
sportingbet.com Heritage Handicap (Newmarket) 12th
Rose Bowl Stakes - Sponsored By Compton Beauchamp Estates Ltd (Newbury) 13th
Etihad Airways Falmouth Stakes (British Champions' Series) (Newmarket) 13th
Irish Thoroughbred Marketing Cherry Hinton Stakes (Newmarket) 13th
totesport.com Stakes (Heritage Handicap) (Newmarket) 13th
tyregiant.com Summer Stakes (York) 13th
totepool City Plate (Chester) 14th
Shadwell Stakes (Registered as The Hackwood Stakes) (Newbury) 14th
Shadwell Beech House Stud Stakes (Registered as The Steventon Stakes) (Newbury) 14th
Weatherbys Super Sprint (Newbury) 14th
Darley July Cup (British Champions' Series & Global Sprint Challenge) (Newmarket) 14th
32Red.com Superlative Stakes (Newmarket) 14th
32Red Bunbury Cup Handicap (Heritage Handicap) (Newmarket) 14th
John Smith's City Walls Stakes (York) 14th
John Smith's Silver Cup Stakes (Handicap) (York) 14th
John Smith's Cup (Heritage Handicap) (York) 14th
Tipperary Stakes (Tipperary) 14th

Juddmonte Grand Prix de Paris (Longchamp) ... 14th
Belgrave Stakes (Fairyhouse) ... 15th
totepool Glasgow Stakes (Hamilton Park) ... 19th
Silver Flash Stakes (Leopardstown) ... 19th
Challenge Stakes (Leopardstown) ... 19th
King George VI and Queen Elizabeth Stakes (Sponsored by Betfair) (British Champions' Series) (Ascot) ... 21st
totesport.com Summer Mile Stakes (Ascot) ... 21st
Jaguar XKR-S Winkfield Stakes (Ascot) ... 21st
Betfair Summer Double First Leg International Stakes (Heritage Handicap) (Ascot) ... 21st
totesport.com Summer Plate (A Handicap Steeple Chase) (Market Rasen) ... 21st
totescoop6 Summer Hurdle Race (A Handicap) (Market Rasen) ... 21st
Newsells Park Stud Stakes (Registered as The Aphrodite Stakes) (Newmarket) ... 21st
Minstrel Stakes (Curragh) ... 21st
Darley Irish Oaks (Curragh) ... 22nd
Jebel Ali Anglesey Stakes (Curragh) ... 22nd
Kilboy Estate Stakes (Curragh) ... 22nd
Grimes Hurdle (Tipperary) ... 22nd
Sweet Mimosa Stakes (Naas) ... 25th
Weatherbys VAT Services Star Stakes (Sandown Park) ... 26th
Meld Stakes (Leopardstown) ... 26th
Tyros Stakes (Leopardstown) ... 26th
Woodcote Stud E.B.F. "Halling" Valiant Stakes (Ascot) ... 27th
E.B.F. 'Authorized' Lyric Fillies' Stakes (York) ... 27th
Princess Margaret Juddmonte Stakes (Ascot) ... 28th
Sky Bet York Stakes (York) ... 28th
Sky Bet Dash (Handicap) (York) ... 28th
Skybet Supporting Yorkshire Racing Summer Festival (Pontefract) ... 29th
Prix Rothschild (Deauville) ... 29th
bet365 Lennox Stakes (Goodwood) ... 31st
bet365 Gordon Stakes (Goodwood) ... 31st
bet365 Molecomb Stakes (Goodwood) ... 31st
bet365.com Stakes (Handicap) (Goodwood) ... 31st

AUGUST

Qipco Sussex Stakes (British Champions' Series) (Goodwood) ... 1st
Veuve Clicquot Vintage Stakes (Goodwood) ... 1st
UBS Stakes (Handicap) (Goodwood) ... 1st
Goodwood Stakes (Handicap) (Goodwood) ... 1st
thetote.com Galway Plate (Handicap Chase) (Galway) ... 1st
Artemis Goodwood Cup (British Champions' Series) (Goodwood) ... 2nd
Audi King George Stakes (Goodwood) ... 2nd
i-Shares Fillies' Stakes (Registered as The Lillie Langtry Stakes) (Goodwood) ... 2nd
Guinness Galway Hurdle (Handicap) (Galway) ... 2nd
Tanqueray Richmond Stakes (Goodwood) ... 3rd
Coutts Glorious Stakes (Goodwood) ... 3rd
Oak Tree Stakes (Goodwood) ... 3rd
RSA Thoroughbred Stakes (Goodwood) ... 3rd
totesport Mile (Heritage Handicap) (formerly known as The Golden Mile) (Goodwood) ... 3rd
Markel Insurance Nassau Stakes (British Champions' Series) (Goodwood) ... 4th
Blue Square Stewards' Cup (Heritage Handicap) (Goodwood) ... 4th
Colin Kersley Queensferry Stakes (Chester) ... 5th
European Breeders' Fund 'Paco Boy' Chalice Stakes (Newbury) ... 5th
Give Thanks Stakes (Cork) ... 5th
Platinum Stakes (Cork) ... 5th
Prix Maurice de Gheest (Deauville) ... 5th
Ballyroan Stakes (Leopardstown) ... 9th
El Gran Senor Stakes (Tipperary) ... 10th
Abergwaun Stakes (Tipperary) ... 10th
Dubai Duty Free Shergar Cup Day (Ascot) ... 11th
Betfred Rose of Lancaster Stakes (Haydock Park) ... 11th
E.B.F. 'Kayf Tara' Dick Hern Fillies' Stakes (Haydock Park) ... 11th
Watch Races Live at racinguk.com Handicap Stakes (Heritage Handicap) (Haydock Park) ... 11th
German-Thoroughbred.com Sweet Solera Stakes (Newmarket) ... 11th
Keeneland Phoenix Stakes (Curragh) ... 12th
Keeneland Debutante Stakes (Curragh) ... 12th
Keeneland Royal Whip Stakes (Curragh) ... 12th
Patrick O'Leary Memorial Phoenix Sprint (Curragh) ... 12th
Prix du Haras de Fresnay-le-Buffard-Jacques Le Marois (Deauville) ... 12th
E.B.F. 'Exceed And Excel' Upavon Fillies' Stakes (Salisbury) ... 15th
Hurry Harriet Stakes (Gowran Park) ... 15th
totepool Sovereign Stakes (Salisbury) ... 16th
Desmond Stakes (Leopardstown) ... 16th
Bathwick Tyres St Hugh's Stakes (Newbury) ... 17th
CGA Hungerford Stakes (Newbury) ... 18th
CGA Geoffrey Freer Stakes (Newbury) ... 18th

Denford Stud Stakes (Registered as The Washington Singer Stakes) (Newbury)..18th
William Hill Great St Wilfrid Stakes (Heritage Handicap) (Ripon)...18th
E.B.F. 'Showcasing' Flying Fillies' Stakes (Pontefract)..19th
Darley Prix Morny (Deauville)..19th
Darley Prix Jean Romanet (Deauville)...19th
Juddmonte International Stakes (British Champions' Series) (York)...22nd
sportingbet.com Great Voltigeur Stakes (York)..22nd
sportingbet.com Acomb Stakes (York)..22nd
Darley Yorkshire Oaks (British Champions' Series) (York)..23rd
Irish Thoroughbred Marketing Gimcrack Stakes (York)...23rd
Jaguar Cars Lowther Stakes (York)..23rd
E.B.F. 'Selkirk' Galtres Stakes (York)..23rd
Addleshaw Goddard Stakes (Handicap) (York)..23rd
DBS Premier Yearling Stakes (York)...23rd
Fairy Bridge Stakes (Tipperary)..23rd
Peter Willett Stakes (Registered as The Stardom Stakes) (Goodwood)..24th
Betfred Starlit Stakes (Goodwood)..24th
Coolmore Nunthorpe Stakes (British Champions' Series) (York)..24th
Sky Bet Mobile Strensall Stakes (York)...24th
Betfair Celebration Mile (Goodwood)..25th
Whiteley Clinic Prestige Stakes (Goodwood)...25th
Windflower March Stakes (Goodwood)...25th
Betfair Summer Double Second Leg Stakes (Heritage Handicap) (Goodwood)..25th
Chris Blackwell Memorial Hopeful Stakes (Newmarket)..25th
totepool Winter Hill Stakes (Windsor)..25th
toteexacta August Stakes (Windsor)...25th
Weatherbys Insurance Lonsdale Cup (British Champions' Series) (York)..25th
Julia Graves Roses Stakes (York)...25th
Debenhams City Of York Stakes (York)...25th
Sky Bet Mobile Strensall Stakes (York)...25th
Betfred Ebor (Heritage Handicap) (York)..25th
Betfred Melrose Stakes (Handicap) (York)...25th
Curragh Stakes (Curragh)...25th
Galileo EBF Futurity Stakes (Curragh)..25th
Ballycullen Stakes (Curragh)...25th
Supreme Stakes (Goodwood)..26th
Flying Five Stakes (Curragh)...26th
Round Tower Stakes (Curragh)...26th
Dance Design Stakes (Curragh)..26th
Ripon Champion Two-Year-Old Trophy (Ripon)...27th
Ruby Stakes (Killarney)..29th
Weatherbys Bank Stonehenge Stakes (Salisbury)..31st
Brandon Handicap Hurdle (Killarney)..31st
Denny Handicap Chase (Killarney)...31st

SEPTEMBER

totepool Beverley Bullet Sprint Stakes (Beverley)...1st
totepool Chester Stakes (Handicap) (Chester)..1st
Sunshine Coach Solario Stakes (Sandown Park)..1st
De Vere Venues Atalanta Stakes (Sandown Park)...1st
Lord Mildmay Memorial Handicap Steeple Chase (Newton Abbot)...2nd
Irish Stallion Farms E.B.F. Dick Poole Fillies' Stakes (Salisbury)..6th
Betfred Sprint Cup (British Champions' Series) (Haydock Park)...8th
Betfred Treble Odds On All Lucky's Stakes (Registered as The Ascendent Stakes) (Haydock Park)...................................8th
Betfred 'Goals Galore' Superior Mile (Haydock Park)..8th
Betfred Bundles Old Borough Cup (Heritage Handicap) (Haydock Park)...8th
Betfred September Stakes (Kempton Park)..8th
Betfred Bonus King Sirenia Stakes (Kempton Park)...8th
Betfred London Mile Handicap Stakes (Series Final) (Kempton Park)..8th
Red Mills Irish Champion Stakes (Leopardstown)...8th
Coolmore Matron Stakes (Leopardstown)..8th
Kilternan Stakes (Leopardstown)..8th
Golden Fleece Stakes (Leopardstown)..8th
Moyglare Stud Stakes (Curragh)...9th
Solonoway Stakes (Curragh)...9th
Renaissance Stakes (Curragh)...9th
Blandford Stakes (Curragh)...9th
Scarbrough Stakes (Doncaster)..12th
Oyster Stakes (Galway)...12th
DFS Park Hill Stakes (Doncaster)...13th
Japan Racing Association Sceptre Stakes (Doncaster)..13th
Weatherbys Insurance £300,000 2-Y-O Stakes (Doncaster)...13th
Barrett Steel May Hill Stakes (Doncaster)..14th
Stobart Doncaster Cup (British Champions' Series) (Doncaster)..14th
Polypipe Flying Childers Stakes (Doncaster)..14th

Ladbrokes Mallard Stakes (Handicap) (Doncaster) 14th
Star Sports Stand Cup (Chester) 15th
Ladbrokes St Leger Stakes (British Champions' Series) (Doncaster) 15th
APC Industrial Services Park Stakes (Doncaster) 15th
One Call Insurance Champagne Stakes (Doncaster) 15th
Ladbrokes Portland (Heritage Handicap) (Doncaster) 15th
Irish Field St Leger Stakes (Curragh) 15th
Goffs National Stakes (Curragh) 15th
Flame Of Tara Stakes (Curragh) 15th
Qatar Prix du Moulin de Longchamp (Longchamp) 16th
Qatar Prix Vermeille (Longchamp) 16th
Lafrigue 4yo Handicap Hurdle (Listowel) 18th
Fortune Stakes (Sandown Park) 19th
Irish E.B.F. At The Races John Musker Fillies' Stakes (Yarmouth) 19th
Guinness Kerry National (Handicap Chase) (Listowel) 19th
Listowel Stakes (Listowel) 19th
Guinness Handicap Hurdle (Listowel) 20th
BAM Properties Harry Rosebery Stakes (Ayr) 21st
Dubai Duty Free Cup (Newbury) 21st
Laundry Cottage Stud Firth of Clyde Stakes (Ayr) 22nd
williamhill.com Doonside Cup Stakes (Ayr) 22nd
William Hill (Ayr) Silver Cup (Handicap) (Ayr) 22nd
William Hill (Ayr) Gold Cup (Heritage Handicap) (Ayr) 22nd
Dubai Duty Free Mill Reef Stakes (Newbury) 22nd
Dubai Duty Free Arc Trial (Newbury) 22nd
Dubai International World Trophy (Newbury) 22nd
Dubai Duty Free Handicap Stakes (Heritage Handicap) (Newbury) 22nd
£100,000 Tattersalls Millions Median Auction Trophy (Newmarket) 22nd
£100,000 Tattersalls Millions Fillies' Median Auction Stakes (Newmarket) 22nd
Tanqueray Stakes (Registered as The Foundation Stakes) (Goodwood) 26th
Princess Royal Richard Hambro E.B.F. Stakes (Newmarket) 27th
Somerville Tattersall Stakes (Newmarket) 27th
Jockey Club Rose Bowl (Newmarket) 27th
Shadwell Fillies' Mile (Newmarket) 28th
Sakhee Oh So Sharp Stakes (Newmarket) 28th
Nayef Joel Stakes (British Champions' Series) (Newmarket) 28th
Aqlaam Godolphin Stakes (Newmarket) 28th
Mawatheeq Rosemary Stakes (Newmarket) 28th
totepool 'Prelude' Handicap Steeple Chase (Market Rasen) 29th
totescoop6 'Prelude' Hurdle Race (A Handicap) (Market Rasen) 29th
Jaguar Cars Cheveley Park Stakes (Newmarket) 29th
Kingdom of Bahrain Sun Chariot Stakes (Newmarket) 29th
Juddmonte Royal Lodge Stakes (Newmarket) 29th
Betfred Cambridgeshire (Heritage Handicap) (Newmarket) 29th
Juddmonte Beresford Stakes (Curragh) 30th
CL Weld Park Stakes (Curragh) 30th
Blenheim Stakes (Curragh) 30th

OCTOBER

Kilbegnet Novices' Chase (Roscommon) 1st
Keltbray Noel Murless Stakes (Ascot) 5th
Diamond Stakes (Dundalk) 5th
Kilkenny Racing Festival Handicap Hurdle (Gowran Park) 5th
Grosvenor Casinos Cumberland Lodge Stakes (Ascot) 6th
Miles & Morrison E.B.F. October Stakes (Ascot) 6th
Macquarie Group Rous Stakes (Ascot) 6th
John Guest Bengough Stakes (Ascot) 6th
totescooop6 Challenge Cup (Heritage Handicap) (Ascot) 6th
Jaguar XJ Cornwallis Stakes (Newmarket) 6th
TRM Severals Stakes (Newmarket) 6th
E.B.F. Bahamian Bounty Boadicea Fillies' Stakes (Newmarket) 6th
£500,000 Tattersalls Millions 2YO Trophy (Newmarket) 6th
£300,000 Tattersalls Millions 2YO Fillies' Trophy (Newmarket) 6th
Guisborough Stakes (Redcar) 6th
totepool Two-Year-Old Trophy (Redcar) 6th
Cordell Lavarack Stakes (Gowran Park) 6th
Gowran Champion Chase (Gowran Park) 6th
Concorde Stakes (Tipperary) 7th
Tipperary Hurdle (Tipperary) 7th
Joe Mac Novices' Hurdle (Tipperary) 7th
Like A Butterfly Novices' Chase (Tipperary) 7th
Qatar Prix de La Foret (Longchamp) 7th
Qatar Prix du Cadran (Longchamp) 7th
Qatar Prix de l'Abbaye de Longchamp (Longchamp) 7th
Qatar Prix de l'Arc de Triomphe (Longchamp) 7th

Qatar Prix Jean Luc Lagardere (Grand Criterium) (Longchamp) 7th
Qatar Prix Marcel Boussac (Longchamp) 7th
Qatar Prix de l'Opera (Longchamp) 7th
Star Appeal Stakes (Dundalk) 12th
Emaar Middle Park Stakes (Newmarket) 13th
Dubai Dewhurst Stakes (Newmarket) 13th
Vision.ae Rockfel Stakes (Newmarket) 13th
Burj Khalifa Challenge Stakes (Newmarket) 13th
Darley Stakes (Newmarket) 13th
Autumn Stakes (Newmarket) 13th
Betfred Cesarewitch (Heritage Handicap) (Newmarket) 13th
coral.co.uk Rockingham Stakes (York) 13th
Coral Sprint Trophy (Heritage Handicap) (York) 13th
Finale Stakes (Curragh) 14th
Waterford Testimonial Stakes (Curragh) 14th
Lanwades & Staffordstown Studs Silken Glider Stakes (Curragh) 14th
Ladbrokes Munster National Handicap Chase (Limerick) 14th
Pricewaterhouse Cooper Chase (Limerick) 14th
Greenmount Park Novices' Hurdle (Limerick) 14th
Carvills Hill Chase (Punchestown) 18th
Buck House Novices' Chase (Punchestown) 18th
Sheilas Cottage Hurdle (Punchestown) 18th
Grabel Mares Hurdle (Punchestown) 18th
Queen Elizabeth II Stakes Sponsored by Qipco (British Champions Mile) (Ascot) 20th
Qipco Champion Stakes (British Champions Middle Distance) (Ascot) 20th
Qipco British Champions' Sprint Stakes (Ascot) 20th
Qipco British Champions' Fillies' and Mares' Stakes (Ascot) 20th
Qipco British Champions Long Distance Cup (Ascot) 20th
Zeturf.com Handicap Steeple Chase (Cheltenham) 20th
Navigation Stakes (Cork) 20th
williamhill.com - The Home of Betting Novices' Hurdle Race (Kempton Park) 21st
Kinsale Handicap Chase (Cork) 21st
Garnet Stakes (Naas) 21st
totepool Silver Tankard Stakes (Pontefract) 22nd
Mercury Stakes (Dundalk) 26th
Betfred Monet's Garden Old Roan Steeple Chase (A Limited Handicap) (Aintree) 27th
totetentofollow Persian War Novices' Hurdle Race (Chepstow) 27th
totepool Silver Trophy Handicap Hurdle Race (Chepstow) 27th
Racing Post Trophy (Doncaster) 27th
Bet Through The Racing Post App Stakes (Registered as The Doncaster Stakes) (Doncaster) ... 27th
Join racingpost.com Members' Club Handicap Stakes (Doncaster) 27th
Worthington's Highfield Social Club Stakes (Registered as The Horris Hill Stakes) (Newbury) ... 27th
Worthington's Champion Shield Stakes (Registered as The St Simon Stakes) (Newbury) 27th
totepool Stakes (Registered as The Radley Stakes) (Newbury) 27th
Killavullan Stakes (Leopardstown) 27th
Trigo Stakes (Leopardstown) 27th
Prix Royal Oak (Longchamp) 28th
Byrne Group Handicap Steeple Chase (Ascot) 29th
United House Gold Cup Handicap Steeple Chase (Ascot) 29th
williamhill.com Handicap Hurdle Race (Ascot) 29th
Ballybrit Novices' Chase (Galway) 29th
Poplar Square Chase (Naas) 29th
Brown Lad Handicap Hurdle (Naas) 29th

NOVEMBER

E.B.F. Normandie Stud Fleur De Lys Fillies' Stakes (Lingfield Park) 1st
E.B.F. Cockney Rebel - A Leading First Season Sire River Eden Fillies' Stakes (Lingfield Park) ... 1st
Criterium International (Saint-Cloud) 1st
Dubawi' E.B.F. Bosra Sham Fillies' Stakes (Newmarket) 2nd
Weatherbys Bank Wensleydale Juvenile Hurdle Race (Wetherby) 2nd
WKD Hurdle (Down Royal) 2nd
Hamptons EBF Mares' Novices' Hurdle (Down Royal) 2nd
United House Gold Cup Handicap Steeple Chase (Ascot) 3rd
James Seymour Stakes (Newmarket) 3rd
Novae Bloodstock Insurance Ben Marshall Stakes (Newmarket) 3rd
E.B.F. 'Mount Nelson' Montrose Fillies' Stakes (Newmarket) 3rd
bet365 Charlie Hall Steeple Chase (Wetherby) 3rd
John Smith's Hurdle Race (Registered as The West Yorkshire Hurdle Race) (Wetherby) 3rd
bet365 Mares' Hurdle Race (Wetherby) 3rd
JNwine Champion Chase (Down Royal) 3rd
Ladbrokes Skymas Chase (Down Royal) 3rd
Cumberland Handicap Steeple Chase (Carlisle) 4th
Paddy Power Cork Grand National Handicap Chase (Cork) 4th
Paddy Power EBF Novices' Hurdle (Cork) 4th
Paddy Power EBF Novices' Chase (Cork) 4th

Eyrefield Stakes (Leopardstown) 4th
Knockaire Stakes (Leopardstown) 4th
Betfred Haldon Gold Cup Steeple Chase (A Limited Handicap) (Exeter) 6th
Betdaq Mobile Apps Floodlit Stakes (Kempton Park) 7th
Thurles Chase (Thurles) 8th
Cooley Stakes (Dundalk) 9th
Betfred Goals Galore E.B.F. 'Sir Percy' Gillies Fillies' Stakes (Doncaster) 10th
Betfred 1350 Shops Nationwide Wentworth Stakes (Doncaster) 10th
Betfred November Handicap Stakes (Heritage Handicap) (Doncaster) 10th
totetentofollow.co.uk Rising Stars Novices' Steeple Chase (Wincanton) 10th
totepool Elite Hurdle Race (Wincanton) 10th
Badger Ales Trophy (A Handicap Steeple Chase) (Wincanton) 10th
Fishery Lane Stakes (Naas) 10th
Criterium de Saint Cloud (Saint-Cloud) 10th
Fortria Chase (Navan) 11th
Lismullen Hurdle (Navan) 11th
For Auction Novices' Hurdle (Navan) 11th
Clonmel Oil Chase (Clonmel) 15th
EBF TA Morris Memorial Mares Chase (Clonmel) 15th
Opus Energy Novices' Hurdle Race (Registered as The Sharp Novices' Hurdle) (Cheltenham) 16th
paddypower.com On Mobile Handicap Steeple Chase (Cheltenham) 16th
Steel Plate and Sections Novices' Steeple Chase (Cheltenham) 16th
Carlingford Stakes (Dundalk) 16th
JCB Triumph Hurdle Trial (Registered as The Prestbury Juvenile Hurdle Race) (Cheltenham) 17th
Paddy Power Gold Cup Steeple Chase (A Handicap) (Cheltenham) 17th
Rewards4Racing Handicap Steeple Chase (Cheltenham) 17th
Jardine Lloyd Thompson Handicap Hurdle Race (Cheltenham) 17th
Blue Square Churchill Stakes (Lingfield Park) 17th
Blue Square Golden Rose Stakes (Lingfield Park) 17th
Neptune Investment Management Novices' Hurdle Race (Registered as The Hyde Novices' Hurdle Race) (Cheltenham) .. 18th
Independent Newspaper Novices' Steeple Chase (Registered as The November Novices' Steeple Chase) (Cheltenham) .. 18th
Greatwood Handicap Hurdle Race (Cheltenham) 18th
Cleanevent Standard Open National Hunt Flat Race (Cheltenham) 18th
Blackwater Handicap Hurdle (Cork) 18th
Florida Pearl Novices' Chase (Punchestown) 18th
Morgiana Hurdle (Punchestown) 18th
Craddockstown Novices' Chase (Punchestown) 18th
Come to Kempton on Boxing Day Hyde Stakes (Kempton Park) 21st
timeform.betfair.com Novices' Hurdle Race (Registered as The Newton Novices' Hurdle) (Haydock Park) .. 23rd
Amlin 1965 Steeple Chase (Ascot) 24th
Coral Hurdle Race (Registered as The Ascot Hurdle Race) (Ascot) 24th
Betfair Steeple Chase (Registered as The Lancashire Chase) (Haydock Park) 24th
betfair/paulnicholls "Fixed Brush" Handicap Hurdle Race (Haydock Park) 24th
Monksfield Novices' Hurdle (Navan) 25th
Troytown Handicap Chase (Navan) 25th
Mares Bumper (Navan) 25th
Coolmore NH Sires "Ask and Getaway" Mares' Hurdle Race (Kempton Park) 26th
Back or Lay at betdaq.com Wild Flower Stakes (Kempton Park) 28th
GPG Novices' Steeple Chase (Registered as The Worcester Novices' Steeple Chase) (Newbury) 29th
Fuller's London Pride Novices' Steeple Chase (Registered as The Berkshire Novices' Steeple Chase) (Newbury) .. 30th

DECEMBER

Sportingbet Long Distance Hurdle Race (Newbury) 1st
Hennessy Gold Cup Steeple Chase (A Handicap) (Newbury) 1st
Sportingbet Handicap Steeple Chase (Newbury) 1st
Sportingbet Intermediate Hurdle Race (A Limited Handicap) (Registered as The Gerry Feilden Hurdle) (Newbury) .. 1st
StanJames.com Fighting Fifth Hurdle Race (Newcastle) 1st
At The Races Rehearsal Steeple Chase (A Handicap) (Newcastle) 1st
New Stand Handicap Hurdle (Fairyhouse) 1st
Ballyhack Handicap Chase (Fairyhouse) 1st
Porterstown Handicap Chase (Fairyhouse) 2nd
Bar One Drinmore Novices' Chase (Fairyhouse) 2nd
Bar One Hattons Grace Hurdle (Fairyhouse) 2nd
Bar One Royal Bond Novices' Hurdle (Fairyhouse) 2nd
Winter Festival Juvenile Hurdle (Fairyhouse) 2nd
Neptune Investment Management Novices' Hurdle Race (Registered as The Winter Novices' Hurdle Race) (Sandown Park) .. 7th
Sportingbet Future Stars Steeple Chase (Sandown Park) 7th
Betfred Becher Handicap Steeple Chase (Aintree) 8th
Betfred Grand Sefton Handicap Steeple Chase (Aintree) 8th
Sportingbet Tingle Creek Steeple Chase (Sandown Park) 8th
Markel Insurance Henry VIII Novices' Steeple Chase (Sandown Park) 8th
Bavaria Imported Premium Lager Handicap Hurdle Race (Sandown Park) 8th
Proudstown Handicap Hurdle (Navan) 8th
Hilly Way Chase (Cork) 9th
Cork Stayers Novices' Hurdle (Cork) 9th

Lombardstown Mares Novices' Chase (Cork)..9th
John Durkan Memorial Chase (Punchestown)...9th
EBF Novices Hurdle (Punchestown)...9th
Betfred Peterborough Steeple Chase (Huntingdon)...13th
Majordomo Hospitality Handicap Steeple Chase (Cheltenham)..14th
Albert Bartlett Novices' Hurdle Race (Registered as The Bristol Novices' Hurdle Race) (Cheltenham)......................15th
StanJames.com International Hurdle Race (Cheltenham)...15th
Unicoin Homes Relkeel Hurdle Race (Cheltenham)..15th
December Gold Cup (A Handicap Steeple Chase) (Cheltenham)...15th
Victor Chandler Summit Juvenile Hurdle Race (Doncaster)...15th
December Novices' Steeple Chase (Lingfield Park)..15th
Navan Novices' Hurdle (Navan)..16th
Tara Hurdle (Navan)..16th
Future Champions Bumper (Navan)..16th
totepool Novices' Steeple Chase (Registered as The Noel Novices' Steeple Chase) (Ascot)....................................21st
Mitie Kennel Gate Novices' Hurdle Race (Ascot)..21st
Championship Standard Open National Hunt Flat Race (Ascot)..21st
Long Walk Hurdle Race (Ascot)...22nd
The Ladbroke (A Handicap Hurdle Race) (Ascot)..22nd
GL Events Owen Brown Silver Cup Handicap Steeple Chase (Ascot)..22nd
Betfred Quebec Stakes (Lingfield Park)..22nd
Horse and Jockey Hurdle (Thurles)..23rd
williamhill.com Feltham Novices' Steeple Chase (In memory of Nigel Clark) (Kempton Park).................................26th
williamhill.com Christmas Hurdle Race (Kempton Park)..26th
William Hill King George VI Steeple Chase (Kempton Park)..26th
Rowland Meyrick Handicap Steeple Chase (Wetherby)..26th
Bord Na Mona Novices' Chase (Leopardstown)..26th
inforthenight.ie Juvenile Hurdle (Leopardstown)...26th
Guinness Greenmount Park Novices' Chase (Limerick)..26th
Coral Future Champions Finale Juvenile Hurdle Race (Chepstow)...27th
Coral Welsh National (A Handicap Steeple Chase) (Chepstow)...27th
williamhill.com Desert Orchid Steeple Chase (Kempton Park)...27th
williamhill.com Novices' Steeple Chase (Registered as The Wayward Lad Novices' Steeple Chase) (Kempton Park)............27th
Paddy Power Dial A Bet Chase (Leopardstown)..27th
Paddy Power Future Champions Novices' Hurdle (Leopardstown)..27th
Paddy Power Handicap Chase (Leopardstown)...27th
Tim Duggan Memorial Handicap Chase (Limerick)...27th
Lexus Chase (Leopardstown)..28th
Woodies DIY Christmas Hurdle (Leopardstown)...28th
Fort Leney Novices' Chase (Leopardstown)..28th
Dorans Pride Novices' Hurdle (Limerick)...28th
Bathwick Tyres Challow Novices' Hurdle Race (Newbury)..29th
Leopardstown Golf Centre December Hurdle (Leopardstown)...29th
EBF Mares Hurdle (Leopardstown)...29th

The list of Principal Races has been supplied by the BHA and is provisional. In all cases, the dates, venues and names of sponsors are correct at the time of going to press, but also subject to possible alteration.

INDEX TO TRAINERS

†denotes Permit to train under N.H. Rules only

Name	Team No.	Name	Team No.
A			
ADIELSSON, MR HANS	001	BARY, MR P.	029
AKEHURST, MR JOHN	002	BASTIMAN, MR ROBIN	030
AL ZAROONI, MR MAHMOOD	003	BATCHELOR, MRS ALISON	031
ALEXANDER, MR N. W.	004	BAUGH, MR BRIAN	032
ALLAN, MISS LOUISE	005	BEALBY, MR CHRIS	033
ALLEN, MR JIM.	006	BECKETT, MR RALPH	034
ALSTON, MR ERIC	007	BELL, MR MICHAEL	035
AMOS, MR WILLIAM	008	†BENNETT, MR CLIVE	036
APPLEBY, MR MICHAEL	009	†BENNETT, MR JAMES	037
ARBUTHNOT, MR DAVID	010	BERRY, MR ALAN	038
†ATKINSON, MR PETER	011	BERRY, MR J. A.	039
ATTWATER, MR MICHAEL	012	BERRY, MR JOHN	040
AYLIFFE, MR NICK	013	†BERWICK, MR JOHN	041
		BEST, MR JIM	042
		BEST, MR JOHN	043
B		BEST, MRS LOUISE	044
BAILEY, MR ALAN	014	BETHELL, MR JAMES	045
BAILEY, MRS CAROLINE	015	BEVAN, MR EDWARD	046
BAILEY, MR KIM	016	BEWLEY, MR GEORGE	047
BAKER, MISS EMMA	017	†BEWLEY, MR JOSEPH	048
BAKER, MR GEORGE	018	BIN SUROOR, MR SAEED	049
BALDING, MR ANDREW	019	BISHOP, MR KEVIN	050
BALDING, MR JOHN	020	BLACKFORD, MISS LINDA	051
†BANKS, MR MICHAEL	021	†BLACKMORE, MR ALAN	052
†BARCLAY, MRS ALTHEA	022	BLAKE, MR MICHAEL	053
BARFOOT-SAUNT, MRS TRACEY	023	BLANSHARD, MR MICHAEL	054
BARNES, MR MAURICE	024	BOLGER, MR J. S.	055
BARR, MR BRIAN	025	BOLLACK-BADEL, MRS MYRIAM	056
BARR, MR RON	026	BOSLEY, MR MARTIN	057
BARRON, MR DAVID	027	BOTTI, MR MARCO	058
†BARTON, MR FRANK	028	BOWEN, MR PETER	059
		BOWRING, MR ROY	060

Name	Team No.
BOYLE, MR JIM	061
†BRACE, MR DAVID	062
BRADBURNE, MRS SUE	063
BRADLEY, MR MILTON	064
BRADSTOCK, MR MARK	065
†BRAMALL, MISS ANNA	066
BRAVERY, MR GILES	067
BRENNAN, MR BARRY	068
BRENNAN, MR OWEN	069
†BREWIS, MISS RHONA	070
BRIDGER, MR JOHN	071
BRIDGWATER, MR DAVID	072
BRISBOURNE, MR MARK	073
BRITTAIN, MR CLIVE	074
BRITTAIN, MR MEL	075
BROOKS, MRS ANNA	076
BROOKS, MR CHARLIE	077
BROTHERTON, MR ROY	078
BROWN, MR ALAN	079
BROWN, MR DAVID	080
BROWN, MR GARY	081
†BROWN, MR IAN	082
†BROWN, MR REGINALD	083
†BRYANT, MISS MICHELLE	084
†BUCKETT, MRS KATE	085
BUCKLER, MR BOB	086
BUCKLEY, MR MARK	087
†BULL, MR PETER	088
BURCHELL, MR DAI	089
BURGOYNE, MR PAUL	090
BURKE, MRS E. M.	091
BURKE, MR KEIRAN	092
BURROUGH, MR SIMON	093
BUTLER, MR JOHN	094
BUTLER, MR PADDY	095
†BUTTERWORTH, MRS BARBARA	096
BYCROFT, MR NEVILLE	097
BYRNES, MR CHARLES	098

C

Name	Team No.
CAMACHO, MISS JULIE	099
CAMPION, MR MARK	100
CANAVAN, MR T. J.	100a
CANDLISH, MS JENNIE	101
CANDY, MR HENRY	102
CANN, MR GRANT	103
CANTILLON, MR DON	104
†CARR, MR DAVID	105
CARR, MRS RUTH	106
CARROLL, MR DECLAN	107
CARROLL, MR TONY	108
CARSON, MR TONY	109
CASE, MR BEN	110
CECIL, SIR HENRY	111
CHAMINGS, MR PATRICK	113
CHANCE, MR NOEL	114
CHAPMAN, MR MICHAEL	115
CHAPPLE-HYAM, MS JANE	116
CHAPPLE-HYAM, MR PETER	117
CHARLTON, MR GEORGE	118
CHARLTON, MR ROGER	119
CHISMAN, MR HARRY	120
†CLARKE, MRS ANGELA	121
CLAY, MR WILLIAM	122
CLEMENT, MR NICOLAS	123
CLEMENT, MR TERRY	124
CLINTON, MR PATRICK	125
CLUTTERBUCK, MR K. F.	126
COAKLEY, MR DENIS J.	127
†COBB, MRS HEATHER	128
COLE, MR PAUL	129
COLES, MR TOBIAS B. P.	130
COLTHERD, MR STUART	131
†CONNELL, LADY ANNE	132
COOGAN, MR ALAN	133
COOMBE, MR JOHN	134
†CORBETT, MRS SUSAN	135
CORCORAN, MR LIAM	136
CORNWALL, MR JOHN	137
†COSGRIFF, MR ANTHONY	138
COWELL, MR ROBERT	139
COWLEY, MR PAUL	140

Name	Team No.		Name	Team No.
COX, MR CLIVE	141		DODS, MR MICHAEL	180
COYLE, MR TONY	142		DONOVAN, MR DESMOND	181
CRAGGS, MR RAY	143		DORE, MR CONOR	182
CRATE, MR PETER	144		DOUMEN, MR FRANCOIS	183
CROOK, MR ANDREW	145		DOW, MR SIMON	184
CROWLEY, MISS JO	146		DOWN, MR CHRIS	185
CUMANI, MR LUCA	147		DREW, MR CLIVE	186
CUNNINGHAM, MR MICHAEL	148		†DU PLESSIS, MISS JACKIE	187
CURLEY, MR BARNEY	149		DUFFIELD, MRS ANN	188
CURTIS, MISS REBECCA	150		DUNCAN, MR IAN	189
CURTIS, MR ROGER	151		†DUNGER, MR NIGEL	190
CUTHBERT, MR TOM	152		DUNLOP, MR ED	191
			DUNLOP, MR HARRY	192
			DUNLOP, MR JOHN	193
D			DUNNETT, MRS CHRISTINE	194
D'ARCY, MR PAUL	153		DURACK, MR SEAMUS	195
DACE, MR LUKE	154		DUTFIELD, MRS NERYS	196
DALGLEISH, MR KEITH	155		DWYER, MR CHRIS	197
DALTON, MR NEALE	156		DYSON, MISS CLAIRE	198
DALY, MR HENRY	157			
†DANAHAR, MR JAMES	158			
†DANDO, MR PHILLIP	159		**E**	
DARTNALL, MR VICTOR	160		EARLE, MR SIMON	199
DASCOMBE, MR TOM	161		EASTERBY, MR MICHAEL	200
DAVIES, MR JOHN	162		EASTERBY, MR TIM	201
†DAVIES, MR PAUL	163		†ECKLEY, MR BRIAN	202
DAVIS, MISS JOANNA	164		EDDERY, MR PAT	203
†DAVIS, MISS LOUISE	165		EDDERY, MR ROBERT	204
DAVISON, MISS ZOE	166		†EDWARDS, MR GORDON	205
DAY, MR ANTHONY	167		EGERTON, MR CHARLES	206
†DAY, MISS LISA	168		ELLISON, MR BRIAN	207
DE GILES, MR ED	169		ELSWORTH, MR DAVID	208
DE GILES, MR JONATHEN	170		EMBIRICOS, MS A. E.	209
DE HAAN, MR BEN	171		†ENGLAND, MISS EVELYN	210
DEACON, MR GEOFFREY	172		ENRIGHT, MR GERRY	211
†DENNIS, MR TIM	173		ETHERINGTON, MR TIM	212
DICKIN, MR ROBIN	174		EUSTACE, MR JAMES	213
†DIXON, MR JOHN	175		EVANS, MR DAVID	214
DIXON, MR SCOTT	176		EVANS, MR JAMES	215
†DIXON, MR STEVEN	177		†EVANS, MRS MARY	216
DOBBIN, MRS ROSE	178		EVANS, MRS NIKKI	217
†DODGSON, MR ASHLEY	179		EWART, MR JAMES	218

Name	Team No.

F

FABRE, MR ANDRE......219
FAHEY, MR RICHARD......220
FAHEY, MR SEAMUS......221
FAIRHURST, MR CHRIS......222
FANSHAWE, MR JAMES......223
FEATHERSTONE, MS LUCINDA...224
FEILDEN, MISS JULIA......225
FENTON, MR PHILIP......226
†FERGUSON, MR JOHN......227
FFRENCH DAVIS, MR DOMINIC...228
FIERRO, MR GIUSEPPE......229
FIFE, MRS MARJORIE......230
FITZGERALD, MR TIM......231
FITZSIMONS, MR PAUL......232
FLINT, MR JOHN......233
FLOOD, MR DAVID......234
†FORBES, MR TONY......235
FORD, MRS PAM......236
FORD, MR RICHARD......237
†FORD, MRS RICHENDA......238
FORSEY, MR BRIAN......239
FORSTER, MISS SANDY......240
FOSTER, MR GEORGE......241
FOSTER, MISS JOANNE......242
FOX, MR JIMMY......243
FRANCE, MISS SUZZANNE......244
†FRANKLAND, MR DEREK......245
FROST, MR JAMES......246

G

GALLAGHER, MR JOHN......247
GARDNER, MRS SUSAN......248
GASK, MR JEREMY......249
†GASSON, MRS ROSEMARY......250
†GATES, MR MICHAEL......251
GEAKE, MR JONATHAN......252
GEORGE, MISS KAREN......253
GEORGE, MR TOM......254
†GIBSON, MRS THERESA......255
GIFFORD, MR NICK......256

GILLARD, MR MARK......257
GILLIGAN, MR PATRICK......258
GIVEN, MR JAMES......259
GOLDIE, MR JIM......260
†GOLDIE, MR ROBERT......261
GOLDSWORTHY, MR KEITH......262
GOLLINGS, MR STEVE......263
GORDON, MR CHRISTOPHER......264
GORMAN, MR J T......265
GOSDEN, MR JOHN......266
GRAHAM, MRS HARRIET......267
GRANT, MR CHRIS......268
GRASSICK, MR LIAM......269
GRASSICK, MR M. J.......270
GRAY, MR CARROLL......271
GRAYSON, MR PETER......272
GREEN, MR PAUL......273
GRETTON, MR TOM......274
GRIFFIN, MR PATRICK......275
GRIFFITHS, MR DAVID C.......276
GRIFFITHS, MR SIMON......277
†GRIFFITHS, MR SIRRELL......278
GRISSELL, MRS DIANA......279
GROUCOTT, MR JOHN BRYAN......280
GUBBY, MR BRIAN......281
GUEST, MR RAE......282
GUEST, MR RICHARD......283
GUNDRY, MISS POLLY......284

H

HAGGAS, MR WILLIAM......285
HALES, MR ALEX......286
HALFORD, MR MICHAEL......287
HALL, MR LES......288
HALL, MISS SALLY......289
HAM, MR GERALD......290
HAMBRO, MRS MARY......291
HAMER, MRS DEBRA......292
†HAMILTON, MRS ALISON......293
HAMILTON, MRS ANN......294
†HAMILTON, MRS CATHY......295

Name	Team No.	Name	Team No.
HAMMOND, MR MICKY	296	HOLMES, MR PATRICK	337
HAMMOND, MR MIKE	297	HOLT, MR JOHN	338
HANLON, MR JOHN JOSEPH	298	HONEYBALL, MR ANTHONY	339
HANNON, MR RICHARD	299	HOURIGAN, MR MICHAEL	340
HARKER, MR GEOFFREY	300	HOWE, MR STUART	341
†HARKIN, MRS PAULINE	301	HOWLING, MR PAUL	342
HARNEY, MR W.	302	HUGHES, MR D. T.	343
†HARPER, MR RICHARD	303	HUGHES, MRS JO	344
HARRINGTON, MRS JESSICA	304	†HUGHES, MR STEPHEN	345
HARRIS, MR JOHN	305	†HUGHES, MR V. J.	346
HARRIS, MR RONALD	306	HUMPHREY, MRS SARAH	347
HARRIS, MR SHAUN	307	†HUNTER, MR JOHN	348
HARRISON, MR GARY	308	†HURLEY, MISS LAURA	349
HARRISON, MISS LISA	309		
HASLAM, MR BEN	310		
HASSETT, MR P. J.	311	**I**	
HAWKE, MR NIGEL	312	†IKIN, MRS CAROLE	350
HAWKER, MR RICHARD	313	INGRAM, MR ROGER	351
HAYDEN, MR JOHN C.	314	IVORY, MR DEAN	352
HAYDN JONES, MR DEREK	315		
†HAYNES, MR JONATHAN	316		
HAYNES, MR TED	317	**J**	
HEAD-MAAREK, MRS C.	318	JACKSON, MISS TINA	353
HEARD, MR COLIN	319	†JACKSON, MRS VALERIE	354
HEDGER, MR PETER	320	JAMES, MR LEE	355
HENDERSON, MR NICKY	321	JARDINE, MR IAIN	356
HENDERSON, MR PAUL	322	JARVIS, MR ALAN	357
HERRIES, LADY	323	JARVIS, MR WILLIAM	358
HERRINGTON, MR MICHAEL	324	JEFFERSON, MR MALCOLM	359
HIATT, MR PETER	325	JENKINS, MR J. R.	360
HILL, MRS LAWNEY	326	†JESSOP, MR ALAN	361
HILL, MR MARTIN	327	JEWELL, MRS LINDA	362
HILLS, MR CHARLES	328	JOHNSON, MR BRETT	363
HILLS, MR J. W.	329	JOHNSON HOUGHTON, MISS EVE	364
HOAD, MR MARK	330	JOHNSON, MR ROBERT	365
HOBBS, MR PHILIP	331	JOHNSTON, MR MARK	366
HOBBS, MRS RACHEL	332	JONES, MR ALAN	367
HODGES, MR RON	333	JONES, MR GEORGE	368
†HOGARTH, MR HENRY	334	†JONES, MR GRUFFYDD	369
HOLLINGSWORTH, MR ALAN	335	JONES, MS LUCY	370
HOLLINSHEAD, MR REG	336	JORDAN, MRS VIOLET M.	371

Name	Team No.
K	
KEDDY, MR TOM	372
KEEVIL, MRS CAROLINE	373
KEIGHLEY, MR MARTIN	374
KELLETT, MR CHRISTOPHER	375
KELLEWAY, MISS GAY	376
KELLY, MR G. P.	377
†KENDALL, MISS LYNSEY	378
KENT, MR NICK	379
KING, MR ALAN	380
KING, MR NEIL	381
†KING, MR RICHARD	382
KIRBY, MR PHILIP	383
KIRK, MR SYLVESTER	384
KITTOW, MR STUART	385
KNIGHT, MISS HENRIETTA	386
KNIGHT, MR WILLIAM	387
L	
LAFFON-PARIAS, MR C.	388
LAMPARD, MR NICK	389
LANIGAN, MR DAVID	390
LAVELLE, MISS EMMA	391
LE BROCQ, MS JOAN L.	392
LEAVY, MR BARRY	393
LEE, MR RICHARD	394
LEECH, MRS SOPHIE	395
LEWIS, MR DAVID	396
LIDDERDALE, MR ALASTAIR	397
LINES, MR CLIFFORD	398
LITTMODEN, MR NICK	399
LLEWELLYN, MR BERNARD	400
LLOYD-BEAVIS, MISS NATALIE	401
LOCKWOOD, MR ALAN	402
LONG, MR JOHN E.	403
LONGSDON, MR CHARLIE	404
LOUGHNANE, MR DANIEL MARK	405
LYCETT, MR SHAUN	406
LYONS, MR G. M.	407

Name	Team No.
M	
MACAIRE, MR GUILLAUME	408
†MACDONALD, MR R.	409
MACKIE, MR JOHN	410
†MACTAGGART, MR ALAN	411
MACTAGGART, MR BRUCE	412
†MADDISON, MR PETER	413
MADGWICK, MR MICHAEL	414
MAGNUSSON, MR MIKAEL	415
MAIN, MRS HEATHER	416
MAKIN, MR PETER	417
MALZARD, MRS ALYSON	418
MANGAN, MR JAMES JOSEPH	419
MANN, MR CHARLIE	420
MANNERS, MRS AUDREY	421
MARGARSON, MR GEORGE	422
†MARSHALL, MR STEPHEN	423
MARTIN, MR A. J.	424
MASON, MRS JENNIFER	425
†MATHEW, MR ROBIN	426
†MATHIAS, MISS JANE	427
†MAUNDRELL, MR G. C.	428
MAYLAM, MISS OLIVIA	429
MCAULEY, MR JAMES	430
MCAULIFFE, MR KEVIN	431
MCBRIDE, MR CHARLIE	432
MCCABE, MR ALAN	433
MCCAIN, MR DONALD	434
MCCARTHY, MR TIM	435
MCCREERY, MR WILLIE	436
MCENTEE, MR PHIL	437
MCGRATH, MR MURTY	438
MCGREGOR, MRS JEAN	439
MCINNES, MR IAN	440
MCLINTOCK, MS KAREN	441
MCMAHON, MR ED	442
MCMATH, MR BRIAN	443
MCPHERSON, MR GRAEME	444
MCWILLIAMS, MR HUGH	445
MEADE, MR NOEL	446
MEEHAN, MR BRIAN	447

Name	Team No.	Name	Team No.
MIDDLETON, MR ANTHONY	448	NEWTON-SMITH, MISS ANNA	487
†MIDDLETON, MR PHILIP	449	NICHOLLS, MR DAVID	488
MIDGLEY, MR PAUL	450	NICHOLLS, MR PAUL	489
MILLMAN, MR ROD	451	NIVEN, MR PETER	490
MILLS, MR ROBERT	452	†NIXON, MR GEORGE	491
†MITCHELL, MR COLIN	453	†NOCK, MRS SUSAN	492
MITCHELL, MR NICK	454	NOLAN, MR DONAL	493
MITCHELL, MR RICHARD	455	NORMILE, MRS LUCY	494
MOFFATT, MR JAMES	456	NORTON, MR JOHN	495
MONGAN, MRS LAURA	457	NOSEDA, MR JEREMY	496
MOORE, MR ARTHUR	458		
MOORE, MR BILL	459		
MOORE, MR GARY	460	**O**	
MOORE, MR GEORGE	461	O'BRIEN, MR DANIEL	497
MOORE, MR J. S.	462	O'BRIEN, MR FERGAL	498
MORGAN, MR KEVIN	463	O'GRADY, MR EDWARD J.	499
MORRIS, MR DAVE	464	O'KEEFFE, MR JEDD	500
MORRIS, MR M. F.	465	O'MEARA, MR DAVID.	501
MORRISON, MR HUGHIE	466	†O'NEILL, MR JOHN	502
MUIR, MR WILLIAM	467	O'NEILL, MR JONJO	503
MULHALL, MR CLIVE	468	O'SHEA, MR JOHN	504
MULHOLLAND, MR NEIL	469	OLD, MR JIM	505
MULLANEY, MR LAWRENCE	470	OLDROYD, MR GEOFFREY	506
MULLINEAUX, MR MICHAEL	471	OSBORNE, MR JAMIE	507
MULLINS, MR SEAMUS	472	OXX, MR JOHN M.	508
MULLINS, MR WILLIAM P.	473		
MURPHY, MRS ANABEL	474		
MURPHY, MR COLM	475	**P**	
MURPHY, MR FERDY	476	PALLING, MR BRYN	509
MURPHY, MR MIKE	477	PALMER, MR HUGO	510
MURPHY, MR PAT	478	PANTALL, MR H. A.	511
MURTAGH, MR BARRY	479	PANVERT, MR JOHN	512
MUSSON, MR WILLIE	480	PARKER, MR ANDREW	513
		†PAYNE, MR JAMES	514
		PEACOCK, MR RAY	515
N		PEARCE, MRS LYDIA	516
NAYLOR, DR JEREMY	481	PEARS, MR OLLIE	517
†NEEDHAM, MR JOHN	482	†PEARSON, MR DAVID	518
NELMES, MRS HELEN	483	PERRATT, MISS LINDA	519
†NENADICH, MR CHRIS	484	PERRETT, MRS AMANDA	520
NEWCOMBE, MR TONY	485	PHELAN, MR PAT	521
NEWLAND, DR RICHARD	486	PHILLIPS, MR RICHARD	522

Name	Team No.	Name	Team No.
PICKERING, MR JOHN	523	†ROBERTS, MR DAVE	559
PINDER, MR DAVID	524	ROBERTS, MR MICHAEL	560
PIPE, MR DAVID	525	ROBESON, MRS RENEE	561
PITT, MR TIM	526	ROBINSON, MISS SARAH	562
POGSON, MR CHARLES	527	ROBSON, MISS PAULINE	563
POMFRET, MR NICHOLAS	528	ROHAUT, MR FRANCOIS	564
PORTMAN, MR JONATHAN	529	ROPER, MR W. M.	565
POULTON, MR JAMIE	530	ROTHWELL, MR BRIAN	566
POWELL, MR BRENDAN	531	ROWE, MR RICHARD	567
POWELL, MR TED	532	ROWLAND, MISS MANDY	568
PRENDERGAST, MR KEVIN M.	533	ROYER-DUPRE, MR A. DE	569
PRESCOTT BT, SIR MARK	534	RUSSELL, MRS LUCINDA	570
PRICE, MR ANDREW	535	RYALL, MR JOHN	571
†PRICE, MRS ANN	536	RYAN, MR JOHN	572
†PRICE, MR JOHN	537	RYAN, MR KEVIN	573
PRICE, MR RICHARD	538		
PRITCHARD, MR PETER	539		
PRODROMOU, MR GEORGE	540	**S**	
PURDY, MR PETER	541	SADIK, MR AYTACH	574
		SALMON, MR PETER	575
		SANDERSON, MRS DEBORAH	576
Q		†SANDERSON, MRS KATHLEEN	577
QUINLAN, MR NOEL	542	SAUNDERS, MR MALCOLM	578
QUINN, MR JOHN	543	SAYER, MRS DIANNE	579
QUINN, MR MICHAEL	544	SCARGILL, DR JON	580
		†SCOTT, MR DERRICK	581
		†SCOTT, MRS ELIZABETH	582
R		SCOTT, MR JEREMY	583
†RATCLIFFE, MR C. I.	545	†SCRIVEN, MR BERNARD	584
†REED, MR WILLIAM	546	SCUDAMORE, MR MICHAEL	585
REES, MR DAVID	547	SEMPLE, MR IAN	586
†REES, MRS HELEN	548	†SHARP, MR PHILIP	587
REGAN, MR SEAN	549	SHAW, MR DEREK	588
REID, MR ANDREW	550	†SHAW, MRS FIONA	589
†RETTER, MRS JACQUELINE	551	†SHEPPARD, MR JAMES	590
REVELEY, MR KEITH	552	SHEPPARD, MR MATT	591
†RICH, MR PAUL	553	SHERIDAN, MR FRANK	592
†RICHARDS, MR DAVID	554	SHERWOOD, MR OLIVER	593
RICHARDS, MRS LYDIA	555	†SHIELS, MR RAYMOND	594
RICHARDS, MR NICKY	556	SHIRLEY-BEAVAN, MR SIMON	595
RIMELL, MR MARK	557	SIDDALL, MISS LYNN	596
RIMMER, MR MARK	558	SIMCOCK, MR DAVID	597

Name	Team No.	Name	Team No.
†SLACK, MRS EVELYN	598	TIERNEY, MR RUAIDHRI J.	638
SLY, MRS PAM	599	TIZZARD, MR COLIN	639
SMAGA, MR DAVID	600	TODHUNTER, MR MARTIN	640
SMART, MR BRYAN	601	TOLLER, MR JAMES	641
SMITH, MR CHARLES	602	TOMPKINS, MR MARK	642
SMITH, MR JULIAN	603	TREGONING, MR MARCUS	643
SMITH, MR MICHAEL	604	TUER, MR EDWIN	644
†SMITH, MR ROBERT	605	TUITE, MR JOSEPH	645
SMITH, MRS SUE	606	TURNELL, MR ANDY	646
SMITH, MISS SUZY	607	TURNER, MR BILL	647
SMYLY, MR GILES	608	TURNER, MR JAMES	648
SMYTH, MR HARRY	609	TUTTY, MRS KAREN	649
SNOWDEN, MR JAMIE	610	TWISTON-DAVIES, MR NIGEL	650
SOWERSBY, MR MIKE	611		
SPEARING, MR JOHN	612		
SQUANCE, MR MICHAEL	613	**U**	
STACK, MR TOMMY	614	UNETT, MR JAMES	651
STIMPSON, MR JOHN	615	UPSON, MR JOHN	652
STONE, MR WILLIAM	616	USHER, MR MARK	653
STOREY, MR BRIAN	617		
STOREY, MR WILF	618		
STOUTE, SIR MICHAEL	619	**V**	
STUBBS, MRS LINDA	620	VARIAN, MR ROGER	654
SUMMERS, MR ROB	622	VAUGHAN, MR EDWARD	655
†SUNTER, MRS S.	623	VAUGHAN, MR NICKY	656
SUPPLE, MR JOHN A.	624	VAUGHAN, MR TIM	657
SWINBANK, MR ALAN	625	VON DER RECKE, MR CHRISTIAN	658
SYMONDS, MR TOM	626		
		W	
		WADE, MR JOHN	659
T		WADHAM, MRS LUCY	660
TALLIS, MR PATRICK	627	WAGGOTT, MISS TRACY	661
TATE, MR JAMES	628	WAINWRIGHT, MR JOHN	662
TATE, MR TOM	629	†WALEY-COHEN, MR R. B.	663
†TAYLOR, MRS SUSAN	630	WALFORD, MR TIM	664
TEAGUE, MR COLIN	631	WALKER, MR ED	665
TEAL, MR ROGER	632	WALL, MR CHRIS	666
†THOMAS, MRS D.	633	†WALL, MRS SARAH	667
THOMPSON, MR DAVID	634	WALL, MR TREVOR	668
†THOMPSON, MR VICTOR	635	†WALTON, MR JAMES	669
†THOMSON, MR SANDY	636	WALTON, MRS JANE	670
THORPE, MRS ALISON	637	WALTON, MRS KATE	671

Name	Team No.
WALTON, MRS SHEENA	672
WARD, MR JASON	673
†WAREHAM, MR GEORGE	674
†WATKINS, MISS TRACY	675
WATSON, MR FREDERICK	676
WATT, MRS SHARON	677
WAUGH, MR SIMON	678
WEAVER, MISS AMY	679
†WEBB-BOWEN, MR ROBERT	680
WEBBER, MR PAUL	681
WELD, MR D. K.	682
WELLINGS, MR MARK	683
WEST, MISS SHEENA	684
WEST, MR SIMON	685
WEYMES, MR JOHN	686
WHEELER, MR ERIC	687
WHILLANS, MR ALISTAIR	688
WHILLANS, MR DONALD	689
WHITAKER, MR RICHARD	690
†WHITEHEAD, MR ARTHUR	691
†WHITING, MR ARTHUR	692
WIGHAM, MR MICHAEL	693
WILESMITH, MR MARTIN	694
WILLIAMS, MR EVAN	695
WILLIAMS, MR IAN	696
WILLIAMS, MR NICK	697
WILLIAMS, MR STUART	698
WILLIAMS, MISS VENETIA	699
WILLIAMSON, MRS LISA	700
†WILSON, MR ANDREW	701
WILSON, MR CHRISTOPHER	702
WILSON, MR JIM	703
†WILSON, MISS MAIRI	704
WILSON, MR NOEL	705
WINGROVE, MR KEN	706
†WINTLE, MR ADRIAN	707
WOOD, MR IAN	708
WOODMAN, MR STEVE	709
†WOODROW, MRS A. M.	710
WOODWARD, MR GARRY	711
WYLIE, MR ROBERT	712

Y

Name	Team No.
YORK, MR RAYMOND	713
YOUNG, MRS LAURA	714
†YOUNG, MR WILLIAM	715

PROPERTY OF HER MAJESTY

The Queen

Colours: Purple, gold braid, scarlet sleeves, black velvet cap with gold fringe

Trained by **Sir Michael Stoute**, Newmarket

1 CARLTON HOUSE (USA), 4, b c Street Cry (IRE)-Talented

THREE-YEAR-OLDS

2 ESTIMATE (IRE), b f Monsun (GER)-Ebaziya (IRE)
3 GALLEON, b c Galileo (IRE)-Tempting Prospect
4 GLITTERING GOLD, b c Galileo (IRE)-Phantom Gold
5 SEQUENCE (IRE), b f Selkirk (USA)-Sinntara (IRE)

TWO-YEAR-OLDS

6 CIRCUS TURN (USA), b c 19/2 Street Cry (IRE)-Showlady (USA) (Theatrical)
7 B c 19/1 Street Cry (IRE)-Dream Ticket (USA) (Danzig (USA))

Trained by **Richard Hannon**, Marlborough

THREE-YEAR-OLDS

8 FREE VERSE, b f Danehill Dancer (IRE)-Fictitious
9 TRAVELLER'S TALES, b f Cape Cross (IRE)-Lost In Wonder (USA)

TWO-YEAR-OLDS

10 PRINCE'S TRUST, b c 21/2 Invincible Spirit (IRE)-Lost In Wonder (USA) (Galileo (IRE))
11 SEA SHANTY (USA), b c 23/1 Elusive Quality (USA)-Medley (Danehill Dancer (IRE))

Trained by **Roger Charlton**, Beckhampton

THREE-YEAR-OLDS

12 BORDER LEGEND, ch g Selkirk (USA)-Bonnie Doon (IRE)
13 DAWN GLORY, b f Oasis Dream-Fairy Godmother
14 MOIDORE, b c Galileo (IRE)-Flash of Gold

TWO-YEAR-OLDS

15 CANDOLUMINESCENCE b br f 11/3 Dansili-Flash of Gold (Darshaan)

Trained by **Michael Bell**, Newmarket

16 SET TO MUSIC (IRE), 4, b f Danehill Dancer (IRE)-Zarabaya (IRE)
17 TACTICIAN, 5, b g Motivator-Tempting Prospect

THREE-YEAR-OLDS

18 MOMENTARY, b f Nayef (USA)-Fleeting Memory
19 SIGN MANUAL, b g Motivator-New Assembly (IRE)

TWO-YEAR-OLDS

20 DALLIEFOUR (IRE), b f 14/3 Cape Cross (IRE)-Daliyana (IRE) (Cadeaux Genereux)
21 GAMBLE, ch f 19/3 Galileo (IRE)-Pretty Face (Rainbow Quest (USA))
22 SOUVENIR, b f 1/2 Cape Cross (IRE)-Trianon (Nayef (USA))

PROPERTY OF HER MAJESTY

The Queen

Trained by **Andrew Balding**, Kingsclere

THREE-YEAR-OLDS

23 AUTUMN FIRE, b f Avonbridge-Brand
24 BANK BONUS, b g Motivator-Small Fortune
25 PRICE LIST (USA), b f Red Ransom (USA)-Film Script

Trained by **Nicky Henderson**, Lambourn

26 BARBERS SHOP, 10, b g Sadlers' Hall (IRE) - Close Harmony
27 CLOSE TOUCH, 4, ch g Generous (IRE)- Romantic Dream
28 KILLIECRANKIE, 4, b g Kayf Tara - Bella Macrae
29 OPEN HEARTED, 5, b g Generous (IRE)- Romantic Dream

Trained by **Miss Henrietta Knight**, Wantage

30 HARVEST SONG (IRE), 6, b g Sadler's Wells (USA)- La Mouline (IRE)

To be allocated

TWO-YEAR-OLDS

31 AUGUSTINIAN, b c 16/4 Holy Roman Emperor (IRE)-Aurore (IRE) (Fasliyev (USA))
32 BOLD SNIPER, b c 21/1 New Approach (IRE)-Daring Aim (Daylami (IRE))
33 BOOKMARK, ch g 22/4 Dylan Thomas (IRE)-Fictitious (Machiavellian (USA))
34 DOMESDAY BOOK (USA), b c 13/4 Street Cry (IRE)-Film Script (Unfuwain (USA))
35 ENDORSE, b f 28/1 Royal Applause-Provision (Cadeaux Genereux)
36 HANDIWORK, ch c 18/2 Motivator-Spinning Top (Alzao (USA))
37 INAUGURAL, b c 20/5 Invincible Spirit (IRE)-Anasazi (IRE) (Sadler's Wells (USA))
38 KEW PALACE, ch g 26/3 Kheleyf (USA)-New Assembly (IRE) (Machiavellian (USA))
39 SWEET AS HONEY, b f 19/3 Duke of Marmalade (IRE)-Tempting Prospect (Shirley Heights)
40 VAPOUR TRAIL, b f 4/5 Dalakhani (IRE)-Fleeting Memory (Danehill (USA))
41 WHITE MONTH, b c 13/2 Tiger Hill (IRE)-Purple Heather (USA) (Rahy (USA))

All Registered trainers and permit holders were contacted to appear in
Horses In Training, those who do not appear declined.

1
MR HANS ADIELSSON, Kingston Lisle
Postal: Manor Farm Stables, Kingston Lisle Business Centre, Kingston Lisle,
Oxfordshire, OX12 9QX
Contacts: PHONE (01367) 820690 FAX (01367) 820690
E-MAIL manorstables@btconnect.com

1 **BEAUCHAMP XERXES**, 6, ch g Compton Admiral—Compton Astoria (USA) **Mr Erik Penser**
2 **KARATE (IRE)**, 4, ch g Exceed And Excel (AUS)—La Belle Katherine (USA) **Mr Erik Penser**
3 **SAND SKIER**, 5, b g Shamardal (USA)—Dubai Surprise (IRE) **Mr Erik Penser**
4 **STRIDING EDGE (IRE)**, 6, b br g Rock of Gibraltar (IRE)—For Criquette (IRE) **Mr Erik Penser**

MR HANS ADIELSSON—continued

THREE-YEAR-OLDS

  5 **BEAUCHAMP AQUA,** ch f Compton Admiral—Aquarelle **Mr Erik Penser**
  6 **BEAUCHAMP BEST,** ch f Compton Admiral—Bestemor **Mr Erik Penser**
  7 **BEAUCHAMP CASTLE,** b f Motivator—Ashford Castle (USA) **Mr Erik Penser**
  8 **BEAUCHAMP ORANGE,** ch f Green Tune (USA)—Orange Sunset (IRE) **Mr Erik Penser**
  9 **COMPTON AIR (USA),** b g Langfuhr (CAN)—Air Kiss **Mr Erik Penser**
10 **COMPTON ASHDOWN,** b g Proclamation (IRE)—Ashlinn (IRE) **Mr Erik Penser**
11 **COMPTON BABY,** b f Proud Citizen (USA)—Baby Victory (BRZ) **Mr Erik Penser**
12 **COMPTON BELL,** b g Shirocco (GER)—Bela-M (IRE) **Mr Erik Penser**
13 **COMPTON BIRD,** b f Motivator—Noble Peregrine **Mr Erik Penser**
14 **COMPTON CROFTER,** ch g Sleeping Indian—Crofters Ceilidh **Mr Erik Penser**
15 **COMPTON MONARCH,** b g Red Ransom (USA)—Monaiya **Mr Erik Penser**
16 **COMPTON RAINBOW,** b f Exceed And Excel (AUS)—Rainbow Goddess **Mr Erik Penser**
17 **COMPTON SHUTTLE (IRE),** b f Shirocco (GER)—Shuheb **Mr Erik Penser**
18 **COMPTON TARGET (IRE),** b g Strategic Prince—Tarakana (USA) **Mr Erik Penser**
19 **HOLLY MARTINS,** b g Rail Link—Pretty Girl (IRE) **The Third Man**
20 **KARIM,** b g Cape Cross (IRE)—Green Room (FR) **XSNRJ Holding**
21 **LITTLESUZIE,** b f Kyllachy—Golubitsa (IRE) **Mrs Paul Tengquist**

TWO-YEAR-OLDS

22 **BEAUCHAMP ASTRA,** b f 13/4 Observatory (USA)—Ashford Castle (USA) (Bates Motel (USA)) **Mr Erik Penser**
23 **BEAUCHAMP BELLA,** b f 9/5 Manduro (GER)—Baharah (USA) (Elusive Quality (USA)) **Mr Erik Penser**
24 **BEAUCHAMP BOLD,** b g 21/3 Byron—Bestemor (Selkirk (USA)) **Mr Erik Penser**
25 **BEAUCHAMP ELLE,** b f 27/2 Cockney Rebel (IRE)—Aquarelle (Kenmare (FR)) **Mr Erik Penser**
26 **BEAUCHAMP REBEL,** b g 17/4 Cockney Rebel (IRE)—Beauchamp Jade (Kalaglow) **Mr Erik Penser**
27 **BEAUCHAMP SUNSET,** b g 15/3 Tiger Hill (IRE)—Orange Sunset (IRE) (Roanoke (USA)) **Mr Erik Penser**
28 **CATCH THE CIDER,** b c 16/3 Medicean—Zanna (FR) (Soviet Star (USA)) (14285) **P & D Bronsman AB**
29 **COMPTON SILVER,** ch g 21/3 Haafhd—Anna Oleanda (IRE) (Old Vic) (34285) **Mr Erik Penser**

Apprentice: Nicole Nordblad.

---

2 | **MR JOHN AKEHURST, Epsom**
Postal: **The Old Yard, Clear Height Stables, Derby Stables Road, Epsom, Surrey, KT18 5LB**
Contacts: PHONE (01372) 740878 FAX (01372) 740898
E-MAIL john.akehurst@tiscali.co.uk WEBSITE www.jakehurst.co.uk

1 **BLUE DEER (IRE),** 4, b g Bahamian Bounty—Jaywick (UAE) **Mrs I. Marshall**
2 **CHILLI GREEN,** 5, b m Desert Sun—Jade Pet **P. M. Crane**
3 **EDGEWATER (IRE),** 5, b g Bahamian Bounty—Esteemed Lady (IRE) **One More Bid Partnership**
4 **MARY'S PET,** 5, b m Where Or When (IRE)—Contrary Mary **Mrs I. Marshall**
5 **PRINCE OF SORRENTO,** 5, ch g Doyen (IRE)—Princess Galadriel **J. Akehurst**

THREE-YEAR-OLDS

6 **KING'S FUTURE,** b g King's Best (USA)—Las Beatas **The Green Pastures Partnership II**

Other Owners: P. A. Allard, N. Boyce, J. D. A. Gordon, W. R. Hinge, Mr S. A. Lockyer, Mrs S. Sheldon.

---

3 | **MR MAHMOOD AL ZAROONI, Newmarket**
Postal: **Godolphin Management Co Ltd, Godolphin Stables, Snailwell Road, Newmarket, Suffolk, CB8 7YE**
The following list has not been supplied by the trainer and is as accurate as possible at the time of going to press. Some horses listed may not return to Britain from Dubai. Details of 2yos were not available.
For the latest information visit www.godolphin.com

1 **AHTOUG,** 4, b c Byron—Cherokee Rose (IRE)
2 **AICHI (AUS),** 7, b g Strategic (AUS)—Nagoya (AUS)
3 **ANATOLIAN,** 4, ch c Pivotal—Poseidon's Bride (USA)
4 **BE FABULOUS (GER),** 5, b m Samum (GER)—Bandeira (GER)
5 **BIONDETTI (USA),** 4, b c Bernardini—Lyphard's Delta (USA)
6 **BRIDGEFIELD (USA),** 4, ch c Speightstown—Treysta (USA)
7 **BRIDGEFIELD (USA),** 4, ch c Speightstown—Treysta (USA)
8 **CALVADOS BLUES (FR),** 6, ch h Lando (GER)—Persian Belle

MR MAHMOOD AL ZAROONI—continued

9 **CAPPONI (IRE)**, 5, ch h Medicean—Nawaiet (USA)
10 **CASAMENTO (IRE)**, 4, ch c Shamardal (USA)—Wedding Gift (FR)
11 **CITY STYLE (USA)**, 6, ch g City Zip (USA)—Brattothecore (CAN)
12 **DEBUSSY (IRE)**, 6, b br h Diesis—Opera Comique (FR)
13 **DOUBLE DEALER**, 4, b c Dubawi (IRE)—Infiel
14 **DUBAI PRINCE (IRE)**, 4, b c Shamardal (USA)—Desert Frolic (IRE)
15 **ECLIPTIC (USA)**, 4, ch c Kingmambo (USA)—Indy Five Hundred (USA)
16 **FRENCH NAVY**, 4, b c Shamardal (USA)—First Fleet (USA)
17 **GENIUS BEAST (USA)**, 4, b c Kingmambo (USA)—Shawanda (IRE)
18 **HAMAN (CAN)**, 4, b br c Street Cry (IRE)—Penny Perfect (CAN)
19 **HIGH TWELVE (IRE)**, 5, b g Montjeu (IRE)—Much Faster (IRE)
20 **INLER (IRE)**, 5, br g Red Ransom (USA)—Wedding Gift (FR)
21 **INTROVERT (IRE)**, 4, b c Iffraaj—Isana (JPN)
22 **LAAJOOJ (IRE)**, 4, b c Azamour (IRE)—Flanders (IRE)
23 **LEGISLATION**, 7, b g Oasis Dream—Kite Mark
24 **LIFE AND TIMES (USA)**, 4, b br c Medaglia d'oro (USA)—Sur Ma Vie (USA)
25 **MAYWOOD**, 4, b c Cape Cross (IRE)—Murrieta
26 **MEEZNAH (USA)**, 5, b m Dynaformer (USA)—String Quartet (IRE)
27 **MODERN HISTORY (IRE)**, 4, b c Shamardal (USA)—Fatefully (USA)
28 **MONTEROSSO**, 5, b h Dubawi (IRE)—Porto Roca (AUS)
29 **NAMECHECK (GER)**, 5, ch h Shamardal (USA)—Nadia
30 **OCEAN WAR**, 4, gr g Dalakhani (IRE)—Atlantic Destiny (IRE)
31 **OPINION POLL (IRE)**, 6, b h Halling (USA)—Ahead
32 **PARLOUR GAMES**, 4, ch c Monsun (GER)—Petrushka (IRE)
33 **PRIZEFIGHTING (USA)**, 5, ch g Smart Strike (CAN)—Allencat (USA)
34 **RILEYSKEEPINGFAITH**, 4, b g Hunting Lion (USA)—Keeping The Faith (IRE)
35 **ROSTRUM (FR)**, 5, b h Shamardal (USA)—En Public (IRE)
36 **SADEEK'S SONG (USA)**, 4, ch c Kingmambo (USA)—New Morning (IRE)
37 **SAMURAI SWORD**, 4, b c Motivator—Japanese Whisper (UAE)
38 **SANDUSKY**, 4, b c Tiger Hill (IRE)—Red Carnation (IRE)
39 **SEA LORD (IRE)**, 5, b h Cape Cross (IRE)—First Fleet (USA)
40 **SPLASH POINT (USA)**, 4, b c Street Cry (IRE)—Dianehill (IRE)
41 **TAKE TEN**, 5, b g Bahamian Bounty—See You Later
42 **TIME PRISONER (USA)**, 5, gr ro h Elusive Quality (USA)—Zelanda (IRE)
43 **TIMELINE**, 4, b c Elusive Quality (USA)—Last Second (IRE)
44 **XIN XU LIN (BRZ)**, 5, b h Wondertross (USA)—Barbiera (BRZ)

THREE-YEAR-OLDS

45 **ACCREDIT (IRE)**, b c Authorized (IRE)—Sharp Mode (USA)
46 **ALDGATE (USA)**, ch c Street Cry (IRE)—Adonesque (IRE)
47 **ANOMALY**, ch c Pivotal—Anna Palariva (IRE)
48 **AUTUMNUS (IRE)**, b c Manduro (GER)—Turning Light (GER)
49 **BRAILSFORD (IRE)**, b c Dubawi (IRE)—Meynell
50 **CAPORETTO (USA)**, b c Street Sense (USA)—Crimson Conquest (USA)
51 **CIRCUS MONDAO (USA)**, b g Hard Spun (USA)—Dominique's Show (USA)
52 **COMMISSAR**, b c Soviet Star (USA)—Sari
53 **COTTESMORE (USA)**, b br c Medaglia d'oro (USA)—Racing Heart (USA)
54 **COUNTERGLOW (IRE)**, b g Echo of Light—Quintellina
55 **COUNTERSIGN**, b c Authorized (IRE)—Circle of Love
56 **CRYING WOLF (USA)**, b br c Street Cry (IRE)—Don't Tacha Me (USA)
57 **CURZON LINE**, b c Dubawi (IRE)—Polska (IRE)
58 **DISCOURSE (USA)**, b br f Street Cry (IRE)—Divine Dixie (USA)
59 **DUBAWI ISLAND (FR)**, b c Dubawi (IRE)—Housa Dancer (FR)
60 **ECHO OF DREAM**, br c Echo of Light—Rahcak (IRE)
61 **EDUCATE**, b c Echo of Light—Pasithea (IRE)
62 **ELUDING**, b f Street Cry (IRE)—Without A Trace (IRE)
63 **ENCKE (USA)**, b c Kingmambo (USA)—Shawanda (IRE)
64 **ETON DORNEY (USA)**, b c Medaglia d'oro (USA)—Sweet and Firm (USA)
65 **EUROPE (IRE)**, ch c Manduro (GER)—Twiggy's Sister (IRE)
66 **FALLS OF LORA (IRE)**, b f Street Cry (IRE)—Firth of Lorne (IRE)
67 **FITFUL SKIES (IRE)**, b f Dubawi (IRE)—Wajd (USA)
68 **GAMILATI**, b f Bernardini—Illustrious Miss (USA)
69 **GOLD RALLY (USA)**, gr c Medaglia d'oro (USA)—Beright (USA)
70 **GREEK WAR (IRE)**, ch g Monsun (GER)—Gonfilia (GER)
71 **GRIZZLE**, b c Shamardal (USA)—Pearl Grey

MR MAHMOOD AL ZAROONI—continued

72 **GUARDI (IRE)**, gr c Dalakhani (IRE)—Grizel
73 **HELLENISTIC**, ch f Street Cry (IRE)—Rahiyah (USA)
74 **INDIAN PETAL**, ch f Singspiel (IRE)—Wood Vine (USA)
75 **IPTISAM**, ch c Rahy (USA)—Grain of Truth
76 **KAILANI**, b f Monsun (GER)—Kazzia (GER)
77 **KINGLET (USA)**, b br c Kingmambo (USA)—Karen's Caper (USA)
78 **KIZ KULESI**, ch c Street Cry (IRE)—Maiden Tower
79 **KUNOOZ (IRE)**, b f Hard Spun (USA)—Aviacion (BRZ)
80 **LACILY (USA)**, b f Elusive Quality (USA)—Lailani
81 **LIGHT BURST (USA)**, b c Hard Spun (USA)—Kew Garden (USA)
82 **MANDAEAN**, b c Manduro (GER)—Summertime Legacy
83 **MARINER'S CROSS (IRE)**, b c Dubawi (IRE)—Trilemma
84 **MIGHTY AMBITION (USA)**, b c Street Cry (IRE)—New Morning (IRE)
85 **MINIDRESS**, br f Street Cry (IRE)—Short Skirt
86 **MOJAVE (IRE)**, b c Dubawi (IRE)—Desert Frolic (IRE)
87 **MORROW**, ch f Pivotal—Morning Pride (IRE)
88 **MR CHURCHILL (IRE)**, b c Invincible Spirit (IRE)—Mayoress
89 **MY DESTINATION (IRE)**, b c Dubai Destination (USA)—Gossamer
90 **OKIMONO**, b c Invincible Spirit (IRE)—Ivory Gala (FR)
91 **OSCAN (USA)**, b c Street Cry (IRE)—Moyesii (USA)
92 **OXBOW (IRE)**, b g Shirocco (GER)—Maeander (FR)
93 **PACIFIC ISLANDS (IRE)**, ch c Teofilo (IRE)—Tropical Lady (IRE)
94 **PALADIN (IRE)**, b g Dubawi (IRE)—Palwina (FR)
95 **PEMBREY**, b c Teofilo (IRE)—Miss Penton
96 **PERIPHERY (USA)**, b c Elusive Quality (USA)—Punctilious
97 **PIMPERNEL (IRE)**, b f Invincible Spirit (IRE)—Anna Pallida
98 **POLICE FORCE (USA)**, b c Street Sense (USA)—Land of Dreams
99 **PRINCE OF ORANGE (IRE)**, b c Shamardal (USA)—Cox Orange (USA)
100 **PUNITA (USA)**, ch f Distorted Humor (USA)—Indy Five Hundred (USA)
101 **PURPLE BAY (IRE)**, b c Dubawi (IRE)—Velvet Lady
102 **QUERNSTONE (USA)**, b g Smart Strike (CAN)—Sluice (USA)
103 **REBEL SONG (IRE)**, b c Refuse To Bend (IRE)—Dubai Opera (USA)
104 **REPRESENTATION (USA)**, ch c Street Cry (IRE)—Portrayal (USA)
105 **RUBAN (IRE)**, ch c Dubawi (IRE)—Piece Unique
106 **RUSLAND (IRE)**, b c Shamardal (USA)—Rosia (IRE)
107 **SALACIA (IRE)**, b f Echo of Light (IRE)—Neptune's Bride (USA)
108 **SAMBA KING**, b g Dubai Destination (USA)—Dance of Leaves
109 **SPECIFIC (IRE)**, b f Dubawi (IRE)—Miss Particular (IRE)
110 **SWEDISH SAILOR**, b c Monsun (GER)—Epitome (IRE)
111 **TACTFULLY (IRE)**, b f Discreet Cat (USA)—Kydd Gloves (USA)
112 **TAILORING (IRE)**, br c Dansili—Subtle Charm
113 **TROIS VALLEES (USA)**, b br c Elusive Quality (USA)—Chamrousse (USA)
114 **UNIVERSAL (IRE)**, ch c Dubawi (IRE)—Winesong (IRE)
115 **VEZZALI (USA)**, b br f Medaglia d'oro (USA)—Dirty Rush (USA)
116 **WINTER SUN (IRE)**, b c Cape Cross (IRE)—Bright Morning
117 **WITNESSED**, b f Authorized (IRE)—Magic Mission
118 **YAA SALAM**, ch c Any Given Saturday (USA)—Alizes (NZ)
119 **ZAEEM**, b c Echo of Light—Across (ARG)
120 **ZIP TOP (IRE)**, b c Smart Strike (CAN)—Zofzig (USA)

4

MR N. W. ALEXANDER, Glenrothes
Postal: **Kinneston, Leslie, Glenrothes, Fife, KY6 3JJ**
Contacts: PHONE **(01592) 840774** MOBILE **(07831) 488210**
E-MAIL kinneston@aol.com WEBSITE www.kinneston.com

1 **AMULREE**, 9, b m Dancing High—Harrietfield **Alexander Family**
2 **BUFFALO BALLET**, 6, b g Kayf Tara—Minora (IRE) **Alexander Family**
3 **CAPITAL VENTURE (IRE)**, 6, b g Moscow Society (USA)—
Benrue Adventure (IRE) **Mrs Ray Calder & Mrs Jan Scott**
4 **COMMERCIAL EXPRESS**, 11, b g Oscar (IRE)—Biddy Earley (IRE) **Alexander Family**
5 **FORCEFIELD**, 6, b g Kalanisi (IRE)—Force of Nature (USA) **Kinneston Racing**
6 **FOUR FIDDLERS (IRE)**, 7, br g Accordion—Folle Idee De Luz (FR) **Dan & Michelle Macdonald**
7 **HERE'S TO HARRY**, 5, b g Helissio (FR)—Harrietfield **Mrs R. C. Calder**
8 **ISLA PATRIOT**, 6, b g Silver Patriarch (IRE)—Salem Beach **Mrs P. M. Gammell**
9 **ISLA PEARL FISHER**, 9, br g Supreme Sound—Salem Beach **Mrs P. M. Gammell**

MR N. W. ALEXANDER—continued

10 **NORTHERN FLAME (IRE)**, 7, b g Luso—Gails Gift (IRE) **Alexander Family**
11 **OCARINA (FR)**, 10, b g Bulington (FR)—Alconea (FR) **Mrs R. C. Calder**
12 **PAPAMOA**, 7, gr g Terimon—Larksmore **The Papamoans**
13 **SEEKING POWER (IRE)**, 11, b g Supreme Leader—Seeking Gold (IRE) **Alexander Family**
14 **SYDNEY COVE (IRE)**, 6, b g Cape Cross (IRE)—First Fleet (USA) **Mrs L. A. Ogilvie**
15 **THE PADDY PREMIUM (IRE)**, 12, b g Glacial Storm (USA)—Miss Cripps (IRE) **Mr M. R. D. Fleming**

Other Owners: Mr Nicholas Alexander, Mr Jamie Alexander, Mrs Ray Calder, Ms Jane Cameron, Mrs Margaret M. Henderson, Mr Dan Macdonald, Mrs Jan Scott.

Conditional: Lucy Alexander. **Apprentice:** Lucy Alexander. **Amateur:** Mr Kit Alexander.

5

MISS LOUISE ALLAN, Newmarket
Postal: Flat 2, Brickfields Stud, Cemetery Hill, Exning, Newmarket, Suffolk, CB8 7JH

1 **FLYING TRUMP**, 5, b m First Trump—Cold Blow **Mrs K. E. Abel-Smith & Mr G. Belcher**
2 **PRESSTHEREDBUTTON**, 7, b m Deploy—Mid Day Chaser (IRE) **F. Allan**
3 **ROMPER STOMPER**, 11, b g Sir Harry Lewis (USA)—Joley Blake **A. M. Smith**
4 **ROYAL CITY**, 4, b g Val Royal (FR)—City Gambler **J. J. May**
5 **THEREDBALLOON**, 6, ch g Sulamani (IRE)—Sovana (FR) **F. Allan**

Other Owners: Mr G. A. G. Belcher, Mrs K. E. Collie.

6

MR JIM ALLEN, Tiverton
Postal: West Steart Farm, Stoodleigh, Tiverton, Devon, EX16 9QA

1 **BEACH RHYTHM (USA)**, 5, ch g Footstepsinthesand—Queen's Music (USA) **J. P. Allen**
2 **GLADSTONE (IRE)**, 4, b g Dansili—Rockerlong **J. P. Allen**

7

MR ERIC ALSTON, Preston
Postal: Edges Farm Stables, Chapel Lane, Longton, Preston, Lancashire, PR4 5NA
Contacts: **PHONE (01772) 612120 FAX (01772) 619600 MOBILE (07879) 641660**
E-MAIL eric1943@supanet.com

1 **BALLARINA**, 6, b m Compton Place—Miss Uluwatu (IRE) **Mrs P. O. Morris**
2 **BARKSTON ASH**, 4, b g Kyllachy—Ae Kae Ae (USA) **The Selebians**
3 **CEREJEIRA (IRE)**, 4, b f Exceed And Excel (AUS)—Camassina (IRE) **D. Mossop**
4 **DIMAN WATERS (IRE)**, 5, br g Namid—Phantom Waters **Buist, Long, Thompson**
5 **DOCTOR PARKES**, 6, b g Diktat—Lucky Parkes **J. Heler**
6 **FLIPPING**, 5, br g Kheleyf (USA)—Felona **R. S. E. Gifford**
7 **FOXY MUSIC**, 8, b g Foxhound (USA)—Primum Tempus **Mr G. M. & Mrs C. Baillie**
8 **KING OF EDEN (IRE)**, 6, b g Royal Applause—Moonlight Paradise (USA) **The Grumpy Old Geezers**
9 **SALLY'S SWANSONG**, 6, b m Mind Games—Sister Sal **Miss F. D. Fenley**
10 **SONG OF PARKES**, 5, b m Fantastic Light (USA)—My Melody Parkes **J. Heler**
11 **SPAVENTO (IRE)**, 6, gr m Verglas (IRE)—Lanasara **Whitehills Racing Syndicate**
12 **TENHOO**, 6, b g Reset (AUS)—Bella Bambina **Buist, Long, Thompson**
13 **VINTAGE GRAPE (IRE)**, 4, b f Exceed And Excel (AUS)—
Begin The Beguine (IRE) **Edges Farm Racing Stables Ltd**

THREE-YEAR-OLDS

14 **CHESTER ARISTOCRAT**, ch g Sakhee (USA)—New Light **Buist, Long, Thompson**
15 **KING OF PARADISE (IRE)**, b g Hurricane Run (IRE)—Silly Game (IRE) **P. G. Buist**
16 **LORD FRANKLIN**, ch g Iceman—Zell (IRE) **Liam & Tony Ferguson**
17 **RED BARON (IRE)**, b c Moss Vale (IRE)—Twinberry (IRE) **J. W. Stephenson**

TWO-YEAR-OLDS

18 **CANTARA**, b f 22/2 Piccolo—Damalis (IRE) (Mukaddamah (USA)) **Liam & Tony Ferguson**
19 **COLOURS OF NATURE**, b g 13/4 Lucky Story (USA)—Sweetly Sharp (IRE) (Daggers Drawn (USA))
20 **DON JUAN**, b g 7/5 Byron—Zell (IRE) (Lend A Hand) **Liam & Tony Ferguson**

MR ERIC ALSTON—continued

21 B g 29/3 Green Desert (USA)—Princess Ellis (Compton Place) **J. E. Jackson**
22 B g 13/2 Multiplex—Springtime Parkes (Medicean) **Mr Nigel Leadbeater Mrs Val Leadbeater**

Other Owners: Mr G. M. Baillie, Mrs C. Baillie, Mrs J. E. Buist, M. L. Ferguson, Mr C. A. Ferguson, M. S. Kelly, Mr N. G. Leadbeater, Mrs V. A. Leadbeater, Mr G. W. Long, Mrs A. Long, J. Thompson.

Assistant Trainer: Mrs Sue Alston

Jockey (flat): David Allan.

MR WILLIAM AMOS, Hawick
Postal: **Broadhaugh Farm, Newmill on Teviot, Hawick, Roxburghshire, TD9 0JX**
Contacts: **PHONE (01450) 850323 MOBILE (07810) 738149**

1 ALL FOR A BUZZ, 7, ch m Alflora (IRE)—G'ime a Buzz **Aitchison Amos Hall Stenhouse**
2 ALSO JO, 9, gr g Cloudings (IRE)—Forgotten Empress **Mrs S. Gray, Mr I. Gray**
3 BILLSGREY (IRE), 10, gr g Pistolet Bleu (IRE)—Grouse-N-Heather **John & Mary Stenhouse**
4 BOB'S DREAM (IRE), 10, b g Bob's Return (IRE)—Back In Kansas (IRE) **Kyle, Elliott & Crook**
5 BORDER FLORA, 7, br m Alflora (IRE)—Faucon **Mrs E. H. Aitchison**
6 BRIERYHILL BOY, 5, gr g Terimon—Bella Mary **Mr & Mrs D. S. Byers**
7 CHESTER RIDGE, 8, b g Alflora (IRE)—Scarlet Ember **Miss R. G. Brewis**
8 DANTE'S FROLIC, 4, b f Overbury (IRE)—Dusky Dante (IRE) **East-West Partnership**
9 EUROHUNTER (IRE), 8, b g Bishop of Cashel—Prestissimo **J. W. Stephenson**
10 FAIRLEE DUTCH, 5, gr m Fair Mix (IRE)—Dutch Dyane **J. L. Gledson**
11 JULIA TOO, 5, b m King's Theatre (IRE)—Candello **J. L. Gledson**
12 LIE FORRIT (IRE), 8, b g Subtle Power (IRE)—Ben Roseler (IRE) **Mr JW McNeill Mr C McNeill Ms L Gillies**
13 LOCHORE (IRE), 6, b g Morozov (USA)—Fulgina (FR) **Mr I. A. Gauld**
14 MALIBU DANCER (IRE), 4, b g Malibu Moon (USA)—Capilla Bonita (USA) **J. W. Stephenson**
15 NAMED AFTER NINA, 5, b m Helissio (FR)—Gilston Lass
16 NEVILLE WOODS, 5, b g Alflora (IRE)—Angie Marinie **J. L. Gledson**
17 PRINCE BLACKTHORN (IRE), 6, b g Desert Prince (IRE)—Notable Dear (ITY) **J. W. Stephenson**
18 RAVENSBILL (IRE), 10, b g Sea Raven (IRE)—Two Hills Folly (IRE) **John & Mary Stenhouse**
19 RINGAROUND, 7, b m Karinga Bay—Waffling **Imperial Racing Partnership**
20 ROLL OVER ROSE (IRE), 7, b m Beneficial—Rockport Rosa (IRE) **Six Men & Mare**
21 SCARLET RUBY, 5, ch m Grape Tree Road—Scarlet Ember **Miss R. G. Brewis**
22 TEVIOT LASS, 10, b m Minster Son—Here Comes Tibby **S. Bonney**
23 TURBO ISLAND, 7, b g Turbo Speed—Island Path (IRE) **C Davidson J Crichton L Burnett D Waugh**
24 VIVONA HILL, 8, b g Overbury (IRE)—Lets Go Dutch **Mrs F. Crone & Mrs V. Birnie**
25 WHAT A DREAM, 6, ch g Supreme Sound—Ben Roseler (IRE) **R. J. Kyle, D. & J. Byers**
26 WILLIE HALL, 8, b g Alflora (IRE)—G'ime a Buzz **R. H. Hall**

Other Owners: W. M. Aitchison, W. Amos, Mrs V. A. Birnie, Mrs L. M. Burnett, D. S. Byers, Mrs M. J. Byers, J. M. Crichton, Mrs F. H. Crone, Mr J. R. Crook, Mr C. Davidson, K. R. Elliott, Ms L. M. Gillies, Mr I. J. B. Gray, Mrs S. I. Gray, R. J. Kyle, J. W. McNeill, Mr J. C. McNeill, Mr W. J. Muir, I. Robinson, Mrs G. C. Robinson, A. Robson, Mr J. M. Stenhouse, Mrs M. Stenhouse, R. W. Thomson, Mr D. Waugh.

MR MICHAEL APPLEBY, Newark
Postal: **Stubby Nook Lodge Bungalow, Danethorpe Lane, Danethorpe, Newark, Nottinghamshire, NG24 2PD**
Contacts: **MOBILE (07884) 366421**
E-MAIL appleby477@aol.com

1 AGGBAG, 8, b g Fath (USA)—Emaura **M. Appleby**
2 AL SIRAT, 6, b g Josr Algarhoud (IRE)—Toleration **Julia Abrahams & Juliet Reed**
3 ART SCHOLAR (IRE), 5, b g Pyrus (USA)—Marigold (FR) **Mrs J. Scrivens**
4 ART THIEF, 4, b g Catcher In The Rye (IRE)—Eurolink Sundance **T. R. Pryke**
5 BALLINACUBBY LASS (IRE), 8, b m Poltarf (USA)—Ballinacubby Pride (IRE) **Mr D. J. Lewin**
6 BAY OF NAPLES (IRE), 4, b g Holy Roman Emperor (IRE)—Kalidasa (USA) **Zodiac Racing**
7 BEATING HARMONY, 4, b g Beat Hollow—Heart's Harmony **Dennis & Andy Deacon**
8 BERTIE BOO, 7, b g Where Or When (IRE)—Lucy Boo **Mr P. A. Voce**
9 BEYEH (IRE), 4, b f King's Best (USA)—Cradle Rock (IRE) **T. R. Pryke**
10 BRIDGETOWN, 4, gr g Beat All (USA)—Moon Magic **Woodhaven Stud**
11 CLAIMANT (IRE), 5, b g Acclamation—Between The Winds (USA) **Dallas Racing**
12 CORVETTE, 4, b f Araafa (IRE)—Clipper **Mr T. J. Cunnane**

MR MICHAEL APPLEBY—continued

13 **COUNTRY ROAD (IRE)**, 6, b g Montjeu (IRE)—Souffle **S. Hussain & P. O'Neill**
14 **ELEGANT MUSE**, 4, b f Fraam—Georgianna (IRE) **T. R. Pryke**
15 **FAVORITE GIRL (GER)**, 4, b f Shirocco (GER)—Favorite (GER) **T. R. Pryke**
16 **FROSTY RECEPTION**, 4, b f Iceman—Toleration **C. Greenall, M. Truan & J. Reed**
17 **HARDWICK BAY**, 6, ch m Karinga Bay—Silver Madam **P. G. Hepworth**
18 5, B g Alflora (IRE)—La Bella Villa **Kim Pugh**
19 **LIEUTENANT DAN (IRE)**, 5, b g Danroad (AUS)—Dakhira **M. Appleby**
20 **LOCKANTANKS**, 5, ch g Compton Place—Locharia **Dallas Racing**
21 **MECOX BAY (IRE)**, 5, b g Noverre (USA)—Birdsong (IRE) **Dallas Racing**
22 **MIDNIGHT FUN**, 7, b m Midnight Legend—More Laughter **M. Appleby**
23 **MINSKY MINE (IRE)**, 5, b g Montjeu (IRE)—Summer Trysting (USA) **T. R. Pryke**
24 **NHA TRANG (IRE)**, 5, b g Indian Danehill (IRE)—Baileys On Line **The Giggle Factor Partnership**
25 **NO DIAMOND**, 5, b g Helissio (FR)—Diamond Swan **Mrs V. Kinder**
26 **NORTHERN GENES (AUS)**, 6, b g Refuse To Bend (IRE)—Cotswold Dancer (AUS) **Mrs E. Morris**
27 **OSSIE ARDILES (IRE)**, 4, gr g Aussie Rules (USA)—Look Who's Dancing **Dallas Racing**
28 **PONTE DI ROSA**, 4, b f Avonbridge—Ridgewood Ruby (IRE) **Reed, Mould, Gorley & Spershott**
29 **PRONOUNCE**, 4, b g Denounce—Ivy Bridge (IRE) **J. Branson**
30 **REALITY SHOW (IRE)**, 5, b g Cape Cross (IRE)—Really (IRE) **Mr J. Singh**
31 **SIR IKE (IRE)**, 7, b g Xaar—Iktidar **Mrs J. Scrivens**
32 **ST IGNATIUS**, 5, b g Ishiguru (IRE)—Branston Berry (IRE) **Cheshire Elite Racing**
33 **THE LOCK MASTER (IRE)**, 5, b g Key of Luck (USA)—Pitrizza (IRE) **Kenneth George Kitchen**
34 **TYSOE LAD**, 4, br g Zafeen (FR)—Nicholas Mistress **P. G. Hepworth**
35 **VALENTINO SWING (IRE)**, 9, ch g Titus Livius (FR)—Farmers Swing (IRE) **Zodiac Racing**

THREE-YEAR-OLDS

36 **DEMORA**, b f Deportivo—Danzanora **Dallas Racing**
37 **DEREK THE DIAMOND**, b c Araafa (IRE)—West One **Mr T. J. Cunnane**
38 **DEWALA**, b f Deportivo—Fuwala **Dallas Racing**
39 **DUBAI RYTHM**, b c Echo of Light—Slave To The Rythm (IRE) **M. Appleby**
40 **FIRST GLANCE**, br g Passing Glance—Lady Santana (IRE) **Sarnian Racing**
41 **FLEETING FASHION**, b f Alhaarth (IRE)—Sempre Sorriso **P. J. & Mrs J. P. Haycock**
42 **FOURACRES**, ch f Firebreak—Capponicus (IRE) **Brooklands Racing**
43 **LOOKING TANNED**, b g Passing Glance—Tanning **Sarnian Racing**
44 **MAGGIE PINK**, b f Beat All (USA)—Top Notch **Mr A. W. Bult**
45 B g Tillerman—Magical Music **The Giggle Factor Partnership**
46 **OUR IVOR**, gr c Cape Town (IRE)—Caprice **J&G Bacciochi, A Taylor, Bruce W. Wyatt**
47 Ch f Araafa (IRE)—Puzzling
48 **SIOUXIES DREAM**, b f Zafeen (FR)—Lady de Londres **M. Appleby**
49 **STELLAR EXPRESS (IRE)**, b f Royal Applause—Aitch (IRE) **Mr & Mrs James Sumsion**
50 **TRESABELLA**, b f Firebreak—Bella Tutrice (IRE) **Brooklands Racing**

TWO-YEAR-OLDS

51 B c 1/4 Mount Nelson—Purple Rain (IRE) (Celtic Swing) **Matthew Sharkey**

Other Owners: Ms Julia Abrahams, Mr Michael Appleby, Mr J. Bacciochi, Mr Simon Ballard, Mr M. H. Bates, Mr A. D. Burke, Mr Dennis Deacon, Mr Andy Deacon, Mr J. Glassett, Mrs K. Glassett, Mr Mark A. Glassett, Mr Antony Gorley, Mr Christopher Greenall, Mr P.J. Haycock, Mrs J. P. Haycock, Mr James Holt, Mr S. Hussain, Mr D. S. Lovatt, Mrs A. M. Mercs, Mr Jeff Mould, Mr Paul O'Neill, Miss Juliet E. Reed, Miss D. Scragg, Mr Nigel Sennett, Mr David Spershott, Mr James Sumsion, Mrs Beth Sumsion, Michael Truan, Mr Bruce W. Wyatt.

Assistant Trainer: Mr Jonathan Clayton **Head Lad:** Jason Parkhouse

Jockey (flat): Neil Chalmers, Luke Morris, Robbie Fitzpatrick, Liam Jones. **Jockey (NH):** Will Kennedy, Rhys Flint. **Conditional:** Richie Killoran. **Apprentice:** Jack Duern. **Amateur:** Miss Leanne Masterton.

---

10 **MR DAVID ARBUTHNOT**, Dorking
Postal: **Henfold House Cottage, Henfold Lane, Beare Green, Dorking, Surrey, RH5 4RW**
Contacts: **PHONE (01306) 631529 FAX (01306) 631529 MOBILE (07836) 276464**
E-MAIL **dwparbuthnot@hotmail.com** WEBSITE **www.henfoldracing.co.uk**

1 **AATHER (IRE)**, 7, b g Key of Luck (USA)—Alkaffeyeh (IRE) **A. T. A. Wates**
2 **BEDARRA BOY**, 6, ch g Needwood Blade—Roonah Quay (IRE) **Mr P. M. Claydon**
3 **BOB RUN (IRE)**, 8, ch g Bob Back (USA)—Rith Ar Aghaidh (IRE) **Mr P. Fry & Miss S. Richards**
4 **CAROLE'S DESTINY**, 5, ch m Hernando (FR)—Carole's Crusader **Mr P. Murphy**

MR DAVID ARBUTHNOT—continued

5 **DON POOLEONI (IRE)**, 7, b g Catcher In The Rye (IRE)—Liss Rua (IRE) **The Dons**
6 **FEEL THE FORCE (IRE)**, 8, br g Presenting—Shipping News (IRE) **A. T. A. Wates**
7 **FIREITFROMYE (IRE)**, 7, b g Milan—Sweet Merenda (IRE) **Mr J. G. M. Wates & Mr A. T. A. Wates**
8 **GANDALFE (FR)**, 7, b br g Laveron—Goldville (FR) **A. T. A. Wates**
9 **HIGH VILLE (IRE)**, 6, b g Beneficial—Brenny's Pearl (IRE) **Mr Geoff Thompson**
10 **LEELU**, 6, b m Largesse—Strat's Quest **P. Banfield**
11 **ON BORROWED WINGS (IRE)**, 9, br g Quws—Ann's Pet **A. T. A. Wates**
12 **PREUTY BOY (FR)**, 7, b g Saint Preuil (FR)—Titian Queen **A. T. A. Wates**
13 **ROCKY ELSOM (USA)**, 5, b g Rock of Gibraltar (IRE)—Bowstring (IRE) **Mr J. G. M. Wates & Mr A. T. A. Wates**
14 5, Gr g Alderbrook—Rosafi (IRE) **Mr Fry & Mr P. Claydon**
15 5, B g Oscar (IRE)—Rose of Salome (IRE) **A. T. A. Wates**
16 **SHUIL ROYALE (IRE)**, 7, b g King's Theatre (IRE)—Shuil Na Lee (IRE) **Mr Phil Fry & Mr Geoff Thompson**
17 **SILVER DOLLARS (FR)**, 11, gr g Great Palm (USA)—Marie Olga (FR) **A. R. Parrish**
18 **STARLUCK (IRE)**, 7, gr g Key of Luck (USA)—Sarifa (IRE) **A. T. A. Wates**
19 **THE STRAWBERRY ONE**, 7, ch m Kadastrof (FR)—Peppermint Plod **Miss C. A. B. Allsopp**
20 **TOPOLSKI (IRE)**, 6, b g Peintre Celebre (USA)—Witching Hour (USA) **Mr P. M. Claydon**
21 5, Ch g Shantou (USA)—Warning Cry (IRE) **A. T. A. Wates**
22 **YESYOUCAN (IRE)**, 7, b g Beneficial—Except Alice (IRE) **A. T. A. Wates**

THREE-YEAR-OLDS

23 **TINGO IN THE TALE (IRE)**, b g Oratorio (IRE)—Sunlit Skies **G. S. Thompson**

Other Owners: Mr Phil Fry, Mrs Denise Sheasby, Mr G. Thompson.

Jockey (NH): Daryl Jacob. **Conditional:** Ross Wishart, Tom Cannon.

---

11 **MR PETER ATKINSON, Northallerton**
Postal: **Yafforth Hill Farm, Yafforth, Northallerton, North Yorkshire, DL7 0LT**
Contacts: **PHONE (01609) 772598 MOBILE (07751) 131215**

1 **CROCO BAY (IRE)**, 5, b g Croco Rouge (IRE)—April Thistle (IRE) **Mr P. G. Atkinson**
2 **SPARKLING HAND**, 6, b m Lend A Hand—Sparkling Yasmin **Mr P. G. Atkinson**

Jockey (NH): Phil Kinsella.

---

12 **MR MICHAEL ATTWATER, Epsom**
Postal: **Tattenham Corner Stables, Tattenham Corner Road, Epsom Downs, Surrey, KT18 5PP**
Contacts: **PHONE (01737) 360066 MOBILE (07725) 423633**
E-MAIL **Attwaterracing@hotmail.co.uk** WEBSITE **www.attwaterracing.com**

1 **AIN'T TALKIN'**, 6, ch g Zaha (CAN)—Royal Ivy **Canisbay Bloodstock**
2 **ALL WE KNOW**, 8, b g Green Desert (USA)—Anniversary **Mr S. Byrne**
3 **BATTLEOFTRAFALGAR**, 5, b g Galileo (USA)—Pink Stone (FR) **Bagden Wood Building Services Limited**
4 **BEAT ROUTE**, 5, ch g Beat Hollow—Steppin Out **Canisbay Bloodstock**
5 **BRAVO ECHO**, 6, b g Oasis Dream—Bold Empress (USA) **Canisbay Bloodstock**
6 **CASTLEMORRIS KING**, 4, br c And Beyond (IRE)—Brookshield Baby (IRE) **Mr C. O'Connell**
7 **DISPATCH BOX**, 8, b g Dansili—Division Bell **Canisbay Bloodstock**
8 **GEORGE GURU**, 5, b g Ishiguru (USA)—Waraqa (USA) **T. M. Jones**
9 **HOLYFIELD WARRIOR (IRE)**, 8, b g Princely Heir (IRE)—Perugino Lady (IRE) **A. J Syndicate**
10 **L'HIRONDELLE (IRE)**, 8, b g Anabaa (USA)—Auratum (USA) **Canisbay Bloodstock**
11 **LYSSIO (GER)**, 5, b g Motivator—Lysuna (GER) **Bagden Wood Building Services Limited**
12 4, B f Royal Applause—Mo Stopher **Canisbay Bloodstock**
13 **PRINCE OF THEBES (IRE)**, 11, b g Desert Prince (IRE)—Persian Walk (FR) **Canisbay Bloodstock**
14 **PYTHEAS (USA)**, 5, b g Seeking The Gold (USA)—
Neptune's Bride (USA) **Bagden Wood Building Services Limited**
15 **QUEENIE'S STAR (IRE)**, 5, b m Arakan (USA)—Starway To Heaven (ITY) **The Attwater Partnership**
16 **SAHARIA (IRE)**, 5, b g Oratorio (IRE)—Inchiri **Brooklands Racing**
17 **SALIENT**, 8, b g Fasliyev (USA)—Savannah Belle **Canisbay Bloodstock**
18 4, Ch f Zamindar (USA)—Steppin Out **Canisbay Bloodstock**
19 **SUHAILAH**, 6, ch m Sulamani (IRE)—Vrennan **Canisbay Bloodstock**
20 **TIRADITO (USA)**, 5, b br g Tale of The Cat (USA)—
Saratoga Sugar (USA) **Bagden Wood Building Services Limited**
21 **TRAFALGAR SQUARE**, 10, b g King's Best (USA)—Pat Or Else **Canisbay Bloodstock**

MR MICHAEL ATTWATER—continued

22 **UNEX RENOIR**, 4, b c Nayef (USA)—Simacota (GER) **Bagden Wood Building Services Limited**
23 **YMIR**, 6, b g Zaha (CAN)—Anastasia Venture **Canisbay Bloodstock**

THREE-YEAR-OLDS

24 B f Sakhee (USA)—Anastasia Venture **Canisbay Bloodstock**
25 **AURENS (IRE)**, b g One Cool Cat (USA)—Al Aqabah (IRE) **B. Gubby**
26 B f Iceman—Steppin Out **Canisbay Bloodstock**
27 Ch f Doyen (IRE)—Vrennan **Canisbay Bloodstock**

Other Owners: Mr B. M. Attwater, Mr M. J. Attwater, Mr M. H. Bates, Mr R. F. Kilby, Mr D. S. Lovatt, Mrs A. M. Mercs, Miss Maureen Stopher.

Assistant Trainer: K. F. Latchford

Jockey (flat): Mark Coumbe. **Apprentice:** Aaron Chave.

---

13 **MR NICK AYLIFFE, Minehead**
Postal: Glebe Stables, Little Ham, Winsford, Minehead, Somerset, TA24 7JH
Contacts: **PHONE (01643) 851265 MOBILE (07975) 657839**

1 **HOLDEN CAULFIELD (IRE)**, 7, b g Catcher In The Rye (IRE)—God Speed Her **R. Allatt**
2 **SHUFFLEWING (IRE)**, 5, ch m Sakhee (USA)—Hen Harrier **D. T. Hooper**
3 **SI BIEN (FR)**, 7, b g Solon (GER)—Secret Gold (GER) **Hooper, Barrett, Young & Brown**
4 **STELLAR CAUSE (USA)**, 6, ch g Giant's Causeway (USA)—Stellar (USA) **Mrs M A Barrett & Mr David Mileham**
5 **TRANSVESTITE (IRE)**, 10, b g Trans Island—Christoph's Girl **Barrett, Winzer, Brown & Saunders**
6 5, B g Oscar (IRE)—Winter Break (IRE) **D. Jones**

Other Owners: Mrs M. A. Barrett, Mrs K. Brown, Mr D. T. Hooper, Mr David Mileham, Mr A. Saunders, Mr G. Winzer, Mrs J. J. Young.

---

14 **MR ALAN BAILEY, Newmarket**
Postal: Cavendish Stables, Hamilton Road, Newmarket, Suffolk, CB8 7JQ
Contacts: **PHONE (01638) 664546 FAX (01638) 664546 MOBILE (07808) 734223**
WEBSITE www.alanbaileyracing.co.uk

1 **BARBICAN**, 4, b g Hurricane Run (IRE)—The Faraway Tree **Mr J. F. Stocker**
2 **DAZZLING VALENTINE**, 4, b f Oratorio (IRE)—Bedazzling (IRE) **The Glenbuccaneers**
3 **GRANNY MCPHEE**, 6, b m Bahri (USA)—Allumette **Middleham Park Racing XXVI & Alan Bailey**
4 **IMPRIMIS TAGULA (IRE)**, 8, b g Tagula (IRE)—Strelitzia (IRE) **Middleham Park Racing XLI & Alan Bailey**
5 **KIDLAT**, 7, b g Cape Cross (IRE)—Arruhan (IRE) **Mr J. F. Stocker**
6 **LOVES THEME (IRE)**, 4, ch f Iffraaj—Bauci (IRE) **R. Gomersall**
7 **MAZ**, 4, ch f Needwood Blade—Lady Mytton **AB Racing Limited**
8 **NEWBY LODGE (IRE)**, 4, b f Intikhab (USA)—Titans Clash (IRE) **A. J. H.**
9 **OUTPOST (IRE)**, 4, ch c Giant's Causeway (USA)—Southern Migration (USA) **Rathordan Partnership**
10 **SO IS SHE (IRE)**, 4, b f Kheleyf (USA)—River Beau (IRE) **A. J. McNamee**
11 **STRICTLY PINK (IRE)**, 4, b f Kodiac—Church Mice (IRE) **A. J. H.**
12 **TEWIN WOOD**, 5, ch g Zaha (CAN)—Green Run (IRE) **North Cheshire Trading & Storage Ltd**
13 **TURJUMAN (USA)**, 7, ch g Swain (IRE)—Hachiyah (IRE) **AB Racing Limited**

THREE-YEAR-OLDS

14 **BUBBLY BALLERINA**, ch f Footstepsinthesand—Pain Perdu (IRE) **The Champagne Club**
15 **BUBBLY BOUNTY**, b f Bahamian Bounty—Eljariha **The Champagne Club**
16 **STORMING BERNARD (USA)**, b br g Stormy Atlantic (USA)—Anguilla (USA) **Mr J. F. Stocker**
17 **STREET ANGEL (IRE)**, b f Kodiac—Perfectionist
18 **STRICTLY SILVER (IRE)**, gr c Dalakhani (IRE)—Miss Chaussini (IRE) **A. J. H.**
19 **SUDDEN WISH (IRE)**, b f Jeremy (USA)—Fun Time **M&R Refurbishments Ltd**

TWO-YEAR-OLDS

20 B c 17/2 Bertolini (USA)—Baddi Heights (FR) (Shirley Heights) (13333) **Mrs A Shone & Mrs V Hubbard**

MR ALAN BAILEY—continued

Other Owners: A. Bailey, Mr M. Heffernan, Mr H. Herne, Mrs V. Hubbard, Mr P. M. Murphy, T. S. Palin, M. Prince, Mr M. Quirke, Mrs M. Shone.

Assistant Trainer: Mrs J. P. Bailey

Apprentice: Natasha Eaton.

---

15 MRS CAROLINE BAILEY, Northampton

Postal: **37 Eastfield Road, Brixworth, Northampton, Northamptonshire, NN6 9ED**
Contacts: **PHONE (01604) 883729 (Home) (01604) 770234 (Yard) FAX (01604) 770423**
MOBILE (07831) 373340
E-MAIL caroline.bailey4@btinternet.com WEBSITE www.carolinebaileyracing.co.uk

1 **BATTLEFIELD BOB (IRE)**, 8, b g Bob's Return (IRE)—Comkilred (IRE) **G. T. H. Bailey**
2 **BOHEMIAN ROCK**, 8, b g Alflora (IRE)—Karolina (FR) **Mr W. Persse & Mr C. Flinton**
3 **BREAK THE CHAIN**, 6, b g Barathea (IRE)—Mesange Royale (IRE) **Mr & Mrs R. Scott**
4 **DERMATOLOGISTE**, 9, b m Kayf Tara—Poor Skin (IRE) **Mrs L. C. Taylor**
5 **EARL OF THOMOND (IRE)**, 7, b g Milan—Jodella (IRE) **Mr G Bailey & Mr A Wootton**
6 **GLOBAL FLYER**, 8, b g Sir Harry Lewis (USA)—Flicker **Mrs S. Carsberg**
7 **INDIAN RIVER (IRE)**, 7, b g Loup Sauvage (USA)—Wingfield Lady **G. T. H. Bailey**
8 **MAYOLYNN (USA)**, 6, ch m Johannesburg (USA)—Civilynn (USA) **Mr & Mrs R. Scott**
9 **MISS HILTON**, 6, gr m Silver Patriarch (IRE)—Emily-Mou (IRE) **A. S. Reid**
10 **MORNING MOMENT**, 10, b g Killer Instinct—Golf World (IRE) **C Flinton R Lloyd G Bailey**
11 **NOBLE LEGEND**, 5, b g Midnight Legend—Elmside Katie **Mr P. Dixon Smith**
12 **PRINCE DES MARAIS (FR)**, 9, b br g Network (GER)—Djeba Royale (FR) **C. W. Booth**
13 4, B f King's Theatre (IRE)—Queen's Leader **Mr R. Hunnisett**
14 **REFUSAL**, 4, b g Teofilio (IRE)—Frankie Fair (IRE) **A. S. Reid**
15 **THE LAODICEAN**, 6, b g Midnight Legend—Sea Pearl **G. T. H. Bailey**
16 **WHINSTONE BOY (IRE)**, 11, b g Supreme Leader—Deemiss (IRE) **Exit 36 Racing Club**

Other Owners: C. Flinton, Mr E. J. Franklin, Mr R. B. Lloyd, Mr W. W. Persse, R. Scott, Mrs P. M. Scott, Mr H. J. W. Tregoning, Mr A. L. Wootton.

Jockey (NH): Tom Messenger, Adam Pogson, Andrew Thornton. **Amateur:** Mr Jonathan Bailey.

---

16 MR KIM BAILEY, Cheltenham

Postal: **Thorndale Farm, Withington Road, Andoversford, Cheltenham, Gloucestershire, GL54 4LL**
Contacts: **PHONE (01242) 890241 FAX (01242) 890193 MOBILE (07831) 416859**
E-MAIL info@kimbaileyracing.com WEBSITE www.kimbaileyracing.com

1 **ABLE DEPUTY**, 5, b g Lomitas—Island Colony (USA) **Campbell Carter Osborne James Foylan**
2 **ALFIE WILLS**, 5, b g Alflora (IRE)—Inesse **Mr P. J. H. Wills**
3 **ALL FOR CASH**, 7, b g Alflora (IRE)—Mrs Moneypenny **Mrs P. A. Perriss**
4 **ALLFORMARY**, 6, b m Tobougg (IRE)—Bollin Rita **J. F. Perriss**
5 **BALLYWATT (IRE)**, 6, b g Kayf Tara—Lady Arpel (IRE) **Mrs V. W. H. Johnson**
6 **BASODA**, 9, b g Karinga Bay—Another Wag **Angie & Michael Storey**
7 **BISHOPHILL JACK (IRE)**, 6, b g Tikkanen (USA)—Kerrys Cross (IRE) **The On The Bridle Partnership**
8 **BONNE FEE**, 5, b m Karinga Bay—Jolika (FR) **Mrs Julie Martin & David R. Martin**
9 **BUFFALO BOB (IRE)**, 9, b g Bob's Return (IRE)—Back In Kansas (IRE) **The GFH Partnership**
10 **CHARLES**, 6, b g Loup Sauvage (USA)—Broom Isle **Mr T. D. Rowe**
11 **CHERRY LADY**, 5, br m Doyen (IRE)—Cullen Bay (IRE) **Mr C. H. Bothway**
12 **CHERRY VINE**, 6, b m Grape Tree Road—Rachel C (IRE) **Lucky Bin Racing**
13 **CINDERELLA ROSE**, 6, ch m Midnight Legend—Miniature Rose **Mrs N. Jones**
14 **DANCE TEMPO**, 5, b g Dansili—Musical Twist (USA) **A. N. Solomons**
15 **DARNA**, 6, b g Alflora (IRE)—Dutch Dyane **Mrs Julie Martin & David R. Martin**
16 **HANDSOME HARRY (IRE)**, 6, b g Broadway Flyer (USA)—Whistful Suzie (IRE) **Mrs E. A. Kellar**
17 **HARRY TOPPER**, 5, b g Sir Harry Lewis (USA)—Indeed To Goodness (IRE) **D. J. Keyte**
18 **JACALOU**, 7, b m Exit To Nowhere (USA)—Dalticia (USA) **Kim Bailey Racing Partnership III**
19 **KAFFIE**, 7, b m Kayf Tara—Galix (FR) **D. H. Morgan**
20 **LION ON THE PROWL (IRE)**, 8, b g Sadler's Wells (USA)—Ballerina (IRE) **Kim Bailey Racing Partnership II**
21 **LORD TOMNODDY**, 10, b g Tragic Role (USA)—Rosemoss **David Jenks**
22 **MALLUSK (IRE)**, 7, b g Exit To Nowhere (USA)—Saucy Nun (IRE) **A. N. Solomons**
23 **MARINESIDE (FR)**, 5, b g Enrique—Valgreen (FR) **Don Churston**

MR KIM BAILEY—continued

24 **MARK TWAIN (IRE)**, 5, b g Rock of Gibraltar (IRE)—Lady Windermere (IRE) **Mrs V. W. H. Johnson**
25 **MAX BYGRAVES**, 9, ch g Midnight Legend—Smokey Diva (IRE) **J. F. Perriss**
26 **MIDNIGHT HAZE**, 10, b g Midnight Legend—Gypsy Haze **Kim Bailey Racing Partnership**
27 **MIDNIGHT OSCAR (IRE)**, 5, br g Oscar (IRE)—Midnight Light (IRE) **The Oscar Partnership**
28 **MRS PEACHEY (IRE)**, 5, b m Brian Boru—Maracana (IRE)
29 **MULDOON'S PICNIC (IRE)**, 6, b g King's Theatre (IRE)—Going My Way **Mr C. A. Washbourn**
30 **MYSORTOFMAN**, 8, gr g Alflora (IRE)—Charlotte Gray **Mrs C. Bailey**
31 **NORTH STACK**, 6, ch g Alflora (IRE)—Mandy Chat (IRE) **Mrs Julie Martin & David R. Martin**
32 **OSCAR'S SECRET (IRE)**, 5, b g Oscar (IRE)—Black Flora (IRE) **Mrs J. Shipp**
33 **POLARBROOK (IRE)**, 5, br g Alderbrook—Frozen Cello (IRE) **Lucky Bin Racing**
34 **QUEENSWOOD BAY**, 6, b m Karinga Bay—Forest Maze **Woodcocks Racing Optimists**
35 **QUIET WHISPER (IRE)**, 6, b g Quiet American (USA)—Relish (IRE) **W. J. Ives**
36 **RANNOCH MOOR**, 5, b g Hernando (FR)—Stormy Weather **Mrs Mark Horne & Partners**
37 **RUBY CROWN**, 10, b m Rakaposhi King—Suilven **I. F. W. Buchan**
38 **SAVANT BLEU (FR)**, 6, ch g Agent Bleu (FR)—Avane Iii (FR) **Kim Bailey Racing Partnership III**
39 **SET IN HER WAYS (IRE)**, 6, b m Old Vic—Yes Your Honour **Have Fun Racing Partnership**
40 **SIRIUS CHESNUT**, 4, ch g Domedriver (IRE)—Heart **Have Fun Racing Partnership**
41 **SMOKEY GEORGE**, 7, ch g Kadastrof (FR)—Smokey Diva (IRE) **Mrs P. A. Perriss**
42 **THE RAINBOW HUNTER**, 8, b g Rainbow High—Sobranie **The Hon Mrs A. M. Cookson**
43 **TOP BENEFIT (IRE)**, 10, gr g Beneficial—Cottage Lass (IRE) **The H & H Partnership**
44 **TWELVE ROSES**, 4, ch g Midnight Legend—Miniature Rose **Jones Broughtons Wilson Weaver**
45 **VALENTO**, 7, ch g Noverre (USA)—My Valentina **Mr & Mrs Nigel Blackwell**
46 **VIKING RIDGE (IRE)**, 5, gr g Cloudings (IRE)—Lady Newmill (IRE) **J. W. Hardy**
47 **WEDGER PARDY (IRE)**, 11, b g Zaffaran (USA)—Raise The Bells **Lord Leigh**

Other Owners: Mr K. C. Bailey, Mrs Kim Bailey, Mr G. W. Bennett, Mr Michael J. Campbell, Mr J. De Lisle Wells, Mr Bill Foylan, Mr Ian C. Griffiths, Mr Chris Guy, Mrs Lisa Hall, Mr P. Hall, Mr Peter James, Mr N. R. Jennings, Mr P. S. Kerr, Ms Susan Livesey, Mrs Julie Martin, Mr David R. Martin, Mrs P. O. Perry, Mr B. Robbins, Miss C. Shipp, Mr A. N. Solomons, Mrs Sandra Steer-Fowler, Mr G. D. W. Swire, Mrs C. A. T. Swire, Mr Rob Withecombe.

Assistant Trainer: Mathew Nicholls

Conditional: Ed Cookson, Charles Greene. **Amateur:** Mr M. McIntyre.

---

17 **MISS EMMA BAKER, Cheltenham**
Postal: **Brockhill, Naunton, Cheltenham, Gloucestershire, GL54 3BA**
Contacts: **PHONE (01451) 851986 (Home) FAX (01451) 850199 MOBILE (07887) 845970**
E-MAIL emmajbakerracing@hotmail.co.uk

1 **BALLYDONAGH (IRE)**, 9, b g Accordion—Little Elk (IRE) **Mrs J. Arnold**
2 **CRACKERJACK**, 5, ch g Lahib (USA)—Tidesong **Mrs J. Arnold**
3 **FEN FARM**, 7, b g Luso—Regan (USA) **Mrs J. Arnold**
4 **MASTER CARDOR VISA (IRE)**, 7, br g Alderbrook—Princess Moodyshoe **Mrs J. Arnold**
5 **MIDNIGHT CHARMER**, 6, b g Midnight Legend—Dickies Girl **Mrs J. Arnold**
6 **PADDLEYOUROWNCANOE (IRE)**, 11, b g Saddlers' Hall (IRE)—
Little Paddle (IRE) **Miss E. J. Baker & Mrs J. Arnold**
7 **PETRARCHICK (USA)**, 5, b m Arch (USA)—Tustin (USA) **Mr P. G. Horrocks**
8 **SUBTLE APPROACH (IRE)**, 7, b g Subtle Power (IRE)—Rotoruasprings (IRE) **Mrs J. Arnold**
9 **TIGNELLO (IRE)**, 7, b g Kendor (FR)—La Genereuse **Mrs J. Arnold**

---

18 **MR GEORGE BAKER, Fordingbridge**
Postal: **Whitsbury Manor Racing Stables, Whitsbury, Fordingbridge, Hampshire, SP6 3QQ**
Contacts: **PHONE OFFICE: (01725) 518889 FAX (01725) 518747 MOBILE (07889) 514881**
E-MAIL gbakerracing@gmail.com WEBSITE www.georgebakerracing.com

1 **ANCIENT GREECE**, 5, b g Pivotal—Classicism (USA) **Inkin, Inkin, Byng, Baker & Partners**
2 **AQUA ARDENS (GER)**, 4, b g Nayef (USA)—Arduinna (GER) **M Khan X2**
3 **BALDADASH (IRE)**, 7, b g Beneficial—Balda Girl **Mr R. Cooper**
4 **BELGIAN BILL**, 4, b c Exceed And Excel (AUS)—Gay Romance **PJL, Cooper & Heath**
5 **BELLE DE FONTENAY (FR)**, 7, b m Spadoun (FR)—Friendly Hostess **George Baker & Partners**
6 **BENHEGO**, 7, ch g Act One—Sadaka (USA) **Mr G. Baker**
7 **BUGSY'S BOY**, 8, b g Double Trigger (IRE)—Bugsy's Sister **Seaton Partnership**
8 **CAPE MELODY**, 6, b m Piccolo—Cape Charlotte **M Khan X2**
9 **CONTRADIKTIVE (IRE)**, 6, b g Diktat—Additive (USA) **M Khan X2**

MR GEORGE BAKER—continued

10 DINNER GUEST, 6, b g Beat All (USA)—Come To Tea (IRE) Mrs C. E. Cone
11 DIVY (FR), 7, b g Highest Honor (FR)—Divination (FR) PJL Racing
12 FAIRMILE, 10, b g Spectrum (IRE)—Juno Marlowe (IRE) The Fairmile Partnership
13 GEORGE BAKER (IRE), 5, b g Camacho—Petite Maxine George Baker & Partners
14 GOOD OLD PAUL (IRE), 7, b g Snurge—La Kabyle (FR) Coleman, Wand, Baker Partnership
15 HUMIDOR (IRE), 5, b g Camacho—Miss Indigo M Khan X2
16 I'M FRAAM GOVAN, 4, ch g Fraam—Urban Dancer (USA) Sir Alex Ferguson
17 IF I HAD HIM (IRE), 8, b g City Honours (USA)—Our Valentine (IRE) Sir Alex Ferguson
18 IRONS ON FIRE (USA), 4, ch g Tale of The Cat (USA)—One and Twenty (USA) George Baker & Partners
19 JACK'S REVENGE (IRE), 4, br g Footstepsinthesand—Spirit of Age (IRE) PJL Racing
20 KLEBB (USA), 4, b g Aptitude (USA)—Single Market (USA) Mr C. Palmer
21 LITTLE COTTONSOCKS, 4, b f Sulamani (IRE)—Caytinga Mrs Sandra Fox
22 MARTYR, 7, bay g Cape Cross (IRE)—Sudeley PJL Racing
23 MAWSEM (IRE), 6, ch g Monsun (GER)—Irtifa The Mawsem Racing Partnership
24 MONDEGO (GER), 10, b g Big Shuffle (USA)—Molto In Forma (GER) Lady Forwood & Partners
25 MUCHMORDASH, 6, b m Tamure (IRE)—Dashing Executive (IRE) Mrs P. A. Scott-Dunn
26 NATIONAL HOPE (IRE), 4, b f Exceed And Excel (AUS)—Zandaka (FR) The No Hope Partnership
27 NOT SO SURE DICK (IRE), 7, b g Flemensfirth (USA)—
                                   The Peckaloo (IRE) Peter Earl, Lin Baker & Irene Paterson
28 OSCAR CLOSE (IRE), 7, br g Oscar (IRE)—Upham Close Mr W. Hennessey
29 QUEEN OF EPIRUS, 4, ch f Kirkwall—Andromache J. T. Brown
30 SERGEANT TROY (IRE), 4, gr g Aussie Rules (USA)—Et Dona Ferentes M Khan X2
31 SINBAD THE SAILOR, 7, b g Cape Cross (IRE)—Sinead (USA) Sir Alex Ferguson
32 THUNDERING HOME, 5, gr g Storming Home—Citrine Spirit (IRE) Mr G. Baker
33 TISH BAY, 6, ch g Karinga Bay—Tisho Mrs P. A. Scott-Dunn
34 WARNEFORD, 4, b g Dansili—Maramba M Khan X2
35 YENSI, 5, b m Doyen (USA)—Sifat Mr W. Hennessey

THREE-YEAR-OLDS

36 BEGGAR'S BANQUET (IRE), b c Dubawi (IRE)—Colour Splash MGH
37 BILLYRAYVALENTINE (CAN), b c Elusive Quality (USA)—
                                   Sweet and Careless (USA) Russell, Wheeler, Vail Partnership
38 B f Beat Hollow—Broken Romance (IRE) L. Lillingston
39 CHARLES TYRWHITT, b c Iffraaj—Riverside Dancer (USA) Wheeler, Russell, Vail Partnership
40 DANA'S PRESENT, ch g Osorio (USA)—Euro Empire (USA) Mr Mike Wilson & Mr Victor Chandler
41 DARK AGES (IRE), bl f Dark Angel (IRE)—Prosaic Star (IRE) A & J Racing Ltd
42 FINAL DELIVERY, b g Three Valleys—Bowled Out (GER) M Khan X2
43 GUNNER WILL (IRE), b g Le Vie Dei Colori—Ros The Boss (IRE) M M Racing
44 IT'S A GIRL THING (IRE), ch f Hurricane Run (IRE)—Princess Magdalena Gottaluvit Partnership
45 JAKE'S DESTINY (IRE), b g Desert Style (IRE)—
                                   Skehana (IRE) Delancey Real Estate Asset Management Limited
46 KING'S CIEL, ch g Septieme Ciel (USA)—King's Jewel Miss Z. Sims
47 MISSUS MILLS (IRE), ch f Notnowcato—Putout Mr Bob Cooper
48 MOUNT ST MISTRESS, ch f Zamindar (USA)—Capannina Mr William Asprey
49 PERCYTHEPINTO (IRE), b g Tiger Hill (IRE)—Tullawadgeen (IRE) Seaton Partnership
50 PIERS GAVESTON (IRE), b g Amadeus Wolf—Dancing Tempo Marcus Edwards-Jones & Friends
51 PLACE IN MY HEART, ch f Compton Place—Lonely Heart Turf Club 2010
52 POKER HOSPITAL, b f Rock of Gibraltar (IRE)—Empress Anna (IRE) The Look Look Partnership
53 PURPLE 'N GOLD (IRE), b c Strategic Prince—Golden Dew (IRE) M Khan X2
54 REFRESHESTHEPARTS (USA), ch f Proud Citizen (USA)—St Francis Wood (USA) Mr M. R. de Carvalho
55 RELENTLESS HARRY (IRE), gr c Excellent Art—Les Alizes (IRE) PJL Racing
56 SAHARAN AIR (IRE), ch g Hurricane Run (IRE)—Haute Volta (FR) M Khan X2
57 STEPTURN, b c Invincible Spirit (IRE)—Gay Gallanta (USA) R. J. Lorenz
58 SWEET OPHELIA, b f Shamardal (USA)—Showery Russell, Wheeler, Vail, Baker

TWO-YEAR-OLDS

59 BOOMSHACKERLACKER (IRE), gr c 16/3 Dark Angel (IRE)—Allegrina (Barathea (IRE)) (65000) PJL Racing
60 BUGSY'S BABE, ch f 20/4 Tobougg (IRE)—Oak Tree Miss (USA) (Woodman (USA)) Seaton Partnership
61 COLOUR THERAPY (IRE), b gr f 7/4 Verglas (IRE)—Colour Splash (Rainbow Quest (USA)) Invictus Racing
62 Gr f 11/5 Sakhee's Secret—Fluttering Rose (Compton Place) Lady Cobham & Mr Giles Irwin
63 B f 23/4 Rail Link—Gay Romance (Singspiel (IRE)) Wickfield Stud & Mr David Jenks
64 B f 18/3 Multiplex—Georgie The Fourth (IRE) (Cadeaux Genereux) (476) Mrs C. E. Cone
65 GEORGINA BAKER, b f 21/4 Camacho—Petite Maxine (Sharpo) (37000) George Baker & Partners
66 Ch f 19/2 Notnowcato—Gib (IRE) (Rock of Gibraltar (IRE)) Jeremy Gompertz
67 B c 9/4 Elusive City (USA)—It's Twilight Time (Royal Applause) (4000) George Baker & Partners

MR GEORGE BAKER—continued

68 B f 25/3 Bahamian Bounty—Madamoiselle Jones (Emperor Jones (USA)) (12000) **The Whitsbury Hopefuls**
69 NENGE MBOKO, b c 25/4 Compton Place—
Floppie (FR) (Law Society (USA)) (21000) **Russell, Wheeler, Vail, Conrad**
70 RUTHERGLEN, b c 27/3 Tiger Hill (IRE)—Hanella (IRE) (Galileo (IRE)) (40000) **F. Brady**
71 SECRET BEAU, gr c 13/2 Sakhee's Secret—Belle Reine (King of Kings (IRE)) (23809) **Mrs H. I. Slade**
72 B c 30/4 Lawman (FR)—Silver Bandana (USA) (Silver Buck (USA)) (22000) **Mr G. Baker**
73 SUTTON SID, ch c 7/3 Dutch Art—Drastic Measure (Pivotal) (49261) **Paul Bowden**

Other Owners: Mrs C. E. S. Baker, Mrs Lin Baker, Mr Danny Baker, Mrs Holly Bigmore, Mr James Bowditch, Mrs Angela Bray, The Earl Of Brecknock, Mr Robert Byng, Mr Victor Chandler, Mrs J. Clevely, Mr A. Coleman, Mr R. Cooper, Mr Patrick Delaney, Mr J. Dougall, Mr John Dwyer, Mr Peter Earl, Mr Marcus Edwards-Jones, Mrs Clare Evans, Mrs R. S. Evans, Mr Richard Evans, Mr D. Heath, Mr David Heath, Mrs Carvalho Heineken, Mr Brendan Holland, Miss L. Hurley, Mr Piers Inkin, Mrs Janet Jukes, Mr Diarmaid Kelly, Mr M. Khan, Mr Mustafa Khan, Mr Adam Knox, Mr Marcus Locock, Mr L. Lugg, Mr R. J. McAlpine, Mr Patrick Milmo, Mr & Mrs Jeremy Minchin, Mr Nat Parker, Mr Iraj Parvizi, Mr Nick Patsiledes, Mrs Ginny Pratt, Mrs Susan Roy, Mr W. A. B. Russell, Mrs Carolyn Russell, Mr D. I. Russell, Mr Ned Sangster, Mr T. Sheringham, Mr Edward Spurrier, Mr Robbie Streatfield, Mrs Kathleen Street, Mrs Sally Turnbull, Mr Tony Verrier, Mr Adam Wain, Mr Dan Wain, Mr & Mrs William Wallis, Mr Toby Wand, Mr W. S. Watt, Mr Michael Wilson, Yeomanstown Stud.

Assistant Trainers: Patrick Murphy, Valerie Murphy

Jockey (flat): Tony Culhane, Ted Durcan, Daragh O'Donohoe. **Jockey (NH):** Andrew Tinkler. **Conditional:** Trevor Whelan. **Apprentice:** Matthew Davies, David Kenny. **Amateur:** Mr J. Goss.

---

19 MR ANDREW BALDING, Kingsclere
Postal: **Park House Stables, Kingsclere, Newbury, Berkshire, RG20 5PY**
Contacts: **PHONE (01635) 298210 FAX (01635) 298305 MOBILE (07774) 633791**
E-MAIL admin@kingsclere.com WEBSITE www.kingsclere.com

1 ANGELIC UPSTART (IRE), 4, b g Singspiel (IRE)—Rada (IRE) **Mr B. Burdett**
2 ARABIAN STAR (IRE), 4, b g Green Desert (USA)—Kassiopeia (IRE) **Jackie & George Smith**
3 ASTRAGAL, 4, b f Shamardal (USA)—Landinium (ITY) **Lord J. Blyth**
4 BERNIE THE BOLT (IRE), 6, br g Milan—Chaparral Lady (IRE) **Mr B. P. McGuire**
5 BILLY BUTTONS, 4, gr g Act One—Dolce Thundera (USA) **W.V. & Mrs E.S. Robins**
6 CHIBERTA KING, 6, b g King's Best (USA)—Glam Rock **The Pink Hat Racing Partnership**
7 COMMUNICATOR, 4, b g Motivator—Goodie Twosues **Lady S. Davis**
8 DECENT FELLA (IRE), 6, b g Marju—Mac Melody (IRE) **One Carat Partnership**
9 DESERT LAW (IRE), 4, b c Oasis Dream—Speed Cop **J. C. Smith**
10 DREAMSPEED (IRE), 5, b h Barathea (IRE)—Kapria (FR) **J. C. Smith**
11 DUNGANNON, 5, b g Monsieur Bond (IRE)—May Light **I. G. Burbidge**
12 GOLD MINE, 4, b g Diktat—Memsahib **Sir Gordon Brunton**
13 HIDDEN VALLEY, 4, b f Haafhd—Spurned (USA) **Kingsclere Racing Club**
14 HIGHLAND KNIGHT (IRE), 5, b g Night Shift (USA)—Highland Shot **J. C. Smith**
15 I LOVE ME, 4, b f Cape Cross (IRE)—Garanciere (FR) **Mr N. N. Botica**
16 JOHN BISCUIT (IRE), 4, ch g Hawk Wing (USA)—Princess Magdalena **Dr P. J. Brown**
17 KAKATOSI, 5, br g Pastoral Pursuits—Ladywell Blaise (IRE) **Mr R. E. Tillett**
18 LAY TIME, 4, b f Galileo (IRE)—Time Saved **R. Barnett**
19 MEGAN'S MOTIVATOR, 4, ch g Motivator—Top Sauce **Mr E.M. Sutherland**
20 MOMENT OF TIME, 4, b f Rainbow Quest (USA)—Not Before Time (IRE) **R. Barnett**
21 NIGHT CARNATION, 4, ch f Sleeping Indian—Rimba (USA) **G. Strawbridge**
22 OPERA GAL (IRE), 5, b m Galileo (IRE)—Opera Glass **J. C. Smith**
23 PERFECT MISSION, 4, b g Bertolini (USA)—Sharp Secret (IRE) **Mildmay Racing & D. H. Caslon**
24 RAWAKI (IRE), 4, b g Phoenix Reach (IRE)—Averami **Kingsclere Racing Club**
25 SEA SOLDIER (IRE), 4, b g Red Ransom (USA)—Marajuana **Kingsclere Racing Club**
26 SIDE GLANCE, 5, br g Passing Glance—Averami **Pearl Bloodstock Limited**
27 SIRIUS SUPERSTAR, 4, b c Galileo (IRE)—Brightest **J. L. C. Pearce**
28 STAGE ATTRACTION (IRE), 4, b g Royal Applause—Mona Em (IRE) **Miss A. V. Hill**
29 TAPPANAPPA (IRE), 5, b g High Chaparral (IRE)—Itsibitsi (IRE) **McMahon/Gorell/Pausewang**
30 TARTAN TRIP, 5, b g Selkirk (USA)—Marajuana **Kingsclere Racing Club**
31 THELADYINQUESTION, 5, b m Dubawi (IRE)—Whazzat **D. H. Caslon & Mildmay Racing**
32 TULLIUS (IRE), 4, ch g Le Vie Dei Colori—Whipped Queen (USA) **Kennet Valley Thoroughbreds VI**
33 TWIN SOUL (IRE), 4, br f Singspiel (IRE)—Kirk Wynd **Mr N. N. Botica**
34 WHIPLASH WILLIE, 4, ch c Phoenix Reach (IRE)—Santa Isobel **J. C. & S. R. Hitchins**

MR ANDREW BALDING—continued

THREE-YEAR-OLDS

35 **AMPHORA**, b f Oasis Dream—Carafe **Highclere Thoroughbred Racing - Minoru**
36 **ARCHINA (IRE)**, b f Arch (USA)—Cross Your Fingers (USA) **Dr P. J. Brown**
37 **AUNTIE MABEL**, b f Tagula (IRE)—Vive La Chasse (IRE) **Kingsclere Racing Club**
38 **AUTUMN FIRE**, b f Avonbridge—Brand **Her Majesty The Queen**
39 **BACKTRADE (IRE)**, b g Holy Roman Emperor (IRE)—Braari (USA) **Birkdale Racing Syndicate**
40 **BANA WU**, ch f Shirocco (GER)—My Way (IRE) **G. B. Russell**
41 **BANK BONUS**, b g Motivator—Small Fortune **Her Majesty The Queen**
42 **BASINGSTOKE (IRE)**, b c Elusive City (USA)—Ryninch (IRE) **Kingsclere Racing Club**
43 **BEAU DUKE (IRE)**, b g Bachelor Duke (USA)—Xema **The Ten Gallon Partnership I**
44 **BENZANNO (IRE)**, b g Refuse To Bend (IRE)—Crossanza (IRE) **Martin & Valerie Slade & Partner**
45 **BIG NOTE (IRE)**, b c Amadeus Wolf—Double Vie (IRE) **Mr N. N. Botica**
46 **BONFIRE**, b c Manduro (GER)—Night Frolic **Highclere Thoroughbred Racing - Pocahontas**
47 **BYPASS**, br f Passing Glance—Florida Heart **Kingsclere Racing Club**
48 **CADES REEF (IRE)**, gr g Dalakhani (IRE)—Just Special **Mick and Janice Mariscotti**
49 **CAITLIN**, b f Dylan Thomas (IRE)—Kassiopeia (IRE) **Jackie & George Smith**
50 **CAPE CROSSING**, br f Cape Cross (IRE)—Dame Hester (IRE) **Mildmay Racing & D. H. Caslon**
51 **CARMEN'S CONCERTO**, b f Singspiel (IRE)—Lady McNair **J. M. Brown**
52 **CHERRY STREET**, b c Alhaarth (IRE)—Weqaar (USA) **James/Michaelson/Greenwood 1**
53 **DANCE WITH ME (IRE)**, b g Danehill Dancer (IRE)—
                        Perpetual Time **Mr & Mrs R. Gorell / Mr & Mrs P. Pausewang**
54 **DANDY (GER)**, b c Nayef (USA)—Diacada (GER) **Mr R. E. Tillett**
55 **DISTANT LOVE (IRE)**, b f Halling (USA)—Conference (IRE) **Mr L. L. Register**
56 **DOLLAR BILL**, ch g Medicean—Jardin **Mrs C. L. Kyle**
57 **DUTCH MASTER**, b g Dutch Art—Duena **Mr A. N. Brooke Rankin**
58 **EMPEROR VESPASIAN**, b g Royal Applause—Flavian **The Emperor Syndicate**
59 **EXPENSE CLAIM (IRE)**, b g Intikhab (USA)—Indolente (IRE) **Another Bottle Racing 2**
60 **FINE RESOLVE**, b g Refuse To Bend (IRE)—Papillon de Bronze (IRE) **Lord J. Blyth**
61 **FLAXEN FLARE (IRE)**, ch g Windsor Knot (IRE)—Golden Angel (USA) **Kennet Valley Thoroughbreds VIII**
62 **FORTROSE ACADEMY (IRE)**, b c Iceman—Auspicious **Mr E.M. Sutherland**
63 **GOLDONI (IRE)**, ch g Dylan Thomas (IRE)—Lasso **Mick and Janice Mariscotti**
64 **HALLINGS COMET**, ch c Halling (USA)—Landinium (ITY) **Lord J. Blyth**
65 **HINT OF MINT**, b f Passing Glance—Juno Mint **Mrs J. S. Newton**
66 **INTRANSIGENT**, b g Trans Island—Mara River **Kingsclere Racing Club**
67 **JUST WHEN**, b c Dalakhani (IRE)—Cape Grace (IRE) **G. Strawbridge**
68 **LOVE TATOO (IRE)**, b f Acclamation—Kapria (FR) **Can't Do 10st Partnership**
69 **MAGMA**, b f Singspiel (IRE)—Rakata (USA) **H. Robinson**
70 **MARIET**, ch f Dr Fong (USA)—Medway (IRE) **Pollards Stables**
71 **MICQUUS (IRE)**, b g High Chaparral (IRE)—My Potters (USA) **Shooting Star Racing**
72 **MINIMISE RISK**, b c Galileo (IRE)—Dararita (IRE) **Mrs F. H. Hay**
73 **MISS CAP ESTEL**, b f Hernando (FR)—Miss Cap Ferrat **J. L. C. Pearce**
74 **MYSTERIOUS MAN (IRE)**, b c Manduro (GER)—Edabiya (IRE) **Mr & Mrs R. Gorell / Mr & Mrs P. Pausewang**
75 **NATASHA ROSTOVA**, b f Beat Hollow—Putuna **J. C. & S. R. Hitchins**
76 **NORTHERN OUTLOOK**, b c Selkirk (USA)—Casual Glance **Kingsclere Racing Club**
77 **OCEANA DREAMER (IRE)**, b c Oasis Dream—Arbella **The C H F Partnership**
78 **OMAR KHAYYAM**, b c Pivotal—Kithanga (IRE) **J. L. C. Pearce**
79 **OPEN WATER (FR)**, b c Orpen (USA)—So Stream (ITY) **Thurloe Thoroughbreds XXVI**
80 **PARQUE ATLANTICO**, b br g Piccolo—Silken Dalliance **The C H F Partnership**
81 **PERFECT RESPONSE**, b f Royal Applause—Perfect Solution (IRE) **Mildmay Racing**
82 **PRICE LIST (USA)**, b f Red Ransom (USA)—Film Script **Her Majesty The Queen**
83 **PROFIT AGAIN (IRE)**, b c Tagula (IRE)—Baileys First (IRE) **Another Bottle Racing 2**
84 **QUEEN'S STAR**, ch f With Approval (CAN)—Memsahib **Sir Gordon Brunton**
85 **RAHY'S PROMISE (USA)**, ch c Rahy (USA)—Promise Me This **Mr E.M. Sutherland**
86 **RENEGOTIATE**, ch g Trade Fair—L'extra Honor (USA) **Birkdale Racing Syndicate**
87 **RESTAURATEUR (IRE)**, b c Excellent Art—Velvet Appeal (IRE) **Brook Farm Bloodstock**
88 **ROCKY REEF**, b c Danbird (AUS)—Leah's Pride **I. A. Balding**
89 **ROSERROW**, ch c Beat Hollow—Sabah **Sir R. J. Buckley**
90 **SEA ANEMONE**, b f Phoenix Reach (IRE)—Seaflower Reef (IRE) **Kingsclere Racing Club**
91 **SHOT IN THE DARK (IRE)**, ch g Dr Fong (USA)—Highland Shot **J. C. Smith**
92 **SILVER SAMBA**, gr f Dalakhani (IRE)—Fancy Dance **BA Racing**
93 **SIR QUINTIN (IRE)**, b g Dixie Union (USA)—No Frills (IRE) **Dr P. J. Brown**
94 **SPIRITUAL STAR (IRE)**, b c Soviet Star (USA)—Million Spirits (IRE) **Thurloe Thoroughbreds XXIX**
95 **STATURE (IRE)**, b g Montjeu (IRE)—Pescia (IRE) **Mr N. N. Botica**
96 **STIRRING BALLAD**, ch f Compton Place—Balnaha **G. Strawbridge**
97 **SUNNY BANK**, b c Notnowcato—Sweet Mandolin **J. C., J R & S. R. Hitchins**

MR ANDREW BALDING—continued

  98 **SWAN SONG**, br f Green Desert (USA)—Lochsong **J. C. Smith**
  99 **SWEET LIBERTA (IRE)**, b f Cape Cross (IRE)—Hendrina (IRE) **Mick and Janice Mariscotti**
100 **TAGLIETELLE**, b g Tagula (IRE)—Averami **Kingsclere Racing Club**
101 **TOP COP**, b c Acclamation—Speed Cop **J. C. Smith**
102 **TOPANGA CANYON**, b g Nayef (USA)—Classical Dancer **Mick and Janice Mariscotti**
103 **UNDERWRITTEN**, b g Authorized (IRE)—Grain of Gold **R. Barnett**
104 **VISCOUNT VERT (IRE)**, br g Kheleyf (USA)—Viscountess Brave (IRE) **Martin & Valerie Slade**
105 **VIVACIOUS WAY**, b f Holy Roman Emperor (IRE)—Dance Lively (USA) **Mrs J. Chandris**

TWO-YEAR-OLDS

106 **ABSOLUTELY SO (IRE)**, b c 14/1 Acclamation—Week End (Selkirk (USA)) (230000) **Jackie & George Smith**
107 Ch f 6/5 Dylan Thomas (IRE)—Almarai (USA) (Vaguely Noble) (15000) **R. Wilmot-Smith**
108 B c 4/4 Lucarno (USA)—Balnaha (Lomond (USA)) **G. Strawbridge**
109 B c 8/4 Holy Roman Emperor (IRE)—Blue Iris (Petong) (114941) **Dr P. Brown**
110 Ch c 21/2 Pivotal—Blue Siren (Bluebird (USA)) **J. C. Smith**
111 **BUONA FORTUNA**, b f 18/3 Oasis Dream—
                          Sadie Thompson (IRE) (King's Best (USA)) (55000) **Mick and Janice Mariscotti**
112 B f 14/3 Phoenix Reach (IRE)—Casual Glance (Sinndar (IRE)) **Kingsclere Racing Club**
113 Ch c 8/4 Phoenix Reach (IRE)—Comtesse Noire (CAN) (Woodman) (7000) **Brick Racing**
114 **CUISINE (IRE)**, b c 1/4 Holy Roman Emperor (IRE)—
                          Samorra (IRE) (In The Wings) (40000) **Brook Farm Bloodstock**
115 **DAYLIGHT**, ch c 10/2 Firebreak—Dayville (USA) (Dayjur (USA)) (70000) **Kennet Valley Thoroughbreds V**
116 **DESERT DONKEY**, b c 25/1 Acclamation—Honky Tonk Sally (Dansili) (34481) **G. A. D. Partnership**
117 **DOCTOR'S GIFT**, b c 14/2 Motivator—Josie May (USA) (Aljabr (USA)) **D. E. Brownlow**
118 B c 27/4 Refuse To Bend (IRE)—Dona Royale (IRE) (Darshaan) (18882) **Mr P. Brend & Mr J. Dwyer**
119 Ch f 20/3 Rock of Gibraltar (IRE)—Etizaan (IRE) (Unfuwain (USA)) (16420) **Mrs F. H. Hay**
120 B f 11/2 Sakhee (USA)—Exorcet (FR) (Selkirk (USA)) **J. C. Smith**
121 Ch c 10/3 Singspiel (IRE)—Flamjica (USA) (Real Quiet (USA)) **Cadagan Partnership**
122 Br c 2/3 Passing Glance—Florida Heart (First Trump) **Kingsclere Racing Club**
123 B br f 28/4 Red Clubs (IRE)—Guajira (IRE) (Mtoto) (38000) **Kennet Valley Thoroughbreds**
124 B f 29/4 Sakhee's Secret—Harryana (Efisio) (21904) **Hot To Trot Racing Club**
125 **HAVANA BEAT (IRE)**, b c 2/3 Teofilo (IRE)—
                          Sweet Home Alabama (IRE) (Desert Prince (IRE)) (65000) **Mick and Janice Mariscotti**
126 **HERE COMES WHEN (IRE)**, b c 29/4 Danehill Dancer (IRE)—
                          Quad's Melody (USA) (Spinning World (USA)) (139572) **Mrs F. H. Hay**
127 B f 9/4 Teofilo (IRE)—Island Destiny (Kris) (22000) **C. H. F. Partnership**
128 B c 26/4 Passing Glance—Juno Mint (Sula Bula) **Mrs J. S. Newton**
129 **LIZZIE TUDOR**, ch f 16/3 Tamayuz—Silca Destination (Dubai Destination (USA)) (30000) **Ms K. Gough**
130 B c 24/4 Acclamation—Lyca Ballerina (Marju (IRE)) (109523) **Highclere Thoroughbred Racing-JohnPorter**
131 Ch f 3/4 Manduro (GER)—Marika (Marju (IRE)) (50000) **Mr & Mrs R Gorell / Mr & Mrs P Pausewang**
132 **MARTIAL ART (IRE)**, ch c 9/4 Compton Place—
                          Brush Strokes (Cadeaux Genereux) (26000) **Jackie & George Smith**
133 **MELVIN THE GRATE (IRE)**, b c 20/4 Danehill Dancer (IRE)—Hawala (IRE) (Warning) (200000) **Mrs F. H. Hay**
134 **MUSIKHANI**, b f 15/2 Dalakhani (IRE)—Musicanna (Cape Cross (IRE)) (72000) **Mrs K. Holmes**
135 **NELLIE FORBUSH**, b f 28/1 Phoenix Reach (IRE)—Santa Isobel (Nashwan (USA)) J. C. & S. R. Hitchins
136 B f 26/1 Royal Applause—Never A Doubt (Night Shift (USA)) (260000) **Jackie & George Smith**
137 **NEW FFOREST**, b f 3/4 Oasis Dream—Ffestiniog (IRE) (Efisio) **Elite Racing**
138 B c 11/4 Montjeu (IRE)—No Frills (IRE) (Darshaan) **Dr P. J. Brown**
139 **NOT RIGG (USA)**, b c 23/1 Henrythenavigator (USA)—
                          St Helens Shadow (USA) (Septieme Ciel (USA)) (95000) **Mrs F. H. Hay**
140 **OASIS SPIRIT**, b f 22/3 Oasis Dream—Fearless Spirit (USA) (Spinning World (USA)) **G. S. Strawbridge**
141 B f 14/3 Sir Percy—Oblige (Robellino (USA)) (17240) **Birkdale Racing**
142 B c 24/4 High Chaparral (IRE)—Palatine Dancer (IRE) (Namid) (45000) **Thurloe Thoroughbreds**
143 **PEARL BOUNTY (IRE)**, ch c 14/2 Bahamian Bounty—
                          Roslea Lady (IRE) (Alhaarth (IRE)) (120000) **Pearl Bloodstock Limited**
144 **PEARL CASTLE (IRE)**, b c 14/1 Montjeu (IRE)—
                          Ghurra (USA) (War Chant (USA)) (150000) **Pearl Bloodstock Limited**
145 Ch c 21/2 Halling (USA)—Perfect Treasure (IRE) (Night Shift (USA)) **Mildmay Bloodstock**
146 B f 9/2 Zamindar (USA)—Pure Song (Singspiel (IRE)) **R. Barnett**
147 **RACE AND STATUS (IRE)**, b c 3/2 Raven's Pass (USA)—
                          Love Excelling (FR) (Polish Precedent (USA)) (240000) **Jackie & George Smith**
148 **REFECTORY (IRE)**, b c 23/5 Danehill Dancer (IRE)—
                          Akuna Bay (USA) (Mr Prospector (USA)) (61576) **Brook Farm Bloodstock**
149 Ch c 22/3 Kyllachy—Reputable (Medicean) (59112) **Dr P. Brown**
150 B f 15/3 Passing Glance—Sankaty Light (USA) (Summer Squall (USA)) (476) **Kingsclere Racing Club**

MR ANDREW BALDING—continued

151 B f 11/3 Invincible Spirit (IRE)—Scripture (IRE) (Sadler's Wells (USA)) (57470) **Dr P. Brown**
152 Br c 2/3 Footstepsinthesand—
               Shenkara (IRE) (Night Shift (USA)) (45000) **Mr & Mrs R Gorell / Mr & Mrs P Pausewang**
153 SIGNATURE DISH (IRE), b f 12/1 Galileo (IRE)—Magic Carpet (IRE) (Danehill (USA)) **Brook Farm Bloodstock**
154 B f 14/3 Piccolo—Silken Dalliance (Rambo Dancer (CAN)) (476) **C. H. F. Partnership**
155 SOVIET ROCK (IRE), b c 25/3 Rock of Gibraltar (IRE)—
                     Anna Karenina (USA) (Atticus (USA)) (180000) **Jackie & George Smith**
156 B c 12/4 Shirocco (GER)—
               Special Touch (IRE) (Spinning World (USA)) (35000) **James / Michaelson / Greenwood 1**
157 B c 17/2 Oasis Dream—Speed Cop (Cadeaux Genereux) **J. C. Smith**
158 STORMING (IRE), b c 5/5 Stormy Atlantic (USA)—French Lady (NZ) (Entrepreneur) (28735) **CJJR Partnership**
159 SUBTLE DIFFERENCE, b f 19/3 Vita Rosa (JPN)—Sulitelma (USA) (The Minstrel (CAN)) **K. Rausing**
160 B f 22/3 Beat Hollow—Sweet Mandolin (Soviet Star (USA)) **J. C., J. R. & S. R. Hitchins**
161 THE WIZARD OF AUS (IRE), b c 2/3 Aussie Rules (USA)—
               Dyness (USA) (Dynaformer (USA)) (32000) **The Pink Star Racing Partnership**
162 Ch f 27/3 New Approach (IRE)—Time Away (IRE) (Darshaan) (100000) **R. Barnett**
163 B c 27/3 Halling (USA)—Ushindi (IRE) (Montjeu (IRE)) (35000) **Mr P. Brend & Mr J. Dwyer**
164 VAN PERCY, b c 24/4 Sir Percy—
               Enforce (USA) (Kalanisi (IRE)) (27000) **Mrs L. E. Ramsden & Richard Morecombe**
165 VICKSBURG, b f 3/4 Cape Cross (IRE)—Totality (Dancing Brave (USA)) (50000) **Mr R. J. C. Wilmot-Smith**
166 WALTER WHITE (IRE), b c 11/4 Dark Angel (IRE)—Fun Time (Fraam) (30476) **G. A. D. Partnership**
167 ZANETTO, b c 9/2 Medicean—Play Bouzouki (Halling (USA)) (40000) **Mick and Janice Mariscotti**

Other Owners: Mr Richard Starczewski, Mrs C. S. Whitaker, Mr I. A. Balding, Mr Richard Wilmot-Smith, Mr D. H. Back, Mrs I. A. Balding, Mr Paul Blaydon, Mr Peter Box, Mr John Bridgman, Mr John Bromfield, Mr D. H. Caslon, Mr P. Coates, Mr Paul Darling, Mr E. Dedman, Dr Bridget Drew, Mr John Drew, Mr P. E. Felton, Mr K. H. Fischer, Mr C. H. Fischer, Mr R. Gorell, Mrs W. Gorell, Mr P. Green, Mr B. Greenwood, Mr Peter W. Haddock, Mr P. G. L. Hall, Mrs S. Harding, Mr N. G. R. Harris, The Hon H. Herbert, Highclere Thoroughbred Racing Ltd, Mr J. C. Hitchins, Mr J. Hitchins, Mr S. R. Hitchins, Mr G. R. Ireland, Ms S. Johnson, Mr Bob Knight, Mr Luke Lillingston, Mr Mick Mariscotti, Mrs Janice Mariscotti, Mr P. C. McMahon, Mrs J. A. McMahon, Mr R. P. B. Michaelson, Mr G. Middlebrook, Mrs L. Middlebrook, Mr J. G. Moore, Mr D. Nicholson, Mr Peter Pausewang, Mrs Peter Pausewang, Mr O. J. W. Pawle, Miss N. J. Randall, Mrs P. A. Reading, Mr G. E. J. Reading, Mr W. V. Robins, Mrs Shirley Robins, Mr N. J. F. Robinson, Mr J. Rodosthenous, Mr D. M. Slade, Mrs V. J. M. Slade, Mrs G. A. E. Smith, Mr G. A. E. Smith, Mr J. A. B. Stafford, Mr A. J. Viall.

Assistant Trainer: C. Bonner

Jockey (flat): Liam Keniry, David Probert, Neil Chalmers, Jimmy Fortune. **Apprentice:** Thomas Brown, Simon Pearce. **Amateur:** Mr A. Rawlinson.

MR JOHN BALDING, Doncaster

Postal: **Mayflower Stables, Saracens Lane, Scrooby, Doncaster, South Yorkshire, DN10 6AS**
Contacts: **HOME (01302) 710096 FAX (01302) 710096 MOBILE (07816) 612631**
E-MAIL j.balding@btconnect.com

1 IRISH LAW, 4, b g Redoubtable (USA)—Largs **Mayflower Syndicate**
2 POINT NORTH (IRE), 5, b g Danehill Dancer (IRE)—Briolette (IRE) **Mr W. Herring**
3 SECRET VIRTUE, 4, b f Iceman—Leominda **Mr P. Balding**
4 SLEEPY BLUE OCEAN, 6, b g Oasis Dream—Esteemed Lady (IRE) **Tykes & Terriers Racing Club**
5 THE MAGIC OF RIO, 6, b m Captain Rio—Good Health **J. E. Abbey**
6 THIS ONES FOR EDDY, 7, b g Kyllachy—Skirt Around **Mr W. Herring**

TWO-YEAR-OLDS

7 Ch c 2/4 Tobougg (IRE)—Homeoftheclassics (Tate Gallery (USA)) (3809) **Mr S. Massarella**

Other Owners: Mr K. Ackroyd, Mr Fred Aram, Mr M. V. Firth, Mrs Sharon O'Neil-Watters.

Assistant Trainers: Claire Edmunds, Jason Edmunds.

21 MR MICHAEL BANKS, Sandy
Postal: **Manor Farm, Manor Farm Road, Waresley, Sandy, Bedfordshire, SG19 3BX**
Contacts: **PHONE (01767) 650563 FAX (01767) 652988 MOBILE (07860) 627370**
E-MAIL waresleyfarms@btconnect.com

1 LOMBARDY BOY (IRE), 7, b g Milan—Horner Water (IRE) **M. C. Banks**
2 MAX LAURIE (FR), 7, bl g Ungaro (GER)—Laurie Mercurialle (FR) **Mrs R. L. Banks**
3 PLAY IT SAM, 6, b g Bahamian Bounty—Bombalarina (IRE) **M. C. Banks**
4 ROGUE DANCER (FR), 7, b g Dark Moondancer—Esperanza IV (FR) **M. C. Banks**
5 TRANSFORMER (IRE), 6, b g Trans Island—Lady At War **M. C. Banks**

22 MRS ALTHEA BARCLAY, Moreton-in-Marsh
Postal: **Fotherop, Oddington, Moreton-In-Marsh, Gloucestershire, GL56 0XF**
Contacts: **PHONE (01451) 830680 FAX (01451) 870572 MOBILE (07850) 729000**

1 GERRARD (IRE), 14, b g Jurado (USA)—Vienna Waltz (IRE) **Mrs A. Barclay**
2 QUAPRILAND (FR), 8, br m Dark Moondancer—Falkland III (FR) **Mrs A. Barclay**
3 RIVER EXIT (IRE), 5, b g Exit To Nowhere (USA)—Kilbricken Sunset (IRE) **Mrs A. Barclay**

23 MRS TRACEY BARFOOT-SAUNT, Wotton-under-Edge
Postal: **Cosy Farm, Huntingford, Charfield, Wotton-under-Edge, Gloucestershire, GL12 8EY**
Contacts: **PHONE (01453) 520312 FAX (01453) 520312 MOBILE (07976) 360626**

1 BARRY THE BARBER (IRE), 6, b g Flemensfirth (USA)—Dining Hall (IRE) **Six Of The Very Best**
2 PRESENTING DR T (IRE), 6, b g Luso—Halfway Home **T. Jewitt**
3 ROCKANDAHARDPLACE (IRE), 9, b g Rock Hopper—Field of Smiles (IRE) **A Good Days Racing**
4 ST MARYS HALL, 4, b g Librettist (USA)—Bella Cantata **A Good Days Racing**
5 TOP BOB (IRE), 7, b m Bob Back (USA)—Top Ar Aghaidh (IRE) **Mrs T. M. Barfoot-Saunt**

Other Owners: Mr G. C. Barfoot-Saunt.

Jockey (NH): Henry Oliver. Amateur: Mr Geoff Barfoot-Saunt.

24 MR MAURICE BARNES, Brampton
Postal: **Tarnside, Farlam, Brampton, Cumbria, CA8 1LA**
Contacts: **PHONE/FAX (01697) 746675 MOBILE (07760) 433191**
E-MAIL anne.barnes1@btinternet.com

1 ABOUT THYNE (IRE), 7, ch g Anshan—Down The Garden (IRE) **Mr K. Greenwell & Mr R. Briggs**
2 ACROSS THE TWEED (IRE), 6, b br g Alderbrook—Cash Chase (IRE) **J. W. Stephenson**
3 ATTYCRAN (IRE), 7, b g Snurge—Baltimore Lass (IRE) **Miss A. P. Lee**
4 BAMPTON BECKS, 6, ch g Supreme Sound—Suka Ramai **Evergreen Racing**
5 CURRAHEE, 8, b g Efisio—Dixie Favor (USA) **Abbadis Racing Club**
6 DORSET DORA, 4, b f Exit To Nowhere (USA)—Pems Gift **Mr W. J. Muir**
7 FOLLOW ON, 10, b h Barathea (IRE)—Handora (IRE) **M. A. Barnes**
8 GARLETON (IRE), 11, b g Anshan—Another Grouse **East-West Partnership**
9 GOODLUKIN LUCY, 5, ch m Supreme Sound—Suka Ramai **Evergreen Racing**
10 HOWIZEE, 6, gr g Baryshnikov (AUS)—Sendai **Mr G. Baird**
11 I'LL BE FRANK, 7, b g Fraam—Miss Opulence **Mr M. D. Townson**
12 L'EMINENCE GRISE (IRE), 5, gr g Kahyasi—Belle Innocence (FR) **East-West Partnership**
13 LOCKALANE, 5, b g Olden Times—Daylight Dreams **Miss A. P. Lee**
14 LYRICAL INTENT, 6, ch g Imperial Dancer—Magical Flute **Mr N. Haughan**
15 MY IDEA, 6, b g Golan (IRE)—Ghana (GER) **J. W. Stephenson**
16 ODDSMAKER (IRE), 11, b g Barathea (IRE)—Archipova (IRE) **M. A. Barnes**
17 OVERPRICED, 6, b m Chocolat de Meguro (USA)—Vacaria (SWI) **M. A. Barnes**
18 PAS TROP TARD (FR), 5, b g Caballo Raptor (CAN)—This Melody (FR) **East-West Partnership**
19 SAGA SURPRISE (FR), 7, b g Sagacity (FR)—Vacaria (SWI) **M. A. Barnes**
20 SOFT SPOKEN GUY (IRE), 9, b g Saddlers' Hall (IRE)—Pisa (IRE) **Mr Scott Lowther & The Whisperers**
21 STILL CALM, 8, b g Zamindar (USA)—Shining Water **M. A. Barnes**
22 STORMONT BRIDGE, 4, b g Avonbridge—Stormont Castle (USA) **Minstrel's Double Racing**
23 TOLEDO GOLD (IRE), 6, ch g Needwood Blade—Eman's Joy **J. W. Stephenson**
24 WATCHMEGO, 4, b f Supreme Sound—One Stop **M. A. Barnes**

MR MAURICE BARNES—continued

25 **WEETFROMTHECHAFF**, 7, gr g Weet-A-Minute (IRE)—Weet Ees Girl (IRE) **J. M. Carlyle**
26 **WESTENDJACK**, 5, b g Piccolo—Everdene

THREE-YEAR-OLDS

27 B g Zafeen (FR)—Flying Wind **East-West Partnership**
28 B g Dylan Thomas (IRE)—Keyaki (IRE) **East-West Partnership**
29 B f Fantastic View (USA)—Little Cascade **M. A. Barnes**
30 B br g Kheleyf (USA)—Millymix (FR) **East-West Partnership**

Other Owners: Mr M. A. Barnes, Mr R. H. Briggs, Mr C. Davidson, Mr J. H. Gibson, Mr J. G. Graham, Mr Keith Greenwell, Mr Robert Jackson, Mr S. G. Johnston, Mr Scott Lowther, Mr William Muir.

Assistant Trainer: Angela Barnes

Jockey (NH): Michael McAlister. **Conditional:** Stephen Mulqueen. **Amateur:** Miss Angela Barnes.

25
MR BRIAN BARR, Sherborne
Postal: **Tall Trees Stud, Longburton, Sherborne, Dorset, DT9 5PH**
Contacts: **PHONE (07826) 867881**
E-MAIL brianbarr2@hotmail.co.uk

1 **DON'T LOOK BACH (IRE)**, 7, b g Bach (IRE)—Buckalong (IRE) **Miss D. Hitchins**
2 **FLOWERBUD**, 7, b m Fantastic Light (USA)—Maidment **Miss D. Hitchins**
3 **FORGOTTEN PROMISE**, 5, b m Revoque (IRE)—Ivory's Promise **Miss D. Hitchins**
4 **SWISS ART (IRE)**, 6, b g One Cool Cat (USA)—Alpine Park (IRE) **Miss D. Hitchins**
5 **TOUCH OF STYLE (IRE)**, 8, b g Desert Style (IRE)—No Hard Feelings (IRE) **Miss D. Hitchins**
6 **VACARIO (GER)**, 8, br g Acatenango (GER)—Vaillance (GER) **Miss D. Hitchins**
7 **VILLAGE SECRET**, 6, ch g Pasternak—Daphne Odora **Miss D. Hitchins**

THREE-YEAR-OLDS

8 **SALEAL**, br g Gentleman's Deal (IRE)—Sales Flow **Miss D. Hitchins**

Assistant Trainer: Daisy Hitchins (07975) 754622

Conditional: Gary Derham, Darren O'Keeffe, Gavin Sheehan.

26
MR RON BARR, Middlesbrough
Postal: **Carr House Farm, Seamer, Stokesley, Middlesbrough, Cleveland, TS9 5LL**
Contacts: **PHONE (01642) 710687 MOBILE (07711) 895309**
E-MAIL christinebarr1@aol.com

1 **AL FURAT (USA)**, 4, b g El Prado (IRE)—No Frills (IRE) **P. Cartmell**
2 **BAYBSHAMBLES (IRE)**, 8, b g Compton Admiral—Payvashooz **R. E. Barr**
3 **BRAVE BATTLE**, 4, b g Compton Place—War Shanty **R. E. Barr**
4 **FOREIGN RHYTHM (IRE)**, 7, ch m Distant Music (USA)—Happy Talk (IRE) **P. Cartmell**
5 **ISLE OF ELLIS (IRE)**, 5, b g Statue of Liberty (USA)—Fable **R. E. Barr**
6 **IZZET**, 4, b g Cadeaux Genereux—Asbo **A. Suddes**
7 **KARATE QUEEN**, 7, b m King's Best (USA)—Black Belt Shopper (IRE) **Mrs C. Barr**
8 **KYZER CHIEF**, 7, b g Rouvres (FR)—Payvashooz **R. E. Barr**
9 **SEA SALT**, 9, b g Titus Livius (FR)—Carati **R. E. Barr**
10 **SILLY GILLY (IRE)**, 8, b m Mull of Kintyre (USA)—Richly Deserved (IRE) **D. Thomson**
11 **TOFFEE NOSE**, 5, b m Ishiguru (USA)—The Synergist **Mrs C. Barr**
12 **TROPICAL DUKE (IRE)**, 6, ch g Bachelor Duke (USA)—Tropical Dance (USA) **Mrs C. Barr**
13 **TUDOR BEAT**, 6, br m Beat All (USA)—Help Yourself (IRE) **Mr G. J. Pearson**

Other Owners: M. Mullins, B. Cunningham.

Assistant Trainer: Mrs C. Barr

Amateur: Miss V. Barr.

27 MR DAVID BARRON, Thirsk
Postal: **Maunby House, Maunby, Thirsk, North Yorkshire, YO7 4HD**
Contacts: **PHONE (01845) 587435 FAX (01845) 587331**
E-MAIL david@harrowgate.wanadoo.co.uk

1 **AMAZING AMORAY (IRE)**, 4, b g Tagula (IRE)—Amistad (GER) **R. C. Miquel**
2 **AMITOLA (IRE)**, 5, ch m Choisir (AUS)—Emly Express (IRE) **J. O. Browne**
3 **BEAT THE BELL**, 7, b g Beat All (USA)—Bella Beguine **Mr D. Pryde & Mr J. Cringan**
4 **BERTIEWHITTLE**, 4, ch g Bahamian Bounty—Minette **Norton Common Farm Racing II**
5 **BOSUN BREESE**, 7, b g Bahamian Bounty—Nellie Melba **Harrowgate Bloodstock Ltd**
6 **CHESHIRE LADY (IRE)**, 5, b m Marju (IRE)—Kiris World **Four Cheshire Gents**
7 **COLONEL MAK**, 5, br g Makbul—Colonel's Daughter **Norton Common Farm Racing,O'Kane,Murphy**
8 **ELIJAH PEPPER (USA)**, 7, ch g Crafty Prospector (USA)—Dovie Dee (USA) **Wensleydale Bacon Limited**
9 **ELUSIVE PRINCE**, 4, b g Storming Home—Ewenny **Bridge Extraction Systems Ltd**
10 **EZRA CHURCH (IRE)**, 5, br g Viking Ruler (AUS)—Redrightreturning **Mr C. A. Washbourn**
11 **FASTNET STORM (IRE)**, 6, br g Rock of Gibraltar (IRE)—Dreams **The Kittywake Partnership**
12 **FIELDGUNNER KIRKUP (GER)**, 4, b g Acclamation—Fire Finch **K. Kirkup**
13 **FRED WILLETTS (IRE)**, 4, b g Noverre (USA)—Intaglia (GER) **24 - 7 Recruitment/ Mr Allan Jones**
14 **GOTTCHER**, 4, b g Fasliyev (USA)—Danalia (USA) **Twinacre Nurseries Ltd**
15 **HILLS OF DAKOTA**, 4, b g Sleeping Indian—Pontressina (USA) **Mr J. Cringan & Mr D. Pryde**
16 **HITCHENS (IRE)**, 7, b g Acclamation—Royal Fizz (IRE) **Mr Laurence O'Kane & Mr Paul Murphy**
17 **INGLEBY ARCH (USA)**, 9, b g Arch (USA)—Inca Dove (USA) **Mr D. Scott**
18 **JACOB MCCANDLES**, 5, br g Trade Fair—Feather Circle (IRE) **Harrowgate Bloodstock Ltd**
19 **MAGICAL MACEY (IRE)**, 5, ch g Rossini (USA)—Spring's Glory (USA) **Harrowgate Bloodstock Ltd**
20 **MICHAEL'S NOOK**, 5, b g Intikhab (USA)—Mysterious Plans (IRE) **R. S. E. Gifford**
21 **MUFFIN MCLEAY (IRE)**, 4, b g Hawk Wing—Youngus (USA) **Harrowgate Bloodstock Ltd**
22 **POET'S PLACE (USA)**, 7, b g Mutakddim (USA)—Legion of Merit (USA) **Mrs E. Russell**
23 **ROYAL PROFILE**, 4, b g Royal Applause—Romantic Drama (IRE) **Profile Storage Ltd**
24 **SIRVINO**, 7, b g Vettori (IRE)—Zenita (USA) **Mr Theo Williams & Mr Charles Mocatta**
25 **SOHCAHTOA (IRE)**, 6, b g Val Royal (FR)—Stroke of Six (IRE) **Douglas Pryde Jim Beaumont**
26 **SPES NOSTRA**, 4, b g Ad Valorem (USA)—Millagros (IRE) **Mr J. Cringan & Mr D. Pryde**
27 **SUITS ME**, 9, ch g Bertolini (USA)—Fancier Bit **D. E. Cook**
28 **TIMELESS ELEGANCE (IRE)**, 5, b m Invincible Spirit (IRE)—Tidy Wager (IRE) **Douglas Pryde Jim Beaumont**
29 **TRES CORONAS (IRE)**, 5, b g Key of Luck (USA)—Almansa (IRE) **Mr J. Cringan & Mr D. Pryde**
30 **WAFFLE (IRE)**, 6, ch g Kheleyf (USA)—Saphire **Mr Laurence O'Kane & Mr Paul Murphy**

THREE-YEAR-OLDS

31 **ANNIE BEACH (IRE)**, ch f Redback—Kiva **Mrs S. C. Barron**
32 **CLON BRULEE (IRE)**, ch g Modigliani (USA)—Cloneden (IRE) **Ms Colette Twomey**
33 **DANSILI DUTCH (IRE)**, gr f Dutch Art—Joyful Leap **R. C. Miquel**
34 **DORRY K (IRE)**, b f Ad Valorem (USA)—Ashtaroute (USA) **Twinacre Nurseries Ltd**
35 **GYPSY WEDDING**, b f Ishiguru (USA)—Gypsy Fair **Harrowgate Bloodstock Ltd**
36 **JUST PERFECT (IRE)**, b f Elusive City (USA)—Miss Sandy Claws (IRE) **Wensleydale Bacon Limited**
37 **LA SALIDA**, b f Proclamation (IRE)—Anapola (GER) **J. G. Brown**
38 **LUPIN POOTER**, b g Bertolini (USA)—Carrie Pooter **Liam & Dermot Kelly**
39 **MAGILINI (IRE)**, b f Bertolini (USA)—Magic Annemarie (IRE) **T. D. Barron**
40 **MITCHUM**, b c Elnadim (USA)—Maid To Matter **A. J. Duffield**
41 **PEARL SECRET**, ch c Compton Place—Our Little Secret (IRE) **Pearl Bloodstock Limited**
42 **PROFILE STAR (IRE)**, b g Kodiac—Fingal Nights (IRE) **Profile Storage Ltd**
43 **PROFILE STORM (IRE)**, b g Footstepsinthesand—Mataji (IRE) **Profile Storage Ltd**
44 **THE CLAN MACDONALD**, b f Intikhab (USA)—Song of Passion (IRE)
45 **VITAL CALLING**, b g Vital Equine (IRE)—Crosby Millie **J. E. Raper**

TWO-YEAR-OLDS

46 **A J COOK (IRE)**, b g 1/4 Mujadil (USA)—
Undertone (IRE) (Noverre (USA)) (13136) **Norton Common Farm Racing Ltd**
47 B c 25/4 Redback—Alexander Composer (IRE) (Mozart (IRE)) (11493) **Mrs J. Hazell**
48 **HITHERTO**, b g 21/4 Bertolini (USA)—Princess Almora (Pivotal) (6157) **Mrs J. Hazell**
49 **MITCHELL**, ch c 25/2 Haafhd—Maid To Matter (Pivotal) (19047) **A. J. Duffield**
50 **PEARL NOTE**, b c 21/2 Elnadim (USA)—Selkirk Rose (IRE) (Pips Pride) (78095) **Pearl Bloodstock Limited**
51 **RED OCTOBER (IRE)**, b g 10/4 Red Clubs (IRE)—
Sakkara Star (IRE) (Mozart (IRE)) (5336) **Norton Common Farm Racing Ltd**
52 Ch f 19/3 Kheleyf (USA)—Robema (Cadeaux Genereux) (7388) **Liam & Dermot Kelly**

MR DAVID BARRON—continued

Other Owners: J. J. Beaumont, Mr N. J. E. Cook, J. A. Cringan, P. J. Huntbach, Peter Jones, A. Jones, Mr L. Kelly, Mr D. Kelly, Mr J. P. Lakin, Mr C. T. Mocatta, Mr P. A. Murphy, L. G. O'Kane, D. G. Pryde, D. C. Rutter, A. Sturman, Twenty Four Seven Recruitment Services Ltd, T. Williams.

Assistant Trainer: Nicola-Jo Barron

Apprentice: Luke McNiff.

---

28 | **MR FRANK BARTON, Tarporley**
Postal: **Radley Wood Farm, Whitchurch Road, Spurstow, Tarporley, Cheshire, CW6 9TD**
Contacts: **PHONE (01829) 260453 MOBILE (07833) 960632**

1 RINCE DONN (IRE), 10, b g Imperial Ballet (IRE)—Arrow Field (USA) **F. M. Barton**

Amateur: Miss S. Sharratt.

---

29 | **MR P. BARY, Chantilly**
Postal: **5 Chemin des Aigles, 60500 Chantilly, France**
Contacts: **PHONE (0033) 3445 71403 FAX (0033) 3446 72015 MOBILE (0033) 6075 80241**
E-MAIL p-bary@wanadoo.fr

1 ALCHIMIA (FR), 4, gr f Trade Fair—Alchimiste (FR) **Jalobey Stud**
2 BALADA SALE (ARG), 4, b f Not For Sale (ARG)—La Balada (ARG) **K. Yoshida**
3 DEVOIR DE MEMOIRE (FR), 6, gr g Anabaa Blue—Tashira (FR) **M-A Berghgracht**
4 DORMELLO (IRE), 4, b c Dansili—Field of Hope (IRE) **Ecurie J. L. Bouchard**
5 EIGHTFOLD PATH (USA), 5, b h Giant's Causeway (USA)—Divine Proportions (USA) **Niarchos Family**
6 LET IT SLIP (FR), 5, gr h Verglas (IRE)—Lunaska (FR) **Laghi SNC II**
7 MINAKSHI (FR), 4, b f Footstepsinthesand—Maria de la Luz **Mrs Ehrnrooth**
8 PERENNITE (FR), 4, b f Vespone (FR)—Aaliyah (GER) **M-A Berghgracht**
9 PLANET ELDER, 4, b g Cape Cross (IRE)—Celestial Lagoon (JPN) **Niarchos Family**
10 RICH COAST, 4, b c King's Best (USA)—Costa Rica (IRE) **K. Abdulla**
11 ROATAN, 7, b g Daylami (IRE)—Celestial Lagoon (JPN) **Laghi SNC II**
12 ROCK'N'ROLL DREAM (FR), 6, ch h Lomitas—Vignola **Mrs L. Bary**
13 SHAYALINA (FR), 4, gr f Sagamix (FR)—Shayanne (FR) **Ecurie La Boetie**
14 SPEARTOOTH, 5, b g Hernando (FR)—Napoli **Niarchos Family**
15 UNNEFER (FR), 7, b h Danehill Dancer (IRE)—Mimalia (USA) **Niarchos Family**

THREE-YEAR-OLDS

16 ABSENT MINDED, b f Medicean—Divergence (USA) **J. R. Treptow**
17 ADJUDICATE, b f Dansili—Cochin (USA) **K. Abdulla**
18 ALAMARIE (FR), b f Acclamation—Marie Rheinberg (GER) **Mr & Mrs R. Woolcott**
19 ATOMIC WAVES, ch c Hernando (FR)—Atlantic Blue (USA) **Skymarc Farm Inc.**
20 BOATHOUSE, ch f Dylan Thomas (IRE)—Blue Fern (USA) **Skymarc Farm Inc.**
21 BOLDOGSAG (FR), ro f Layman (USA)—Belga Wood (USA) **G. Sandor**
22 BONBONNIERE (USA), b f Mizzen Mast (USA)—Helstra (USA) **K. Abdulla**
23 BONNE JOURNEE (FR), b f Great Journey (JPN)—Kathmara (FR) **L. Bary**
24 CITY ON SEA (IRE), b f Monsun (GER)—Napoli **Niarchos Family**
25 DAWNING (USA), b f War Chant (USA)—Sun Is Up (JPN) **Niarchos Family**
26 DELTA SCUTI (USA), b c A P Indy (USA)—Denebola (USA) **Niarchos Family**
27 DIVINE PRESENCE (USA), b f A P Indy (USA)—Divine Proportions (USA) **Niarchos Family**
28 DUKHAN (USA), b c Cadeaux Genereux—Lunevision (FR) **M. Al Naemi**
29 ECLAIR CLASSIC (FR), b c Shirocco (GER)—Waconda (USA) **T. Li Chu Kwan**
30 EUROZONE, b c Rail Link—Questa Nova **K. Abdulla**
31 FIRST DATE, b c Selkirk (USA)—Valentine Girl **K. Abdulla**
32 FLANDRE (USA), b f Elusive Quality (USA)—Fresnay **Grundy Bloodstock Ltd**
33 GALLANT LEADER (USA), b c Zamindar (USA)—Real Trust (USA) **K. Abdulla**
34 GASPROM'S BRINED (IRE), b c Hurricane Run (IRE)—Alivera (FR) **Red Square**
35 HASNA (FR), ch f American Post—Harriet (FR) **G. Sandor**
36 KALAMOS (USA), b c Empire Maker (USA)—Kithira **K. Abdulla**
37 LE BILBOQUET, b c Holy Roman Emperor (FR)—La Balagna **Ecurie J. L. Bouchard**
38 LIGOVKA (FR), b f Anabaa (USA)—Idria (GER) **Red Square**
39 MAGIQ RIO (IRE), ch c Captain Rio—Margie Queen (GER) **Ecurie J. L. Bouchard**

MR P. BARY—continued

40 **MAINSAIL**, b c Oasis Dream—Docklands (USA) **K. Abdulla**
41 **MARIUS (FR)**, b c Panis (USA)—Malaba (FR) **M. Ohana**
42 **MENARDAIS (FR)**, b c Canyon Creek—Madeleine's Blush **G. Sandor**
43 **MORTGA (FR)**, b c Anabaa (USA)—Cornelia (FR) **Saeed Nasser Al Romaithi**
44 **MUSCAT**, b f Green Desert (USA)—Saga River (FR) **Michele Solbiati**
45 **MYCENAEAN (USA)**, b f King's Best (USA)—Caillech **J. R. Treptow**
46 **NIMBUS STAR**, b f Nayef (USA)—Starfan (USA) **K. Abdulla**
47 **PANAMAX (IRE)**, br c Dansili—Lune d'or (FR) **Haras du Mezeray**
48 **PARAMITA (FR)**, b f Galileo (IRE)—Six Perfections (FR) **Niarchos Family**
49 **POUPEE FLASH (USA)**, b f Elusive Quality (USA)—Modesty Blaise (USA) **Niarchos Family**
50 **RAHEB**, b c Red Ransom (USA)—Jarhes (IRE) **Saeed Nasser Al Romaithi**
51 **REARRANGE**, b f Rail Link—New Order **K. Abdulla**
52 **RED HURRICANE (IRE)**, b c Hurricane Run (IRE)—Red Blossom (USA) **J-M Hegesippe**
53 **REEMAS (FR)**, b f Anabaa (USA)—New Jersey (USA) **Saeed Nasser Al Romaithi**
54 **ROSE ET NOIRE (IRE)**, b f Dansili—Royal Highness (GER) **Ecurie des Monceaux**
55 **SATOPANTH**, b f Medicean—Alakananda **Niarchos Family**
56 **SMOKING SUN (USA)**, b br c Smart Strike (CAN)—Burning Sunset **Niarchos Family**
57 **STELLA DIVINE (FR)**, gr f Verglas (IRE)—Noblesse de Robe (FR) **D. Jacob**
58 **STELWAY (FR)**, ch c Gold Away (IRE)—Hill Tiger (IRE) **D. Jacob**
59 **TARTESSIAN (IRE)**, b f Lawman (FR)—Coconut Show **J. R. Treptow**
60 **TETBURY (USA)**, b c Giant's Causeway (USA)—Fanzine (USA) **K. Abdulla**
61 **THAT'S THE SPIRIT (FR)**, bl f Country Reel (USA)—Risque de Verglas (FR) **Ecurie J. L. Bouchard**
62 **TOUR EIFFEL (FR)**, gr f Stormy River (FR)—Dance Or Romance (USA) **J. Beres**
63 **TRIPLE WITCHING (USA)**, b f Pulpit (USA)—Witching Hour (FR) **Niarchos Family**
64 **WAY OF LOVE (FR)**, ch c Gold Away (IRE)—Love Affair (FR) **M. Al Naemi**
65 **YOUDA (IRE)**, gr f Verglas (IRE)—Carraigoona (IRE) **M. Al Naemi**
66 **ZERO GRAVITY**, b f Dansili—Imbabala **K. Abdulla**

TWO-YEAR-OLDS

67 **ACHERNAR (USA)**, ch c 26/2 Lemon Drop Kid (USA)—Ikat (IRE) (Pivotal) **Niarchos Family**
68 B c 21/5 Nayef (USA)—Aiglonne (USA) (Silver Hawk (USA)) (41050) **Skymarc Farm Inc. & Mme de Moussac**
69 Ch c 1/1 Turtle Bowl—Alsu **Red Square**
70 **APHRODITE (FR)**, b f 1/1 Whipper (USA)—Roseanna (FR) (Anabaa (USA)) (57471) **Ecurie La Boetie**
71 **ARLY (FR)**, b f 1/1 Zamindar—Samya **M. Solbiati**
72 **ART COMTEMPORAIN (USA)**, gr c 18/4 Smart Strike (CAN)—
Super Lina (FR) (Linamix (FR)) (131362) **Ecurie J. L. Bouchard**
73 **BARSAM (FR)**, b c 1/1 Tomorrows Cat (USA)—Belga Wood (USA) (Woodman (USA)) **G. Sandor**
74 B c 18/3 Henrythenavigator (USA)—Burning Sunset (Caerleon (USA)) **Niarchos Family**
75 **CELESTIAL SEA (FR)**, b f 15/2 Dalakhani (IRE)—
Celestial Lagoon (JPN) (Sunday Silence (USA)) **Niarchos Family**
76 B c 12/4 Empire Maker (USA)—Cheyenne Dream (Dancing Brave (USA)) **K. Abdulla**
77 B c 19/3 Dansili—Colza (USA) (Alleged (USA)) **Niarchos Family**
78 B c 15/3 Oasis Dream—Condition (Deploy) **K. Abdulla**
79 **CUCUMA (FR)**, b f 31/1 Invincible Spirit (IRE)—Cumin (USA) (Fusaichi Pegasus (USA)) (36945) **M. Randelli**
80 **DAIVIKA (USA)**, b f 1/1 Dynaformer (USA)—Divine Proportions (USA) (Kingmambo (USA)) **Niarchos Family**
81 B f 8/5 Street Cry (IRE)—Denebola (USA) (Storm Cat (USA)) **Niarchos Family**
82 **ELITISTE (IRE)**, b f 6/5 Danehill Dancer (IRE)—Alpha Lupi (IRE) (Rahy (USA)) (217569) **Ecurie La Boetie**
83 **FIRST MANDURO (FR)**, b f 4/2 Manduro (GER)—Avant Premiere (USA) (Vindication (USA)) (22167) **M. Al Naemi**
84 **HER STAR (USA)**, b f 17/2 Harlan's Holiday (USA)—Silver Comic (USA) (Silver Hawk (USA)) **Niarchos Family**
85 **HIPPOLYTO (FR)**, b c 26/3 Galileo (IRE)—
Fountain of Peace (USA) (Kris S (USA)) (82101) **Ecurie J. L. Bouchard**
86 Br f 8/5 Dansili—Imbabala (Zafonic (USA)) **K. Abdulla**
87 B f 6/2 Raven's Pass (USA)—Khumba Mela (IRE) (Hero's Honor (USA)) (69786) **Ecurie des Monceaux**
88 B f 16/5 Oasis Dream—Krisia (Kris) **K. Abdulla**
89 **LAURELINE (FR)**, b f 1/1 Canyon Creek—Leila **G. Sandor**
90 **LEGITIMITE (FR)**, b f 16/4 Lando (GER)—Alcidiana (FR) (Linamix (FR)) (18062) **M. Ohana**
91 B f 7/4 Cape Cross (IRE)—Mirina (FR) (Pursuit of Love) **Lady O'Reilly**
92 **MISRAI (IRE)**, gr c 25/4 Dalakhani (IRE)—Altruiste (USA) (Diesis) (106732) **Ecurie J. L. Bouchard**
93 **MODESTY'S WAY (USA)**, b f 1/1 Giant's Causeway (USA)—
Modesty Blaise (USA) (A P Indy (USA)) **Niarchos Family**
94 B c 7/5 Dalakhani (IRE)—Naissance Royale (IRE) (Giant's Causeway (USA)) (39408) **Ecurie des Monceaux**
95 **NERVI (FR)**, b c 17/4 Orpen (USA)—O' Keefe (IRE) (Be My Guest (USA)) (24630) **L. Dassault**
96 **NOLENE (FR)**, ch f 1/1 Layman—Noemie **G. Sandor**
97 B f 21/1 Dansili—Ombrie (Zafonic (USA)) **Mme de Moussac**
98 B c 16/2 Medaglia d'oro (USA)—Orellana (USA) (With Approval (CAN)) **Mme de Moussac**

MR P. BARY—continued

99 PARLE MOI (IRE), b f 14/3 Montjeu (IRE)—Di Moi Oui (Warning) (98522) **Grundy Bloodstock Ltd**
100 B c 13/3 Dansili—Perfect Hand (Barathea (IRE)) **K. Abdulla**
101 PILGRIM SOUL (FR), b f 4/4 Rock of Gibraltar (IRE)—Ramita (Fasliyev (USA)) (67323) **M. Al Naemi**
102 PROVENCE VERTE (IRE), b f 24/2 Dylan Thomas (IRE)—

                                                 Coup d'eclat (IRE) (Rainbow Quest (USA)) **Ecurie J. L. Bouchard**
103 Ch f 14/4 New Approach (IRE)—Raisonnable (Common Grounds) **Niarchos Family**
104 Ch f 9/4 Monsun (GER)—Remote Romance (USA) (Irish River (FR)) **Niarchos Family**
105 SAINT THOMAS (FR), b c 1/1 Dansili—Metisse (USA) (Kingmambo (USA)) (164203) **Ecurie La Boetie**
106 Br c 6/4 Rock of Gibraltar (IRE)—Se La Vie (FR) (Highest Honor (FR)) (73891) **Saeed Nasser Al Romaithi**
107 SEA OF LAUGHTER (USA), ch f 4/3 Distorted Humor (USA)—

                                       Sea of Showers (USA) (Seattle Slew (USA)) **Niarchos Family**
108 SINDIANA (FR), b f 14/3 Indian Rocket—Sumatra (IRE) (Mukaddamah (USA)) (2463) **M. Al Naemi**
109 SPIRITJIM (FR), b c 1/1 Galileo (IRE)—Hidden Silver (Anabaa (USA)) (254515) **J-M. Hegesippe**
110 Bl f 1/1 Diableneyev—Stella Berine **Haras du Mezeray**
111 B f 20/2 Rail Link—Strike Lightly (Rainbow Quest (USA)) **K. Abdulla**
112 STRIX, ch c 22/3 Muhtathir—Serandine (IRE) (Hernando (FR)) (32840) **M. Solbiati**
113 B f 27/4 Beat Hollow—Summer Breeze (Rainbow Quest (USA)) **K. Abdulla**
114 SYNCHRONIC (IRE), b f 20/4 Dansili—Platonic (Zafonic (USA)) (410509) **Niarchos Family**
115 TANTRIS (FR), ch c 1/1 Turtle Bowl—Tianshan **G. Sandor**
116 US LAW (IRE), gr c 18/2 Lawman (FR)—Dookus (IRE) (Linamix (FR)) (94417) **Ecurie J. L. Bouchard**
117 B c 20/2 Zamindar (USA)—Winter Solstice (Unfuwain (USA)) **K. Abdulla**

Assistant Trainer: Miss Charlotte De Rouglle

Jockey (flat): S. Pasquier.

---

30 **MR ROBIN BASTIMAN, Wetherby**
Postal: **Goosemoor Farm, Warfield Lane, Cowthorpe, Wetherby, West Yorkshire, LS22 5EU**
Contacts: **PHONE (01423) 359397 MOBILE (07976) 282976**
WEBSITE www.rbastimanracing.com

1 BORDERLESCOTT, 10, b g Compton Place—Jeewan **James Edgar & William Donaldson**
2 CANNON BOLT (IRE), 4, b g Chineur (FR)—Prime Time Girl **R. Bastiman**
3 DOTTY DARROCH, 4, b f Ad Valorem (USA)—Sensible Idea **The McMaster Springford Partnership**
4 FANTASTIC STORM, 5, b g Fantastic Light (USA)—Answered Prayer **R. Bastiman**
5 FOXLEY (IRE), 4, ch f Indian Haven—Maidford (IRE) **Mr C. J. Harris**
6 GREEN HOWARD, 4, ch g Bahamian Bounty—Dash of Lime **Ms M. Austerfield**
7 KWIK TIME, 4, b g Avonbridge—Never Away **R. Bastiman**
8 KYLLACHYKOV (IRE), 4, ch g Kyllachy—Dance On **Ms M. Austerfield**
9 LIZZY'S DREAM, 4, ch g Choisir (AUS)—Flyingit (USA) **R. Bastiman**
10 MISS BLINK, 5, ch m Compton Place—Tawny Way **J. A. Reed**
11 MISS POLLY ANYA, 4, b f Where Or When (IRE)—Fledge **Ms L. M. K. Pollinger**
12 MONSIEUR PONTAVEN, 5, b g Avonbridge—Take Heart **Ms M. Austerfield**
13 NOVALIST, 4, ch g Avonbridge—Malelane (IRE) **Ms M. Austerfield**
14 ROMAN SIOUX (IRE), 5, b g Antonius Pius (USA)—Blue Sioux **Ms M. Austerfield**
15 SECRET CITY (IRE), 6, b g City On A Hill (USA)—Secret Combe (IRE) **Ms M. Austerfield**
16 SEE VERMONT, 4, b g Kyllachy—Orange Lily **Mr J. Smith**
17 SINGEUR (IRE), 5, b g Chineur (FR)—Singitta **Ms M. Austerfield**
18 SISTER SIOUX (IRE), 4, b f Antonius Pius (USA)—Blue Sioux **Ms M. Austerfield**

THREE-YEAR-OLDS

19 BORDER HILL JACK, b g Danbird (AUS)—Edge of Darkness **Mr J. M. Barraclough**
20 JACK BARKER, b g Danbird (AUS)—Smiddy Hill **I. B. Barker**

TWO-YEAR-OLDS

21 B c 27/3 Choisir (AUS)—Love Thing (Phountzi (USA)) (12000)
22 MASAI KING (IRE), b c 21/3 Kheleyf (USA)—Masai Queen (IRE) (Mujadil (USA)) (23809)
23 B f 28/3 Bertolini (USA)—Smiddy Hill (Factual (USA))
24 B c 29/4 Amadeus Wolf—Sudden Interest (FR) (Highest Honor (FR)) (5000)
25 TROOPER ROYAL, b g 2/5 Zafeen (FR)—Faithful Beauty (IRE) (Last Tycoon)

MR ROBIN BASTIMAN—continued

Other Owners: Mr I. B. Barker, Mrs P. Bastiman, Mr Robin Bastiman, Mr William Donaldson, Mr James Edgar, Mr Brown McMaster, Mrs Jean McMaster.

Assistant Trainers: H. Bastiman & Miss R. Bastiman

Jockey (flat): Lee Newman, Robert Winston, Daniel Tudhope. **Amateur:** Miss R. Bastiman.

---

31 | **MRS ALISON BATCHELOR, Petworth**
Postal: **Down View Farm, Burton Park Road, Petworth, West Sussex, GU28 0JT**
Contacts: **PHONE (01798) 343090 FAX (01798) 343090**
E-MAIL alison@alisonbatchelorracing.com WEBSITE www.alisonbatchelorracing.com

1 **BALAJO (FR)**, 6, ch g Kendor (FR)—Dareen (IRE) **Mrs A. M. Batchelor**
2 **BOLLYWOOD (IRE)**, 9, ch g Indian Rocket—La Fille de Cirque **Mrs A. M. Batchelor**
3 **BORDER STATION (IRE)**, 6, b g Shantou (USA)—Telemania (IRE) **Mrs A. M. Batchelor**
4 **CAPISCI (IRE)**, 7, br g Tikkanen (USA)—Dolce Notte (IRE) **Mrs A. M. Batchelor**
5 **GOLAN GUY (IRE)**, 7, b g Golan (IRE)—Countess Marengo (IRE) **Mrs A. M. Batchelor**
6 **LAMBRO RIVER (IRE)**, 7, b g Milan—Chaparral Reef (IRE) **Mrs A. M. Batchelor**
7 **MINNEAPOLIS**, 7, b g Sadler's Wells (USA)—Teggiano (IRE) **Mrs A. M. Batchelor**
8 **SIOUXME (IRE)**, 10, b m Little Bighorn—Winter Sunset **Mrs A. M. Batchelor**
9 **STAGECOACH DANMAN (IRE)**, 4, b g Montjeu (IRE)—Gothic Dream (IRE) **Mrs A. M. Batchelor**
10 **STRAWBERRY VILLA**, 7, b m Alflora (IRE)—Square One (IRE) **Mrs A. M. Batchelor**
11 **TARASS D'ALBEN (FR)**, 4, b g Policy Maker (IRE)—Passe Du Diable (FR) **Mrs A. M. Batchelor**
12 **TRY CATCH ME (IRE)**, 7, b g Commander Collins—Misty River (IRE) **Mrs A. M. Batchelor**
13 **UPTON MEAD (IRE)**, 5, b g Jimble (FR)—Inchinnan **Mrs A. M. Batchelor**

Conditional: Mark Quinlan.

---

32 | **MR BRIAN BAUGH, Stoke on Trent**
Postal: **Brooklands Farm, Park Lane, Audley, Stoke on Trent**
Contacts: **HOME (01782) 723144 MOBILE (07771) 693666**

1 **AVONCREEK**, 8, b g Tipsy Creek (USA)—Avondale Girl (IRE) **Messrs Chrimes, Winn & Wilson**
2 **AVONLINI**, 6, b m Bertolini (USA)—Avondale Girl (IRE) **J. H. Chrimes**
3 **BENTLEY**, 8, b g Piccolo—April Lee **The Flying Spur Racing Partnership**
4 **BRET MAVERICK (IRE)**, 8, b g Josr Algarhoud (IRE)—
Shady Street (USA) **Mr J.H.Chrimes & Mr & Mrs G.W.Hannam**
5 **CONSISTANT**, 4, b g Reel Buddy (USA)—Compact Disc (IRE) **Miss J. A. Price**
6 **FIREBALL EXPRESS**, 4, ch g Firebreak—Ashfield **Mr G. B. Hignett**
7 **GOLDSTORM**, 4, ch f Storming Home—Antonia Bertolini **Magnate Racing**
8 **HILBRE COURT (USA)**, 7, br g Doneraile Court (USA)—Glasgow's Gold (USA) **Saddle Up Racing**
9 **JOHN POTTS**, 4, b g Josr Algarhoud (IRE)—Crown City (USA) **Miss S. M. Potts**
10 **JULY DAYS (IRE)**, 6, b m Exceed And Excel (AUS)—Tocade (IRE) **Miss S. M. Potts**
11 **JUST TIMMY MARCUS**, 6, ch g Ishiguru (USA)—Grandads Dream **Mr C. R. Watts**
12 **KIELTY'S FOLLY**, 8, gr g Weet-A-Minute (IRE)—Three Sweeties **Saddle Up Racing**
13 **KYLE OF BUTE**, 6, ch g Kyllachy—Blinding Mission (IRE) **Mr J.H.Chrimes & Mr & Mrs G.W.Hannam**
14 **LOVE CLUB**, 4, ch g Kheleyf (USA)—Avondale Girl (IRE) **Mr J.H.Chrimes & Mr & Mrs G.W.Hannam**
15 **LUV U NOO**, 5, b m Needwood Blade—Lady Suesanne (IRE) **21C Telecom.co.uk**
16 **MAGNITUDE**, 7, ch g Pivotal—Miswaki Belle (USA) **Mr J.H.Chrimes & Mr & Mrs G.W.Hannam**
17 **MASTER OF DISGUISE**, 6, b g Kyllachy—St James's Antigua (IRE) **21C Telecom.co.uk**
18 **MISSHOLLYGOLIGHTLY**, 4, b f Kheleyf (USA)—Crown City (USA) **F. Gillespie**
19 **PASSING MOMENT**, 4, b f Fraam—Passing Fancy **S. M. Mercer**
20 **PICCOLO EXPRESS**, 6, b g Piccolo—Ashfield **Mr G. B. Hignett**
21 **SCAMPERDALE**, 10, br g Compton Place—Miss Up N Go **Saddle Up Racing**
22 **SUPASTARQUEEN (USA)**, 4, b br f El Corredor (USA)—Supamova (USA) **Mr G. B. Hignett**
23 **SYMPHONIC DANCER (USA)**, 5, ch m Smart Strike (CAN)—Summer Exhibition (USA) **Mr G. B. Hignett**
24 **TANFORAN**, 10, b g Mujahid (USA)—Florentynna Bay **Miss S. M. Potts**

THREE-YEAR-OLDS

25 **BUDS BRUVVER**, ch g Reel Buddy (USA)—Spectrum Queen (IRE) **Mr G. B. Hignett**
26 **DEAR BEN**, b g Echo of Light—Miss Up N Go **C. Turner**

MR BRIAN BAUGH—continued

Other Owners: Mr B. P. J. Baugh, W. G. Hannam, Mrs C. Hannam, Mr R. A. Hunt, Mrs N. Hunt, Mrs M. Robinson, Mr K. V. Robinson, R. W. Sansom, J. Tomlinson, Mrs L. E. Tomlinson, J. M. Winn.

Assistant Trainer: S Potts

---

33 **MR CHRIS BEALBY, Grantham**
Postal: **North Lodge, Barrowby, Grantham, Lincolnshire, NG32 1DH**
Contacts: **OFFICE (01476) 564568 FAX (01476) 572391 MOBILE (07831) 538689**
E-MAIL chris@northlodgeracing.co.uk WEBSITE www.northlodgeracing.co.uk

1 AWAREINESS (IRE), 6, b g Flemensfirth (USA)—Special Case (IRE) **R. A. Jenkinson**
2 BENNYNTHEJETS (IRE), 10, b g Beneficial—Lucky Adventure (IRE) **Payplan Partnership**
3 BLACK SAMBUCA, 5, b g Samraan (USA)—Derring Floss **R. P. Kernohan**
4 CHAC DU CADRAN (FR), 6, b g Passing Sale (FR)—L'indienne (FR) **Bingley, Williams & Pepperdine**
5 COUNTESS COMET (IRE), 5, b m Medicean—Countess Sybil **Payplan Partnership II**
6 DUSHY LADY (IRE), 8, b m Dushyantor (USA)—Shoidin (IRE) **Payplan Partnership II**
7 FOXINTHECOTS, 6, b g Beat All (USA)—Ardeal **C. C. Bealby**
8 IFONLYALFIE, 7, b g Alflora (IRE)—Ifni du Luc (FR) **Triumph In Mind**
9 L'ELDORADO (FR), 7, b g Urban Ocean (FR)—Little Warden **Mrs C. M. Radford**
10 LEGENDARY HOP, 6, b m Midnight Legend—Hopping Mad **Messrs Duke,Umpleby,Holmes & Bealby**
11 LEYTE GULF (USA), 9, b g Cozzene (USA)—Gabacha (USA) **R. A. Jenkinson**
12 M'LADY ROUSSEAU (IRE), 6, ch m Selkirk (USA)—Millay **Payplan Partnership II**
13 MASS HYSTERIA (IRE), 6, b g Dr Massini (IRE)—Tear Away Katie (IRE) **Mrs J. Bullas**
14 ORDELIA, 8, b m Overbury (IRE)—Ardeal **C. C. Bealby**
15 PERSIAN GATES (IRE), 8, ch g Anshan—Mrs Jenks **Mrs Robert Bingley & Mrs Bryan Spooner**
16 POLLEN JOCK (IRE), 8, ch g Loup Sauvage (USA)—Rollinginit (IRE) **Keen Racing**
17 RAKTIMAN (IRE), 5, ch g Rakti—Wish List (IRE) **Michael Hill**
18 REELWILL (FR), 7, gr m Dom Alco (FR)—Jeep Will (FR) **C. C. Bealby**
19 ROCKY REBEL, 4, b g Norse Dancer (IRE)—Gulchina (USA) **R. A. Jenkinson**
20 TANGO IN THE NIGHT, 5, b g Fleetwood (IRE)—Secret Dance **C. C. Bealby**
21 VINTAGE RED, 4, ch g Grape Tree Road—Simply Stunning **C. C. Bealby**

Other Owners: Mrs E. A. Bingley, Mr J. W. H. Brown, Mr M. W. L. Brown, Mr D. M. Cook, B. G. Duke, F. M. Holmes, Mrs M. J. Pepperdine, Mr G. P. D. Rann, Mrs L. E. Rann, Mrs B. M. Spooner, Mrs L. E. Tapson, Mr P. Umpleby, Mr T. Wendels, Mrs A. M. Williams, R. F. Wright.

Jockey (flat): Dane O'Neill. **Jockey (NH):** Tom Messenger, Noel Fehily. **Conditional:** Adam Wedge. **Amateur:** Mr Olly Murphy, Mr Matt Stanley.

---

34 **MR RALPH BECKETT, Andover**
Postal: **Kimpton Down Stables, Old Coach Road, Kimpton Down, Andover, Hampshire, SP11**
Contacts: **PHONE (01264) 772278 FAX (01264) 771221 MOBILE (07802) 219022**
E-MAIL trainer@rbeckett.com WEBSITE www.rbeckett.com

1 ALBERT BRIDGE, 4, gr g Hernando (FR)—Alvarita **The Cheyne Walkers**
2 DEVOTED (IRE), 4, gr f Dalakhani (IRE)—Wavertree Girl (IRE) **Landmark Racing Limited**
3 FARLOW (IRE), 4, ch g Exceed And Excel (AUS)—Emly Express (IRE) **Lawrence, Deal & Carolyn Thornton**
4 GREEN PEARL (IRE), 4, b g Green Desert (USA)—Kinnaird (IRE) **Mrs I. M. Beckett**
5 HAYAKU (USA), 4, b f Arch (USA)—Promptly (IRE) **G. B. Partnership**
6 MAVERIK, 4, ch g Iceman—Nouvelle Lune **Athos, Cooper, Quinn, EPL**
7 MOONE'S MY NAME, 4, gr f Intikhab (USA)—The Manx Touch (IRE) **McDonagh Murphy & Nixon**
8 MORETTA BLANCHE, 5, br m Dansili—Cotton House (IRE) **P. K. Gardner T/A Springcombe Park Stud**
9 OASIS DANCER, 5, br gr g Oasis Dream—Good Enough (FR) **Mrs H. I. Slade**
10 PABUSAR, 4, b g Oasis Dream—Autumn Pearl **Mr & Mrs Kevan Watts**
11 POYLE TODREAM, 4, b c Oasis Dream—Lost In Lucca **Cecil and Miss Alison Wiggins**
12 RUBY BROOK, 4, b g Sakhee (USA)—Highbrook (USA) **Mr A. E. Frost & Mr A. R. Adams**
13 SANDBANKS SIZZLER (IRE), 4, ch g Soviet Star (USA)—Isticanna (USA) **I. J. Heseltine**
14 SEASIDE SIZZLER, 5, ch g Rahy (USA)—Via Borghese (USA) **I. J. Heseltine**
15 SNOW RIDGE, 4, b g Iceman—Confetti **The Villains**
16 WESTERN PRIZE, 4, br g High Chaparral (IRE)—Spot Prize (USA) **J. C. Smith**

THREE-YEAR-OLDS

17 ASTRA HALL, ch f Halling (USA)—Star Precision **G. B. Balding**

MR RALPH BECKETT—continued

18 **BY INVITATION (USA)**, b f Van Nistelrooy (USA)—Sahara Star **Clipper Group Holdings Ltd**
19 **COLIMA (IRE)**, b f Authorized (IRE)—Coyote **Mr & Mrs David Aykroyd**
20 **COMPTON**, ch g Compton Place—Look So **J. H. Richmond-Watson**
21 **CUBANITA**, ch f Selkirk (USA)—Caribana **Miss K. Rausing**
22 **DESPATCH**, b f Nayef (USA)—Time Saved **R. Barnett**
23 **ELECTRELANE**, ch f Dubawi (IRE)—Imperialistic (IRE) **Clipper Group Holdings Ltd**
24 B f Medicean—Fancy Rose (USA) **Mrs E. Kennedy**
25 **FINESSE**, ch f Shamardal (USA)—Clare Hills (IRE) **P. K. Gardner T/A Springcombe Park Stud**
26 **FLEUR DE LA VIE (IRE)**, ch f Primary (USA)—Francophilia **Prime Of Life 3**
27 **FROG HOLLOW**, gr g Intikhab (USA)—The Manx Touch (IRE) **R. A. Pegum**
28 **HAAF A SIXPENCE**, b g Haafhd—Melody Maker **Melody Racing**
29 **HURRY UP GEORGE**, b g Intikhab (USA)—Digamist Girl (IRE) **A. E. Frost**
30 **IT'S A PRIVILEGE**, gr g Verglas (IRE)—No Rehearsal (FR) **Mr R. J. Roberts**
31 **MATURED**, b f Manduro (GER)—Time Away (IRE) **R. Barnett**
32 **MONOPOLI**, ch f Cadeaux Genereux—Jump Ship **Mark & Emma Dixon**
33 **MOON PEARL (USA)**, b br g Johannesburg (USA)—Moonavvara (USA) **Pearl Bloodstock Limited**
34 **MOONSTONE MAGIC**, b f Trade Fair—Woodcock Moon **Lady S. K. Marchwood**
35 **NAPOLEON'S MUSE (IRE)**, b f Peintre Celebre (USA)—Art Work **Mrs E. Kennedy**
36 **NICEOFYOUTOTELLME**, b c Hernando (FR)—Swain's Gold (USA) **Mr R. J. Roberts**
37 **NOOSA BOY**, b c Pivotal—Maroochydore **R. A. Pegum**
38 **NORLANDER**, b f Royal Applause—Arrivato **Miss R. C. Tregaskes**
39 **PEARL FROST**, gr g Verglas (IRE)—Eternelle **Mrs I. M. Beckett**
40 **PEARL MIX (IRE)**, gr c Oratorio (IRE)—Rosamixa (FR) **Pearl Bloodstock Limited**
41 **PENINSULA**, b f Rock of Gibraltar (IRE)—Kayah **J. H. Richmond-Watson**
42 **PERFECT POLICY**, b f Kyllachy—Perfect Cover (IRE) **J. R. Drew**
43 **PICURA**, ch f King's Best—Picolette **Dulverton Equine**
44 **PINK TEQUILA**, b f Teofilo—Puce **Newsells Park Stud Limited**
45 **RADIOACTIVE**, b f Haafhd—Toxique (IRE) **P. K. Gardner T/A Springcombe Park Stud**
46 **RHAGORI**, b f Exceed And Excel (AUS)—Cresta Gold **Landmark Racing Limited**
47 **RIOT OF COLOUR**, b f Excellent Art—Riotous Applause **The Eclipse Partnership**
48 **SAKHEERA**, b f Sakhee (USA)—Shona (USA) **Belmore Lane Stud Racing Partnership**
49 B g Hurricane Run (IRE)—Shallika (IRE) **D & J Newell**
50 **STEREOTYPICAL**, ch g Notnowcato—Delightful Rhythm (USA) **The Anagram Partnership**
51 **SUPERCILIARY**, b g Dansili—Supereva (IRE) **The Prince of Wales & The Duchess of Cornwall**
52 **TAKEITFROMALADY (IRE)**, b g Intikhab (USA)—Pinheiros (IRE) **Mr R. J. Roberts**
53 **TANGO SKY**, b g Namid—Sky Galaxy (USA) **A.W.A. Partnership**
54 **VICKERS VIMY**, b f Montjeu (IRE)—First Bloom (USA) **Lady N. F. Cobham**
55 **WAYNE MANOR**, br c Cape Cross (IRE)—Inchmahome **Tullpark Limited**

TWO-YEAR-OLDS

56 **ALDBOROUGH (IRE)**, b c 14/4 Danehill Dancer (IRE)—
                                   Kitty O'shea (Sadler's Wells (USA)) **Mr & Mrs David Aykroyd**
57 **ANNA'S PEARL**, ch c 18/4 Pivotal—Mi Anna (GER) (Lake Coniston (IRE)) (80000) **Pearl Bloodstock Limited**
58 **BIRDLOVER**, ch f 5/3 Byron—Bird Over (Bold Edge)
59 **CASTA DIAMANTE**, b c 13/3 Dutch Art—Casterossa (Rossini (USA)) (952) **D. P. Barrie**
60 B f 24/2 Cape Cross (IRE)—Catherine Palace (Grand Lodge (USA)) **J. H. Richmond-Watson**
61 B f 1/3 Dutch Art—Classic Vision (Classic Cliche (IRE)) (32000) **W. E. A. Fox**
62 B c 14/3 Notnowcato—Cockatrice (Petong) (31000) **P. Hickey**
63 B c 20/3 Baltic King—
            Greta d'argent (IRE) (Great Commotion (USA)) (8000) **Hillier, Lawrence, Turney & Goddard**
64 **HELLO SAILOR**, b c 6/5 Mount Nelson—Fairy Queen (IRE) (Fairy King (USA)) (8000)
65 B f 26/3 Tobougg (IRE)—Hilarious (IRE) (Petorius)
66 B c 25/3 Kingsalsa (USA)—Hip (Pivotal) **Mr R. J. Roberts**
67 **INGOT OF GOLD**, b f 29/1 Dubawi (IRE)—Cresta Gold (Halling (USA))
68 Ch f 3/4 Sakhee (USA)—La Dangeville (Danehill) (41050) **Newsells Park Stud Limited**
69 **LADY WHO**, b f 14/4 Sir Percy—Herminoe (Rainbow Quest (USA)) **Dulverton Equine**
70 **LEMON PEARL**, ch f 12/4 Singspiel (IRE)—
                     Basemah (FR) (Lemon Drop Kid (USA)) (55000) **Pearl Bloodstock Limited**
71 B f 26/2 Elusive City (USA)—Lochridge (Indian Ridge) **J. C. Smith**
72 **MME SANS GENE**, gr f 11/2 Verglas (IRE)—Diablerette (Green Desert (USA)) **Miss K. Rausing**
73 Ch f 21/3 Exceed And Excel (AUS)—Paradise Isle (Bahamian Bounty) (80000)
74 **PEARL BRIDGE**, b c 21/3 Avonbridge—Our Little Secret (IRE) (Rossini (USA)) (26666) **Pearl Bloodstock Limited**
75 **POMPEIA**, ch f 22/4 Singspiel (IRE)—Caesarea (GER) (Generous (IRE)) **J. L. Rowsell**
76 **PROSPERA (IRE)**, b f 20/3 Cape Cross (IRE)—Opera (Forzando) **The Millennium Madness Partnership**
77 **RIO'S PEARL**, b f 24/2 Captain Rio—Agony Aunt (Formidable (USA)) (47619) **Pearl Bloodstock Limited**

MR RALPH BECKETT—continued

78 **SECRET ART (IRE)**, ch c 27/2 Excellent Art—Ivy Queen (IRE) (Green Desert (USA)) (16000) **Circuit Racing**
79 B f 1/4 Sakhee's Secret—See You Later (Emarati (USA))
80 B c 27/4 Marju (IRE)—Shallow Ground (IRE) (Common Grounds) (40000) **Brook House**
81 B f 22/1 Galileo (IRE)—Shastye (IRE) (Danehill (USA)) (230000) **Newsells Park Stud Limited**
82 **SILVER RIDGE (IRE)**, gr c 26/2 Verglas (IRE)
          Jacaranda Ridge (Indian Ridge) (20952) **The Pickford Hill Partnership**
83 **SIZZLER**, ch c 18/3 Hernando (FR)—Gino's Spirits (Perugino (USA)) (60000) **Heseltine, Henley & Jones**
84 Ch c 12/3 Nayef (USA)—Spot Prize (Seattle Dancer (USA)) **J. C. Smith**
85 B c 7/3 Intikhab (USA)—Sweet Surprise (IRE) (Danetime (IRE)) (6157) **McDonagh Murphy & Nixon**
86 **TALENT**, ch f 25/2 New Approach (IRE)—Prowess (IRE) (Peintre Celebre (USA))
87 B c 18/2 Ishiguru (USA)—Tharwa (Last Tycoon) (25000) **The Quick Fill Partnership**
88 **THORPE (IRE)**, b c 8/4 Danehill Dancer (IRE)—Minkova (IRE) (Sadler's Wells (USA)) **Mr & Mrs David Aykroyd**
89 **THWART**, ch f 2/4 Refuse To Bend (IRE)—Jump Ship (Night Shift (USA)) **M. H. Dixon**
90 B c 7/2 Intikhab (USA)—United Passion (Emarati (USA)) (23000)

Other Owners: Mr A. R. Adams, Mrs L. M. Aykroyd, D. P. Aykroyd, Mr R. D. Beckett, Duchess of Cornwall, P. A. Deal, D. W. Dennis, Miss E. J. Dixon, N. J. Forman Hardy, R. Frisby, Mr M. P. Gibbens, Mr P Gregg, Mrs M. R. Gregory, M. G. H. Heald, Mr A. M. H. Heald, Mr K. Lawrence, Mr O. C. S. Lazenby, Mr E. A. M. Leatham, Mrs S. E. Leatham, Mr J. Makin, Mr P. G. Murphy, D. J. M. Newell, Mrs J. Newell, Mr B. O'Brien, Mrs G. R. Pembroke, S. J. Pembroke, Mr S. A. J. Penny, G. R. Pooley, Mr J. W. Randall, Mrs H. L. Smyly, Mr B. P. J. Spiers, Mr R. W. Stirling, L. R. Turland, H.R.H. The Prince Of Wales, Mr K. Watts, Mrs P. M. L. Watts, Mr R. Weston, C. Wiggins, Miss A. J. Wiggins, Mrs P. H. Williams, Miss C. J. Wills.

Assistant Trainer: Charlie Duckworth

Jockey (flat): Jim Crowley. **Apprentice:** Emmet McNamara.

---

35 MR MICHAEL BELL, Newmarket
Postal: **Fitzroy House, Newmarket, Suffolk, CB8 0JT**
Contacts: **PHONE (01638) 666567 FAX (01638) 668000 MOBILE (07802) 264514**
E-MAIL office@fitzroyhouse.co.uk WEBSITE www.michaelbellracing.co.uk

1 **ALLIED POWERS (IRE)**, 7, b g Invincible Spirit (IRE)—Always Friendly **Mr David Fish & Mr Edward Ware**
2 **BOUNCY BOUNCY (IRE)**, 5, ch m Chineur (FR)—Wunderbra (IRE) **A. Scotney, D.Asplin, A.Symonds**
3 **CREME ANGLAISE**, 4, b f Motivator—Reading Habit (USA) **Mrs G. E. Rowland-Clark**
4 **JO BOY**, 5, b g Royal Applause—Bad Kitty (USA) **Karmaa Racing Limited**
5 **KING OF JAZZ (IRE)**, 4, b g Acclamation—Grand Slam Maria (FR) **Mr R. Upshall**
6 **MARGOT DID (IRE)**, 4, b f Exceed And Excel (AUS)—Special Dancer **Mr T Redman & Mr P Philipps**
7 **MISS AIX**, 4, b f Selkirk (USA)—Miss Provence **J. L. C. Pearce**
8 **MYSTIC EDGE**, 4, ch f Needwood Blade—Magic Flo **Herts & Hinds Racing Syndicate**
9 **RISHIKESH**, 4, b c Cape Cross (IRE)—Maycocks Bay **Lady Bamford**
10 **SET TO MUSIC (IRE)**, 4, b f Danehill Dancer (IRE)—Zarabaya (IRE) **Her Majesty The Queen**
11 **STRONG VIGILANCE**, 5, ch g Mr Greeley (USA)—Zabadani **Mr L. J. Inman**
12 **TACTICIAN**, 5, b g Motivator—Tempting Prospect **Her Majesty The Queen**
13 **TWINKLED**, 4, ch g Bahamian Bounty—Panic Stations **D. W. & L. Y. Payne**
14 **WIGMORE HALL (IRE)**, 5, b g High Chaparral (IRE)—Love And Laughter (IRE) **M. B. Hawtin**

THREE-YEAR-OLDS

15 **ADVERSE (IRE)**, b f Refuse To Bend (IRE)—Shadow Roll (IRE) **Sheikh Marwan Al Maktoum**
16 **ALASKAN BULLET (IRE)**, b g Kodiac—Czars Princess (IRE) **Partners In Crime**
17 **APOSTLE (IRE)**, gr g Dark Angel (IRE)—Rosy Dudley (IRE) **Highclere Thoroughbred Racing - Jackson**
18 **BACKCOURT (USA)**, ch f Street Cry (IRE)—Badminton **Sheikh Marwan Al Maktoum**
19 **BITE OF THE CHERRY**, br f Dalakhani (IRE)—Bianca Nera **R. Frisby**
20 **BITTER HARVEST**, b g Singspiel—Queen of Norway **R. Frisby**
21 **BLACK MOTIVE**, b c Motivator—Special Dancer **TSEGA Horses Company Ltd**
22 **BORN TO SURPRISE**, b c Exceed And Excel (AUS)—Dubai Surprise (IRE) **Dr A. Ridha**
23 **BRIDGEHAMPTON**, b c Lando (GER)—Gaze **M. B. Hawtin**
24 **BRYANT PARK (USA)**, ch g Street Cry (IRE)—Cala (FR) **Sheikh Marwan Al Maktoum**
25 **CANDYCAKES (IRE)**, b f Cape Cross (IRE)—Charita (IRE) **Mr J. Acheson**
26 **DELMA (IRE)**, b f Authorized (IRE)—Contradictive (USA) **Saleh Al Homaizi & Imad Al Sagar**
27 **DESERT RED (IRE)**, b f Green Desert (USA)—Penicuik **M M Racing**
28 **DUBAI SPRING (USA)**, b br f E Dubai (USA)—Best Mover (USA) **N. Mourad**
29 **DUBAI SUNSHINE (IRE)**, b g Dubawi (USA)—Star Express **Dr A. Ridha**
30 **EIGHT LETTERS (USA)**, b br f Mr Greeley (USA)—Thara (USA) **Mr C. Wright & The Hon Mrs J.M.Corbett**
31 **EXCEEDEXPECTATIONS (IRE)**, b g Intikhab (USA)—Jazan (IRE) **Mr M. Caine**

MR MICHAEL BELL—continued

32 **EXTREMELY ALERT,** ch c Nayef (USA)—Megdale (IRE) **Mr L. J. Inman**
33 **FORTIETH AND FIFTH (IRE),** b g Lemon Drop Kid (USA)—Maugusta (USA) **C. Bryce**
34 **GABRIAL THE GREAT (IRE),** b c Montjeu (IRE)—Bayourida (USA) **Dr Marwan Koukash**
35 **HOLY EMPRESS (IRE),** b f Holy Roman Emperor (IRE)—Kahira (IRE) **Tamdown Group Limited**
36 **INTENT (IRE),** b f Jeremy (USA)—Cant Hurry Love **The Royal Ascot Racing Club**
37 **KAI,** b g Kyllachy—Belle Ile (USA) **R. C. Tooth**
38 **KASHGAR,** b c Hernando (FR)—Miss Katmandu (IRE) **J. L. C. Pearce**
39 **LOOKS LIKE RAIN,** ch f Medicean—Hippogator (USA) **Mr D. J. Burke & Mr Peter Alderson**
40 **LOVE GROWS WILD (USA),** gr ro f Cozzene (USA)—Dierks Timber (USA) **W. H. Ponsonby**
41 **MECOX MEADOW (USA),** gr ro g El Prado (IRE)—Chalamont (IRE) **M. B. Hawtin**
42 **MEXICAN WAVE,** b c Rock of Gibraltar (IRE)—La Belga (ARG) **W. Maguire**
43 **MOMENTARY,** b f Nayef (USA)—Fleeting Memory **Her Majesty The Queen**
44 **ONE KOOL DUDE,** ch g Iceman—Hiraeth **M. L. W. Bell Racing Ltd**
45 **OPERATION TRACER,** ch g Rock of Gibraltar (IRE)—Quite Elusive (USA) **R. N. Frosell**
46 **ROCK OF MONET,** b c Kyllachy—Level Pegging (IRE) **Karmaa Racing Limited**
47 **ROSE MADDER,** b f Singspiel (IRE)—Crimson Year (USA) **Sheikh Marwan Al Maktoum**
48 **RUACANA,** b c Cape Cross (IRE)—Farrfesheena (USA) **Sheikh Marwan Al Maktoum**
49 **RUBY NIGHT (IRE),** b g Red Clubs (IRE)—Stop Out **Timeform Betfair Racing Club Ltd**
50 **SHOW ME THE LINE (IRE),** b c Teofilo (IRE)—Extreme Beauty (USA) **Dr A. Ridha**
51 **SIGN MANUAL,** b g Motivator—New Assembly (IRE) **Her Majesty The Queen**
52 **SOVEREIGN DEBT (IRE),** br c Dark Angel (IRE)—Kelsey Rose **Mr L. J. Inman**
53 **SURAJ,** ch c Galileo (IRE)—Maid of Killeen (IRE) **Lady Bamford**
54 **TAHLIA REE (IRE),** b f Acclamation—Dora Carrington (IRE) **P. E. Barrett**
55 **UNEX BOSCH,** b g Haafhd—Bering Up (IRE) **W. J. Gredley**
56 **WIDOW FLOWER (IRE),** b f Moss Vale (IRE)—Satin Rose **R. I. Morris**
57 B br f Henny Hughes (USA)—Zanoubia (USA) **N. Mourad**

TWO-YEAR-OLDS

58 B f 20/4 Kyllachy—Bijou A Moi (Rainbow Quest (USA)) (52000) **R. Frisby**
59 B f 31/3 Holy Roman Emperor (IRE)—Blessing (Dubai Millennium) **Lordship Stud**
60 B c 1/3 Kheleyf (USA)—Blue Echo (Kyllachy) (220000) **Saleh Al Homaizi & Imad Al Sagar**
61 B c 2/3 Street Sense (USA)—Cala (FR) (Desert Prince (IRE)) **Sheikh Marwan Al Maktoum**
62 **CAPELLA'S SONG (IRE),** b f 14/2 Oratorio (IRE)—
                                    Bright Bank (IRE) (Sadler's Wells (USA)) (34481) **P. A. Philipps & C. E. L. Philipps**
63 Ch c 5/3 Sleeping Indian—Carla (FR) (Cardoun (FR)) (49523) **Thurloe Thoroughbreds XXX**
64 B f 18/4 Duke of Marmalade (IRE)—
      Crystal Curling (IRE) (Peintre Celebre (USA)) (32840) **Mrs John Magnier, Mr Michael Tabor & Mr Derek Smith**
65 B f 19/3 Motivator—Crystal Swan (IRE) (Dalakhani (IRE)) **Saleh Al Homaizi & Imad Al Sagar**
66 B f 14/3 Cape Cross (IRE)—Daliyana (IRE) (Cadeaux Genereux) **Her Majesty The Queen**
67 B f 9/3 Oasis Dream—Dancing Abbie (USA) (Theatrical) **Sheikh Marwan Al Maktoum**
68 **DIVERGENCE (IRE),** b f 19/4 Teofilo (IRE)—Min Alhawa (USA) (Riverman (USA)) (98521) **Mr L. J. Inman**
69 **FILS ANGES (IRE),** gr c 16/2 Dark Angel (IRE)—La Piaf (FR) (Fabulous Dancer (USA)) (33333) **Mr D. Hanafin**
70 B f 17/4 High Chaparral (IRE)—Freezing Love (USA) (Danzig (USA)) (40000) **E. J. Ware**
71 **GAMBLE,** ch f 19/3 Galileo (IRE)—Pretty Face (Rainbow Quest (USA)) **Her Majesty The Queen**
72 **GEORGE CINQ,** b c 24/1 Pastoral Pursuits—Fairnilee (Selkirk (USA)) (42000) **Tamdown Group Limited**
73 B f 18/3 Kheleyf (USA)—Heavenly Bay (USA) (Rahy (USA)) **Sheikh Marwan Al Maktoum**
74 **HISPANIA (IRE),** b f 17/4 Teofilo (IRE)—Badalona (Cape Cross (IRE)) **Sheikh Marwan Al Maktoum**
75 **HOT MUSTARD,** b c 20/2 Pastoral Pursuits—Lihou Island (Beveled (USA)) (55000) **Mrs G. Rowland-Clark**
76 **HUNTSMANS CLOSE,** b c 20/4 Elusive Quality (USA)—Badminton (Zieten (USA)) **Sheikh Marwan Al Maktoum**
77 **JADESNUMBERONE (IRE),** b f 23/2 Authorized (IRE)—
                                    Gabriella (Cape Cross (IRE)) (34481) **Sir Alex Ferguson & Mr Mike Dawson**
78 B c 20/2 Refuse To Bend (IRE)—Juniper Girl (IRE) (Revoque (IRE)) (13000) **M. B. Hawtin**
79 **KENSINGTON GARDENS,** b f 28/2 Oasis Dream—
                                    Wendylina (IRE) (In The Wings) **Mrs Julia Scott & Mr James Dean**
80 **KIMBERELLA,** b c 15/4 Kyllachy—Gleam of Light (IRE) (Danehill) (80952) **Mr K. J. P. Gundlach**
81 Ch f 9/2 Exceed And Excel (AUS)—Local Spirit (USA) (Lion Cavern (USA)) **Sheikh Marwan Al Maktoum**
82 B c 26/4 Elusive City (USA)—Lucky Norwegian (IRE) (Almutawakel) (52544) **The Royal Ascot Racing Club**
83 B c 15/4 Danehill Dancer (IRE)—Lucky Spin (Pivotal) (100000) **Mr K. J. P. Gundlach**
84 **OILINDA,** b f 23/2 Nayef (USA)—Loyal Love (USA) (Danzig (USA)) (50000) **Karmaa Racing Limited**
85 **POINT OF CONTROL,** b f 29/1 Pivotal—Finlaggan (Be My Chief (USA)) (250000) **Mr L. J. Inman**
86 **RISKIT FORA BISKIT (IRE),** b f 9/4 Kodiac—
                                    Miss Brief (IRE) (Brief Truce (USA)) (57142) **Mr C. Wright & The Hon Mrs J.M.Corbett**
87 **SABRE (IRE),** br c 16/2 Kheleyf (USA)—
                                    Spiritual Air (Royal Applause) (66666) **Highclere Thoroughbred Racing - Herbert Jones**
88 **SEEMENOMORE,** b c 27/2 Bahamian Bounty—Rise (Polar Falcon (USA)) (95000) **Mr K. J. P. Gundlach**

MR MICHAEL BELL—continued

89 B f 12/5 Cape Cross (IRE)—Shadow Roll (IRE) (Mark of Esteem (IRE)) **Sheikh Marwan Al Maktoum**
90 B c 22/4 Kyllachy—Some Diva (Dr Fong (USA)) (49260) **Mrs S. M. Roy**
91 SOUVENIR, b f 1/2 Cape Cross (IRE)—Trianon (Nayef (USA)) **Her Majesty The Queen**
92 STAR OF ROHM, ch c 13/2 Exceed And Excel (AUS)—
        Noble Desert (FR) (Green Desert (USA)) (32000) **Mrs Louise Whitehead & Mr Chris Lomas**
93 B c 17/4 Danehill Dancer (IRE)—Tanami Desert (Lycius (USA)) (340000) **Mr L. J. Inman**
94 THE MANX MISSILE, ch c 25/1 Sakhee's Secret—Careless Freedom (Bertolini (USA)) (25000) **P. J. Ransley**
95 B c 15/3 Sir Percy—Tiger Spice (Royal Applause) (110000) **Saleh Al Homaizi & Imad Al Sagar**
96 Gr c 24/4 Dalakhani (IRE)—Venturi (Danehill Dancer (IRE)) (140000) **Mr L. J. Inman**
97 WE ARE CITY, b f 7/3 Elusive City (USA)—
        Musique Magique (IRE) (Mozart (IRE)) (22000) **Middleham Park Racing VI & Partner**

Assistant Trainer: George Scott

Jockey (flat): Hayley Turner, Jamie Spencer. **Apprentice:** Ian Burns, Thomas Hemsley.

---

36   MR CLIVE BENNETT, Dymock
Postal: Blacklands Farm, Normansland, Dymock, Gloucestershire, GL18 2BE
Contacts: **PHONE (01531) 890206 MOBILE (07775) 763000**

1 RYE CROSS (IRE), 5, b g Catcher In The Rye (IRE)—Jeanette Hall (IRE) **C. J. Bennett**
2 5, B g Vinnie Roe (IRE)—Soy Alegre (IRE) **C. J. Bennett**

Assistant Trainer: Emma Alvis

---

37   MR JAMES BENNETT, Wantage
Postal: 2 Filley Alley, Letcombe Bassett, Wantage, Oxfordshire, OX12 9LT
Contacts: **PHONE (01235) 762163 FAX (01235) 762163 MOBILE (07771) 523076**
E-MAIL jabennett@tiscali.co.uk

1 KING'S ALCHEMIST, 7, b g Slickly (FR)—Pure Gold **Miss J. C. Blackwell**
2 PRINCESSE KATIE (IRE), 6, b m Presenting—Another Shot (IRE) **Miss J. C. Blackwell**

Assistant Trainer: Miss J. Blackwell

Amateur: Mr M. T. Stanley.

---

38   MR ALAN BERRY, Cockerham
Postal: Moss Side Racing Stables, Crimbles Lane, Cockerham, Lancashire, LA2 0ES
Contacts: **PHONE (01524) 791179 FAX (01524) 791958 MOBILE (07880) 553515**
E-MAIL mosssideracing@tiscali.co.uk WEBSITE www.alanberryracing.co.uk

1 ANDRASTA, 7, b m Bertolini (USA)—Real Popcorn (IRE) **A. Berry**
2 BYGONES FOR COINS (IRE), 4, ch f Danroad (AUS)—Reservation (IRE) **A. Berry**
3 DAWN MYSTERY, 8, gr m Daylami (IRE)—Frustration **A. Berry**
4 DE LESSEPS (USA), 4, ch c Selkirk (USA)—Suez **J. W. Barrett**
5 GRETHEL (IRE), 8, b m Fruits of Love (USA)—Stay Sharpe (USA) **A. Berry**
6 KING BERTOLINI (IRE), 5, b h Bertolini (USA)—Bareilly (USA) **A. Berry**
7 MYFOURTHBOY, 5, b g Grape Tree Road—Firedancer **Ms S. A. Crossman**
8 ONE MORE CENT, 7, b m Karinga Bay—One More Dime (IRE)
9 ROYAL BLADE (IRE), 5, ch g Needwood Blade—Royal Dream **A. B. Parr**
10 SPREAD BOY (IRE), 5, b g Tagula (IRE)—Marinka **A. Berry**

THREE-YEAR-OLDS

11 ESSEXVALE (IRE), b f Moss Vale (IRE)—Danccalli (IRE) **A. B. Parr**
12 NEVER IN (IRE), b f Elusive City (USA)—Priceoflove (IRE) **Mr J. P. Smith**
13 RIVER NOVA, b f Avonbridge—Assistacat (IRE) **A. B. Parr**
14 SCRIPT, b f Firebreak—Signs And Wonders **Mr T. G. & Mrs M. E. Holdcroft**

Jockey (flat): Franny Norton. **Apprentice:** Billy Cray. **Amateur:** Miss Sarah Richardson.

39 MR J. A. BERRY, Blackwater
Postal: Ballyroe, Blackwater, Enniscorthy, Co. Wexford, Ireland
Contacts: **PHONE (00353) 53 9127205 MOBILE (00353) 53 8625 57537**

1 **ACRIVEEN (IRE)**, 10, ch g Accordion—Raheen River (IRE) **M. Devine**
2 **ANGLES HILL (IRE)**, 5, b g Heron Island (IRE)—No Tails Told (IRE) **D. Roche**
3 **BACK IN A FLASH (IRE)**, 6, ch m Pilsudski (IRE)—Classic Enough **Ballyroe Syndicate**
4 **BALLYROE RAMBLER (IRE)**, 5, br g Lahib (USA)—Victoria's Rose (IRE) **J. A. Berry**
5 **CIVENA (IRE)**, 6, b m Oscar (IRE)—The Village Merc (IRE) **Go For It Syndicate**
6 **COOTAMUNDRA (IRE)**, 9, ch g Broken Hearted—Sigginstown **Turbine Syndicate**
7 **FAMOUS BALLERINA (IRE)**, 4, b f Golan (IRE)—World of Ballet (IRE) **Mrs Anna Berry**
8 **GIVE US A HAND (IRE)**, 10, br g Anshan—Desperado Dawn (IRE) **Mrs Joan Berry**
9 **HOT OR WHAT (IRE)**, 8, br m Bob's Return (IRE)—Takeaway Curry **Mrs Joan Berry**
10 **LIVE ACT (IRE)**, 6, ch m Snurge—Crosschild (IRE) **M. Berry**
11 **MICK THE TOOTH (IRE)**, 9, ch g Broken Hearted—Strong Edition (IRE) **J. P. McManus**
12 **PARNELL STREET (IRE)**, 8, gr g Great Palm (USA)—Fashionista (IRE) **J.P. McManus**
13 **PRETTY HAPPY (IRE)**, 10, b m Shernazar—Cash It In (IRE) **Mrs Joan Berry**
14 **RATHER CURIOUS (IRE)**, 8, b g Corrouge (USA)—Imlistening (IRE) **Mrs Anna Berry**
15 **SAVELLO (IRE)**, 6, ch g Anshan—Fontaine Frances (IRE) **Go For It Syndicate**
16 **SILVER CAVALIER (IRE)**, 6, gr g Sonus (IRE)—Benaughlin (IRE) **Not For Friends Syndicate**
17 **SWEET MARIA (IRE)**, 6, b m Luso—Over The Sands (IRE) **Mrs Anna Berry**
18 **VILLAGE WHISPERS (IRE)**, 5, b g Classic Cliche (IRE)—Raheen River (IRE) **P. Byrne**
19 **WHATS ON THE MENU (IRE)**, 8, ch g Anshan—Leading Dream (IRE) **Mrs Joan Berry**

Assistant Trainer: Blain Parnell

Jockey (NH): R. Moran. **Amateur:** Mr M. J. Scallan, Miss S.K. McCarthy, Mr A. O'Neill.

40 MR JOHN BERRY, Newmarket
Postal: Beverley House Stables, Exeter Road, Newmarket, Suffolk, CB8 8LR
Contacts: **PHONE (01638) 660663**
WEBSITE www.beverleyhousestables.com

1 **ALCALDE**, 6, b g Hernando (FR)—Alexandrine (IRE) **The Alhambra Partnership**
2 **ASTERISK**, 5, b m Fantastic Light (USA)—Sydney Star **J. C. De P. Berry**
3 **BATGIRL**, 5, ch m Mark of Esteem (IRE)—Serriera (FR) **Mr Tony Fordham**
4 **DOUCHKIRK (FR)**, 5, b g Prince Kirk (FR)—Douchka (FR) **The Beverley Hillbillies**
5 **DR DARCEY**, 4, b g Dr Fong (USA)—Ballet **Aristotle's Elements**
6 **ETHICS GIRL (IRE)**, 6, b m Hernando (FR)—Palinisa (FR) **The 1997 Partnership**
7 **EXTREME CONVICTION (IRE)**, 8, b g Danehill Dancer (IRE)—Nousaiyra (IRE) **All Points West Partnership**
8 **FIRST PRESSING**, 4, b f Bertolini (USA)—Lady Donatella **The Oil & Water Partnership**
9 **KADOUCHSKI (FR)**, 8, b g Ski Chief (USA)—Douchka (FR) **J. C. De P. Berry**
10 **OSCAR BERNADOTTE**, 4, b g Sulamani (IRE)—Desiree (IRE) **Mrs Emma Berry**
11 **RUBY IN THE DUST**, 5, b m Doyen (IRE)—Nijmah **Mrs Emma Berry**
12 **SILKEN THOUGHTS**, 4, b f Tobougg (IRE)—The Jotter **The Renewal Partnership**

THREE-YEAR-OLDS

13 **GIFT OF SILENCE**, gr f Cadeaux Genereux—Not A Word **Mr H. R. Moszkowicz**
14 **GRAND LIAISON**, b f Sir Percy—Dancinginthedark (IRE) **Barrie Catchpole & Michael Meaney**
15 **KARMA CHAMELEON**, b g Haafhd—Mrs Snaffles (IRE) **EERC**
16 **SAIL PAST**, b f Beat Hollow—Serriera (FR) **Mrs M. L. Parry & Mr P. M. Steele-Mortimer**
17 **WASABI (IRE)**, b f Tiger Hill (USA)—Quinzey (JPN) **Mr Tony Fordham**
18 **ZAROSA**, b f Barathea (IRE)—Shantalla Peak (IRE) **Mr R. G. Vicarage**

TWO-YEAR-OLDS

19 **JACK IRISH**, b g 3/5 Bertolini (USA)—Desiree (IRE) (Desert Story (IRE))
20 **MANY LEVELS**, br c 3/3 Nayef (USA)—Polygueza (FR) (Be My Guest (USA)) (24000) **Mr J. Hathorn**
21 **ROY ROCKET (FR)**, gr g 2/4 Layman (USA)—Minnie's Mystery (FR) (Highest Honor (FR)) **J. C. De P. Berry**

Other Owners: Mr C. Aarons, Mr W. F. Benter, Mr Claude Berry, Mr Jeremy Bond, Mr Stuart Bradie, Mrs Jane Braithwaite, Mr Andrew Brannon, Mrs Rebecca Byrne, Mr Justin Byrne, Ms Jane Duscherer, Mr Richard Fleck, Mr Ken Gibbs, Mr G. Grimstone, Mrs Fiona Hathorn, Mr Philip Holden, Mr D. J. Huelin, Mr Richard Jones, Mr Steve Jones, Mr Luke Kingston, Mr Steve Lee, Mr Kevan Leggett, Miss L. McCarthy, Mrs I. McCarthy, Mr S. McCormack, Mr L. Norris, Mr P. Onslow, Mrs M. L. Parry, Mr P. Steele-Mortimer, Ms J. Strong, Mr P. Temple, Mr Graham P. Triefus, Mrs Roxana S. Triefus, Mr Tim Trounce, Mr Matt Trounce, Mr Colin Vautier, Mr L. C. Wadey, Ms Sarah Louise Williams, Mrs D. Williams.

MR JOHN BERRY—continued

Assistant Trainer: Hugh Fraser

Jockey (flat): Cathy Gannon, Robert Havlin, Tom McLaughlin, Iva Milickova, Franny Norton. **Jockey (NH):** Will Kennedy. **Apprentice:** Hannah Nunn. **Amateur:** Mr J. Insole.

 MR JOHN BERWICK, North Bovey
Postal: **Cullensmoor, North Bovey, Newton Abbot, Devon, TQ13 8RB**
Contacts: **PHONE (01647) 440192 MOBILE (07710) 406605**
E-MAIL john.berwick224@btinternet.com

1 BLAKENEYS PET (IRE), 6, b m Celtic Swing—Kathryn's Pet **J. H. Berwick**

Jockey (NH): Tom O'Connor.

 MR JIM BEST, Lewes
Postal: **Grandstand Stables, The Old Racecourse, Lewes, East Sussex, BN7 1UR**
Contacts: **PHONE (01435) 882073 (01273) 480249 FAX (01435) 882073 MOBILE (07968) 743272**
E-MAIL jimandtombest@btinternet.com WEBSITE www.jimandtombestracing.co.uk

1 ACE FIGHTER PILOT, 6, b g Silver Patriarch (IRE)—Vedra (IRE) **Odds On Racing**
2 BALLYTURN BOY (IRE), 6, b g Alderbrook—Sakina (IRE) **Mr B. Reilly**
3 BEGGAR'S OPERA (IRE), 5, b g Singspiel (IRE)—Hannda (IRE) **David & Jane George**
4 BLUELAND (IRE), 13, b m Bigstone (IRE)—Legally Delicious **L. Best**
5 BOLLIN JUDITH, 6, br m Bollin Eric—Bollin Nellie **Mr J. J. Callaghan**
6 CASTLE MYTH (USA), 6, b br g Johannesburg (USA)—Castlemania (CAN) **Fruits Incorporated**
7 CAVE OF THE GIANT (IRE), 10, b g Giant's Causeway (USA)—Maroussie (FR) **Mr J. D. Maskell**
8 COMMANCHE DAWN, 10, b m Commanche Run—Charlycia **Goodwood Starlight Partnership**
9 DOT'S DELIGHT, 8, b m Golden Snake (USA)—Hotel California (IRE) **M. G. Rimell**
10 DUBAWI DANCER, 4, ch f Dubawi (IRE)—Adees Dancer **Mr F W Golding & E Kirtland**
11 FREE SPEECH, 9, b g King's Best (USA)—Daring Miss **Mr B. Reilly**
12 GOODWOOD STARLIGHT (IRE), 7, br g Mtoto—Starring (FR) **Goodwood Starlight Partnership**
13 ICE BELLINI, 7, ch m Erhaab (USA)—Peach Sorbet (IRE) **Palace Brewers**
14 KING OF CASTILE, 8, ch g Hernando (FR)—Pato **Silverton Racing Inc**
15 MANGONEL, 8, ch m Beckett (IRE)—Apachee Flower **Mr J. J. Callaghan**
16 MURCHAN HIGH (IRE), 7, b m Rainbow High—Murchan Tyne (IRE) **C. F. Harrington**
17 ONLY HOPE, 8, b m Marju (IRE)—Sellette (IRE) **Mr S. A. Jones**
18 PERFECT SHOT (IRE), 6, b g High Chaparral (IRE)—Zoom Lens (IRE) **Mr C. Hui**
19 ROCKY RYAN (IRE), 9, b g Even Top (IRE)—The Dara Queen **Mr & Mrs F. W. Golding**
20 SCHOOL FOR SCANDAL (IRE), 4, b g Pivotal—Sensation **Goodwood Starlight Partnership**
21 SHARAKTI (IRE), 5, b g Rakti—Easter Parade **The Sharakti Partnership**
22 SUDDEN LIGHT (IRE), 6, b m Presenting—Coolshamrock (IRE) **M&R Refurbishments Ltd**
23 TUSCANY STAR (IRE), 9, ch g Fourstars Allstar (USA)—Merendas Sister **The Prophets**
24 WAYWARD GLANCE, 4, b g Sadler's Wells (USA)—Daring Aim **Mr J. J. Callaghan**
25 WESTERN HIGH, 7, b g Rainbow High—Western Ploy **Fruits Incorporated**

Other Owners: Mr S. B. Bull, G. E. Butters, Mr J. Cumber, Mr J. Cumber, Mr P. E. Gardener, Mr P. J. Gardner, Mr D. W. George, Mrs J. George, Mrs M. J. Golding, Mr F. W. Golding, Mr T. J. Good, S. P. Graham, Mr R. Grice, E. M. Kirtland, Mr S. Ratcliff, Mrs S. Ratcliff, Mr G. C. Sales.

Assistant Trainer: Mr T. Best

Jockey (NH): Marc Goldstein, A. P. McCoy.

 MR JOHN BEST, Maidstone
Postal: **Scragged Oak Farm, Scragged Oak Road, Hucking, Maidstone, Kent, ME17 1QU**
Contacts: **PHONE (01622) 880276 FAX (01622) 880525 MOBILE (07889) 362154**
E-MAIL john.best@johnbestracing.com WEBSITE www.johnbestracing.com

1 ALFRESCO, 8, b g Mtoto—Maureena (IRE) **Mrs A. M. Riney**
2 ARCTIC LYNX (IRE), 5, b g One Cool Cat (USA)—Baldemara (FR) **Heading For The Rocks Partnership**
3 BAHRI SHEEN (IRE), 4, b g Bahri (USA)—Kama's Wheel **Kingsgate Racing 2**
4 CASUAL MOVER (IRE), 4, b c Diamond Green (FR)—Baileys On Line **Brian Goodyear & Rhonda Wilson**

MR JOHN BEST—continued

5 **EREKA (IRE)**, 4, ch f Tau Ceti—Most-Saucy **Mrs A. M. Riney**
6 **GETCARTER**, 6, b g Fasliyev (USA)—Pourquoi Pas (IRE) **Mrs J. K. Powell**
7 **HECTON LAD (USA)**, 5, b br g Posse (USA)—Foxy Queen **H. J. Jarvis**
8 **MANCUNIAN (IRE)**, 4, b c Motivator—Winesong (IRE) **Mr S. D. Malcolm**
9 **PRINCE AYOOB**, 4, b g Noverre (USA)—Santiburi Girl **Mr J. R. Best**
10 **SKETCHY EVIDENCE (USA)**, 4, ch c Officer (USA)—Drawing A Blank (USA) **Splinter Group**
11 **SONNY G (IRE)**, 5, ch h Desert Sun—Broughton Zest **Mr J. R. Best**
12 **SOWETO STAR (IRE)**, 4, ch g Johannesburg (USA)—Lady of Talent (USA) **Mr J. R. Best**
13 **STONE OF FOLCA**, 4, b g Kodiac—Soyalang (FR) **Folkestone Racecourse Owners Group**
14 **STREWTH (IRE)**, 4, ch c Encosta de Lago (AUS)—Alpine Park (IRE) **Mr S. Malcolm & Mr J. Foulger**

THREE-YEAR-OLDS

15 **ARCTIC STRYKER**, b c Iceman—Khafayif (USA) **H. J. Jarvis**
16 **BAREBACK (IRE)**, b c Redback—Lady Lucia (IRE) **Malt, Malcolm & Gabriel**
17 **BAYLEYF (IRE)**, b c Kheleyf (USA)—Hi Katriona (IRE) **Graham Jones & Partners**
18 **BORIS THE BOLD**, b c Librettist (USA)—Santiburi Girl **Folkestone Racecourse Owners Group II**
19 **EL CALAFATE (USA)**, ch c Mr Greeley—Jive Talk (USA) **Mr S. D. Malcolm**
20 **GUNG HO JACK**, b g Moss Vale (IRE)—Bijan (IRE) **Mr J. Fletcher**
21 **INSTRUMENTALIST (IRE)**, b c Amadeus Wolf—Kobalt Sea (FR) **Kingsgate Racing 4**
22 **LOTARESPECT**, b f Byron—Epineuse **Mr J. R. Best**
23 **LUPO D'ORO (IRE)**, b g Amadeus Wolf—Vital Laser (USA) **Mr S. Malcolm, Mr M. Winwright & Mr P. Tindall**
24 **MISTER MACKENZIE**, br c Kodiac—Dazzling View (USA) **H. J. Jarvis**
25 **RED RAMESSES (IRE)**, br c Red Clubs (IRE)—Marasem **H. J. Jarvis**
26 **RETROMANIA (IRE)**, b g Moss Vale (IRE)—Vade Retro (IRE) **Wellbelove & Partners**
27 **SAFFRON PARK**, ch c Compton Place—Beacon Silver **Kingsgate Racing 3**
28 **SAUCY CAT (IRE)**, br f One Cool Cat (USA)—Most-Saucy **Mrs A. M. Riney**
29 **SHEIKH THE REINS (IRE)**, b c Iffraaj—Wychwood Wanderer (IRE) **Splinter Group**
30 **VALE OF LINGFIELD (IRE)**, b c Moss Vale (IRE)—Celtic Guest (IRE) **Lingfield Park Owners Club II**
31 **YALDING DANCER**, b f Zafeen (FR)—Daughters World **Mrs Bennett & Mr Schabacker**

TWO-YEAR-OLDS

32 Ch f 30/4 Dutch Art—Break of Dawn (USA) (Mt Livermore (USA)) (16000) **Mr S. Malcolm & Mr J. Foulger**
33 B c 1/1 Azamour (IRE)—Brixa (FR) (Linamix (FR)) (21346)
34 B c 17/2 Mujadil (USA)—Caro Mio (IRE) (Danehill Dancer (IRE)) (12380) **H. J. Jarvis**
35 B c 3/5 Pastoral Pursuits—Epineuse (Gorse) **Mr J. R. Best**
36 Ch c 2/4 Assertive—Fanciful Dancer (Groom Dancer (USA)) (4761) **Hucking Horses V**
37 **FEARLESS LAD (IRE)**, b c 17/4 Excellent Art—Souffle (Zafonic (USA)) (15599) **Mrs J. O. Jones**
38 **HATS OFF**, b c 10/3 Royal Applause—Miriam (Forzando) (31428) **Malt, Longman & Goulding**
39 Br f 3/3 Pastoral Pursuits—Hucking Harmony (IRE) (Spartacus (IRE)) **Five In Harmony**
40 **LE DELUGE (FR)**, b c 16/2 Oratorio (IRE)—
                                          Princess Sofia (UAE) (Pennekamp (USA)) (34482) **Goulding, Longman & Malt**
41 B c 10/2 Elusive Quality (USA)—Lilium (Nashwan (USA)) (22987) **Fuller, Demarco & Perkins**
42 Ch c 31/3 Muhtathir—Lumiere Rouge (FR) (Indian Ridge) (55829) **C. B. Goodyear**
43 B c 26/1 Holy Roman Emperor (IRE)—
                                          Paquita (IRE) (Sadler's Wells (USA)) (12315) **Longman, Goulding, Malt & Fuller**
44 B c 6/4 Moss Vale (IRE)—Perovskia (USA) (Stravinsky (USA)) (14285) **Hucking Horses V**
45 B c 17/3 Dubawi (IRE)—Retainage (USA) (Polish Numbers (USA)) **J. H. Mayne**
46 B c 24/3 Royal Applause—Sancia (IRE) (Docksider (USA)) (18882) **Malt, Howland, Sharp & Partners**
47 B f 27/3 Dubawi (IRE)—Santiburi Girl (Casteddu) **Laura Malcolm & Bob Malt**
48 B f 28/4 Pastoral Pursuits—Silver Miss (FR) (Numerous (USA)) (11428) **Mr J. R. Best**
49 B c 20/2 Amadeus Wolf—Thai Dye (UAE) (Jade Robbery (USA)) (18883) **C. B. Goodyear**
50 Ch c 25/3 Refuse To Bend (IRE)—Woodmaven (USA) (Woodman (USA)) (12380) **S. Nunn**
51 **YALDING DUTCH**, b c 17/4 Dutch Art—Daughters World (Agnes World (USA)) **Mrs J. A. Bennett**
52 B f 4/4 Pastoral Pursuits—Zaynah (IRE) (Kahyasi) **Watson & Malyon**

Other Owners: Mr J. Foulger, D. J. Goulding, Mr G. R. Jones, A. Longman, Mrs L. C. G. Malcolm, Mr R. C. Malt, Mr C. M. Newing, Mr P. Schabacker, M. J. Ward, Mr A. Watson, Mr M. J. Wellbelove, Mr S. Wellbelove, Mr S. J. Whelan, Miss H. J. Williams, Ms R. L. Wilson, Mr M. J. Winwright.

Assistant Trainer: Malcolm Ward

Jockey (flat): Steve Drowne, Luke Morris.

44 **MRS LOUISE BEST, Maidstone**
Postal: **Northdown Croft, Broad Street Hill, Hollingbourne, Maidstone, Kent, ME17 1QY**

THREE-YEAR-OLDS

1 **AWESOME ROCK (IRE)**, ch c Rock of Gibraltar (IRE)—Dangerous Diva (IRE) **Rock On Racing Partnership**
2 **JUSTBOOKIES DOTNET**, b g Kheleyf (USA)—Moly **Louise Best Racing & Martyn Cruse**

Other Owners: Mrs L. A. Best, Mr M. F. Cruse.

45 **MR JAMES BETHELL, Middleham**
Postal: **Thorngill, Coverham, Middleham, North Yorkshire, DL8 4TJ**
Contacts: PHONE **(01969) 640360** FAX **(01969) 640360** MOBILE **(07831) 683528**
E-MAIL jamesbethell@aol.com
WEBSITE www.clarendonracing.co.uk and www.jamesbethell.co.uk

1 **ALIVE AND KICKING**, 4, b g Compton Place—Strawberry Dale (IRE) **M. J. Dawson**
2 **APRESLEPETITBOIS**, 4, b f Proclamation (IRE)—Scotland The Brave **R. F. Gibbons**
3 **BRADBURY (IRE)**, 4, ch g Redback—Simonaventura (IRE) **Clarendon Thoroughbred Racing**
4 **CHARLCOT**, 4, ch g Monsieur Bond (IRE)—Miss Apricot **Mrs S. Bethell**
5 **DAMASCUS SYMPHONY**, 4, b f Pastoral Pursuits—Syrian Queen **Clarendon Thoroughbred Racing**
6 **FOSSGATE**, 11, ch g Halling (USA)—Peryllys **Mrs S. Bethell**
7 **GRANSTON (IRE)**, 11, gr g Revoque (IRE)—Gracious Gretclo **R. T. Vickers**
8 **HARTFORTH**, 4, ch g Haafhd—St Edith (IRE) **Clarendon Thoroughbred Racing**
9 **LITTLE BOB**, 11, ch g Zilzal (USA)—Hunters of Brora (IRE) **R. F. Gibbons**
10 **PINTRADA**, 4, b g Tiger Hill (IRE)—Ballymore Celebre (IRE) **Scotyork Partnership I**
11 **SPEY SONG (IRE)**, 4, b f Singspiel (IRE)—All Embracing (IRE) **Clarendon Thoroughbred Racing**
12 **WILL NOT**, 4, ch f Where Or When (IRE)—La Notte **L. B. Holliday**

THREE-YEAR-OLDS

13 **BOBS HER UNCLE**, b f Fair Mix (IRE)—Shazana **R. F. Gibbons**
14 **HOW SWEET IT IS (IRE)**, b f Kodiac—Yaqootah (USA) **Mr C. Wright & The Hon Mrs J.M.Corbett**
15 **LAST SUPPER**, b f Echo of Light—Scotland The Brave **R. F. Gibbons**
16 **MISTER BOB (GER)**, ch c Black Sam Bellamy (IRE)—Mosquera (GER) **R. F. Gibbons**
17 **RICH AGAIN (IRE)**, b g Amadeus Wolf—Fully Fashioned (IRE) **R. T. Vickers**
18 **RIGHT RESULT (IRE)**, b g Acclamation—Mist And Stone (IRE) **Chris Wright**
19 **SEVEN YEAR ITCH (IRE)**, b f Lawman (FR)—Stella Del Mattino (USA) **Clarendon Thoroughbred Racing**
20 B f Lucky Story (USA)—The Pen

TWO-YEAR-OLDS

21 **FAB LOLLY (IRE)**, b f 28/4 Rock of Gibraltar (IRE)—Violet Ballerina (IRE) (Namid) (24000)
22 Ch c 25/4 Byron—Hoh Hedsor (Singspiel (IRE)) (2857)
23 Ch c 28/3 Sakhee's Secret—Marakabei (Hernando (FR)) (18000)
24 B c 30/3 Iffraaj—Numerus Clausus (FR) (Numerous (USA)) (22000)
25 **RICH FOREVER (IRE)**, b c 13/3 Camacho—Sixfields Flyer (IRE) (Desert Style (IRE)) (24761) **R. T. Vickers**
26 B c 20/2 Motivator—Selkirk Sky (Selkirk (USA)) (10000)
27 **STARBOTTON**, b f 22/3 Kyllachy—Bonne Etoile (Diesis) (11000) **Clarendon Thoroughbred Racing**

Other Owners: Mrs James Bethell, Mr J. D. Bethell, The Hon Mrs J. M. Corbett, Mr Christopher Wright.

Assistant Trainer: Jessica Bethell

46 **MR EDWARD BEVAN, Hereford**
Postal: **Pullen Farm, Ullingswick, Herefordshire, HR1 3JQ**
Contacts: PHONE/FAX **(01432) 820370** MOBILE **(07970) 650347**

1 **BOLD CROSS (IRE)**, 9, b g Cape Cross (IRE)—Machicane Akaiito (IRE) **E. G. Bevan**
2 **BOLD DUKE**, 4, b g Sulamani (IRE)—Dominant Duchess **E. G. Bevan**
3 **REINETTE O'BRY**, 6, b m Sulamani (IRE)—Dominant Duchess **E. G. Bevan**

Assistant Trainer: I Pickard

47 MR GEORGE BEWLEY, Hawick
Postal: **South Dean Farm, Bonchester Bridge, Hawick, Roxburghshire, TD9 8TP**
Contacts: **PHONE (01450) 860651 MOBILE (07704) 924783**
E-MAIL southdean.farm@btconnect.com

1 **DIAMOND D'AMOUR (IRE)**, 6, gr g Danehill Dancer (IRE)—
Diamond Line (FR) **Mr J. Hope, Mr K. Twentyman & Mr J. Gibson**
2 **EASEMENT**, 9, b g Kayf Tara—Raspberry Sauce **G. T. Bewley**
3 **HOCKENHEIM (IRE)**, 11, b g Kadalko (FR)—Linka (FR) **WEB Racing & K. Twentyman**
4 **INOOGOO (IRE)**, 7, b g Great Palm (USA)—Ballindante (IRE) **EBB Racing**
5 **SOUTH LEINSTER (IRE)**, 7, b g Chevalier (IRE)—Easy To Please **Lucy Forbes & G. T. Bewley**
6 **TEERIE EXPRESS**, 11, b g Sir Harry Lewis (USA)—Trecento **G. T. Bewley**
7 **VENITZIA (IRE)**, 6, b br g Presenting—Bloom Berry **Hadrian's Warriors**

Other Owners: Mr Gordon Adamson, Mr G. T. Bewley, Mr R. H. Brown, Mr H. Brydon, Mr K. Carruthers, Mr Gary Etheridge, Mrs Lucy Forbes, Mr J. H. Gibson, Mr J. Hope, Mr Kevin Twentyman.

Conditional: Jonathon Bewley.

48 MR JOSEPH BEWLEY, Jedburgh
Postal: **Newhouse Cottage, Camptown, Jedburgh, Roxburghshire, TD8 6RW**
Contacts: **PHONE (01835) 840273 MOBILE (07758) 783910**
E-MAIL bewley18@tiscali.co.uk

1 **BURY PARADE (IRE)**, 6, br g Overbury (IRE)—Alexandra Parade (IRE) **J. R. Bewley**
2 6, B g Pasternak—Carousel Music **J. R. Bewley**

Assistant Trainer: Mrs K Bewley

Conditional: Ryan Mania. **Amateur:** Mr Callum Bewley.

49 MR SAEED BIN SUROOR, Newmarket
Postal: **Godolphin Office, Snailwell Road, Newmarket, Suffolk, CB8 7YE**
The following list has not been supplied by the trainer and is as accurate as possible at the time of going to press. Some horses listed may not return to Britain from Dubai. Only 2yos entered in the 2013 Derby are shown. **For the latest information visit www.godolphin.com**

1 **AFRICAN STORY**, 5, ch h Pivotal—Blixen (USA)
2 **AL AASIFH (IRE)**, 4, b g Invincible Spirit (IRE)—Urgele (FR)
3 **ALKIMOS (IRE)**, 4, b c High Chaparral (IRE)—Bali Breeze (IRE)
4 **BAB AL SALAM (USA)**, 6, b h Seeking The Gold (USA)—Encandiladora (ARG)
5 **BANK MERGER (USA)**, 5, ch h Consolidator (USA)—Lucrative (USA)
6 **BIG AUDIO (IRE)**, 5, b g Oratorio (IRE)—Tarbela (IRE)
7 **BUFFUM (USA)**, 4, b c Bernardini (USA)—Storm Beauty (USA)
8 **BURJ HATTA (USA)**, 4, b br g Kingmambo (USA)—Vadahilla (FR)
9 **BURJ NAHAR**, 5, b h Shamardal (USA)—Melikah (IRE)
10 **CAMPANOLOGIST (USA)**, 7, b h Kingmambo (USA)—Ring of Music
11 **CAVALRYMAN**, 6, b h Halling (USA)—Silversword (FR)
12 **CAYMANS (AUS)**, 7, b g Secret Savings (USA)—Easy Out (AUS)
13 **CHABAL (IRE)**, 5, b g Galileo (IRE)—Vagary (IRE)
14 **CHOCK A BLOCK (IRE)**, 6, gr g Dalakhani (IRE)—Choc Ice (IRE)
15 **COLONIAL (IRE)**, 5, b h Cape Cross (IRE)—Elizabeth Bay (USA)
16 **COLOUR VISION (FR)**, 4, gr g Rainbow Quest (USA)—Give Me Five (GER)
17 **CON ARTIST (IRE)**, 5, b h Invincible Spirit (IRE)—Hoodwink (USA)
18 **DARLEY SUN (IRE)**, 6, b h Tiger Hill (IRE)—Sagamartha
19 **DELEGATOR**, 6, b h Dansili—Indian Love Bird
20 **DO IT ALL (USA)**, 5, b br h Distorted Humor (USA)—Stupendous Miss (USA)
21 **EMERALD COMMANDER (IRE)**, 5, b h Pivotal—Brigitta (IRE)
22 **EMIRATES CHAMPION**, 6, b h Haafhd—Janaat
23 **EMIRATES DREAM (USA)**, 5, b g Kingmambo (USA)—My Boston Gal (USA)
24 **ENAK (ARG)**, 6, b h Orpen (USA)—Enfeite (ARG)
25 **ESTOURAH (IRE)**, 4, b g Dalakhani (IRE)—Canouan (IRE)
26 **FALLEN IDOL**, 5, b h Pivotal—Fallen Star
27 **FARHH**, 4, b c Pivotal—Gonbarda (GER)
28 **FLAG OFFICER**, 4, b g Dubai Destination (USA)—Dusty Answer

MR SAEED BIN SUROOR—continued

29 **GLOBAL CITY (IRE)**, 6, b h Exceed And Excel (AUS)—Victory Peak
30 **GRAND VENT (IRE)**, 4, b c Shirocco (GER)—Housa Dancer (FR)
31 **HOLBERG (UAE)**, 6, b h Halling (USA)—Sweet Willa (USA)
32 **HONOUR SYSTEM (IRE)**, 5, ch g King's Best (USA)—Rawabi
33 **HUNTER'S LIGHT (IRE)**, 4, ch c Dubawi (IRE)—Portmanteau
34 **INVISIBLE MAN**, 6, ch g Elusive Quality (USA)—Eternal Reve (USA)
35 **KHAWLAH (IRE)**, 4, b f Cape Cross (IRE)—Villarrica (USA)
36 **KIDNAPPED (AUS)**, 6, b g Viscount (AUS)—Youthful Presence (AUS)
37 **LAATAFREET (IRE)**, 4, ch c Singspiel (IRE)—Cerulean Sky (IRE)
38 **LES TROYENS**, 4, b c Librettist (USA)—Native Blue
39 **LEY HUNTER (USA)**, 5, b h Kingmambo (USA)—Lailani
40 **LOST IN THE MOMENT (IRE)**, 5, b h Danehill Dancer (IRE)—Streetcar (IRE)
41 **MAN OF ACTION (USA)**, 5, ch g Elusive Quality (USA)—Dixie Melody (USA)
42 **MASTEROFTHEROLLS (IRE)**, 4, b c Refuse To Bend (IRE)—Miss Sally (IRE)
43 **MENDIP (USA)**, 5, b br h Harlan's Holiday (USA)—Well Spring (USA)
44 **MODEYRA**, 5, br m Shamardal (USA)—Zahrat Dubai
45 **MODUN (IRE)**, 5, br g King's Best (USA)—Olympienne (IRE)
46 **MY FREEDOM (IRE)**, 4, b g Invincible Spirit (IRE)—Priere
47 **PISCO SOUR (USA)**, 4, b br c Lemon Drop Kid (USA)—Lynnwood Chase (USA)
48 **PRINCE BISHOP (IRE)**, 5, ch g Dubawi (IRE)—North East Bay (USA)
49 **PRINCE SIEGFRIED (FR)**, 6, b g Royal Applause—Intrum Morshaan (IRE)
50 **QUICK WIT**, 5, b h Oasis Dream—Roo
51 **RETRIEVE (USA)**, 5, b h Rahy (USA)—Hold To Ransom (USA)
52 **RIO DE LA PLATA (USA)**, 7, ch h Rahy (USA)—Express Way (ARG)
53 **ROAYH (USA)**, 4, ch g Speightstown (USA)—Most Remarkable (USA)
54 **RUMH (GER)**, 4, ch f Monsun (GER)—Royal Dancer (GER)
55 **SAAMIDD**, 4, b c Street Cry (IRE)—Aryaamm (IRE)
56 **SAJJHAA**, 5, b m King's Best (USA)—Anaamil (IRE)
57 **SARRSAR**, 5, b g Shamardal (USA)—Bahr
58 **SECRECY**, 6, b g King's Best (USA)—Wink
59 **SONGCRAFT (IRE)**, 4, b g Singspiel (IRE)—Baya (USA)
60 **SPRING OF FAME (USA)**, 6, b h Grand Slam (USA)—Bloomy (USA)
61 **START RIGHT**, 5, b g Footstepsinthesand—Time Crystal (IRE)
62 **TAHAAMAH**, 4, ch c King's Best (USA)—Russian Snows (IRE)
63 **TERDAAD (IRE)**, 4, ch g Shamardal (USA)—Akrmina
64 **WEALTHY (IRE)**, 5, b g Refuse To Bend (IRE)—Enrich (USA)
65 **WILLING FOE (USA)**, 5, b br g Dynaformer (USA)—Thunder Kitten (USA)
66 **YAA WAYL (IRE)**, 5, b g Whipper—Lidanna
67 **YASIR (USA)**, 4, b c Dynaformer (USA)—Khazayin (USA)

THREE-YEAR-OLDS

68 **A'JUBA**, b c Kingmambo (USA)—Arlette (IRE)
69 **AHZEEMAH (IRE)**, b g Dubawi (IRE)—Swiss Roll (IRE)
70 **AJAWEED (IRE)**, b f Singspiel (IRE)—Almansoora (USA)
71 **AL SAHAM**, b c Authorized (IRE)—Local Spirit (USA)
72 **ALMAAS (USA)**, ch c Hard Spun (USA)—Summer Dream Girl (USA)
73 **ANJAZ (USA)**, b f Street Cry (USA)—Playful Act (IRE)
74 **ASATIR (USA)**, b c Elusive Quality (USA)—Valid Warning (USA)
75 **ASIFA (IRE)**, b c Green Desert (USA)—Agata (FR)
76 **BLUE TIGER**, b g Pivotal—Poised (USA)
77 **DAMAR (IRE)**, b g Authorized (IRE)—North East Bay (USA)
78 **DESERT GAZELLE (USA)**, ch f Smart Strike (CAN)—Code Book (USA)
79 **EHKAM (USA)**, ch c Seeking The Gold (USA)—Ishtak
80 **EHTEDAAM (USA)**, b c Arch (USA)—Bow River Gold
81 **ESTIQBAAL**, b f Oasis Dream—Manayer (IRE)
82 **EXPERT FIGHTER (USA)**, ch c Dubai Destination (USA)—Porto Roca (AUS)
83 **FAMOUS POET (IRE)**, b c Exceed And Excel (AUS)—Asfurah (USA)
84 **FUTURE SECURITY (IRE)**, ch c Dalakhani (IRE)—Schust Madame (IRE)
85 **GOLD CITY (IRE)**, b c Pivotal—Storm Lily (USA)
86 **GOZLAN (USA)**, b br f Tiznow (USA)—Issaqueena (USA)
87 **GREAT TIMES (USA)**, b c Smart Strike (CAN)—Geminiani (USA)
88 **HANDSOME MAN (IRE)**, ch c Nayef (USA)—Danceabout
89 **IBTAHAJ**, b c Invincible Spirit (IRE)—Maroussies Wings (IRE)
90 **IHSAS (USA)**, ch f Rahy (USA)—Express Way (ARG)
91 **IHTIFAL**, b f Dansili—Zaeema

MR SAEED BIN SUROOR—continued

92 **IHTIRAAM (IRE)**, b f Teofilo (IRE)—Park Romance (IRE)
93 **INQADH (USA)**, b g Invasor (ARG)—Saywaan (USA)
94 **INTHAR (USA)**, ch c Medicean—Mont Étoile (IRE)
95 **INVISIBLE HUNTER (USA)**, ch c Rahy (USA)—Madeline P (USA)
96 **ITTASAL**, b f Any Given Saturday (USA)—Journalist (IRE)
97 **LAST FIGHTER (IRE)**, b g Cape Cross (IRE)—Launch Time (USA)
98 **LAYALI DUBAI (USA)**, b f Street Sense (USA)—Make My Heart Sing (USA)
99 **MAHKAMA (USA)**, b f Bernardini (USA)—Rahy Rose (USA)
100 **MIZBAH**, b g Dubai Destination (USA)—Candice (IRE)
101 **MIZWAAJ (IRE)**, b c Invincible Spirit (IRE)—My Dubai (IRE)
102 **MUHAMEE (IRE)**, ch c Proud Citizen (USA)—Santolina (USA)
103 **MUNTASIR (IRE)**, b c Distorted Humor (USA)—Mansfield Park
104 **MUTARJIM (USA)**, b c Dynaformer (USA)—Thunder Kitten (USA)
105 **MY LEADER (USA)**, b c Discreet Cat (USA)—Thousand Islands
106 **RASSAM (IRE)**, b br c Dansili—Vantive (USA)
107 **SADMA**, gr c Street Cry (IRE)—Blue Dress (USA)
108 **SAYTARA (IRE)**, b f Nayef (USA)—Celtic Silhouette (FR)
109 **SHIHAB (IRE)**, b c Dubawi (IRE)—Baya (USA)
110 **SHUJA (USA)**, b c Street Sense (USA)—Seba
111 **SILENT MOMENT (USA)**, ch f Giant's Causeway (USA)—Mari's Sheba (USA)
112 **TADMIR (USA)**, b br c Bernardini (USA)—Owsley (USA)
113 **TAJRIBA (IRE)**, b f Teofilo (IRE)—Caumshinaun (IRE)
114 **TAMARRUD**, b c Authorized (IRE)—Miss Hepburn (USA)
115 **TUMOOH (IRE)**, b f Authorized (IRE)—Sulaalah (IRE)

TWO-YEAR-OLDS

116 B c 23/2 Marju (IRE)—Almansoora (USA) (Bahri (USA))
117 B c 8/5 Nayef (USA)—Anna Palariva (IRE) (Caerleon (USA))
118 B c 13/3 New Approach (IRE)—Athreyaa (Singspiel (IRE))
119 B c 2/4 Raven's Pass (USA)—Aviacion (BRZ) (Know Heights (IRE))
120 B c 19/3 Street Cry (IRE)—Be Happy (BRZ) (Ghadeer (FR))
121 B c 15/5 Bernardini (USA)—Caffe Latte (IRE) (Seattle Dancer (USA))
122 B c 22/3 Dalakhani (IRE)—Carisolo (Dubai Millennium)
123 B c 28/1 Shamardal (USA)—Castaway Queen (IRE) (Selkirk (USA)) (110000)
124 B c 12/2 Authorized (IRE)—Chaturanga (Night Shift (USA)) (61576)
125 B c 1/2 New Approach (IRE)—Dress Uniform (USA) (Red Ransom (USA)) (190000)
126 Ch c 17/5 Singspiel (IRE)—Ejlaal (IRE) (Caerleon (USA))
127 B c 9/3 Distorted Humor (USA)—Emotion Parade (ARG) (Parade Marshal (USA))
128 B c 18/1 Street Cry (IRE)—Evil Empire (GER) (Acatenango (GER))
129 B c 9/3 Teofilo (IRE)—Fann (USA) (Diesis) (240000)
130 B c 21/3 New Approach (IRE)—Flashing Green (Green Desert (USA)) (86206)
131 B c 2/4 New Approach (IRE)—Gonbarda (GER) (Lando (GER))
132 B br c 21/3 Dubawi (IRE)—La Vinchina (GER) (Oasis Dream) (77996)
133 Ch c 10/2 Dubawi (IRE)—Laurena (GER) (Acatenango (GER)) (250000)
134 B c 8/2 Shamardal (USA)—Line Ahead (IRE) (Sadler's Wells (USA))
135 Ch c 4/5 Monsun (GER)—Mandellicht (IRE) (Be My Guest (USA))
136 B c 29/1 Teofilo (IRE)—Mawaakeb (USA) (Diesis)
137 Ch c 18/5 Raven's Pass (USA)—Mike's Wildcat (USA) (Forest Wildcat (USA))
138 B c 2/3 Raven's Pass (USA)—Mysterial (USA) (Alleged (USA))
139 B c 25/4 Shamardal (USA)—Neshla (Singspiel (IRE)) (160000)
140 B c 22/2 Nayef (USA)—Northern Melody (IRE) (Singspiel (IRE))
141 Ch c 12/4 New Approach (IRE)—One So Marvellous (Nashwan (USA)) (120000)
142 B c 5/2 Singspiel (IRE)—Oriental Dance (Fantastic Light (USA))
143 B c 29/3 Teofilo (IRE)—Ramona (Desert King (IRE)) (250000)
144 B c 2/3 Dubawi (IRE)—Reine Zao (FR) (Alzao (USA)) (98522)
145 B c 15/4 Teofilo (IRE)—Ruby Affair (IRE) (Night Shift (USA)) (85000)
146 B c 7/3 Street Cry (IRE)—Secret Charm (IRE) (Green Desert (USA))
147 Ch c 19/1 Hard Spun (USA)—Vague (USA) (Elusive Quality (USA))

50 **MR KEVIN BISHOP, Bridgwater**
Postal: **Barford Park Stables, Spaxton, Bridgwater, Somerset, TA5 1AF**
Contacts: **PHONE/FAX (01278) 671437 MOBILE (07816) 837610**
E-MAIL hevbishop@hotmail.com

1 CHILBURY HILL (IRE), 9, b g Bahhare (USA)—Fire Goddess **Mrs E. K. Ellis**
2 CRUISE IN STYLE (IRE), 6, b m Definite Article—Henrietta Street (IRE) **K. Bishop**
3 JUST SPOT, 5, ch m Baryshnikov (AUS)—Just Jasmine **Mrs E. K. Ellis**
4 QUEEN'S GROVE, 6, gr m Baryshnikov (AUS)—Just Jasmine **Mrs E. K. Ellis**
5 REDGRAVE DANCER, 6, gr m Baryshnikov (AUS)—Redgrave Bay **W. Davies**
6 STRATEGIC PLAN (FR), 9, ch g Pivotal—Peony Girl (FR) **Mr K. G. Evett**
7 SWAINS MEADOW, 7, ch m First Trump—Level Headed **Mr S. G. Atkinson**
8 WILD GROUND (IRE), 11, ch m Simply Great—Rapid Ground **Jim Kilduff & Ken Jones**
9 WITHY MILLS, 7, gr m Baryshnikov (AUS)—Gipsy Rose **Slabs & Lucan**

Other Owners: Mr Ken Jones, Mr K. J. Kilduff, Mr C. J. Macey, Mr C. H. Roberts.

Assistant Trainer: Heather Bishop

Jockey (NH): Johnny Farrelly. **Conditional:** James Best. **Amateur:** Mr Jo Park.

51 **MISS LINDA BLACKFORD, Tiverton**
Postal: **Shortlane Stables, Rackenford, Tiverton, Devon, EX16 8EH**
Contacts: **PHONE (01884) 881589 MOBILE (07887) 947832**
E-MAIL overthelast@talktalk.net WEBSITE www.overthelast.com

1 ARTIC JOURNEY (IRE), 8, b g Kasmayo—Bella Blue **Bridgehouse Bloodstock**
2 CHANCE ENCOUNTER (IRE), 6, gr g Anshan—Glittering Grit (IRE) **Bridgehouse Bloodstock**
3 EDWARD LEAR, 5, b g Refuse to Bend (IRE)—Darrery **Over De Last Racing**
4 ON THE BRIDGE (IRE), 7, b g Milan—Bay Dove **Mr Kit James**
5 ROMANY QUEST, 5, b g Nomadic Way (USA)—Dinkies Quest **D. J. Cocks**
6 ROOFTOP RAINBOW (IRE), 8, b g Lord Americo—Rulleena (IRE) **Bridgehouse Bloodstock**
7 SHADES OF AUTUMN (IRE), 7, ch g Anshan—Be Right (IRE) **Bridgehouse Bloodstock**

Other Owners: Miss L. A. Blackford, Bridgehouse Bloodstock, Mr David Cocks, Mr Kit James, Over De Last Racing, Mr Rob Pitcher, Exors of the late Mrs B. C. Pocock, Mr R. G. Ross, The Profile Partnership, Mr M. J. Vanstone, Mr Terry Wheatley.

Assistant Trainer: M J Vanstone

Jockey (NH): Nick Scholfield, Andrew Glassonbury. **Conditional:** John Kington. **Amateur:** Mr Joshua Guerriero.

52 **MR ALAN BLACKMORE, Hertford**
Postal: **'Chasers', Stockings Lane, Little Berkhamsted, Hertford, SG13 8LW**
Contacts: **PHONE (01707) 875060 MOBILE (07803) 711453**

1 MONROE PARK (IRE), 7, b g Spectrum (IRE)—Paloma Bay (IRE) **A. G. Blackmore**
2 OCCASIONALLY YOURS (IRE), 8, b g Moscow Society (USA)—Kristina's Lady (IRE) **A. G. Blackmore**

THREE-YEAR-OLDS

3 B g Sleeping Indian—Be Bop Aloha **A. G. Blackmore**

Assistant Trainer: Mrs P M Blackmore

Jockey (NH): Marc Goldstein. **Amateur:** Miss Emily Crossman.

53 **MR MICHAEL BLAKE, Trowbridge**
Postal: **Staverton Farm, Trowbridge, Wiltshire, BA14 6PE**

1 AKSOUN (IRE), 4, b g Red Ransom (USA)—Akdara (IRE) **Mrs V. A. Butcher**
2 ANNELKO, 5, b g Sulamani (IRE)—Creeking **Mr D. Prosser**
3 COME OUT FIRING (IRE), 10, b g Supreme Leader—Thegirlfromslane (IRE) **Staverton Owners Group**
4 DOLLY COLMAN (IRE), 4, br gr f Diamond Green (FR)—Absolutely Cool (IRE) **Mr K. Corke**

MR MICHAEL BLAKE—continued

5 **GORMANSTOWN CUCKOO**, 8, b g King's Theatre (IRE)—Cloud Cuckoo **Mrs V. A. Butcher**
6 **HASSADIN**, 6, ch g Reset (AUS)—Crocolat **H. M. W. Clifford**
7 **LAMPS**, 5, b g Dynaformer (USA)—Conspiring (USA) **Mrs V. A. Butcher**
8 **PACHA D'OUDAIRIES (FR)**, 9, b g Ungaro (GER)—Forlane V (FR) **Mrs J. M. Haines**
9 **ROYAL CHATELIER (FR)**, 7, b g Video Rock (FR)—Attualita (FR) **Mrs V. A. Butcher**
10 **SADLER'S STAR (GER)**, 9, b g Alwuhush (USA)—Sadlerella (IRE) **Mrs J. M. Haines**
11 **SAHRATI**, 8, ch g In The Wings—Shimna **Mark Holder Racing Limited**
13 **SAMUEL GEORGE**, 5, ch g Generous (IRE)—Digyourheelsin (IRE) **Muddiman & Hatchard**
13 **SOVEREIGN SPIRIT (IRE)**, 10, b g Desert Prince (FR)—Sheer Spirit (IRE) **Mark Holder Racing Limited**
14 **SPORTING BOY (IRE)**, 4, b g Barathea (IRE)—Sportsticketing (IRE) **H. M. W. Clifford**
15 **TORRENTIAL RAINE**, 4, b g Storming Home—La Riveraine (USA) **H. M. W. Clifford**
16 **WADSWICK BEN**, 10, b g El Conquistador—Country Town **Tim & Carolyn Barton Wadswick countrystore Ltd**

THREE-YEAR-OLDS

17 **MIDNIGHT SEQUEL**, b f Midnight Legend—Silver Sequel **Dajam Ltd**

Other Owners: T. Barton, Mrs C. A. Barton, M. J. Blake, Mrs S. E. Blake, Mr G. H. Hatchard, Mr M. A. Muddiman.

---

54   MR MICHAEL BLANSHARD, Upper Lambourn
Postal: **Lethornes Stables, Upper Lambourn, Hungerford, Berkshire, RG17 8QP**
Contacts: **PHONE (01488) 71091 (01488) 71315 (Home) FAX (01488) 73497
MOBILE (07785) 370093**
E-MAIL blanshard.racing@virgin.net WEBSITE www.michaelblanshard.co.uk

1 **ARCTIC MIRAGE**, 4, b g Iceman—Marysienka **J. Gale, J. Oliver & V. Ward**
2 **BAJAN BEAR**, 4, ch g Compton Place—Bajan Rose **C. McKenna**
3 **COPPERWOOD**, 7, ch g Bahamian Bounty—Sophielu **Mrs R. K. Wilkerson**
4 **HARVEST MIST (IRE)**, 4, ch f Captain Rio—Thaw **Mr C. C. Buckingham**
5 **KATCHMORE (IRE)**, 5, br g Catcher In The Rye (IRE)—One For Me **Sara Collie, Nigel Kelly & Alison Auvray**
6 **MAE CIGAN (FR)**, 9, gr g Medaaly—Concert **A. D. Jones**
7 **ROMAN STRAIT**, 4, b c Refuse To Bend (IRE)—Oman Sea (USA) **J. M. Beever**
8 **SAMMYMAN**, 5, b g Tamure (IRE)—Bajan Rose **C. McKenna**
9 **SECOND TO NUN (IRE)**, 6, b m Bishop of Cashel—One For Me **The Dragon Partnership No.2**
10 **SENTOSA**, 5, b m Dansili—Katrina (IRE) **Lady E. Mays-Smith**
11 **THE COMPOSER**, 10, b g Royal Applause—Superspring **A. D. Jones**

THREE-YEAR-OLDS

12 B c Lucky Story (USA)—Bajan Rose **C. McKenna**
13 B g Iceman—Bowden Rose
14 **DISHY GURU**, ch c Ishiguru (USA)—Pick A Nice Name **Clifton Partners**
15 **DOC HILL**, ch c Dr Fong (USA)—Cultural Role **S. Hinton**
16 **ICE LOCH**, gr c Avonbridge—Bountiful **Lady Bland**
17 **ICED OPAL**, ch f Iceman—Marysienka **J K Racing Club**
18 **LADY HEARTBEAT**, b f Avonbridge—Take Heart **A. D. Jones**
19 **POETRY WRITER**, ch g Byron—Away To Me **J K Racing Club**
20 **SAINT IRENE**, ch f Halling—Santorini (USA) **The Breeze-in Partnership**

TWO-YEAR-OLDS

21 B f 11/2 Sleeping Indian—Blaenavon (Cadeaux Genereux)
22 B f 22/3 Ad Valorem (USA)—Churn Dat Butter (USA) (Unbridled (USA)) (1000)
23 B f 17/2 Tamayuz—Cliche (IRE) (Diktat)
24 B f 9/2 Sakhee's Secret—Greensand (Green Desert (USA)) (952) **Mrs C. Ward**
25 B f 5/5 Beat Hollow—Shangazi (USA) (Miswaki (USA))
26 Br f 17/4 Danehill Dancer (IRE)—Speak Softly To Me (USA) (Ogygian (USA)) (27000) **J. M. Beever**

Other Owners: Mrs A. L. Auvray, Miss Sara E. Collie, Mr R. C. C. Gait, Mrs Hannah Gait, Mr John K. Gale, Mr N. R. Kelly, Mr Stuart McPhee, Mr M. J. Prescott, Mr C. D. Pritchard, Dr Mike Webley.

55 MR J. S. BOLGER, Carlow

Postal: Glebe House, Coolcullen, Carlow, Ireland
Contacts: PHONE (00353) 56 4443150 / (00353) 56 4443158 / (00353) 56 4443168
FAX (00353) 56 4443256
E-MAIL racing@jsb.ie

1 DANCING ON TURF (IRE), 4, b f Dalakhani (IRE)—Irish Question (IRE)
2 EMPRESS OF ROME (IRE), 4, b f Holy Roman Emperor (IRE)—Altarejos (IRE) Mrs J. Bolger
3 GLOR NA MARA (IRE), 4, b c Leroidesanimaux (BRZ)—Sister Angelina (USA) Mrs J. Bolger
4 GORT NA MONA (USA), 4, b br f Aldebaran (USA)—Autumn Rhythm Brian O'Connor
5 NAOISE (IRE), 4, ch c Stormy Atlantic (USA)—Machinale (USA) Mrs J. Bolger
6 QUILL AND VELLUM (IRE), 4, b g High Chaparral (IRE)—Arjooch (USA) Mrs J. Bolger
7 SINGE THE TURF (IRE), 4, ch c Galileo (IRE)—Affianced (IRE) Mrs J. Bolger
8 STATESMANSHIP, 4, b c Dubawi (IRE)—State Secret Sheikh Mohammed
9 WHIPLESS (IRE), 4, b c Whipper (USA)—Kimola (IRE) Mrs J. Bolger

THREE-YEAR-OLDS

10 ALLA SPERANZA, gr f Sir Percy—Alvarita Kirsten Rausing
11 AMHRASACH (IRE), b f Teofilo (IRE)—Irish Question (IRE) Mrs J. Bolger
12 AN GHALANTA (IRE), b f Holy Roman Emperor (IRE)—Alamanta (IRE) Mrs J. Bolger
13 AN SAINCHEANN (IRE), b f Dylan Thomas (IRE)—Uimhir A Haon (IRE) Mr M. D. Ryan
14 AQUILONIUS (IRE), b c Soviet Star (USA)—Via Verbano (IRE) Mrs J. Bolger
15 ASTEROID BELT (IRE), ch g Heliostatic (IRE)—Affaire Royale (IRE) Mrs J. Bolger
16 AURIFODINA (IRE), ch c Dylan Thomas (IRE)—Ovazione Mrs J. Bolger
17 BOUNDLESS HOPE (IRE), b c Teofilo (IRE)—Yukon Hope (USA) Mrs J. Bolger
18 CLEOFILA (IRE), b f Teofilo (IRE)—Altarejos (IRE) Mrs J. Bolger
19 CLOGHER COVE (IRE), b f Teofilo (IRE)—Shining Hour (USA) Ennistown Stud
20 CRUINNEAS (IRE), b f Westerner—Grinneas (IRE) Mrs J. Bolger
21 DAYRINA (IRE), b f Whipper (USA)—Darina (IRE) Mrs J. Bolger
22 DINARA (IRE), b f Bachelor Duke (USA)—Groves Royal (USA) Mrs J. Bolger
23 DYNAMITE DIXIE (IRE), b c Dylan Thomas (IRE)—Lavender Blue Mrs June Judd
24 EDGE OF SANITY (IRE), b c Invincible Spirit (IRE)—Saor Sinn (IRE) Mrs June Judd
25 FERE GRANDIS (USA), b f Mr Greeley (USA)—Unbridled Treasure (USA) Mrs J. Bolger
26 FERRYCARRIG (IRE), b c Manduro (GER)—Scribonia (GER) Mrs June Judd
27 FIONNUAR (IRE), b f Teofilo (IRE)—Six Nations (USA) Mrs J. Bolger
28 FOINSE (IRE), b f Teofilo (IRE)—Machinale (USA) Mrs J. Bolger
29 GOLDIROCKS (IRE), ch c Manduro (GER)—Gold Bust Mrs J. Bolger
30 HANNAH'S SMILE (IRE), br f Cape Cross (IRE)—Hannah Wiggles (USA) Mrs June Judd
31 HEAVY WEIGHT (IRE), b c Teofilo (IRE)—Sister Angelina (USA) Mrs J. Bolger
32 HIGHWATER EXPRESS (IRE), b c Holy Roman Emperor (IRE)—Fainne (IRE) Mrs June Judd
33 INVINCIBLE VINCE (IRE), b c Invincible Spirit (IRE)—Christmas Letter (IRE) Mrs June Judd
34 IVETA (IRE), b f Invincible Spirit (IRE)—Heir Today (IRE) Mrs J. Bolger
35 JANEY MUDDLES (IRE), b f Lawman (FR)—Slip Dance (IRE) Mrs June Judd & Mrs J S Bolger
36 LEGAL FARCE (IRE), b f Lawman (FR)—Manger Square (IRE) Mrs J. Bolger
37 LIGHT HEAVY (IRE), ch c Teofilo (IRE)—Siamsa (USA) Mrs J. Bolger
38 LIVIA GALILEI (IRE), b f Galileo (IRE)—Mohican Princess K. J. Molloy
39 LONRACH (IRE), b f Holy Roman Emperor (IRE)—Luminous One (IRE) Mrs J. Bolger
40 MANALISA (IRE), br f Manduro (GER)—Dark Indian (IRE) Mrs J. Bolger
41 MANALIVE (IRE), b c Manduro (GER)—Senora Galilei (IRE) Mrs J. Bolger
42 MIRACLE CURE (IRE), b c Whipper (USA)—Bring Back Matron (IRE) Mrs J. Bolger
43 MISS DYLAN (IRE), b f Dylan Thomas (IRE)—Marette (IRE) Mrs J. Bolger
44 MISS EKATERINA (IRE), b f Teofilo (IRE)—Najmati Mrs J. Bolger
45 MISTEIREACH (IRE), b f Cherokee Run (USA)—Wild Heaven (IRE) Mrs J. Bolger
46 MY FERE LADY (USA), ch f Mr Greeley (USA)—Saintly Hertfield (USA) Mrs J. Bolger
47 NATIONAL FIBRE (IRE), b c Invincible Spirit (IRE)—Geal Mo Chroi (IRE) Mrs J. Bolger
48 NIGHT INVADER (IRE), b c Teofilo (IRE)—Night Visit Mrs June Judd
49 OICHE GHEALAI (IRE), ch f Galileo (IRE)—Affianced (IRE) Mrs J. Bolger
50 PAENE MAGNUS (IRE), ch c Teofilo (IRE)—Luminaria (IRE) Mrs J. Bolger
51 PARISH HALL (IRE), b c Teofilo (IRE)—Halla Siamsa (IRE) Mrs J. Bolger
52 PATRIMONIUM (IRE), b f Green Desert (USA)—Patrimony Mrs J. Bolger
53 RIGOLETTA (IRE), b f Teofilo (IRE)—Zavaleta (IRE) Mrs J. Bolger
54 SIANSA (IRE), b f Teofilo (IRE)—Arjooch (IRE) Mrs J. Bolger
55 SOMETHING GRACEFUL, ch f Galileo (IRE)—Que Puntual (ARG) Mrs June Judd
56 STEADY HAND (IRE), b c Dylan Thomas (IRE)—April Evening (IRE) Mrs J. Bolger
57 TEODOLITE (IRE), ch f Teofilo (IRE)—Tamra Delight (USA) Mrs J. Bolger
58 TEOFOLINA (IRE), b f Teofilo (IRE)—Moon Unit (IRE) Mrs J. Bolger

MR J. S. BOLGER—continued

59 **TEOLANE (IRE)**, ch f Teofilo (IRE)—Masnada (IRE) **Mrs J. Bolger**
60 **THOMAS DYLAN (IRE)**, b c Dylan Thomas (IRE)—Virginia Rose (IRE) **Mrs June Judd**
61 **TIFFILIA (IRE)**, b f Macho Uno (USA)—Tiffed (USA) **Mrs J. Bolger**
62 **TIGER AT HEART (IRE)**, ch c Teofilo (IRE)—Julie Girl (USA) **Mrs June Judd**
63 **TWIN FOCUS (IRE)**, b c Galileo (IRE)—Twin Sails (USA) **Mrs J. Bolger**
64 **VASANTA NAVARATRI (IRE)**, b c Hurricane Run (IRE)—Vasanta (IRE) **Mrs June Judd**
65 **WHILE YOU WAIT (IRE)**, b c Whipper (USA)—Azra (IRE) **Mrs June Judd**
66 B f Holy Roman Emperor (IRE)—Witch of Fife (USA) **Mrs Joan Brosnan**

TWO-YEAR-OLDS

67 **ALPINIST**, b c 25/4 New Approach (IRE)—Alouette (Darshaan) **Mrs J. Bolger**
68 **BEDECKED (IRE)**, b f 7/3 Holy Roman Emperor (IRE)—Fainne (IRE) (Peintre Celebre (USA)) (820) **Mrs J. Bolger**
69 **BEYOND THANKFUL (IRE)**, b c 21/2 Whipper (USA)—Beyond Compare (IRE) (Galileo (IRE)) **Mrs J. Bolger**
70 **BUNAIRGEAD (IRE)**, b f 5/5 New Approach (IRE)—Montecito (Seeking The Gold (USA)) **Mrs J. Bolger**
71 **BUNREACHT (USA)**, gr c 21/3 Mr Greeley (USA)—
        Unbridled Treasure (USA) (Unbridled's Song (USA)) **Mrs J. Bolger**
72 B c 30/4 Teofilo (IRE)—Cache Creek (IRE) (Marju (IRE)) **Sheikh Mohammed**
73 **CHANCE TO DANCE (IRE)**, b c 19/5 Teofilo (IRE)—Crystal Ballet (IRE) (Royal Academy (USA)) **Mrs J. Bolger**
74 **CITY SQUARE (IRE)**, b f 10/3 Lawman (FR)—Manger Square (IRE) (Danehill (USA)) **Mrs J. Bolger**
75 **CLOCH CHORA (IRE)**, b c 8/5 Hurricane Run (IRE)—Vasanta (IRE) (Indian Ridge) **Mrs J. Bolger**
76 **DAWN APPROACH (IRE)**, ch c 23/4 New Approach (IRE)—
        Hymn of The Dawn (USA) (Phone Trick (USA)) **Mrs J. Bolger**
77 **EINSTEINS FOLLY (IRE)**, b c 8/5 Whipper (USA)—Azra (IRE) (Danehill (USA)) **Mrs J. Bolger**
78 **ELUSIVE MARETTE (IRE)**, b f 30/4 Elusive City (USA)—Marette (IRE) (Soviet Star (USA)) **Mrs J. Bolger**
79 **ERE YESTERDAY (IRE)**, b f 7/5 Invincible Spirit (IRE)—Heir Today (IRE) (Princely Heir (IRE)) **Mrs J. Bolger**
80 **FEILE BRIDE (IRE)**, b f 6/3 Dylan Thomas (IRE)—Teacht An Earraig (USA) (Galileo (IRE)) **Mrs J. Bolger**
81 **FEILE NA MBAN (IRE)**, b f 4/2 New Approach (IRE)—Ard Fheis (IRE) (Lil's Boy (USA)) **Mrs J. Bolger**
82 **GLOBAL REACH (IRE)**, ch f 20/3 Galileo (IRE)—Luminaria (IRE) (Danehill (USA)) **Mrs J. Bolger**
83 **GLOVE SMITH (IRE)**, b c 18/5 Teofilo (IRE)—Sukeena (IRE) (Brief Truce (USA)) **Mrs J. Bolger**
84 **GOLD BAND (IRE)**, ch c 27/2 Teofilo (IRE)—Gold Bust (Nashwan (USA)) **Mrs J. Bolger**
85 **HALLA NA SAOIRE (IRE)**, ch f 5/5 Teofilo (IRE)—Siamsa (USA) (Quest For Fame) **Mrs J. Bolger**
86 **IRISH BULLETIN (IRE)**, b c 20/5 Invincible Spirit (IRE)—Geal Mo Chroi (IRE) (Galileo (IRE)) **Mrs J. Bolger**
87 **LEARGAS (IRE)**, b c 20/3 Kheleyf (USA)—Derpat (IRE) (Invincible Spirit (IRE)) **Mrs J. Bolger**
88 **LEGS ON DISPLAY (IRE)**, b c 2/5 Duke of Marmalade (IRE)—Elida (IRE) (Royal Academy (USA)) **Mrs J. Bolger**
89 **LEITIR MOR (IRE)**, b c 27/1 Holy Roman Emperor (IRE)—Christinas Letter (IRE) (Galileo (IRE)) **Mrs J. Bolger**
90 **LOCH GARMAN (IRE)**, b c 12/4 Teofilo (IRE)—Irish Question (IRE) (Giant's Causeway (USA)) **Mrs J. Bolger**
91 **MAC LIR (USA)**, ch c 7/5 Majestic Warrior (USA)—Saintly Hertfield (USA) (Saint Ballado (CAN)) **Mrs J. Bolger**
92 **MIDFIELD GENERAL (IRE)**, gr c 26/5 Aussie Rules (USA)—
        High Stool Lady (USA) (Distant View (USA)) **Mrs J. Bolger**
93 **MONTFERRAT (IRE)**, b c 1/5 Invincible Spirit (IRE)—Alessandria (Sunday Silence (USA)) **Sheikh Mohammed**
94 **MORNING WITH IVAN (IRE)**, b f 29/1 Ivan Denisovich (IRE)—Grinneas (IRE) (Barathea (USA)) **Mrs J. Bolger**
95 **MOVE TO STRIKE (IRE)**, b c 5/5 Lawman (FR)—Alamanta (IRE) (Ali-Royal (IRE)) **Mrs J. Bolger**
96 **NEOPHILIA (IRE)**, b f 22/1 Teofilo (IRE)—Tiffed (USA) (Seattle Slew (USA)) **Mrs J. Bolger**
97 **NEW REGALIA (IRE)**, b f 15/2 New Approach (IRE)—Simonetta (IRE) (Lil's Boy (USA)) **Mrs J. Bolger**
98 **NEWS AT SIX (IRE)**, ch c 26/3 New Approach (IRE)—Dublin Six (USA) (Kingmambo (USA)) **Mrs J. Bolger**
99 **PACK THE PUNCH (IRE)**, b c 5/5 Teofilo (IRE)—Zavaleta (IRE) (Kahyasi) **Mrs J. Bolger**
100 **PEN TO PAPER (IRE)**, b c 18/5 Lawman (FR)—Aoibhneas (USA) (Dehere (USA)) **Mrs J. Bolger**
101 **PERFUME DAYS (IRE)**, b f 8/3 New Approach (IRE)—Marionnaud (IRE) (Spectrum (IRE)) **Mrs J. Bolger**
102 **PITCH 'N TOSS (IRE)**, b c 29/4 Teofilo (IRE)—Darina (IRE) (Danehill (USA)) **Mrs J. Bolger**
103 B f 20/4 Hannouma (IRE)—Prototype (Beat Hollow) **Sylvian Benillouche**
104 **QUICK FIZZ (IRE)**, b f 24/1 Bachelor Duke (USA)—Sherbet (IRE) (Alzao (USA)) (820) **Mrs J. Bolger**
105 **RAPID APPROACH (IRE)**, b c 2/5 New Approach (IRE)—Blas Ceoil (USA) (Mr Greeley (USA)) **Mrs J. Bolger**
106 **RING CRAFT (IRE)**, b c 8/5 Teofilo (IRE)—Masnada (IRE) (Erins Isle) **Mrs J. Bolger**
107 **RUNAIOCHT (IRE)**, ch c 7/3 Teofilo (IRE)—Julie Girl (USA) (Jules (USA)) **Mrs J. Bolger**
108 B c 22/3 Bachelor Duke (USA)—Saana (IRE) (Erins Isle) **Mrs J. Bolger**
109 **SCEILG (IRE)**, b f 17/4 Rock Hard Ten (USA)—Intriguing Humor (CAN) (Distorted Humor (USA)) **Mrs J. Bolger**
110 **SCINTILLULA (IRE)**, b f 15/5 Galileo (IRE)—Scribonia (USA) (Danehill (USA)) **Kirsten Rausing**
111 **SOLAR OUTBURST (IRE)**, ch f 31/5 Galileo (IRE)—Twin Sails (USA) (Boston Harbor (USA)) **Mrs J. Bolger**
112 B br f 22/4 Authorized (IRE)—Solas Na Greine (IRE) (Galileo (IRE)) **Mrs J. Bolger**
113 **SOPHISTICATED HEIR (IRE)**, b c 14/2 New Approach (IRE)—
        My Girl Sophie (USA) (Danzig (USA)) **Mrs June Judd**
114 B c 13/3 Hannouma (IRE)—Spark Sept (FR) (Septieme Ciel (USA)) (4105) **Sylvian Benillouche**
115 **STARLAND (IRE)**, b f 25/3 Galileo (IRE)—Key To Coolcullen (IRE) (Royal Academy (USA)) **Mrs J. Bolger**
116 **STRAPLESS (IRE)**, b f 21/5 Whipper (USA)—
        Bring Back Matron (IRE) (Rock of Gibraltar (IRE)) (820) **Mrs J. Bolger**

MR J. S. BOLGER—continued

117 **SUN ON THE RUN (IRE)**, b c 30/4 Whipper (USA)—Gaisce (IRE) (Bluebird (USA)) **Patrick Bolger**
118 B c 20/4 Hannouma (IRE)—Sweet Shop (Grand Lodge (USA)) (2463) **Sylvian Benillouche**
119 **TEOCHRIOS (IRE)**, b f 22/2 Teofilo (IRE)—Tamra Delight (USA) (Diesis) **Mrs J. Bolger**
120 **TEOCHT (IRE)**, b f 3/4 Teofilo (IRE)—Machinale (USA) (Kingmambo (USA)) **Mrs J. Bolger**
121 **TEOIRICIUIL (IRE)**, b f 14/5 Teofilo (IRE)—National Swagger (IRE) (Giant's Causeway (USA)) **Mrs J. Bolger**
122 **TEOIRIM (IRE)**, ch f 20/4 Teofilo (IRE)—Groves Royal (Royal Academy (USA)) **Mrs J. Bolger**
123 **TEORAINN (IRE)**, b f 30/5 Teofilo (IRE)—Six Nations (USA) (Danzig (USA)) **Mrs J. Bolger**
124 **TEORANTA (IRE)**, b f 30/4 Teofilo (IRE)—Arjooch (IRE) (Marju (IRE)) **Mrs J. Bolger**
125 **THE VISITOR (IRE)**, b c 5/4 Invincible Spirit (IRE)—Aeraiocht (IRE) (Tenby) **Mrs J. Bolger**
126 **THUS FAR (USA)**, b f 27/4 Cuvee (USA)—Fardus (IRE) (Danehill (USA)) **Mrs J. Bolger**
127 **TOBANN (IRE)**, b f 8/5 Teofilo (IRE)—Precipitous (IRE) (Indian Ridge) **Mrs J. Bolger**
128 **TOQUETTE (IRE)**, b f 13/3 Acclamation—Tariysha (IRE) (Daylami (IRE)) **John Corcoran**
129 **TRADING LEATHER (IRE)**, b c 20/3 Teofilo (IRE)—Night Visit (Sinndar (IRE)) **Mrs J. Bolger**
130 **VERBAL HONESTY (IRE)**, b f 13/4 Elusive City (USA)—Tus Maith (IRE) (Entrepreneur) (1641) **Mrs J. Bolger**
131 **WE'LL GO WALKING (IRE)**, b f 2/3 Authorized (IRE)—Senora Galilei (IRE) (Galileo (IRE)) **Mrs J. Bolger**
132 **WEXFORD OPERA (IRE)**, b br c 26/4 New Approach (IRE)—
                                         Sister Angelina (USA) (Saint Ballado (CAN)) **Mrs J. Bolger**
133 **WHIP STORM (IRE)**, b c 25/3 Whipper (USA)—Danemarque (AUS) (Danehill (USA)) (14778) **Mrs J. Bolger**
134 **ZELIE MARTIN (IRE)**, b f 6/5 Invincible Spirit (IRE)—Saor Sinn (IRE) (Galileo (IRE)) **Mrs J. Bolger**

Jockey (flat): K.J. Manning, R. P. Cleary. **Apprentice:** David Parkes, Conor Walsh, Ronan Whelan.

---

56   **MRS MYRIAM BOLLACK-BADEL, Lamorlaye**
Postal: **20 Rue Blanche, 60260 Lamorlaye, France**
Contacts: **(0033) 9600 53602 FAX (0033) 3442 13367 MOBILE (0033) 6108 09347**
E-MAIL myriam.bollack@gmail.com WEBSITE www.myriam-bollack.com

1 **BREAD LOFT (FR)**, 4, ch c Touch of The Blues (FR)—Jamouna (FR)
2 **EL MARIACHI (FR)**, 4, gr g Chichicastenango (FR)—Marviah (USA)
3 **GLASCLUNE (IRE)**, 5, b br h Slickly (FR)—Guanhumara
4 **HELIODORO (FR)**, 4, b g Miesque's Son (USA)—Hokey Pokey (FR)
5 **HENRY MORGANN (FR)**, 8, gr g Take Risks (FR)—Hokhmah
6 **KANOTIER (FR)**, 4, b c Daliapour (IRE)—Knout (FR)
7 **KATMANDOUNE (FR)**, 4, b f Country Reel (USA)—Louvardie (FR)
8 **KAZAYA (IRE)**, 5, b m Kahyasi—Sanagora (IRE)
9 **LONG JOHN SILVER (FR)**, 7, b g Marchand de Sable (USA)—Lune Et L'autre
10 **NUMEROLOGIE (FR)**, 6, b m Numerous (USA)—Operam
11 **OH OH (FR)**, 5, b m Vettori (IRE)—Anna Francesca (FR)
12 **PASSING CLOUD (FR)**, 4, b f Barathea (IRE)—Dance Treat (USA)
13 **PEACE KEEPER (FR)**, 6, b g Namid—Desirous of Peace
14 **SUCH A MAJ (FR)**, 4, ch c Soave (GER)—Kapi Creek (FR)
15 **ZEGODLESSMAN (FR)**, 6, b g Lord of Men—Zayine (IRE)
16 **ZEMIRO (FR)**, 4, b c Daliapour (IRE)—Zython (FR)
17 **ZIMRI (FR)**, 8, b g Take Risks (FR)—Zayine (IRE)

THREE-YEAR-OLDS

18 **AVIATOR (FR)**, b c Motivator—Summer Wave (IRE)
19 **BLUE RAPIDS (FR)**, b f Anabaa Blue—Orkney Rapids
20 **EASTERN GLOW (FR)**, b f Cape Cross (IRE)—Come What May
21 **HESIONE (IRE)**, gr f Aussie Rules (USA)—Hortanse (FR)
22 **JABBERWOCKY**, b f Catcher In The Rye (IRE)—Thunderbaby (USA)
23 **KATHERINE DEUX (FR)**, b f Poliglote—Knout (FR)
24 **LISA POST (FR)**, b f American Post—Lisatine (FR)
25 **LOS ABRIGOS (FR)**, b c Kingsalsa (USA)—Perspective (FR)
26 **MESSIRE CHIPIE (FR)**, b c Enrique—Royale Chipie (FR)
27 **NORSE KING (FR)**, ch c Norse Dancer (IRE)—Angel Wing
28 **NORSE WARRIOR (FR)**, ch c Norse Dancer (IRE)—Speed of Sound
29 **SKHOLANTA (FR)**, ch c Gold Away (IRE)—Secret Formula
30 **TCHERNICHEVA (FR)**, b f Early March—Indiena
31 **TEMPO FELICE**, b c Lando (GER)—Teresa Balbi

TWO-YEAR-OLDS

32 **ANNABEL LEE (FR)**, ch f 4/2 Starcraft (NZ)—Ashley River (Ashkalani (IRE))
33 **CANDY BUBBLE**, b f 7/4 American Post—Hay Amor (ARG) (Candy Stripes)

MRS MYRIAM BOLLACK-BADEL—continued

34 **CINDER'S POST (FR)**, b f 25/2 American Post—Cinders' Prize (Sinndar (IRE))
35 B f 23/3 Desert Style (IRE)—Hokey Pokey (FR) (Lead On Time (USA))
36 **KUKURUN (FR)**, b c 18/5 Kouroun (FR)—Knout (FR) (Kendor (FR))
37 B c 13/4 Medicean—Sambala (IRE) (Danehill Dancer (IRE))
38 B f 27/3 Sinndar (IRE)—Summer Wave (IRE) (King's Best (USA))
39 **WINGLAND (FR)**, b f 25/3 Lando (GER)—Angel Wing (Barathea (IRE))
40 **ZAAFRAN (FR)**, b f 6/4 Medecis—Zython (FR) (Kabool)

Assistant Trainer: Alain Badel

57

MR MARTIN BOSLEY, Chalfont St Giles
Postal: **Bowstridge Farm, Bowstridge Lane, Chalfont St. Giles, Buckinghamshire, HP8 4RF**
Contacts: **PHONE (01494) 875533 FAX (01494) 875533 MOBILE (07778) 938040**
E-MAIL martin@martinbosley.com WEBSITE www.martinbosleyracing.com

1 **BEECH VIEW (IRE)**, 7, b m Desert Prince (IRE)—Karakapa (FR) **Mr J. Carey**
2 **BOB'S LEGEND (IRE)**, 6, b g Bob's Return (IRE)—Pepsi Starlet (IRE) **K. Quinn/ C. Benham/ I. Saunders**
3 **BURNT CREAM**, 5, b m Exceed And Excel (AUS)—Basbousate Nadia **Mrs P. M. Brown**
4 5, B m Westerner—Dantes Term (IRE) **Mr J. Carey**
5 **DUALAGI**, 8, b m Royal Applause—Lady Melbourne (IRE) **Inca Financial Services**
6 **FIORDALINDA**, 6, b m Tamure (IRE)—Bellacaccia (IRE) **Mr D. B. Dennison**
7 **GLENDUN ANNIE (IRE)**, 5, b m Beneficial—Discerning Air **Mr A. McKay**
8 **HIGHCLIFFE**, 4, ch f Bertolini (USA)—Galapagar (USA) **Mrs J. M. O'Connor**
9 **JUST SAY PLEASE**, 5, ch m Needwood Blade—Roonah Quay (IRE) **K. J. Quinn**
10 5, Ch g Fahris (IRE)—Kit Kat Kate (IRE) **Mr J. Carey**
11 5, B m Oscar (IRE)—Legendsofthefall (IRE) **Mr J. Carey**
12 **LISSELTON CROSS**, 4, ch g Compton Place—Sweet Myrtle (USA) **Mrs J. M. O'Connor**
13 **MIDNIGHT SPIRIT**, 12, b g Midnight Legend—West-Hatch-Spirit **Mr M. Bosley**
14 **MISEFI**, 4, b f Nayef (USA)—Simonida (IRE) **M. R. Bosley**
15 **MY SUMMER DAY**, 5, ch m Umistim—Summer Passion **Mr S. Day**
16 **SPACEMAN**, 9, b g In The Wings—Souk (IRE) **Mr J. Carey**
17 **VINNIE'S GIRL (IRE)**, 5, b m Vinnie Roe (IRE)—Keralba (USA) **Mr J. Carey**

THREE-YEAR-OLDS

18 **ANNIESUELLA (IRE)**, b f Whipper (USA)—Viking Fair **The Jamasitr Partnership**
19 B f Red Clubs (IRE)—Naughty Nell **Mr L. M. Quinn**
20 **NOTNOWIVORHEADACHE**, b f Notnowcato—Inchcoonan **The Jamasitr Partnership**
21 **ROMAN SENATE (IRE)**, b c Holy Roman Emperor (IRE)—Indian Fun **Jamasitr Racing (Chalfont)**

TWO-YEAR-OLDS

22 Ch f 10/4 Sakhee's Secret—Regal Curtsy (Royal Applause) (7619)
23 B c 6/2 Indesatchel (IRE)—Today's The Day (Alhaarth (IRE)) (11428)

Other Owners: Mr Troy Attwood, Mr Chris Benham, Mr M. R. Bosley, Mr G. H. Carson, Mr S. J. Coggon, Mr Simon K. I. Double, Mr M. G. Edwards, Mr J. Neville, Mr Kevin Quinn, Mr Ian Saunders.

Jockey (flat): George Baker. **Apprentice:** Kirsten Smith. **Amateur:** Mr Zac Baker.

58

MR MARCO BOTTI, Newmarket
Postal: **Green Ridge Stables, Hamilton Road, Newmarket, Suffolk, CB8 7JQ**
Contacts: **PHONE (01638) 662416 FAX (01638) 662417 MOBILE (07775) 803007**
E-MAIL office@marcobotti.co.uk WEBSITE www.marcobotti.co.uk

1 **ARMOISE**, 4, b f Sadler's Wells (USA)—Di Moi Oui **Scuderia Vittadini SRL**
2 **BOHEMIAN MELODY**, 5, b g Desert Sun—Chamonis (USA) **Mrs L. Botti**
3 **CEREMONIAL JADE (UAE)**, 9, b g Jade Robbery (USA)—Talah **G. Manfredini**
4 **COCOZZA (USA)**, 4, b c Elusive Quality (USA)—Watership Crystal (IRE) **Byerley Racing Limited**
5 **ENTHUSIASTIC**, 4, b c Galileo (IRE)—Que Puntual (ARG) **E. I. Mack**
6 **FAMUSA**, 5, b m Medicean—Step Danzer (IRE) **Scuderia Rencati Srl**
7 **FANUNALTER**, 6, b g Falbrav (IRE)—Step Danzer (IRE) **Scuderia Rencati Srl**
8 **FATTSOTA**, 4, b g Oasis Dream—Gift of The Night (USA) **Scuderia Rencati Srl**
9 **HALFSIN (IRE)**, 4, b g Haafhd—Firesteed (IRE) **G. Manfredini**
10 **INKLET**, 4, b f Intikhab (USA)—Digamist Girl (IRE) **Mrs A. J. Nicol**

MR MARCO BOTTI—continued

11 **JAKKALBERRY (IRE)**, 6, b h Storming Home—Claba di San Jore (IRE) **Effevi Snc Di Villa Felice & C.**
12 **JOSHUA TREE (IRE)**, 5, b h Montjeu—Madeira Mist (IRE) **Mr K K Al Nabooda & Mr K Albahou**
13 **LAW OF THE RANGE**, 5, b m Alhaarth (IRE)—Mountain Law (USA) **Mr C. McHale**
14 **LITTLE GARCON (USA)**, 5, b g Bernstein (USA)—Demure **J. Barton**
15 **MARCRET (ITY)**, 5, b h Martino Alonso (IRE)—Love Secret (USA) **Az. Agr. Antezzate SRL**
16 **RAGDA**, 4, b f Invincible Spirit (IRE)—Junior Council (IRE) **Saleh Al Homaizi & Imad Al Sagar**
17 **SCIAMPIN**, 4, b g Invincible Spirit (IRE)—Gracious **Scuderia Rencati Srl**
18 **STRAWBERRYMYSTIQUE**, 4, b f Motivator—Strawberry Morn (CAN) **Mr C. McHale**
19 **WHAILEYY (IRE)**, 4, b g Holy Roman Emperor (IRE)—Alshoowg (USA) **Saleh Al Homaizi & Imad Al Sagar**

THREE-YEAR-OLDS

20 **APPEALING (IRE)**, b f Bertolini (USA)—Radiant Energy (IRE) **Miss Y. M. G. Jacques**
21 **AZERODEGREE (IRE)**, b g Azamour (IRE)—Fairy (USA) **G. Manfredini**
22 **BARBARELLA BLUE (IRE)**, b f Iffraaj—Ditton Dancer **Miss A. Bonito**
23 **BARTOLOMEU**, b g Footstepsinthesand—Catch Us (FR) **HE Sheikh Sultan Bin Khalifa Al Nahyan**
24 **BEOGRAD SNIPER**, b g Cape Cross (IRE)—Messelina **Op - Center**
25 **CALIFORNIA ENGLISH (IRE)**, b g Oasis Dream—Muwali (USA) **California English Partnership**
26 **CANARY WHARF (IRE)**, b c Danehill Dancer (IRE)—Wedding Morn (IRE) **Mr G Manfredini & Mr J Allison**
27 **COLORFUL NOTION (IRE)**, b f Danehill Dancer (IRE)—
Red Yellow Blue (USA) **HE Sheikh Sultan Bin Khalifa Al Nahyan**
28 **DROPZONE (USA)**, b g Smart Strike (CAN)—Dalisay (IRE) **P. Newton**
29 **EASTERN AMOUR (IRE)**, b g Azamour (IRE)—Eastern Appeal (IRE) **Mr W. A. Tinkler**
30 **FOUR LEAVES (IRE)**, ch f Singspiel (IRE)—My Heart's Deelite (USA) **HE Sheikh Sultan Bin Khalifa Al Nahyan**
31 **FROSTY BERRY**, gr f Proclamation (IRE)—Star Entry **J. H. Widdows**
32 **GOLDEN SHARE (USA)**, b br c Medaglia d'oro (USA)—Siempre Asi (USA) **Unregistered Partnership**
33 **GREY MIRAGE**, b c Oasis Dream—Grey Way (USA) **Scuderia Vittadini SRL**
34 **GUEST OF HONOUR (IRE)**, b c Cape Cross (IRE)—Risera (IRE) **E. I. Mack**
35 **INFORTUAL (TUR)**, b f Acclamation—Asafa (IRE)
36 **KINGSDESIRE (IRE)**, b c King's Best (USA)—Lucky Clio (IRE) **G. Manfredini**
37 **KLANG VALLEY**, ch f Dubai Destination (USA)—Kelang **Grundy Bloodstock Ltd**
38 **KOKO LOCA (IRE)**, b g f Kodiac—Pure Folly (IRE) **Mrs L. Botti**
39 **LELAPS (USA)**, ch c Mr Greeley (USA)—Rebecca Parisi (IRE) **Team Valor LLC**
40 **LIKE THE NIGHT**, ch f Byron—Twitch Hill **Fortunati Partnership**
41 **MARIA VEZZERA**, b f Authorized (IRE)—La Virtu (IRE) **Scuderia Rencati Srl**
42 **MEZZOTINT (IRE)**, b c Diamond Green (FR)—Aquatint **Miss A. Bonito**
43 **MUNIFICENCE**, ch g Bahamian Bounty—Snake's Head **The Stondon Beeez**
44 **OGARITMO**, ch f Manduro (GER)—Querida **Mrs O. Carlini Cozzi**
45 **RAVING MONSUN**, ch f Monsun (GER)—Rave Reviews (IRE) **Newsells Park Stud Limited**
46 **REDCLUE (IRE)**, br g Red Clubs (IRE)—Stratospheric **G. Manfredini**
47 **ROCKGOAT (IRE)**, b g Rock of Gibraltar (IRE)—Queveda (IRE) **G. Manfredini**
48 **SECRETS AWAY (IRE)**, ch f Refuse To Bend (IRE)—Lady Zonda **HE Sheikh Sultan Bin Khalifa Al Nahyan**
49 **SOLAR DEITY (IRE)**, b c Exceed And Excel (AUS)—Dawn Raid (IRE) **Mr W. A. Tinkler**
50 **SPANISH WEDDING**, ch g Hernando (FR)—I Do **K. A. Dasmal**
51 **SUEGIOO (FR)**, ch c Manduro (GER)—Mantesera (IRE) **Scuderia Rencati Srl**
52 **SWALLOW (TUR)**, ch f Dubawi (IRE)—Rewarding
53 **TRAVELLING**, b f Dubai Destination (USA)—Attune **Longview Stud & Bloodstock Ltd**

TWO-YEAR-OLDS

54 **ADMIRABLE ART (IRE)**, b c 13/4 Excellent Art—Demi Voix (Halling (USA)) **Longview Stud & Bloodstock Ltd**
55 B c 18/3 Danehill Dancer (IRE)—Al Saqiya (Woodman (USA))
56 **ALGA REH (IRE)**, b c 3/4 Invincible Spirit (IRE)—Mosaique Beauty (IRE) (Sadler's Wells (USA)) (45714) **S. Ali**
57 **AUTSPREAD**, b c 1/3 Authorized (IRE)—Ridotto (Salse (USA)) (15000) **G. Manfredini**
58 B c 14/5 Lawman (FR)—Caerlina (IRE) (Caerleon (USA)) (18061) **Mr A. N. Mubarak**
59 **CHEEKTOCHEEK (IRE)**, b c 15/4 Chineur (FR)—Diamond Soles (IRE) (Danetime (IRE)) (5746) **G. Manfredini**
60 **CORINTHIAN CASUAL (IRE)**, b c 2/2 Rock of Gibraltar (IRE)—
Whispering Blues (IRE) (Sadler's Wells (USA)) **P. Newton**
61 B c 6/2 Danehill Dancer (IRE)—Drifting (IRE) (Sadler's Wells (USA)) **HE Sheikh Sultan Bin Khalifa Al Nahyan**
62 B c 27/3 Cape Cross (IRE)—Eternity Ring (Alzao (USA)) (80000) **Scuderia Rencati Srl**
63 **FATHER AND SON (IRE)**, b c 6/4 Duke of Marmalade (IRE)—Slap Shot (IRE) (Lycius (USA)) (30000)
64 B c 16/1 Rock of Gibraltar (IRE)—Ghenwah (FR) (Selkirk (USA)) **HE Sheikh Sultan Bin Khalifa Al Nahyan**
65 B c 8/2 Peintre Celebre (USA)—Homegrown (IRE) (Mujadil (USA)) (41050) **Mr K. J. P. Gundlach**
66 Ch c 12/3 Manduro (GER)—Junior Council (IRE) (Sadler's Wells (USA)) **Saleh Al Homaizi & Imad Al Sagar**
67 B f 14/3 Raven's Pass (USA)—
Lady Elgar (IRE) (Sadler's Wells (USA)) (246305) **HE Sheikh Sultan Bin Khalifa Al Nahyan**
68 B c 19/3 Mizzen Mast (USA)—Lynnwood Chase (USA) (Horse Chestnut (SAF)) (55000) **Mr K. J. P. Gundlach**

MR MARCO BOTTI—continued

- **69** Gr c 22/4 Exceed And Excel (AUS)—Mango Lady (Dalakhani (IRE)) (40000) **Scuderia Rencati Srl**
- **70 MESMERIZED (IRE),** b f 3/3 Duke of Marmalade (IRE)—Margot (Sadler's Wells (USA)) (28571)
- **71** B c 30/4 Dansili—Niner's Home (USA) (Forty Niner (USA)) **HE Sheikh Sultan Bin Khalifa Al Nahyan**
- **72 OPUS CACTUS (USA),** b f 20/1 Johannesburg (USA)—Momix (Selkirk (USA)) (36945) **Scuderia Vittadini SRL**
- **73** B c 1/4 Jeremy (USA)—Princess Leona (IRE) (Naiyli (IRE)) (8209) **Mr A. N. Mubarak**
- **74** B c 20/3 Dutch Art—Princess Raya (Act One) **Rothmere Racing Limited**
- **75 SALFORD EXCEL,** b f 21/4 Exceed And Excel (AUS)—Steeple (Selkirk (USA)) (30000) **A. J. Thompson**
- **76** B f 4/3 Duke of Marmalade (IRE)—Serrenia (IRE) (High Chaparral (IRE)) (41050) **Newsells Park Stud Limited**
- **77** B f 10/4 Byron—Shbakni (USA) (Mr Prospector (USA)) **Mr A. Ali**
- **78** B c 29/4 Danehill Dancer (IRE)—Singing Diva (IRE) (Royal Academy (USA))
- **79** B f 10/4 Dutch Art—Smart Ass (IRE) (Shinko Forest (IRE)) (10476) **Mr A. N. Mubarak**
- **80 SUMMER DREAM (IRE),** b f 16/2 Oasis Dream—
  Star On Stage (Sadler's Wells (USA)) (82101) **Niarchos Family**
- **81 TEOPHILIP (IRE),** b br c 23/4 Teofilo (IRE)—Triomphale (Nureyev (USA)) (24761) **G. Manfredini**
- **82** Ch f 2/4 Kyllachy—Triple Sharp (Selkirk (USA)) (210000) **Saleh Al Homaizi & Imad Al Sagar**
- **83 WAKEUP LITTLE SUZY (IRE),** ch f 27/2 Peintre Celebre (USA)—Maramba (Hussonet (USA)) **P. Newton**

Other Owners: Sheikha H. B. S. Al Nehayan, I. J. Al-Sagar, Mr K. F. Albahou, Mr J. Allison, Mr L. Biffi, A. R. Blackman, Mr D. Bladon, Mr E. Bulgheroni, Mr A. J. Driver, Saleh Al Homaizi, Mr Khalid Khalifa Al Nabooda, Mr I. Montone, M. A. Stein.

Assistant Trainer: Lucie Botti

Apprentice: Toby Atkinson.

59	**MR PETER BOWEN, Haverfordwest**

Postal: Yet-Y-Rhug, Letterston, Haverfordwest, Pembrokeshire, SA62 5TB
Contacts: PHONE (01348) 840486 FAX (01348) 840486 MOBILE (07811) 111234
E-MAIL info@peterbowenracing.com WEBSITE www.peterbowenracing.com

- **1 AL CO (FR),** 7, ch g Dom Alco (FR)—Carama (FR) **F. Lloyd**
- **2 ALWAYS WAINING (IRE),** 11, b g Unfuwain (USA)—Glenarff (USA) **Mr & Mrs P. J. Douglas**
- **3 AMAZING VALOUR (IRE),** 10, b g Sinndar (IRE)—Flabbergasted (IRE) **G. J. Morris**
- **4 BALLYVESEY (IRE),** 7, ch g Anshan—Bridgequarter Lady (IRE) **Roddy Owen & Paul Fullagar**
- **5 BOOK'EM DANNO (IRE),** 6, ch g Moscow Society (USA)—Rifada **Roddy Owen & Paul Fullagar**
- **6 CATCH THE FIRE,** 4, b g Motivator—Salinova (FR) **Roddy Owen & Paul Fullagar**
- **7 CRUISING BYE,** 6, b g Alflora (IRE)—Althrey Flame (IRE) **F. Lloyd**
- **8 DAIS RETURN (IRE),** 8, b g Lahib (USA)—Bayazida **West Coast Haulage Limited**
- **9 DERWEN PRYDE,** 8, b m Hazaaf (USA)—Landsker Pryde **V. T. Beynon**
- **10 FLANAGAN (IRE),** 8, b g Old Vic—Fosterandallen (IRE) **P. Bowling,S.Scott,R.Harvey & K.Bowen**
- **11 FOREVER WAINING (IRE),** 6, b g Choisir (AUS)—Dahoar **Mr & Mrs P. J. Douglas**
- **12 GET HOME NOW,** 4, b g Diktat—Swiftly **D. J. Robbins**
- **13 KIAN'S DELIGHT,** 4, b g Whipper (USA)—Desert Royalty (IRE) **Yeh Man Partnership**
- **14 LAMBORO LAD (IRE),** 7, b g Milan—Orchard Spray (IRE) **Margaret and Raymond John**
- **15 LUCKY THUMB,** 6, gr m Fair Mix (IRE)—Burdens Girl **Five Arms**
- **16 MAGIC SHOW,** 8, b g Marju (IRE)—White Rabbit **Miss Jayne Brace & Mr Gwyn Brace**
- **17 MEZZANISI (IRE),** 7, b g Kalanisi (IRE)—Mezzanine **Yeh Man Partnership**
- **18 MISS KALIFA (IRE),** 5, b m Catcher In The Rye (IRE)—Verbena (IRE) **R. D. J. Swinburne**
- **19 MUMBLES HEAD (IRE),** 11, ch g Flemensfirth (USA)—Extra Mile **Mrs K. Bowen**
- **20 NATURAL ACTION,** 8, b g Diktat—Naskhi **Mrs K. Bowen**
- **21 NORMALLY,** 8, b g Tobougg (IRE)—Constant Delight **Mr T. E. Gibbon**
- **22 PENSION PLAN,** 8, b g Alflora (IRE)—Dalbeattie **The Loppington Five**
- **23 PONTYATES,** 7, ch g Definite Article—Whimsey (IRE) **Ednyfed & Elizabeth Morgan**
- **24 PRANKSTER,** 6, ch g Rock of Gibraltar (IRE)—Coraline **Roddy Owen & Paul Fullagar**
- **25 PURE FAITH,** 8, b g Anshan—Bolaney Girl (IRE) **P. Bowling,S.Scott,R.Harvey & K.Bowen**
- **26 PURLANDO (GER),** 7, b g Lando (GER)—Purple Haze (GER) **Miss H. R. Nelmes**
- **27 RUDANPHAST (IRE),** 7, b g Rudimentary (USA)—Alpha Style (GER) **Mrs T. S. P. Stepney**
- **28 RUN TO FLY (IRE),** 7, b g Milan—Paper Money (IRE) **D. A. Smith**
- **29 SAINT LUKE (IRE),** 7, b g Bob's Return (IRE)—Condonstown (IRE) **Saith O Ni & Ednyfed & Elizabeth Morgan**
- **30 SAINTLY LADY,** 7, b m Old Vic—Ban Ri Ciara (IRE) **The Hedonists**
- **31 SANSILI,** 5, gr g Dansili—Salinova (FR) **Saith O Ni**
- **32 SANTAMINA (IRE),** 6, ch g Anshan—Capotaormina (IRE) **Roddy Owen & Paul Fullagar**
- **33 SERANWEN (IRE),** 5, b g Old Vic—Glenarb Molly (IRE) **Walters Plant Hire Ltd Egan Waste Ltd**
- **34 SIR JOHNSON,** 6, ch g Deploy—Little Daphne **Steve & Jackie Fleetham**
- **35 STRUMBLE HEAD (IRE),** 7, b g Anshan—Milan Moss **Mr J. A. Martin**
- **36 SUNDAY CITY (JPN),** 11, ch g Sunday Silence (USA)—Diamond City (USA) **C. E. R. Greenway**

MR PETER BOWEN—continued

Other Owners: Mr A. W. Barker, Mr B. G. Bowen, P. G. A. Bowling, Miss M. J. Brace, D. G. Brace, W. Bryan, Mr R. D. Burden, P. J. Douglas, Mrs L. Douglas, Egan Waste Services Ltd, Mr S. Fleetham, Mrs J. Fleetham, P. G. Fullagar, Mrs R. Harvey, Mrs M. B. A. John, Mr R. D. John, Mr E. O. Morgan, Mrs E. Morgan, R. R. Owen, B. S. Port, S. D. Reeve, Mr S. J. Scott, Mr R. K. Shingler, Walters Plant Hire Ltd, Mr P. R. Williams.

Assistant Trainer: K Bowen

Jockey (NH): Tom O'Brien, Jamie Moore. **Conditional:** Donal Devereux. **Amateur:** Mr Alan Johns.

MR ROY BOWRING, Edwinstowe
Postal: **Fir Tree Farm, Edwinstowe, Mansfield, Nottinghamshire, NG21 9JG**
Contacts: **PHONE (01623) 822451 MOBILE (07973) 712942**
E-MAIL bowrings@btconnect.co.uk

1 **ACE MASTER,** 4, ch g Ballet Master (USA)—Ace Maite **S. R. Bowring**
2 **BLONDE MAITE,** 6, ch g Ballet Master (USA)—Ace Maite **S. R. Bowring**
3 **DANCING MAITE,** 7, ch g Ballet Master (USA)—Ace Maite **S. R. Bowring**
4 **DIVERTIMENTI (IRE),** 8, b g Green Desert (USA)—Ballet Shoes (IRE) **K. Nicholls**
5 **FLYING APPLAUSE,** 7, b g Royal Applause—Mrs Gray **K. Nicholls**
6 **HIGH FIVE SOCIETY,** 8, b g Compton Admiral—Sarah Madeline **S. R. Bowring**
7 **MARINA BALLERINA,** 4, b br f Ballet Master (USA)—Marinaite **S. R. Bowring**
8 **MARINA'S OCEAN,** 8, b m Beat All (USA)—Ocean Song **S. R. Bowring**
9 **MASTER OF SONG,** 5, ch g Ballet Master (USA)—Ocean Song **S. R. Bowring**
10 **SEAWOOD,** 6, b g Needwood Blade—Ocean Song **S. R. Bowring**
11 **SOFIAS NUMBER ONE (USA),** 4, b br g Silver Deputy (CAN)—Storidawn (USA) **S. R. Bowring**
12 **WEST END LAD,** 9, b g Tomba—Cliburnel News (IRE) **K. Nicholls**
13 **XPRES MAITE,** 9, b g Komaite (USA)—Antonias Melody **Charterhouse Holdings Plc**

THREE-YEAR-OLDS

14 **SOLARMAITE,** b f Needwood Blade—Marinaite **S. R. Bowring**

MR JIM BOYLE, Epsom
Postal: **South Hatch Stables, Burgh Heath Road, Epsom, Surrey, KT17 4LX**
Contacts: **PHONE (01372) 748800 FAX (01372) 739410 MOBILE (07719) 554147**
E-MAIL info@jamesboyle.co.uk & jimboylesec@hotmail.co.uk (Secretary)
WEBSITE www.jamesboyle.co.uk

1 **BATCHELORS STAR (IRE),** 4, ch g Fath (USA)—Batchelor's Button (FR) **Mrs Anne Cowley**
2 **CRISTALIYEV,** 4, b g Fasliyev (USA)—Desert Cristal (IRE) **The Talbot Boys**
3 **GRAND THEFT EQUINE,** 4, b g Piccolo—Red Storm **Mrs P. Boyle**
4 **HOOVER,** 4, b g Sleeping Indian—Spring Clean (FR) **Hoover Partnership**
5 **IN THE LONG GRASS (IRE),** 4, b g Ivan Denisovich (IRE)—Dabtiyra (IRE) **Mr H. Brown Kerr**
6 **ISINGY RED (FR),** 4, ch g Chichicastenango—Loving Smile (FR) **The Idle B'S**
7 **LLEWELLYN,** 4, b g Shamardal (USA)—Ffestiniog (IRE) **Elite Racing Club**
8 **MARCUS ANTONIUS,** 5, b g Mark of Esteem (IRE)—Star of The Course (USA) **The Grosvenor Club**
9 **PERFECT PASTIME,** 4, ch g Pastoral Pursuits—Puritanical (IRE) **Country Friends**
10 **REE'S RASCAL (IRE),** 4, gr g Verglas—Night Scent (USA) **Mr W. J. Hayford**
11 **REGAL APPROVAL,** 4, br g Royal Applause—Enthralled **The Splendid Partnership**
12 **RODRIGO DE FREITAS (IRE),** 5, b g Captain Rio—Brazilian Sun (IRE) **The Rodrigo De Freitas Partnership**
13 **ROWAN RIDGE,** 4, ch g Compton Place—Lemon Tree (USA) **Rowan Stud Partnership 1**
14 **SEEK THE FAIR LAND,** 6, b g Noverre (USA)—Duchcov **Chris Watkins & David N. Reynolds**
15 **SIOUX CITY SUE,** 6, b m Noverre (USA)—Sartigila **S. C. Gollogly**
16 **SPEAK THE TRUTH (IRE),** 6, b g Statue of Liberty (USA)—Brave Truth (IRE) **Inside Track Racing Club**
17 **THE RECTIFIER,** 5, b br h Langfuhr (CAN)—Western Vision (USA) **Mrs A. Cowley**

THREE-YEAR-OLDS

18 B c High Chaparral (IRE)—Van de Cappelle (IRE)
19 **ATLANTIS CROSSING (IRE),** b c Elusive City (USA)—Back At de Front (IRE) **The "In Recovery" Partnership**
20 **AVAILABLE (IRE),** b f Moss Vale (IRE)—Divert (IRE) **M Khan X2**
21 **DIVINE PAMINA (IRE),** br f Dark Angel (IRE)—Greek Symphony (IRE) **Pippbrook Ltd**
22 **ESPRIT DANSEUR,** b f Invincible Spirit (IRE)—Oulianovsk (IRE) **The "In Recovery" Partnership**
23 **ILLUSTRIOUS LAD (IRE),** ch g Bertolini (USA)—Squeak **Inside Track Racing Club**

MR JIM BOYLE—continued

24 INTOMIST (IRE), ch c Strategic Prince—Fast Temper (USA) **The Clueless Syndicate**
25 KING OF WING (IRE), b c Hawk Wing (USA)—Miss Shivvy (IRE) **Chris Watkins & David N. Reynolds**
26 LOOK AT ME NOW, ch c Choisir (AUS)—Sweet Pickle **M Khan X2**
27 MR KNIGHTLEY (IRE), b c Strategic Prince—Emma's Surprise **M Khan X2**
28 NORTHERN TERRITORY (IRE), b c Choisir (AUS)—Krasivaya (IRE) **Poppinghole Racing Partnership**
29 PALOMA'S PRINCE (IRE), ch c Nayef (USA)—Ma Paloma (FR) **Serendipity Syndicate 2006**
30 ROWAN RHAPSODY, ch f Araafa (IRE)—Filippa (GER) **Rowan Stud**
31 SCOUTING FOR GIRLS, b g Sleeping Indian—Concubine (IRE) **Mrs P. Boyle**
32 STRIKE A POSE (IRE), b f Mujadil (USA)—Naked Poser (IRE) **M Khan X2**
33 SUPREME ROCK, b br c Rock of Gibraltar (IRE)—Izadore (IRE)
34 TITUS BOLT (IRE), b g Titus Livius (FR)—Megan's Bay **The Vine Associates**

TWO-YEAR-OLDS

35 B f 9/3 Bahamian Bounty—Complication (Compton Place) (13136) **The "In Recovery" Partnership**
36 B c 9/3 Piccolo—Concubine (IRE) (Danehill (USA))
37 Ch f 17/3 Sleeping Indian—Desert Cristal (IRE) (Desert King (IRE))
38 B c 30/3 Captain Marvelous (IRE)—Jezyah (USA) Chief's Crown) (22857) **The "In Recovery" Partnership**
39 B c 3/3 Oratorio (IRE)—Prayers For Rain (IRE) (Darshaan) (13136) **Tahi Stud**
40 B c 16/4 High Chaparral (IRE)—Reem One (IRE) (Rainbow Quest (USA)) (28000) **M Khan X2**
41 ROWAN LIGHTENING, b f 1/4 Compton Place—Lemon Tree (USA) (Zilzal (USA)) **Rowan Stud**
42 B f 28/2 Dylan Thomas (IRE)—
                    Southern Migration (USA) (Kingmambo (USA)) (21345) **The "In Recovery" Partnership**
43 Br f 19/2 Sleeping Indian—Spring Clean (FR) (Danehill (USA)) (11428)
44 B f 3/3 Sakhee (USA)—Sweet Pickle (Piccolo) **M Khan X2**
45 B f 7/4 Kyllachy—Validate (Alhaarth (IRE)) (16000) **The National Sporting Club**

Other Owners: Mr K. Booth, Mr A. Chambers, Mr Kevin Ferguson, Mr D. Ferguson, Ms Julie Harrison, Mr Dennis Hegarty, Mr John Hillier, Mr John Hopkins, Mr. M. Khan, Mr Mustafa Khan, Mr R. Kolien, Mr K. J. Mackie, Mr P. O. Mooney, Mr Sean O'Connell, Mr R. O'Dwyer, Mr David N. Reynolds, Mrs Rosalind Ridout, Mr J. S. Ridout, Mr E. Sames, Mrs M. E. Sandford, Mr Paul Taylor, Mr David Tobin, Mr C. D. Watkins.

Apprentice: Nathan Alison, Daniel Cremin.

MR DAVID BRACE, Bridgend
Postal: **Llanmihangel Farm, Pyle, Bridgend, Mid-Glamorgan, CF33 6RL**
Contacts: **PHONE (01656) 742313**

1 ASK THE THATCHER (IRE), 8, b g Witness Box (USA)—African Lily (IRE) **D. Brace**
2 DIRECT LINE (IRE), 7, ch g Moscow Society (USA)—Try Another Rose (IRE) **D. Brace**
3 EDIESKAIA (IRE), 6, b g Exit To Nowhere (USA)—Friendly Craic (IRE) **D. Brace**
4 JOHNNY OWEN (IRE), 6, b g Danehill Dancer (IRE)—Makarova (IRE) **D. Brace**
5 JUMPJACK FLINT, 6, b g Definite Article—Bajan Girl (FR) **D. Brace**
6 KHACHATURIAN (IRE), 9, b g Spectrum (IRE)—On Air (FR) **D. Brace**
7 KNIGHT BLAZE, 5, b m Bach (IRE)—Braceys Girl (IRE) **D. Brace**
8 MASTER'N COMMANDER, 10, ch g Zafonic (USA)—Magical Retreat (USA) **D. Brace**
9 MOON STREAM, 5, b g Kayf Tara—Moon Catcher **D. Brace**
10 PRINCE N POACHERS, 5, b g Bach (IRE)—Sister Kit (IRE) **D. Brace**
11 SON OF SWALLOW (IRE), 6, b g Swallow Flight (IRE)—Heresheis **D. Brace**
12 WHISPERING WIND (IRE), 9, b m Sunshine Street (USA)—Soul Fire (IRE) **D. Brace**

Assistant Trainer: Miss Jessica Roberts

MRS SUE BRADBURNE, Cupar
Postal: **Cunnoquhie Cottage, 1 Ladybank, Cupar, Fife, KY15 7RU**
Contacts: **PHONE (01337) 810325 FAX (01337) 810486 MOBILE (07769) 711064/(07768) 705722**
E-MAIL susanbradburne@aol.com

1 BATTLE HONOUR, 5, b g Mark of Esteem (IRE)—Proserpine **Quandt & Cochrane**
2 BERTIE MILAN (IRE), 7, b g Milan—Miss Bertaine (IRE) **Turcan Barber Douglas Miller Dunning**
3 CAUGHT IN THE ACT (IRE), 5, br g Overbury (IRE)—Catch Those Kisses **Turcan Barber Fletcher Dunning**
4 CHEATINGSIDEOFTOWN (IRE), 6, b g Flemensfirth (USA)—My Baloo **Mr HW Turcan & Sir Simon Dunning**
5 JET MASTER (IRE), 6, b g Brian Boru—Whats The Reason (IRE) **Mr HW Turcan & Sir Simon Dunning**
6 5, B g Elmaamul (USA)—Noble Tiger (IRE) **Mark Fleming**

MRS SUE BRADBURNE—continued

7 **NORTHERN ACRES**, 6, b g Mtoto—Bunting **C. Lysaght Media, Quandt & Cochrane**
8 **OR DE GRUGY (FR)**, 10, b g April Night (FR)—Girlish (FR) **Lord Cochrane & Partners**
9 **ROSSINI'S DANCER**, 7, b g Rossini (USA)—Bint Alhabib **Turcan Barber Fletcher Dunning**

Other Owners: J. M. Barber, The Hon T. H. V. Cochrane, Lord Cochrane of Cults, Mrs J. Douglas Miller, Sir Simon Dunning, Miss F. M. Fletcher, C. Lysaght, Miss S. Quandt, H. W. Turcan.

Assistant Trainer: J. G. Bradburne

---

64 MR MILTON BRADLEY, Chepstow
Postal: **Meads Farm, Sedbury Park, Chepstow, Gwent, NP16 7HN**
Contacts: **PHONE (01291) 622486 FAX (01291) 626939**
E-MAIL j.m.bradley@virgin.net

1 **ATLANTIC BEACH**, 7, ch g Kyllachy—Amused **E. A. Hayward**
2 **ATLANTIC CYCLE (IRE)**, 5, ch m Stormy Atlantic (USA)—Cycle of Life (USA) **G. S. Thompson**
3 **AVON LIGHT**, 4, ch g Avonbridge—Veronese (USA) **Ms S. A. Howell**
4 **COLOURBEARER (IRE)**, 5, ch g Pivotal—Centifolia (USA) **E. A. Hayward**
5 **DANCING WELCOME**, 6, b m Kyllachy—Highland Gait **J. M. Bradley**
6 **DEVEZE (IRE)**, 4, b f Kyllachy—La Caprice (USA) **J. M. Bradley**
7 **DIVINE CALL**, 5, b g Pivotal—Pious **E. A. Hayward**
8 **EMIRATESDOTCOM**, 6, b g Pivotal—Teggiano (USA) **Ms S. A. Howell**
9 **EXCELLENT VISION**, 5, b g Exceed And Excel (AUS)—Classic Vision **E. A. Hayward**
10 **FLAXEN LAKE**, 5, b g Sampower Star—Cloudy Reef **Asterix Partnership**
11 **FLEETWOODSANDS (IRE)**, 5, b g Footstepsinthesand—Litchfield Hills (USA) **E. R. Griffiths**
12 **ISLAND LEGEND (IRE)**, 6, b g Trans Island—Legand of Tara (USA) **J. M. Bradley**
13 **KHATEER**, 5, ch g Shamardal (USA)—Polly Perkins (IRE) **J. M. Bradley**
14 **LOYAL ROYAL (IRE)**, 9, b g King Charlemagne (USA)—Supportive (IRE) **Mr D. Hudson-Wood**
15 **PETRARCHAN**, 4, ch g Rainbow—Summer Sonnet **E. A. Hayward**
16 **REGENCY ART (IRE)**, 5, b g Titus Livius (FR)—Honey Storm (IRE) **Banfield, Thompson**
17 **ROODEE QUEEN**, 4, b f Kyllachy—Hilites (IRE) **Mr T Godbert & Mr P Banfield**
18 **SOLE DANSER (IRE)**, 4, b g Dansili—Plymsole (USA) **E. A. Hayward**
19 **SOLEMN**, 7, b g Pivotal—Pious **E. A. Hayward**
20 **SPIRIT OF GONDREE (IRE)**, 4, b g Invincible Spirit (IRE)—Kristal's Paradise (IRE) **J. M. Bradley**
21 **TEMPLE ROAD (IRE)**, 4, b g Street Cry (IRE)—Sugarhoneybaby (IRE) **J. M. Bradley**
22 **THE GREY ONE (IRE)**, 9, gr g Dansili—Marie Dora **Mr R. Miles Mr T. Stamp**
23 **TRADE CENTRE**, 7, b g Dubai Destination (USA)—Khubza **R. Williams**
24 **TRIPLE DREAM**, 7, ch g Vision of Night—Triple Joy **J. M. Bradley**
25 **VOLCANIC DUST (IRE)**, 4, b f Ivan Denisovich (IRE)—Top of The Form (IRE) **Miss D. Hill**

THREE-YEAR-OLDS

26 **HATHA ZAIN (IRE)**, b g Bahamian Bounty—Arabian Dancer **J. M. Bradley**
27 B f Helissio (FR)—Legand of Tara (USA) **J. M. Bradley**

TWO-YEAR-OLDS

28 B c 25/2 Sleeping Indian—Rare Fling (USA) (Kris S (USA)) **J. M. Bradley**
29 B c 23/4 Zahran (IRE)—Royal Supremacy (IRE) (Desert Prince (IRE)) **J. M. Bradley**

Other Owners: Mr Philip Banfield, Mr J. M. Bradley, Mrs J. K. Bradley, Mr T. A. Godbert, Mr Clifton Hunt, Mr Stephen McAvoy, Mr R. Miles, Mr Tony Stamp, Mr George S. Thompson.

Assistant Trainer: Miss Hayley Davies

Jockey (flat): Liam Keniry, Russ Kennemore, Richard Kingscote. Jockey (NH): Richard Johnson. Conditional: Chris Davies, Charlie Wallis. Apprentice: Ryan Clark. Amateur: Miss Sarah-Jayne Bradley, Miss Hayley Davies.

---

65 MR MARK BRADSTOCK, Wantage
Postal: **The Old Manor Stables, Letcombe Bassett, Wantage, Oxfordshire, OX12 9NB**
Contacts: **PHONE (01235) 760780 FAX (01235) 760754 MOBILE (07887) 686697**
E-MAIL mark.bradstock@btconnect.com

1 4, Ch g Shantou (USA)—Bit of A Chance
2 **CARRUTHERS**, 9, b g Kayf Tara—Plaid Maid (IRE) **The Oaksey Partnership**

MR MARK BRADSTOCK—continued

3 **CONEYGREE**, 5, b g Karinga Bay—Plaid Maid (IRE) **The Max Partnership**
4 **CUCKOO PEN**, 8, b g Alflora (IRE)—Plaid Maid (IRE) **The Hill Farm Partnership**
5 **DAHTESTE**, 4, b f Overbury (IRE)—Sunday News'n'echo (USA) **The Elgram Club**
6 **MEGASTYLE**, 5, b g Kayf Tara—Shoptillyoudrop **Happy Valley Racing (2009)**
7 **PROPER VILLAN (IRE)**, 7, b br g Naheez (USA)—Nativa Negra (IRE) **Simple Lorry Drivers**
8 **RADETSKY MARCH (IRE)**, 9, b g Taipan (IRE)—Jane Jones (IRE) **P. J. D. Pottinger**
9 **ROYAL VILLAN (IRE)**, 6, b g Luso—Frantesa **Simple Lorry Drivers**
10 **UBIQUE (IRE)**, 5, ch g Flemensfirth (USA)—Clamper (IRE) **P. J. D. Pottinger**

Other Owners: Mr Martyn Butler, Mr S. Darvall, Lady Dundas, Mr C. Elgram, Mrs D. Elgram, Mr Duncan King, Miss Amy Marshall, Mrs H. Marshall, Lord Oaksey, Mr Mark Tamburro, Mr Alan Waller.

Assistant Trainer: Sara Bradstock

Jockey (NH): Mattie Batchelor. **Amateur:** Mr Alfie Bradstock.

66 MISS ANNA BRAMALL, Boltby
Postal: **Merry Hall, Boltby, North Yorkshire, YO7 2DY**

1 **CHINK OF LIGHT**, 5, ch g Dr Fong (USA)—Isle of Flame **Miss A. Bramall**
2 **NEXT EDITION (IRE)**, 4, b g Antonius Pius (USA)—Starfish (IRE) **Miss A. Bramall**
3 **SACRE TOI (FR)**, 6, b g Network (GER)—Magicielle (FR) **Miss A. Bramall**
4 **SLEEP IN FIRST (FR)**, 6, b br g Sleeping Car (FR)—First Union (FR) **Miss A. Bramall**
5 **SLEEPING POLICEMAN (FR)**, 6, b br g Sleeping Car (FR)—Furika (FR) **Miss A. Bramall**
6 **TAX BENEFIT (IRE)**, 7, b g Beneficial—Sweedy (IRE) **Miss A. Bramall**
7 **TRESOR DE L'ISLE (FR)**, 5, br g Dark Moondancer—Ad Vitam Eternam (FR) **Miss A. Bramall**

67 MR GILES BRAVERY, Newmarket
Postal: **2 Charnwood Stables, Hamilton Road, Newmarket, Suffolk, CB8 7JQ**
Contacts: PHONE (01638) 454044 MOBILE (07711) 112345
E-MAIL Braverygc@aol.com

1 **CANTOR**, 4, b g Iceman—Choir Mistress **Mr J. F. Tew**
2 **GOLDEN COMPASS**, 4, ch f Sakhee (USA)—Northern Bows **Mr J. P. Carrington**
3 **JEMIMAVILLE (IRE)**, 5, b m Fasliyev (USA)—Sparkling Isle **Midbras Group Holdings Ltd**
4 **TIN PAN ALLEY**, 4, b c Singspiel (IRE)—Tazmeen **Miss K. McManus**
5 **ZIGGY LEE**, 6, b g Lujain (USA)—Mary O'grady (USA) **Rothmere Racing Limited**

THREE-YEAR-OLDS

6 **CLEAR WONDER**, gr f Verglas (IRE)—Pure Wonder (IRE) **Mrs R. Mason**
7 **PRINCESS PALMER**, b f Iceman—Tapas En Bal (FR) **Rothmere Racing Limited**
8 **SUBTLE KNIFE**, ch f Needwood Blade—Northern Bows **D. B. Clark**

TWO-YEAR-OLDS

9 **AMBER SPYGLASS**, ch c 6/4 Act One—Northern Bows (Bertolini) (USA) **Hyphen Racing & Mrs F E Bravery**
10 Ch f 22/3 Notnowcato—La Gazzetta (IRE) (Rossini) (USA) **Mrs F. E. Bravery**
11 B c 19/3 Halling (USA)—Secret Blend (Pivotal) **Mr J. P. Carrington**

Other Owners: J. Peter-Hoblyn, Mrs I. Peter-Hoblyn, Mr P. J. Singleton.

68 MR BARRY BRENNAN, Lambourn
Postal: **Flemington Stables (Small Barn), Upper Lambourn, Hungerford, Berkshire, RG17 8QH**

1 **BATHCOUNTY (IRE)**, 5, ch g Tobougg (IRE)—Seasons Estates **Seasons Holidays**
2 **BIN END**, 6, b g King's Best (USA)—Overboard (IRE) **D. R. T. Gibbons**
3 **BRIXEN (IRE)**, 8, b m Heron Island (IRE)—Rythem Ofthe Night (IRE) **T. E. Ford**
4 **CANADIAN DIAMOND (IRE)**, 5, ch g Halling (USA)—Six Nations (USA) **Nicholls Family**
5 **HOBACK JUNCTION (IRE)**, 8, b g Heron Island (IRE)—Lizzie Simms (IRE) **T. E. Ford**
6 **LUCKY VIC (IRE)**, 6, b g Old Vic—Graphic Lady (IRE) **F. J. Brennan**
7 **OFFICIER DE RESERVE (FR)**, 10, br g Sleeping Car (FR)—Royaute (FR) **Seasons Holidays**

MR BARRY BRENNAN—continued

   8 **QRACKERS (FR),** 8, b g Lahint (USA)—Babolna (FR) **Seasons Holidays**
   9 **RUDINERO (IRE),** 10, gr g Rudimentary (USA)—Cash Chase (IRE) **D. R. T. Gibbons**
 10 **SING SING SING (FR),** 6, b m Passing Sale (FR)—Caline So (FR) **Mr R. J. Haines**
 11 **THEATRELANDS,** 4, ch g Beat Hollow—Dance Dress (USA) **Mr N Davies & Mr S Crowley**
 12 **WORDINESS,** 4, br c Dansili—Verbose (USA) **F. J. Brennan**

Other Owners: Mr S. Crowley, Mr N. Davies, Mr R. Nicholls, Mrs E. Nicholls.

---

69   **MR OWEN BRENNAN, Worksop**
Postal: **22 Wheeldon Avenue, Derby, Derbyshire, DE22 1HN**
Contacts: **PHONE (01909) 473950 MOBILE (07891) 402648**
E-MAIL **patsyb13@live.co.uk**

   1 **AMAZINGREYCE,** 7, gr m Rainbow High—Lightning Belle **Mrs P. N. Brennan**
   2 **CIRCUS POLKA (USA),** 8, br g Stravinsky (USA)—Far Wiser (USA) **Miss S. L. Bailey**
   3 **ELLERSLIE POSH,** 6, b m Alflora (IRE)—Crepe de Chine (FR) **Mr P. Mina**
   4 **FREDA'S ROSE (IRE),** 8, b m Rossini (USA)—African Scene (IRE) **Mrs V. J. Hannigan**
   5 **IRISH SYMPHONY (IRE),** 8, ch m Bach (IRE)—Conna Dodger (IRE) **Mr O. Brennan**
   6 **LOWRY MAHER (IRE),** 8, b g Flying Legend (USA)—Tirol's Luck (IRE) **Mr O. Brennan**
   7 **MARINA BAY,** 7, b m Karinga Bay—Marina Bird **Mr K. & Mr A. K. Smith**
   8 **MORE FOR LESS,** 5, b g Danbird (AUS)—Patricia Philomena (IRE) **Mrs P. N. Brennan**
   9 **NORTHUMBERLAND,** 6, b g Bertolini (USA)—Cal Norma's Lady (IRE) **Dr A. Shubsachs**
 10 **REBEL NELL,** 4, ch f Needwood Blade—Prima Casa **Mrs J. Woods**
 11 **SILVER DIVO,** 5, gr g Silver Patriarch (IRE)—Deep C Diva (IRE) **J. S. Harlow**

Other Owners: Mr K. Smith, A. K. Smith.

Jockey (NH): Noel Fehily.

---

70   **MISS RHONA BREWIS, Belford**
Postal: **Chester Hill, Belford, Northumberland, NE70 7EF**
Contacts: **PHONE (01668) 213239/213281**

   1 **BURGUNDY BEAU,** 6, br g Grape Tree Road—Chantilly Rose **Miss R. G. Brewis**
   2 **CONJOLA,** 5, b m Grape Tree Road—Conchita **Mrs G. E. Brewis**
   3 **SCARLET RUBY,** 5, ch m Grape Tree Road—Scarlet Ember **Miss R. G. Brewis**

---

71   **MR JOHN BRIDGER, Liphook**
Postal: **Upper Hatch Farm, Wheatsheaf Enclosure, Liphook, Hampshire, GU30 7EL**
Contacts: **PHONE (01428) 722528 MOBILE (07785) 716614**
E-MAIL **jbridger@btconnect.com**

   1 **A B CELEBRATION,** 4, ch gr f Sleeping Indian—Silver Louie (IRE) **Mr & Mrs K. Finch**
   2 **BONDIE,** 4, ch g Monsieur Bond (IRE)—Mockingbird **Mr J. J. Bridger**
   3 **CHORAL FESTIVAL,** 6, b m Pivotal—Choirgirl **Mrs E. Gardner**
   4 **COMMANDINGPRESENCE (USA),** 6, b br m Thunder Gulch (USA)—Sehra (USA) **Mrs E. Gardner**
   5 **DUNE ISLAND,** 4, b f Compton Admiral—Desert Island Disc **Mr W. A. Wood**
   6 **ESCAPE ARTIST,** 5, gr g Act One—Free At Last **Mrs E. Gardner**
   7 **GOWER RULES (IRE),** 4, gr g Aussie Rules (USA)—Holy Norma **Mrs E. Gardner**
   8 **INQUISITRESS,** 8, b m Hernando (FR)—Caribbean Star **Mr C. Marshall, Mr T. Wallace, Mr J. J. Bridger**
   9 **MEGALALA (IRE),** 11, b g Petardia—Avionne **T. Ware**
 10 **ONE COOL CHICK,** 4, b f Iceman—Barrantes **Mr & Mrs K. Finch**
 11 **RATHER COOL,** 4, b f Iceman—Kowthar **Mr W. A. Wood**
 12 **SHIFTING STAR (IRE),** 7, ch g Night Shift—Ahshado **Night Shadow Syndicate**
 13 **SILVEE,** 5, ch gr m Avonbridge—Silver Louie (IRE) **Mr & Mrs K. Finch**
 14 **STARWATCH,** 5, b g Observatory—Trinity Reef **Mr J. J. Bridger**
 15 **WELSH INLET (IRE),** 4, br f Kheleyf (USA)—Ervedya (USA) **Mr J. J. Bridger**
 16 **ZAZOUS,** 11, b g Zafonic (USA)—Confidentiality (USA) **Mr J. J. Bridger**

THREE-YEAR-OLDS

 17 **ARABIAN FLIGHT,** b f Exceed And Excel (AUS)—Emirates First (IRE) **Mrs E. Gardner**
 18 **FLYING KITTY,** b f One Cool Cat (USA)—Flying Millie (IRE) **Mr J. J. Bridger**

MR JOHN BRIDGER—continued

19 **THE PLOUGHMAN**, gr g Tillerman—Kilmovee **Mr & Mrs K. Finch**

TWO-YEAR-OLDS

20 **DARK RUMOUR (IRE)**, b f 27/4 Azamour (IRE)—Adjisa (IRE) (Doyoun) (2500) **Mr & Mrs K. Finch**

Other Owners: Mrs Diane Ellison, Mr K. Finch, Mrs Daphne Finch, Mrs Diane Stewart.

Assistant Trainer: Rachel Cook

---

72 **MR DAVID BRIDGWATER, Stow-on-the-Wold**
Postal: **Wyck Hill Farm, Wyck Hill, Stow-on-the-Wold, Cheltenham, Gloucestershire, GL54 1HT**
Contacts: **PHONE** (01451) 830349 **FAX** (01451) 830349 **MOBILE** (07831) 635817
E-MAIL **dg.bridgwater@yahoo.co.uk**

1 **BIG TALK**, 5, b g Selkirk (USA)—Common Request (USA) **Deauville Daze Partnership**
2 **DAVERON (IRE)**, 4, b g Winged Love (IRE)—Double Doc (IRE)
3 **DEVON DIVA**, 6, b m Systematic—General Jane **Miss J. S. Dorey**
4 **DIRTY BERTIE (FR)**, 6, ch g Dream Well (FR)—Ma Reilly (FR) **Mr R. P. Russell**
5 **EDGEWORTH (IRE)**, 6, b g Pyrus (USA)—Credibility **Mrs M. B. Carre**
6 **ENGAI (GER)**, 6, b g Noroit (GER)—Enigma (GER) **Building Bridgies**
7 **ESCARDO (GER)**, 9, b g Silvano (GER)—Epik (GER) **J. Star**
8 **INDIAN DUMAANI**, 5, gr m Indian Ridge—Mubadalah (USA) **Botany Bay**
9 **NINFEA (IRE)**, 4, b f Le Vie Dei Colori—Attymon Lill (IRE) **Mr G. White**
10 **RED FLASH (IRE)**, 5, b g Red Ransom—Mar Blue (FR) **M. J. Rowe**
11 **REG'S RUBY**, 6, b m Pursuit of Love—Sweets (IRE) **Mrs M. A. Bridgwater**
12 **RUNSHAN (IRE)**, 12, ch g Anshan—Whitebarn Run **Terry & Sarah Amos**
13 **THE GIANT BOLSTER**, 7, b g Black Sam Bellamy (IRE)—Divisa (GER) **Mr S. Hunt**
14 **TRIOMPHAL (FR)**, 5, b g Passing Sale (FR)—Iwo Shima (FR) **Terry & Sarah Amos**
15 **VINEMAN**, 5, b g Grape Tree Road—Great Ovation (FR) **Mr A. A. Wright**
16 **WYCK HILL (IRE)**, 8, b g Pierre—Willow Rose (IRE) **SAB Partnership**

Other Owners: T. P. Amos, Mrs S. P. Amos, R. J. Brennan, Mr R. J. Bridgeman, D. G. Bridgwater, Mr R. W. Frost, Mr M. V. Hill, Mr A. J. Kincaid, Mr T. J. Payton, Mr S. J. Raybould, Mr D. J. Smith.

Jockey (NH): Robert Thornton.

---

73 **MR MARK BRISBOURNE, Nesscliffe**
Postal: **Ness Strange Stables, Great Ness, Shrewsbury, Shropshire, SY4 2LE**
Contacts: **PHONE** (01743) 741536/741360 **FAX** (01743) 741285 **MOBILE** (07803) 019651

1 **AMANA (USA)**, 8, b m Diesis—Ma-Arif (IRE) **Mr Greig Coleman**
2 4, Gr g Iceman—Amarella (FR) **Mr Phil Evans**
3 **BLACK COFFEE**, 7, br g Vettori (IRE)—In The Woods **Mr Derek & Mrs Marie Dean**
4 **CRUISE TOTHELIMIT (IRE)**, 4, b g Le Vie Dei Colori—Kiva **Odysian Limited**
5 **DANCING PRIMO**, 6, b m Primo Valentino—Tycoon's Last **L. R. Owen**
6 **DOWNHILL SKIER (IRE)**, 8, ch g Danehill Dancer (IRE)—Duchy of Cornwall (USA) **Miss P. D. Insull**
7 **ELLIELUSIVE (IRE)**, 5, b m Elusive City (USA)—Danzolin **Mr Derek & Mrs Marie Dean**
8 **HARRYS YER MAN**, 8, b g Nomadic Way (USA)—Barden Lady **D. G. Blagden**
9 **HATHAWAY (IRE)**, 5, ch m Redback—Finty (IRE) **Mr W. M. Clare**
10 4, Gr f Silver Patriarch (IRE)—Hill Farm Dancer **Mark Brisbourne**
11 **ITSTHURSDAYALREADY**, 5, b g Exceed And Excel (AUS)—Succinct **Mr W. Hennessey**
12 **JOIN UP**, 6, b g Green Desert (USA)—Rise **P. R. Kirk**
13 **LAURA LAND**, 5, b m Lujain (USA)—Perdicula (IRE) **Law Abiding Citizens**
14 **LORD OF THE DANCE (IRE)**, 6, ch g Indian Haven—Maine Lobster (USA) **Mr H. Clewlow**
15 **MARKET PUZZLE (IRE)**, 5, ch g Bahamian Bounty—Trempjane **Mark Brisbourne**
16 **MARKSBURY**, 5, b m Mark of Esteem (IRE)—Penelewey **Mr W. Hennessey**
17 **OUR EM**, 6, gr m Fair Mix (IRE)—Andy Coin **Mr R. J. R. Moseley**
18 **PORT HILL**, 5, ch g Deportivo—Hill Farm Dancer **Mr Derek & Mrs Marie Dean**
19 **PRINCESS GAIL**, 4, b f Ad Valorem (USA)—First Musical **R. O. Rickett**
20 **QEETHAARA (IRE)**, 8, gr m Aljabr (USA)—Aghsaan (USA) **Crewe & Nantwich Racing Club**
21 **RAGGED STAFF (IRE)**, 8, b g Desert Style (IRE)—Hardshan **Mr Greig Coleman**
22 **ROWAN SPIRIT (IRE)**, 4, gr g Captain Rio—Secret Justice (USA) **Deva Racing Captain Rio Partnership**

MR MARK BRISBOURNE—continued

23 **TAKAJAN (IRE)**, 5, b g Barathea (IRE)—Takaliya (IRE) **Mr S. W. Jones**
24 **WHIPPHOUND**, 4, b g Whipper (USA)—Golden Symbol **H. Clewlow**

THREE-YEAR-OLDS

25 **APRIL LEYF (IRE)**, b f Kheleyf (USA)—Maroussies Rock **Mr P. L. Mort**
26 **BRANDY SNAPPING**, ch f Needwood Blade—Sunisa (IRE) **Mr Greaves/Mr R. Kent**
27 **GO COURCHEVAL**, b f Three Valleys (USA)—Hasten (USA) **Chester Racing Club Ltd**
28 **LADY TYCOON**, b f Indesatchel (IRE)—Tycoon's Last **L. R. Owen**
29 **MRS AWKWARD**, b f Primo Valentino (IRE)—Musical Chimes **Mr John Jones**
30 **MULTIPOWER**, b g Multiplex—River Ensign **Mrs Mary Brisbourne**
31 **NOVA NIMPH**, ch f Avonbridge—Nimphida **The Antique Partnership**
32 **PENDLE LADY (IRE)**, b f Chineur (FR)—Rose of Battle **Mr P. L. Mort**
33 **PRINCESS TAMINA (IRE)**, b br f Strategic Prince—Taffeta And Tulle (IRE) **The Bubblino Boys**
34 **SILENT AMBITION**, b f Striking Ambition—Hi Rock **Mr J. Holcombe**
35 **SILVAS ROMANA (IRE)**, b f Holy Roman Emperor (IRE)—Triple Wood (USA) **The Bourne Connection**
36 **SKYERON**, b f Byron—Song of Skye **W. M. Brisbourne**
37 **VERY FIRST BLADE**, b g Needwood Blade—Dispol Verity **L. R. Owen**

TWO-YEAR-OLDS

38 B f 27/2 Indian Haven—Condilessa (IRE) (Key of Luck (USA)) (952) **Crewe & Nantwich Racing Club**
39 **ELLE REBELLE**, b f 7/2 Cockney Rebel (IRE)—Lille Ida (Hawk Wing (USA)) (3500) **The Bourne Connection**
40 **GIFTED SPIRIT**, b f 26/4 Indesatchel (IRE)—Dispol Verity (Averti (IRE)) (761) **Mr L. R. Owen**
41 **WINDSOR ROSE (IRE)**, ch f 13/4 Windsor Knot (IRE)—Rose of Battle (Averti (IRE)) (6000) **Mr P. L. Mort**

Other Owners: Mr A. J. Banton, Mr Peter Bowden, Mr P. Clare, Mr Derek Dean, Mrs Marie Dean, Mrs J. Foster, Mr M. Foster, Mr Ian Knight, Mr Brendan McLoughlin, Mr A. Pitt.

Assistant Trainer: Antony Brisbourne

Jockey (flat): Liam Jones, Tom McLaughlin, Eddie Ahern, Shane Kelly. **Jockey (NH):** Liam Treadwell. **Apprentice:** Ryan Clark, Jack Duern, Racheal Kneller. **Amateur:** Miss Becky Brisbourne.

---

74   MR CLIVE BRITTAIN, Newmarket
Postal: **'Carlburg', 49 Bury Road, Newmarket, Suffolk, CB8 7BY**
Contacts: **OFFICE (01638) 664347 HOME (01638) 663739 FAX (01638) 661744**
MOBILE (07785) 302121
E-MAIL carlburgst@aol.com

1 **A'FAAL (IRE)**, 4, ch f Dr Fong (USA)—Golubitsa (IRE) **A. M. A. Al Shorafa**
2 **AFKAR (IRE)**, 4, b g Invincible Spirit (IRE)—Indienne (IRE) **C. E. Brittain**
3 **BAHIANO (IRE)**, 11, ch g Barathea (IRE)—Trystero **C. E. Brittain**
4 **BASHAMA**, 4, ch f Dubai Destination (USA)—My Amalie (IRE) **S. Manana**
5 **BRIGHT GIRL (IRE)**, 4, b f Invincible Spirit (IRE)—Honour Bright (IRE) **S. Manana**
6 **DIPLOMASI**, 4, b g Iceman—Piper's Ash (USA) **C. E. Brittain**
7 **ELJOWZAH (IRE)**, 4, b f Acclamation—Express Logic **S. Manana**
8 **ELSHABAKIYA (IRE)**, 4, b f Diktat—Amalie (IRE) **S. Manana**
9 **FAKHUUR**, 4, b f Dansili—Halska **S. Manana**
10 **GHAR SHOOP (IRE)**, 4, b f Dubai Destination (USA)—Lunda (IRE) **S. Manana**
11 **HUBOOD**, 4, b f Refuse To Bend (IRE)—Shuheb **S. Manana**
12 **HUWAYIT (IRE)**, 4, ch f Dalakhani (IRE)—Matin de Tempete (FR) **S. Manana**
13 **JIBOUTI (IRE)**, 4, b g Exceed And Excel (AUS)—Treble Seven (USA) **C. E. Brittain**
14 **JOLAH**, 4, b f Oasis Dream—Fanny's Fancy **S. Manana**
15 **MASAYA**, 4, b f Dansili—Anbella (FR) **S. Manana**
16 **METHAYEL (IRE)**, 4, b f Araafa (IRE)—First Breeze (USA) **S. Manana**
17 **MUDHISH (IRE)**, 7, b g Lujain (USA)—Silver Satire **C. E. Brittain**
18 **NAJRAAN**, 4, b f Cadeaux Genereux—Madam Ninette **S. Manana**
19 **PASTORAL PRIDE**, 4, ch f Pastoral Pursuits—Off By Heart **S. Manana**
20 **SAWAHILL**, 4, b f Diktat—Youm Jadeed (IRE) **S. Manana**
21 **SIMAYILL**, 4, b f Oasis Dream—Triennial (IRE) **S. Manana**
22 **THINK FAST (IRE)**, 4, br f Songandaprayer (USA)—Think (FR) **S. Manana**
23 **ZIRAUN**, 4, b f Cadeaux Genereux—Eternal Beauty (USA) **S. Manana**

MR CLIVE BRITTAIN—continued

THREE-YEAR-OLDS

24 **ABSHIR ZAIN (IRE)**, b c Green Desert (USA)—O Fourlunda **S. Manana**
25 **AHUQD (IRE)**, ch f Manduro (GER)—Daruliyya (IRE) **S. Manana**
26 **AL KARLOVYYH (IRE)**, b f Authorized (IRE)—Karlovy **S. Ali**
27 **AL KARTUZYYH (IRE)**, b f Authorized (IRE)—Kartuzy (JPN) **S. Ali**
28 **AMTHAL (IRE)**, b f Dalakhani (IRE)—Al Ihtithar (IRE) **A. M. A. Al Shorafa**
29 **ANABEDWEYAH (IRE)**, b f Authorized (IRE)—Al Kamah (USA) **S. Manana**
30 **ATMANNA**, br f Manduro (GER)—Samdaniya **S. Manana**
31 **BLUE TREASURE**, b f Shamardal (USA)—Blue Parade (IRE) **S. Ali**
32 **CAPE ALEX**, b f Cape Cross (IRE)—Alexander Three D (IRE) **S. Manana**
33 **DAGHASH**, b c Tiger Hill (IRE)—Zibet **M. Al Nabouda**
34 **DAGHASHAH**, b f Authorized (IRE)—Bunting **M. Al Nabouda**
35 **DARAA (IRE)**, b f Cape Cross (IRE)—Guarantia **S. Manana**
36 **ECHO OF DUBAI (IRE)**, b f Echo of Light—Papabile (USA) **Mr A. Al Mansoori**
37 **FAURAN (IRE)**, b f Shamardal (USA)—Zamhrear **S. Manana**
38 **HADAJ**, b c Green Desert (USA)—My Amalie (IRE) **S. Manana**
39 **HARAQAAN**, b f Manduro (GER)—Amalie (IRE) **S. Manana**
40 **HAZAZ (IRE)**, b c Dubawi (IRE)—Treble Seven (USA) **S. Manana**
41 **JAMHARA**, b f Authorized (IRE)—Wimple (USA) **S. Manana**
42 B f Singspiel (IRE)—Lady Hen **S. Manana**
43 **LAZEEZ (USA)**, b f Green Desert (USA)—Ballet School (IRE) **S. Manana**
44 **MANOMINE**, b g Manduro (GER)—Fascinating Hill (FR) **Mrs C. E. Brittain**
45 **MIBLISH**, b c Teofilo (IRE)—Triton Dance (IRE) **S. Manana**
46 **MISHHAR (IRE)**, b f Authorized (IRE)—Jakarta (IRE) **S. Manana**
47 **MUZHIL (IRE)**, b f Manduro (GER)—Mazuna (IRE) **S. Manana**
48 **QUIXOTE**, ch g Singspiel (IRE)—Rainbow Queen (FR) **C. E. Brittain**
49 **RED AGGRESSOR (IRE)**, b c Red Clubs (IRE)—Snap Crackle Pop (IRE) **C. E. Brittain**
50 **SAREEAH (IRE)**, b f Cadeaux Genereux—Jules (IRE) **S. Manana**
51 **SEMAYYEL (IRE)**, b f Green Desert (USA)—Lii Najma **S. Manana**
52 **SINGSPIEL SPIRIT**, ch g Singspiel (IRE)—Aberavon **Mr A. Al Mansoori**
53 **WAHYLAH (IRE)**, b f Shamardal (USA)—Neshla **S. Manana**
54 **WATANEE**, ch f Shamardal (USA)—Fascinating Rhythm **S. Manana**
55 **WEOOD (IRE)**, b f Dubawi (IRE)—Fawaayid (USA) **Mr M. Al Shafar**

TWO-YEAR-OLDS

56 B c 8/2 Byron—Al Hawa (USA) (Gulch (USA)) (12000) **S. Manana**
57 B f 4/3 Green Desert (USA)—Amalie (IRE) (Fasliyev (USA)) **S. Manana**
58 B f 14/4 Manduro (GER)—Bunting (Shaadi (USA)) **M. Al Nabouda**
59 B c 19/4 Notnowcato—Coconut Queen (IRE (Alhaarth (IRE)) (36000) **S. Manana**
60 B f 2/5 Rail Link—Dance Solo (Sadler's Wells (USA)) (26000) **S. Manana**
61 B f 19/2 Cape Cross (IRE)—Fragrancy (IRE) (Singspiel (IRE)) **M. Al Nabouda**
62 B f 8/3 Compton Place—Golubitsa (IRE) (Bluebird (USA)) (9000) **S. Manana**
63 B c 25/3 Authorized (IRE)—Lady Zonda (Lion Cavern (USA)) **M. Al Nabouda**
64 B c 1/5 Bernardini (USA)—Love of Dubai (USA) (More Than Ready (USA)) **Mr M. Al Shafar**
65 B f 30/3 Cadeaux Genereux—Pachanga (Inchinor) (18000) **S. Manana**
66 B f 28/3 Oratorio (IRE)—Pivotting (Pivotal) (32000) **C. E. Brittain**
67 B f 19/3 Medicean—Regal Riband (Fantastic Light) (36000) **S. Manana**
68 **SINAADI (IRE)**, b f 5/3 Kyllachy—Quantum (IRE) (Alhaarth (IRE)) (65000) **S. Manana**
69 Ch c 27/3 Dubawi (IRE)—Songbook (Singspiel (IRE)) (15000) **C. E. Brittain**
70 B f 1/4 Teofilo (IRE)—Valse Mystique (IRE) (Grand Lodge (USA)) (30000) **S. Manana**
71 B f 19/2 Singspiel (IRE)—Zibet (Kris)

Assistant Trainer: Mrs C. E. Brittain

Jockey (flat): Seb Sanders, Neil Callan. **Apprentice:** Debra England.

---

75   MR MEL BRITTAIN, Warthill
Postal: Northgate Lodge, Warthill, York, YO19 5XR
Contacts: PHONE (01759) 371472 FAX (01759) 372915
E-MAIL email@melbrittain.co.uk **WEBSITE** www.melbrittain.co.uk

1 **AVONCHARM**, 4, b f Avonbridge—Be My Charm **M. A. Brittain**
2 **BROCKFIELD**, 6, ch g Falbrav (IRE)—Irish Light (USA) **M. A. Brittain**

MR MEL BRITTAIN—continued

3 **CARANBOLA**, 6, br m Lucky Story (USA)—Ladywell Blaise (IRE) **M. A. Brittain**
4 **CARRAGOLD**, 6, b g Diktat—Shadow Roll (IRE) **M. A. Brittain**
5 **COTTAM DONNY**, 4, ch g Doyen (IRE)—Northern Bird **P. Easterby**
6 **COTTAM STELLA**, 4, br f Diktat—Flower Breeze (USA) **P. Easterby**
7 **DEFENCE COUNCIL (IRE)**, 4, b g Kheleyf (USA)—Miss Gally (IRE) **R. J. Mustill**
8 **GOSFORTH PARK**, 6, ch g Generous (IRE)—Love And Kisses **M. A. Brittain**
9 **GREY COMMAND (USA)**, 7, gr g Daylami (IRE)—Shmoose (IRE) **M. A. Brittain**
10 **KAYF COMMANDER**, 9, b g Kayf Tara—Silk Stockings (FR) **M. A. Brittain**
11 **MOZAYADA (USA)**, 8, ch m Street Cry (IRE)—Fatina **M. A. Brittain**
12 **SELDOM (IRE)**, 6, b g Sesaro (USA)—Daisy Dancer (IRE) **M. A. Brittain**
13 **STEEL STOCKHOLDER**, 6, b g Mark of Esteem (IRE)—Pompey Blue **M. A. Brittain**
14 **TOBRATA**, 6, ch g Tobougg (IRE)—Sabrata (IRE) **M. A. Brittain**
15 **TRADE SECRET**, 5, b g Trade Fair—Kastaway **M. A. Brittain**

THREE-YEAR-OLDS

16 B g Gentleman's Deal (IRE)—First Harmony
17 **FIRST PHASE**, b f First Trump—Melandre **M. A. Brittain**

TWO-YEAR-OLDS

18 Ch c 17/4 Lucky Story (USA)—Eurolink Cafe (Grand Lodge (USA)) (1600)
19 B f 30/4 Bahamian Bounty—Eurolinka (IRE) (Tirol) (2095) **Northgate Partnerships**
20 B f 18/4 Lucky Story (USA)—Guadaloup (Loup Sauvage (USA)) (1523) **Northgate Partnerships**
21 B f 24/4 Lucky Story (USA)—Mana Pools (IRE) (Brief Truce (USA)) (2857)
22 **MARABOUT (IRE)**, b c 21/4 Haafhd—Nirvana (Marju (IRE)) (5714)
23 B c 22/4 Lucky Story (USA)—Melandre (Lujain (USA)) (1904)
24 **MISTER MARCASITE**, gr c 23/4 Verglas (IRE)—No Rehearsal (FR) (Baillamont (USA)) (6000) **S. J. Box**
25 Gr c 15/5 Desideratum—Mother Corrigan (IRE) (Paris House) (1523)
26 B f 13/3 One Cool Cat (USA)—Musicology (Singspiel (IRE)) (3800)
27 B f 15/4 Araafa (IRE)—Notjustaprettyface (USA) (Red Ransom (USA)) (7500) **Northgate Partnerships**
28 Br f 6/3 One Cool Cat (USA)—Rose of Mooncoin (IRE) (Brief Truce (USA)) (10500)

Other Owners: Mr R. Adams, Mr J. Allan, Mr P. Chambers, Mrs C. Dobbs, Mr N. Dobbs, Mrs F. Godson, Mr J. Gunn, Mr S. Harrison, Mr S. Imeson, Mr J. Jarvis, Mr G. Pritchard, Mr D. Raymont, Mr H. Redhead, Mr C. Sim, Mr S. Taylor, Mr D. White, Mr N. Wilson.

Assistant Trainer: Paul Sedgwick, **Head Lad** - Neil Jordan

Apprentice: Jordan Hibberd.

MRS ANNA BROOKS, Towcester
Postal: **Horton House, Alderton, Towcester, Northamptonshire, NN12 7LN**
Contacts: **PHONE (01327) 811354 FAX (01327) 811496 MOBILE (07802) 541294**
E-MAIL onespotracing@hotmail.com

1 **ALTERNATOR (IRE)**, 10, ch g Pistolet Bleu (IRE)—Marello **Brooks & Robinson**
2 **CARRIG AN UISCE (IRE)**, 11, ch g Portrait Gallery (IRE)—Yarra Glen **Brooks & Robinson**
3 **DEVILS RIVER (IRE)**, 10, b g Anabaa (USA)—Riviere du Diable (USA) **Lloyd & Linda**
4 **DUKE OF ORMOND (IRE)**, 9, ch g Flemensfirth (USA)—Supreme Alannah (IRE) **Woz 5 Now 4**
5 **MIDNIGHT MAISIE**, 5, ch m Midnight Legend—Persian Silk (IRE) **T. L. Brooks**
6 **MUDITA MOMENT (IRE)**, 7, b g Heron Island (IRE)—Woodville Leader (IRE) **Mr J. H. Moorhouse**
7 **NO BUTS**, 4, b g Kayf Tara—Wontcostalotbut **Wontcostalot Partnership**
8 **ROSSBRIN (IRE)**, 7, b g Flemensfirth (USA)—Mustard Mor (IRE) **Mr J. H. Moorhouse**

Other Owners: A. A. Clifford, R. L. Clifford, Mr D. P. Gascoigne, Mrs L. M. Pestell, Mr C. N. Reynolds, Mr J. L. Robinson.

MR CHARLIE BROOKS, Chipping Norton
Postal: **Castle Barn Farm, Churchill, Chipping Norton, Oxfordshire, OX7 6RA**

1 **BECKHANI**, 5, b g Flemensfirth (USA)—Nicklup **Mr T. F. Lacey**
2 **CAVITE ALPHA (IRE)**, 6, b g Oscar (IRE)—The Purple Penguin **Mr C. P. E. Brooks**
3 **CAVITE GAMMA (IRE)**, 6, b g Beneficial—Follow Mama (IRE) **Mr C. P. E. Brooks**

78 MR ROY BROTHERTON, Pershore
Postal: Mill End Racing Stables, Netherton Road, Elmley Castle, Pershore, Worcestershire, WR10 3JF
Contacts: PHONE/FAX (01386) 710772 MOBILE (07973) 877280

1 CAPE OF STORMS, 9, b g Cape Cross (IRE)—Lloc **Mr A. T. L. Clayton**
2 CRIMSON QUEEN, 5, ch m Red Ransom (USA)—Rainbow Queen **Mr A. T. L. Clayton**
3 FLOTATION (USA), 5, b br m Chapel Royal (USA)—Storm Dove (USA) **Mrs T. J. Byrne**
4 JACKIE KIELY, 11, ch g Vettori (IRE)—Fudge **Mrs C. A. Newman**
5 LADYDOLLY, 4, b f Kyllachy—Lady Pekan **P. S. J. Croft**
6 LOVE IN THE PARK, 7, b m Pivotal—Naughty Crown (USA) **Mr A. T. L. Clayton**
7 PIE POUDRE, 5, ch g Zafeen (FR)—Eglantine (IRE) **Bredon Hill Racing Club**
8 STAR BELUCKY, 4, b f Overbury (IRE)—Herecomespapin (IRE) **M. D. Coulson**
9 TAWSEEF (IRE), 4, b g Monsun (GER)—Sahool **Millend Racing Club**
10 WAR OF THE ROSES (IRE), 9, b g Singspiel (IRE)—Calvia Rose **Millend Racing Club**
11 WEST COAST DREAM, 5, b g Oasis Dream—Californie (IRE) **Miss E. J. Byrd**

Other Owners: Mr Roy Brotherton, Mr T. L. Martin.

Assistant Trainer: Justin Brotherton

Jockey (flat): Paul Mulrennan, Tom Eaves, Phillip Makin. **Jockey (NH):** Wayne Kavanagh.

79 MR ALAN BROWN, Malton
Postal: Lilac Farm, Yedingham, Malton, North Yorkshire, YO17 8SS
Contacts: PHONE (01944) 728090 FAX (01944) 728071 MOBILE (07970) 672845
E-MAIL ad.brownn@globaluk.net

1 AUBURN LADY, 4, ch f Tobougg (IRE)—Carati **Mr D. Tate**
2 BARBARIAN, 6, b g Noverre (USA)—Love In The Mist (USA) **Mr F. E. Reay**
3 FITZWARREN, 11, b g Presidium—Coney Hills **Mrs S. Johnson**
4 HEAD TO HEAD (IRE), 8, gr g Mull of Kintyre (USA)—Shoka (FR) **A. Brown**
5 INDIAN OASIS, 4, b g Indian Haven—Royalty (IRE) **S. E. Pedersen**
6 O CROTAIGH (IRE), 8, b g Beneficial—Jerpoint Rose (IRE) **Mr D. J. Sturdy**
7 OUR GOLDEN BOY (IRE), 6, b g Milan—Just Little **The Golden Boys Partnership**
8 SKIDDAW VIEW, 4, b f Goodricke—Skiddaw Wolf **Mr D. J. Ellis**
9 VALDEMAR, 6, ch g Tobougg (IRE)—Stealthy Times **J. R. Wills**

TWO-YEAR-OLDS

10 ONLY FOR YOU, b f 16/4 Elusive City (USA)—
Enlisted (IRE) (Sadler's Wells (USA)) (1714) **B Selective Partnership**

Other Owners: Mrs W. A. D. Craven, Mr T. P. Curry, R. Hartley, Mr M. Lovett, Mr M. White.

Jockey (flat): Silvestre De Sousa. **Apprentice:** Terence Fury.

80 MR DAVID BROWN, Averham
Postal: The Old Stables, Averham Park, Newark, Nottinghamshire, NG23 5RU
Contacts: PHONE (01636) 613793 MOBILE (07889) 132931
E-MAIL david@davidbrownracing.com

1 ANRHEG, 4, b f Diktat—Dim Ots **Mrs D. J. Hughes**
2 BELLAPAIS ABBEY (IRE), 6, b g Shernazar—Wealthy And Wise (IRE) **N. P. Ender**
3 DONCASTER ROVER (USA), 6, b h War Chant (USA)—
Rebridled Dreams (USA) **P. Holling, I. Raeburn, S. Halsall & S. Bolland**
4 GOOD TIMIN', 4, b g Royal Applause—Record Time **P. Onslow**
5 4, B g Overbury (IRE)—Luneray (FR) **D. H. Brown**
6 ONELADYOWNER, 4, b c Auction House (USA)—Inya Lake **Bolland, Watson, Gregory, Lloyd & Oades**

THREE-YEAR-OLDS

7 CATCHY TUNE (IRE), ch c Redback—Magic Melody **J. C. Fretwell**
8 GRIPPA, ch g Avonbridge—Easy Mover (IRE) **Mr & Mrs Halsall & Partner**
9 MINNE WA WA, b f Bahamian Bounty—Crimson Dancer **Mr D. M. Brooke**
10 REGAL LADY, b f Captain Rio—Alvarinho Lady **Brown, Dyson, Tomlinson & Raper**

MR DAVID BROWN—continued

11 **SWEET GRACE**, b f Echo of Light—Sydney Star **P. Onslow**
12 **WHISKY BRAVO**, b g Byron—Dress Design (IRE) **S. Bolland & C. Watson**

TWO-YEAR-OLDS

13 Ch c 24/3 Medicean—Choir Gallery (Pivotal) (20952) **J. C. Fretwell**
14 Ch c 6/3 Kheleyf (USA)—Coffee Cream (Common Grounds) (38000) **J. C. Fretwell**
15 Ch c 12/2 Pastoral Pursuits—Dunloe (IRE) (Shaadi (USA)) (3809) **J. C. Fretwell**
16 B c 29/3 Footstepsinthesand—Dunya (Unfuwain (USA)) (30000) **J. C. Fretwell**
17 **FIDGET**, ch f 29/3 Bertolini (USA)—Record Time (Clantime) **P. Onslow**
18 **HOLLOWINA**, ch f 9/3 Beat Hollow—Trick Or Treat (Lomitas) **P. Onslow**
19 Ch f 29/1 Compton Place—Jodrell Bank (IRE) (Observatory (USA)) (11428) **Kilbride, Watson, Hughs**
20 **NEW PEARL (IRE)**, gr c 28/3 Acclamation—New Deal (Rainbow Quest (USA)) (71428) **Pearl Bloodstock**
21 B c 11/2 Byron—Oatcake (Selkirk (USA)) (37000) **J. C. Fretwell**
22 B c 10/5 Red Clubs (IRE)—Ossiana (IRE) (Polish Precedent (USA)) (12857) **Mr D. H. Brown**
23 B c 3/2 Compton Place—Passing Hour (USA) (Red Ransom (USA)) (29000) **J. C. Fretwell**
24 **PEARL SEA (IRE)**, b f 26/3 Elusive City (USA)—Catch The Sea (Barathea (IRE)) (32840) **Pearl Bloodstock**
25 B c 29/3 Royal Applause—Rock Lily (Rock of Gibraltar (IRE)) (33333) **J. C. Fretwell**
26 B br f 6/3 Street Boss (USA)—Strike Hard (IRE) (Green Desert (USA)) (30476) **J. C. Fretwell**
27 B c 19/3 Elusive City (USA)—Vanitycase (IRE) (Editor's Note (USA)) (36190) **J. C. Fretwell**

Other Owners: Mr Steve Bolland, Mr D. H. Brown, Mr P. J. Dyson, Mr J. Fretwell, Mrs K. Halsall, Mr S. Halsall, Mr P. Holling, Peter Onslow, Pearl Bloodstock, Mr J. Raper, Mr D. M. Tomlinson, Mr Clive Watson.

Assistant Trainer: Dushyant Dooyea

Jockey (flat): Philip Makin, Richard Mullen, Michael Stainton. **Apprentice:** Claire Murray. **Amateur:** Miss Paige Brown.

 MR GARY BROWN, Lambourn
Postal: **Lodge Down, Baydon, Berkshire, RG17 7BJ**
Contacts: **MOBILE (07545) 915253**
E-MAIL gbrownracing@hotmail.co.uk

1 **CHASING ACES**, 6, ch g Definite Article—Daprika (FR) **E. Wettern**
2 **CHESTNUT BEN (IRE)**, 7, ch g Ridgewood Ben—Betseale (IRE) **Mr J. Bourke**
3 **CORSICAN BOY**, 4, gr g Tobougg (IRE)—Madiyla **G. Brown**
4 **HIGHBYRY HIGH (IRE)**, 5, gr g Salford Express (IRE)—Betseale (IRE) **Mr J. Bourke**
5 **ILEWIN DUNDEE**, 6, b g Loup Sauvage (USA)—Ilewin Janine (IRE) **T. J. Segrue**
6 5, B g Generous (IRE)—Ilewin Janine (IRE) **T. J. Segrue**
7 **ILEWIN KIM**, 6, b g Grape Tree Road—Bridepark Rose (IRE) **T. J. Segrue**
8 **MAD GEORGE (IRE)**, 5, b g High Chaparral—Like My Style (IRE) **Mr G. E. Hickmott**
9 **SENIORS PET (IRE)**, 4, gr g Antonius Pius (USA)—Adelaide Pearl (USA) **M. H. Burke**
10 **TIME TO PLAY**, 7, b g Best of The Bests (IRE)—Primavera **Miss E. H. Wettern**

THREE-YEAR-OLDS

11 **HILALI (IRE)**, b g Sakhee (USA)—Mufradat (IRE) **Miss E. H. Wettern**

Jockey (flat): Liam Keniry. **Jockey (NH):** Jamie Moore. **Conditional:** Joshua Moore.

 MR IAN BROWN, Nawton
Postal: **Pasture House Farm, Nawton, York, YO62 7TU**
Contacts: **YARD/HOME (01439) 771250 MOBILE (07840) 842281**

1 **ANDY VIC (IRE)**, 9, b g Old Vic—Garranard Ros (IRE) **I. A. Brown**

Amateur: Mrs Joanne Brown.

 MR REGINALD BROWN, Abergavenny
Postal: **The Firs, Grosmont, Abergavenny, Gwent, NP7 8LY**

1 **ROSES LEGEND**, 7, b g Midnight Legend—Graig Hill Rose **S. R. Brown**
2 **UMORISTIC (FR)**, 4, gr g Baroud d'honneur (FR)—Canlastou (FR) **R. L. Brown**

84 MISS MICHELLE BRYANT, Lewes
Postal: Bevern Bridge Farm Cottage, South Chailey, Lewes, East Sussex, BN8 4QH
Contacts: PHONE/FAX (01273) 400638 MOBILE (07976) 217542
E-MAIL Bear_2009@live.co.uk

1 HAWK GOLD (IRE), 8, ch g Tendulkar (USA)—Heiress of Meath (IRE) Miss M. P. Bryant
2 MONASH LAD (IRE), 10, ch g General Monash (USA)—Story Time (IRE) Miss M. P. Bryant
3 NIGHT GROOVE (IRE), 9, b g Night Shift (USA)—Taysala (IRE) Miss M. P. Bryant
4 USQUAEBACH, 5, b m Trade Fair—Mashmoum Miss M. P. Bryant

Amateur: Miss M. P. Bryant.

85 MRS KATE BUCKETT, Bishops Waltham
Postal: Woodlocks Down Farm, Upham, Bishops Waltham, Hampshire, SO32 1JN

1 UPHAM ATOM, 9, b g Silver Patriarch (IRE)—Upham Lady Mrs K. A. Buckett

Jockey (NH): Liam Treadwell. Amateur: Miss Chloe Boxall.

86 MR BOB BUCKLER, Crewkerne
Postal: Higher Peckmoor, Henley, Crewkerne, Somerset, TA18 8PQ
Contacts: PHONE (01460) 75922 FAX (01460) 74851 MOBILE (07785) 773957
E-MAIL rbuckler@btconnect.com WEBSITE www.robertbucklerracing.co.uk

1 ASHBOURNE FOLLY (IRE), 6, b g Milan—Time To Ask (IRE) Mrs H R Dunn & Mr & Mrs C Collier
2 BALLYEGAN (IRE), 7, b g Saddlers' Hall (IRE)—Knapping Princess (IRE) Ballyegan Partnership
3 CHAMPAGNE ROSIE, 6, b m Shambo—Sharp Dance J. A. G. Meaden
4 CULLAHILL (IRE), 10, b br g Good Thyne (USA)—Rossacrowe Gale (IRE) N. Elliott
5 DIFFERENT TRADES (IRE), 8, b g Oscar (IRE)—Gale Tan (IRE) R. H. Buckler
6 DIGGER'S MATE, 4, b g General Gambul—Miss Diskin (IRE) M. J. Forrester
7 DONTSAYATHING (IRE), 8, br g Sayarshan (FR)—Executive Lass (IRE) D. R. Fear
8 DOUBLE DIZZY, 11, b g Double Trigger (IRE)—Miss Diskin (IRE) M. J. Forrester
9 ETHIOPIA, 9, b g Silver Patriarch (IRE)—Anhaar N. Elliott
10 GLENWOOD PRESENT (IRE), 5, ch g Presenting—Chancy Lass (IRE) N. Elliott
11 INCA CAVE (IRE), 7, b g Court Cave (IRE)—Inca Hill (IRE) Miss S. A. Hiscox
12 LA MADONNINA (IRE), 4, b f Milan—Supreme Nova Mrs H. R. Dunn
13 MALIN HEAD (IRE), 7, b g Presenting—Dedham Gale (IRE) Strictly Come Racing
14 MIZZURKA, 8, b m Alflora (IRE)—Miss Diskin (IRE) Golden Cap
15 4, B g Tamure (IRE)—Quick Exit Mr R. Hall
16 QUIX, 6, gr g Fair Mix (IRE)—Teeno Nell Golden Cap
17 READY OR NOT (IRE), 9, b g Oscar (IRE)—Ou La La (IRE) Mr Christopher and Anne Collier
18 SAINT PERAY (FR), 6, b g Fragrant Mix (IRE)—Gintonique (FR) Strictly Come Racing
19 SMALL FLY (IRE), 8, b g Humbel (USA)—Tworow (IRE) R. H. Buckler
20 SULPIUS (GER), 7, b g Tertullian (USA)—Suva (GER) R. H. Buckler
21 THE HAPPY WARRIOR, 4, b g Luso—Martomick N. Elliott
22 THE SAWYER (BEL), 12, ch g Fleetwood (IRE)—Green Land (BEL) D. R. Fear
23 TRENCHANT, 7, b g Medicean—Tromond Mr P. Harding & Mr S. Williams
24 WELD'S PRIDE, 5, ch m Weld—Connaught's Pride J. A. G. Meaden

Other Owners: Mr C. E. G. Collier, Mrs A. C. E. Collier, P.M. Harding, Mrs C. Lewis, Mr N. C. Robinson, Mrs H. E. Shane, S. P. Williams.

Head Lad: Giles Scott

Jockey (NH): Andrew Glassonbury, Will Kennedy. Conditional: Nathan Sweeney.

87 MR MARK BUCKLEY, Stamford
Postal: Potters Hill Stables, Morkery Lane, Castle Bytham, Stamford, Lincolnshire, NG33 4SP
Contacts: OFFICE (01780) 411158 MOBILE (07808) 360488
E-MAIL markbuckley215@btinternet.com

1 LIBERTY SHIP, 7, b g Statue of Liberty (USA)—Flag David Lockwood & Fred Lockwood
2 MATERIANA (IRE), 4, b br f Presenting—Jay Lo (IRE)

MR MARK BUCKLEY—continued

3 **ORIENTAL CAVALIER**, 6, ch g Ishiguru (USA)—Gurleigh (IRE) **X8 Racing Partnership 2**

Other Owners: M. A. Buckley, Mr P. Edwards, D. J. Lockwood.

---

88 MR PETER BULL, Wadhurst
Postal: Buss's Green Farm, Cousley Wood, Wadhurst, East Sussex, TN5 6QU

1 **MASTER T (USA)**, 13, b g Trempolino (USA)—Our Little C (USA) **P. A. Bull**

---

89 MR DAI BURCHELL, Ebbw Vale
Postal: Drysiog Farm, Briery Hill, Ebbw Vale, Gwent, NP23 6BU
Contacts: PHONE (01495) 302551 MOBILE (07980) 482860

1 **ACAPULCO BAY**, 8, b g Pursuit of Love—Lapu-Lapu **J. Parfitt**
2 **BEAT ALL OUT**, 7, b g Beat All (USA)—Help Yourself (IRE) **The Beefeaters**
3 **CAPTAIN LOUI (IRE)**, 4, gr g Verglas (IRE)—Miss Corinne **T. R. Pearson**
4 **COMMERCE**, 5, b m Trade Fair—Well Away (IRE) **B. J. Williams**
5 **CRUCHAIN (IRE)**, 9, ch g Shernazar—Mack Tack (IRE) **Mr & Mrs A. J. Mutch**
6 **FLYING PHOENIX**, 4, b f Phoenix Reach (IRE)—Rasmalai **B. J. Williams**
7 **NOTABOTHERONME (IRE)**, 10, b br g Religiously (USA)—Kylogue's Delight **J. E. Mutch**
8 **REBECCAS CHOICE (IRE)**, 9, b g Religiously (USA)—Carolin Lass **J. E. Mutch**
9 **ROYAL BOX**, 5, b g Royal Applause—Diamond Lodge **T. R. Pearson**
10 **SPINNING WATERS**, 6, b g Vettori (IRE)—Secret Waters **B. M. G. Group**

TWO-YEAR-OLDS

11 **SYMPHONY OF DREAMS**, b f 4/3 Primo Valentino (IRE)—Flying Lion (Hunting Lion (IRE)) **T. R. Pearson**
12 **SYMPHONY OF LIGHT**, b f 20/2 Primo Valentino (IRE)—Echostar (Observatory (USA)) **T. R. Pearson**

Other Owners: Mr L. Coulton, Mr W. R. A. Davies, Mrs S. Mutch, Mr A. J. Mutch, Mr D. H. Protheroe.

Assistant Trainer: Ruth Burchell

Jockey (flat): Kelly Harrison, Sam Hitchcott. **Jockey (NH):** Christian Williams. **Amateur:** Mr Nick Williams, Mr Robert Williams.

---

90 MR PAUL BURGOYNE, Wincanton
Postal: Knowle Rock, Shepton Montague, Wincanton, Somerset, BA9 8JA
Contacts: PHONE (01963) 32138 MOBILE (07894) 081008
E-MAIL knowlerockracing@hotmail.co.uk

1 **METROPOLITAN CHIEF**, 8, b g Compton Place—Miss Up N Go **L. E. Tomlin**
2 **MISS BOOTYLISHES**, 7, b m Mujahid (USA)—Moxby **Mrs Helen Adams**
3 **RUPERT BRUSH**, 11, b g Thornberry (USA)—O K Sohrar **Mr M. A. Bickell**
4 **SIR LOIN**, 11, ch g Compton Place—Charnwood Queen **Mrs C Leigh-Turner**
5 **SUHAYL STAR (IRE)**, 8, b g Trans Island—Miss Odlum (IRE) **Mrs C. Leigh-Turner & Mr Kris Clark**
6 **TEEN AGER (FR)**, 8, b g Invincible Spirit (IRE)—Tarwiya (IRE) **L. E. Tomlin**
7 **WEE BUNS**, 7, b g Piccolo—Gigetta (IRE) **Mrs C. Leigh-Turner**
8 **WEST LEAKE (IRE)**, 6, b g Acclamation—Kilshanny **L. E. Tomlin**

Other Owners: Mrs H. Adams, Mr M. A. Bickell, Mr Kris Clark, Mrs C. Leigh-Turner.

Assistant Trainer: Mr Gareth Charles-Jones

---

91 MRS E. M. BURKE, Leyburn
Postal: Spigot Lodge, Middleham, Leyburn, North Yorkshire, DL8 4TL
Contacts: PHONE (01969) 625088 FAX (01969) 625099 MOBILE (07778) 458777
E-MAIL karl@karlburke.co.uk WEBSITE www.karlburke.co.uk

1 **AQUILIFER (IRE)**, 4, b g Holy Roman Emperor (IRE)—Sassy Bird (USA) **J. Kelsey-Fry**
2 **BAVARIAN PRINCESS (USA)**, 4, b f Invincible Spirit (IRE)—Lileagh (IRE) **Aricabeau Syndicate II & Partners**

MRS E. M. BURKE—continued

3 **BELLA NOIR**, 5, b m Kyllachy—Lady Broughton (IRE) **John & Sally Kelsey-Fry**
4 **BOLD MARC (IRE)**, 10, b g Bold Fact (USA)—Zara's Birthday (IRE) **Mrs E. M. Burke**
5 **BUZZ LAW (IRE)**, 4, b g Fasliyev (USA)—Buzz Two (IRE) **Mr Mark James & Mrs Elaine Burke**
6 **DOYNOSAUR**, 5, b m Doyen (IRE)—Daring Destiny **Mrs E. M. Burke**
7 **FINEFRENZYROLLING (IRE)**, 4, ch f Refuse To Bend (IRE)—
Oasis Star (IRE) **Mr Mark James & Mrs Elaine Burke**
8 **FRONTLINE PHANTOM (IRE)**, 5, b g Noverre (USA)—Daisy Hill **Mrs E. M. Burke**
9 **MAGIC CAT**, 6, b g One Cool Cat (USA)—Magic Music (IRE) **R. Bailey**
10 **MEDIA HYPE**, 5, b h Tiger Hill (IRE)—Hyperspectra **Light Valley Stud & Mrs E Burke**
11 **MIAMI GATOR (IRE)**, 5, ch g Titus Livius (FR)—Lovere **Mrs E. M. Burke**
12 **OLLON (USA)**, 4, b br g Mr Greeley (USA)—Town Branch (USA) **Keep Racing**
13 **PARADISE SPECTRE**, 5, b g Firebreak—Amber's Bluff **The Paradise Partnership**
14 **RED JADE**, 7, ch g Dubai Destination (USA)—Red Slippers (USA) **Keep Racing**
15 **REIGNIER**, 5, b g Kheleyf (USA)—Komena **W. P. Richards**
16 **RODRIGO DE TORRES**, 5, ch g Bahamian Bounty—Leonica **Mr M Gittins & Mrs E Burke**
17 **SILENCEOFTHEWIND (USA)**, 5, b g Eddington (USA)—Betty's Solutions (USA) **Mrs E. M. Burke**
18 **TEPMOKEA (IRE)**, 6, ch g Noverre (USA)—Eroica (GER) **Keep Racing**
19 **URSULA (IRE)**, 6, b m Namid—Fritta Mista (IRE) **The Ursula Partnership**
20 **VANTAA (IRE)**, 4, ch g Shamardal (USA)—Indian Express **Mrs E. M. Burke**
21 **WINGS OF APOLLO (IRE)**, 4, b g Librettist (USA)—Niobe **Aricabeau Syndicate II & Partners**

THREE-YEAR-OLDS

22 **BALTIC FIZZ (IRE)**, b f Baltic King—Holly Springs **Mr Mark James & Mrs Elaine Burke**
23 **BOOTS AND SPURS**, b g Oasis Dream—Arctic Char **C. Bryce**
24 **CLASS MONITOR**, b f Indesatchel (IRE)—First Tarf **Leydens Farm Stud & Mrs E Burke**
25 **DANCHEUR (IRE)**, ch f Chineur (FR)—Daneville (FR) **Mr Mark James & Mrs Elaine Burke**
26 **FICELLE (IRE)**, b f Chineur (FR)—Petite Boulangere (IRE) **Mr D Simpson & Mrs E Burke**
27 **GANGSTERBANKSTERS (FR)**, b c High Chaparral (IRE)—Pantelleria (GER) **Mr W Chow & Mrs E Burke**
28 **GURU GIRL**, b f Ishiguru—Startori **Mr D Redvers & Mrs E Burke**
29 **HAWAIIAN STORM**, b f Jeremy (USA)—Malahini (UAE) **The Storm Partnership**
30 **LISIERE (IRE)**, b f Excellent Art—Sahara Sky (IRE) **David & Yvonne Blunt**
31 **PRIESTLEY'S REWARD (IRE)**, b g Whipper—Prima Figlia (IRE) **Mr P Dean & Mrs E Burke**
32 **ROSSELLI (IRE)**, b c Iffraaj—Special Ellie (FR) **W. P. Richards**
33 **SPYKES BAY (USA)**, ch c Speightstown (USA)—She's a Rich Girl (USA) **Mr M. T. Gittins**
34 **STORMY GLAZ (FR)**, b g Stormy River (FR)—South Island (IRE) **The Storm Partnership**
35 **YEEOOW (IRE)**, b c Holy Roman Emperor (IRE)—Taraya (IRE) **Mr R. Lee & Mrs E. Burke**

Other Owners: Aricabeau Racing Limited, Mr A. W. Barlow, Mr D. Blunt, Mrs Y. Blunt, Mrs V. Brazier, J. Burley, Mr W. W. K. Chow, Mr B. Dahl, Mrs A. Dahl, P. Dean, Dr C. I. Emmerson, I. Goldsmith, Mrs M. R. Goldsmith, Mr E. J. Hughes, Mr M. J. James, Mrs S. Kelsey-Fry, Mr R. Lee, S. P. Marley, Mr R. C. McKeown, Mr D. P. Meagher, Mr D. Redvers, Mr M. A. Roden, D. Simpson, Mr A. Watson.

Assistant Trainer: Mr Karl Burke

Jockey (flat): Martin Harley. **Conditional:** Alexander Voy. **Apprentice:** Richard Old.

---

92 MR KEIRAN BURKE, Martock
Postal: **Lavenoak Racing Stables, Burrough Street, Ash, Martock, Somerset, TA12 6NZ**

1 **FORTIFICATION (USA)**, 9, gr g With Approval (CAN)—Palisade (USA) **Mr C. P. Rudd**
2 **GARDINER HARTE (IRE)**, 8, b g Beneficial—Mirasel **W. A. Harrison-Allan**
3 **HOLMWOOD LEGEND**, 11, b g Midnight Legend—West-Hatch-Spirit **B. A. Derrick**
4 **HUNT BALL (IRE)**, 7, b g Winged Love (IRE)—La Fandango (IRE) **A. C. W. Knott**
5 **KIRBYS GLEN (IRE)**, 10, b g Charente River (IRE)—Silence To Silence (IRE) **P. R. Rodford**
6 **OPTIMISTIC DUKE (IRE)**, 5, ch g Bachelor Duke (USA)—Gronchi Rosa (IRE) **J. H. W. Finch**
7 **REYMYSTERIO (IRE)**, 11, b g Luso—Rehey Lady **P. R. Rodford**
8 **SPARKY MAY**, 7, b m Midnight Legend—Glassy Appeal (USA) **Mr W. F. Muddyman**
9 **TENITEMSPLUSTOAST**, 6, ch g Midnight Legend—Ultra Pontem **Mr L. Kirkwood**
10 **TIMMIES GONE (IRE)**, 7, b g Saddlers' Hall—Gaye Artiste (IRE) **Gimme Notise**
11 **TRUQ CHOUET (FR)**, 5, ch g Valanour (IRE)—Tulipp D'avril (FR) **Graham, Kate & Paul Darby**

Other Owners: Mrs S. L. Bender, Mrs C. G. Cruddace, Mr G. A. Darby, Mrs K. A. Darby, Mr P. Darby.

93 MR SIMON BURROUGH, Chard
Postal: **7 Peacocks Close, West Buckland, Wellington, Somerset, TA21 9JY**
Contacts: PHONE **(01823) 660223** MOBILE **(07887) 958131**

1 **ARMAGNAC REBEL,** 4, b g Grape Tree Road—Charm Offensive **Mr A P Helliar & Mr A J W Hill**
2 **CRIDDA BOY,** 6, ch g Mark of Esteem (IRE)—Second Affair (IRE) **D. G. Staddon**
3 **DADS BIRTHDAY,** 6, b gr g Baryshnikov (AUS)—Keysmith **G. W. Giddings**
4 **FOLLY FARM (IRE),** 4, gr g Definite Article—West Hill Rose (IRE) **D. G. Staddon**
5 **GREAT KICKER (IRE),** 7, b g Great Palm (IRE)—Keep The Change (IRE) **John & Greer Norman**
6 **KRUSEMAN,** 5, b g Doyen (IRE)—Polar Charge **Mr M. Gomm**
7 **LAVENOAK LAD,** 12, b g Cloudings (IRE)—Halona **Mrs Elizabeth Heal & Mrs Heather Heal**
8 **SAFFRON SAM,** 5, b g Zamindar (USA)—Sally Gardens **Mrs C. A. Lewis-Jones**
9 **TAHITI DANCER,** 4, b f Tamure (IRE)—Rosevear (IRE) **N. J. McMullan & S. H. Bryant**
10 **THUNDER CHILD,** 12, gr g Cloudings (IRE)—Double Dutch **R. J. Weeks**
11 **TREGONY BRIDGE,** 5, b g Avonbridge—Serotina (IRE) **H. J. W. Davies**
12 **VICTORIA ROSE (IRE),** 7, b m Old Vic—West Hill Rose (IRE) **D. G. Staddon**
13 **YELLOW JERSEY,** 10, b m Mark of Esteem (IRE)—La Bicyclette (FR) **S. Burrough**

Other Owners: S. H. Bryant, Mrs E. A. Heal, Mrs H. A. Heal, A. P. Helliar, A. J. W. Hill, N. J. McMullan, John Norman, Mrs G. O. Norman.

Conditional: Ben Clarke.

94 MR JOHN BUTLER, Newmarket
Postal: **I Have a Dream Stables, Hamilton Road, Newmarket, Suffolk, CB8 7JQ**

1 **ALL ABOUT YOU (IRE),** 6, b g Mind Games—Expectation (IRE) **Mrs H. F. Prendergast**
2 **CLEAR SAILING,** 9, b g Selkirk (USA)—Welsh Autumn **Mr C. Owen**
3 **DOUZE POINTS (IRE),** 6, b g Redback—Grade A Star (IRE) **Mr J. Butler**
4 **ENSNARE,** 7, b g Pivotal—Entrap (USA) **Mrs H. F. Prendergast**
5 **FUTURE IMPACT (IRE),** 4, b g Kheleyf (USA)—Daring Imp (IRE) **The Chicken On A Chain Partnership**
6 **HOLCOMBE BOY,** 4, b g Intikhab (USA)—Lady Lindsay (IRE) **Circle Of Trust Racing**
7 **PETROGLYPH,** 8, ch g Indian Ridge—Madame Dubois **Mrs H. F. Prendergast**
8 **RAISE THE RAFTERS (IRE),** 7, ch g Monashee Mountain (USA)—
Zolube (IRE) **The Chicken On A Chain Partnership**
9 **SILVER LINNET (IRE),** 5, gr m Acclamation—Nadeema (FR) **The Chicken On A Chain Partnership**
10 **STAND GUARD,** 8, b g Danehill (USA)—Protectress **Mr C. Owen**
11 **THE BAY BANDIT,** 5, b g Highest Honor (FR)—Pescara (IRE) **The Chicken On A Chain Partnership**

THREE-YEAR-OLDS

12 B c Elusive City (USA)—Hi Lyla (IRE) **Mrs H. F. Prendergast**
13 **PAYBACK (GER),** b c Shirocco (GER)—Panagia (USA) **The Chicken On A Chain Partnership**

Other Owners: Mr P. Babe, Mrs J. D. Owen.

95 MR PADDY BUTLER, Lewes
Postal: **Homewood Gate Racing Stables, Novington Lane, East Chiltington, Lewes, East Sussex, BN7 3AU**
Contacts: PHONE/FAX **(01273) 890124** MOBILE **(07973) 873846**
E-MAIL **homewoodgate@aol.com**

1 **CARLTON SCROOP (FR),** 9, ch g Priolo (USA)—Elms Schooldays **Miss M. P. Bryant**
2 **CORLOUGH MOUNTAIN,** 8, ch g Inchinor—Two Step **Miss M. P. Bryant**
3 **CURRAGH DANCER (FR),** 9, ch g Grand Lodge (USA)—Native Twine **Miss M. P. Bryant**
4 **GUILDED WARRIOR,** 9, b g Mujahid (USA)—Pearly River **Miss M. P. Bryant**
5 **HEADING TO FIRST,** 5, b g Sulamani (IRE)—Bahirah **Homewoodgate Racing Club**
6 **QUERIDO (GER),** 8, b g Acatenango (GER)—Quest of Fire (FR) **Homewoodgate Racing Club**
7 **SUNSET BOULEVARD (IRE),** 9, b g Montjeu (IRE)—Lucy In The Sky (IRE) **Mrs E. Lucey-Butler**
8 **WHAT'S FOR TEA,** 7, b m Beat All (USA)—Come To Tea (IRE) **Mrs E. Lucey-Butler**

MR PADDY BUTLER—continued

TWO-YEAR-OLDS

9 **SWEET PICCOLO**, ch c 4/4 Piccolo—Quality Street (Fraam) **Mr D. M. Whatmough**

Other Owners: Mr P. J. Charman, Mrs A. Horrell, C. W. Wilson.

Assistant Trainer: Mrs E Lucey-Butler

Jockey (flat): Robert L. Butler. Amateur: Miss Zoe Lilly, Miss M. Bryant.

---

96 **MRS BARBARA BUTTERWORTH, Appleby**
Postal: **Bolton Mill, Bolton, Appleby-in-Westmorland, Cumbria, CA16 6AL**
Contacts: **PHONE (01768) 361363**

1 **BELOW THE DECK (IRE)**, 9, b m Stowaway—Clear Bid (IRE) **Mrs B. Butterworth**
2 **KNICKERBOKERGLORY**, 6, b m Saddlers' Hall (IRE)—Cashmere Lady **Miss E. Butterworth**
3 **KNIGHT VALLIANT**, 9, gr g Dansili—Aristocratique **Mrs B. Butterworth**
4 **THE BRAVETRAVELLER (IRE)**, 9, b g Bravefoot—Morning Nurse (IRE) **Mrs B. Butterworth**

Assistant Trainer: Miss Elizabeth Butterworth

Jockey (NH): James O'Farrell. Amateur: Miss Elizabeth Butterworth.

---

97 **MR NEVILLE BYCROFT, Malton**
Postal: **Cotman Rise, Brandsby, York, YO61 4RN**
Contacts: **PHONE (01347) 888641 MOBILE (07802) 763227**

1 **AUTO MAC**, 4, b g Auction House (USA)—Charlottevalentina (IRE) **Mrs C. M. Whatley**
2 **BABY MAC**, 4, b g Presidium—Nishara
3 **BEDLOE'S ISLAND (IRE)**, 7, b g Statue of Liberty (USA)—Scenaria (IRE) **Mr J. G. Lumsden & Mr M. F. Hogan**
4 **EENY MAC (IRE)**, 5, ch g Redback—Sally Green (IRE) **Mrs J. Dickinson**
5 **FAMA MAC**, 5, b g Fraam—Umbrian Gold (IRE) **Mrs C. M. Whatley**
6 **MAYBEME**, 6, b m Lujain (USA)—Malvadilla (IRE) **N. Bycroft**
7 **SHOTLEY MAC**, 8, ch g Abou Zouz (USA)—Julie's Gift **J. A. Swinburne**
8 **VALENTINE'S GIFT**, 4, b g Presidium—Efipetite **Hambleton Racing Partnership**
9 **WILLBEME**, 4, b f Kyllachy—Befriend (USA) **Mr P. D. Burrow**

THREE-YEAR-OLDS

10 **EIUM MAC**, b g Presidium—Efipetite **N. Bycroft**
11 **SHOTLEY MUSIC**, b g Amadeus Wolf—Silca Key **Mr J A Swinburne & Mrs C M Whatley**

Other Owners: Mr N. Bycroft, Mr R. C. Crawford, Mr J. H. Hemy, Mr M. F. Hogan, Mrs E. Hughes, Mr J. G. Lumsden, Mr J. A. Swinburne, Mrs C. M. Whatley.

Assistant Trainer: Seb Spencer

Jockey (flat): Jimmy Quinn, Franny Norton. Amateur: Mr Seb Spencer.

---

98 **MR CHARLES BYRNES, Ballingarry**
Postal: **Ballynoe, Ballingarry, Co. Limerick, Ireland**
Contacts: **PHONE (00353) 69 68473 FAX (00353) 69 68473 MOBILE (00353) 8783 16111**
E-MAIL ballynoestables@yahoo.co.uk

1 **ADROPAUPEP (IRE)**, 6, gr m Amilynx (FR)—Floribunda Rose **David Speiran**
2 **ARNAUD (IRE)**, 4, b g Chevalier (IRE)—Jumbo Romance (IRE) **Gigginstown House Stud**
3 **CAPTAIN DANCER (IRE)**, 6, ch g Danehill Dancer (IRE)—Rain Flower (IRE) **Relic Pride Partnership**
4 **DOMINATION**, 5, b g Motivator—Soliza (IRE) **Patrick Wilmott**
5 **FISTS OF FURY (IRE)**, 8, ch g Beneficial—Shean Alainn (IRE) **Gigginstown House Stud**
6 **IN A NUTSHELL (IRE)**, 5, b g Xaar—Trilemma **Pat & Mary O'Hanlon**
7 **JACK COOL (IRE)**, 6, b g One Cool Cat (USA)—Rachrush (IRE) **Relic Pride Partnership**
8 **KNOCKFIERNA (IRE)**, 7, b m Flemensfirth (USA)—Garden Town (IRE) **Knockfierna Syndicate**
9 **MAZAGEE (FR)**, 4, b f Muhtathir—Zafonia (FR) **Patrick Wilmott**

MR CHARLES BYRNES—continued

10 **OUR VINNIE (IRE)**, 5, b br g Vinnie Roe (IRE)—Boopsey (IRE) **P. Ennis**
11 **PITTONI (IRE)**, 6, b g Peintre Celebre (USA)—Key Change (IRE) **Patrick Wilmott**
12 **ROYAL VIC (IRE)**, 5, b g Old Vic—Harelda **Flor McCarthy**
13 **SCOTTISH BOOGIE (IRE)**, 5, b g Tobougg (IRE)—Scottish Spice **Patrick Willmott**
14 **SEA OF THUNDER (IRE)**, 7, b g Old Vic—Snob's Supreme (IRE) **Gigginstown House Stud**
15 **SHRAPNEL (IRE)**, 6, b br g Flemensfirth (USA)—Victoria Theatre (IRE) **Gigginstown House Stud**
16 **SKIBABE (IRE)**, 8, ch g Pilsudski (IRE)—Furry Baby **Nay Syndicate**
17 **SOLWHIT (FR)**, 8, b g Solon (GER)—Toowhit Towhee (USA) **Top Of The Hill Syndicate**
18 **TRIFOLIUM (FR)**, 5, b g Goldneyev (USA)—Opium des Mottes (FR) **Gigginstown House Stud**
19 **WEAPON'S AMNESTY (IRE)**, 9, ch g Presenting—Victoria Theatre (IRE) **Gigginstown House Stud**
20 **WOLF HALL (IRE)**, 5, br g Presenting—Water Rock **Gigginstown House Stud**

Assistant Trainer: Patrick Byrnes

Jockey (flat): F. M. Berry. **Jockey (NH):** D.N. Russell.

---

99 MISS JULIE CAMACHO, Malton
Postal: **Star Cottage, Welham Road, Norton, Malton, North Yorkshire, YO17 9QE**
Contacts: **PHONE (01653) 696205 FAX (01653) 696205 MOBILE (07779) 318135 / (07950) 356440**
E-MAIL julie@jacracing.co.uk WEBSITE www.juliecamacho.com

1 **BEAT THE RUSH**, 5, b g Tobougg (IRE)—Rush Hour (IRE) **Axom (XX)**
2 **BELINSKY (IRE)**, 5, b g Compton Place—Westwood (FR) **Wentdale Ltd**
3 **BERNIX**, 10, gr g Linamix (FR)—Bernique (USA) **Wentdale Ltd**
4 **BILLY CADIZ**, 7, b g Zilzal (USA)—Faraway Moon **Wentdale Ltd**
5 **DANDARRELL**, 5, b g Makbul—Dress Design (IRE) **Mr J. S. De W. Waller**
6 **DIESCENTRIC (USA)**, 5, b g Diesis—Hawzah **Axom (XVIII)**
7 **DUBAI CELEBRATION**, 4, b g Dubai Destination (USA)—Pretty Poppy **Julie Camacho**
8 **EDITORS STORY**, 6, ch g Lucky Story (USA)—Midnight Break **Wentdale Ltd**
9 **MY SINGLE MALT (IRE)**, 4, b g Danehill Dancer (IRE)—Slip Dance (IRE) **R. Walker, S. Brown & J. Camacho**
10 **NOBLE ATTITUDE**, 6, b m Best of The Bests (IRE)—Charming Lotte **Wentdale Ltd**
11 **PUNTA BALUARTE**, 6, b m Lahib (USA)—Calachuchi **J. S. Spence**
12 **ROCK OF DEAUVILLE (IRE)**, 5, b g Rock of Gibraltar (IRE)—Ruff Shod (USA) **T. Warner**
13 **SIR NOD**, 10, b g Tagula (IRE)—Nordan Raider **Julie Camacho**
14 **TOM SAWYER**, 4, b g Dansili—Cayman Sunset (IRE) **Bolingbroke J Howard FAO Mersey R & Ptns**
15 **TROJAN GIFT (USA)**, 5, b br g War Chant (USA)—Extry (USA) **Axom (XIX)**
16 **WEBBOW (IRE)**, 10, b g Dr Devious (IRE)—Ower (IRE) **Wentdale Ltd**
17 **ZAKATAL**, 6, gr g Kalanisi (IRE)—Zankara (FR) **J. Sugarman & D. Furman**

THREE-YEAR-OLDS

18 **ARTLANA**, b f Dutch Art—Latanazul **Julie Camacho**
19 **ISTAN STAR (USA)**, b g Istan (USA)—Migygian (USA) **Axom XXVIII**
20 **JUSTINE TIME (IRE)**, b f Kodiac—Sinn Time (IRE) **N R T Ltd**
21 **LAST OF THE DIXIES**, ch f Halling (USA)—Dixie Favor (USA) **J. Spence**
22 **NEW ROMANTIC**, b f Singspiel (IRE)—Kalinova (IRE) **Elite Racing Club**
23 **SPANISH LEGACY**, b f Dr Fong (USA)—Spanish Lace **Julie Camacho**

Other Owners: Axom, Mr Lee Bolingbroke, Mr Tony Bruce, Mr S. Burrows, Miss Julie Camacho, Mr Dan Downie, Mr Brian Hankey, Mr Tony Hill, Mr Graeme Howard, Ms S. M. Jamieson, Mrs Faith O'Connor, Mr J. E. Townend.

Assistant Trainer: Mr S. Brown

Jockey (flat): Tom Eaves, Barry McHugh.

---

100 MR MARK CAMPION, Malton
Postal: **Whitewell House Stables, Whitewall, Malton, North Yorkshire, YO17 9EH**
Contacts: **PHONE (01653) 692729 FAX (01653) 600066 MOBILE (07973) 178311**
E-MAIL info@markcampion-racing.com WEBSITE www.markcampion-racing.com

1 **BELINSKY (IRE)**, 5, b g Compton Place—Westwood (FR) **Wentdale Limited**
2 **BERNIX**, 10, gr g Linamix (FR)—Bernique (USA) **Wentdale Limited**
3 **BILLY CADIZ**, 7, b g Zilzal (USA)—Faraway Moon **Wentdale Limited**
4 **CHARMING GRACE (IRE)**, 6, b m Flemensfirth (USA)—Lady Laureate **The Saddlers' Flyers**

MR MARK CAMPION—continued

5 DESERT NOVA (IRE), 10, ch g Desert King (IRE)—Assafiyah (IRE) **Whitewall Racing**
6 EDITORS STORY, 6, ch g Lucky Story (USA)—Midnight Break
7 MINKIE MOON (IRE), 4, b g Danehill Dancer (IRE)—Minkova (IRE) **Faulkner West & Co Ltd**
8 PANASHKA (IRE), 7, ch m Ashkalani (IRE)—Dressed In Style (IRE) **Pan's People**
9 SADDLERS' SECRET (IRE), 7, b m Saddlers' Hall (IRE)—Birdless Bush (IRE) **The Saddlers' Flyers**
10 6, B m Bob Back (USA)—Storm In Front (IRE) **A. M. Campion**
11 WEBBOW (IRE), 10, b g Dr Devious (IRE)—Ower (IRE) **Wentdale Limited**

Other Owners: Mrs L. Beale, Mrs J. Boutell, Mr A. C. Brett, Mr Jason Button, Mr A. M. Campion, Mr Barrie Coleman, Mr C. Laws, Mr Glenn Nurse.

Assistant Trainer: Mrs F Campion

MR T. J. CANAVAN, Belfast
Postal: **8 Glenholm Drive, Belfast, BT8 6LW**
Contacts: **PHONE (07989) 233670**

1 DOUBLE TWIST (IRE), 7, b g Double Eclipse (IRE)—Hawaiian Goddess (USA) **T. J. Canavan**
2 LUSO'S GIRL (IRE), 9, b m Luso—Orchards Beauty (IRE) **T. J. Canavan**
3 POLAR LASS (IRE), 5, ch m Vinnie Roe (IRE)—Polar Crash **T. J. Canavan**

Assistant Trainer: John Canavan

MS JENNIE CANDLISH, Leek
Postal: **Basford Grange Racing Stables, Basford, Leek, Staffordshire, ST13 7ET**
Contacts: **PHONE (01538) 360324 (07779) 047826 FAX (01538) 360324 MOBILE (07889) 413639**
E-MAIL jenniecandlish@yahoo.co.uk WEBSITE www.jenniecandlishracing.co.uk

1 AMROTH BAY, 8, b g Alflora (IRE)—La Bella Villa **West Mercia Fork Trucks Ltd**
2 BASFORD BOB (IRE), 7, b g Bob's Return (IRE)—El Monica (IRE) **A. J. Baxter**
3 CRESCENT BEACH (IRE), 5, b g Presenting—Angelas Choice (IRE) **Mr P. & Mrs G. A. Clarke**
4 CROSS KENNON (IRE), 8, b g Craigsteel—Gaelic Million (IRE) **Mr P. & Mrs G. A. Clarke**
5 DECENT LORD (IRE), 8, b g Lord of Appeal—Otorum (IRE) **Mrs J. M. Ratcliff**
6 DETOUR AHEAD, 4, ch f Needwood Blade—My Tern (IRE) **Mr Phillip Dutton**
7 5, Gr g Cloudings (IRE)—Different Dee (IRE) **A. J. Baxter**
8 DONT TELL SAILOR (IRE), 6, b g Saddlers' Hall (IRE)—Pharlen's Dream (IRE) **Mr P. & Mrs G. A. Clarke**
9 DOWNWARD SPIRAL (IRE), 7, br g Windsor Castle—Misty Links (IRE) **Keith O. Warner**
10 EBONY RIVER (IRE), 6, b g Alderbrook—Dishy (IRE) **Mr & Mrs R. Hall & Mrs W. Glazebrook**
11 FAIR REFLECTION, 4, gr f Fair Mix (IRE)—Eller's Reflection **Mr L. A. Taylor**
12 FIENDISH FLAME (IRE), 8, ch g Beneficial—Deenish (IRE) **Mr & Mrs R. N. C. Hall**
13 FLAME OF DIXIE (IRE), 6, b m Beneficial—Deenish (IRE) **Mr & Mrs R. N. C. Hall**
14 FRENCH TIES (IRE), 10, ch g John French—No Ties (IRE) **A. J. Baxter**
15 GRANVILLE ISLAND (IRE), 5, b g Flemensfirth (USA)—Fox Glen **Mr P. & Mrs G. A. Clarke**
16 GRAYCLIFFE (IRE), 6, gr g Val Royal (FR)—Popiplu (USA) **Mr M. M. Allen**
17 HIT THE SWITCH, 6, b g Reset (AUS)—Scenic Venture (IRE) **Mr M. M. Allen**
18 LADY IDA, 7, b m Dolpour—La Princesse **Mr R. J. Cant**
19 LUCKY LUKEY, 6, gr g Cape Town (IRE)—Imprevue (IRE) **John Pointon & Sons**
20 LUKEYS LUCK, 5, b g Cape Town (IRE)—Vitelucy **John Pointon & Sons**
21 MAOI CHINN TIRE (IRE), 5, b g Mull of Kintyre (USA)—Primrose And Rose **A. J. Baxter**
22 OLD STYLE (IRE), 7, b g Classic Cliche (IRE)—Granny Smith (IRE) **Mr S. J. Bryant**
23 PYRACANTHA, 7, b g Muhtarram (USA)—Forsythia **A. J. Baxter**
24 RARE RUBY (IRE), 8, b m Dilshaan—Ruby Setting **Mrs J. M. Ratcliff**
25 4, B g Oscar (IRE)—Rose Karanja
26 4, Ch g Sir Harry Lewis (USA)—Scottish Clover **Mr P. & Mrs G. A. Clarke**
27 4, B g Milan—Stratosphere
28 TARN HOWS (IRE), 6, ch g Old Vic—Orchardstown Lady **Mr P. & Mrs G. A. Clarke**
29 YIPPEE KIYAY (IRE), 6, b g Heron Island (IRE)—Winter Utopia (IRE) **Christine Hunter**

THREE-YEAR-OLDS

30 BOB'S WORLD, b g Multiplex—Vocation (IRE) **Mr R. J. Cant**
31 SNOWED IN (IRE), gr g Dark Angel (IRE)—Spinning Gold **A. J. Baxter**

MS JENNIE CANDLISH—continued

Other Owners: Mr S. Bryant, Mr Peter Clarke, Mrs Gwenda Ann Clarke, Mrs Sara Glazebrook, Mr R. N. C. Hall, Mrs R. N. C. Hall.

Assistant Trainer: Alan O'Keeffe

Jockey (flat): Joe Fanning, Jimmy Fortune, Paul Hanagan. **Jockey (NH):** Alan O'Keeffe, Sam Thomas, Sean Quinlan.
Conditional: Peter Carberry.

---

102 MR HENRY CANDY, Wantage
Postal: **Kingston Warren, Wantage, Oxfordshire, OX12 9QF**
Contacts: **PHONE (01367) 820276 / 820514 FAX (01367) 820500 MOBILE (07836) 211264**
E-MAIL henrycandy@btconnect.com

1 AMOUR PROPRE, 6, ch g Paris House—Miss Prim **Simon Broke & Partners**
2 BALLINLINA, 4, ch f Iceman—Competa **Balding, Rayment, Starczewski, Whitaker**
3 BEAUCHAMP ZORRO, 4, ch g Zamindar (USA)—Aquarelle **E. Penser**
4 BLESS YOU, 4, b f Bahamian Bounty—Follow Flanders **T. A. F. Frost**
5 COLLOQUIAL, 11, b g Classic Cliche (IRE)—Celia Brady **Mrs M. Blackburn**
6 DINKUM DIAMOND (IRE), 4, b c Aussie Rules (USA)—Moving Diamonds **Eight Star Syndicate**
7 EFFIGY, 8, b g Efisio—Hymne d'amour (USA) **Henry D. N. B. Candy**
8 GOSBECK, 4, ch f Dubawi (IRE)—Goslar **Major M. G. Wyatt**
9 GOURAY GIRL (IRE), 5, b m Redback—Brillano (FR) **Mr A. Le Herissier**
10 HOOLIGAN SEAN, 4, ch g Ishiguru (USA)—Sheesha (USA) **Henry D. N. B. Candy**
11 L'AMI LOUIS (IRE), 4, b g Elusive City (USA)—Princess Electra (IRE) **First Of Many Partnership**
12 LOOKING ON, 4, b g Observatory (USA)—Dove Tree (FR) **Girsonfield Ltd**
13 MA QUILLET, 4, gr f Tumbleweed Ridge—Raffelina (USA) **Mr G. E. Buck**
14 MARKAB, 9, b g Green Desert (USA)—Hawafiz **Mosaic Racing**
15 NO LARKING (IRE), 4, b g Refuse To Bend (IRE)—Dawn Chorus (IRE) **Burley & Candy**
16 RUPEETOUPS, 4, b g Deportivo—Rock Flower **The Rupert Partnership**
17 SEAL ROCK, 4, b g Ishiguru (USA)—Satin Doll **P. A. Deal / H. Candy**
18 SEAMUS SHINDIG, 10, b g Aragon—Sheesha (USA) **Henry D. N. B. Candy**
19 THE CALLING CURLEW, 4, b g Soviet Star (USA)—The Lady Mandarin **Mrs F. A. Veasey & Mr J. Porteous**
20 THE CONFESSOR, 5, b g Piccolo—Twilight Mistress **Six Too Many**
21 WIGGY SMITH, 13, ch g Master Willie—Monsoon **Mrs G. M. Tricks**

THREE-YEAR-OLDS

22 BRUNDON, ch f Refuse To Bend (IRE)—Anna of Brunswick **Major M. G. Wyatt**
23 BYTON, b f Byron—Arculinge **Major M. G. Wyatt**
24 CHORAL BEE, b f Oratorio (IRE)—Chief Bee **Henry D. N. B. Candy**
25 FLY ON BY, b g Byron—High Bird **Henry D. N. B. Candy**
26 GIFTED DANCER, b f Cadeaux Genereux—Puteri Sas (IRE) **Dale / Deal / Candy**
27 GULL ROCK, b f Ishiguru (USA)—Petrovna (IRE) **Henry D. N. B. Candy**
28 JOCASTA DAWN, b f Kyllachy—Jubilee Dawn **Mrs M. J. Blackburn**
29 JOLI SOLEIL, b g Kyllachy—Jolie (IRE) **Mrs C. S. Baylis**
30 LARWOOD (IRE), gr g Aussie Rules (USA)—Ashbilya (USA) **Six Too Many**
31 LONDON SILVER, b g Zafeen (FR)—Princess Londis **J. Simms**
32 MABEL'S SONG, b f Sakhee (USA)—War Shanty **Lady Whent**
33 MADAME FEU, ch f Tumbleweed Ridge—Raffelina (USA) **Mr G. E. Buck**
34 MR OPULENCE, ch g Generous (IRE)—Miss Opulence (IRE) **S. M. Smith**
35 MRS HUFFEY, b f Acclamation—Passing Hour (USA) **John Joseph Byrne**
36 RUGGED CROSS, b c Cape Cross (IRE)—Lunda (IRE) **T. Barr**
37 SCHOOL FEES, b f Royal Applause—Cankara (IRE) **Elias, Bennett, Mitchell & Newton**
38 SELKIE'S FRIEND, b g Elnadim (USA)—T G's Girl **Henry D. N. B. Candy**
39 SIENA STREET, b f Strategic Prince—Savoy Street **Mr D. Clark**
40 B g Royal Applause—Tart And A Half **Lady Whent**
41 TIME FOR A TIGER, b f Tiger Hill (IRE)—Last Slipper **Mr D. Clark**
42 ZHIGGY'S STARDUST, b g Zafeen (FR)—Lady Natilda **I. Higginson**

TWO-YEAR-OLDS

43 Br f 28/2 Clodovil (IRE)—Alenushka (Soviet Star (USA)) (7000) **Mrs Fiona Gordon**
44 ANNAWI, b f 21/3 Dubawi (IRE)—Anna of Brunswick (Rainbow Quest (USA)) **Major M. G. Wyatt**
45 APRICOT SKY, ch c 20/4 Pastoral Pursuits—Miss Apricot (Indian Ridge) (3809) **Henry D. N. B. Candy**
46 BENONI, b c 19/3 Bertolini (USA)—Ladykirk (Slip Anchor) (9523) **Henry D. N. B. Candy**

MR HENRY CANDY—continued

47 B g 27/3 Byron—Cankara (IRE) (Daggers Drawn (USA)) (380) **Giles, McCarthy, Stephens & Newton**
48 CAPE PERON, b c 27/1 Beat Hollow—Free Offer (Generous (IRE)) **The Earl Cadogan**
49 DALGIG, b c 16/2 New Approach (IRE)—Bright Halo (IRE) (Bigstone (IRE)) (70000) **T. Barr**
50 GALILAHI, b f 7/2 Sleeping Indian—Tittle (Tobougg (IRE)) (5000) **T A Frost/ H Candy**
51 GREY'S ELEGY, gr c 23/3 Ishiguru (USA)—Christmas Rose (Absalom) (16000) **Simon Broke & Partners III**
52 HERBALIST, ch g 27/3 Haafhd—Puya (Kris) **Girsonfield Ltd**
53 MUSKAT LINK, b c 17/2 Rail Link—Muskat Rose (One Cool Cat (USA)) **The Muskateers**
54 PEARL STREET (USA), b f 12/2 Street Sense (USA)—
                           Pretty Meadow (USA) (Meadowlake (USA)) (177045) **Pearl Bloodstock**
55 SECRETLY, ch f 28/2 Sakhee's Secret—
                  The Cat's Whiskers (NZ) (Tale of The Cat (USA)) **Henrietta, Duchess Of Bedford**
56 B c 28/3 Footstepsinthesand—Shaiyadima (IRE) (Zamindar (USA)) (42000) **Six Too Many**
57 SILK ROUTE, ch f 11/4 Dubai Destination (USA)—Crinolette (IRE) (Sadler's Wells (USA)) **Mr D. Clark**
58 B c 1/3 Piccolo—Siryena (Oasis Dream) (18000) **Mrs A D Bourne/ Mr H Candy**
59 SPEEDY WRITER, b c 28/3 Byron—Merch Rhyd-Y-Grug (Sabrehill (USA)) (5238) **Henry Candy & Partners II**
60 TIGHT FIT, ch f 18/3 Assertive—Bikini (Trans Island) **W. M. Lidsey / H. Candy**
61 B c 25/3 Piccolo—Twilight Mistress (Bin Ajwaad (IRE)) **Caroline Wilson**
62 B c 25/4 Zafeen (FR)—Verbal Intrigue (USA) (Dahar (USA)) (60000) **Clark / Byrne**
63 VIENNESE VERSE, b g 18/4 Byron—Teller (ARG) (Southern Halo (USA)) **The Chevaliers**

Other Owners: Mr C. J. Burley, Mr J. J. Byrne, Mr Henry Candy, Mr J. B. Clark, Mr W. R. Collins, Mr J. S. Dale, Mr P. A. Deal, Mr Alexander Frost, Mr T. Gould, Mrs Jo Slogrove, Mr R. Turkington, Mrs C. S. Whitaker.

Jockey (flat): Fergus Sweeney, Frankie McDonald, Dane O'Neill. **Apprentice:** Amy Scott.

---

103   MR GRANT CANN, Cullompton
Postal: **Newlands Farm, Cullompton, Devon, EX15 1QQ**

1 ARCTIC WATCH, 7, gr g Accondy (IRE)—Watcha (USA) **P. J. Cave**
2 HOW'S MY FRIEND, 7, b g Karinga Bay—Friendly Lady **J. G. Cann**
3 MOLLY ROUND (IRE), 8, b m Old Vic—Mondeo Rose (IRE) **Mr A. R. M. M. Kavanagh**
4 SHE'S ON THE CASE (IRE), 7, b m Witness Box (USA)—New Line (IRE) **J. G. Cann**

---

104   MR DON CANTILLON, Newmarket
Postal: **10 Rous Road, Newmarket, Suffolk, CB8 8DL**
Contacts: **PHONE (01638) 668507 MOBILE (07709) 377601**

1 ALPINE BREEZE (IRE), 6, b m King's Theatre (IRE)—Alpine Gale (IRE) **D. E. Cantillon**
2 AS I AM (IRE), 4, b f Old Vic—Faucon **D. E. Cantillon**
3 AVRUMI, 6, b g Kayf Tara—Bit of A Citizen (IRE) **Mr L. Cohen**
4 DANCING JACK (FR), 8, b br g True Brave (USA)—Line Saj (FR) **D. E. Cantillon**
5 DON'T CALL ME TINY (IRE), 4, b f Acclamation—Holly Rose **Mrs C. Reed**
6 GREEN TO GOLD (IRE), 7, gr g Daylami (IRE)—Alonsa (IRE) **D. E. Cantillon**
7 HIGHTOWN (IRE), 5, b g King's Theatre (IRE)—Faucon **D. E. Cantillon**
8 LA ESTRELLA (USA), 9, b g Theatrical—Princess Ellen **D. E. Cantillon**
9 MILITARY MAN, 4, br g Dubai Destination (USA)—Cyclonic Storm **D. E. Cantillon**
10 THIS IS ME, 4, b g Presenting—Shayzara (IRE) **D. E. Cantillon**

---

105   MR DAVID CARR, Hexham
Postal: **Highwood Farm, Hexham, Northumberland, NE46 3RR**

1 ARDNACLANCY (IRE), 9, br g Darnay—Ardnataggle (IRE) **D. Carr**
2 COASTLEY (IRE), 10, b g Lord Americo—Cosima (IRE) **D. Carr**
3 COOL STAR (IRE), 6, b g One Cool Cat (USA)—Pack Ice (USA) **D. Carr**
4 COOL VIC (IRE), 8, b g Old Vic—Winterland Gale (IRE) **D. Carr**
5 INDIAN VOYAGE (IRE), 4, b g Indian Haven—Voyage of Dreams (USA) **D. Carr**
6 WINCES WELL (IRE), 5, b g Helissio (FR)—Cardinal Press

106 MRS RUTH CARR, Stillington
Postal: **Risedale, Easingwold Road, Huby, York, North Yorkshire, YO61 1HN**
Contacts: PHONE **(01347) 811719 (home) (01347) 821683 (yard) MOBILE (07721) 926772**
E-MAIL **ruth@ruthcarrracing.co.uk** WEBSITE **www.ruthcarrracing.co.uk**

1 **CHOSEN ONE (IRE)**, 7, ch g Choisir (AUS)—Copious (IRE) **Bridget Houlston & Marion Chapman**
2 **LIGHT THE CITY (IRE)**, 5, b g Fantastic Light (USA)—Marine City (JPN) **Atkins Legal Services**
3 **MOHEEBB (IRE)**, 8, b g Machiavellian (USA)—Rockerlong **Reach For The Moon & Mrs R Carr**
4 **MYRAID**, 5, b g Danbird (AUS)—My Desire **Mr J. D. Spensley & Mrs M. A. Spensley**
5 **ORPSIE BOY (IRE)**, 9, b g Orpen (USA)—Nordicolini (IRE) **Miss V. A. Church**
6 **RED CAPE (FR)**, 9, b g Cape Cross (IRE)—Muirfield (FR) **Middleham Park Racing LVI**
7 **VIKING DANCER**, 5, b g Danehill Dancer (IRE)—Blue Siren **Michael Hill**

THREE-YEAR-OLDS

8 **WOLF SPIRIT (IRE)**, b g Amadeus Wolf—Nasharaat (IRE) **Michael Hill**

Other Owners: Mr M. J. Atkins, T. J. E. Brereton, Mrs R. A. Carr, Mrs M. Chapman, S. B. Clark, Mr A. R. G. Harris, Miss B. J. Houlston, T. S. Palin, A. Riaz, Mrs M. A. Spensley, Mr J. D. Spensley.

Assistant Trainer: David Chapman

107 MR DECLAN CARROLL, Sledmere
Postal: **Sledmere House Stables, Sledmere, Driffield, East Yorkshire, YO25 3XG**
Contacts: PHONE **(01377) 236161 FAX (01377) 236161 MOBILE (07801) 553779**
E-MAIL **sledmereracing@hotmail.com**

1 **AENEID**, 7, b g Rainbow Quest (USA)—Grecian Slipper **Mr M. Stewart**
2 **AMAZING STAR (IRE)**, 7, b g Soviet Star (USA)—Sadika (IRE) **Mr K. McConnell**
3 **BOUCHER GARCON (IRE)**, 4, b g Spartacus (IRE)—Valamander (IRE) **M. Cunningham & P. Cunningham**
4 **CATALLOUT (IRE)**, 4, b f One Cool Cat (USA)—America Lontana (FR) **Ferrari Racing**
5 **COME HERE YEW (IRE)**, 4, ch g Refuse To Bend (IRE)—Red Zinger (USA) **K. Mackay & L. Ibbotson**
6 **GRAND STITCH (USA)**, 5, b g Grand Slam (USA)—Lil Sister Stich (USA) **Mr D. K. Fantom**
7 **GREEN PARK (IRE)**, 9, b g Shinko Forest (IRE)—Danccini (IRE) **G. A. Fixings Ltd**
8 **HITS ONLY JUDE (IRE)**, 4, gr g Bold Fact (USA)—Grey Goddess **Dreams**
9 **ILLUSTRIOUS PRINCE (IRE)**, 5, b g Acclamation—Sacred Love (IRE) **Mr P. J. Dolan**
10 **INVINCIBLE HERO (IRE)**, 5, b g Invincible Spirit (IRE)—Bridelina (FR) **Mrs S. A. Bryan**
11 **LAC A DANCER (IRE)**, 6, b m Danehill Dancer (IRE)—Lac Dessert (USA) **Ferrari Racing**
12 **MISS BEAT (IRE)**, 6, b m Beat Hollow—Bolas **Mr J. Harney**
13 **POPPY GOLIGHTLY**, 5, ch m Compton Place—Popocatepetl (FR) **Denis Hardy, Christian Wroe**
14 **SAVE THE BEES**, 4, b g Royal Applause—Rock Concert **Mr S. P. Ryan**
15 **SWIFTLY DONE (IRE)**, 5, b g Whipper (USA)—Ziffany **Mr D. Watts, Miss C. King, J. Syme & M. Syme**
16 **WATTS UP SON**, 4, b g Diktat—Local Fancy **L. Ibbotson, D. Watts & J. Syme**
17 **WHATS FOR PUDDING (IRE)**, 4, ch f Kheleyf (USA)—Margaret's Dream (IRE) **Mr R. J. Ball**
18 **WHOZTHECAT (IRE)**, 5, b g One Cool Cat (USA)—Intaglia (GER) **Ninerus**
19 **YAHRAB (IRE)**, 7, gr g Dalakhani (IRE)—Loire Valley (IRE) **I. D. Woolfitt**

THREE-YEAR-OLDS

20 **ALNAIR (IRE)**, b c Red Clubs (IRE)—Danccini (IRE) **Mr K. McConnell**
21 **BAILE ATHA CLIATH (IRE)**, b g Barathea (IRE)—Danielli (IRE) **Dreams**
22 **FARANG KONDIEW**, ch c Selkirk (USA)—Passiflora **Kenny Mackay & Lee Ibbotson**
23 **HOPES REBELLION**, b g Royal Applause—Relativity (IRE) **Mr R. Close**
24 **MICK SLATES (IRE)**, b g Moss Vale (IRE)—Sonic Night (IRE) **Ormskirk**
25 **PROPHESY (IRE)**, ch c Excellent Art—Race The Wild Wind (USA) **Mr M. Stewart**

TWO-YEAR-OLDS

26 B c 22/4 Compton Place—Fancy Rose (USA) (Joyeux Danseur (USA)) (13136) **K. McConnell**
27 **LASTCHANCELUCAS**, b g 24/4 Ishiguru (USA)—Light of Aragon (Aragon) **Mr C. H. Stephenson**
28 Ch c 19/3 Ad Valorem (USA)—Love Valentine (IRE) (Fruits of Love (USA)) (5336) **Dreams**
29 Gr c 31/1 Verglas (IRE)—Miss St Tropez (Danehill Dancer (IRE)) (13957) **Dreams**
30 **SANTRY**, ch c 27/4 Ishiguru (USA)—Mis Chicaf (IRE) (Prince Sabo) **Dreams**

Head Girl - Kym Dee

Apprentice: Neil Farley, Jason Hart, Michael Kenny.

108 **MR TONY CARROLL, Cropthorne**
Postal: **The Cropthorne Stud, Field Barn Lane, Cropthorne, Pershore, Worcestershire, WR10 3LY**
Contacts: PHONE **(01386) 861020** FAX **(01386) 861628** MOBILE **(07770) 472431**
E-MAIL **a.w.carroll@btconnect.com** WEBSITE **www.awcarroll.co.uk**

1 **ARCTIC WINGS (IRE)**, 8, b g In The Wings—Arctic Hunt (IRE) **Mr P. A. Downing**
2 **BENGAL TIGER**, 6, ch g Tagula (IRE)—Floriana **Centaur Global Partnership I**
3 **BLAZING BUCK**, 6, ch g Fraam—Anapola (GER) **Mill House Racing Syndicate**
4 **BOSTON BLUE**, 5, b g Halling—City of Gold (IRE) **Mr B. J. Millen**
5 **CANE CAT (IRE)**, 5, b br m One Cool Cat (USA)—Seven Wonders (USA) **J. W. Egan**
6 **CARR HALL (IRE)**, 9, b g Rossini (USA)—Pidgeon Bay (IRE) **The Cropthorne Boys**
7 **CRAZY BOLD (GER)**, 9, ch g Erminius (GER)—Crazy Love (GER) **Mrs S. R. Keable**
8 **DRACO BOY**, 5, gr g Silver Patriarch (IRE)—Miss Tehente (FR) **Mayden Stud**
9 **EASYDOESIT (IRE)**, 4, b g Iffraaj—Fawaayid (USA) **T. R. Pearson**
10 **FLYFORD PRINCE**, 7, b g Superior Premium—Bisquet-de-Bouche **L. T. Cheshire**
11 **FLYFORD PRINCESS**, 4, b m Superior Premium—Bisquet-de-Bouche **L. T. Cheshire**
12 **GAMBATTE**, 5, b m One Cool Cat (USA)—Dahshah **Balding, Taylor & Bathwick Tyres**
13 **GENEROUS KENNY**, 6, ch g Generous (IRE)—Lady Franpalm (IRE) **Mrs E. V. A. Trotman**
14 **GRACCHUS (USA)**, 6, b g Black Minnaloushe (USA)—Montessa **A. W. Carroll**
15 **HUCKLEBERRY (IRE)**, 10, b g Hubbly Bubbly (USA)—Laur's Melody (IRE) **T. Mennell & K. Gwilliam**
16 **JOLIE ETOILE**, 4, b f Choisir (AUS)—Jolie (IRE) **Mrs C. S. Baylis**
17 **KING OLAV (UAE)**, 7, ch g Halling (USA)—Karamzin (USA) **Cover Point Racing**
18 **KINKEEL (IRE)**, 13, b g Hubbly Bubbly (USA)—Bubbly Beau **Group 1 Racing (1994) Ltd**
19 **LAUGHING JACK**, 4, b g Beat Hollow—Bronzewing **Mr P. A. Downing**
20 **LAYLA'S DANCER**, 5, b g Danehill Dancer (IRE)—Crumpetsfortea (IRE) **S. Hussain & P. O'Neill**
21 **LE CORVEE (IRE)**, 10, b g Rossini (USA)—Elupa (IRE) **A. W. Carroll**
22 **LUGGERS HALL (IRE)**, 4, b g Cape Cross (IRE)—Saabga (USA) **Mr M. S. Cooke**
23 **MALANOS (IRE)**, 4, b br g Lord of England (GER)—Majorata (GER) **Mr B. J. Millen**
24 **MAYAN FLIGHT (IRE)**, 4, b g Hawk Wing (USA)—Balimaya (IRE) **A. W. Carroll**
25 **MISSIONAIRE (USA)**, 5, b br g El Corredor (USA)—Fapindy (USA) **Mr B. J. Millen**
26 **MY BEST MAN**, 6, b g Forzando—Victoria Sioux **D. J. Lowe**
27 **MY MATE LES (IRE)**, 4, b g High Chaparral (IRE)—Precedence (IRE)
28 **OCEAN COUNTESS (IRE)**, 6, b m Storming Home—Pennycairn **Mr W. McLuskey**
29 **OCEAN LEGEND (IRE)**, 7, b g Night Shift (USA)—Rose of Mooncoin (IRE) **Mr W. McLuskey**
30 **PAHENTE**, 4, br gr g Silver Patriarch (IRE)—Miss Tehente (FR) **Mayden Stud**
31 **POLAR AURORAS**, 4, b f Iceman—Noor El Houdah (IRE) **Balding, Davenport, Hayman, Prestwich**
32 **RIGID**, 5, ch g Refuse To Bend (IRE)—Supersonic **Mr & Mrs J. B.**
33 **RIO MILAN (IRE)**, 6, b g Milan—Lady Medina (IRE) **Mrs J. Cumiskey Mr T. Joyce**
34 **SALFORD ROSE (IRE)**, 5, ch m Salford Express (IRE)—
                    Toppagale (IRE) **Let's Give It A Go Racing & Mr D. A. Jervis**
35 **SANNIBEL**, 4, ch f Needwood Blade—Socialise **Mr P. & Mrs V. Williams**
36 **SANTERA (IRE)**, 8, br m Gold Away (IRE)—Sainte Gig (FR) **Mr J. Tucker**
37 **SHALAMBAR (IRE)**, 6, gr g Dalakhani (IRE)—Shalama (IRE) **Mr B. J. Millen**
38 **SHARE OPTION**, 10, b g Polish Precedent (USA)—Quota **Last Day Racing Partnership**
39 **SMART CATCH (IRE)**, 6, b g Pivotal—Zafaraniya (IRE) **Cover Point Racing**
40 **SOUTER POINT (USA)**, 6, b br g Giant's Causeway (USA)—
                    Wires Crossed (USA) **The Centaur Group Partnership III**
41 **SUN DREAM**, 5, b m Desert Sun—I Have A Dream (SWE) **Mayden Stud**
42 **SUPA SEEKER (USA)**, 6, b br g Petionville (USA)—Supamova (USA) **A. W. Carroll**
43 **THE DERRY**, 4, gr g Terimon—Dancing Danoli **Mrs S. Davies**
44 **THE RIGHT TIME**, 4, b f Val Royal (FR)—Esligier (IRE) **The Cropthorne Boys**
45 **TIME MEDICEAN**, 6, gr g Medicean—Ribbons And Bows (IRE) **A. W. Carroll**
46 **TIME SQUARE (FR)**, 5, b g Westerner—Sainte Parfaite (FR) **Mr M. S. Cooke**
47 **TRECASE (IRE)**, 5, b g Zafeen (FR)—Pewter Lass **Mr S. Agodino**
48 **TROUBLETIMESTWO (FR)**, 6, gr g Linamix (FR)—Time of Trouble (FR) **Mill House Racing Syndicate**
49 **UNLIMITED**, 10, b g Bold Edge—Cabcharge Blue **Mr M. B. Clarke**
50 **VALMINA**, 5, b g Val Royal (FR)—Minnina (IRE) **Mayden Stud**
51 **VERTUEUX (FR)**, 7, gr g Verglas (IRE)—Shahrazad (FR) **Mr J. Rutter**
52 **WALDEN PRINCE (IRE)**, 5, b g Saffron Walden (FR)—Kahyasi Princess (IRE) **Mr G. Attwood**
53 , Ch m Umistim—Wilming
54 **ZAFRANAGAR (IRE)**, 7, b g Cape Cross (IRE)—Zafaraniya (IRE) **Mr P. A. Downing**

THREE-YEAR-OLDS

55 B f Byron—Noor El Houdah (IRE)
56 **THE YANK**, b g Trade Fair—Silver Gyre (IRE) **Mr G. Attwood**
57 **TOOLEY WOODS (IRE)**, b f Cape Cross (IRE)—Kondakova (IRE) **Hodgson, Jarvis, Louch**

MR TONY CARROLL—continued

TWO-YEAR-OLDS

58 **AMIRAH (IRE)**, b f 31/1 Holy Roman Emperor (IRE)—
Nadwah (USA) (Shadeed (USA)) (19047) **Hodgson, Jarvis, Louch**

Other Owners: Mr J. Bacciochi, Mrs J. Bacciochi, Mr Peter Balding, Mrs M. Bayley, Mr A. W. Carroll, Mrs Carolyn Chamberlain, Mr W. Clifford, Mr A. J. Cork, Mr A. M. Cosnett, Mrs J. Cumiskey, Mr John Daniell, Mr M. S. Day, Mr J. Dewhurst, Mrs D. S. Dewhurst, Mr J. Hayman, Mr Carl Hodgson, Mr S. Hussain, Mr Kevin Jarvis, Mr D. A. Jervis, Mr T. Joyce, Mr J. Loftus, Mr Stephen Louch, Mr Bob Millen, Mr B. J. Millen, Mr Paul O'Neill, Dr A. D. Rogers, Mr David Shorthouse, Mr K. Sobey, Mr M. G. Taylor, Mr Trevor Turner, Mrs I. Whitehead, Mrs V. Williams, Mr P. Williams.

Conditional: Lee Edwards. **Apprentice:** George Downing. **Amateur:** Mr Mark J. J. Smith, Mr Charles Carroll.

---

109 **MR TONY CARSON, Newmarket**
Postal: **5 Churchill Avenue, Newmarket, Suffolk, CB8 0BZ**
Contacts: **PHONE (01638) 660947 MOBILE (07837) 601867**
E-MAIL topcatcarson@gmail.com

1 **CONSIDER YOURSELF (USA)**, 5, gr ro m Afleet Alex (USA)—
Champagne Royale (USA) **Chris Wright & Minster Stud**
2 **DASHWOOD**, 5, b h Pivotal—Most Charming (FR) **Macattack**
3 **DEBBIE DOO**, 4, b f Beat Hollow—Pleasing **W. Carson**
4 **HORATIAN**, 4, b br c Medaglia d'oro (USA)—
Swift and Classy (USA) **Mr Chris Wright & Mr David Murrell**
5 **LYRIC POET (USA)**, 5, b br g Distorted Humor (USA)—Baltic Nations (USA) **G. Houghton**
6 **MUNCHKIN**, 4, b f Tiger Hill (IRE)—Baranquilla **Macattack**
7 **PEACE SEEKER**, 4, b g Oasis Dream—Mina **Neville Chamberlain Syndicate**
8 **STATUS SYMBOL (IRE)**, 7, ch g Polish Precedent (USA)—Desired **W. Carson**

THREE-YEAR-OLDS

9 **AMIS REUNIS**, b f Bahamian Bounty—Spring Clean (FR) **W. Carson**
10 **ARABIAN RANCHES**, b g Echo of Light—Deira (USA) **Neville Chamberlain Syndicate**
11 **BRIMSTONE HILL (IRE)**, b c Royal Applause—Right As Rain **G. Houghton, S. Ebanks-Blake & K. P. Foley**
12 **CHAUD LAPIN**, ch c Haafhd—Culture Queen **Chris Wright & Minster Stud**
13 **GEEAITCH**, ch g Cockney Rebel (IRE)—Grand Rebecca (IRE) **G. Houghton**
14 **NADEMA ROSE (IRE)**, b f Elnadim—Noctilucent (JPN) **W. Carson**
15 **PARANDIH (USA)**, b c Dubai Destination (USA)—Princess Nada **W. Carson**
16 **ROUNDELAY**, b f Tiger Hill (IRE)—Cercle d'amour (USA) **G. R. Poole, B. Clover, M. Doughty**
17 **SANAD (IRE)**, br c Red Clubs (IRE)—Knockatotaun **Athos Racing**

TWO-YEAR-OLDS

18 Ch f 31/3 Three Valleys (USA)—Tanasie (Cadeaux Genereux) **Minster Stud**
19 B f 12/2 Oratorio (IRE)—Theebah (Bahamian Bounty) (7000) **Mr S. Ebanks-Blake & Mr K. P. Foley**
20 B f 30/3 Dubai Destination (USA)—Trounce (Barathea (IRE)) **Minster Stud**

Assistant Trainer: Graham Carson

Jockey (flat): William Carson. **Apprentice:** Emma Dawe. **Amateur:** Mr Graham Carson.

---

110 **MR BEN CASE, Banbury**
Postal: **Wardington Gate Farm, Edgcote, Banbury, Oxfordshire, OX17 1AG**
Contacts: **PHONE (01295) 750959 FAX (01295) 758840 MOBILE (07808) 061223**
E-MAIL info@bencaseracing.com WEBSITE www.bencaseracing.com

1 **APPLAUSE FOR AMY (IRE)**, 5, b m King's Theatre (IRE)—Amathea (IRE) **D. C. R. Allen**
2 **BRASS TAX (IRE)**, 6, b g Morozov (USA)—Cry Before Dawn (IRE) **Mrs C. Kendrick**
3 **DANCE ISLAND (IRE)**, 9, b g Turtle Island (IRE)—Inse Na Rince (IRE) **Lady Jane Grosvenor**
4 **EDGEFOUR (IRE)**, 8, b m King's Best (USA)—Highshaan **D. C. R. Allen**
5 **EVERDON BROOK (IRE)**, 7, br g Laveron—Shean Rose **Biggs Case Case & Brun**
6 **FINNS REFLECTION**, 4, b g Overbury (IRE)—Tudor Thyne (IRE) **Mrs C.J.C. Bailey**
7 **GAME HALL (IRE)**, 5, b g Gamut (IRE)—Downbytheglenside (IRE) **Mr S.F. Cooper**
8 **GINGER FIZZ**, 5, ch m Haafhd—Valagalore **Itchen Valley Stud**
9 **HANDTHEPRIZEOVER**, 7, b g Exit To Nowhere (USA)—Main Dans La Main (FR) **D. C. R. Allen**

MR BEN CASE—continued

10 **INKY MISS**, 6, bl m Erhaab (USA)—Scarlet Miss **Mrs W. M. D. Moore**
11 **KERNEL VICTOR**, 4, b g Old Vic—Noisetine (FR) **D. C. R. Allen**
12 **MARK THE BOOK (IRE)**, 11, b g Mister Lord (USA)—Boardroom Belle (IRE) **D. C. R. Allen**
13 4, Br g Overbury (IRE)—Mimis Bonnet (FR) **Steve Hemstock**
14 **MY NOSY ROSY**, 4, b f Alflora (IRE)—Quiz Night **Mr I. A. Low & Mr J. S. English**
15 4, B g Court Cave (IRE)—No More Trouble (IRE) **Lady Jane Grosvenor**
16 **ORANGEADAY**, 5, b g Kayf Tara—One of Those Days **D. C. R. Allen**
17 **PHARE ISLE (IRE)**, 7, b g Turtle Island (IRE)—Pharenna (IRE) **Nicholson Family Moore Moore & Kendrick**
18 **RAINBOW DANCER (IRE)**, 5, b g Presenting—Tavildara (IRE) **Lady Jane Grosvenor**
19 **RUSH CAD (FR)**, 7, b g Cadoudal (FR)—Hanoi City (FR) **Sir Peter & Lady Gibbings**
20 **TEMPEST RIVER (IRE)**, 6, b m Old Vic—Dee-One-O-One **Fly Like The Wind Partnership**
21 **THORESBY (IRE)**, 6, b g Milan—I Remember It Well (IRE) **D. C. R. Allen**
22 **TOP DANCER (FR)**, 5, b g Dark Moondancer—Latitude (FR) **Case Racing Partnership**
23 **TOPENHALL (IRE)**, 11, b g Topanoora—Jrred Up (IRE) **S. F. Cooper**
24 **TRIBAL DANCE (IRE)**, 6, br g Flemensfirth (USA)—Native Sparkle (IRE) **Lady Jane Grosvenor**
25 **USSEE (FR)**, 4, gr f Vangelis (USA)—Duchesse Pierji (FR) **J. Wright**
26 **WATER ROSE**, 5, b m Exit To Nowhere (USA)—Rhapsody Rose **D. C. R. Allen**

THREE-YEAR-OLDS

27 B g Midnight Legend—Half Inch **Mrs M. Howlett**

TWO-YEAR-OLDS

28 **MY RENAISSANCE**, b br g 29/3 Medicean—Lebenstanz (Singspiel (IRE)) (10000) **N. S. Hutley**

Other Owners: Mr & Mrs D. Baines, Mr N. Biggs, Mrs A. D. Bourne, Mr T. Boylan, Mrs E. Brun, Mrs S. Case, Mrs R. Case, Mr A. Case, Mrs A. Charlton, Mr C K Crossley Cooke, Mr & Mrs B. Derbyshire, Mr J. S. English, Sir Peter Gibbings, Lady Gibbings, Mr A. Goodsir, Mr Douglas Green, Mrs T. Grindlay, Mrs S. Harrison, Miss R. Hoskin, Mrs M. Howlett, Mr J. Hulse, Mrs Carolyn Kendrick, Mrs C. Lawrence, Mr I. A. Low, Mr P. Lush, Mr T. W. Moore, Mrs Wendy Moore, Mr Grahame Nicholson, Mr & Mrs C. Nixey, Mr J. Nowell-Smith, Mr & Mrs G. D. Payne, Mrs K. Perrem, Dr & Mrs L. Watson, Mrs P. Williams, Mr M. Wise.

---

111 SIR HENRY CECIL, Newmarket
Postal: Warren Place, Newmarket, Suffolk, CB8 8QQ
Contacts: OFFICE (01638) 662192 FAX (01638) 669005
E-MAIL henry@henrycecil.co.uk WEBSITE www.henrycecil.com

1 **AIR TRAFFIC**, 4, b c Dansili—Emplane (USA) **K. Abdulla**
2 **AJAAN**, 8, br h Machiavellian (USA)—Alakananda **Niarchos Family**
3 **ALL TIME**, 4, br f Dansili—Clepsydra **K. Abdulla**
4 **BULLET TRAIN**, 5, b h Sadler's Wells—Kind (IRE) **K. Abdulla**
5 **CHACHAMAIDEE (IRE)**, 5, b m Footstepsinthesand—Canterbury Lace (USA) **R. A. H. Evans**
6 **DURANTE ALIGHIERI**, 4, b c Galileo (IRE)—Puce **HE Sheikh Sultan Bin Khalifa Al Nahyan**
7 **EMILIO LARGO**, 4, b g Cadeaux Genereux—Gloved Hand **M. C. Denmark**
8 **FIRST MOHICAN**, 4, ch g Tobougg (IRE)—Mohican Girl **W. H. Ponsonby**
9 **FRANKEL**, 4, b c Galileo (IRE)—Kind (IRE) **K. Abdulla**
10 **JET AWAY**, 5, b h Cape Cross (IRE)—Kalima **K. Abdulla**
11 **LATE TELEGRAPH (IRE)**, 4, b c Montjeu (IRE)—Bywayofthestars **T. Barr**
12 **MIDSUMMER SUN**, 4, b c Monsun (GER)—Midsummer **K. Abdulla**
13 **ROYAL PECULIAR**, 4, b c Galileo (IRE)—Distinctive Look (IRE) **De La Warr Racing & Newsells Park Stud**
14 **SEARING HEAT (USA)**, 4, b br c Empire Maker (USA)—Valentine Band (USA) **K. Abdulla**
15 **SOLAR SKY**, 4, ch c Galileo (IRE)—La Sky (IRE) **Lordship Stud**
16 **SPECIFIC GRAVITY (FR)**, 4, b g Dansili—Colza (USA) **Niarchos Family**
17 **TIMEPIECE**, 5, b m Zamindar (USA)—Clepsydra **K. Abdulla**
18 **TRANQUIL TIGER**, 8, ch h Selkirk (USA)—Serene View (USA) **K. Abdulla**
19 **TWICE OVER**, 7, b br h Observatory (USA)—Double Crossed **K. Abdulla**
20 **VITA NOVA (IRE)**, 5, b m Galileo (IRE)—Treca (IRE) **HE Sheikh Sultan Bin Khalifa Al Nahyan**
21 **WILD COCO (GER)**, 4, ch f Shirocco (GER)—Wild Side (GER) **Gestut Rottgen**
22 **WORLD DOMINATION (USA)**, 4, b c Empire Maker (USA)—Reams of Verse (USA) **K. Abdulla**

THREE-YEAR-OLDS

23 **ACE OF VALHALLA**, b c Authorized (IRE)—Trick of Ace (USA) **Mr I. Wilson**
24 **ALL THAT RULES**, b c Galileo (IRE)—Alba Stella **Mr W. A. Tinkler**
25 **ALMASE (USA)**, b f Giant's Causeway (USA)—Net Worth (USA) **HE Sheikh Sultan Bin Khalifa Al Nahyan**

SIR HENRY CECIL—continued

26 **AMARAJA (GER)**, b f Galileo (IRE)—Apsara (FR) **Niarchos Family**
27 **AQUILA (IRE)**, b f Teofilo (IRE)—Dance Troupe **HE Sheikh Sultan Bin Khalifa Al Nahyan**
28 **AYSHEA**, b f Mr Greeley (USA)—Be My Queen (IRE) **Lady Bamford**
29 **BE JOYFUL (IRE)**, ch f Teofilo (IRE)—Angelic Sounds (IRE) **Mrs S. L. Richardson**
30 **BON ALLUMAGE**, b f Nayef (USA)—Brisk Breeze (GER) **Ennismore Racing I**
31 **CHECKPOINT**, ch c Zamindar (USA)—Kalima **K. Abdulla**
32 **CHIGNON (IRE)**, b f Dalakhani (IRE)—Fringe **Miss Y. M. G. Jacques**
33 **CHIGUN**, b f Oasis Dream—Stormy Weather **Mr V. I. Araci**
34 **CONTINUUM**, b br c Dansili—Clepsydra **K. Abdulla**
35 **CORSETRY (USA)**, b f Distorted Humor (USA)—Lingerie **Niarchos Family**
36 **CRYSTAL MONARCH (IRE)**, b c Dalakhani (IRE)—Top Crystal (IRE) **M. D. Poland**
37 **DEFY THE ODDS**, b f Galileo (IRE)—Fully Invested (USA) **K. Abdulla**
38 **DR YES (FR)**, b c Dansili—Light Shift (USA) **Niarchos Family**
39 **ELBE**, b f Dansili—Imroz (USA) **K. Abdulla**
40 **EPOQUE (USA)**, b f Empire Maker (USA)—Dock Leaf (USA) **K. Abdulla**
41 **FEELTHEDIFFERENCE**, b f Iceman—Miss McGuire **Mandy Whitlock**
42 **FRAGONARD**, ch f Teofilo (IRE)—Delicieuse Lady **Sir R. Ogden C.B.E., LLD**
43 **HIGHLY SKILLED**, b c Exceed And Excel (AUS)—Mint Royale (IRE) **The Duchess of Sutherland**
44 **HOLOGRAM**, b c Teofilo (IRE)—Love Divine **Lordship Stud**
45 **INTERLOCKING (USA)**, b f Awesome Again (CAN)—Engaging (USA) **Niarchos Family**
46 **INTERVALE**, ch f Three Valleys (USA)—Intervene **Mr M. A. Colgan**
47 **INTIMACY (IRE)**, ch f Teofilo (IRE)—Skiphall **Miss Y. M. G. Jacques**
48 **ISATIS**, ch f Zamindar (USA)—Isis (USA) **Dr Catherine Wills**
49 **JORUM**, b f Dansili—Grail (USA) **Mrs S. M. Rogers**
50 **JOYRIDE (GER)**, ch f Samum (GER)—Jumble **Mr G. Schoeningh**
51 **KEEPING TIME**, b c Observatory (USA)—Sandglass **K. Abdulla**
52 **KING OF DUDES**, b c Dansili—Leto (USA) **Mr W. A. Tinkler**
53 **LORD NANDI**, b c Oasis Dream—Pink Cristal **Lady Bamford**
54 **MALEKOV (IRE)**, b c Dansili—Young and Daring (USA) **HE Sheikh Sultan Bin Khalifa Al Nahyan**
55 **MARINE GIRL**, ch f Shamardal (USA)—Aquamarine **Black Type Partnership II**
56 **MEREVALE**, b c Selkirk (USA)—A Thousand Smiles (IRE) **Gillian, Lady Howard de Walden**
57 **MIXORA (USA)**, gr ro f Mizzen Mast (USA)—Ixora (USA) **K. Abdulla**
58 **MORANT BAY (IRE)**, b f Montjeu (IRE)—Quad's Melody (IRE) **Mr N. Martin**
59 **NARLA**, b f Nayef (USA)—Polygueza (FR) **Mrs S. L. Richardson**
60 **NATURAL BLOOM (IRE)**, b f Galileo (IRE)—Dedicated Lady (IRE) **Sir R. Ogden C.B.E., LLD**
61 **NOBLE MISSION**, b c Galileo (IRE)—Kind (IRE) **K. Abdulla**
62 **POPULAR**, b f Oasis Dream—Midsummer **K. Abdulla**
63 **PORTRAITOFMYLOVE (IRE)**, b f Azamour (IRE)—Flashing Green **Mr W. A. Tinkler**
64 **REGENCY (GER)**, ch c Galileo (IRE)—Reem Dubai (IRE) **Gestut Etzean**
65 **RIDDLE MASTER**, ch c Observatory (USA)—Quandary (USA) **K. Abdulla**
66 **ROMANTIC (IRE)**, b c Holy Roman Emperor (IRE)—Welsh Love **Miss Y. M. G. Jacques**
67 **RUNNING DEER (IRE)**, b f Hurricane Run (IRE)—Sweet Sioux **W. H. Ponsonby**
68 **SEPTENARIUS (USA)**, b c Empire Maker (USA)—Reams of Verse (USA) **K. Abdulla**
69 **SET DREAMS (FR)**, b f Galileo (IRE)—Seven Magicians (USA) **Niarchos Family**
70 **SONGBIRD (IRE)**, ch f Danehill Dancer (IRE)—Mine Excavation (FR) **Sir R. Ogden C.B.E., LLD**
71 **SPIRITOFTOMINTOUL**, gr c Authorized (IRE)—Diamond Line (FR) **Angus Dundee Distillers Plc**
72 **SRINAGAR GIRL**, b f Shamardal (USA)—Adees Dancer **A. Parker**
73 **STIPULATE**, b c Dansili—Indication **K. Abdulla**
74 **SYMPOSIA**, ch f Galileo (IRE)—Emplane (USA) **K. Abdulla**
75 **THOMAS CHIPPENDALE (IRE)**, br c Dansili—All My Loving (IRE) **Sir R. Ogden C.B.E., LLD**
76 **TICKLED PINK (IRE)**, gr f Invincible Spirit (IRE)—Cassandra Go (IRE) **T. C. Stewart**
77 **TIGER CLIFF (IRE)**, b c Tiger Hill (IRE)—Verbania **W. H. Ponsonby**
78 **TOUCH GOLD (IRE)**, b c Oasis Dream—Seek Easy (USA) **HE Sheikh Sultan Bin Khalifa Al Nahyan**
79 **UKRAINIAN PRINCESS**, ch f Medicean—Unquenchable (USA) **Gestut Ammerland**
80 **VARIETY SHOW (IRE)**, b f Royal Applause—Sensasse (IRE) **De La Warr Racing**
81 **VASTLY (USA)**, gr ro c Mizzen Mast (USA)—Valentine Band (USA) **K. Abdulla**
82 **WROTHAM HEATH**, b c Dansili—Native Justice (USA) **K. Abdulla**
83 **ZEYRAN (IRE)**, ch f Galileo (IRE)—Chervil **Miss Z. Araci**

TWO-YEAR-OLDS

84 **ALEGRA**, gr f 28/2 Galileo (IRE)—Altitude (Green Desert (USA)) (246304) **Sir R. Ogden C.B.E., LLD**
85 B f 21/4 Tamayuz—All Time Great (Night Shift (USA)) (16000) **Gestut Ammerland**
86 **AMELIORATE (IRE)**, b f 16/3 Galileo (IRE)—Arkadina (IRE) (Danehill (USA)) **Merry Fox Stud Limited**
87 Ch c 15/2 Danehill Dancer (IRE)—Aunt Julia (In The Wings) (61576) **Mr A. N. Mubarak**
88 B c 26/3 Dutch Art—Bella Bertolini (Bertolini (USA)) (26666) **Mr A. N. Mubarak**

SIR HENRY CECIL—continued

89 B c 29/1 Dansili—Bionic (Zafonic (USA)) **K. Abdulla**
90 Ch f 13/2 Galileo (IRE)—Breathe (FR) (Ocean of Wisdom (USA)) **Niarchos Family**
91 Ch c 3/4 Beat Hollow—Brisk Breeze (GER) (Monsun (GER)) **Ennismore Racing I**
92 **BUCHANAN**, b c 26/1 Dansili—Because (IRE) (Sadler's Wells (USA)) (50000) **T. Barr**
93 B f 12/3 Dalakhani (IRE)—Camaret (IRE) (Danehill (USA)) (14000) **Andrew Bull**
94 Ch f 24/2 Bahamian Bounty—
                       Cefira (USA) (Distant View (USA)) (30000) **Mr Mehernosh H Deboo & Mrs C. Glenn**
95 B c 13/4 Jeremy (USA)—Collada (IRE) (Desert Prince (IRE)) (60000) **Mr A. N. Mubarak**
96 **CONSERVE (IRE)**, b f 14/3 Duke of Marmalade (IRE)—
                       Minor Point (Selkirk (USA)) (80000) **Highclere Thoroughbred Racing-Lord Mayor**
97 **COSMIC CURIOUS (GER)**, gr c 16/3 Rock of Gibraltar (IRE)—
                       Cosmic Fire (FR) (Dalakhani (IRE)) **Niarchos Family**
98 **COURT PASTORAL**, b f 27/4 Mount Nelson—Teggiano (IRE) (Mujtahid (USA)) (16000) **J. Shack**
99 **CRYOSPHERE (USA)**, b f 12/3 Candy Ride (ARG)—
                       Polar Circle (USA) (Royal Academy (USA)) (115995) **Niarchos Family**
100 B c 19/3 New Approach (IRE)—Dame's Violet (GER) (Groom Dancer (USA)) (42000) **De La Warr Racing**
101 **DARIA (IRE)**, ch f 27/2 Rock of Gibraltar (IRE)—Desabina (IRE) (Big Shuffle (USA)) **Gestut Rottgen**
102 Ch c 25/3 Byron—Diliza (Dilum (USA)) (14000) **Mr A. N. Mubarak**
103 B c 5/4 Teofilo (IRE)—Easy To Love (USA) (Diesis) (22000) **Maze Rattan Ltd**
104 B f 28/1 Mount Nelson—Entente Cordiale (IRE) (Ela-Mana-Mou) (120000) **Newsells Park Stud Limited**
105 **FAFA O O (IRE)**, b f 31/1 Galileo (IRE)—Witch of Fife (USA) (Lear Fan (USA)) (850000) **Sir R. Ogden C.B.E., LLD**
106 **FINGER POPPIN**, b c 26/3 Haafhd—Quest For Freedom (Falbrav (IRE)) **Mr J. A. Coleman**
107 B g 3/4 Iffraaj—Flash And Dazzle (IRE) (Bertolini (USA)) **Mr A. N. Mubarak**
108 **FLOW (USA)**, b br c 18/2 Medaglia d'oro (USA)—Enthused (USA) (Seeking The Gold (USA)) **Niarchos Family**
109 Br f 23/4 Rock of Gibraltar (IRE)—Gems of Araby (Zafonic (USA)) (65000) **Mr V. I. Araci**
110 B c 6/3 Invincible Spirit (IRE)—Ghazal (USA) (Gone West (USA)) (240000) **Ms A. Quinn**
111 **GHOST RUNNER (IRE)**, b c 23/4 Tagula (IRE)—
                       Ball Cat (FR) (Cricket Ball (USA)) (55000) **Middleham Park Racing L**
112 B f 4/3 Dansili—Grail (USA) (Quest For Fame) (50000) **Mr Mehernosh H Deboo & Mrs C. Glenn**
113 B c 13/5 Lawman (FR)—Green Lassy (FR) (Green Tune (USA)) (21345) **Mr A. N. Mubarak**
114 Ch c 22/2 Hernando (FR)—Heat of The Night (Lear Fan (USA)) (18061) **Mr A. N. Mubarak**
115 **IBERIS**, b f 18/3 Nayef (USA)—Isis (USA) (Royal Academy (USA)) **Dr C. M. H. Wills**
116 Ch f 12/3 Zamindar (USA)—Imroz (USA) (Nureyev (USA)) **K. Abdulla**
117 B f 28/2 Authorized (IRE)—Incoming Call (USA) (Red Ransom (USA)) (75000) **M. C. Denmark**
118 B c 14/5 Oasis Dream—Kalima (Kahyasi) **K. Abdulla**
119 B c 24/3 Shirocco (GER)—Katariya (IRE) (Barathea (IRE)) (28735) **Mr A. N. Mubarak**
120 **KELVINGROVE (IRE)**, b c 28/4 Hurricane Run (IRE)—Silversword (FR) (Highest Honor (FR)) (180000) **T. Barr**
121 B f 13/5 Oasis Dream—Kid Gloves (In The Wings) **K. Abdulla**
122 B c 13/3 Oasis Dream—Kind (IRE) (Danehill (USA)) **K. Abdulla**
123 B c 25/3 Cape Cross (IRE)—Kissing (Grand Lodge (USA)) **Lordship Stud**
124 B c 10/3 Mr Greeley (USA)—Kushnarenkovo (Sadler's Wells (USA)) (100000) **Paul Hickman**
125 **KYLLACHY RISE**, b c 10/4 Kyllachy—Up And About (Barathea (IRE)) (100000) **Mr Arjun Waney**
126 B c 31/3 Cape Cross (IRE)—Love Divine (Diesis) **Lordship Stud**
127 B f 15/2 Oasis Dream—Maid To Believe (Galileo (IRE)) (150000) **Niarchos Family**
128 **MAJESTY (IRE)**, gr c 13/2 Shamardal (USA)—
                       Princess Serena (USA) (Unbridled's Song (USA)) (110000) **Highclere Thoroughbred Racing - Archer**
129 Ch f 29/3 Pivotal—Midsummer (Kingmambo (USA)) **K. Abdulla**
130 **MIGHTY YAR (IRE)**, gr c 5/4 Teofilo (IRE)—Karaliyfa (IRE) (Kahyasi) (45000) **R. A. H. Evans**
131 B c 10/2 Galileo (IRE)—Miss Beatrix (IRE) (Danehill Dancer (IRE)) **Mr V. I. Araci**
132 B f 9/3 Dansili—Modesta (IRE) (Sadler's Wells (USA)) **K. Abdulla**
133 B c 21/4 Exceed And Excel (AUS)—
                       Monnavanna (IRE) (Machiavellian (USA)) (70000) **The Johnson & Ives Families**
134 Ch f 16/4 Halling (USA)—My Mariam (Salse (USA)) (5000) **Andrew Bull**
135 B c 23/1 Dansili—Novellara (Sadler's Wells (USA)) **K. Abdulla**
136 B c 17/4 Afleet Alex (USA)—Nyramba (Night Shift (USA)) **Gestut Ammerland**
137 **PARALLAX (IRE)**, b c 11/5 Galileo (IRE)—Moonlight's Box (USA) (Nureyev (USA)) (200000) **K. Abdulla**
138 B br c 6/2 Monsun (GER)—Passage of Time (Dansili) **K. Abdulla**
139 **PASSING PARADE**, b f 30/3 Cape Cross (IRE)—
                       Model Queen (Kingmambo (USA)) (500000) **Merry Fox Stud Limited**
140 **PHAENOMENA (IRE)**, ch f 1/4 Galileo (IRE)—Caumshinaun (IRE) (Indian Ridge) (700000) **Niarchos Family**
141 **PHOSPHORESCENCE (IRE)**, b c 19/3 Sakhee (USA)—Eccentricity (USA) (Kingmambo (USA)) **Niarchos Family**
142 B f 5/4 High Chaparral (IRE)—Power of Future (GER) (Definite Article) **Mr G. Schoeningh**
143 B f 10/2 Invincible Spirit (IRE)—Quan Yin (IRE) (Sadler's Wells (USA)) **Niarchos Family**
144 B f 25/2 Dansili—Rainbow Lake (Rainbow Quest (USA)) **K. Abdulla**
145 **RAJARATNA (IRE)**, b f 4/6 Galileo (IRE)—Coup de Genie (USA) (Mr Prospector (USA)) **Niarchos Family**
146 **REMINISCE (IRE)**, b c 15/3 Oasis Dream—Sedna (IRE) (Priolo (USA)) (100000) **Miss Y. M. G. Jacques**

SIR HENRY CECIL—continued

147 **RIDGEWAY STORM (IRE)**, b c 22/3 Hurricane Run (IRE)—Hesperia (Slip Anchor) (37000) **Henry Ponsonby**
148 **ROME**, b c 23/3 Holy Roman Emperor (IRE)—Magical Cliche (USA) (Affirmed (USA)) (40000) **John Penny**
149 B f 4/3 Dansili—Sacred Song (USA) (Diesis) **Niarchos Family**
150 B f 4/2 Oasis Dream—Sandglass (Zafonic (USA)) **K. Abdulla**
151 B c 19/2 Empire Maker (USA)—Sense of Joy (Dansili) **K. Abdulla**
152 B c 27/1 Nayef (USA)—Seven Magicians (USA) (Silver Hawk (USA)) **Niarchos Family**
153 **SLEEK**, b f 29/1 Oasis Dream—Slink (Selkirk (USA)) **Miss Y. M. G. Jacques**
154 **TOMINTOUL MAGIC (IRE)**, b f 2/5 Holy Roman Emperor (IRE)—
Trois Graces (USA) (Alysheba (USA)) (52000) **Angus Dundee Distillers Plc**
155 **VOX POP**, ch f 4/2 Dylan Thomas (IRE)—Pentatonic (Giant's Causeway (USA)) (15000) **J. Shack**
156 B c 16/4 Teofilo (IRE)—Water Fountain (Mark of Esteem (IRE)) (70000) **Lady Cecil**
157 B c 9/2 Zamindar (USA)—Zarannda (IRE) (Last Tycoon) (38000) **M. C. Denmark**

Other Owners: Mubarak Al Naemi, H E Sheikh Sultan bin Khalifa al Nahyan (Al Asayl), Mr G. Barnard, Mrs Andrew Bull, Mrs Andrew Bull, Mr S. Bullard, Lady Cecil, Lord De La Warr, Lady De La Warr, Mr Mehernosh H. Deboo, Mrs Christaline Glenn, Mrs S. Grassick, Mr T. F. Harris, Mrs E. A. Harris, Henry Cecil and Company Limited, The Hon H. Herbert, Mr P Hickman, Highclere Thoroughbred Racing Ltd, Mr D. L. Ives, Mr K. R. Ives, Mr D. A. Johnson, Maze Rattan Ltd, Mr T. S. Palin, Mr M. Prince, Mr G. Schoeningh.

Assistant Trainer: Michael Marshall

Jockey (flat): Tom Queally, Ian Mongan, Eddie Ahern.

---

113 **MR PATRICK CHAMINGS, Basingstoke**
Postal: **Inhurst Farm Stables, Baughurst, Tadley, Hampshire, RG26 5JS**
Contacts: **PHONE (01189) 814494 FAX (01189) 820454 MOBILE (07831) 360970**
E-MAIL chamingsracing@talk21.com

1 **AYE AYE DIGBY (IRE)**, 7, b g Captain Rio—Jane Digby (IRE) **Trolley Action**
2 **BEAT UP**, 6, b g Beat Hollow—Whitgift Rose **R Lyon, P Hayton & P Chamings**
3 **BOLACHOIR (IRE)**, 10, b g Hubbly Bubbly (USA)—Boolindrum Lady (IRE) **R. V. Shaw**
4 **CAPE BRETON**, 6, b g Cape Cross (IRE)—Red Bouquet **Mrs A. J. Chandris**
5 **CUCURRI**, 5, gr m Silver Patriarch (IRE)—Dawn Romance (IRE) **Mr & Mrs R. H. F. Fuller**
6 **DIRECTORSHIP**, 6, br g Diktat—Away To Me **Mrs R Lyon,Mrs P Hayton,Mr P R Chamings**
7 **DISCO DOLL**, 4, b f Diktat—Cookie Cutter (IRE) **Mrs R. Lyon**
8 **EAGER TO BOW (IRE)**, 6, b g Acclamation—Tullawadgeen (IRE) **Mrs J. E. L. Wright**
9 **ELSIE'S ORPHAN**, 5, br m Pastoral Pursuits—Elsie Plunkett **Mrs J. E. L. Wright**
10 **FIRESCENT**, 5, b g Firebreak—Milliscent **Mr G. T. Broadbank**
11 **FOXHAVEN**, 10, ch g Unfuwain (USA)—Dancing Mirage (IRE) **Inhurst Players**
12 **GIANT ACT**, 7, gr g Act One—Giant Nipper **P.Chamings F.Lee P.Bowler N.Robinson**
13 **MIDAS WAY**, 12, ch g Halling (USA)—Arietta's Way (IRE) **P. R. Chamings**
14 **MONASHEE ROCK (IRE)**, 7, b m Monashee Mountain (USA)—Polar Rock **P. R. Chamings**
15 **OSIRIS WAY**, 10, ch g Indian Ridge—Heady **Mrs A. J. Chandris**
16 **RONDEAU (GR)**, 7, ch g Harmonic Way—Areti (GR) **The Foxford House Partnership**
17 **SCOTTISH GLEN**, 6, ch g Kyllachy—Dance For Fun **The Foxford House Partnership**
18 **THE NAMES JAMES**, 4, ch g Monsieur Bond (IRE)—Bob's Princess **P. R. Chamings**
19 **TREASURE ACT**, 4, ch f Act One—Benjarong **Mrs J. E. L. Wright**
20 **UNCLE FRED**, 7, b g Royal Applause—Karla June **Inhurst Players**
21 **WOODCOTE PLACE**, 9, b g Lujain (USA)—Giant Nipper **The Foxford House Partnership**

THREE-YEAR-OLDS

22 **KILLORGLIN**, b g Araafa (IRE)—Regal Curtsy **P. R. Chamings**
23 **TAKE A NOTE**, b c Singspiel (IRE)—Ela Paparouna **P. J. L. Wright**

Other Owners: Mr P. O. Bowler, R. H. F. Fuller, Mrs C. Fuller, Mrs P. L. Hayton, F. T. Lee, Mr I. J. Matthews, Mr N. R. Robinson, Mr M. R. Stewart, K. W. Tyrrell.

Assistant Trainer: Phillippa Chamings

114 MR NOEL CHANCE, Upper Lambourn
Postal: **Upshire House Racing Stables, Greenways, Lambourn, Hungerford, Berkshire, RG17 7LE**
Contacts: **OFFICE (01488) 73436 FAX (01488) 72296 MOBILE (07785) 300168**
E-MAIL info@noelchanceracing.com WEBSITE www.noelchanceracing.com

1 **ATHWAAB**, 5, b m Cadeaux Genereux—Ahdaaf (USA) **Mr N. P. Horsfall**
2 **BRACKLOON HIGH (IRE)**, 7, b g Bob Back (USA)—Homebird (IRE) **Mr T Conway,Mrs Conway&Mr T G Warren**
3 **FABULOUS FRED (IRE)**, 8, b g Beneficial—Roseabel (IRE) **T. F. C. Partnership**
4 **GORES ISLAND (IRE)**, 6, b g Beneficial—Just Leader (IRE) **Collins, Horsfall, Michael & O'Sullivan**
5 **I KNOW THE CODE (IRE)**, 7, b g Viking Ruler (AUS)—Gentle Papoose **Noel Chance Racing Club**
6 **I'M A COLLEGE BOY (IRE)**, 6, b g Winged Love (IRE)—Hatherley **Mr Conway & Mrs Conway & Mr T G Warren**
7 **I'M SO SPECIAL (IRE)**, 6, b m Milan—Hudson Hope (IRE) **Mrs M. Chance**
8 **ICANSEECLEARLYNOW**, 4, ch g Bold Edge—Helens Last (IRE) **Mrs M. C. Sweeney**
9 **PRIZE POPPY**, 5, b m Kayf Tara—Just Jodi (IRE) **Mrs R. F. Greener**
10 **SUGAR AND SPICE**, 6, b m Alflora (IRE)—Sound Appeal **R. W. & J. R. Fidler**
11 **TIGER BAY (IRE)**, 8, b g Goldmark (USA)—Roussanne (IRE) **Mr D. C. Hitchins**
12 5, B g Old Vic—Water Stratford (IRE) **J. P. McManus**

Other Owners: Miss E. Chance, Mr J. A. Collins, T. Conway, Mrs M. Conway, J. P. Craughwell, R. J. Fairlie, Mr R. W. Fidler, Mrs J. R. Fidler, Mr S. A. Michael, K. P. Trowbridge, T. G. Warren.

Assistant Trainer: Eimear Chance

Jockey (NH): Tom Siddall, Richard Johnson, Will Kennedy. **Conditional:** Ryan Raftery.

115 MR MICHAEL CHAPMAN, Market Rasen
Postal: **Woodlands Racing Stables, Woodlands Lane, Willingham Road, Market Rasen, Lincolnshire, LN8 3RE**
Contacts: **PHONE/FAX (01673) 843663 MOBILE (07971) 940087**
E-MAIL mcc@marketrasen.net WEBSITE www.woodlandsracingstables.co.uk

1 **DANCING WAVE**, 6, b m Baryshnikov (AUS)—Wavet **Mr R. Gowans**
2 **FEELING PECKISH (USA)**, 8, ch g Point Given (USA)—Sunday Bazaar (USA) **J. E. Reed**
3 **FINNEGANS RAINBOW**, 10, ch g Spectrum (IRE)—Fairy Story (IRE) **J. E. Reed**
4 **GALLEY SLAVE (IRE)**, 7, b g Spartacus (IRE)—Cimeterre (IRE) **Mrs M. M. Chapman**
5 **HERESELLIE (IRE)**, 4, b f Clodovil (IRE)—Special Dissident **Mrs M. M. Chapman**
6 **KATHINDI (IRE)**, 5, ch g Pearl of Love (IRE)—Turfcare Flight (IRE) **Mrs M. M. Chapman**
7 **KHESKIANTO (IRE)**, 6, b m Kheleyf (USA)—Gently (IRE) **F. A. Dickinson**
8 **LENDERKING (IRE)**, 4, b g Sleeping Indian—Roses From Ridey (IRE) **Mrs M. M. Chapman**
9 **MAZOVIAN (USA)**, 4, b g E Dubai (USA)—Polish Style (USA) **Mrs M. M. Chapman**
10 **MONZINO (USA)**, 4, b br g More Than Ready (USA)—Tasso's Magic Roo (USA) **Mrs M. M. Chapman**
11 **NIGHT REVELLER (IRE)**, 9, b m Night Shift (USA)—Tir-An-Oir (IRE) **J. E. Reed**
12 **ORPEN WIDE (IRE)**, 10, b g Orpen (USA)—Melba (IRE) **Mrs M. M. Chapman**
13 **PEAK SEASONS (IRE)**, 9, ch g Raise A Grand (IRE)—Teresian Girl (IRE) **J. E. Reed**
14 **SIMPLIFIED**, 9, b m Lend A Hand—Houston Heiress (USA) **R. A. Gadd**
15 **SOPHIE'S BEAU (IRE)**, 5, b g Stormy Atlantic (USA)—Lady Buttercup (USA) **Mrs M. M. Chapman**
16 **TAYARAT (IRE)**, 7, b g Noverre (USA)—Sincere (IRE) **Mrs M. M. Chapman**
17 **THE MIGHTY MOD (USA)**, 5, b g Gone West (USA)—Michelle's Monarch (USA) **Mrs M. M. Chapman**
18 **TROPICAL SKY (IRE)**, 4, b g Librettist (USA)—Tropical Breeze (IRE) **Mrs M. M. Chapman**
19 **VOGARTH**, 8, ch g Arkadian Hero (USA)—Skara Brae **Mrs M. M. Chapman**

Assistant Trainer: Mr S. Petch

116 MS JANE CHAPPLE-HYAM, Newmarket
Postal: **Rose Cottage, The Street, Dalham, Newmarket, Suffolk, CB8 8TF**
Contacts: **PHONE (01638) 500451 FAX (01638) 663576 MOBILE (07899) 000555**

1 **ARTEUS**, 6, b g Fantastic Light (USA)—Enchanted **Norcroft Park Stud**
2 **BIG BAY (USA)**, 6, b g Horse Chestnut (SAF)—Takipy (USA) **Mrs J. Chapple-Hyam & Mrs B. J. Hirst**
3 **FORKS**, 5, ch g Fraam—Balinsky (USA) **Mrs J. M. T. Martin**
4 **GO GO GADGET (GER)**, 5, b h Areion (GER)—Globuli (GER) **Stall Trick Or Treat**
5 **GRANDAD MAC**, 4, b g Invincible Spirit (IRE)—No Rehearsal (FR) **Mrs Jane Chapple-Hyam**
6 **JUNGLE BAY**, 5, b g Oasis Dream—Dominica **Mr S. Brewster**
7 **MULL OF KILLOUGH (IRE)**, 6, b g Mull of Kintyre (USA)—Sun Shower (IRE) **Invictus Racing Partnership**
8 **REACHFORTHEBUCKS**, 4, ch g Phoenix Reach (IRE)—Miles **Reach For The Bucks Racing Partnership**

MS JANE CHAPPLE-HYAM—continued

9 **RUFUS STONE (USA)**, 4, ch g Henny Hughes (USA)—Jive Talk (USA) **L. Sheridan**
10 **SASKIA'S DREAM**, 4, b f Oasis Dream—Swynford Pleasure **Mr Peter Bottomley & Mrs Jane Chapple-Hyam**
11 **SECRET ASSET (IRE)**, 7, gr g Clodovil (IRE)—Skerray **Mr & Mrs S. Pierpoint & Mr P. Salisbury**
12 **SPYDER**, 4, b g Resplendent Glory (IRE)—Collect **Miss C. Blockley**
13 **TRUE SATIRE**, 4, b f Oasis Dream—Native Justice (USA) **Mrs Jane Chapple-Hyam**

THREE-YEAR-OLDS

14 **ANGELS WILL FLY (IRE)**, b f Tiger Hill (IRE)—Lady Naomi (USA) **The Hon A. S. Peacock**
15 **BULL BAY**, b c Bahamian Bounty—Buffy Boo **Mrs J. M. T. Martin**
16 **COACH MONTANA (IRE)**, b g Proud Citizen (USA)—Market Day **Mr C. R. Moore**
17 **COCKNEY ROCKER**, br c Cockney Rebel (IRE)—Fur Will Fly **Mr Chris Fahy & Mr Lee Jordan**
18 **DAHAB GOLD (IRE)**, gr f Clodovil (IRE)—Desert Alchemy (IRE) **Mr Liam Sheridan & Miss Victoria Sheridan**
19 **FLYING TRADER (USA)**, gr ro c Mizzen Mast (USA)—Remediate (USA) **Mr Greg Secker - Unlimited Racing**
20 **FROSTY SECRET**, b f Echo of Light—Raze **Mr S. Brewster**
21 **LADY CAPRICE**, b f Kyllachy—Lady Betambeau (IRE) **Mrs A. Cantillon**
22 **MAN OF ICE**, br g Iceman—Never Enough (GER) **Mrs A. Cantillon**
23 **OTTAVINO (IRE)**, b g Piccolo—Indian's Feather (IRE) **Mr Y. W. Wu**
24 **RED BAY**, b c Haafhd—Red Zinnia **Mrs J. M. T. Martin**
25 **SALUTARY**, b g Kyllachy—Leonica **Mr Y. W. Wu**

TWO-YEAR-OLDS

26 B f 17/3 Mount Nelson—Cruinn A Bhord (Inchinor) (5000)
27 **INKA EXPRESS**, b f 20/4 Rail Link—Coolberry (USA) (Rahy (USA)) (1600) **Invictus Racing Partnership**
28 **MISTY SECRET (IRE)**, b f 20/3 Clodovil (IRE)—
    Villafranca (IRE) (In The Wings) (11000) **Mr & Mrs S. Pierpoint & Mr P. Salisbury**
29 B c 19/3 Delta Dancer—Russian Silk (Fasliyev (USA)) **Mr Joe Loveridge**
30 **SKATING OVER (USA)**, ch f 24/3 Giant's Causeway (USA)—
    Annie Skates (Mr Greeley (USA)) (32000) **Mr Richard Morecombe & Mrs L. E. Ramsden**
31 **TOMMY'S SECRET**, gr g 25/4 Sakhee's Secret—La Gessa (Largesse) (952) **Mrs Jane Chapple-Hyam**

Assistant Trainer: Abigail Harrison

---

117   **MR PETER CHAPPLE-HYAM, Newmarket**
Postal: St Gatien Stables, All Saints Road, Newmarket, Suffolk, CB8 8HJ
Contacts: PHONE (01638) 560827 FAX (01638) 561908 MOBILE (07770) 472774
E-MAIL pchapplehyam@yahoo.com WEBSITE www.peterchapplehyam.com

1 **CARAVAN ROLLS ON**, 4, b c Hernando (FR)—Grain Only **Pearl Bloodstock Limited**
2 **CHEDDAR GEORGE**, 6, ch g Pivotal—Grandeala **The Comic Strip Heroes**
3 **RED SPADES (IRE)**, 4, b c Kyllachy—Queveda (IRE) **R. J. Arculli**
4 **TREND LINE (IRE)**, 4, b f Holy Roman Emperor (IRE)—Dabiliya **Mr L. J. Inman**
5 **WHEY SAUCE (JPN)**, 4, gr f Kurofune (JPN)—Histoire (JPN) **A. W. Black**

THREE-YEAR-OLDS

6 **AL KHAN (IRE)**, b c Elnadim (USA)—Popolo (IRE) **Ziad A. Galadari**
7 **BONNET DE DOUCHE (IRE)**, ch f Modigliani (USA)—Isadora Duncan (IRE) **Mr Tony Elliott**
8 **CAPE SAMBA**, b c Cape Cross (IRE)—Dancing Feather **A. J. Driver**
9 **CHUNKY DIAMOND (IRE)**, b c Diamond Green (FR)—Balance The Books **Rebel Racing**
10 **COCKNEY SPARROW**, b f Cockney Rebel (IRE)—Compose **P. Cunningham**
11 **DARK ORCHID**, br f Shamardal (USA)—Misty Waters (IRE) **Mrs C. Hassett**
12 **DICK BOS**, ch c Dutch Art—Cosmic Countess (IRE) **The Comic Strip Heroes**
13 **EVERLONG**, b f Authorized (IRE)—Crooked Wood (USA) **C. G. P. Wyatt**
14 **FLAMING FERRARI (IRE)**, b f Authorized (IRE)—Spirit of Pearl (IRE) **P. D. Rogers**
15 **FUGITIVE MOTEL (IRE)**, b g Holy Roman Emperor (IRE)—Zing Ping (IRE) **Joseph Barton**
16 B c High Chaparral (IRE)—Lady Marshall (FR) **Coleman Bloodstock Limited**
17 **LITTLE RED MINX (IRE)**, b f Red Clubs (IRE)—Bid Dancer **John C. Davies**
18 Ch f Hawk Wing (USA)—Lovealot **Coleman Bloodstock Limited**
19 **MY BODY IS A CAGE (IRE)**, ch f Strategic Prince—Moonlight Wish (IRE) **Joseph Barton**
20 **MY PROPELLER (IRE)**, b f Holy Roman Emperor (IRE)—Incise **J. Barton**
21 **OTTO THE GREAT**, b g Holy Roman Emperor (IRE)—Vayavaig **Mrs D. M. Swinburn**
22 **PALUS SAN MARCO (IRE)**, b g Holy Roman Emperor (IRE)—Kylemore (IRE) **Eledy SRL**
23 **PEARL DIVA (IRE)**, b f Acclamation—Lassie's Gold (USA) **John C. Davies**
24 **PERFECT EXAMPLE (IRE)**, b f Cape Cross (IRE)—Shining Debut (IRE) **Mr A. J. Driver**

MR PETER CHAPPLE-HYAM—continued

25 **POSSIBLY**, b f Exceed And Excel (AUS)—One of The Family **Miss Susanna Ballinger**
26 **RIGHT EXPECTATION (IRE)**, b c Holy Roman Emperor (IRE)—Palacoona (FR) **Right Tack Partnership**
27 **SAMMINDER (IRE)**, b c Red Ransom (USA)—Gimasha **Ziad A. Galadari**
28 **SCARABOCIO**, b c Shamardal (USA)—My Sara **Eledy SRL**
29 **SUBURBAN WAR**, b c Dutch Art—Nedwa **J. Barton**
30 **SUNDAY TIMES**, b f Holy Roman Emperor (IRE)—Forever Times **Allan Belshaw**
31 **TELWAAR**, ch c Haafhd—Waafiah **Ziad A. Galadari**
32 **VENEGAZZU (IRE)**, br c Dubawi (IRE)—Vintage Tipple (IRE) **Eledy SRL**

TWO-YEAR-OLDS

33 **BOITE (IRE)**, b c 26/4 Authorized (IRE)—Albiatra (USA) (Dixieland Band (USA)) **Eledy SRL**
34 B c 27/3 Cape Cross (IRE)—Bright Hope (IRE) (Danehill (USA)) (75000) **Eledy SRL**
35 Br f 3/2 Kheleyf (USA)—Elegant Times (IRE) (Dansili) **Allan Belshaw**
36 B f 30/3 Acclamation—Etica (IRE) (Barathea (IRE)) (19047) **Eledy SRL**
37 B f 1/1 Rock of Gibraltar (IRE)—Forever Times **Allan Belshaw**
38 B f 24/1 Cape Cross (IRE)—Gimasha (Cadeaux Genereux) **Ziad A. Galadari**
39 **GRANULE**, b f 26/2 Hernando (FR)—Grain Only (Machiavellian (USA)) **Miss K. Rausing**
40 B c 7/2 Holy Roman Emperor (IRE)—Guantanamera (IRE) (Sadler's Wells (USA)) (7619) **Mr Tony Elliott**
41 **HOT DIGGITY (IRE)**, b c 1/4 Whipper (USA)—Como (USA) (Cozzene (USA)) (28735) **The Horse Players Two**
42 B f 10/4 Dutch Art—Loquacity (Diktat) (20952)
43 **MARIELLA**, ch f 28/3 Piccolo—Viva Maria (Hernando (FR)) **Miss K. Rausing**
44 **MOCENIGO (IRE)**, ch c 9/3 Refuse To Bend (USA)—Doregan (IRE) (Bahhare (USA)) **Eledy SRL**
45 B f 14/4 Holy Roman Emperor (IRE)—Parvenue (FR) (Ezzoud (IRE)) (4761) **Chelston**
46 B c 20/3 Elnadim (USA)—Popolo (IRE) (Fasliyev (USA)) **Ziad A. Galadari**
47 B c 26/2 Exceed And Excel (AUS)—Sakhya (IRE) (Barathea (IRE)) **Ziad A. Galadari**
48 B c 26/3 Lawman (FR)—Stella Del Mattino (USA) (Golden Gear (USA)) (17142) **Pearl Bloodstock Limited**
49 B f 19/3 Royal Applause—Waafiah (Anabaa (USA)) **Ziad A. Galadari**

Other Owners: Mr James Barber, Mrs Jonathan Blacklock, Mr Tim Bostwick, Mr Phil Cunningham, Mr Philip Ellick, Fullbury Limited, Mr D. Hanafin, Mr Hung Yat Fai, Mr Stewart Jones, Mr Benson Lo, Lynch Bages Limited, Mrs Johnny McKeever, Mr C. Pizarro, Mr J. Wray.

---

118 MR GEORGE CHARLTON, Stocksfield
Postal: **Mickley Grange Farm, Stocksfield, Northumberland, NE43 7TB**
Contacts: PHONE **(01661) 843247** MOBILE **(07808) 955029**
E-MAIL gcharlton@fsmail.net

1 **BALIVERNIER**, 6, b g Beat All (USA)—Keep Ikis **G. A. G. Charlton**
2 **BALLYMACDUFF (IRE)**, 8, b g Strategic Choice (USA)—Ashpark Rose (IRE) **G. A. G. Charlton**
3 **BALLYVOQUE (IRE)**, 6, b g Revoque (IRE)—Timissa (IRE) **J. I. A. Charlton**
4 **BOGSIDE (IRE)**, 8, ch g Commander Collins (IRE)—Miss Henrietta (IRE) **Mrs S. M. Wood**
5 **BREMER BAY (IRE)**, 6, b g Tikkanen (USA)—Luciamaria (IRE) **M. H. Walton**
6 **CITY PLAYER (IRE)**, 6, ch g City Honours (USA)—Taketheblameagain **G. A. G. Charlton**
7 **DANEBROOK LAD (IRE)**, 6, b g Indian Danehill (IRE)—Lady Brookvale (IRE) **Charlton Proud Gillies**
8 **DARK EXILE (IRE)**, 7, b g Expelled (USA)—Schwartz Story (IRE) **The Gathering & George A. Charlton**
9 **DARKAN ROAD**, 7, b br g Beat All (USA)—Sister Seven (IRE) **M. H. Walton & G. A. Charlton**
10 **FREDDIE BROWN**, 8, b g Missed Flight—Some Shiela **J. R. Jeffreys**
11 **HEEZ A STEEL (IRE)**, 11, b g Naheez (USA)—Ari's Fashion **J. I. A. Charlton**
12 **ICE IMAGE (IRE)**, 10, b g Darnay—Ice Trix (IRE) **Sydney Ramsey & Partners**
13 **KNOCKARA BEAU (IRE)**, 9, b g Leading Counsel (USA)—Clairabell (IRE) **W. F. Trueman**
14 **MASTER BEAU**, 8, b g Beat All (USA)—Golden Aureole **J. I. A. Charlton**
15 **MELANGE (USA)**, 6, b g Alphabet Soup (USA)—Garendare **Northumbria Leisure Ltd/ G. A. Charlton**
16 **MONASHEE (IRE)**, 7, b br g Monashee Mountain (USA)—On The Bridle (IRE) **G. A. G. Charlton**
17 **MURKLE BOY (IRE)**, 6, b g Tikkanen (USA)—Simple Mind **Mr & Mrs Raymond Anderson Green**
18 **NEMI (CZE)**, 5, b g Look Honey (IRE)—Non Pareille (GER) **G. A. G. Charlton**
19 **SHANNAGARRY (IRE)**, 6, b g Presenting—Tikrara (USA) **M. H. Walton & G. A. Charlton**
20 **SHERIFF HALL (IRE)**, 7, b g Saddlers' Hall (IRE)—Derravarra Breeze (IRE) **Mr & Mrs Raymond Anderson Green**
21 **WINSTONE (IRE)**, 7, b g Pierre—Cushenstown Best (IRE) **G. A. G. Charlton**

Other Owners: Mr George A. Charlton, Mr Alan Davies, Mr M. C. Gillies, Mr Raymond Anderson Green, Mrs Anita Green, Mr R. Hamilton, Northumbria Leisure Ltd, Mr H. Proud, Mr Syd Ramsey, Mr J. T. Stobbs, Mr M. H. Walton.

Assistant Trainer: Mr J I A Charlton

Jockey (NH): Jan Faltejsek, Alistair J. Findlay.

119 MR ROGER CHARLTON, Beckhampton

Postal: Beckhampton House, Marlborough, Wiltshire, SN8 1QR
Contacts: **OFFICE** (01672) 539533 **HOME** (01672) 539330 **FAX** (01672) 539456
MOBILE (07710) 784511
E-MAIL r.charlton@virgin.net **WEBSITE** www.rogercharlton.com

1 **AL KAZEEM**, 4, b c Dubawi (IRE)—Kazeem **D. J. Deer**
2 **BATED BREATH**, 5, b h Dansili—Tantina (USA) **K. Abdulla**
3 **CAMBERLEY TWO**, 4, b gr g Invincible Spirit (IRE)—Diamond Line (FR) **H.R.H. Sultan Ahmad Shah**
4 **CITYSCAPE**, 6, ch h Selkirk (USA)—Tantina (USA) **K. Abdulla**
5 **CRY FURY**, 4, b g Beat Hollow—Cantarna **K. Abdulla**
6 **DEFINIGHTLY**, 6, b br g Diktat—Perfect Night **Mr S. Emmet & Miss R. Emmet**
7 **GENKI (IRE)**, 8, ch g Shinko Forest (IRE)—Emma's Star (ITY) **Ms G. F. Khosla**
8 **MAC LOVE**, 11, b g Cape Cross (IRE)—My Lass **V. Khosla**
9 **MARZANTE (USA)**, 4, gr ro g Maria's Mon (USA)—Danzante (USA) **K. Abdulla**
10 **PRIMEVERE (IRE)**, 4, ch f Singspiel (IRE)—Tree Peony **A. E. Oppenheimer**
11 **PROPONENT (IRE)**, 8, b g Peintre Celebre (USA)—Pont Audemer (USA) **B. E. Nielsen**
12 **SEA OF HEARTBREAK (IRE)**, 5, b m Rock of Gibraltar (IRE)—Top Forty **D. G. Hardisty Bloodstock**
13 **THISTLE BIRD**, 4, b f Selkirk (USA)—Dolma (FR) **Lady Rothschild**
14 **ZERO MONEY (IRE)**, 6, ch g Bachelor Duke (USA)—Dawn Chorus (IRE) **Ms G. F. Khosla**

THREE-YEAR-OLDS

15 **ALVITUDE (USA)**, b g Aptitude (USA)—Alvernia (USA) **K. Abdulla**
16 B g Lawman (FR)—Beech Gardens **H.R.H. Sultan Ahmad Shah**
17 **BISHOP ROKO**, b g Rock of Gibraltar (IRE)—Kirk **M. Pescod**
18 **BORDER LEGEND**, ch g Selkirk (USA)—Bonnie Doon (USA) **K. Abdulla**
19 **CAPTAIN CAT (IRE)**, b br g Dylan Thomas (IRE)—Mother of Pearl (IRE) **Seasons Holidays**
20 **CLOWANCE ESTATE (IRE)**, b g Teofilo (IRE)—Whirly Bird **Seasons Holidays**
21 **CONSENTING**, ch f Refuse To Bend (IRE)—Perfect Night **Mr S. Emmet & Miss R. Emmet**
22 **DAFFYD**, b g Green Desert (USA)—Ffestiniog (IRE) **Elite Racing Club**
23 **DAWN GLORY**, b f Oasis Dream—Fairy Godmother **Her Majesty The Queen**
24 **DEDICATION**, b f Beat Hollow—Total Devotion **K. Abdulla**
25 **DOGSTAR (IRE)**, b f Nayef (USA)—Dolma (FR) **Lady Rothschild**
26 **DOURO**, b f Manduro (GER)—Tamso (IRE) **Lady Rothschild**
27 **ESPAGNOLETTE**, b f Oasis Dream—Valencia **K. Abdulla**
28 **ESTRELA**, b f Authorized (IRE)—Wannabe Grand (IRE) **Seasons Holidays**
29 **FRANK MORGAN**, b g Iceman—Maystock **P. Dean**
30 **HABITA (IRE)**, b f Montjeu (IRE)—Minnie Habit **D. J. Deer**
31 **HINT OF PROMISE**, b f Beat Hollow—Marching West (USA) **K. Abdulla**
32 **INCHINA**, b f Montjeu (IRE)—Incheni (USA) **A. E. Oppenheimer**
33 **INVESTIGATE**, b g Dansili—Bionic **K. Abdulla**
34 B g Authorized (IRE)—Kazeem **D. J. Deer**
35 **LOVAGE**, b f Exceed And Excel (AUS)—Name of Love (IRE) **Lady Rothschild**
36 **MINCE**, ch f Medicean—Strut **Lady Rothschild**
37 **MOIDORE**, b c Galileo (IRE)—Flash of Gold **Her Majesty The Queen**
38 **NEWNTON LODGE**, b c Rail Link—Widescreen (USA) **K. Abdulla**
39 **NIMBLE THIMBLE (USA)**, ch f Mizzen Mast (USA)—Skiable (IRE) **K. Abdulla**
40 **PICK THREE**, ch c Three Valleys (USA)—Magic Number **K. Abdulla**
41 **PRICELESS JEWEL**, b f Selkirk (USA)—My Branch **B. E. Nielsen**
42 **REVERT (USA)**, b f Rail Link—Chaminade (USA) **K. Abdulla**
43 **REX IMPERATOR**, b g Royal Applause—Elidore **M. Pescod**
44 **ROSIE PROBERT**, b f Dylan Thomas (IRE)—Corsican Sunset (USA) **Seasons Holidays**
45 **ROSSLYN CASTLE**, ch c Selkirk (USA)—Margarula (IRE) **Lady Rothschild**
46 **RUNWAY GIRL (IRE)**, b f Dansili—Fashion Model **B. E. Nielsen**
47 **SELFARA**, b f Oasis Dream—Rustic (IRE) **K. Abdulla**
48 **SILVER LIME (USA)**, b c Mizzen Mast (USA)—Red Dot (USA) **K. Abdulla**
49 **STIR TRADER (IRE)**, b g Titus Livius (FR)—Changari (USA) **Mr D. M. Carter**
50 **SUPREME QUEST**, ch f Exceed And Excel (AUS)—Spanish Quest **Inglett, Allen, Carter and Kennedy**
51 **TANTAMOUNT**, b f Observatory (USA)—Cantarna **K. Abdulla**
52 **TIOMAN LEGEND**, b g Kyllachy—Elegant Times (IRE) **H.R.H. Sultan Ahmad Shah**
53 **TOP OFFER**, b c Dansili—Zante **K. Abdulla**
54 **TRADER JACK**, b c Trade Fair—Azeema (IRE) **D. J. Deer**
55 **VALIANT GIRL**, b f Lemon Drop Kid (USA)—Victoria Cross (IRE) **A. E. Oppenheimer**
56 **WATERCLOCK (IRE)**, ch g Notnowcato—Waterfall One **Lady Rothschild**
57 **ZAMARELLE**, b f Zamindar (USA)—Kardelle **Beckhampton Stables Ltd**

MR ROGER CHARLTON—continued

TWO-YEAR-OLDS

58 B f 24/2 First Defence (USA)—Alvernia (USA) (Alydar (USA)) **K. Abdulla**
59 **CANDOLUMINESCENCE**, b br f 11/3 Dansili—Flash of Gold (Darshaan) **Her Majesty The Queen**
60 B c 26/4 Three Valleys—Dansara (Dancing Brave (USA)) **K. Abdulla**
61 B f 4/2 Empire Maker (USA)—Didina (Nashwan (USA)) **K. Abdulla**
62 **DON MARCO**, b c 11/2 Choisir (AUS)—Dolma (FR) (Marchand de Sable (USA)) **Lady Rothschild**
63 B c 30/1 First Defence (USA)—Family (Danzig (USA)) **K. Abdulla**
64 **FIRST SECRETARY**, b f 7/2 Nayef (USA)—Spinning Queen (Spinning World (USA)) **Lady Rothschild**
65 B f 21/3 Montjeu (IRE)—Freni (GER) (Sternkoenig (IRE)) **Seasons Holidays**
66 B c 20/4 Oasis Dream—Global Trend (Bluebird (USA)) **K. Abdulla**
67 B c 12/3 Oasis Dream—Hypoteneuse (IRE) (Sadler's Wells (USA)) **K. Abdulla**
68 B f 19/3 Sakhee's Secret—Isobel Rose (IRE) (Royal Applause) (14285) **Beckhampton Stables Ltd**
69 **KALITHEA**, b f 24/3 Kheleyf (USA)—Baralinka (IRE) (Barathea (IRE)) **Elite Racing Club**
70 Gr c 27/3 Dark Angel (IRE)—Knapton Hill (Zamindar (USA)) (24761) **Mr P. Inglett & Mr D. Carter**
71 **MAGOG**, b c 21/3 Dansili—Margarula (IRE) (Doyoun) **Lady Rothschild**
72 Gr f 8/3 Excellent Art—Molly Mello (GER) (Big Shuffle (USA)) **Seasons Holidays**
73 Ch c 26/4 Compton Place—Muffled (USA) (Mizaaya) (40000) **Mr D. Carter & Mr P. Inglett**
74 B c 3/5 Teofilo (IRE)—No Quest (IRE) (Rainbow Quest (USA)) (58000) **H.R.H. Sultan Ahmad Shah**
75 **ROCKPOOL**, b f 6/2 Rock of Gibraltar (IRE)—Waterfall One (Nashwan (USA)) **Lady Rothschild**
76 B c 4/4 Mizzen Mast (USA)—Skiable (IRE) (Niniski (USA)) **K. Abdulla**
77 **SPIRAEA**, ch f 16/3 Bahamian Bounty—Salvia (Pivotal) **Mr Nicholas Jones**
78 B f 11/5 Dansili—Tantina (USA) (Distant View (USA)) **K. Abdulla**
79 **TARTARY (IRE)**, b c 10/4 Oasis Dream—Tamso (USA) (Seeking The Gold (USA)) **Lady Rothschild**
80 **TELAMON (IRE)**, b c 30/3 Rock of Gibraltar (IRE)—Laureldean Express (Inchinor) (45000) **M. Pescod**
81 B br f 15/3 Exchange Rate (USA)—Trekking (USA) (Gone West (USA)) **K. Abdulla**
82 B c 30/4 Dansili—Valencia (Kenmare (FR)) **K. Abdulla**

Other Owners: Mr S. Emmet, Miss Rosalind Emmet, Mr Tony Hill.

Assistant Trainer: Tom Grantham

---

120   **MR HARRY CHISMAN, Cheltenham**
Postal: **The Retreat Stables, Maugersbury, Cheltenham, Gloucestershire, GL54 1HP**
Contacts: **PHONE (07787) 516723**

1 **AUGHCARRA (IRE)**, 7, b g High Chaparral (IRE)—Pearly Brooks **Waggott Lowe Flowers Byrne Bell**
2 **CROSSGUARD (USA)**, 9, b g Royal Anthem (USA)—Foible (USA) **Mr H. J. Chisman**
3 **GAINSBOROUGH'S ART (IRE)**, 7, ch g Desert Prince (IRE)—
                                               Cathy Garcia (IRE) **Wood Appleyard Latta Byrne Goodall Welch**

Other Owners: Mr H. J. Appleyard, Mr Terry Bell, Mrs H. Byrne, Mr Harry Chisman, Mr V. R. Cooke, Mr M. J. Flowers, Mr Ray Goodall, Mr R. Latta, Mr David Lowe, Mr M. Slingsby, Mr J. W. Waggott, Mr D. Welch, Mr Duncan Wood.

Jockey (NH): Sean Quinlan, Tom O'Brien, David England. **Amateur:** Miss Claire Hulse.

---

121   **MRS ANGELA CLARKE, Llangadog**
Postal: **Marlands, Llangadog, Dyfed, SA19 9EW**

1 **PICOT DE SAY**, 10, b g Largesse—Facsimile **Dr S. R. Clarke**

---

122   **MR WILLIAM CLAY, Stoke-on-Trent**
Postal: **Saverley House Farm, Saverley Green, Fulford, Stoke-On-Trent, Staffordshire, ST11 9QX**

1 **MONTEVETRO**, 7, b g Galileo (IRE)—Three Piece **Mrs L. B. Clay**
2 **MORNING FAREWELL**, 8, br g Daylami (IRE)—Got To Go **Mrs L. B. Clay, Mr D. Holmes**
3 **SMOOTH SOVEREIGN (IRE)**, 7, ch g King's Best (USA)—Mellow Park (IRE) **Mrs L. B. Clay**

Other Owners: D. B. Holmes.

123 MR NICOLAS CLEMENT, Chantilly

Postal: **37, Avenue de Joinville, 60500 Chantilly, France**
Contacts: PHONE **(0033) 3445 75960** FAX **(0033) 3445 77084** MOBILE **(0033) 6072 34640**
E-MAIL **clementoffice@wanadoo.fr** WEBSITE **www.nicolasclement.com**

1 **AKARLINA (FR)**, 6, gr m Martaline—Akaralda (FR)
2 **CONSTANT DESIRE (IRE)**, 4, ch gr g Shirocco (GER)—Saudade (GER)
3 **FORT TICONDEROGA (IRE)**, 4, b g Marju (IRE)—Forewarned (IRE)
4 **GALIPEA (FR)**, 4, ch f Galileo (IRE)—Vanishing Prairie (USA)
5 **ICEBRAKER (IRE)**, 4, ch c Iffraaj—Stash The Ice (IRE)
6 **IRIS GLORIA (FR)**, 4, b f Iron Mask (USA)—Lost Ring (FR)
7 **LAST ATTEMPT (IRE)**, 4, b c Cape Cross (IRE)—Majestic Role (FR)
8 **LION KING (FR)**, 4, bl c Xaar—Lion's Bride (FR)
9 **PANFILO**, 17, b h Thatching—Reveuse du Soir
10 **PERSISTE ET SIGNE (FR)**, 5, b h With Approval (CAN)—Mahima (FR)
11 **PLAYLAND**, 4, b f Cape Cross (IRE)—Playact (IRE)
12 **REASONS (USA)**, 8, b g Malabar Gold (USA)—Anbella (FR)
13 **SEA FIGHT (USA)**, 6, ch g Smart Strike (CAN)—Incredulous (USA)
14 **TWO FOR TWO (IRE)**, 4, b g Danehill Dancer (IRE)—D'articleshore (USA)

THREE-YEAR-OLDS

15 **AIGUE MARINE**, b f Galileo (IRE)—Aiglonne (USA)
16 **ASSAULT ROYAL**, ch c Royal Assault—Vetority
17 **BECQUANIS (FR)**, bl c Panis (USA)—Berangele (FR)
18 **BENWAKI (FR)**, b c Sandwaki (USA)—Benghor (GER)
19 **BORDER SONG (FR)**, b c Stormy River (FR)—Tanea (FR)
20 **BRIONNE (GER)**, ch f Pivotal—Baltic Gift
21 **BROCOTTES (FR)**, b f Lando (GER)—Macotte (FR)
22 **CARNOUSTIE (FR)**, b f Acclamation—Matin de Tempete (FR)
23 **CLICQUOT (USA)**, b f Elusive Quality (USA)—Bushra (USA)
24 **CORSAGE (USA)**, b f Exchange Rate—Gingivere
25 **DIEPPE (IRE)**, gr c Dutch Art—Spinamix
26 **FRENCH FIFTEEN (FR)**, ch c Turtle Bowl (IRE)—Spring Morning (FR)
27 **GREEN FEES (IRE)**, gr c Clodovil (IRE)—Green Lassy (FR)
28 **GRIMOD (FR)**, b c Vespone (IRE)—Metaline (FR)
29 **HI YA PAL (USA)**, b c Pulpit (USA)—Cloon (USA)
30 **HIGH ENDEAVOUR (IRE)**, b f High Chaparral (IRE)—Green Tambourine
31 **IZODAR (FR)**, ch c Zamindar (USA)—Ice Dream (GER)
32 **KANDYKAINE (IRE)**, b f Montjeu (IRE)—Madura (GER)
33 **KANEL (FR)**, ch f Zamindar (USA)—Marie Vison (IRE)
34 **KASLICKY (FR)**, b c Slickly (FR)—Kacsa (FR)
35 **LA ZAM (FR)**, b f Zamindar (USA)—Francais
36 **LAC FONTANA (FR)**, b c Shirocco (GER)—Fontaine Riant (FR)
37 **LADY ANA (FR)**, b f Anabaa (USA)—The Wise Lady (FR)
38 **MARINA PICCOLA (IRE)**, ch f Halling (USA)—Marine Bleue (IRE)
39 **MOONSAIL (USA)**, b br f Malibu Moon (USA)—Eternity
40 **NOW WE CAN**, b c Martillo (GER)—Notre Dame (GER)
41 **RAQUETTE**, ch f Muhtathir—Racoon (FR)
42 **SAGA BOREALE (USA)**, b f Arch (USA)—Scarlett's Pride (FR)
43 **SAVE HER NAME (FR)**, b f One Cool Cat (USA)—Save Me The Waltz (FR)
44 **SIBERIAN FREEZE (IRE)**, b gr c Verglas (IRE)—Debbie's Next (USA)
45 **SNAKESTONE**, b f Sakhee (USA)—Moidart
46 **STATU QUO (FR)**, b c American Post—Porza (FR)
47 **STRONGER (FR)**, bl f Early March—Ballade Viennoise (FR)
48 **SURVEYANCE (USA)**, b f Broken Vow (USA)—Succession
49 **TOREODORA (IRE)**, b f Teofilo (IRE)—Amandian (IRE)
50 **VANILOQUIO (IRE)**, b c Acclamation—Trinity Joy
51 **YELLOW AND GREEN**, br f Monsun (GER)—Green Swallow (FR)

TWO-YEAR-OLDS

52 B f 19/4 Tale of The Cat (USA)—A Party For Two (USA) (Lear Fan (USA))
53 Gr c 15/2 Verglas (IRE)—Afra Tsitsi (FR) (Belong To Me (USA)) (65681)
54 B c 4/5 Green Tune—Arbalette (Anabaa)
55 Br c 16/3 Dark Angel (IRE)—Bellacoola (GER) (Lomitas) (119047)
56 B c 2/5 Stormy River (FR)—Coastline (Night Shift (USA)) (102627)
57 f 1/1 Elnadim (USA)—Didn't I Tell You (IRE) (Docksider (USA))

MR NICOLAS CLEMENT—continued

58 **FANDEE (IRE),** b c 1/3 Oasis Dream—Priere (Machiavellian (USA)) (90311)
59 B c 5/3 Rock of Gibraltar (IRE)—Forewarned (IRE) (Grand Lodge (USA)) (36945)
60 B f 23/2 Invincible Spirit (IRE)—Laramie (USA) (Gulch (USA))
61 **LOWER LAKE (FR),** b c 20/4 Medecis—Black Dahlia (Sanglamore)
62 B c 9/4 Stormy River (FR)—Mixture (Linamix (FR)) (36945)
63 **SEREZ (IRE),** b c 19/5 Shamardal (USA)—Afya (Oasis Dream) (59113)
64 **SHAREEL (FR),** b f 1/2 Country Reel—Shaking (Linamix)
65 B f 15/2 Gold Away (IRE)—Street Lightning (FR) (Best of The Bests (IRE)) (27093)
66 **STYLE VENDOME (FR),** b c 25/2 Anabaa (USA)—Place Vendome (FR) (Dr Fong (USA)) (75533)
67 B f 1/1 Giant's Causeway (USA)—Titian Time (USA) (Red Ransom (USA))
68 B c 3/4 Stormy River (FR)—Yes My Love (FR) (Anabaa (USA)) (32840)

---

124 **MR TERRY CLEMENT, Newmarket**
Postal: **Calder Park, Hamilton Road, Newmarket, Suffolk, CB8 0NY**
Contacts: **MOBILE (07885) 674474**

1 **BOBBY'S DOLL,** 5, ch m Needwood Blade—Nine To Five **Ms S. K. Jensen**
2 **BOBBYOW,** 4, b g Bertolini (USA)—Brooklyn's Sky **The Bill & Ben Partnership**
3 **DADO MUSH,** 9, b g Almushtarak (IRE)—Princess of Spain **Mrs C. Clement**
4 **HAMILTON HILL,** 5, b g Groom Dancer (USA)—Loriner's Lass **Mrs C. Clement**
5 **HARLEQUIN GIRL,** 4, ch f Where Or When (IRE)—Lauren Louise **The Quin's Racing Partnership**
6 **HISCANO,** 4, ch c Paolini (GER)—Hollywood Love (GER) **Mr M. Dyke**
7 **HURRICANE SPIRIT (IRE),** 8, b g Invincible Spirit (IRE)—Gale Warning (IRE) **The Little House Partnership**
8 **JAMAICA GRANDE,** 4, ch g Doyen (IRE)—Mary Sea (FR) **Mr E. Rayner**
9 **MAXIYOW (IRE),** 4, b f Royal Applause—Fudge **The Bill & Ben Partnership**
10 **MOLLYOW (IRE),** 4, ch f Iceman—Corryvreckan (IRE) **The Bill & Ben Partnership**
11 **MR SKIPITON (IRE),** 7, b g Statue of Liberty (USA)—Salty Air (IRE) **Miss C. J. Bishop**
12 **MR WILLIS,** 6, b g Desert Sun—Santiburi Girl **Mr C. R. Brister**
13 **MUMMYOW (IRE),** 4, b f Darsi (FR)—A Two (IRE) **The Bill & Ben Partnership**
14 **NGINA,** 4, b f Iceman—Nairobi (FR) **Mr M. Dyke**
15 4, B f Needwood Blade—Nine To Five **Ms S.K.Jensen**
16 **SOS BRILLANTE (CHI),** 7, b m Dance Brightly (CAN)—Strike Out (CHI) **R.F.Dale**
17 **THE MIGHTIE QUIN,** 5, b h Reset (AUS)—Dance Light (IRE) **The Quin's Racing Partnership**

THREE-YEAR-OLDS

18 **CANNIZARO HOUSE (IRE),** ch c Dutch Art—Travel On (USA) **Mr C. R. Brister**
19 **GIANTSTEPSAHEAD (IRE),** br c Footstepsinthesand—Salty Air (IRE) **Mr K. R. Hills**
20 **KINGSHILL LAD (IRE),** b br c Marju (IRE)—Brogan's Well (IRE) **Mr M. Dyke**
21 **NAVAHO SPIRIT,** ch g Sleeping Indian—Sefemm **Brister & Waddingham**
22 **PACK OF CARDS (IRE),** b g Red Clubs—Truly A Gift (IRE) **Mr M. Dyke**
23 **PRINCESS ALESSIA,** b f Byron—Break of Dawn (USA) **Mr M. Dyke**
24 **SILKY BLEU,** b f Elnadim (USA)—Tattling **Mr C. R. Brister**
25 **THARAWAL (IRE),** b c Moss Vale (IRE)—Notanother **Brister & Waddingham**
26 **YAJBER (USA),** gr ro c Aljabr (USA)—Futuh (USA) **Mr M. Dyke**

Other Owners: Mr P. G. Amos, Mr C. R. Brister, Mrs C. Clement, Ms Sarah Jensen, Mr William McGregor (Hendon), Mr D. T. Norton, Mr P. Ragan, Mr M. C. Waddingham.

Apprentice: Georgean Buckell, Jessica Steven.

---

125 **MR PATRICK CLINTON, Doveridge**
Postal: **Lordlea Farm, Marston Lane, Doveridge, Ashbourne, Derbyshire, DE6 5JS**
Contacts: **PHONE (01889) 566356 MOBILE (07815) 142642**

1 **BUSINESS BAY (USA),** 5, b br g Salt Lake (USA)—Jeweled Lady (USA) **In The Clear Racing**
2 **IMPERIAL ROYALE (IRE),** 11, ch g Ali-Royal (IRE)—God Speed Her **In The Clear Racing**
3 7, B m Beat All (USA)—Salska **P. L. Clinton**
4 6, B g Beat All (USA)—Salska **In The Clear Racing**
5 **TOFFEEPOT,** 5, ch m Generous (IRE)—Recipe **Moorland Racing**

Other Owners: S. A. Mace, Mrs A. M. Mace, G. Worrall.

126   MR K. F. CLUTTERBUCK, Newmarket
Postal: **Pond House Stables, Church Lane, Exning, Newmarket, Suffolk, CB8 7HF**
Contacts: **PHONE (01638) 577043 MOBILE (07868) 605995**

1 ALWAYS DE ONE, 5, b m Fruits of Love (USA)—Yes Virginia (USA) **K. F. Clutterbuck**
2 CAPTAIN SMOOTHY, 12, b g Charmer—The Lady Captain **A. J. White**
3 CERISE EN BLEU (FR), 8, ch g Goldneyev (USA)—Wild Rita **K. F. Clutterbuck**
4 DANCE TO DESTINY, 4, ch f Carnival Dancer—Java Dawn (IRE) **K. F. Clutterbuck**
5 JASMIN RAI, 5, b m Doyen (IRE)—Ella's Wish (IRE) **K. F. Clutterbuck**
6 TWENTYNINEBLACK (FR), 8, b br g Valanour (IRE)—Grange Cunault (FR) **K. F. Clutterbuck**
7 UNCLE PELDER (IRE), 5, b g Pelder (IRE)—Aunt Annie (IRE) **K. F. Clutterbuck**

THREE-YEAR-OLDS

8 BUCKLEY BOY, b g Araafa (IRE)—Waseyla (IRE) **K Clutterbuck & Mr P & Mrs A Pearce**

Other Owners: Mr C. J. Baldwin, Mr W. I. McKay, Mr A. White.

Assistant Trainer: James Clutterbuck

Conditional: Emma Clutterbuck.

127   MR DENIS J. COAKLEY, West Ilsley
Postal: **Keeper's Stables, West Ilsley, Newbury, Berkshire, RG20 7AH**
Contacts: **PHONE (01635) 281622 MOBILE (07768) 658056**
E-MAIL racing@deniscoakley.com WEBSITE www.deniscoakley.com

1 CAMACHE QUEEN (IRE), 4, b f Camacho—Alinda (IRE) **Keeper's 12**
2 CHIEF OF MEN, 4, b g Sleeping Indian—Hidden Meaning **C. T. Van Hoorn**
3 FANNY MAY, b f Nayef (USA)—Sweet Wilhelmina **C. T. Van Hoorn**
4 HUYGENS, 5, b g Zafeen (FR)—Lindfield Belle (IRE) **C. T. Van Hoorn**
5 PEARL OPERA, 4, b f Librettist (USA)—Letsimpress (IRE) **J. C. Kerr**
6 REBECCA ROMERO, 5, b m Exceed And Excel (AUS)—Cloud Dancer **Keepers Racing II**
7 ROCKFELLA, 6, ch g Rock of Gibraltar (IRE)—Afreeta (USA) **Mrs B. Coakley**
8 TIPSY GIRL, 4, b f Haafhd—Disco Lights **Mr L. M. Alkin**

THREE-YEAR-OLDS

9 ENTHRALL (IRE), b f Holy Roman Emperor (IRE)—Intriguing (IRE) **Miss Y. M. G. Jacques**
10 GABRIEL'S LAD (IRE), b g Dark Angel (IRE)—Catherine Wheel **Killoran Ennis Conway**
11 HARDY PLUME, ch g Manduro (GER)—Macleya (GER) **Cheviot Partnership**
12 HURRICANE IN DUBAI (IRE), ch g Hurricane Run (IRE)—In Dubai (USA) **Mr J. O'Riordan**
13 ROYAL DUTCH, ch g Nayef (USA)—Shersha (IRE) **C. T. Van Hoorn**

TWO-YEAR-OLDS

14 ALCANDO (IRE), ch c 10/4 Alhaarth (IRE)—Cantando (IRE) (Hamas (IRE)) (6190) **The Good Mixers**
15 B f 15/4 Steppe Dancer (IRE)—Carmencita (Rock of Gibraltar (IRE)) (492) **Mrs B. Coakley**
16 INDIGO MOON, b b 11/3 Sleeping Indian—Ewenny (Warrshan (USA)) (9000) **Count Calypso Racing**
17 KASTINI, b c 6/4 Halling (USA)—Toucantini (Inchinor) (10000) **West Ilsley Racing**
18 NORPHIN, b c 1/5 Norse Dancer (IRE)—Orphina (Orpen (USA)) **Mr J. A. Mould**
19 PERCY'S GIFT (IRE), b c 1/4 Hurricane Run (IRE)—Bysshe (Linamix (FR)) (22000) **Count Calypso Racing**
20 STUPENDA, b f 24/1 Misu Bond (IRE)—Opera Babe (IRE) (Kahyasi) (6000) **Finders Keepers Partnership**
21 THOMASINA, b f 23/2 One Cool Cat (USA)—Jemiliah (Dubai Destination (USA)) **N. J. Stafford**

Other Owners: Mr A. P. Bloor, R. J. Bolam, G. Callegari, P. M. Emery, J. T. Ennis, Mr E. P. L. Faulks, M. Kerr-Dineen, Mr T. A. Killoran, J. G. Ross, R. D. Whitehead.

128   MRS HEATHER COBB, Pulborough
Postal: **Kilbrannan Stud Farm, Gay Street, Pulborough, West Sussex, RH20 2HJ**
Contacts: **PHONE (01798) 812541 FAX (01798) 817371 MOBILE (07764) 942854**
E-MAIL kilbrannanstud@aol.com

1 MASTER ALF (IRE), 12, ch g Anshan—The Little Bag **Miss G. Cobb**
2 SAN JOSE (IRE), 9, b g Frimaire—Leinster Lady (IRE) **Mrs H. J. Cobb**

129 MR PAUL COLE, Whatcombe
Postal: **Whatcombe Estate, Whatcombe, Wantage, Oxfordshire, OX12 9NW**
Contacts: **PHONE (01488) 638433 FAX (01488) 638609**
E-MAIL jenny@paulcole.co.uk WEBSITE www.paulcole.co.uk

1 **CIRCUMVENT**, 5, ch g Tobougg (IRE)—Seren Devious **The Fairy Story Partnership**
2 **FLASHBANG**, 4, ch f Dubawi (IRE)—Colourflash (IRE) **A. H. Robinson**
3 **MONS CALPE (IRE)**, 6, b g Rock of Gibraltar (IRE)—Taking Liberties (IRE) **H.R.H. Sultan Ahmad Shah**
4 **MOYNAHAN (USA)**, 7, ch g Johannesburg (USA)—Lakab (USA) **Mr D. S. Lee**
5 **STRATEGIC MOUNT**, 9, b g Montjeu (IRE)—Danlu (USA) **P. F. I. Cole Ltd**
6 **ZING WING**, 4, ch f Hawk Wing (USA)—Zietory **The Fairy Story Partnership**

THREE-YEAR-OLDS

7 **DARING DAMSEL (IRE)**, b f Van Nistelrooy (USA)—Serengeti Day (USA) **Sisters Syndicate**
8 **DON LIBRE**, b c Librettist (USA)—Darwinia (GER) **Mrs E. A. Bass**
9 **GEM OF WIZDOM (IRE)**, b f Kheleyf (USA)—Sandy Lady (IRE) **Mrs Jill Haines & PFI Cole Ltd**
10 **GIFTED GIRL (IRE)**, b f Azamour (IRE)—Hoodwink (IRE) **A. D. Spence**
11 **HUNT A MISTRESS (IRE)**, ch f Teofilo (IRE)—Arctic Hunt (IRE) **K Dhunjibhoy, V Shirke, A Chudasama**
12 **JOY TO THE WORLD (IRE)**, ch f Dylan Thomas (IRE)—Speciale (USA) **Mr & Mrs Christopher Wright**
13 **KAISER WILHELM (IRE)**, b c Hurricane Run (IRE)—Luana **Mr D. S. Lee**
14 **MYSTIC MELODY (IRE)**, b f Montjeu (IRE)—Three Owls (IRE) **Mr D. S. Lee**
15 **PEARLS FROM SYDNEY (IRE)**, b f Librettist (USA)—Cultured Pearl (IRE) **Mr & Mrs Christopher Wright**
16 **SILVERHEELS (IRE)**, gr c Verglas (IRE)—Vasilia **Goldswain Hunter Jefferson Williams**
17 **STORMBOUND (IRE)**, b c Galileo (IRE)—A Footstep Away (USA) **P. F. I. Cole Ltd**
18 **SWINGLAND**, b f Pivotal—Farfala (FR) **Ben & Sir Martyn Arbib**
19 **UNEX CANALETTO**, b g Motivator—Logic
20 **VELVET STAR (IRE)**, b f Galileo (USA)—Velvet Moon (IRE) **Racing Club UK LLP**
21 **WITCHY MOMENTS (IRE)**, b f Excellent Art—Souffle **Mrs M. Bryce**
22 **ZIEFHD**, b f Haafhd—Zietory **The Fairy Story Partnership**

TWO-YEAR-OLDS

23 **BELOVA (IRE)**, ch f 10/3 Soviet Star (USA)—Slieve (Selkirk (USA)) (20000) **A. H. Robinson**
24 B c 13/2 Intikhab (USA)—Bermuxa (FR) (Linamix (FR)) (10000)
25 B f 11/3 Duke of Marmalade (IRE)—Blessyourpinksox (IRE) (Cadeaux Genereux) (28735) **C. Shiacolas**
26 **CARLTON BLUE (IRE)**, gr c 19/2 Aussie Rules (USA)—
                         Nurama (Daylami (IRE)) (26666) **Sir G. Meyrick & Sir M. Dunnington-Jefferson**
27 B c 16/2 Sakhee's Secret—Cheeky Girl (College Chapel) (30000)
28 **CUT NO ICE (IRE)**, gr f 29/4 Verglas (IRE)—Limpopo (Green Desert (USA)) (172413) **Denford Stud Limited**
29 B gr c 19/4 Dark Angel (IRE)—Dear Catch (IRE) (Bluebird (USA)) (36190)
30 B c 9/4 Namid—Duck Over (Warning) (22987)
31 **FALUKA (IRE)**, ch f 14/4 Iffraaj—Tortue (Turtle Island (IRE)) (55000) **Denford Stud Limited**
32 B c 30/3 Duke of Marmalade (IRE)—Farfala (FR) (Linamix (FR)) **Ben Arbib & Sir M. Arbib**
33 Br c 8/4 Bahamian Bounty—Heather Mix (Linamix (FR)) (30000)
34 **LOOK AT LULU**, ch f 13/3 Kyllachy—Sari (Faustus) (30000) **R. A. Instone**
35 B c 20/4 Exceed And Excel (AUS)—Magic Music (IRE) (Magic Ring (IRE)) (67000) **A. D. Spence**
36 **MONETS SECRET**, ch c 15/4 Excellent Art—Queen Isabella (El Prado (IRE)) (11000) **Whatcombe Partnership**
37 B c 1/4 Red Clubs (IRE)—Pure Gold (Dilum (USA)) (40000)
38 B c 18/3 Strategic Prince—Puteri Wentworth (Sadler's Wells (USA)) **H.R.H. Sultan Ahmad Shah**
39 B c 17/2 Oratorio (IRE)—Ring The Relatives (Bering) (65680)
40 **SERENATA (IRE)**, b f 7/5 Oratorio (IRE)—Seren Devious (Dr Devious (IRE)) **The Fairy Story Partnership**
41 **STANDING BEAR (IRE)**, b c 18/2 Excellent Art—Sweet Sioux (Halling (USA)) (22857) **W. H. Ponsonby**
42 B c 30/4 Strategic Prince—Starfish (IRE) (Galileo (USA)) (150000) **H.R.H. Sultan Ahmad Shah**
43 B c 30/4 Royal Applause—Tafiya (Bahri (USA)) (32000) **Mrs Jill Haines**

Other Owners: Mr T. M. Bird, Mr A. Chudasama, Mr P. F. I. Cole, Mrs P. F. I. Cole, Mr K. Dhunjibhoy, Sir Mervyn Dunnington-Jefferson, Mr Brian Goldswain, Mr E. R. Goodwin, Mrs J. M. Haines, Mr A. W. Hunter, Mr Richard Lane, Mr D. R. McLaughlan, Sir George Meyrick, P. F. I. Cole Ltd, Miss C. S. Scott-Balls, Mr Vijay Shirke, Mr Nicholas Williams, Mr N. F. J. Wood, Mr Christopher Wright, Mrs Chris Wright.

Assistant Trainer: Oliver Cole

Apprentice: Raul Da Silva.

130 MR TOBIAS B. P. COLES, Newmarket
Postal: **16 Doris Street, Newmarket, Suffolk, CB8 0LD**
Contacts: **MOBILE (07904) 779222**

1 **BRENT PELHAM**, 5, b h Royal Applause—Little Firefly (IRE)
2 **COTTON KING**, 5, b g Dubawi (IRE)—Spinning The Yarn
3 **DEAR MAURICE**, 8, b g Indian Ridge—Shamaiel (IRE)
4 **ICY QUIET**, 4, b f Shirocco (GER)—Winter Silence
5 **MAIN BEACH**, 5, ch g Starcraft (NZ)—Ocean View (USA)
6 **OBLIGADA (IRE)**, 4, ch f Beat Hollow—Oblique (IRE)
7 **RHYMING SKY**, 5, b m Erhaab (USA)—Rhyming Moppet

THREE-YEAR-OLDS

8 **CAMELOPARDALIS**, b f Tobougg (IRE)—Bonne Etoile
9 **HUGENOT (IRE)**, ch c Choisir (AUS)—All Elegance (IRE)
10 **INDIAN MOON**, gr f Royal Applause—In The Pink (IRE)
11 **LYCIDAS (GER)**, b c Zamindar (USA)—La Felicita
12 **SKYBLUE**, b f Royal Applause—Fiina

TWO-YEAR-OLDS

13 B f 3/4 Red Clubs (IRE)—Champion Tipster (Pursuit of Love)
14 B f 24/1 Mount Nelson—French Quartet (IRE) (Lycius (USA)) (2500)
15 Br f 9/2 Araafa (IRE)—Lekka Ding (IRE) (Raise A Grand (IRE))
16 B f 6/3 Tamayuz—Sandtime (Green Desert (USA)) (15000)
17 Ch c 5/4 Dubai Destination (USA)—Sefemm (Alhaarth (USA))
18 B c 31/3 Byron—Sovereign Seal (Royal Applause)

Owners: Mr P. Bamford, Mr J. Broughton, Miss H. Budgett, Mr C. Budgett, Mr M. Coleman, Mrs R. Coles, Mr T. Coles, Mr D. Cullinan, Miss K. Dalborg, Mr P. Deal, Mr M. Fitzroy, Miss D. Fleming, Mr Peter Foster, Mr Paul Foster, Mrs Sarah Hamilton, Mr R. S. Hoskins, Mr J. E. Micklethwait, Mr M. Tillbrook, Graf & Grafin Philip Schenk von Stauffenberg.

Assistant Trainer: Mrs J. O'Neill

Jockey (flat): Stevie Donohoe. **Jockey (NH):** Dominic Elsworth.

131 MR STUART COLTHERD, Selkirk
Postal: **Clarilawmuir Farm, Selkirk, Selkirkshire, TD7 4QA**
Contacts: **PHONE (01750) 21251 FAX (01750) 21251 MOBILE (07801) 398199**
E-MAIL wscoltherd@clarilawmuir.wanadoo.co.uk

1 **AWMAN**, 5, b g Grape Tree Road—Dubelle **Richard Nixon**
2 **AYE WELL**, 7, b g Overbury (IRE)—Squeeze Box (IRE) **J. Hogg**
3 **MAN OF PRINCIPLES (IRE)**, 9, b br g Bob Back (USA)—Shuil Le Gaoth (IRE) **Coltherd, Jeffrey & Hall**
4 **OVERLADY**, 10, b br m Overbury (IRE)—Chief Lady Nicola **W. F. Jeffrey**
5 **PADDYS UNYOKE (IRE)**, 11, b g Carroll House—Paddy's Dancer **J. F. W. Muir**
6 **ROYAL CURTSY**, 9, b m Pivotal—Fen Princess (IRE) **W. S. Coltherd**
7 **SHARNEY SIKE**, 6, ch g And Beyond (IRE)—Squeeze Box (IRE) **J. Hogg**
8 **SUPRISE VENDOR (IRE)**, 6, ch g Fath (USA)—Dispol Jazz **W. S. Coltherd**
9 **TALKIN SENCE (IRE)**, 7, b g Heron Island (IRE)—Catatonia (IRE) **W. S. Coltherd**
10 **TARTAN SNOW**, 12, b g Valseur (USA)—Whitemoss Leader (IRE) **Whitemoss Golf Syndicate**

Other Owners: Mr T. Conchar, Mr I. Hall, Mr N. Hancock, J. B. Jeffrey, R. V. Westwood, Mrs E. M. Westwood.

Jockey (NH): Richie McGrath, Fearghal Davis, Graham Lee. **Conditional:** Gary Rutherford.

132 LADY ANNE CONNELL, Brackley
Postal: **Steane Park, Brackley, Northamptonshire, NN13 6DP**
Contacts: **PHONE (01280) 705899 FAX (01280) 700873**

1 **COURT AGAIN**, 8, b g Alflora (IRE)—Southern Survivor (IRE) **Sir Michael Connell**
2 **COURT BEHIND**, 5, gr g Zafeen (FR)—Lightning Fork (IRE) **Sir Michael Connell**
3 **LEGAL LEGEND**, 5, b g Midnight Legend—Calamintha **Sir Michael Connell**

LADY ANNE CONNELL—continued

4 **RICH LIVE (FR)**, 7, b g Subotica (FR)—Iona Will (FR) **Sir Michael Connell**
5 **THE FAST FROG (FR)**, 11, b g Kadalko (FR)—Alba Terra (FR) **J. E. Connell**

Assistant Trainer: Mr Christopher Henn

Apprentice: Robert Spencer.

---

133   MR ALAN COOGAN, Ely
Postal: **31 Hasse Road, Soham, Ely, Cambridgeshire, CB7 5UW**
Contacts: **PHONE (01353) 721673 FAX (01353) 721117**

1 **CAPE SCHANCK**, 8, b g Observatory (USA)—Sally Gardens **A. B. Coogan**
2 **NOUS VOILA (FR)**, 11, b g Video Rock (FR)—Ability (FR) **A. B. Coogan**

---

134   MR JOHN COOMBE, Weymouth
Postal: **Sea Barn Farm, Fleet, Weymouth, Dorset, DT3 4ED**
Contacts: **PHONE (01305) 761745 (0780) 3752831 FAX (01305) 775396 MOBILE (07796) 990760**
E-MAIL wib@seabarnracing.com WEBSITE www.seabarnracing.com

1 **CHESIL BEACH BOY**, 9, b g Commanche Run—Eatons **C. C. Pugsley**
2 **FLEET DAWN**, 6, b g Polish Precedent (USA)—Wychnor Dawn (IRE) **M. J. Coombe**
3 **GAY SLOANE (IRE)**, 8, b g Anabaa (USA)—Seattle's Wood (USA) **J. D. Roberts**
4 **JUST WATCH OLLIE (IRE)**, 6, b g Indian Danehill (IRE)—Westgate Run **M. J. Coombe**
5 6, B g Olden Times—Pequenita **M. J. Coombe**
6 **SAN MARINO (FR)**, 9, ch g Bering—Sienne (FR) **M. J. Coombe**
7 **SHANNONS BOY (IRE)**, 10, b g Anshan—Dusky Lady **M. J. Coombe**

Assistant Trainer: Mr John Roberts

Amateur: Mrs M. Roberts.

---

135   MRS SUSAN CORBETT, Otterburn
Postal: **Girsonfield, Otterburn, Newcastle upon Tyne, Tyne and Wear, NE19 1NT**

1 **CLARESBURN**, 8, b m Milieu—Make The Grade **Mr W. F. Corbett**
2 **DEFINITE APPEAL (IRE)**, 9, ch g Definite Article—Marian's Wish (IRE) **Mr W. F. Corbett**
3 **DESTINY RULES**, 5, br m Endoli (USA)—Up The Order **Mr W. F. Corbett**
4 **DODGE THE BULLET**, 6, ch g Endoli (USA)—Leighten Lass (IRE) **Mr W. F. Corbett**
5 **FAWDON**, 5, br m Lahib (USA)—Piracy **Mrs S. Corbett**
6 **JUST JORDAN**, 6, b m Bollin Eric—Piracy **Mrs S. Corbett**

---

136   MR LIAM CORCORAN, Castle Cary
Postal: **Lovington Racing Stables, Ashview Farm, Lovington, Castle Cary, Somerset, BA7 7PU**
Contacts: **MOBILE (07789) 368234**
E-MAIL corcoranracing@aol.co.uk

1 **AURORA SKY (IRE)**, 6, gr m Hawk Wing (USA)—To The Skies (USA) **M. Chandler**
2 **BAILEYS AGINCOURT (IRE)**, 4, ch g Beat Hollow—Numberonedance (USA) **Miss C. L. Bowles**
3 **BLITZED ECKIE (IRE)**, 6, b g Zagreb (USA)—Glasson Storm (IRE) **B. Walsh**
4 **BRAVE HEART (IRE)**, 9, b g Broken Hearted—Belladoon (IRE) **Miss C. L. Bowles**
5 **CATCHING DREAMS (IRE)**, 6, b g Catcher In The Rye (IRE)—Kadarassa (IRE) **Miss C. L. Bowles**
6 **CONVERTI**, 8, b g Averti (IRE)—Conquestadora **Mrs E. A. Heal**
7 **DRUMADOON (IRE)**, 4, b c Hawk Wing (USA)—Lady Taufan (IRE) **GD Building & Roofing Contractors Ltd**
8 **JANUARY**, 9, gr g Daylami (IRE)—Noushkey **L. Gilbert**
9 4, B g Tamure (IRE)—Montagnette **Mrs J. M. O'Connor**
10 **RIO CARLOS (IRE)**, 5, ch g Captain Rio—Opalescent (IRE) **J. Clements**
11 4, B f Exit To Nowhere (USA)—Securon Lady **Mrs J. M. O'Connor**
12 **TEGAN LEE**, 9, b m Midnight Legend—What Chance (IRE) **Home Corp. Limited**
13 **YOUR TURN NOW (IRE)**, 7, b g Van Dantzig (USA)—Luso's Temple (IRE) **Home Corp. Limited**

Jockey (NH): Timmy Murphy. **Amateur:** Mr Louis Muspratt.

137 MR JOHN CORNWALL, Melton Mowbray
Postal: **April Cottage, Pasture Lane, Hose, Melton Mowbray, Leicestershire, LE14 4LB**
Contacts: **PHONE (01664) 444453 FAX (01664) 444754 MOBILE (07939) 557091**

1 FLICHITY (IRE), 7, br g Turtle Island (IRE)—Chancy Gal **J. R. Cornwall**
2 GRENOLI (FR), 11, b g Garde Royale—Pietrosella (FR) **J. R. Cornwall**
3 KERCABELLEC (FR), 14, b br g Useful (FR)—Marie De Geneve (FR) **J. R. Cornwall**
4 MAD PROFESSOR (IRE), 9, b g Mull of Kintyre (USA)—Fancy Theory (USA) **J. R. Cornwall**
5 ORTEGA (FR), 10, b g Useful (FR)—Madame Dabrovine (FR) **J. R. Cornwall**
6 PHOENIX DES MOTTES (FR), 9, b g Useful (FR)—Camille des Mottes (FR) **J. R. Cornwall**
7 RESTER VRAI (FR), 7, gr g Cadoudal (FR)—Moulouya (FR) **J. R. Cornwall**
8 THAT'S THE DEAL (IRE), 8, b br g Turtle Island (IRE)—Sister Swing **J. R. Cornwall**

Conditional: Joe Cornwall.

138 MR ANTHONY COSGRIFF, Malpas
Postal: **1 Lower Farm Court, Duckington, Malpas, Cheshire, SY14 8LQ**

1 GORGE (AUS), 10, b g Thunder Gulch (USA)—Heed Zamelina (AUS) **Mrs R. N. Cosgriff**

139 MR ROBERT COWELL, Newmarket
Postal: **Bottisham Heath Stud, Six Mile Bottom, Newmarket, Suffolk, CB8 0TT**
Contacts: **PHONE (01638) 570330 FAX (01638) 570330 MOBILE (07785) 512463**
E-MAIL cowellracing@aol.com WEBSITE www.robertcowellracing.co.uk

1 BRAVE DECISION, 5, gr g With Approval (CAN)—Brave Vanessa (USA) **Bottisham Heath Stud**
2 CANADIAN DANEHILL (IRE), 10, b g Indian Danehill (IRE)—San Jovita (CAN) **T. W. Morley**
3 CARDINAL, 7, ch h Pivotal—Fictitious **Mrs J. May**
4 CHANTILLY JEWEL (USA), 7, b m Century City (IRE)—Betty's Star (USA) **Bottisham Heath Stud**
5 CLERICAL (USA), 6, b g Yes It's True (USA)—Clerical Etoile (ARG) **Mr J. Sargeant**
6 DEAD COOL, 4, ch f Kyllachy—Dead Certain **K. A. Dasmal**
7 DIKANTA, 4, b g Diktat—Frascati **Lord Crawshaw**
8 EMERALD WILDERNESS (IRE), 8, b g Green Desert (USA)—Simla Bibi **Mrs J Morley & Mr Khalifa Dasmal**
9 FANTASY GLADIATOR, 6, b g Ishiguru (USA)—Fancier Bit **The Fantasy Fellowship**
10 FOUR WINDS, 6, b g Red Ransom (USA)—Fairy Godmother **T. W. Morley**
11 INSTRUCTRESS, 4, b f Diktat—Two Step **Bottisham Heath Stud**
12 JAMEELA GIRL, 4, ch f Haafhd—Peach Sorbet (IRE) **Lone Oak Stud/ Mrs J Morley/ Foulkes**
13 LUI REI (ITY), 6, b g Reinaldo (IRE)—My Luigia (IRE) **Rei Of Sunshine Partnership**
14 MONSIEUR JOE (IRE), 5, b g Choisir (AUS)—Pascali **Mrs H. Checkley**
15 PROHIBIT, 7, b g Oasis Dream—Well Warned **Dasmal, Rix, Barr, Morley, Mrs Penney**

THREE-YEAR-OLDS

16 CATS EYES, b f Echo of Light—Desert Lynx (IRE) **Manor Farm Stud (Rutland)**
17 FLASH CRASH, b c Val Royal (FR)—Tessara (GER) **J. R. Furlong**
18 INDIAN TINKER, b g Sleeping Indian—Breakfast Creek **Mr J. Sargeant**
19 JWALA, b f Oasis Dream—Kangra Valley **Manor Farm Stud & Miss S. Hoare**
20 KARA'S VISION, b f Kyllachy—Classic Vision **Hercules Horseracing Syndicate & Partner**
21 LOVE TO TARA, b f Notnowcato—Sparkling Clear **Mr G. A. G. Belcher**
22 MARMALADE MOON, ch f Shamardal (USA)—Frascati **Lord Crawshaw**
23 OSSIE'S DANCER, ch g Osorio (GER)—Nina Ballerina **Mrs J. May**
24 PETER'S PLEASURE, ch f Medicean—Swynford Pleasure **Mr P. Bottomley**
25 SILKEN EXPRESS (IRE), ch f Speightstown (USA)—Laureldean Express **Malih L. Al Basti**
26 WHEN WE COLLIDE, b f Fraam—Arinaga **Mrs J. May**

TWO-YEAR-OLDS

27 B f 18/3 Elusive City (USA)—Black Tribal (IRE) (Mukaddamah (USA)) **K. A. Dasmal**
28 DARK DIAMOND (IRE), b c 14/3 Dark Angel (IRE)—Moon Diamond (Unfuwain (USA)) (36190) **K. A. Dasmal**
29 IMMEDIATELY, b f 20/3 Notnowcato—Two Step (Mujtahid (USA)) (19047) **Bottisham Heath Stud**
30 NELINA, b f 21/1 Mount Nelson—Naralina (Linamix (FR)) (19000) **Newsells Park Stud & Mr A Rix**
31 B c 11/4 Three Valleys (USA)—Overwing (IRE) (Fasliyev (USA)) **Mr K. R. Robinson**
32 B f 20/3 Kyllachy—Poly Blue (IRE) (Thatching) (10476) **Mr Khalifa Dasmal & Bottisham Heath Stud**

MR ROBERT COWELL—continued

Other Owners: Malih Al Basti, Mr F. G. Barr, Mr G. Belcher, A. M. Blewitt, Bottisham Heath Stud, Mr P. Bottomley, Mrs H. Checkley, Lord Crawshaw, Mr Khalifa Dasmal, Mr Richard Foulkes, Mrs C. A. Foulkes, Mr J. Furlong, Mrs V. Garner, Mr F. Gorman, T. F. Harris, Miss S. Hoare, Lone Oak Stud Limited, Manor Farm Stud (Rutland), Mrs J. May, Mrs J. Morley, Mr T. W. Morley, Newsells Park Stud Limited, Ms E. O'Brien, Mrs J. M. Penney, Allen Rix, Mr K. Robinson, Mr J. Sargeant.

Assistant Trainer: Mr Nikki Himsworth

---

140 MR PAUL COWLEY, Banbury
Postal: **Lodge Farm Barn, Culworth, Banbury, Oxfordshire, OX17 2HL**
Contacts: **PHONE (01295) 768998 MOBILE (07775) 943346**
E-MAIL **paulcowleyequine@yahoo.co.uk**

1 **BILL THE LAD (IRE)**, 5, b g Classic Cliche (IRE)—Quilty's Rose Bud (IRE) **S. G. West**
2 **BILLY MURPHY**, 9, gr g Silver Patriarch (IRE)—Sperrin View **The BMWs**
3 **GRAND ARTICLE (IRE)**, 8, ch g Definite Article—Grand Morning (IRE) **S. G. West**

Other Owners: Mr R. J. Batchelor, Mr D. E. Wilson.

---

141 MR CLIVE COX, Hungerford
Postal: **Beechdown Farm, Sheepdrove Road, Lambourn, Hungerford, Berkshire, RG17 7UN**
Contacts: **OFFICE (01488) 73072 FAX 01488 73500 MOBILE (07740) 630521**
E-MAIL **clive@clivecox.com WEBSITE www.clivecox.com**

1 **ALWAYS THE LADY**, 4, ch f Halling (USA)—Hector's Girl **A. D. Spence**
2 **APOLLO D'NEGRO (IRE)**, 4, br g Fasliyev (USA)—Special One **Gwyn Powell & Peter Ridgers**
3 **BLACK SPIRIT (USA)**, 5, b g Black Minnaloushe (USA)—L'extra Honor (USA) **A. D. Spence**
4 **BLAZING FIELD**, 4, ch f Halling (USA)—Autumn Wealth (IRE) **Whitley Stud**
5 **CARRICK A REDE (IRE)**, 4, b g Footstepsinthesand—Intricate Design **S. W. Barrow**
6 **CHOKUREI (IRE)**, 4, b f Bertolini (USA)—Catch Us (FR) **HE Sheikh Sultan Bin Khalifa Al Nahyan**
7 **COVERT DECREE**, 4, ch f Proclamation (IRE)—Armada Grove **Lakes Bathrooms Ltd**
8 **DEN'S GIFT (IRE)**, 8, gr ro g City On A Hill (USA)—Romanylei (IRE) **Mrs O. A. Shaw**
9 **DRAKES DRUM**, 4, b g Dansili—Perfect Echo **R. J. Vines**
10 **ELECTROLYSER (IRE)**, 7, gr g Daylami (IRE)—Iviza (IRE) **Mr & Mrs P. Hargreaves**
11 **GANAS (IRE)**, 4, b g Oasis Dream—Hollow Dynasty (USA) **HE Sheikh Sultan Bin Khalifa Al Nahyan**
12 **HAAFACHANCE**, 4, b c Haafhd—Iviza (IRE) **Mr D. Shaw**
13 **JIMMY STYLES**, 8, ch g Inchinnor—Inya Lake **Gwyn Powell & Peter Ridgers**
14 **LITTLE COTTONSOCKS**, 4, b f Sulamani (IRE)—Caytinga **Mrs S. A. Fox**
15 **NIGHT AND DANCE (IRE)**, 4, b f Danehill Dancer (IRE)—
Evensong (GER) **HE Sheikh Sultan Bin Khalifa Al Nahyan**
16 **NINA ROSE**, 5, ro m Pastoral Pursuits—Magnolia **Martin C. Oliver**
17 **OH MY DAYS (IRE)**, 4, ch g Bahamian Bounty—Princess Speedfit (FR) **Miss J. Deadman & Mr S. Barrow**
18 **PERFECT CRACKER**, 4, ch g Dubai Destination (USA)—Perfect Story (IRE) **Mildmay Racing**
19 **PERFECT SILENCE**, 7, b m Dansili—Perfect Echo **Wild Beef Racing (Mr & Mrs R.J. Vines)**
20 **PERFECT TRIBUTE**, 4, b f Dubawi (IRE)—Perfect Spirit (USA) **Mildmay Racing & D. H. Caslon**
21 **POET**, 7, b h Pivotal—Hyabella **HE Sheikh Sultan Bin Khalifa Al Nahyan**
22 **SEEKING MAGIC**, 4, b g Haafhd—Atnab (USA) **The Seekers**
23 **SHADES OF GREY**, 5, gr m Dr Fong (USA)—Twosixtythreewest (FR) **Dr & Mrs John Merrington**
24 **WINTER'S NIGHT (IRE)**, 4, b f Night Shift (USA)—Woodland Glade **Mr J. T. Thomas**

THREE-YEAR-OLDS

25 **ACCESSION (IRE)**, b c Acclamation—Pivotal's Princess (IRE) **Brighthelm Racing**
26 **COMPTON PRINCE**, ch c Compton Place—Malelane (IRE) **The Beechdown Allstars**
27 **CYNTHIA CALHOUN**, b f Exceed And Excel (AUS)—The Jotter **T. P. Bostwick**
28 **DANCE EXPRESS (IRE)**, b f Rail Link—Swingsky (IRE) **Mrs T. L. Cox**
29 **DEVDAS (IRE)**, b c Dylan Thomas (IRE)—Drifting (IRE) **HE Sheikh Sultan Bin Khalifa Al Nahyan**
30 **DONT TAKE ME ALIVE**, b c Araafa (IRE)—Up At Dawn **Mr Jim Bostwick**
31 **DREAM TUNE**, b c Oasis Dream—Play Bouzouki **HE Sheikh Sultan Bin Khalifa Al Nahyan**
32 **DRUMMOND**, b g Zamindar (USA)—Alrisha (IRE) **Old Peartree Stud**
33 **FABLED CITY (USA)**, ch c Johannesburg (USA)—Fabulous Fairy (USA) **The Tenners**
34 **FAR EAST**, b f Cape Cross (IRE)—Hollow Dynasty (USA) **HE Sheikh Sultan Bin Khalifa Al Nahyan**
35 **FOREST ROW**, b c Cockney Rebel (IRE)—Forest Fire (SWE) **The Bodkins**
36 **HASSLE (IRE)**, b c Montjeu (IRE)—Canterbury Lace (USA) **A. D. Spence**
37 **HIGHLAND DUKE (IRE)**, b c Dansili—House In Wood (FR) **Highland Thoroughbred Ltd**

MR CLIVE COX—continued

38 **JINKER NOBLE,** b c Green Desert (USA)—Depressed **Gwyn Powell & Peter Ridgers**
39 **KUDOZ,** ch c Three Valleys (USA)—Rosapenna (IRE) **HE Sheikh Sultan Bin Khalifa Al Nahyan**
40 **KYANIGHT (IRE),** b f Kodiac—Blue Holly (IRE) **HE Sheikh Sultan Bin Khalifa Al Nahyan**
41 **LETHAL FORCE (IRE),** gr c Dark Angel (IRE)—Land Army (IRE) **Mr Alan G. Craddock**
42 **LITTLE DUTCH GIRL,** ch f Dutch Art—Photographie (USA) **Mrs J. F. Maitland-Jones**
43 **LITTLE RAINBOW,** ch f King's Best (USA)—Little Nymph **Mrs S. A. Fox**
44 **LUCKY HENRY,** br c Lucky Story (USA)—Seldemosa **T. P. Bostwick**
45 **LUNA ROSA (IRE),** b f Marju (IRE)—Lone Spirit **Mr Alan Le Herissier**
46 **MIRACLE MAID,** b f Selkirk (USA)—Miracle **Whitley Stud**
47 **MORILLES,** b f Montjeu (USA)—Niner's Home (USA) **HE Sheikh Sultan Bin Khalifa Al Nahyan**
48 **MY ESPOIR,** b f Oasis Dream—Eden (USA) **HE Sheikh Sultan Bin Khalifa Al Nahyan**
49 **PERFECT DELIGHT,** b f Dubai Destination (USA)—Perfect Spirit (IRE) **Mildmay Racing & D. H. Caslon**
50 **PERFECT FANTASY (IRE),** b f Oratorio (IRE)—Petite Fantasy **Mr John Drew & Mr Ian M. Brown**
51 **PINDROP,** ch f Exceed And Excel (AUS)—Why So Silent **The Quiet Alliance**
52 **POETIC DANCER,** ch f Byron—Crozon **The Laureates**
53 **POSEIDON GREY (IRE),** gr g Kheleyf (USA)—Elitista (IRE) **The Grey Goosers**
54 **PRESENT DAY,** gr f Cadeaux Genereux—Crackle **Mr A. Parker & Mr S. Bullard**
55 **ROYALE RANSOM,** b f Red Ransom (USA)—Prayer (IRE) **Mr S. Shorland**
56 **TINA'S SPIRIT (IRE),** gr f Invincible Spirit (IRE)—Dundel (IRE) **Mr S. R. Hope & Mr S. W. Barrow**
57 **TONLE SAP (IRE),** b f Manduro (GER)—Badee'a (IRE) **Miss B. M. S. Egan**
58 **TOP FROCK (IRE),** b f Acclamation—Silk Dress (IRE) **Mr A. McIver**
59 **YOUR WORD,** b f Monsieur Bond (IRE)—Only Yours **Wood Street Syndicate V & Mr C.J. Harper**

TWO-YEAR-OLDS

60 B c 20/4 Redback—Amber's Bluff (Mind Games) (20524) **Mr D. Shaw**
61 B c 7/3 Kheleyf (USA)—Balladonia (Primo Dominie) (76190) **HE Sheikh Sultan Bin Khalifa Al Nahyan**
62 B f 20/3 Elusive City (USA)—Corryvreckan (IRE) (Night Shift) (6666) **Elusive City Syndicate**
63 **GRAND DENIAL (IRE),** b c 16/4 Thousand Words—
    The Oldladysays No (IRE) (Perugino (USA)) (10672) **Lakes Bathrooms Ltd**
64 Ch c 4/4 Haafhd—Ha'penny Beacon (Erhaab) (30000) **Mr D. Shaw**
65 B f 29/4 Byron—Jolies Dee (Diktat) (4761) **The City & Provincial Partnership**
66 B f 16/2 Antonius Pius—Kotdiji (Mtoto) (13136) **Wickham Stud**
67 Br c 13/4 Red Clubs (IRE)—La Bataille (USA) (Out of Place (USA)) (3283) **Mr D. Shaw**
68 **LITTLE CHOOSEY,** ch f 5/3 Cadeaux Genereux—Little Nymph (Emperor Fountain) **Mrs S. A. Fox**
69 **MILLY'S GIFT,** b f 17/3 Trade Fair—Milly's Lass (Mind Games) (4000) **Ken Lock Racing**
70 B f 30/3 Authorized (IRE)—
    Mountain Chain (USA) (Royal Academy (USA)) **HE Sheikh Sultan Bin Khalifa Al Nahyan**
71 **RECKLESS ABANDON,** b c 28/3 Exchange Rate (USA)—
    Sant Elena (Efisio) (22857) **Miss J. Deadman & Mr S. Barrow**
72 Ch f 1/5 Galileo (IRE)—Red Yellow Blue (USA) (Sky Classic (CAN)) **HE Sheikh Sultan Bin Khalifa Al Nahyan**
73 Gr c 22/3 Holy Roman Emperor (IRE)—
    Rosamixa (FR) (Linamix (FR)) (127257) **HE Sheikh Sultan Bin Khalifa Al Nahyan**
74 B f 13/5 Footstepsinthesand—Stratospheric (Slip Anchor) (4925)
75 B c 30/1 Orientate (USA)—Stunning Rose (IRE) (Sadler's Wells (USA)) (28571) **Orientate Colt Syndicate**
76 Ch f 5/5 Sakhee's Secret—Tahara (IRE) (Caerleon (USA)) **Wood Street Syndicate & Mr C. J. Harper**
77 B f 16/5 Danehill Dancer (IRE)—
    Young and Daring (USA) (Woodman (USA)) **HE Sheikh Sultan Bin Khalifa Al Nahyan**

Other Owners: Mr Stephen W. Barrow, Mr J. D. Brynteson, Mr C. G. Cox, Mrs T. L. Cox, Dr Bridget Drew, Mr John Drew, Mr G. W. Elphick, Mr M. R. Flitton, Mr Mark Goodall, Mrs R. J. Hargreaves, Mr P. K. Hargreaves, Mr John Hetherington, Mr S. R. Hope, Ms Diane Jones, Mr A. McIver, Dr J. Merrington, Mrs U. Merrington, Mr Gwyn Powell, Mr Peter Ridgers, Mr R. J. Vines, Mrs R. J. Vines, Mr J. Wilkinson.

Assistant Trainer: Andrew Llewellyn

Jockey (flat): Luke Morris, John Fahy, Adam Kirby. **Apprentice:** Thomas Dyer, Lucy Barry. **Amateur:** Miss Rachel King.

---

142 **MR TONY COYLE, Norton**
Postal: **Long Row Stables, Beverley Road, Norton, Malton, North Yorkshire, YO17 9PJ**
Contacts: MOBILE **(07976) 621425**
E-MAIL **tonycoyleracing@hotmail.co.uk**

1 **BETTERAS BERTIE,** 9, gr g Paris House—Suffolk Girl **Mrs V. C. Sugden**
2 **DUBAIANSWER,** 4, b f Dubawi (IRE)—Answered Prayer **C. E. Whiteley**

MR TONY COYLE—continued

3 **EQTIRAAB (IRE)**, 4, b g Dalakhani (IRE)—Mayara (IRE) **Mr T. Coyle**
4 **FOREVER HOPE**, 5, b m Mark of Esteem (IRE)—Polar Dancer **Mr M. Kelly**
5 **LUCKY LANDING (IRE)**, 6, b br g Well Chosen—Melville Rose (IRE) **Gap Parsonnel**
6 **NIALLY NOO**, 4, b g Oasis Dream—Millyant **Mr B. Dunn**
7 **PILGRIM DANCER (IRE)**, 5, b g Danehill Dancer (IRE)—Pilgrim's Way (USA) **Chris Green**
8 **RICHIE ROB**, 6, b g Robellino (USA)—Friend For Life **C. E. Whiteley**
9 **RIO'S GIRL**, 5, b m Captain Rio—African Breeze **W. P. S. Johnson**
10 **RIVER DRAGON (IRE)**, 7, b g Sadler's Wells (USA)—Diarshana (GER) **Mr B. Kerr**
11 **SHARWAKOM (IRE)**, 4, b f Dansili—Candelabra **Mr B. Kerr**
12 **THATCHERITE (IRE)**, 4, gr g Verglas (IRE)—Damiana (IRE) **Mr B. Kerr**
13 **THE CARDEN ARMS**, 4, gr f Act One—Lapu-Lapu **Gap Personnel**
14 **YORKSTERS PRINCE (IRE)**, 5, b g Beat Hollow—Odalisque (IRE) **Mr B. Kerr**

THREE-YEAR-OLDS

15 B g Dylan Thomas (IRE)—Silk (IRE) **Mr T. Coyle**

TWO-YEAR-OLDS

16 B f 11/4 Sir Percy—Gwen John (USA) (Peintre Celebre (USA)) (1500) **Paul Inman**
17 Ch f 29/4 Beat Hollow—Lothian Lass (IRE) (Daylami (IRE)) (2500) **Mr T. Coyle**
18 **NIKNAD**, b f 5/4 Zafeen (FR)—Eau Rouge (Grand Lodge (USA)) (3000) **Market Avenue Racing Club**

Assistant Trainer: Jaimie Kerr

Jockey (flat): Stephen Craine, Barry McHugh. **Jockey (NH):** Brian Toomey. **Amateur:** Miss Harriet Dukes.

---

143 MR RAY CRAGGS, Sedgefield
Postal: **East Close Farm, Sedgefield, Stockton-On-Tees, Cleveland, TS21 3HW**
Contacts: **PHONE (01740) 620239 FAX (01740) 623476**

1 **BELLINGO**, 5, b m Danroad (AUS)—Rasin Luck **R. Craggs**
2 **DOWNTOWN BOY (IRE)**, 4, br g Kheleyf (USA)—Uptown (IRE) **R. Craggs**
3 **NEEDWOOD PARK**, 4, br g Needwood Blade—Waterpark **R. Craggs**
4 **STANROAD**, 5, b g Danroad (AUS)—Distinctly Laura (IRE) **R. Craggs**

THREE-YEAR-OLDS

5 B f Tillerman—Miss Fleurie **R. Craggs**

Assistant Trainer: Miss J N Craggs

Amateur: Miss Nicola Craggs.

---

144 MR PETER CRATE, Dorking
Postal: **Springfield Farm, Parkgate Road, Newdigate, Dorking, Surrey, RH5 5DZ**
Contacts: **PHONE (01737) 842311 MOBILE (07775) 821560**
E-MAIL peterdcrate@jandjfranks.com

1 **ELNA BRIGHT**, 7, b g Elnadim (USA)—Acicula (IRE) **P. D. Crate**
2 **PICANSORT**, 5, b g Piccolo—Running Glimpse (IRE) **P. D. Crate**
3 **TAAJUB (IRE)**, 5, b g Exceed And Excel (AUS)—Purple Tiger (IRE) **P. D. Crate**

THREE-YEAR-OLDS

4 **SANDFRANKSKIPSGO**, ch g Piccolo—Alhufoof (USA) **P. D. Crate**

TWO-YEAR-OLDS

5 B f 7/4 Royal Applause—Alhufoof (USA) (Dayjur (USA)) **P. D. Crate**

145 MR ANDREW CROOK, Leyburn

Postal: **Ashgill Stables (Yard 2), Tupgill Park, Coverham, Middleham, North Yorkshire, DL8 4TJ**
Contacts: PHONE **(01969) 640303** MOBILE **(07764) 158899**
E-MAIL **andycrookracing@fsmail.net** WEBSITE **www.andrewcrookracing.co.uk**

1 **AGESILAS (FR)**, 4, gr g Ultimately Lucky (IRE)—Aimessa du Berlais (FR) **R. P. E. Berry**
2 **ALONG CAME ROSIE**, 8, b m Alflora (IRE)—Seraphim (FR) **Friends Of Rosie & Select Racing Club**
3 **ALWAYS DIXIE (IRE)**, 5, b m Lucky Story (USA)—Jerre Jo Glanville (USA) **Mr R. Jones**
4 **ARIZONA HIGH**, 4, ch g Phoenix Reach (IRE)—Floriana **Mr G. P. Clarkson**
5 **BERWAAZ (GER)**, 4, b g Tertullian (USA)—Birthday Night (USA) **The Select Racing Club Limited**
6 **BOCAMIX (FR)**, 6, gr g Linamix (FR)—Bocanegra (FR) **Mrs H. Sinclair**
7 **CABAL**, 5, br m Kyllachy—Secret Flame **Leeds Plywood & Doors Ltd**
8 **DEERHURST**, 6, b g Dalakhani (IRE)—Cape Grace (IRE) **Mr G. P. Clarkson**
9 **FORTYSECOND STREET (IRE)**, 8, ch g Flemensfirth (USA)—Miss Murtle (IRE) **Mr G. Heap**
10 **GRAND DAY OUT (IRE)**, 4, ch g Byron—Maria Isabella (USA) **The 100 Club**
11 **MATMATA DE TENDRON (FR)**, 12, gr g Badolato (USA)—Cora des Tamarix (FR) **Lucky Catch Partnership**
12 **RANGEFINDER**, 8, gr g Linamix (FR)—Risen Raven (USA) **Leeds Plywood & Doors Ltd**
13 **STRATHAIRD (IRE)**, 8, b g Medicean—Heed My Warning (IRE) **Mrs K. M. Savage**
14 **WHITE FUSION**, 4, gr g Oratorio (IRE)—Divine Grace (IRE) **G Clarkson, D Dodsworth, K Looney**
15 **ZAZAMIX (FR)**, 7, b g Sagamix (FR)—Ombre Bleue (FR) **Mrs C. Hopper**

Other Owners: Mr Geoffrey Clarkson, Mr A. Crook, Mr David Dodsworth, Mr G. Heap, Mr E. W. Lerigo, Dr Kieran Looney, www.Select-Racing-Club.co.uk.

Jockey (NH): Brian Hughes, Keith Mercer.

146 MISS JO CROWLEY, Whitcombe

Postal: **Whitcombe Monymusk Racing Stables, Whitcombe, Dorchester, Dorset, DT2 8NY**
Contacts: PHONE **(01305) 265300** FAX **(01305) 265499** MOBILE **(07918) 735219**
E-MAIL **jocrowley61@hotmail.co.uk**

1 **COMADOIR (IRE)**, 6, ch g Medecis—Hymn of The Dawn (USA) **Mrs E. A. M. Nelson**
2 **DEORAI (IRE)**, 4, ch g Choisir (AUS)—Tropical Lake (IRE) **Kilstone Ltd**
3 **DESTINY OF DREAMS**, 4, b f Dubai Destination (USA)—Valjarv (IRE) **Kilstone Ltd**
4 **DUBARSHI**, 4, gr g Dubawi (IRE)—Asheyana (IRE) **Kilstone Ltd**
5 **EBONY SONG (USA)**, 4, b br g Songandaprayer (USA)—Thiscatsforcaryl (USA) **Kilstone Ltd**
6 **EVERYBODY KNOWS**, 7, b g King's Best (USA)—Logic **Mrs E. A. M. Nelson**
7 **PATAVIUM PRINCE (IRE)**, 9, ch g Titus Livius (FR)—Hoyland Common (IRE) **Mrs E. A. M. Nelson**
8 **PRINCESS ICICLE**, 4, b f Iceman—Sarabah (IRE) **Kilstone Ltd**
9 **RUNNING MATE (IRE)**, 5, b g Acclamation—It Takes Two (IRE) **Kilstone Ltd**
10 **SAKHEE'S PEARL**, 6, gr m Sakhee (USA)—Grey Pearl **The Peregrina Partnership**
11 **SHAMIR**, 5, b g Dubai Destination (USA)—Lake Nyasa (IRE) **Kilstone Ltd**
12 **SHELAGH (IRE)**, 4, b f Aussie Rules (USA)—Viburnum (USA) **Kilstone Ltd**
13 **SONDRAY**, 4, b f Diktat—Hoh Dancer **Kilstone Ltd**
14 **THE HOLYMAN (IRE)**, 4, ch c Footstepsinthesand—Sunset (IRE) **Kilstone Ltd**
15 **TICK TOCK LOVER**, 4, gr g Tikkanen (USA)—Ivory's Promise **Kilstone Ltd**
16 **WILFRED PICKLES (IRE)**, 6, ch g Cadeaux Genereux—Living Daylights (IRE) **Kilstone Ltd**

THREE-YEAR-OLDS

17 **DRESSED IN LACE**, b f Dark Angel (IRE)—Pure Speculation **Mrs E. A. M. Nelson**
18 **KALOKAGATHIA (IRE)**, b c Kodiac—Seabound **Kilstone Ltd**
19 **MANDIANNA (IRE)**, b f Manduro (GER)—Lock's Heath (CAN) **Mrs E. A. M. Nelson**
20 **PRINCESS MAYA**, b f Royal Applause—Secret Blend **Mrs E. A. M. Nelson**
21 **REGAL ART**, ch c Dutch Art—Grey Pearl **Regally Artful Partnership**
22 **THRASOS (IRE)**, b c Invincible Spirit (IRE)—Plymsole (USA) **Kilstone Ltd**

TWO-YEAR-OLDS

23 **CAPTAIN STARLIGHT (IRE)**, b c 28/3 Captain Marvelous (IRE)—
    Jewell In The Sky (IRE) (Sinndar (IRE)) (8209) **Kilstone Ltd**
24 **EMPEROR JULIUS (IRE)**, b c 21/3 Antonius Pius (USA)—Queen's Victory (Mujadil (USA)) (6567) **Kilstone Ltd**
25 **LADY TABITHA (IRE)**, b f 24/3 Tamayuz—Kimola (IRE) (King's Theatre (IRE)) (14778) **Mrs E. A. M. Nelson**
26 **MADAME SCARLETT (IRE)**, br f 27/1 Red Clubs (IRE)—
    Shining Desert (IRE) (Green Desert (USA)) (5746) **Mrs E. A. M. Nelson**
27 **MISS LEGAL EAGLE (IRE)**, b f 20/4 Authorized (IRE)—
    Pride of My Heart (Lion Cavern (USA)) (18882) **Mrs E. A. M. Nelson**

MISS JO CROWLEY—continued

28 **MUSIC MAN (IRE)**, b g 22/2 Oratorio (IRE)—Chanter (Lomitas) (21345) **Kilstone Ltd**
29 **MYSTICAL SAPPHIRE**, b f 25/3 Sakhee's Secret—Nadyma (IRE) (Daylami (IRE)) (476) **Mrs E. A. M. Nelson**
30 **SWEET MARWELL (IRE)**, b f 5/4 Excellent Art—
　　　　　　Bee Eater (IRE) (Green Desert (USA)) (13136) **Mrs E. A. M. Nelson**

Other Owners: Miss C. J. Davies, T. A. Edwards, Mr J. E. Gardner, Mrs L. Kellaway, Mr J. Luck, Mrs A. P. Wilkinson, C. J. Wilkinson.

Assistant Trainer: Anthony Clark

Jockey (flat): Dane O'Neill, Ian Mongan, Fergus Sweeney.

---

147 | **MR LUCA CUMANI, Newmarket**
Postal: **Bedford House Stables, Bury Road, Newmarket, Suffolk, CB8 7BX**
Contacts: **PHONE (01638) 665432 FAX (01638) 667160 MOBILE (07801) 225300**
E-MAIL **luca@lucacumani.com** WEBSITE **www.lucacumani.com**

1 **AFSARE**, 5, b g Dubawi (IRE)—Jumaireyah **Sheikh Mohammed Obaid Al Maktoum**
2 **DANADANA (IRE)**, 4, b c Dubawi (IRE)—Zeeba (IRE) **Sheikh Mohammed Obaid Al Maktoum**
3 **FIERY LAD (IRE)**, 7, b g Mull of Kintyre (USA)—Forget Paris (IRE) **Samanda Racing**
4 **FRANCISCAN**, 4, b g Medicean—Frangy **Dr M. B. Q. S. Koukash**
5 **FULGUR**, 4, b c High Chaparral (IRE)—Selebela **Scuderia Rencati Srl**
6 **IPPIOS**, 4, b c Cadeaux Genereux—Siena Gold **L. Marinopoulos & Partners**
7 **KIRTHILL (IRE)**, 4, b c Danehill Dancer (IRE)—Kirtle **L. Marinopoulos & Partners**
8 **MOHEDIAN LADY (IRE)**, 4, b f Hurricane Run (IRE)—Amathia (IRE) **Mrs O. Hoare**
9 **PRESVIS**, 8, b g Sakhee (USA)—Forest Fire (SWE) **L. Marinopoulos & Partners**
10 **QAHRIMAN**, 4, b c Tiger Hill (IRE)—Jumaireyah **Sheikh Mohammed Obaid Al Maktoum**
11 **QUEST FOR PEACE (IRE)**, 4, b c Galileo (IRE)—Play Misty For Me **O.T.I. Racing**
12 **SPIFER (IRE)**, 4, gr c Motivator—Zarawa (IRE) **Scuderia Rencati Srl**
13 **STOICAL**, 5, b g Galileo (IRE)—Stefania (IRE) **O.T.I. Racing**
14 **SUMMIT SURGE (IRE)**, 8, b g Noverre—Lady Peculiar (CAN) **Mr W. P. Bellew**
15 **SWOP (IRE)**, 9, b g Shinko Forest (IRE)—Changing Partners **Mrs A. S. Silver**

THREE-YEAR-OLDS

16 **ALEKSANDAR**, ch c Medicean—Alexander Celebre (IRE) **Fittocks Stud Ltd**
17 **ASHYANE (IRE)**, b f Dubawi (IRE)—Tarabaya (IRE) **Sheikh Mohammed Obaid Al Maktoum**
18 **AVALANCHE**, gr c Three Valleys (USA)—Silent Waters **Mrs A. S. Silver**
19 **AWAKE MY SOUL (IRE)**, ch c Teofilo (IRE)—Field of Hope (IRE) **J. Barton**
20 **BARKIS**, ch c Selkirk (USA)—Batik (IRE) **Aston House Stud**
21 **BATU (IRE)**, b c Lawman (FR)—Expectation (IRE) **The Kurultai Group**
22 **BINT ALMUKHTAR (IRE)**, b f Halling (USA)—Dabawiyah (IRE) **Sheikh Mohammed Obaid Al Maktoum**
23 **BLASH**, b f Dylan Thomas (IRE)—Heady **Mrs M. Marinopoulos**
24 **CITY OF CANTON (IRE)**, b c Monsun (GER)—Snow Crystal (IRE) **Mr S. A. Stuckey**
25 **COMMITMENT**, b c Motivator—Courting Highclere Racing - Diamond Jubilee
26 **DONATIA**, b f Shamardal (USA)—Donna Anna **Lady Juliet Tadgell**
27 **DULARAME (IRE)**, b f Pivotal—Easy Sunshine (IRE) **Sheikh Mohammed Obaid Al Maktoum**
28 **DULKASHE (IRE)**, br f Pivotal—Saik (USA) **Sheikh Mohammed Obaid Al Maktoum**
29 **EMIRATES QUEEN (IRE)**, b f Street Cry (IRE)—Zomaradah **Sheikh Mohammed Obaid Al Maktoum**
30 **FERLADIN**, ch c Selkirk (USA)—Selebela **Scuderia Rencati Srl**
31 **FRANCESCANA**, b f Dylan Thomas (IRE)—Frottola **Scuderia Rencati Srl**
32 **FURZANAH**, b f Dubawi (IRE)—Latent Lover (IRE) **Sheikh Mohammed Obaid Al Maktoum**
33 **GALLETTO (IRE)**, b c Azamour (IRE)—Galleta (IRE) **L. Marinopoulos & Partners**
34 **GOLDREAM**, br c Oasis Dream—Clizia (IRE) **TSEGA Horses Company Ltd**
35 **HIGH STRATOS**, b c Montjeu (IRE)—Hyabella **Castle Down Racing**
36 **HIPPY HIPPY SHAKE**, b f Danehill Dancer (IRE)—Hyperspectra **Helena Springfield Ltd**
37 **I STAND CORRECTED**, b f Exceed And Excel (AUS)—Forever Fine (USA) **J. Barton**
38 **INFINITE HOPE (USA)**, b br f Dynaformer (USA)—Shared Dreams **Miss S. J. E. Leigh**
39 **KALILY**, b c Dubawi (IRE)—Mail Express (IRE) **Sheikh Mohammed Obaid Al Maktoum**
40 **KEEP IT DARK**, b c Invincible Spirit (IRE)—Tarneem (USA) **L. Marinopoulos & Partners**
41 **KHIONE**, b f Dalakhani (IRE)—Sularina (IRE) **Aston House Stud**
42 **KIWAYU**, b c Medicean—Kibara **Fittocks Stud Ltd**
43 **KONA STORM**, b c Selkirk (USA)—Frabjous **L. Marinopoulos & Partners**
44 **MAISTRO (IRE)**, b c Excellent Art—Kicking Bird (FR) **Rathordan Partnership & Partners**
45 **MANKINI (IRE)**, b c Dansili—Fashion Statement **L. Marinopoulos & Partners**

MR LUCA CUMANI—continued

46 **MEDICI MUSIC**, b c Medicean—Balalaika **Mr S. A. Stuckey**
47 **OUT DO**, ch c Exceed And Excel (AUS)—Ludynosa (USA) **L. Marinopoulos & Partners**
48 **PARAMYTHI (IRE)**, ch c Peintre Celebre (USA)—The Spirit of Pace (IRE) **L. Marinopoulos & Partners**
49 **PETROL**, ch c Danehill Dancer (IRE)—Pongee **Fittocks Stud Ltd**
50 **POCKET WATCH**, gr f Pivotal—Dali's Grey **Mr S. A. Stuckey**
51 **QANAN**, b c Green Desert (USA)—Strings **Mr S. A. Stuckey**
52 **QUALITY PEARL (USA)**, b f Elusive Quality (USA)—Marianka (USA) **Pearl Bloodstock Limited**
53 **REQUIRE**, b f Montjeu (IRE)—Request **The Duke of Devonshire**
54 **ROCKALONG (IRE)**, b c Rock of Gibraltar (IRE)—High Spot **Mr Nagy El Azar**
55 **RUBRICS (IRE)**, gr c High Chaparral (IRE)—Inner Strength (FR) **Mr W. P. Bellew**
56 **SCRUPUL (IRE)**, b c Dylan Thomas (IRE)—Pearl Quest **Scuderia Rencati Srl**
57 **SEA FEVER (IRE)**, b c Footstepsinthesand—Love And Laughter (IRE) **De La Warr Racing**
58 **SEA SMOKE (IRE)**, gr g Dalakhani (IRE)—Tochar Ban (USA) **Mr J. S. Kelly**
59 **SECRET ENVOY**, b c Nayef (USA)—Bella Lambada **Castle Down Racing**
60 **SEMEEN**, b c Dubawi (IRE)—Zeeba (IRE) **Sheikh Mohammed Obaid Al Maktoum**
61 **SOUTHERLY**, ch c Shirocco (GER)—Jetbeeah (IRE) **L. Marinopoulos & Partners**
62 **STRADA FACENDO (USA)**, ch c Street Cry (IRE)—What A Treasure (USA) **Scuderia Archi Romani**
63 **SUBTRACTION (IRE)**, b c Pivotal—Attraction **Mrs M. Marinopoulos & The Duke of Roxburghe**
64 **SYNCOPATE**, b c Oratorio (IRE)—Millistar **L. Marinopoulos & Partners**
65 **TOTALIZE**, b g Authorized (IRE)—You Too **Castle Down Racing**
66 **TWELVE STRINGS (IRE)**, b g Iffraaj—Favoritely (USA) **Mr S. A. Stuckey**
67 **UTOPIAN**, b c Rock of Gibraltar (IRE)—Idealistic **Fittocks Stud Ltd**
68 **VALIDUS**, b c Zamindar (USA)—Victoire Finale **Mr S. A. Stuckey**
69 **VITALIZE**, b c Authorized (IRE)—Ventura Highway **Castle Down Racing**

TWO-YEAR-OLDS

70 **AJMAN BRIDGE**, ch c 7/4 Dubawi (IRE)—
        Rice Mother (IRE) (Indian Ridge) (125000) **Sheikh Mohammed Obaid Al Maktoum**
71 **AJMANY (IRE)**, b c 9/2 Kheleyf (USA)—
        Passerelle (USA) (In The Wings) (53365) **Sheikh Mohammed Obaid Al Maktoum**
72 Ch f 27/4 Medicean—Alexander Celebre (IRE) (Peintre Celebre (USA)) **Fittocks Stud Ltd**
73 **BARTACK (IRE)**, b c 16/3 Acclamation—Bentley's Bush (IRE) (Barathea (IRE)) (78000) **B. Corman**
74 **BLACK ROLLER**, b c 31/3 Kavafi (IRE)—Vallota (Polish Precedent (USA)) **Mrs L. Marinopoulos**
75 **CANON LAW (IRE)**, b c 6/4 Holy Roman Emperor (IRE)—Delisha (Salse (USA)) (98000) **Mr S. A. Stuckey**
76 Ch f 25/2 Pivotal—Cartimandua (Medicean) (90311) **Qatar Bloodstock Ltd**
77 B c 4/2 Motivator—Corinium (IRE) (Turtle Island (IRE)) (34000) **Scuderia Rencati Srl**
78 **DESERTED**, b f 2/2 Oasis Dream—Tentpole (USA) (Rainbow Quest (USA)) **Fittocks Stud Ltd**
79 **DIAMOND MINE**, br gr c 14/4 Rock of Gibraltar (IRE)—Kassiyra (IRE) (Kendor (FR)) **Fittocks Stud Ltd**
80 B c 2/5 Dylan Thomas (IRE)—Dubious (Darshaan) (87000) **Scuderia Rencati Srl**
81 **DUKE OF PERTH**, b c 4/5 Danehill Dancer (IRE)—Frangy (Sadler's Wells (USA)) **Fittocks Stud Ltd**
82 **ELHAAME (IRE)**, b c 17/3 Acclamation—
        Gold Hush (USA) (Seeking The Gold (USA)) (160000) **Sheikh Mohammed Obaid Al Maktoum**
83 **GREATWOOD**, b c 1/3 Manduro (GER)—Gaze (Galileo (IRE)) (85000) **Highclere Thoroughbred Racing - Archer**
84 B c 10/3 Mount Nelson—Hoh Chi Min (Efisio) (45000) **L. Marinopoulos & Partners**
85 **JAZZ MASTER**, b c 30/4 Singspiel (IRE)—Turn of A Century (Halling (USA)) **Castle Down Racing**
86 **KIKONGA**, b f 16/4 Danehill Dancer (IRE)—Kibara (Sadler's Wells (USA)) **Fittocks Stud Ltd**
87 **KINDU**, b f 23/5 Pivotal—Kithanga (IRE) (Darshaan) **Fittocks Stud Ltd**
88 **KRAKEN**, br c 15/2 Notnowcato—
        Madame Claude (IRE) (Paris House) (42000) **L. Marinopoulos & Partners**
89 **LIONHEART**, ch c 5/4 Zamindar (USA)—
        Victoire Celebre (USA) (Stravinsky (USA)) **Fittocks Stud & Andrew Bengough**
90 **MAKAFEH**, b c 29/1 Elusive Quality (USA)—
        Demisemiquaver (Singspiel (IRE)) (190000) **Sheikh Mohammed Obaid Al Maktoum**
91 **MALLORY HEIGHTS (IRE)**, b c 27/2 Dalakhani (IRE)—My Dark Rosaleen (Sadler's Wells (USA)) **Merry Fox Stud**
92 **MARKTTAG**, b c 12/2 Manduro (GER)—Makhsusah (IRE) (Darshaan) (82000) **Mr S. A. Stuckey**
93 B f 15/4 Giant's Causeway (USA)—Measure (USA) (Seeking The Gold (USA))
94 **MONAWER**, b c 10/3 Teofilo (IRE)—
        Israar (Machiavellian (USA)) (115000) **Sheikh Mohammed Obaid Al Maktoum**
95 **MOUNT MACEDON**, b c 18/4 Hernando (FR)—White Palace (Shirley Heights) (38000) **Mr S. A. Stuckey**
96 **NARGYS (IRE)**, b f 3/3 Lawman (FR)—
        Spesialta (Indian Ridge) (102626) **Sheikh Mohammed Obaid Al Maktoum**
97 B c 18/4 Royal Applause—Ocean View (USA) (Gone West (USA)) (70000) **L. Marinopoulos & Partners**
98 B br c 24/4 High Chaparral (IRE)—Pay The Bank (High Top) (105000) **L. Marinopoulos & Partners**
99 **PLEASURE BENT**, b c 21/2 Dansili—Nitya (FR) (Indian Ridge) (150000) **C. Bennett**
100 B c 8/2 Mount Nelson—Regal Step (Royal Applause) (55000) **L. Marinopoulos & Partners**

MR LUCA CUMANI—continued

101 Br c 20/1 Red Clubs (IRE)—Rejuvenation (IRE) (Singspiel (IRE)) (45000) **L. Marinopoulos & Partners**
102 **ROMANOFF (IRE),** b c 6/3 Holy Roman Emperor (IRE)—
                    Alexander Anapolis (IRE) (Spectrum (IRE)) (50000) **Mrs A. Silver & Partners**
103 **ROYAL BALLET,** ch c 2/4 Pivotal—
         Dance A Dream (Sadler's Wells (USA)) (85000) **Highclere Thoroughbred Racing - Lord Mayor**
104 **SHARAREH,** b f 23/2 Sir Percy—You Too (Monsun (GER)) (40000) **Sheikh Mohammed Obaid Al Maktoum**
105 **SHARQAWIYAH,** b f 25/4 Dubawi (IRE)—
             Pompey Girl (Rainbow Quest (USA)) (50000) **Sheikh Mohammed Obaid Al Maktoum**
106 **SHUTTLE,** b f 14/5 Peintre Celebre (USA)—Cosmodrome (USA) (Bahri (USA)) **Fittocks Stud Ltd**
107 **SILK SARI,** b f 16/3 Dalakhani (IRE)—So Silk (Rainbow Quest (USA)) **Fittocks Stud & Andrew Bengough**
108 **SORYAH (IRE),** b f 6/4 Shamardal (USA)—Dirtybirdie (Diktat) (110000) **Sheikh Mohammed Obaid Al Maktoum**
109 **SPIETA (IRE),** gr f 20/3 Shirocco (GER)—Zarawa (Kahyasi) (40000) **Scuderia Rencati Srl & Partners**
110 **TOMAHAWK CHIEF (IRE),** b c 5/5 High Chaparral (IRE)—
              Moore's Melody (IRE) (Marju (IRE)) (135000) **Mr S. A. Stuckey**
111 Ch c 14/3 Hurricane Run (IRE)—Unquenchable (USA) (Kingmambo (USA)) (30000) **L. Marinopoulos & Partners**
112 **VELOX,** b c 29/4 Zamindar (USA)—Victoire Finale (Peintre Celebre (USA)) **Mr S. A. Stuckey**
113 B br f 4/2 Footstepsinthesand—Zee Zee Gee (Galileo (IRE)) (65000) **Helena Springfield Ltd**

Other Owners: Scuderia Rencati Srl, Mr Paolo Agostini, Mrs Emma Agostini, Mr S. Al Ansari, Mr K. B. Bailey, Mr Joseph Barton, Mr A. N. C. Bengough, Mr Daniel Boorer, Mr P. Booth, Mr W. F. Charnley, The Hon Mrs J. M. Corbett, Mrs Luca Cumani, Ms Naomi Davis, Lord De La Warr, Lady De La Warr, Mr Alexander Frost, Mr T. Henderson, Prof John Hunter, Mrs Melissa Kay, Mr Paul Moulton, Mr S. O'Donnell, Mr Andrew Patey, Mr C. Pizarro, Mr M. Quirke, Mrs L. E. Ramsden, Duke of Roxburghe, Scuderia Blueberry S. R. L., Mr Paul G. S. Silver, Miss Amanda Staveley, Mr M. Weinfeld, Mr Christopher Wright.

Assistant Trainers: Charles Henson (Abroad), Matthew Cumani (Home)

Jockey (flat): Kieren Fallon, J-P Guillambert. **Apprentice:** Talib Hussain, Hayley Burton, Jordan Taylor. **Amateur:** Miss F. Cumani.

148
MR MICHAEL CUNNINGHAM, Navan
Postal: Gormanstown Stables, Kildalkey, Navan, Co.Meath, Ireland
Contacts: **PHONE (00353) 4694 31672 FAX (00353) 4694 31467 MOBILE (00353) 8625 93962
E-MAIL cunninghamstables@gmail.com**

1 **CROWDED ROOM (IRE),** 6, b g Oscar (IRE)—Leadamurraydance (IRE) **Mrs Michael Cunningham**
2 **MARTIN CASH (IRE),** 6, b g Oscar (IRE)—Native Singer (IRE) **Mrs Paul Shanahan**
3 5, B g Shantou (USA)—Nancys Bridge (IRE) **Canal Racing Syndicate**
4 4, B f Westerner—Penny Farthing **Mayoco Syndicate**
5 **TIERNAN'S TERROR,** 10, br g Overbury (IRE)—Snitton Lane **Herb M. Stanley**

149
MR BARNEY CURLEY, Newmarket
Postal: Cleveland House Stables, Hamilton Road, Newmarket, Suffolk, CB8 7JQ
Contacts: **PHONE (01638) 668755**

1 **AGAPANTHUS (GER),** 7, b g Tiger Hill (IRE)—Astilbe (GER) **Curley Leisure Limited**
2 **ALLANIT (GER),** 8, b g Tiger Hill (IRE)—Astilbe (GER) **Curley Leisure Limited**
3 **ELUSIVE HAWK (IRE),** 8, b g Noverre (USA)—Two Clubs **Curley Leisure Limited**
4 **KASSIODOR (GER),** 5, b g Tiger Hill (IRE)—Kitcat (GER) **Curley Leisure Limited**
5 **MARY KATE O'BRIEN,** 5, b m Tiger Hill (IRE)—Glorosia (FR) **Curley Leisure Limited**
6 **ME FEIN,** 8, gr g Desert Prince (IRE)—Attachment (USA) **Curley Leisure Limited**
7 **SAVARONOLA (USA),** 7, ch g Pulpit (USA)—Running Debate (USA) **Curley Leisure Limited**
8 **SHOUDA (IRE),** 6, b g Tiger Hill (IRE)—Sommernacht (GER) **Curley Leisure Limited**
9 **SIR MOZART (IRE),** 9, b g Mozart (IRE)—Lady Silver Hawk (USA) **Curley Leisure Limited**
10 **SOMMERSTURM (GER),** 8, b g Tiger Hill (IRE)—Sommernacht (GER) **Curley Leisure Limited**

THREE-YEAR-OLDS

11 **HEARDUTHEFIRSTTIME (IRE),** b g Tiger Hill (IRE)—Caona (USA) **Mr A. R. Purvis**

Assistant Trainer: Andrew Stringer

Jockey (flat): Tom Queally. **Jockey (NH):** Paul Moloney.

150 MISS REBECCA CURTIS, Newport
Postal: **Fforest Farm, Newport, Pembrokeshire, SA42 0UG**
Contacts: **PHONE (01348) 811489 MOBILE (07970) 710690**
E-MAIL rebcurtis@hotmail.com

1 ALWAARY (USA), 6, b g Dynaformer (USA)—Tabrir (IRE) **Mr C. Noell**
2 5, B g Flemensfirth (USA)—Ballyclough Gale **G. Costelloe**
3 BENHEIR (IRE), 6, b g Beneficial—Vicford (IRE) **G. Costelloe**
4 4, B g King's Theatre (IRE)—Blast Freeze (IRE) **G. Costelloe**
5 CODDINGTON BOY, 4, br g Fair Mix (IRE)—Coddington Girl **G. Costelloe**
6 CORSICAN BOY, 4, gr g Tobougg (IRE)—Madiyla **I. S. Naylor**
7 FAMILY THREE (IRE), 7, b g Dushyantor (USA)—Leaping Three (IRE) **Mr M. A. Sherwood & G. Costelloe**
8 FIRST QUARTER, 5, b g Old Vic—Webb Find (IRE) **J. P. McManus**
9 FISHOUTOFWATER (IRE), 8, ch g Old Vic—Frost Bound **J. P. McManus**
10 GOD OF THE KOP (IRE), 5, ch g Old Vic—Liss Rua (IRE) **G. Costelloe**
11 HERONS WELL, 9, b g Heron Island (IRE)—The Storm Bell (IRE) **Mr J. Halley**
12 HIGH STORM (IRE), 5, b g High Chaparral (IRE)—Lady Storm (IRE) **Mr D. R. James**
13 HODGSON (IRE), 7, gr g Oscar (IRE)—Gairha Grey (IRE) **G. Costelloe**
14 IN THE POST (IRE), 7, b g Oscar (IRE)—Watch Your Step (IRE) **G. Costelloe**
15 4, B g Definite Article—Love The Lord (IRE) **Mr A. J. Rhead**
16 MADE IN TIME (IRE), 7, b br g Zagreb (USA)—No Easy Way (IRE) **J. P. McManus**
17 MEISTER ECKHART (IRE), 6, b br g Flemensfirth (USA)—Carrabawn **G. Costelloe**
18 MONTE CAVALLO (SAF), 7, b g Saumarez—Mufski (SAF) **D. R. Morrison**
19 NEARBY, 8, b g King's Best (USA)—Contiguous (USA) **I. S. Naylor**
20 OLD WIGMORE (IRE), 7, ch g Old Vic—Wigmore (IRE) **Sea Partnership**
21 ONE TERM (IRE), 5, b g Beneficial—One Edge (IRE) **L Reid, W A Thomas & G Costelloe**
22 ROYAL REVERIE, 4, b g Royal Applause—Christina's Dream **Miss R. Curtis**
23 SCOTER FONTAINE (FR), 6, b g Sleeping Car (FR)—Blanche Fontaine (FR) **J. P. McManus**
24 SIR BERE (IRE), 6, b g Della Francesca (USA)—Known Alibi (USA) **Ms Diane Morgan**
25 SNOW BLIZZARD (IRE), 5, b g Sadler's Wells (USA)—Pescia (USA) **Davies & Price**
26 TAKE OF SHOC'S (IRE), 8, ch g Beneficial—Dear Dunleer (IRE) **Sharp As A Beachball Partnership**
27 TEAFORTHREE (IRE), 8, b g Oscar (IRE)—Ethel's Bay (IRE) **T437**
28 THE BEAR TRAP (IRE), 5, b g Westerner—Calendula **J. P. McManus**
29 THE JIGSAW MAN (IRE), 8, ch g Bob Back (USA)—Native Sunset (IRE) **LI.R.P.Racing**
30 THE JUGOPOLIST (IRE), 5, b g Oscar (IRE)—Chance My Native (IRE) **C. R. Trembath**
31 THE PLAYFUL PRIEST (IRE), 5, ch g Presenting—First Strike (IRE) **Mr P. P. Elliott**
32 THE ROMFORD PELE (IRE), 5, b g Accordion—Back And Fore (IRE) **G. Costelloe**

Other Owners: Mr J. Conyers, R. A. Davies, Mr J. M. I. Evetts, Mr C. J. Guyver, T. G. Jones, Mr C. J. O'Reilly, Mr J. P. O'Reilly, Mr P. J. Owen, Mr A. G. Price, Mr J. L. Rees, Miss L. Reid, Mr N. M. Roddis, M. A. Sherwood, Mr W. A. Thomas, Mr A. Wright, D. C. Zeffman.

Assistant Trainer: Paul Sheldrake

151 MR ROGER CURTIS, Lambourn
Postal: **Delamere Stables, Baydon Road, Lambourn, Hungerford, Berkshire, RG17 8NT**
Contacts: **PHONE (01488) 73007 FAX (01488) 73909 MOBILE (07836) 320690**
E-MAIL rcurtislambourn@aol.com WEBSITE www.rogercurtis.com

1 BALLY GUNNER, 7, br g Needle Gun (IRE)—Rich Pickings **The Bally Gunners**
2 BRAVE ENOUGH (USA), 5, b g Yes It's True (USA)—Courageous (USA) **The Racing 4 Fun Partnership**
3 ELEGANT OLIVE, 9, b m Alflora (IRE)—Strong Cloth (USA) **Collective Dreamers**
4 KAYCEE (IRE), 7, ch g King Charlemagne (USA)—Bollicina (USA) **R. M. Carson**
5 KILCOMMON PRIDE (IRE), 7, br g Catcher In The Rye (IRE)—Ballyhookeen Lass (IRE) **Healycoyle & Partners**
6 MADERSON BLUE (IRE), 10, b g Pistolet Bleu (IRE)—Not A Bid (IRE) **The Maderson Blue Partnership**
7 NEAR GERMANY (IRE), 12, b g Germany (USA)—Night Year (IRE) **R. Curtis**
8 QUAM CELERRIME, 7, b g Xaar—Divine Secret **The Maderson Blue Partnership**
9 ROMNEY MARSH, 11, br m Glacial Storm (USA)—Mirador **The Romney Marsh Partnership**

THREE-YEAR-OLDS

10 RAINBOW RICHES (IRE), b f Princely Heir (IRE)—Another Rainbow (IRE) **The Racing 4 Fun Partnership**

Other Owners: Miss A. Atkin, Ms L. M. Barton, Mr T. N. Coyle, Mrs D. S. Gibbs, Mrs P. McCluskey, B. Newman, Mr D. N. Thurlow, Dr P. G. Walker.

MR ROGER CURTIS—continued

Assistant Trainer: Dawn Gibbs

Jockey (flat): Dane O'Neill, James Doyle. **Jockey (NH):** Dave Crosse, Hadden Frost. **Amateur:** Mr Jos Curtis, Mr Freddy Tett.

---

152 MR TOM CUTHBERT, Brampton
Postal: **Woodlands, Cowranbridge, How Mill, Brampton, Cumbria, CA8 9LH**
Contacts: **PHONE (01228) 560822 FAX (01228) 560822 MOBILE (07747) 843344**
E-MAIL **cuthbertracing@fsmail.net**

1 EDAS, 10, b g Celtic Swing—Eden (IRE) **Mrs J. Cuthbert**
2 SECOND REEF, 10, b g Second Empire (IRE)—Vax Lady **Mrs J. Cuthbert**
3 SKYLARKER (USA), 14, b g Sky Classic (CAN)—O My Darling (USA) **Mrs J. Cuthbert**

Assistant Trainer: Helen Cuthbert

Amateur: Miss H. Cuthbert.

---

153 MR PAUL D'ARCY, Newmarket
Postal: **Charnwood Stables, Hamilton Road, Newmarket, Suffolk, CB8 7JQ**
Contacts: **PHONE (01638) 662000 FAX (01638) 661100 MOBILE (07768) 807653**
E-MAIL **pauldarcy@fsmail.net WEBSITE www.pauldarcyracing.com**

1 EDINBURGH KNIGHT (IRE), 5, b g Selkirk (USA)—Pippas Song **Knights Racing**
2 GRANNY ANNE (IRE), 4, ch f Redback—Krayyalei (IRE) **C. M. Wilson**
3 LITTLE JAZZ, 4, b f Doyen (IRE)—Meddle **Mr K. Snell**
4 MCBIRNEY (USA), 5, b g Danehill Dancer (IRE)—Dear Girl (IRE) **P. W. D'Arcy**
5 NELSON'S BOUNTY, 5, b g Bahamian Bounty—Santisima Trinidad (IRE) **The Newmarket Pirates**
6 NIGHT LILY (IRE), 6, b m Night Shift (USA)—Kedross (IRE) **Mr K. Snell**
7 ONGOODFORM (IRE), 5, b h Invincible Spirit (IRE)—Elfin Queen (IRE) **Dr J. S. Kinnear**
8 POLLY HOLDER (IRE), 4, b f Peintre Celebre (USA)—Love Emerald (USA) **C. M. Wilson**

THREE-YEAR-OLDS

9 COME ON BLUE CHIP (IRE), b g Holy Roman Emperor (IRE)—Rapid Action (USA) **Blue Chip Feed Ltd**
10 COOL AS CASH, ch g Notnowcato—Coconut Queen (IRE) **Rowley Racing**
11 COOL FANTASY (IRE), b g One Cool Cat (USA)—Regal Fantasy (IRE) **Stapleford Racing Ltd**
12 DARNATHEAN, b g Librettist (USA)—Meddle **Mr K. Snell**
13 FAIRYINTHEWIND (IRE), ch f Indian Haven—Blue Daze **Spittinginthewind Partnership**
14 SONG OF JOY (IRE), b f Oratorio (IRE)—Wondrous Joy **Mr M. J. Hyson**
15 SYMPHONY STAR (IRE), b f Amadeus Wolf—Bezant (IRE) **Mr K. Snell**

TWO-YEAR-OLDS

16 GLOBAL LEADER (IRE), b c 17/3 Dark Angel (IRE)—
Headborough Lass (IRE) (Invincible Spirit (IRE)) (98521) **Dr J. S. Kinnear**
17 KROSSKINA (IRE), b f 19/4 Cape Cross (IRE)—
Dievotchkina (IRE) (Bluebird (USA)) (72000) **Stapleford Racing Ltd**
18 SPIRIT MAN, b c 19/2 Manduro (GER)—World Spirit (Agnes World (USA)) (25000) **Stapleford Racing Ltd**
19 TRUE SPIRIT, b c 16/3 Shamardal (USA)—Petonellajill (Petong) (65000) **Mr K. Snell**

Other Owners: Mr A. P. Burlton, Mrs S. I. D'Arcy, Mr R. J. Delnevo, Mrs J. Harris, P. Lupson, Mr J. W. Lupson, Mrs D. L. Smyth.

Assistant Trainer: Sue D'Arcy

---

154 MR LUKE DACE, Billingshurst
Postal: **Copped Hall Farm, Okehurst Lane, Billingshurst, West Sussex, RH14 9HR**
Contacts: **OFFICE (01403) 780889 FAX (01403) 780889 MOBILE (07949) 401085**
E-MAIL **lukedace@yahoo.co.uk WEBSITE www.lukedace.co.uk**

1 AMERICAN SPIN, 8, ch g Groom Dancer (USA)—Sea Vixen **Mr G. Collacott**
2 DALHAAN (USA), 7, b g Fusaichi Pegasus (USA)—Khazayin (USA) **Copped Hall Farm & Stud**

MR LUKE DACE—continued

   3 EASTER LAD, 8, b g Shahrastani (USA)—Frozen Pipe **Copped Hall Farm & Stud**
   4 HIP HIP HOORAY, 6, ch m Monsieur Bond (IRE)—Birthday Belle **M. C. S. D. Racing Partnership**
   5 NUBA (IRE), 4, b f Exceed And Excel (AUS)—Little Doll **Copped Hall Farm & Stud**
   6 SPIRITUAL ART, 6, b m Invincible Spirit (IRE)—Oatey **Miss R. Kennedy**
   7 TARGET SCORE, 4, b g Zamindar (USA)—Shoot **J. D. Sells**
   8 WHERE'S JOSIE, 5, b m Josr Algarhoud (IRE)—Just Warning **Miss J. W. Hawkins**

Other Owners: L. A. Dace, Mrs L. J. Dace, B. J. McClean, Mrs M. B. McClean.

Assistant Trainer: Mrs L Dace

---

155 MR KEITH DALGLEISH, Carluke
Postal: **Belstane Racing Stables, Carluke, Lanarkshire, ML8 5HN**
Contacts: **PHONE (01555) 773335 FAX (01555) 772243 MOBILE (07584) 092939**
E-MAIL keith@belstaneracing.net

   1 BLOWN IT (USA), 6, b br g More Than Ready (USA)—Short Shadow (USA) **David Savala**
   2 CADGERS BRIG, 4, ch g Halling (USA)—Burghmuir (IRE) **J. F. Allan**
   3 CHOOKIE AVON, 5, ch g Avonbridge—Lady of Windsor (IRE) **Carleton Boys Of Carlisle**
   4 CHOOKIE HAMILTON, 8, ch g Compton Place—Lady of Windsor (IRE) **Raeburn Brick Limited**
   5 CHOOKIE ROYALE, 4, ch g Monsieur Bond (IRE)—Lady of Windsor (IRE) **Raeburn Brick Limited**
   6 DOC HAY (USA), 5, b br g Elusive Quality (USA)—Coherent (USA) **Mr S. Laffan**
   7 FREQUENCY, 5, br g Starcraft (NZ)—Soundwave **Mrs F. E. Mitchell**
   8 HINTON ADMIRAL, 8, b g Spectrum (IRE)—Shawanni **William Brand & Gordon Mcdowall**
   9 KHANDAQ (USA), 5, b g Gulch (USA)—Jadarah (USA) **G. McDowall**
  10 MASTER OF DANCE (IRE), 5, ch h Noverre (USA)—Shambodia (USA) **G. McDowall**
  11 MUNSARIM (IRE), 5, b g Shamardal (USA)—Etizaaz (USA) **Gordon Leckie**
  12 MUSTAFEED (USA), 4, b br g Distorted Humor (USA)—Word of Mouth (USA) **Mr Thamer Al Daihani**
  13 SO WISE (USA), 4, b g Elusive Quality (USA)—Intercontinental **Mr S. Laffan**

THREE-YEAR-OLDS

  14 ACT YOUR SHOE SIZE, b f Librettist (USA)—Howards Heroine (IRE) **G. McDowall**
  15 JOSHUA THE FIRST, br c Kheleyf (USA)—Newkeylets **Newkeylets**
  16 LUCTOR EMERGO (IRE), b g Amadeus Wolf—Batilde (IRE) **G. McDowall**
  17 SONSIE LASS, b f Refuse To Bend (IRE)—Rapsgate (IRE) **S. Morrison**
  18 SOUND ADVICE, b c Echo of Light—Flylowflylong (IRE) **G L S Partnership**
  19 STONEFIELD FLYER, b c Kheleyf (USA)—Majestic Diva (IRE) **Mr G. R. Leckie**

TWO-YEAR-OLDS

  20 Ch f 13/4 Sakhee's Secret—Flylowflylong (IRE) (Danetime (IRE)) **G L S Partnership**
  21 HELLO GORGEOUS, b f 29/1 Phoenix Reach (IRE)—Roman Fun (IRE) (Peintre Celebre (USA)) **Mr R Hyndman**
  22 B c 11/4 Byron—Howards Heroine (IRE) (Danehill Dancer (USA)) **Mr G. McDowall**
  23 Ch f 18/4 Sakhee's Secret—Lady of Windsor (IRE) (Woods of Windsor (USA)) **Raeburn Brick Limited**
  24 Gr f 17/1 Royal Applause—Lady Xara (Xaar) (4500) **The Crown Lanark**
  25 B c 10/4 Refuse To Bend (IRE)—Rapsgate (IRE) (Mozart (IRE)) **S. Morrison**
  26 B c 17/2 Strategic Prince—Silk Meadow (IRE) (Barathea (IRE)) (25000) **Mrs Janice MacPherson**
  27 B c 26/2 Jeremy—Twilight Belle (IRE) (Fasliyev (USA)) (12000) **Mrs Janice MacPherson**

Other Owners: William Brand, Colin Davidson, Pat Docherty, Alisdair Fletcher, Robin Galbraith, John Hutton, Robert Hyndman, Janice MacPherson, Billy McNeil, Billy Muir, David Raeburn, Jim Raeburn.

Assistant Trainer: Kevin Dalgleish

Jockey (flat): Joe Fanning.

---

156 MR NEALE DALTON, Shifnal
Postal: **Sutton House Farm, Sutton Maddock, Shifnal, Shropshire, TF11 9NF**
Contacts: **PHONE (01952) 730656 FAX (01952) 730261 MOBILE (07831) 555351**
E-MAIL neale.dalton@farming.co.uk

   1 CELTIC BALLAD (IRE), 6, br g Celtic Swing—Birdsong (IRE) **J. N. Dalton**
   2 GLIDEWELL, 10, b g Gildoran—Throw In Your Hand **J. N. Dalton**
   3 HIHARRY, 4, b g Sir Harry Lewis (USA)—Ryoshi **J. N. Dalton**

MR NEALE DALTON—continued

  4 PLAYFUL GIRL (IRE), 4, b f Byron—Feminine Touch (IRE) **J. N. Dalton**
  5 PRIME DESIGN (IRE), 7, b m Blueprint (IRE)—Rare Vintage (IRE) **J. N. Dalton**

Other Owners: A.N. Dalton, Mrs C.A. Dalton.

---

157   **MR HENRY DALY, Ludlow**
Postal: **Downton Hall Stables, Ludlow, Shropshire, SY8 3DX**
Contacts: OFFICE (01584) 873688 FAX (01584) 873525 MOBILE (07720) 074544
E-MAIL henry@henrydaly.co.uk WEBSITE www.henrydaly.co.uk

  1 AMA JIMA, 5, b m Bollin Eric—Silken Pearls **P. E. Truscott**
  2 ARCTIC BEN (IRE), 8, gr g Beneficial—Hurst Flyer **Mrs A. W. Timpson**
  3 ART BROKER (IRE), 6, b g Pivotal—La Gandilie (FR) **M. C. Stoddart**
  4 ARTICULATE (IRE), 7, b g Definite Article—Quare Dream's (IRE) **H. D. J. Daly**
  5 CASTLE CONFLICT (IRE), 7, b g Close Conflict (USA)—Renty (IRE) **Strachan, Clarke, Gabb, Corbett & Salwey**
  6 COBBLER'S QUEEN (IRE), 8, br m Presenting—Lareine d'anjou (FR) **Mrs A. W. Timpson**
  7 5, B g Heron Island (IRE)—Cool Merenda (IRE) **Mrs R. Strachan**
  8 FENNEY MILL, 5, b m Presenting—Fenney Spring **The Wadeley Partnership**
  9 FIDELOR (FR), 6, b g Sagacity (FR)—Fille Fidele (FR) **R. M. Kirkland**
10 FRANCESA, 7, b m Silver Patriarch (IRE)—Franciscaine (FR) **The Glazeley Partnership 2**
11 GROVE PRIDE, 7, b g Double Trigger (IRE)—Dara's Pride (IRE) **T. J. Hemmings**
12 INGA BIRD, 7, ch g Karinga Bay—Girlzone (IRE) **Mr M. Stoddart & The Hon Mr A. Vestey**
13 KINGSMERE, 7, b g King's Theatre (IRE)—Lady Emily **Hamer & Hawkes**
14 LONGITUDE, 5, b g Kayf Tara—Sail By The Stars **T. F. F. Nixon**
15 LORD GRANTHAM (IRE), 5, b g Definite Article—Last of Her Line **T. F. F. Nixon**
16 MASTER SOMERVILLE, 10, b g Alflora (IRE)—Lucy Glitters **Mrs A. Churton**
17 MR ROBINSON (FR), 5, b g Robin des Pres (FR)—Alberade (FR) **Neville Statham & Family**
18 NO DUFFER, 5, ch g Karinga Bay—Dolly Duff **Mr D. C. Robey**
19 ORDRE DE BATAILLE (FR), 10, gr g Ungaro (GER)—Hache de Guerre (FR) **Mrs A. W. Timpson**
20 PEARLYSTEPS, 9, ch g Alflora (IRE)—Pearly-B (FR) **The Glazeley Partnership**
21 PICKAMUS (FR), 9, gr g April Night (FR)—Duchesse du Cochet (FR) **Neville Statham & Family**
22 POSSOL (FR), 9, b g Robin des Pres (FR)—Alberade (FR) **Neville Statham & Family**
23 QUENTIN COLLONGES (FR), 8, gr g Dom Alco (FR)—Grace Collonges (FR) **Neville Statham & Family**
24 ROCKITEER (IRE), 9, b g Rudimentary (USA)—Party Woman (IRE) **Michael O'Flynn & John Nesbitt**
25 SAFRAN DE COTTE (FR), 6, gr g Dom Alco (FR)—Vanille de Cotte (FR) **Mrs A. W. Timpson**
26 SANDYNOW (IRE), 7, ch g Old Vic—Kasterlee (FR) **The Hon Mrs M. J. Heber-Percy**
27 4, B g Bollin Eric—Silken Pearls **P.E. Truscott**
28 STACCATO VALTAT (FR), 6, gr g Fragrant Mix (IRE)—Harmonie de Valtat (FR) **H. D. J. Daly**
29 SUNSETTEN (IRE), 8, b g Tendulkar (USA)—Rosy Affair (IRE) **M. C. Stoddart**
30 SURE THING (FR), 6, b g Ragmar (FR)—Harpe (FR) **H. D. J. Daly**
31 4, B g Oscar (IRE)—Taneys Leader (IRE) **Henry Daly**
32 THE FALKLANDER, 8, gr g Silver Patriarch (IRE)—Island Mist **J. B. Sumner**
33 TIMPO (FR), 9, ch g Baby Turk—Faensa (FR) **Mrs A. W. Timpson**
34 TOBY BELCH (IRE), 9, ch g Presenting—Peptic Lady (IRE) **Strachan, Griffith, Gabb, Lewis & Lawson**
35 TOOT SWEET (IRE), 5, b m Generous (IRE)—Cresswell Native (IRE) **A. J. Haden**
36 UP TO THE MARK, 7, b g Mark of Esteem (IRE)—Villella **Strachan, Gabb, Griffith, Harford, Lewis & Graham**
37 UPBEAT COBBLER (FR), 4, gr f Brier Creek (USA)—Jade de Chalamont (FR) **Mrs A. W. Timpson**
38 WESSEX KING (IRE), 8, b g Second Empire (IRE)—Winchester Queen (IRE) **Mrs D. P. G. Flory**
39 WILD CARD, 5, b g First Trump—Vanina II (FR) **E. R. Hanbury**
40 WINDS AND WAVES (IRE), 6, b g Alflora (IRE)—Sail By The Stars **T. F. F. Nixon**
41 YOUM JAMIL (USA), 5, gr ro g Mizzen Mast (USA)—
                           Millie's Choice (IRE) **Strachan, Stephens, Gabb, Griffith, Todd**
42 ZAHIRAH MOON, 5, b m Grape Tree Road—Lunasa (IRE) **Ludlow Racing Partnership**

THREE-YEAR-OLDS

43 KAYFLEUR, b f Kayf Tara—Combe Florey **Neville Statham, Bart Hellyer**
44 VICE ET VERTU (FR), b g Network (GER)—Duchesse du Cochet (FR) **Neville Statham & Family**

Other Owners: Mrs S. T. Clarke, Mrs P Corbett, Mrs Henry Daly, Lord Daresbury, Mrs Roger Gabb, Mrs Douglas Graham, Mrs J. G. Griffith, Mr C. M. Hamer, Mr H. Harford, Mr M. Hawkes, Mr Peter Holt, Mr W. Jenks, Mrs A. S. Lawson, Mrs David Lewis, Mr Richard Mapp, Mr John Nesbitt, Mr Michael O'Flynn, Mr H. Salwey, Mr Neville Statham, Mrs P. Statham, Mrs Nicholas Stephens, Mr Michael Stoddart, Mrs Richard Strachan, The Hon Mrs A. H. Todd, The Hon. Arthur Vestey.

Assistant Trainer: Alastair Ralph

Jockey (NH): Richard Johnson, Andrew Tinkler. **Conditional:** Jake Greenall.

158 MR JAMES DANAHAR, Tirley
Postal: **Walkers Slough, Ledbury Road, Tirley, Gloucestershire, GL19 4EU**

1 MAYOR OF KILCOCK, 9, b g King's Theatre (IRE)—Disallowed (IRE) **J. A. Danahar**
2 MEMORIES OF GOLD (IRE), 12, b m Carroll House—Sweet Harmony (IRE) **J. A. Danahar**

159 MR PHILLIP DANDO, Peterston-Super-Ely
Postal: **Springfield Court, Peterston-Super-Ely, Cardiff, South Glamorgan, CF5 6LG**
Contacts: PHONE **(01446) 760012** MOBILE **(07872) 965395**

1 AUTUMN HAZE, 7, b g Chaddleworth (IRE)—Kristal Haze **P. C. Dando**
2 ILLEGALE (IRE), 6, b m Poliglote—Pinkai (IRE) **Hanford's Chemist Ltd**
3 MOORLANDS JACK, 7, b g Cloudings (IRE)—Sandford Springs (USA) **Mrs L. M. Williams**
4 MOORLANDS MIST, 5, gr g Fair Mix (IRE)—Sandford Springs (USA) **Mrs L. M. Williams**
5 RAINBOW HAZE, 6, b g Rainbow High—Kristal Haze **Mr Phillip Dando & Dr Michael Armitage**

Other Owners: Dr M. G. Armitage.

Assistant Trainer: Miss Rebecca Dando

160 MR VICTOR DARTNALL, Barnstaple
Postal: **Higher Shutscombe Farm, Charles, Brayford, Barnstaple, Devon, EX32 7PU**
Contacts: PHONE **(01598) 710280** FAX **(01598) 710708** MOBILE **(07974) 374272**
E-MAIL **victor@victordartnallracing.com** WEBSITE **www.victordartnallracing.com**

1 ACE HIGH, 8, b g Kayf Tara—Celtic Native (IRE) **All The Aces**
2 AMBION WOOD, 8, b g Oscar (IRE)—Dorans Grove **Mr O. C. R. Wynne & Mrs S. J. Wynne**
3 5, B m Milan—Blackwater Bay (IRE) **Mrs L. M. Northover**
4 5, B h Waky Nao—Broadcast **Unregistered Partnership**
5 CALICO ROSE, 8, ch m Karinga Bay—Sprig Muslin **D. G. Staddon**
6 CONNAK (IRE), 10, ch g Pasternak—Call Me Connie (IRE) **Mr W. O. P. Miles**
7 DANCING MIST (IRE), 9, gr g Shernazar—Daddy's Girl (IRE) **Willis, Rich & Russian Partners**
8 EXMOOR RANGER (IRE), 10, ch g Grand Plaisir—Slyguff Torus (IRE) **The Rangers Partnership**
9 FLOWER HAVEN, 10, b m Dr Fong (USA)—Daisy May **Gentlemen Don't Work on Mondays**
10 FRESHER FISHING (IRE), 8, gr g Luso—Turbet Lass (IRE) **Victor Dartnall Racing Club**
11 GENEROUS BEAUTY, 6, b m Generous (IRE)—Ruby Star (IRE) **A. Hordle**
12 GILES CROSS (IRE), 10, b g Saddlers' Hall (IRE)—Mystockings **K.C.M.S Partnership**
13 GREAT GUSTO (IRE), 6, ch g Moscow Society (USA)—Warm Front **Bray Valley Partners**
14 HENRY HOOK (IRE), 8, ch g Presenting—Swing The Lead (IRE) **Under The Radar**
15 HENRY KING (IRE), 8, gr g Great Palm (USA)—Presenting Shares (IRE) **Mrs C. M. Barber**
16 HONOURABLE ARTHUR (IRE), 9, br g Presenting—Ronkino (IRE) **Miss A. J. Woolley**
17 5, B g Baryshnikov (AUS)—Kimmeridge Bay **Mr G. Dartnall**
18 MAGOT DE GRUGY (FR), 12, b g Tzar Rodney (FR)—Hirlish (FR) **Mrs S. De Wilde**
19 MIC'S DELIGHT (IRE), 8, b g Witness Box (USA)—Warrior Princess (IRE) **The Higos Hopefuls**
20 MIGHTY MONTY, 7, br g Overbury (IRE)—Ruby Star (IRE) **A. Hordle**
21 MOLESKIN (IRE), 9, b g Saddlers' Hall (IRE)—Magic Gale (IRE) **Mrs C. M. Barber**
22 MR BACHSTER (IRE), 7, b g Bach (IRE)—Warrior Princess (IRE) **The Second Brayford Partnership**
23 MR HOOPER, 6, b g Karinga Bay—Rempstone **Mrs J. E. Purdie**
24 MYSOCKS, 6, ch g Lahib (USA)—Mystockings **Mrs K. Birchenhough**
25 NEMETAN (FR), 11, ch g Port Lyautey (FR)—Annabelle Treveene (FR) **Mrs S. De Wilde**
26 NICTO DE BEAUCHENE (FR), 11, b g Nashamaa—Chipie d'angron (FR) **Mrs S. De Wilde**
27 PHILADELPHUS, 7, ch g Dancing Spree (USA)—Mandalay Miss **Dorset Racing**
28 6, B g Karinga Bay—Quiet Confidence (IRE) **Unregistered Partnership**
29 RANDJO (IRE), 7, b g Network (GER)—Daytona II (FR) **Mrs S. De Wilde**
30 REGAL PRESENCE (IRE), 5, ch g Presenting—Lucy Lodge (IRE)
31 REQUIN (FR), 7, b br g Video Rock (FR)—Funkia (FR) **Mrs S. De Wilde**
32 RICHARD'S SUNDANCE (IRE), 10, b g Saddlers' Hall (IRE)—
Celestial Rose (IRE) **Elizabeth Masterman & Sara Vernon**
33 ROUDOUDOU VILLE (FR), 7, b br g Winning Smile (FR)—Jadoudy Ville (FR) **Mrs S. De Wilde**
34 RUGGED JACK (FR), 5, b g Bonbon Rose (FR)—A Plus Ma Puce (FR) **G. D. Hake**
35 SEEBRIGHT, 5, b g Milan—Aranga (IRE) **Mr G. Dartnall**
36 SEIGNEUR DE GUERRE (FR), 6, b b g Alberto Giacometti (IRE)—
Hache de Guerre (FR) **T D J Syder & Richard Hobson**
37 SHAMMICK BOY (IRE), 7, b g Craigsteel—Dulcet Music (IRE) **First Brayford Partnership**

MR VICTOR DARTNALL—continued

38 **SIR WINSTON (IRE)**, 10, b g Supreme Leader—Aliandbet Jewel (IRE) **D. G. Staddon**
39 **SLEEPING CITY (FR)**, 5, b br g Sleeping Car (FR)—City Prospect (FR) **Victor Dartnall Racing Club**
40 **STARSKY DES MOTTES (FR)**, 6, b g Useful (FR)—Camille des Mottes (FR) **O. P. J. Meli**
41 **SWALING (IRE)**, 6, b g Oscar (IRE)—Princess Supreme (IRE) **Mrs C. M. Barber**
42 **TOLKEINS TANGO (IRE)**, 4, ch g Beneficial—Aule (FR)
43 **TUROYAL (FR)**, 4, gr g Turgeon (USA)—Quelle Est Belle (FR) **Unregistered Partnership**

Other Owners: Mr M. Bevan, Mrs Kay Birchenhough, Mrs Jean Browning, Mr Neil Buckland, Mr T. G. Cowell, Mr M. W. Cox, Mr V. R. A. Dartnall, Mr G. A. Dartnall, Mr Jeffery Edelman, Mr Peter Emery, Mrs Jill Emery, Mrs Carolyn Fisher, Mrs D. J. Fleming, Mrs Mary Fletcher, Mrs P. P. S. Forbes, Mr I. F. Gosden, Mrs James Grazebrook, Mr B. Greening, Mr G. D. Hake, Mr J. M. Haley, Mr N. P. Haley, Mrs Janine Hillary, Mr Bill Hinge, Mr Robert Hobson, Mr G. Leatherbarrow, Mr Herbert Malek, Mrs Elizabeth Masterman, Mr J. de Meo, Mr Paul Nicholls, Mrs L. M. Northover, Mrs Rowan Peto, Mr Nigel Rich, Mr M. W. Richards, Mr P. A. Roberts, Mr T. Saye, Mr John Searchfield, Mr Romilly Stuart-Jervis, Mr T. D. J. Syder, Mrs Sara Vernon, Mr R. Watts, Mr C. R. Wilde, Mr David Willis, Mrs S. J. Wynne, Mr O. C. R. Wynne.

Assistant Trainer: G A Dartnall

Jockey (NH): Denis O'Regan, Andrew Glassonbury. **Conditional:** Ed Glassonbury. **Amateur:** Mr Josh Guerriero.

---

161 MR TOM DASCOMBE, Malpas
Postal: **Manor House Stables, Malpas, Cheshire, SY14 8AD**
Contacts: **PHONE (01948) 820485 FAX (01948) 820495 MOBILE (07973) 511664**
E-MAIL tom@manorhousestables.com WEBSITE www.manorhousestables.com

1 **ADORABLE CHOICE (IRE)**, 4, b br f Choisir (AUS)—Burnin' Memories (USA) **Mr J. D. Brown**
2 **BALLISTA (IRE)**, 4, b g Majestic Missile (IRE)—Ancient Secret **Well Done Top Man Partnership**
3 **BLUE JACK**, 7, b g Cadeaux Genereux—Fairy Flight (IRE) **A. Black & M. Owen**
4 **BROUHAHA**, 8, b g Bahhare (USA)—Top of The Morning **Manor House Racing Club**
5 **BROWN PANTHER**, 4, b c Shirocco (GER)—Treble Heights (IRE) **Owen Promotions Limited**
6 **CHOSEN CHARACTER (IRE)**, 4, b c Choisir (AUS)—Out of Thanks (IRE) **Aykroyd & Sons Limited**
7 **FANTASY FRY**, 4, b g Avonbridge—Footlight Fantasy (USA) **A. D. Solomon**
8 **HUNG PARLIAMENT (FR)**, 4, b g Numerous (USA)—Sensational Mover (USA) **The Tipperary Partners**
9 **JONNY MUDBALL**, 6, b g Oasis Dream—Waypoint **Woodgate Family**
10 **JULIUS GEEZER (IRE)**, 4, b g Antonius Pius (USA)—Victoria's Secret (IRE) **Basing Bellman Stroud**
11 **JUNOOB**, 4, b g Haafhd—Faydah (USA) **A. D. Solomon**
12 **LIBYS DREAM (IRE)**, 4, b f Invincible Spirit (IRE)—Perilous Pursuit (USA) **Ms A. Quinn**
13 **OLLIANNA (IRE)**, 4, b f Majestic Missile (IRE)—Aspired (IRE) **T. G. Dascombe**
14 **RHYTHM OF LIGHT**, 4, b f Beat Hollow—Luminda (IRE) **Lowe Silver Deal**
15 **RICZAR**, 4, b f Intikhab (USA)—Tharwa (IRE) **Mr R. Woods**

THREE-YEAR-OLDS

16 **ANACONDA (FR)**, b c Anabaa (USA)—Porretta (IRE) **The MHS 8X8 Partnership**
17 **ANTON CHIGURH**, b c Oasis Dream—Barathiki **Panarea Racing**
18 **BASANTEE**, ch f Lucky Story (USA)—Soft Touch (IRE) **The MHS 8X8 Partnership**
19 **BEAR BEHIND (IRE)**, b c Kodiac—Gerobies Girl (USA) **Bellman Black Marantelli Owen**
20 **BROCKWELL**, b c Singspiel (IRE)—Noble Plum (IRE) **South Wind Racing 3**
21 **BRUBECK (IRE)**, b c Red Clubs (IRE)—Cheeky Weeky **Mrs P. Good**
22 **CABOODLE**, b f Bahamian Bounty—Bowness **Mr & Mrs G. Middlebrook**
23 **CHOCOLATE PURSUITS**, ch f Pastoral Pursuits—Yes Dear **S. E. Roberts**
24 **COOL HAND LUKE (IRE)**, br g Le Vie Dei Colori—Thelma Louise (IRE) **Mr P. L. Mousley**
25 **DALIANCE (IRE)**, ch c Dalakhani (IRE)—Everlasting Love **The Illusionists**
26 **DECISION BY ONE**, ch c Bahamian Bounty—Intellibet One **The Half A Third Partnership**
27 **ELECTRIC QATAR**, b c Pastoral Pursuits—Valandraud (USA) **A. Black & M. Owen**
28 **EQUALIZER**, b c Authorized (IRE)—Octaluna **L. A. Bellman**
29 **GAUL WOOD (IRE)**, b c Amadeus Wolf—Emly Express (IRE) **Star Sports**
30 **GIN TWIST**, b f Invincible Spirit (IRE)—Winding (USA) **Manor House Stables LLP**
31 **KENNY POWERS**, b c Vital Equine (IRE)—Alexander Ballet **First Manor**
32 **MARFORD MISSILE (IRE)**, b g Majestic Missile (IRE)—Khawafi **The MHS 4X10 Partnership**
33 **MY PRETTY**, b f Byron—Veiled Beauty (USA) **A. W. Black**
34 **PELICAN ROCK (IRE)**, b g Amadeus Wolf—Darby Shaw (IRE) **L. A. Bellman**
35 **ROMAN SEAL (IRE)**, b f Holy Roman Emperor (IRE)—Gilded Vanity (IRE) **Bellman Black Owen**

MR TOM DASCOMBE—continued

36 **SIR TREVOR (IRE)**, b g Refuse To Bend (IRE)—Joyfullness (USA) **Mr D. R. Passant**
37 **SWITCHER (IRE)**, b f Whipper (USA)—Bahamamia **The Whipper Partnership**
38 **TOMWAY**, b c Kyllachy—Lake Melody **Mr & Mrs W. Rooney**
39 **VIOLA D'AMOUR (IRE)**, b f Teofilo (IRE)—Dame's Violet (IRE) **L. A. Bellman**
40 **WINTER HILL**, b f Three Valleys (USA)—White Turf (GER) **The MHS 4X10 Partnership**

TWO-YEAR-OLDS

41 Ch c 29/4 Mount Nelson—Alexia Reveuse (IRE) (Dr Devious (IRE)) (52380) **Manor House Stables LLP**
42 B c 5/3 Bahamian Bounty—Amazon Beauty (IRE) (Wolfhound (USA)) (60000) **Mr & Mrs W. Rooney**
43 **ATTENSHUN (IRE)**, ch c 15/3 Salute The Sarge (USA)—
                            Southern House (IRE) (Paris House) (26272) **The Folly Racers**
44 B f 4/2 Red Clubs (IRE)—Baldovina (Tale of The Cat (USA)) (16000) **A. W. Black**
45 **BARRACUDA BOY (IRE)**, b c 13/2 Bahamian Bounty—
                           Madame Boulangere (Royal Applause) (64761) **L. A. Bellman**
46 **BONNE AMIE (FR)**, b f 6/3 Elusive City (USA)—Sintra (IRE) (Kris) (28735) **L. A. Bellman**
47 **BRAVE ACCLAIM (IRE)**, b c 30/4 Acclamation—
                         Indienne (IRE) (Indian Ridge) (57470) **Manor House Stables LLP**
48 **CANADIAN RED**, b c 4/3 Sleeping Indian—
                         Pontressina (USA) (St Jovite (USA)) (7619) **The MHS 4X10 Partnership**
49 Ch c 27/3 Captain Rio—Chaukao (IRE) (Inchinor) (7388) **The MHS 2012 Olympic Partnership**
50 **COOL RUNNINGS (IRE)**, gr c 15/3 Dalakhani (IRE)—
                         Aguinaga (USA) (Machiavellian) (40000) **Siwan & David Ward**
51 **CUBAN TASH**, b c 3/4 Exceed And Excel (AUS)—Crinkle (IRE) (Distant Relative) (53365) **The Cuban Partnership**
52 **DOUBLE DISCOUNT (IRE)**, b c 26/1 Invincible Spirit (IRE)—
                         Bryanstown Girl (IRE) (Kalanisi) (57470) **L. A. Bellman**
53 B c 6/4 Majestic Missile (IRE)—
                         Ginger Not Blonde (USA) (Atticus (USA)) (16420) **The MHS 2012 Olympic Partnership**
54 **HURRY HOME POPPA (IRE)**, b c 2/3 Holy Roman Emperor (IRE)—
                         My Renee (USA) (Kris S (USA)) (28735) **Mr D. Ward**
55 B f 9/2 Dutch Art—Ile Deserte (Green Desert (USA)) (38095) **M. Owen & M. Williams**
56 B f 21/3 Rakti—Italian Affair (Fumo di Londra (IRE)) (3500) **J. A. Duffy**
57 B c 15/3 Elusive City (USA)—Jamrah (IRE) (Danehill (USA)) (13546) **Manor House Stables LLP**
58 **LORD ASHLEY (IRE)**, ch c 20/3 Iffraaj—Mrs Dalloway (IRE) (Key of Luck (USA)) (29556) **Mr D. R. Passant**
59 Ch f 4/3 Sakhee's Secret—Martha (IRE) (Alhaarth (IRE)) (66297) **Mr P. A. Deal & Mr A. Black**
60 B c 14/2 Pastoral Pursuits—Miss Wells (IRE) (Sadler's Wells) (38095) **Manor House Stables LLP**
61 B f 15/3 Refuse To Bend (IRE)—Munaawashat (IRE) (Marju (IRE)) **J. A. Duffy**
62 Ch c 5/4 Dutch Art—Naomi Wildman (USA) (Kingmambo (USA)) (42857) **Manor House Stables LLP**
63 **NORTHERN STAR (IRE)**, b f 6/2 Montjeu (IRE)—Slow Sand (USA) (Dixieland Band (USA)) (41050) **Mr D. Ward**
64 Ch f 31/3 Nayef (USA)—Patacake Patacake (USA) (Bahri (USA)) **A. W. Black**
65 Ch f 4/3 Bahamian Bounty—Pointed Arch (IRE) (Rock of Gibraltar (IRE)) (9523) **Manor House Stables LLP**
66 **PREMIER STEPS (IRE)**, b f 19/3 Footstepsinthesand—
                         Primissima (GER) (Second Set (IRE)) (22857) **Attenborough Bellman Ingram Lowe**
67 Gr c 9/3 Verglas—Ragtime Blues (IRE) (Grand Lodge (USA)) (13136) **Panarea Racing**
68 Ch c 25/2 Pastoral Pursuits—Rainy Day Song (Persian Bold) (6500) **The MHS 2012 Olympic Partnership**
69 **SAGA LOUT**, b c 2/4 Assertive—Intellibet One (Compton Place) (15238) **L. A. Bellman**
70 B c 31/1 Three Valleys (USA)—Sambarina (IRE) (Victory Note) (9030) **London Market Racing Club**
71 B c 20/4 Red Clubs (IRE)—Satin Cape (IRE) (Cape Cross (IRE)) (11493) **Deva Racing Red Clubs Partnership**
72 **SPIRIT OF PARKES**, gr c 9/4 Fair Mix (IRE)—Lucky Parkes (Full Extent (USA)) **J. Heler**
73 B f 4/4 Mount Nelson—Statua (IRE) (Statoblest) (49260) **Manor House Stables LLP**
74 **STRIPPED BEAR (IRE)**, b f 9/2 Kodiac—
                         Triple Zero (IRE) (Raise A Grand (IRE)) (17142) **The MHS 4X10 Partnership**
75 B c 20/4 Firebreak—Suzie Fong (Dr Fong (USA)) (2500) **The MHS 2012 Olympic Partnership**
76 Ch c 5/2 Dutch Art—Suzuki (IRE) (Barathea (USA)) (27914) **Manor House Stables LLP**
77 **TAMALETTA (IRE)**, ch f 6/3 Tamayuz—Annaletta (Belmez (USA)) (18061) **L. A. Bellman**
78 **THIS IS NICE (IRE)**, ch f 10/3 Exceed And Excel (AUS)—
                         Spanish Quest (Rainbow Quest (USA)) (30476) **L. A. Bellman**
79 B c 28/3 Manduro (GER)—Treble Heights (Unfuwain (USA)) **Owen Promotions Limited**
80 B f 7/5 Singspiel (IRE)—Veiled Beauty (USA) (Royal Academy (USA)) **A. W. Black**
81 B c 25/4 Acclamation—Vintage Tipple (IRE) (Entrepreneur) (47619) **Lowe Silver Deal**
82 Ch f 27/2 Teofilo (IRE)—Welsh Cake (Fantastic Light (USA)) (60000) **Manor House Stables LLP**
83 B f 12/2 Montjeu (IRE)—Wing Stealth (IRE) (Hawk Wing (USA)) (30000) **Manor House Stables LLP**
84 **ZARLA**, b f 2/5 Zamindar (USA)—Ikhteyaar (USA) (Mr Prospector (USA)) (40000) **K. P. Trowbridge**

MR TOM DASCOMBE—continued

Other Owners: N. B. Attenborough, A. M. Basing, R. H. Coombe, Mrs M. Coxon, G. J. Dascombe, Mrs S. A. E. Dascombe, P. A. Deal, M. D. Foster, Mrs J. Foster, Mr D. J. Haddrell, S. J. High, Mrs C. L. Ingram, Mr M. A. Jones, Mr B. Keith, Mr M. J. Lilley, Mr D. J. Lowe, G. A. Lowe, Mr D. I. Lubert, Mr A. K. MacCormack, Mr B. Marantelli, G. Middlebrook, Mrs L. A. Middlebrook, Mr G. Nicholas, Mr D. O'Sullivan, Mrs R. O'Sullivan, Mr M. Owen, Mr C. D. Pritchard, Mr C. R. Pugh, Mr W. Rooney, P. Scholes, Mr G. Shepherd, M. J. Silver, Stoneygate 48 Limited, Mr S. J. Stroud, Ms S. A. Ward, Mr D. A. Ward, Mr M. K. Williams, Mr J. Woodgate, Mr A. W. Woodgate.

Assistant Trainer: Colin Gorman

Jockey (flat): Richard Kingscote, Richard Smith. **Apprentice:** Ross Atkinson. **Amateur:** Mr Nuno Santos.

---

162 MR JOHN DAVIES, Darlington
Postal: Denton Grange, Piercebridge, Darlington, Co. Durham DL2 3TZ
Contacts: **PHONE (01325) 374366 MOBILE (07746) 292782**
E-MAIL johndavieshorses@live.co.uk

1 EVELITH REGENT (IRE), 9, b g Imperial Ballet (IRE)—No Avail (IRE) **J. J. Davies**
2 FINBAR FLYNN, 8, b g Dapper—Clohamon Gossip (IRE) **J. J. Davies**
3 4, B gr f Doyen (IRE)—Nearly Decent **Mr Phillip Taylor**
4 THE OSTEOPATH (IRE), 9, ch g Danehill Dancer (IRE)—Miss Margate (IRE) **Mr Kevin Kirkup**

TWO-YEAR-OLDS

5 Ch f 20/2 Halling (USA)—Crimson Topaz (Hernando (FR)) **Mr Phillip Taylor**
6 Ch f 7/5 Great Palm (USA)—Pleasant Dreams (Sabrehill (USA)) **Mr Christopher Davies**
7 B g 22/4 Millkom—Wedgewood Star (Bishop of Cashel) (1904) **Mr Kevin Kirkup**

Jockey (flat): Paddy Aspell. **Jockey (NH):** Andrew Tinkler.

---

163 MR PAUL DAVIES, Bromyard
Postal: **20 Hatton Park, Bromyard, Herefordshire, HR7 4EY**

1 EMMA SODA, 7, b m Milan—Ms Trude (IRE) **Mr P. S. Davies**

---

164 MISS JOANNA DAVIS, East Garston
Postal: South Cottage, Pounds Farm, East Garston, Hungerford, Berkshire, RG17 7HU
Contacts: **PHONE (01488) 649977 FAX (01488) 649977 MOBILE (07879) 811535**
E-MAIL davisjo_007@hotmail.com WEBSITE www.jodavisracing.com

1 BILLION DOLLAR KID, 7, br g Averti (IRE)—Fredora **Who's The Daddy**
2 BRIGHT DECISION, 6, b g Thowra (FR)—Bright Spangle (IRE) **Miss J. S. Davis**
3 ELIXIR DU LAC, 5, gr m Fair Mix (IRE)—Hutcel Loch **V. R. Bedley**
4 FESTIVAL DREAMS, 7, ch g Largesse—Bright Spangle (IRE) **Oakhedge Racing**
5 GO ANNIE, 4, gr f Proclamation (IRE)—Bright Spangle (IRE) **Lockstone Business Services Ltd**
6 4, B g Let The Lion Roar—Leane (IRE) **Joe Bloggs**
7 NATAANI (IRE), 9, br g Presenting—Clahada Rose (IRE) **Mr A. G. Worth**
8 PASSATO (GER), 8, b g Lando (GER)—Passata (FR) **P. J. Ponting**
9 SGT ROBERTS (IRE), 6, b g Diktat—Ann's Annie (IRE) **Tony Hutchinson & Dave Clayton**

THREE-YEAR-OLDS

10 Gr ro f Proclamation (IRE)—Bright Spangle (IRE) **Lockstone**

Other Owners: Mr M. Bloomfield, Mrs J. Bloomfield, Mr Dave Clayton, Miss J. Davis, Mr A. D. Hutchinson, Mr L. M. Power, Mr Chris Webb.

165 MISS LOUISE DAVIS, Stafford
Postal: **The Stables, Hillcrest, Bradley Lane, Levedale, Stafford, ST18 9AH**
Contacts: **MOBILE (07760) 457293**
E-MAIL vky1971@yahoo.co.uk WEBSITE www.louisedavisracing.co.uk

1 CRYING GAME (IRE), 7, b m Akbar (IRE)—Broken Spirit (IRE) **Miss L. V. Davis**
2 EQUITY RELEASE (IRE), 11, b g Supreme Leader—Loshian (IRE) **Miss L. V. Davis**
3 I'M IN THE PINK (FR), 8, b g Garuda (IRE)—Ahwaki (FR) **Miss L. V. Davis**
4 SECOND BROOK (IRE), 5, b g Celtic Swing—Mur Taasha (USA) **Miss L. V. Davis**
5 SUPREME TEAM (IRE), 9, b g Supreme Leader—La Gazelle (IRE) **Miss L. V. Davis**
6 WELCOME STRANGER, 12, b g Most Welcome—Just Julia **Miss L. V. Davis**

Assistant Trainer: Mr J. Freeman

Conditional: Peter Hatton.

166 MISS ZOE DAVISON, East Grinstead
Postal: **Shovelstrode Racing Stables, Shovelstrode Lane, Ashurstwood, East Grinstead, West Sussex, RH19 3PN**
Contacts: FAX (01342) 323153 MOBILE (07970) 839357 & (07812) 007554
E-MAIL andy01031976@yahoo.co.uk WEBSITE www.shovelstroderacing.co.uk

1 AJOOL (USA), 5, ch m Aljabr (USA)—Tamgeed (USA) **Curl and Newman Partnership**
2 AROWANA (IRE), 4, b f Kodiac—Bali Royal **A. J. Irvine**
3 CANNI THINKAAR (IRE), 11, b g Alhaarth (IRE)—Cannikin (IRE) **B. Ward**
4 CARBIS BAY, 6, b g Deploy—Hi Lily **A. J. Irvine**
5 EJEED (USA), 7, b g Rahy (USA)—Lahan **Mrs J. A. Irvine**
6 FLIXTER, 5, b g King O' The Mana (IRE)—Freedom Weekend (USA) **Mrs D. L. Smith-Hooper**
7 HAMMERWOOD, 6, br g Makbul—Havantadoubt (IRE) **Mr D. P. O'Keeffe**
8 HONORINE DE DUCY (FR), 5, b m Beat All (USA)—Tootsie Galore (USA) **Curl and Newman Partnership**
9 JOHN'S GEM, 7, ch g Silver Patriarch (IRE)—Hollow Legs **Golfguard Limited**
10 JUMEIRAH LIBERTY, 4, ch g Proclamation (IRE)—Gleam of Light (USA) **A. J. Irvine**
11 JUST BEWARE, 10, b m Makbul—Bewails (IRE) **The Secret Circle**
12 LINDSAY'S DREAM, 6, b m Montjeu (IRE)—Lady Lindsay (IRE) **A. J. Irvine**
13 LOSTAYER (IRE), 8, gr g Luso—Kamlass (IRE) **Mr D. P. O'Keeffe**
14 NOZIC (FR), 11, b g Port Lyautey (FR)—Grizilh (FR) **The Lump O'Clock Syndicate**
15 RIVIERE RUBY, 5, b m King O' The Mana (IRE)—Madonna da Rossi **Mrs D. L. Smith-Hooper**
16 SHERJAWY (IRE), 8, b g Diktat—Arruhan (IRE) **Charlie's Starrs**
17 SID, 4, ch g Needwood Blade—Easter Moon (FR) **The Vodka Racing Partnership**
18 SUPER FRANK (IRE), 9, b g Cape Cross (IRE)—Lady Joshua (IRE) **Mr M Sharp Mr T Brightwell**
19 SUSSEX LASS, 7, b m Beat All (USA)—Emma-Lyne **Sussex Racing**
20 TCHANG GOON (FR), 8, b g Marathon (USA)—Royal Hostess (IRE) **J. E. Belsey**
21 TOMS RIVER TESS (IRE), 4, b f Kodiac—Sonorous (IRE) **Charlie's Starrs**
22 TURBULENT PRIEST, 4, b c Storming Home—Hymn Book (IRE) **Miss P. I. Westbrook**

THREE-YEAR-OLDS

23 MARIE'S FANTASY, b f Whipper (USA)—My American Beauty **D. J. Bearman**

Other Owners: Mr S. W. Bain, Mr A. W. Bain, Mr A. R. Brightwell, S. J. Clare, Miss Z. C. Davison, L. D. Hand, Mrs A. Lyndoe-Tavistock, Mr R. F. Newman, Mr M. Sharp, A. N. Waters, Mr J. Whinfield-Curl.

Assistant Trainer: A. Irvine

Jockey (flat): Sam Hitchcott. **Conditional:** Gemma Gracey-Davison. **Apprentice:** Ross Atkinson. **Amateur:** Mr H. G. Miller.

167 MR ANTHONY DAY, Hinckley
Postal: **Wolvey Fields Farm, Coalpit Lane, Wolvey, Hinckley, Leicestershire, LE10 3HD**
Contacts: PHONE (01455) 220225 MOBILE (07546) 593485
E-MAIL kathy197@btinternet.com

1 OHMS LAW, 7, b g Overbury (IRE)—Polly Live Wire **Mrs K. D. Day**
2 SHESLIKETHEWIND, 4, b f Central Park (IRE)—Velvet Leaf **Mr A.A. Day**
3 STARLIT EVE, 4, br f Samraan (USA)—Kissed By Moonlite **Mrs K. D. Day**

Assistant Trainer: Mrs K.D. Day

168 **MISS LISA DAY, Pontypool**
Postal: Well Cottage, Penyhroel, Pontypool, Gwent

1 BABE HEFFRON (IRE), 11, ch g Topanoora—Yellow Ochre (IRE) **Miss L. Day**
2 BOBBYBOARD (IRE), 6, b g Chevalier—Nilousha **Miss L. Day**
3 STRAND LINE (IRE), 12, b g Supreme Leader—Good Credentials **Miss L. Day**

169 **MR ED DE GILES, Ledbury**
Postal: Lilly Hall Farm, Little Marcle, Ledbury, Herefordshire, HR8 2LD
Contacts: PHONE (01531) 637369 MOBILE (07811) 388345

1 A HEART BEATS ON (IRE), 6, b g Kaieteur (USA)—Helen's Sisters (IRE) **GLMM**
2 AJZAL (IRE), 8, b g Alhaarth (IRE)—Alkaffeyeh (IRE) **John Manser & Claire de Giles**
3 BIOGRAPHICAL (USA), 4, b br g Dynaformer (USA)—Tell It (USA) **T. Gould**
4 BY IMPLICATION, 4, br g Cacique (IRE)—Insinuate (USA) **Chester Racing Club Ltd**
5 COLORADO GOLD, 4, ch g Dubawi (IRE)—Yanka (USA) **Mr P. J. Manser**
6 COMMAND MARSHAL (FR), 9, b g Commands (AUS)—Marsakara (IRE) **E. B. de Giles**
7 DAY ONE, 11, ch g Daylami (IRE)—Myself **E. B. de Giles**
8 FLAMEOFTHEFOREST (IRE), 5, b g Danehill Dancer (IRE)—Coralita (IRE) **Mrs H. McAlister**
9 GALLANT EAGLE (IRE), 5, ch g Hawk Wing (USA)—Generous Gesture (IRE) **Mr S. R. Sandat**
10 GENTLEMAN IS BACK (USA), 4, b br g Johannesburg (USA)—Torros Straits (USA) **T. Gould**
11 GO NANI GO, 6, b g Kyllachy—Go Between **T. Gould**
12 GREEK ISLANDS (IRE), 4, b g Oasis Dream—Serisia (FR) **Mr A. Frost**
13 HANDHELD, 5, ch g Observatory (USA)—Kid Gloves **Mrs S. Smith**
14 KINGSGATE CHOICE (IRE), 5, b g Choisir (AUS)—Kenema (IRE) **T. Gould**
15 LIVING IT LARGE (FR), 5, ch g Bertolini (USA)—Dilag (IRE) **T. Gould**
16 LUCKY BREEZE (IRE), 5, b m Key of Luck (USA)—Lasting Chance (USA) **C. C. Shand Kydd**
17 MAHADEE (IRE), 7, br g Cape Cross (IRE)—Rafiya **2 1/2 - 3 1/2 Club**
18 MINGUN BELL (USA), 5, b g Mingun (USA)—Miss Tippins (USA) **Blackham & Gould Partnership**
19 MUTANAKER (IRE), 5, b g Cape Cross (IRE)—Purple Haze (IRE) **Mr D. J. Greenall**
20 NAABEGHA, 5, ch g Muhtathir—Hawafiz **Tight Lines Partnership**
21 ORTHODOX LAD, 4, ch g Monsieur Bond (IRE)—Ashantiana **T. Gould**
22 PRESENT TO YOU (IRE), 7, ch g Presenting—Charm of Toulon (IRE) **The Centaur Group Partnership III**
23 PRINCE OF DREAMS, 5, b g Sadler's Wells (USA)—Questina (FR) **Jennifer & Alex Viall**
24 SPA'S DANCER (IRE), 5, b g Danehill Dancer (USA)—Serisia **Spa T. Gould**
25 STYLE MARGI (IRE), 4, b f Desert Style (IRE)—Margi (FR) **E. B. de Giles**
26 SUMMERINTHECITY (IRE), 5, ch g Indian Ridge—Miss Assertive **Mr A. Mortazavi**

THREE-YEAR-OLDS

27 CHESTER'SLITTLEGEM (IRE), b f Atraf—Ceylon Round (FR) **Chester Racing Club Ltd**
28 CROQUEMBOUCHE (IRE), b c Acclamation—Wedding Cake **E. B. de Giles**
29 MEN DON'T CRY (IRE), b g Street Cry (USA)—Naissance Royale (IRE) **Clarke, King & Lewis**
30 TIJUCA (IRE), b f Captain Rio—Some Forest (IRE) **E. B. de Giles**
31 TWENTY ONE CHOICE (IRE), ch g Choisir (AUS)—Midnight Lace **Penna Racing**

Other Owners: Mr K. Blackham, Mr D. Clarke, Mr A. J. Cork, Mr M. J. Gibbons, I. W. Gibson, C. J. King, Mrs E. V. Lewis, Mr C. Morris, Mr M. C. Penna, K. Sobey, A. J. Viall, Mrs C. R. de Giles.

170 **MR JONATHEN DE GILES, Highworth**
Postal: South Farm, Stanton Fitzwarren, Swindon, Wiltshire, SN6 7RZ
Contacts: PHONE (01793) 763094 FAX (01793) 763109

1 DAARTH, 7, b g Alhaarth (IRE)—Glamorous Girl (IRE) **Mr J. A. T. de Giles**
2 PRINCE NAMID, 10, b g Namid—Fen Princess (IRE) **Mr J. A. T. de Giles**
3 RED LANCER, 11, ch g Deploy—Miss Bussell **Mr J. A. T. de Giles**
4 SCALLEYS RUN, 11, gr g Commanche Run—Scally Belle **D. J. Shorey**

171 MR BEN DE HAAN, Lambourn
Postal: **Fair View, Long Hedge, Lambourn, Newbury, Berkshire, RG17 8NA**
Contacts: **PHONE (01488) 72163 FAX (01488) 71306 MOBILE (07831) 104574**
E-MAIL bendehaanracing@aol.com WEBSITE www.bendehaanracing.com

1 **ACT OF KINDNESS (IRE)**, 7, b g Beneficial—Kemche **B. D. Heath**
2 **DECIDING MOMENT (IRE)**, 6, b g Zagreb (USA)—Fontaine Jewel (IRE) **W. A. Tyrer**
3 **EDUCATED SON**, 4, br g Diktat—Spring Sunrise **Mrs D. Vaughan**
4 **FIDELIS (IRE)**, 8, gr g Great Palm (USA)—Americo Rescue (IRE) **Mr & Mrs Nicholas Tatman**
5 **LOOKS LIKE SLIM**, 5, b g Passing Glance—Slims Lady **Mr M. Butler**
6 4, B g Fleetwood (IRE)—Moor Hampshire (IRE) **B. De Haan**
7 **NATIVE GALLERY (IRE)**, 7, gr g Portrait Gallery (IRE)—Native Bev (IRE) **W. A. Tyrer**
8 **NOM DE GUERRE (IRE)**, 10, b g Presenting—Asklynn (IRE) **Mr & Mrs Nicholas Tatman**
9 **OCULIST**, 4, b g Dr Fong (USA)—Eyes Wide Open **Mrs F. Walwyn**
10 **UFFA FOX (IRE)**, 9, b g Bravefoot—Ocean Mist (IRE) **Lady Aitken Mrs F Walwyn Mr D Heath**

THREE-YEAR-OLDS

11 **GENERALYSE**, b c Cadeaux Genereux—Dance To The Blues (IRE) **Mrs D. Vaughan**

TWO-YEAR-OLDS

12 B f 17/4 Sixties Icon—Dance To The Blues (IRE) (Danehill Dancer (IRE)) (476) **Mrs D. Vaughan**

Other Owners: Lady Aitken, Mr Duncan Heath, Mr Nicholas Tatman, Mrs Elizabeth Tatman, Mrs F. Walwyn.

Jockey (flat): Adam Kirby. **Jockey (NH):** Noel Fehily, Daryl Jacob.

172 MR GEOFFREY DEACON, Reading
Postal: **Blandys Farm Cottage, Blandys Lane, Upper Basildon, Reading, Berkshire, RG8 8PH**
Contacts: **PHONE (01491) 671958 MOBILE (07967) 626757**
E-MAIL geoffdeacon@aol.com WEBSITE www.geoffreydeacontraining.co.uk

1 **ACCUMULUS**, 12, b g Cloudings (IRE)—Norstock **Mr Ian Murray & Mr Nick Quesnel**
2 **AFFILIATE**, 4, ch f Nayef (USA)—Allied Cause **Woodhall, Nicol & Co**
3 **ARCTIC GUNNER**, 8, gr g Alflora (IRE)—Arctic Chick **D. Teevan**
4 **BANKS ROAD (IRE)**, 7, b g Beneficial—Cecelia's Charm (IRE) **Mrs J. M. Duckett**
5 **BURNT ORCHID (IRE)**, 7, ch m Subtle Power (IRE)—Native Orchid (IRE) **White Star Racing Syndicate**
6 **CONN MAN (IRE)**, 7, ch g Whitmore's Conn (USA)—Special Artist (IRE) **White Star Racing Syndicate**
7 **ESEEJ (USA)**, 7, ch g Aljabr (USA)—Jinaan (USA) **Miss S. J. Duckett**
8 **FUHGEDDABOUDIT**, 5, ch g Generous (IRE)—Serraval (IRE) **J. T. Brown**
9 **GLASTONBERRY**, 4, gr f Piccolo—Elderberry **Mr J. J. Kelly**
10 **PILKAYSKI**, 4, b f Pilsudski (IRE)—Ann's Mill **The White Horse Of Hermitage Syndicate**
11 **VICTORIAN NUMBER (FR)**, 4, ch c Numerous (USA)—Malaisia (FR) **Mr A. R. Pittman**

TWO-YEAR-OLDS

12 B c 25/1 Bertolini (USA)—Fleeting Moon (Fleetwood (IRE)) (8000) **Mr J. J. Kelly**

Other Owners: Mr Ken Anidjah, Mr Geoffrey Deacon, Miss Sally Duckett, Mrs A. Nicol, Mr D. Woodhall, Mrs H. Woodhall.

Assistant Trainer: Sally Duckett

Jockey (flat): Sophie Doyle. **Jockey (NH):** Jimmy McCarthy. **Amateur:** Miss Emily Macmahon.

173 MR TIM DENNIS, Bude
Postal: **Thorne Farm, Bude, Cornwall, EX23 0LU**

1 **WISHES AND STARS (IRE)**, 6, b m Old Vic—She's No Trouble (IRE) **Mrs J. E. Dennis**

174 MR ROBIN DICKIN, Stratford-Upon-Avon

Postal: Alscot Racing Stables, Alscot Park, Atherstone On Stour, Stratford-Upon-Avon, Warwickshire, CV37 8BL
Contacts: **PHONE** (01789) 450052 **FAX** (01789) 450053 **MOBILE** (07979) 518593 / (07979) 518594
E-MAIL robin@robindickinracing.org.uk **WEBSITE** www.robindickinracing.org.uk

1 **ATHERSTONE HILL (IRE)**, 10, b g Presenting—Mystic Madam (IRE) **Colin & Co**
2 **AUTUMN SPIRIT**, 8, ch m Kadastrof (FR)—Dickies Girl **The Lordy Racing Partnership**
3 **BADGERS COVE (IRE)**, 8, b g Witness Box (USA)—Celestial Rose (IRE) **E. R. C. Beech & B. Wilkinson**
4 **BALLYHOOLEY BOY (IRE)**, 5, b g Oscar (IRE)—Nivalf **The Tricksters 2010**
5 5, Ch g Denounce—Bay Maid **Gannaway Racing Club**
6 **CORNISH ICE**, 8, b g Dolpour—Icelandic Poppy **R. G. Whitehead**
7 **CYDONIA (IRE)**, 5, b g Westerner—Keen Gale (IRE) **P. R. Armour**
8 **DAN'S MARTHA**, 4, b f Tagula (IRE)—Piedmont (UAE) **D. G. O. Partnership**
9 **DANCE FOR LIVVY (IRE)**, 4, br f Kodiac—Dancing Steps **The Tricksters & Mark James**
10 **DANCING DAFFODIL**, 7, ch m Kadastrof (FR)—Whistling Song **Mr & Mrs J. Cooper**
11 **DROM**, 9, b g Gildoran—Sabre Drom **Mark Hingley & David Doolittle**
12 **ENTERTAIN ME**, 8, b m Kadastrof (FR)—Just The Ticket **Mrs A. L. Merry**
13 4, Ch f Kadastrof (FR)—Fair Cruise **Mrs C. M. Dickin**
14 **GRAYLYN AMBER**, 7, b m Nomadic Way (USA)—State Lady (IRE) **Graham Knight**
15 **GRAYLYN RUBY (FR)**, 7, b g Limnos (JPN)—Nandi (IRE) **Graham Knight**
16 **GUNS OF LOVE (IRE)**, 10, b g Lord of Appeal—Golden Seekers **Whoops 72!**
17 **JUST KATES GIRL**, 6, b m Alflora (IRE)—Just Kate **R. G. Whitehead**
18 **KADUNA**, 7, b m Kadastrof (FR)—Mystic Legacy **Miss C. A. B. Allsopp**
19 **KATHLEENS PRIDE (IRE)**, 12, b g Broken Hearted—Cyprus Hill (IRE) **Mrs C. M. Dickin**
20 **KAWA (FR)**, 6, gr g Kouroun (FR)—Kulitch (FR) **P. R. Armour**
21 **LADY VALTAS**, 4, b f Val Royal (FR)—Phantasmagoria **Mr J. Patton**
22 **LAIDBACK LEO**, 4, ch g Golden Snake (USA)—Rockstine (IRE) **The Jameson & Elbro Partnership**
23 **MISS LADYBIRD (USA)**, 11, b br m Labeeb—Bird Dance (USA) **William Wyatt, Eleanor Wright & Robin Dickin**
24 **MISS MORN (IRE)**, 8, b m Loup Sauvage (USA)—Frosty Morn
25 **MUSIC IN THE AIR**, 8, ch m Kadastrof (FR)—Makin Whoopee (IRE) **Mrs A. L. Merry**
26 **NICKS POWER (IRE)**, 6, b g Luso—Shii-Take's Girl **J. F. R. Stainer**
27 **OSCAR TOM (IRE)**, 8, b g Oscar (IRE)—Duffys Dream **R. G. Whitehead**
28 **PLAYING WITH FIRE (IRE)**, 8, gr m Witness Box (USA)—Smokey Path (IRE) **Mrs A. L. Merry**
29 **RAPHIELL (IRE)**, 8, b g Turtle Island (IRE)—Glenwood Lass **R. G. Whitehead**
30 **RESTLESS HARRY**, 8, b g Sir Harry Lewis (USA)—Restless Native (IRE) **R. G. Whitehead**
31 **RIPOFF**, 7, b g Kadastrof (FR)—Just The Ticket **Mrs A. L. Merry**
32 **ROTHRES (FR)**, 8, b m Lavirco (GER)—Academic Dance (FR) **Law & Disorder**
33 **ROXANE BRUERE (FR)**, 7, b m Loup Solitaire (USA)—Ifranne (FR) **Mr R. E. Hill**
34 **RUSSIAN ROMANCE (IRE)**, 7, b m Moscow Society (USA)—My Romance **Mrs A. L. Merry**
35 **SCARLETT O'TARA**, 4, b m Kayf Tara—Lynoso **J. F. R. Stainer**
36 **THE ABSENT MARE**, 4, gr f Fair Mix (IRE)—Precious Lucy (FR) **Mr J. C. Clemmow**
37 **THE DE THAIX (FR)**, 5, b g Polish Summer—Etoile de Thaix (FR) **John Priday**
38 **THE QUANTUM KID**, 8, b g Desert Prince (IRE)—Al Hasnaa **Eleanor Wright**
39 **THOMAS CRAPPER**, 5, b g Tamure (IRE)—Mollycarrs Gambul **Apis.uk.com**
40 **TILT DU CHATELIER (FR)**, 5, ch g Arnaqueur (USA)—Une Du Chatelier (FR) **Mrs C M. Dickin**
41 **TOM O'TARA**, 8, b g Kayf Tara—Mrs May **G. Knight, D. Ward & C. Marriott**
42 **TOP ROSE**, 6, b m Sleeping Car (FR)—Quark Top (FR) **The Apostles**
43 **TROYAN (IRE)**, 5, b g King's Theatre (IRE)—Talk The Talk **John Priday**
44 **UNFORGETTABLE (IRE)**, 9, b g Norwich—Miss Lulu (IRE) **J. Rogers**
45 **VALRENE**, 6, b m Grape Tree Road—Across The Water **Mike Mifflin & John Priday**
46 **WESTERLY BREEZE (IRE)**, 4, b g Westerner—Sup A Whiskey (IRE) **Paul Armour**

THREE-YEAR-OLDS

47 Ch f Kadastrof (FR)—Fair Cruise **Mrs C. M. Dickin**
48 **GRAYLYN VALENTINO**, b g Primo Valentino (IRE)—Rhuby River (IRE) **Graham & Lynn Knight**
49 **YOUNG LOU**, b f Kadastrof (FR)—Wanna Shout **E. R. C. Beech & B. Wilkinson**

Other Owners: Mr N. Austin, Mr E. R. Clifford Beech, Ms Joanne Clark, Mr R. A. Cockrell, Mrs C. M. Dickin, Mrs Jan Gibson, Mr B. M. R. Haslam, Mr Mark James, Mrs V. Jameson, Mr S. Kirby, Mr G. Knight, Mr L. C. Knight, Mr C. D. Marriott, Mrs M. Payne, Miss B. Sykes, Mr Alan Varey, Mr P. Venvell, Mr Derek J. Ward, Mr Steve Webb, Mr R. G. Whitehead, Mr B. Wilkinson, Mr Brian Wilson.

Assistant Trainer: Claire Dickin

Jockey (flat): Luke Morris, Martin Lane. **Jockey (NH):** Charlie Poste, Wayne Kavanagh. **Conditional:** Chris Ward, Arron Kennedy. **Amateur:** Mr F. Green.

175 MR JOHN DIXON, Carlisle
Postal: **Moorend, Thursby, Carlisle, Cumbria, CA5 6QP**
Contacts: PHONE **(01228) 711019**

1 **CROFTON ARCH,** 12, b g Jumbo Hirt (USA)—Joyful Imp **Mrs E. M. Dixon**
2 **CROFTON LANE,** 6, b g And Beyond (IRE)—Joyful Imp **Mrs S. F. Dixon**
3 **DANIEL'S DREAM,** 12, b g Prince Daniel (USA)—Amber Holly **Mrs E. M. Dixon**

Amateur: Mr J. J. Dixon.

176 MR SCOTT DIXON, Retford
Postal: **Haygarth House Stud, Haygarth House, Babworth, Retford, Nottinghamshire, DN22 8ES**

1 **ABSOLUTE PRINCESS,** 4, b f Avonbridge—Park Ave Princess (IRE) **P. J. Dixon**
2 **ASKAUD (IRE),** 4, b f Iffraaj—Tarabaya (IRE) **P. J. Dixon**
3 **CADEAUX PEARL,** 4, b g Acclamation—Anneliina **P. J. Dixon**
4 **CAPONE (IRE),** 7, b g Daggers Drawn (USA)—Order of The Day (USA) **Brooklands Racing**
5 **DOCOFTHEBAY (IRE),** 8, ch g Docksider (USA)—Baize **P. J. Dixon**
6 **DREAM LODGE (IRE),** 8, ch g Grand Lodge (USA)—Secret Dream (IRE) **Mr P J Dixon & Mr A Baker**
7 **EVEN STEVENS,** 4, br g Ishiguru (USA)—Promised (IRE) **P. J. Dixon**
8 **FIELD FINNER,** 4, ch f Goodricke—Princess Carranita (IRE) **J. P. Burton**
9 **LA CAPRIOSA,** 6, ch m Kyllachy—La Caprice (USA) **P. J. Dixon**
10 **LUSCIVIOUS,** 8, ch g Kyllachy—Lloc **Paul J. Dixon & Mr Brian Morton**
11 **PICENO (IRE),** 4, b g Camacho—Ascoli **P. J. Dixon**
12 **SACROSANCTUS,** 4, ch g Sakhee (USA)—Catalonia (IRE) **P. J. Dixon**
13 **SIR GEOFFREY (IRE),** 6, b g Captain Rio—Disarm (IRE) **Dixon, Howlett & The Chrystal Maze Ptn**
14 **SIX WIVES,** 5, b m Kingsalsa (USA)—Regina **Sexy Six Partnership**
15 **SUDDENLY SUSAN (IRE),** 4, b f Acclamation—Westerly Gale (USA) **P. J. Dixon**
16 **SWINGER,** 4, ch g Singspiel (IRE)—Helen Bradley (IRE) **P. J. Dixon**
17 **THUNDERBALL,** 4, ch g Haafhd—Trustthunder **Paul J. Dixon & Mr Brian Morton**
18 **THUNDERSTRUCK,** 7, b g Bertolini (USA)—Trustthunder **The Doncaster Racing Club**

THREE-YEAR-OLDS
19 **BENGALINE,** b c Bahamian Bounty—Indian Silk (IRE) **P. J. Dixon & The Nulli Secundus Friends**
20 **BURNHOPE,** b g Choisir (AUS)—Isengard (USA) **Mrs S. M. Roy**
21 **MAN OF MY WORD,** b g Milk It Mick—Promised (IRE) **P J Dixon & Partners**
22 **MONNOYER,** ch g Dutch Art—Ellebanna **Mrs S Roy, Mr P Dixon & Mr B Morton**
23 **VAN GO GO,** b f Dutch Art—Baldovina **A Black & Partners**

Other Owners: Mr A. D. Baker, M. H. Bates, A. W. Black, P. G. Dawson, Mrs Y. Dixon, General Sir G. H. W. Howlett, D. S. Lovatt, Mrs A. M. Mercs, B. Morton, Mr K. J. Newsome, Mr A. C. Timms.

177 MR STEVEN DIXON, Salisbury
Postal: **Apple Tree Barn, Livery Road, Winterslow, Nr Salisbury, Wiltshire, SP5 1RJ**
Contacts: PHONE **(01980) 862930** MOBILE **(07771) 963011**
E-MAIL **sarahjdixon@hotmail.co.uk**

1 4, B f General Gambul—Pink Lady **Mr S. D. Dixon**
2 **POWER MAN (IRE),** 7, ch g Subtle Power (IRE)—Karinga Duff **Mr S. D. Dixon**
3 **SUN QUEST,** 8, b g Groom Dancer (USA)—Icaressa **Mr S. D. Dixon**
4 **WARSAW PACT (IRE),** 9, b g Polish Precedent (USA)—Always Friendly **Mr S. D. Dixon**

Assistant Trainer: Mrs Sarah Dixon

Conditional: Robert Kirk, Wayne Kavanagh.

178 MRS ROSE DOBBIN, Alnwick
Postal: **South Hazelrigg Farm, Chatton, Alnwick, Northumberland, NE66 5RZ**
Contacts: PHONE **(01668) 215395 (office) (01668) 215151 (house)** FAX **(01668) 215114**
MOBILE **(07969) 993563**
E-MAIL **hazelriggracing1@btconnect.com** WEBSITE **www.rosedobbinracing.co.uk**

1 **ALWAYS BEST,** 8, b g Best of The Bests (IRE)—Come To The Point **Mr J. L. Dickson**
2 **ANOTHER DIMENSION (IRE),** 6, b g Overbury (IRE)—Freshwater (IRE) **Arkle Recruitment Limited**

MRS ROSE DOBBIN—continued

3 **BANOGE (IRE)**, 10, b g Flemensfirth (USA)—Prove It (IRE) **The Hookers**
4 **BELLA VENEZIA (IRE)**, 5, b m Milan—Fairy Native (IRE) **Mr & Mrs Duncan Davidson**
5 **CAERLAVEROCK (IRE)**, 7, br g Statue of Liberty (USA)—Daziyra (IRE) **Mr & Mrs Duncan Davidson**
6 5, Ch g Pentire—Eastern Bazzaar (IRE)
7 **FLYING SQUAD (UAE)**, 8, b g Jade Robbery (USA)—Sandova (IRE) **Major-Gen C. A. Ramsay**
8 **FORTUNI (IRE)**, 6, b g Montjeu (IRE)—Desert Ease (IRE) **Mr & Mrs Duncan Davidson**
9 **GROOVY DANCER**, 5, ch m Groom Dancer (USA)—Cita Verda (FR) **Mr & Mrs Raymond Anderson Green**
10 **HARRY HANDSOME**, 7, b g Sir Harry Lewis (USA)—Fair Cruise **J P H Wight & J J Cockburn**
11 **MAGIC ECHO**, 8, b m Wizard King—Sunday News'n'echo (USA) **F. Watson**
12 **MARSHMALLOW**, 4, b f Tiger Hill (IRE)—Gooseberry Pie **Mr & Mrs Duncan Davidson**
13 **MIRAGE DORE (FR)**, 9, b g Muhtathir—Rose Venitien (FR) **Mr & Mrs Duncan Davidson**
14 **MOUNTSKIP**, 8, b g Beat All (USA)—Roman Uproar **Mrs R. Dobbin**
15 **MYSTIC ECHO**, 6, b m Overbury (IRE)—Sunday News'n'echo (USA) **F. Watson**
16 **OSCAR STANLEY (IRE)**, 5, b g Oscar (IRE)—Mujavail (IRE) **Another Fine Mess Partnership**
17 **PURCELL'S BRIDGE (FR)**, 5, b g Trempolino (USA)—Theatrical Lady (USA) **Mr J. A. F. Filmer-Wilson**
18 **PYJAMA GAME (FR)**, 6, b g Hernando (FR)—Princess Claudia (IRE) **Mr & Mrs Duncan Davidson**
19 **ROBIN'S COMMAND (IRE)**, 5, gr g Tikkanen (USA)—Marian's Wish (IRE) **M Hunter, J Matterson & R Jacobs**
20 **ROLE ON (IRE)**, 10, gr g Bob's Return (IRE)—Banderole (IRE) **Mr & Mrs Duncan Davidson**
21 **ROS CASTLE (IRE)**, 6, ch g Flemensfirth (USA)—Castlehaven (IRE) **Mr & Mrs Duncan Davidson**
22 **SARABELLE (FR)**, 6, b br m Sleeping Car (FR)—Jonque (FR) **Mrs R. Dobbin**
23 **SNOOKER (GER)**, 6, ch g Acambaro (GER)—Sheraton (RE) **Mr & Mrs Duncan Davidson**
24 **TWEEDO PARADISO (NZ)**, 5, br g Golan (IRE)—Buzz (NZ) **The Friday Lions**
25 **VINNY GAMBINI (IRE)**, 5, b g Vinnie Roe (IRE)—Red Velvet **Mr & Mrs Duncan Davidson**
26 **WHY ARE YOU ASKING (IRE)**, 7, b g Needle Gun (IRE)—Tyrilda (FR) **Major-Gen C. A. Ramsay**

Other Owners: R. H. T. Barber, Mr J. J. Cockburn, Mrs C. M. T. Cunningham-Jardine, D. H. Davidson, Mrs S. K. Davidson, Lady Duncan, R. A. Green, Mrs A. Green, M. S. Hunter, Mr R. A. Jacobs, J. R. Jeffreys, Miss J. G. K. Matterson, Mr M. T. Ord, J. P. H. Wight.

Assistant Trainer: Tony Dobbin (07775) 680894

Jockey (NH): Graham Lee, Wilson Renwick. **Amateur:** Mr Nick Orpwood, Miss Joanna Walton.

---

179 **MR ASHLEY DODGSON, Thirsk**
Postal: **Southerby House, Catton, Thirsk, North Yorkshire, YO7 4SQ**

1 **CANDLEFORD**, 7, b g Vettori (IRE)—Second Affair (IRE) **Mr A. C. Dodgson**
2 **RICH HILL**, 10, b g Environment Friend—Tapua Taranata (IRE) **Mr A. C. Dodgson**

---

180 **MR MICHAEL DODS, Darlington**
Postal: **Denton Hall Farm, Piercebridge, Darlington, Co. Durham, DL2 3TY**
Contacts: **PHONE (01325) 374270 FAX (01325) 374020**
MOBILE (07860) 411590/(07773) 290830 C Dods
E-MAIL dods@michaeldodsracing.co.uk WEBSITE www.michaeldodsracing.co.uk

1 4, Ch g Dr Fong (USA)—Aikaterine
2 **ASHVA (USA)**, 4, b g Quiet American (USA)—Pondicherry (USA) **Mr W. A. Tinkler**
3 **BARNEY MCGREW (IRE)**, 9, b g Mark of Esteem (IRE)—Success Story **Mr W. A. Tinkler**
4 **BROOK STAR (IRE)**, 4, b f Refuse To Bend (IRE)—Star of Cayman (IRE) **D. Neale**
5 **CHEATING TIGER (IRE)**, 4, b g Tiger Hill (IRE)—Chita Rivera **D. C. Batey**
6 **COMMANCHE RAIDER (IRE)**, 5, b g Tale of The Cat (USA)—Alsharq (IRE) **D. R. Graham**
7 **DEEP APPLAUSE**, 4, b g Royal Applause—Deep Deep Blue **Appleton - Davison - Spinks**
8 **HENRYS GIFT (IRE)**, 4, b g Titus Livius (FR)—Xania **Mrs C. M. Hewitson**
9 **KIWI BAY**, 7, b g Mujahid (USA)—Bay of Plenty (IRE) **Kiwi Racing**
10 **LADY CHAPARRAL**, 5, b m High Chaparral (IRE)—La Sylphide
11 **LE CHAT D'OR**, 4, b g One Cool Cat (USA)—Oh So Well (IRE) **Calum Stewart Anne Gillespie**
12 **MARVELLOUS VALUE (IRE)**, 7, b g Danetime (IRE)—Despondent (IRE) **A. J. Henderson**
13 **MASS RALLY (IRE)**, 5, b g Kheleyf (USA)—Reunion (IRE) **Business Development Consultants Limited**
14 **MAXAMILLION BOUNTY**, 4, ch g Bahamian Bounty—Never Say Deya **Denton Hall Racing Ltd**
15 **MECCA'S TEAM**, 4, ch f Ishiguru (USA)—Clancassie **Mr David T.J. Metcalfe & Mr D.W. Barker**
16 **MOHAWK RIDGE**, 4, b g Storming Home—Ipsa Loquitur **D. R. Graham**
17 **ORBIT THE MOON (IRE)**, 4, b c Oratorio (IRE)—Catch The Moon (IRE) **Mr W. A. Tinkler**
18 **OSTEOPATHIC REMEDY (IRE)**, 8, ch g Inchinor—Dolce Vita (IRE) **K. Kirkup**

MR MICHAEL DODS—continued

19 **SHAMDARLEY (IRE)**, 4, b g Shamardal (USA)—Siphon Melody (USA) **Mr W. A. Tinkler**
20 **SPINATRIX**, 4, b f Diktat—Shrink **Mrs J. W. Hutchinson & Mrs P. A. Knox**
21 **SWEET LIGHTNING**, 7, b g Fantastic Light (USA)—Sweetness Herself **Mr W. A. Tinkler**
22 **THE OIL MAGNATE**, 7, ch g Dr Fong (USA)—Bob's Princess **Smith & Allan Racing**
23 **TIGER REIGNS**, 6, b g Tiger Hill (IRE)—Showery **J. Buzzeo**
24 **VIKING WARRIOR (IRE)**, 5, ch g Halling (USA)—Powder Paint **Transpennine Partnership**

THREE-YEAR-OLDS

25 **AMADEUS DENTON (IRE)**, b g Amadeus Wolf—Wood Sorrel (IRE) **Denton Hall Racing Ltd**
26 **DARTRIX**, b f Dutch Art—Shrink **T. K. Knox**
27 **DOS AMIGOS (IRE)**, b c Clodovil (IRE)—Ide Say (IRE) **Doug Graham,Roger Stokell,Michael Dods**
28 **FINE ALTOMIS**, b g Lomitas—Mi Anna (GER) **Steve Catchpole & Keith Hanson**
29 **FINE KINGDOM**, b g King's Best—Eurolink Sundance **Mr S. L. Catchpole & Mr K. Hanson**
30 **HALF A BILLION (IRE)**, b g Acclamation—Amankila (IRE) **I. Galletley, B. Stenson, M Dods**
31 **IFFRAAM (IRE)**, b c Iffraaj—Madamaa (IRE) **Mr W. A. Tinkler**
32 **MASTER CHIPPER**, ch g Medicean—Spiralling **N. A. Riddell**
33 **MISTRESS OF ROME**, b f Holy Roman Emperor (IRE)—Fairy Dance (IRE) **K. Kirkup**
34 **ODDYSEY (IRE)**, b f Acclamation—Darling Smile (IRE) **Pearson, Lowthian & Coburn**
35 **ROCKTHERUNWAY (IRE)**, ch g Nayef (USA)—Femme Fatale **The Sedgewick And Dods Racing Partnership**
36 **SPRINGINMYSTEP (IRE)**, b c Footstepsinthesand—Joyful (IRE) **Mr W. A. Tinkler**
37 **STAR CITY (IRE)**, b g Elusive City (USA)—Teacher Preacher (IRE) **Appleton Davison Dods**
38 B g Compton Place—Surrealist (ITY) **Mrs C. E. Dods**
39 **TIME TO EXCEL**, ch g Exceed And Excel (AUS)—Treacle (USA) **A Wynn-Williams, D Graham, D Neale**
40 B f Marju—Uluwatu (IRE) **K. Kirkup**
41 **VERA RICHARDSON (IRE)**, b f Dutch Art—Play With Fire (FR)

TWO-YEAR-OLDS

42 **AERONWYN BRYN (IRE)**, b f 8/3 Dylan Thomas (IRE)—
　　　　　　　　　　　Hecuba (Hector Protector (USA)) (18061) **Mr W. A. Tinkler**
43 B g 16/4 Footstepsinthesand—Appleblossom Pearl (IRE) (Peintre Celebre (USA)) (13000) **Mrs C. E. Dods**
44 **CRACKING CHOICE (IRE)**, ch c 28/2 Choisir (AUS)—Champagne Cracker (Up And At 'em) (8209)
45 B f 14/3 Amadeus Wolf—Dane Blue (IRE) (Danehill Dancer (IRE)) (1231) **Mrs C. E. Dods**
46 **ELLE WOODS (IRE)**, b f 25/2 Lawman (FR)—Lady Livius (IRE) (Titus Livius (FR)) (65000) **Mr W. A. Tinkler**
47 Ch f 20/3 Araafa (IRE)—Locharia (Wolfhound (USA)) (4500) **M. J. K. Dods**
48 Ch f 30/3 Iffraaj—Lucies Pride (IRE) (Noverre (USA)) (11493) **Business Development Consultants Limited**
49 **MUNICIPAL (IRE)**, b c 27/4 Elusive City (USA)—Ripalong (IRE) (Revoque (IRE)) (48000) **Mr W. A. Tinkler**
50 **NEW RICH**, b c 1/4 Bahamian Bounty—Bling Bling (IRE) (Indian Ridge) (75000) **Mr W. A. Tinkler**
51 B c 7/5 Black Sam Bellamy (IRE)—Sablonne (USA) (Silver Hawk (USA)) (22000) **J. A. Wynn-Williams**
52 B g 26/4 Whipper (USA)—Salva (Grand Lodge (USA)) (15238) **Bennett Potatoes Ltd**
53 B c 5/3 Dr Fong (USA)—Strawberry Lolly (Lomitas) (6978) **K. Kirkup**
54 B g 16/3 Multiplex—Subtle Move (USA) (Known Fact (USA)) (10476) **Mrs C. E. Dods**
55 Ch c 15/2 Rock of Gibraltar (IRE)—
　　　　　　　　　　Toorah Laura La (USA) (Black Minnaloushe (USA)) (21345) **Mr & Mrs G. Turnbull**
56 Ch c 26/3 Captain Rio—Walk In My Shadow (IRE) (Orpen (USA)) (9030) **K. Kirkup**

Other Owners: Mr P. Appleton, D. W. Barker, Mr S. L. Catchpole, G. Coburn, Mr J. Cockcroft, R. Davison, Mr I. Galletley, Dr A. J. F. Gillespie, Mr K. Hanson, W. S. D. Lamb, S. R. Lowthian, D. T. J. Metcalfe, Mr M. D. Pearson, Mr M. J. Sedgewick, V. J. Spinks, J. W. Stenson, Mr C. M. Stewart, R. Stokell, D. J. Stokell, Mr G. Turnbull, Mrs S. E. Turnbull, D. Watts, D. G. A. E. Woods, Mr B. Yeadon.

Assistant Trainers: C Dods, Steve Alderson (07533) 401887, Greg Carroll

Jockey (flat): Tom Eaves.

MR DESMOND DONOVAN, Newmarket
Postal: **Harraton Stables, Chapel Street, Exning, Newmarket, Suffolk, CB8 7HA**
Contacts: **PHONE (01638) 578494 FAX (01638) 578494 MOBILE (07761) 841285**
E-MAIL **hareparkbloodstock@yahoo.co.uk** WEBSITE **www.desdonovan.co.uk**

1 **DAZZLING BEGUM**, 7, b m Okawango (USA)—Dream On Me **Mr J. T. Mangan**
2 **INDUS VALLEY (IRE)**, 5, ch g Indian Ridge—Gloriously Bright (USA) **River Racing**
3 **MOSCOW OZNICK**, 7, br g Auction House (USA)—Cozette (IRE) **W. P. Flynn**
4 **SAVARONOLA (USA)**, 7, ch g Pulpit (USA)—Running Debate (USA) **River Racing**

MR DESMOND DONOVAN—continued

    5 TEVEZ, 7, b g Sakhee (USA)—Sosumi **River Racing**
    6 TORTILLA (IRE), 4, ch f Choisir (AUS)—Alifandango (IRE) **River Racing**

THREE-YEAR-OLDS

    7 CAN DO LES (IRE), b g Modigliani (USA)—Yulara (IRE) **W. P. Flynn**
    8 THE COULBECK KID, b g Tobougg (IRE)—Billiard **The Overdraft Partnership**

Other Owners: Mrs R. P. Aggio, Mrs R. Cioffi, Mr J. D. Donovan, P. P. Mclaughlin.

---

182   MR CONOR DORE, Frampton Fen
Postal: **Barford Farm, Swinehead Road, Frampton Fen, Boston, Lincolnshire, PE20 1SG**

    1 ACE OF SPIES (IRE), 7, br g Machiavellian (USA)—Nadia **Mrs L. J. Marsh**
    2 ANJOMARBA (IRE), 5, b m Tillerman—Golden Charm (IRE) **C. D. Marsh**
    3 CHJIMES (IRE), 8, b g Fath (USA)—Radiance (IRE) **Mrs L. J. Marsh**
    4 EFISTORM, 11, b g Efisio—Abundance **Sean J. Murphy**
    5 ELHAMRI, 8, b br g Noverre (USA)—Seamstress (IRE) **C. D. Marsh**
    6 GRUDGE, 7, b g Timeless Times (USA)—Envy (IRE) **Mrs J. R. Marsh**
    7 ISTIQDAAM, 7, b g Pivotal—Auspicious **Mr C. McHugh & Mr C. Eliades**
    8 KIPCHAK (IRE), 7, b g Soviet Star (USA)—Khawafi **L. Breslin**
    9 LASTKINGOFSCOTLAND (IRE), 6, b g Danehill Dancer (IRE)—Arcade **Mrs J. R. Marsh**
    10 LUCKY ART (USA), 6, b g Johannesburg (USA)—Syrian Summer (USA) **C. J. McHugh**
    11 OPUS MAXIMUS (IRE), 7, ch g Titus Livius (FR)—Law Review (IRE) **Mrs L. J. Marsh**
    12 PUNCHING, 8, b g Kyllachy—Candescent **L. Breslin**

Other Owners: Mr C. T. Eliades, Mr M. Fitzsimons.

---

183   MR FRANCOIS DOUMEN, Bouce
Postal: **Le Gue, 61570 Bouce, France**
Contacts: PHONE **(0033) 2 33 67 11 59** FAX **(0033) 2 33 67 82 37** MOBILE **(0033) 6 07 42 33 58**
E-MAIL **doumenecouves@orange.fr**

    1 AIR BLOND, 5, ch g Green Tune (USA)—Cover Look (SAF)
    2 BRONCOLI (FR), 7, b g Observatory (USA)—Balouchina (IRE)
    3 CABARETUNE (FR), 7, b g Green Tune (USA)—Cabaret Club (FR)
    4 CAPITAINE COURAGE (IRE), 7, ch g Bering—Four Green (FR)
    5 CELTIC CELEB (IRE), 5, ch h Peintre Celebre (USA)—Gaelic Bird (FR)
    6 CIPRIANI (FR), 4, b g Until Sundown—Coureuse
    7 CROIX MADAME (FR), 5, b m Forestier (FR)—She Runs (FR)
    8 DIABLE DE JIM (FR), 6, b g Diableneyev (USA)—Jolie Jim (FR)
    9 GOLD EXCHANGE (FR), 6, ch g Gold Away (IRE)—Chop And Change (FR)
    10 GOLD SAVE THE KING (IRE), 5, ch g King's Best (USA)—Beringold
    11 GREEN BANANAS (FR), 6, b m Green Tune (USA)—Anabaa Republic (FR)
    12 GRISE LEIGH, 4, ch f Green Tune—Vezina
    13 JOLIE NOCE (FR), 4, b f Muhtathir—Jolie Jim
    14 KASBAH BLISS (FR), 10, b g Kahyasi—Marital Bliss (FR)
    15 KEYED UP (FR), 4, b f Key Of Luck—Tipsy Topsy
    16 KINGS BLISS (FR), 4, b g Kingsalsa—Marital Bliss
    17 KIROCCO (FR), 4, b f Shirrocco—Killgra
    18 KUSTER BEATON (FR), 4, gr g Chichicastenango—Chop And Change
    19 LE GRENELLE (FR), 5, b g Green Tune (USA)—L'annee Folle (FR)
    20 RAGEUR (FR), 4, b g Iffraaj—Ethelinda
    21 SALUT L'AMI (FR), 6, b g Subotica—Voltige De Nievre (FR)
    22 SIYOUMA(IRE), 4, b f Medicean—Sichilla (IRE)
    23 STEED (FR), 10, b g Double Bed (FR)—River Tweed
    24 SUNRISE SPIRIT (FR), 11, b g Double Bed (FR)—Belle Chaumiere
    25 TANIN, 5, b g Le Malemoretois—Vodkatonique
    26 TASTEVIN (FR), 5, ch g Dark Moondancer—Donitille (FR)
    27 TIP TOE (FR), 5, b h Footstepsinthesand—Midnight Queen (GER)
    28 TRUQUE (FR), 4, b g Enrique—The Trollop
    29 UHLAN BUTE (FR), 4, b g Brier Creek (USA)—Jonquiere (FR)
    30 UKISSDAWINNA (FR), 4, b f Bedawin (FR)—French Kiss IV (FR)

MR FRANCOIS DOUMEN—continued

31 UMBRAGE (FR), 4, b f Astarabad—Ma'am (FR)
32 VOYAGE A VENISE (FR), 4, b g Della Francesca—Ashley

THREE-YEAR-OLDS

33 ART ROCK (FR), b f Rock Of Gibraltar—Armanda
34 AUTORITAIRE (FR), b f Authorized (IRE)—Castilly
35 CASCO MOJADO (IRE), b c Footstepsinthesand—Acqua Verde
36 CHARLIZE (FR), b f Bedawin—Dauphine
37 CHICHITEUSE (FR), b f Chichicastenango—Gigawatt
38 FAST FLIGHT (FR), b c Anabaa (USA)—Flight Night
39 GOLDIE JOLIE (FR), b f Gold Away—Jolie Jim
40 HOLD MY HAND (FR), b f Hold That Tiger—Carte Blanche
41 HUMHUM, b f Medicean—Danehill Dreamer (USA)
42 KASBAH BISS (FR), b g Kahyasi—Marital Bliss
43 KHASMA (IRE), b f Rock of Gibraltar (IRE)—Kassana (IRE)
44 MIEUXDARQUEJAMAIS (FR), b g Sinndar—Mieux Mieux
45 PHIL MAN (IRE), b c Manduro (GER)—Fureau (GER)
46 QUAND REVERRAIJE (FR), b f Enrique—She Runs (FR)
47 THORZIEN (FR), b c Muhtathir—Hertzienne
48 TOP TRIP, b c Dubai Destination (USA)—Topka (FR)
49 TUNE IN (FR), b g Green Tune (USA)—Irunari (FR)
50 VOUS MEME (FR), b g Le Fou—Ma'am
51 XPO UNIVERSEL, b c Poliglote—Xanadu Bliss
52 ZARNIT (FR), b f Invincible Spirit (IRE)—Zarnitza (USA)

TWO-YEAR-OLDS

53 COQUERELLE'S BEST, b f 27/1 Galileo (IRE)—Coquerelle (IRE) (Zamindar (USA)) (164203)
54 DAUPHINE RUSSE (FR), b f 26/2 Russian Blue—Dauphine
55 DERNIERE CARTE (FR), b f 21/4 Sunday Break—Carte Blanche
56 DYLAN PHILLY (IRE), b f 13/2 Dylan Thomas (IRE)—Titillate (IRE) (Barathea (IRE)) (82101)
57 FIRST TO RISE (FR), ch f 9/2 Bedawin—Next Sunrise
58 JUNZI (FR), ch g 20/2 Muhtathir—Gigana
59 KAPSTADT (FR), b c 26/2 Country Reel (USA)—King's Parody (IRE) (King's Best (USA)) (24630)
60 LIBRARY (FR), b c 24/4 Librettist—Irunarri
61 MIDNIGHT MIRACLE (IRE), b f 9/2 Danehill Dancer (IRE)—Beyond Belief (IRE) (Sadler's Wells (USA)) (131362)
62 QUATRE ARPENTS (FR), b c 11/3 Bedawin—Queen Aida
63 TOPZA (FR), b f 3/5 Zamindar (USA)—Topka (FR) (Kahyasi)

Owners: Mr Dermot Cantillon, Mr Xavier Doumen, Gold and Blue Ltd, Mr Edward Goodwin, Haras D'Ecouves, Mr Robert Jeffcock, Mr William Jeffcock, Marquise de Moratalla, Mr Eric Puerari, Mr Gerard Rollain, Mr Anthony Smurfit, Mr Michael Somerset-Leeke, Mr Joerg Vasicek, Mr Hans Peter Vogt, Conte Henri de Pracomtal.

Jockey (flat): Thomas Huet, Gerald Mosse.

---

184   MR SIMON DOW, Epsom
Postal: **Clear Height Stables, Derby Stables Road, Epsom, Surrey, KT18 5LB**
Contacts: PHONE (01372) 721490 FAX (01372) 748099 MOBILE (07860) 800109
E-MAIL simon@simondow.co.uk Office: mary@simondow.co.uk WEBSITE www.simondow.co.uk

1 CLEAR PRAISE (USA), 5, b g Songandaprayer (USA)—Pretty Clear (USA) **Chua, Moore, Goalen & Warner**
2 DIAMOND CHARLIE (IRE), 4, br g Diamond Green (FR)—Rosy Lydgate **David & Stanley Adams**
3 FAIR VALUE (IRE), 4, b f Compton Place—Intriguing Glimpse **E. Hyde**
4 FORCEFUL APPEAL (USA), 4, b br c Successful Appeal (USA)—Kinetic Force (USA) **Mr S. A. Caunce**
5 GOLDEN DESERT (IRE), 8, b g Desert Prince (IRE)—Jules (IRE) **T. G. Parker**
6 JUHD (IRE), 4, gr g Nayef (USA)—Norfolk Lavender (CAN) **P. G. Jacobs**
7 NECESSITY, 5, b g Empire Maker (USA)—Fully Invested (USA) **P. G. Jacobs**
8 NORTHERN SPY (USA), 8, b g War Chant (USA)—Sunray Superstar **S. L. Dow**
9 NOTABADLAD, 5, br g Denounce—Lady Jo **K. F. Butler**
10 OUT OF THE STORM, 4, b f Elmhurst Boy—Night Storm **R. E. Anderson**
11 RENOIR'S LADY, 4, b f Peintre Celebre (USA)—Marie de Blois (IRE) **Malcolm & Alicia Aldis**
12 SOTTOVOCE, 4, b f Oratorio (IRE)—In A Silent Way (IRE) **Malcolm & Alicia Aldis**
13 SPACE STATION, 6, b g Anabaa (USA)—Spacecraft (USA) **Mr & Mrs Chua, Moore & Ong**
14 SQUAD, 6, ch g Choisir (AUS)—Widescreen (USA) **Sarah Snell & Anne Devine**
15 SUMANI (FR), 6, b g Della Francesca (USA)—Sumatra (IRE) **T. G. Parker**

MR SIMON DOW—continued

THREE-YEAR-OLDS

16 **BESSICHKA**, b f Exceed And Excel (AUS)—Jouet **J. D. Manley**
17 **CHRISTOPHER CHUA (IRE)**, gr g Clodovil (IRE)—Pearls of Wisdom **C. G. J. Chua**
18 **JOE M**, ch g Araafa (IRE)—Ambonnay **P. Green and A. Malone**
19 **KAYPEA**, br f Imperial Dancer—Cape Maya **L P R Partnership**
20 **KERFUFFLE (IRE)**, b f Kheleyf—Chiosina (IRE) **J Taylor L Robinson & W J Taylor**
21 **NOTABADGIRL**, ch f Denounce—Lady Jo **K. F. Butler**
22 **TRISHA'S BOY (IRE)**, ch g Exceed And Excel (AUS)—Golden Anthem (USA) **Mr J. P. D. Stead**

TWO-YEAR-OLDS

23 **MARJONG**, b f 22/1 Mount Nelson—Vermilliann (IRE) (Mujadil (USA)) (27000) **Mr J. L. Marsden**
24 B f 6/3 Rock of Gibraltar (IRE)—Ommadawn (IRE) (Montjeu (IRE)) (26000) **Malcolm & Alicia Aldis**
25 **PRESUMIDO (IRE)**, b c 13/4 Iffraaj—Miss Megs (IRE) (Croco Rouge (IRE)) (19000) **R. Moss & J. Page**
26 B f 31/3 Lawman (FR)—Silca Key (Inchinor) (14000) **P. G. Jacobs**
27 B c 12/2 Anabaa (USA)—Sourire (Domedriver) (IRE) (25000) **Mr M. McAllister**

Other Owners: Mrs F. Abbott, Mr D. Adams, Mr S. J. Adams, Mrs A. Aldis, Mr M. S. Aldis, Mrs A. M. Devine, Mr N. Gordon, Mr P. T. Green, Mrs B. D. Hall, Mr A. J. Malone, Mr R. Moore, Mr R. J. Moss, Mr J. W. Page, Ms E. Robinson, Ms S. A. Snell, Miss J. E. Taylor, Mr W. J. Taylor.

Assistant Trainer: Daniel Hutchison

---

185 | **MR CHRIS DOWN, Cullompton**
Postal: **Upton, Cullompton, Devon, EX15 1RA**
Contacts: **PHONE (01884) 33097 FAX (01884) 33097 MOBILE (07828) 021232**
E-MAIL **cjdownracing@gmail.com**

1 **BOB LEWIS**, 6, b g Sir Harry Lewis (USA)—Teelyna **Mrs L. M. Edwards**
2 **DE LUAIN GORM (IRE)**, 14, b g Beneficial—Call Catherine (IRE) **Mrs M. Trueman**
3 **DOLLY PENROSE**, 7, b m Hernando (FR)—Mistinguett (IRE) **G. M. Rowe**
4 **DRAGON'S DEN (IRE)**, 5, b g Antonius Pius (USA)—Tallassee **G. R. Waterman**
5 **KEY TO MILAN**, 6, b g Milan—Key West (FR) **M. R. Lavis & C. J. Down**
6 **LEGION D'HONNEUR (UAE)**, 7, b g Halling (USA)—
Renowned (IRE) **P Holland, JT Measures, AV Price, V Holland**
7 **LOYAUTE (FR)**, 5, ch m Green Tune (USA)—Iles Marquises (IRE) **C. J. Down**
8 **MASTER COBBLER (IRE)**, 10, b g Alhaarth (IRE)—Lady Joshua (IRE) **G. R. Waterman**
9 **MISTER SNOWBALL (FR)**, 5, ch g Ballingarry (IRE)—
No Coincidence (IRE) **P Holland, JT Measures, AV Price, V Holland**
10 **NATIVE BRIAN (IRE)**, 6, b g Brian Boru—Gentle Native (IRE) **Miss S. J. Lock**
11 **NEW CHRISTMAS (USA)**, 5, gr ro g Smoke Glacken (USA)—Occhi Verdi (IRE) **Dr M. J. Dixon**
12 **RACEY LACEY**, 5, b m Loup Sauvage (USA)—La Feuillarde (FR) **G. M. Rowe**
13 **RUSSIE WITH LOVE**, 6, b m Alflora (IRE)—Vieille Russie **Howzat Partnership**
14 **THEDEBOFTHEYEAR**, 8, b m Sir Harry Lewis (USA)—Juste Belle (FR) **Culm Valley Racing**
15 **UPTON OAKS**, 6, b g Sir Harry Lewis (USA)—Copper Valley **Upton Racing**
16 **WATS ON LUCKY**, 8, b m Beckett (IRE)—Grande Dame (IRE) **Mrs A. Denny**

Other Owners: Mrs F. Down, P. D. Holland, Mrs V. Holland, M. R. Lavis, Mr J. T. Measures, Mrs S. E. Norman, Mr J. A. G. Norman, Mrs A. V. Price, Mr C. B. Stevens, K. W. Tyrrell.

Jockey (flat): Steve Drowne. **Jockey (NH):** James Davies, Andrew Glassonbury. **Conditional:** Giles Hawkins.

---

186 | **MR CLIVE DREW, Rampton**
Postal: **Fox End Stables, 83 King Street, Rampton, Cambridgeshire, CB24 8QD**
Contacts: **PHONE/FAX (01954) 250772 MOBILE (07917) 718127**

1 **MAISON BRILLET (IRE)**, 5, b g Pyrus (USA)—Stormchaser (IRE) **Mr C. Drew**
2 **MY SILVER LILLY**, 5, b m Silver Patriarch (IRE)—Myumi **Miss P. Drew & Mrs J. Bland**
3 **MYTARA**, 7, br m Kayf Tara—Myumi **Mrs J. K. Burt**
4 **SMILE FOR US**, 9, b g Whittingham (IRE)—Don't Smile **Miss P. Drew**

Other Owners: Mrs J. Bland, Mr A. Plumb, Mr M. M. Brown, Mr C. Drew, Mr J. D. Paull.

Assistant Trainer: Miss Polly Drew

187 **MISS JACKIE DU PLESSIS, Saltash**
Postal: **Burell Farm, Longlands, Saltash, Cornwall, PL12 4QH**
Contacts: **PHONE (01752) 842362 MOBILE (07970) 871505**
E-MAIL ziggerson@aol.com

1 **COOL GEORGE**, 4, b g Pastoral Pursuits—Magic Valentine **Mr R. J. Reip**
2 **JAYJAY VALENTINE**, 9, b g Double Trigger (IRE)—Magic Valentine **R. J. Reip, M. Stevenson**
3 **THEATRE DIVA (IRE)**, 11, b m King's Theatre (IRE)—Rigobertha (IRE) **Miss J. M. du Plessis**
4 **TRIPLE BLUFF**, 9, b g Medicean—Trinity Reef **Mr T. J. G. Martin**

188 **MRS ANN DUFFIELD, Leyburn**
Postal: **Sun Hill Racing Stables, Sun Hill Farm, Constable Burton, Leyburn,
North Yorkshire, DL8 5RL**
Contacts: **PHONE (01677) 450303 FAX (01677) 450993 MOBILE (07802) 496332**
E-MAIL ann@annduffield.co.uk WEBSITE www.annduffield.co.uk

1 **ANGELO POLIZIANO**, 6, ch g Medicean—Helen Sharp **Middleham Park Racing XXVIII**
2 **INCA CHIEF**, 4, b g Sleeping Indian—Queen of Havana (USA) **D. K. Barker**
3 **INDIESLAD**, 4, b g Indesatchel (IRE)—Sontime **Mr T. Wilson**
4 **JUST LILLE (IRE)**, 9, b m Mull of Kintyre (IRE)—Tamasriya (IRE) **Middleham Park Racing XLVI**
5 **SALEROSA (IRE)**, 7, b m Monashee Mountain (USA)—Sainte Gig (FR) **Mr David K. Barker & Mr Phil White**
6 **SHARP SHOES**, 5, br g Needwood Blade—Mary Jane **Mr T. P. McMahon & Mr D. McMahon**
7 **SOVEREIGN STREET**, 4, ch f Compton Place—Mint Royale (IRE) **The Duchess of Sutherland**

THREE-YEAR-OLDS

8 **DUBIOUS ESCAPADE (IRE)**, b f Dubawi (IRE)—Brief Escapade (IRE) **Mr C. L. Stirling**
9 **ELUSIVE ISLAND (USA)**, b g Elusive Quality (USA)—Quiet Word (USA) **Mr Peter Odle & Mr James Pak**
10 **FERNDALE**, b f Royal Applause—Carradale **The Duchess of Sutherland**
11 **GIVEHERACHANCE**, b f Bachelor Duke (USA)—Apple Sauce **Mrs B. Skinner**
12 **GOODFELLOWS QUEST (IRE)**, ch c Intikhab (USA)—Poppys Footprint (IRE) **Mr J. Gatenby**
13 **HEIDI'S DELIGHT (IRE)**, b f Red Clubs (IRE)—Alexander Confranc (IRE) **David & Carole Mcmahon**
14 **ICE (IRE)**, b c Elusive City (USA)—Ice Box (USA) **Sir R. Ogden C.B.E., LLD**
15 **JESSIE'S SPIRIT (IRE)**, gr f Clodovil (IRE)—Alexander Anapolis (IRE) **David & Carole Mcmahon**
16 **MIDNIGHT TRYST**, ch f Cockney Rebel (IRE)—Shaken And Stirred **Middleham Park Racing XXXVII**
17 **NO TIME TO CRY**, b f Josr Algarhoud (IRE)—Autumn Bloom (IRE) **Middleham Park Racing XXXVII**
18 **OAKBROOK**, b g Indesatchel (IRE)—Statuette **James Warrender & Mrs Elaine Culf**
19 **OUTBACK (IRE)**, b g Kodiac—Florida City (IRE) **Sir R. Ogden C.B.E., LLD**
20 B c Diamond Green (FR)—Pivotal Role
21 **RIO GRANDE**, b g Invincible Spirit (IRE)—Pharma West (USA) **Sir R. Ogden C.B.E., LLD**
22 **SEATTLE SOUNDER (IRE)**, b g Choisir (AUS)—Bea's Ruby (IRE) **Phil Cunningham & Harry Redknapp**
23 **SILKEN SATINWOOD (IRE)**, b f Refuse To Bend (IRE)—Reine de Neige **Ms J. Grimes**
24 **SPRINGHEEL JAKE**, b g Lawman (FR)—Rye (IRE) **Mr J. A. Kay**
25 **SWIFT ENCOUNTER (IRE)**, b g Antonius Pius (USA)—Eucalyptus (USA) **Middleham Park Racing VII**
26 **TARO TYWOD (IRE)**, br f Footstepsinthesand—Run To Jane (IRE) **Rasio Cymru Racing 1**
27 **TWO CITIES (IRE)**, b g Excellent Art—Rock Dove (IRE) **Sir R. Ogden C.B.E., LLD**

TWO-YEAR-OLDS

28 **CHANT (IRE)**, b g 1/3 Oratorio (IRE)—Akarita (IRE) (Akarad (FR)) (11904) **Mrs A. Starkie**
29 **CHLOE'S DREAM (IRE)**, gr f 12/4 Clodovil (IRE)—Extravagance (IRE) (King's Best (USA)) (6000) **Mr P. A. Bowles**
30 **DENBIGH RAUR (IRE)**, b br f 9/4 Footstepsinthesand—
Gate Lodge (IRE) (Grand Lodge (USA)) (3809) **Rasio Cymru Racing 1**
31 B c 5/4 Sleeping Indian—Desert Gold (IRE) (Desert Prince (IRE)) (6567)
32 B f 30/4 Firebreak—Eloquent Isle (IRE) (Mull of Kintyre (IRE)) (4571) **Mrs D. Addison**
33 Gr f 2/2 Jeremy (USA)—Lady Georgina (Linamix (FR)) (4925)
34 **MYANNE**, b f 4/2 Indesatchel (IRE)—Mookhlesa (Marju (IRE)) (8095) **Jimmy Kay & Lovely Bubbly Racing**
35 B f 20/5 Holy Roman Emperor (IRE)—Opera Ridge (FR) (Indian Ridge) (5500) **The Four Fat Bellies Racing Club**
36 B f 10/3 Tobougg (IRE)—Prairie Sun (GER) (Law Society (USA)) **Mrs A. Duffield**
37 **RANGOONED**, gr f 18/2 Bahamian Bounty—Dansa Queen (Dansili) (19047) **Morecool Racing & David Redvers**
38 **RED CHARMER**, b g 29/4 Red Clubs (IRE)—
Golden Charm (IRE) (Common Grounds) (17240) **Mr I Farrington & Mr R Chapman**
39 **RED HIGHLITES (IRE)**, b f 21/2 Red Clubs (IRE)—
High Lite (Observatory) (13333) **Middleham Park Racing XL**
40 **RUST (IRE)**, b c 15/2 Elnadim (USA)—Reddening (Blushing Flame (USA)) (24630) **The Duchess of Sutherland**
41 B f 20/3 Celtic Swing—Saying Grace (IRE) (Brief Truce (USA)) (5746) **David & Carole Mcmahon**
42 **SCENTPASTPARADISE**, b f 13/5 Pastoral Pursuits—Centenerola (USA) (Century City (IRE)) (9523) **Mr M. Curtis**

MRS ANN DUFFIELD—continued

43 **TIGER PRINCE (IRE)**, b g 21/2 Strategic Prince—
Tiger Desert (GER) (Desert King (IRE)) (16190) **Middleham Park Racing XLII**
44 B c 2/2 Kheleyf (USA)—Tropical Breeze (IRE) (Kris) (13000)
45 **YORKSHIRE ICON**, b c 1/4 Sixties Icon—Evanesce (Lujain (USA)) (5238) **Middleham Park Racing XXIX**

Other Owners: Mr S. Bland, Mr R. P. Chapman, Mrs E. Culf, P. M. Cunningham, Mr A. W. Ellis, Mr I. J. Farrington, Mr D. McMahon, Mr T. P. McMahon, Mrs C. A. McMahon, Dr M. J. O'Brien, Mr P. J. Odle, Mr J. Pak, T. S. Palin, Mr J. D. Pierce, M. Prince, H. Redknapp, Mr D. Redvers, R. B. Rosenberg, Mr M. Sykes, Mr J. Warrender, Mr P. M. White.

Assistant Trainer: G Duffield

---

189 **MR IAN DUNCAN, Coylton**
Postal: **Sandhill Farm, Coylton, Ayr, Ayrshire, KA6 6HE**

1 **BALLYCOLIN**, 9, ch g Alflora (IRE)—Shift Changeover **Michael Kearney, Stephen Sinclair, Ian Duncan**
2 **DESSIE GRAY (IRE)**, 5, gr g Hawk Wing (USA)—Innocentines (FR) **Dr S. Sinclair**
3 **DODGEY DREAM**, 10, ch g Zaffaran (USA)—Dinnys Dream (IRE) **Miss H. A. Cross**
4 **GOLDEN SPARKLE (IRE)**, 6, ch m Samraan (USA)—Bye For Now **I. A. Duncan**
5 **INVERLOCHY LAD (IRE)**, 11, b g Mister Lord (USA)—Brogue Melody (IRE) **I. A. Duncan**
6 **MY UNCLE JACK**, 6, b g Fair Mix (IRE)—Sing And Dance **Mr A. J. R. Lilley**

Other Owners: Mr M. Kearney.

---

190 **MR NIGEL DUNGER, Pulborough**
Postal: **Generation House, Coombelands Stables, Pulborough, West Sussex, RH20 1BP**
Contacts: **PHONE (01798) 872194 MOBILE (07790) 631962**

1 **RICH MAID (IRE)**, 6, b m Flemensfirth (USA)—Richs Mermaid (IRE) **N. A. Dunger**
2 **SNOW PATROL**, 11, gr g Linamix (FR)—Overcast (IRE) **N. A. Dunger**

Assistant Trainer: Mrs D Dunger

---

191 **MR ED DUNLOP, Newmarket**
Postal: **La Grange Stables, Fordham Road, Newmarket, Suffolk, CB8 7AA**
Contacts: **PHONE (01638) 661998 FAX (01638) 667394 MOBILE (07785) 328537**
E-MAIL edunlop@eddunloppracing.co.uk WEBSITE www.edunlop.com

1 **DRAGONERA**, 4, b f Doyen (IRE)—Time Will Show (FR) **J. Weatherby, Champneys**
2 **LYRIC STREET (IRE)**, 4, b g Hurricane Run (IRE)—Elle Danzig (GER) **E. I. Mack**
3 **MOMENT JUSTE**, 4, b f Pivotal—Place de L'opera **Cliveden Stud**
4 **RED CADEAUX**, 6, ch g Cadeaux Genereux—Artisia (IRE) **R. J. Arculli**
5 **RED LOVER**, 4, b g Azamour (IRE)—Love Me Tender **R. J. Arculli**
6 **ROMEO MONTAGUE**, 4, b g Montjeu (IRE)—Issa **Mrs G. A. Rupert**
7 **ROYAL RAZZINI**, 4, b g Royal Applause—Shaken And Stirred **E. A. L. Dunlop**
8 **SNOW FAIRY (IRE)**, 5, b m Intikhab (USA)—Woodland Dream (IRE) **Anamoine Ltd**
9 **SWIFT GIFT**, 7, b g Cadeaux Genereux—Got To Go **Anamoine Ltd**
10 **TESTOSTERONE (IRE)**, 4, br f Dansili—Epopee (IRE) **N. Bizakov**
11 **THE TIGER**, 4, b g Tiger Hill (IRE)—Rafiya **J. Weatherby**
12 **VOODOO PRINCE**, 4, b g Kingmambo (USA)—Ouija Board **The Earl Of Derby**

THREE-YEAR-OLDS

13 **AEGAEUS**, b c Monsun (GER)—Ouija Board **The Earl Of Derby**
14 **ALMUDER**, b c Intikhab (USA)—Adraaj (USA) **Hamdan Al Maktoum**
15 **ALMUFTARRIS (USA)**, b c Smart Strike (CAN)—Ranin **Hamdan Al Maktoum**
16 **ALUSHTA**, b f Royal Applause—Degree **Miss P. Araci**
17 **AMORALIST**, b c Tobougg (IRE)—Ellablue **Mrs S. M. Roy**
18 **BASHAASH (USA)**, b f Dixie Union (USA)—Destination (USA) **Hamdan Al Maktoum**
19 **BURSTING BUBBLES (IRE)**, br f Big Bad Bob (IRE)—Ski For Gold **Anamoine Ltd**
20 **BURWAAZ**, b c Exceed And Excel (AUS)—Nidhaal (IRE) **Hamdan Al Maktoum**
21 **CARTHAGINIAN (IRE)**, b c Azamour (IRE)—Khayrat (IRE) **Sir Robert Ogden C.B.E., LLD**
22 **CYRUS SOD**, b g Nayef (USA)—Tahirah **C. J. Murfitt**
23 **ESHAAB (USA)**, b br c Dynaformer (USA)—Jaish (USA) **Hamdan Al Maktoum**
24 **FOURTH OF JUNE (IRE)**, b c Amadeus Wolf—Our Joia **Mrs S. M. Roy**

MR ED DUNLOP—continued

25 **GOLD LACE (IRE)**, b f Invincible Spirit (IRE)—Brigitta (IRE) **Mr R. Barnes**
26 **HOMERIC (IRE)**, b c Montjeu (IRE)—Al Saqiya (USA) **Highclere Thoroughbred Racing - Jackson**
27 **KHUBALA (IRE)**, b c Acclamation—Raghida (IRE) **Mr V. I. Araci**
28 B c Dansili—Lady Elgar (IRE) **Mr V. I. Araci**
29 **MAWAAL**, b g Shamardal (USA)—Perfect Plum (IRE) **Hamdan Al Maktoum**
30 **MIKDAAR (IRE)**, b c Elnadim (USA)—Jeed (USA) **Hamdan Al Maktoum**
31 **MUARRAB**, b c Oasis Dream—Licence To Thrill **Hamdan Al Maktoum**
32 **MUGAZALA (IRE)**, ch f Sakhee (USA)—Nasij (USA) **Hamdan Al Maktoum**
33 **NARCISSIST (IRE)**, b c Dylan Thomas (IRE)—Gabare (FR) **E. I. Mack**
34 B c Royal Applause—Nebraska Lady (IRE) **Sir Robert Ogden C.B.E., LLD**
35 **NEGIN**, b f Selkirk (USA)—Snow Goose **M. Jaber**
36 B f Bahamian Bounty—Ripples Maid **Saleh Al Homaizi & Imad Al Sagar**
37 B c Red Clubs (IRE)—Sacred Love (IRE) **R. J. Arculli**
38 **SKY KHAN**, b c Cape Cross (IRE)—Starlit Sky **Mr V. I. Araci**
39 **SPIRIT OF THE LAW (IRE)**, b c Lawman (FR)—Passion Bleue **R. J. Arculli**
40 **STRATHNAVER**, b f Oasis Dream—River Belle **St Albans Bloodstock LLP**
41 **TURAMA**, ch f Pivotal—Our Queen of Kings **Saleh Al Homaizi & Imad Al Sagar**
42 **WASPY**, ch f King's Best (USA)—Gib (IRE) **Miltil Consortium**
43 **ZIMIRA (IRE)**, b f Invincible Spirit (IRE)—Zibilene **N. Bizakov**

TWO-YEAR-OLDS

44 **ABRAQ**, b c 20/2 Danehill Dancer (IRE)—Nordhock (USA) (Luhuk (USA)) (130000) **Royal Cavalry Oman**
45 Ch f 27/3 Pivotal—Aiming (Highest Honor (FR)) (310000) **Saleh Al Homaizi & Imad Al Sagar**
46 B f 9/3 Proud Citizen (USA)—Alabaq (USA) (Riverman (USA)) **Hamdan Al Maktoum**
47 B br f 30/1 Cape Cross (IRE)—Alzaroof (USA) (Kingmambo (USA)) **Hamdan Al Maktoum**
48 **AMAZONAS (IRE)**, b f 24/2 Cape Cross (IRE)—
            Francesca d'gorgio (USA) (Proud Citizen (USA)) **Sir Robert Ogden C.B.E., LLD**
49 **AUCTION (IRE)**, b f 23/2 Mr Greeley (USA)—
            Exhibit One (USA) (Silver Hawk (USA)) (65681) **Highclere Thoroughbred Racing - Coventry**
50 **BANTAM (IRE)**, b f 25/4 Teofilo (IRE)—Firecrest (IRE) (Darshaan) (16420)
51 B f 19/1 More Than Ready (USA)—Betty Johanne (USA) (Johannesburg (USA)) (57142) **Mrs S. M. Roy**
52 Ch f 5/4 Notnowcato—Brazilian Terrace (Zilzal (USA)) (10000) **A Partnership**
53 B c 27/4 New Approach (IRE)—Claxon (Caerleon (USA)) (80000) **Bluehills Racing**
54 B f 15/4 Lemon Drop Kid (USA)—Cut Short (USA) (Diesis) (155000) **Cliveden Stud / St Albans Bloodstock**
55 B f 21/2 Manduro (GER)—Desert Royalty (IRE) (Alhaarth (IRE)) **Mrs Janice Quy**
56 B f 25/1 Hurricane Run (IRE)—Grable (IRE) (Sadler's Wells (USA)) (23000) **A Partnership**
57 Ch c 18/4 Medicean—Gretna (Groom Dancer (USA)) (50000) **R. J. Arculli**
58 **GWORN**, b c 3/3 Aussie Rules (USA)—Crochet (IRE) (Mark of Esteem (IRE)) **N. Martin**
59 **HANZADA (USA)**, b f 17/3 Arch (USA)—Chocolate Mauk (USA) (Cozzene (USA)) (225000) **N. Bizakov**
60 B c 14/3 Street Cry (IRE)—Henderson Band (USA) (Chimes Band (USA)) (183150) **Hamdan Al Maktoum**
61 B c 25/2 Acclamation—Intrepid Queen (USA) (Theatrical (USA)) (180000) **Hamdan Al Maktoum**
62 B f 5/2 Hard Spun (USA)—Ishraak (USA) (Sahm (USA)) **Hamdan Al Maktoum**
63 B c 12/3 Distorted Humor (USA)—Jaish (USA) (Seeking The Gold (USA)) **Hamdan Al Maktoum**
64 B f 7/5 Tiger Hill (IRE)—Kozmina (USA) (Sadler's Wells (USA)) **Lowe, Silver, Deal**
65 **NABAT SEIF (USA)**, b f 11/2 Street Sense (USA)—Sierra Madre (FR) (Baillamont (USA)) **Hamdan Al Maktoum**
66 B f 1/3 Invincible Spirit (IRE)—
            Needles And Pins (Fasliyev (USA)) (120000) **Saleh Al Homaizi & Imad Al Sagar**
67 B f 26/2 Oasis Dream—Nidhaal (IRE) (Observatory (USA)) **Hamdan Al Maktoum**
68 B f 20/2 Galileo (IRE)—Ouija Board (Cape Cross (IRE)) **The Earl Of Derby**
69 B c 19/2 Choisir (AUS)—Pairumani Princess (IRE) (Pairumani Star (IRE)) (1231) **Anamoine Ltd**
70 B c 3/3 Exceed And Excel (AUS)—Prayer (IRE) (Rainbow Quest (USA)) (63809) **Mrs S. M. Roy**
71 Ch c 1/3 Halling (USA)—Prithee (Barathea (IRE)) (10000) **A Partnership**
72 B c 21/4 Invasor (ARG)—Ranin (Unfuwain (USA)) **Hamdan Al Maktoum**
73 **SAXON SOLDIER**, br c 11/4 Kyllachy—Gwyneth (Zafonic (USA)) (26000) **H. Channon**
74 **SINGERSONGWRITER**, ch f 23/2 Raven's Pass (USA)—Independence (Selkirk (USA)) **Cliveden Stud**
75 **SPECKLED HILL**, b c 25/3 Oasis Dream—World's Heroine (IRE) (Spinning World (USA)) (75000) **H. Channon**
76 B f 20/4 Exceed And Excel (AUS)—Summers Lease (Pivotal) (50000)
77 B f 25/4 Royal Applause—Third Party (Terimon) (90000) **Hamdan Al Maktoum**
78 Ch f 25/2 Dalakhani (IRE)—Whazzis (Desert Prince (IRE)) (65000) **A Partnership**

Other Owners: Mr Imad Al-Sagar, Adie Bamboye, Duke of Bedford, Andrew Bengough, W. J. Gredley, The Hon. H. Herbert, Highclere Thoroughbred Racing Ltd, Mr Saleh Al Homaizi, Mark Horne, Tony Hurley, Mike Kean, Chris Kilroy, Martin Mitchell, Wendy O'Leary, Mr O. J. W. Pawle, Mr S. J. Purdew, Mr J. A. B. Stafford, The Hon. Peter Stanley, Mr Andrew Stone, Mrs M. F. Stone, Mr J. R. Weatherby.

Assistant Trainer: Mr George Peckham

192 **MR HARRY DUNLOP, Lambourn**
Postal: Windsor House Stables, Crowle Road, Lambourn, Berkshire, RG17 8NR
Contacts: PHONE (01488) 73584 FAX (01488) 674172 MOBILE (07880) 791895
E-MAIL info@harrydunloparacing.com WEBSITE www.harrydunloparacing.com

1 **BENARTIC (IRE)**, 8, b g Beneficial—Glacial Queen (IRE) **Sir Eric Parker & Mary Anne Parker**
2 **CHHOTA NAA**, 4, b g Calcutta—Ceilidh Band **Penny & Adrian Burton, Bob & Angela Lampard**
3 **SAINT HELENA (IRE)**, 4, b f Holy Roman Emperor (IRE)—Tafseer (IRE) **W R B Racing 47**
4 **VIKING STORM**, 4, b g Hurricane Run (IRE)—Danehill's Dream (IRE) **Be Hopeful Partnership**

THREE-YEAR-OLDS

5 **AIRBORNE AGAIN (IRE)**, gr g Acclamation—Bunditten (IRE) **A Partnership**
6 **BROADWAY BABE (IRE)**, br f Big Bad Bob (IRE)—Lady Sharp Shot (IRE) **Anamoine Ltd**
7 **HESPERIDES**, ch f Halling (USA)—Nando's Dream **Bluehills Racing Limited**
8 **HOUSE LIMIT (IRE)**, br c Red Clubs (IRE)—Fritillary **The Blue Bar Partnership**
9 **INDIAN BLOSSOM**, b f Sakhee (USA)—Al Corniche (IRE) **W R B Racing 42**
10 **MITCH RAPP (USA)**, b g Yankee Gentleman (USA)—Foolish Party (USA) **Mr Michael Buckley**
11 **NIC NOK**, b c Iceman—Past 'n' Present **Penny & Adrian Burton, Bob & Angela Lampard**
12 **OUR PHYLLI VERA (IRE)**, b f Motivator—With Colour **Kieron Drake & Simon Withers**
13 **POLYDAMOS**, b g Nayef (USA)—Spotlight **Mr Michael Buckley**
14 **RED MISCHIEF (IRE)**, b f Red Clubs (IRE)—Mujadilly **Harry Dunlop Racing Partnership**
15 B c Refuse To Bend (IRE)—Renowned **Racing UK Partnership**
16 **STICKLEBACK**, ch f Manduro (GER)—The Stick **Darby, Gehring, Marsden, McCreery**
17 **SUBTLE EMBRACE (IRE)**, b f Acclamation—Subtle Affair (IRE) **Dean Woodley & Partners**
18 **VILLA ROYALE**, b f Val Royal (FR)—Villa Carlotta **J. H. Richmond-Watson**

TWO-YEAR-OLDS

19 Gr c 18/3 Astronomer Royal (USA)—America Nova (FR) (Verglas (IRE)) (13136) **A Partnership**
20 **BAY LAUREL (IRE)**, b f 24/8 Baltic King—Bayleaf (Efisio) (18500) **Susan Abbott Racing**
21 B c 1/4 Pastoral Pursuits—Eishin Eleuthera (IRE) (Sadler's Wells (USA)) **The Bow Wave Partnership**
22 B f 18/4 Thousand Words—Es Que (Inchinor) (18000) **The Wigwam Partnership**
23 B gr f 11/3 Holy Roman Emperor (IRE)—Feather (USA) (Unbridled's Song (USA)) (4500) **A Partnership**
24 B f 23/5 Exceed And Excel (AUS)—Hiddendale (IRE) (Indian Ridge) **Mr Paul Roy**
25 **LE GRANDE CHEVAL (IRE)**, b c 25/3 Jeremy (USA)—Theory of Law (Generous (IRE)) (9523) **Mr Dean Woodley**
26 B f 18/4 Motivator—Nando's Dream (Hernando (FR)) (6500) **Bluehills Racing Limited**
27 B c 22/4 Elusive City—Ouliianovsk (IRE) (Peintre Celebre (USA)) **Mrs Mary-Anne Parker**
28 B f 30/1 Kheleyf (USA)—Port Providence (Red Ransom (USA)) **David Hearson & Paul Hearson**
29 **ROZ**, b f 23/4 Teofilo—Debonnaire (Anabaa (USA)) (16000) **Mrs Mary-Anne Parker**
30 Br gr f 15/4 Dalakhani (IRE)—Snow Crystal (IRE) (Kingmambo (USA)) (40000) **Kieron Drake & Simon Withers**
31 B f 23/4 Sakhee (USA)—Tenable (Polish Precedent (USA)) **Mrs Mary-Anne Parker**
32 B f 24/3 Tiger Hill (GER)—Waitingonacloud (In The Wings) **Mr D. Hearson**

Other Owners: Mr Andrew Bates, Miss Christina Blockley, Mrs Harry Dunlop, Sir David Sieff, Lady Sieff.

193 **MR JOHN DUNLOP, Arundel**
Postal: Castle Stables, Arundel, West Sussex, BN18 9AB
Contacts: PHONE (01903) 882194 FAX (01903) 884173 MOBILE (07860) 339805
E-MAIL jldunlop@jldunlop.co.uk WEBSITE www.jldunlop.co.uk

1 **AJEEL (IRE)**, 13, b g Green Desert (USA)—Samheh (USA) **Hamdan Al Maktoum**
2 **ANTON DOLIN (IRE)**, 4, ch g Danehill Dancer (IRE)—Ski For Gold **Windflower Overseas Holdings Inc**
3 **BEATRICE AURORE (IRE)**, 4, b f Danehill Dancer (IRE)—Mondschein **B. Andersson**
4 **BERLING (IRE)**, 5, gr h Montjeu (IRE)—Danaskaya (IRE) **B. Andersson**
5 **DOWNHILLER (IRE)**, 7, ch g Alhaarth (IRE)—Ski For Gold **Windflower Overseas Holdings Inc**
6 **HARLESTONE TIMES**, 5, b g Olden Times—Harlestone Lady **J. L. Dunlop**
7 **HOT SPICE**, 4, b g Kodiac—Harlestone Lady **J. L. Dunlop**
8 **KNIGHTLY ESCAPADE**, 4, ch g Sakhee (USA)—Queen of Iceni **Mrs I. H. Stewart-Brown**
9 **KORNGOLD**, 4, b c Dansili—Eve **B. Andersson**
10 **MAFETENG**, 4, b f Nayef (USA)—Marakabei **Mrs J. A. M. Poulter**
11 **MANY A SLIP**, 5, gr g Verglas (IRE)—Tri Pac (IRE) **J. L. Dunlop**
12 **MISK KHITAAM (USA)**, 4, b g Distorted Humor (USA)—Tashawak (IRE) **J. L. Dunlop**
13 **MISS TOPSY TURVY (IRE)**, 4, br f Mr Greeley (USA)—Cara Fantasy (IRE) **Windflower Overseas Holdings Inc**
14 **MOUNTAIN RANGE (IRE)**, 4, b g High Chaparral (IRE)—Tuscany Lady **Sir Philip Wroughton**
15 **PHONIC (IRE)**, 5, ch g Green Tune (USA)—Superfonic (FR) **J. L. Dunlop**
16 **SPANISH DUKE (IRE)**, 5, b g Big Bad Bob (IRE)—Spanish Lady (IRE) **Windflower Overseas Holdings Inc**

MR JOHN DUNLOP—continued

17 **SWINGKEEL (IRE)**, 7, ch g Singspiel (IRE)—Anniversary **Mrs H. I. Slade**
18 **TIMES UP**, 6, b g Olden Times—Princess Genista **Mrs I. H. Stewart-Brown**
19 **WARLU WAY**, 5, b h Sakhee (USA)—Conspiracy **The Earl Cadogan**
20 **YAIR HILL (IRE)**, 4, b g Selkirk (USA)—Conspiracy **The Earl Cadogan**

THREE-YEAR-OLDS

21 **AAZIF (IRE)**, ch c Nayef (USA)—Ayun (USA) **Hamdan Al Maktoum**
22 **AFNOON (USA)**, b f Street Cry (IRE)—Tashawak (IRE) **Hamdan Al Maktoum**
23 **ALRAASED (USA)**, br c Exchange Rate (USA)—Alabaq (USA) **Hamdan Al Maktoum**
24 **BALADY (IRE)**, b f Zamindar (USA)—Faydah (USA) **Hamdan Al Maktoum**
25 **BETTER BE MINE (IRE)**, br f Big Bad Bob (IRE)—Cara Fantasy (IRE) **Windflower Overseas Holdings Inc**
26 **BIG JOHNNY D (IRE)**, ch c Alhaarth (IRE)—Bakiya (USA) **Mr C. A. Washbourn**
27 **CAPHENE**, b f Sakhee (USA)—Claxon **Bluehills Racing Limited**
28 **ESTEBSAAL (IRE)**, b c Dansili—Bunood (IRE) **Hamdan Al Maktoum**
29 **FAREEDHA (IRE)**, b f Green Desert (USA)—Shahaamah (IRE) **Hamdan Al Maktoum**
30 **FARHAAN (USA)**, b c Jazil (USA)—Alshadiyah (USA) **Hamdan Al Maktoum**
31 **GOODWOOD ATLANTIS (IRE)**, b c Elusive City (USA)—
Kayak **Goodwood Racehorse Owners Group (Eighteen) Ltd**
32 **HARLESTONE WOOD**, b c Olden Times—Harlestone Lady **J. L. Dunlop**
33 **HIGHLY LIKELY (IRE)**, b g Elnadim (USA)—Height of Fantasy (IRE) **Windflower Overseas Holdings Inc**
34 **JOYFUL SPIRIT (IRE)**, b f Invincible Spirit (IRE)—Pershaan (IRE) **Windflower Overseas Holdings Inc**
35 **LADY OCARINA**, b f Piccolo—Queen of Iceni **Mrs I. H. Stewart-Brown**
36 **MAN OF PLENTY**, ch g Manduro (GER)—Credit-A-Plenty **Bluehills Racing Limited**
37 **MANBAA (USA)**, b f Jazil (USA)—Itnab **Hamdan Al Maktoum**
38 **MARHOONA (USA)**, b f Elusive Quality (USA)—Elrehaan **Hamdan Al Maktoum**
39 **MARIANNES**, br f Piccolo—Madurai **J. L. Dunlop**
40 **MUBARAZA (IRE)**, ch c Dalakhani (IRE)—Mokaraba **Hamdan Al Maktoum**
41 **NAWWAAR (USA)**, ch c Distorted Humor (USA)—Mostaqeleh (USA) **Hamdan Al Maktoum**
42 **SHOWMEPOWER (IRE)**, ch g Choisir (AUS)—Spanish Rainbow (IRE) **Windflower Overseas Holdings Inc**
43 **ZAAHYA (IRE)**, ch f Shamardal (USA)—Najah (IRE) **Hamdan Al Maktoum**

TWO-YEAR-OLDS

44 **ALPINE MYSTERIES (IRE)**, b f 17/4 Elusive City (USA)—
Alpine Gold (Montjeu (IRE)) **Windflower Overseas Holdings Inc**
45 B f 2/5 Invasor (ARG)—Alshadiyah (USA) (Danzig (USA)) **Hamdan Al Maktoum**
46 B f 3/3 Cape Cross (IRE)—Ayun (USA) (Swain (IRE)) **Hamdan Al Maktoum**
47 **ESTIRDAAD (USA)**, b c 4/2 Intikhab (USA)—Elmaleeha (Galileo (IRE)) **Hamdan Al Maktoum**
48 B c 9/4 Tamayuz—Etizaaz (USA) (Diesis) **Hamdan Al Maktoum**
49 **GOODWOOD MIRAGE (IRE)**, b c 22/3 Jeremy (USA)—
Phantom Waters (Pharly (FR)) (27000) **Goodwood Racehorse Owners Group (Nineteen) Ltd**
50 **INVINCIBLE CARA (IRE)**, b f 2/4 Invincible Spirit (IRE)—
Cara Fantasy (IRE) (Sadler's Wells (USA)) **Windflower Overseas Holdings Inc**
51 B f 5/3 Lemon Drop Kid (USA)—Itnab (Green Desert (USA)) **Hamdan Al Maktoum**
52 B f 3/4 Shamardal (USA)—Jules (Danehill (USA)) **Mr M. Stewkesbury**
53 Br c 30/3 Kheleyf (USA)—Laqataat (IRE) (Alhaarth (IRE)) **Hamdan Al Maktoum**
54 B f 2/2 Singspiel (IRE)—Lysandra (IRE) (Danehill (USA)) (16000) **The Earl Cadogan**
55 B f 16/2 Tamayuz—Miracolia (IRE) (Montjeu (IRE)) (130000) **Hamdan Al Maktoum**
56 B f 22/4 Dalakhani (IRE)—Mokaraba (Unfuwain (USA)) **Hamdan Al Maktoum**
57 **MOMBASA**, b c 15/4 Dubawi (IRE)—Limuru (Salse (USA)) **Wis Green Partners**
58 B c 15/3 Dansili—Mondschein (Rainbow Quest (USA)) **B. Andersson**
59 B f 6/4 Nayef (USA)—Muthabara (IRE) (Red Ransom (USA)) **Hamdan Al Maktoum**
60 **NOBLE GIFT**, ch c 9/5 Cadeaux Genereux—Noble Penny (Pennekamp (USA)) (18000) **Gail Brown Racing**
61 **ROSA BURN**, ch f 19/4 Notnowcato—Les Hurlants (IRE) (Barathea (IRE)) (10000) **Mrs J. P. R. Boscawen**
62 B f 9/2 Manduro (GER)—Special Moment (IRE) (Sadler's Wells (USA)) (11000)
63 B c 5/2 Shirocco (GER)—Tanaghum (Darshaan) **Hamdan Al Maktoum**
64 B c 12/3 Jazil (USA)—Tarteel (USA) (Bahri (USA)) **Hamdan Al Maktoum**
65 B c 3/4 Mr Greeley (USA)—Tashawak (IRE) (Night Shift (USA)) **Hamdan Al Maktoum**
66 **VELVETINA (IRE)**, b f 16/2 Barathea (IRE)—Pershaan (IRE) (Darshaan) **Windflower Overseas Holdings Inc**
67 Br f 7/2 Kheleyf (USA)—Winsa (USA) (Riverman (USA)) **Hamdan Al Maktoum**

Other Owners: Lord Balfour, Mrs M. Burrell, Mrs Emma Gregson-Williams, Mrs Sarah Lakin, M. J. Meacock, Mr M. Slade, A. J. Struthers, Mrs Valerie Thrower.

Assistant Trainer: David Menuisier

194 **MRS CHRISTINE DUNNETT, Norwich**
Postal: **College Farm, Hingham, Norwich, Norfolk, NR9 4PP**
Contacts: **PHONE (01953) 850596 FAX (01953) 851364 MOBILE (07775) 793523**
E-MAIL christine@christinedunnett.com WEBSITE www.christinedunnett.com

1 **AVEC MOI**, 5, b m Reset (AUS)—Pardon Moi **Christine Dunnett Racing (Avec Moi)**
2 **BLAZING APOSTLE (IRE)**, 4, ch f Redback—Salonika Sky **Mr A. Machin & Mrs C. Dunnett**
3 **CAPTAINRISK (IRE)**, 6, b g Captain Rio—Helderberg (USA) **Mr P. West**
4 **DANZOE (IRE)**, 5, br g Kheleyf (USA)—Fiaba **Mrs C. A. Dunnett**
5 **GIVE OR TAKE**, 4, ch g Where Or When (IRE)—Tata Naka **Christine Dunnett Racing (Avec Moi)**
6 **HOT TUB**, 4, b g Iceman—Starminda **Mrs C. Dunnett, Mr R. Spore & Mr P. West**
7 **IF AND WHEN**, 4, ch g Where Or When (IRE)—Pardon Moi **Mary Benjafield & Christine Dunnett**
8 **ITUM**, 5, ch g Bahamian Bounty—Petomi **Mary Benjafield & Christine Dunnett**
9 **NORCROFT**, 10, b g Fasliyev (USA)—Norcroft Joy **Mrs C. A. Dunnett**
10 **ONWARDS'N'UPWARDS**, 4, b g Diktat—Lunar Goddess **S. K. Crane, C. A. Dunnett, P. D. West**
11 **PATIENCE**, 4, b f Kyllachy—Capstick (JPN) **P. D. West, A. S. Machin & C. A. Dunnett**
12 **PATRICK DEE**, 7, gr g Silver Patriarch (IRE)—Bunty **The Daydreamers**
13 5, b m Reset (AUS)—Pinini **Mrs C. A. Dunnett**
14 4, Ch f Storming Home—Possessive Lady **Mrs C. A. Dunnett**
15 **SOUTHWARK NEWSMAN**, 5, b g Sulamani (IRE)—Another Nightmare (IRE) **Mrs C. A. Dunnett**
16 **SPEEDYFIX**, 5, b g Chineur (FR)—Zonnebeke **Mrs C. A. Dunnett**
17 **YAKAMA (IRE)**, 7, b g Indian Danehill (IRE)—Working Progress (IRE) **Mrs C. A. Dunnett**

THREE-YEAR-OLDS

18 B g Kheleyf (USA)—Bajan Belle (IRE) **Mrs C. A. Dunnett, Mr D. Cooper, Mr F. Butler**
19 B f Iceman—Capstick (JPN) **Mrs C. A. Dunnett**
20 **LATER IN LIFE**, ch f Notnowcato—Life's A Whirl **Life's a Whirl Partnership**
21 **MYSTICAL WITCH**, b f Kyllachy—Shifty Night (IRE) **Mrs C. A. Dunnett & Mr P. D. West**
22 Ch f Piccolo—Southwarknewsflash **Mrs C. A. Dunnett**

Other Owners: Mrs Mary Benjafield, Mr M. L. Clements, Mr D. Cooper, Mrs Christine Dunnett, Miss Karen Everitt, Mr A. S. Machin, Mr Ron Spore, Mr P. D. West.

195 **MR SEAMUS DURACK, Lambourn**
Postal: **16 Downsmead, Baydon, Marlborough, Wiltshire, SN8 2LQ**
Contacts: **PHONE (01488) 686581 MOBILE (07770) 537971**
E-MAIL sd111@btinternet.com

1 **AMORELIMONCELLO (IRE)**, 6, ch g Shantou (USA)—Eluna **Dale & Mick White**
2 **LAKOTA GHOST (USA)**, 4, b g Rockport Harbor (USA)—Political Alert (USA) **G. R. Poole**

THREE-YEAR-OLDS

3 **ZENAAD (USA)**, b br g Henny Hughes (USA)—Lady Cruella (USA) **Maze Rattan Limited**

Other Owners: J. J. Blackshaw, M. E. White, Mr D. White.

196 **MRS NERYS DUTFIELD, Seaton**
Postal: **Crabhayne Farm, Axmouth, Seaton, Devon, EX12 4BW**
Contacts: **PHONE (01297) 553560 FAX (01297) 551185**
E-MAIL nerys.dutfield@tiscali.co.uk WEBSITE www.nerysdutfield.com

1 **COLONEL FLAY**, 8, ch g Danehill Dancer (IRE)—Bobbie Dee **Mrs P. N. Dutfield**
2 **ELLE DIVA (IRE)**, 6, ch m Quws—Elle **S. J. Dutfield**
3 **HIDDEN PLEASURE**, 7, b m Karinga Bay—Girl of Pleasure (IRE) **Mrs P. N. Dutfield**
4 **LADY ON TOP (IRE)**, 4, b f Oratorio (IRE)—Ascot Lady (IRE) **S. J. Dutfield**
5 **LAID BARE**, 5, b m Barathea (IRE)—Lady Eberspacher (IRE) **Mrs P. N. Dutfield**
6 **MAN OF LEISURE**, 8, b g Karinga Bay—Girl of Pleasure (IRE) **Mrs P. N. Dutfield**
7 **PRESENT ACCEPTED**, 5, b g Presenting—Kwaheri **S. J. Dutfield**

197 MR CHRIS DWYER, Newmarket

Postal: **1 Hare Park, Six Mile Bottom, Newmarket, Suffolk, CB8 0UU**
Contacts: **PHONE (01638) 570074 FAX (01638) 570074 MOBILE (07831) 579844**
E-MAIL getadwyer@aol.com

1 **DURING THE WAR (USA)**, 5, b g Lion Heart (USA)—Carson's Star (USA) **Mr P. Venner**
2 **HENRY'S HERO**, 6, b g Mujahid (USA)—Primavera **Mrs I. L. Sneath**
3 **IMPERIAL FONG**, 4, b f Dr Fong (USA)—Chine **Mrs S. Dwyer**
4 **MIA'S BOY**, 8, b g Pivotal—Bint Zamayem (IRE) **Mrs S. Dwyer**
5 **MISS POLLY PLUM**, 5, b m Doyen (IRE)—Mrs Plum **Mrs J. Hughes & Miss C. Hughes**
6 **ONWARD**, 4, b g Doyen (IRE)—Crochet (IRE) **Mrs I. L. Sneath**
7 **PATRIOTIC (IRE)**, 4, b g Pivotal—Pescara (IRE) **M. M. Foulger**

THREE-YEAR-OLDS

8 **JENNDALE**, b g Common World (USA)—Jennelle **Mrs J. A. Cornwell**
9 **MORMORAN**, b f Proclamation (IRE)—Split Briefs (IRE) **Mrs S. Dwyer**
10 **RING FOR BAILEYS**, ch f Kyllachy—Ring of Love **G. R. Bailey Ltd**
11 **TATTING**, ch g Street Cry (IRE)—Needlecraft (IRE)
12 **TECTONIC (IRE)**, b g Dylan Thomas (IRE)—Pine Chip (USA) **I. Parvizi**

TWO-YEAR-OLDS

13 Gr g 25/3 Paris House—Clunie (Inchinor) **Mrs S. Dwyer**
14 Ch f 23/4 Notnowcato—Gretel (Hansel (USA)) (4000)

Other Owners: Mrs J. V. Hughes, Miss C. J. Hughes.

Assistant Trainer: Shelley Dwyer

Jockey (flat): Jimmy Quinn, Franny Norton, Cathy Gannon, Andrea Atzeni. **Conditional:** Charlie Wallis. **Apprentice:** Josh Crane. **Amateur:** Mr Matthew Smith.

198 MISS CLAIRE DYSON, Evesham

Postal: **Froglands Stud Farm, Froglands Lane, Cleeve Prior, Evesham, Worcestershire, WR11 8LB**
Contacts: **PHONE (07803) 720183 (01789) 774000 FAX (01789) 774000**
E-MAIL cdyson@live.co.uk WEBSITE www.clairedysonracing.co.uk

1 4, Gr g Overbury (IRE)—Altesse de Sou (FR) **D. J. Dyson**
2 **BOOMTOWN**, 7, b g Fantastic Light (USA)—Ville d'amore (USA) **Miss L. J. Hales**
3 **BURNTHILL**, 8, b g Winged Love (IRE)—Kilcorig (IRE) **Mr J. W. Wigglesworth**
4 **CILRHIWRON**, 8, b g Laverlon—Trefelyn Snowdrop **Ms I. Heritage**
5 **DADDY'SLITTLEGIRL**, 7, b m Midnight Legend—Lochnagold **Mr K. Elvins**
6 5, Br g Needwood Blade—Dudleys Delight **FSF Racing**
7 **DUNCANTHOMAS**, 8, gr g Executive Perk—Scallymill **N. J. Allen**
8 5, Ch gr g Danroad (AUS)—Eurolis (IRE) **C. R. Green**
9 **GIVEITACHANCE (IRE)**, 5, b g Clerkenwell (USA)—Native Lisa (IRE) **FSF Racing**
10 **INCHLOCH**, 10, ch g Inchinor—Lake Pleasant (IRE) **FSF Racing**
11 **LINDENGROVE**, 7, ch g Executive Perk—Lady Blakeney **Mr J. W. Wigglesworth**
12 **MUD MONKEY**, 8, ch g Muhtarram (USA)—Tenderfoot **B & S Vaughan & Partner**
13 **MUSICAL WEDGE**, 8, ch g Sir Harry Lewis—Wedge Musical **D. J. Dyson**
14 **MYSULA**, 5, b m Sulamani (IRE)—Air of Affection **Miss S. J. Turner**
15 **NELTARA**, 8, b g Kayf Tara—Lucia Forte **D. J. Dyson**
16 **PEQENO DIABLO (IRE)**, 7, br g Alexius (IRE)—Miss Huro (IRE) **Miss C. Dyson**
17 **PERGAMON (IRE)**, 6, b g Dalakhani (IRE)—Pinaflore (FR) **Team Arrow**
18 **PHAR AGAIN (IRE)**, 9, b g Beneficial—Phar From Men (IRE) **B & S Vaughan**
19 4, B g Beat All (USA)—Plus Tu Mets (FR) **D. J. Dyson**
20 **QUALITEE**, 7, b m Superior Premium—Coco Loco **C. R. Green**
21 **QUAYSIDE COURT (IRE)**, 8, ch g Anshan—Rustic Court (IRE) **Guy Sainsbury & Carl Mason**
22 **ROBOUGG (IRE)**, 6, b g Tobougg (IRE)—Robin Lane **FSF Racing**
23 **SLEEPING DU GRANIT (FR)**, 6, b g Sleeping Car (FR)—Broceliande Fine (FR) **Harborne House Syndicate**
24 **WHEELAVIT (IRE)**, 9, b g Elnadim (USA)—Storm River (USA) **FSF Racing**

Other Owners: Mr Reginald J. Coade, Miss C. Dyson, Mr D. J. Dyson, Miss L. Hales, Mr I. N. Jones, Mr Carl Mason, B. Rowland, Mr Guy Sainsbury, Mrs S. Vaughan, Mr B. Vaughan, Wilf Wigglesworth.

Assistant Trainer: John Dyson

Jockey (NH): Tom O'Brien, Nick Scholfield. **Conditional:** Ian Popham, Joe Cornwall. **Amateur:** Mr Jake Hodson.

199 MR SIMON EARLE, Warminster
Postal: **Little Croft, Tytherington, Warminster, Wiltshire, BA12 7AD**
Contacts: **PHONE** (01985) 840450 **FAX** (01985) 840450 **MOBILE** (07850) 350116
E-MAIL simon@simonearleracing.com **WEBSITE** www.simonearleracing.com

1 **BEMUSED (IRE)**, 7, b g Spartacus (IRE)—Arab Scimetar (IRE) **R. L. Dacombe**
2 **CHORD**, 8, ch g Pivotal—Choirgirl **The Plum Merchants**
3 **HEADLY'S BRIDGE (IRE)**, 6, b g Tillerman—Brockton Flame **Mrs P. L. Bridel**
4 **LISSELAN AMAZON (IRE)**, 5, b m Golan (IRE)—Amazonian (CAN) **Mr J. R. Powell**
5 **OPERA PRINCE**, 7, b g Kyllachy—Optaria **R. L. Dacombe**
6 **OUTSIDE THE BOX**, 8, b g Karinga Bay—Maydoo (IRE) **Mrs B. O'Flynn**
7 **RED NOT BLUE (IRE)**, 9, b g Blueprint (IRE)—Silent Valley **The Plum Merchants**
8 **SHILPA (IRE)**, 7, b m Medicean—Nature Girl (USA) **EPDS Racing Partnership I**

THREE-YEAR-OLDS

9 **SNOWY VALLEY**, ch g Three Valleys (USA)—Rasseem (IRE) **P & M Racing**
10 **STARLIGHT SECRET**, b g Exceed And Excel (AUS)—Caribbean Star **P & M Racing**
11 **WATER RAIL**, b g Manipulator (IRE)—Madame Mozaik (USA) **Mrs S. Earle**

Other Owners: Mr A. C. Clift, Mr T. M. Santry.

Jockey (flat): George Baker. Jockey (NH): Andrew Thornton, Gerard Tumelty. Amateur: Mr Luke Kilgarriff.

200 MR MICHAEL EASTERBY, Sheriff Hutton
Postal: **New House Farm, Sheriff Hutton, York, North Yorkshire, YO60 6TN**
Contacts: **PHONE** (01347) 878368 **FAX** (01347) 878204 **MOBILE** (07831) 347481
E-MAIL enquiries@mickeasterby-racing.co.uk **WEBSITE** www.mickeasterby-racing.co.uk

1 **AERODYNAMIC (IRE)**, 5, b g Oratorio (IRE)—Willowbridge **M. W. Easterby**
2 **ALLURING STAR**, 4, b f Gentleman's Deal (IRE)—Alustar **Jeff Hamer & Bernard Bargh**
3 **ANCIENT CROSS**, 8, b g Machiavellian (USA)—
　　　　　　　　　　　　　　　　　Magna Graecia (IRE) **Mr Pete Bown, Backup Technology & Steve Hull**
4 **ATLANTIC STORY (USA)**, 10, b br g Stormy Atlantic (USA)—Story Book Girl (USA) **Mr M. Green**
5 **BARREN BROOK**, 5, b g Beat Hollow—Carinthia (IRE) **Mr D Scott, Mrs E Wright & Mr J Clark**
6 **BLACK ANNIS BOWER**, 4, gr f Proclamation (IRE)—Bow Bridge **Mrs A. Jarvis**
7 **CHRISTMAS CARNIVAL**, 5, ch g Cadeaux Genereux—Ellebanna **Mrs L. J. Turpin**
8 **CITY GROUND (USA)**, 5, b br g Orientate (USA)—Magnet (USA) **Wiendiola**
9 **DAY OF THE EAGLE (IRE)**, 6, b g Danehill Dancer (IRE)—Puck's Castle **S. Hull**
10 **DESERT VISION**, 8, b g Alhaarth (IRE)—Fragrant Oasis **A Black, R Edmonds, J Holdroyd, J Quickfall**
11 **DEVIL YOU KNOW (IRE)**, 6, b g Elusive City (USA)—Certainly Brave **Mrs L. J. Turpin**
12 **DUCHESS THEATRE (IRE)**, 4, b f King's Theatre (IRE)—Avitta (IRE) **P. A. Deal**
13 **FEW AND FAR**, 6, gr g Fair Mix (IRE)—Dutch Czarina **Mr N W A Bannister & Mr N H T Wrigley**
14 **FIGHTER BOY (IRE)**, 5, b g Rock of Gibraltar (IRE)—In My Life (IRE) **Mr A. G. Greenwood**
15 **FRIDAYTHORPE (IRE)**, 7, b g Flemensfirth (USA)—Calm Waters (IRE) **N. H. T. Wrigley**
16 **GOLD RULES**, 5, ch g Gold Away (IRE)—Raphaela (FR) **Mr B. Padgett**
17 **HALLMARK HARRY**, 6, b g Silver Patriarch (IRE)—Society Girl **N. W. A. Bannister**
18 **HERNANDO TORRES**, 4, b g Iffraaj—Espana **N. W. A. Bannister**
19 **HOOF IT**, 5, b g Monsieur Bond (IRE)—Forever Bond **Mr A. Chandler & Mr L. Westwood**
20 **ICEBLAST**, 4, b g Iceman—Medici Princess **Mr B. Padgett**
21 **IT'S ME AND YOU**, 4, b g Dubai Destination (USA)—Time Crystal (IRE) **A. J. Duke**
22 **ITLAAQ**, 6, b g Alhaarth (IRE)—Hathrah (IRE) **Mrs L. J. Turpin**
23 **JANET'S PEARL (IRE)**, 4, ch f Refuse To Bend (IRE)—Sassari (IRE) **Lord Daresbury**
24 **JEER (IRE)**, 8, ch g Selkirk (USA)—Purring (USA) **Mrs L. J. Turpin**
25 **KALK BAY (IRE)**, 5, b g Hawk Wing (USA)—Politesse (USA) **Mrs L. J. Turpin**
26 **KINYRAS (IRE)**, 4, ch g Peintre Celebre (USA)—Amathusia **Backup Technology & Steve Hull 1**
27 **L'ASTRE DE CHOISIR (IRE)**, 4, ch g Choisir (AUS)—Starring (FR) **Mr A Simpson & Mr B Hoggarth**
28 **LIGHTENING ROD**, 7, b g Storming Home—Bolero **N. W. A. Bannister**
29 **MAJESTIC DREAM (IRE)**, 4, b g Exceed And Excel (AUS)—Tallassee **Mr A Simpson & Mr B Hoggarth**
30 **NACHO LIBRE**, 7, b g Kyllachy—Expectation (IRE) **Tri Nations Racing Syndicate**
31 **OIL STRIKE**, 5, b g Lucky Story (USA)—Willisa **Mr A. Saha**
32 **ONE OF TWINS**, 4, b g Gentleman's Deal (IRE)—Miss Twiddles (IRE) **Clark Industrial Services Partnership**
33 **PERTEMPS NETWORKS**, 8, b g Golden Snake (USA)—Society Girl **E. A. Brook**
34 **PITKIN**, 4, b g Proclamation (IRE)—Princess Oberon (IRE) **Steve Hull & Backup Technology**
35 **POLITBUREAU**, 5, b g Red Ransom (USA)—Tereshkova (USA) **W. H. & Mrs J. A. Tinning**
36 **PRICES LANE**, 5, b m Gentleman's Deal (IRE)—Prime Property (IRE) **A. G. Black**

MR MICHAEL EASTERBY—continued

37 **PRINCE JAMES**, 5, b g Danroad (AUS)—Lawless Bridget **Mr A. Saha**
38 **SHADOWS LENGTHEN**, 6, b g Dansili—Bay Shade (USA) **T. A. F. Frost**
39 **SHAN VALLEY (IRE)**, 6, ch m Shantou (USA)—Statim **C. F. Spence**
40 **SINGZAK**, 4, ch g Singspiel (IRE)—Zakuska **Clark Industrial Services Partnership**
41 **SPACE WAR**, 5, b g Elusive City (USA)—Princess Luna (GER) **Mr B. Padgett**
42 **SPECIAL MIX**, 4, b g Proclamation (IRE)—Flaming Spirt **E. A. Brook**
43 **SWITCHBACK**, 4, b g Medicean—Hooplah **Backup Technology & Steve Hull 1**
44 **TAPIS LIBRE**, 4, b g Librettist (USA)—Stella Manuela (FR) **Carpet Kings Syndicate**
45 **THE WAYWARD LORD**, 7, b g Emperor Fountain—Last House **Mr Andrew Chandler & Mr Lee Westwood**
46 **THIRTEEN SHIVERS**, 4, b g Iceman—Thirteen Tricks (USA) **Keith Wreglesworth & Andre Fordham**
47 **TIGER WEBB**, 4, b g Hurricane Run (IRE)—Wonderful Desert **Backup Technology & Steve Hull 1**
48 **WE'LL DEAL AGAIN**, 5, b g Gentleman's Deal (IRE)—Emma Amour **K. Wreglesworth**
49 **WIGRAM'S TURN (USA)**, 7, ch g Hussonet (USA)—Stacey's Relic (USA) **S. Hull**
50 **WITHOUT PREJUDICE (USA)**, 7, ch g Johannesburg (USA)—
                    Awesome Strike (USA) **Tri Nations Racing Syndicate**

THREE-YEAR-OLDS

51 **AUNTIE JOY**, b f Pursuit of Love—Aunt Hilda **Mrs A. L. Blanchard**
52 **BALTI'S SISTER (IRE)**, b f Tiger Hill (IRE)—Itsibitsi (IRE) **Steve Hull & David Swales**
53 **BE CALM**, b f Gentleman's Deal (IRE)—Flower O'cannie (IRE) **C. F. Spence**
54 **BORIS GRIGORIEV (IRE)**, b br g Excellent Art—Strategy **Mrs L. Ward**
55 **BURNING PASSION**, b g Gentleman's Deal—Search For Love (FR) **M. Pollitt**
56 **DICKY MINT**, ch g Osorio (GER)—Oh Bej Oh Bej (IRE) **Backup Technology & Steve Hull**
57 **LAST ZAK**, b g Lucky Story (USA)—Zakuska **Clark Industrial Services Partnership**
58 **LOW PASTURES**, ch g Lucky Story (USA)—Ring of Roses **Aricabeau Syndicate II**
59 **MARTHA'S WAY**, b f Tiger Hill (IRE)—Pilgrim's Way (USA) **Mr P. Morrison**
60 **MILLYMONKIN**, b f Gentleman's Deal (IRE)—Royal Distant (USA) **Mr T. Dewhirst & Mr R. Moore**
61 **NAMEITWHATYOULIKE**, b g Trade Fair—Emma Peel **S. J. Bowett**
62 **ON THE HOOF**, gr g Monsieur Bond (IRE)—Smart Hostess **Mr A. Chandler & Mr L. Westwood**
63 **PIPER CHEROKEE**, ch f Lucky Story (USA)—Miss Twiddles (IRE) **Clark Industrial Services Partnership**
64 **SIRIOUS OSS**, b g Sir Percy—Groom Landing (PR) **Backup Technology Racing**
65 **TOWBEE**, b g Doyen—Bow Bridge **Mrs A. Jarvis**
66 **UP TEN DOWN TWO (IRE)**, b g Hurricane Run (IRE)—Darabela (IRE) **B Delaney, A Duke & Backup Technology**

TWO-YEAR-OLDS

67 B f 1/4 Pastoral Pursuits—Alustar (Emarati (USA)) (7619) **Mr B. Bargh**
68 B c 8/5 Bollin Eric—Amalfi Storm (Slip Anchor) **Lucky 5 Partnership**
69 B f 27/4 Pastoral Pursuits—Answered Prayer (Green Desert (USA)) (7809) **Subiaco Racing**
70 B c 30/4 Pastoral Pursuits—Baymist (Mind Games) (11428) **Mr L. Westwood, Mr A. Chandler & Mr D. Blunt**
71 B f 8/4 Sleeping Indian—Bow Bridge (Bertolini (USA)) **Mrs Anne Jarvis**
72 Ch c 21/4 Pastoral Pursuits—Bow Peep (IRE) (Shalford (IRE)) **Mrs Anne Jarvis**
73 Ch f 15/3 Choisir (AUS)—Danifah (IRE) (Perugino (USA)) (1904) **Mr A. Morgans**
74 B f 23/1 Royal Applause—Forest Prize (Charnwood Forest (IRE)) (16666) **Mr D. Scott & Mrs E. Wright**
75 Ch c 9/3 Rock of Gibraltar (IRE)—Frambroise (Diesis) (14000) **Mr R. Armitage**
76 **HAAF'N HAAF**, ch c 10/3 Haafhd—Sweet Ludy (IRE) (Be My Guest (USA)) (4761) **Dachel Stud**
77 **MILL END DANCER**, b f 20/3 Antonius Pius (USA)—
                    Five Lakes (USA) (Coronado's Quest (USA)) (5714) **Lady Manton & Mr W Allgood**
78 B c 8/2 Trade Fair—Night Owl (Night Shift (USA)) (7619) **Mr Andrew Simpson**
79 B f 7/2 Indesatchel (IRE)—On The Brink (Mind Games) (29000) **Mr B. Padgett**
80 **PERFECT PASTURE**, b c 14/3 Pastoral Pursuits—Word Perfect (Diktat) (10476) **Mrs J. Turpin**
81 B c 14/2 Dutch Art—Pious (Bishop of Cashel) (65000) **Mrs L. Ward**
82 Ch c 15/4 Lucarno (USA)—Royal Distant (USA) (Distant View (USA)) **Mr T. Dewhirst & Mr R. Moore**
83 Ch f 29/3 Kyllachy—Spritzeria (Bigstone (IRE)) (12000) **Mr B. Sangster & Mr M. Green**
84 B c 19/4 Ishiguru (USA)—Sumitra (Tragic Role (USA)) (6666) **Mr D. Scott & Mr E. Brook**
85 Ch c 16/3 Sleeping Indian—Summer Dew (USA) (Swain (IRE)) (2380) **Sparsholt Stud**
86 B f 24/4 Sleeping Indian—Vagabond Chanteuse (Sanglamore (USA)) (10000) **Mr D. Scott**

Other Owners: Aricabeau Racing Limited, Mr R. Armitage, Mr J. Babbs, Mr Bernard Bargh, Mr Andy Barlow, Mr A. G. Black, Mr P. J. Bown, Mr John Bryan, Mr Andrew Chandler, Mr S. Chappell, Mr Jim Clark, Mr A. W. Clark, Lord Daresbury, Mr P. A. Davies, Mr Peter Davies, Mr Bill Delaney, Mr T. C. Dewhirst, Mr A. Duke, Mr M. W. Easterby, Mr Ray Edmonds, Mr Andre Fordham, Mr M. Gelber, Mr Matthew Green, Mr John L. Holdroyd, Mr S. A. Hollings, Mr Malcolm Hoyle, Mr Steve Hull, Mr J. R. Moore, Mr J. E. H. Quickfall, Mr B. V. Sangster, Mr G. E. Sangster, Mr David Scott, Mr John Southway, Mr G. H. Sparkes, Mr D. Swales, Mrs J. A. Tinning, Mr W. H. Tinning, Mr K. Wreglesworth, Mrs E. Wright, Mrs A. M. Wright.

MR MICHAEL EASTERBY—continued

Assistant Trainer: D. M. Easterby

Jockey (flat): Graham Gibbons, Paddy Aspell, Paul Mulrennan, James Sullivan. **Conditional:** Jake Greenall. **Apprentice:** David Simmonson. **Amateur:** Miss S. Brotherton, Miss J. Coward, Miss Joanna Mason, Mr H. Bannister, Mr T. Greenall, Mr O. Greenall.

---

201 **MR TIM EASTERBY, Malton**
Postal: **Habton Grange, Great Habton, Malton, North Yorkshire, YO17 6TY**
Contacts: **PHONE (01653) 668566 FAX (01653) 668621**

1 **ANOTHER CITIZEN (IRE)**, 4, b g Byron—Royal Rival (IRE) **Middleham Park Racing V & Partners**
2 **ANOTHER SUNSET**, 5, b m Doyen (IRE)—Sienna Sunset (IRE) **R. Bailey**
3 **BOLLIN FELIX**, 8, br g Generous (IRE)—Bollin Magdalene **T. D. Easterby**
4 **BOLLIN GRETA**, 7, b br m Mtoto—Bollin Zola **Habton Farms**
5 **BORDER REIVER**, 8, ch g Erhaab (USA)—Cumbrian Rhapsody **C. H. Stevens**
6 **BOUNDARIES**, 4, b g Indesatchel (IRE)—On The Brink **Bon Accord Racing & Partner**
7 **BUCKSHEE**, 4, b g Sulamani (IRE)—Cumbrian Rhapsody **Habton Farms**
8 **CAPTAIN DUNNE (IRE)**, 7, b g Captain Rio—Queen Bodicea (IRE) **Middleham Park Racing XV & Partners**
9 **CHEERS FOR THEA (IRE)**, 7, gr m Distant Music (USA)—Popiplu (USA) **R. A. George**
10 **CLOCKMAKER (IRE)**, 6, b g Danetime (IRE)—Lady Ingabelle (IRE) **Middleham Park Racing XI & Partners**
11 **CLOUD HAWK (IRE)**, 4, b f Hawk Wing (USA)—Grey Clouds **T. J. Hemmings**
12 **COCKTAIL CHARLIE**, 4, b g Danbird (AUS)—Royal Punch **C. H. Stevens**
13 **COLLATERAL DAMAGE (IRE)**, 9, b g Orpen (USA)—Jay Gee (IRE) **Middleham Park Racing XXV & Partners**
14 **CRACKENTORP**, 7, b g Generous (IRE)—Raspberry Sauce **C. H. Stevens**
15 **DARK DUNE (IRE)**, 4, b g Diamond Green (FR)—Panpipes (USA) **Miss B. C. Duxbury**
16 **DEAUVILLE FLYER**, 4, b g Dubai Destination (USA)—Reaf **Mr & Mrs J. D. Cotton**
17 **DISCANTI (IRE)**, 7, ch g Distant Music (USA)—Gertie Laurie
18 **FAST SHOT**, 4, b g Fasliyev (USA)—Final Pursuit **Ontoawinner & Partners**
19 **FAVOURITE GIRL (IRE)**, 6, b m Refuse To Bend (IRE)—Zuccini Wind (IRE) **P. C. J. Bourke**
20 **FAVOURS BRAVE**, 6, b g Galileo (IRE)—Tuning **Mrs J. M. Bowser**
21 **FIRST CLASS FAVOUR (IRE)**, 4, b f Exceed And Excel (AUS)—Lamh Eile (IRE) **S. A. Heley**
22 **GETABUZZ**, 4, b g Beat Hollow—Ailincala (IRE) **Langham Hall Stud Three**
23 **GRISSOM (IRE)**, 6, b g Desert Prince (IRE)—Misty Peak (IRE) **Jim & Helen Bowers**
24 **HAMISH MCGONAGALL**, 7, b g Namid—Anatase **Reality Partnerships I**
25 **HAYEK**, 5, b g Royal Applause—Salagama (IRE) **Habton Farms**
26 **HAZELRIGG (IRE)**, 7, b g Namid—Emma's Star (ITY) **The Senators**
27 **JONNY LESTERS HAIR (IRE)**, 7, b g Danetime (IRE)—Jupiter Inlet (IRE) **Reality Partnerships II**
28 **KING OF THE CELTS (IRE)**, 4, b g Celtic Swing—Flamands (USA) **Mrs B. Oughtred**
29 **LEASE LEND**, 9, ch g Zilzal (USA)—Moogie **C. H. Stevens**
30 **LITTLE JIMMY ODSOX (IRE)**, 4, b g Namid—September Tide (IRE) **Reality Partnerships III**
31 **LIZZIE (IRE)**, 4, b f Acclamation—Sky Galaxy (USA) **Mrs J. P. Connew**
32 **LOST IN PARIS (IRE)**, 6, b g Elusive City (USA)—Brazilia **W. H. Ponsonby**
33 **LOUKOUMI**, 4, b f Iffraaj—Odalisque (IRE) **Legard Sidebottom & Sykes**
34 **MALCHEEK (IRE)**, 10, br g Lend A Hand—Russland (GER) **Habton Farms**
35 **MAPPIN TIME (IRE)**, 4, b g Orientate (USA)—Different Story (USA) **P. Baillie**
36 **MARIACHI MAN**, 4, b f Doyen (IRE)—Popocatepetl (FR) **A. J. J. Gompertz**
37 **MAVEN**, 4, b f Doyen (IRE)—Bollin Jeannie **Habton Farms**
38 **MEDICI TIME**, 7, gr g Medicean—Pendulum **Mrs C. A. Hodgetts**
39 **MIDNIGHT MARTINI**, 5, b m Night Shift (USA)—Shaken And Stirred **D. A. West**
40 **MIRRORED**, 6, b g Dansili—Reflections **Middleham Park Racing XXX**
41 **MOJOLIKA**, 4, ch g Motivator—Kalandika **Mr A. Brannon & Habton Farms**
42 **MONSIEUR JOURDAIN (IRE)**, 6, b g Royal Applause—Palwina (FR) **C. H. Stevens**
43 **NO POPPY (IRE)**, 4, b f Chineur (FR)—Capetown Girl **Mrs P. M. Easterby**
44 **OFF CHANCE**, 6, b m Olden Times—La Notte **L. B. Holliday**
45 **OLD TESTAMENT**, 4, b g Olden Times—Birsay **L. B. Holliday**
46 **ONE FOR LUCK**, 5, b g Bollin Eric—One For Terry (IRE) **Ryedale Partners No 8**
47 **OSCAR ROMEO (IRE)**, 6, or g Environment Friend—Oscar Leader (IRE) **C. H. Stevens**
48 **PEBBLEGLEN (IRE)**, 6, b g Milan—Strong Profit (IRE) **T. J. Hemmings**
49 **REDMOLLY (IRE)**, 4, b f Namid—Molly Marie (IRE) **T. J. Hemmings**
50 **RESIDENCE AND SPA (IRE)**, 4, b g Dubai Destination (USA)—Toffee Nosed **Mr J. C. McGrath**
51 **ROYAL COMPOSER (IRE)**, 9, b g Mozart (IRE)—Susun Kelapa (USA) **Mrs B. Oughtred**
52 **RYEDANE (IRE)**, 10, b g Danetime (IRE)—Miss Valediction (IRE) **Ryedale Partners No 5**
53 **SEA FLOWER (IRE)**, 4, b f Acclamation—Rebel Clan (IRE) **Miss B. C. Duxbury**
54 **SILVERY MOON (IRE)**, 5, gr g Verglas (IRE)—Starry Night **Mr R. J. Swinbourne**

MR TIM EASTERBY—continued

55 **STEAL THE CURTAIN,** 4, b f Royal Applause—Ellebanna **D. J. Brown**
56 **THE FUN CRUSHER,** 4, ch g Halling (USA)—South Rock **Mr J. C. McGrath**
57 **THINKING,** 5, b g Makbul—Concentration (IRE) **Habton Farms**
58 **TILLIEMINT (IRE),** 4, b f Acclamation—Phantom Act (USA) **A. H. Arton**
59 **TIPTOEAWAY (IRE),** 7, b g Insan (USA)—My Blackbird (IRE) **T. J. Hemmings**
60 **TOP BID,** 8, b g Auction House (USA)—Trump Street
61 **TRANSMIT (IRE),** 5, ch g Trans Island—Apple Brandy (USA) **Habton Farms**
62 **TRUSTAN TIMES (IRE),** 6, b g Heron Island (IRE)—

Ballytrustan Maid (IRE) **Mrs M E Armitage & Mr Peter Armitage**
63 **VINTAGE TIMES (IRE),** 5, b g Croco Rouge (IRE)—Rare Vintage (IRE) **T. J. Hemmings**
64 **ZITENKA (IRE),** 10, b g Beneficial—Volobollea (IRE) **Mrs J. E. Pallister**

THREE-YEAR-OLDS

65 **ALABANDA (IRE),** b f Camacho—Alinda (IRE) **D. A. West**
66 **ART DZEKO,** b g Acclamation—Delitme (IRE) **Middleham Park Racing LIX & Partners**
67 **BEDLAM,** b f Auction House (USA)—Frantic **J. Musgrave**
68 **BLUE SHOES (IRE),** b f Kodiac—Alexander Capetown (IRE) **C. H. Stevens**
69 **BOLLIN TOMMY,** ch g Carnival Dancer—Bollin Ann **Habton Farms**
70 **BROTHER SUPERIOR,** b g Vital Equine (IRE)—Amber Mill **Ryedale Partners No 7**
71 **CHOISAN (IRE),** b g Choisir (AUS)—Attanagh (IRE) **Croft, Taylor, Hebdon & Hernon**
72 **CRIED FOR YOU (IRE),** b f Moss Vale—Baywood **Lease Terminated**
73 **DAZZLIN BLUEBELL (IRE),** b f Strategic Prince—Sharamaine (IRE) **Mr C. Wilson**
74 **DEEPSAND (IRE),** b c Footstepsinthesand—Sinamay (USA) **T. J. Hemmings**
75 **DUBAI DESTINY,** b g Dubai Destination (USA)—Ukraine (IRE)
76 **DUCHESSE SATIN (IRE),** b f Baratea—Carmona **Mr Colin Conway & Mr Jean-Michel Elbeze**
77 **DYLAN'S DREAM (IRE),** b f Dark Angel (IRE)—Catherinofaragon (USA) **R. A. George**
78 **ELEGANT GIRL (IRE),** b f Amadeus Wolf—Zuccini Wind (IRE) **P. C. J. Bourke**
79 **FAYR FALL (IRE),** b g Fayruz—Keshena Falls (IRE) **Reality Partnerships**
80 **HADRIANS RULE (IRE),** b g Holy Roman Emperor (IRE)—Farbenspiel (IRE) **Mrs J. E. Pallister**
81 **HAREBY (IRE),** b g Strategic Prince—Red Beach (IRE) **Mrs J. M. Bowser**
82 **HELLO STRANGER (IRE),** ch c Redback—Bobbydazzle **N. A. Jackson**
83 **HOLY ANGEL (IRE),** b g Dark Angel (IRE)—Bakewell Tart (IRE) **Three Jolly Farmers**
84 **JUST LIKE HEAVEN (IRE),** b g Kodiac—Night Beauty **Lease Terminated**
85 **LADY ADVOCATE (IRE),** b f Lawman (FR)—Shalev (GER) **S. A. Heley**
86 B g Jeremy (USA)—Lady Ellen
87 **LAST BID,** b f Vital Equine (IRE)—Manderina **C. H. Stevens**
88 **MAGIC BOUNTY,** ch g Bahamian Bounty—Magic Myth (IRE) **Habton Farms**
89 **MAYBEAGREY,** b f Shamardal (USA)—Grey Again **Habton Farms**
90 **NEARLY A GIFT (IRE),** b f Tagula—Chaukao (IRE) **A. H. Arton**
91 **PEARL CATCHER (IRE),** b g Catcher In The Rye (IRE)—Midnight Pearl (USA) **D. B. Lamplough**
92 **PONTY ACCLAIM (IRE),** b f Acclamation—Leopard Creek **Rapcalone**
93 **PREMIER CHOICE,** b g Exceed And Excel (AUS)—Simply Times (USA) **Sir Alex Ferguson & Mr J Hanson**
94 **QUEENS REVENGE,** b f Multiplex—Retaliator **W. H. Ponsonby**
95 **REGAL ACCLAIM (IRE),** b g Acclamation—Certain Charm (USA)
96 **ROGER SEZ (IRE),** b f Red Clubs (IRE)—Stately Princess **R. Sidebottom**
97 **SAFFA HILL (IRE),** b g Tiger Hill—Saffa Garden (IRE) **C. H. Stevens**
98 **SEE CLEARLY,** b f Bertolini (USA)—True Vision (IRE) **Ryedale Partners No 4**
99 **SOLANGE (IRE),** ch f Van Nistelrooy (USA)—Bank On Her (USA) **Mr Trevor C Stewart & Mrs Sheila Grassick**
100 **TRUST FUND BABE (IRE),** b f Captain Rio—Perfect Order (USA) **The Mutineers & Habton Farms**
101 **WARRICK BROWN,** b g Tagula (IRE)—Katie Boo (IRE) **Jim & Helen Bowers**
102 **ZAFFY (IRE),** b f Iffraaj—Silkie Smooth (IRE) **Mrs J. P. Connew**

TWO-YEAR-OLDS

103 **ANNIE GOGH,** b f 21/1 Dutch Art—Spunger (Fraam) (10000) **Mrs J. P. Connew**
104 B c 26/2 Ivan Denisovich (IRE)—Attanagh (IRE) (Darnay) (2052) **R. Taylor & Mr P. Hebdon**
105 **BANNOCKBURN BOY,** b c 20/2 Motivator—Senta's Dream (Danehill (USA)) (22000) **Numac Engineering Ltd**
106 B f 11/4 Pastoral Pursuits—Branston Gem (So Factual (USA)) (6666) **Habton Farms**
107 B f 26/4 Sleeping Indian—Camp Fire (IRE) (Lahib (USA)) (16190) **Habton Farms**
108 B f 2/4 Dark Angel (IRE)—Capetown Girl (Danzero (AUS)) (4761) **J & P Baillie & C & G Baillie**
109 Ch f 19/4 Medicean—Dance Away (Pivotal) (17142) **Ryedale Partners No 3**
110 B f 23/1 Captain Rio—Goodwood March (Foxhound (USA)) (7142) **Habton Farms**
111 B c 17/3 Haatef (USA)—Hazardous (Night Shift (USA)) **Habton Farms**
112 **HEIGHTS RIDGE,** b c 29/4 Sleeping Indian—Ellebana (Tina's Pet) (14000) **Miss B. C. Duxbury**
113 B f 5/4 Royal Applause—Icing (Polar Falcon (USA)) (13333) **J. Musgrave**
114 **INCHY COO,** br f 14/3 Pastoral Pursuits—Inchcoonan (Emperor Jones (USA)) (19047) **R. Sidebottom**

MR TIM EASTERBY—continued

115 B f 30/4 Captain Marvelous (IRE)—Lilac Mist (Spectrum (IRE)) (3283) **Habton Farms**
116 B c 2/3 One Cool Cat (USA)—Manon's Song (IRE) (Sadler's Wells (USA)) (6978) **Habton Farms**
117 **MARBLE SILVER (IRE),** gr f 2/2 Notnowcato—
                                    Serena's Storm (IRE) (Statue of Liberty (USA)) (7000) **Miss B. C. Duxbury**
118 Ch c 14/4 Dutch Art—Off Camera (Efisio) (2857) **D. B. Lamplough**
119 Ch c 19/2 Three Valleys (USA)—Phi Phi (IRE) (Fasliyev (USA)) (4761) **Ryedale Partners No 9**
120 B c 6/4 Byron—Piper's Ash (USA) (Royal Academy (USA)) (11000) **Reality Partnerships IV**
121 **RELIGHT MY FIRE,** ch c 5/4 Firebreak—Making Music (Makbul) (1523) **J. Gill**
122 Ch c 5/2 Elnadim (USA)—Saffa Garden (IRE) (King's Best (USA)) (9851) **Habton Farms**
123 **SANTA FE STINGER,** b f 26/2 Rail Link—Highly Liquid (Entrepreneur) (800)
124 B f 24/1 Aussie Rules (USA)—Stroppy (IRE) (Xaar) (4515) **Habton Farms**
125 **TOBACCO,** b c 29/4 Manduro (GER)—Wonderful Desert (Green Desert (USA)) (12500) **P. H. Milmo**
126 **VALETTO (IRE),** br c 14/2 Moss Vale (IRE)—Uhud (Mujtahid (USA)) (9523) **R. Taylor & Mr P. Hebdon**
127 Ch c 13/4 Pastoral Pursuits—Woodcock Moon (Kyllachy) (20000) **J. Musgrave**

Other Owners: Mrs M. E. Armitage, P. Armitage, Mr G. M. Baillie, Mr P. M. Baillie, P. J. W. Botham, J. F. Bowers, Mrs H. M. Bowers, Mr A. Brannon, Mr C. Conway, J. D. Cotton, Mrs B. Cotton, Mrs P. D. Croft, Mr H. Easterby, Mr J. Elbeze, Sir A. Ferguson, Mr S. R. Fraser, Mr G. C. Gilroy, Mr P. M. Goldsmith, Mrs S. Grassick, J. Hanson, Mr P. F. Hebdon, Mr P. J. Hernon, Mr R. A. Jacobs, Miss Y. M. G. Jacques, Mr C. Jones, Miss E. A. Lake, Lady Legard, Mr M. J. Lewendon, Mr J. Mounsey, Mr P. E. Nodding, N. J. O'Brien, Mr M. O'Neill, T. S. Palin, Mr M. Pearson, Mr D. Pearson, Mr J. Preston, M. Prince, A. H. Raby, Mr A. Reid, Mrs F. C. Saint Jean, T. C. Stewart, B. G. Swallow, Sir T. Sykes, R. Taylor, Miss S. J. Turner, J. R. Weatherby, Mr N. Yeoman.

202
MR BRIAN ECKLEY, Brecon
Postal: **Closcedi Farm, Llanspyddid, Brecon, Powys, LD3 8NS**
Contacts: PHONE (01874) 622422 MOBILE (07891) 445409
E-MAIL brian.eckley@live.co.uk

1 4, B g Revoque (IRE)—Fenella **B. J. Eckley**
2 **LUCKY PRINCE,** 5, b g Lucky Owners (NZ)—Sun Bonnet **B. J. Eckley**
3 **LUCKY SUN,** 6, b g Lucky Owners (NZ)—Sun Bonnet **B. J. Eckley**
4 **TIMEFORAGIN,** 5, b m Pasternak—Little Time **B. J. Eckley**
5 5, B m Oscar (IRE)—Tina Thyne (IRE) **B. J. Eckley**

203
MR PAT EDDERY, Nether Winchendon
Postal: **Musk Hill Stud, Nether Winchendon, Aylesbury, Buckinghamshire, HP18 OEB**
Contacts: RACING OFFICE: (01844) 296153 FAX (01844) 290282
MOBILE (07725) 616164/(07718)984799
E-MAIL info@patedderyracing.com WEBSITE www.patedderyracing.com

1 **ASCALON,** 8, ch h Galileo (IRE)—Leaping Flame (USA) **P J J Eddery, Mrs John Magnier, M. Tabor**
2 **AVALON BAY,** 4, b g Avonbridge—Feeling Blue **Pat Eddery Racing (Reference Point)**
3 **KENSWICK,** 5, b m Avonbridge—The Jotter **P. J. J. Eddery**
4 **STORM HAWK (IRE),** 5, b g Hawk Wing (USA)—Stormy Larissa (IRE) **Storm Hawk Partnership**
5 **SWEET POSSESSION (USA),** 6, b m Belong To Me (USA)—Bingo Meeting (USA) **Miss E. L. Owen**
6 **TWILIGHT ANGEL,** 4, ch f Compton Place—Leaping Flame (USA) **P. J. J. Eddery**
7 **WRENINGHAM,** 7, br g Diktat—Slave To The Rythm (IRE) **Miss E. L. Owen**

THREE-YEAR-OLDS

8 **BARNACLE,** b c Compton Place—Bombalarina (IRE) **Miss E.L. Owen**
9 **COOLER CLIMES,** ch c Three Valleys (USA)—Balmy **K. Abdulla**
10 **KHAZIUM (IRE),** br c Kheleyf (USA)—Hazium (IRE) **The Hill Top Partnership**
11 **KINGSCOMBE (USA),** gr ro c Mizzen Mast (USA)—Gombeen (USA) **P. W. Middleton**
12 **NEVAEH,** b f Firebreak—Mitsuki **Patrick Eddery & Emma L Owen**

TWO-YEAR-OLDS

13 B c 15/2 Captain Marvelous (IRE)—Aimee's Delight (Robellino (USA)) (12380)
14 B f 15/4 Excellent Art—Capriole (Noverre (USA)) (19047)
15 B c 4/5 Manduro (GER)—Opening Ceremony (USA) (Quest For Fame (USA)) (19047)
16 B f 29/4 Key of Luck (USA)—Rosewater (GER) (Winged Love (IRE)) (761)

MR PAT EDDERY—continued

Other Owners: Mr P. Burgoyne, Mr P. J. J. Eddery, Mrs John Magnier, Mr Doug Martin, Mr Peter Oppenheimer, Miss Emma L. Owen, Pat Eddery Racing Limited, Mr M. Tabor.

Assistant Trainer: Miss Emma L Owen (07718984799)

Jockey (flat): Ryan Clark. **Apprentice:** David Warren. **Amateur:** Mr D. Gannon, Miss E.L. Owen.

---

204 MR ROBERT EDDERY, Newmarket
Postal: **Robert Eddery Racing, Heywood Place, Hamilton Road, Newmarket, Suffolk, CB8 7JQ**
Contacts: **PHONE** (01638) 428001 **MOBILE** (07938) 898455
E-MAIL info@roberteddery racing.com **WEBSITE** www.robberteddery racing.com

1 **INVENT**, 4, b g Dansili—Fantasize **Robert Eddery**
2 **RAFAAF (IRE)**, 4, b g Royal Applause—Sciunfona (IRE) **Mrs P. Aitken & Eddie Phillips**
3 **VASILY**, 4, b c Sadler's Wells (USA)—Red Bloom **Owen O'Brien & David Bannon**
4 **WORLD HERITAGE**, 6, b g Kahyasi—Imbabala **Eddie Phillips & The Giggles Partnership**

THREE-YEAR-OLDS

5 **BALTIC FLYER (IRE)**, b f Baltic King—Negria (IRE) **Eddie Phillips**
6 **CASTALIAN SPRING (IRE)**, b f Oasis Dream—Lady Lafitte (USA) **Mrs Pat Phillips et Al**
7 **GRAYLYN OLIVAA**, b g Cockney Rebel (IRE)—Gaelic Roulette (IRE) **Mr & Mrs G. Knight**
8 **HEYWARD GIRL (IRE)**, ch f Bertolini (USA)—Rancho Cucamonga (IRE) **Mrs Pat Phillips et Al**
9 **LUNA VALE**, b f Dubai Destination (USA)—Fly Me To The Moon (GER) **Mrs Pat Phillips et Al**
10 **RED QUARTET (IRE)**, b c Red Clubs (IRE)—Nans Lady (IRE) **Trisha Keane et Al**

TWO-YEAR-OLDS

11 Ch f 21/2 Assertive—Branston Berry (IRE) (Mukaddamah (USA)) (7619) **Colin Gurnett et Al**
12 B f 10/2 Compton Place—Graceful Lass (Sadler's Wells (USA)) (5500)
13 Ch c 16/5 Assertive—Noor El Houdah (IRE) (Fayruz) (4761) **Michael Moss et Al**
14 **SPESSARTINE (IRE)**, b c 14/4 Duke of Marmalade (IRE)—
Lasting Chance (USA) (American Chance (USA)) (22000) **Eddie Phillips**

Other Owners: Mr Ian Anderson (Edinburgh), Mr Peter Collins, Mrs Natalie Donaldson, Mrs Sue Johnson, Mr Maris Kerve, Mrs Millicent Matthews, Mrs Julia Rayment, Mr Stuart Smith.

Jockey (flat): Andrea Atzeni.

---

205 MR GORDON EDWARDS, Minehead
Postal: **Summering, Wheddon Cross, Minehead, Somerset, TA24 7AT**
Contacts: **PHONE** (01643) 831549 **FAX** (01643) 831549 **MOBILE** (07970) 059297
E-MAIL dazjock001@hotmail.com

1 **BRIEFCASE (IRE)**, 7, b g Witness Box (USA)—Another Tycoon (IRE) **G. F. Edwards**
2 **CONSULATE (IRE)**, 8, b g Rock of Gibraltar (IRE)—Soha (USA) **G. F. Edwards**
3 **SHANANN STAR (IRE)**, 6, br m Anshan—Baile An Droichid (IRE) **G. F. Edwards**

Amateur: Mr D. Edwards.

---

206 MR CHARLES EGERTON, Chaddleworth
Postal: **Heads Farm Stables, Chaddleworth, Newbury, Berkshire, RG20 7EU**
Contacts: **PHONE HOME** (01488) 639786 **OFFICE** (01488) 638771 **FAX** (01488) 638832
MOBILE (07795) 220630
E-MAIL charles@charlesegerton.co.uk **WEBSITE** www.charlesegerton.co.uk

1 **ABBEVILLIAN (IRE)**, 8, b g Definite Article—Imminent Approach (IRE) **A & J Allison, D Thomas & Partners**
2 **LOMBARD LIGHT (IRE)** 6, b g Milan—All The Roses (IRE) **Equis**
3 **AVOCA PROMISE (IRE)**, 7, b g Oscar (IRE)—High Ace (IRE) **Bailey-Carvill Equine**
4 **CAPELLINI**, 5, b g Cape Cross (IRE)—Red Stella (FR) **Bruce Pomford & Malcolm Frost**
5 **CARRIBS LEAP (IRE)**, 7, b g Old Vic—Majister Ludi (IRE) **Equis**
6 **CATSPAN (FR)**, 6, gr g Turgeon (USA)—Royale Pour Moi (FR) **Bailey-Carvill Equine**
7 **DIXIE BULL (IRE)**, 7, br g Milan—Calora (USA) **Bailey-Carvill Equine**

MR CHARLES EGERTON—continued

8 GEE HI (IRE), 6, b g Milan—Curzon Street **Equis**
9 GREAT ESTEEM (IRE), 7, b g Carnival Dancer—California Dreamin **Bailey-Carvill Equine**
10 JOHN GULLY (IRE), 5, b g High Chaparral (IRE)—Desperate Virgin (BEL) **Equis**
11 JUST WALKING JACK, 4, ch f Old Vic—Lady Llancillo (IRE) **R. F. Bailey**
12 MONNOW MADE (IRE), 7, b m Bob Back (USA)—Lady Llancillo (IRE) **R. F. Bailey**
13 POLURRIAN (IRE), 5, b g Oasis Dream—Kincob (USA) **A Allison, D Thomas & Partners**
14 SEEDSMAN, 5, ch g Sulamani (IRE)—Unseeded **Christopher Spence & Partners**
15 VERY EDGY (IRE), 8, ch g Accordion—Lady Llancillo (IRE) **Bailey-Carvill Equine**

Other Owners: Mr R. K. Carvill, Mr J. Cavanagh, Mr Malcolm Davidson, Mr D. J. Erwin, Mr Tod Floyd, Mr Andrew Jones, Mr M. B. J. Kimmins, Mr Chris Taylor, Mr Rupert Villiers.

Assistant Trainer: David Plunkett (07778) 379341

Jockey (NH): Jimmy McCarthy (W.A.), A. P. McCoy (W.A.), Sam Twiston-Davies (W.A.)

---

207   **MR BRIAN ELLISON, Malton**
Postal: Spring Cottage Stables, Langton Road, Norton, Malton, North Yorkshire, YO17 9PY
Contacts: OFFICE (01653) 690004 FAX (01653) 690008 MOBILE (07785) 747426
E-MAIL ellisonracing@aol.com WEBSITE www.brianellisonracing.co.uk

1 ABERGAVENNY, 5, b g Dubai Destination (USA)—Welsh Dawn **Dan Gilbert & Kristian Strangeway**
2 AMTIRED, 6, gr g Beauchamp King—Rising Talisker **Mr G. Smith**
3 ANANDA KANDA (USA), 5, b br m Hero's Tribute (USA)—Roja (USA) **Koo's Racing Club**
4 ANDREO BAMBALEO, 8, ch g Silver Patriarch (IRE)—Time And A Place (IRE) **P. C. Andries**
5 ARTISAN, 4, ch g Medicean—Artisia (IRE) **Mr L. S. Keys & Kristian Strangeway**
6 BOCCIANI (GER), 7, b g Banyumanik (IRE)—Baila **J. D. Macgregor**
7 BRING SWEETS (IRE), 5, b g Firebreak—Missperon (IRE) **Racing Management & Training Ltd**
8 DAAWEITZA, 9, ch g Daawe (USA)—Chichen Itza **Mrs A. M. Mallinson**
9 DANE COTTAGE, 5, ch m Beat Hollow—Lady Soleas **Koo's Racing Club**
10 DIZZY RIVER (IRE), 7, ch g Flemensfirth (USA)—Dizzy Dealer **Mr D. R. Gilbert**
11 DONTPAYTHEFERRYMAN (USA), 7, ch g Wiseman's Ferry (USA)—Expletive Deleted (USA) **Koo's Racing Club**
12 DUSKY BOB (IRE), 7, br g Bob Back (USA)—Sunsets Girl (IRE) **Mr D. R. Gilbert**
13 FLORIO VINCITORE (IRE), 5, b g High Chaparral (IRE)—Salome's Attack **Mr L. S. Keys & Kristian Strangeway**
14 GLOBAL, 6, ch g Bahamian Bounty—Tuppenny Blue **Koo's Racing Club**
15 GLOBAL VILLAGE (IRE), 7, b g Dubai Destination (USA)—Zelding (IRE) **Jack Racing Melksham**
16 GOLDEN DREAM (IRE), 8, ch g Golden Tornado (IRE)—Orion Dream **Koo's Racing Club**
17 GREYFRIARSCHORISTA, 5, ch g King's Best (USA)—Misty Heights **Sekura Trade Frames Ltd**
18 HAKUNA MATATA, 5, b g Dubai Destination (USA)—Green Song (FR) **Sekura Trade Frames Ltd**
19 4, B g Key of Luck (USA)—Imdina (IRE) **Mr J. M. Basquill**
20 JOHN FORBES, 10, b g High Estate—Mavourneen (USA) **Brian Ellison**
21 KINGSWINFORD (IRE), 6, b g Noverre (USA)—Berenica (IRE) **Mr L. S. Keys**
22 KOO AND THE GANG (IRE), 5, b g Le Vie Dei Colori—Entertain **Koo's Racing Club**
23 4, Ch c Night Shift (USA)—Lady Hawk (USA) **Brian Ellison**
24 LAKEMAN (IRE), 6, b g Tillerman—Bishop's Lake **The Country Stayers**
25 LIFETIME (IRE), 4, b g Shamardal (USA)—La Vita E Bella (IRE) **Koo's Racing Club**
26 LITEUP MY WORLD (USA), 6, ch g Hennessy (USA)—Liteup My Life (USA) **Liteup Partnership**
27 MAHFAL (FR), 4, b g Dalakhani (IRE)—Peace Talk (FR) **Mr D. R. Gilbert**
28 MARSH WARBLER, 5, ch g Barathea (IRE)—Echo River **Dan Gilbert & Kristian Strangeway**
29 MAWJOODAH, 4, ch f Cadeaux Genereux—Isis (USA) **Mr D. R. Gilbert**
30 MEMORY CLOTH, 5, b g Cape Cross (IRE)—Gossamer **Racing Management & Training Ltd**
31 MUSNAD (USA), 4, ch g Mr Greeley (USA)—Jadarah (USA) **Mr D. R. Gilbert**
32 NEPTUNE EQUESTER, 9, b g Sovereign Water (FR)—All Things Nice **Koo's Racing Club**
33 OPTIMIST (GER), 4, ch g Liquido (GER)—Optik (GER) **Brian Ellison**
34 OVERRULE (USA), 8, b g Diesis—Her Own Way (USA) **Mr S. May**
35 PENDRAGON (USA), 9, ch g Rahy (USA)—Turning Wheel (USA) **Dan Gilbert & Kristian Strangeway**
36 POWERFUL AMBITION (IRE), 6, b g Bob Back (USA)—Native Shore (IRE) **Koo's Racing Club**
37 PRAVDA STREET, 7, ch g Soviet Star (USA)—Sari **Ms Z. Hatcher**
38 RAVI RIVER (IRE), 8, ch g Barathea (IRE)—Echo River (USA) **Koo's Racing Club**
39 RED INCA, 4, ch g Pivotal—Magicalmysterykate (USA) **D Gilbert, M Lawrence, A Bruce**
40 ROYAL OPERA, 4, b g Acclamation—Desert Gold (IRE) **Dan Gilbert & Kristian Strangeway**
41 SANDS OF VATERSAY, 6, b m Milan—Reflective Way **J. D. Macgregor**
42 SIMONSIDE, 9, b g Shahrastani (USA)—Only So Far **Racing Management & Training Ltd**
43 STORMY WEATHER (FR), 6, gr g Highest Honor (FR)—
                                         Stormy Moud (USA) **Mr S. L. Catchpole & Mr K. Hanson**

MR BRIAN ELLISON—continued

44 **THREE WHITE SOCKS (IRE)**, 5, b g Whipper (USA)—Halesia (USA) **Racing Management & Training Ltd**
45 **TILOS GEM (IRE)**, 6, ch g Trans Island—Alpine Flair (IRE) **G. Mercer**
46 **ULTIMATE**, 6, b g Anabaa (USA)—Nirvana **Mr D. R. Gilbert**
47 **UNION ISLAND (IRE)**, 6, b g Rock of Gibraltar (IRE)—Daftiyna (IRE) **Union Of Friends**
48 **WESTLIN' WINDS (IRE)**, 6, b g Montjeu (IRE)—Uliana (USA) **The Go 90 Partnership**

THREE-YEAR-OLDS

49 **ADILI (IRE)**, ch c Dubai Destination (USA)—Adirika (IRE) **Brian Ellison**
50 **DILIZAN (IRE)**, b c Dubai Destination (USA)—Dibiya (IRE) **Brian Ellison**
51 **FEELING GOOD**, b c Shamardal (USA)—Lady Golan (IRE) **Koo's Racing Club**

Other Owners: Mr J. M. Basquill, Mr S. L. Catchpole, Mr K. J. Corcoran, Mr T. Cosgrove, Mr Chris Duggan, Mr Brian Ellison, Mr Dan Gilbert, Mr Brendan Gilligan, Mr K. Hanson, Mr B. Hickson, Mr L. S. Keys, Mr Mark Lawrence, Mr A. Marucci, Mr A. Pierce, Mr Kristian Strangeway, Mr C. E. Weare.

Assistant Trainer: Mrs Claire Ellison, Mobile (07979) 570652

Jockey (flat): Tom Eaves. **Jockey (NH):** Fearghal Davis. **Apprentice:** Dale Swift. **Amateur:** Mr Jacob Butterfield, Miss Harriet Bethell, Mr David Cottle, Mr John Willey.

---

208 MR DAVID ELSWORTH, Newmarket
Postal: **Kings Yard, Egerton House Stables, Cambridge Road, Newmarket, Suffolk, CB8 0TH**
Contacts: **PHONE (01638) 665511 FAX (01638) 665310 MOBILE (07771) 804828**
E-MAIL david.elsworth@virgin.net

1 **BONNIE BRAE**, 5, b m Mujahid (USA)—Skara Brae **Mrs T. A. Foreman**
2 **CLASSIC PUNCH (IRE)**, 9, b g Mozart (IRE)—Rum Cay (USA) **The Classic Bunch**
3 **HIGHLAND CASTLE**, 4, b g Halling (USA)—Reciprocal (IRE) **Mr J Wotherspoon & Mr W Harrison-Allan**
4 4, B f Haafhd—However (IRE) **Mrs T. A. Foreman**
5 **HURSLEY HOPE (IRE)**, 4, b f Baratrea (IRE)—Hendrina (IRE) **J. C. Smith**
6 **ODIN (IRE)**, 4, b g Norse Dancer (IRE)—Dimelight **J. C. Smith**
7 **SALFORD PRINCE (IRE)**, 4, b g Invincible Spirit (IRE)—Bring Plenty (USA) **D. R. C. Elsworth**
8 **SWISS DREAM**, 4, b f Oasis Dream—Swiss Lake (USA) **Lordship Stud**
9 **SWISS FRANC**, 7, br g Mr Greeley (USA)—Swiss Lake (USA) **Lordship Stud**
10 **VIVA VETTORI**, 8, ch h Vettori (IRE)—Cruinn A Bhord **Mr M. Watson**

THREE-YEAR-OLDS

11 **ARTE DEL CALCIO**, b g Manduro (GER)—Movie Queen **M. R. Green**
12 **BRAVE KISS**, b f Manipulator (IRE)—Brave Vanessa (USA) **Miss Kay Russell**
13 **CHEWOREE**, b f Milk It Mick—Jodrell Bank (IRE) **S Stoneham, E Van Cutsem, A Hoctor-Duncan**
14 **ELUSIVE FLAME**, b f Elusive City (USA)—Dimelight **J. C. Smith**
15 **ENCOURAGING (IRE)**, ch g Rock of Gibraltar (IRE)—Unreachable Star **Mr B. C. M. Wong**
16 **ENGROSSING**, b g Tiger Hill (IRE)—Pan Galactic (USA) **Mr B. C. M. Wong**
17 **FLASHYFRANK**, b g Franklins Gardens—White Flash **D. R. C. Elsworth**
18 **GOLDEN SONG**, ch f Singspiel (IRE)—Premier Prize **J. C. Smith**
19 **HANDSOME MOLLY**, b f Halling (USA)—However (IRE) **Mrs T. A. Foreman**
20 **MONYMUSK**, b g Norse Dancer (IRE)—Bee One (IRE) **Mr J Wotherspoon & D Elsworth**
21 **NORSE SONG**, b f Norse Dancer (IRE)—Blue Lullaby (IRE) **D and C Bloodstock**
22 B g Dr Fong (USA)—Odabella's Charm **Peter Kelly**
23 **PLUM BAY**, ch f Nayef (USA)—Pelican Key (IRE) **K. A. Dasmal**
24 **POETIC POWER (IRE)**, b g Dylan Thomas (IRE)—Chalice Wells **J. C. Smith**
25 **SALFORD ART (IRE)**, ch f Sir Percy—Millay **A J Thompson & Matthew Green**
26 **SALFORD DREAM**, ch g Halling (USA)—Spitting Image (IRE) **A. J. Thompson**
27 **SWISS SPIRIT**, b c Invincible Spirit (IRE)—Swiss Lake (USA) **Lordship Stud**

TWO-YEAR-OLDS

28 B g 6/5 Avonbridge—Blaina (Compton Place) (10000) **McPabb Racing**
29 B c 15/3 Echo of Light—Blue Lullaby (IRE) (Fasliyev (USA)) **D & C Bloodstock**
30 B c 28/1 Teofilo (IRE)—Dashiba (Dashing Blade) **J. C. Smith**
31 B f 16/1 Royal Applause—Dodo (IRE) (Alzao (USA)) (50000) **Usk Valley Stud 1**
32 **FRIENDSHIP IS LOVE**, ch f 31/3 Byron—Silver Sail (Daylami (IRE)) **Mrs T. A. Foreman**
33 B f 26/3 New Approach (IRE)—Gower Song (Singspiel (IRE)) (23000) **G. B. Partnership**
34 B c 14/4 Bernstein (USA)—Hangin Withmy Buds (USA) (Roar (USA)) (68000) **Jiang XI Friends Ltd**

MR DAVID ELSWORTH—continued

35 B c 2/2 Kheleyf (USA)—Kissing Time (Lugana Beach) (66666) **Lordship Stud 1**
36 B f 22/3 Milk It Mick—Lamarita (Emarati (USA)) (9523) **Hilborough Racing**
37 B c 17/2 Kheleyf (USA)—Morality (Elusive Quality (USA)) (27000) **Corrigan, Dwyer & Partners**
38 B c 25/3 Mount Nelson—Pan Galactic (USA) (Lear Fan (USA)) (65000) **Mr B. C. M. Wong**
39 B f 7/3 Kyllachy—Poldhu (Cape Cross (IRE)) (30000) **K. A. Dasmal**
40 B f 19/2 Motivator—Premier Prize (Selkirk (USA)) **J. C. Smith**
41 Ch c 13/5 Halling (USA)—Rainbow End (Botanic (USA)) **P. A. Deal**
42 B c 5/4 Montjeu (IRE)—Seattle Ribbon (Seattle Dancer (USA)) **J. C. Smith**
43 **SENATOR BONG**, ch c 6/3 Dutch Art—Sunley Gift (Cadeaux Genereux) (40000) **J. Dwyer**
44 B c 17/1 Intikhab (USA)—Sopran Marida (IRE) (Darshaan) (8209) **Mr S. O'Keefe & Sean O'Sullivan**
45 **SORCELLERIE**, ch f 12/2 Sir Percy—Souvenance (Hernando (FR)) (15000) **Miss K. Rausing**
46 B c 25/1 Dylan Thomas (IRE)—Tango Tonic (IRE) (Trans Island) (36945) **D. Elsworth**
47 B f 29/3 Antonius Pius (USA)—Tochar Ban (USA) (Assert) (6978) **D. Elsworth**

Other Owners: Mr D. R. C. Elsworth, Mr T. F. Harris, Mrs E. A. Harris, Mr D. D. Sutherland, Mr Charles Wilson.

Assistant Trainer: Mr Paul Holley

---

209 **MS A. E. EMBIRICOS, Bury St Edmunds**
Postal: **St. Clare Hall, Bradfield St. Clare, Bury St. Edmunds, Suffolk, IP30 0EJ**
Contacts: **PHONE (01284) 386926 MOBILE (07876) 592308**

1 **JOHN'S DELIGHT (IRE),** 9, b g Luso—Be My Betty (IRE) **Ms A. E. Embiricos**
2 **OLD SI (IRE),** 9, b g Saddlers' Hall (IRE)—Shaping **Mr & Mrs S. N. J. Embiricos**
3 **RED BURN,** 6, b g Silver Patriarch (IRE)—Highland Rose (IRE) **Mr & Mrs S. N. J. Embiricos**

Assistant Trainer: Tim Bryce

Amateur: Ms A. E. Embiricos.

---

210 **MISS EVELYN ENGLAND, Rugby**
Postal: **Grove Cottage, Priors Hardwick, Southam, Warwickshire, CV47 7SN**
Contacts: **PHONE (01327) 260437**

1 **GIVE A LOT,** 8, b m Generous (IRE)—Gevity **Miss E. M. V. England**

Jockey (NH): Charlie Poste.

---

211 **MR GERRY ENRIGHT, Lewes**
Postal: **The Oaks, Old Lewes Racecourse, Lewes, East Sussex, BN7 1UR**
Contacts: **PHONE/FAX (01273) 479183 MOBILE (07922) 085875**
E-MAIL enright@btinternet.com

1 **DROMBEG PRIDE (IRE),** 8, b g High Account (USA)—Proserpina **Blue & Silver Partnership**
2 **KEEP A WELCOME,** 9, ch g Most Welcome—Celtic Chimes **Homebred Racing**

Other Owners: Mrs M. Enright, Miss P. A. Ross, C. M. Wall, Mrs S. Wall.

Assistant Trainer: Mrs M Enright

Jockey (NH): Robert Thornton.

---

212 **MR TIM ETHERINGTON, Malton**
Postal: **Wold House Stables, Langton Road, Norton, Malton, North Yorkshire, YO17 9QG**
Contacts: **OFFICE (01653) 692842 HOME (01653) 693049**

1 **ALIS AQUILAE (IRE),** 6, b g Captain Rio—
                        Garnock Academy (USA) **R. Hogton R.Bradley Training At Woldhouse**
2 **BAILADEIRA,** 4, b br f Intikhab (USA)—Sainte Gig (FR) **World Wide Racing Partners**
3 **CRANWORTH QUEST (IRE),** 4, b f Royal Applause—Seven of Nine (IRE) **Mr Chris Clark Mr Tim Etherington**
4 **EMBRA (IRE),** 7, b g Monashee Mountain (USA)—Ivory Turner

MR TIM ETHERINGTON—continued

    5 **RULER'S HONOUR (IRE)**, 5, b g Antonius Pius (USA)—Naughty Reputation (IRE) **I. T. Smith**
    6 **RUSSIAN WINTER**, 4, b g Tobougg (IRE)—Karminskey Park **Miss M. V. Greenwood**

THREE-YEAR-OLDS

    7 **ABSOLUTE BEARING (IRE)**, b g Majestic Missile (IRE)—Garnock Academy (USA) **T. J. Etherington**
    8 **PHOENICIAN BLAZE**, b f Phoenix Reach (IRE)—Chelsea (USA) **Lease Terminated**
    9 **ROYAL GIG**, br f Val Royal (FR)—Sainte Gig (FR) **World Wide Racing Partners**

Other Owners: R. Bradley, Mr J. Brierley, C. J. Clark, Mr P. N. Dowding, Mrs N. Dowding, B. Freer, Mr R. Hogton, Miss Z. C. Willis.

---

213   **MR JAMES EUSTACE, Newmarket**
          Postal: **Park Lodge Stables, Park Lane, Newmarket, Suffolk, CB8 8AX**
          Contacts: **PHONE (01638) 664277 FAX (01638) 664156 MOBILE (07802) 243764**
          E-MAIL jameseustace@tiscali.co.uk WEBSITE www.jameseustace.com

    1 **A BOY NAMED SUZI**, 4, b g Medecis—Classic Coral (USA) **Greenstead Hall Racing Ltd**
    2 **BAAN (USA)**, 9, ch g Diesis—Madaen (USA) **Mrs G. R. Eustace**
    3 **GO SET GO**, 5, b g Reset (AUS)—Dragon Star **T. H. Barma**
    4 **IRON CONDOR**, 5, b g Tobougg (IRE)—Coh Sho No **H. D. Nass**
    5 **SCOTTISH STAR**, 4, gr g Kirkwall—Child Star (USA) **J. C. Smith**
    6 **STORMING REDD**, 5, gr g Storming Home—Bogus Mix (IRE) **Sherin Lloyd & Friends**
    7 **SUZI'S A CLASS ACT**, 4, gr f Act One—Latour **Greenstead Hall Racing Ltd**
    8 **THE CAT CREATION (HOL)**, 4, b br g Kreator (POL)—Legal Cat (IRE) **Mrs H. Georganas**
    9 **TORRAN SOUND**, 5, b g Tobougg (IRE)—Velvet Waters **The MacDougall Two**
   10 **VIKING ROSE (IRE)**, 4, ch f Norse Dancer (IRE)—Rosy Outlook (USA) **J. C. Smith**
   11 **WILY FOX**, 5, ch g Observatory (USA)—Kamkova (USA) **Blue Peter Racing 10**

THREE-YEAR-OLDS

   12 **BALCARY BAY**, ch g Zamindar (USA)—Chantress **The MacDougall Two**
   13 **CARIBBEAN ACE (IRE)**, b f Red Clubs (IRE)—Caribbean Escape **J. C. Smith**
   14 **DENTON DANCER**, b br g Halling (USA)—Rapid Revelation **Mr A. E. B. Wiegman**
   15 **FULNEY**, b f Dr Fong (USA)—Postage Stampe **Major M. G. Wyatt**
   16 **HESTON SOUND**, ch g Nayef (USA)—Complimentary Pass **The MacDougall Two**
   17 **IRON BUTTERFLY**, b f Shirocco (GER)—Coh Sho No **H. D. Nass**
   18 **SAMBA NIGHT (IRE)**, b g Dark Angel (IRE)—Brazilia **G. N. Carstairs**
   19 **TIGHT LIPPED (IRE)**, gr g Dark Angel (IRE)—Kayoko (IRE) **Blue Peter Racing 11**

TWO-YEAR-OLDS

   20 B f 19/3 Cadeaux Genereux—Loch Verdi (Green Desert (USA)) **J. C. Smith**
   21 **LONDON SKOLAR**, b c 15/4 Tobougg (IRE)—Coh Sho No (Old Vic) **H. D. Nass**
   22 **PENNYWEIGHT**, ch c 24/3 Hernando (FR)—Penelewey (Groom Dancer (USA)) **Major M. G. Wyatt**
   23 **PRECINCT**, b f 3/3 Refuse To Bend (IRE)—Preceder (Polish Precedent (USA)) **Major M. G. Wyatt**
   24 B c 11/4 Tiger Hill (GER)—Rosy Outlook (USA) (Trempolino (USA)) **J. C. Smith**

Other Owners: Mr A. R. E. Ash, Mr D. F. Ballheimer, Mr B. M. Cimmering, C. Z. Curtis, Mr A. C. Frost, Mrs L. R. Lawson, Mrs S. A. Lloyd, R. E. Lloyd, Mrs K. A. McGladdery.

Amateur: Mr D. J. Eustace.

---

214   **MR DAVID EVANS, Abergavenny**
          Postal: **Ty Derlwyn Farm, Pandy, Abergavenny, Monmouthshire, NP7 8DR**
          Contacts: **PHONE (01873) 890837 (07834) 834775 E. Evans FAX (01873) 890837**
          MOBILE (07860) 668499
          E-MAIL pdevansracing@uwclub.net WEBSITE www.pdevansracing.co.uk

    1 **AVISO (GER)**, 8, b g Tertullian (USA)—Akasma (GER) **Mrs E. Evans**
    2 **BATHWICK BEAR (IRE)**, 4, b g Kodiac—Bayleaf **H. M. W. Clifford**
    3 **BAWAARDI (IRE)**, 6, b g Acclamation—Global Trend **Exors of the Late Mrs S. E. Edwards**
    4 **BOBBLE BORU (IRE)**, 4, b f Brian Boru—Balreask Lady (IRE) **Mrs B. B. Grainger**
    5 **BUSSA**, 4, b g Iceman—Maid To Dance **N. Shutts**
    6 **CANOPY OF STARS**, 6, gr g Fair Mix (IRE)—Maid Equal **Walters Plant Hire Ltd**

MR DAVID EVANS—continued

7 **CAPTAIN DIMITRIOS**, 4, b g Dubai Destination (USA)—Tripti (IRE) **H. M. W. Clifford**
8 **COOTEHILL LASS (IRE)**, 4, b f Ivan Denisovich (IRE)—Heat Alert (USA) **Mr N Shutts & Mrs E Evans**
9 **DAISY DAZE**, 4, ch f Dr Fong (USA)—Halcyon Daze **J. E. Rose**
10 **DELIGHTFUL SLEEP**, 4, b g Sulamani (IRE)—Naemi (GER)
11 **DREAM OF FORTUNE (IRE)**, 8, b g Danehill Dancer (IRE)—Tootling (IRE) **Mrs E. Evans**
12 **ESHTYAAQ**, 5, b g Mark of Esteem (IRE)—Fleet Hill (IRE) **T. H. Gallienne**
13 **ESTEEM**, 9, b g Mark of Esteem (IRE)—Please **N. Shutts**
14 **GRACEFUL SPIRIT**, 5, b m Reset (AUS)—Naemi (GER) **L. Audus**
15 **HONEY OF A KITTEN (USA)**, 4, b g Kitten's Joy (USA)—Sweet Baby Jane (USA) **Mrs E. Evans**
16 **INA POINT**, 6, b m Karinga Bay—Aranga (IRE) **Mrs B. B. Grainger**
17 **JACK MY BOY (IRE)**, 5, b g Tagula (IRE)—Bobanlyn **Mr G Evans & Mr T Earle**
18 **JUSTBOOKIE DOT COM (IRE)**, 4, ch g Fath (USA)—Dream On Deya (IRE) **J A & S Wilcox**
19 **KINGSWINFORD (IRE)**, 6, b g Noverre (USA)—Berenica (IRE) **J. E. Abbey**
20 **MEMPHIS MAN**, 9, b g Bertolini (USA)—Something Blue **Mrs I. M. Folkes**
21 **NORVILLE (IRE)**, 5, b h Elusive City (USA)—Saraposa (IRE) **R. N. Auld**
22 **NOVIKOV**, 8, ch g Danehill Dancer (IRE)—Ardisia (USA) **N. Shutts**
23 **NUBAR BOY**, 5, ch g Compton Place—Out Like Magic **Mr P. Slater**
24 **ONE WAY OR ANOTHER (AUS)**, 9, b g Carnegie (IRE)—True Blonde (AUS) **Mrs E. Evans**
25 **PENANG CINTA**, 9, b g Halling (USA)—Penang Pearl (FR) **T. H. Gallienne**
26 **RED DAGGER (IRE)**, 6, b g Daggers Drawn (USA)—Dash of Red **G. Byard**
27 **SCARLET ROCKS (IRE)**, 4, b f Chineur (FR)—Alexander Duchess (IRE) **N. Shutts**
28 **SCOTSBROOK CLOUD**, 7, gr g Cloudings (IRE)—Angie Marinie **Walters Plant Hire Ltd**
29 **SCRIBE (IRE)**, 4, b c Montjeu—Crafty Example (USA) **Shropshire Wolves/John Wilcox**
30 **STAR GALAXY (IRE)**, 12, b g Fourstars Allstar (USA)—Raven Night (IRE) **Don Gould, Wendy Herring**
31 **STAR ROVER (IRE)**, 5, ch g Camacho—Charlene Lacy (IRE) **Mr C. Leo**
32 **STEELCUT**, 8, b g Iron Mask (USA)—Apple Sauce **Shropshire Wolves 3**
33 **STYLE AND PANACHE (IRE)**, 4, b f Trans Island—El Corazon (IRE) **Roger Ambrose,Sean Ambrose & Bill Reilly**
34 **THE MONGOOSE**, 4, b g Montjeu (IRE)—Angara **Mr G Evans & Mr P D Evans**
35 **VALDAN (IRE)**, 8, b g Val Royal (FR)—Danedrop (IRE) **Diamond Racing Ltd**

THREE-YEAR-OLDS

36 **AL'S MEMORY (IRE)**, b c Red Clubs (IRE)—Consensus (IRE) **Mr W. R. J. Dawson**
37 **ALJOSAN**, b f Compton Place—Little Caroline (IRE) **J A & S Wilcox**
38 **ANGINOLA (IRE)**, b f Kodiac—Lady Montekin **Mrs E. Evans**
39 **ANNALUNA (IRE)**, b f Whipper—Annaletta **N. Shutts**
40 **AQUASULIS (IRE)**, ch f Titus Livius (FR)—Christoph's Girl **Bathwick Gold Partnership**
41 **BAJAN HERO**, b g Haafhd—Maid To Dance **Mrs E. Evans**
42 **BATHWICK STREET**, ch g Compton Place—Bahawir Pour (USA) **H. M. W. Clifford**
43 **CAMROCK STAR (IRE)**, b f Rock of Gibraltar (IRE)—Night Cam (IRE) **Dukes Head Racing**
44 **CAPTAIN KENDALL (IRE)**, b g Clodovil (IRE)—Queen's Lace (IRE) **J. G. K. White**
45 **CHOISIREZ (IRE)**, b f Choisir (AUS)—Filimeala (IRE) **N. Shutts**
46 **COCKNEY FIRE**, ch f Cockney Rebel (IRE)—Camp Fire (IRE) **Mr G Amey & Mr P D Evans**
47 **COMPLEX**, b f Multiplex—Dockside Strike **Mr S. Michael & Mr A. Stennett**
48 **COTES DU RHONE (IRE)**, b g Catcher In The Rye (IRE)—La Vie En Rouge (IRE) **Mrs E. Evans**
49 **COURTLAND KING (IRE)**, b g Baltic King—Red Rabbit **H. M. W. Clifford**
50 **DINGLE TWO (IRE)**, br f Mujadil (USA)—Puerto Oro (IRE) **Mr B. J. Mould**
51 **FOREST EDGE (IRE)**, b g Amadeus Wolf—Compass Light (USA) **Mr P. B. Swinnerton**
52 **JACK WHO'S HE (IRE)**, b g Red Clubs—Annus Iucundus (IRE) **Mr B. McCabe**
53 **JAWKING**, b g Compton Place—Just Down The Road (IRE) **J A & S Wilcox**
54 **KING'S WHARF (IRE)**, gr g Clodovil—Global Tour (USA) **R. N. Auld**
55 **KNOCKER KNOWLES (IRE)**, b g Refuse To Bend (IRE)—Yomalo (IRE) **Shropshire Wolves**
56 **LANA (IRE)**, b f Amadeus Wolf—Carn Lady (IRE) **Mr W. R. J. Dawson**
57 **MEET JOE BLACK (IRE)**, br b g Red Clubs (IRE)—Pascali **Mrs E. Evans**
58 **MISS PURITY PINKER (IRE)**, b f One Cool Cat (USA)—Consultant Stylist (IRE) **Mr J Abbey & Mr J Lomas**
59 **ORTEA**, b c Vital Equine (IRE)—Artistic (IRE) **Mr P. Slater**
60 **PALE ORCHID (IRE)**, b f Invincible Spirit (IRE)—Chelsea Rose (IRE) **Mrs E. Evans**
61 **PICALILY**, b f Piccolo—Kaylianni **W. A. Harrison-Allan**
62 **REDAIR (IRE)**, b f Redback—Alexander Goldmine **Mr & Mrs J. Potter & Exors of the Late Mrs S. E. Edwards**
63 **SI SEALY (IRE)**, b g Lawman (FR)—Sharpville (USA) **Mrs E. Evans**
64 **UMPH (IRE)**, b g Kodiac—Baraloti (IRE) **Mrs E. Evans**
65 **VERSE OF LOVE**, b g Byron—Lovellian **Bathwick Gold Partnership**
66 **ZIGAZAG (IRE)**, b g Refuse To Bend (IRE)—Most Charming (FR) **H. M. W. Clifford**

MR DAVID EVANS—continued

TWO-YEAR-OLDS

67 Ch c 4/3 Thousand Words—Autumn Star (IRE) (Mujadil (USA)) (7388) **Mrs E. Evans**
68 B c 5/4 Misu Bond (IRE)—Desert Sceptre (Desert Story (IRE)) (761) **Mrs E. Evans**
69 DREAMY CIARA, b f 13/3 Multiplex—Billie Holiday (Fairy King (USA)) (952) **Mrs E. P. Ambrose**
70 ED, b c 26/4 One Cool Cat (USA)—Danjet (IRE) (Danehill Dancer (IRE)) (2857) **E. A. R. Morgans**
71 B c 20/4 Indesatchel (IRE)—Happy Omen (Warning)
72 B c 1/5 Jeremy (USA)—Karinski (USA) (Palace Music (USA)) **Mr J. A. Wilcox**
73 B c 30/3 Tagula (IRE)—Polish Belle (Polish Precedent (USA)) **Mrs E. Evans**
74 B c 31/3 Multiplex—Samadilla (IRE) (Mujadil (USA)) (5336) **R. Kent**
75 B f 26/4 Camacho—Savvy Shopper (USA) (Stravinsky (USA)) (1333) **Mrs E. Evans**
76 B c 18/2 Iffraaj—Spanish Needle (Green Desert (USA)) **Mrs E. Evans**

Other Owners: Mr R. D. Ambrose, Mr S. Ambrose, G. E. Amey, Mr J. Babb, J. L. Collins, Mr P. G. Dalton, Mr T. H. Earle, P. D. Evans, Mr G. G. Evans, D. I. Gould, Miss P. W. Herring, Mr J. Lomas, Mr S. R. P. Michael, Mrs M. J. Potter, J. E. Potter, Mr W. J. Reilly, R. Simpson, A. Stennett, N. E. Webb, Mrs S. Wilcox.

Assistant Trainer: Mrs Emma Evans

Jockey (flat): Cathy Gannon. **Conditional:** Peter Hatton. **Apprentice:** Richard Evans, Kevin Lundie, Matthew Cosham. **Amateur:** Mrs E. Evans, Miss Megan Evans.

---

215 **MR JAMES EVANS, Worcester**
Postal: **Stone Farm, Broadwas on Teme, Worcester, Worcestershire, WR6 5NE**
Contacts: **PHONE (01886) 822054 FAX (01886) 821303 MOBILE (07813) 166430**
E-MAIL **herbie_evans@hotmail.com WEBSITE www.hjamesevans.co.uk**

1 CALDERCRUIX (USA), 5, ch g Rahy (USA)—Al Theraab (USA) **Mr D. C. Mantle**
2 CARBON PRINT (USA), 7, ch g Johannesburg (USA)—Caithness (USA) **Mrs J. Evans**
3 CARD LOVER, b m First Trump—American Pie **Mr R. J. Davis**
4 ESTATES RECOVERY (IRE), 7, b g Luso—Jendam (IRE) **Threemorelargeones**
5 FRIENDSHIP BAY, 8, b g Midnight Legend—Friendly Fairy **Mrs J. Evans**
6 GHOSTWING, 5, gr g Kheleyf (USA)—Someone's Angel (USA) **M. J. Benton**
7 HEEZAGREY (IRE), 9, gr g Naheez (USA)—Silver Belle (IRE) **Miss S. Troughton**
8 MEXICAN BOB, 9, b g Atraf—Eskimo Nel (IRE) **M. J. Benton**
9 MIDNIGHT CHOICE, 7, b g Midnight Legend—Pearl's Choice (IRE) **Mrs O. H. Stewart**
10 MNARANI (IRE), 5, b g Oasis Dream—Finity (USA) **Mrs J. Evans**
11 NAMIR (IRE), 10, b g Namid—Danalia (IRE) **Shakespeare Racing**
12 NEIGHBOURHOOD (USA), 4, b br g Street Cry (IRE)—Miznah (IRE) **James Evans Racing**
13 PHOENIX FLIGHT (IRE), 7, b g Hawk Wing (USA)—Firecrest (IRE) **Mr D. T. Ross**
14 PROPHETE DE GUYE (FR), 9, b g Apple Tree (FR)—Kasibelle de Guye (FR) **Elegant Clutter Ltd**
15 REVUPCLOVER (IRE), 5, gr g Revoque (IRE)—Kingsfield Clover **Miss S. Troughton**
16 ROC DE GUYE (FR), 7, b g Video Rock (FR)—Kasibelle de Guye (FR) **S. Crawley, T. Crawley**
17 TRACKMATE, 6, b g Muhtarram (USA)—Cruz Santa **Mr B. W. Preece**

Other Owners: Mrs S. E. Crawley, Mr T. P. M. Crawley, Mr H. J. Evans, Mr N. Higginson, Mr T. Lively, J. F. Long, B. J. McClean.

Assistant Trainer: Mrs Jane Evans

---

216 **MRS MARY EVANS, Haverfordwest**
Postal: **Hengoed, Clarbeston Road, Haverfordwest, Pembrokeshire, SA63 4QL**
Contacts: **PHONE (01437) 731336**

1 MAIZY MISSILE (IRE), 10, b m Executive Perk—Landsker Missile **Mary & Billy Evans**

Other Owners: Mrs M. Evans, W. J. Evans.

Assistant Trainer: W J Evans

217 MRS NIKKI EVANS, Abergavenny

Postal: Penbiddle Farm, Penbidwal, Pandy, Abergavenny, Gwent, NP7 8EA
Contacts: **(01873) 890957 FAX** (01873) 890957 **MOBILE** (07977) 753437
E-MAIL nikki@penbiddle.fsnet.co.uk **WEBSITE** www.nikki-evans-racing.co.uk

1 **DUNEEN DREAM (USA)**, 7, ch g Hennessy (USA)—T N T Red (USA) **Mr J. Berry**
2 **GLACIAL HARRY**, 6, b g Sir Harry Lewis (USA)—Glacial Wonder (IRE) **B. Hatton**
3 **HECTOR'S HOUSE**, 6, b g Tobougg (IRE)—Thrasher **Iwantaracehorse.Com**
4 **KAYFTON PETE**, 6, b g Kayf Tara—Jonchee (FR) **B. Hatton**
5 **LILEO (IRE)**, 5, b g Galileo (IRE)—Jabali (FR) **Mr J. Berry**
6 **MARATIB (USA)**, 4, b g Street Cry (IRE)—Colcon (USA) **Mr J. Berry**
7 **MAYTHETENTH (IRE)**, 6, b m Dr Massini (IRE)—Maythefifth **P. T. Evans**
8 **MINELLA BLISS (IRE)**, 7, gr g Old Vic—Carraigrose **Running Dragon Racing 2**
9 **OAK LEAVES**, 5, b m Mark of Esteem (IRE)—Exotic Forest **Girlsjustwannahavefun**
10 **SASSANIAN (IRE)**, 5, b g Clodovil (IRE)—Persian Sally (IRE) **Mr M. Llewelyn**
11 **STEEL RAIN**, 4, b g Striking Ambition—Concentration (IRE) **Mr J. Berry**

THREE-YEAR-OLDS

12 **BOGEY HOLE (IRE)**, gr f Aussie Rules (USA)—Sticky Green **Mr J. Berry**
13 B f Sakhee (USA)—Exotic Forest **Mrs N. S. Evans**

Other Owners: Mr John Berry (Gwent), Mr P. T. Evans, Mrs G. Gittings-Watt, Mr Martin Llewelyn, Mrs Helen Llewelyn, Mr L. W. Merrick.

Assistant Trainer: Mr P. T. Evans

Conditional: Peter Hatton.

218 MR JAMES EWART, Langholm

Postal: James Ewart Racing Limited, Craig Farm, Westerkirk, Langholm, Dumfriesshire, DG13 0NZ
Contacts: **PHONE** (01387) 370707 **FAX** (01387) 370733 **MOBILE** (07786) 995073
E-MAIL office@jeracing.co.uk **WEBSITE** www.jamesewartracing.com

1 **AIKMAN (IRE)**, 8, b g Rudimentary (USA)—Omas Lady (IRE) **J. D. Gordon**
2 **AIREY SCAREY**, 9, b m Missed Flight—Terrorisa **Mrs J. D. Percy**
3 **ALLOW ME**, 7, b g Daylami (USA)—Time Honoured **The South Hayrigg Partnership**
4 **BENEFICIAL REFORM (IRE)**, 7, ch g Beneficial—Miss Performance (IRE) **Mr M. J. Tedham**
5 **BEST LOVER (FR)**, 10, ch g Great Palm (USA)—Droid (FR) **The Best Lovers**
6 **BEYOND THE TWEED**, 6, b g And Beyond (IRE)—Over The Tweed **Mrs Hugh Fraser**
7 **BISHOPS HEIR**, 7, b g Turbo Speed—
                    Linns Heir **Mr G. Reid, Mrs A.G. Humbert, Mr W. Graham, Richard Barrie, Scott White**
8 **CAPTAIN AMERICO (IRE)**, 10, b g Lord Americo—Excitable Lady **Mr M. J. Tedham**
9 **CIVIL UNREST (IRE)**, 6, ch g Blueprint (IRE)—Yore (IRE) **Halliday,Carruthers,Optimists & Ancrum**
10 **CLASSIC CUT**, 8, b g Classic Cliche (IRE)—Leading Line **J. D. Gordon**
11 **DISCOVERIE**, 4, b g Runyon (IRE)—Sri (IRE) **D. Coppola, J. Ewart**
12 **FRONTIER BOY (IRE)**, 8, b g New Frontier (IRE)—
                    Mary Bridie (IRE) **Main, Conneely, Palmer, Ritson, Mr J. P. L. Ewart**
13 **HERON'S MILL (IRE)**, 4, b g Heron Island (IRE)—Princess Vic (IRE) **Jump Racing Up North**
14 **HIGH EXPECTATION**, 5, b m Kayf Tara—Hazel Bank Lass (IRE) **Mr M. J. Tedham**
15 **LORD WISHES (IRE)**, 5, b g Milan—Strong Wishes (IRE) **Leeds Plywood & Doors Ltd**
16 **OPEN DE L'ISLE (FR)**, 10, b br g Funny Baby (FR)—
                    Gabatine (FR) **Dr C. Kesson, Mr/Mrs Reid, Mr R. Carruthers**
17 **PLUS JAMAIS (FR)**, 5, b g Caballo Raptor (CAN)—Branceilles (FR) **Alba-Eire Syndicate**
18 **PREMIER GRAND CRU (FR)**, 6, b g Kaldounevees (FR)—Last Harvest (FR) **Leeds Plywood & Doors Ltd**
19 **QUICUYO (GER)**, 9, ch g Acatenango—Quila (IRE) **D. Coppola, J. Ewart**
20 **RAINING HORSE (FR)**, 10, b g Rainbow Reef—
                    C. Kesson, T. Lockhart Smith, G. & J. Reid & Mrs A. G. Humbert
21 **SA SUFFIT (FR)**, 9, b g Dolpour—Branceilles (FR) **Alba-Eire Syndicate**
22 **SIGNALMAN**, 8, gr g Silver Patriarch (IRE)—Kairine (IRE) **Margaret Coppola, J. Ewart**
23 **SNUKER**, 5, b g Snurge—Briar Rose (IRE) **N. M. L. Ewart & R. Finlay**
24 **SOLIS (GER)**, 9, ch g In The Wings—Seringa (GER) **D. Coppola, J. Ewart**
25 **SUPER BABY (FR)**, 10, b g Baby Turk—Norma Jane (FR) **Mr R. M. Boyd**
26 **SWALLOW (FR)**, 6, b br g Lavirco (GER)—Pocahontas (FR) **Roy & Linda Geddes**
27 **THINK GREEN**, 6, b m Montjeu (IRE)—Hasty Words (IRE) **Mr R. M. Boyd**
28 **THORLAK (FR)**, 5, b h Caballo Raptor (CAN)—Temara (FR) **J. Ewart**

MR JAMES EWART—continued

29 **TIME OUT (IRE)**, 9, b g Alhaarth (IRE)—Waif **W. H. Whitley**
30 **TOUCH OF TWEED (IRE)**, 5, b m Helissio (FR)—Over The Tweed **Mrs Hugh Fraser**
31 **UEUETEOTL (FR)**, 4, gr g Tikkanen (USA)—Azturk (FR) **Going Grey**
32 **UNEX VALADON**, 4, b f Red Ransom (USA)—Way O'gold (USA) **The South Hayrigg Partnership**
33 **VOSGES (FR)**, 5, b g Turgeon (USA)—Vanilla Sky (FR) **Mrs A. G. Humbert, Mr N. A. Sperling & Mrs L. Drew**
34 **WILDE PASTURES (IRE)**, 7, gr g Oscar (IRE)—Kingsfield Clover **Border Pastures**
35 **ZAFRITA**, 5, b m Zafeen (FR)—Lady Lenor **Longlands Racing**
36 **ZARU (FR)**, 6, b br g Laveron—Zianini (FR) **Mrs A. G. Humbert, Mrs L. Drew**

Other Owners: Mr James. D. Allen, Mrs D. Blythe, Mr R. Carruthers, Mr Allan Cartner, Mr G. Chamberlain, Mr T. Cobain, Mr B. Conneely, Mr Dennis J. Coppola, Mrs Margaret Coppola, Mr M. T. Cowen, Mr Gerry Davidson, Mr J. Doherty, Lord Donegall, Mrs Lavinia Drew, Mr J. P. L. Ewart, Mr N. M. L. Ewart, Mrs G. B. Fairbairn, Mr Maurice Friel, Mrs L. Gander, Mr Roy Geddes, Mrs M. Graham, Mr W. Graham, Miss S. A. M. Graham, Mr J. U. Hales, Mr Rob Halliday, Mrs A. G. Humbert, Dr Colin Kesson, Mrs P. Lockhart Smith, Mr Rod Main, Mr A. Manson, Mr John David Mason, Mrs Linda Geddes, Lady Milburn, Mr Peter Ogilvie, Mr Roy Palmer, Mrs Janie Reid, Mr Graeme Reid, Capt T. W. Ritson, Mr Barry Robinson, Mr Robert Smith, Mr N. A. Sperling, Mr G. Taitt, Ms Heather K. Walker, Mr James Westoll.

Jockey (NH): Brian Hughes. **Conditional:** Nathan Moscrop. **Amateur:** Mr Dale Irving.

---

219 MR ANDRE FABRE, Chantilly
Postal: **14 Avenue de Bourbon, 60500 Chantilly, France**
Contacts: **PHONE (0033) 3445 70498 FAX (0033) 3445 81415**

1 **ALKANIA**, 4, gr f Dalakhani (IRE)—Altruiste (USA) **Rothschild**
2 **ASULAYANA**, 5, b m Sulamani (IRE)—Aiyana (GER) **Mrs Fabre**
3 **BATAHOLA (USA)**, 4, ch f Bluegrass Cat (USA)—Beauty Halo (ARG) **Mrs Fabre**
4 **BRIGANTIN (USA)**, 5, ch h Cozzene (USA)—Banyu Dewi (GER) **Team Valor LLC**
5 **BYWORD**, 6, ch h Peintre Celebre (USA)—Binche (USA) **K. Abdulla**
6 **CHASING HALOS (USA)**, 5, b h Elusive Quality (USA)—Ballado's Halo (USA) **Godolphin**
7 **CHIEF OF STAFF**, 4, ch c Pivotal—Melikah (IRE) **Sheikh Mohammed**
8 **CONSTELLATION**, 4, b f Cape Cross (IRE)—White Star (IRE) **Sheikh Mohammed**
9 **DANCE MOVES**, 4, b c Dansili—Dance Routine **K. Abdulla**
10 **EGOTIST (IRE)**, 4, ch c Halling (USA)—Devil's Imp (IRE) **Sheikh Mohammed**
11 **FORT BELVEDERE**, 4, ch c King's Best (USA)—Sweet Folly (USA) **Sheikh Mohammed**
12 **GALLERIA**, 4, b f Dalakhani (IRE)—Galatee (FR) **Sheikh Mohammed**
13 **GOLDEN LILAC (IRE)**, 4, b f Galileo (IRE)—Grey Lilas (IRE) **Gestut Ammerland**
14 **HOMILY**, 4, ch f Singspiel (IRE)—Last Resort **Sheikh Mohammed**
15 **INTARSIA (GER)**, 5, ch m Pentire—Iphianassa (GER) **Mrs Fabre**
16 **KING OF ARNOR**, 4, b c Monsun (GER)—Luce (IRE) **Ballygallon Stud**
17 **LITIGANT**, 4, b c Sinndar (IRE)—Jomana (IRE) **Godolphin**
18 **MEANDRE (FR)**, 4, gr c Slickly (FR)—Penne (FR) **Rothschild Family**
19 **MEXICALI (IRE)**, 4, b f Tiger Hill (USA)—Guadalajara (GER) **Sheikh Mohammed**
20 **PAVIE (USA)**, 4, b f Lomitas—Proudeyes (GER) **Mrs Fabre**
21 **PINE CREEK**, 4, b c Doyen (IRE)—Valley of Gold (FR) **Sheikh Mohammed**
22 **PIRIKA (IRE)**, 4, b br f Monsun (GER)—Paita **T. Yoshida**
23 **POLYTECHNICIEN (USA)**, 6, ch h Royal Academy (USA)—Golden Party (USA) **Wertheimer et Frere**
24 **ROCK MY SOUL (IRE)**, 6, b m Clodovil (IRE)—Rondinay (FR) **Mrs Fabre**
25 **UFOLOGUE (IRE)**, 5, gr g Xaar—Up To Date (FR) **Mrs Fabre**
26 **UIGHUR (FR)**, 4, gr g Verglas (IRE)—Up To Date (FR) **Mrs Fabre**

THREE-YEAR-OLDS

27 **AESOP'S FABLES (USA)**, b c Distorted Humor (USA)—Abhisheka (IRE) **Godolphin**
28 **ALBION**, br gr c With Approval (CAN)—Alborada **Miss K. Rausing**
29 **AMIENS**, b c Galileo (IRE)—Dordogne (USA) **Smith's**
30 **ARC LIGHTER (USA)**, b g Street Cry (IRE)—Flamelet (USA) **Sheikh Mohammed**
31 **ARIBAA**, b c Halling (USA)—Arrivee (FR) **Wertheimer et Frere**
32 **ASSAGIE (IRE)**, b f Dansili—Altruiste (USA) **Lady O'Reilly**
33 **BANDIDAZO (USA)**, ch c Van Nistelrooy (USA)—Bailongaras (ARG) **Mrs Fabre**
34 **BE STILL (USA)**, b f Street Cry (IRE)—Banksia **Sheikh Mohammed**
35 **BEST LOVED (IRE)**, ch f Dubai Destination (USA)—Rosa Parks **Sheikh Mohammed**
36 **BISCAYA BAY**, b f Dansili—Borgia (GER) **Gestut Ammerland**
37 **BLUE PETREL (USA)**, b f Distorted Humor (USA)—Kotuku **Sheikh Mohammed**
38 **BOLINGBROKE (IRE)**, b c King's Best (USA)—Noble Rose (IRE) **Sheikh Mohammed**
39 **CALLE FLORA (USA)**, b f Street Sense (USA)—In A Bound (AUS) **Sheikh Mohammed**

MR ANDRE FABRE—continued

40 **CASERTA**, b f Dansili—Daring Miss **K. Abdulla**
41 **COMEDY AWARD (USA)**, b c Distorted Humor (USA)—Composure (USA) **Sheikh Mohammed**
42 **CONSERVATOIRE (USA)**, b f Street Cry (IRE)—Mezzo Soprano (USA) **Sheikh Mohammed**
43 **CRANACH**, b c Rail Link—Hachita (USA) **K. Abdulla**
44 **DARK ORCHID (USA)**, b f Dansili—Pleione (FR) **Sheikh Mohammed**
45 **DISCOPHILIA**, b f Teofilo (IRE)—Electric Society (IRE) **Sheikh Mohammed**
46 **DRAGON FALLS (IRE)**, b c Distorted Humor (USA)—Tizdubai (USA) **Sheikh Mohammed**
47 **EAST FIFTEEN**, b f Cape Cross (IRE)—Dramatique **Sheikh Mohammed**
48 **ENCIPHER (USA)**, b c Elusive Quality (USA)—Secret Charm (IRE) **Sheikh Mohammed**
49 **ENDELLION (USA)**, ch f Monsun (GER)—Dunnes River (USA) **Sheikh Mohammed**
50 **ESSENTIELLE (USA)**, b f North Light (IRE)—Polysheba (FR) **Wertheimer et Frere**
51 **EVADING (USA)**, b f Street Sense (USA)—Ever Love (BRZ) **Sheikh Mohammed**
52 **FAIRY WINGS (USA)**, b f Dynaformer (USA)—Lady Pegasus (USA) **Sheikh Mohammed**
53 **FARRUCA (FR)**, b c Montjeu (USA)—Dancing Lady (FR) **Waratah Thoroughbreds**
54 **FRACTIONAL (IRE)**, b c Manduro (GER)—Sharp Point (USA) **Sheikh Mohammed**
55 **GATERIE (USA)**, b f Dubai Destination (USA)—Galatee (FR) **Sheikh Mohammed**
56 **GHOST ARMY (IRE)**, b c Elusive Quality (USA)—Pure Illusion (IRE) **Sheikh Mohammed**
57 **GIACINTA (IRE)**, b f Hurricane Run (IRE)—Grosgrain (USA) **Mrs Fabre**
58 **GOLDEN AQUILA (IRE)**, ch c Singspiel (IRE)—Oiseau Rare (FR) **Sheikh Mohammed**
59 **GRAN MAESTRO (USA)**, ch c Medicean—Red Slippers (USA) **Sheikh Mohammed**
60 **GURUTZIA**, b f Hernando (FR)—Danseuse Indienne (FR) **Rothschild**
61 **HISTORIC FIND**, ch c Pivotal—Philae (USA) **Sheikh Mohammed**
62 **HOULEUSE (USA)**, b f Dynaformer (USA)—Sea Hill (USA) **Wertheimer et Frere**
63 **HUSSAR BALLAD (USA)**, b br c Hard Spun (USA)—Country Melody (USA) **Sheikh Mohammed**
64 **INSOUCIANTE (IRE)**, ch f Pivotal—Insijaam (USA) **Sheikh Mohammed**
65 **ISPANKA**, b f Invincible Spirit (IRE)—Russian Love (IRE) **Rothschild**
66 **KEEGSQUAW (IRE)**, ch f Street Cry (IRE)—Kentucky Rose (FR) **Mrs Fabre**
67 **LA ARENOSA (IRE)**, b f Exceed And Excel (AUS)—Baranquilla **Sheikh Mohammed**
68 **LA POLONAISE (USA)**, b f Smart Strike (CAN)—Soldera (USA) **Wertheimer et Frere**
69 **LA TOUR ROUGE**, ch f Monsun (GER)—Dream Play (IRE) **Sheikh Mohammed**
70 **LAST BORN (FR)**, ch f Monsun (GER)—America (IRE) **Wertheimer et Frere**
71 **LAST TRAIN**, b c Rail Link—Rainbow Lake **K. Abdulla**
72 **LAUSANNE (IRE)**, b f Lawman (FR)—Lupa Romana (IRE) **Mrs Fabre**
73 **LINDA RADLETT (IRE)**, b f Manduro (GER)—Portmanteau **Sheikh Mohammed**
74 **LOCKWOOD**, gr g Invincible Spirit (IRE)—Emily Bronte **Sheikh Mohammed**
75 **LOOKING**, ch c Gold Away (IRE)—Gold Round (USA) **Wertheimer et Frere**
76 **LOUISA M ALCOTT**, ch f King's Best (USA)—Nabati (USA) **Sheikh Mohammed**
77 **MAGIC MOTIF (USA)**, b br f Giant's Causeway (USA)—Silver Star **K. Abdulla**
78 **MAHNAZ**, b f Dansili—Minaccia (GER) **Mrs Fabre**
79 **MALICHO**, ch c Manduro (GER)—Shane (GER) **Sheikh Mohammed**
80 **MANDORE (IRE)**, b c Rock of Gibraltar (IRE)—Olimpic Girl (IRE) **Rothschild**
81 **MANTILLA (USA)**, ch f Gone West (USA)—Didina **K. Abdulla**
82 **MASTERSTROKE (USA)**, b c Monsun (GER)—Melikah (IRE) **Sheikh Mohammed**
83 **MEI (FR)**, gr f Shamardal—Miss Salvador **Mrs Fabre**
84 **MONST (IRE)**, b f Monsun (GER)—First One (ARG) **Wertheimer et Frere**
85 **MYPRECIOUSBLUE**, ch f Peintre Celebre (USA)—Pony Girl (IRE) **Wertheimer et Frere**
86 **MYRTLEWOOD (IRE)**, gr f Montjeu (IRE)—Walkamia (FR) **Ballygallon Stud**
87 **NARUKO (USA)**, b f Street Cry (IRE)—Lake Toya (USA) **Sheikh Mohammed**
88 **NAVARRE**, b c Dansili—Binche (USA) **K. Abdulla**
89 **NEVER ANOTHER (USA)**, b c Manduro (GER)—Discuss (USA) **K. Abdulla**
90 **NIGHT GARDEN (USA)**, b f Redoute's Choice (AUS)—Wild Queen (AUS) **Sheikh Mohammed**
91 **NOBILIS**, b f Rock of Gibraltar (IRE)—Dolydille (IRE) **M. Tabor**
92 **NOVELTY SEEKER (USA)**, b c Street Sense (USA)—Nawaiet (USA) **Sheikh Mohammed**
93 **ONDOYANTE (IRE)**, b f Slickly (FR)—Penne (FR) **Rothschild Family**
94 **ONLY A PLEASURE (IRE)**, b c Montjeu (USA)—Sense of Style (USA) **Smith's**
95 **OPPOSITE (IRE)**, b c Dansili—Silver Rain (FR) **Wertheimer et Frere**
96 **PETITE NOBLESSE (FR)**, b f Galileo (IRE)—Flower Bowl (FR) **Smith's**
97 **ROMANTICA**, b f Galileo (IRE)—Banks Hill **K. Abdulla**
98 **SAINT BAUDOLINO (IRE)**, b c Pivotal—Alessandria **Sheikh Mohammed**
99 **SAMANA CAY (USA)**, b f Authorized (IRE)—Tessa Reef (IRE) **Sheikh Mohammed**
100 **SECRETE (FR)**, b f Cape Cross (IRE)—Featherquest **Wertheimer et Frere**
101 **SOLENSI (GER)**, b c Montjeu (USA)—Stormina (USA) **Wertheimer et Frere**
102 **SOMALIAN (IRE)**, b c Tiger Hill (GER)—Somoushe (FR) **Sheikh Mohammed**
103 **SPELLWORK (USA)**, b f Hard Spun (USA)—Satin Kiss **Sheikh Mohammed**
104 **SPIRAL SEA (IRE)**, b f Hard Spun (USA)—Forest Pearl (USA) **Sheikh Mohammed**
105 **SYLVAN SONG (USA)**, b f Street Cry (IRE)—Forest Heiress (USA) **Godolphin**

MR ANDRE FABRE—continued

106 **THANDISWA (FR)**, b f Zamindar (USA)—Themba (USA) **Mrs Fabre**
107 **TULIPS (IRE)**, b f Pivotal—Hint of Spring **Sheikh Mohammed**
108 **UCCELLINA (FR)**, b f Great Journey (JPN)—Up To Date (FR) **Mrs Fabre**
109 **UPPER HOUSE (IRE)**, ch c Barathea (IRE)—Uryale (FR) **Rothschild Family**
110 **URANY**, b f King's Best (USA)—Double Green (IRE) **Wertheimer et Frere**
111 **VICTORIAN BEAUTY (USA)**, b f Rahy (USA)—Jood (USA) **Sheikh Mohammed**
112 **WALDLERCHE**, ch f Monsun (GER)—Waldmark (GER) **Gestut Benried**
113 **WATCHFUL EYES (IRE)**, b f Street Sense (USA)—French Bid (AUS) **Sheikh Mohammed**
114 **WILLOW BREEZE**, b f Hard Spun (USA)—Island Babe (USA) **Sheikh Mohammed**
115 **WINTERGREEN (IRE)**, b c Authorized (IRE)—Spring Oak **Mrs Fabre**
116 **WOVEN LACE**, br f Hard Spun (USA)—Do The Honours (IRE) **Sheikh Mohammed**
117 **WYBORNE**, ch g Halling (USA)—Coraline **K. Abdulla**
118 **ZOUBROVKA (USA)**, b f Proud Citizen (USA)—Zinziberine (USA) **Mrs Fabre**

TWO-YEAR-OLDS

119 **ALBEMARLE**, b f 11/2 King's Best (USA)—Adonita (Singspiel (IRE)) **Sheikh Mohammed**
120 **ALUMNA (USA)**, b f 3/3 Mr Greeley (USA)—Alma Mater (Sadler's Wells (USA)) **Miss K. Rausing**
121 **ALZUBRA**, b f 3/5 Dansili—Azabara (Pivotal) **Mrs Fabre**
122 **ANGEL OAK**, b f 17/4 Teofilo (IRE)—Spring Oak (Mark of Esteem (IRE)) **Sheikh Mohammed**
123 **ARKANSAS**, b c 6/5 Pivotal—Aynthia (USA) (Zafonic (USA)) **Sheikh Mohammed**
124 Ch c 4/2 Three Valleys (USA)—Atlantic High (Nashwan (USA)) **Gestut Ammerland**
125 B f 8/5 Oasis Dream—Banks Hill (Danehill (USA)) **K. Abdulla**
126 **BAYARGAL (USA)**, b f 8/4 Bernstein (USA)—Bailonguera (ARG) (Southern Halo (USA)) **Mrs Fabre**
127 **BELONGING**, ch f 5/2 Raven's Pass (USA)—Desired (Rainbow Quest (USA)) **Sheikh Mohammed**
128 B c 20/3 Montjeu (IRE)—Beyond The Dream (Fusaichi Pegasus (USA)) (200000) **Magnier**
129 B f 5/4 Oasis Dream—Binche (USA) (Woodman (USA)) **K. Abdulla**
130 **BLUE RAMBLER**, b c 30/3 Monsun (GER)—La Nuit Rose (FR) (Rainbow Quest (USA)) **Sheikh Mohammed**
131 **BOOK OF MANNERS**, ch f 11/4 King's Best (USA)—Elegant Way (IRE) (Cape Cross (IRE)) **Sheikh Mohammed**
132 Ch c 20/3 Medicean—Borghesa (GER) (Galileo (IRE)) **Gestut Ammerland**
133 B f 1/1 Shamardal—Born Wild **Gestut Ammerland**
134 B c 25/1 Montjeu (IRE)—Catherine Linton (IRE) (Machiavellian (USA)) **M. Tabor**
135 B f 7/5 Dansili—Cinnamon Bay (Zamindar (USA)) **K. Abdulla**
136 B f 19/1 Dansili—Concentric (Sadler's Wells (USA)) **K. Abdulla**
137 **COUNTERFEITER**, b c 10/2 Singspiel (IRE)—Grain of Truth (Gulch (USA)) **Sheikh Mohammed**
138 B c 4/4 Dansili—Dance Routine (Sadler's Wells (USA)) **K. Abdulla**
139 B c 23/1 Three Valleys (USA)—Diamond Reef (Alzao (USA)) **K. Abdulla**
140 B f 4/4 Danehill Dancer (IRE)—Dievotchka (Dancing Brave (USA)) **Rothschild**
141 **FALCOMIX (FR)**, ch c 3/3 Falco—Beautifix (Bering) **Wertheimer et Frere**
142 B c 12/3 Singspiel (IRE)—First (Highest Honor (USA)) **Magnier**
143 **FORESTAN**, b c 5/4 King's Best (USA)—Snow Ballerina (Sadler's Wells (USA)) **Sheikh Mohammed**
144 **GEORGETOWN**, ch c 8/4 Manduro (GER)—Summertime Legacy (Darshaan) **Sheikh Mohammed**
145 **GERMANIC**, b c 18/2 Manduro (GER)—White Star (IRE) (Darshaan) **Sheikh Mohammed**
146 **GOLBAHAR (IRE)**, b f 14/1 Holy Roman Emperor (IRE)—Grosgrain (USA) (Diesis) **Mrs Fabre**
147 Ch c 24/2 Giant's Causeway (USA)—Golden Antigua (USA) (Hansel (USA)) (201465) **Magnier**
148 Ch f 23/3 Manduro (GER)—Guadalajara (GER) (Acatenango (GER)) **Sheikh Mohammed**
149 B c 25/2 Rail Link—Hachita (Gone West (USA)) **K. Abdulla**
150 **HERMINIA (IRE)**, b f 16/4 Hernando (FR)—Danseuse Indienne (IRE) (Danehill (USA)) **Rothschild**
151 **HOKKAIDO**, b f 23/4 Street Cry (IRE)—Lake Toya (USA) (Darshaan) **Sheikh Mohammed**
152 **INTELLO (FR)**, b c 1/1 Galileo (IRE)—Impressionnante (Danehill (USA)) **Wertheimer et Frere**
153 **ISTRIANE (IRE)**, gr f 28/2 Slickly (FR)—Rumored (USA) (Royal Academy (USA)) (197044) **Rothschild**
154 **ITALIAN**, b c 25/2 Dansili—Taranto (Machiavellian (USA)) **Sheikh Mohammed**
155 **KEY TO PEACE (IRE)**, b f 19/5 Kheleyf (USA)—African Peace (USA) (Roberto (USA)) **Sheikh Mohammed**
156 **KING OF ENGLAND**, ch c 28/3 Galileo (IRE)—
    Royal Highness (GER) (Monsun (GER)) (410509) **Waratah Thoroughbreds**
157 **L'ORFEO**, ch c 11/2 Singspiel (IRE)—Limeira (Bertolini (USA)) (147783) **Sheikh Mohammed**
158 **LADY ELLIOTT**, b f 22/3 Authorized (IRE)—Madame Arcati (IRE) (Sinndar (IRE)) **Sheikh Mohammed**
159 Ch f 19/1 New Approach (IRE)—Last Rhapsody (Kris) **Sheikh Mohammed**
160 B c 28/2 Montjeu (IRE)—Llia (Shirley Heights) (150000) **Smith's**
161 **LOOKING AT GLORY (IRE)**, b gr c 13/1 Selkirk (USA)—
    Trip To Glory (FR) (Where Or When (IRE)) **Rothschild Family**
162 **LOU SALOME (GER)**, ch f 20/3 Giant's Causeway (USA)—Cicerole (FR) (Barathea (IRE)) **Rothschild Family**
163 **LUCUMON (GER)**, b c 22/3 Cape Cross (IRE)—Lasira (GER) (Vettori (IRE)) (69786) **Sheikh Mohammed**
164 **MATRIARCHY (IRE)**, b f 11/5 Doyen (IRE)—Criquette (Shirley Heights) **Sheikh Mohammed**
165 B c 10/4 Danehill Dancer (IRE)—Mer de Corail (IRE) (Sadler's Wells (USA)) **Magnier**
166 B c 1/1 Clodovil (IRE)—Montagne Magique (IRE) (King's Best (USA)) (36945) **Baron Van Gysel**

MR ANDRE FABRE—continued

167 **MONTCLAIR (IRE)**, b c 7/4 Montjeu (IRE)—Minaccia (GER) (Platini (GER)) (279146) **M. Tabor**
168 Ch f 15/4 Dalakhani (IRE)—Mount Elbrus (Barathea (IRE)) **Sheikh Mohammed**
169 B f 11/1 Hurricane Run (IRE)—Mysterix (IRE) (Linamix (FR)) **Gestut Ammerland**
170 **OCEANLINER (USA)**, b c 1/1 Dynaformer (USA)—Sweet Travel (Ger) (Danzig (USA)) **Wertheimer et Frere**
171 **PENGLAI PAVILION (USA)**, b br c 28/4 Monsun (GER)—
Maiden Tower (Groom Dancer (USA)) **Sheikh Mohammed**
172 **PIEPOWDER COURT (IRE)**, ch c 24/5 Pivotal—Chercheuse (USA) (Seeking The Gold (USA)) **Sheikh Mohammed**
173 **PLUMBA**, b f 10/1 Anabaa (USA)—Featherquest (Rainbow Quest (USA)) **Wertheimer et Frere**
174 Gr f 13/5 Shamardal (USA)—Princess Taise (USA) (Cozzene (USA)) **Sheikh Mohammed**
175 **QUIET DIPLOMACY**, b c 1/3 New Approach (IRE)—Coy (IRE) (Danehill (USA)) (34481) **Sheikh Mohammed**
176 B c 1/4 Manduro (GER)—Russian Snows (IRE) (Sadler's Wells (USA)) **Sheikh Mohammed**
177 B c 12/2 Sinndar (IRE)—Russian Society (Darshaan) **Sheikh Mohammed**
178 B f 20/1 Galileo (IRE)—Sanjida (IRE) (Polish Precedent (USA)) (1395730) **Waratah Thoroughbreds**
179 Ch f 4/1 New Approach (IRE)—Scatina (IRE) (Samum (GER)) **Sheikh Mohammed**
180 B f 4/5 Montjeu (IRE)—Sense of Style (USA) (Thunder Gulch (USA)) **M. Tabor**
181 B gr f 13/3 Dalakhani (IRE)—Shinko Hermes (IRE) (Sadler's Wells (USA)) **Sheikh Mohammed**
182 **SILENT FIRE (IRE)**, b c 3/5 Street Cry (IRE)—Flamelet (USA) (Theatrical) **Sheikh Mohammed**
183 **SILVER PEARL**, b f 27/3 Authorized (IRE)—Jomana (IRE) (Darshaan) **Sheikh Mohammed**
184 **SKY HUNTER**, b c 26/4 Motivator—Pearl Kite (USA) (Silver Hawk (USA)) **Sheikh Mohammed**
185 **SOBLUE (IRE)**, b c 8/3 Invincible Spirit (IRE)—Never Green (IRE) (Halling (USA)) **Wertheimer et Frere**
186 **SPARKLE PLENTY (IRE)**, b f 3/4 Galileo (IRE)—Gwynn (IRE) (Darshaan) (800000) **P. Makin**
187 B c 26/3 Montjeu (IRE)—Spritza (IRE) (Spectrum (IRE)) (164202) **Smith's**
188 Ch f 5/5 Any Given Saturday (USA)—Surf Club (USA) (Ocean Crest (USA)) **Sheikh Mohammed**
189 B c 29/4 Dylan Thomas (IRE)—Tadorne (FR) (Inchinor) **Rothschild Family**
190 Gr ro f 22/2 Nayef (USA)—Tashelka (FR) (Mujahid (USA)) **Sheikh Mohammed**
191 B f 22/4 Montjeu (IRE)—Tree Tops (Grand Lodge (USA)) (150000) **Smith's**
192 **TRIPLE THREAT (FR)**, b c 3/4 Monsun (GER)—Drei (USA) (Lyphard (USA)) **Team Valor Int**
193 Ch c 19/2 Teofilo (IRE)—Uryale (FR) (Kendor (FR)) **Rothschild Family**
194 **USHANA (FR)**, br f 1/1 Great Journey—Up To Date **Mrs Fabre**
195 **VARSOVIAN**, ch c 10/3 Refuse To Bend (IRE)—Queen of Poland (Halling (USA)) **Sheikh Mohammed**
196 B c 2/3 Dansili—Villarrica (USA) (Selkirk (USA)) **Sheikh Mohammed**
197 **ZENJI (USA)**, b c 1/1 Hat Trick (JPN)—Zinziberine (USA) (Zieten (USA)) **Mrs Fabre**
198 **ZIMBALI (FR)**, b c 1/1 Hurricane Run—Zaltana **Mrs Fabre**

---

220 **MR RICHARD FAHEY, Malton**
Postal: RF Racing Ltd, Mews House, Musley Bank, Malton, North Yorkshire, YO17 6TD
Contacts: **PHONE (01653) 698915 FAX (01653) 699735 MOBILE (07713) 478079**
E-MAIL enquiries@richardfahey.com WEBSITE www.richardfahey.com

1 **ABOVE THE STARS**, 4, b f Piccolo—Swindling **Mrs K. R. Scaife**
2 **ALBEN STAR (IRE)**, 4, b g Clodovil (IRE)—Secret Circle **Mr J. K. Shannon & Mr M. A. Scaife**
3 **ANTIGUA SUNRISE (IRE)**, 6, b m Noverre (USA)—Staff Approved **David & Jackie Knaggs**
4 **AQUARIAN SPIRIT**, 5, b g Fantastic Light (USA)—Notable Lady (IRE) **P. S. Cresswell & Mrs P. A. Morrison**
5 **ARABIAN SPIRIT**, 7, b g Oasis Dream—Royal Flame (IRE) **Timeform Betfair Racing Club Ltd**
6 **AVISON (IRE)**, 4, b g Diamond Green (FR)—Actoris (USA) **Havelock Racing 2**
7 **BAWAARDI (IRE)**, 6, b g Acclamation—Global Trend **The Matthewman One Partnership**
8 **CASTLES IN THE AIR**, 7, b g Oasis Dream—Dance Parade (USA) **Mr J. C. McGrath**
9 **CUNNING CLARETS (IRE)**, 7, ch g Trans Island—Ellistown Lady (IRE) **The Matthewman One Partnership**
10 **DUNMORE BOY (IRE)**, 4, ch g Iffraaj—Night Club **Mr T. M. Flaherty**
11 **GLEN'S DIAMOND**, 4, b g Intikhab (USA)—Posta Vecchia (USA) **S & G Clayton**
12 **GOLDENVEIL (IRE)**, 4, b f Iffraaj—Line Ahead (IRE) **Mrs H. Steel**
13 **GRITSTONE**, 5, b g Dansili—Cape Trafalgar (IRE) **The Living Legend Racing Partnership**
14 **HAADEETH**, 5, b g Oasis Dream—Musical Key **Mr J. Gaffney**
15 **HALLA SAN**, 10, b g Halling (USA)—St Radegund **Mrs U. Towell**
16 **HIGH OFFICE**, 4, b g High Chaparral (IRE)—White House **J. C. Parsons**
17 **INGLEBY SPIRIT**, 5, b g Avonbridge—Encore du Cristal **Percy/Green Racing**
18 **JUSTONEFORTHEROAD**, 6, b g Domedriver (IRE)—Lavinia's Grace (USA) **The Pontoon Partnership**
19 **KINGDOM OF MUNSTER (IRE)**, 5, b g Danehill Dancer (IRE)—Kitty O'shea (IRE) **J. D. Clark & Partners I**
20 **LESANDA**, 6, b m Hernando (FR)—Wardeh **Collins, Medawar, Nash & Whyatt I**
21 **MAJESTIC MYLES (IRE)**, 4, b g Majestic Missile (IRE)—Gala Style (IRE) **Mr J. Gaffney**
22 **MAYSON**, 4, b c Invincible Spirit (IRE)—Mayleaf **D. W. Armstrong**
23 **MICA MIKA (IRE)**, 4, ch g Needwood Blade—Happy Talk (IRE) **Mrs U. Towell**
24 **MIGHTY CLARETS (IRE)**, 5, br g Whipper—Collected (IRE) **The Matthewman Partnership**
25 **OUR JOE MAC (IRE)**, 5, b g Celtic Swing—Vade Retro (IRE) **A. Long**
26 **PHILHARMONIC HALL**, 4, b g Victory Note (USA)—Lambast **R. Cowie**

MR RICHARD FAHEY—continued

27 **PODGIES BOY (IRE)**, 4, b g Statue of Liberty (USA)—Lake Victoria (IRE) **Mr S. Duffy**
28 **PURSUIT OF PASSION**, 4, b f Pastoral Pursuits—Marisa (GER) **Mr Mel Roberts & Ms Nicola Meese 1**
29 **SIR LOUIS**, 5, b g Compton Place—Heuston Station (IRE) **Mr P. Ashton**
30 **SIR REGINALD**, 4, b g Compton Place—Clincher Club **Mr J. C. McGrath**
31 **STANLEY RIGBY**, 6, b g Dr Fong (USA)—Crystal (IRE) **Mr D. Hardman & Mrs S. Hardman**
32 **TAMAREEN (IRE)**, 4, b g Bahamian Bounty—Damjanich (IRE) **Dr M. B. Q. S. Koukash**
33 **TAROOQ (USA)**, 6, b g War Chant (USA)—Rose of Zollern (IRE) **Mr Y. M. Nasib**
34 **TINY TEMPER (IRE)**, 4, b f Montjeu (IRE)—Lady Storm (IRE) **Mrs P. Davies**
35 **VALLEY TIGER**, 4, b g Tiger Hill (IRE)—Nantyglo **Dr M. B. Q. S. Koukash**
36 **VENTURA COVE (IRE)**, 5, ch g Bahamian Bounty—Baby Bunting **Mr K. Denham**
37 **VIVA RONALDO (IRE)**, 6, b g Xaar—Papaha (FR) **Aykroyd & Sons Limited**
38 **WHAT ABOUT YOU (IRE)**, 4, b g Statue of Liberty (USA)—Why Now **Errigal Racing**
39 **WIND SHUFFLE (GER)**, 9, b g Big Shuffle (USA)—Wiesensturmerin (GER) **Mrs S. Bruce & Mrs L. Mackay**
40 **WOOD FAIRY**, 6, b m Haafhd—Woodbeck **Mrs P. B. E. P. Farr**

THREE-YEAR-OLDS

41 **ANYTHING (IRE)**, b f Rock of Gibraltar (IRE)—Sharapova (IRE) **Mrs S Grassick & Mr Matthew Duffy**
42 **BACCARAT (IRE)**, ch c Dutch Art—Zut Alors (IRE) **Sir R. Ogden C.B.E., LLD**
43 **BALDASSARRE (IRE)**, ch c Medicean—Cleide da Silva (USA) **Sir R. Ogden C.B.E., LLD**
44 **CLARETINTHEBLOOD (IRE)**, b c Elusive City (USA)—River Abouali **The Matthewman Partnership**
45 **COLBYOR**, ch g Orientor—College Maid (IRE) **E. Bruce**
46 **COSMIC HALO**, ch f Halling (USA)—Cosmic Case **The Cosmic Cases**
47 **DUBAWI CHEETAH (IRE)**, b f Dubawi (IRE)—Magical Cliche (USA) **Sheikh M. B. K. Al Maktoum**
48 **FLASHMAN**, ch g Doyen (IRE)—Si Si Si **The G-Guck Group**
49 **GABRIAL'S LEXI (IRE)**, b f Dubawi (IRE)—Lady Causeway (USA) **Dr M. B. Q. S. Koukash**
50 **GOING GREY (IRE)**, ro c Diamond Green (FR)—Incendio **Mrs H. Steel**
51 **GONE BY SUNRISE**, b c Three Valleys (USA)—Quadrophenia **Market Avenue Racing & Tremousser**
52 **HAWKS REEF**, b g Bahamian Bounty—Karisal (IRE) **J. E. M. Hawkins Ltd**
53 **HENRY BEE**, b g Cadeaux Genereux—Emerald Fire **Wildcard Racing Syndicate X2**
54 **HURLER AND FARMER (IRE)**, b c Red Clubs (IRE)—Undercover Glamour (USA) **G. Devlin**
55 **LADY AUTHOR**, b f Authorized (IRE)—Kelucia (IRE) **F. Brady**
56 **LADY LOCH**, b f Dutch Art—Locharia **D. W. Armstrong**
57 **LITTLE MR SUNSHINE**, b c Azamour (IRE)—Tagula Sunrise (IRE) **Mr Mel Roberts & Ms Nicola Meese**
58 **LOST CITY (IRE)**, b g Elusive City (USA)—Farthing (IRE) **Sir Alex Ferguson & Jack Hanson**
59 **MFIFTYTHREE FORD (IRE)**, b f Royal Applause—Maid For Romance **M53 Motors Ltd T/A M53 Ford**
60 **MOORSIDE MAGIC**, b f Dubai Destination (USA)—Parsonagehotelyork (IRE) **P. D. Smith Holdings Ltd**
61 **PINOT**, b g Desert Style (IRE)—Rosablanca (IRE) **The G-Guck Group**
62 **POONTOON (IRE)**, gr c Clodovil (IRE)—Tahtheeb (IRE) **M. F. Browne**
63 **RIVINGTON**, b c Oasis Dream—Kiralik **D. W. Armstrong**
64 **SABORE**, br f Orientor—Annie Gee **F. Brady**
65 **SHERRY CHERIE (IRE)**, b f Footstepsinthesand—Tipsy Lady **Mrs H. Steel**
66 **SHEVINGTON**, b g Choisir (AUS)—Miss Dixie **D. W. Armstrong**
67 **SHOWSINGER**, b f Singspiel (IRE)—Very Agreeable **R. A. Fahey**
68 **SNOOKY**, b c Exceed And Excel (AUS)—Quintrell **Mrs J. M. MacPherson**
69 **SPARKLING PORTRAIT**, b c Excellent Art—Time Crystal **M. F. Browne**
70 **SUFFICE (IRE)**, b g Iffraaj—Shallat (IRE) **Highclere Thoroughbred Racing-Iffraaj I**
71 **SUNNY SIDE UP (IRE)**, b f Refuse To Bend (IRE)—
Feeling Wonderful (IRE) **Jim McGrath, Roger & Dianne Trevitt**
72 **WARCROWN (IRE)**, b c Azamour (IRE)—Alikhlas (USA) **Mrs H. Steel**
73 **YEOMANOFTHEGUARD**, b g Librettist (USA)—Red Blooded Woman (USA) **H. J. P. Farr**

Other Owners: Sheik M. B. K. Al Maktoum, Mr Mike J. Beadle, Mr Andy Bonarius, Mr N. J. Bonarius, Mr Stuart Brown, Mr John Browne, Mrs S. E. Bruce, Mr I. T. Buchanan, Mr G. Calder, Mrs J. Calder, Mr John D. Clark, Mr Steven Clayton, Mrs G. A. Clayton, Mr N. T. Collins, Mr N. Collins, Mr A. E. Corbett, Mr P. S. Cresswell, Mr Michael Cunningham, Mr L. Duddy, Mr Matthew Duffy, Mr R. A. Fahey, Sir Alex Ferguson, Mr David M. Fulton, Mr Brian W. Goodall, Mr J. D. Gordon, Mrs S. Grassick, Mr David A. Green, Mr J. Hanson, Mr Dean Hardman, Mrs Stella Hardman, Mr John Harris, The Hon H. Herbert, Highclere Thoroughbred Racing Ltd, Mr K. Hubery, Mr G. R. Hunnam, Mr R. F. Johnson, Mr D. M. Knaggs, Mrs Jackie Knaggs, Mrs Christine Lally, Mrs Lisa Mackay, Market Avenue Racing Club Ltd, Mr Bill Martin (Fife), Mr P. McBride, Mrs Sandra McCarthy, Mr Jim McGrath, Mr D. J. P. McWilliams, Ms Nicola Meese, Mrs P. A. Morrison, Mr Terry Nash, Mr C. O'Keeffe, Mr D. Pearson, Mr Alan Pirie, Mr Mel Roberts, Mr M. A. Scaife, Mr Dave Scott, Mr J. K. Shannon, Mr Steve Shaughnessy, Mr A. Shearer, Mrs Doreen M. Swinburn, Mr Steve Taplin, Mr A. Tattersall, Mr Roger Trevitt, Mrs Dianne Trevitt, Exors of the late Mr M. Wassall, Mr A. Watson, Mrs Norman Williamson.

MR RICHARD FAHEY—continued

Assistant Trainer: Robin O'Ryan

Jockey (flat): Tony Hamilton, Paul Hanagan, Frederik Tylicki, Barry McHugh. **Jockey (NH):** Brian Hughes. **Apprentice:** George Chaloner, Laura Barry, Shane B. Kelly, Lee Topliss. **Amateur:** Miss Phillipa Tutty, Miss Alyson Deniel, Mr Jamie Hamilton, Mr Sean Huggan, Miss Toni Syddall.

221   MR SEAMUS FAHEY, Co. Kildare
Postal: **Cloneygath, Monasterevin, Co. Kildare, Ireland**
Contacts: **PHONE (00 353) 45 523586 FAX (00 353) 45 523586 MOBILE (00 353) 87 2200262**
E-MAIL **seamusfahey_14@hotmail.com**

1 **INDIAN ST JOVITE (IRE),** 5, b g Indian Haven—Meritorious (USA) **Mr D. Considine**
2 **IT'S FREEZING (IRE),** 4, b g High Chaparral (IRE)—Freezing Love (USA) **Mrs S. Dempsey**
3 **ORPENS PEACH (IRE),** 5, b m Orpen (USA)—Shes A Peach (IRE) **Mrs V. Maxwell**
4 **RAYBERTS PET (IRE),** 4, b f Orpen (USA)—Shes A Peach (IRE) **Mrs V. Maxwell**
5 **SENOR TOMMIE (IRE),** 6, b g Statue of Liberty (USA)—La Luna (USA) **Hubert Maxwell**
6 **SONGJIANG,** 4, b g Tiger Hill (IRE)—Showery **Seamus Fahey**
7 **TIDAL STAR,** 4, b g Kyllachy—Tidal **Mrs B. Quinn**
8 **TINAS EXHIBITION (IRE),** 5, ch m Great Exhibition (USA)—El Tina **James Colgan**

THREE-YEAR-OLDS

9 **AUSSIE BOUND (IRE),** b g Robert Emmet (IRE)—Rochambelle (IRE) **Mr B. Woods**
10 **ELLELL DUKE (IRE),** b c Kheleyf (USA)—Any Ellells (IRE) **Mrs M. Lawless & S. Fahey**
11 **FAST ON (IRE),** gr g Verglas (IRE)—Dream State (IRE) **Mr Liam Tolland**
12 **GREAT SUMMER (IRE),** b f Great Exhibition (USA)—Summer Cloud (IRE) **Mrs B. Fahey**

Assistant Trainer: James Fahey

Jockey (flat): Shane Foley, Gary Carroll. **Conditional:** Shane Butler. **Apprentice:** K. C. Sexton, C. P. Hoban. **Amateur:** Mr J. A. Fahey, Mr Mark Fahey, Mr B. P. Fahey, Miss C. Fahey.

222   MR CHRIS FAIRHURST, Middleham
Postal: **Glasgow House, Middleham, Leyburn, North Yorkshire, DL8 4QG**
Contacts: **PHONE/FAX (01969) 622039 MOBILE (07889) 410840**
E-MAIL **cfairhurst@tiscali.co.uk WEBSITE www.chrisfairhurstracing.com**

1 4, B g Doyen (IRE)—Dombeya (IRE) **S. K. McPhee**
2 **FERNEY BOY,** 6, b g Courteous—Jendorcet **Mrs P. J. Taylor-Garthwaite**
3 **LADY ANNE NEVILL,** 8, b m Nomadic Way (USA)—Prudent Pet **Mrs C. Arnold**
4 **MOOTABAR (IRE),** 5, gr g Verglas (IRE)—Melanzane **Mrs A. M. Leggett**
5 **ROMAN RULER (IRE),** 4, gr g Antonius Pius (USA)—Way of Truth **S Leggott & S Atkinson**
6 **SHIRLS SON SAM,** 4, b g Rambling Bear—Shirl **Mrs S. France**
7 **SPRUZZO,** 6, b g Emperor Fountain—Ryewater Dream **980 Racing**
8 **THACKERAY,** 5, b g Fasliyev (USA)—Chinon (IRE) **Mrs C. Arnold**
9 **TIGERINO (IRE),** 4, b g Tiger Hill (IRE)—Golden Shadow (IRE) **980 Racing**
10 **WHO'S SHIRL,** 6, b m Shinko Forest (IRE)—Shirl **Mrs S. France**

THREE-YEAR-OLDS

11 **HURRICANE MAX (IRE),** b c Oratorio (IRE)—Perfect Peach **Mrs A. Morris**
12 **MAJESTIC BOUNTY,** b f Bahamian Bounty—Princess Louise **The PQD Partnership**

TWO-YEAR-OLDS

13 B f 7/2 Misu Bond (IRE)—Matilda Peace (Namaqualand (USA)) **North Cheshire Trading & Storage Ltd**
14 B f 3/2 Misu Bond (IRE)—Peyto Princess (Bold Arrangement) **North Cheshire Trading & Storage Ltd**

223   MR JAMES FANSHAWE, Newmarket
Postal: **Pegasus Stables, Snailwell Road, Newmarket, Suffolk, CB8 7DJ**
Contacts: **PHONE (01638) 664525 / 660153 FAX (01638) 664523**
E-MAIL **james@jamesfanshawe.com WEBSITE www.jamesfanshawe.com**

1 **ABBRACCIO,** 4, b g Pivotal—Embraced **Cheveley Park Stud**
2 **ALDEDASH (USA),** 4, b g Aldebaran (USA)—Hawzah **Axom XXVII**

MR JAMES FANSHAWE—continued

3 **CAPTIVATOR**, 5, gr m Motivator—Cashew **Lord Vestey**
4 **COCO ROUGE (IRE)**, 4, ch f Shamardal (USA)—Coquette Rouge (IRE) **Carivalis, Eady & Swinburn**
5 **DANDINO**, 5, br h Dansili—Generous Diana **Elite Racing Club**
6 **DEACON BLUES**, 5, b g Compton Place—Persario **Jan & Peter Hopper & Michelle Morris**
7 **DIMENSION**, 4, b g Medicean—Palatial **Cheveley Park Stud**
8 **GLASS MOUNTAIN (IRE)**, 4, gr g Verglas (IRE)—Exotic Mix (FR) **Mr Simon Gibson**
9 **HALLELUJAH**, 4, b f Avonbridge—My Golly **Chippenham Lodge Stud**
10 **HIGH JINX (IRE)**, 4, b c High Chaparral (IRE)—Leonara (GER) **Mr & Mrs W. J. Williams**
11 **INCENDO**, 6, ch g King's Best (USA)—Kindle **Andrew & Julia Turner**
12 **MAC'S POWER (IRE)**, 6, b g Exceed And Excel (AUS)—Easter Girl **Mr Michael McDonnell**
13 **NOVIRAK (IRE)**, 4, gr g Noverre (USA)—Manchaca (FR) **Mr Norman Brunskill**
14 **OLD HUNDRED (IRE)**, 5, b g Tiger Hill (IRE)—Bordighera (USA) **Lael Stable**
15 **PRIMAEVAL**, 6, ch g Pivotal—Langoustine (AUS) **The Foncey Syndicate**
16 **REFRACTOR (IRE)**, 4, ch g Refuse To Bend (IRE)—Fancy Intense **Mr & Mrs W. J. Williams**
17 **ROSSETTI**, 4, gr g Dansili—Snowdrops **Dragon Gate**
18 **SOCIETY ROCK (IRE)**, 5, br h Rock of Gibraltar (IRE)—High Society (IRE) **Mr Simon Gibson**
19 **SPENSLEY (IRE)**, 6, ch g Dr Fong (USA)—Genoa **Axom XV**

THREE-YEAR-OLDS

20 **AQUA JETER (IRE)**, b g Dansili—Silk And Scarlet **Dragon Gate**
21 **ARABIC**, b g Dubai Destination (USA)—Artifice **Dr Catherine Wills**
22 **BEDAZZLED**, b f Authorized (IRE)—Dazzle **Cheveley Park Stud**
23 **BLAZING SPEED**, b g Dylan Thomas (IRE)—Leukippids (IRE) **Dragon Gate**
24 **CAPACIOUS**, b f Nayef (USA)—Palatial **Cheveley Park Stud**
25 **CATWALK (IRE)**, ch f Pivotal—Mona Em (IRE) **Cheveley Park Stud**
26 **EAGLE POWER (IRE)**, b g Teofilo (IRE)—Changeable **Dragon Gate**
27 **ENTITLEMENT**, br f Authorized (IRE)—Applecross **Dr Catherine Wills**
28 **EXNING HALT**, b g Rail Link—Phi Phi (IRE) **Mr Simon Gibson**
29 **GREY SEAL (IRE)**, gr f Cape Cross (IRE)—Mundus Novus (USA) **Lord Vestey**
30 **IF SO**, b f Iffraaj—Persario **Hopper, Grundy, Handscombe**
31 **ISOLA VERDE**, b f Oasis Dream—Firenze **Jan & Peter Hopper**
32 **KEPT**, ch c Pivotal—Possessed **Cheveley Park Stud**
33 **KUNEGUNDA**, b f Pivotal—Panna **Lord Halifax**
34 **LEVI DRAPER**, b g Rock of Gibraltar (IRE)—Splice **Andrew & Julia Turner**
35 **LURCHER**, gr g With Approval (CAN)—Pitcroy **Dr Catherine Wills**
36 **MISS DASHWOOD**, b f Dylan Thomas (IRE)—Dash To The Front **Helena Springfield Ltd**
37 **MOHAIR**, b f Motivator—Cashmere **Lady Halifax**
38 **OPENLY**, b f Singspiel (IRE)—Grand Opening (IRE) **Mr J. H. Richmond-Watson**
39 **SEAL OF APPROVAL**, b f Authorized (IRE)—Hannda (IRE) **Mr T. R. G. Vestey**
40 **SECRET QUEST**, br f Pivotal—Secret Flame **Cheveley Park Stud**
41 **SOVIET DREAM**, b c Oasis Dream—Soviet Song (IRE) **Elite Racing Club**
42 **SUPERSTICION**, b f Red Ransom (USA)—Go Supersonic **Helena Springfield Ltd**
43 **TWIN SHADOW (IRE)**, ch f Dubawi (IRE)—Its On The Air (IRE) **Clipper Logistics**
44 **WIJAYA**, ch f Haafhd—First Fantasy **Nigel & Carolyn Elwes**

TWO-YEAR-OLDS

45 Ch f 19/4 Dubai Destination (USA)—Allied Cause (Giant's Causeway (USA)) **Helena Springfield Ltd**
46 Br c 30/3 Authorized (IRE)—Blue Lightning (Machiavellian (USA)) **Mr Mohamed Obaida**
47 B f 6/2 Teofilo (IRE)—Carinae (USA) (Nureyev (USA)) (36000) **Mr Salem Bel Obaida**
48 B c 12/3 Hurricane Run (IRE)—Close Regards (IRE) (Danehill (USA)) (82100) **Dragon Gate**
49 **COSSETED**, b f 24/1 Pivotal—Fondled (Selkirk (USA)) **Cheveley Park Stud**
50 B f 20/2 Acclamation—Dani Ridge (Indian Ridge) (90000) **Mr Mohamed Obaida**
51 B c 24/4 Marju (IRE)—Donnai (IRE) (Soviet Star (USA)) (28000) **Mr Salem Bel Obaida**
52 B c 15/4 Green Desert (USA)—Firenze (Efisio) **Mr & Mrs P Hopper, Mr & Mrs M Morris**
53 B f 28/3 Nayef (USA)—Galaxy Highflyer (Galileo (IRE)) (55000) **Helena Springfield Ltd**
54 **GLANELY (IRE)**, b c 18/2 Exceed And Excel (AUS)—
                    Bon Ton Roulet (Hawk Wing (USA)) (100000) **Mr Simon Gibson**
55 Ch f 19/3 Nayef (USA)—Ivory Gala (FR) (Galileo (IRE)) (10000) **Mr T. R. G. Vestey**
56 **KNIGHT OWL**, b c 20/3 Rock of Gibraltar (IRE)—
                    Miss Ivanhoe (Selkirk (USA)) (155000) **Miss Annabelle Condon**
57 **KOALA BEAR**, b f 14/2 Oasis Dream—Birthday Suit (IRE) (Daylami (IRE)) **Lady Halifax**
58 Ch c 12/2 Manduro (GER)—Lady Stardust (Spinning World (USA)) (95000) **Mrs Martin Armstrong**
59 **LOVED ONE**, b f 27/4 Medicean—Embraced (Pursuit of Love) (14000) **Cheveley Park Stud**
60 **MAC'S SUPERSTAR (FR)**, b c 20/2 Elusive City (USA)—
                    Diamond Light (USA) (Fantastic Light (USA)) (75000) **Mr Michael McDonnell**

MR JAMES FANSHAWE—continued

61 Ch c 4/2 Sakhee (USA)—Maghya (IRE) (Mujahid (USA)) (17000) **Mr Mohamed Obaida**
62 Ch c 11/2 Singspiel (IRE)—Moonmaiden (Selkirk (USA)) (115000) **Mr Saeed bel Obaida**
63 B br c 18/2 Street Boss (USA)—Pad The Wallet (USA) (Skip Away (USA)) **Axom XXXIV**
64 B c 5/5 Intikhab (USA)—Pattimech (USA) (Nureyev (USA)) (36000) **Mr Saeed bel Obaida**
65 Ch c 28/3 Pivotal—Pediment (Desert Prince (IRE)) (55000) **Mr Mohamed Obaida**
66 RIBBONS, ch f 19/4 Manduro (GER)—Sister Act (Marju (IRE)) **Elite Racing Club**
67 ROUBLE, b f 21/4 Royal Applause—Mycenae (Inchinor) **Dr Catherine Wills**
68 B c 26/2 Rock of Gibraltar (IRE)—Siren Sound (Singspiel (IRE)) (90000) **Dragon Gate**
69 SORN (IRE), ch c 28/4 Galileo (IRE)—Dame Again (AUS) (Danehill (USA)) (75000) **Mr T. Barr**

Other Owners: Mr D. Donnelly, Mrs H. S. Ellingsen, Mr R. Jackson, Mrs G. S. Jackson, Mr A. McPartlin, Mr T. Mohan, Mrs G. Thompson, Miss G. Thompson, Mr M. Weinfeld, Mr B. York.

Assistant Trainer: Charlie Fellowes

---

 224   **MS LUCINDA FEATHERSTONE, Ashbourne**
Postal: **Closes Farm, Atlow, Ashbourne, Derbyshire, DE6 1PZ**
Contacts: PHONE **(01335) 372108 MOBILE (07977) 930801**
E-MAIL **pedro74321@hotmail.co.uk** WEBSITE **www.heartofenglandracing.co.uk**

1 PATRICIAS PRIDE, 5, ch g Silver Patriarch (IRE)—Anniversary Guest (IRE)
2 SNOWBERRY HILL (USA), 9, b g Woodman (USA)—Class Skipper (USA)

THREE-YEAR-OLDS

3 B f Pastoral Pursuits—Flighty Dancer
4 JAY PEAS JACKO, b g Pastoral Pursuits—Anniversary Guest (IRE)

Assistant Trainer: J. P. Featherstone, M. Connors (Head Lad)

Amateur: Mr J. P. Featherstone, Mr W. R. Featherstone.

---

 225   **MISS JULIA FEILDEN, Newmarket**
Postal: **Harraton Stud, Laceys Lane, Exning, Newmarket, Suffolk, CB8 7HW**
Contacts: PHONE **(01638) 577470 FAX (01638) 578628 MOBILE (07924) 817694**
E-MAIL **hoofbeatstours@aol.com** WEBSITE **www.juliafeildenracing.com**

1 ANGEL OF MERCY, 4, b f Green Tune (USA)—Hula Queen (USA) **J. & S. Montague**
2 AUTOMOTIVE, 4, b g Beat Hollow—Bina Ridge **Stowstowquickquickstow Partnership**
3 BESEECH, 5, gr ro m Maria's Mon (USA)—Concert Hall (USA) **Miss J. D. Feilden**
4 BLACKMORE, 5, b g Rainbow Quest (USA)—Waki Music (USA) **Good Company Partnership**
5 DOLLY BAY, 4, ch f Kyllachy—Loblolly Bay **Mrs S. McGuiness**
6 EMMA'S GIFT (IRE), 4, gr f Aussie Rules—Rose of Mooncoin (IRE) **Mrs E. M. Raffan**
7 ENTRANCE, 4, ch f Iceman—Enrapture (USA) **Hoofbeats Racing Club**
8 EXOPUNTIA, 6, b m Sure Blade (USA)—Opuntia **J. W. Ford**
9 FARAWAY LAND (USA), 4, b f Empire Maker (USA)—Out of Reach **Miss J. Feilden**
10 GENEROUS GENELLA, 4, b f Cape Cross (IRE)—Gombay Girl (USA) **The Sultans of Speed**
11 KAMPAI, 4, b f Sakhee (USA)—Green Supreme **Peter M. Crane**
12 KHAJAALY (IRE), 5, b g Kheleyf (USA)—Joyfullness (USA) **Geegeez.co.uk**
13 SAIL HOME, 5, b m Mizzen Mast (USA)—Bristol Channel **Hoofbeats Racing Club**
14 SANCHO PANZA, 5, b g Zafeen (FR)—Malvadilla (IRE) **Carol Bushnell & Partners**
15 SILVER ALLIANCE, 4, gr g Proclamation (IRE)—Aimee Vibert **In It To Win Partnership**
16 SPIRIT OF SHARJAH (IRE), 7, b g Invincible Spirit (IRE)—Rathbawn Realm **Mr A. Dee**
17 THE DUCKING STOOL, 5, ch m Where Or When (IRE)—Dance Sequel **Mrs S. McGuiness**

THREE-YEAR-OLDS

18 ACER DIAMONDS (IRE), b c Red Clubs (IRE)—Tree House (USA) **Grabupenn Racing**
19 ARGANTE CLAUDIUS (FR), gr g Keltos (FR)—Balle De Golf (FR) **Mr A. Dee & Miss J. Feilden**
20 ATTAIN, b c Dansili—Achieve **The Attainables**
21 CANNING VALE, ch f Araafa (IRE)—Elegant Beauty **R. J. Creese**
22 B f Halling (USA)—In Luck **John W. Ford & Peter J. Skinn**
23 LEA VALLEY, b f Araafa (IRE)—Guaranda **R. J. Creese**
24 VERONA BAY (FR), b g Della Francesca (USA)—Verone (USA) **Hoofbeats Racing Club**

MISS JULIA FEILDEN—continued

TWO-YEAR-OLDS

25 **BELIEVE IN ME**, b f 10/3 Bertolini (USA)—Zephrina (Zafonic (USA)) (4000) **Hoofbeats Racing Club**
26 **TIGER'S HOME**, b f 9/4 Tiger Hill (IRE)—Homeward (IRE) (Kris) **Hoofbeats Racing Club**

Other Owners: Mr J. Birkett, Mr M. Bisogno, Miss J. Feilden, Mrs Jackie Olkowicz, Mr Chris Page, Mrs A. S. Styles.

Assistant Trainer: John Birkett

Apprentice: Adam Beschizza. **Amateur:** Mr R. Birkett, Miss Shelley Birkett.

---

226 **MR PHILIP FENTON, Carrick-On-Suir**
Postal: **Glenbower Stables Ltd., Garryduff, South Lodge, Carrick-On-Suir, Co. Tipperary, Ireland**
Contacts: **PHONE (00 353) 51 647901 FAX (00 353) 51 647901 MOBILE (00 353) 87 2581048**
E-MAIL glenbowerstables@gmail.com WEBSITE www.glenbowerstables.com

1 5, B g Bishop of Cashel—Academy Jane (IRE) **P. Fenton**
2 5, B m Oscar (IRE)—Boro Supreme (IRE) **J. Luttrell**
3 **BRIGHTON ROAD (IRE)**, 5, b g Milan—Grand Quest **Barry Connell**
4 **CAIM HILL (IRE)**, 9, b g Deploy—Glen's Gale (IRE) **Dempsey Construction**
5 **CHILLY CHOCOLATE (IRE)**, 5, b g Norwich—Gurthravin Lass (IRE) **J. Glynn**
6 **DRIVE ON LOCKY (IRE)**, 5, b g Milan—Husyans Beauty (IRE) **Keep on Dreaming Syndicate**
7 4, B g Bienamado (USA)—Duneavey (IRE) **K. Fenton**
8 **DUNGUIB (IRE)**, 9, b g Presenting—Edermine Berry (IRE) **Daniel Harnett/Mrs E. A. Lawlor**
9 **FAIR OF CAPPAMORE (IRE)**, 7, b g Oscar (IRE)—Quinnsboro Ice (IRE) **J. P. McManus**
10 **FIVE POINT PLAN (IRE)**, 6, b g Rashar (USA)—Grangeway **J. Moran**
11 **HOUNDSCOURT (IRE)**, 5, b g Court Cave (IRE)—Broken Rein (IRE) **Kevin Power**
12 **KILFLORA (IRE)**, 9, b g Alflora (IRE)—Stac-Pollaidh **Patsy O'Brien**
13 **LAST INSTALMENT (IRE)**, 7, ch g Anshan—Final Instalment (IRE) **Gigginstown House**
14 **LOUDMOUTH (IRE)**, 5, br g Milan—Grandy Invader (IRE) **Gigginstown House**
15 **LOWANBEHOLD (IRE)**, 5, gr g Cloudings (IRE)—Marble Quest (IRE) **T. O'Dwyer**
16 6, B g Flemensfirth (USA)—Mounthenry Lady (IRE) **Moanmore Stables**
17 5, B g Broadway Flyer (USA)—My Delight (IRE) **Patsy O'Brien**
18 4, Gr g Pierre—Nancymar (IRE) **Innovotec**
19 **ON MY OWN (IRE)**, 8, b g Shernazar—Bloomfield (IRE) **J. Sayers**
20 **ORAN FLYER (IRE)**, 11, b g Safety Catch (USA)—Mill Dancer (IRE) **P. Fenton**
21 **PASSING THROUGH**, 8, b g Exit To Nowhere (USA)—Island Hopper **Border Macs Syndicate**
22 **PINEAU DE RE (FR)**, 9, b g Maresca Sorrento (FR)—Elfe du Perche (FR) **B. Connell**
23 4, B br g Golan (IRE)—Pinkeen Lady (IRE) **M. Daly**
24 **RESOLUTE BAY (IRE)**, 6, br g Presenting—Anniesthyne (IRE) **Gigginstown House**
25 **SCAMALLACH (IRE)**, 6, b g Overbury (IRE)—Tell No One (IRE) **All Kyne Syndicate**
26 4, Ch g Alflora (IRE)—Sequin Slippers (IRE) **P. Fenton**
27 **SHANIV (IRE)**, 6, b g Definite Article—Miss Amy (IRE) **Patsy O'Brien**
28 **STRANGE ENCOUNTER (IRE)**, 8, b g Witness Box (USA)—Lilymare (IRE) **W. O'Neill**
29 **SUPREME BOB (IRE)**, 6, b g Bob's Return (IRE)—Suprememories (IRE) **Coole Tavern Syndicate**
30 4, B g Moscow Society (USA)—Supreme Favour (IRE) **C. Heron**
31 **TETE A QUEUE (FR)**, 5, b g Robin des Champs (FR)—Macadoun (FR) **Gigginstown House**
32 **TOMMIE MILAN (IRE)**, 6, b g Milan—Damers Venture (IRE) **M. V. O'Gorman**
33 **UTRILLO'S ART (IRE)**, 7, ch m Medecis—Theory of Law **Tom Coleman**
34 **VENTURE CAPITAL (IRE)**, 5, b g Presenting—Dare To Venture (IRE) **J. P. McManus**
35 **WAY TO SUCCESS (IRE)**, 6, b g Pilsudski (IRE)—Failte Na Heireann (USA) **Donica Gray**
36 **WOODBINE WILLIE (IRE)**, 11, b g Zaffaran (USA)—Good Foundation (IRE) **Elizabeth Lawlor**
37 **WRIGHT FLYER (IRE)**, 10, ch g Accordion—Deep Estee (IRE) **Mrs Cotter**

Jockey (NH): Brian O'Connell. **Amateur:** Mr R. J. Kiely.

---

227 **MR JOHN FERGUSON, Newmarket**
Postal: **Bloomfields, Cowlinge, Newmarket, Suffolk, CB8 9HN**
Contacts: **PHONE (01638) 500423 FAX (01638) 500387**

1 **ART HISTORY (IRE)**, 4, gr c Dalakhani (IRE)—What A Picture (FR) **Bloomfields**
2 **ASAID**, 4, b g Singspiel (IRE)—Forum Floozie (NZ) **Bloomfields**
3 **BIRDWATCHER (IRE)**, 4, ch g Cadeaux Genereux—Dancing Feather **Bloomfields**
4 **CAPE DUTCH (IRE)**, 5, b g Cape Cross (IRE)—Rosia (IRE) **Bloomfields**

MR JOHN FERGUSON—continued

5 **CAYMAN ISLANDS**, 4, b g Shirocco (GER)—Barbuda **Bloomfields**
6 **COTTON MILL**, 5, b g Tiger Hill (IRE)—Mill Line **Bloomfields**
7 **CREEKSIDE**, 4, b g Dubai Destination (USA)—Khubza **Bloomfields**
8 **CRY OF FREEDOM (USA)**, 6, b g Street Cry (IRE)—Tustarta (USA) **Bloomfields**
9 **DONATORIO**, 4, b g King's Best (USA)—Relish (IRE) **Bloomfields**
10 **GIREVOLE**, 4, b g Tiger Hill (IRE)—Taranto **Bloomfields**
11 **HALIFAX (IRE)**, 4, ch c Halling (USA)—Lady Zonda **Bloomfields**
12 **HOUSEPARTY**, 4, b g Invincible Spirit (IRE)—Amusing Time (IRE) **Bloomfields**
13 **JAMEEL (USA)**, 4, b g Monsun (GER)—Maids Causeway (IRE) **Bloomfields**
14 **KADOODD (IRE)**, 4, b g Motivator—Briery (IRE) **Bloomfields**
15 **MEMORABILIA**, 4, b g Dansili—Sentimental Value (USA) **Bloomfields**
16 **MONARCH'S WAY**, 5, b g King's Best (USA)—La Bayadere **Bloomfields**
17 **NEW YEAR'S EVE**, 4, b g Motivator—Midnight Angel (GER) **Bloomfields**
18 **PERE BLANC (IRE)**, 7, b g King's Theatre (IRE)—Sunset Leader (IRE) **Bloomfields**
19 **PERPETUALLY (IRE)**, 6, b g Singspiel (IRE)—Set In Motion (USA) **Bloomfields**
20 **POPULATION**, 5, ch g Noverre (USA)—Ville d'amore (USA) **Bloomfields**
21 **PRIMARIES (IRE)**, 4, b g Selkirk (USA)—First of Many **Bloomfields**
22 **PROOF (IRE)**, 4, b g Monsun (GER)—Foolish Act (IRE) **Bloomfields**
23 **RED DEVIL BOYS (IRE)**, 5, b g Oscar (IRE)—Lohort Castle (IRE) **Bloomfields**
24 **SHALLOON (IRE)**, 4, b c Cape Cross (IRE)—Sun Silk (USA) **Bloomfields**
25 **TRESPASSER (IRE)**, 4, b g Cape Cross (IRE)—Tamarillo **Bloomfields**
26 **ULLSWATER (IRE)**, 4, b c Singspiel (IRE)—Uluwatu (IRE) **Bloomfields**

---

228 | **MR DOMINIC FFRENCH DAVIS, Lambourn**
Postal: Windy Hollow Stables, Sheepdrove, Lambourn, Hungerford, Berkshire, RG17 7XA
Contacts: YARD (01488) 73675 HOME (01488) 72342 FAX (01488) 73675 MOBILE (07831) 118764
E-MAIL ffrenchdavis@btinternet.com WEBSITE www.ffrenchdavis.com

1 **ADMIRABLE DUCHESS**, 5, gr m Compton Place—Smart Hostess **Exors of the Late Mr B. W. Taylor**
2 **ADMIRABLE DUQUE (IRE)**, 6, b g Selkirk (USA)—Stunning (USA) **Exors of the Late Mr B. W. Taylor**
3 **BLUECROP BOY**, 8, b g Zaha (CAN)—Pearl Dawn (IRE) **Mrs J. E. Taylor**
4 **BRANDYWELL BOY (IRE)**, 9, b g Danetime (IRE)—Alexander Eliott (IRE) **D. J. S. Ffrench Davis**
5 **GAELIC WIZARD (IRE)**, 4, b c Fasliyev (USA)—Fife (IRE) **Mr T. Dawson**
6 **IF I WERE A BOY**, 5, b m Invincible Spirit (IRE)—Attymon Lill (IRE) **Mr R. F. Haynes**
7 **JUSTCALLMEHANDSOME**, 10, ch g Handsome Ridge—Pearl Dawn (IRE) **Mrs J. E. Taylor**
8 **LONDON AVENUE (IRE)**, 4, ch g Compton Place—Great Joy (IRE) **Mrs J. H. Burn**
9 **ORLA (IRE)**, 4, b f Hawk Wing (USA)—Irish Ensign (SAF) **Ms Angela Clifford/Mrs Caryl Clifford**

THREE-YEAR-OLDS

10 **ABSOLUTELY ME (IRE)**, ch f Barathea (IRE)—Attymon Lill (IRE) **Miss Alison Jones**
11 **BOJANGLE (IRE)**, b f Namid—Fine Detail (IRE) **Miss Alison Jones**
12 B c Barathea (IRE)—Cream Tease **Mr S. J. Edwards**
13 **DELISHUSS**, gr f Aussie Rules (USA)—Effie **Dynamik Duo & Mr Gary Black**
14 **DREAM WHISPERER**, b f Piccolo—Sweet Whisper **Mrs M. A. M. Norwood**

TWO-YEAR-OLDS

15 B f 19/3 Three Valleys (USA)—Breathing Space (USA) (Expelled (USA)) **Miss A. Jones**
16 B f 7/4 Avonbridge—Cinciallegra (Royal Applause) (1000) **Mr S. J. Edwards**
17 B g 20/4 Holy Roman Emperor (IRE)—Palwina (FR) (Unfuwain (USA)) (5000) **Miss A. Jones**

Other Owners: G. H. Black, Ms A. Clifford, Mr Alan Coleing, Dynamik Duo Limited, Mr Stephen Leppard.

Assistant Trainer: Avery Ffrench Davis

Jockey (flat): James Doyle. **Jockey (NH):** Mark Grant.

---

229 | **MR GIUSEPPE FIERRO, Hednesford**
Postal: Bentley Brook House, Rawnsley Road, Hednesford, Cannock, Staffordshire, WS12 1RB
Contacts: (01543) 879611 MOBILE (07976) 321468

1 **FRANKIE FALCO**, 6, br h Bollin Eric—Marsh Marigold **G. Fierro**
2 **GO ON JACK**, 14, ch g Saint Keyne—Swift Messenger **G. Fierro**
3 **PEHERA BOY**, 5, b g Fleetwood (IRE)—Abbiejo (IRE) **G. Fierro**

Assistant Trainer: M Fierro

230 **MRS MARJORIE FIFE, Stillington**
Postal: **White Thorn Farm, Stillington, Easingwold, York, YO61 1LT**

1 **JUST THE TONIC,** 5, ch m Medicean—Goodwood Blizzard **R. W. Fife**
2 **KING MAK,** 10, gr g Makbul—Miss Nova **Mrs M. Turner**
3 **LADY DEL SOL,** 4, b f Monsieur Bond (IRE)—Villa Del Sol **Mrs S. Johnson**
4 **LADY OGLIER,** 4, b f Tamayaz (CAN)—Chanteuse **Lerigo Family**
5 **LAWGIVER (IRE),** 11, b g Definite Article—Marylou Whitney (USA) **R. W. Fife**
6 **LUCKY FOR SOME,** 5, b m Lucky Owners (NZ)—Countess Elton (IRE) **Mrs M. Turner**
7 **MANDALAY KING (IRE),** 7, b g King's Best (USA)—Mahamuni (IRE) **R. W. Fife**
8 **WHISKY MAGIC (FR),** 8, b g Maresca Sorrento (FR)—Winska Girl (FR) **Fellowship Of The Rose Partnership**

THREE-YEAR-OLDS

9 **TWIN IVAN (IRE),** b g Ivan Denisovich (IRE)—Twin Logic (USA) **Mr T. W. Fife**

Other Owners: P. Allison, E. W. Lerigo, Mr J. A. Lerigo, Mr J. G. Lerigo, Mr S. D. Lerigo, Mr P. R. Woodcock-Jones.

231 **MR TIM FITZGERALD, Malton**
Postal: **Norton Grange, Norton, Malton, North Yorkshire, YO17 9EA**
Contacts: **OFFICE (01653) 692718 FAX (01653) 600214 MOBILE (07950) 356437**
E-MAIL fitzgeraldracing@hotmail.com

1 **ACRAI RUA (IRE),** 9, ch g Rock Hopper—Dontbelieveaword (IRE) **T. J. Fitzgerald**
2 **CAPTAIN LING,** 8, ch g Presidium—Giffoine **T. J. Fitzgerald**
3 **COMERAGH KING,** 8, b g Kayf Tara—Velcro Girl (IRE) **Halewood International Ltd**
4 **EMPEROR OF ROME (IRE),** 4, b g Antonius Pius (USA)—Fire Flower **Mr J. M. & Mrs E. E. Ranson**
5 **FRENCH HOLLOW,** 7, b g Beat Hollow—Campaspe **T. J. Fitzgerald**
6 **MR SYNTAX (IRE),** 8, b g King's Theatre (IRE)—Smile Awhile (USA) **Regalmist Associates Ltd**
7 **STRIKING PRIORITE,** 4, b g Striking Ambition—Priorite (IRE) **Mr P. Coulter**

Other Owners: M. J. K. Dods, J. M. Ranson, Mrs E. E. Ranson.

232 **MR PAUL FITZSIMONS, Upper Lambourn**
Postal: **Saxon Gate Stables, Malt Shovel Lane, Lambourn, Berkshire, RG17 8QH**

THREE-YEAR-OLDS

1 **CHANDIGARH (IRE),** b f Moss Vale (IRE)—Secret Justice (USA) **Mr B. Sohal**
2 **FU FIC FAS,** b f Multiplex—Sarcita **R. C. Tooth**

TWO-YEAR-OLDS

3 B c 27/4 Camacho—Lucky Dancer (FR) (Groom Dancer (USA)) (14367) **Mr B. Sohal**
4 B c 10/3 Red Clubs (IRE)—Tabrina (IRE) (Fasliyev (USA)) (12315) **Mr B. Sohal**
5 Ch c 28/4 Choisir (AUS)—Wood White (UAE) (Timber Country (USA)) (6567) **Mr B. Sohal**

233 **MR JOHN FLINT, Bridgend**
Postal: **Cherry Tree, 71 Woodlands Park, Kenfig Hill, Bridgend, Mid-Glamorgan, CF33 6EB**
Contacts: **PHONE (01656) 744347 FAX (01656) 744347 MOBILE (07581) 428173**
E-MAIL johnl.flint@talktalk.net

1 **BATHWICK JUNIOR,** 5, b m Reset (AUS)—Bathwick Babe (IRE) **H. M. W. Clifford**
2 **CABO ROCHE,** 5, ch m Alflora (IRE)—Pougatcheva (FR) **T. Reffell**
3 **CAPTAIN SCARLETT (IRE),** 6, b g Milan—Count My Blessings (IRE) **J. L. Flint**
4 **DREAM ALLIANCE,** 11, ch g Bien Bien (USA)—Rewbell **The Alliance Partnership**
5 **DULCEMARA (IRE),** 4, b f Bahri (USA)—Almnadia (IRE) **Mr J. Hennessy**
6 **GRAMS AND OUNCES,** 5, b g Royal Applause—Ashdown Princess (IRE) **Mr R. C. Williams**
7 **HEAVENSTOWN (IRE),** 6, ch g Bienamado (USA)—Little Bliss (IRE) **Mr M. Page**
8 **HELENS VISION,** 9, b m Alflora (IRE)—Kinlet Vision (IRE) **Mr W. D. Morris**
9 **HERE COMES MOSS,** 5, b g Karinga Bay—Madam Mosso **Mr A. R. Evans**
10 **ONE FOR JOULES (IRE),** 5, b m Choisir (AUS)—Stuttgart **J. L. Flint**

MR JOHN FLINT—continued

11 **RIGHT OPTION (IRE)**, 8, b g Daylami (IRE)—Option (IRE) **Mr R. E. Mathias**
12 **ROWLESTONE LAD**, 5, b g Sulamani (IRE)—Charmante Femme **Mr R. C. Williams**
13 **ROYAL ENCHANTRESS**, 4, b f Goodricke—Fairlee Royal **The Ever Hopeful Partnership**
14 **ROYBUOY**, 5, b g Royal Applause—Wavy Up (IRE) **J. L. Flint**
15 **SILVA FLINT**, 4, gr f Generous (IRE)—Senna da Silva **J. L. Flint**
16 **TARMAC GIRL**, 4, b f Alflora (IRE)—Cool Spice **Mr B. M. Jones**
17 **WESTERN KATE (IRE)**, 5, b m Westerner—Golden Odyssey (IRE) **Mr R. Stafford**

THREE-YEAR-OLDS

18 **HENDRY TRIGGER**, ch g Double Trigger (IRE)—Denise Best (IRE) **T. Reffell**
19 **KHATELLA (IRE)**, b f Generous (IRE)—Triple Dash (GER) **Miss V. Mack**
20 **LADY LECTRA**, b f Multiplex—Coronation Queen **Mr R. Quinn**
21 B f Fair Mix (IRE)—Senna da Silva **J. L. Flint**

Other Owners: H. B. Davies, Mr K. French, Mr A. Jones, Mr C. McFee.

Assistant Trainer: Mrs Martine Louise Flint (07968) 044487

Jockey (NH): Rhys Flint. **Conditional:** Thomas Flint.

---

234 MR DAVID FLOOD, Newmarket
Postal: **Exeter Stables, Church Street, Exning, Newmarket, Suffolk, CB8 7EH**
Contacts: **PHONE (07919) 340619**
E-MAIL **davidflood1@hotmail.co.uk**

1 **BUAITEOIR (FR)**, 6, b g Mineshaft (USA)—Witching Hour (FR) **Mr L. J. Mann**
2 **MISTER GREEN (FR)**, 6, b g Green Desert (USA)—Summertime Legacy **Flood Family Racing Limited**
3 **TIGER WHO**, 4, b f Tiger Hill (IRE)—Aunt Susan **Flood Family Racing Limited**

THREE-YEAR-OLDS

4 Ch f Bahamian Bounty—Bel Tempo **Flood Family Racing Limited**
5 **EQUATION OF TIME**, gr c Proclamation (IRE)—Winter Ice **Mr L. J. Mann**
6 **RED PROTECTOR (IRE)**, ch g Haafhd—Red Ray **Mr L. J. Mann**

TWO-YEAR-OLDS

7 B f 30/3 Royal Applause—Winter Ice (Wolfhound (USA)) (40000)

Jockey (flat): James Doyle, Stephen Craine, Tony Culhane, John Egan. **Apprentice:** Sophie Doyle.

---

235 MR TONY FORBES, Uttoxeter
Postal: **Hill House Farm, Poppits Lane, Stramshall, Uttoxeter, Staffordshire, ST14 5EX**
Contacts: **PHONE (01889) 569568 MOBILE (07963) 246571**
E-MAIL **tony@thimble.net**

1 **ASTRONOMICAL (IRE)**, 10, b g Mister Baileys—Charm The Stars **Mr A. L. Forbes**
2 **SPIRIT CALLING (IRE)**, 11, br g Lord Americo—Satco Street (IRE) **Mr A. L. Forbes**

Assistant Trainer: Mr Tim Eley

---

236 MRS PAM FORD, Hereford
Postal: **Stone House Stables, Preston Wynne, Hereford, Herefordshire, HR1 3PB**
Contacts: **HOME/FAX (01432) 820604 MOBILE (07733) 152051**
E-MAIL **pam_ford@hotmail.co.uk**

1 **BUSSELL ALONG (IRE)**, 6, b m Mujadil (USA)—Waaedah (USA) **R. S. Herbert**
2 7, B gr m M'bebe—Candy Copper
3 **CAPTAIN OATS (IRE)**, 9, b g Bahhare (USA)—Adarika **K. R. Ford**
4 **HIGHLAND CADETT**, 5, ch g Putra Sandhurst (IRE)—Highland Rossie **R. S. Herbert**
5 **RACING WITH ANGELS**, 10, ch g Alflora (IRE)—Murphy's Angel **D. H. Godfrey**
6 **RUSSELLSTOWN BOY (IRE)**, 12, b br g Arctic Lord—Lough Borough (IRE) **R. S. Herbert**

MRS PAM FORD—continued

Assistant Trainer: Mr K Ford

Jockey (flat): Hayley Turner, Royston Ffrench. **Jockey (NH):** J. Davies. **Amateur:** Mr K. Ford.

---

237 MR RICHARD FORD, Garstang
Postal: The Paddocks, Strickens Lane, Barnacre, Garstang, Lancashire, PR3 1UD
(Satellite Yard: Butterton Racing Stables, Park Road, Butterton, Newcastle-Under-Lyme, Staffs.)
Contacts: PHONE (01995) 605790 (07802) 7644094 FAX (01995) 605245 MOBILE (07976) 522768
E-MAIL lrs@lancashireracingstables.co.uk WEBSITE www.lancashireracingstables.co.uk

1 ALAGHIRAAR (IRE), 8, b g Act One—Tarsheeh (USA) **D. W. Watson**
2 BEAR WITH RUPERT, 5, ch g Act One—Rose Bay **The Coz Syndicate**
3 BIG SAM, 7, b g Conclude (USA)—Geegee Emmarr **The Gazetters**
4 BOO'S BOUNTY, 4, b f Kyllachy—Sosumi **Jason Carver**
5 CALCULAITE, 11, b g Komaite (USA)—Miss Calculate **The Hexham Handicappers**
6 CHAMBERS (IRE), 6, b g Green Desert (USA)—Court Lane (USA) **P.M. Clarkson**
7 CHEERY CAT (USA), 8, b br g Catienus (USA)—Olinka (USA) **The Cataractonium Racing Syndicate**
8 COLDITZ (IRE), 8, ch g Noverre (USA)—West Escape **R. J. Hewitt**
9 DULALLY, 4, b f Dubawi (IRE)—Rose Bounty **Mrs Stella Barclay & Andrew Bell**
10 FLYNN'S ISLAND (IRE), 6, b g Trans Island—Cappuccino (IRE) **Steve & Helen Manning**
11 GARSTANG, 9, ch g Atraf—Approved Quality (IRE) **The Foulrice Twenty**
12 GOLDEN DREAM (IRE), 8, ch g Golden Tornado (IRE)—Orion Dream **Winks Racing**
13 INSOLENCEOFOFFICE (IRE), 4, b g Kodiac—Sharp Diversion (USA) **CCCNLP**
14 4, Ch f Alflora (IRE)—Island Hopper **Mrs S. E. Barclay**
15 ISLAND SPRITE (IRE), 8, b m Heron Island (IRE)—Saucy Sprite **Brandsby Racing**
16 MARK OF MEYDAN, 7, ch g Mark of Esteem (IRE)—Rose Bounty **The Bounty Hunters**
17 MCCROHAN (IRE), 7, b g Alderbrook—Tidal Princess (IRE) **D. W. Watson**
18 MEYDAN STYLE (USA), 6, b g Essence of Dubai (USA)—Polish Ruby (USA) **The Style Council**
19 MIDNIGHT RETURN (IRE), 6, b m Midnight Legend—By Return (IRE) **Harpers Brook Racing**
20 MINISTEROFINTERIOR, 9, b g Nayef (USA)—Maureen's Hope (USA) **D. E. Simpson & R. Farrington-Kirkham**
21 MORNING SUNSHINE (IRE), 9, b g Presenting—Culfadda Girl (IRE) **Tarporley Turf Club II**
22 RED DANGER ANGEL, 4, ch f Sulamani (IRE)—Synergie (IRE) **Network Racing**
23 RIGHT CREDENTIALS, 4, b f Diktat—Approved Quality (IRE) **Mrs S. E. Barclay**
24 ROYAL LADYBIRD, 4, b f Danbird (AUS)—Royal Shepley **P B J Racing**
25 ROYAL PREMIUM, 4, b h Superior Premium—Royal Shepley **P B J Racing**
26 RUSTIC GOLD, 8, ch g Tobougg (IRE)—Suave Shot **D. W. Watson**
27 SADDLERS' SUPREME (IRE), 10, b m Saddlers' Hall (IRE)—
Festival Leader (IRE) **The Northern Echo Partnership**
28 SEAMSTER, 5, ch g Pivotal—Needles And Pins (IRE) **Dave Watson & David Sibson**
29 SHARP AND CHIC, 5, b m Needwood Blade—Moreover (IRE) **Ms N Taylor**
30 SILVER STEEL (FR), 9, b g Robin des Pres (FR)—Oliver's Queen (FR) **Mrs Julie Gordon & Mr Keith Hesketh**
31 THETASTEOFPARADISE, 5, b m Act One—Rose Bounty **Winks Racing**
32 TROPICAL BACHELOR (IRE), 6, b g Bachelor Duke (USA)—Tropical Coral (IRE) **Mrs P. F. Bickerton**
33 4, B g Bachelor Duke (USA)—Tropical Coral (IRE) **Mrs P. F. Bickerton**
34 TUNZA THE LION, 5, b g Trade Fair—Bella Helena **The Most Wanted Partnership**
35 YOU'RELIKEMEFRANK, 6, ch g Bahamian Bounty—
Proudfoot (IRE) **Mrs K. E. Barrett, Mr P. Clarkson & Mr D. Clarkson**

THREE-YEAR-OLDS

36 AWAYWITHFAIRIES, b f Courteous—Shahadah (IRE) **Mr P. Metcalfe**
37 BLACKAMOOR ZARA, b f Haafhd—Sara Mana Mou **F M Racing**
38 BRIAN'S BEST, ch g Tobougg (IRE)—Approved Quality (IRE) **Mr B. Hartley**
39 BYRON GET ONE FREE, b g Byron—Ishela (IRE) **The Cartmel Race Club**
40 CHORISTER GIRL, b f Acclamation—Hazelhurst (IRE) **R. Ford**
41 B g And Beyond (IRE)—Cotton Easter **Mrs Stella Barclay & Mr Andrew Bailey**
42 NANI JANI, ch f Halling (USA)—Betty's Pride **Betty's Brigade**
43 B g Tobougg (IRE)—No Comebacks **Mrs S. E. Barclay**
44 PRINCEOFPERFECTION, b g Tobougg (IRE)—Princess Perfect (IRE) **Winks Racing**
45 Ch g Tobougg (IRE)—Synergie (IRE) **Mrs S. E. Barclay**

TWO-YEAR-OLDS

46 B f 20/5 Proclamation (IRE)—Approved Quality (IRE) (Persian Heights) **Mrs S. E. Barclay**
47 B f 22/2 Zafeen (FR)—Betty's Pride (Lion Cavern (USA)) **Mrs S. E. Barclay**

MR RICHARD FORD—continued

48 B g 17/3 Byron—Hasty Lady (Dubai Destination (USA)) **Mrs S. E. Barclay**
49 **JONNY WOMBAT**, b g 20/4 Avonbridge—Moonlight Angel (Kyllachy) **Mr B. Hartley**
50 B f 19/3 Kyllachy—Magic Peak (IRE) (Danehill (USA)) **Mrs Stella Barclay**
51 B f 13/3 Zafeen (FR)—Monica Geller (Komaite (USA)) **Mrs S. E. Barclay**
52 B f 8/6 Proclamation (IRE)—No Comebacks (Last Tycoon) **Mrs S. E. Barclay**
53 B g 13/5 Tiger Hill (IRE)—Rose Bounty (Polar Falcon (USA)) **Mrs S. E. Barclay**
54 Ch g 22/4 Proclamation (IRE)—Synergie (IRE) (Exit To Nowhere (USA)) **Mrs S. E. Barclay**

Other Owners: Mrs Leslie Buckley, Mr Neil Burbridge, Mr J. Calderbank, Mr A. Calderbank, John & Lyn Campion, W. R. Chudley, Mrs R. Farrington-Kirkham, Mr L.J. Fielding, Mrs J. E. Gordon, Mr Robert Hall, Mrs Irene Hall, K. M. Hesketh, H. Kirkham, Lancashire Racing Stables, Mr Richard Mattinson, D. E. Simpson, Mrs Paula Smith, S. A. Stokes, Mr T. R. Vaughan, Mr Matt Watkinson, C. G. Wilson, Mr Mike Wright.

Assistant Trainer: Stella Barclay

Jockey (flat): Frederik Tylicki. **Jockey (NH):** Graham Lee, Richie McGrath. **Conditional:** Harry Challoner. **Amateur:** Miss Caroline Hurley, Miss Nicky Stead.

---

238 MRS RICHENDA FORD, Dorchester
Postal: **Cross Farm, Brockhampton, Buckland Newton, Dorchester, Dorset, DT2 7DJ**

1 **ABAYAAN**, 6, gr g Sadler's Wells (USA)—Showdown **Mr & Mrs K. B. Snook**
2 **SOMERBY (IRE)**, 9, b g Sadler's Wells (USA)—Oriental Mystique **Mrs R. Ford**

Other Owners: K. B. Snook, Mrs M. Snook.

---

239 MR BRIAN FORSEY, Taunton
Postal: **Three Oaks, Ash Priors, Taunton, Somerset, TA4 3NQ**
Contacts: PHONE (01823) 433914 MOBILE (07747) 392760
E-MAIL forsey2001@yahoo.com

1 **AUREATE**, 8, ch g Jade Robbery (USA)—Anne d'autriche (IRE) **Mr K. C. Jago**
2 **BARISTA (IRE)**, 4, b g Titus Livius (FR)—Cappuccino (IRE) **Mr K. C. Jago**
3 **FOLLOW THE MASTER**, 6, b g Alflora (IRE)—Daisy May **Mrs P. M. Bosley**
4 **KILLING ME SOFTLY**, 11, b g Kingsinger (IRE)—Slims Lady **B. Forsey, Pam Bosley**
5 **RIGHT MOVE (IRE)**, 7, b g Golan (IRE)—Need You Badly **Mr K. C. Jago**
6 **SOFTLY KILLING ME**, 7, b m Umistim—Slims Lady **Mr R. W. Haynes**
7 **SOLITARY PALM (IRE)**, 9, gr ro g Great Palm (USA)—
                                            Grande Solitaire (FR) **W. McKibbin, A. Stevens & N. Samuel**

Other Owners: B. Forsey, W. McKibbin, Mr N. Samuel, A. G. Stevens.

Assistant Trainer: Susan Forsey

---

240 MISS SANDY FORSTER, Kelso
Postal: **Halterburn Head, Yetholm, Kelso, Roxburghshire, TD5 8PP**
Contacts: PHONE/FAX (01573) 420615 FAX (01573) 420615
MOBILE (07880) 727877 or (07976) 587315
E-MAIL clivestorey@btinternet.com

1 **BEVERLY HILL BILLY**, 8, b g Primo Valentino (IRE)—Miss Beverley **Miss S. E. Forster**
2 **JOLLYGOODWELLDONE**, 9, b g Dancing High—Merimbula **J. R. Jeffreys**
3 **NISAAL (IRE)**, 7, b g Indian Ridge—Kahalah (USA) **Anne & Tony Howarth**
4 **SEE THE LEGEND**, 7, b m Midnight Legend—Amys Delight **The Border Racers**
5 **SOUL ANGEL**, 8, ch g Tipsy Creek (USA)—Over Keen **Soul Searchers**
6 **STORYMAKER**, 11, b g Midnight Legend—Amys Delight **J M & Miss H M Crichton, Miss S Forster**
7 **TAKE A SPIN**, 4, ch g Bahamian Bounty—Regal Run (USA) **Miss S. E. Forster**
8 **WELL OILED (IRE)**, 11, b g Supreme Leader—Mightyatom **Miss S. E. Forster**

Other Owners: F. Berry, Mrs H. M. Crichton, J. M. Crichton, Mr A. J. Howarth, D. A. Skeldon, Mr M. Smith, C. Storey.

Assistant Trainer: C. Storey

Jockey (NH): Tom Messenger. **Conditional:** Jakob Kocman. **Amateur:** Mr C. Storey.

241 MR GEORGE FOSTER, Haddington
Postal: **Stoneypath Tower Farm, Haddington, East Lothian, EH41 4QB**
Contacts: PHONE **(01620) 830233** MOBILE **(07855) 374346**
E-MAIL **georgefosterracing@gmail.com** WEBSITE **www.stoneypathracing.co.uk**

1 **ACOL**, 5, ch g Domedriver (IRE)—Bridge Pal **Miss E. G. MacGregor**
2 **BALLADE DE LA MER**, 6, b m Ishiguru (USA)—Riviere Rouge **Highland Racing 6**
3 **CATCHER OF DREAMS (IRE)**, 6, b g Catcher In The Rye (IRE)—No Islands **Stoneypath Racing Club**
4 **CLANACHY**, 6, b m Kyllachy—Antonia's Dream **Stoneypath Racing Club**
5 **EILEAN EEVE**, 6, b m And Beyond (IRE)—Yeveed (IRE) **Highland Racing 6**
6 **GEORGIAN SILVER**, 4, ch f Auction House (USA)—Proud Titania (IRE) **D. W. Shaw**
7 **HELLBENDER (IRE)**, 6, ch g Exceed And Excel (AUS)—Desert Rose **A. G. Foster**
8 **HOTGREW BOY**, 5, b g Tobougg (IRE)—Tanwir **Mr S. F. Cawkwell**
9 **MANGHAM (IRE)**, 7, b g Montjeu (IRE)—Lovisa (USA) **A. G. Foster**
10 **MERRION TIGER (IRE)**, 7, ch g Choisir (AUS)—Akita (IRE) **Save The Tiger**
11 **NAAFETHA (IRE)**, 4, b f Alhaarth (IRE)—Doctrine **Mr F. E. Snowie**
12 4, B g Doyen (IRE)—Sally's Twins **D. W. Shaw**
13 **SANDWITH**, 9, ch g Perryston View—Bodfari Times **Stoneypath Racing Club**
14 **SQUIRE TRELAWNEY**, 6, b g Domedriver (IRE)—Crockadore (USA) **P. J. Haycock**
15 **TWIN EDGE**, 7, ch m Bold Edge—Sally's Twins **D. W. Shaw**

THREE-YEAR-OLDS

16 B f Rainbow High—Big Betty **D. W. Shaw**

TWO-YEAR-OLDS

17 Ch f 28/3 Auction House (USA)—Immortelle (Arazi (USA)) (2095) **A. G. Foster**
18 Ch f 12/2 Bertolini (USA)—Music In Exile (USA) (Diesis) **A. G. Foster**
19 **PASTORAL PREY**, b c 15/5 Pastoral Pursuits—Bird of Prey (IRE) (Last Tycoon) (2380) **A. G. Foster**
20 B c 4/4 Needwood Blade—Scarlet Woman (Sri Pekan (USA)) **A. G. Foster**
21 Ch f 14/3 Dubai Destination—Tab's Gift (Bijou d'inde) (857) **A. G. Foster**

Other Owners: Dr T. I. Brown, S. E. Kennedy, W. A. Powrie.

Jockey (flat): Tom Eaves, Andrew Mullen. **Conditional:** Ryan Mania. **Amateur:** Mr M. Ennis.

242 MISS JOANNE FOSTER, Ilkley
Postal: **Brookleigh Farm, Burley Road, Menston, Ilkley, West Yorkshire, LS29 6NS**
Contacts: PHONE **(07980) 301808 (01943) 864116** MOBILE **(07980) 301808**
E-MAIL **info@jofosterracing.co.uk** WEBSITE **www.jofosterracing.co.uk**

1 **MARINO PRINCE (FR)**, 7, b g Dr Fong (USA)—Hula Queen (USA) **The Golden Syndicate**
2 **NOUNOU**, 11, b g Starborough—Watheeqah (USA) **The Smash Block Partnership**
3 **UMVERTI**, 7, b m Averti (IRE)—Umbrian Gold (IRE) **S Hollings & Partners**
4 **WINGED FARASI**, 8, b g Desert Style (IRE)—Clara Vale (IRE) **The Smash Block Partnership**

Other Owners: P. J. Deakin, Miss J. E. Foster, P. Foster, Mr S. A. Hollings.

Amateur: Miss J. Foster, Mr Oliver Greenall.

243 MR JIMMY FOX, Marlborough
Postal: **Highlands Farm Stables, Herridge, Collingbourne Ducis, Marlborough, Wiltshire, SN8 3EG**
Contacts: PHONE **(01264) 850218 (07931) 724358** MOBILE **(07702) 880010**
E-MAIL **jcfoxtrainer@aol.com**

1 **ANNES ROCKET (IRE)**, 7, b h Fasliyev (USA)—Aguilas Perla (IRE) **The Cross Keys Racing Club**
2 **BIG JAKE**, 6, b g Karinga Bay—Spellbinder (IRE) **G. B. Balding**
3 **HENRY HURST (IRE)**, 6, b g Bob's Return (IRE)—Proper Primitive **G. B. Balding**
4 **MARTIN'S SHADOW**, 6, br m Tamure (IRE)—Anns Girl **Mrs J. A. Cleary**
5 **MAYDREAM**, 5, b m Sea Freedom—Maedance **The Dancing Partners**
6 **MY JEANIE (IRE)**, 8, ch m King Charlemagne (USA)—Home Comforts **R. E. Kavanagh**
7 **ORPEN'ARRY (IRE)**, 4, b g Orpen (USA)—Closing Time (IRE) **Mrs B. A. Fuller**
8 **PEVERIL PANDORA**, 9, b m Kayf Tara—Spellbinder (IRE) **G. B. Balding**
9 **THE WEE CHIEF (IRE)**, 6, ch g King Charlemagne (USA)—La Belle Clare (IRE) **R. E. Kavanagh**
10 **TORRES DEL PAINE**, 5, b h Compton Place—Noble Story **Mrs S. J. Fox**

MR JIMMY FOX—continued

THREE-YEAR-OLDS

11 **BOLD DAVID,** b g Bold Edge—Veverka **Mrs M. Morrow**

TWO-YEAR-OLDS

12 **GRACIOUS GEORGE (IRE),** b c 25/3 Oratorio (IRE)—Little Miss Gracie (Efisio) **Mrs B. A. Fuller**
13 Ch c 5/5 Kheleyf (USA)—Sacred Pearl (IRE) (Daylami (IRE))

Other Owners: Mrs E. Estall, M. J. McAuley, A. Slattery.

Assistant Trainer: Sarah-Jane Fox

Jockey (flat): Pat Dobbs. **Amateur:** Mrs Sarah-Jane Fox.

---

244 | **MISS SUZZANNE FRANCE, Norton on Derwent**
Postal: Newstart Racing, Cheesecake Hill House, Cheesecake Hill, Beverley Road,
Norton on Derwent, North Yorkshire, YO17 9PJ
Contacts: PHONE (01653) 691947 FAX (01653) 691947 MOBILE (07904) 117531
E-MAIL suzzannemunchie@talk21.com

1 **BACHELOR KNIGHT (IRE),** 4, b g Bachelor Duke (USA)—Labetera **Newstart Partnership**
2 **STAMP DUTY (IRE),** 4, b g Ad Valorem (USA)—Lothian Lass (IRE) **Newstart Partnership**

Other Owners: Mrs P. France, Mr P. R. France.

Amateur: Mr Aaron James.

---

245 | **MR DEREK FRANKLAND, Brackley**
Postal: Springfields, Mixbury, Brackley, Northamptonshire, NN13 5RR
Contacts: FAX (01280) 847334 MOBILE (07763) 020406
E-MAIL dsfrankland@aol.com

1 **CLOONAVERY (IRE),** 10, b g Xaar—Hero's Pride (FR) **D. S. Frankland & D. J. Trott**
2 **MULAAZEM,** 9, b g King's Best (USA)—Harayir (USA) **D. S. Frankland & D. J. Trott**
3 **REBEL HIGH (IRE),** 8, ch g Hymns On High—Celia's Fountain (IRE) **D. S. Frankland & D. J. Trott**

Other Owners: Mr D. Frankland, Mr D. Trott.

Jockey (NH): Liam Treadwell.

---

246 | **MR JAMES FROST, Buckfastleigh**
Postal: Hawson Stables, Buckfastleigh, Devon, TQ11 0HP
Contacts: YARD (01364) 642267 HOME (01364) 642332 FAX (01364) 643182
MOBILE (07860) 220229

1 **ALL FOR EVE,** 6, ch g Alflora (IRE)—Evening Scent **P. M. Tosh**
2 **CANSHEBEMINE,** 8, b m Morpeth—Pigeon Loft (IRE) **Dr D. Edwards**
3 **CAPTAIN BECKET,** 9, b g Access Ski—Sporting Annie **Share My Dream**
4 **CHASE GATE,** 7, ch g Arkadian Hero (USA)—Carlingford Lass (IRE) **Mrs J. Bury**
5 **DANEVA (IRE),** 8, b m Turtle Island (IRE)—Testaway (IRE) **Mr C. Johnston**
6 **FASINATOR,** 5, b m Morpeth—Serena Pride (IRE) **J. D. Frost**
7 **HAYDENS MOUNT,** 7, ch g Bahamian Bounty—Tenderfoot **Share My Dream**
8 **HAZELWOOD,** 5, b m Morpeth—Imperial Jewel (FR) **J. D. Frost**
9 **KILDERRY DEAN (IRE),** 5, b g Croco Rouge (IRE)—Perkalette (IRE) **Miss M. D. Wheaton**
10 **NORTH LONDON,** 5, b g Morpeth—Miss Grace **Mr T. G. Russell**
11 **ROLANTA (FR),** 7, b m Maresca Sorrento (FR)—Gazelle de Sou (FR) **Mrs J. McCormack**
12 **SARENICE (FR),** 6, gr g April Night (FR)—Delice du Soleil (FR) **Mrs J. Bury**

Other Owners: Mr M. Kay, Ms H. M. Vernon-Jones.

Assistant Trainer: G. Frost

Jockey (NH): Hadden Frost, Tom O'Connor. **Amateur:** Mr Ben Robarts.

247 MR JOHN GALLAGHER, Moreton-In-Marsh
Postal: **Grove Farm, Chastleton, Moreton-In-Marsh, Gloucestershire, GL56 0SZ**
Contacts: **PHONE/FAX** (01608) 674492 **MOBILE** (07780) 972663
E-MAIL gallagherracing@phonecoop.coop **WEBSITE** www.gallagherracing.com

1 ALPHA DELTA WHISKY, 4, ch g Intikhab (USA)—Chispa **Adweb Ltd**
2 FAYRE BELLA, 5, ch m Zafeen (FR)—Hollybell **John Gallagher**
3 MAC GILLE EOIN, 8, b h Bertolini (USA)—Peruvian Jade **M. C. S. D. Racing Partnership**
4 MENHA, 4, ch f Dubawi (IRE)—Tessara (GER) **C. R. Marks (Banbury)**
5 SHARED MOMENT (IRE), 6, ch m Tagula—Good Thought (IRE) **M. J. Benton**
6 SOUNDBYTE, 7, b g Beat All (USA)—Gloaming **M. C. S. D. Racing & Mark Benton**

THREE-YEAR-OLDS
7 CHICARITO, b g Striking Ambition—Mary Jane **Mucky Duck Partnership**
8 DIAMOND MARKS (IRE), b g Diamond Green (FR)—Miss Megs (IRE) **C. R. Marks (Banbury)**
9 EMMAN BEE, gr f Dark Angel (IRE)—Two Sets To Love (IRE) **M. J. Benton**
10 HEARTSONG (IRE), b f Kheleyf (USA)—Semiquaver (IRE) **C. Rashbrook**
11 ONE COOL DANCER (IRE), br f One Cool Cat (USA)—Dancing Duchess (IRE) **C. R. Marks (Banbury)**
12 PIUS PARKER (IRE), b g Antonius Pius (USA)—Parker's Cove (USA) **C. R. Marks (Banbury)**

TWO-YEAR-OLDS
13 B c 1/3 Sleeping Indian—Chispa (Imperial Frontier (USA)) (1714) **John Gallagher**
14 ECHO BRAVA, b gr g 27/2 Proclamation (IRE)—Snake Skin (Golden Snake (USA)) (1714) **Adweb Ltd**
15 FLETCHER CHRISTIAN, b c 29/3 Bahamian Bounty—
Lady Dominatrix (IRE) (Danehill Dancer (IRE)) (30476) **C. R. Marks (Banbury)**
16 LADWEB, ch c 19/5 Bertolini (USA)—Adweb (Muhtarram (USA)) (1333) **Adweb Ltd**

Other Owners: Mr J. Gallagher, Mr J. M. Buob-Aldorf, Mr C. Cory, Mr J. F. Long, Mrs B. A. Long, Mr Barry J. McClean, Mrs
Maggie McClean.

Assistant Trainer: Mrs R. Gallagher

Jockey (flat): Neil Callan, Jamie Spencer, Chris Catlin, Martin Lane.

248 MRS SUSAN GARDNER, Longdown
Postal: **Woodhayes Farm, Longdown, Exeter, Devon, EX6 7SB**
Contacts: **PHONE/FAX** (01392) 811213 **MOBILE** (07971) 097936
E-MAIL woodhayesstudfarm@btinternet.com

1 BREAKOUTTHEBOOZE (IRE), 4, b g Tiger Hill (IRE)—Quantum (IRE) **D. V. Gardner**
2 CLOVERS BOY, 7, b g First Trump—Persian Clover **R. W. Mitchell**
3 FLYING AWARD (IRE), 8, br g Oscar (IRE)—Kates Machine (IRE) **Mr & Mrs P. George & Mrs B. Russell**
4 MEDIC MAN (IRE), 6, b g Dr Massini (IRE)—Tina Torus (IRE) **D. V. Gardner**
5 MISS SAFFRON, 9, br m Access Ski—Saffron Lake **P. A. Tylor & G. N. Noye**
6 MR REDWOOD, 10, ch g Romany Rye—Wood Corner **P. A. Tylor**
7 ORION EXPRESS, 11, gr h Bahhare (USA)—Kaprisky (IRE) **The Barley Mow Syndicate**
8 SALUT L'AS (FR), 6, ch g Kaldou Star—Kayas (FR) **D. V. Gardner**
9 SEA SAFFRON, 11, b g Sea Raven (IRE)—Saffron Lake **G. N. Noye & P. A. Tylor**
10 SOUTHWAY STAR, 7, b m Morpeth—Nearly A Score **T. R. Watts**
11 STORM ALERT, 5, ch g Karinga Bay—Rash-Gale (IRE) **D. V. Gardner**

Other Owners: Mr D. V. Gardner, Mrs P. George, Mr P. George, Mr G. Gray, Mr D. Layfield, Mr G. N. Noye, Mrs Brenda Russell,
Mr P. A. Tylor.

Assistant Trainer: D. V. Gardner

Jockey (NH): Aidan Coleman, Sam Thomas. Amateur: Miss L. Gardner.

249 MR JEREMY GASK, Warminster
Postal: **The Beeches, Deverill Road, Sutton Veny, Warminster, Wiltshire, BA12 7BY**
Contacts: **PHONE** (01985) 841166 **FAX** (01985) 840474 **MOBILE** (07507) 555303
E-MAIL info@horsesfirstracing.com **WEBSITE** www.horsesfirstracing.com

1 BERBERANA (IRE), 4, b f Acclamation—Barbera (GER) **Horses First Racing Ltd**
2 BUNKERED AGAIN, 5, b m Footstepsinthesand—Cragreen **P. W. Urquhart**
3 CREW CUT (IRE), 4, b gr g Acclamation—Carabine (USA) **R. L. Page**

MR JEREMY GASK—continued

4 **DAN DONNELLY (IRE)**, 4, b g Antonius Pius (USA)—Lacinia **Mr K. Blake**
5 **DOMINIUM (USA)**, 5, b g E Dubai (USA)—Sudenlylastsummer (USA) **R. L. Page**
6 **HIGH STANDING (USA)**, 7, b br g High Yield (USA)—Nena Maka **Mr A. G. Bloom**
7 **IVORY SILK**, 7, b m Diktat—Ivory's Joy **Miss K. M. Dobb**
8 **LASER BLAZER**, 4, b g Zafeen (FR)—Sashay **Calne Engineering Ltd**
9 **LEWYN**, 5, b m Exceed And Excel (AUS)—Panoramic View **The Nobles**
10 **LUCKY ROYALE**, 4, b f Lucky Story (USA)—Bella Bertolini **Gracelands Stud Partnership**
11 **LUCKY TRICKS**, 4, ch f Lucky Story (USA)—Miss Madame (IRE) **Gracelands Stud Partnership**
12 **MEDICEAN MAN**, 6, ch g Medicean—Kalindi **Mr Stuart Dobb & Miss Kate Dobb**
13 **NICE STYLE (IRE)**, 7, b g Desert Style (IRE)—Great Idea (IRE) **Mr A. G. Bloom**
14 **PERFECT OUTLOOK**, 4, b f Doyen (IRE)—Cautiously (USA)
15 **PRINCE OF BURMA (IRE)**, 4, b c Mujadil (USA)—Spinning Ruby **The Nobles**
16 **SASHEEN**, 5, b m Zafeen (FR)—Sashay **Sasheen Partnership**
17 **SILVER TURN**, 4, ch f Shamardal (USA)—Mambo Mistress (USA) **The Nobles**
18 **STREET POWER (IRE)**, 7, b br g Street Cry (IRE)—Javana (USA) **Horses First Racing Ltd**
19 **SULIS MINERVA (IRE)**, 5, b m Arakan (USA)—Lacinia **R. L. Page**
20 **SUTTON VENY (IRE)**, 6, gr m Acclamation—Carabine (USA) **The Sutton Veny Syndicate**
21 **SWEET SECRET**, 5, ch m Singspiel (IRE)—Ballymore Celebre **140 Characters**
22 **TITUS GENT**, 7, ch g Tumbleweed Ridge—Genteel (IRE) **Mr A. G. Bloom**
23 **TOGA TIGER (IRE)**, 5, b g Antonius Pius (USA)—Minerwa (GER) **For Sale**
24 **TRIPLE ASPECT (IRE)**, 6, b g Danetime (IRE)—Wicken Wonder (IRE) **Mr A. G. Bloom**

THREE-YEAR-OLDS

25 **ANNA'S STORM**, b f Milk It Mick—Habibi **Mr S. Y. Sun**
26 B f Namid—Carabine (USA) **Horses First Racing Ltd**
27 **ECLAT ROYALE**, b f Royal Applause—Maramkova (USA) **Five Horses Ltd**
28 **EXKALIBER**, b g Exceed And Excel (AUS)—Kalindi **The Exkaliber Partnership**
29 **GABBIANO**, b g Zafeen (FR)—Hollybell **Mr A. G. Bloom**
30 **GONE TO GROUND**, ch g Grape Tree Road—Chase The Fox **C. R. Withers**
31 **MISS SOCIALITE**, b gr f Nayef (USA)—Miss Satamixa (FR) **140 Characters**
32 **PHENOMENA**, b c Galileo (IRE)—Something Exciting **Trebles Holford Thoroughbreds**
33 **PRECISION FIVE**, b f Proclamation (IRE)—Sashay **Calne Engineering Ltd**
34 **ROCKME COCKNEY**, ch f Cockney Rebel (IRE)—Rock Lily **The Kathryn Stud Limited**
35 **TALYA'S STORM**, b c Milk It Mick—Absolutely Soaked (IRE) **Mr S. Y. Sun**
36 **TOPFLIGHT PRINCESS**, b f Cockney Rebel (IRE)—Topflightcoolracer **P. Bamford**
37 **TRENDING (IRE)**, gr g Dark Angel (IRE)—Call Later (USA) **The Twitterati**
38 **WILTSHIRE LIFE (IRE)**, b f Camacho—Miss Indigo **Mr M. Allen**
39 **YOU GOT THE LOVE**, ch f Hawk Wing (USA)—Precedence (IRE) **SN Racing IV**

TWO-YEAR-OLDS

40 **MAP OF LOVE (IRE)**, b f 13/2 Dylan Thomas (IRE)—Maramba (Rainbow Quest (USA)) **Five Horses Ltd**
41 B f 27/1 Sakhee's Secret—Maramkova (USA) (Danehill Dancer (IRE)) **Five Horses Ltd**
42 B c 8/3 Green Desert (USA)—Millyant (Primo Dominie) (30000)
43 B f 26/3 Milk It Mick—Salalah (Lion Cavern (USA)) **Mr S. Y. Sun**
44 Ch c 15/4 Kheleyf (USA)—Silver Quest (Rainbow Quest (USA)) (15000) **P. H. Morgan**

Other Owners: Mr M. J. Board, Miss N. F. Davey, Mr I. Hebbard, J. A. Knight, S. Nunn, A. C. Pickford, E. Wilmott, Mrs O. J. Wilmott, Mr A. S. Wood, R. V. Young, Mrs K. M. Young.

Apprentice: Raul da Silva

MRS ROSEMARY GASSON, Banbury
Postal: Alkerton Grounds, Balscote, Banbury, Oxfordshire, OX15 6JS
Contacts: PHONE (01295) 730248 MOBILE (07769) 798430
E-MAIL arb@aqf.myzen.co.uk

1 **ADIOS ALONSO (IRE)**, 6, b g Saffron Walden (FR)—Rosy Rockford (IRE) **Mrs R. Gasson**
2 **ALWAYS WILLING (IRE)**, 8, b g Darnay—Anniepepp (IRE) **Mrs R. Gasson**
3 **CROCO MISTER (IRE)**, 5, ch g Croco Rouge (IRE)—Nimrods Dream (IRE) **Mrs R. Gasson**
4 **ELITE BENEFICIAL (IRE)**, 7, ch g Beneficial—A Fine Romance (IRE) **Mrs R. Gasson**
5 **GENTLEMAN ANSHAN (IRE)**, 8, b g Anshan—Second Violin (IRE) **Mrs R. Gasson**
6 **JOLLY BOYS OUTING (IRE)**, 9, b g Glacial Storm (USA)—St Carol (IRE) **Mrs R. Gasson**
7 **KILCASCAN**, 8, b g Alflora (IRE)—Peasedown Tofana **Mrs R. Gasson**
8 **OFFICIALLY MODERN (IRE)**, 5, ch g Beneficial—Musical Millie (IRE) **Mrs R. Gasson**

Amateur: Miss Hannah Watson, Mr Ben Poste.

251 MR MICHAEL GATES, Stratford-on-Avon
Postal: **Comfort Park Stud, Campden Road, Clifford Chambers, Stratford-on-Avon, CV37 8LW**
Contacts: **MOBILE (07581) 246070**
E-MAIL comfortparkstud@hotmail.co.uk

1 CAMISKY, 12, b g Minster Son—Jamimo (IRE) **M. Gates**
2 CRACK AT DAWN (IRE), 11, b br g Insan (USA)—Ten Quid Short (IRE) **M. Gates**
3 FULL OV BEANS, 8, ch g Midnight Legend—Scarlet Baroness **M. Gates**
4 HANDSOME BUDDY (IRE), 5, br g Presenting—Moya's Magic (IRE) **Mrs Karin Gates**
5 IMPERIAL LAIDY (IRE), 8, b br m Corrouge (USA)—Encalchoise (FR) **M. Gates**
6 MEZARAT (ITY), 7, ch g Dream Well (FR)—Dayara (GER) **M. Gates**
7 PEACE CORPS, 6, ch g Medicean—Tromond **M. Gates**
8 TOUGH COOKIE (IRE), 9, b g Rashar (USA)—Vam Cas (IRE) **M. Gates**
9 WATCH HOUSE (IRE), 7, ch g Deploy—Derby Affair **M. Gates**

252 MR JONATHAN GEAKE, Marlborough
Postal: **Harestone House, East Kennett, Marlborough, Wiltshire, SN8 4EY**
Contacts: **PHONE (01672) 861784 MOBILE (07768) 350738**
E-MAIL jageake@yahoo.co.uk

1 ACROSS THE STRAITS (FR), 8, b g Dansili—Skipnight **Dr & Mrs Peter Leftley**
2 ANABAA'S DANCE (IRE), 5, ch m Tobougg (IRE)—Anabaa's Music **Double Kings Partnership**
3 BALLYMAN (IRE), 11, gr g Accordion—Sliabhin Rose **Dr & Mrs Peter Leftley**
4 BEWARE CHALK PIT (IRE), 8, b g Anshan—Rakiura (IRE) **Dr & Mrs Peter Leftley**
5 GOLDEN CELEBRATION, 6, ch g Double Trigger (IRE)—Rose Thyne (IRE) **Double Kings Partnership**
6 KELTIC CRISIS (IRE), 8, b g Needle Gun (IRE)—Catch Ball **Mr T. Geake & Mr D. J. Erwin**
7 LADY BLING BLING, 11, b m Midnight Legend—Slipmatic **P. J. Jones & G. D. Blagbrough**
8 MAELSTROM SEA, 7, b g Sea Freedom—Maedance **Mrs E. Estall**
9 RAMBRIDGE COPSE, 5, b g Terimon—Copper Rose Hill **Mr H. M. F. McCall**
10 5, ch g Best of The Bests (IRE)—Rose Thyne (IRE) **Mr T. Geake**
11 SILKY LADY (IRE), 5, b m Barathea (IRE)—Promising Lady **Double Kings Partnership**
12 STAN'S THE MAN, 4, b g Statue of Liberty (USA)—Anabaa's Music **D. J. Erwin**
13 STRIPE ME BLUE, 10, b g Miner's Lamp—Slipmatic **Mrs A. H. Jones & G. D. Blagbrough**
14 SUNSET PLACE, 5, ch g Compton Place—Manhattan Sunset (USA) **Jag Racing 1**

Other Owners: Mr G. D. Blagbrough, Mr D. J. Erwin, Mr Tony Geake, Mr J. A. Geake, Mrs P. D. Gulliver, Mr P. J. Jones, Mrs A. H. Jones, Dr Peter Leftley, Mrs Ann Leftley.

Assistant Trainer: Mrs S A Geake **Pupil Assistant:** Mr Sam Geake

Jockey (flat): Richard Thomas. **Jockey (NH):** Jimmy McCarthy, Andrew Thornton.

253 MISS KAREN GEORGE, Crediton
Postal: **Higher Eastington Stables, Lapford, Crediton, Devon, EX17 6NE**

1 BARNEY THE BEAR, 5, br g Best of The Bests (IRE)—Aquavita **P. J. H. George**
2 BELLE PARK, 5, b m Hamairi (IRE)—Cape Siren **R. A. Bimson**
3 CALL ME APRIL, 4, b f Generous (IRE)—Anyhow (IRE) **P. J. H. George**
4 GOOD AUTHORITY (IRE), 5, b g Chineur (FR)—Lady Alexander (IRE) **Adrian Parr & Karen George**
5 JOG ON KITTY, 4, b f Generous (IRE)—Storm Kitten (USA) **P. J. H. George**
6 MULBERRY BRITE, 4, b f Librettist (USA)—Thea (USA) **P. J. H. George**
7 NOTHING PERSONAL, 5, b g Double Trigger (IRE)—Nothings Forever **P. J. H. George**
8 ROYAL SELECTION (IRE), 4, ch f Choisir (AUS)—Rustic Princess (IRE) **A. T. Still**
9 SPIRIT OF LAKE (IRE), 10, b g Sheer Danzig (IRE)—Rosheen (IRE) **R. A. Bimson**
10 TOP DESIGN, 4, b g Zafeen (FR)—Dress Design (IRE) **Sharpened Newt Racing**

THREE-YEAR-OLDS

11 TRICOR, b f Medicean—Insinuation (IRE) **Tricor Partnership**

Other Owners: Mr A. J. Dickinson, Miss K. M. George, A. B. Parr.

254 **MR TOM GEORGE, Slad**

Postal: **Down Farm, Slad, Stroud, Gloucestershire, GL6 7QE**
Contacts: PHONE **(01452) 814267** FAX **(01452) 814246** MOBILE **(07850) 793483**
E-MAIL **tom@trgeorge.com** WEBSITE **www.tomgeorgeracing.co.uk**

1 **ARTHUR'S PASS**, 8, b g Midnight Legend—Bella Coola **Vicki Robinson & James Williams**
2 **BABY MIX (FR)**, 4, gr g Al Namix (FR)—Douchka (FR) **GDM Partnership**
3 **BACK BOB BACK (IRE)**, 7, b g Bob Back (USA)—Joyney **Power Panels Electrical Systems Ltd**
4 **BALLYALLIA MAN (IRE)**, 7, b g Flemensfirth (USA)—
                     Hatch Away (IRE) **H S Smith, R&M Gabbertas and Doone Hulse**
5 **BE DEFINITE (IRE)**, 8, b g Definite Article—Etoile Margot (FR) **Mr S. W. Clarke**
6 **BETTY BROWNEYES**, 7, b br m Classic Cliche (IRE)—Corn Bunting **Capt & Mrs J. A. George**
7 **BIG SOCIETY (IRE)**, 6, b g Flemensfirth (USA)—Choice of Kings (IRE) **Simon Clarke & David Thorpe**
8 **BLOSSOM KING (FR)**, 8, b g King's Best (USA)—Red Blossom (FR) **Silkword Racing Partnership**
9 **BLUE SIGNAL (IRE)**, 7, b g Blueprint (IRE)—Signal Lizzy (IRE) **Silkword Racing Partnership**
10 **CELTIC INTRIGUE (IRE)**, 5, b g Celtic Swing—Macca Luna (IRE) **O'Donohoe, Nelson, Stratford & Barlow**
11 **CESIUM (FR)**, 7, b g Green Tune (USA)—Tantatura (FR) **Miss J. A. Hoskins**
12 **COEUR DE FOU (FR)**, 7, ch g Limnos (JPN)—Folly Lady (FR) **Lady H. J. Clarke**
13 **COOLBEG (IRE)**, 6, b g Oscar (IRE)—Dianeme **R. P. Foden**
14 **COTTAGE ACRE (IRE)**, 9, b g Shernazar—Quits (IRE) **Thoroughbred Ladies**
15 **CROOKSHANKS (IRE)**, 6, b g Catcher In The Rye (IRE)—Sunset Park (IRE) **T. George**
16 **FORGOTTEN GOLD (IRE)**, 6, b g Dr Massini (IRE)—Ardnataggle (IRE) **Mr & Mrs R. Cornock**
17 **GENTLE BOB (IRE)**, 7, b g Bob's Return (IRE)—Maraniza (IRE) **David Thorpe & Simon Clarke**
18 **GOOD ORDER**, 7, b g Alflora (IRE)—Twinnings Grove (IRE) **Sharon C. Nelson & Dermot O'Donohoe**
19 **HALLEY (FR)**, 5, b g Loup Solitaire (USA)—Moon Glow (FR) **PJL Racing & Mr T R George**
20 **HIGH HO SHERIFF (IRE)**, 6, ch g Presenting—Miss Snapdragon (IRE) **Simon Clarke & David Thorpe**
21 **HOARE ABBEY (IRE)**, 6, ch g Definite Article—Tourist Attraction (IRE) **Mr S. W. Clarke**
22 **KINGS QUEEN (IRE)**, 6, b m Wizard King—Muharib Lady (IRE) **Five Valleys Racing Partnership**
23 **LEXICON LAD (IRE)**, 7, ch g Presenting—Hazel's Glory (IRE) **C. B. Compton**
24 **LORD RYEFORD (IRE)**, 12, br g Arctic Lord—Killoskehan Queen **T. W. C. Edwards**
25 **MAJAALES (USA)**, 9, b g Diesis—Roseate Tern **S Nelson, J Bowen-Rees, D O'Donohoe**
26 **MAJALA (FR)**, 6, b g Lavirco (GER)—Majae (FR) **Sharon Nelson Jayne Taylor Darren Taylor**
27 **MASTER CYNK**, 5, ch g Diableneyev (USA)—Model View (USA) **Barlow, Nelson, O'Donohoe & Stratford**
28 **MODULE (FR)**, 5, b g Panoramic—Before Royale (FR) **Mr S. W. Clarke**
29 **MONSIEUR CADOU (FR)**, 7, b g Cadoudal (FR)—Dame De Trefles (FR) **The 'Ye Of Little Faith' Partnership**
30 **MOONLIGHT MAGGIE**, 5, b m Pasternak—Moyliscar **Capt & Mrs J. A. George**
31 **MORENITO (FR)**, 9, b g Nononito (FR)—Cohiba (FR) **Mr C. B. Compton Mr B. D. Johnston**
32 **MOSCOW CHANCER (IRE)**, 6, b g Moscow Society (USA)—I'll See You Again (IRE) **T. D. J. Syder**
33 **MY INHERITANCE (IRE)**, 4, b g Araafa (IRE)—Glory Days (GER) **Miss J. A. Hoskins**
34 **NACARAT (FR)**, 11, gr g Smadoun (FR)—Gerbora (FR) **Mr S. W. Clarke**
35 **NODEBATEABOUTIT (IRE)**, 7, b g Alflora (IRE)—Mystere (IRE) **Sharon C. Nelson & Dermot O'Donohoe**
36 **OLOFI (FR)**, 6, gr g Slickly (FR)—Dona Bella (FR) **R&L Channing S&F Roberts McNeill Family**
37 **ON THE CASE (GB)**, 4, ch g Generous (IRE)—Tulipa (POL) **Sharon C. Nelson and John Fielding**
38 **ON THE MONEY**, 5, ch g Karinga Bay—Clover Coin **Sharon C. Nelson & Julie Natala**
39 **OVERNIGHT FAME (IRE)**, 8, b m Kayf Tara—Best of The Girls (IRE) **Mr & Mrs R. Cornock**
40 **PARSNIP PETE**, 6, b g Pasternak—Bella Coola **The Parsnips**
41 **PLEASURE ISLAND (IRE)**, 5, b g Heron Island (IRE)—Deep Satisfaction **D. A. Thorpe**
42 **PRIEST ISLAND (IRE)**, 6, b g Heron Island (IRE)—Chapel Field (IRE) **Thoroughbred Ladies**
43 **RING BO REE (IRE)**, 9, b g Topanoora—La Ronde **Miss J. D. Wilson**
44 **RODY (FR)**, 7, ch g Colonel Collins (USA)—Hamelie II (FR) **R A Dalton & J C E Laing**
45 **SAPHIRE NIGHT**, 11, b m Sir Harry Lewis (USA)—Tyrilda (USA) **Simon W. Clarke & David Zeffman**
46 **SHAKE THE BARLEY (IRE)**, 9, ch g Marignan (USA)—Glengarra Princess **Slad Valley Racing Partnership**
47 **SIVOLA DE SIVOLA (FR)**, 6, gr g Martaline—Kerrana (FR) **D O'Donohoe, S & P Nelson & D Sylvester**
48 **SLAM**, 7, b g Beat Hollow—House Hunting **J. T. Warner**
49 **TARTAK (FR)**, 9, b g Akhdari (USA)—Tartamuda (FR) **Power Panels Electrical Systems Ltd**
50 **THE DARLING BOY**, 7, b g Medicean—Silver Top Hat (USA) **The Hon Mrs D. Hulse**
51 **THECIRCLEOFTRUST (FR)**, 7, ch g Gold Away (IRE)—Dash (FR) **Mike Stratford & Steve Hurn**
52 **TIRE LARIGOT (FR)**, 5, b g Muhtathir—Rhaetia (IRE) **Mr Tom George**
53 **TORY MASSINI (IRE)**, 5, b g Dr Massini (IRE)—Star Mover **Simon Clarke & David Thorpe**
54 **TRIANGULAR (USA)**, 7, b g Diesis—Salchow (USA) **Mrs H. Charlet**
55 **VIVRE LIBRE**, 5, b g Sadler's Wells (USA)—Vallee Enchantee (IRE) **PJL Racing & Mr & Mrs R E R Rumboll**
56 **WATLEDGE (FR)**, 5, b g Lando (GER)—Flower of Freedom (FR) **Stratford, Nelson, O'Donohoe & Barlow**
57 **WESTON LODGE (IRE)**, 6, b g Aahsaylad—Slip Me Fippence **Miss G. I. G. McCormick**

MR TOM GEORGE—continued

THREE-YEAR-OLDS

58 **ABSOLUTE RETURN**, b g Kayf Tara—Kitty Wong (IRE) **Mr & Mrs R. E. R. Rumboll**

Other Owners: Mrs D. M. Barker, Mr M. H. D. Barlow, Mrs C. D. Chamberlain, Mrs Lisa Channing, Mr Simon W. Clarke, Mr C. B. Compton, Mr R. Cornock, Mrs Michele Cornock, Mr R. A. Dalton, Mr Peter Duffy, Mr R. K. Gabbertas, Mrs C. M. George, Capt. J. A. George, Mr E. Henriksen, Mrs A. Henriksen, Mrs Doone Hulse, Mr Steve Hurn, Mr Bruce Johnston, Miss Jennifer Laing, Mr John B. Lawson, McNeill Family, Mrs Sharon C. Nelson, Mr J. R. S. Newiss, Mr D. J. O'Donohoe, Mr P.T. Petrie, Mr Simon Roberts, Ms Vicki Robinson, Mrs Robin Rumboll, Mr H. Stephen Smith, Mr Mike Stratford, Mr Jeremy Taylor, Mr Darren Taylor, Mr D. A. Thorpe, Mr R. F. Tromans, Mr Michael Watkins, Mr David Zeffman.

Jockey (NH): Liam Heard, Paddy Brennan.

---

255 **MRS THERESA GIBSON, Hexham**
Postal: **Embley, Steel, Hexham, Northumberland, NE47 0HW**
Contacts: **PHONE (01434) 673334**
E-MAIL theresagibson356@btinternet.com

1 **RUGGED JEM (IRE)**, 11, b g Humbel (USA)—Glenastar VII **Mrs T. M. Gibson**
2 **SUNSET SONG**, 8, b m Supreme Sound—Cudder Or Shudder (IRE) **Mrs T. M. Gibson**

---

256 **MR NICK GIFFORD, Findon**
Postal: **The Downs, Stable Lane, Findon, West Sussex, BN14 0RT**
Contacts: **OFFICE (01903) 872226 FAX (01903) 877232 MOBILE (07940) 518077**
E-MAIL downs.stables@btconnect.com WEBSITE www.nickgiffordracing.co.uk

1 **ACCORDING TO THEM (IRE)**, 8, ch g Quws—Any Old Music (IRE) **Mr D. R. Steele**
2 **BOUGUEREAU**, 7, b g Alhaarth (IRE)—Blessed Honour **A. W. Black**
3 **CHESTHAM LAD**, 6, gr h Exit To Nowhere (USA)—Petale de Rose (IRE) **Mrs T. J. Stone-Brown**
4 **CHRISTOPHER WREN (USA)**, 5, ch g D'wildcat (USA)—Ashley's Coy (USA) **J. P. McManus**
5 **DEE EE WILLIAMS (IRE)**, 9, b g Dushyantor (USA)—Fainne Oir (IRE) **Give Every Man His Due**
6 **EL PADRINO (IRE)**, 7, b g Definite Article—Nova Rose **Mrs T. J. Stone-Brown**
7 **FAIRY RATH (IRE)**, 6, ch g Accordion—Killoughey Fairy (IRE) **Mrs C. L. Kyle**
8 **GENERAL KUTUZOV (IRE)**, 8, b g Moscow Society (USA)—Bonnie Thynes (IRE) **Barkfold Manor Stud**
9 **KUILSRIVER (IRE)**, 5, b g Cape Cross (IRE)—Ripple of Pride (IRE) **Mrs T. J. Stone-Brown**
10 **MADAME PAPILLON**, 5, b m Generous (IRE)—Scarlet Poppy **Mrs T. J. Stone-Brown**
11 **MAJOR BELLAMY (GER)**, 6, ch g Black Sam Bellamy (IRE)—Marie Claire (GER) **Sir Christopher Wates**
12 **MOY RIVER (IRE)**, 5, b g Indian River (FR)—Slowly Does It (IRE) **F. A. Hutsby**
13 **NICEBOY (IRE)**, 8, br g Environment Friend—Take The Catch **Mr D. R. Steele**
14 **NOMECHEKI (FR)**, 10, b g Kalmoss (FR)—Kan A Dare (FR) **The Stewart Family**
15 **OLD DREAMS (IRE)**, 6, b m Old Vic—I Can Imagine (IRE)
16 **ON TREND (IRE)**, 6, b g Jammaal—Comrun (IRE) **Ham Manor Farms Ltd**
17 **OSCAR PAPA**, 7, ch g Presenting—Oso Special **Mrs C. J. Zetter-Wells**
18 **PALE RIDER (FR)**, 9, gr g Linamix (FR)—Grove Daffodil (IRE) **P. H. Betts**
19 **PARIGINO (FR)**, 4, b g Panis (USA)—Loretta Gianni (FR) **Bayonet Partners**
20 **PASCHA BERE (FR)**, 9, gr g Verglas (IRE)—Ephelide (FR) **Mr & Mrs Mark Tracey**
21 4, Ch g Generous (IRE)—Penneyrose Bay **Sir Christopher Wates**
22 **RESTE JEUNE (FR)**, 6, ch g Reste Tranquille (FR)—Rosy Junior (FR) **Lady Wates**
23 **SPECIALAGENT ALFIE**, 6, b g Alflora (IRE)—Oso Special **Mr M. K. O'Shea**
24 **TULLAMORE DEW (IRE)**, 10, ch g Pistolet Bleu (IRE)—Heather Point **Give Every Man His Due**
25 **UTOPIAN (FR)**, 4, ch g Kapgarde (FR)—Djeti (FR) **Coldunell Limited**
26 **WHAT WILL YOU SAY**, 5, gr g Kayf Tara—Janiture (FR) **D. Dunsdon**
27 **WHOLELOTTALOVE**, 4, b g Doyen (IRE)—Janiture (FR) **D. Dunsdon**

THREE-YEAR-OLDS

28 **IN RAINBOWS**, gr c Shirocco (GER)—Janiture (FR) **D. Dunsdon**

Other Owners: Mr A. Bradley, Mr D. Ellis, Mrs S. N. J. Embiricos, S. N. Embiricos, Mr L. Horvath, Mr A. Stewart, Mrs J. A. Stewart, Mr M. J. Tracey, Mrs I. M. Tracey.

Jockey (NH): Liam Treadwell. **Amateur:** Mr D. H. Dunsdon.

257 MR MARK GILLARD, Sherborne
Postal: Elm Tree Stud, Holwell, Sherborne, Dorset, DT9 5LL
Contacts: PHONE (01963) 23026 FAX (01963) 23297 MOBILE (07970) 700605
E-MAIL Mark@thegillards.co.uk WEBSITE markgillardracing.com

1 BOOGIE KNIGHT, 4, ch g Tobougg (IRE)—Brave Vanessa (USA) **Miss Kay Russell**
2 CATHOLIC HILL (USA), 7, gr ro g Pleasant Tap (USA)—Celestial Bliss (USA) **Miss Kay Russell**
3 FORCRYINGOUTLOUD (IRE), 8, ch g Old Vic—Bijubu (IRE) **Pippa Grace**
4 LADY BRIDGET, 4, b f Hawk Wing (USA)—Change Partners (IRE) **T. J. C. Seegar**
5 LADY WILLA (IRE), 5, b m Footstepsinthesand—Change Partners (IRE) **T. J. C. Seegar**
6 PETITO (IRE), 9, b g Imperial Ballet (IRE)—Fallacy **D. E. Hazzard**
7 RED LAW (IRE), 8, b g Reprimand—Trouville Lass (IRE) **Mr T J C Seegar & Mrs T Connor**
8 REVAADER, 4, b f Revoque (IRE)—Wave Rider **Miss Kay Russell**
9 THE NAME IS FRANK, 7, b g Lujain (USA)—Zaragossa **D. E. Hazzard**
10 YELLOW PRINTER, 6, b g Royal Applause—Robsart (IRE) **Ms T. Connor**

THREE-YEAR-OLDS

11 THE NAME IS DON (IRE), b g One Cool Cat (USA)—Waroonga (IRE) **D. E. Hazzard**

TWO-YEAR-OLDS

12 Ch f 25/2 Assertive—Bint Baddi (FR) (Shareef Dancer (USA)) (3000) **M. C. Denning**

Assistant Trainer: Pippa Grace

Jockey (flat): Liam Keniry. **Jockey (NH):** Tommy Phelan.

258 MR PATRICK GILLIGAN, Newmarket
Postal: Sackville House, Sackville Street, Newmarket, Suffolk, CB8 8DX
Contacts: PHONE (01638) 669151 MOBILE (07881) 796612
E-MAIL gilliganmax@aol.com WEBSITE www.patrickgilligan.org

1 REPLICATOR, 7, b g Mujahid (USA)—Valldemosa **Mr L. J. Doolan**
2 UNA VITA PIUS (IRE), 4, b f Antonius Pius (USA)—Avit (IRE) **Treasure Seekers**

THREE-YEAR-OLDS

3 SHAHRAZAD (IRE), b f Cape Cross (IRE)—Khulasah (IRE) **F. Brian Barnes**

Other Owners: Mr P. J. Crowe, Mr S. Gilligan.

Assistant Trainer: Jack Gilligan

259 MR JAMES GIVEN, Willoughton
Postal: Mount House Stables, Long Lane, Willoughton, Gainsborough, Lincolnshire, DN21 5SQ
Contacts: PHONE (01427) 667618 FAX (01427) 667734 MOBILE (07801) 100496
E-MAIL james@jamesgivenracing.com WEBSITE www.jamesgivenracing.com

1 CLUMBER PLACE, 6, ch m Compton Place—Inquirendo (USA) **Carl Stocks & Julie Walsh**
2 GLENRIDDING, 8, b g Averti (IRE)—Appelone **Tremousser Partnership**
3 HIDDEN GLORY, 5, b g Mujahid (USA)—Leominda **Danethorpe Racing Partnership**
4 INDIAN DAYS, 7, ch h Daylami (IRE)—Cap Coz (IRE) **Mr D. J. Fish**
5 JACK SMUDGE, 4, br g One Cool Cat (USA)—Forever Fine (USA) **Danethorpe Racing Partnership**
6 MY MATE JAKE (IRE), 4, ch g Captain Rio—Jam (IRE) **Mr A. Owen**
7 NELLA SOFIA, 4, bl f Diktat—Night Symphonie **Mrs L. J. Daykin**
8 ROYAL BAJAN (USA), 4, gr ro g Speightstown (USA)—Crown You (USA) **Danethorpe Racing Partnership**
9 ROYAL TROOPER (IRE), 6, b g Hawk Wing (USA)—Strawberry Roan (IRE) **Mr J. A. Barson**
10 SERGEANT ABLETT (IRE), 4, b g Danehill Dancer (IRE)—Dolydille (IRE) **Mr J. A. Barson**
11 STILETTOESINTHEMUD (IRE), 4, ch f Footstepsinthesand—The Stick **Mr A. C. Gray**
12 TARTAN GUNNA, 6, b g Anabaa (USA)—Embraced **Simply Racing Limited**
13 TOYMAKER, 5, b g Starcraft (NZ)—Eurolink Raindance (IRE) **Antoniades Family**
14 VEROON (IRE), 6, b g Noverre (USA)—Waroonga (IRE) **Danethorpe Racing Partnership**

MR JAMES GIVEN—continued

THREE-YEAR-OLDS

15 **BAILEYS BIGISHU,** ch g Ishiguru (USA)—Jane Jubilee (IRE) **G. R. Bailey Ltd (Baileys Horse Feed)**
16 **BAILEYS OVER ICE,** b f Iceman—Exhibitor (USA) **G. R. Bailey Ltd (Baileys Horse Feed)**
17 **BUSTER BROWN (IRE),** ch c Singspiel (IRE)—Gold Dodger (USA) **Mrs L. P. Fish**
18 **CHOCCYWOCCYDOODAH,** b f Dr Fong (USA)—Galaxy of Stars **Danethorpe Racing Partnership**
19 **FINBAR,** b c Nayef (USA)—Baralinka (IRE) **Elite Racing Club**
20 **FIRST BID,** b c Kyllachy—Toucantini **P. Swann**
21 **FIRST VOICE (IRE),** ch g Dylan Thomas (IRE)—Prealpina (IRE) **Danethorpe Racing Partnership**
22 **HALOGEN,** b g Halling (USA)—Trompette (USA) **Elite Racing Club**
23 **HARBOUR SANDS,** b c Bahamian Bounty—Sahara Silk (IRE) **Danethorpe Racing Partnership**
24 **HUNTING GONK,** b c Amadeus Wolf—Para Siempre **R. C. Spore**
25 **KUNG HEI FAT CHOY (USA),** b g Elusive Quality (USA)—Lady Succeed (JPN) **Danethorpe Racing Partnership**
26 **MALINDI,** b f Compton Place—Mana Pools (IRE) **H. J. P. Farr**
27 **MEDLAUR,** ch f Medicean—Laurena (GER) **C. G. Rowles Nicholson**
28 **NIGHT FLASH (GER),** b c Oratorio—Night Woman (GER) **Danethorpe Racing Partnership**
29 **NO DOMINION (IRE),** b c Dylan Thomas (IRE)—Boast **Mr J. A. Barson**
30 **RED ALEX,** b c Nayef (USA)—Expedience (USA) **Mr A. Owen**
31 **RHYME ROYAL,** b f Byron—Burton Ash **Mrs S. M. Lee**
32 **SALLY PEPPER (USA),** b br f Rock Hard Ten (USA)—La Sila (USA) **Danethorpe Racing Partnership**
33 **SEASON SPIRIT,** ch c Shirocco (GER)—Shadow Dancing **Mr D. J. Fish**
34 **SINGALAT,** b g Singspiel (IRE)—Crocolat **Danethorpe Racing Partnership**
35 **SKY CROSSING,** b c Cape Cross (IRE)—Sky Wonder **Bolton Grange**
36 **SPARTILLA,** b c Teofilo (IRE)—Wunders Dream (IRE) **Bolton Grange**
37 **STORMY WHATEVER (FR),** gr c Stormy River (FR)—Evening Serenade (IRE) **Simply Racing Limited**
38 **TAFFE,** b c Byron—Blorenge **Ingram Racing**
39 **TRIOOMPH,** b f Three Valleys—Oomph **C. G. Rowles Nicholson**

TWO-YEAR-OLDS

40 **AMANDA WOLF (IRE),** b f 14/4 Amadeus Wolf—
    Alexander Phantom (Soviet Star (USA)) (33000) **Danethorpe Racing Partnership**
41 **AQUILA CARINA,** b f 20/3 Cockney Rebel (IRE)—
    Galaxy of Stars (Observatory (USA)) **Danethorpe Racing Partnership**
42 B c 18/4 Jeremy (USA)—Compradore (Mujtahid (USA)) (49523) **Simply Racing Limited**
43 **CRYSTAL PEAKS,** b f 6/4 Intikhab (USA)—
    Crozon (Peintre Celebre (USA)) (12000) **Danethorpe Racing Partnership**
44 Ch c 19/5 Redback—Flames (Blushing Flame (USA)) (24630) **Simply Racing Limited**
45 **JADANNA (IRE),** b f 13/3 Mujadil (USA)—
    Savannah Poppy (IRE) (Statue of Liberty (USA)) (25000) **Danethorpe Racing Partnership**
46 Ch c 2/4 Byron—Molly Pitcher (IRE) (Halling (USA)) **Ingram Racing**
47 Ch c 4/3 Mount Nelson—Oomph (Shareef Dancer (USA)) **C. G. Rowles Nicholson**
48 Br f 5/5 Kheleyf (USA)—Pizzicato (Statoblest) (70000) **Bolton Grange**
49 Ch c 19/2 Dutch Art—Royal Nashkova (Mujahid (USA)) **Ingram Racing**
50 **THE POWER OF ONE (IRE),** b c 17/1 Duke of Marmalade (IRE)—
    Mustique Dream (Don't Forget Me) (52000) **Nigel & Suzanne Williams**
51 **WOODY BAY,** b c 26/2 New Approach (IRE)—Dublino (USA) (Lear Fan (USA)) (60000) **Mr J. A. Barson**

Other Owners: Mr Mike J. Beadle, Mr J. A. Ellis, Mrs M. E. Ellis, Mr Tony Hill, Mr P. A. Horton, Mr R. H. Jennings, Miss M. Noden, Mr Peter Swann, Mrs B. E. Wilkinson, Mr G. Wilson.

Jockey (flat): Paul Mulrennan.

---

260   **MR JIM GOLDIE, Glasgow**
Postal: **Libo Hill Farm, Uplawmoor, Glasgow, Lanarkshire, G78 4BA**
Contacts: **PHONE (01505) 850212 MOBILE (07778) 241522**
WEBSITE www.jimgoldieracingclub.co.uk

1 **ARCTIC COURT (IRE),** 8, b g Arctic Lord—Polls Joy **Mr & Mrs Raymond Anderson Green**
2 **BAAHER (USA),** 8, b g War Chant (USA)—Raajiya (USA) **Alfred Chadwick**
3 **BENE LAD (IRE),** 10, b br g Beneficial—Sandwell Old Rose (IRE) **Mr & Mrs Raymond Anderson Green**
4 **CIRCUS CLOWN (IRE),** 7, b g Vettori (IRE)—Comic (IRE) **D. L. McKenzie**
5 **DHAULAR DHAR (IRE),** 10, b h Indian Ridge—Pescara (IRE) **Jim Goldie Racing Club**
6 **FULL TOSS,** 6, b g Nayef (USA)—Spinning Top **Discovery Racing Club 2**
7 **GO GO GREEN (IRE),** 6, b g Acclamation—Preponderance (IRE) **Jim Goldie Racing Club**

MR JIM GOLDIE—continued

8 **GONINODAETHAT**, 4, b g Proclamation (IRE)—Big Mystery (IRE) **Jim Goldie Racing Club**
9 **GRAND DIAMOND (IRE)**, 8, b g Grand Lodge (USA)—Winona (IRE) **Jim Goldie Racing Club**
10 **HIGGS BOSON**, 7, b g Overbury (IRE)—Evening Splash (IRE) **J. S. Goldie**
11 **HILLVIEW BOY (IRE)**, 8, b br g Bishop of Cashel—Arandora Star (USA) **Connor & Dunne**
12 **I GOT SUNSHINE**, 4, b g Grape Tree Road—I Got Rhythm **Thomson & Fyffe Racing**
13 **JONNY DELTA**, 5, ch g Sulamani (IRE)—Send Me An Angel (IRE) **Johnnie Delta Racing**
14 **KAOLAK (USA)**, 6, b br h Action This Day (USA)—Cerita (USA) **Thomson & Fyffe Racing**
15 **LATIN REBEL (IRE)**, 5, b g Spartacus (IRE)—Dance To The Beat **Mr R. W. C. McLachlan**
16 **LAYBACH (IRE)**, 8, br g Bach (IRE)—River Breeze (IRE) **Alan & Barry Macdonald**
17 **LILLIOFTHEBALLET (IRE)**, 5, b m Rakti—Lillibits (USA) **The Dregs Of Humanity**
18 **LOS NADIS (GER)**, 8, ch g Hernando (FR)—La Estrella (GER) **I. G. M. Dalgleish**
19 **MERCHANT OF DUBAI**, 7, b g Dubai Destination (USA)—Chameleon **Highland Racing 2**
20 **NAMWAHJOBO (IRE)**, 4, b c Namid—Notley Park **A. R. Turnbull**
21 **POKFULHAM (IRE)**, 6, b g Mull of Kintyre (USA)—Marjinal **A. R. Turnbull**
22 **PURKAB**, 4, ch g Intikhab (USA)—Pure Misk **Whitestonecliffe Racing Partnership**
23 **RONALD GEE (IRE)**, 5, ch g Garuda (IRE)—Panache Lady (IRE) **Mrs J. Perratt**
24 **SEVEN IS LUCKY (IRE)**, 10, b g Old Vic—Green Legend (IRE) **The Dregs Of Humanity**
25 **SOMETHING SILVER**, 11, gr g Silver Patriarch—Phantom Singer **Happy Sundays Racing Club 1**
26 **SOPRANO (IRE)**, 10, b g Sendawar (IRE)—Spirit Lake (GER) **Johnnie Delta Racing**
27 **TOSHI (USA)**, 10, b g Kingmambo (USA)—Majestic Role (FR) **E. R. H. Nisbet**
28 **WATERCOLOURS (IRE)**, 7, b m High Chaparral (IRE)—Emerald Waters **Johnnie Delta Racing**
29 **WINDFIELD TRICK (IRE)**, 5, b g Wizard King—Windfields Native (IRE) **Mrs J. Perratt**
30 **WYSE HILL TEABAGS**, 7, b g Theatrical Charmer—Mrs Tea **Mr & Mrs Philip C. Smith**

Other Owners: R. M. S. Allison, Mr E. N. Barber, Mr F. J. Connor, Mr H. G. Connor, Mr G. Dunne, Mrs L. Dyer, Mr J. Frew, Mr S. Fyffe, Mr J. Fyffe, Mrs D. I. Goldie, R. A. Green, Mrs A. Green, A. G. Guthrie, P Hampshire, Mr P. Harrison, Mr G. Illingworth, Mr B. N. MacDonald, Mr A. G. MacDonald, A. McManus, W. A. Powrie, Mr W. Robinson, Mr P. C. Smith, Mrs J. W. Smith, G. M. Thomson.

Assistant Trainers: James & George Goldie

Jockey (flat): D. Tudhope, G. Bartley. **Jockey (NH):** Graham Lee, Ryan Mania, Denis O'Regan. **Amateur:** Mrs Carol Bartley, Mrs I. Goldie.

---

261   **MR ROBERT GOLDIE, Kilmarnock**
Postal: **Harpercroft, Old Loans Road, Dundonald, Kilmarnock, Ayrshire, KA2 9DD**
Contacts: **PHONE (01292) 317222 FAX (01292) 313585 MOBILE (07801) 922552**

1 **ALEXANDER OATS**, 9, b g Insan (IRE)—Easter Oats **R. H. Goldie**
2 **ALFRED OATS**, 8, b g Alflora (IRE)—Easter Oats **R. H. Goldie**
3 **EASTER QUEEN**, 10, b m Rakaposhi King—Easter Oats **R. H. Goldie**
4 **EASTER VIC**, 11, b m Old Vic—Easter Oats **R. H. Goldie**

Assistant Trainer: Mrs R H Goldie

---

262   **MR KEITH GOLDSWORTHY, Kilgetty**
Postal: **Grumbly Bush Farm, Yerbeston, Kilgetty, Pembrokeshire, SA68 0NS**
Contacts: **PHONE/FAX (01834) 891343 MOBILE (07796) 497733**
E-MAIL **grumbly@supanet.com** WEBSITE **www.keithgoldsworthyracing.co.uk**

1 **ALESANDRO MANTEGNA (IRE)**, 7, b g Peintre Celebre (USA)—
                                    Mantua **M. Duthie, P. Fisher, P. Gough, Hughes, Barrack**
2 **BEREA BORU (IRE)**, 4, b g Brian Boru—Wayward Venture (IRE) **Berea Stud**
3 **BEREA COURT (IRE)**, 5, ch g Pierre—Tournore Court (IRE) **Berea Stud**
4 **BEREA VENTURE (IRE)**, 4, b g Indian Danehill (IRE)—Ballinard Lady (IRE) **Berea Stud**
5 **BOB CASEY (IRE)**, 10, b g Bob Back (USA)—Casey Jane (IRE) **Mrs P. A. Gough**
6 **BOBS LAW (IRE)**, 8, b g Bob Back (USA)—Retinue (IRE) **The Big Dreamers Partnership**
7 **COCK OF THE ROCK (IRE)**, 7, b g Pierre—Glynn View (IRE) **The Rooster Partnership**
8 **CRANNAGHMORE BOY (IRE)**, 7, b g Pilsudski (IRE)—Glencairn Mist (IRE) **Racing Coast Ltd**
9 **FREE ADVICE (IRE)**, 5, b g Milan—Coco Opera (IRE) **Greenacre Racing Partnership Ltd**
10 **GEORGIE WHALE**, 6, b m Milan—Baby Whale (IRE) **Mr A. J. R. Hart**
11 **JUMP UP**, 6, b g Carnival Dancer—Taylor Green (USA) **Mr A. J. R. Hart**

MR KEITH GOLDSWORTHY—continued

12 **KANTURK (IRE)**, 6, b g Wareed (IRE)—Kanturk Belle (IRE) **Mr A. J. R. Hart**
13 **MERCURY BAY (IRE)**, 7, ch g Karinga Bay—Jolie Landaise (FR) **Mr E. C. Jones**
14 **MILANEEN**, 6, b m Milan—Kosheen (IRE) **Mr A. Roberts**
15 **MOON DEVIL (IRE)**, 5, b g Muhtarram (USA)—Mandys Moynavely (IRE) **Mr A. J. R. Hart**
16 **ROAD SHOW**, 5, b g Sadler's Wells (USA)—Danilova (USA) **Racing Coast Ltd**
17 **SIR BENFRO**, 6, b g Runyon (IRE)—Dunrowan **Pembrokeshire Racing**
18 **STREET DANCE (IRE)**, 6, b g Beneficial—Zvezda (IRE) **Racing Coast Ltd**
19 **TENBY JEWEL (IRE)**, 7, ch g Pilsudski (IRE)—Supreme Delight (IRE) **Racing Coast Ltd**
20 **WILLIAM HOGARTH**, 7, b g High Chaparral (IRE)—Mountain Holly **ROL Plant Hire Ltd**

Other Owners: Mr R. J. Barrack, Mr Joe Boland, Mr G. Braun, Mr M. Duthie, Mr Paul Fisher, Mr K. Goldsworthy, Mrs Petra Gough, Greenacre Racing Partnership Ltd, Mr Ashley Hart, Mr D. B. T. Hughes, Mr Grant Lewis, Mrs Frances Miller, Mr Gethyn Mills, Mr Patrick O'Leary, ROL Plant Hire Ltd, Racing Coast, Mr Mortimer Reidy, Mr Mike Skidmore, Mr Iwan Thomas, Mr G. Williams, Mr John H. Williams.

Assistant Trainer: Mrs L. A. Goldsworthy

Amateur: Miss Charlotte Evans, Miss Rebecca Bockhart.

---

263 MR STEVE GOLLINGS, Louth
Postal: **Highfield House, Scamblesby, Louth, Lincolnshire, LN11 9XT**
Contacts: **YARD (01507) 343204 HOME/FAX (01507) 343213 MOBILE (07860) 218910**
E-MAIL stevegollings@aol.com WEBSITE www.stevegollings.com

1 **ALL THAT REMAINS (IRE)**, 7, b g King's Theatre (IRE)—Morning Breeze (IRE) **P. J. Martin**
2 **ALLIED ANSWER**, 4, gr g Danehill Dancer (IRE)—Hotelgenie Dot Com **P. J. Martin**
3 **ANDHAAR**, 6, b g Bahri (USA)—Deraasaat **P. J. Martin**
4 **BAR DE LIGNE (FR)**, 6, b g Martaline—Treekle Toffee (FR) **P. J. Martin**
5 **BRUNSWICK GOLD (IRE)**, 7, ch g Moscow Society (USA)—Tranbu (IRE) **P. J. Martin**
6 **CONQUISTO**, 9, ch g Hernando (FR)—Seal Indigo (IRE) **P. J. Martin**
7 **HONEST JOHN**, 8, b g Alzao (USA)—Tintera (IRE) **P. J. Martin**
8 **INTO WAIN (USA)**, 5, b g Eddington (USA)—Serene Nobility (USA) **P. J. Martin**
9 **JAMARJO (IRE)**, 5, b g Marju (IRE)—Athlumney Lady **Northern Bloodstock Racing**
10 **KYLLADDIE**, 5, ch g Kyllachy—Chance For Romance **Mr P. S. Walter**
11 **LANDESHERR (GER)**, 5, b g Black Sam Bellamy (IRE)—Lutte Marie (GER) **P. J. Martin**
12 **LATERLY (IRE)**, 7, b g Tiger Hill (IRE)—La Candela (GER) **P. J. Martin**
13 **LOCAL HERO (GER)**, 5, b g Lomitas—Lolli Pop (GER) **P. J. Martin**
14 **ROCKWEILLER**, 5, b h Rock of Gibraltar (IRE)—Ballerina Suprema (IRE) **P. Whinham**
15 **RUSSIAN GEORGE (IRE)**, 6, ch g Sendawar (IRE)—Mannsara (IRE) **Northern Bloodstock Racing**
16 **SHAN BLUE (IRE)**, 7, ch g Anshan—River Runs Blue (IRE) **P. J. Martin**
17 **SIBLING RIVALRY**, 4, b g Cacique (IRE)—Persian Walk (FR) **Mrs M A Hall & Mr P J Martin**
18 **SOUDAIN (FR)**, 6, ch g Dom Alco (FR)—Ebene d'avril (FR) **P. J. Martin**
19 **SPRINGFIELD RAKI**, 8, b g Rakaposhi King—Springfield Rhyme **Mrs M. A. Hall**
20 **THEOLOGY**, 5, b g Galileo (IRE)—Biographie **P. J. Martin**
21 **TROOPINGTHECOLOUR**, 6, b g Nayef (USA)—Hyperspectra **Northern Bloodstock Racing**
22 **VISCOUNT VICTOR (IRE)**, 6, b g Wizard King—Minstrels Daughter (IRE) **Richard Atterby & Christine Atterby**
23 **WALKABOUT CREEK (IRE)**, 5, b g Alderbrook—La Mouette (FR) **P. J. Martin**

THREE-YEAR-OLDS

24 Gr f Clodovil (IRE)—Five of Wands **Mr R. Swift**
25 **REMEMBER ROCKY**, ch c Haafhd—Flower Market **Mr R. Swift**

Other Owners: Mr Richard Atterby, Mrs Christine Atterby, Mr S. Gollings, Mrs Jayne M. Gollings, Mrs M. A. Hall, Mr P. J. Martin.

Assistant Trainer: Mrs J M Gollings

Jockey (flat): Darryll Holland, Ian Mongan, Jamie Spencer. **Jockey (NH):** Keith Mercer, Brian Hughes, Timmy Murphy, A. P. McCoy, Tom Scudamore. **Amateur:** Mr Matthew Rochford.

264 MR CHRISTOPHER GORDON, Winchester
Postal: **Morestead Farm Stables, Morestead, Winchester, Hampshire, SO21 1JD**
Contacts: **PHONE (01962) 712774 FAX (01962) 712774 MOBILE (07713) 082392**
E-MAIL chrisgordon68@hotmail.com WEBSITE www.chrisgordonracing.com

1 BALUSTRADE (IRE), 6, b g Barathea (IRE)—Haladiya (IRE) **Gordon Racing**
2 BON SPIEL, 8, b g Singspiel (IRE)—L'affaire Monique **Chris Gordon Racing Club**
3 CHILWORTH SCREAMER, 4, b f Imperial Dancer—The Screamer (IRE) **7RUS**
4 DAYS OF PLEASURE (IRE), 7, b g Fraam—Altizaf **E. J. Farrant**
5 FREDERICK WILLIAM, 4, b g Tobougg (IRE)—Bisaat (USA) **Mrs K. Digweed**
6 GILDED AGE, 6, b g Cape Cross (IRE)—Sweet Folly (IRE) **Draper Edmonds Draper**
7 HERECOMESTHETRUTH (IRE), 10, ch g Presenting—Beagan Rose (IRE) **The Not Over Big Partnership**
8 HIBBA (USA), 5, b br m Sahm (USA)—Nuzooa (USA) **Runs In The Family**
9 KING EDMUND, 9, b g Roi de Rome (USA)—Cadbury Castle **A. C. Ward-Thomas**
10 LAUNDE (IRE), 13, b g Norwich—Carbia's Last **A. C. Ward-Thomas**
11 MARIE DEJA LA (FR), 6, b m Daliapour (IRE)—Comedie Divine (FR) **Chris Gordon Racing Club**
12 MATTORAL, 4, b c High Chaparral (IRE)—Angry Bark (USA) **The Not Over Big Partnership**
13 OSMOSIA (FR), 7, b m Mansonnien (FR)—Osmose (FR) **Mr B. Ryder**
14 OWNER OCCUPIER, 7, ch g Foxhound (USA)—Miss Beverley **Mrs D. M. Lawes**
15 PROMISED WINGS (GER), 5, ch g Monsun (GER)—Panagia (USA) **Mrs K. Digweed**
16 ROANSTAR, 5, gr g Act One—Dolce Thundera (USA) **Mr A. J. O' Gorman**

Other Owners: J. Draper, Mr M. J. Draper, T. W. Edmonds, Mrs C. M. Foster, C. E. Gordon, Mrs J. L. Gordon, Mrs A. J. Hamilton-Fairley, Mrs Satu Marks, Mrs A. B. Plummer, P. J. H. Rowe, Mr M. Swallow, Simon Trant, R. M. Venn, Mr J. A. M. Wechsler.

Assistant Trainer: Jenny Gordon

Jockey (NH): Colin Bolger.

265 MR J. T. GORMAN, Curragh
Postal: **Maddenstown Lodge Stables, Maddenstown, Curragh, Co. Kildare, Ireland**
Contacts: **PHONE (00353) 45 441404 FAX (00353) 45 441404 MOBILE (00353) 872 599603**
E-MAIL jtgorman1@hotmail.com

1 ALL ABOUT TIMING (IRE), 7, b g Val Royal (FR)—Albula (FR) **J. M. G. Andrews**
2 BLUE EYED MISS (IRE), 7, b m Statue of Liberty (USA)—Classic Jenny (IRE) **J. T. Gorman**
3 CHAPTER NINE (IRE), 6, b g Expelled (USA)—Abbey Ever After **Miss M. McWey**
4 COLONUS (IRE), 5, b g Westerner—Shvera (IRE) **Miss M. McWey**
5 DE VESCI (IRE), 4, b g Statue of Liberty (USA)—Goldenfort Queen (IRE) **Miss M. McWey**
6 ELUSIVE GENT (IRE), 5, b g Elusive City (USA)—Satin Cape (IRE) **Mrs Wendy O'Leary**
7 GABH MO LEITHSCEAL (IRE), 4, b c Aussie Rules (USA)—Lady Windermere (IRE) **Mrs J. S. Bolger**
8 GOLDEN SHOE (IRE), 4, br g Footstepsinthesand—Goldilocks (IRE) **Mrs P. A. Foley**
9 LIBERTY TO ROCK (IRE), 6, b g Statue of Liberty (USA)—Polynesian Goddess (IRE) **Mrs P. A. Foley**
10 LOVEINASANDDUNE, 4, b g Oasis Dream—Windy Gulch (USA) **Mrs P. A. Foley**
11 MR ROCKNROLL, 5, b g Monsieur Bond (IRE)—Stream **Mrs P. A. Foley**
12 RIGID ROCK (IRE), 5, b g Refuse To Bend (IRE)—Delia (IRE) **Mrs P. A. Foley**
13 ROCK OF FIRE (IRE), 4, b g Statue of Liberty (USA)—Polynesian Goddess (IRE) **Mrs P. A. Foley**
14 ROCKIN N REELIN (USA), 5, b g Forest Camp (USA)—Dusti's Tune (USA) **Mrs P. A. Foley**
15 THREE WAY STRETCH (IRE), 6, b g Intikhab (USA)—Chapka (IRE) **Mrs P.A. Foley**
16 WATERHOUSE (IRE), 5, b g Key of Luck (USA)—Blue Mantle (IRE) **Miss M. McWey**
17 WREKIN ROCK (IRE), 4, br c Statue of Liberty (USA)—Orpendonna (IRE) **Mrs P. A. Foley**

THREE-YEAR-OLDS

18 BURNELL (IRE), br g Baltic King—Silver Fizz (IRE) **Miss M. McWey**
19 CONAN'S ROCK (IRE), b c Shamardal (USA)—Reeling N' Rocking (IRE) **Mrs P. A. Foley**
20 I FOUGHT THE LAW (IRE), b c Lawman (FR)—Indian Express **Mrs P. A. Foley**
21 KINGDOMFORTHEBRIDE (IRE), b f Titus Livius (FR)—Desert Bride (USA) **Miss M. McWey**
22 LOOK NOBLE, b c Byron—Stream **Mrs P. A. Foley**
23 PIERRE D'OR (IRE), ch c Rock of Gibraltar (IRE)—Gilded Edge **Mrs P. A. Foley**

TWO-YEAR-OLDS

24 C'EST MA SOEUR (IRE), b f 4/4 Oratorio (IRE)—Gilded Edge (Cadeaux Genereux) (76190) **Mrs P. A. Foley**
25 CEST NOTRE GRIS (IRE), gr c 27/2 Verglas (IRE)—Alikhlas (Lahib (USA)) (50902) **Mrs P. A. Foley**

Jockey (flat): Kevin Manning, C. D. Hayes. **Jockey (NH):** Ben Dalton, Ian McCarthy.

266   MR JOHN GOSDEN, Newmarket
Postal: **Clarehaven, Bury Road, Newmarket, Suffolk, CB8 7BY**
Contacts: **PHONE (01638) 565400 FAX (01638) 565401**
E-MAIL jhmg@johngosden.com

1 **AIKEN,** 4, b c Selkirk (USA)—Las Flores (IRE)
2 **ALMAGEST,** 4, b g Galileo (IRE)—Arabesque
3 **ARCTIC COSMOS (USA),** 5, b h North Light (IRE)—Fifth Avenue Doll (USA)
4 **BEACHFIRE,** 5, ch g Indian Haven—Maine Lobster (USA)
5 **BUTHELEZI (USA),** 4, br g Dynaformer (USA)—Ntombi (USA)
6 **CAMBORNE,** 4, b g Doyen (IRE)—Dumnoni
7 **CAUCUS,** 5, b g Cape Cross (IRE)—Maid To Perfection
8 **COLOMBIAN (IRE),** 4, b br c Azamour (IRE)—Clodora (FR)
9 **DICK DOUGHTYWYLIE,** 4, b g Oasis Dream—Sugar Mill (FR)
10 **ESHTIBAAK (IRE),** 4, b c Dalakhani (IRE)—Nanabanana (IRE)
11 **GATEWOOD,** 4, b c Galileo (IRE)—Felicity (IRE)
12 **HEZMAH,** 4, b f Oasis Dream—Bright Moll
13 **INVESTISSEMENT,** 6, b g Singspiel (IRE)—Underwater (USA)
14 **IZZI TOP,** 4, b f Pivotal—Zee Zee Top
15 **JOVIALITY,** 4, b f Cape Cross (IRE)—Night Frolic
16 **KING OF WANDS,** 6, b g Galileo (IRE)—Maid To Treasure (IRE)
17 **MASKED MARVEL,** 4, b c Montjeu (IRE)—Waldmark (GER)
18 **MORNING CHARM (USA),** 4, b f North Light (IRE)—Vignette (USA)
19 **NATHANIEL (IRE),** 4, b c Galileo (IRE)—Magnificient Style (USA)
20 **NEHAAM,** 6, b g Nayef (USA)—Charm The Stars
21 **PALAZZO BIANCO,** 4, b c Shirocco (GER)—White Palace
22 **POLYGON (USA),** 4, b f Dynaformer (USA)—Polaire (IRE)
23 **PURIFICATION (IRE),** 4, b g Hurricane Run (IRE)—Ceanothus (IRE)
24 **QUESTIONING (USA),** 4, b c Elusive Quality (USA)—Am I (USA)
25 **ROBEMAKER,** 4, b c Oasis Dream—Regal Velvet
26 **SKILFUL,** 4, ch c Selkirk (USA)—Prowess (IRE)
27 **SPLENDID LIGHT,** 4, gr ro g Selkirk (USA)—Light of Morn
28 **THIMAAR (USA),** 4, b g Dynaformer (USA)—Jinaan (USA)
29 **TRADE COMMISSIONER (IRE),** 4, b g Montjeu (IRE)—Spinning Queen
30 **TROPICAL BEAT,** 4, b g Beat Hollow—Tropical Heights (FR)
31 **ZUIDER ZEE (GER),** 5, b g Sakhee (USA)—Zephyrine (IRE)

THREE-YEAR-OLDS

32 **ALSHMEMI (USA),** br c Bernardini (USA)—Capote's Crown (USA)
33 **APOTHECARY,** br f Manduro (GER)—Sister Maria (USA)
34 **AQUANAUT,** br f Dansili—Love The Rain
35 **ASTRONOMY DOMINE,** b f Galileo (IRE)—Platonic
36 **BINABEE,** b f Galileo (IRE)—Quenched
37 **COTTON TRADER (USA),** b c Hard Spun (USA)—Saytarra (USA)
38 **DANEKING,** b c Dylan Thomas (IRE)—Sadie Thompson (IRE)
39 **DARK STRANGER (USA),** b c Stormy Atlantic (USA)—Vivacious Vivian (USA)
40 **DARTFORD (USA),** ch c Giant's Causeway (USA)—Apple of Kent (USA)
41 **DEIA SUNRISE (IRE),** gr g Clodovil (IRE)—Hedera (USA)
42 **DERIVATIVES (IRE),** b f Dansili—Favourable Terms
43 **DINVAR DIVA,** gr f Dalakhani (IRE)—Musique Magique (IRE)
44 **DISCOVERER (IRE),** b c Bernardini (USA)—Danuta (USA)
45 **DISPOSITION,** ch f Selkirk (USA)—Far Shores (USA)
46 **DUTCH DIAMOND,** ch f Dutch Art—Treasure Trove (USA)
47 **EASTERN SUN (IRE),** b c Kodiac—Always Friendly
48 **ELECTRICIAN,** b g Echo of Light—Primrose Lane (JPN)
49 **ELTIQAA (IRE),** b f Oasis Dream—Dream Valley (IRE)
50 **ELUSIVE KATE (USA),** b f Elusive Quality (USA)—Gout de Terroir (USA)
51 **EX ORIENTE (IRE),** b g Azamour (IRE)—Little Whisper (IRE)
52 **EXPRESSIONISM,** ch f Pivotal—Easy Option (IRE)
53 **FALKLAND (IRE),** b c Rock of Gibraltar (IRE)—Evita
54 **FALLEN FOR YOU,** b f Dansili—Fallen Star
55 **FANOOS,** b f Dutch Art—Miss Otis
56 **FAWAAYED (IRE),** b f Singspiel (IRE)—Eshaadeh (USA)
57 **FEARLESS DREAM,** b f Oasis Dream—Fearless Spirit (USA)
58 **FENCING (USA),** ch c Street Cry (IRE)—Latice (IRE)
59 **FLUCTUATE (USA),** ch c Exchange Rate (USA)—Cut Short (USA)

MR JOHN GOSDEN—continued

60 **FOREVER AND EVER (IRE),** b f Monsun (GER)—Time Ahead
61 **GALLIPOT,** b f Galileo (IRE)—Spinning Queen
62 **GATHERING (USA),** b f Street Cry (IRE)—Seebe (USA)
63 **GHUSOON,** b f Red Ransom (USA)—Sundus (USA)
64 **GINGERNUT,** ch c Galileo (IRE)—Foodbroker Fancy (IRE)
65 **GRAVITATE,** ch c Pivotal—Spacecraft (USA)
66 **GREAT HEAVENS,** b f Galileo (IRE)—Magnificient Style (USA)
67 **GREGORIAN (IRE),** b c Clodovil (IRE)—Three Days In May
68 **HANDSOME RANSOM,** b c Red Ransom (USA)—Maid For The Hills
69 **HANSEATIC,** b c Galileo (IRE)—Insinuate (USA)
70 **HEPWORTH,** b f Singspiel (IRE)—Annalina (USA)
71 **HILL STREET (IRE),** ch c Street Cry (IRE)—Utrecht
72 **INFINITUM,** gr f Dalakhani (IRE)—Time Honoured
73 **JUNGLE BEAT (IRE),** ch c Galileo (IRE)—Flamingo Guitar (USA)
74 **LASCAUX,** ch f Pivotal—Tora Bora
75 **LIGHT SHINE,** gr f Dansili—Light of Morn
76 **LOWNDES,** b f Rail Link—New Abbey
77 **MANAAR (USA),** b f Invasor (ARG)—Ruby Summer (USA)
78 **MARIA LETIZIA,** b f Galileo (IRE)—Napoleon's Sister (IRE)
79 **MERRY JAUNT (USA),** b f Street Sense (USA)—Light Jig
80 **MICHELANGELO,** b c Galileo (IRE)—Intrigued
81 **MINWAH (IRE),** b f Oasis Dream—Cephalonie (USA)
82 **MISSOURI BELLE,** gr f Invincible Spirit (IRE)—Mussoorie (FR)
83 **MOONGLOW,** b f Nayef (USA)—Mystic Goddess (USA)
84 **MOROCCO,** b c Rock of Gibraltar (IRE)—Shanghai Lily (IRE)
85 **MOSHAAGIB (USA),** b c Dynaformer (USA)—Ensenada (USA)
86 **MUTAFAAKIR (IRE),** b c Oasis Dream—Moon's Whisper (USA)
87 **NEWS DESK,** b f Cape Cross (IRE)—La Presse (USA)
88 **PALMETTE,** b f Oasis Dream—Arabesque
89 **PANZANELLA,** b f Dansili—Zenda
90 **PATEGONIA,** b c Oasis Dream—Cozy Maria (USA)
91 **PROOFREADER,** b c Authorized (IRE)—Blixen (USA)
92 **QAADIRA (USA),** b f Mr Greeley (USA)—Makderah (IRE)
93 **RED HAND (USA),** br f Mr Greeley (USA)—Helena Molony (IRE)
94 **REGAL AURA,** b f Teofilo (IRE)—Regal Velvet
95 **RIPPLED,** gr f Dalakhani (IRE)—Last Dance
96 **SEE EMILY PLAY (IRE),** b f Galileo (IRE)—Tree Tops
97 **SHANTARAM,** b c Galileo (IRE)—All's Forgotten (USA)
98 **STARBOARD,** b c Zamindar (USA)—Summer Shower
99 **STARSCOPE,** ch f Selkirk (USA)—Moon Goddess
100 **STUNNING VIEW (USA),** br f Dynaformer (USA)—No Matter What (USA)
101 **SUNPASS,** ch c Pivotal—Tebee
102 **TEMPEST FUGIT (IRE),** b f High Chaparral (IRE)—Diary (IRE)
103 **THE FUGUE,** br f Dansili—Twyla Tharp (IRE)
104 **THE NILE,** ch c Three Valleys (USA)—Delta
105 **THETURNOFTHESUN (IRE),** ch c Galileo (IRE)—Something Mon (USA)
106 **THOUGHT WORTHY (USA),** b c Dynaformer (USA)—Vignette (USA)
107 **TIGHTLACED (USA),** b f Tiznow (USA)—Polaire (IRE)
108 **TRAIL OF TEARS (IRE),** b f Exceed And Excel (AUS)—Cherokee Rose (IRE)
109 **UMAYYAD (IRE),** b c Montjeu (IRE)—Janoubi
110 **UTTERANCE,** b c Dansili—Valentine Waltz (IRE)
111 **WANNABE LOVED,** b f Pivotal—Wannabe Posh (IRE)
112 **WIDYAAN (IRE),** b g Lawman (FR)—Lady Livius (IRE)
113 **WILLOW BECK,** b f Shamardal (USA)—Woodbeck

TWO-YEAR-OLDS

114 **ALL BLACK ROSE,** b f 18/2 Vita Rosa (JPN)—All A Dream (Desert Story (IRE))
115 Ch f 15/5 Three Valleys (USA)—Arabesque (Zafonic (USA))
116 B c 26/2 Oasis Dream—Bahja (USA) (Seeking The Gold (USA))
117 Br f 17/1 Raven's Pass (USA)—Bauble (USA) (Tale of The Cat (USA)) (85470)
118 B f 14/4 Duke of Marmalade (IRE)—Boast (Most Welcome) (160000)
119 B c 25/3 Dansili—Bonash (Rainbow Quest (USA))
120 **CAPE ELIZABETH (IRE),** b f 20/2 Invincible Spirit (IRE)—Maine Lobster (USA) (Woodman (USA)) (180000)
121 **CHERRY MALOTTE,** b f 22/2 Pivotal—Shanghai Lily (IRE) (King's Best (USA))
122 Ch c 13/3 Elusive Quality (USA)—Cloudspin (USA) (Storm Cat (USA))

MR JOHN GOSDEN—continued

123 Ch f 1/3 Raven's Pass (USA)—Contentious (USA) (Giant's Causeway (USA)) (167887)
124 **CORNROW,** ch c 6/3 New Approach (IRE)—Needlecraft (IRE) (Mark of Esteem (IRE))
125 **DEBORAH,** b f 16/4 New Approach (IRE)—Danelissima (IRE) (Danehill (USA))
126 **DREAM TO BE MAID,** b f 16/4 Oasis Dream—Maid For The Hills (Indian Ridge)
127 **ETHEL,** b f 19/3 Exceed And Excel (AUS)—Agnus (IRE) (In The Wings)
128 B f 29/1 Shamardal (USA)—Fashion Trade (Dansili) (80000)
129 **FLIRTINI,** b f 8/3 Nayef (USA)—Frappe (Inchinor)
130 B f 25/3 Dansili—High Praise (USA) (Quest For Fame)
131 B f 14/3 Dansili—Hureya (USA) (Woodman (USA))
132 B c 19/2 Dansili—Innocent Air (Galileo (IRE))
133 B c 19/4 Halling (USA)—La Spezia (IRE) (Danehill Dancer (IRE)) (35000)
134 Ch c 13/4 Speightstown (USA)—Light Jig (Danehill (USA))
135 B c 26/2 Kheleyf (USA)—Madam Ninette (Mark of Esteem (IRE)) (71428)
136 B f 21/4 Singspiel (IRE)—Magic Tree (UAE) (Timber Country (USA)) (70000)
137 B f 13/2 Harlan's Holiday (USA)—Mirabilis (USA) (Lear Fan (USA))
138 B c 8/5 Exceed And Excel (AUS)—Miss Meltemi (IRE) (Miswaki Tern (USA)) (160000)
139 Ch f 6/4 Pivotal—Miss Penton (Primo Dominie) (240000)
140 Ch c 15/4 New Approach (IRE)—Miss Queen (USA) (Miswaki (USA)) (125000)
141 Ch c 11/3 Raven's Pass (USA)—Multicolour Wave (IRE) (Rainbow Quest (USA)) (170000)
142 **NICKELS AND DIMES (IRE),** b f 15/4 Teofilo (IRE)—Neat Shilling (IRE) (Bob Back (USA)) (57000)
143 B f 11/5 Galileo (IRE)—Peace Time (GER) (Surumu (GER)) (600000)
144 **POMEROL,** ch c 18/4 Kyllachy—Clinet (USA) (Docksider (USA)) (145000)
145 **POMODORO,** ch c 1/3 Pivotal—Foodbroker Fancy (IRE) (Halling (USA))
146 Br c 16/3 Monsun (GER)—Quenched (Dansili)
147 **SHE'S LATE,** ch c 24/4 Pivotal—Courting (Pursuit of Love) (120000)
148 **SLIP FREE,** ch f 2/4 Pivotal—Abandon (USA) (Rahy (USA))
149 **SNOWBRIGHT,** b f 13/2 Pivotal—Snow Gretel (Green Desert (USA)) (110000)
150 **SOLACE (USA),** ch f 1/3 Langfuhr (CAN)—Songerie (Hernando (FR))
151 **STREAMER,** b f 3/2 Medicean—Striving (Danehill Dancer (IRE))
152 **TROPICAL SONG,** b c 13/3 Beat Hollow—Tropical Heights (FR) (Shirley Heights)
153 B f 27/2 Pivotal—Ulfah (USA) (Danzig (USA))
154 B f 6/3 Dubawi (IRE)—Valjarv (IRE) (Bluebird (USA)) (125000)
155 B c 18/5 Galileo (IRE)—Vallee des Reves (USA) (Kingmambo (USA))
156 B c 17/3 Rock of Gibraltar (IRE)—Waldmark (GER) (Mark of Esteem (IRE)) (85000)
157 **WANNABE YOUR MAN,** b c 8/2 Halling (USA)—Wannabe Posh (IRE) (Grand Lodge (USA))
158 Ch c 26/3 Raven's Pass (USA)—Waterways (IRE) (Alhaarth (IRE)) (72000)
159 B c 30/3 Elusive Quality (USA)—What A Treasure (IRE) (Cadeaux Genereux) (91575)
160 B f 1/2 Dansili—Winter Sunrise (Pivotal)
161 B c 22/2 Dansili—Zenda (Zamindar (USA))

Jockey (flat): William Buick, Robert Havlin, Nicky Mackay, Saleem Golam, Marc Halford.

---

267 ## MRS HARRIET GRAHAM, Jedburgh
Postal: **Brundeanlaws Cottage, Camptown, Jedburgh, Roxburghshire, TD8 6NW**
Contacts: PHONE (01835) 840354 MOBILE (07843) 380401
E-MAIL hgrahamracing@aol.com WEBSITE www.harrietgrahamracing.co.uk

1 **DUKE OF MALFI,** 9, b g Alflora (IRE)—Princess Maxine (IRE) **Miss G. Joughin**
2 **HOOKY'S DIAMOND,** 6, b g Endoli (USA)—Hooky's Treat **H G Racing**
3 **HURRY UP HARRY,** 6, b g Bandmaster (USA)—Lady Harriet Luis **H G Racing**
4 **MAGGIE BLUE (IRE),** 4, b f Beneficial—Top Ar Aghaidh (IRE) **R. S. Hamilton**
5 **MR WOODS,** 10, b g Then Again—Lucky Lievre **Laumar Racing**
6 **PRINCE TAM,** 8, gr g Terimon—Princess Maxine (IRE) **Mrs L. R. Joughin**
7 4, B f Beat All (USA)—Ruby Joy **R. S. Hamilton**
8 **SCOTSWELL,** 6, b g Endoli (USA)—Tofino Swell **H G Racing**
9 **SOUL MAGIC (IRE),** 10, b g Flemensfirth (USA)—Indian Legend (IRE) **H G Racing**

Other Owners: L. H. Gilmurray, Mrs H. O. Graham, R. D. Graham.

Assistant Trainer: R D Graham

Jockey (NH): James Reveley. **Conditional:** Gary Rutherford.

268 MR CHRIS GRANT, Billingham
Postal: **Low Burntoft Farm, Wolviston, Billingham, Cleveland, TS22 5PD**
Contacts: **PHONE/FAX (01740) 644054 MOBILE (07860) 577998**
E-MAIL chrisgrantracing@gmail.com WEBSITE www.chrisgrantracing.co.uk

1 ALPHA ONE (IRE), 6, b g Fruits of Love (USA)—Dunedin Lass (IRE) **J. Wade**
2 BEAUMONT'S PARTY (IRE), 5, b g High Chaparral (IRE)—Miss Champagne (FR) **Elliott Brothers And Peacock**
3 BRAVE SPARTACUS (IRE), 6, b g Spartacus (IRE)—Peaches Polly **R. Collins**
4 BROCKWELL ABBEY, 6, ch m Central Park (IRE)—Little Brockwell (IRE) **The Roper Family**
5 BROKETHEGATE, 7, b g Presenting—Briery Ann **T. J. Hemmings**
6 CAPTAIN NASH (IRE), 9, b g Dushyantor (USA)—Castle Carrig (IRE) **Mr D. Armstrong**
7 DANCING DIK, 7, b g Diktat—Maureena (IRE) **Panther Racing Limited**
8 DARK GLACIER (IRE), 7, b g Flemensfirth (USA)—Glacier Lilly (IRE) **T. J. Hemmings**
9 DESTINY BLUE (IRE), 5, b g Danehill Dancer (IRE)—Arpege (IRE) **Elliott Brothers And Peacock**
10 DICE (IRE), 6, b g Kalanisi (IRE)—Rain Dancer (IRE) **Straightline Construction Ltd**
11 DOUBLE EXPRESSO, 8, b g Kayf Tara—Sallys Lodge **Mr D. Armstrong**
12 EMIRATE ISLE, 8, b g Cois Na Tine (IRE)—Emmajoun **Bell Bridge Racing**
13 FASHION STAKES, 8, ch m Fleetwood (IRE)—Glamour Game **Division Bell Partnership**
14 FLAYGRAY, 8, gr g Terimon—I'll Skin Them (IRE) **Miss A. P. Lee**
15 FLAYMORE, 6, b g Grape Tree Road—I'll Skin Them (IRE) **Miss A. P. Lee**
16 GENTLEMAN JEFF (USA), 8, ch g Mr Greeley (USA)—Wooing (USA) **Woodgate Family**
17 KINDER SCOUT, 5, b m Tamure (IRE)—Riviere **Dr R. G. Fairs**
18 KOSTA BRAVA (FR), 8, ch g Nikos—Tamana (USA) **Mr D. Armstrong**
19 LUCEMATIC, 6, b m Systematic—Soldier's Song **Mrs P. C. Stirling**
20 LUTIN DU MOULIN (FR), 13, br g Saint Preuil (FR)—Emeraude du Moulin (FR) **N. E. M. Jones**
21 MARDOOD, 7, b g Oasis Dream—Gaelic Swan (IRE) **W. Raw**
22 MICRO MISSION (IRE), 6, b m Flemensfirth (USA)—Micro Villa (IRE) **Mr D. Armstrong**
23 MILANS MAN (IRE), 7, b g Milan—Montanara (IRE) **David Armstrong & Nigel E M Jones**
24 MINSTER SHADOW, 13, b g Minster Son—Polar Belle **Anne Cairns & Partners**
25 MONOCO MAN (IRE), 5, b g Revoque (IRE)—Lady Monoco (IRE) **T. J. Hemmings**
26 MONTOYA'S SON (IRE), 7, ch g Flemensfirth (USA)—Over The Grand (IRE) **Straightline Construction Ltd**
27 MUWALLA, 5, b g Bahri (USA)—Easy Sunshine (IRE) **Elliott Brothers And Peacock**
28 NINE STORIES (IRE), 7, b g Catcher In The Rye (IRE)—Irinatinvidio **Straightline Construction Ltd**
29 OVERYOU, 7, b m Overbury (IRE)—Keep The Treasure (IRE) **D. Mossop**
30 PAPILLON PARC, 6, b g Central Park (IRE)—Persian Butterfly **D. Mossop**
31 PHOENIX LADY, 9, ch m Minster Son—Moorfield Lady **Mrs E. Dresser**
32 ROCK RELIEF (IRE), 6, gr g Daylami (IRE)—Sheer Bliss (IRE) **Mr D. Armstrong**
33 SENDALI (FR), 8, b g Daliapour (IRE)—Lady Senk (FR) **Elliott Brothers And Peacock**
34 SILVER BY CHOICE, 6, b g Silver Patriarch (IRE)—Poor Celt **Mrs S. Johnson**
35 SOUL BID (IRE), 6, b g Luso—Bid For Fun (IRE) **J. Wade**
36 STOP ON, 7, b g Fraam—Tourmalet **D. M. P. R. Racing**
37 TEARS FROM HEAVEN (USA), 6, b br g Street Cry (IRE)—Heavenly Aura (USA) **Mrs S. Sunter**

Other Owners: A. Cairns, Mrs A. Cairns, T. Cunningham, J. M. Elliott, C. R. Elliott, C. Grant, Miss L. V. Horner, Mr D. A. Lofthouse, A. Meale, Mrs L. Monkhouse, Mr J. H. Monkhouse, Mrs M. Nicholas, J. K. Roper, Mrs E. M. Roper, Mr J. Woodgate, Mr A. W. Woodgate, A. D. Wright.

Assistant Trainer: Mrs S. Grant

Jockey (NH): Denis O'Regan. **Conditional:** Alexander Voy.

269 MR LIAM GRASSICK, Cheltenham
Postal: **Postlip Racing Stables, Winchcombe, Cheltenham, Gloucestershire, GL54 5AQ**
Contacts: **PHONE (01242) 603124 YARD (01242) 603919 MOBILE (07816) 930423**
E-MAIL mark.grassick@btopenworld.com

1 CLEEVE CLOUD (IRE), 6, b g Noverre (USA)—La Galeisa (IRE) **Mrs T. A. Macey**
2 DAZZLING RITA, 6, b m Midnight Legend—Pytchley Dawn **The Atkin Partnership**
3 FATHER PAT, 9, br g Chaddleworth—Lady Crusty **L. P. Grassick**
4 RICARDO'S CHANCE, 13, b g Alflora (IRE)—Jims Sister **The Atkin Partnership**
5 ROSE DE RITA, 7, br m Superior Premium—Rita's Rock Ape **L. P. Grassick**

Other Owners: J. A. Atkin, T. J. Atkin.

Assistant Trainer: Mark Grassick

270 MR M. J. GRASSICK, Curragh
Postal: Fenpark Stables, Pollardstown, Curragh, Co. Kildare, Ireland
Contacts: PHONE (00353) 4543 4483 FAX (00353) 4543 7895 MOBILE (00353) 8724 31923
E-MAIL mjgrassick2@eircom.net

1 **ARGENTINIAN TANGO (IRE)**, 4, ch f Prince Arch (USA)—Tordasia (IRE) **Crowley Family**
2 **BOULAY (IRE)**, 6, b m Montjeu (IRE)—Gamra (IRE) **Mrs C. Grassick**
3 **CASIMIR ROAD (IRE)**, 4, b g High Chaparral (USA)—Six Nations (USA) **Patrick McKeown**
4 **CELTIC CHARM (IRE)**, 4, b f Celtic Swing—Antapoura (IRE) **J. Malone**
5 **CHAPATTI (IRE)**, 4, b f High Chaparral (USA)—Tropical Lass (IRE) **A Goonan**
6 **HARD ROCK CITY (USA)**, 12, b g Danzig (USA)—All The Moves (USA) **J. Dolan**
7 **KING OF ARAN (IRE)**, 5, b br g Val Royal (FR)—Innishmore (IRE) **Dont Tell The Missus Syndicate**
8 **LAUREL CREEK (IRE)**, 7, b g Sakura Laurel (JPN)—Eastern Sky (AUS) **Patrick McKeown**
9 **SOUL CUSTODY (CAN)**, 5, b m Perfect Soul (IRE)—Halo's Gleam (USA) **Matt Duffy**
10 **TRIKIRK (IRE)**, 11, b g Selkirk (USA)—Shastri (USA) **M. C. Grassick**

THREE-YEAR-OLDS
11 **ALLUSIVE POWER (IRE)**, gr f Verglas (IRE)—Fernanda **J. Higgins**
12 **BELLE INDIGO (IRE)**, b f Jeremy (USA)—Miami Sands (IRE) **Mrs S. Grassick**
13 B f Dylan Thomas (IRE)—Bounce (FR) **Mrs C. Grassick**
14 **ELUSIVE IN PARIS (IRE)**, b g Elusive City (USA)—Bradwell (IRE) **J. Keeling**
15 **INVELITE**, b f Whipper (USA)—On The Wind (IRE) **Marquesa de Moratalla**
16 B f Dylan Thomas (IRE)—Jinskys Gift (IRE) **Mrs N. Moore**
17 **LINENHALL LADY (IRE)**, ch f Indian Haven—Gentle Wind (USA) **A. Goonan**
18 **LOTUS ROOTS (IRE)**, b f Whipper (USA)—Star of Akkar **Marquesa de Moratalla**
19 **LOVING KIND (IRE)**, b f Jeremy (USA)—Linette (GER) **Mrs S. Grassick**
20 **ONLY EXCEPTION (IRE)**, b f Jeremy (USA)—Misaayef (USA) **A. Goonan**
21 **UNESCORTED (IRE)**, b f Holy Roman Emperor (IRE)—Eadaoin (USA) **Mrs N. Moore**

TWO-YEAR-OLDS
22 Ch g 13/3 Indian Haven—Porto Venere (IRE) (Ashkalani (IRE)) (4104) **J. Kavanagh**

Other Owners: Barouche Stud, P. Boyle, B. Cooke, T. Dwyer, Miss P. F. O'Kelly, R. Weiss.

Assistant Trainer: M. C. Grassick

Jockey (flat): N. G. McCullagh.

---

271 MR CARROLL GRAY, Bridgwater
Postal: Horlake, Moorland, Bridgwater, Somerset, TA7 0AT
Contacts: HOME (01278) 691359 MOBILE (07989) 768163

1 **DIAMOND VISION (IRE)**, 4, b g Diamond Green (FR)—Tranquil Sky **E. T. Wey**
2 **GLEANNACREIM (IRE)**, 9, ch g Old Vic—Rosie Brook (IRE) **optimumracing.co.uk**
3 **MEDICINAL (IRE)**, 11, gr g Linamix (FR)—Pharmacist (IRE) **S. C. Botham**
4 **MON CHEVALIER (IRE)**, 9, b g Montjeu (IRE)—Kumta (IRE) **S. C. Botham**
5 **NOMAD (FR)**, 11, b g Brier Creek (USA)—Fortune V (FR) **A. P. Helliar**
6 **THE CONJURER (FR)**, 5, b g Kaldounevees (FR)—Gee Whizz (FR) **Mr K. J. Legg**

THREE-YEAR-OLDS
7 **BOVS CASTLE**, gr f Proclamation (IRE)—Focosa (ITY) **S. C. Botham**
8 Ch g Needwood Blade—Hayden Grace
9 B f Lucky Story (USA)—Richenda **S. C. Botham**

Other Owners: Mrs A. Birch, Mr R. G. Botham, Mrs Christine Gray, Mr K. J. Legg, Mr Andrew Lowrie, Mrs J. Lowrie, Riverdance Consortium.

Assistant Trainer: Mrs C M L Gray

Jockey (NH): Harry Skelton. **Amateur:** Mr M. G. Nolan.

272 **MR PETER GRAYSON, Formby**
Postal: **South Moss Stud, Pasture Lane, Formby, Merseyside, L37 0AP**
Contacts: PHONE **01704 830668** FAX **01704 830668**
E-MAIL **info@pgr.uk.com** WEBSITE **www.pgr.uk.com**

1 AVONVALLEY, 5, b m Avonbridge—Piper's Ash (USA) **R. S. Teatum**
2 DINGAAN (IRE), 9, b g Tagula (IRE)—Boughtbyphone **R. S. Teatum**
3 EGYPTIAN LORD, 9, ch g Bold Edge—Calypso Lady (IRE) **Mr E. Grayson**
4 FLOW CHART (IRE), 5, b g Acclamation—Free Flow **Mr E. Grayson**
5 ISHETOO, 8, b g Ishiguru (USA)—Ticcatoo (IRE) **R. S. Teatum**
6 LADY BROOKIE, 4, br f Makbul—Miss Brookie **R. S. Teatum**
7 RIGHTCAR, 5, b g Bertolini (USA)—Loblolly Bay **R. S. Teatum**
8 RIGHTCAR DOMINIC, 7, b g Kyllachy—Vallauris **R. S. Teatum**
9 STONEACRE JOE JOE, 4, b g Proclamation (IRE)—It's So Easy **R. S. Teatum**
10 STONEACRE LAD (IRE), 9, b h Bluebird (USA)—Jay And-A (IRE) **R. S. Teatum**
11 VHUJON (IRE), 7, b g Mujadil (USA)—Livius Lady (IRE) **R. S. Teatum**

THREE-YEAR-OLDS

12 B f Baltic King—Golden Charm (IRE)
13 B f Doyen (IRE)—Jodeeka **R. S. Teatum**
14 B c Refuse To Bend (IRE)—Kaveri (USA)
15 Gr f Verglas (IRE)—Melody Island (IRE)
16 Ch f Haafhd—Peryllys
17 STONEACRE THIRSK (IRE), br f Red Clubs (IRE)—Alexander Eliott (IRE) **R. S. Teatum**

Assistant Trainer: Mrs S. Grayson

273 **MR PAUL GREEN, Lydiate**
Postal: **Oak Lea, Southport Road, Lydiate, Liverpool, Merseyside, L31 4HH**
Contacts: PHONE **(0151) 526 0093** FAX **(0151) 520 0299** MOBILE **(07748) 630685**
E-MAIL **paulgreen@mitchell-james.com**

1 BERTIE BLU BOY, 4, b g Central Park (IRE)—Shaymee's Girl **B & B Hygiene Limited**
2 C P JOE (IRE), 4, br g One Cool Cat (USA)—Trinity Fair **G. Williams**
3 DUBARA REEF (IRE), 5, ch g Dubawi (IRE)—Mamara Reef **Oaklea Aces**
4 ELEGANT DANCER (IRE), 5, ch m Choisir (AUS)—Sofistication (IRE) **Mr D. A. Howard**
5 INVINCIBLE FORCE (IRE), 8, b g Invincible Spirit (IRE)—Highly Respected (IRE) **Mr D. A. Howard**
6 LEGAL EAGLE (IRE), 7, b g Invincible Spirit (IRE)—Lupulina (CAN) **I. P. Mason**
7 LUCKY DAN (IRE), 6, b g Danetime (IRE)—Katherine Gorge (USA) **P. Green**
8 LUCKY NUMBERS (IRE), 6, b g Key of Luck (USA)—Pure Folly (IRE) **Men Behaving Badly Two**

THREE-YEAR-OLDS

9 BEAU MISTRAL (IRE), ch f Windsor Knot (IRE)—Carpet Lover (IRE) **The Winsor Not Group**
10 FERDY (IRE), b c Antonius Pius (USA)—Trinity Fair **Mr E. Sciarrillo**
11 FOREVER JANEY, b f Indesatchel (IRE)—Nee Lemon Left **Mr A. Mills**
12 M J WOODWARD, b c Needwood Blade—Canina **Mr E. Sciarrillo**
13 MY NEW ANGEL (IRE), gr f Dark Angel (IRE)—Mynu Girl **Mr C. J. Dingwall**
14 PUNTA LARA LADY (IRE), b f Desert Style (IRE)—Mine Hostess (IRE) **M. F. Nolan**
15 RUSTY ROCKET (IRE), ch c Majestic Missile (IRE)—Sweet Compliance **Seven Stars Racing**

Other Owners: Mr G. Barton, Mr A. Fellows, P. Lavin.

Assistant Trainer: Fiona Ford

274 **MR TOM GRETTON, Inkberrow**
Postal: **c/o Gretton & Co Ltd, Middle Bouts Farm, Bouts Lane, Inkberrow, Worcester, WR7 4HP**
Contacts: PHONE **(01386) 792240** FAX **(01386) 792472** MOBILE **(07866) 116928**
E-MAIL **tomgretton@hotmail.co.uk** WEBSITE **www.tomgrettonracing.com**

1 ANA BUACHAILL DANA, 10, b g Spadoun (FR)—Silva Linda **Yorton Farm**
2 ARMEDANDDANGEROUS (IRE), 7, b g Kris Kin (USA)—Lucky Fountain (IRE) **The Beats Working Partnership**
3 CARDINAL RICHELIEU (IRE), 4, b g King's Theatre (IRE)—Vol de Minuit (FR) **Duncey Dees**

MR TOM GRETTON—continued

4 **CONTADOR (IRE)**, 6, ch g Right Win (IRE)—Norton Gale (IRE) **Mrs Laura Gretton**
5 **DAPPLE PRINCE (IRE)**, 7, gr g Environment Friend—Mitsy (IRE) **Ms A. S. Potze**
6 **DEIANIRA (IRE)**, 5, b m King's Theatre (IRE)—Zenith **Mr E. M. O'Connor**
7 **DRAGON MASTER**, 6, b g Green Card (USA)—The Pedlar **Old Moat Lane**
8 5, Ch m Erhaab (USA)—Four Vallies (IRE) **Mr Edward Gretton**
9 4, B f Oscar (IRE)—Grey Mistral **The Beats Working Partnership**
10 **HARRYS GUNNER**, 7, ch g Sir Harry Lewis (USA)—Little Starlight **Ms Heather Bell**
11 **INKBERROW ROSE (IRE)**, 8, b m Glacial Storm (USA)—Inuit (IRE) **The Clarke Girls**
12 **LITTLE JIMMY**, 5, br g Passing Glance—Sementina (USA) **The Archers Partnership**
13 **MISS POWDERKEG**, 5, b m Beat All (USA)—Worth Waitin For **The Morris McCurrich Partnership**
14 **PRIZE POINT**, 6, ch g Bahamian Bounty—Golden Symbol **The Archers Partnership**

Other Owners: Mr Alan S. Clarke, Mr R. K. Edwards, Mrs J. M. Edwards, Mr C. M. C. Edwards, Mrs T. Futter, Mr T. R. Gretton, Mrs Laura Gretton, Mr J. Hynes, Mrs Fran Mathison, Mr Eamonn O'Connor, Mr Kevin O'Connor, Mr Robert Pope.

Assistant Trainer: Laura Gretton (07789) 754806

Jockey (NH): Tommy Phelan.

---

275 **MR PATRICK GRIFFIN, Co Dublin**
Postal: **Killeen House, Oldtown, Co. Dublin, Ireland**
Contacts: **PHONE 00353 18433128 FAX 00353 18433128 MOBILE 00353 871301719**
E-MAIL pggriffin@live.ie

1 **DICA (FR)**, 6, ch g Kapgarde (FR)—Easy World (FR) **Mr M. Deren**
2 **DONTCALLERTHAT (IRE)**, 9, ch m Anshan—Smash N Lass **Mrs F. Griffin**
3 **DRISHOGUE LAD (IRE)**, 8, ch g Naheez (USA)—Astronomer Lady (IRE) **J. A. Griffin**
4 **INCA KOLA**, 4, gr g Verglas (IRE)—Palm Reef (USA) **J Griffin & M. Deren**
5 **LISBON (IRE)**, 4, b g Cape Cross (IRE)—Caraiyma (IRE) **Mr M. Deren**
6 **MAGGIO (FR)**, 7, b g Trempolino (USA)—La Musardiere (FR) **Mr M. Deren**
7 **SEA CLIFF (IRE)**, 8, b g Golan (IRE)—Prosaic Star (IRE) **Mr J. A. Griffin**
8 **STRONGPOINT (IRE)**, 8, b br g Bob Back (USA)—Ceo Draiochta (IRE) **P. Griffin**
9 **TORTUEUSE (IRE)**, 5, b m Indian Danehill (IRE)—Taffety **Mr M. Deren**
10 **TWENTYPOUNDLUCK (IRE)**, 7, ch g Beneficial—Guitane Lady (IRE) **Mr M. Deren**

THREE-YEAR-OLDS

11 Br f Beneficial—Kigali (IRE) **B. Griffin**

TWO-YEAR-OLDS

12 B g 25/4 Poliglote—Place d'armes (IRE) (Spinning World (USA)) (4926) **Mr M. Deren**
13 B f 1/1 Balmont (USA)—Quay Moment (IRE) (Definite Article) **P. Griffin**
14 **SORROW (FR)**, b g 18/5 Early March—Cochinchine (IRE) (Namaqualand (USA)) (3284) **Mr M. Deren**
15 Br g 6/5 Arcadio (GER)—Soviet Princess (IRE) (Soviet Lad (USA)) **Mrs F. Griffin**

Other Owners: Liam Heron, Andy Hulme, Paul Scholes, Alan Kirkham, Clarricien Syndicate, M. D. Fitzpatrick, R. T. Griffin, Mrs C. Kelly, Colm White.

Assistant Trainer: James Griffin

Jockey (NH): James Reveley, Brian Hughes, Robbie Colgan. **Conditional:** C. D. Maxwell. **Apprentice:** E. J. McNamara.

---

276 **MR DAVID C. GRIFFITHS, Bawtry**
Postal: **Martin Hall, Martin Common, Bawtry, Doncaster, South Yorkshire, DN10 6DA**
Contacts: **PHONE (01302) 714247 MOBILE (07816) 924621**
E-MAIL davidgriffiths250@hotmail.com WEBSITE www.dcgracing.co.uk

1 **AY TAY TATE (IRE)**, 6, b g Catcher In The Rye (IRE)—Vintage Belle (IRE) **Mr A. J. Langan**
2 **CHEERS BUDDY (IRE)**, 4, b g Acclamation—Victorian Dancer (IRE)
3 **CYFLYMDER (IRE)**, 6, b g Mujadil (USA)—Nashwan Star (IRE) **Mr S. Young**
4 **GORGEOUS GOBLIN (IRE)**, 5, b m Lujain (USA)—Tama (IRE) **K Humphries & Sons Roofing Contractors Ltd**
5 **LADY LIBBY LAMB**, 4, bl f Statue of Liberty (USA)—
Lady Caroline Lamb (IRE) **K Humphries & Sons Roofing Contractors Ltd**
6 **LEGAL LEGACY**, 6, ch g Beat Hollow—Dan's Delight **Eros Bloodstock**

MR DAVID C. GRIFFITHS—continued

7 **MUNAAWIB**, 4, b c Haafhd—Mouwadh (USA) **Mrs J. C. Lumb**
8 **NOT MY CHOICE (IRE)**, 7, ch g Choisir (AUS)—Northgate Raver **C. D. K. Racing**
9 **YUNGABURRA (IRE)**, 8, b g Fath (USA)—Nordic Living (IRE) **Mr D. W. Noble**

THREE-YEAR-OLDS

10 **ADRANIAN (IRE)**, gr g Dark Angel (IRE)—Make Me Blush (USA) **Eros Bloodstock**
11 B g Cape Town (IRE)—Leave It To Lib
12 B f Ferrule (IRE)—Lets Get It On (IRE) **K Humphries & Sons Roofing Contractors Ltd**
13 **WAKE UP SIOUX (IRE)**, b f Sleeping Indian—Dubious **Mr D Clarke, R P B Michaelson, D Griffiths**

TWO-YEAR-OLDS

14 B c 28/3 Phoenix Reach (IRE)—Antigoni (IRE) (Grand Lodge (USA)) (3809) **Winterbeck Manor Stud**
15 Ch c 7/4 Sir Percy—Caribana (Hernando (FR)) (410) **Norton Common Farm Racing Ltd**
16 **MACE THE ACE**, b f 31/3 Phoenix Reach (IRE)—Lady Soleas (Be My Guest (USA)) (3333) **Mr C. Midson**
17 B f 2/4 Croco Rouge (IRE)—Reveur (Rossini (USA)) **Mr & Mrs A. Jones**
18 B f 3/4 Antonius Pius (USA)—Spinning Gold (Spinning World (USA)) (327) **Norton Common Farm Racing Ltd**
19 B c 11/3 Byron—Tripti (IRE) (Sesaro (USA)) (2857)

Other Owners: Mr J. Adlam, Mr D. J. Clarke, D. C. Griffiths, Mr A. Jones, R. P. B. Michaelson, Mrs S. Noble, Mr P. Sutherland.

Assistant Trainer: Mrs S. E. Griffiths

---

277 **MR SIMON GRIFFITHS, Easingwold**
Postal: **Hazel Hill Farm, Blackwoods, Easingwold, York, North Yorkshire, YO61 3ER**
Contacts: **PHONE (01347) 823589 MOBILE (07967) 039208**
E-MAIL elizabeth.grant@grantsvets.co.uk

1 **CARLTON MAC**, 7, ch g Timeless Times (USA)—Julie's Gift **S. D. Rose**
2 **CHARLES PARNELL (IRE)**, 9, b g Elnadim (USA)—Titania **Mr J. N. Griffiths**

Assistant Trainer: Elizabeth Grant

---

278 **MR SIRRELL GRIFFITHS, Carmarthen**
Postal: **Rwyth Farm, Nantgaredig, Carmarthen, Dyfed, SA32 7LG**
Contacts: **PHONE (01267) 290321/290120**

1 **CLORAN JACK (IRE)**, 8, ch g Moonax—Kerry Leitrim (IRE) **S. G. Griffiths**
2 **HARRY WESTON**, 7, b g Sir Harry Lewis (USA)—Fractious **S. G. Griffiths**
3 **U B CAREFULL**, 9, ch g Roi de Rome (USA)—Harry's Bride **S. G. Griffiths**

Assistant Trainer: Martyn Roger Griffiths

---

279 **MRS DIANA GRISSELL, Brightling**
Postal: **Brightling Park, Robertsbridge, East Sussex, TN32 5HH**
Contacts: **PHONE (01424) 838241 MOBILE (07950) 312 610**
E-MAIL digrissell@aol.com WEBSITE www.grissellracing.co.uk

1 **ARBEO (IRE)**, 6, b g Brian Boru—Don't Waste It (IRE) **Nigel & Barbara Collison**
2 **BOY OF BORU (IRE)**, 5, b g Brian Boru—Don't Waste It (IRE) **The Wasteinit Partnership**
3 **CAPTAIN CRACKERS (IRE)**, 8, b g King's Theatre (IRE)—Love The Lord (IRE) **Mrs L. P. Baker**
4 **DOUBLE BUD**, 5, b m Double Trigger (IRE)—Little Bud **Mrs P. A. Wilkins**
5 **DOWNE PAYMENT (IRE)**, 7, b m Saddlers' Hall (IRE)—Waterloo Park (IRE) **Blackdowne Racing**
6 **MAXIMIX**, 9, gr g Linamix (FR)—Time Will Show (FR) **Mrs S. M. Russell**
7 **OSCAR BABY (IRE)**, 6, b m Oscar (IRE)—Snowbaby (IRE) **Mr R. E. Halley**
8 **PRE RAPHAELITE (FR)**, 6, b g Spadoun (FR)—Final Moment **J. B. Robinson**
9 **REAR GUNNER (IRE)**, 10, b g Pistolet Bleu (IRE)—Nethertara **Cockerell Cowing Racing**
10 **ROPARTA AVENUE**, 5, b g Nomadic Way (USA)—Miss Fizz **Mrs D. M. Grissell**
11 **SOLE AGENT (IRE)**, 10, b g Trans Island—Seattle Siren (USA) **Mrs S. M. Russell**

Other Owners: B. J. Cockerell, Mr N. Collison, Mrs B. Collison, A. Cowing, Mr M. Cutler, K. P. Hewstone, M. Lynch.

Jockey (NH): Robert Thornton, Jamie Moore, Alex Merriam. **Amateur:** Miss Hannah Grissell.

280 MR JOHN BRYAN GROUCOTT, Much Wenlock
Postal: **11 Bourton Cottages, Much Wenlock, Shropshire, TF13 6QF**
Contacts: **PHONE** (01746) 785603 **FAX** (01746) 785603 **MOBILE** (07866) 480830
E-MAIL lisajmwillis@aol.com

1 **ONE MORE DINAR**, 9, b g Kayf Tara—One More Dime (IRE) **Mrs A. V. Winwood**
2 **PRET A THOU (FR)**, 9, ch g Funny Baby (FR)—Va Thou Line (FR) **C. J. Tipton**
3 **SUMMER DE BAUNE (FR)**, 7, b g Saint Cyrien (FR)—Fee de Baune (FR) **C. J. Tipton**
4 **WAYWOOD PRINCESS**, 7, b m Sir Harry Lewis (USA)—First Bee **Three Counties Racing 2**

Other Owners: Mr P. Price, N. Scanlan.

281 MR BRIAN GUBBY, Bagshot
Postal: **Dukes Wood, Bracknell Road, Bagshot, Surrey, GU19 5HX**
Contacts: **OFFICE** (01276) 850513 **FAX** (01276) 479859 **MOBILE** (07768) 867368

1 **AL AQABAH (IRE)**, 7, ch m Redback—Snow Eagle (IRE) **B. Gubby**
2 **SON OF THE CAT (USA)**, 6, b g Tale of The Cat (USA)—Dixieland Gal (USA) **B. Gubby**

THREE-YEAR-OLDS

3 **AURENS (IRE)**, b g One Cool Cat (USA)—Al Aqabah (IRE) **B. Gubby**
4 **KINGLAMI**, b c Kingsalsa (USA)—Red Japonica **B. Gubby**

TWO-YEAR-OLDS

5 Ch c 13/3 Choisir (AUS)—Evenstorm (USA) (Stephen Got Even (USA)) **B. Gubby**

Assistant Trainer: Larry Wilkins

282 MR RAE GUEST, Newmarket
Postal: **Chestnut Tree Stables, Hamilton Road, Newmarket, Suffolk, CB8 0NY**
Contacts: **PHONE** (01638) 661508 **FAX** (01638) 667317 **MOBILE** (07711) 301095
E-MAIL raeguest@raeguest.com **WEBSITE** www.raeguest.com

1 **FIRST CLASS**, 4, b g Oasis Dream—Break Point **Mr B. Cooper & Miss E. Reffo**

THREE-YEAR-OLDS

2 **GUILETTA (IRE)**, gr f Dalakhani (IRE)—Guilia **The Hornets**
3 **KICKINGTHELILLY**, ch f Byron—Teller (ARG) **T. Hirschfeld**
4 **MISS CATO**, ch f Notnowcato—Regal Fairy (IRE) **A. H. Bennett**
5 B c Peintre Celebre (USA)—Sambala (IRE) **Mr C. Artam**

TWO-YEAR-OLDS

6 Gr f 21/2 Dark Angel (IRE)—Downland (USA) (El Prado (IRE)) (18000) **The Calm Again Partnership**
7 Ch c 22/2 Pivotal—Poppy Carew (IRE) (Danehill (USA)) (30000) **E. P. Duggan**
8 B f 27/3 Medicean—Rhumba Rage (USA) (Nureyev (USA)) (14000) **The Calm Again Partnership**
9 Ch f 20/4 Dutch Art—Turban Heights (IRE) (Golan (IRE)) (19000) **The Calm Again Partnership**

Other Owners: Mr D. M. Carter, B. A. Cooper, B. J. Flahive, R. Guest, L. K. Piggott Ltd, S. J. Piper, Ms E. M. B. A. Reffo, D. I. Scott, Mrs P. Smith, B. Stewart, D. J. Willis.

Assistant Trainer: Nicholas McKee **Head Lad:** Stephen Davis

Apprentice: Noel Garbutt.

283 MR RICHARD GUEST, Stainforth
Postal: **Maggswood Racing Stables, Stainforth, Doncaster, South Yorkshire, DN7 5PS**
Contacts: **PHONE** (07760) 755741 **MOBILE** (07760) 755742
E-MAIL future-racing@hotmail.com **WEBSITE** www.richardguest.co.uk

1 **ALPHA TAURI (USA)**, 6, b g Aldebaran (USA)—Seven Moons (JPN) **W. McKay**
2 **ALQAAHIR (USA)**, 10, b h Swain (IRE)—Crafty Example (USA) **Rakebackmypoker.com**
3 **ARRIVADERCI**, 4, b f Kyllachy—Arrivato **Future Racing (Notts) Limited**

MR RICHARD GUEST—continued

4 **ATHENIAN GARDEN (USA)**, 5, b m Royal Academy (USA)—Webee (USA) **Rakebackmypoker.com**
5 **BAHARAT (IRE)**, 4, b g Iffraaj—Gharam (USA) **Willie McKay & Alison Ibbotson**
6 **BARNET FAIR**, 4, br g Iceman—Pavement Gates **Mr D. Wheatley**
7 **BE MY DEPUTY (IRE)**, 7, b g Oscar (IRE)—Have A Myth (IRE) **Malcolm Penney & Miss Alison Ibbotson**
8 **BEFORTYFOUR**, 7, b g Kyllachy—Ivania **W. McKay**
9 **BEST TRIP (IRE)**, 5, b g Whipper (USA)—Tereed Elhawa **P. J. Duffen & P. Brown**
10 **BRAVO KING (IRE)**, 4, b g Sakhee (USA)—Ashbilya (USA) **Rakebackmypoker.com**
11 **BROWN PETE (IRE)**, 4, b br g Aussie Rules (USA)—Banba (IRE) **Rakebackmypoker.com**
12 **CAPTAIN SCOOBY**, 6, b g Captain Rio—Scooby Dooby Do **Future Racing (Notts) Limited**
13 **CASHELGAR (IRE)**, 6, b g Anabaa (USA)—Tropical Barth (IRE) **Future Racing (Notts) Limited**
14 **CATALYZE**, 4, b g Tumblebrutus (USA)—Clarita Dear (CHI) **W. McKay**
15 **CATAWOLLOW**, 5, b m Beat Hollow—Catalonia (IRE) **Miss C. Fordham**
16 **CLASSICAL CHLOE**, 4, b f Sleeping Indian—Mana Pools **Miss A. L. Ibbotson**
17 **COASTAL PASSAGE**, 4, b g Ishiguru (USA)—Ellcon (IRE) **W. McKay**
18 **CROCODILE BAY (IRE)**, 9, b g Spectrum (IRE)—Shenkara (IRE) **Future Racing (Notts) Limited**
19 **CUT THE CACKLE (IRE)**, 6, b m Danetime (IRE)—Alexander Anapolis (IRE) **Rakebackmypoker.com**
20 **DANCING FREDDY (IRE)**, 5, b g Chineur (FR)—Majesty's Dancer **Rakebackmypoker.com**
21 **DANIEL THOMAS (IRE)**, 10, b g Dansili—Last Look **Rakebackmypoker.com**
22 **DIAMOND FAY (IRE)**, 4, ch f Fayruz—Waroonga (IRE) **Mr C. J. Penney**
23 **DICKIE LE DAVOIR**, 8, b g Kyllachy—Downeaster Alexa (USA) **M. E. White**
24 **DUNASKIN (IRE)**, 12, b g Bahhare (USA)—Mirwara (IRE) **Miss A. L. Ibbotson**
25 **DZESMIN (POL)**, 10, b g Professional (IRE)—Dzakarta (POL) **S. Miller**
26 **EL DECECY (USA)**, 8, b g Seeking The Gold (USA)—Ashraakat (USA) **W. McKay**
27 **EMERALD GIRL (IRE)**, 5, b m Chineur (FR)—Faypool (IRE) **Rakebackmypoker.com**
28 **EUROPEAN DREAM (IRE)**, 9, br g Kalanisi (IRE)—Tereed Elhawa **You Trotters**
29 **FROGNAL (IRE)**, 6, b g Khelyf (USA)—Shannon Dore (IRE) **Rakebackmypoker.com**
30 **GEORGEBERNARDSHAW (IRE)**, 7, b g Danehill Dancer (IRE)—Khamseh **Future Racing (Notts) Limited**
31 **GOAL (IRE)**, 4, b g Mujadil (USA)—Classic Lin (FR) **W. McKay**
32 **GORDY BEE (USA)**, 6, b g More Than Ready (USA)—Honoria (USA) **Mrs Rita Bailey, Mr Mick White**
33 **GRACIE'S GIFT (IRE)**, 10, b g Imperial Ballet (IRE)—Settle Petal (IRE) **S. E. Hussey**
34 **GREEN WARRIOR**, 4, b g Invincible Spirit (IRE)—Starlit Sky **Future Racing (Notts) Limited**
35 **IMOGEN LOUISE (IRE)**, 4, gr f Verglas (IRE)—Strina (IRE) **Rakebackmypoker.com**
36 **IVAN THE TERRIBLE (IRE)**, 4, b g Ivan Denisovich (IRE)—Pussie Willow (IRE) **Miss C. Fordham**
37 **IVORY JAZZ**, 5, b g Dubai Destination (USA)—Slow Jazz (USA) **W. McKay**
38 **JAWAAB (IRE)**, 8, ch g King's Best (USA)—Canis Star **L & D Interiors Ltd**
39 **JOYOUSLY**, 4, ch f Needwood Blade—Lambadora **Rakebackmypoker.com**
40 **KAMES PARK (IRE)**, 10, b g Desert Sun—Persian Sally (IRE) **Future Racing (Notts) Limited**
41 **LE REVEUR**, 10, b g Machiavellian (USA)—Brooklyn's Dance (FR) **Future Racing (Notts) Limited**
42 **LITTLEPORTNBRANDY (IRE)**, 4, ch f Camacho—Sharplaw Destiny (IRE) **Rakebackmypoker.com**
43 **MAJURO (IRE)**, 8, b g Danetime (IRE)—First Fling (IRE) **W. McKay**
44 **MANANA MANANA**, 6, b g Tobougg (IRE)—Midnight Allure **W. McKay**
45 **MCCONNELL (USA)**, 7, ch g Petionville (USA)—Warsaw Girl (IRE) **Rakebackmypoker.com**
46 **MICKY'S KNOCK OFF (IRE)**, 5, b g Camacho—La Grace **Miss Alison Ibbotson**
47 **MILTON OF CAMPSIE**, 7, ch m Medicean—La Caprice (USA) **W. McKay**
48 **MOTTLEY CREWE**, 5, b g Mujahid (USA)—Ticcatoo (IRE) **Rakebackmypoker.com**
49 **MUKTASB (USA)**, 11, b g Bahri (USA)—Maghaarb **Miss C. S. Comery**
50 **NINE BEFORE TEN (IRE)**, 4, ch f Captain Rio—Sagaing **W. McKay**
51 **NOLECCE**, 5, ch g Reset (AUS)—Ghassanah **Future Racing (Notts) Limited**
52 **ON THE CUSP (IRE)**, 5, b g Footstepsinthesand—Roman Love (IRE) **Rakebackmypoker.com**
53 **PAVEMENT GAMES**, 5, b m Mind Games—Pavement Gates **S. E. Hussey**
54 **PETOMIC (IRE)**, 7, ch g Dubai Destination (USA)—Petomi **Johnson Racing**
55 **POBS TROPHY**, 5, b g Umistim—Admonish **Miss C. Fordham**
56 **QUALITY ART (USA)**, 4, b g Elusive Quality (USA)—Katherine Seymour **Maze Rattan Limited**
57 **ROYAL INTRUDER**, 7, b g Royal Applause—Surprise Visitor (IRE) **Rakebackmypoker.com**
58 **RYEDALE DANCER (IRE)**, 4, ch f Refuse To Bend (IRE)—Saik (USA) **Future Racing (Notts) Limited**
59 **RYLEE MOOCH**, 4, gr g Choisir (AUS)—Negligee **Katie Hughes, Sheila White, Julie McCarlie**
60 **SIX DIAMONDS**, 5, b m Exceed And Excel (AUS)—Daltak **Rakebackmypoker.com**
61 **SLATEY HEN (IRE)**, 4, b f Acclamation—Silver Arrow (USA) **Rakebackmypoker.com**
62 **TED'S BROTHER (IRE)**, 4, b g Fath (USA)—Estertide (IRE) **Maze Rattan Limited**
63 **THE WHICH DOCTOR**, 7, b g Medicean—Oomph **Rakebackmypoker.com**
64 **UNBREAK MY HEART (IRE)**, 7, ch g Bahamian Bounty—Golden Heart **Rakebackmypoker.com**
65 **VELVET VIC (IRE)**, 6, b g Old Vic—Elleena Rose (IRE) **R. Collins**
66 **VISIONS OF JOHANNA (USA)**, 7, b g Johannesburg (USA)—Belle Turquoise (FR) **Willie McKay & Brian Carey**
67 **WAABEL**, 5, b br g Green Desert (USA)—Najah (USA) **Rakebackmypoker.com**
68 **YOSSI (IRE)**, 8, b g Montjeu (IRE)—Raindancing (IRE) **Miss A. L. Ibbotson**

MR RICHARD GUEST—continued

THREE-YEAR-OLDS

69 **AMBITIOUS ICARUS**, b g Striking Ambition—Nesting Box **Future Racing (Notts) Limited**
70 **CONCORDIA NOTTE (IRE)**, b f Elusive City (USA)—Laylati (IRE) **Rakebackmypoker.com**
71 **GEORGE FENTON**, ch g Piccolo—Mashmoum **Maze Rattan Limited**
72 **JOHNNY CAVAGIN**, b g Superior Premium—Beyond The Rainbow **A. Bell**
73 **JOHNSON'S CAT (IRE)**, b g One Cool Cat (USA)—Takanewa (IRE) **Johnson Racing**
74 **JULY SPECIALISTS**, b f Josr Algarhoud (IRE)—La Corujera **Future Racing (Notts) Limited**
75 **LORD BUFFHEAD**, br g Iceman—Royal Pardon **Brooklands Racing & Partners**
76 **MISERERE MEI (IRE)**, b f Moss Vale (IRE)—Flying Clouds **Future Racing (Notts) Limited**
77 **NURSE DOMINATRIX (IRE)**, b br f Whipper (USA)—Medica Boba **Mr C. J. Penney**
78 **OUTLAW TORN (IRE)**, ch g Iffraaj—Touch And Love (IRE) **Future Racing (Notts) Limited**
79 **SLEEPY LUCY**, b f Multiplex—Millie The Filly **Mr A. K. Elton**
80 **THERE'S NO RULES**, br g Authorized (IRE)—Excellent **Miss A. L. Ibbotson**
81 Gr f Librettist (USA)—Zilkha **Mr C. J. Penney**

TWO-YEAR-OLDS

82 Ch g 25/2 Bahamian Bounty—Croeso Bach (Bertolini (USA)) (9523)
83 B g 4/4 Multiplex—Dockside Strike (Docksider (USA)) (11428)
84 Br f 19/3 Cockney Rebel (IRE)—Korolieva (IRE) (Xaar) (5714)
85 B f 6/3 Bertolini (USA)—Lady Natilda (First Trump) (15238)
86 Gr f 9/3 Aussie Rules (USA)—River Grand (IRE) (Grand Lodge (USA)) (2857)
87 Br f 2/3 Royal Applause—Wood Chorus (Singspiel (IRE)) (7619)
88 B g 4/4 Kyllachy—Woodbeck (Terimon) (14285) **Maze Rattan Limited**
89 Br g 27/5 Jeremy (USA)—Zagaleta (Sri Pekan (USA)) (10000)

Other Owners: Mr Sam Allardyce, Mr S. Arnold, Mr M. H. Bates, Mr Phil Brown, Mr Paul J. Duffen, Future Racing (Notts) Limited, Miss Alison Ibbotson, Mr David Kilpatrick, Mr D. S. Lovatt, Mrs E. Lucey-Butler, Mr John Lynch, Maze Rattan Limited, Mr Willie McKay, Mrs A. M. Mercs, Mr Mick White, Mrs S. White, Mr C. Wing.

Assistant Trainers Mr Ronald Thompson, Mr Stephen Arnold

Jockey (flat): Robert L. Butler. **Apprentice:** Charles Eddery, Jamie Jones. **Amateur:** Mrs A. Guest.

---

284 **MISS POLLY GUNDRY, Ottery St Mary**
Postal: Holcombe Brook, Holcombe Lane, Ottery St. Mary, Devon, EX11 1PH
Contacts: PHONE (01404) 811181 MOBILE (07932) 780621
E-MAIL polly.gundry@live.co.uk

1 **FOLIE A DEUX (IRE)**, 10, b g Anshan—Flynn's Girl (IRE) **G. N. Carstairs**
2 **FORT VIEW (IRE)**, 8, b g Ashley Park (IRE)—Laurens Pride (IRE) **Guy and Sophie Henderson**
3 **FREDDY'S STAR (IRE)**, 10, ch g Kris—Kutaisi (IRE) **F. A. Clegg**
4 **KABIRA**, 4, b f Exit To Nowhere (USA)—Fleeting Vision (IRE) **Ashley House Stud**
5 **LORD RAGNAR (IRE)**, 9, b g King's Theatre (IRE)—Shaiymara (IRE) **Mr & Mrs R. G. Kelvin Hughes**
6 **MIX N MATCH**, 8, b g Royal Applause—South Wind **F. A. Clegg**
7 **NOTCANTDOIT (IRE)**, 5, ch g Classic Cliche (IRE)—Tanya Thyne (IRE) **G. N. Carstairs**
8 **PENDOUN**, 10, b g Spadoun (FR)—Last Penny **Mrs J. Alford**
9 **TEENAGE KICKS (IRE)**, 7, ch g Giant's Causeway (USA)—Ruissec (USA) **G. Carstairs**
10 **TULLOW BOY**, 8, b g Double Trigger (IRE)—Pollys Perk (IRE) **Mr R. E. Stuart-Jervis**

Assistant Trainer: Edward Walker

Jockey (NH): Hadden Frost, Tom O'Brien. **Conditional:** Matt Griffiths. **Amateur:** Mr Ed Barrett, Mr Robbie Henderson.

---

285 **MR WILLIAM HAGGAS, Newmarket**
Postal: Somerville Lodge, Fordham Road, Newmarket, Suffolk, CB8 7AA
Contacts: PHONE (01638) 667013 FAX (01638) 660534 MOBILE (07860) 282281
E-MAIL william@somerville-lodge.co.uk

1 **BEATEN UP**, 4, b g Beat Hollow—Frog **Mr B. Haggas**
2 **CAPE CLASSIC (IRE)**, 4, b c Cape Cross (IRE)—Politesse (USA) **Mr B. Kantor**
3 **DANCING RAIN (IRE)**, 4, ch f Danehill Dancer (IRE)—Rain Flower (IRE) **M J Taylor & L A Taylor**
4 **EXPOSE**, 4, ch g Compton Place—Show Off **The Royal Ascot Racing Club**

MR WILLIAM HAGGAS—continued

5 **FIGARO**, 4, ch g Medicean—Chorist **Mr A. Duke & Mr R. Smith**
6 **FIREBEAM**, 4, b g Cadeaux Genereux—Firebelly **Highclere Thoroughbred Racing - Blue Peter**
7 **FURY**, 4, b ro g Invincible Spirit (IRE)—Courting **Cheveley Park Stud**
8 **HAAMAAT (IRE)**, 4, b f Shamardal (USA)—Exultate Jubilate (USA) **Hamdan Al Maktoum**
9 **HARRIS TWEED**, 5, b g Hernando (FR)—Frog **Mr B. Haggas**
10 **JAWHAR (IRE)**, 4, ch g Halling (USA)—Kawn **Hamdan Al Maktoum**
11 **LORDOFTHEHOUSE (IRE)**, 4, ch g Danehill Dancer (IRE)—Bordighera (USA) **Lael Stable**

THREE-YEAR-OLDS

12 **AARTI (IRE)**, b f Oasis Dream—Sewards Folly **Saleh Al Homaizi & Imad Al Sagar**
13 **AFAAL (USA)**, b g Hard Spun (USA)—Alattrah (USA) **Hamdan Al Maktoum**
14 **AL JABREIAH**, b f Bertolini (USA)—Nihal (IRE) **Mohammed Jaber**
15 **AL QATARI (USA)**, b br c Dynaformer (USA)—Where's The Church (USA) **H.E. S. M. B. H. B. K. Al Thani**
16 **AL WAJBA (USA)**, ch f Ghostzapper (USA)—Crystal Symphony (USA) **Khalifa Bin Sheail Al Kuwari**
17 **ANISEED (IRE)**, gr f Dalakhani (IRE)—Anna Karenina (USA) **M J Taylor & L A Taylor**
18 **ARSAADI (IRE)**, b f Dubawi (IRE)—Arsad (IRE) **Sultan Ali & Saeed Misleh**
19 **ASIAN TRADER**, b c Acclamation—Tiger Waltz **M S Bloodstock Ltd**
20 **BORNHOLM (IRE)**, b g Oasis Dream—Barbuda **David & Paul Hearson**
21 **CARDIGAN (IRE)**, ch f Barathea (IRE)—Precipitous (IRE) **R. C. Tooth**
22 **CELLIST**, b g Halling (USA)—Ae Kae Ae (USA) **The Royal Ascot Racing Club**
23 **CHRISTINGLE**, b f Iceman—Pious **Cheveley Park Stud**
24 **CLASSIC FALCON (IRE)**, ch f Dubawi (IRE)—Livius Lady (IRE) **Sheikh Hamdan Bin Maktoum Al Maktoum**
25 **COUNTESS FERRAMA**, ch f Authorized (IRE)—Madame Dubois **B. Kantor & M. Jooste**
26 **DANCHAI**, gr c Authorized (IRE)—Scarlet Empire (IRE) **Saleh Al Homaizi & Imad Al Sagar**
27 **DARLING GRACE**, b f Nayef (USA)—Lady Grace (IRE) **Mrs D. J. James**
28 **DIALA (IRE)**, b f Iffraaj—Quaich **Abdulla Al Khalifa**
29 **DISTRICT ATTORNEY (IRE)**, b c Lawman (FR)—Mood Indigo (IRE) **M. Jooste & B. Kantor**
30 **ENTIFAADHA**, b c Dansili—Model Queen (USA) **Hamdan Al Maktoum**
31 **FAST OR FREE**, ch c Notnowcato—Ewenny **Ian & Christine Beard**
32 **GUARANTEE**, b c Authorized (IRE)—Zuleika Dobson **Highclere Thoroughbred Racing-Authorized**
33 **GUARDA PAMPA**, b f Dansili—Factice (USA) **Mr & Mrs C. Bryce**
34 **HEERAAT (IRE)**, b c Dark Angel (IRE)—Thawrah (IRE) **Hamdan Al Maktoum**
35 **HUMMINGBIRD**, b f Nayef (USA)—Artistic Blue (USA) **Mrs P. Eddis**
36 **JAFOOL (IRE)**, b f Cape Cross (IRE)—Ghazal (USA) **Hamdan Al Maktoum**
37 **JUSTINEO**, b c Oasis Dream—Loulwa (IRE) **Saleh Al Homaizi & Imad Al Sagar**
38 **KAHRUMAN (USA)**, b br c Mr Greeley—Jaleela (USA) **Hamdan Al Maktoum**
39 **KHAZEENA**, b f Oasis Dream—Shamaiel (IRE) **Hamdan Al Maktoum**
40 **LEITRIM KING (IRE)**, b c High Chaparral (IRE)—Therry Girl (IRE) **Gallagher Equine Ltd**
41 **MABAANY**, b c Exceed And Excel (AUS)—Tarbiyah **Hamdan Al Maktoum**
42 **MAMA QUILLA (USA)**, ch f Smart Strike (CAN)—Myth To Reality (FR) **Mr & Mrs G. Middlebrook**
43 **MEDHYAAR**, b f Bahri—Kawn **Hamdan Al Maktoum**
44 **MUJANNADA (USA)**, b f Jazil (USA)—Wasnah (USA) **Hamdan Al Maktoum**
45 **MUKHADRAM**, b c Shamardal (USA)—Magic Tree (UAE) **Hamdan Al Maktoum**
46 **NINE REALMS**, b c Green Desert (USA)—Bourbonella **Mr & Mrs D. Hearson**
47 **PAWPRINTS (IRE)**, ch f Footstepsinthesand—Samphire Red (IRE) **Bill Eason, Michael Pallett & Partners**
48 **PEARL WAR (USA)**, b f War Front (USA)—B W Chargit (USA) **Pearl Bloodstock Limited**
49 **POLAR VENTURE**, b g Invincible Spirit (IRE)—Sharplaw Venture **Cheveley Park Stud**
50 **PURSUE**, b g Pivotal—Entrap (USA) **Cheveley Park Stud**
51 **RIGHT TO RULE (IRE)**, b g Rock of Gibraltar (IRE)—Epistoliere (IRE) **Right Tack Partnership**
52 **SAITARA**, b f Shamardal (USA)—Neila (GER) **Sheikh Ahmed Al Maktoum**
53 **SENTARIL**, b f Danehill Dancer (IRE)—Superstar Leo (IRE) **Lael Stable**
54 **SEVENTH SIGN**, b c Pivotal—Rahayeb **Mr A. Tinkler**
55 **SHATTER (IRE)**, b f Mr Greeley (USA)—Watership Crystal (IRE) **Cheveley Park Stud**
56 **SHOLAAN (IRE)**, b c Invincible Spirit (IRE)—Jazz Up **Sheikh Ahmed Al Maktoum**
57 **SHORE PERFORMER (IRE)**, b f Footstepsinthesand—Dancing Eclipse (IRE) **Mr D I Scott & Mr M Kerr-Dineen**
58 **SIGURWANA (USA)**, b br f Arch (USA)—Nyarhini **A. E. Oppenheimer**
59 **SIR PALOMIDES (USA)**, ch c Mr Greeley (USA)—Glatisant (USA) **A. E. Oppenheimer**
60 **STENCIVE**, b c Dansili—Madeira Mist (IRE) **B. Kantor & M. Jooste**
61 **SUN CENTRAL (IRE)**, ch c Galileo (IRE)—Bordighera (USA) **Lael Stable**
62 **SWNYMOR (IRE)**, b c Dylan Thomas (IRE)—
Propaganda (IRE) **Roberts Green Watson Savidge Whittal-Williams**
63 **TA AJABB**, b g Pastoral Pursuits—First Eclipse (IRE) **Sheikh Ahmed Al Maktoum**
64 **TAWAASUL**, b f Haafhd—Muwakleh **Hamdan Al Maktoum**
65 **TEACHER (IRE)**, ch g Danehill Dancer (IRE)—Lac Dessert (USA) **Highclere Thoroughbred Racing - Minoru**
66 **VALIANT**, ch c Galileo (IRE)—Whazzis **Highclere Thoroughbred Racing - Herring**

MR WILLIAM HAGGAS—continued

67 **VIVID BLUE,** ch f Haafhd—Vivianna **Mrs F Woodd & Mrs Julia Scott**
68 **VOW,** b f Motivator—Frog **Highclere Thoroughbred Racing - Pocahontas**
69 **WELL PAINTED (IRE),** ch g Excellent Art—Aoife (IRE) **Options O Syndicate**
70 **WESTWITHTHENIGHT (IRE),** b f Cape Cross (IRE)—Hidden Hope **A. E. Oppenheimer**
71 **WINDY LANE,** b f Dubai Destination (USA)—Wendylina (IRE) **M. Jooste & B. Kantor**

TWO-YEAR-OLDS

72 **ARAQELLA,** b f 23/4 Oasis Dream—Bourbonella (Rainbow Quest (USA)) **Mr & Mrs D. Hearson**
73 Ch c 19/2 Haatef (USA)—Bezant (IRE) (Zamindar (USA)) (82100) **Hamdan Al Maktoum**
74 **BUTTERFLY DREAM,** ch f 9/3 Kyllachy—Dream Again (Medicean) **Cheveley Park Stud**
75 **CARA GINA,** b f 4/3 Bahamian Bounty—Princess Georgina (Royal Applause) (50000) **Mrs D. J. James**
76 B c 7/3 Manduro (GER)—Central Force (Pivotal) **Mohammed Jaber**
77 Ch c 11/4 Kyllachy—Constitute (Gone West (USA)) (85000) **Highclere Thoroughbred Racing - Coventry**
78 **CRY PEARL (USA),** b f 11/4 Street Cry (IRE)—
 Onda Nova (Keos (USA)) (85470) **Pearl Bloodstock Limited**
79 B c 13/4 Tiger Hill (IRE)—Cyclone Connie (Dr Devious (IRE)) (3000) **Mrs C. A. Cyzer**
80 **DANAT AL ATHEER,** ch f 19/3 Shamardal (USA)—Height of Vanity (Erhaab (USA)) **Jaber Abdullah**
81 **DUBAI AIRSHOW,** b c 28/2 Kheleyf (USA)—Danidh Dubai (IRE) (Noverre (USA)) **Jaber Abdullah**
82 B f 9/4 Invincible Spirit (IRE)—Emily Blake (IRE) (Lend A Hand) **Mr & Mrs R. Scott**
83 **EMPRESS ADELAIDE,** ch f 21/2 Pivotal—Emperice (USA) (Empire Maker (USA)) **Cheveley Park Stud**
84 B c 23/2 Danehill Dancer—Enticing (IRE) (Pivotal) **Lael Stable**
85 B f 9/2 Nayef (USA)—Ethaara (Green Desert (USA)) **Hamdan Al Maktoum**
86 B c 14/3 Invincible Spirit (IRE)—Fairy of The Night (IRE) (Danehill) (130000) **Hamdan Al Maktoum**
87 B c 22/2 Teofilo (IRE)—Fantastic Spring (USA) (Fantastic Light (USA)) (72000) **Mr Liam Sheridan**
88 **GARDEN ROW,** b gr f 1/4 Invincible Spirit (IRE)—Gladstone Street (IRE) (Waajib) **Cheveley Park Stud**
89 B f 3/2 Invincible Spirit (IRE)—Harayir (USA) (Gulch (USA)) **Hamdan Al Maktoum**
90 **I SAY (IRE),** b f 3/3 Oratorio (IRE)—Lisieux Orchid (IRE) (Sadler's Wells (USA)) (40000) **R. C. Tooth**
91 B f 16/2 Kheleyf (USA)—Insaaf (Averti (IRE)) **Hamdan Al Maktoum**
92 B f 16/2 Dynaformer (USA)—Jaleela (USA) (Kingmambo (USA)) **Hamdan Al Maktoum**
93 Ch c 27/4 Tamayuz—Kawn (Cadeaux Genereux) **Hamdan Al Maktoum**
94 **LADY MALET,** b f 18/3 Azamour (IRE)—Miss Rochester (IRE) (Montjeu (IRE)) (18000) **Cheveley Park Stud**
95 **LIGHTNING DEBUT,** b f 5/4 Pivotal—Dance of Light (USA) (Sadler's Wells (USA)) (80000) **Cheveley Park Stud**
96 B f 3/2 Royal Applause—Lumiere Noire (FR) (Dashing Blade) (139573) **St Albans Bloodstock Ltd**
97 B f 3/2 Teofilo (IRE)—Majestic Sakeena (IRE) (King's Best (USA)) **Saleh Al Homaizi & Imad Al Sagar**
98 **MARTIAN,** b c 13/3 Duke of Marmalade (IRE)—Starship (Galileo (IRE)) **Scott/Magnier/Piggott**
99 **MOMALORKA,** ch f 21/3 Dutch Art—Scarlet Royal (Red Ransom (USA)) (761) **The Duchess Syndicate**
100 B c 20/2 Excellent Art—Mrs Marsh (Marju (IRE)) (210000) **Highclere Thoroughbred Racing -Wavertree**
101 Ch c 21/1 Duke of Marmalade (IRE)—
 Mubkera (IRE) (Nashwan (USA)) (120000) **Saleh Al Homaizi & Imad Al Sagar**
102 **MUJADORA (IRE),** b f 26/1 Mujadil (USA)—Golden Ora (ITY) (Nordance (USA)) (23000) **Mr & Mrs Ian Beard**
103 B c 8/2 Galileo (IRE)—Mussoorie (FR) (Linamix (FR)) (50000) **B. Kantor & M. Jooste**
104 B f 6/3 Dansili—Muwakleh (Machiavellian) (USA) **Hamdan Al Maktoum**
105 B f 10/5 Kyllachy—Nausicaa (USA) (Diesis) (61904) **Wood Hall Stud Ltd**
106 **NOBLE DEED,** ch c 14/2 Kyllachy—Noble One (Primo Dominie) **Cheveley Park Stud**
107 B c 4/3 Elusive City (USA)—Parakopi (IRE) (Green Desert (USA)) (125000) **Sheikh Ahmed Al Maktoum**
108 **PARIS ROSE,** b f 14/3 Cape Cross (IRE)—Samira Gold (FR) (Gold Away (IRE)) **Jaber Abdullah**
109 B f 2/4 Oasis Dream—Politesse (USA) (Barathea (IRE)) (400000) **Lael Stable**
110 B c 7/3 Nayef (USA)—Red Camellia (Polar Falcon (USA)) (110000) **Sheikh Ahmed Al Maktoum**
111 **RESILIENT (IRE),** b c 11/2 Shamardal (USA)—Zither (Zafonic (USA)) (350000) **Silver Arrow Racing**
112 **ROCK CHOIR,** b f 27/3 Pivotal—Choir Mistress (Chief Singer) **Cheveley Park Stud**
113 B c 16/1 Distorted Humor (USA)—Rockcide (USA) (Personal Flag (USA)) (335775) **Hamdan Al Maktoum**
114 B f 28/4 Echo of Light—Romantic Retreat (Rainbow Quest (USA)) (2500) **Mrs C. A. Cyzer**
115 Br f 27/3 Manduro (GER)—Royal Secrets (IRE) (Highest Honor (FR)) **Mohammed Jaber**
116 B c 17/5 Excellent Art—Royale Figurine (IRE) (Dominion Royale) **D. I. Scott**
117 B f 29/4 Sakhee's Secret—Sacre Coeur (Compton Place) **Hot To Trot Partnership**
118 B c 24/4 Lucky Story (USA)—Seed Al Maha (USA) (Seeking The Gold (USA)) **Mohammed Jaber**
119 B c 17/2 Pivotal—Shabiba (USA) (Seeking The Gold (USA)) **Hamdan Al Maktoum**
120 **SONG AND DANCE MAN,** b c 15/3 Danehill Dancer—Song (IRE) (Sadler's Wells (USA)) **Paulyn Ltd**
121 Ch c 15/2 New Approach (IRE)—
 Spotlight (Dr Fong (USA)) (135000) **Highclere Thoroughbred Racing - Dalmeny**
122 B c 31/3 Cape Cross (IRE)—Street Star (USA) (Street Cry (IRE)) (75000) **Hamdan Al Maktoum**
123 B f 13/2 Acclamation—Superstar Leo (IRE) (College Chapel) **Lael Stable**
124 B c 25/2 Royal Applause—Take The Plunge (Benny The Dip (USA)) (31000) **Options O Syndicate**
125 Ch f 6/2 Muhtathir—Tiger Mist (IRE) (Galileo (IRE)) **M S Bloodstock Ltd**
126 **TWEED,** b f 6/5 Sakhee (USA)—Frog (Akarad (FR)) **Mr B. Haggas**

MR WILLIAM HAGGAS—continued

127 **VALTINA**, b f 22/4 Teofilo (IRE)—Vassiana (FR) (Anabaa (USA)) (160000) **M. J. & L. A. Taylor**
128 **VEERAYA**, b c 27/3 Rail Link—Follow Flanders (Pursuit of Love) (18000) **Mr Reyaz Farook**
129 B f 21/3 Singspiel (IRE)—Winds of Time (IRE) (Danehill (USA)) **Mr & Mrs R. Scott**
130 B c 18/2 Acclamation—Wrong Key (IRE) (Key of Luck (USA)) (220000) **Saleh Al Homaizi & Imad Al Sagar**

Other Owners: Mr Imad Al-Sagar, Mr James Barber, Mr Ian Beard, Mrs Christine Beard, Mrs Jonathan Blacklock, Mr Tim Bostwick, Mr N. A. Callaghan, Mr Peter Crate, Mrs A. Cruz, Mr T. Da Cruz, Mr William Eason, Mr J. Flannery, Gallagher Equine Ltd, Mr F. M. Green, Mr D. Hearson, Mrs David Hearson, Mr Paul Hearson, The Hon H. Herbert, Highclere Thoroughbred Racing Ltd, Mr Tony Hirschfeld, Mr Saleh Al Homaizi, Mr R. Jackson, Mrs G. S. Jackson, Mr M. J. Jooste, Mr Bernard Kantor, Mr Michael Kerr-Dineen, L. K. Piggott Ltd, Mrs Johnny McKeever, Mr G. Middlebrook, Mrs L. Middlebrook, Mr M. J. Pallett, Mr G. A. Roberts, Mr Mark Savidge, Mr D. I. Scott, Mrs Julia Scott, Mr M. J. Taylor, Mr L. Taylor, Mr C. P. Watson, Mr E. B. Whittal-Williams, Mr S. Wignall, Mrs David Woodd.

Assistant Trainers: Robert Stephens, Gail Hacking & Jason Favell

---

286 MR ALEX HALES, Banbury
Postal: **Trafford Bridge Stables, Edgcote, Banbury OX17 1AG**
Contacts: **PHONE (01295) 660131 FAX (01295) 660128 MOBILE (07771) 511652**
E-MAIL **alex@alexhalesracing.co.uk** WEBSITE **www.alexhalesracing.co.uk**

1 **BANKCITY (FR)**, 5, b g Sagacity (FR)—Eclipse de Lune (USA) **Not A Bunch Of Bankers**
2 **BLINKA ME**, 5, b g Tiger Hill (IRE)—Easy To Love (USA) **Edging Ahead**
3 **COOL STRIKE (UAE)**, 6, b g Halling (USA)—Velour **A. L. Cohen**
4 **DAKOTA BOY**, 10, ch g Flying Legend (USA)—Lisaleen River **Edging Ahead**
5 **DINARIUS**, 7, b g Bertolini (USA)—Ambassadress **A. S. Helaissi**
6 **FAREWELLATMIDNIGHT**, 6, b m Midnight Legend—Fond Farewell (IRE) **Mrs J. Way**
7 **HANAHOE**, 7, b g Diktat—Shortfall **A Group Of Eight**
8 **ICONOCLAST**, 11, b br g Topanoora—La Cigale (GER) **John & Lorraine Barlow**
9 **LILAC BELLE**, 6, b m Robellino (USA)—Lilac Dreams **The Of-Ten Racing Partnership**
10 **LORD KENNEDY (IRE)**, 7, b g Saddlers' Hall (IRE)—Minstrel Madame (IRE) **The Patient Partnership**
11 **PENANGDOUBLE O ONE**, 5, ch g Starcraft (NZ)—Penang Pearl (FR) **Edging Ahead**
12 **RIF (FR)**, 7, b g Byzantium (FR)—Isabellita (FR) **The Patient Partnership**
13 **ROSENEATH (IRE)**, 8, b g Saddlers' Hall (IRE)—Vital Approach (IRE) **The Strathclyders**
14 **ROYAUME BLEU (FR)**, 7, ch g Kapgarde (FR)—Dear Blue (FR) **The Royaume Bleu Racing Partnership**
15 **SAINT DENIS (FR)**, 6, b g Saint des Saints (FR)—Imprevue (FR) **Mr D Hunter & Mr S Brown**
16 **SALUT HONORE (FR)**, 6, b g Lost World (IRE)—Kadalkote (FR) **The Hexagon Racing Partnership**
17 **SANDOFTHECOLOSSEUM (IRE)**, 7, b g Bob Back (USA)—Shuil Again (IRE) **The Old Relics Partnership**
18 **SOUND ACCORD (IRE)**, 11, br g Accordion—Shuil Na Lee (IRE) **Mr Andrew Cohen & Mr Alan Kaplan**
19 **VENCEREMOS**, 5, b m Generous (IRE)—Miss Orchestra **D. M. Huglin**

Other Owners: Mrs L. Barlow, Mr J. K. Barlow, T. B. Brown, Miss S. Burnell, Mr J. Cleary, A. M. Hales, Mr D. Hunter, Alan Kaplan, R. E. Morris-Adams, Mrs H. Steele, I. R. Taylor, Mr A. M. Warren, Mrs J. Wood.

---

287 MR MICHAEL HALFORD, Kildare
Postal: **Copper Beech Stables, Doneaney, Kildangan Road, Kildare, Co. Kildare, Ireland**
Contacts: **PHONE (00 353) 45 526119 FAX (00 353) 45 526157 MOBILE (00 353) 87 2579204**
E-MAIL **info@michaelhalford.com** WEBSITE **www.michaelhalford.com**

1 **ALVAR (USA)**, 4, ch c Forest Danger (USA)—Diameter (USA) **Mr P. Rooney**
2 **BANNA BOIRCHE (IRE)**, 6, b g Lucky Owners (NZ)—Ziet d'alsace (FR) **Mr P. Rooney**
3 **BARROW ISLAND (IRE)**, 5, b g Chevalier (IRE)—Shelini **Mrs H. M. Smith**
4 **CEBUANO**, 7, ch g Fraam—Ideal Figure **Mr P. McMahon**
5 **CERTERACH (IRE)**, 4, b g Halling (USA)—Chartres (IRE) **Mr P. Rooney**
6 **CHAPARRO (IRE)**, 7, b g High Chaparral (IRE)—Star's Proud Penny (USA) **Mr P. Rooney**
7 **DANICK OF TIME (IRE)**, 4, b g Iffraaj—Serious Delight **Mr N. Hartery**
8 **DEFINING YEAR (IRE)**, 4, b g Hawk Wing (USA)—Tajaathub (USA) **Ms C. Riordan**
9 **DEVONELLI (IRE)**, 4, b f Mujadil (USA)—Ann's Annie (IRE) **Mrs C. Roper**
10 **EASTERN RULES (IRE)**, 4, b c Golden Snake (USA)—Eastern Ember **Coleman Bloodstock**
11 **ELIZABETH COFFEE (IRE)**, 4, b f Byron—Queens Wharf (IRE) **Mr D. Carey**
12 **EXHILARATOR (IRE)**, 4, b g Ivan Denisovich (IRE)—Shaanbar (IRE) **Ms A. Keane**
13 **HUJAYLEA (IRE)**, 9, b g Almutawakel—Red Eagle (IRE) **Mr G. M. O'Leary**
14 **IF PER CHANCE (IRE)**, 7, b g Danetime (IRE)—Zafaraya (IRE) **CGE Partnership**
15 **INVINCIBLE ASH (IRE)**, 7, b m Invincible Spirit (IRE)—Fully Fashioned (IRE) **Mr P. Condron**
16 **LORD KENMARE (USA)**, 6, b g Hold That Tiger (USA)—The Fur Flew (USA) **Mr B. Gallivan**
17 **ONDEAFEARS (IRE)**, 5, b m Chineur (FR)—Irma La Douce (IRE) **Mrs C. Roper**

MR MICHAEL HALFORD—continued

18 PADDY THE CELEB (IRE), 6, ch g Peintre Celebre (USA)—On The Razz (USA) **Mr P. McMahon**
19 PIPERS CHOICE (IRE), 4, b g Choisir (AUS)—Pipewell (IRE) **Sin A Bhfuil Syndicate**
20 QUINMASTER (USA), 10, gr g Linamix (FR)—Sherkiya (IRE) **Mrs L. Halford**
21 RIDAYEF (IRE), 5, b g Dr Fong (USA)—Ridakiya (IRE) **Mr R. McNally**
22 RUMMAGING (IRE), 4, ch g Chineur (FR)—Roundabout Girl (IRE) **Mr P. E. I. Newell**
23 SAINT BY DAY (IRE), 6, b g Marju (IRE)—Spring To Light (USA) **Mr P. Rooney**
24 SHANROD (IRE), 6, b g Bachelor Duke (USA)—Classic Colleen (IRE) **Mr P. Rooney**
25 THE LAST DON (IRE), 6, b g Redback—Banco Solo **Mr P. J. McMahon**
26 THE MUNSTER MAORI (IRE), 4, br g Footstepsinthesand—Kilmore Princess (IRE) **Boys Four Fun Syndicate**
27 TROTTING WEASEL (IRE), 9, b g Bold Fact (USA)—Eves Temptation (IRE) **Mrs C. Roper**

THREE-YEAR-OLDS

28 BENSOON, b g Refuse To Bend (IRE)—Monsoon Wedding **Mrs G. McDonald**
29 BLUE CORNER (IRE), b c Teofilo (IRE)—Indian Belle (IRE) **H. H. Sheikh Mohammed (Darley)**
30 B c Hurricane Run (IRE)—Cute Cait **Ms J. Hogan**
31 DALIYAN (IRE), b c Red Ransom (USA)—Daliyana (IRE) **H. H. Aga Khan**
32 DANZERINI (USA), b g Bernardini (USA)—Lucifer's Stone (USA) **Barouche Stud**
33 DENOMINATOR (IRE), b g Diamond Green (FR)—Molomo **Barouche Stud**
34 DIYALA (IRE), b f Tiger Hill (IRE)—Daliya (IRE) **H. H. Aga Khan**
35 HAYLOFT (IRE), b f Clodovil (IRE)—Lucky Norwegian (IRE) **Barouche Stud**
36 HONOUR AND OBEY (IRE), ch f Hurricane Run (IRE)—Miss Intimate (USA) **Gigginstown House Stud**
37 KARKASAR (IRE), b c Rock of Gibraltar (IRE)—Karkiyla (IRE) **H. H. Aga Khan**
38 KHAREZI (IRE), b c Bachelor Duke (USA)—Kharsaka (IRE) **H. H. Aga Khan**
39 Gr f Verglas (IRE)—Lahiba (IRE) **Mrs C. Roper**
40 MADAMOISELLE H (IRE), br f Footstepsinthesand—Kilmore Princess (IRE) **Mr J. Hennessy**
41 MASSIYN (IRE), ch c Zamindar (USA)—Masilia (IRE) **H. H. Aga Khan**
42 MAZARAK (IRE), b c Amadeus Wolf—Masakala (USA) **H. H. Aga Khan**
43 MEA PARVITAS (IRE), b f Oasis Dream—Red Rita (IRE) **Mr J. Zindel**
44 MIZANI (IRE), gr c Bachelor Duke (USA)—Miss Sazanica (FR) **Les Haras De Son Alteese L'Aga Khan**
45 MULTITASKING, b g Multiplex—Ryan's Quest (IRE) **Mrs V. Osborne**
46 RED LASER (IRE), br g Red Clubs (IRE)—Prancing **Mr M. Phelan**
47 REGULATION (IRE), br c Danehill Dancer (IRE)—Source of Life (IRE) **Barouche Stud**
48 SHARP AND SMART (IRE), b f Dark Angel (IRE)—Church Road (IRE) **J. Harley/R. Boland Partnership**
49 SINETTA (IRE), b f Red Ransom (USA)—Siniyya (IRE) **H. H. Aga Khan**
50 B f Red Clubs (IRE)—Sister Sox (IRE) **Mrs C. Roper**
51 STEELY GRACE (IRE), b f Refuse To Bend (IRE)—Daganya (IRE) **Mr J. Claque**
52 SUNRISE SONG (IRE), b f Invincible Spirit (IRE)—Interpose **Gigginstown House Stud**
53 TAWARIYKA (USA), b br f Forest Wildcat (USA)—Tawaria (FR) **H. H. Aga Khan**
54 VIA BALLYCROY (IRE), b f Lawman (FR)—Via Milano (FR) **Rollx Syndicate**
55 ZALANGA (IRE), b f Azamour (IRE)—Zanara (IRE) **H. H. Aga Khan**
56 ZARIYNA (IRE), b f Marju (IRE)—Zariliya (IRE) **H. H. Aga Khan**

TWO-YEAR-OLDS

57 ADELA (IRE), ch f 29/3 Dr Fong (USA)—Adelfia (IRE) (Sinndar (IRE)) **H. H. Aga Khan**
58 B c 23/2 Iffraaj—Causeway Song (USA) (Giant's Causeway (USA)) **H. H. Sheikh Mohammed (Darley)**
59 B f 1/4 Dalakhani (IRE)—Chan Tong (BRZ) (Hampstead (URU)) **H. H. Sheikh Mohammed (Darley)**
60 DABADIYAN (IRE), b c 20/4 Zamindar (USA)—Dabista (IRE) (Highest Honor (FR)) **H. H. Aga Khan**
61 B c 1/3 Shamardal (USA)—Dibiya (IRE) (Caerleon (USA)) **H. H. Aga Khan**
62 MIZZAVA (IRE), b br f 9/4 Cape Cross (IRE)—Flamanda (Niniski (USA)) **Mr G. M. O'Leary**
63 B f 4/4 Danehill Dancer (IRE)—Mount Klinovec (IRE) (Mujadil (USA)) (115000) **Gigginstown House Stud**
64 B f 19/1 Cape Cross (IRE)—Nick's Nikita (IRE) (Pivotal) (40000) **Mr N. Hartery**
65 B c 18/4 Observatory—Siniyya (IRE) (Grand Lodge (USA)) **H. H. Aga Khan**
66 B c 10/3 Clodovil (IRE)—Smoken Rosa (USA) (Smoke Glacken (USA)) **Mr N. Hartery**
67 B c 27/1 Footstepsinthesand—Your Village (IRE) (Be My Guest (USA)) (28735) **Dr K. Swanick**
68 B c 25/2 Acclamation—Zarkalia (IRE) (Red Ransom (USA)) **H. H. Aga Khan**

Other Owners: H. H. Sheikh Mohammed (Darley), Barouche Stud, Boys Four Fun Syndicate, CGE Partnership, Mr D. Carey, Mr J. Claque, Coleman Bloodstock, Mr P. J. Condron, Mr B. Gallivan, Gigginstown House Stud, H. H. Aga Khan, Mrs L. Halford, Mr N. Hartery, Mr J. Hennessy, Ms J. Hogan, J. Harley/R. Boland Partnership, Ms A. Keane, Les Haras De Son Alteese L'Aga Khan, Mrs G. McDonald, Mr P. McMahon, Mr R. McNally, Mr P. E. I. Newell, Mr G. M. O'Leary, Mrs V. Osborne, Mr M. Phelan, Ms C. Riordan, Rollx Syndicate, Mr P Rooney, Mrs C. Roper, Sin A Bhfuil Syndicate, Mrs H. M. Smith, Dr K. Swanick, Mr J. Zindel.

Assistant Trainer: Louise Halford

Jockey (flat): Gary Carroll, Shane Foley. **Apprentice:** Conor Hoban, Jonathan Killahena, Peter Donnelly, Marc Monaghan.

288 MR LES HALL, Tadworth
Postal: **17 Thurnham Way, Tadworth, Surrey, KT20 5PR**
Contacts: **PHONE (07990) 707014**

1 AMOR PATRICE, 4, b g Ransom O'war (USA)—Sweet Stormy (IRE) **Mrs J R Green and Mr D A Docherty**
2 AYAARAH (IRE), 4, b f Cape Cross (IRE)—La Jwaab **Surrey Horseracing - Deirdre Ann**
3 BURNBRAKE, 7, b g Mujahid (USA)—Duena **B. H. Page**
4 EYE FOR THE GIRLS, 6, ch g Bertolini (USA)—Aunt Ruby (USA) **Mrs P. L. Capper**
5 RIVIERA RED (IRE), 12, b g Rainbow Quest (USA)—Banquise (IRE) **M. S. Green**
6 SAOI (USA), 5, ch g Wiseman's Ferry (USA)—Careyes (IRE) **Surrey Horseracing Limited**
7 THALIA GRACE, 5, ch m Zafeen (FR)—Days of Grace **Surrey Horseracing - Maria Jane**

Other Owners: Mrs M. M. Boyd, Mr P. D. Denny, Mr D. A. Docherty, Mrs M. J. Docherty, Mrs J. R. Green.

289 MISS SALLY HALL, Middleham
Postal: **Brecongill, Coverham, Leyburn, North Yorkshire, DL8 4TJ**
Contacts: **PHONE (01969) 640422 FAX (0800) 066 4274**
E-MAIL sally@brecongill.co.uk

1 COUNTRYCRAFT, 5, b g Pastoral Pursuits—Turn Back **Colin Platts**
2 MAGIC HAZE, 6, b g Makbul—Turn Back **Mrs J. Hodgson**
3 OAKWELL (IRE), 4, b g Antonius Pius (USA)—Cindy's Star (IRE) **Colin Platts**
4 4, Ch gr f Act One—Second Affair (IRE) **Miss S. E. Hall**

Assistant Trainer: Colin Platts

Jockey (NH): Richard Johnson. **Amateur:** Mrs D.S. Wilkinson.

290 MR GERALD HAM, Bridgwater
Postal: **Rose Farm, Rooksbridge, Axbridge, Somerset, BS26 2TH**
Contacts: **HOME (01934) 750331 FAX (01934) 750331 MOBILE (07732) 979962**
E-MAIL geraldham@btinternet.com

1 CASPAR OF TARSUS (IRE), 9, ch g Moonax (IRE)—Another Thurn (IRE) **The Holmes Office Limited**
2 CASTLEBOY WARRIOR (IRE), 6, b g Tikkanen (USA)—Spring Beauty (IRE) **Isle Of Frogs Partnership**
3 FLUTERS HOUSE, 8, b g Piccolo—Little Tumbler (IRE) **The Lansdowners**
4 LANSDOWNE PRINCESS, 10, b m Cloudings (IRE)—Premier Princess **The Lansdowners**
5 MAID IN ENGLAND, 9, b m Mujadil (USA)—Lalique (IRE) **Mr G. Holmes**
6 4, B g Grape Tree Road—Premier Princess **Mr D. M. Drury**
7 TARABELA, 9, b m Kayf Tara—Rocky Revival **G2 Recruitment Solutions Ltd**
8 ZAYDAR (IRE), 12, b br g Dr Devious (IRE)—Zayana (IRE) **Mrs B. Ham**

THREE-YEAR-OLDS

9 B f Kentucky Dynamite (USA)—Maid In England **The Holmes Office Ltd**

TWO-YEAR-OLDS

10 B f 24/3 Ishiguru (USA)—Maid In England (Mujadil (USA)) **The Holmes Office Ltd**

Other Owners: J. F. Baldwin, R. T. Wilkins.

Assistant Trainer: Jonathan Ham

Jockey (NH): Paddy Brennan, Andrew Thornton. **Conditional:** David Bass.

291 MRS MARY HAMBRO, Cheltenham
Postal: **Cotswold Stud, Sezincote, Moreton-In-Marsh, Gloucestershire, GL56 9TB**
Contacts: **PHONE (01386) 700700 FAX (01386) 700701 MOBILE (07860) 632990**
E-MAIL maryhambro@mac.com

1 DOVER'S HILL, 10, b g Pistolet Bleu (IRE)—Classic Beauty (IRE) **Mrs M. C. Hambro**
2 SQUIRREL WOOD (IRE), 4, b f Sadler's Wells (USA)—Didbrook **Mrs Richard Hambro & Mr Chris Palmer**

MRS MARY HAMBRO—continued

THREE-YEAR-OLDS

   3 HAZEL BROOK, b f High Chaparral (IRE)—Didbrook **Mrs M. C. Hambro**

Other Owners: Mrs Richard Hambro.

292
MRS DEBRA HAMER, Carmarthen
Postal: **Bryngors Uchaf, Nantycaws, Carmarthen, Dyfed, SA32 8EY**
Contacts: **HOME (01267) 234585 MOBILE (07870) 643185**

   1 BENDANT, 7, b g Beat All (USA)—Rendita (IRE) **T. L. Cooper**
   2 CELTIC FELLA (IRE), 5, br g Kahtan—Mens Business (IRE) **Mr T M & Mrs S M Morse**
   3 CLASSIC EURO (IRE), 6, b g Classic Cliche (IRE)—Native Euro (IRE) **Mr B. M. Jones**
   4 HIGHMEAD HARRY, 7, b g Sir Harry Lewis (USA)—Princess Pool **Mr D. E. J. Harries**
   5 KINGDOM OF HEAVEN (IRE), 7, b m Heron Island (IRE)—Heavenly Hill **W. J. Cole**
   6 MAGICAL MAN, 5, b g Lahib (USA)—Majestic Di (IRE) **Mr C. A. Hanbury**
   7 MICHIGAN ASSASSIN (IRE), 10, b g King's Theatre (IRE)—Shuil Ar Aghaidh **Mr C. A. Hanbury**
   8 PRIME EDITION (IRE), 7, b g Publisher (USA)—Oneoftheclan (IRE) **Formula One Racing**
   9 SIGNE D'ESTRUVAL (FR), 6, b g Lavirco (GER)—Balbeck (FR) **Hanford's Chemist Ltd**
10 WYNN DARWI (IRE), 7, b g Anshan—Noughtynova **Mrs P. A. Davies**

Other Owners: Mrs D. A. Hamer, Mr T. M. Morse, Mrs S. M. Morse, Mrs J. Taylor, Mr A. Yorke.

Assistant Trainer: Mr M P Hamer

293
MRS ALISON HAMILTON, Hawick
Postal: **The Dykes, Denholm, Hawick, Roxburghshire, TD9 8TB**
Contacts: **PHONE (01450) 870323 MOBILE (07885) 477349**
E-MAIL Alisonhamilton53@yahoo.com

   1 AGGIE'S LAD (IRE), 10, b g Saddlers' Hall (IRE)—Grangemills **J. P. G. Hamilton**
   2 BOW SCHOOL (IRE), 11, b g New Frontier (IRE)—Sallaghan (IRE) **J. P. G. Hamilton**
   3 MOONWIND (IRE), 7, b g Bach (IRE)—Rixdale (FR) **J. P. G. Hamilton**
   4 SOME LAD (IRE), 7, b g Beneficial—Some News (IRE) **J. P. G. Hamilton**
   5 TOPAZ BAY, 7, ch g Karinga Bay—Princess Topaz **J. P. G. Hamilton**
   6 WINTERWOOD (IRE), 9, b g Definite Article—Miss Dolly (IRE) **J. P. G. Hamilton**

Assistant Trainer: Mr G. Hamilton

294
MRS ANN HAMILTON, Newcastle Upon Tyne
Postal: **Claywalls Farm, Capheaton, Newcastle Upon Tyne, NE19 2BP**
Contacts: **PHONE (01830) 530219**
E-MAIL annhamilton1952@hotmail.com

   1 DR FLYNN (IRE), 7, b g Tikkanen (USA)—Tallaquale (IRE) **I. Hamilton**
   2 EDMUND (IRE), 5, b g Indian River (FR)—Awomansdream (IRE) **I. Hamilton**
   3 FARM PIXIE (IRE), 6, b g Snurge—Blue Bobby (IRE) **I. Hamilton**
   4 FRED BOJANGALS (IRE), 10, b g Scribano—Southern Princess **I. Hamilton**
   5 LOCKSTOWN, 9, ch g Exit To Nowhere (USA)—Slaney Rose (IRE) **Hedley Walton & Ian Hamilton**
   6 4, Br g Generous (IRE)—Miss Royello **I. Hamilton**
   7 ROLECARR (IRE), 9, b g Tragic Role (USA)—Nuit d'ete (USA) **I. Hamilton**
   8 TREEHOUSE, 9, b g Nomadic Way (USA)—Swift Reward **I. Hamilton**

TWO-YEAR-OLDS

   9 B f 10/4 Great Palm (USA)—Miss Royello (Royal Fountain) **I. Hamilton**

Other Owners: Mr Ian Hamilton, Mr Hedley Walton.

Assistant Trainer: Ian Hamilton

295 **MRS CATHY HAMILTON, Gillingham**
Postal: **New Town Farm, New Town, Kington Magna, Gillingham, Dorset, SP8 5EU**
Contacts: **MOBILE (07875) 092134**

1 **DEEP PEARL**, 9, br m Roi de Rome (USA)—Pearl's Choice (IRE) **Family Goes Racing**
2 **GUNSHIP (IRE)**, 11, b g Needle Gun (IRE)—Teejay's Future **Mr M. W. Hoskins**
3 **KEYNEEMA**, 10, b g Kayf Tara—Nothings Forever **Family Goes Racing**
4 **MOVING WINGS (IRE)**, 7, b g Winged Love (IRE)—Gene of The Glen (IRE) **Mr M. W. Hoskins**
5 **SIR BATHWICK (IRE)**, 13, b g Oscar (IRE)—Karenda **Family Goes Racing**

Jockey (NH): Danny Cook, Jimmy Derham, Mark Quinlan. **Conditional:** Tom Cannon, D. E. Mullins. **Amateur:** Miss Emma Hamilton, Mr R. G. Henderson, Miss Katy Squires.

296 **MR MICKY HAMMOND, Middleham**
Postal: **Oakwood Stables, East Witton Road, Middleham, Leyburn, North Yorkshire, DL8 4PT**
Contacts: **PHONE (01969) 625223 FAX (01969) 625224 MOBILE (07808) 572777**
E-MAIL mdhammondracing@tiscali.com WEBSITE www.mickyhammondracing.co.uk

1 **AD VITAM (IRE)**, 4, ch g Ad Valorem (USA)—Love Sonnet **Mr David Green**
2 **ALSAHIL (USA)**, 6, ch g Diesis—Tayibah (IRE) **R. D. Bickenson**
3 **AMIR PASHA (UAE)**, 7, br g Halling (USA)—Clarinda (IRE) **The Steven Kay Partnership**
4 **ARAMINTE**, 4, b f One Cool Cat (USA)—Persian Song **Mrs L. Peacock**
5 **ARCHIE'S WISH**, 8, br g Beat All (USA)—Marlands **The Black Bull Partnership**
6 **BACH PEDDLING (IRE)**, 6, b m Bach (IRE)—Amourus **M. D. Hammond**
7 **CHERNIK (IRE)**, 11, b g Norwich—Sue Pickering (IRE) **Bendery Properties Holdings Ltd**
8 **DANCEINTOTHELIGHT**, 5, gr g Dansili—Kali **The Family Of Roland Roper**
9 **DAWN RIDE (IRE)**, 11, b g New Frontier (IRE)—Atlantic Dawn (IRE) **Belarus 2 Partnership**
10 **DESERT HUNTER (IRE)**, 9, b g Desert Story (IRE)—She-Wolff (IRE) **R. Cabrera-Vargas**
11 **FAIR SPIN**, 12, ch g Pivotal—Frankie Fair (IRE) **Bendery Properties Holdings Ltd**
12 **FALCUN**, 5, b g Danehill Dancer (IRE)—Fanofadiga (IRE) **J. Buzzeo**
13 **FRANK THE SLINK**, 6, b g Central Park (IRE)—Kadari **F. Hanson**
14 **FRANKS A MILLION (IRE)**, 5, b g Blueprint (IRE)—Ballys Baby (IRE) **F. Hanson**
15 **GONOW**, 4, b g Red Ransom (USA)—Isotta (GER) **Mike & Eileen Newbould**
16 **HEART OF DUBAI (USA)**, 7, b g Outofthebox (USA)—Diablo's Blend (USA) **The Kings Swingers**
17 **HIGH RANSOM**, 5, b m Red Ransom (USA)—Shortfall **Mike & Eileen Newbould**
18 **HOLLIS**, 8, b g Lost Soldier (USA)—Cutting Reef (USA) **R. D. Bickenson**
19 **HONG KONG ISLAND (IRE)**, 5, br g Alhaarth (IRE)—Three Owls (IRE) **Miss T. A. Nixon**
20 **IDEALISM**, 5, b g Motivator—Fickle **Hope Springs Eternal**
21 **JUSTJOE (IRE)**, 6, b g Carroll House—Made of Marble (IRE) **J. Buzzeo**
22 **KATHLATINO**, 5, b m Danbird (AUS)—Silver Rhythm **M. D. Hammond**
23 **LA PANTERA ROSA (IRE)**, 9, ch g Tragic Role (USA)—
Fortune Cookie **Thomas, Hattie, Gabby, Paul & Vicky Snook**
24 **MAJOR DOMO (FR)**, 4, ch g Domedriver (IRE)—Raphaela (FR) **M. D. Hammond**
25 **MEETINGS MAN (IRE)**, 5, gr g Footstepsinthesand—Missella (IRE) **Paul, Vicky, Gabby, Tom & Hattie Snook**
26 **MERCHANT OF MEDICI**, 5, b g Medicean—Regal Rose **Mr John F. Wilson**
27 **MOTAFARRED (IRE)**, 10, ch g Machiavellian (USA)—Thurayya **R. D. Bickenson**
28 **MR CRYSTAL (FR)**, 8, ch g Trempolino (USA)—Iyrbila (FR) **Champagne Ascent Partnership**
29 **MR PERCEPTIVE**, 4, b g Iffraaj—Astuti (IRE) **MHOG**
30 **MR TALLYMAN**, 6, b g Auction House (USA)—Island Colony (USA) **The County Set (Two)**
31 **PERTUIS (IRE)**, 6, gr g Verglas—Lady Killeen (IRE) **D. Gennard**
32 **RALEIGH QUAY (IRE)**, 5, b g Bachelor Duke (USA)—Speedbird (USA) **S. T. Brankin & J. Zuppinger**
33 **RAPTUROUS APPLAUSE**, 4, b g Royal Applause—Rapturous **Bendery Properties Holdings Ltd**
34 **RED RHYTHM**, 5, ch g Starcraft (NZ)—Araguaia (IRE) **Miss Terri Anne Nixon**
35 **RONNIE RHINO**, 4, b g Darsi (FR)—Pondimari (FR) **Mike & Eileen Newbould**
36 **ROSAIRLIE (IRE)**, 4, ch f Halling (USA)—Mrs Mason (IRE) **The Bay Horse - Masham**
37 **SWALEDALE LAD (IRE)**, 5, b g Arakan (USA)—Tadjnama (USA) **D. Gennard**
38 **SWERVINIRVIN**, 4, b g Noverre (USA)—Saada One (IRE) **F. Hanson**
39 **SWISH DISH (CAN)**, 5, b br m El Corredor (USA)—Amelia Saratoga (JPN) **Bendery Properties Holdings Ltd**
40 4, B g Darsi (FR)—Taipans Girl (IRE) **M. D. Hammond**
41 **TERENZIUM (IRE)**, 10, br g Cape Cross (USA)—Tatanka (ITY) **O'Sunburn Partnership**
42 **XCLAIM**, 4, ch g Proclamation (IRE)—Tahara (IRE) **Mike & Eileen Newbould**
43 **YORKIST (IRE)**, 4, ch g Urban Ocean (FR)—Kilbarry Demon (IRE) **Mike & Eileen Newbould**

MR MICKY HAMMOND—continued

THREE-YEAR-OLDS

44 **EASTLANDS LAD (IRE)**, b br g Strategic Prince—Uisce Tine (IRE) **Mr J. F. Wilson**
45 **FIVE FRANKS (USA)**, b br g More Than Ready (USA)—Salchow (USA) **F. Hanson**
46 **MA KELLYS (IRE)**, ch g Compton Place—Western Sal **M. D. Hammond**
47 **MARGO CHANNING**, ch f Three Valleys (USA)—Charlotte Vale **Mr Peter J. Davies & Mrs Gemma Hogg**
48 **ONLY A ROUND (IRE)**, b g Tagula (IRE)—Scepter'd Isle **The Foundry Boys**
49 **ONLY ORSENFOOLSIES**, b g Trade Fair—Desert Gold (IRE) **This Time Next Year Partnership**
50 **TALLULA (IRE)**, b f Tagula (IRE)—Talara (IRE) **Mr A. J. Snook, Mr E. Tasker & Mr J. Cox**

TWO-YEAR-OLDS

51 Ch c 20/3 Notnowcato—Charlotte Vale (Pivotal) **Mr P. J. Davies**

Other Owners: Mr P. H. Bell, Bendery Properties Holdings Ltd, Mr Andrew Duckworth, Mr M. D. Hammond, Mr Steven Kay, Mr Mike Newbould, Mrs E. E. Newbould, Mr R. M. Roper, Mr R. S. Roper, Mr Nick Rust, Mr Paul Sellars, Mr Paul R. Snook.

Assistant Trainer: Mrs. G. Hogg (07809) 428117

Conditional: Joe Colliver. **Apprentice:** Katie Dowson. **Amateur:** Miss R. Smith.

---

297 **MR MIKE HAMMOND, Abberley**
Postal: **Cherry Ash, Bank Lane, Abberley, Worcester, Worcestershire, WR6 6BQ**
Contacts: **PHONE (01299) 896057 MOBILE 07894 050183**
E-MAIL mphatwellcottage@aol.com WEBSITE www.hammondracing.co.uk

1 **BRAVERY SCOTCH (IRE)**, 10, b g Gothland (FR)—Aokay (IRE) **Mr J. D. Perry**
2 **FOREIGN KING (USA)**, 8, b g Kingmambo (USA)—Foreign Aid (USA) **Mr J. M. T. Court**
3 **LADY JOJO (IRE)**, 4, br f Sonus (IRE)—Sword Lady **Mr J. M. T. Court**
4 4, B g Whitmore's Conn (USA)—River Salts (IRE) **Mr M. P. Hammond**
5 **WILLIAM MORGAN (IRE)**, 5, ch g Arakan (USA)—Dry Lightning **Mr M. P. Hammond**

Assistant Trainer: Zoe Hammond

---

298 **MR JOHN JOSEPH HANLON, Co. Carlow**
Postal: **Fennis Court, Bagenalstown, Co. Carlow, Ireland**
Contacts: **PHONE (00353) 87 6924831 FAX (00353) 59 9723613 MOBILE (00353) 87 6924831**
E-MAIL johnjhanlon@hotmail.com

1 **ADMIRAL HAWKE (IRE)**, 6, b g Stoway—Classical Rachel (IRE) **Mrs A. F. Mee**
2 **ALFA BEAT (IRE)**, 8, gr g Environment Friend—Belle d'anjou (FR) **Irvin S. Naylor**
3 **BLOOD DIAMOND (IRE)**, 7, b g Mujadil (USA)—Betelgeuse **Alan D. Gray**
4 **BUACHAILL ALAINN (IRE)**, 5, b g Oscar (IRE)—Bottle A Knock (IRE) **Barry Connell**
5 **CARIBBEAN SEA**, 5, br g Galileo (IRE)—Numidie (FR) **Alan D. Gray**
6 **CLONDAW WARRIOR (IRE)**, 5, br g Overbury (IRE)—Thespian (IRE) **Mr P. J. McMahon**
7 **COOLKING**, 5, b g King's Theatre (IRE)—Osocool **Mrs A. N. Durkan**
8 **COOSAN BELLE (IRE)**, 6, b m Definite Article—Princess of Zurich (IRE) **Dunk Again Syndicate**
9 **CRANKY CORNER**, 8, b g Classic Cliche (IRE)—Pondimari **Treaty Pals Syndicate**
10 **DARENJAN (IRE)**, 9, br g Alhaarth (IRE)—Darariyna (IRE) **Mrs T. C. Collins**
11 **DE' ORO (IRE)**, 7, b g Old Vic—Shabra Princess **Forever Never Syndicate**
12 **GRAY HESSION (IRE)**, 5, b g Vinnie Roe (IRE)—Little Paddle (IRE) **Alan D. Gray**
13 **HARANGUE (IRE)**, 4, b g Street Cry (USA)—Splendeur (FR) **Sean Conroy**
14 **HIDDEN CYCLONE (IRE)**, 7, b g Stoway—Hurricane Debbie (IRE) **Mrs A. F. Mee**
15 **ILISSOS (USA)**, 4, b g Mineshaft (USA)—Ema Bovary (CHI) **P. Holden**
16 **JULIMARK (IRE)**, 5, b m Accordion—Dannkalia (IRE) **Mrs A. N. Durkan**
17 **LUSKA LAD (IRE)**, 8, ch g Flemensfirth (USA)—Notsophar (IRE) **Barry Connell**
18 **MART LANE (IRE)**, 7, br g Stoway—Western Whisper (IRE) **B. Connell**
19 **MURCHU (IRE)**, 6, b g Oscar (IRE)—Bottle A Knock (IRE) **Paul McMahon**
20 **OBSESSION (IRE)**, 4, b g Marju (IRE)—Athlumney Lady **Paul Holden**
21 **OSCAR GALE (IRE)**, 8, b g Oscar (IRE)—Gales Way **Patrick Kelly**
22 **SILVER CIRCLE (IRE)**, 6, b g Where Or When (IRE)—Silver Bubble (USA) **Silver Chain Syndicate**
23 **STAR NEUVILLE (FR)**, 6, bl g East of Heaven (IRE)—Danystar (FR) **B. Connell**
24 **STREETS OF NEWYORK**, 5, b g Dalakhani (IRE)—Minute Waltz **Mrs A. F. Mee**
25 **SUNSET STANZA**, 4, b g Oasis Dream—Musical Horizon (USA) **Sean Hehir**

JOHN JOSEPH HANLON—continued

26 **SUPER COLLIDER**, 5, b g Montjeu (IRE)—Astorg (USA) **Manhattan Racing Syndicate**
27 **SUPREME BUILDER**, 11, b g Supreme Leader—Osocool **A. Cullen**
28 **THEGONDOLIER (IRE)**, 4, b g Captain Rio—Sandy Fitzgerald (IRE) **Sean Lyons**
29 **THREE MOUNTAINVIEW (IRE)**, 5, b g Heron Island (IRE)—Park Belle (IRE) **Paul McMahon**
30 **TRABAJO (IRE)**, 7, b g King's Theatre (IRE)—My Native Gesture (IRE) **Forever Never Syndicate**
31 **TRUCKERS DELIGHT (IRE)**, 11, b g Darazari (IRE)—Windmill Star (IRE) **Mrs A. F. Mee**
32 **VIKING SPLASH (IRE)**, 9, b g Stowaway—Honey Mustard (IRE) **B. Connell**
33 **WAKHAN (IRE)**, 4, b g Dalakhani (IRE)—Wrapitraise (USA) **William Hanlon**
34 **WARRIOR ONE**, 6, gr g Act One—River Cara (USA) **Patrick Kelly**
35 **WATCH AMIGO (IRE)**, 6, b g Royal Applause—Miss Red Ink (USA) **Mr S. Lyons**
36 **WESTERN LEADER (IRE)**, 8, b g Stowaway—Western Whisper (IRE) **B. Connell**

THREE-YEAR-OLDS

37 **ANDREA BELLEVICA (IRE)**, gr f Aussie Rules (USA)—Fire West (USA) **Alan D. Gray**
38 **GOLDEN CLUBS (IRE)**, b g Red Clubs (IRE)—Gold Strike (IRE) **C. A. Lynch**

Jockey (NH): A J McNamara, Ken Whelan. **Conditional:** Brian Hayes. **Amateur:** Miss R Blackmore, Mr J T Carroll.

---

299 **MR RICHARD HANNON, Marlborough**
Postal: East Everleigh Stables, Everleigh, Marlborough, Wiltshire, SN8 3EY
Contacts: PHONE (01264) 850 254 FAX (01264) 850 820
E-MAIL richard.hannon@btopenworld.com WEBSITE www.richardhannonracing.tv

1 **ALDWICK BAY (IRE)**, 4, b g Danehill Dancer (IRE)—Josie Doocey (IRE) **Mrs A. Williams**
2 **AVONMORE STAR**, 4, b g Avonbridge—Pooka's Daughter (IRE) **Mr K. Geering**
3 **CAI SHEN (IRE)**, 4, ch c Iffraaj—Collada (IRE) **Mrs J. Wood**
4 **CHORAL**, 4, b f Oratorio (IRE)—Sierra **Longview Stud & Bloodstock Ltd**
5 **DUBAWI GOLD**, 4, b c Dubawi (IRE)—Savannah Belle **Mr W. A. Tinkler**
6 **INDIAN ART (IRE)**, 6, b g Choisir (AUS)—Eastern Ember **R. Hannon**
7 **INVINCIBLE RIDGE (IRE)**, 4, b c Invincible Spirit (IRE)—Dani Ridge (IRE) **C. F. Harrington**
8 **JEHANBUX (USA)**, 4, b c Giant's Causeway (USA)—
                                    Harlan Honey (USA) **K N Dhunjibhoy, V B Shirke, B M Desai**
9 **KING SUPREME (IRE)**, 7, b g King's Best (USA)—Oregon Trail (USA) **B. C. Oakley**
10 **KING TORUS (IRE)**, 4, b c Oratorio (IRE)—Dipterous (IRE) **Sir R. Ogden C.B.E., LLD**
11 **LIBRANNO**, 4, b c Librettist (USA)—Annabelle Ja (FR) **McDowell Racing Ltd**
12 **MON AMI JOLIE (USA)**, 4, gr ro c Maria's Mon (USA)—Lasting Pleasure (USA) **Mr W. A. Tinkler**
13 **NUMERAL (IRE)**, 4, b g Holy Roman Emperor (IRE)—
                                    Savieres (IRE) **Highclere Thoroughbred Racing-Flying Fox**
14 **PALAIS GLIDE**, 4, gr f Proclamation (IRE)—Careful Dancer **G. Reed**
15 **REFLECT (IRE)**, 4, b c Hurricane Run (IRE)—Raphimix (FR) **Mrs J. Wood**
16 **SHEWALKSINBEAUTY (IRE)**, 4, b f Byron—Election Special **Mrs J. Wood**
17 **SILENZIO**, 4, b c Cadeaux Genereux—All Quiet **White Beech Farm**
18 **SINFONICO (IRE)**, 4, b g Iffraaj—Zinstar **White Beech Farm**
19 **STRONG SUIT (USA)**, 4, ch c Rahy (USA)—Helwa (USA) **Qatar Bloodstock Ltd**

THREE-YEAR-OLDS

20 **AL MAHMEYAH**, b f Teofilo (IRE)—Aguilas Perla (IRE) **Mr H. R. Bin Ghadayer**
21 **AMAZING STORM (IRE)**, b c Clodovil (IRE)—Forest Storm (USA) **Mr W. P. Drew**
22 **BEACH CANDY (IRE)**, ch f Footstepsinthesand—Endure (IRE) **S. Mahal, R. Morecombe & D. Anderson**
23 **BELLE DE CRECY (IRE)**, b f Rock of Gibraltar (IRE)—Bloemfontain (IRE) **Mr W. A. Tinkler**
24 **BLACK MASCARA (IRE)**, br f Authorized (IRE)—Pina Colada **Mrs J. Wood**
25 **BLONDE (IRE)**, ch f Pivotal—Sister Golden Hair (IRE) **Mrs J. Wood**
26 **BRONTERRE**, b c Oasis Dream—Wondrous Story (USA) **M. Pescod**
27 **CAMPANOLOGY**, b c Royal Applause—Savannah Belle **Mr W. A. Tinkler**
28 **CAPE JOY (IRE)**, b f Cape Cross (IRE)—Perils of Joy (IRE) **Mrs N. F. Lee**
29 **CHANDLERY (IRE)**, b c Choisir (AUS)—Masai Queen (IRE) **Mrs J. Wood**
30 **CITY DAZZLER (IRE)**, b f Elusive City (USA)—Shady Nook (USA) **Ms E. C. Chivers**
31 **COPLOW**, ch f Manduro (GER)—Anna Oleanda (IRE) **R J McCreery & Pall Mall Partners**
32 **COUPE DE VILLE (IRE)**, b c Clodovil (IRE)—Fantastic Account **Macdonald,Wright,Creed,Smith & Jiggins**
33 **CRESTA STAR**, b f Teofilo (IRE)—Fleet Hill (USA) **P. T. Tellwright**
34 **CRIUS (IRE)**, b c Heliostatic (IRE)—Fearless Flyer (IRE) **Titan Assets**
35 **CROWN DEPENDENCY (IRE)**, b g Acclamation—Top Row **Coriolan Links Partnership III**
36 **DALKOVA**, b f Galileo (IRE)—Dalasyla (IRE) **Mr W. A. Tinkler**
37 **DARE TO DREAM**, b f Exceed And Excel (AUS)—Secret History (USA) **Carmel Stud**

MR RICHARD HANNON—continued

38 **DAUNT (IRE)**, ch c Namid—Pearl Egg (IRE) **Highclere Thoroughbred Racing - Namid**
39 **DEMOCRETES**, ch c Cadeaux Genereux—Petite Epaulette **The High Flyers**
40 B c Cape Cross (IRE)—Desertion (IRE) **Mrs J. K. Powell**
41 **DIXIE'S DREAM (IRE)**, b c Hawk Wing (USA)—Hams (USA) **Mr W. Stobart**
42 **DOWNTON ABBEY (IRE)**, b f Dubai Destination (USA)—Morality **Mrs J. Wood**
43 **DREAMWRITER (USA)**, ch f Tale of The Cat (USA)—Rebridled Dreams (USA) **Axom XXIX**
44 **DUKE OF CLARENCE (IRE)**, gr c Verglas (IRE)—Special Lady (FR) **D Dixon J Stunt J Fiyaz**
45 **DYNAMIC DUO (IRE)**, ch c Iffraaj—Collada (IRE) **Mrs J. Wood**
46 **DYNASTIC**, b c Dynaformer (USA)—Demure **Mr W. A. Tinkler**
47 **EL DIAMANTE (FR)**, b f Royal Applause—Lumiere Rouge (FR) **Sir R. Ogden C.B.E., LLD**
48 **EMMUSKA**, b f Sir Percy—Tintac **Mr M. A. Collins**
49 **ENERGIZE (FR)**, ch c Pivotal—Breathe (FR) **Mr W. A. Tinkler**
50 **EURYSTHEUS (IRE)**, b c Acclamation—Dust Flicker **A Ferguson, G Mason, S Hassiakos, P Nicholls**
51 **FLAVIUS VICTOR (IRE)**, b c Holy Roman Emperor (IRE)—Teslemi (USA) **Mr W. A. Tinkler**
52 **FORGIVE**, b f Pivotal—Amira **Highclere Thoroughbred Racing -Spearmint**
53 **FORT BASTION (IRE)**, b c Lawman (FR)—French Fern (IRE) **Sir R. Ogden C.B.E., LLD**
54 **FREDDY Q (IRE)**, ch c Iffraaj—Barnabas (ITY) **H. Hunt**
55 **FREE VERSE**, b f Danehill Dancer (IRE)—Fictitious **Her Majesty The Queen**
56 **GOLD SCEPTRE (FR)**, b g Gold Away (IRE)—Cap Serena (FR) **Mr John Manley & Mr N A Woodcock**
57 **GOLDEN JUBILEE (USA)**, b br c Zavata (USA)—Love Play (USA) **Mrs J. K. Powell**
58 **GRAPHIC (IRE)**, ch c Excellent Art—Follow My Lead **The Royal Ascot Racing Club**
59 **GUSTO**, b c Oasis Dream—Pickle **Highclere Thoroughbred Racing - Rock Sand**
60 **HAAFHD HANDSOME**, ch c Haafhd—Lines of Beauty (USA) **Fairway Racing**
61 **HARBOUR WATCH (IRE)**, b c Acclamation—Gorband (USA) **Mr H Robin Heffer & Qatar Bloodstock**
62 **HEFNER (IRE)**, b c Tagula (IRE)—Classic Style (IRE) **Mrs J. Wood**
63 **HUMUNGOSAUR**, b c Red Ransom (USA)—Fabulously Fast (USA) **Potensis Limited & Mr Chris Giles**
64 **IMPEL (IRE)**, b c Excellent Art—Tencarola (IRE) **Miss Y. M. G. Jacques**
65 **INJUNCTION (USA)**, b br c Vindication (USA)—Ivy Leaf (IRE) **Mr W. A. Tinkler**
66 **INTUITION**, b c Multiplex—Shallow Ground (IRE) **Sir R. Ogden C.B.E., LLD**
67 **JACOB CATS**, b c Dutch Art—Ballet **Mr Michael Pescod & Mr Justin Dowley**
68 **JOSAM (IRE)**, b c Montjeu (IRE)—Bella Miranda **J. R. May**
69 **JUMEIRAH PALM STAR**, b f Invincible Spirit (IRE)—Golden Flyer (FR) **Mr H. R. Bin Ghadayer**
70 **JUVENAL (IRE)**, b c Holy Roman Emperor (IRE)—Final Opinion (IRE) **Noodles Racing**
71 **KARUGA**, ch f Kyllachy—Bolshaya **Fairway Racing**
72 **KID SUITOR (IRE)**, ch c Choisir (AUS)—Fancy Intense **Byerley Racing Limited**
73 **LORD OFTHE SHADOWS (IRE)**, ch c Kyllachy—Golden Shadow (IRE) **Richard Hitchcock Alan King**
74 **MADGENTA (IRE)**, br f Manduro (GER)—Ruby Affair (IRE) **Arlington Bloodstock**
75 **MAGIC CITY (IRE)**, b g Elusive City (USA)—
Annmarie's Magic (IRE) **Barker, Ferguson, Mason, Hassiakos, Done**
76 **MALIGNED (USA)**, ch f El Corredor (USA)—Sue Warner (USA) **J. Wigan**
77 **MISDEMEANOUR (IRE)**, b f Azamour (IRE)—Miss Takeortwo (IRE) **Thurloe Thoroughbreds XXIX**
78 **MISS ASTRAGAL (IRE)**, b f Oratorio (IRE)—Mansiya **Richard Hitchcock Alan King**
79 **MORE THAN WORDS (IRE)**, b f Lawman (FR)—Gilded (IRE) **Mrs J. Wood**
80 **MY QUEENIE (IRE)**, b f Nayef (USA)—Margay (IRE) **N. A. Woodcock**
81 **NETLEY MARSH**, ch g Haafhd—Ha'penny Beacon **The Major Shear**
82 **NEXT CRY (USA)**, b br c Street Cry (IRE)—Storm Alert (USA) **Mr W. Stobart**
83 **NORTH STAR BOY (IRE)**, b c Acclamation—Isla Azul (IRE) **Mr R. W. Tyrrell**
84 **NOT BAD FOR A BOY (IRE)**, b c Elusive City (USA)—Reign of Fire (IRE) **Middleham Park Racing XXI**
85 **OPERA FLUTE (IRE)**, b c Amadeus Wolf—Southern Queen **The Great Partnership**
86 **ORTAC ROCK (IRE)**, b c Aussie Rules—Fashion Guide (IRE) **Coriolan Links Partnership III**
87 **PHILIPSTOWN (IRE)**, b c Notnowcato—Tahara (IRE) **Dragon Gate Development Limited**
88 **PILGRIMS REST (IRE)**, b c Rock of Gibraltar (IRE)—Holly Blue **M. Jooste & B. Kantor**
89 **POETIC LORD**, b c Byron—Jumairah Sun (IRE) **Mrs N. F. Lee**
90 **POLY POMONA**, b f Green Desert (USA)—Maganda (IRE) **Mr W. A. Tinkler**
91 **POOLE HARBOUR (IRE)**, b c Elusive City (USA)—Free Lance (IRE) **The Heffer Syndicate**
92 **PRETTY PRIMO (IRE)**, ch f Kyllachy—Balladonia **Mr W. A. Tinkler**
93 **PRODUCER**, ch c Dutch Art—River Saint (USA) **J. Palmer-Brown**
94 **RED SEVENTY**, b c Sakhee (USA)—Dimakya (USA) **T. Neill**
95 **REDACT (IRE)**, b c Strategic Prince—Rainbow Java (IRE) **Kennet Valley Thoroughbreds III**
96 **REIGNS OF GLORY (IRE)**, b c Dylan Thomas (IRE)—Lolita's Gold (USA) **Mr M. S. Al Shahi**
97 **ROCK BAND**, b c Rock of Gibraltar (IRE)—Decision Maid (USA) **Mrs J. Wood**
98 **ROCK SUPREME (IRE)**, b c Rock of Gibraltar (IRE)—Love And Affection (USA) **Mr W. A. Tinkler**
99 **ROCKINANTE (FR)**, ch c Rock of Gibraltar (IRE)—Nantes (USA) **Coriolan Links Partnership III**
100 **ROUGEMONT (IRE)**, b c Montjeu (IRE)—Spritza (IRE) **Mrs J. Wood**
101 **RULE BOOK (IRE)**, gr c Aussie Rules (USA)—Open Book **Mr W. A. Tinkler**
102 **SANTARINI (IRE)**, b f Lawman (FR)—Lapland (FR) **Mr W. A. Tinkler**

MR RICHARD HANNON—continued

103 **SHAMAAL NIBRAS (USA),** b c First Samurai (USA)—Sashay Away (USA) **Mr T. S. Al Tayer**
104 **SILKEE SUPREME,** b c Primo Valentino (IRE)—Sodelk **B. C. Oakley**
105 **SIZE (IRE),** b c Oratorio (IRE)—Primissima (GER) **Sir R. Ogden C.B.E., LLD**
106 **SO CHEEKY,** ch f Fantastic View (USA)—Fallujah **Malih L. Al Basti**
107 **SPUTNIK SWEETHEART,** b f Oasis Dream—Sachet (USA) **M. Pescod**
108 **STRINGER BELL,** ch c Cockney Rebel (IRE)—Heckle **M. Pescod**
109 **SYNCHRONICITY (IRE),** b c High Chaparral (IRE)—Sea of Time (USA) **Mrs J. Wood**
110 **THREE AM TOUR (IRE),** b f Strategic Prince—Murani (IRE) **Mr A. Victor**
111 **TOTALLY DOMINANT (USA),** b c War Chant (USA)—Miss Kilroy (USA) **Mr M. S. Al Shahi**
112 **TRAVELLER'S TALES,** b f Cape Cross (IRE)—Lost In Wonder (USA) **Her Majesty The Queen**
113 **TRUMPET MAJOR (IRE),** b c Arakan (USA)—Ashford Cross **J. D. Manley**
114 **USAIN COLT,** b c Royal Applause—Bright Vision **Betfair/Birdcage Racing Club**
115 **VALLEY OF DESTINY,** ch c Three Valleys (USA)—Nouvelle Lune **Mr W. P. Drew**
116 B c High Chaparral (IRE)—Van de Cappelle (IRE)
117 **VIEWPOINT (IRE),** b c Exceed And Excel (AUS)—Lady's View (USA) **The Heffer Syndicate**
118 **WHIMSICAL (IRE),** b f Strategic Prince—Sweet Namibia (USA) **Miss Y. M. G. Jacques**
119 **WREATHS OF EMPIRE (IRE),** b c Dalakhani (IRE)—Eyrecourt (IRE) **Mrs J. Wood**
   BEST TERMS, b f Exceed And Excel (AUS)—Sharp Terms **Mr R. Barnett**

TWO-YEAR-OLDS

120 **A LADIES MAN (IRE),** b c 17/2 Kyllachy—Ego (Green Desert (USA)) (220000) **Mrs J. Wood**
121 B c 19/2 Thousand Words—Aces Dancing (GER) (Big Shuffle (USA)) (21904) **Byerley Racing Limited**
122 B c 27/3 Choisir (AUS)—Acidanthera (Alzao (USA)) (61904) **Mrs J. Wood**
123 B f 12/3 Teofilo (IRE)—Alessia (GER) (Warning) (94417) **Mr A. T. J. Russell**
124 B c 8/2 Kheleyf (USA)—Aphorism (Halling (USA)) (30000) **Dragon Gate Development Limited**
125 Ch c 20/2 English Channel (USA)—Arabian Peninsula (Mr Prospector (USA)) (53333) **Mr A. Al Mansoori**
126 **ARCTIC ADMIRAL (IRE),** gr c 28/4 Verglas (IRE)—Fag End (IRE) (Treasure Kay) (50000) **Mr P. D. Merritt**
127 **ARROWSMITH,** b c 27/5 Duke of Marmalade (IRE)—
                                    Danseuse du Soir (IRE) (Thatching) (25000) **Woodcote Stud Ltd**
128 **ASK DAD,** b c 15/2 Intikhab (USA)—Don't Tell Mum (IRE) (Dansili) (115000) **Mr W. A. Tinkler**
129 **AZELLE,** b f 26/1 Starcraft (NZ)—Zola (NZ) (Volksraad)
130 **BE VERY CAREFUL,** b f 20/2 Misu Bond (IRE)—Lady In The Bath (Forzando) **David H. Cox**
131 Ch c 16/2 Byron—Beechnut (IRE) (Mujadil (USA)) (15238) **Malih L. Al Basti**
132 **BLACK MONK (IRE),** b c 26/2 Dark Angel (IRE)—
                                    Double Eight (IRE) (Common Grounds) (62857) **Mr Michael Pescod & Mr Justin Dowley**
133 B c 26/3 Lando (GER)—Blackberry Pie (USA) (Gulch (USA)) (60000) **Mr A. Al Mansoori**
134 B c 16/4 Duke of Marmalade (IRE)—Blue Azure (USA) (American Chance (USA)) (80000) **P. A. Byrne**
135 **BRANSON (IRE),** b c 12/3 Mujadil (USA)—Rorkes Drift (IRE) (Royal Abjar (USA)) (19047) **Mr W. A. Tinkler**
136 B c 25/1 Iffraaj—Brave Madam (IRE) (Invincible Spirit (IRE)) (68571) **Mrs J. Wood**
137 **BRIGADE (IRE),** b c 14/5 Mujadil (USA)—Ela Tina (IRE) (Ela-Mana-Mou) **Mr M. S. Al Shahi**
138 **BROADWAY DUCHESS (IRE),** ch f 22/3 New Approach (IRE)—
                                    Annee Lumiere (IRE) (Giant's Causeway (USA)) (120000) **M. Pescod**
139 B c 27/4 Lawman (FR)—Broken Spectre (Rainbow Quest (USA)) (17142) **Mr M. S. Al Shahi**
140 **BURSLEDON (IRE),** b c 9/3 Jeremy (USA)—Desert Drama (IRE) (Green Desert (USA)) **Mrs J. Wood**
141 **CALIFANTE,** b f 8/3 Kyllachy—Call Mariah (USA) (Dixie Union (USA)) **Rockcliffe Stud**
142 **CAPE APPEAL,** b f 21/3 Cape Cross (IRE)—
                                    Sheboygan (IRE) (Grand Lodge (USA)) (53365) **Longview Stud & Bloodstock Ltd**
143 **CARRY ON CLAPPING (IRE),** b f 11/3 Acclamation—Embassy Belle (IRE) (Marju (IRE)) (53365) **Mr W. A. Tinkler**
144 **CEELO,** b c 25/4 Green Desert (USA)—Mindsharp (USA) (Gone West (USA)) (35000) **Mr W. A. Tinkler**
145 B f 26/3 Pastoral Pursuits—Clarice Orsini (Common Grounds) (61904) **Coriolan Links Partnership III**
146 **COLLINGBOURNEDUCIS (IRE),** b c 18/4 Bahamian Bounty—
                                    Quickstyx (Night Shift (USA)) (62857) **Mr W. A. Tinkler**
147 **CORNICHE (FR),** b c 18/2 Manduro (GER)—Halska (Unfuwain (USA))
148 **CORREGGIO,** ch c 26/2 Bertolini (USA)—Arian Da (Superlative) (75000) **J. D. Manley**
149 **CURL (IRE),** b f 3/2 Duke of Marmalade (IRE)—Fringe (In The Wings) (32840) **Mr W. A. Tinkler**
150 **CYCLONE,** b c 21/4 Teofilo (IRE)—Ascot Cyclone (Rahy (USA)) (62000) **Mr W. A. Tinkler**
151 B f 14/3 Teofilo (IRE)—Dabawiyah (IRE) (Intikhab (USA)) (69786) **Mr H. R. Bin Ghadayer**
152 **DALANDRA,** b f 15/2 Montjeu (IRE)—Dalasyla (IRE) (Marju (IRE)) (200000) **Mr W. A. Tinkler**
153 B c 29/3 Choisir (AUS)—Dancing Debut (Polar Falcon (USA)) **Mrs J. Wood**
154 **DANSILI DUAL (IRE),** b c 29/3 Dansili—Jewel In The Sand (IRE) (Bluebird (USA)) (66666) **Mr W. A. Tinkler**
155 Ch c 24/4 Sakhee's Secret—Disco Lights (Spectrum) (95000) **Hamdan Al Maktoum**
156 B c 14/2 Red Clubs (IRE)—Dreamalot (Falbrav (IRE)) (52380) **R. Hannon**
157 B c 6/3 Bahamian Bounty—Dust (Green Desert (USA)) (40000) **D. W. Barker**
158 **EAST TEXAS RED (IRE),** ch c 2/3 Danehill Dancer (IRE)—Evangeline (Sadler's Wells (USA)) **G. Howard-Spink**

MR RICHARD HANNON—continued

159 EMPOWERMENT (IRE), b c 7/4 Elusive City (USA)—
Maimana (IRE) (Desert King (IRE)) (42857) **Mr M. S. Al Shahi**

160 B c 24/4 Shamardal (USA)—Encouragement (Royal Applause) **Dragon Gate Development Limited**

161 B f 10/2 Alhaarth (IRE)—Endis (IRE) (Distant Relative) (14285) **Mr A. Al Mansoori**

162 EQUITISSA (IRE), b f 18/4 Chevalier (IRE)—Westcote (USA) (Gone West (USA)) (21345) **Mrs J. I. Snow**

163 ERODIUM, b c 23/3 Kyllachy—Alovera (IRE) (King's Best (USA)) **Rockcliffe Stud**

164 EVERLEIGH, b f 29/1 Bahamian Bounty—Blur (Oasis Dream) (35000) **Noodles Racing**

165 B c 9/2 Acclamation—Fathoming (USA) (Gulch (USA)) (66666) **Mr A. T. J. Russell**

166 B f 30/3 Elnadim (USA)—Fawaayid (USA) (Vaguely Noble) (37000) **Ms E. C. Chivers**

167 B c 18/5 Elusive City (USA)—Feld Marechale (FR) (Deputy Minister (CAN)) (98522) **D. J. Barry**

168 B c 5/4 Mount Nelson—Fidelio's Miracle (USA) (Mountain Cat (USA)) (40000)

169 B c 15/5 Medaglia d'oro (USA)—
First Glimmer (USA) (Glitterman (USA)) (85000) **Macdonald, Wright, Creed, Smith & Jiggins**

170 FOLLOWEVERYRAINBOW, b f 9/2 Oasis Dream—Absolute Precision (USA) (Irish River (FR)) **Mrs J. Wood**

171 FORT KNOX, b c 30/3 Dubawi (IRE)—Savannah Belle (Green Desert (USA)) (190000) **Mr W. A. Tinkler**

172 FOXY DANCER (IRE), b f 19/3 Jeremy (USA)—
Date Mate (USA) (Thorn Dance (USA)) (29000) **Fox Inn Syndicate 4**

173 B c 18/3 Dylan Thomas (IRE)—Gently (IRE) (Darshaan) (50000) **Mr B. C. M. Wong**

174 GERRARDS CROSS (IRE), b c 30/1 Cape Cross (IRE)—Shin Feign (USA) (El Prado (IRE)) **Mrs J. Wood**

175 B c 30/5 Elusive City (USA)—Glamadour (IRE) (Sanglamore (USA)) (62000) **Mrs J. Wood**

176 B c 6/4 Leroidesanimaux (BRZ)—Gliding Light (USA) (Always A Classic (CAN)) (41050)

177 B c 31/1 Ishiguro (USA)—Glittering Prize (UAE) (Cadeaux Genereux) **Titan Assets**

178 GLOBAL ICON, b c 12/3 Green Desert (USA)—Maganda (IRE) (Sadler's Wells (USA)) (50000) **Mr W. A. Tinkler**

179 GLOSSY POSSE, b f 27/4 Dubawi (IRE)—Nouvelle Lune (Fantastic Light) (USA) **Woodcote Stud Ltd**

180 B c 22/2 Acclamation—Grand Slam Maria (FR) (Anabaa (USA)) (165000) **Hamdan Al Maktoum**

181 GROUNDWORK, b f 8/3 Sleeping Indian—Roxy (Rock City) (800) **B. Bull**

182 HAIRY ROCKET, b f 12/5 Pivotal—Asaawir (Royal Applause) **Rockcliffe Stud**

183 Ch c 13/2 Compton Place—Hasten (USA) (Lear Fan (USA)) (80000) **Mr S. Wong**

184 HAVANA GOLD (IRE), b c 13/4 Teofilo (IRE)—
Jessica's Dream (IRE) (Desert Style (IRE)) (80000) **Coriolan Links Partnership III**

185 HEADING NORTH, b f 4/3 Teofilo (IRE)—Round The Cape (Cape Cross (IRE)) **P. T. Tellwright**

186 Ch f 5/2 Teofilo (IRE)—Hundred Year Flood (IRE) (Giant's Causeway (USA)) (50000) **S. Manana**

187 INDIGNANT, ch f 24/4 Gold Away (IRE)—Moiava (FR) (Bering) **Theakston Stud Syndicate**

188 B c 24/2 Kyllachy—Ivania (First Trump) (76190) **Mr R. T. Mahtani**

189 JUBILEE DIAMOND (IRE), b f 1/4 Redback—Nice One Clare (IRE) (Mukaddamah (USA)) (30476) **Mrs J. Wood**

190 B c 28/4 Sakhee's Secret—Just In Love (FR) (Highest Honor (FR)) (38000) **Richard Hitchcock Alan King**

191 KING OF KUDOS (IRE), b c 17/3 Acclamation—Perugina (FR) (Highest Honor (FR)) (51428) **Mr W. A. Tinkler**

192 KING OLIVER, ch c 24/3 Kyllachy—Confetti (Groom Dancer (USA)) (35000) **M. Pescod**

193 LADY CALANTHA, b f 19/2 Byron—Brooklyn's Sky (Septieme Ciel (USA)) (16190) **W. H. Ponsonby**

194 B c 12/2 Dutch Art—Lady Darayna (Polish Precedent (USA)) (60000)

195 B c 4/2 Compton Place—Lake Nayasa (Nayef (USA)) (38095) **R. Hannon**

196 B c 1/3 Dutch Art—Lalectra (King Charlemagne (USA)) (55000) **S. Manana**

197 LISA'S LEGACY, b c 26/3 Kyllachy—Lisathedaddy (Darnay) **Mrs P. S. Wilson**

198 B f 18/4 Lawman (FR)—Lolita's Gold (USA) (Royal Academy (USA)) (25000) **Mr M. A. Adams**

199 LUCKY SUIT (IRE), b f 3/2 Red Clubs (IRE)—Alexander Family (IRE) (Danetime (IRE)) (8209) **B. Bull**

200 B c 22/3 Notnowcato—Luminda (IRE) (Danehill) (90000) **S. H. Altayer**

201 Ch c 20/2 Tamayuz—Magical Peace (IRE) (Magical Wonder (USA)) (58000) **Mr A. Al Mansoori**

202 MANDEVILLE (IRE), b f 10/3 Kodiac—Olympia Theatre (Galileo (USA)) (22000) **Mr W. A. Tinkler**

203 B c 16/2 Dansili—Maroussie (FR) (Saumarez) (52000) **Mr I. Murphy**

204 MASTER OF WAR, ch c 16/2 Compton Place—Mamma Morton (FR) (Elnadim (USA)) **Mr M. S. Al Shahi**

205 B f 21/3 Invincible Spirit (IRE)—Matikanehamatidori (JPN) (Sunday Silence (USA)) (75000) **Mrs J. Wood**

206 B c 29/1 War Chant (USA)—Mayaar (USA) (Grand Slam (USA)) (36000) **Richard Hitchcock Alan King**

207 Ch c 12/2 Manduro (GER)—Meon Mix (Kayf Tara) (32840) **J. Palmer-Brown**

208 MESHARDAL (GER), b c 10/2 Shamardal (USA)—
Melody Fair (IRE) (Montjeu (IRE)) (220000) **Hamdan Al Maktoum**

209 B c 28/4 Elusive City (USA)—Midnight Partner (IRE) (Marju (IRE)) (31198) **Mr A. T. J. Russell**

210 MIRAAJ (IRE), b c 24/4 Iffraaj—My-Lorraine (FR) (Mac's Imp (USA)) (34285) **Mr W. A. Tinkler**

211 B c 8/2 Acclamation—Miss Corinne (Mark of Esteem (IRE)) (200000)

212 Gr c 27/3 Dark Angel (IRE)—Miss Indigo (Indian Ridge) (170000) **Hamdan Al Maktoum**

213 B c 14/3 Oratorio (IRE)—Miss Sacha (IRE) (Last Tycoon) (55000) **The Heffer Syndicate**

214 B f 17/4 Invincible Spirit (IRE)—Miss Serendipity (IRE) (Bel Esprit) (55000) **Mr W. A. Tinkler**

215 Ch c 16/4 Tamayuz—Mistress Thames (Sharpo) (40000) **Knockainey Stud Limited**

216 MONTIRIDGE (IRE), b c 14/3 Ramonti (FR)—
Elegant Ridge (IRE) (Indian Ridge) (52380) **M Clarke, J Jeffries, R Ambrose, B Reilly**

217 B f 7/3 Sir Percy—Moody Margaret (Bahamian Bounty) (1904)

218 MOONVALE (IRE), gr f 13/3 Verglas (IRE)—Artistry (Night Shift (USA)) **Longview Stud & Bloodstock Ltd**

MR RICHARD HANNON—continued

219 B f 7/4 Dubawi (IRE)—Mountain Holly (Shirley Heights) (30377) **Mr H. R. Bin Ghadayer**
220 **MYSTERIAL,** b c 13/2 Invincible Spirit (IRE)—
             Diamond Dilemma (IRE) (Sinndar (IRE)) (150000) **Highclere Thoroughbred Racing - Sloan**
221 **MYSTICAL MOMENT,** ch f 13/3 Dutch Art—Tinnarinka (Observatory (USA)) (30000) **Mrs A. Turner**
222 B f 9/2 Nayef (USA)—Natagora (FR) (Divine Light (JPN)) **Hamdan Al Maktoum**
223 B c 13/2 Baltic King—Night of Joy (IRE) (King's Best (USA)) (50000) **Thurloe Thoroughbreds XXX**
224 B f 31/3 Cape Cross (IRE)—Noyelles (IRE) (Docksider (USA)) (72000) **S. H. Altayer**
225 **PAELLA (IRE),** b f 8/2 Oasis Dream—Chibola (ARG) (Roy (USA)) **Mrs A. Wigan**
226 **PEARL ACCLAIM (IRE),** b c 18/3 Acclamation—
             With Colour (Rainbow Quest (USA)) (165000) **Pearl Bloodstock Limited**
227 **PERFECT POSE (IRE),** b f 7/4 Amadeus Wolf—Interpose (Indian Ridge) (22987) **Mr W. A. Tinkler**
228 **PETHER'S MOON (IRE),** b c 15/4 Dylan Thomas (IRE)—Softly Tread (IRE) (Tirol) (42692) **J. D. Manley**
229 Ch f 4/3 Barathea (IRE)—Petite Spectre (Spectrum (IRE)) (73891) **Mrs J. Wood**
230 **PRINCE'S TRUST,** b c 21/2 Invincible Spirit (IRE)—Lost In Wonder (USA) (Galileo (IRE)) **Her Majesty The Queen**
231 Ch c 26/4 Sakhee's Secret—Queen's Pudding (USA) (Royal Applause) (49260)
232 **RAFALE,** b c 25/1 Sleeping Indian—Sweet Coincidence (Mujahid (USA)) (20952) **Mr M. S. Al Shahi**
233 **REBEL MAGIC,** b f 17/2 Cockney Rebel (IRE)—Aastral Magic (Magic Ring (IRE)) (952) **A. Pitt**
234 **RED ADAIR (IRE),** ch c 9/3 Redback—Daanaat (IRE) (Kheleyf (USA)) (16190) **Mrs S. A. F. Brendish**
235 Gr c 20/4 Clodovil (IRE)—Red Empress (Nashwan (USA)) (26000) **Mrs V. Hubbard**
236 **RELAY,** b f 2/4 Clodovil (IRE)—Figlette (Darshaan) (7000) **B. Bull**
237 **REMBRANDT (IRE),** b c 21/3 Dutch Art—Holy Norma (Nashwan (USA)) **Mrs J. Wood**
238 **RHAMNUS,** b c 28/3 Sakhee's Secret—Happy Lady (FR) (Cadeaux Genereux) (28000) **Rockcliffe Stud**
239 **RICHARD SENIOR,** b c 7/4 Cape Cross (IRE)—Sabria (USA) (Miswaki (USA)) (160000) **Mr W. A. Tinkler**
240 **RISING LEGEND,** ch c 20/2 Rock of Gibraltar (IRE)—Miswaki Belle (USA) (Miswaki (USA)) **Mr M. S. Al Shahi**
241 Ch c 19/4 Notnowcato—River Fantasy (IRE) (Irish River (FR)) (20000)
242 B c 25/2 Proclamation (IRE)—Rockburst (Xaar) (29523) **Middleham Park Racing XXXIX & James Pak**
243 B c 28/4 Choisir (AUS)—Roselyn (Efisio) (45000) **The Heffer Syndicate**
244 B c 26/2 Dutch Art—Rotunda (Pivotal) (75000) **Hamdan Al Maktoum**
245 **ROYAL CHALLIS,** b c 15/5 Royal Applause—Oh Hebe (IRE) (Night Shift (USA)) **Longview Stud & Bloodstock Ltd**
246 **SEA SHANTY (USA),** b c 23/1 Elusive Quality (USA)—Medley (Danehill Dancer (IRE)) **Her Majesty The Queen**
247 Ch c 16/1 Pivotal—Selinka (Selkirk (USA)) (280000) **Sir A Ferguson, G Mason, R Wood & P Done**
248 **SENSUAL,** b f 4/2 Kyllachy—
             Xtrasensory (Royal Applause) (40000) **Highclere Thoroughbred Racing- Herbert Jones**
249 B f 18/3 Zamindar (USA)—Shine Like A Star (Fantastic Light) (23000) **D. Boocock**
250 **SIGN OF THE ZODIAC (IRE),** gr c 28/3 Clodovil (IRE)—Auriga (Belmez (USA)) **Mrs J. Wood**
251 **SIR PRANCEALOT (IRE),** b c 14/4 Tamayuz—Mona Em (IRE) (Catrail (USA)) (114941) **Mr W. A. Tinkler**
252 **SKY LANTERN (IRE),** gr f 27/1 Red Clubs (IRE)—Shawanni (Shareef Dancer (USA)) (61576) **Mr B. W. Keswick**
253 B c 16/3 Dylan Thomas (IRE)—Sogno Verde (IRE) (Green Desert (USA)) **Mrs J. Wood**
254 **SPANISH ART,** b c 6/3 Byron—Spanish Gold (Vettori (USA)) (24761) **Mr W. A. Tinkler**
255 B c 23/4 Jeremy (USA)—Spring Glory (Dr Fong (USA)) (52000) **Macdonald, Wright, Creed, Smith & Jiggins**
256 B f 27/3 Duke of Marmalade (IRE)—Square Pants (USA) (King of Kings (IRE)) (100000) **R. Hannon**
257 B c 31/3 Dubawi (IRE)—Strings (Unfuwain (USA)) (190000) **Hamdan Al Maktoum**
258 B c 19/3 Rock of Gibraltar (IRE)—Swynford Lady (IRE) (Invincible Spirit (IRE)) (82100) **Mr A. T. J. Russell**
259 **THE GATLING BOY (IRE),** ch c 4/4 Tamayuz—
             Miniver (IRE) (Mujtahid (USA)) (32000) **Kennet Valley Thoroughbreds I**
260 **THE MASCOT,** b c 17/3 Assertive—All Business (Entrepreneur) (23809) **Mason Brown Partnership**
261 **THREE CHOIRS (IRE),** br f 21/3 Rock of Gibraltar (IRE)—Three Owls (IRE) (Warning) **Mrs J. Wood**
262 **TILSTARR (IRE),** b f 1/2 Shamardal (USA)—Vampire Queen (IRE) (General Monash (USA)) (70000) **H. Hunt**
263 **TOBACCO ROAD (IRE),** b c 3/3 Westerner—Virginias Best (King's Best (USA)) (38000) **Noodles Racing**
264 **TORONADO (IRE),** b c 20/2 High Chaparral (IRE)—
             Wana Doo (USA) (Grand Slam (USA)) (45155) **Coriolan Links Partnership III**
265 Ch f 12/2 Dalakhani (IRE)—Unreachable Star (Halling (USA)) (11000) **Ms V. O'Sullivan**
266 B c 25/2 Cadeaux Genereux—Valiantly (Anabaa (USA)) (50000) **The Heffer Syndicate**
267 B c 27/4 Pivotal—Virtuous (Exit To Nowhere (USA)) (150000) **S. H. Altayer**
268 B c 2/2 Acclamation—Wildsplash (USA) (Deputy Minister (CAN)) (105000) **S. H. Altayer**
269 **WINTER WHITE (IRE),** gr f 26/3 Oratorio (IRE)—Miss Shaan (FR) (Darshaan) **Mrs J. Wood**
270 B c 18/4 High Chaparral (IRE)—Woodwin (IRE) (Woodman (USA)) **Mrs J. Wood**

Other Owners: Mr R. D. Ambrose, Mr D. J. Anderson, Axom Ltd, Mr P. A. Bland, Mr R. J. Blunt, Mr D. P. N. Brown, Mr S. Brown, Mrs L. Bull, Mrs F. J. Carmichael, Exors of the Late L. Cashman, Miss C. I. Chivers, Ms L. D. Chivers, Mr M. Clarke, M. E. T. Davies, Mr B. M. Desai, Mr K. Dhunjibhoy, Mr D. J. Dixon, Mr P. E. Done, Mr L. J. Dowley, Mr D. Downie, Mrs A. M. Doyle, Family Amusements Ltd, Sir A. Ferguson, Mr J. Fiyaz, Mr R. J. Fowler, Mr C. M. Giles, J. K. Grimes, P. W. Haddock, Mrs F. M. Hallett, S. Hassiakos, Mr R. P Heffer, Mr H. R. Heffer, The Hon H. M. Herbert, Highclere Thoroughbred Racing Ltd, A. J. Hill, R. G. Hitchcock, Mr P. G. P Hodgson, Mrs N. Hodgson, Mr T. K. Hulse, Mr C. M. Humber, K. T. Ivory, J. B. R. Leisure Ltd, T. Jackson, Mr J. Jeffries, Mr M. J. Jooste, Mr B. Kantor, Mr M. J. Kershaw, Mr S. L. Keswick, A. S. Kilpatrick, A. E. King, Mr S. G. Lake, Mr A. T. Macdonald, Mr S. Mahal, G. A. Mason, Mr A. Mason, Mr P. J. Mayhew, R. J. McCreery, Mr A. McIntyre,

MR RICHARD HANNON—continued

Miss C. McIntyre, R. P. B. Michaelson, Mr M. J. Mitchell, R. H. W. Morecombe, P. H. Morgan, Mrs M. E. Morgan, P. F. Nicholls, Mrs M. O'Sullivan, Mr J. Pak, T. S. Palin, A. Panetta, O. J. W. Pawle, Potensis Limited, M. Prince, Mr J. J. Reddington, Mr P. W. Reglar, Mr A. Reid, Mr W. J. Reilly, Mr W. A. Rice, Mr N. M. S. Rich, N. J. F. Robinson, Mr H. S. Sharpstone, Mr V. Shirke, R. A. Simmons, Mrs A. C. Simmons, Mr J. A. B. Stafford, Star Pointe Ltd, Mr J. R. F. Stunt, Mr J. J. Sullivan, Mr J. A. Taylor, G. P. Triefus, Mr R. J. Wood, C. N. Wright.

Assistant Trainer: Richard Hannon Jnr

Jockey (flat): Richard Hughes, Pat Dobbs, Ryan Moore, Dane O'Neill. **Apprentice:** Kieran O'Neill.

---

300 **MR GEOFFREY HARKER, Thirsk**
Postal: **Stockhill Green, York Rd, Thirkelby, Thirsk, North Yorkshire, YO7 3AS**
Contacts: **PHONE (01845) 501117 FAX (01845) 501614 MOBILE (07803) 116412/(07930) 125544**
E-MAIL gandjhome@aol.com

1 **BORN TO BE ACHAMP (BRZ),** 6, ch g Redattore (BRZ)—Small High Plain (BRZ) **Mr M. Reay**
2 4, Br f Rock City—Eileen's Girl (IRE)
3 **I CONFESS,** 7, br g Fantastic Light (USA)—Vadsagreya (FR) **Mr B. Harker**
4 **MOUNTAIN CAT (IRE),** 8, b g Red Ransom (USA)—Timewee (USA) **S. Rudolf**
5 **ORATORY (IRE),** 6, b g Danehill Dancer (IRE)—Gentle Night **The Unique Partnership**
6 **PRECIOUS LASS (IRE),** 4, b f Gold Well—Ardrina
7 **WENDY'SGREYHORSE,** 6, gr m Beneficial—Nearly Decent **Mrs W. Taylor**
8 **WHITE DEER (USA),** 8, b g Stravinsky (USA)—Brookshield Baby (IRE) **A. S. Ward**
9 **YKIKAMOOCOW,** 6, b m Cape Town (IRE)—Pigeon **P. Benson**

Other Owners: Mr A. R. Findlay, Mrs G. Findlay.

Assistant Trainer: Jenny Harker

Jockey (flat): Silvestre De Sousa. **Jockey (NH):** W. T. Kennedy.

---

301 **MRS PAULINE HARKIN, Edgcote**
Postal: **Blackgrounds Farm, Culworth Road, Chipping Warden, Banbury, Oxfordshire, OX17 1LZ**
Contacts: **PHONE (01327) 704223 FAX (01327) 872927 MOBILE (07970) 770236**
E-MAIL sales@velvetenergy.com WEBSITE www.velvetenergy.com

1 **BLUE MONOAKA,** 7, b g Alflora (IRE)—Double Romier **Miss W. D. M. Mills**
2 **DOCTOR KINGSLEY,** 10, ch g Classic Cliche (IRE)—Query Line **D. C. Harkin**
3 **MON ROMIER,** 8, b m Terimon—Double Romier **Miss W. D. M. Mills**
4 **QUAND JE REVE DE TOI (FR),** 8, ch m Evening World (FR)—Betty Royale (FR) **Mrs P. E. Harkin**
5 **UNOITMAKESSENSE (IRE),** 10, b g Pistolet Bleu (IRE)—Tara The Grey (IRE) **Mrs P. E. Harkin**
6 **WE NEVER GIVE UP (IRE),** 6, b m Mull of Kintyre (USA)—Parker's Cove (USA) **Mrs P. E. Harkin**

Assistant Trainer: Doug Harkin

---

302 **MR W. HARNEY, Co. Tipperary**
Postal: **Manna Cottage, Templemore, Co. Tipperary, Ireland**
Contacts: **PHONE (00353) 504 31534 FAX (00353) 504 31534 MOBILE (00353) 86 2498836**
E-MAIL harneyvet@eircom.net

1 **BRUACH NA MARA (IRE),** 9, ch g Pasternak—Slievenanee **Premier Bunch Syndicate**
2 **FISCAL NOMAD (IRE),** 5, b g Flemensfirth (USA)—Tradaree (IRE) **Mr Patrick Harney**
3 **FLAMING POP (IRE),** 6, b m Flemensfirth (USA)—Pops Princess (IRE) **Ms I. M. Fielding**
4 **HUSTLE 'N' FLOW (IRE),** 10, b br g Supreme Leader—Clobanna Native (IRE) **Stephen Brolan**
5 **JOXER (IRE),** 5, b g Gold Well—Tender Return (IRE) **Mrs W. Harney**
6 **KAKAGH (IRE),** 8, b g Tel Quel (FR)—Pheisty **Liam Breslin**
7 **KILLTILANE ROSE (IRE),** 7, ch m Flemensfirth (USA)—Miss Rose (IRE) **L. C. D. Syndicate**
8 **LADY BOULEA (IRE),** 7, b m Windsor Castle—Manna Fairy (IRE) **Michael Barrett**
9 **LEANNE (IRE),** 10, ch m Alderbrook—Nagillah (IRE) **Mrs W. Harney**
10 6, Ch m Beneficial—Puff of Magic (IRE) **Mrs W. Harney**
11 5, B g Quws—Sceal Siog (IRE) **Mrs W. Harney**
12 4, B g Gold Well—She's A Dreamer (IRE) **Mrs W. Harney**

MR W. HARNEY—continued

Assistant Trainer: Rachel Harney

Jockey (NH): Bryan J. Cooper. **Conditional:** M. P. Butler.

---

303 **MR RICHARD HARPER, Banbury**
Postal: **Home Farm, Kings Sutton, Banbury, Oxfordshire, OX17 3RS**
Contacts: **PHONE** (01295) 810997 **FAX** (01295) 812787 **MOBILE** (07970) 223481
E-MAIL rharper@freeuk.com

1 **CHAPEL HOUSE,** 9, b g Beneficial—My Moona **R. C. Harper**
2 **THE IRON GIANT (IRE),** 10, b g Giant's Causeway (USA)—Shalimar (IRE) **R. C. Harper**

Assistant Trainer: C. Harper

Conditional: M. Nicholls.

---

304 **MRS JESSICA HARRINGTON, Kildare**
Postal: **Commonstown Racing Stables Ltd., Moone, Co. Kildare, Ireland**
Contacts: **PHONE** (00353) 5986 24153 **FAX** (00353) 5986 24292 **MOBILE** (00353) 8725 66129
E-MAIL jessica@jessicaharringtonracing.com **WEBSITE** www.jessicaharringtonracing.com

1 **ALDERWAY (IRE),** 5, b g Alderbrook—Masriyna (IRE) **Sevens Racing Club**
2 **ALPINE EAGLE (IRE),** 8, b g Golan (IRE)—Alpine Symphony **J. P. McManus**
3 **BACK BURNER (IRE),** 4, br g Big Bad Bob (IRE)—Marl **Anamoine Ltd**
4 **BEACHDALE LAD (IRE),** 5, ch g Carroll House—Morning Clare (IRE) **Mr Geoffrey Ruddock**
5 **BEIR BUA (IRE),** 6, b g Oscar (IRE)—Quennie Mo Ghra (IRE) **Say Nothing Syndicate**
6 **BIBLE BELT (IRE),** 4, br f Big Bad Bob (IRE)—Shine Silently (IRE) **Anamoine Ltd**
7 **BOB LE BEAU (IRE),** 5, br g Big Bad Bob (IRE)—Shine Silently (IRE) **Anamoine Ltd**
8 **BORN TO BENEFIT (IRE),** 6, b m Beneficial—Sister Superior (IRE) **Mr Stephen Hemstock**
9 **BOSTONS ANGEL (IRE),** 8, b g Winged Love—Lady Boston (FR) **Mr E. A. P. Scouller**
10 **BULLOCK HARBOUR (IRE),** 8, b g Second Empire (IRE)—Coteri Run **Mr Barry Connell**
11 **BURN AND TURN (IRE),** 6, b m Flemensfirth—Pescetto Lady (IRE) **Mr Joe O'Flaherty**
12 **CELTIC CAILIN (IRE),** 6, b m Beneficial—Distant Dreams (IRE) **MJK Syndicate**
13 **CHAPERONED (IRE),** 5, b m High Chaparral (USA)—La Stravaganza (USA) **Mr John Harrington**
14 **CITIZENSHIP,** 6, b g Beat Hollow—Three More (USA) **Fresh By Nature Syndicate**
15 **CLOUDED THOUGHTS (IRE),** 6, br g Definite Article—
Native Design (IRE) **Mr Howard Spooner & Mr Nick Wellington**
16 **CREATIVE PURSUIT (IRE),** 5, b g Orpen (USA)—Sue N Win (IRE) **Mr Des Donegan**
17 **CRYSTAL MORNING (IRE),** 4, b f Cape Cross (IRE)—Follow My Lead **Mr Kevin Cullen**
18 **DAVID'S DREAM,** 5, b m Exit To Nowhere (USA)—Armorine (FR) **Miss Stephanie Robinson**
19 **DIRECTOR'S FORUM (IRE),** 4, ch g Pivotal—Stage Struck (IRE) **Ballymacoll Stud Farm Ltd**
20 **DON'T KNOW (IRE),** 5, b g Lahib (USA)—Corcullentra Lass (IRE) **Mr Pat Convery**
21 **DUNDRUM (IRE),** 8, b g Marju (IRE)—Tertia (IRE) **Mr John Hennessy**
22 **ESPRESSO LADY (IRE),** 6, b m Shantou—Katie's Cracker **Mr John Harrington**
23 **FAIRY WING (IRE),** 5, b g Hawk Wing (USA)—Mintaka (IRE) **Mrs Rose Vaughan**
24 **FEABHRA (IRE),** 6, ch m Beneficial—Gales Hill (IRE) **Mr Eamonn Phelan**
25 **FOREVER GLORY (IRE),** 4, ch f Shamardal (USA)—Morning Welcome (IRE) **Mr Kevin Cullen**
26 **GALZIG (IRE),** 8, b m King's Theatre (IRE)—St Cristoph **The Star Racing Syndicate**
27 **GIMLI'S RETURN (IRE),** 5, b br g Flemensfirth (USA)—I Remember It Well (IRE) **Mr Geoffrey Ruddock**
28 **GIMLI'S ROCK (IRE),** 6, b g Rock of Gibraltar (IRE)—Beltisaal (FR) **Mr Geoffrey Ruddock**
29 **GIVING ORDERS (IRE),** 4, gr f Encosta de Lago (AUS)—My Girl Lisa (IRE) **Mr Peter Queally**
30 **GLAMOROUS (GER),** 5, b m Red Ransom (USA)—Gambada (GER) **Mr John Harrington**
31 **GREEN ENERGY,** 5, b g Rainbow Quest (USA)—Carambola (IRE) **Mr Stephen McCormack**
32 **GREENBELT STAR,** 6, ch g Generous (IRE)—Dusty Shoes **Green Belt Partnership**
33 **HUGO DE VINDECY (FR),** 8, b g Robin des Champs (FR)—High Light (FR) **Macs J Syndicate**
34 **HUNDRED SEN,** 4, b g Rainbow Quest (USA)—Silver Yen (USA) **Mr Howard Spooner & Mr Mark Hawtin**
35 **IMPERIAL CASCADE (IRE),** 7, b g Imperial Ballet (IRE)—Shawiya (IRE) **Mrs Judy Wilson**
36 **JENARI (IRE),** 5, b g Milan—La Noire (IRE) **J. P. McManus**
37 **JETSON (IRE),** 7, b g Oscar (IRE)—La Noire (IRE) **Mr Gerard McGrath**
38 **JEZKI (IRE),** 4, b g Milan—La Noire (IRE) **Mr Gerard McGrath**
39 **JOHNNYS LEGACY (IRE),** 5, b g Ecton Park (USA)—Lexy May (USA) **Mr John Hennessy**
40 **JOVIAL QUEEN (IRE),** 5, b m St Jovite (USA)—Fire Queen (IRE) **T. F. McDonald & T. J. McDonald**
41 **KING FERDINAND,** 4, b g Tobougg (IRE)—Spanish Gold **Mr Eamonn McEvoy**

MRS JESSICA HARRINGTON—continued

42 **LAW REBEL (IRE)**, 6, b g High Chaparral (IRE)—Rubenco (IRE) **J. P. McManus**
43 **MAGGIE NEARY (IRE)**, 4, b f Hurricane Run (IRE)—Pleiade (FR) **Mrs Robert Duprey**
44 **MAGICAL MEMOIR (IRE)**, 5, ch m Barathea (IRE)—All To Easy **Mr Des Donegan**
45 **MALLER TREE**, 5, b g Karinga Bay—Annaberg (IRE) **Favourite Racing Ltd**
46 **MELLIFONT ABBEY (IRE)**, 5, b h Alhaarth (IRE)—Carroll's Canyon (IRE) **Miss Christine Kiernan**
47 **MOSSTOWN (IRE)**, 6, b g Dilshaan—Tavildara (IRE) **BB Horse Racing Club**
48 **MYSTIC DESIR (FR)**, 5, ch g Ballingarry (IRE)—Aubane (FR) **Mr Michael Buckley**
49 **NATIVE PALM (IRE)**, 6, gr g Great Palm (USA)—Neath Native Sky (USA) **Palm Tree Syndicate**
50 **OPERATING (IRE)**, 5, b g Milan—Seymourswift **Mr George Hartigan**
51 **OSCARS WELL (IRE)**, 7, b br g Oscar (IRE)—Placid Willow (IRE) **Molley Malone Syndicate**
52 **PARADIS DE THAIX (FR)**, 9, ch g April Night (FR)—Etoile de Thaix (FR) **Hard to Get Syndicate**
53 **PARRAMATTA (IRE)**, 4, gr f Aussie Rules (USA)—Aspasias Tizzy (USA) **Mr Gittins**
54 **PEGGARTY (USA)**, 4, b br f Speightstown (USA)—Social Director (CAN) **Mr Gittins**
55 **PLAY THE MARKET (IRE)**, 5, b g King's Theatre (IRE)—Market Lass (IRE) **Mrs Judy Wilson**
56 **PONTIAC (FR)**, 9, ch g Ragmar (FR)—Tarantelle II (FR) **Mrs Kathleen Quinn**
57 **REAR VIEW (IRE)**, 5, b g Alhaarth (IRE)—Sadinga (IRE) **Mr Howard Spooner**
58 **ROYAL BLUE STAR (IRE)**, 4, b f Dalakhani (IRE)—Etizaan (IRE) **Mr Noel Carter**
59 **SALUDOS (IRE)**, 8, b g Bob Back (USA)—Katie's Cracker **Mr Tom Curran**
60 **SAVILLE ROW (IRE)**, 7, b g Snurge—Designer Lady (IRE) **Mrs Gina Galvin**
61 **SCHOLARS PRINCESS (IRE)**, 5, b m King's Theatre (IRE)—
Belle Provence (FR) **Glassdrummon Racing Syndicate**
62 **SEREIN (IRE)**, 6, b g Definite Article—Sejour (IRE) **Mr Brendan Scully**
63 **SOMETHINGDIFFERENT (IRE)**, 6, b g Distant Music (USA)—Valleya (FR) **Mr Geoffrey Ruddock**
64 **SPACE RACE**, 7, b g Singspiel (IRE)—Tereshkova (USA) **Mr Gerry Byrne**
65 **SPANISH AURIGA (IRE)**, 7, b g Pairumani Star (IRE)—Spanish Lady (IRE) **J. P. McManus**
66 **STARLING LADY**, 7, b m Tamure (IRE)—Ryewater Dream **Mr John Harrington**
67 **STEPS TO FREEDOM (IRE)**, 6, b g Statue of Liberty (USA)—Dhakhirah (IRE) **Mrs Elizabeth Hussey**
68 **STOP ROAD LAD (IRE)**, 6, ch g Definite Article—Masriyna (IRE) **Sevens Racing Club**
69 **TAKEYOURCAPOFF (IRE)**, 7, b m King's Theatre (IRE)—Masriyna's Article (IRE) **Sport Racing Club**
70 **THE BIG EASY (IRE)**, 4, b g Hurricane Run (IRE)—
Flaming Song (IRE) **Mrs P. K. Cooper, Mrs Adam Gurney and Ronchalon Ireland Partnership**
71 **THE BULL HAYES (IRE)**, 6, b g Sadler's Wells (USA)—No Review (USA) **Mr John Wholey**
72 **THE QUIET HAWK (IRE)**, 4, ch f Hawk Wing (USA)—The Quiet Woman (IRE) **Sock and Share Syndicate**
73 **TRASNAGH (IRE)**, 6, b g King's Theatre (IRE)—Stormy (IRE) **Mr E. Hamilton**
74 **TRUE CHARACTER (IRE)**, 6, b g Catcher In The Rye (USA)—Harvest Gold (IRE) **Mrs Margaret Keyes**
75 **WHAT AN ARTICLE (IRE)**, 7, ch g Definite Article—Pescetto Lady (IRE) **Mr Peter Queally**
76 **WHY BUT WHY (USA)**, 4, b g Whywhywhy (USA)—Miss Orah **Mr John Harrington**

THREE-YEAR-OLDS

77 **ABSOLUTE CRACKERS (IRE)**, ch f Giant's Causeway (USA)—El Laoob (USA) **Mr John Harrington**
78 **ACT OF ATTRITION**, b f Acclamation—Ahdaaf (USA) **Mr David Minton**
79 **BACKBENCH BLUES (IRE)**, b g Big Bad Bob (IRE)—Heroine **Anamoine Ltd**
80 **BAFFLES BRAINS (IRE)**, b g Big Bad Bob (IRE)—Marl **Anamoine Ltd**
81 **CAPE VIOLET (IRE)**, b f Cape Cross (IRE)—Violet Ballerina (IRE) **Mr James Hanley**
82 **COLLECTABLE**, b f Excellent Art—Tiriana **Mrs Juliet Minton**
83 Br f Holy Roman Emperor—Colour Coordinated (IRE) **Mr Joe Keappock**
84 **COSMIC RHYTHM (IRE)**, b g Rock of Gibraltar (IRE)—Novelina (IRE) **Mr Kevin Cullen**
85 **DANE STREET (USA)**, b br f Street Cry (IRE)—Daneleta (IRE) **Mrs Sonia Rogers**
86 **DORMERS GIRL (IRE)**, b f Trans Island—Rashida **The Ryan Partnership**
87 **DRAGON PULSE (IRE)**, b c Kyllachy—Poetical (IRE) **Dr Kai Chah Tan**
88 **FLUTTERING LASHES (USA)**, b f Rock Hard Ten—Spectacular Day (USA) **McElroy Racing Syndicate**
89 **GREEN CHORUS (IRE)**, b f Oratorio (IRE)—Green Castle (IRE) **Stonethorn Stud Farm Ltd**
90 **GUSH (USA)**, b f Empire Maker (USA)—Enthused (USA) **Niarchos Family**
91 **HEROIC ENDEAVOUR (IRE)**, b g Ishiguru (USA)—Enchantment **Lady Janet Brookeborough**
92 **HURRICANE RIDGE (IRE)**, b c Hurricane Run (IRE)—Warrior Wings **Mrs P. K. Cooper**
93 **LADY GERONIMO (IRE)**, b f Hawk Wing (USA)—Birthday (IRE) **West Offaly Syndicate**
94 **MAID TO MASTER (IRE)**, ch f Danehill Dancer (USA)—Starlight Dreams (USA) **SF Racing**
95 **NEPALI PRINCESS (IRE)**, b f Mr Greeley (USA)—Ghurra (USA) **Mr Gittins**
96 **ONE FINE DAY (IRE)**, b f Choisir (AUS)—Night Eyes (IRE) **Mr John Harrington**
97 **POSH FROCK (IRE)**, b f Oratorio (IRE)—Opera Ridge (FR) **Dean Fleming Thoroughbreds**
98 **PRINCESS SINEAD (IRE)**, b br f Jeremy (USA)—Princess Atoosa (USA) **Mrs J. Maxwell Moran**
99 **REMEMBER ALEXANDER**, b f Teofilo (IRE)—Nausicaa (USA) **Persian Properties**
100 **SILVER SYCAMORE (USA)**, gr ro f Exchange Rate (USA)—Miss Forest City (USA) **Runnymede Farm**
101 **SISTER ROCKS (USA)**, b f Rock Hard Ten (USA)—Serena's Sister (USA) **Sister Rocks Syndicate**
102 **VIOLET LASHES (USA)**, b f Badge of Silver (USA)—Purple (USA) **McElroy Racing Syndicate**

MRS JESSICA HARRINGTON—continued

TWO-YEAR-OLDS

103 CALISSA (IRE), b f 27/2 Danehill Dancer (IRE)—Mauralakana (FR) (Muhtathir) **Mr Robert Scarborough**
104 B f 2/3 Acclamation—Claustra (FR) (Green Desert (USA)) (69785) **Niarchos Family**
105 EMPRESS CATHERINE (IRE), b f 7/2 Holy Roman Emperor (IRE)—
Dalal (Cadeaux Genereux) **The Wheery Syndicate**
106 B f 25/2 Danehill Dancer (IRE)—
Lace (IRE) (Sadler's Wells (USA)) **Orpendale, Mr Robert Scarborough & Chelston**
107 NO PROBLEM (IRE), b c 5/4 Holy Roman Emperor (IRE)—
Two Marks (USA) (Woodman (USA)) (34481) **Mr John Wholey**
108 POLISHED ROCK (IRE), ch c 11/5 Rock of Gibraltar (IRE)—
Where We Left Off (Dr Devious (IRE)) (18061) **Mr Robert Ryan**
109 B f 27/3 Iffraaj—
Ros The Boss (IRE) (Danehill (USA)) (24630) **Mr Peter Barnett, Mrs Yvonne Nicoll & Mr Joe Throsby**
110 Br c 2/2 Intikhab (USA)—Xaviera (IRE) (Xaar) (7388) **Favourite Racing Ltd**

Assistant Trainer: Mr Eamonn Leigh

Jockey (flat): Fran Berry, Shane Foley. **Jockey (NH):** Robert Power, Andrew Leigh. **Conditional:** Mark Bolger, Kevin Sexton. **Apprentice:** Kevin Sexton. **Amateur:** Mr M. Fahey, Miss K. Harrington.

305 **MR JOHN HARRIS, Melton Mowbray**
Postal: **Eastwell Hall Stables, Eastwell, Melton Mowbray, Leicestershire, LE14 4EE**
Contacts: **YARD/FAX (01949) 860671 HOME (01400) 282819 MOBILE (07989) 947712**

1 OLIVER'S GOLD, 4, b g Danehill Dancer (IRE)—Gemini Gold (IRE) **Mrs A. E. Harris**
2 RICHARD THE THIRD, 8, b g King's Best (USA)—Larousse **Mr V. Kara**
3 RISING KHELEYF (IRE), 6, ch g Kheleyf (USA)—Rising Spirits **Mrs A. E. Harris**
4 TOM WADE (IRE), 5, b g Rakti—Plutonia **Mr P. Tonks**

Assistant Trainer: Miss Vicki M. Harris, Mrs A. E. Harris

Jockey (flat): S. Sanders, Chris Catlin, Mark Coumbe. **Jockey (NH):** Andrew Thornton.

306 **MR RONALD HARRIS, Chepstow**
Postal: **Ridge House Stables, Earlswood, Chepstow, Monmouthshire, NP16 6AN**
Contacts: **PHONE (01291) 641689 FAX (01291) 641258 MOBILE (07831) 770899**
E-MAIL ridgehousestables.ltd@btinternet.com WEBSITE www.ronharrisracing.co.uk

1 ALHABAN (IRE), 6, gr g Verglas (IRE)—Anne Tudor (IRE) **R. M. Bailey**
2 APRIL FOOL, 8, ch g Pivotal—Palace Affair **S. & A. Mares**
3 ATHAAKEEL (IRE), 6, b m Almutawakel—Asaafeer (USA) **Drag Star On Swan**
4 BARACHIEL, 4, b c Pivotal—Coveted **M. J. Benton**
5 BELLE BAYARDO (IRE), 4, b g Le Vie Dei Colori—Heres The Plan (IRE) **William Jones Lisa Harrington**
6 BEST ONE, 8, ch g Best of The Bests (IRE)—Nasaieb (IRE) **Ridge House Stables Ltd**
7 DECIDER (USA), 9, ch g High Yield (USA)—Nikita Moon (USA) **R. M. Bailey**
8 DIAMOND VINE (IRE), 4, b c Diamond Green (FR)—Glasnas Giant **Ridge House Stables Ltd**
9 EBRAAM (IRE), 9, b g Red Ransom (USA)—Futuh (USA) **Robert & Nina Bailey**
10 ECHOS OF MOTIVATOR, 4, ch c Motivator—Echo River (USA) **S. & A. Mares**
11 FAITHFUL RULER (USA), 8, b br g Elusive Quality (USA)—Fancy Ruler (USA) **Ridge House Stables Ltd**
12 ITALIAN TOM (IRE), 5, b h Le Vie Dei Colori—Brave Cat (IRE) **S. & A. Mares**
13 JUDGE 'N JURY, 8, ch g Pivotal—Cyclone Connie **Robert & Nina Bailey**
14 LADY MANGO (IRE), 4, ch f Bahamian Bounty—Opera **Mr L. Scadding & Mrs S. Peachey-Scadding**
15 LUTINE CHARLIE (IRE), 5, b g Kheleyf (USA)—Silvery Halo (USA) **Mr J. Tucker**
16 MY LORD, 4, br g Ishiguru (USA)—Lady Smith **M. J. Benton**
17 NIGHT TRADE (IRE), 5, b m Trade Fair—Compton Girl **Alan & Adam Darlow, A Darlow Productions**
18 NOVERRE TO GO (IRE), 6, ch g Noverre (USA)—Ukraine Venture **Robert & Nina Bailey**
19 PERLACHY, 8, b g Kyllachy—Perfect Dream **Mrs N. J. Macauley**
20 PRODIGALITY, 4, ch g Pivotal—Lady Bountiful **P. Moulton**
21 RIFLESSIONE, 6, ch g Captain Rio—Hilites (IRE) **Mrs J. E. F. Adams**
22 SECRET WITNESS, 6, ch g Pivotal—It's A Secret **P. Moulton**
23 SPINNING RIDGE (IRE), 7, ch g Spinning World (USA)—Summer Style (IRE) **Robert & Nina Bailey**
24 SUGAR BEET, 4, b f Beat Hollow—Satin Bell **Ridge House Stables Ltd**
25 WELSH DANCER, 4, b c Dubawi (IRE)—Rosie's Posy (IRE) **David & Gwyn Joseph**

MR RONALD HARRIS—continued

THREE-YEAR-OLDS

26 **COMMON CENTS**, ch c Pivotal—Small Change (IRE) **Ridge House Stables Ltd**
27 **FANTASY HERO**, br c Notnowcato—Pearly River **The Fantasy Fellowship B**
28 **IMAGERY**, ch c Pivotal—Fantasize **Ridge House Stables Ltd**
29 **IMMORTOTALITY**, ch f Refuse To Bend—Immortelle **Ridge House Stables Ltd**
30 **LADY CRESTA (IRE)**, b f Choisir (AUS)—Dancing Drop **Ridge House Stables Ltd**
31 **MISRED MELISSA (IRE)**, b f Red Clubs (IRE)—Almasa **M. J. Benton**
32 **MY NAME IS SAM**, b c Green Desert (USA)—Caught You Looking **Ridge House Stables Ltd**
33 **PERFECTO TIEMPO (IRE)**, b c Le Vie Dei Colori—Majolica **Ridge House Stables Ltd**
34 **SILENT ENERGY (IRE)**, b c Le Vie Dei Colori—Ghada (USA) **David & Gwyn Joseph/Ridge House Stables**
35 **SIR DYLAN**, b g Dylan Thomas (IRE)—Monteleone (IRE) **David & Gwyn Joseph/Ridge House Stables**

TWO-YEAR-OLDS

36 B c 26/3 Dutch Art—Bella Bertolini (Bertolini (USA)) (26666) **Mr A. N. Mubarak**
37 Gr c 22/4 Verglas (IRE)—Brazilian Style (Exit To Nowhere (USA)) (4761) **Ridge House Stables Ltd**
38 Ch f 22/4 Excellent Art—Cozzene's Pride (USA) (Cozzene (USA)) (15238) **David & Gwyn Joseph**
39 B c 8/4 Auction House (USA)—Fabuleux Cherie (Noverre (USA)) (380) **David & Gwyn Joseph**
40 B g 11/2 Diamond Green (FR)—Golden (FR) (Sanglamore (USA)) (5714) **Mr A. N. Mubarak**

Other Owners: Mr Robert Bailey, Mrs Nina Bailey, Mr A. Baker, Mr A. M. Blewitt, Mr Chris Coley, Mr Peter Coll, Mr Alan Darlow, Mr Adam Darlow, Ms Lisa Harrington, Mr A. Holdsworth, Mr William Jones, Mr D. M. Joseph, Mr D. G. Joseph, Mr S. Mares, Mrs A. Mares, Mr L. A. McGuinness, Mrs S. M. E. Peachey-Scadding, Mr A. J. Powell, Ridge House Stables Ltd, Mr G. Wheeler.

---

307 MR SHAUN HARRIS, Worksop
Postal: **Pinewood Stables, Carburton, Worksop, Nottinghamshire, S80 3BT**
Contacts: **PHONE (01909) 470936 FAX (01909) 470936 MOBILE (07768) 950460**
E-MAIL **shaunharris.racing@hotmail.com** WEBSITE **www.shaunharrisracing.co.uk**

1 **HENRY BOND**, 4, ch g Monsieur Bond (IRE)—Decatur **Mr P. Birley**
2 **MARK ANTHONY (IRE)**, 5, b g Antonius Pius (USA)—Zuniga's Date (USA) **Mr C. Harris**
3 **MIEREVELD**, 5, b g Red Ransom (USA)—Mythic **Mrs A. Kenny**
4 **MUSICAL LEAP**, 4, b g Superior Premium—Musical Fair **Mr W. Hobson**
5 **SEDGWICK**, 10, b g Nashwan (USA)—Imperial Bailiwick (IRE) **Mr W. Hobson**
6 **SWEET VERA**, 7, ch m Double Trigger (IRE)—Inesse **Mrs A. Kenny**
7 **TENANCY (IRE)**, 8, b g Rock of Gibraltar (IRE)—Brush Strokes **Mr W. Hobson**

THREE-YEAR-OLDS

8 **BEA PERSUASIVE**, b f Whipper (USA)—Thrasher **Wilf Hobson & Ciaran Harris**
9 **MEDAM**, b f Medicean—Mamounia (IRE) **Burton Agnes Bloodstock**
10 **MUSICAL STRIKE**, b g Striking Ambition—Musical Fair **Mr W. Hobson**
11 **RAZZLE DAZZLE 'EM**, b g Phoenix Reach (IRE)—Rasmani **Winterbeck Manor Stud Ltd**
12 **ROY'S LEGACY**, b c Phoenix Reach (IRE)—Chocolada **Karl Blackwell Steve Mohammed S A Harris**

TWO-YEAR-OLDS

13 **BETTY BOO (IRE)**, ch f 10/4 Thousand Words—Poker Dice (Primo Dominie) **Mr A. K. Elton**
14 B f 8/2 Sleeping Indian—Blue Nile (IRE) (Bluebird (USA))
15 Ch c 30/4 Phoenix Reach (IRE)—Rainbows Guest (IRE) (Indian Lodge (IRE)) (2857)
16 Ch f 1/4 Phoenix Reach (IRE)—Rasmani (Medicean) (571)

Other Owners: Mr K. Blackwell, The Hon Mrs E. S. Cunliffe-Lister, S. A. Harris, Mr S. Mohammed.

---

308 MR GARY HARRISON, Llandeilo
Postal: **Troed Y Rhiw Farm, Ffairfach, Llandeilo, Dyfed, SA19 6PH**
Contacts: **PHONE (01558) 824685 MOBILE (07813) 846899**
E-MAIL **gary.harrison@live.co.uk**

1 **BRIGHT HEART (IRE)**, 4, b f Danroad (AUS)—First Kiss (GER) **W. G. Harrison**
2 **COALBURN**, 4, ch g Captain Rio—Pusey Street Girl **W. G. Harrison**
3 **CRAZY DAISY**, 25, ch m Turn Back The Time (USA)—Nicaline **Lewis Caterers**
4 **DREAMY NIGHTS**, 4, b f Statue of Liberty (USA)—Hairy Night (IRE) **Lewis Caterers**

MR GARY HARRISON—continued

  5 **GO DAN DO,** 6, ch g Golan (IRE)—Daisy Do (IRE) **Lewis Caterers**
  6 **MORNIN RESERVES,** 13, b g Atraf—Pusey Street Girl **W. G. Harrison**
  7 **PRESENT STORY,** 5, b m Lucky Story (USA)—Aziz Presenting (IRE) **Lewis Caterers**
  8 **SARAH'S ART (IRE),** 9, gr g City On A Hill (USA)—Treasure Bleue (IRE) **W. G. Harrison**
  9 **SHE'S UNTOUCHABLE,** 5, b m Hawk Wing (USA)—Zambezi (USA) **Lewis Caterers**
 10 **TRANSEGGSELENCE,** 5, b m Trans Island—Breakfast Bay (IRE) **Lewis Caterers**
 11 4, B g Danroad (AUS)—Visitation **W. G. Harrison**

THREE-YEAR-OLDS

 12 B f Hawk Wing (USA)—Daisy Do (IRE) **Lewis Caterers**
 13 B g Atraf—Gaoth Na Mara (IRE) **W. G. Harrison**
 14 B f Auction House (USA)—Hairy Night (IRE) **Lewis Caterers**
 15 Ch f Danroad (AUS)—High Chart **W. G. Harrison**
 16 Ch f Danroad (AUS)—Jessie **W. G. Harrison**
 17 B g Atraf—Kealbra Lady **W. G. Harrison**
 18 **OUTSIDE ART,** b f Excellent Art—She's My Outsider **Lewis Caterers**
 19 **PRINCESS QUEST,** gr f Clodovil (IRE)—Corniche Quest (IRE) **Lewis Caterers**
 20 B g Footstepsinthesand—Solar Flare (IRE) **Lewis Caterers**
 21 B f Hurricane Run (IRE)—Zambezi (USA) **Lewis Caterers**

Assistant Trainer: Stephanie A Williams 07581 319284

Jockey (flat): Mark Lawson. **Jockey (NH):** Jimmy McCarthy. **Apprentice:** Matthew Lawson.

309
MISS LISA HARRISON, Aldoth
Postal: **Cobble Hall, Aldoth, Nr Silloth, Cumbria, CA7 4NE**

  1 6, Gr m Portrait Gallery (IRE)—Carmels Gift (IRE) **David A. Harrison**
  2 **SOLWAY BAY,** 10, b g Cloudings (IRE)—No Problem Jac **David A. Harrison**
  3 **SOLWAY BROOK (IRE),** 6, b m Alderbrook—The Shining Force (IRE) **David A. Harrison**
  4 **SOLWAY DORNAL,** 7, b g Afflora (IRE)—Solway Donal (IRE) **David A. Harrison**
  5 5, B g Danroad (AUS)—Solway Rose **David A. Harrison**
  6 **SOLWAY SAM,** 9, b g Double Trigger (IRE)—Some Gale **David A. Harrison**
  7 **SOLWAY STAR,** 9, ch g Zaha (CAN)—Cuddle Bunny (IRE) **David A. Harrison**
  8 5, Ch g And Beyond (IRE)—Spicey Cut **David A. Harrison**

310
MR BEN HASLAM, Middleham
Postal: **Castle Hill Stables, Castle Hill, Middleham, Leyburn, North Yorkshire, DL8 4QW**
Contacts: **PHONE (01969) 624351 FAX (01969) 624463 MOBILE (07764) 411660**
E-MAIL office@benhaslamracing.com WEBSITE www.benhaslamracing.com

  1 **ADAM DE BEAULIEU (USA),** 5, b g Broken Vow (USA)—Gambling Champ (USA) **Blue Lion Racing**
  2 **AZZURRA DU CAPRIO (IRE),** 4, ch f Captain Rio—Dunbrody (FR) **Blue Lion Racing IX**
  3 **BALWYLLO (IRE),** 7, ch g Hubbly Bubbly (USA)—Silver Gala **Mr R. Tocher**
  4 **BLAKE DEAN,** 4, b g Halling (USA)—Antediluvian **Widdop Wanderers**
  5 **CROSS THE BOSS (IRE),** 5, b g Cape Cross (IRE)—Lady Salsa (IRE) **Widdop Wanderers**
  6 **EXECUTIVE'S HALL (IRE),** 8, b g Saddlers' Hall (IRE)—Overtime (IRE) **Mrs S. Mason, Mr R. Stipetic**
  7 **FRONT OF HOUSE (IRE),** 10, b g King's Theatre (IRE)—Dancing Line **J. P. McManus**
  8 **HI DANCER,** 9, b g Medicean—Sea Music **Mr R. Tocher**
  9 **OPERATEUR (IRE),** 4, b g Oratorio (IRE)—Kassariya (IRE) **Mrs Alison Royston**
 10 **REASON TO BELIEVE (IRE),** 4, ch g Spartacus (IRE)—Lady Fabiola (USA) **Mrs C. A. Aldridge**

THREE-YEAR-OLDS

 11 **ANGEL WARRIOR (IRE),** b c Dark Angel (IRE)—Red Slipper (IRE) **Mrs Sheila Mason & Mr Robert Stipetic**
 12 **CRIMSON SEA (IRE),** ch f Redback—Fantastic Cee (IRE) **Mrs C. Barclay**
 13 **DANCE FOR GEORGIE,** ch f Motivator—Chetwynd (IRE) **Mr M. J. James**
 14 **DREAMING OF RUBIES,** b f Oasis Dream—Rubies From Burma (USA) **Middleham Park Racing XXVII**
 15 **KING LAERTIS (IRE),** br g Baltic King—Vltava (IRE) **Mr S. Hassiakos & Mr M. C. Mason**
 16 **LILIARGH (IRE),** b f Acclamation—Discover Roma (IRE) **Middleham Park Racing XXVII**
 17 **TUIBAMA (IRE),** ch g Bertolini (USA)—Supportive (IRE) **Alan Zheng & Mark James**

MR BEN HASLAM—continued

TWO-YEAR-OLDS

18 B c 1/4 Byron—Balwarah (IRE) (Soviet Star (USA)) (4761) **Go Alfresco Racing Club**
19 B c 22/3 Byron—City Maiden (USA) (Carson City (USA)) (8000) **Mr B. M. R. Haslam**
20 B f 21/2 Diamond Green (FR)—Dancing Steps (Zafonic (USA)) (9523) **Go Alfresco Racing Club**
21 B c 21/1 Indesatchel (IRE)—Day By Day (Kyllachy) (13333) **Go Alfresco Racing Club**
22 DIAKTOROS (IRE), b c 12/3 Red Clubs (IRE)—
                    Rinneen (IRE) (Bien Bien (USA)) (42000) **Sir Alex Ferguson & Mr S. Hassiakos**
23 B f 7/3 Refuse To Bend (IRE)—Diplomats Daughter (Unfuwain (USA)) (8000) **Mr B. M. R. Haslam**
24 B f 13/4 Bachelor Duke (USA)—Dunbrody (FR) (Jeune Homme (USA)) **Blue Lion Racing**
25 B f 2/4 Clodovil (IRE)—Green Life (Green Desert (USA)) (5714) **Go Alfresco Racing Club**
26 Ch f 2/2 Sakhee's Secret—May Day Queen (IRE) (Danetime (IRE)) (15238) **Miss Karen Theobald**

Other Owners: Mr A. D. Hollinrake, Mr Marc Middlemiss, Mr T. S. Palin, Mr M. Prince, Mrs Judie Short, Mr David Walker (Stafford).

Assistant Trainer: Leanne Kershaw

Jockey (NH): Barry Keniry. Conditional: Craig Gallagher. Amateur: Miss Charlotte Holmes.

---

311 **MR P. J. HASSETT, Quin**
Postal: Parkview House, Moyriesk, Quin, Co. Clare, Ireland
Contacts: **PHONE (00353) 65 6840555 (MAIN HOUSE) (00353) 65 6825006 (OFFICE)**
FAX (00353) 65 6825006 MOBILE (00353) 86 1731002 / (00353) 86 6081148

1 A NEW DAWN (IRE), 6, b g Old Vic—Andros Dawn (IRE) **P. J. Hassett**
2 BOURGELAT (IRE), 5, b g Flemensfirth (USA)—Sister Cinnamon **BallyC Syndicate**
3 CUSTERS FLIGHT (IRE), 9, b g Little Bighorn—Little Helen **M. Holmes**
4 HANDY MANNY (IRE), 6, b g Amilynx (FR)—Roco-Bridge (IRE) **P. M. Hassett**
5 KETTLE STREET (IRE), 7, b m Dushyantor (USA)—Pharavo (IRE) **T. Corbett**
6 MIYAJIMA, 12, b g Polar Prince (IRE)—Patina **BallyC Syndicate**
7 SANITY (IRE), 7, ch g Insan (USA)—Dusty Lane (IRE) **P. McAteer**
8 STOP N STARE (IRE), 5, b g Danetime (IRE)—Ballina Belle **P. McAteer**
9 5, B m Revoque (IRE)—Swing The Lead (IRE) **P. J. Hassett**
10 WIN FOR US (IRE), 7, ch g Rossini (USA)—Noble Flame (IRE) **Wfouryou Syndicate**

THREE-YEAR-OLDS

11 B g Kaieteur (USA)—Bridgeville Queen (IRE) **P. J. Hassett**

Assistant Trainer: G. Hassett

Amateur: Mr P. J. O'Neill, Mr C. J. Murray, Mr T. J. Considine.

---

312 **MR NIGEL HAWKE, Tiverton**
Postal: Thorne Farm, Stoodleigh, Tiverton, Devon, EX16 9QG
Contacts: **MOBILE (07899) 922827**
E-MAIL nigel@nigelhawkeracing.co.uk

1 ANAY TURGE (FR), 7, b g Turgeon (USA)—Anayette (FR) **K & S Wetherall**
2 CALLERLILLY, 8, ch m Double Trigger (IRE)—Callermine **Whitegate Stud & N. J. McMullan**
3 CALYPSO STAR (IRE), 5, ch g Exceed And Excel (AUS)—Reematna **W. E. Donohue**
4 CAUGHT INTHE LIGHT, 7, b g Old Vic—Webb Find (IRE) **Nigel Hawke Racing & Partners**
5 KYOTO (GER), 8, b g Monsun (GER)—Key West (GER) **N. J. McMullan & S. H. Bryant**
6 LE PERGOLESE (FR), 6, b g Sagacity (FR)—Rasinixa (FR) **N. J. Hawke**
7 MANMOON (FR), 9, gr g Mansonnien (FR)—La Voix de La Lune (FR) **Nigel Hawke Racing & Partners**
8 MASTER NEO (FR), 6, gr g Turgeon (USA)—Really Royale (FR) **W. E. Donohue**
9 MISTER WISEMAN, 10, gr g Bal Harbour—Genie Spirit **Nigel Hawke Racing & Partners**
10 ONE AND ALL (IRE), 9, gr g Saddlers' Hall (IRE)—
                    Rostarr (IRE) **RJ & JA Peake & Mrs A Heayns-Kernow Bloodstock**
11 PIRANS CAR, 6, b g Sleeping Car (FR)—Karolina **R. J. & Mrs J. A. Peake**
12 ROBIN OF SPRING (FR), 6, b g Robin des Pres (FR)—Visite Princiere (FR) **Nigel Hawke Racing & Partners**
13 VINTAGE FABRIC (USA), 10, b g Royal Anthem (USA)—Sandalwood (USA) **N. J. McMullan & S. H. Bryant**
14 ZIMBABWE (FR), 12, b g Turgeon (USA)—Razzamatazz (FR) **R. J. & Mrs J. A. Peake**

MR NIGEL HAWKE—continued

Other Owners: Mr G. C. Board, S. H. Bryant, T. O. Heayns, C. J. Heayns, Mrs A. L. Heayns, Ms J. Henly, N. J. McMullan, R. J. Peake, Mrs J. A. Peake, Mr S. R. Pearce, Mrs K. Wetherall, Mr S. Wetherall.

Assistant Trainer: David Judd

---

313 | **MR RICHARD HAWKER, Frome**
Postal: Rode Farm, Rode, Bath, Somerset, BA11 6QQ

1 **ACTION STEEL (IRE)**, 7, b g Craigsteel—Action Plan **Winning Edge Racing**
2 **BENEFIT GAME (IRE)**, 8, b g Beneficial—Glenarb Molly (IRE) **R. G. B. Hawker**
3 **HIGHWAY JACK (IRE)**, 7, bl g Zagreb (USA)—Bubbly Lady (IRE) **R. G. B. Hawker**
4 **OMMEGA (FR)**, 10, gr g Ragmar (FR)—Cathou (FR) **Mrs A. H. Hampton**
5 **SOLAISE EXPRESS**, 7, b g Kayf Tara—Solo Girl (IRE) **R. G. B. Hawker**

Other Owners: Mrs S. E. Hawker.

---

314 | **MR JOHN C. HAYDEN, Kildare**
Postal: Castlemartin Abbey House Stables, Kilcullen, Co. Kildare, Ireland
Contacts: **PHONE (00353) 4548 1598 FAX (00353) 4548 1598 MOBILE (00353) 86 3895636**

1 **BELFIORE (IRE)**, 5, b m Bertolini (USA)—Literary Lover (IRE)
2 **DANEHILL TAPDANCER (IRE)**, 5, br g Indian Danehill (IRE)—Roundstone Dancer (IRE)
3 **EUR ELUSIVE (IRE)**, 5, b m Elusive City (USA)—Europaea (IRE)
4 6, Ch m Definite Article—Hoyland Common (IRE)
5 **ICE BOUND (IRE)**, 6, gr g Verglas (IRE)—Mubadalah (USA)
6 **LITTLE LIVE WIRE (IRE)**, 4, b f Dubawi (IRE)—Dama'a (IRE)
7 **MUTISKA (IRE)**, 5, ch m Muhtarram (USA)—Biasca
8 **PEARLFIELDS (IRE)**, 4, b f Ad Valorem (USA)—Memory Green (USA)
9 **THE SPAILPIN FANAC (IRE)**, 8, b g Lend A Hand—Roundstone Dancer (IRE)

THREE-YEAR-OLDS

10 **DAINTIE DISH (IRE)**, b f Bertolini (USA)—Song of Sixpence (IRE)

TWO-YEAR-OLDS

11 B f 13/2 Jeremy (USA)—Born For Diamonds (IRE) (Night Shift (USA))
12 B f 26/4 Rakti—Ostjessy (IRE) (In The Wings)

Other Owners: Mr & Mrs R. Blake, Dr A. Calnan, Mr F. Campbell, Mr M. Feeney, Mr M. Ferris, Mr G. Grothier, Mr S. Hayden, Mr J. Keeling, Mr P. McAllister, Mr F. O'Toole.

Assistant Trainer: J A Hayden (00 353) 8682 26717

Jockey (flat): Johnny Murtagh, Fran Berry. **Apprentice:** R Dawson.

---

315 | **MR DEREK HAYDN JONES, Pontypridd**
Postal: Garth Paddocks, Efail Isaf, Pontypridd, Mid-Glamorgan, CF38 1SN
Contacts: **PHONE (01443) 202515 FAX (01443) 201877 MOBILE (07967) 680012**

1 **ALL RIGHT NOW**, 5, b g Night Shift (USA)—Cookie Cutter (IRE) **Mr J. Hay**
2 **APPLE BLOSSOM TIME (IRE)**, 5, b m Invincible Spirit (IRE)—Strina (IRE) **J. E. Keeling**
3 **CHIK'S DREAM**, 5, ch g Dreams End—Chik's Secret **Mr T. L. G. Jenkins**
4 **DIMAIRE**, 5, b m Kheleyf (USA)—Dim Ots **G. J. Hicks**
5 **FIRST POST (IRE)**, 5, b g Celtic Swing—Consignia (IRE) **Llewelyn, Runeckles**
6 **PARHELION**, 5, b g Fantastic Light (USA)—Shamaiel (IRE) **Mr R. Williams**
7 **TINSHU (IRE)**, 6, ch m Fantastic Light (USA)—Ring of Esteem **Llewelyn, Runeckles**

THREE-YEAR-OLDS

8 **IONWY**, b f Piccolo—Dim Ots **G. I. D. Llewelyn**
9 **JEREMY SUE**, b f Amadeus Wolf—Dearest Daisy **Mr J. Holt**
10 **MOLLY JONES**, b f Three Valleys (USA)—And Toto Too **North Cheshire Trading & Storage Ltd**

MR DEREK HAYDN JONES—continued

11 **MONTY FAY (IRE)**, b br g Iffraaj—Blast (USA) **Mr R. Williams**
12 **TENBRIDGE**, b f Avonbridge—Tenebrae (IRE) **Mrs E. M. Haydn Jones**

TWO-YEAR-OLDS

13 Ch f 2/2 Pastoral Pursuits—Calligraphy (Kris) (800) **Mrs E. M. Haydn Jones**
14 B f 26/3 Amadeus Wolf—On Point (Kris) (5500) **D. Llewelyn**
15 Gr f 24/2 Verglas (IRE)—Tahtheeb (IRE) (Muhtarram (USA)) (6567) **Mr J. Hay**
16 Ch f 15/4 Three Valleys (USA)—Tenebrae (IRE) (In The Wings) (2800)

Other Owners: Mr Jon Blencowe, Mrs E. M. Haydn Jones, Mrs D. J. Hughes, Mr D. Llewelyn, Mrs M. L. Parry, Mr J. Runeckles, Mr Brian Sheppard, Mr Gordon Vine.

Assistant Trainer: Mrs E. M. Haydn Jones

---

316 **MR JONATHAN HAYNES, Brampton**
Postal: **Cleugh Head, Low Row, Brampton, Cumbria, CA8 2JB**
Contacts: **PHONE (01697) 746253 MOBILE (07771) 511471**

1 **BERTIELICIOUS**, 4, b g And Beyond (IRE)—Pennepoint **J. C. Haynes**
2 6, B br m Loxias (FR)—Caline de Froment (FR) **J. C. Haynes**
3 **FRED GRASS**, 6, ch g And Beyond (IRE)—Tempted (IRE) **J. C. Hayes**
4 **PANTHERS RUN**, 12, b g Jendali (USA)—Dorado Beach **J. C. Haynes**

---

317 **MR TED HAYNES, Highworth**
Postal: **Red Down Farm, Highworth, Wiltshire, SN6 7SH**
Contacts: **PHONE/FAX (01793) 762437 FAX (01793) 762437 MOBILE (07704) 707728**
E-MAIL reddownracing@aol.com

1 5, B g Kayf Tara—Fly Home **Miss S. R. Haynes**
2 **HOT CHERRY**, 8, b m Bertolini (USA)—Cribella (USA) **H. E. Haynes**
3 **PRINCESS KIERA**, 4, b f Kier Park (IRE)—Rupert's Princess (IRE) **Miss S. R. Haynes**
4 **STANWELL**, 4, ch g Kier Park (IRE)—Magical Dancer (IRE) **The Reddown High Explosive Partnership**
5 5, B g Zafeen (FR)—Stormworthy Miss (IRE) **Miss S. R. Haynes**
6 **THE NAMES HARRY**, 7, b g Sir Harry Lewis (USA)—Fly Home **Miss S. R. Haynes**

THREE-YEAR-OLDS

7 Br c Sir Harry Lewis (USA)—Fly Home **Miss S. R. Haynes**
8 B c Kier Park (IRE)—Rupert's Princess (IRE)

TWO-YEAR-OLDS

9 Ch f 23/4 Bertolini (USA)—Magical Dancer (IRE) (Magical Wonder (USA))
10 B c 15/4 Zafeen (FR)—Stormworthy Miss (IRE) (Glacial Storm (USA))

Other Owners: Mr H. Edward Haynes, Mrs H. E. Haynes.

Assistant Trainer: Sally R Haynes (07711) 488341

---

318 **MRS C. HEAD-MAAREK, Chantilly**
Postal: **32 Avenue du General Leclerc, 60500 Chantilly, France**
Contacts: **PHONE (0033) 3445 70101 FAX (0033) 3445 85333 MOBILE (0033) 6073 10505**
E-MAIL christiane.head@wanadoo.fr

1 **AZADE (IRE)**, 4, b f Marchand de Sable (USA)—Far Distance (USA)
2 **DAMELINA (FR)**, 4, b f Green Tune (USA)—Dame Blanche (USA)
3 **DIKTABAMA (FR)**, 5, b m Diktat—Miss Alabama (FR)
4 **DOM TOM (USA)**, 4, b c Anabaa (USA)—Dedication (FR)
5 **GRAND DUC (USA)**, 5, b h Kingmambo (USA)—New Harmony (USA)
6 **INDEX LINKED**, 4, b c Dansili—Fully Invested (USA)
7 4, B c Bering—Lucille
8 **NICE ASSOCIATION (FR)**, 4, b f High Yield (USA)—Pick A Poket (FR)
9 **NITZA (FR)**, 4, b f Indygo Shiner (USA)—Realdad (ARG)

MRS C. HEAD-MAAREK—continued

10 4, B c Iron Mask—Padina
11 **SONNY (FR)**, 4, b c Numerous (USA)—Spenderella (FR)
12 **STANDARD BEARER**, 4, b c Sakhee (USA)—Gerardina

THREE-YEAR-OLDS

13 **ALEXANDRE D'OR (FR)**, b c Gold Away (IRE)—Reine Annicka (FR)
14 **ARENGO (IRE)**, b c Peintre Celebre (USA)—Cortona (IRE)
15 **BERINGONPHEE (FR)**, ch f Bering—Onphee
16 **BLUE SEA (IRE)**, b c Singspiel (IRE)—Height of Vanity (IRE)
17 **BREAK RANK (USA)**, b c Broken Vow (USA)—Divert (USA)
18 **FAUVISM (USA)**, b c Zamindar (USA)—Chaffinch (USA)
19 **FRANCASTEL (FR)**, ch c Gold Away (IRE)—Funny Feerie (FR)
20 **GOLF JUAN (USA)**, b g Invasor (ARG)—Great Buy (USA)
21 **GRAMMAR**, b c Rail Link—Comma (USA)
22 **HAYA (FR)**, b f Panis (USA)—Heritiere (AUS)
23 **KING'S FAREWELL**, ch c King's Best (USA)—Zahour Al Yasmeen
24 **KORTOBA (USA)**, ch f Distorted Humor (USA)—La Sorbonne (ARG)
25 **MIRACOLO (IRE)**, b c Rock of Gibraltar (IRE)—Campiglia (IRE)
26 **PEMBINA (IRE)**, gr f Dalakhani (IRE)—Mahalia (IRE)
27 **POSTALE**, b f Zamindar (USA)—Posteritas (USA)
28 **PREFERENTIAL**, b f Dansili—Jolie Etoile (USA)
29 **REITERATE**, b f Three Valleys (USA)—Rive (USA)
30 **RESURGENT**, b c King's Best (USA)—Change Course
31 **RIVERAIN (FR)**, b c Anabaa (USA)—Riziere (FR)
32 **ROCHELLE (FR)**, b f Anabaa—Roanne
33 **RUNNING DEER (USA)**, b f Rockport Harbor (USA)—Jazz Drummer (USA)
34 **SAFI WAFI (IRE)**, b c Iffraaj—Min Asl Wafi (IRE)
35 **SEA TRIAL (FR)**, b c Panis (USA)—Sea Life (FR)
36 **SHOMOUKH (USA)**, gr ro f Unbridled's Song (USA)—Future Guest (USA)
37 **SHOMUS (USA)**, b f Tiznow (USA)—Island Rhythm (USA)
38 **TARAF (USA)**, b f Montjeu (IRE)—Lorena Wood (USA)
39 **THE BEST LAWYER (USA)**, b c More Than Ready (USA)—Miss Trinidad (USA)
40 **TIBALDI (FR)**, b f Motivator—Treasure Queen
41 **TOUTE ALLURE (USA)**, b f Dynaformer (USA)—Alluring (USA)
42 **VENTOUX**, b f Galileo (IRE)—Quest To Peak (USA)

TWO-YEAR-OLDS

43 **ARTISTE BERE (FR)**, b c 3/3 Della Francesca (USA)—Realdad (ARG) (Victory Speech (USA)) (30377)
44 **AURORE BERE (FR)**, b f 8/4 Peer Gynt (JPN)—Mysterious Land (IRE) (Kaldoun (FR)) (12315)
45 **BEAUTIFUL SY (FR)**, ch f 1/1 Dutch Art—Beautiful Note (USA) (Red Ransom (USA)) (24630)
46 Ch f 8/3 Zamindar (USA)—Coraline (Sadler's Wells (USA))
47 **DECISION (FR)**, ch f 1/1 Kentucky Dynamite—Dame Blanche
48 Gr ro f 9/3 Mizzen Mast (USA)—Flute (USA) (Seattle Slew (USA))
49 **GALVESTON (FR)**, ch c 7/4 Green Tune (USA)—Great News (FR) (Bering) (24630)
50 **HOUGHTON HILL (FR)**, ch g 1/1 Green Tune—Hierarchie
51 B f 30/4 First Defence (USA)—Kinetic Force (USA) (Holy Bull (USA))
52 Gr f 23/3 Zamindar (USA)—Lixian (Linamix (FR))
53 **MADRASA (FR)**, gr f 1/1 Slickly—Matanilla
54 Ch c 4/5 Three Valleys (USA)—Marching West (USA) (Gone West (USA))
55 **MARTINI (GER)**, b c 1/1 Rock of Gibraltar (IRE)—Missing Link (IRE) (Elusive Quality (USA)) (69786)
56 **MUTIN (FR)**, b c 16/3 Kentucky Dynamite (USA)—Mytographie (FR) (Anabaa (USA)) (12315)
57 B c 2/2 Pleasant Tap (USA)—Pretty Clear (USA) (Mr Prospector (USA))
58 **RADIATION (FR)**, b f 1/1 Anabaa—Riziere
59 **ROCAILLE (FR)**, b f 1/1 Anabaa—Rose Rose
60 B c 19/4 Mizzen Mast (USA)—Routine (USA) (Empire Maker (USA))
61 Ch f 1/1 Kentucky Dynamite—Ryde
62 **SAVOIR (FR)**, b c 1/1 Anabaa—Silverware
63 Ch c 17/2 More Than Ready (USA)—Sister Swank (USA) (Skip Away (USA)) (65681)
64 **TECLA (IRE)**, b f 25/3 Whipper (USA)—Mahalia (IRE) (Danehill (USA))
65 **TEMESTIOS (FR)**, b c 1/1 Poliglote—Tonalite (FR)
66 **TREVE (FR)**, b f 7/4 Motivator—Trevise (FR) (Anabaa (USA)) (18062)
67 **TROYA (IRE)**, b f 19/4 Jeremy (USA)—Segesta (IRE) (Vettori (IRE))
68 **VOYAGEUSE (FR)**, b f 1/1 Kentucky Dynamite—Villadolide

Assistant Trainer: Charley Rossi

319 MR COLIN HEARD, Boscastle
Postal: **Lower Pennycrocker Farm, Boscastle, Cornwall, PL35 0BY**
Contacts: PHONE **(01840) 250613** MOBILE **(07967) 605392**

1 **CARHENEY RIVER (IRE)**, 7, b g Flemensfirth (USA)—Odeeka (IRE) **Mrs S. A. White**
2 **LITTLE EAGLET (IRE)**, 8, br g Dushyantor (USA)—Bagatelle (IRE) **Mrs S. A. White**
3 **QUICKLY ORIGNY (FR)**, 8, ch g Agent Bleu (FR)—Coralline (FR) **Mrs K. Heard**
4 **WRAY CASTLE (IRE)**, 7, b g Desert Prince—Blushing Gleam **Mrs K. Heard**

Assistant Trainer: Karyn Heard

Jockey (NH): Liam Heard. **Conditional:** Ian Popham. **Amateur:** Mr Samuel Allwood.

320 MR PETER HEDGER, Dogmersfield
Postal: **P C F Racing Ltd, Peaked Croft Farm, Chalky Lane, Dogmersfield, Hampshire, RG27 8TG**
Contacts: PHONE **(01243) 543863** FAX **(01243) 543913** MOBILE **(07860) 209448**
E-MAIL hedgerlaura@hotmail.com

1 **BARNMORE**, 4, b g Royal Applause—Veronica Franco **P C F Racing Ltd**
2 **BRETT VALE (IRE)**, 6, br g Sinndar (IRE)—Pinta (IRE) **P C F Racing Ltd**
3 **CLASSICALLY (IRE)**, 6, b g Indian Haven—Specifically (USA) **Mr G. Lloyd**
4 **FOXSPUR (IRE)**, 9, b g Flemensfirth (USA)—Ellway Lady (IRE) **P. R. Hedger**
5 **FRANCO IS MY NAME**, 6, b g Namid—Veronica Franco **P C F Racing Ltd**
6 **ICE 'N' EASY (IRE)**, 6, b g Dushyantor (USA)—Glacial Valley (IRE) **R. Jenner & J. Green**
7 **LISAHANE BOG**, 5, b g Royal Applause—Veronica Franco **P C F Racing Ltd**
8 **RAINSBOROUGH**, 5, b g Trans Island—Greeba **I. Hutchins**
9 **REGAL RAVE (USA)**, 5, b g Wild Event (USA)—Golden Crown (USA) **Mr S. J. Ingham**

THREE-YEAR-OLDS

10 **NORWOOD LANE**, b c Kyllachy—Lay A Whisper **Mr W. F. N. Davis**
11 **SISTER GURU**, b f Ishiguru (USA)—Ulysses Daughter (IRE) **Mr J. F. McHale**
12 **WHIPCRACKAWAY (IRE)**, b g Whipper—Former Drama (USA) **P. R. Hedger**

TWO-YEAR-OLDS

13 B c 8/3 Avonbridge—Amazing Dream (IRE) (Thatching) (40000) **P C F Racing Ltd**
14 Ch c 7/4 Monsieur Bond (IRE)—Birthday Belle (Lycius (USA)) (9000) **P C F Racing Ltd**
15 B f 8/2 Araafa (IRE)—Largo (IRE) (Selkirk (USA)) **P C F Racing Ltd**
16 B c 17/4 Duke of Marmalade (IRE)—Liscune (IRE) (King's Best (USA)) (80000) **P C F Racing Ltd**
17 Br f 11/4 Araafa (IRE)—Lucky Date (IRE) (Halling (USA)) **P C F Racing Ltd**
18 B f 23/4 Pastoral Pursuits—Veronica Franco (Darshaan) **P C F Racing Ltd**

Other Owners: Mrs J. Green, Mouse Hamilton-Fairley, Mr Geoffrey Hamilton-Fairley, Simon Holt, Ms R. Jenner, P C F Racing Ltd, Prof D. B. A. Silk, Mr R. J. Vibert, Mr J. L. Winterbourne.

Assistant Trainer: John Swallow

Jockey (flat): Dane O'Neill. **Jockey (NH):** Leighton Aspell. **Amateur:** Mr Liam Jennings.

321 MR NICKY HENDERSON, Lambourn
Postal: **Seven Barrows, Lambourn, Hungerford, Berkshire, RG17 8UH**
Contacts: PHONE **(01488) 72259** FAX **(01488) 72596** MOBILE **(07774) 608168**
E-MAIL nj.henderson@virgin.net

1 **AIGLE D'OR**, 9, b g Halling (USA)—Epistole (IRE) **J. P. McManus**
2 **ALL THE ACES (IRE)**, 5, b g Spartacus (USA)—Lili Cup (FR) **A. D. Spence**
3 **ANQUETTA (IRE)**, 8, b g Anshan—Quetta (IRE) **The Ten From Seven**
4 **ARCTIC ACTRESS**, 5, b m King's Theatre (IRE)—Blast Freeze (IRE) **Let's Live Racing**
5 **BAI ZHU (IRE)**, 8, b br g Anshan—Cool Thistle (IRE) **The Perfect Day Partnership**
6 **BALLYBOUGH GORTA (IRE)**, 5, b g Indian Danehill (IRE)—Eyelet (IRE) **Mr J. Andrews**
7 **BARBERS SHOP**, 10, b g Saddlers' Hall (IRE)—Close Harmony **Her Majesty The Queen**
8 **BARENGER (IRE)**, 5, b g Indian Danehill (IRE)—Build A Dream (USA) **R. A. Bartlett**
9 4, B g Oscar (IRE)—Be My Belle (IRE) **Orpendale Bloodstock**
10 **BE THERE IN FIVE (IRE)**, 8, b g Indian Danehill (IRE)—Marwa (IRE) **S. E. Munir**
11 **BEAR'S AFFAIR (IRE)**, 6, br g Presenting—Gladtogetit **Mr G. Barlow**

234 RACEFORM

MR NICKY HENDERSON—continued

12 **BELLVANO (GER)**, 8, b g Silvano (GER)—Bella Vista (GER) **J. P. McManus**
13 **BILLY TWYFORD (IRE)**, 5, b g Brian Boru—The Distaff Spy **S. E. Munir**
14 **BINOCULAR (FR)**, 8, b g Enrique—Bleu Ciel Et Blanc (FR) **J. P. McManus**
15 **BLACK POND (USA)**, 4, b g Forestry (USA)—Golden Ballet (USA) **A. D. Spence**
16 **BOBS WORTH (IRE)**, 7, b g Bob Back (USA)—Fashionista (IRE) **The Not Afraid Partnership**
17 **BRAVE ALLIANCE (IRE)**, 5, b m Presenting—La Brave (FR) **Let's Live Racing**
18 **BRIGADIER MILLER**, 5, gr g Act One—Tread Carefully **W. H. Ponsonby**
19 **BROADBACKBOB (IRE)**, 7, b g Broadway Flyer (USA)—Back Home (IRE) **Anthony Speelman**
20 **BUCKIE BOY (IRE)**, 6, b g Bahri (USA)—Woodren (USA) **Joyce, Wilson & Hill**
21 **BURTON PORT (IRE)**, 8, b g Bob Back (USA)—Despute (IRE) **T. J. Hemmings**
22 **BUSKER ROYAL**, 9, ch g Shahrastani (USA)—Close Harmony **Mrs R. H. Brown**
23 **CAPE EXPRESS (IRE)**, 7, b g Cape Cross (IRE)—Lilissa (IRE) **A. D. Spence**
24 **CAPTAIN CONAN (FR)**, 5, b g Kingsalsa (USA)—Lavandou **Triermore Stud**
25 **CAPTAIN CUTTER (IRE)**, 5, b g Westerner—Hollygrove Samba (IRE) **Orpendale Bloodstock**
26 **CARABINIER (FR)**, 6, b g Martaline—Incorrigible (FR) **The Girls Syndicate**
27 **CELTUS (FR)**, 5, b br g Keltos (FR)—Infiltrate (IRE) **Mr S. Munir**
28 **CHARLES ONZE (FR)**, 5, b g Epalo (GER)—Karmiva (FR) **H. R. Mould**
29 **CHARLIE WINGNUT (IRE)**, 5, br g Westerner—Back To Stay (IRE) **M. H. Watt**
30 **CHATTERBOX (IRE)**, 4, b g Poliglote—Ney Will (FR) **The Not Afraid Partnership 2**
31 **CHENEY MANOR**, 7, b g Piccolo—One For Philip **S W Group Logistics Limited**
32 **CITY PRESS (IRE)**, 6, b g Presenting—Phargara (IRE) **Gleadhill House Stud**
33 **CLOSE TOUCH**, 4, ch g Generous (IRE)—Romantic Dream **Her Majesty The Queen**
34 **CRUZ ON TED**, 5, b g Helissio—Dublivia **S. Neighbour**
35 **CRYSTAL ROCK (IRE)**, 7, br g Rock of Gibraltar (IRE)—State Crystal (IRE) **Mrs B. A. Hanbury**
36 **CUCUMBER RUN (IRE)**, 7, b g Oscar (IRE)—Back To Roost (IRE) **The Goblyns**
37 **DANCING DUDE (IRE)**, 5, ch g Danehill Dancer (IRE)—Wadud **A. D. Spence**
38 **DARLAN**, 5, br g Milan—Darbela (IRE) **J. P. McManus**
39 **DAVE'S DREAM (IRE)**, 9, b g Anshan—Native Success (IRE) **David Murdoch & Jenny Murdoch**
40 **DEFINITE RUBY (IRE)**, 4, b f Definite Article—Sunset Queen (IRE) **Trevor & Linda Marlow**
41 **DUBAI CREST**, 6, b g Dubai Destination (USA)—On The Brink **A. D. Spence**
42 **EL MONDO (FR)**, 6, b g Lost World (IRE)—Haiya (FR) **J. P. McManus**
43 **ELDRED (IRE)**, 6, b g Beneficial—Miss Executive (IRE) **P. J. D. Pottinger**
44 **ERADICATE (IRE)**, 8, b g Montjeu (IRE)—Coyote **A. D. Spence**
45 **ERICHT (IRE)**, 6, b g Alderbrook—Lady Orla (IRE) **Mrs B. A. Hanbury**
46 **FABRIKA**, 4, b f Presenting—Daprika (FR) **Mr & Mrs R Kelvin Hughes**
47 **FINIAN'S RAINBOW (IRE)**, 9, b g Tiraaz (USA)—Trinity Gale (IRE) **M. A. C. Buckley**
48 **FIREY KING (IRE)**, 5, b g Flemensfirth (USA)—Chapel Queen (IRE) **The Rams Syndicate**
49 **FIRST IN THE QUEUE (IRE)**, 5, b g Azamour (IRE)—Irina (IRE) **L. Breslin**
50 **FLOREAT**, 5, b g Milan—Haudello (FR) **P. J. D. Pottinger**
51 **FOLLOW THE FACTS**, 5, b g Tobougg (IRE)—Fiddling The Facts (IRE) **Mrs E. C. Roberts**
52 **FOR A LAUGH**, 5, b g Westerner—Wicked Crack (IRE) **Mrs S. Magnier**
53 **FOREVER PRESENT (IRE)**, 5, br m Presenting—Sidalcea (IRE) **Lets Live Racing (Tinbar)**
54 **FORZY ORIGNY (FR)**, 10, gr g Sleeping Car (FR)—Forza Malta (FR) **Sir R. Ogden C.B.E., LLD**
55 **FOURTH ESTATE (IRE)**, 6, b g Fantastic Light (USA)—Papering (IRE) **Out The Box Racing**
56 **FRENCH OPERA**, 9, b g Bering—On Fair Stage (IRE) **Mrs Judy Wilson & Martin Landau**
57 **GENERAL MILLER**, 7, b g Karinga Bay—Millers Action **W. H. Ponsonby**
58 **GHIMAAR**, 7, b g Dubai Destination (USA)—Charlecote (IRE) **Mr M. F. George**
59 **GIBB RIVER (IRE)**, 6, ch g Mr Greeley (USA)—Laurentine (USA) **Corbett Stud**
60 **GIORGIO QUERCUS (FR)**, 7, b g Starborough—Winter Breeze (FR) **Sir R. Ogden C.B.E., LLD**
61 **GLOBAL FELLA (IRE)**, 7, b g Chevalier (IRE)—Antapoura (IRE) **T. J. Hemmings**
62 **GLORIOUS TWELFTH (IRE)**, 5, b m Old Vic—Bilboa (FR) **Mr & Mrs R. G. Kelvin Hughes**
63 **GRACEY BELLA (IRE)**, 5, b m Vinnie Roe (IRE)—Chione (IRE) **Mr A. K. Whelan**
64 **GRANDOUET (FR)**, 5, b br g Al Namix (USA)—Virginia River (USA) **S. E. Munir**
65 **GREAT REASON**, 8, b g Alflora (IRE)—Grignette (FR) **E. R. Hanbury**
66 **HADRIAN'S APPROACH (IRE)**, 5, b g High Chaparral (IRE)—
     Gifted Approach (IRE) **Mr & Mrs R. G. Kelvin Hughes**
67 **HAMMERSLY LAKE (FR)**, 4, b g Kapgarde (FR)—Loin de Moi (FR) **M. A. C. Buckley**
68 **HEATHER ROYAL**, 6, ch m Medicean—Close Harmony **Mrs R. H. Brown**
69 **HERONRY (IRE)**, 4, b g Heron Island (IRE)—In A Tizzy **The Ten From Seven**
70 **HIGGY'S RAGAZZO (FR)**, 5, b g Sinndar (USA)—Super Crusty (IRE) **I. Higginson**
71 **HINTON INDIANA**, 7, b g Kayf Tara—Hinton Grace **Mrs N. L. M. Moores**
72 **HIT THE HEADLINES (IRE)**, 6, b g Flemensfirth (USA)—Heather Breeze (IRE) **M. A. C. Buckley**
73 **JACK THE GIANT (IRE)**, 10, b g Giant's Causeway (USA)—State Crystal (IRE) **Hanbury Syndicate**
74 **JUST SIXTY (IRE)**, 6, b g Presenting—Mistric **T. J. Hemmings**
75 **KAKI DE LA PREE (FR)**, 5, b g Kapgarde (FR)—Kica (FR) **M. A. C. Buckley**
76 **KARAZHAN**, 4, b g Dr Fong (USA)—Karasta (IRE) **Pump & Plant Services Ltd**

MR NICKY HENDERSON—continued

77 **KELLS BELLE (IRE)**, 6, b m Alflora (IRE)—Clandestine **Brian,Gwen,Terri & Kelly Griffiths**
78 **KEY TO THE WEST (IRE)**, 5, b g Westerner—Monte Solaro (IRE) **Corbett Stud**
79 **KEYS (IRE)**, 5, b g Doyen (IRE)—Freni (GER) **Seasons Holidays**
80 **KID CASSIDY (IRE)**, 6, b g Beneficial—Shuil Na Lee (IRE) **J. P. McManus**
81 **KILLIECRANKIE**, 4, b g Kayf Tara—Bella Macrae **Her Majesty The Queen**
82 **KINGS DESTINY**, 6, b g Dubai Destination (USA)—Jalousie (IRE) **Mr D. A. Yardy**
83 **KINGS LODGE**, 6, b g King's Theatre (IRE)—Mardello **W. H. Ponsonby**
84 **LA REINE DE RIOGH (IRE)**, 5, b m Presenting—Nas Na Riogh (IRE) **Brian J Griffiths & John Nicholson**
85 **LARKS LAD (IRE)**, 8, b g Bob Back (USA)—Higher Again (IRE) **T. J. Hemmings**
86 **LAUDATORY**, 6, b g Royal Applause—Copy-Cat **Mr Eric Newnham and Mrs Julia Newnham**
87 **LETS GET SERIOUS (IRE)**, 6, b g Overbury (IRE)—Vendimia **M. A. C. Buckley**
88 **LIEUTENANT MILLER**, 6, b g Beat All (USA)—Still Runs Deep **W. H. Ponsonby**
89 **LIFESTYLE**, 6, b m Karinga Bay—Like Manner **The Turf Club & David Ford**
90 **LITTLE FRITZ (FR)**, 5, gr g Turgeon (USA)—Hunorisk (FR) **Mr & Mrs J. D. Cotton**
91 **LONG RUN (FR)**, 7, b br g Cadoudal (FR)—Libertina (FR) **R. B. Waley-Cohen**
92 **LOOKING HOPEFUL (IRE)**, 6, b g Heron Island (IRE)—Mahaasin **M. J. & Mrs T. Padfield**
93 **LOOSE PREFORMER (IRE)**, 6, b g Luso—Out Performer (IRE) **Kerr-Dineen, Lloyd Webber & Nielsen**
94 **LYVIUS**, 6, g g Paolini (GER)—Lysuna (GER) **T. J. Hemmings**
95 **MALT MASTER (IRE)**, 5, b g Milan—Dantes Profit (IRE) **Mr J P McManus**
96 **MASTER FIDDLE**, 7, ch g Alflora (IRE)—Fiddling The Facts (IRE) **Mrs E. C. Roberts**
97 **MASTER OF THE GAME (IRE)**, 6, ch g Bob's Return (IRE)—
Lady Monilousha (IRE) **Mr & Mrs R. G. Kelvin Hughes**
98 **MASTER OF THE HALL (IRE)**, 8, b g Saddlers' Hall (IRE)—
Frankly Native (IRE) **Martin Landau & Jonathan Duffy**
99 **MILANELLA (IRE)**, 6, b m Milan—La Zingarella (IRE) **Let's Live Racing**
100 **MINELLA CLASS (IRE)**, 7, br g Oscar (IRE)—Louisas Dream (IRE) **Deal George Kelvin-Hughes Nicolson**
101 **MINELLA FORFITNESS (IRE)**, 5, b g Westerner—Ring of Water (USA) **M. A. C. Buckley**
102 **MISS BALLANTYNE**, 5, br m Definite Article—Gardana (FR) **Mr & Mrs R. G. Kelvin Hughes**
103 **MISTER DILLON**, 5, b g Sulamani—Kabayil **Elite Racing Club**
104 **MOLOTOF (FR)**, 5, gr g Smadoun (FR)—Memorial (FR) **S. E. Munir**
105 **MONO MAN (IRE)**, 6, b g Old Vic—Quadrennial (IRE) **Mrs B. A. Hanbury**
106 **MOSSLEY (IRE)**, 6, b g Old Vic—Sorivera **M. A. C. Buckley**
107 **MUSH MIR (IRE)**, 5, b g Key of Luck (USA)—Mawaheb (IRE) **M Khan X2**
108 **MY TENT OR YOURS (IRE)**, 5, b g Desert Prince—Spartan Girl (IRE) **The Happy Campers**
109 **NADIYA DE LA VEGA (FR)**, 6, b br m Lost World (USA)—Shinobie (FR) **Mr J P McManus**
110 **NATIVE BEAUTY (IRE)**, 6, b m King's Theatre (IRE)—Woodville Star (IRE) **Weatherbys Racing Club**
111 **NELSON'S BRIDGE (IRE)**, 5, b g Oscar (IRE)—High Park Lady (IRE) **J. P. McManus**
112 **OASIS KNIGHT (IRE)**, 6, b g Oasis Dream—Generous Lady **Lady Tennant**
113 **ONE LUCKY LADY**, 4, b f Lucky Story (USA)—One For Philip **S W Group Logistics Limited**
114 **OPEN HEARTED**, 5, b g Generous (IRE)—Romantic Dream **Her Majesty The Queen**
115 **OSCAR NOMINEE (IRE)**, 5, b g Old Vic—Native Bid (IRE) **M. A. C. Buckley**
116 **OSCAR WHISKY (IRE)**, 7, b g Oscar (IRE)—Ash Baloo (IRE) **Walters Plant Hire Ltd**
117 **OSCARA DARA (IRE)**, 7, b g Oscar (IRE)—Lisa's Storm (IRE) **BG Racing Partnership**
118 **OSRIC (IRE)**, 9, b g Mister Mat (FR)—Miss Ondee (FR) **Mr & Mrs R. G. Kelvin Hughes**
119 **OTTO THE GREAT (FR)**, 4, gr g Turgeon (USA)—Hunorisk (FR) **Mr & Mrs J. D. Cotton**
120 **OWEN GLENDOWER (IRE)**, 7, br g Anshan—Native Success (IRE) **The Ten From Seven**
121 **OZETA (IRE)**, 4, gr f Martaline—Ozehy (USA) **J. P. McManus**
122 **PETIT ROBIN (FR)**, 9, b g Robin des Pres (FR)—Joie de Cotte (FR) **Mr & Mrs John Poynton**
123 **PICTURE POST (USA)**, 5, b g Mr Greeley (USA)—Cherokee (USA) **A K Collins**
124 **POLLY PEACHUM (IRE)**, 4, b f Shantou (USA)—Miss Denman (IRE) **Lady Tennant**
125 **PRINCE OF PIRATES (IRE)**, 7, b g Milan—Call Kate (IRE) **J. P. McManus**
126 **PRISTINE (IRE)**, 5, b m Presenting—Hazlewood (IRE) **The Hon Mrs T Ponsonby**
127 **PROBLEMA TIC (FR)**, 6, b g Kapgarde (FR)—Atreide (FR) **Sir R. Ogden C.B.E., LLD**
128 **PRYDE ROCK**, 5, b g Fair Mix (IRE)—Knight Ryde **Mrs G M Tregaskes**
129 **PUNCHESTOWNS (FR)**, 9, ch g Morespeed—History (FR) **Mrs J. Wilson**
130 **QUANTITATIVEEASING (IRE)**, 7, ch g Anshan—Mazuna (IRE) **J. P. McManus**
131 **RACKHAM LEROUGE (FR)**, 7, b g Fado (FR)—History (FR) **Mrs J. Wilson**
132 **RAJDHANI EXPRESS, 5**, br g Presenting—Violet Express (FR) **R. B. Waley-Cohen**
133 **REMEMBER NOW (IRE)**, 6, ch g Anabaa Blue—Bleu Ciel Et Blanc (FR) **Mr J. P. McManus**
134 **RIVER MAIGUE (IRE)**, 5, b g Zagreb (USA)—Minor Tantrum (IRE) **M. A. C. Buckley**
135 **RIVERSIDE THEATRE**, 8, b g King's Theatre (IRE)—Disallowed (IRE) **Jimmy Nesbitt Partnership**
136 **ROI TOSCAN (FR)**, 7, b br g Useful (FR)—Ame Toscane (FR) **P. E. Delaney**
137 **ROJO VIVO**, 6, b g Deploy—Shareef Walk **The Royal Ascot Racing Club**
138 **SECRET WORLD (IRE)**, 9, ch g Spinning World (USA)—Classic Park **Mrs S. M. Roy**
139 **SEMI COLON (FR)**, 6, ch m Robin des Champs (FR)—Hi Colon (FR) **Mrs C. M. Mould**
140 **SENTRY DUTY (FR)**, 10, b g Kahyasi—Standing Around (FR) **P. Spiller**

MR NICKY HENDERSON—continued

141 **SEVEN WOODS (IRE)**, 6, b g Milan—Charlotte's Moss **Mrs L. M. M. Birley**
142 **SHAKALAKABOOMBOOM (IRE)**, 8, b g Anshan—Tia Maria (IRE) **L. Breslin**
143 **SHERNANDO**, 5, b g Hernando (FR)—Shimmering Sea **Mr & Mrs Sandy Orr**
144 **SIMONSIG**, 6, gr g Fair Mix (IRE)—Dusty Too **R. Bartlett**
145 **SISTINE**, 4, b f Dubai Destination (USA)—Fickle **Elite Racing Club**
146 **SKINT**, 6, b g King's Theatre (IRE)—No More Money **Favourites Racing XX**
147 **SOLDATINO (IRE)**, 6, gr g Graveron (FR)—Malory du Chenay (FR) **S. E. Munir**
148 **SOLIWERY (FR)**, 4, b g Equerry (USA)—Solimade (FR) **M. A. C. Buckley**
149 **SOLIX (FR)**, 6, b br g Al Namix (FR)—Solimade (FR) **M. A. C. Buckley**
150 **SPEED MASTER (IRE)**, 6, b g King's Theatre (IRE)—Handy Lass **Walters Plant Hire Ltd**
151 **SPIRIT RIVER (FR)**, 7, b g Poliglote—Love River (FR) **M. A. C. Buckley**
152 **SPIRIT SON (FR)**, 6, b g Poliglote—Kirzinnia (FR) **M. A. C. Buckley**
153 **SPRINTER SACRE (FR)**, 6, b br g Network (GER)—Fatima III (FR) **Mrs C. M. Mould**
154 **STATE BENEFIT (IRE)**, 7, b g Beneficial—Gifted **M. A. C. Buckley**
155 **STATE SENATOR (USA)**, 4, b br g Mr Greeley (USA)—Summer Night **R. C. Tooth**
156 **SUNGLASSES (IRE)**, 5, b g Fruits of Love (USA)—Penny Haven (IRE) **Bradley Partnership**
157 **SURFING (FR)**, 6, b g Califet (FR)—Hawai de Vonnas (FR) **M. A. C. Buckley**
158 **TANKS FOR THAT (IRE)**, 9, br g Beneficial—Lady Jurado (IRE) **Mrs B. A. Hanbury**
159 **TETLAMI (IRE)**, 6, ch g Daylami (IRE)—Tetou (IRE) **Mrs S. M. Roy**
160 **THANKS FOR COMING**, 6, b g Helissio (FR)—Kyle Rhea **Unchartered Waters**
161 **THE WHITE ADMIRAL (IRE)**, 7, wh g Revoque (IRE)—Stage Debut **Miss E. Reeves Purdie**
162 **TISTORY (FR)**, 5, ch g Epalo (GER)—History (FR) **Mrs J. Wilson**
163 **TITAN DE SARTI (FR)**, 5, b br g Kapgarde (FR)—Copie des Planches (FR) **M. A. C. Buckley**
164 **TONY DINOZZO (FR)**, 5, b g Lavirco (GER)—Arika (FR) **Mr J. Andrews**
165 **TOP OF THE RANGE (IRE)**, 5, br g Presenting—Brenny's Pearl (IRE) **Walters Plant Hire Ltd**
166 **TORNADE D'ESTRUVAL (FR)**, 5, b m Network (GER)—Onde d'estruval (FR) **Million in Mind Partnership**
167 **TOUR D'ARGENT (FR)**, 5, b g Martaline—Keep Well (FR) **M. A. C. Buckley**
168 **TRADEWINDS (FR)**, 4, b g Kapgarde (FR)—Royale Floriane (FR) **M. A. C. Buckley**
169 **TRIOLO D'ALENE (FR)**, 5, ch g Epalo (GER)—Joliette d'alene (FR) **Mr & Mrs Sandy Orr**
170 **TROZULON (FR)**, 5, b g Roli Abi (FR)—Manza (FR) **S. E. Munir**
171 **TSAR ALEXANDRE (FR)**, 5, b g Robin des Champs (FR)—Bertrange (FR) **H. R. Mould**
172 **TWO OSCARS (IRE)**, 6, b g Oscar (IRE)—Coumeenoole Lady **Fortnum Racing**
173 **UNE ARTISTE (FR)**, 4, b f Alberto Giacometti (IRE)—Castagnette III (FR) **S. E. Munir**
174 **VEILED**, 6, b m Sadler's Wells (USA)—Evasive Quality **Pump & Plant Services Ltd**
175 **VODKAONTHEROCKS (IRE)**, 4, b g Oscar (IRE)—My Native (IRE) **Walters Plant Hire Ltd**
176 **WESTERN APPROACHES**, 5, b m Westerner—Bayariyka (IRE) **M. H. Watt**
177 **WESTERN MOVIE**, 4, b g Westerner—Fortune's Girl **M. H. Watt**
178 **WHISPER (FR)**, 4, b g Astarabad (USA)—Belle Yepa (FR) **Walters Plant Hire Ltd**
179 **WINNING HABIT**, 7, b g Beat All (USA)—Nunsdream **Mr & Mrs Sandy Orr & Mr John Jarvis**
180 **WISE MOVE (IRE)**, 6, b g Kalanisi (IRE)—Akariyda (IRE) **M. A. C. Buckley**
181 **WOODBANK**, 5, br g Needwood Blade—Potter's Gale (IRE) **James & Jean Potter**
182 **YOU'RE THE TOP (FR)**, 8, b g Poliglote—Lolly Lodge (FR) **M. A. C. Buckley**
183 **YOUNG HURRICANE (IRE)**, 6, b g Oscar (IRE)—Georgia On My Mind (FR) **Mr J. Andrews**
184 **ZAMA ZAMA**, 5, b g Sakhee (USA)—Insinuation (IRE) **M. A. C. Buckley**

Other Owners: S. G. Adams, Mr R. B. Antell, Mrs V. A. P. Antell, Mrs D. E. Austin, M. Ball, Mrs C. M. Bampfylde, Mr D. Bickerton, Mr P. Boyle, Mrs D. C. Broad, A. R. Bromley, Mr C. P. E. Brooks, B. G. Brown, E. Burke, Mr J. P. Byrne, Mr R. M. Cathery, V. W. Chandler, Mr M. J. S. Cockburn, A. K. Collins, P. J. Cornell, J. D. Cotton, Mrs B. Cotton, R. Cressey, G. M. Davies, P A. Deal, K. H. M. Doyle, Mr P. J. Dudson, J. B. Duffy, Mrs G. J. Edwards, A. T. Eggleton, Mr D. G. Ford, L. R. Frampton, Mr A. J. Garton, Mr D. A. George, Mr I. H. Goldsmith, G. F. Goode, Mr M. J. Gould, B. J. Griffiths, Mrs G. E. A. Griffiths, C. O. P. Hanbury, R. V. Harding, Mr S. Harris, A. J. Hill, Mr B. L. Hiskey, J. Hornsey, Mr E. J. Hughes, R. A. Hurst, Mr R. A. Jacobs, Mrs A. S. Jacobs, Miss Y. M. G. Jacques, J. F. Jarvis, Mr F. Kelleher, R. G. Kelvin-Hughes, Mrs E. A. Kelvin-Hughes, M. Kerr-Dineen, M. Khan, M. Khan, Mr M. B. J. Kimmins, M. R. Landau, The Hon Mrs J. V. Leigh, Lady Lloyd-Webber, Mr J. Lomas, Mr M. J. Lowry, Mr T. G. Marlow, Mrs L. E. Marlow, C. Marner, Miss N. Martin, Mr C. W. Matthews, Mr D. M. Menzies, Mr I. D. Miller, W. D. C. Minton, Mr D. Murdoch, Miss J. S. Murdoch, Mr W. J. Nesbitt, Mr E. R. Newnham, Mrs J. T. Newnham, J. M. Nicholson, Mrs D. C. Nicholson, M. M. Nicolson, B. E. Nielsen, Miss M. Noden, Mr J. O'Keefe, Mrs C. R. Orr, Mr J. A. M. Orr, Mr J. Padfield, Mrs T. Padfield, J. Peter-Hoblyn, Dr C. E. Ponsonby, The Hon Mrs M. H. Ponsonby, J. E. Potter, Mrs M. J. Potter, J. Poynton, Mrs A. Poynton, Mr S. A. Prater, Brig C. K. Price, Mrs D. Pye, Mrs J. Rees, Paul Robson, U. E. Schwarzenbach, W. G. C. Shaw, Mr G. A. Sheppard, Mr J. Simpson, Mr R. H. D. Smith, B. T. Stewart-Brown Esq, D. F. Sumpter, Mr R. Thayne, Turf Club 2010, Mr M. T. Ward, J. R. Weatherby, Mr R. N. Weatherby, Mrs C. Wells, J. Whittle, Miss S. Wilde, Mrs K. L. Yates, Lord de Mauley.

Jockey (NH): Barry Geraghty, Felix De Giles, A. P. McCoy, Andrew Tinkler. **Conditional:** Richard Killoran, David Bass, Gary Derwin, Jeremiah McGrath, Charlie Wallis. **Amateur:** Mr Nico De Boinville, Mr Jack Sherwood.

322 **MR PAUL HENDERSON, Fordingbridge**
Postal: **Furlong Cottage, Down Farm, Rockbourne, Fordingbridge, Hampshire, SP6 3NY**
Contacts: PHONE **(01725) 518113** FAX **(01725) 518113** MOBILE **(07958) 482213**
E-MAIL **phendersonracing@gmail.com**

1 ADMIRAL BOOM (IRE), 6, b g Beneficial—Gleann Na Smaointe (IRE) **P. F. Henderson**
2 CAPDALIGHT (IRE), 9, b g Simply Great (FR)—A Rare One (IRE) **The Rockbourne Partnership**
3 CARLETON PLACE (IRE), 9, b g Beneficial—Beau Belle (IRE) **Mr R. B. Antell**
4 JOHNNY MULLEN (IRE), 9, b g Bishop of Cashel—Native Land **The Rockbourne Partnership**
5 MINELLA SPECIAL (IRE), 6, b g King's Theatre (IRE)—Della Wee (IRE) **Mr R. & Mrs V. Antell**
6 ONCLE KID (FR), 10, b g Kidder (FR)—Hanoi City (FR) **Mrs M. A. Cole**
7 ONLY VINTAGE (USA), 12, b g Diesis—Wild Vintage (USA) **D. S. Dennis**
8 OSCAR CHARLIE (IRE), 7, b g Oscar (IRE)—Leefen Queen **Mrs**
9 TENZING (IRE), 8, b g Luso—Black Dale (IRE) **GLR Racing & Partners**
10 THE SOCIETY MAN (IRE), 5, ch g Moscow Society (USA)—Redruth (IRE) **The Ray Of Hope Partnership**

Other Owners: Mr Ray Antell, Mr Gary Evans, Mr R. J. Galpin, Mr Russ Griffin, Mr Paul Henderson.

323 **LADY HERRIES, Littlehampton**
Postal: **Angmering Park, Littlehampton, West Sussex, BN16 4EX**
Contacts: YARD **(01903) 871605** HOME **(01903) 871421** FAX **(01903) 871609**
MOBILE **(07785) 282996**
E-MAIL **angparkstables@btconnect.com**

1 BOUGGATTI, 4, b g Tobougg (IRE)—Western Sal **Lady S. Clutton**
2 4, B c Arch (USA)—Copper Rose (USA) **Lady S. Clutton**
3 DUMBFOUNDED (FR), 4, b br g Vettori (IRE)—Take The Light (FR) **Lady S. Clutton**
4 EASTER FAYRE, 5, gr m Fair Mix (IRE)—Meant To Be **Lady Mary Mumford**
5 GENEVA GEYSER (GER), 6, b g One Cool Cat (USA)—Genevra (IRE) **Angmering Park**
6 HONOUR HIGH, 10, gr g Cloudings (IRE)—Meant To Be **Lady Mary Mumford**
7 JEWELLED, 6, b m Fantastic Light (USA)—Danemere (IRE) **Seymour Bloodstock (UK) Ltd**
8 SWIFT BLADE (IRE), 4, ch g Exceed And Excel (AUS)—Gold Strike (IRE) **Angmering Park**
9 TOBAGO, 4, ch g Bertolini (USA)—Heavenly Bay (USA) **Angmering Park**

Other Owners: Lady Herries.

324 **MR MICHAEL HERRINGTON, Thirsk**
Postal: **Garbutt Farm, Cold Kirby, Thirsk, North Yorkshire, YO7 2HJ**
Contacts: PHONE **(01845) 597966** MOBILE **(07855) 396858**
E-MAIL **hjlloyd@blackberry.orange.co.uk**

1 CHEYENNE RED (IRE), 6, br g Namid—Red Leggings **Mr J. S. Herrington**
2 DUKE OF RAINFORD, 5, gr g Bahamian Bounty—Night Haven **Mr J. S. Herrington**

Assistant Trainer: Helen Lloyd-Herrington

325 **MR PETER HIATT, Banbury**
Postal: **Six Ash Farm, Hook Norton, Banbury, Oxfordshire, OX15 5DB**
Contacts: PHONE **(01608) 737255** FAX **(01608) 730641** MOBILE **(07973) 751115**

1 BOW RIVER ARCH (USA), 4, b f Arch (USA)—Bow River Gold **M. S. Anderson**
2 FLAG OF GLORY, 5, b g Trade Fair—Rainbow Sky **N. D. Edden**
3 MANDHOOMA, 6, b m Oasis Dream—Shatarah **P. W. Hiatt**
4 MASHDOOD (USA), 6, b g Sinndar (IRE)—Rahayeb **Mr A. D. Swinburne**
5 MASLAK (IRE), 8, b g In The Wings—Jeed (IRE) **P. W. Hiatt**
6 MAZIJ, 4, b f Haafhd—Salim Toto **P. W. Hiatt**
7 MENADATI (USA), 4, b g More Than Ready (USA)—Ramatuelle (CHI) **Mr C. Demczak**
8 MOONSHINE RUBY, 6, ch m Minster Son—Over The Moon **Mr E. P. Spain**
9 RAGHDAAN, 5, ch g Haafhd—Inaaq **P. W. Hiatt**
10 RHINESTONE REBEL, 6, ch g Rashar (USA)—Flute Opera (IRE) **P. Porter**
11 SHIRATAKI (IRE), 4, b g Cape Cross (IRE)—Noodle Soup (USA) **P. W. Hiatt**
12 SPIRITONTHEMOUNT (USA), 7, b br g Pulpit (USA)—Stirling Bridge (USA) **R. N. Coles**
13 TUXEDO, 7, ch g Cadeaux Genereux—Serengeti Bride (USA) **P. Kelly**
14 VERY WELL RED, 9, b m First Trump—Little Scarlett **P. Kelly**

MR PETER HIATT—continued

15 WAAHEJ, 6, b g Haafhd—Madam Ninette **Monarch Hose & Hydraulics / P W Hiatt**
16 WHODUNIT (UAE), 8, b g Mark of Esteem (IRE)—Mystery Play (IRE) **Exors of the Late Mr J. W. Hedges**

Assistant Trainer: Mrs E. Hiatt

Jockey (flat): Chris Catlin, William Carson. **Apprentice:** Ryan Clark. **Amateur:** Miss M. Edden.

---

326 **MRS LAWNEY HILL, Aston Rowant**
Postal: Woodway Farm, Aston Rowant, Watlington, Oxford, OX49 5SJ
Contacts: PHONE (01844) 353051 FAX (01844) 354751 MOBILE (07769) 862648
E-MAIL lawney@lawneyhill.co.uk WEBSITE www.lawneyhill.co.uk

1 ADAMO (GER), 8, ch g Kornado—Ad Augusta (FR) **Alwyn Phillips Robbie Kaiser Mark Chesterton**
2 ANDREW NICK (IRE), 10, b g Riberetto—Legal Tour (IRE) **W. F. Caudwell**
3 BAILY STORM (IRE), 10, br g Anshan—Euroblend (IRE) **Chasing Gold Limited**
4 BETAVIX, 9, br g Cloudings (IRE)—Lay It Off (IRE) **Christopher Shankland & Diana Clark**
5 BROUGH ACADEMY (IRE), 6, b g Key of Luck (USA)—Cantaloupe **W. F. Caudwell**
6 CAP ELORN (FR), 6, b g Kapgarde (FR)—Legretta (USA) **Mr A. J. Weller**
7 CHAMPION VERSIONS (IRE), 5, b g Presenting—Kelly Gales (IRE) **Ms J. Matthews**
8 CHAPOLIMOSS (FR), 8, ch g Trempolino (USA)—Chamoss (FR) **A Barr, J Basquill, A Hill, H Mullineux**
9 DIVINE FOLLY (IRE), 7, b g Kotashaan (FR)—Jennys Grove (IRE) **Mrs H. C. Mullineux**
10 DOCTOR DAVID, 9, gr g Zilzal (USA)—Arantxa **Dr D. S. Myers & Mr A. S. Reid**
11 DOUBLE HANDFUL (GER), 6, bl g Pentire—Durania (GER) **Mr M. Fossey**
12 DUNLOUGH BAY (IRE), 6, ch g Flemensfirth (USA)—Loch Lomond (IRE) **The Horwoods Partnership**
13 FIVEWAYS (IRE), 9, b g Broken Hearted—Kilbricken Star **Mr R. E. Good, Mr C. J. Collins, Mr P. J. Morgan**
14 FRONTIER DANCER (IRE), 8, b g New Frontier (IRE)—All The Gear (IRE) **Jump For Fun Racing**
15 GENUINE PEARL (IRE), 8, b g Desert King (IRE)—Pearl Kite (USA) **The Specials**
16 GIANT O MURCHU (IRE), 8, b g Carroll House—Centralspires Best **A. Hill**
17 MID DIV AND CREEP, 12, b m Sovereign Water (FR)—Knightsbridge Bred **Mrs K. G. Exall**
18 MIGHTY MAMBO, 5, b g Fantastic Light (USA)—Mambo's Melody **Fortnum Racing**
19 MINELLA THEATRE (IRE), 8, b g King's Theatre (IRE)—Ring of Water (USA) **Mr D. R. Gilbert**
20 MY MATILDA, 9, gr m Silver Patriarch (IRE)—Upton Lass (IRE) **L. G. Kimber**
21 MZURI BAY, 7, b g Arkadian Hero (USA)—Eyelet (IRE) **Ms R. Tupper & Mr T. H. Fletcher**
22 ROYAL ETIQUETTE (IRE), 5, b g Royal Applause—Alpine Gold (IRE) **John Bull & Alan Hill**
23 SAFE INVESTMENT (USA), 8, b g Gone West—Fully Invested (USA) **A. Hill**
24 SUPER VILLAN, 7, ch g Alflora (IRE)—Country House **M. S. Tamburro**
25 TURTLETHOMAS (IRE), 6, br g Turtle Island (IRE)—Makingyourmindup (IRE) **Mr A. J. Weller**

Other Owners: Mr Andrew Barr, Mr J. M. Basquill, Mrs Diana Clark, Mr C. J. Collins, Mr T. H. Fletcher, Mr Edwyn Good, Mr Alan Hill, Mr Brian Hiskey, Mr Robbie Kaiser, Mr P. J. Morgan, Mr E. Mulleady, Mrs Helen Mullineux, Dr D. S. Myers, Mr T. Nolan, Mr A. M. Phillips, Mr A. S. Reid, Mr Ian A. Robinson, Mrs Gillian Robinson, Mr Christopher Shankland, Mr R. I. Sims, Mrs Jennifer Smith, Mr D. F. Sumpter, Ms Ruth Tupper.

Jockey (flat): Dane O'Neill. **Jockey (NH):** Aidan Coleman, Harry Skelton. **Conditional:** David Bass. **Amateur:** Mr J. E. Tudor, Mr J. F. Mathias.

---

327 **MR MARTIN HILL, Totnes**
Postal: The Barn, Knaves Ash Stables, Nr Redpost, Littlehempston, Totnes, Devon, TQ9 6NG
Contacts: PHONE (01803) 813102 MOBILE (07980) 490220
E-MAIL info@martinhillracing.co.uk WEBSITE www.martinhillracing.co.uk

1 BEAT THE SYSTEM, 9, b g Beat All (USA)—Ardentinny **M. E. Hill**
2 CALZAGHE (IRE), 8, ch g Galileo (IRE)—Novelette **Mr R. Thomasson**
3 HENRY THE FIRST (IRE), 7, br g Winged Love (IRE)—Overbury Star **M. E. Hill**
4 HIGGSY, 4, ch g Generous (IRE)—Carmel's Joy (IRE) **M. E. Hill**
5 INSPECTOR QICS, 8, b g Alflora (IRE)—Tamergale (IRE) **Hackett & Mascall**
6 IRONPIN, 5, b g Thank Heavens—Kingston Black **M. E. Hill**
7 MAKIN A FUSS, 10, gr g J B Quick—Shadi Lady (IRE) **M. E. Hill**
8 RED RIVER RUN, 5, ch g Central Park (IRE)—Burning Shore (IRE) **2009 BC**
9 RYDON PYNES, 4, b g Beat All (USA)—Persian Smoke **The Rydon Pynes Partnership**
10 SECRET QUEEN, 5, b m Zafeen (FR)—Gold Queen **Mr M. Leach**

MR MARTIN HILL—continued

Other Owners: Mr J. L. Coombs, Mr C. E. Hackett, J. S. Hearne, Ms S. J. Mascall, Mr I. R. Tharby.

Assistant Trainer: Rachel Williams

Jockey (flat): Jimmy Quinn. **Jockey (NH):** Sam Thomas, Nick Scholfield. **Apprentice:** Amy Baker, Ross Atkinson.

---

328 MR CHARLES HILLS, Lambourn
Postal: **Wetherdown House, Lambourn, Hungerford, Berkshire, RG17 8UB**
Contacts: PHONE **(01488) 71548** FAX **(01488) 72823**
E-MAIL info@charleshills.co.uk WEBSITE www.charleshills.com

1 CAPTAIN BERTIE (IRE), 4, ch g Captain Rio—Sadika (IRE) **Mr A. L. R. Morton**
2 COOL MACAVITY (IRE), 4, b g One Cool Cat (USA)—Cause Celebre (IRE) **Triermore Stud**
3 DESERT STRIKE, 6, b g Bertolini (USA)—Mary Jane **Dorsia Racing**
4 EARLY APPLAUSE, 4, b g Royal Applause—Early Evening **Mr C. W. Jenkins**
5 EVELYN MAY (IRE), 6, b m Acclamation—Lady Eberspacher (IRE) **Mrs B. W. Hills**
6 FADHAA (IRE), 4, b c Bahri (USA)—Weqaar (USA) **Hamdan Al Maktoum**
7 FINE THREADS, 4, b f Barathea (IRE)—Pink Cristal **Lady Bamford**
8 RAASEKHA, 4, b f Pivotal—Tahrir (IRE) **Hamdan Al Maktoum**
9 RANSOM NOTE, 5, b h Red Ransom (USA)—Zacheta **Mr H. R. Mould**
10 RED JAZZ (USA), 5, b h Johannesburg (USA)—Now That's Jazz (USA) **Mr R. J. Arculli**
11 REDWOOD, 6, b h High Chaparral (IRE)—Arum Lily (USA) **Mr K. Abdulla**
12 ROUGETTE, 4, b f Red Ransom (USA)—Never A Doubt **Mr D. M. James**
13 SHROPSHIRE (IRE), 4, gr g Shamardal (USA)—Shawanni **The Hon Mrs J. M. Corbett & Mr C. Wright**
14 WHITE FROST (IRE), 4, gr c Verglas (IRE)—Moivouloirtoi (USA) **Mr & Mrs J. D. Cotton**

THREE-YEAR-OLDS

15 AMBER SILK (IRE), b f Lawman (FR)—Faraday Light (IRE) **Mr Jeremy Gompertz**
16 ANGELS WILL FALL (IRE), b f Acclamation—Coconut Squeak **Mrs E. O'Leary**
17 AT THE LIMIT, b c Three Valleys (USA)—Fonage **Mr K. Abdulla**
18 AUSTRALIA FAIR, ch f Pivotal—Australian Dreams **Mr J. Acheson**
19 BALTY BOYS (IRE), b c Cape Cross (IRE)—
     Chatham Islands (USA) **Sir Alex Ferguson, Cavendish Investing Ltd, J. Hanson**
20 BASSETERRE (IRE), b c Cape Cross (IRE)—Higher Love (IRE) **Mr H. R. Mould**
21 BUNRAKU, b f Cacique (IRE)—Wooden Doll (USA) **Mr K. Abdulla**
22 COCKNEY DANCER, ch f Cockney Rebel (IRE)—Roo **Mr Phil Cunningham**
23 CRYPTIC CHOICE (IRE), b g Johannesburg (USA)—Royal Fupeg (USA) **Mr John C. Grant & Mr A. L. R. Morton**
24 DARK DON (IRE), b c Dark Angel (IRE)—
     Bint Al Hammour (IRE) **Cavendish Investing Ltd, Sir Alex Ferguson, J. Hanson**
25 DIVEA, b f Dylan Thomas (IRE)—Cumin (USA) **Lady Bamford**
26 ELLAAL, b c Oasis Dream—Capistrano Day (USA) **Hamdan Al Maktoum**
27 ENSEJAAM (CAN), b br f Dynaformer (USA)—Catch The Ring (CAN) **Hamdan Al Maktoum**
28 FINAL CALL, b f Rail Link—Well Warned **Mr K. Abdulla**
29 FORGOTTEN HERO (IRE), b c High Chaparral (IRE)—
     Sundown **J. Hanson, Cavendish Investing Ltd, Sir Alex Ferguson**
30 GLEN MOSS (IRE), b c Moss Vale (IRE)—Sail With The Wind **Mr John C. Grant**
31 GRAY PEARL, gr f Excellent Art—Divine Grace (IRE) **Mr H. R. Mould**
32 HAZEL LAVERY (IRE), b f Excellent Art—Reprise **R. Morecombe, E. O'Leary, R. Scarborough**
33 HEY FIDDLE FIDDLE (IRE), b f One Cool Cat (USA)—Crystal Valkyrie (IRE) **Triermore Stud**
34 HEYAARAAT (IRE), b f Lawman (FR)—Lanzana (IRE) **Hamdan Al Maktoum**
35 INUNDATE (USA), b c Pleasant Tap (USA)—Tinge (USA) **Mr K. Abdulla**
36 KAAFEL (IRE), b c Nayef (USA)—Tafaani (IRE) **Hamdan Al Maktoum**
37 LAWN JAMIL (USA), b c Jazil (USA)—Khazayin (USA) **Hamdan Al Maktoum**
38 LINKABLE, b c Rail Link—Fashionable **Mr K. Abdulla**
39 LITMUS (USA), ch f Latent Heat (USA)—Fairy Glade (USA) **Mr K. Abdulla**
40 LUNARMON LAD (IRE), b c Red Clubs (IRE)—Blue Crystal (IRE) **Canwales**
41 MARGATE, b f Mizzen Mast (USA)—Cinnamon Bay **Mr K. Abdulla**
42 MEZMAAR, b c Teofilo (IRE)—Bay Tree (IRE) **Hamdan Al Maktoum**
43 MODEL PUPIL, b c Sinndar (IRE)—Modesta (IRE) **Mr K. Abdulla**
44 MOODHILL, b c Dansili—Almurooj **Hamdan Al Maktoum**
45 NEVER SATISFIED, ch g Haafhd—Pirouetting **Mr B. W. Hills**
46 PERENNIAL, ch c Motivator—Arum Lily (USA) **Mr K. Abdulla**
47 PIECE OF CAKE, b f Exceed And Excel (AUS)—Sundae Girl (USA) **Mr Steve Jenkins & Mr Derek James**
48 PRIVATE MEANS, b f Dansili—Market Forces **Mr K. Abdulla**

MR CHARLES HILLS—continued

49 **QANNAAS (USA)**, br c Hard Spun (USA)—Windsong (USA) **Hamdan Al Maktoum**
50 **RAZORBILL (USA)**, b c Speightstown (USA)—High Walden (USA) **Mr K. Abdulla**
51 **RED ART (IRE)**, b c Excellent Art—All Began (IRE) **Mr Des Anderson & Mr R. J. Arculli**
52 **RED DANZIG (IRE)**, b g Desert Style (IRE)—Hemaca **Mr R. J. Arculli & Mr Des Anderson**
53 **RED SENOR (IRE)**, b c Red Clubs (IRE)—Belsay **Mr R. J. Arculli**
54 **RED TRUMP (IRE)**, b c Red Clubs—Wolf Cleugh (IRE) **Mr R. J. Arculli**
55 **REVEAL THE STAR (USA)**, b f Aptitude (USA)—Rouwaki (USA) **Mr K. Abdulla**
56 **REVELETTE (USA)**, b f Mizzen Mast (USA)—Skimble (USA) **Mr K. Abdulla**
57 **RUGOSA**, b f Oasis Dream—Zathonia **Mr K. Abdulla**
58 **SAFARJAL (IRE)**, b f Marju (IRE)—Wijdan (USA) **Hamdan Al Maktoum**
59 **SELF CENTRED**, ch f Medicean—Ego **Mrs E. Roberts**
60 **SEQUOIA**, b c Shamardal (USA)—Atnab (USA) **Mr H. R. Mould**
61 **SHAME ON YOU (IRE)**, ch f Shamardal (USA)—Woodlass (USA) **Cavendish Investing Ltd**
62 **SHAWKA**, b f Oasis Dream—Wissal (USA) **Hamdan Al Maktoum**
63 **SIR FREDLOT (IRE)**, b g Choisir (AUS)—Wurfklinge (GER) **Mr P. Winkworth & Mr Rupert Williams**
64 **SIR PEDRO**, b c Acclamation—Milly-M **R. Morecombe, J. Netherthorpe, C. Wright**
65 **SPACE RAIDER (AUS)**, ch g Starcraft (NZ)—Lacandona (USA) **S W Group Logistics Limited**
66 **TAJAWWUB (USA)**, b c Dynaformer (USA)—Ladue (USA) **Hamdan Al Maktoum**
67 **UNEX MONA LISA**, b f Shamardal (USA)—Friendlier **Mr W. J. Gredley**
68 **VILLAGE GREEN**, b c Green Desert (USA)—Avessia **Mr D. J. Deer**
69 **WEST LEAKE DIMAN (IRE)**, b c Namid—Roselyn **Mr Henry Barton**
70 **WEST LEAKE HARE (IRE)**, b c Choisir (AUS)—March Hare **Mr Henry Barton**
71 **WILLIES WONDER (IRE)**, b c Moss Vale (IRE)—Red Letter **John C. Grant, Ray Harper, B. W. Hills**

TWO-YEAR-OLDS

72 B c 13/2 Daaher (CAN)—Abby Road (IRE) (Danehill (USA))
73 **ALWAYS SATISFIED**, b c 9/4 Haafhd—Pirouetting (Pivotal)
74 B f 21/2 Dansili—Arum Lily (USA) (Woodman (USA))
75 B f 12/2 High Chaparral (IRE)—Attilia (GER) (Tiger Hill (IRE)) (35000)
76 B f 30/3 Excellent Art—Bali Breeze (IRE) (Common Grounds) (86206)
77 **BESPOKE JOE**, b g 24/2 Royal Applause—Spinning Lucy (IRE) (Spinning World (USA)) (5000)
78 **CAMISOLE (IRE)**, br f 12/2 Teofilo (IRE)—Sleeveless (USA) (Fusaichi Pegasus (USA)) (78000)
79 Ch f 29/1 Giant's Causeway (USA)—Cast In Gold (IRE) (Elusive Quality (USA)) (60000)
80 B c 7/4 Dark Angel (IRE)—Charlene Lacy (IRE) (Pips Pride) (36000)
81 B c 27/2 Dixie Union—Daffaash (USA) (Mr Greeley) (60000)
82 B c 2/4 Acclamation—Delphie Queen (IRE) (Desert Sun) (60000)
83 **ENGLISHMAN**, b c 7/2 Royal Applause—Tesary (Danehill (USA)) (34285)
84 B br f 13/3 Henrythenavigator (USA)—Fabulous Fairy (USA) (Alydar (USA))
85 Br f 19/4 Lawman (FR)—Faraday Light (Rainbow Quest (USA)) (41050)
86 B c 22/4 Footstepsinthesand—Farbenspiel (IRE) (Desert Prince (IRE)) (66666)
87 Ch f 12/3 Medicean—Frabjous (Pivotal) (30000)
88 **FUNK SOUL BROTHER**, b c 8/3 Cockney Rebel (IRE)—Sweet Afton (IRE) (Mujadil (USA)) (61904)
89 B c 22/4 Cockney Rebel (IRE)—Fustaan (IRE) (Royal Applause)
90 B c 6/2 Mizzen Mast (USA)—Geographic (USA) (Empire Maker (USA))
91 **GLEN GINNIE (IRE)**, b f 12/4 Red Clubs (IRE)—Belsay (Belmez (USA)) (53365)
92 **GLENARD**, b c 23/2 Arch (USA)—Olaya (USA) (Theatrical) (65000)
93 B c 5/3 Captain Marvelous (IRE)—Glory Days (GER) (Tiger Hill (IRE)) (21000)
94 B c 25/2 Dylan Thomas (IRE)—Golden Dew (IRE) (Montjeu (IRE)) (110000)
95 Ch f 21/4 Bahamian Bounty—Halland Park Girl (IRE) (Primo Dominie) (23280)
96 B c 18/4 Indian Charlie (USA)—Hatpin (USA) (Smart Strike (CAN)) (198412)
97 B c 17/2 Royal Applause—Helen Sharp (Pivotal) (40000)
98 B f 7/3 Excellent Art—Hendrina (IRE) (Daylami (IRE)) (18000)
99 B c 15/4 Royal Applause—Hidden Heart (USA) (Kingmambo (USA)) (31198)
100 B f 30/4 Holy Roman Emperor (IRE)—Le Montrachet (Nashwan (USA)) (20000)
101 **LUCKY BEGGAR (IRE)**, gr c 27/3 Verglas (IRE)—Lucky Clio (IRE) (Key of Luck (USA)) (18061)
102 B c 11/4 Invincible Spirit (IRE)—Lulua (USA) (Bahri (USA)) (280000)
103 B c 22/1 Dixie Union (USA)—Mabaahej (USA) (Belong To Me (USA))
104 **MRS WARREN**, b f 23/1 Kyllachy—Bold Bunny (Piccolo) (42857)
105 B c 22/5 Oasis Dream—Musical Horizon (USA) (Distant View (USA))
106 **MY HEARTS RACING (IRE)**, b f 25/3 Montjeu (IRE)—Nuriva (USA) (Woodman (USA))
107 B f 9/3 Kyllachy—Never Away (Royal Applause) (40000)
108 **NOBLE BULL (IRE)**, b c 2/2 Papal Bull—Fernlawn Hope (IRE) (Danehill Dancer (IRE)) (23000)
109 **ONE WORD MORE (IRE)**, b c 18/3 Thousand Words—Somoushe (IRE) (Black Minnaloushe (USA)) (34285)
110 B f 10/4 Manduro (GER)—Penang Pearl (FR) (Bering)
111 Ch f 22/4 Rock of Gibraltar (IRE)—Penny Cross (Efisio)

MR CHARLES HILLS—continued

112 B c 21/3 Invasor (ARG)—Plenty of Sugar (CAN) (Ascot Knight (CAN))
113 B f 13/5 Lawman (FR)—Portelet (Night Shift (USA)) (42000)
114 B f 11/4 Shirocco (GER)—Portodora (USA) (Kingmambo (USA))
115 B c 20/3 Aussie Rules (USA)—Reinstated (IRE) (Galileo (IRE)) (13957)
116 B c 3/3 Royal Applause—Rolexa (Pursuit of Love) (90000)
117 Ch f 20/2 Mizzen Mast (USA)—Single Market (USA) (Dynaformer (USA))
118 **SOCIETY PEARL (IRE),** b f 12/3 Kheleyf (USA)—Mamonta (Fantastic Light (USA)) (30377)
119 B f 31/3 Pivotal—Speed Song (Fasliyev (USA)) (110000)
120 B c 9/4 Haatef (USA)—Star of Siligo (USA) (Saratoga Six (USA))
121 Br f 10/4 Shirocco (GER)—Starring (FR) (Ashkalani (IRE)) (30000)
122 B f 12/5 Galileo (IRE)—State Crystal (IRE) (High Estate)
123 B f 10/3 Excellent Art—Subito (Darshaan) (53365)
124 **SUNBULA (USA),** ch f 20/3 Singspiel (IRE)—Uroobah (USA) (Dynaformer (USA))
125 B c 7/4 Green Desert (USA)—Sundus (USA) (Sadler's Wells (USA))
126 B f 28/1 Tamayuz—Tafaani (IRE) (Green Desert (USA))
127 B f 1/4 Zamindar (USA)—Tahrir (IRE) (Linamix (FR))
128 B c 18/4 Red Clubs (IRE)—Tifariti (USA) (Elusive Quality (USA)) (92000)
129 B f 25/3 Intikhab (USA)—Viola Royale (IRE) (Royal Academy (USA)) (53365)
130 B f 10/2 Beat Hollow—Western Appeal (USA) (Gone West (USA))
131 Gr c 12/2 Smoke Glacken (USA)—Zaghruta (USA) (Gone West (USA))

Other Owners: AEGIS Partnership, Mr N. N. Browne, Cam Clark, Mr Tony Elliott, Mrs G. Galvin, George Gosbee, Mrs Barbara James, Mr M. V. Magnier, Mr Paul McNamara, Mr & Mrs G. Middlebrook, Mr A. Nicoll, Mrs A. K. H. Ooi, Pearl Bloodstock, Mrs Richard Plummer, Mrs J. K. Powell, Mr David F. Powell, Mr Nicholas Roberts, Mr S. E. Sangster, B. V. Sangster, Mr R. A. Scarborough, Mrs Paul Shanahan, Mr J. A. Wechsler, Lady Wellesley.

Assistant Trainer: Kevin Mooney

Jockey (flat): Michael Hills. **Apprentice:** Matthew Lawson.

---

329 **MR J. W. HILLS, Lambourn**
Postal: **The Croft, Upper Lambourn, Newbury, Berkshire, RG17 8QH**
Contacts: **PHONE (01488) 73144 FAX (01488) 73099 MOBILE (07836) 283091**
E-MAIL john@johnhills.com WEBSITE www.johnhills.com

1 **HYGROVE WELSHLADY (IRE),** 4, b f Langfuhr (CAN)—Milwaukee (FR) **Mr D. H. Francis**
2 **POTENTIALE (IRE),** 8, ch g Singspiel (IRE)—No Frills (IRE) **Tony Waspe & Partners**
3 **SSAFA,** 4, b f Motivator—Orange Sunset (IRE) **Prolinx Limited**

THREE-YEAR-OLDS

4 B FIFTY TWO (IRE), br c Dark Angel (IRE)—Petite Maxine **Gary & Linnet Woodward**
5 **BOHEMIAN RHAPSODY (IRE),** b c Galileo (IRE)—Quiet Mouse (USA) **Hammers & Woodies**
6 **BOOMERANG BOB (IRE),** b c Aussie Rules (USA)—Cozzene's Pride (USA) **R. J. Tufft**
7 **CHA CHING (IRE),** b f Elnadim (USA)—Sudden Interest (FR) **Mrs S. Fenton**
8 **EXCELLENT NEWS (IRE),** ch f Excellent Art—Subito **J W Hills & Partners**
9 B g Lemon Drop Kid (USA)—Faux Pas (IRE)
10 **FEISTY CHAMPION (IRE),** b c Captain Rio—Deylviyna (IRE) **Mr M. C. E. Wong**
11 **INFINITE JEST,** ch c Danehill Dancer—Noelani (IRE) **Abbott Racing Partners**
12 **JOHNNO,** br c Excellent Art—Vert Val (USA) **Gary & Linnet Woodward**
13 **MARIA MONTEZ,** b f Piccolo—Easy Feeling (IRE) **Mr J. M. Cole**
14 **NAUGHTICAL,** ch f Haafhd—Mid Ocean **G. P. Troeller**
15 **PADDYFROMMENLO (IRE),** ch c Hurricane Run (IRE)—Dolce Dovo **Mr S. C. P. McDonagh**
16 **PRESS BARON,** ch c King's Best (USA)—Esteraad (IRE) **Mr J. M. Cole**
17 **REMIX (IRE),** b f Oratorio (IRE)—Miss Lopez (IRE) **Mrs F. Hills**
18 **SEARCH AND RESCUE (USA),** b br c Seeking The Best (IRE)—Pattern Step (USA) **G. P. Troeller**
19 **THE ROYAL (IRE),** b f Exceed And Excel (AUS)—Porthcawl **Glyn Charles & Usk Valley Stud**
20 **VIRGINIA GALLICA (IRE),** b f Galileo (IRE)—Papering (IRE) **Corinthian**
21 **WESTWARD HOPE (USA),** b br c Mr Greeley (USA)—Morning Cry (USA) **Mr P. A. Abberley**
22 **XINBAMA (IRE),** b c Baltic King—Persian Empress (IRE) **Xinbama Partnership**

TWO-YEAR-OLDS

23 B c 24/3 Sixties Icon—Aileen's Gift (IRE) (Rainbow Quest (USA)) (58000) **Gary & Linnet Woodward**
24 B f 2/4 Danehill Dancer (IRE)—Amethyst (IRE) (Sadler's Wells (USA)) **Corinthian**
25 Ch c 22/1 Danehill Dancer (IRE)—Arosa (IRE) (Sadler's Wells (USA)) (50000)

MR J. W. HILLS—continued

26 Br c 14/3 Avonbridge—Belle's Edge (Danehill Dancer (IRE)) (26666) **Mrs D. Abberley**
27 Ch f 5/3 Singspiel (IRE)—Carson Dancer (USA) (Carson City (USA))
28 B c 17/4 Red Clubs (IRE)—Dai E Dai (USA) (Seattle Dancer (USA)) (17500)
29 B f 2/3 Duke of Marmalade (IRE)—Elegant Pride (Beat Hollow) (17000)
30 B c 29/3 Excellent Art—Enchanting Way (Linamix (FR)) (20524)
31 B c 21/3 Galileo (IRE)—Flamingo Guitar (USA) (Storm Cat (USA)) (50000) **Prolinx Limited**
32 B f 4/3 Hurricane Run (IRE)—Foreign Relation (IRE) (Distant Relative) (28735)
33 Ch f 1/2 Excellent Art—Greenvera (USA) (Riverman (USA))
34 B f 9/3 Nayef (USA)—Isle of Spice (USA) (Diesis) **Hills' Angels**
35 KONZERT (ITY), b c 27/3 Hurricane Cat (USA)—Known Alibi (USA) (Known Fact (USA)) (13957)
36 B f 6/4 Elusive City (USA)—Lady Angola (IRE) (Lord At War (ARG)) (11428)
37 B c 28/2 Aussie Rules (USA)—Lucky Oakwood (USA) (Elmaamul (USA)) (16190) **R. J. Tufft**
38 B f 31/3 Montjeu (IRE)—Noble Pearl (GER) (Dashing Blade) **Corinthian**
39 B f 18/4 Danehill Dancer (IRE)—Portentous (Selkirk (USA))
40 B c 2/2 Dutch Art—Red Heaven (Benny The Dip (USA)) (38000) **R. J. Tufft**
41 B c 30/4 Oratorio (IRE)—Red Rita (IRE) (Kefaah (USA)) (49523) **Gary & Linnet Woodward**
42 Ch f 21/3 Danehill Dancer (IRE)—River Flow (USA) (Affirmed (USA)) (61576)
43 Br f 8/3 Sleeping Indian—Rye (IRE) (Charnwood Forest (IRE)) (4761)
44 B f 24/3 Danehill Dancer (IRE)—Snowy Day In La (IRE) (Sadler's Wells (USA)) **Mr Richard Tufft & Partners**
45 B f 28/1 Galileo (IRE)—Tea Break (Daylami (IRE)) (50000)
46 Ch f 24/2 Dutch Art—Toffee Vodka (IRE) (Danehill Dancer (IRE)) (2000) **Gary & Linnet Woodward**
47 Gr f 17/1 Dark Angel (IRE)—Wohaida (IRE) (Kheleyf (USA)) (15599)

Other Owners: Mr J. W. Hills, Mr Daniel Abbott, Mr M. Baxter, Mr N. N. Browne, Mrs Peter Caroe, Mr Glyn Charles, Mr W. Y. Chen, Mr Robert Cottam, Mrs K. A. Ellis, Mr D. Fulford, Mr P. D. Gee, Mrs S. Heinemann, Mrs F. Hills, Mr K. F. Hoh, Mrs M. Kingham, Mr H. P. Mason, Mr K. J. Mercer, Mrs S. Mercer, Mr R. J. Tufft, Mr T. Waspe, Mr Michael Wauchope, Mr Gary Woodward, Mrs Linnet Woodward.

Assistant Trainer: Henry Tett

Jockey (flat): Seb Sanders, Eddie Ahern, Richard Hills, Michael Hills. **Apprentice:** Patrick Hills, Leah-Anne Avery.

---

330 MR MARK HOAD, Lewes
Postal: **Windmill Lodge Stables, Spital Road, Lewes, East Sussex, BN7 1LS**
Contacts: **PHONE (01273) 477124/(01273) 480691 FAX (01273) 477124 MOBILE (07742) 446168**
E-MAIL markhoad@aol.com

1 C'MON YOU IRONS (IRE), 7, b g Orpen (USA)—Laissez Faire (IRE) **The Likely Bunch**
2 CONFIDE IN ME, 8, b g Medicean—Confidante (USA) **Mr I. J. Tarbox**
3 DOCTOR HILARY, 10, b g Mujahid (USA)—Agony Aunt **J. Baden White**
4 FARMERS HILL, 4, ch g Dalakhani (IRE)—Wemyss Bight **Mr P Saunders Mr C Basson Mrs S Tyrrell**
5 MAFI (IRE), 4, b g Modigliani (USA)—Yulara **Mrs J. E. Taylor**
6 MAJESTUEUX (USA), 5, ch g Royal Academy (USA)—Buck Aspen (USA) **G. Brice & R. P. C. Hoad**
7 TOTAL OBSESSION, 5, b m Mujahid (USA)—Buon Amici **Miss H. S. Matthews**

THREE-YEAR-OLDS

8 FRIENDS OF AMA GI, b g Reel Buddy (USA)—Skovshoved (IRE) **The Likely Bunch**

Other Owners: Mr C. R. Basson, G. C. Brice, Mr R. P. Clark, I.R. Headington, R. P. C. Hoad, P. W. Saunders, Mrs S. A. Tyrrell, Mr C. Woolston.

---

331 MR PHILIP HOBBS, Minehead
Postal: **Sandhill, Bilbrook, Minehead, Somerset, TA24 6HA**
Contacts: **PHONE (01984) 640366 FAX (01984) 641124 MOBILE (07860) 729795**
E-MAIL pjhobbs@pjhobbs.com WEBSITE www.pjhobbs.com

1 AL ALFA, 5, ch g Alflora (IRE)—Two For Joy (IRE) **The Hon J. R. Drummond**
2 ALLTHEKINGSHORSES (IRE), 6, b g King's Theatre (IRE)—Penny Brae (IRE) **R Triple H**
3 ARTHURIAN LEGEND, 7, b g Alflora (IRE)—Be My Adelina (IRE) **Mr R. T. Kanter & Mr A. J. Scrimgeour**
4 BALLYQUIN QUEEN (IRE), 6, br m King's Theatre (IRE)—One Swoop (IRE) **Racegoers Club Owners Group**
5 BALTHAZAR KING (IRE), 8, b g King's Theatre (IRE)—Afdala (IRE) **The Brushmakers**
6 BIG EASY (GER), 5, b g Ransom O'war (USA)—Basilea Gold (GER) **J. T. Warner**
7 BILLESLEY ROAD, 4, ch g Zafeen (FR)—Doubletta (IRE) **James & Jean Potter**

MR PHILIP HOBBS—continued

8 **BOLD HENRY**, 6, b g Kayf Tara—Madam Min **Mrs K. V. Vann**
9 **CALUSA CALDERA (IRE)**, 10, b g Presenting—Stormy Sea (IRE) **P. Luff**
10 **CAPPAGH (IRE)**, 7, ch g Presenting—Random Bless (IRE) **J. P. McManus**
11 **CAPTAIN CHRIS (IRE)**, 8, b g King's Theatre (IRE)—Function Dream (IRE) **Mrs D. L. Whateley**
12 **CARRIGMORNA KING (IRE)**, 6, b g King's Theatre (IRE)—Carrigmorna Flyer (IRE) **R. & Mrs J. E. Gibbs**
13 **CAYMAN KIRK (IRE)**, 8, b g Dolpour—Kickles Lass **David & Daphne Walsh**
14 **CHANCE DU ROY (FR)**, 8, ch g Morespeed—La Chance Au Roy (FR) **Miss I. D. Du Pre**
15 **COCKNEY TRUCKER (IRE)**, 10, b g Presenting—Kiltiernan Easter (IRE) **Mrs K. V. Vann**
16 **COLOUR SQUADRON (IRE)**, 6, b g Old Vic—That's The Goose (IRE) **P. A. Bonner**
17 **COURTING WHITNEY (IRE)**, 7, b m Witness Box (USA)—Lady Lamb (IRE) **Total Plumbing Supporters Club**
18 **CROIX DE GUERRE (IRE)**, 12, gr g Highest Honor (FR)—Esclava (USA) **Mrs S. Hobbs**
19 **DANANDY (IRE)**, 5, b g Cloudings (IRE)—Tower Princess (IRE) **Mrs C. J. Walsh**
20 **DANCING ROYAL**, 9, ch g Tobougg (IRE)—Just Kate **W. H. Ponsonby**
21 **DARE ME (IRE)**, 8, b g Bob Back (USA)—Gaye Chatelaine (IRE) **T. J. Hemmings**
22 **DE LA BECH**, 5, ch g Karinga Bay—Vallis Vale **B. K. Peppiatt**
23 **DREAM FUNCTION (IRE)**, 7, b m King's Theatre (IRE)—Function Dream (IRE) **Mr B Cloney & Mr O Cloney**
24 **DUKE OF LUCCA (IRE)**, 7, b g Milan—Derravaragh Native (IRE) **Mrs L. H. Field**
25 **DUNRAVEN STORM (IRE)**, 7, b g Presenting—Foxfire **Mrs K. V. Vann**
26 **FAIR ALONG (GER)**, 10, b g Alkalde (GER)—Fairy Tango (FR) **A. E. Peterson**
27 **FAIROAK LAD (IRE)**, 9, br g Tiraaz (USA)—Flair Dante (IRE) **A. E. Peterson**
28 **FAULTLESS FEELINGS (IRE)**, 6, b g Milan—Duchess of Cork (IRE) **Mrs E. A. Prowting**
29 **FEATHERBED LANE (IRE)**, 7, b g Saddlers' Hall (IRE)—Frankly Native (IRE) **J. T. Warner**
30 **FIGHTING FLYNN (IRE)**, 7, b g Old Vic—Innovate (IRE) **Mrs K. V. Vann**
31 **FILBERT (IRE)**, 6, b g Oscar—Coca's Well (IRE) **R Triple H**
32 **FINGAL BAY (IRE)**, 6, b g King's Theatre (IRE)—Lady Marguerrite **Mrs C. Skan**
33 **GARROW'S LAW**, 5, b g King's Theatre (IRE)—Rocheflamme (FR) **Mrs L. H. Field**
34 **GIORDANO BRUNO (IRE)**, 8, ch g Commander Collins (IRE)—Vinecroft (IRE) **Mr A. G. Bloom**
35 **GO LIMPOPO**, 6, b g Alflora (IRE)—Anamasi **M St Quinton, C Hellyer, A Clark**
36 **GOLDMADCHEN (GER)**, 4, b f Ivan Denisovich (IRE)—Goldkatze (GER) **Hill, Trembath, Bryan & Outhart**
37 **GREAT TUSKER (IRE)**, 8, gr g Great Palm—Tusker Lady **Mrs S. Hobbs**
38 **HERDSMAN (IRE)**, 7, b g Flemensfirth (USA)—My Sunny South **T. J. Hemmings**
39 **IMPERIAL CIRCUS (IRE)**, 6, b g Beneficial—Aunty Dawn **R. A. S. Offer**
40 **IRISH BUCCANEER (IRE)**, 5, b g Milan—Supreme Serenade (IRE) **Mrs K. V. Vann**
41 **JAWHARY**, 5, b br g Pivotal—Moon's Whisper (USA) **A. L. Cohen**
42 **JAYANDBEE (IRE)**, 5, b g Presenting—Christines Gale (IRE) **J & B Gibbs & Sons Ltd**
43 **JOSEPH MERCER (IRE)**, 5, b g Court Cave (IRE)—Vikki's Dream (IRE)
44 **KARTANIAN (IRE)**, 6, br g Kalanisi (IRE)—Katiykha (IRE) **Louisville Syndicate III**
45 **KINGS MUSIC (IRE)**, 6, b g Bach (IRE)—Kings Rose (IRE) **P. J. Hobbs**
46 **LEADING CONTENDER (IRE)**, 11, b g Supreme Leader—Flair Dante (IRE) **Mrs J. J. Peppiatt**
47 **LORD CREWE (IRE)**, 9, b g Sinndar (IRE)—Eurobird **The Country Side**
48 **LUCKY MIX**, 6, b m Fair Mix (IRE)—Nicklup **R. S. Brookhouse**
49 **MAGIC MARMALADE (IRE)**, 9, ch g Mohaajir (USA)—Kylogue's Delight **Racing Magic**
50 **MARCHAND D'ARGENT (FR)**, 9, b h Marchand de Sable (USA)—Masslama (FR) **Mrs C. A. Y. Vaughan**
51 **MARUFO (IRE)**, 10, b g Presenting—Bucks Cregg (IRE) **Mrs M. K. Isaacs**
52 **MENORAH (IRE)**, 7, b g King's Theatre (IRE)—Maid For Adventure (IRE) **Mrs D. L. Whateley**
53 **MILLIE O'BRIEN**, 4, b f Milan—Mrs Philip **Mrs S. Hobbs**
54 **MOSTLY BOB (IRE)**, 9, b g Bob Back—Town Gossip (IRE) **Favourites Racing XXVI**
55 **NATIVE BREEZE (IRE)**, 7, br m Flemensfirth (USA)—Roaming (IRE) **Sally Mutch & Denise Bailey**
56 **NOT SO PRUDENT (IRE)**, 8, b g Flemensfirth (USA)—Prudent Princess **Lady Blyth**
57 **NOVA SAM (FR)**, 4, ch c Black Sam Bellamy (IRE)—Elasili (FR) **Peter Jones**
58 **NUTIN FANCY (IRE)**, 6, br g Oscar—Ennel Lady (IRE) **Mrs J. A. Phillips**
59 **OLDRIK (GER)**, 9, b g Tannenkonig (GER)—Onestep (GER) **D. J. Jones**
60 **OSCAR DAVY (IRE)**, 6, b g Oscar—Galtee Castle (IRE) **Mr A. R. E. Ash**
61 **OUTRAGEOUS REQUEST**, 6, ch g Rainbow Quest (USA)—La Sorrela (IRE) **P. J. Hobbs**
62 **PATEESE (FR)**, 7, b g Priolo (USA)—Flyer (FR) **The Test Valley Partnership**
63 **PAVILLON BLEU (FR)**, 9, b g Vaguely Pleasant (FR)—Isaure de Bussy (FR) **Mrs A. M. Taylor**
64 **PERSIAN SNOW (IRE)**, 6, b g Anshan—Alpine Message **D. R. Peppiatt**
65 **PIROULET (FR)**, 6, b g Slickly (FR)—Pantelleria (IRE) **James & Jean Potter**
66 **PLANET OF SOUND**, 10, b g Kayf Tara—Herald The Dawn **Mr C. G. M. Lloyd-Baker**
67 **PRINCELY PLAYER (IRE)**, 5, b g King's Theatre (IRE)—Temptation (FR) **Thurloe 52**
68 **QASPAL (FR)**, 8, b g Subotica (FR)—Une Du Chatelier (FR) **J. P. McManus**
69 **QROKTOU (IRE)**, 8, b g Fragrant Mix (FR)—Cathou (FR) **P. A. Bonner**
70 **REDBRIDGE REBEL**, 6, b g Beat All (USA)—Arctic Revel **Dr V. M. G. Ferguson**
71 **REDUNDERTHEBED (IRE)**, 7, ch m Moscow Society (USA)—Niat Supreme (IRE) **F. R. Jarvey**
72 **RESTE GOSSE (FR)**, 7, b br g Mad Tax (USA)—Folibeth (FR) **The Country Side**
73 **ROALCO DE FARGES (FR)**, 7, gr g Dom Alco (FR)—Vonaria (FR) **The Brushmakers**

MR PHILIP HOBBS—continued

74 **ROB CONTI (FR)**, 7, b br g Network (GER)—Initiale Royale (FR) **P. J. Hobbs**
75 **ROBIN DE CREUSE (FR)**, 6, b br g Robin des Champs (FR)—Myrolix (FR) **A. L. Cohen**
76 **ROLL THE DICE (IRE)**, 6, b g Oscar (IRE)—Sallowglen Gale (IRE) **The Kingpins**
77 **ROUGHAM**, 6, b g Red Ransom (USA)—Louella (USA) **Mr & Mrs James Wigan**
78 **SADLER'S RISK (IRE)**, 4, b g Sadler's Wells (USA)—Riskaverse (USA) **R. S. Brookhouse**
79 **SAFARI JOURNEY (USA)**, 8, ch h Johannesburg (USA)—Alvernia (USA) **Hill, Trembath, Bryan & Outhart**
80 **SATOU (FR)**, 6, gr g Fragrant Mix (IRE)—Jonquiere (FR) **E. Puerari**
81 **SEVEN DAYS (IRE)**, 7, b g Indian Danehill (IRE)—Majakerta (IRE) **Taylormaid**
82 **SNAP TIE (IRE)**, 10, b g Pistolet Bleu (IRE)—Aries Girl **Mrs D. L. Whateley**
83 **SO FINE (IRE)**, 6, b br g Definite Article—Not So Green (IRE) **Mrs L. R. Lovell**
84 **STATE DEPARTMENT**, 5, b g Doyen (IRE)—Time For Tea (IRE) **P. J. Hobbs**
85 **STORM SHADOW (IRE)**, 6, br g Presenting—Harvest Storm (IRE) **Mrs C. Skan**
86 **SWIFT CHAP**, 6, b g Diktat—Regent's Folly (IRE) **M. A. Swift & A. J. Chapman**
87 **TALKONTHESTREET (IRE)**, 5, b g Milan—Super Size (IRE) **Mrs D. L. Whateley**
88 **TANNERMAN (IRE)**, 6, br g Presenting—Coolsilver (IRE) **T. J. Hemmings**
89 **TEMPLER (IRE)**, 11, ch g Charmer—Ballinamona Lady (IRE) **Mr Tony Staple & Mr N Sutton**
90 **THE DISENGAGER (IRE)**, 8, b g Snurge—The Doctors Wife (IRE) **Govier & Brown**
91 **TONY STAR (FR)**, 5, b g Lone Bid (FR)—Effet de Star (FR) **Thurloe 51**
92 **TRIGGERMAN**, 10, b g Double Trigger (IRE)—Carrikins **M. G. St Quinton**
93 **TULIA DE GRAVELLE (FR)**, 5, b m Port Lyautey (FR)—Memsie de Gravelle (FR) **P. J. Hobbs**
94 **TURANJO BELLO (FR)**, 5, gr g Turgeon (USA)—Tchi Tchi Bang Bang (FR) **Mrs D. L. Whateley**
95 **UNCLE JIMMY (IRE)**, 5, b br g Alderbrook—Carrabawn **Mr A. R. E. Ash**
96 **VILLAGE VIC (IRE)**, 5, b g Old Vic—Etoile Margot (FR) **A. E. Peterson**
97 **VOLADOR (IRE)**, 8, b g Old Vic—She's The One (IRE) **Louisville Syndicate II**
98 **WISHFULL THINKING**, 9, ch g Alflora—Poussetiere Deux (FR) **Mrs D. L. Whateley**
99 **ZAGOVA (IRE)**, 6, b g Zagreb (USA)—Move Over Lucy (IRE) **Mr M. C. Sargent**

Other Owners: Mrs D. A. Bailey, Mr D. J. Baker, G. S. Brown, B. G. Brown, C. J. Butler, Mr A. J. Chapman, M. A. Clark, Mr B. A. Cloney, Mr O. M. Cloney, Mr J. P. Cooper, P. J. Cornell, H. R. Gibbs, Mrs J. E. Gibbs, Mr P. Govier, Mr P. F. Govier, T. M. Hailstone, J. R. Hall, C. E. Handford, C. G. Hellyer, M. Hill, J. R. Holmes, Mr D. Howard, Mr E. J. Hughes, Mr B. R. Ingram, R. T. Kanter, C. G. Mackenzie, R. P. B. Michaelson, Mr I. D. Miller, Mr J. Monaghan, Mr I. D. Moses, Mrs S. Mutch, Mr T. E. Olver, D. M. Parsons, O. J. W. Pawle, N. D. Peppiatt, Mr A. C. Phillips, J. E. Potter, Mrs M. J. Potter, Mr S. A. Prater, Mrs D. Pye, D. A. Rees, Mr G. Royal, Mr A. Saffrin, N. C. Savery, A. J. Scrimgeour, Mr H. S. Sharpstone, Mr J. Simpson, Mr J. A. B. Stafford, A. P. Staple, N. R. A. Sutton, M. A. Swift, Mrs Ann Taylor, C. R. Trembath, C. J. M. Walker, D. R. Walsh, Mrs D M Walsh, J. Wigan, Mrs A. Wigan.

Assistant Trainers: Richard White & Darren O'Dwyer

Jockey (NH): Rhys Flint, Richard Johnson, Tom O'Brien. **Conditional:** Chris Davies, Matt Griffiths, Giles Hawkins, James Best, Chris Geoghegan. **Amateur:** Mr Tom Cheesman, Mr Matt Hampton, Mr Michael Nolan.

---

332 MRS RACHEL HOBBS, Hanley Swan
Postal: Tyre Hill Stables, Hanley Swan, Worcester, WR8 0EQ
Contacts: PHONE (01684) 311760 FAX (01684) 311760 MOBILE (07887) 527032
E-MAIL teamhobbs@btinternet.com WEBSITE www.teamhobbs.co.uk

1 **ABSTRACT ART (USA)**, 9, ch g Distorted Humor (USA)—Code From Heaven (USA) **Mr N. J. Morris**
2 **ARTY FARMER**, 8, b g Karinga Bay—One of Those Days **Mr N. J. Morris**
3 5, B g Vinnie Roe (IRE)—Billie's Mate (IRE) **D. Shorey**
4 **BOOSHA**, 7, ch m Sir Harry Lewis (USA)—Musical Vocation (IRE) **Three Counties Racing 2**
5 **BUYERS PREMIUM**, 5, b m Hazaaf (USA)—Gilly Weet **Mr H. J. Pugh**
6 **ELY BROWN (IRE)**, 7, b g Sunshine Street (USA)—
Browneyed Daughter (IRE) **Countrywide Vehicle Rentals Limited**
7 **GOT ATTITUDE (IRE)**, 9, ch g Beneficial—Ilderton Road **Three Counties Racing & Nigel Morris**
8 **HIGHKINGOFMUNSTER (IRE)**, 6, b g Brian Boru—Belize Tropical (IRE) **Mr N. J. Morris**
9 5, B m Great Palm (USA)—Janet Lindup **M. Molloy**
10 **JOKER OF THE PACK (IRE)**, 7, b g Craigsteel—Callmartel (IRE) **The Bearwood Partnership**
11 **JOMADE (IRE)**, 6, b g Definite Article—Culmore Native (IRE) **The Hobb's Choice Partnership**
12 **KAUTO RELKO (FR)**, 8, b g With The Flow (USA)—Kauto Relka (FR) **Countrywide Vehicle Rentals Limited**
13 **KINGSTON QUEEN (IRE)**, 9, b m Moscow Society (USA)—Lady of Sonas (IRE) **M. Molloy**
14 6, B, B br g Kayf Tara—La Brigantine (IRE) **D. Shorey**
15 **LA FILLE D'OSCAR (IRE)**, 8, b m Oscar (IRE)—Ladoc Et Moi (IRE) **The Hobb's Choice Partnership**
16 5, Ch g Oscar Schindler (IRE)—Pampered Molly (IRE) **D. Shorey**
17 **QUOUSKO DE L'ISOP (FR)**, 8, gr g Balleroy (USA)—Pointissima (FR) **Hills of Ledbury Ltd**
18 **SUZIE GREY (IRE)**, 7, gr m Portrait Gallery (IRE)—Scepter'd Isle **The Full Monty Racing Club**

MRS RACHEL HOBBS—continued

19 **TALK D'ARON (FR)**, 5, b g Ragmar (FR)—Cathou (FR)
20 **TRUCKERS PRINCESS (IRE)**, 8, b m Beneficial—Lady Jurado (IRE) **P. J. Jones**
21 **UNWANTED GIFT (IRE)**, 7, b g Tendulkar (USA)—Slieverue (IRE) **The Hobb's Choice Partnership**
22 **VIN DE ROY (FR)**, 7, gr g Balleroy (USA)—Coup de Rouge (FR) **The Vin de Roy Racing Syndicate**

Other Owners: Mr N. A. Brimble, Mr J. R. Driscoll, Mrs Rachel M. Hobbs, Mr A. G. Hobbs, Mr N. Morris, Mr P. M. Price, Mr N. Scanlan, Mr M. S. Scott, Mr D. J. Smith, Mr Mark Wilson.

Assistant Trainer: Andy Hobbs

Jockey (NH): Sean Quinlan, Christian Williams, Aidan Coleman. **Amateur:** Mr J. Mahot.

---

333 MR RON HODGES, Somerton
Postal: **Bull Brook Stables, West Charlton, Charlton Mackrell, Somerton, Somerset, TA11 7AL**
Contacts: **PHONE (01458) 223922 FAX (01458) 223969 MOBILE (07770) 625846**
E-MAIL mandyhodges@btconnect.com

1 **BOLLIN PIPER**, 4, b g Bollin Terry—Astraliser **The Happy Days Partnership**
2 **BUSHWACKER (IRE)**, 8, b g Top of The World—Tender Pearl **Miss R. J. Dobson**
3 **BUTE STREET**, 7, b g Superior Premium—Hard To Follow **J. W. Mursell**
4 **CANTABILLY (IRE)**, 9, b g Distant Music (USA)—Cantaloupe **Mrs S. G. Clapp**
5 **DON'T PANIC (IRE)**, 8, ch g Fath (USA)—Torrmana (IRE) **Mr A. B. S. Webb**
6 **LOCAL PRESENT (IRE)**, 9, ch g Presenting—Local Issue (IRE) **Miss R. Dobson, P. Hart, R. Hodges**
7 **MISS TENACIOUS**, 5, b m Refuse To Bend (IRE)—Very Speed (USA) **John Frampton & Paul Frampton**
8 **OH DEAR OH DEAR**, 4, b f Pasternak—Post It **Mr J. M. Dare**
9 **ON YOUR MAX**, 4, b g Tobougg (IRE)—Maxilla (IRE) **Mr K. B. Hodges**
10 **POSH EMILY**, 9, b m Rakaposhi King—Persistent Gunner **Racing Demons Partnership**
11 **SETTER'S PRINCESS**, 6, ch m Generous (USA)—Setter Country **Mrs L. Sharpe & Mrs S. G. Clapp**
12 **UNDERLAY UNDERLAY**, 4, b g Namid—Rainbow Nation **K. J. Corcoran**

THREE-YEAR-OLDS

13 **ONE LAST DREAM**, ch g Resplendent Glory (IRE)—Pip's Dream **P. E. Axon**
14 **THE QUARTERJACK**, b g Haafhd—Caressed **P. E. Axon**

Other Owners: Mrs S. G. Clapp, Mr K. J. Corcoran, Miss R. Dobson, Mrs P. Elliot, Mr J. L. Frampton, Mr Paul S. Frampton, Mr Peter Hart, Mr R. J. Hodges, Mr Andrew Midgley, Mrs L. Sharpe, Mr Anthony Shead.

---

334 MR HENRY HOGARTH, Stillington
Postal: **New Grange Farm, Stillington, York, YO61 1LR**
Contacts: **PHONE (01347) 811168 FAX (01347) 811168 MOBILE (07788) 777044**

1 **APACHE BRAVE (IRE)**, 9, ch g Kahtan—Glenstal Forest (IRE) **Hogarth Racing**
2 **DENY**, 4, ch g Mr Greeley (USA)—Sulk (IRE) **Hogarth Racing**
3 **FINBIN (IRE)**, 10, b g Presenting—More Dash (IRE) **Hogarth Racing**
4 **MASTER CONOR (IRE)**, 6, b g Classic Cliche (IRE)—Shuil Iontach (IRE) **Hogarth Racing**
5 **MISTER BLOOM (IRE)**, 11, b g Germany (USA)—Una Juna (IRE) **Hogarth Racing**
6 **MURRELL (IRE)**, 7, b g Dushyantor (USA)—Lady Mayday (IRE) **Hogarth Racing**
7 **MYSTERIOUS WORLD (IRE)**, 8, ch g Desert Prince (IRE)—Salligram **Hogarth Racing**
8 **OVER AND ABOVE (IRE)**, 6, b g Overbury (IRE)—Rose Gold (IRE) **Hogarth Racing**
9 **PAMAK D'AIRY (FR)**, 9, b g Cadoubel (FR)—Gamaska d'airy (FR) **Hogarth Racing**
10 **WATFORD (IRE)**, 6, b g Flemensfirth (USA)—Complainingbut (IRE) **Hogarth Racing**

Other Owners: Mr H. P. Hogarth, Mr P. H. Hogarth, Mr J. Hogarth, Mr J. L. Hogarth.

Assistant Trainer: Fergus King

Jockey (NH): Fearghal Davis. **Conditional:** Robert McCarth.

335 MR ALAN HOLLINGSWORTH, Feckenham
Postal: Lanket House, Crofts Lane, Feckenham, Redditch, Worcestershire, B96 6PU
Contacts: PHONE (01527) 68644/892054 FAX (01527) 60310 MOBILE (07775) 670644
E-MAIL kombined@btconnect.com

1 **AGITATION**, 8, b g Cloudings (IRE)—Shadowgraff **Kombined Motor Services Ltd**
2 **BEE BUMBLE**, 7, b g Alflora (IRE)—Shadowgraff **A. F. Hollingsworth**
3 6, Ch m Alflora (IRE)—Celtic Tore (IRE) **A. F. Hollingsworth**
4 **EMMABEL**, 8, br m Alflora (IRE)—Emmabella **A. F. Hollingsworth**
5 **GEMMASON**, 8, ch g Alflora (IRE)—Gemmabel **Kombined Motor Services Ltd**
6 **ISINGOLD**, 9, ch g Alflora (IRE)—Celtic Tore (IRE) **A. F. Hollingsworth**

Assistant Trainer: Sharon Smith

336 MR REG HOLLINSHEAD, Upper Longdon
Postal: Lodge Farm, Upper Longdon, Rugeley, Staffordshire, WS15 1QF
Contacts: PHONE (01543) 490298 FAX (01543) 490490

1 **ANATHENA**, 4, gr f Act One—Goldeva **Mr M. Pyle & Mrs T. Pyle**
2 **BAHAMIAN LAD**, 7, b g Bahamian Bounty—Danehill Princess (IRE) **Graham Brothers Racing Partnership**
3 **BILASH**, 5, gr h Choisir (AUS)—Goldeva **Mr M. Pyle & Mrs T. Pyle**
4 **BOA**, 7, b m Mtoto—Maradata (IRE) **Mr G. Lloyd**
5 **CADMIUM LOCH**, 4, b g Needwood Blade—Vermilion Creek **M. A. N. Johnson**
6 **CLOUDY SPIRIT**, 7, gr m Silver Patriarch (IRE)—Miss Lacroix **Mrs N. S. Harris**
7 **DESTINY OF A DIVA**, 5, b m Denounce—Royal Fontaine (IRE) **M. Massarella**
8 **DRAWN GOLD**, 8, b g Daggers Drawn (USA)—Gold Belt (IRE) **Mr E. T. D. Leadbeater**
9 **EASTERN MAGIC**, 5, b g Observatory (USA)—Inchtina **Mrs C. A. Stevenson**
10 **ISHISMART**, 8, ch m Ishiguru (USA)—Smartie Lee **Mrs N. S. Harris**
11 **LOOK FOR LOVE**, 4, b g Pursuit of Love—Look Here's May **S. L. Edwards**
12 **MOUNT HOLLOW**, 7, b g Beat Hollow—Lady Lindsay (IRE) **R. Hollinshead**
13 **MY MATE MAX**, 7, b g Fraam—Victory Flip (IRE) **Mr E. T. D. Leadbeater**
14 **NOUAILHAS**, 6, b g Mark of Esteem (IRE)—Barachois Princess (USA) **Mr C. W. Wardle & Mrs J. E. Wardle**
15 **ONE SCOOP OR TWO**, 6, b g Needwood Blade—Rebel County (IRE) **Showtime Ice Cream Concessionaire**
16 **RAINY NIGHT**, 6, b g Kyllachy—Rainy Day Song **N. Chapman**
17 **RED RANI**, 7, ch m Whittingham (IRE)—Crystal Magic **Miss S. E. Smith**
18 **RESTLESS BAY (IRE)**, 4, br g Elusive City (USA)—Argus Gal (IRE) **J. L. Marriott**
19 **SHIPBOARD ROMANCE (IRE)**, 7, b m Captain Rio—In Other Words (IRE) **Fromthestables.Com Racing**
20 **SPANISH PLUME**, 4, b g Ishiguru (USA)—Miss Up N Go **The Three R's**
21 **STANDPOINT**, 6, b g Oasis Dream—Waki Music (USA) **Moores Metals Ltd**
22 **STRAVERSJOY**, 5, b m Kayf Tara—Stravsea **E. Bennion**
23 **TAKE ROOT**, 4, b g Indesatchel (IRE)—Lamarita **R. Hollinshead**
24 **TOMINATOR**, 5, gr g Generous (IRE)—Jucinda **Mrs S. M. H. Haslehurst**

THREE-YEAR-OLDS

25 **AMBITIOUS BOY**, bl g Striking Ambition—Cherished Love (IRE) **Mr C. W. Wardle & Mrs J. E. Wardle**
26 B g Three Valleys (USA)—Appelone **R. Hollinshead**
27 **ASTONISHED HARRY (GER)**, b g Dubai Destination (USA)—Aijala (FR) **D. Coppenhall**
28 **AUREOLIN GULF**, b g Proclamation (IRE)—Vermilion Creek **M. A. N. Johnson**
29 **DYLANS VERSE (IRE)**, b g Dylan Thomas (IRE)—In My Dreams (IRE) **Mr G. Lloyd**
30 **FOURSQUARE FUNTIME**, b g Common World (USA)—Farina (IRE) **T. Kelly**
31 **HYSON**, ch g Hernando (FR)—Be Decisive **Lodge Hyson And Breese Racing**
32 **LADY LYRICIST**, b f Librettist (USA)—Victory Flip (IRE) **Mr E. T. D. Leadbeater**
33 **LANDOWN LITTLEROCK**, b g Sakhee (USA)—Maraha **Landown Racing**
34 **LETS GO PRIMO**, b c Primo Valentino (IRE)—Weet By Far **The Giddy Gang**
35 **LINDEN ROSE**, b f Striking Ambition—Inchtina
36 **PATH FINDER (FR)**, ch g Medecis—Desirous of Peace **J. L. Marriott**
37 **RAPID HEAT LAD (IRE)**, b c Aussie Rules (USA)—Alwiyda (USA) **Graham Brothers Racing Partnership**
38 **TOO AMBITIOUS**, b f Striking Ambition—Ticcatoo (IRE) **The Giddy Gang**

TWO-YEAR-OLDS

39 B c 3/3 Ramonti (FR)—Campiglia (IRE) (Fairy King (USA)) (11000) **R. Hollinshead**
40 B g 12/3 Vitus—Farina (IRE) (Golan (IRE)) **R. Hollinshead**
41 **MADAME ELIZABETH**, b f 21/4 Multiplex—Madame Jones (IRE) (Lycius (USA)) (6666)
42 B f 29/3 Striking Ambition—Parkside Prospect (Piccolo)
43 **SCARLET STRAND**, b f 4/5 Pastoral Pursuits—Vermilion Creek (Makbul)

MR REG HOLLINSHEAD—continued

44 SNOWY DAWN, gr g 8/4 Notnowcato—Tereyna (Terimon) (2500) **Mrs C. A. Stevenson**
45 B c 5/2 Needwood Blade—Waterline Twenty (IRE) (Indian Danehill (IRE)) (476)

Other Owners: Mrs H. Bellingham, Mr D. A. Breese, Mr N. A. Coster, Mr A. M. Graham, Mr M. P Graham, Mrs M. E. Hill, Miss S. A. Hollinshead, D. R. Horne, Mr M. J. Hyson, Mr C. J. Jacob, Mr D. R. Lodge, A. L. Marriott, Mr I. G. Martin, Mr L. A. Penny, M. J. F. Pyle, Mrs T. P. Pyle, R. Robinson, C. W. Wardle, Mrs J. E. Wardle.

Assistant Trainer: A N Hollinshead

Jockey (flat): Russ Kennemore. **Amateur:** Mr S. Harrison.

---

337 MR PATRICK HOLMES, Brandsby
Postal: **The Bungalow, Foulrice Farm, Brandsby, York, North Yorkshire, YO61 4SB**

1 **BOW FIDDLE (IRE)**, 6, br m Anshan—Elite Racing **Mrs A. M. Stirling**
2 **CAPTAIN PAULIE (IRE)**, 9, b g Lahib (USA)—Garvivonne **Foulrice Park Racing Limited**
3 **COAX**, 4, b g Red Ransom (USA)—True Glory (IRE) **Foulrice Park Racing Limited**
4 **DOBERDAN (USA)**, 7, b g Street Cry (IRE)—Sophonisbe **Foulrice Park Racing Limited**
5 **DORLESH WAY (IRE)**, 5, ch g Rakti—Patalavaca (GER) **Di Midwinter Foulrice Park Racing Ltd**
6 **FOOT THE BILL**, 7, b g Generous (IRE)—Proudfoot (IRE) **Mr C. R. Stirling**
7 **GOLDEN GROOM**, 9, b g Groom Dancer (USA)—Reine de Thebes (FR) **Mr C. R. Stirling**
8 **IMPERATOR AUGUSTUS (IRE)**, 4, b g Holy Roman Emperor (IRE)—Coralita (IRE) **Foulrice Park Racing Limited**
9 **LIL ELLA (IRE)**, 5, b m Pearl of Love (IRE)—Royal Jubilee (IRE) **Foulrice Park Racing Limited**
10 **REX ROMANORUM (IRE)**, 4, b g Holy Roman Emperor (IRE)—Willowbridge (IRE) **Foulrice Park Racing Limited**
11 **RIPRISTINI (IRE)**, 4, gr c Aussie Rules (USA)—Oiseau Grise (FR) **Mr R. F. Harries**
12 **SUPREME RULER (IRE)**, 9, b g Supreme Leader—Twin Gale (IRE) **Foulrice Park Racing Limited**
13 **TOOMAN LANE (IRE)**, 8, b g Close Conflict (USA)—
Treasure Forecast (IRE) **Christine Clarke FoulricePark Racing Ltd**

Other Owners: Mrs C. M. Clarke, Miss D. Midwinter.

---

338 MR JOHN HOLT, Peckleton
Postal: **Hall Farm, Church Road, Peckleton, Leicester, LE9 7RA**
Contacts: **PHONE/FAX (01455) 821972 MOBILE (07850) 321059**
E-MAIL hallfarmracing@btconnect.com WEBSITE www.hallfarmracing.co.uk

1 **CHIPPY**, 4, b g Diktat—French Mannequin (IRE) **Mr G. F. Archer**
2 4, B f Nomadic Way (USA)—Deepritive **Ms C. A. Lacey**
3 **HANDFORD HENRY (IRE)**, 6, b g Brian Boru—Second Violin (IRE) **Mr M. Golding**
4 **HERES ACTION MAN**, 4, b g Nomadic Way (USA)—Jesmund **Ms C. A. Lacey**
5 **IZZA DIVA**, 4, b f Nomadic Way (USA)—Pebbles Moonlight (IRE) **Mr P. R. Burgess**
6 4, B g Denounce—Jago's Girl
7 4, Gr f Kayf Tara—Kildee Lass **Mr M. Golding**
8 **MATA HARI BLUE**, 6, ch m Monsieur Bond (IRE)—Feeling Blue **Mr M. Golding**
9 **MINI'S DESTINATION**, 4, b f Dubai Destination (USA)—Heather Mix **J. R. Holt**
10 **MOONLARK**, 4, b f Kodiac—Sophie'jo **Mr E. Boumans**
11 **NOMADIC WARRIOR**, 7, b g Nomadic Way (USA)—Jesmund **Ms C. A. Lacey**
12 **NUMBER THEORY**, 4, b g Halling (USA)—Numanthia (IRE) **Mr M. S. Fonseka**
13 5, Bl m Erhaab (USA)—River Ness
14 **THE SNORER**, 4, b g Diktat—La Chesneraie **J. R. Holt**

THREE-YEAR-OLDS

15 **HIKKADUWA**, br f Sakhee (USA)—Numanthia (IRE) **Mr M. S. Fonseka**
16 **LHOTSE SHERPA**, b c Byron—Soyalang (FR) **J. R. Holt**
17 **SOLERA TIME**, b f Librettist (USA)—Sophie'jo **Mr E. Boumans**

TWO-YEAR-OLDS

18 B f 7/4 Byron—Dazzling View (USA) (Distant View (USA)) (2857) **Mr P. V. Thomas**
19 B f 9/3 Holy Roman Emperor (IRE)—Fairmont (IRE) (Kingmambo (USA)) (15238) **Mr E. Boumans**
20 B f 8/3 Byron—Feeling Blue (Missed Flight) (2380) **Mr M. Golding**
21 B f 24/3 Holy Roman Emperor (IRE)—Inveraray (Selkirk (USA)) (9500) **D. R. Botterill**
22 Ch f 20/3 Three Valleys (USA)—Rabshih (IRE) (Green Desert (USA)) (800) **Mr E. Boumans**

MR JOHN HOLT—continued

23 B c 6/5 Camacho—Soyalang (FR) (Alydeed (CAN)) **D. R. Botterill**
24 B f 27/2 Dutch Art—Spangle (Galileo (IRE)) **Mr E. Boumans**

Assistant Trainer: Jessica Holt

---

339 **MR ANTHONY HONEYBALL, Beaminster**
Postal: **Potwell Farm, Mosterton, Beaminster, Dorset, DT8 3HG**
Contacts: **PHONE (01308) 867452 MOBILE (07815) 898569**
E-MAIL a.honeyball@btinternet.com WEBSITE www.ajhoneyballracing.co.uk

1 **ALPANCHO,** 6, ch g Alflora (IRE)—Run Tiger (IRE) **Apple Pie Partnership**
2 **AS DE FER (FR),** 6, b g Passing Sale (FR)—Miss Hollywood (FR) **Midd Shire Racing**
3 **CRESSWELL CRUSADER,** 8, b g Overbury (IRE)—Sloe Hill **Anthony Honeyball Racing Club Ltd**
4 **DORSET NAGA,** 6, b g Alflora (IRE)—Tellicherry **Steve & Jackie Fleetham**
5 **ELEVEN FIFTY NINE,** 6, b m Midnight Legend—Essex Bird **M. Rowe & B. Wright**
6 4, B c Pasternak—Fountain Crumble **The Fountains Partnership**
7 **GAN ON,** 8, b m Missed Flight—Sayin Nowt **Club Revive**
8 **HES OUR LAD (IRE),** 6, b g Rudimentary (USA)—Polyzar (IRE) **A Smith S E Wall A J Forde**
9 **JACKIES SOLITAIRE,** 4, ch f Generous (IRE)—Bond Solitaire **Steve & Jackie Fleetham**
10 **JIVRY,** 5, ch g Generous (IRE)—Jadidh **Mrs S. L. Brimble**
11 **KALANI KING (IRE),** 5, b g Ashkalani (IRE)—
Supreme Kellycarra (IRE) **S. Brimble, A. J. Forde, S Honeyball, T. Harris**
12 **LA MILANAISE,** 6, b m Milan—Dalticia (FR) **Manor Farm In It For Fun**
13 **MIDNIGHT MINX,** 5, b m Midnight Legend—Phar Breeze (IRE) **Mrs J. M. E. Mann**
14 **MOVE ALONG,** 5, ch m Grape Tree Road—What A Mover **T. Hamlin**
15 **RAFFA,** 5, b g Milan—Westbourne (IRE) **R. C. Mitford-Slade**
16 **REGAL ENCORE (IRE),** 4, b g King's Theatre (IRE)—Go On Eileen (IRE) **James Burley & Anthony Honeyball**
17 **ROUQUINE SAUVAGE,** 4, ch f Loup Sauvage (USA)—No Need For Alarm **Anthony Honeyball Racing Club Ltd**
18 **ROYAL ANNOUNCEMENT,** 5, b g Flemensfirth (USA)—Made For A King **Manor Farm In It For Fun**
19 **ROYAL NATIVE (IRE),** 4, b g King's Theatre (IRE)—Hollygrove Native (IRE) **Michael & Angela Bone**
20 **SIR TYTO (IRE),** 4, b g Fruits of Love (USA)—Sophie May **Mr W. H. Simpson**
21 **STEADY GIRLFRIEND,** 7, ch m Classic Cliche (IRE)—Dame Fonteyn **Mr & Mrs R. Tizzard**
22 **SWINCOMBE STONE,** 5, ch g Best of the Bests (IRE)—Soloism **Yeo Racing Partnership**
23 **TARADREWE,** 5, b m Kayf Tara—Kaream **Frosties Friends II**
24 **UNCLE JOHNNY,** 7, b g Alflora (IRE)—Lady Speckles (IRE) **Mr D. Billington**
25 **VELATOR,** 5, b g Old Vic—Jupiter's Message **Steve & Jackie Fleetham**
26 **VICS STAR (IRE),** 6, ch m Old Vic—Karinga Star (IRE)
27 **VICTORS SERENADE (IRE),** 7, b g Old Vic—Dantes Serenade (IRE) **Michael & Angela Bone**

Other Owners: G. T. Birks, Mrs A. P. Bone, Mr M. J. Bone, Mrs M. H. Bowden, Miss A. J. Brewer, D. F. Briers, J. Burley, Mrs C. A. Eyre, Mrs L. Fielding-Johnson, Mr S. Fleetham, Mrs J. Fleetham, Mrs A. J. Forde, A. R. Franklin, Mr M. N. Franklin, T. C. Frost, Mrs S. Honeyball, A. Honeyball, B. G. Middleton, K. B. W. Parkhouse, Ms S. D. Ravenor, Mrs V. J. Reed, M. W. Rowe, A. J. Shire, Mr A. J. Smith, R. G. Tizzard, Mrs S. L. Tizzard, Mrs S. E. Wall, B. J. C. Wright, Mrs K. D. Yeo.

Assistant Trainers: Rachael Green & Nick Child

Jockey (NH): Sam Thomas, Aidan Coleman, Rachael Green. **Conditional:** Ryan Crawford.

---

340 **MR MICHAEL HOURIGAN, Limerick**
Postal: **Lisaleen, Patrickswell, Co. Limerick, Ireland**
Contacts: **PHONE (00353) 6139 6603 FAX (00353) 6139 6812 MOBILE (00353) 8682 26655**
E-MAIL info@mhourigan.ie WEBSITE www.mhourigan.ie

1 **A NEW STORY (IRE),** 14, b g Fourstars Allstar (USA)—Diyala (FR) **Storey's Over Syndicate**
2 **ADAMS WOOD (IRE),** 5, b g Waky Nao—Hurada (IRE) **Michael P. Hourigan**
3 **AMIGAN LADY (IRE),** 6, b m Alderbrook—Garrisker (IRE) **Miss M. M. Hourigan**
4 **AWKWARD MOMENT (IRE),** 8, ch g Deploy—True Blade **B. J. Craig**
5 **BALLYSTEEN (IRE),** 6, b g Elnadim (USA)—Winning Jenny **Gigginstown House Stud**
6 **BEST SERVED COLD,** 6, b g King's Theatre (IRE)—Mirana (IRE) **Gigginstown House Stud**
7 **BILLYTHEBLACKSMITH (IRE),** 5, ch g Golden Tornado (IRE)—Lady Dante (IRE) **J. P. McManus**
8 **CLEAR HILLS (IRE),** 5, b g Marju (IRE)—Rainbows For All (IRE) **Doran Bros Ltd.**
9 **CLOUGHMILE (IRE),** 9, b m Oscar (IRE)—Pappy's Girlfriend **Castle Six Syndicate**
10 **CRAIGS DREAM (IRE),** 6, b g Craigsteel—Sinead's Dream (IRE) **Donal O'Connor**
11 **CRASH (IRE),** 7, b g Milan—Mary Connors (IRE) **Gigginstown House Stud**

MR M. HOURIGAN—continued

12 **CUTEASAFOX (IRE)**, 5, br m Vinnie Roe (IRE)—Verney Bird (IRE) **Mrs D. P. Magnier**
13 **DANCING TORNADO (IRE)**, 11, ch g Golden Tornado (IRE)—Lady Dante (IRE) **J. P. McManus**
14 **DEBT TO SOCIETY (IRE)**, 5, ch g Moscow Society (USA)—Nobody's Darling (IRE) **H. Williams**
15 **DINGALING (IRE)**, 6, b g Milan—Keralba (USA) **J. P. McManus**
16 **EXCUSE ME MARIA (IRE)**, 7, b m Make No Mistake (IRE)—Mardiya (IRE) **Mrs Maria Fitzgerald**
17 **FALSE ECONOMY (IRE)**, 7, b g Orpen (USA)—Ashanti Dancer (IRE) **Mrs Miriam Murphy**
18 **FALSE MESSENGER (IRE)**, 7, b m Oscar (IRE)—Corcomohide (IRE) **Well In Herself Syndicate**
19 **FINE PRESENTATION (IRE)**, 5, ch g Presenting—Time To Ask (IRE) **J. Carey**
20 **FRIENDLY SOCIETY (IRE)**, 7, ch g Moscow Society (USA)—Friendly Breeze **Virginia Lady Petersham**
21 **GIZZIT (IRE)**, 6, b g Son of Sharp Shot (IRE)—Suez Canal (FR) **Miss Maria Fraser**
22 **GLENELEG (IRE)**, 6, b g Flemensfirth (USA)—Charlies Rising (IRE) **Miss R. Easom**
23 **HANS CRESCENT (FR)**, 7, b g Dansili—Embroider (IRE) **S.Lucey**
24 **HOLEINTHEWALL BAR (IRE)**, 4, b g Westerner—Cockpit Lady (IRE) **S. Fahy**
25 **LEND A HAND SON**, 7, bl g Lend A Hand—Sun Bonnet **Golf at Ballyneety Syndicate**
26 **MADE FOR SHARING (IRE)**, 6, b m Bienamado (USA)—Strong Tide **S. Fahy**
27 **NOBLE CHIC**, 7, ch g Generous (IRE)—Chicodove **Miss K. Hourigan**
28 **RUN WITH THE WIND (IRE)**, 6, b g Sadler's Wells (USA)—Race The Wild Wind (USA) **John B. O'Hagan**
29 **SHERCO SPORTS (IRE)**, 5, br m Fruits of Love (USA)—Vintage Classic (IRE) **Tuffy Ten Syndicate**
30 **THE CRAFTY BUTCHER (IRE)**, 5, b g Vinnie Roe (IRE)—Ivy Queen (IRE) **Cairde Chiarrai Syndicate**
31 **THE FLYING DUSTMAN (IRE)**, 13, b g Supreme Leader—Ballyhouraprincess (IRE) **M. M. Hourigan**
32 **THE JOB IS RIGHT**, 4, gr g With Approval (CAN)—Common Request **Mrs M. Devine**
33 **THE TELAVARA (IRE)**, 7, b g Grand Plaisir (IRE)—All-Together **N. O'Connor**
34 **WHATS HAPPENING (IRE)**, 5, b g Lahib (USA)—Rebeccas Star (IRE) **Misss Karen Hourigan**

Assistant Trainer: Kay Hourigan

Jockey (NH): A. P. Heskin. **Amateur:** Miss L. Hourigan, Mr D. Lordan.

---

341 **MR STUART HOWE, Tiverton**
Postal: **Ringstone Stables, Oakford, Tiverton, Devon, EX16 9EU**
Contacts: **PHONE (01398) 351224 MOBILE (07802) 506344**
E-MAIL hshowe@stuarthoweracing.co.uk

1 **ASHKALARA**, 5, b m Footstepsinthesand—Asheyana (IRE) **C R Hollands Cutting Tools Ltd**
2 **BOOGIE DANCER**, 8, b m Tobougg (IRE)—Bolero **Mrs V. W. Jones**
3 **LONGROW**, 6, ch m Tobougg (IRE)—Stealthy
4 **MY LEGAL LADY**, 7, b m Sir Harry Lewis (USA)—Clifton Mist **H. S. Howe**
5 **PARTY PALACE**, 8, b m Auction House (USA)—Lady-Love **Horses Away Ltd**

---

342 **MR PAUL HOWLING, Bramshill**
Postal: **57 David Newberry Drive, Lee-On-The-Solent, Hampshire, PO13 8FG**
Contacts: **MOBILE (07866) 674469**
E-MAIL billichang@aol.com

1 **A POCKETFUL OF RYE (IRE)**, 5, b m Acclamation—Rye (IRE) **Mr J. M. J. Esau**
2 **BREAKHEART (IRE)**, 5, b g Sakhee (USA)—Exorcet (FR) **Mr J. M. J. Esau**
3 **DVINSKY (IRE)**, 11, b g Stravinsky (USA)—Festive Season (USA) **Mr D. A. Hardaker**
4 **FIGARO FLYER (IRE)**, 9, b g Mozart (IRE)—Ellway Star (IRE) **P. Howling**
5 **GALLANTRY**, 10, b g Green Desert (USA)—Gay Gallanta (USA) **Mr J. Wright, Mr D. Patrick, Mr P. D. Woodward**
6 **GRAND HONOUR (IRE)**, 6, gr g Verglas (IRE)—Rosy Dudley (IRE) **Mr E. W. Gordon**
7 **HIGH ON THE HOG (IRE)**, 4, b c Clodovil (IRE)—Maraami **R. Murphy**
8 **HUZZAH (IRE)**, 7, b g Acclamation—Borders Belle (IRE) **Mr J. M. J. Esau**
9 **LEVANTERA (IRE)**, 4, ch f Hurricane Run (IRE)—Ellway Star (IRE) **Mr P. A. Randall**
10 **LITTLE PERISHER**, 5, b g Desert Sun—Sasperella **Mr Peter Randall**
11 **LOCAL SINGER (IRE)**, 4, b g Elusive City (USA)—Alinga (IRE) **Martin Sellars & Joanne Webster**
12 **MISS WHIPPY**, 5, b m Whipper (USA)—Glorious **Mr N. George**
13 **ROYAL ENVOY (IRE)**, 9, b g Royal Applause—Seven Notes **Mr J. M. J. Esau**
14 **WHITE SHIFT (IRE)**, 6, b m Night Shift (USA)—Ivy Queen (IRE) **Martin Sellars & Joanne Webster**

Other Owners: Mr N. J. Funnell, Mrs J. P. Howling, Mr D. C. Patrick, Mr Martin Sellars, Miss Joanne Webster, Mr P. Woodward, Mr James Wright.

Assistant Trainer: Mrs J. Howling

Jockey (flat): Ian Mongan, Michael Stainton. **Conditional:** James Banks.

343 **MR D. T. HUGHES, Kildare**
Postal: **Osborne Lodge, Kildare, Co. Kildare, Ireland**
Contacts: PHONE **(00353) 4552 1490** FAX **(00353) 4552 1643** MOBILE **(00353) 8625 34098**
E-MAIL **dthughes1@eircom.net**

1 ACTION MASTER, 6, b g Domedriver (IRE)—All Is Fair **All Gone West Syndicate**
2 APACHE JACK (IRE), 4, b br g Oscar (IRE)—Cailin Supreme (IRE) **Mrs P. Sloane**
3 BABY'S HOT (IRE), 8, b m Winged Love (IRE)—Annaelaine (IRE) **Big Hat No Cattle Syndicate**
4 BAFFIN ISLAND (IRE), 9, b g Old Vic—Bellora (IRE) **Tom Curran**
5 BLACK APALACHI (IRE), 13, b g Old Vic—Hattons Dream (IRE) **D. Hughes**
6 BRIGHT LIGHT CITY (IRE), 6, b g Elusive City (USA)—Alajyal (IRE) **L & J Young**
7 BRIGHT NEW DAWN, 5, br g Presenting—Shuil Dorcha (IRE) **Gigginstown House Stud**
8 CAHERONAUN (IRE), 6, b m Milan—Fair Present (IRE) **Dan Corry**
9 CANALY (IRE), 7, b g Bob Back (USA)—Starry Lady (IRE) **Michael Moore**
10 CAPTAIN ARCEUS (IRE), 6, b g Captain Rio—Siana Springs (IRE) **T. O'Driscoll**
11 CHASING SHADOWS (IRE), 6, b m Presenting—Chancy Lass (IRE) **M. Moore**
12 CHILL (IRE), 4, b c Diamond Green (FR)—Time To Relax (IRE) **Essential Supplies Ireland Ltd**
13 CROWNING VIRTUE (IRE), 6, b m Jimble (FR)—Mossy Mistress (IRE) **Mrs W. O'Leary**
14 CUMULUS NIMBUS, 5, ch g Muhtathir—Supreme Talent **Mrs N. F. Lee**
15 DALE STREET (IRE), 6, b g Luso—Black Dale (IRE) **D. Hughes**
16 DEAL DONE (FR), 8, b g Vertical Speed (FR)—Five Rivers (IRE) **Mrs A. N. Durkan**
17 DEFINITE CLASS (IRE), 7, b br m Definite Article—Class Society (IRE) **Three Locks Syndicate**
18 DUN MASC (IRE), 7, b g Right Win (IRE)—Timber Toes (IRE) **Anne Marie Ryan**
19 EL FONTAN (FR), 7, gr g Verglas (IRE)—Valeriane (FR) **Mrs P. Sloane**
20 FRISCO DEPOT, 5, b g King's Theatre (IRE)—Gardana (FR) **D. Hughes**
21 GLENBARROW (IRE), 8, b g Old Vic—Cry In The Dark **Ms Anne Marie Ryan**
22 GLOBALIZED (IRE), 5, b g Alhaarth (IRE)—Piacenza (IRE) **D. Hughes**
23 GREAT VALUE (IRE), 7, b g Revoque—Dame de L'oise (USA) **Value Cabs Ltd**
24 HIGH KINGS (IRE), 5, b g Hernando (FR)—Stay Behind **Gigginstown House Stud**
25 HOWS THE CHAP (IRE), 5, b g Desert Prince (IRE)—Dalkey Dasher (IRE) **Monread Stud**
26 INISH ISLAND (IRE), 6, ch g Trans Island—Ish (IRE) **Susan Flanagan**
27 JEWEL OF THE WEST (IRE), 8, b g Desert Prince (IRE)—Tycooness (IRE) **Munnelley Support Services Ltd**
28 JULIE PRINCE (IRE), 6, b g Desert Prince (IRE)—Daniella Ridge (IRE) **Mr Con Harrington**
29 KNOCKARA ONE (IRE), 5, ch m Snurge—Midnights Daughter (IRE)
30 LADY OF GLENCOE (IRE), 4, b f Marju (IRE)—Nabadhaat (USA) **T. O'Driscoll**
31 LENABANE (IRE), 10, b g Luso—Meelick Lady (IRE) **Kevin McNulty**
32 LYREEN LEGEND (IRE), 5, b g Saint des Saints (FR)—Bint Bladi (FR) **Lyreen Syndicate**
33 MACKEYS FORGE (IRE), 8, b g Mr Combustible—Lucy Walters (IRE) **Seven To Eleven Syndicate**
34 MAGNANIMITY (IRE), 8, b br g Winged Love (IRE)—Mossy Mistress (IRE) **Gigginstown House Stud**
35 MERRYDOWN VINTAGE (IRE), 5, ch g Ballingarry (IRE)—Cure The Blues (IRE) **Mrs P. Sloane**
36 MINSK (IRE), 4, b g Dalakhani (IRE)—Penza **Barry Connell**
37 MISS ACCURATE (IRE), 5, ch m Presenting—Elphis (IRE) **D. Hughes**
38 MR MEANER, 6, b g Beat Hollow—Valnerina (IRE) **Lillyroyal Syndicate**
39 PRINCE OF IVAGH (IRE), 6, br g Brian Boru—Stormy Skies **D. Hughes**
40 RARE BOB (IRE), 10, b br g Bob Back (USA)—Cut Ahead **D. A. Syndicate**
41 RATHFEIGH (IRE), 6, b m Pilsudski (IRE)—Sweet Rocket (IRE) **John Purfield**
42 RAZ DE MAREE (FR), 7, ch g Shaanmer (IRE)—Diyala III (FR) **J. J. Swan**
43 RICK (IRE), 8, b g Astarabad (USA)—Catty Jolie (FR) **J. P. Dunne**
44 RIVAGE D'OR (FR), 7, b g Visionary (FR)—Deesse d'allier (FR) **Gigginstown House Stud**
45 ROBERTO GOLDBACK (IRE), 10, b g Bob Back (USA)—Mandysway (IRE) **J. P. Dunne**
46 ROSS NA RIGH (IRE), 8, b br g Presenting—Gladys May (IRE) **Declan O'Keeffe**
47 SARTEANO (IRE), 9, gr g Kaldounevees (FR)—Sovereign Touch (IRE) **More Busted Sofa's Syndicate**
48 SCHINKEL (IRE), 7, ch g Subtle Power (IRE)—Last Sprite **Mr Gerome Sheehan**
49 SEEFOOD (IRE), 5, b g Kahyasi—Anne Theatre **Lyreen Syndicate**
50 SIMON GRAY, 6, b g Act One—Shardette (IRE) **J. P. McManus**
51 SPORTINGTHEME (IRE), 8, b g Beneficial—Balda Girl (IRE) **Mrs M. O'Toole**
52 STONEMASTER (IRE), 7, br g Old Vic—Rose of Stradbally (IRE) **Gigginstown House Stud**
53 STONEY, 5, b g Stowaway—Classical Rachel (IRE) **Slaneyville Syndicate**
54 STOWREE BUD (IRE), 7, b g Pilsudski (IRE)—Forgotten Star (IRE) **Gigginstown House Stud**
55 SUGAR BULLET (IRE), 8, b m Witness Box (USA)—Deep Inthought (IRE) **Just Friends Syndicate**
56 TALAB, 7, b g Red Ransom (USA)—Raghba (USA) **Fred Kenny**
57 TALES OF MILAN (IRE), 5, b g Milan—The Millers Tale (IRE) **Down To Four Syndicate**
58 THE REAL TARGET (IRE), 6, br g Bishop of Cashel—Coumphar (IRE) **Best Of The Rest Syndicate**
59 TOFINO BAY (IRE), 9, br g Bishop of Cashel—Boyne View (IRE) **Gigginstown House Stud**
60 TROUBLED (IRE), 5, b g Vinnie Roe (IRE)—Tart of Tipp (IRE) **Gigginstown House Stud**
61 TUSA EIRE (IRE), 6, b g Turtle Island (IRE)—Neeto (IRE) **Monread Stud**
62 ULTIMATE RISK (IRE), 6, b g Tamayaz (CAN)—Beechzaff Lady (IRE) **M. F. Burke**

MR D. T. HUGHES—continued

63 **VIC VENTURI (IRE)**, 12, ch g Old Vic—Carmen Lady **Mr J. P. Dunne**
64 **WESTERN CHARMER (IRE)**, 10, b br g Good Thyne (USA)—Tulladante (IRE) **D. Hughes**
65 **WHISPERING HILLS (IRE)**, 7, b g Tiger Hill (IRE)—Wells Whisper (FR) **P. Aspell**
66 **WHITE STAR LINE (IRE)**, 8, b g Saddlers' Hall (IRE)—Fairly Deep **Patsy Byrnes**
67 **YOUNG DALE (IRE)**, 6, b g Craigsteel—Miss Dale (IRE) **Mrs Margaret Walshe**
68 **ZERASHAN (IRE)**, 5, b g Azamour (IRE)—Zarannda (IRE) **Gigginstown House Stud**

THREE-YEAR-OLDS

69 **EVERYTHING ZAIN (IRE)**, b g Cape Cross (IRE)—Chamela Bay (IRE) **D. Hughes**

Jockey (NH): Bryan J. Cooper, Roger Loughran. **Conditional:** Mark Enright. **Amateur:** Mr Robbie McNamara.

---

344 MRS JO HUGHES, Lambourn
Postal: **Hill House, Folly Road, Lambourn, Hungerford, Berkshire, RG17 8QE**
Contacts: **PHONE (01488) 71444 FAX (01488) 71103 MOBILE 07900680189**
E-MAIL johughes3@aol.co.uk WEBSITE www.johughesracing.co.uk

1 5, Ch gr g Silver Patriarch (IRE)—Another Mans Cause (FR) **T. J. Wardle**
2 **BABICH BAY (IRE)**, 4, b g Captain Rio—Ibtihal (IRE) **Bernard Allen & Jo Hughes**
3 **BEACHWOOD BAY**, 4, b g Tobougg (IRE)—The Terrier **Mrs J. F. Hughes**
4 **BEN EVA (IRE)**, 6, b m Beneficial—Little Talk **Mrs P. J. Nye**
5 **CALEDONIA PRINCE**, 4, b g Needwood Blade—Granuaile O'malley (IRE) **Isla & Colin Cage**
6 **CANDELITA**, 5, b m Trade Fair—Gramada (IRE) **P. Rosas**
7 **DAZAKHEE**, 5, ch m Sakhee (USA)—Ziya (IRE) **Mr & Mrs D. Yates**
8 **DOUGLAS**, 7, b g Beat All (USA)—Cromaboo Crown **T. J. Wardle**
9 **DUNSEVERICK (IRE)**, 4, ch g Footstepsintheisand—Theatrale (USA) **Four Nations**
10 **LIGHTS OF BROADWAY (IRE)**, 6, b m Broadway Flyer (USA)—Supreme Call (IRE) **B. W. Parren**
11 **MISS P**, 4, b f Bahamian Bounty—Gitane (FR) **Miss Louise Harbord & Mr Anthony Calver**
12 **MULLINS WAY (USA)**, 4, ch g Mr Greeley (USA)—Aljawza (USA) **Bernard Allen & Jo Hughes**
13 5, Ch m Septieme Ciel (USA)—Nearly A Mildred **Mrs K. M. C. Lundberg-Young**
14 **OOLALA LADY (IRE)**, 4, b f High Chaparral (IRE)—Paris Song (IRE) **R. Kent**
15 **OSCAR FLYER (IRE)**, 5, b g Oscar (IRE)—Cointosser (IRE) **West Coast Haulage Limited**
16 **OSCAR TANNER (IRE)**, 4, br g Oscar (IRE)—Rose Tanner (IRE) **Mrs J. F. Hughes**
17 **PENSNETT BAY**, 7, ch g Karinga Bay—Balmoral Princess **Mr H. S. Maan**
18 **REGAL BROOK**, 6, br m Alderbrook—Cadal Queen (FR) **Mrs K. M. C. Lundberg-Young**
19 **WISHBONE**, 5, b m Danehill Dancer (IRE)—Intricate Design **Four Nations**
20 **ZAFISIO (IRE)**, 6, b g Efisio—Goldthroat (IRE) **Mr D. A. Looney**

THREE-YEAR-OLDS

21 **MAYFORDE JACK**, b g Septieme Ciel (USA)—Jessinca **P. T. Newell**
22 **SON OF MAY**, b g Royal Applause—Second of May **Sterling Racing,Don Bird & Jo Hughes**
23 **WICKED WENCH**, b f Kyllachy—Effervescent **Mr J. M. H. Hearne**

Other Owners: Mr C. G. Adam, B. C. Allen, D. G. Bird, Mrs I. Cage, C. J. Cage, Mr A. Calver, Miss L. A. Harbord, J. E. Mottram, Mr J. F. Simpson, Mr D. Yates, Mrs A. V. Yates.

Assistant Trainer: Paul Blockley

Jockey (flat) Paul Hanagan, Tony Culhane. **(NH):** Mark Grant. **Apprentice:** Josh Baudains.

---

345 MR STEPHEN HUGHES, Gilfach Goch
Postal: **Dusty Forge, 2 Oak Street, Gilfach Goch, Porth, Mid-Glamorgan, CF39 8UG**
Contacts: **PHONE 07823334300 (01443) 672110 FAX (01443) 672110 MOBILE 07823334282**
E-MAIL dustyforge@aol.com

1 **CONVINCE (USA)**, 11, ch g Mt Livermore (USA)—Conical
2 **NOMADIC FAITH**, 4, ch f Nomadic Way (USA)—Fair Kai (IRE)
3 **POUR CHANGER (FR)**, 7, b g Daliapour (IRE)—Chop And Change (FR)

Assistant Trainer: Maggie Kidner Hughes

346 **MR V. J. HUGHES, Bridgend**
Postal: **Mill Field House, Glynogwr, Bridgend, Mid-Glamorgan, CF35 6EN**
Contacts: **PHONE (01443) 672944 MOBILE (07925) 133396**

1 **SHARLENE'S QUEST (IRE)**, 6, b m Revoque (IRE)—Sanka (IRE) **V. J. Hughes**
2 **TIGER'S JACEY (IRE)**, 5, b m Milan—Shes Elite (IRE) **V. J. Hughes**

Assistant Trainer: Miss Lisa J. Llewellyn

347 **MRS SARAH HUMPHREY, West Wratting**
Postal: **Yen Hall Farm, West Wratting, Cambridge, Cambridgeshire, CB21 5LP**
Contacts: **PHONE (01223) 291445 FAX (01223) 291451 MOBILE (07798) 702484**
E-MAIL sarah.yenhallfarm@btinternet.com WEBSITE www.sarahhumphrey.co.uk

1 4, B g Blueprint (IRE)—Authentic Creature (IRE)
2 **BARNHILL BROWNIE (IRE)**, 9, b g Presenting—In The Brownies (IRE) **Mrs S. Humphrey**
3 **BE EXTRAORDINARY (IRE)**, 6, b g Subtle Power (IRE)—Wise Native (IRE) **Mrs S. Humphrey**
4 **BIG KAHUNA**, 5, br g Trade Fair—Pistoia **Redgate Bloodstock**
5 **BUCKS R'US (IRE)**, 5, b g Oscar (IRE)—Princess Kertina (IRE)
6 **CALL AT MIDNIGHT**, 7, b m Midnight Legend—Second Call **Yen Hall Farm Racing**
7 **CARPINCHO (FR)**, 8, b br g Jimble (FR)—La Rapaille (IRE) **W. D. Glover & P. Chapman**
8 4, Ch g Old Vic—Clara's Dream (IRE)
9 **COURT RED HANDED (IRE)**, 7, ch g Flemensfirth (USA)—Desert Gail (IRE) **Mr P. Chapman**
10 **DORSET SQUARE (IRE)**, 8, b g Fantastic Light (USA)—Albula (FR) **Mr J. Waterfall**
11 **FLEMI TWO TOES (IRE)**, 6, b g Flemensfirth (USA)—Silva Venture (IRE) **Mr P. Chapman**
12 **HIBIKI (IRE)**, 8, b g Montjeu (IRE)—White Queen (IRE) **Mrs S. Humphrey**
13 **I NEED A HERO (IRE)**, 7, b g Oscar Schindler (IRE)—Old Fontaine (IRE) **The Bonnie Tyler Partnership**
14 **I'VE BEEN FRAMED (IRE)**, 8, b g Portrait Gallery (IRE)—
Sunday Surprise (IRE) **Mr & Mrs A. Whyte, Mr. P. Edwards, Mr C. Appleton**
15 **INVESTMENT AFFAIR (IRE)**, 12, b g Sesaro (USA)—Superb Investment (IRE) **Mr R. N. Fuller**
16 **KICKING TIME (IRE)**, 6, b g Luso—Fairy Dawn (IRE) **P. & C. Chapman, D. Nott & S. Humphrey**
17 **KNIGHT LEGEND (IRE)**, 13, b g Flying Legend (USA)—Well Trucked (IRE) **Yen Hall Farm Racing**
18 **LADY KARABAYA**, 7, b m Karinga Bay—Supreme Lady (IRE) **The Lady Karabaya Partnership**
19 **LITTLE CARMELA**, 8, gr m Beat Hollow—Carmela Owen **A. Whyte, J. Custerson, R. Swinfen**
20 **MIDNIGHT GAMBLE**, 6, ch g Midnight Legend—Mashwe (IRE) **D. Nott, R. Britton, G. A. Thomas**
21 **SILVER LILY (IRE)**, 10, gr m Gothland (FR)—Imlistening (IRE) **Dr R. Britton & Mr G. Thomas**
22 **THE ROYAL BROMPTON**, 6, b g Kayf Tara—Goldenswift (IRE) **The Brompton Partnership**

THREE-YEAR-OLDS

23 **FEVER FEW**, b f Pastoral Pursuits—Prairie Oyster **Redgate Bloodstock**

Other Owners: Dr. R. Britton, Mr R. J. Burdett, Mr B. Cahill, Mr P. Chapman, Mr D. Flynn, Miss E. Foley, Mr W. D. Glover, Mrs S. J. Humphrey, Mr A. R. Humphrey, Mrs M. J. Kelsey Fry, Mr D. F. Nott, Miss J. Seaman, Mr Garry Thomas, Mrs S. Wise.

Assistant Trainer: Mr A. Humphrey

Jockey (NH): Aidan Coleman, Jack Doyle. **Conditional:** Charlie Huxley, Mark Marris. **Amateur:** Mr M. Ennis.

348 **MR JOHN HUNTER, Natland**
Postal: **Larkrigg, Natland, Cumbria, LA9 7QS**
Contacts: **PHONE (01539) 560245**

1 **CONFLICTOFINTEREST**, 10, b g Saddlers' Hall (IRE)—Fortune's Girl **J. K. Hunter**
2 **LORD ARATAN (GER)**, 5, b g Tiger Hill (IRE)—Luce (IRE) **J. K. Hunter**

349 **MISS LAURA HURLEY, Kineton**
Postal: **Kineton Grange Farm, Kineton, Warwick, Warwickshire, CV35 0EE**

1 **ILÒNGUE (FR)**, 11, b m Nononito (FR)—Marie De Geneve (FR) **Mrs R. Hurley**
2 **LAUGHING GAME**, 8, b m Classic Cliche (IRE)—Ground Game **Mrs R. Hurley**
3 **MOSCOW MULE**, 9, b g Moscow Society (USA)—Madam Advocate **Mrs R. Hurley**
4 **ORANG OUTAN (FR)**, 10, b g Baby Turk—Ellapampa (FR) **Mrs R. Hurley**

350 MRS CAROLE IKIN, Sutton In The Elms
Postal: **Walton Lodge Farm, Sutton In The Elms, Leicestershire, LE9 6RB**
Contacts: **PHONE** (01455) 282321 **MOBILE** (07850) 278491
E-MAIL nevagree@yahoo.co.uk **WEBSITE** www.equinespa.co.uk

1 **MASSAMS LANE**, 8, b g Lahib (USA)—Night Trader (USA) **Mrs C. J. Ikin**
2 **SATINDRA (IRE)**, 8, b g Lil's Boy (USA)—Voronova (IRE) **Mrs C. J. Ikin**
3 **TARKESAR (IRE)**, 10, b g Desert Prince (IRE)—Tarwila (IRE) **Mrs C. J. Ikin**

Assistant Trainer: Mr P. J. Ikin

351 MR ROGER INGRAM, Epsom
Postal: **Wendover Stables, Burgh Heath Road, Epsom, Surrey, KT17 4LX**
Contacts: **PHONE** (01372) 748505 or (01372) 749157 **FAX** (01372) 748505
MOBILE (0777) 3665980
E-MAIL roger.ingram.racing@virgin.net **WEBSITE** www.rogeringramracing.com

1 **BRIDGE THAT GAP**, 4, b c Avonbridge—Figura **The Stargazers**
2 **BUXTON**, 8, b g Auction House (USA)—Dam Certain (IRE) **Mr P. J. Burton**
3 **KAI MOOK**, 5, b gr m Littletown Boy (USA)—Beenaboutabit **Mr G. E. Ley**
4 **LINGTREN**, 4, b g Storming Home—Sunny Times (IRE) **T. H. Barma**
5 **POSE (IRE)**, 5, b m Acclamation—Lyca Ballerina **Mrs E. N. Nield**
6 **RIVER TAFF**, 5, b g Auction House (USA)—Lady Ploy **Mrs C. E. Hallam**

THREE-YEAR-OLDS

7 Ch c Auction House (USA)—Charlottevalentina (IRE)
8 Ch c Auction House (USA)—Dam Certain (IRE)
9 B c Byron—Sea Jade (IRE)

Other Owners: M. W. Joy, Mr D. Ross-Watt.

Assistant Trainer: Sharon Ingram

Amateur: Miss Sarah Sawyer.

352 MR DEAN IVORY, Radlett
Postal: **Harper Lodge Farm, Harper Lane, Radlett, Hertfordshire, WD7 7HU**
Contacts: **PHONE** (01923) 855337 **FAX** (01923) 852470 **MOBILE** (07785) 118658
E-MAIL dean.ivory@virgin.net **WEBSITE** www.deanivoryracing.com

1 **AVON RIVER**, 5, ch g Avonbridge—Night Kiss (FR) **Mr J. J. Reddington**
2 **DARWIN STAR**, 4, gr f Aussie Rules (USA)—Fine Lady **K. T. Ivory**
3 **ELLEMUJIE**, 7, b g Mujahid (USA)—Jennelle **Mrs J. A. Cornwell**
4 **HEREFORD BOY**, 8, ch g Tomba—Grown At Rowan **Recycled Products Limited**
5 **KINGS 'N DREAMS**, 5, b g Royal Applause—Last Dream (IRE) **Mr Ian Gethin & Mr Richard Gethin**
6 **KISS A PRINCE**, 6, b g Fraam—Prancing **Mr A. D. Pryer**
7 **LARKRISE STAR**, 5, b m Where Or When (IRE)—Katy Ivory (IRE) **Radlett Racing**
8 **LUJEANIE**, 6, br g Lujain (USA)—Ivory's Joy **K. T. Ivory**
9 **MACK'S SISTER**, 5, ch m Pastoral Pursuits—Linda's Schoolgirl (IRE) **Recycled Products Limited**
10 **RUSSIAN ICE**, 4, ch f Iceman—Dark Eyed Lady (IRE) **Roger Beadle & Ben Bennett**
11 **SHAUNAS SPIRIT (IRE)**, 4, b f Antonius Pius (USA)—Shaunas Vision (IRE) **John Connolly & Rahul Bajaj**
12 **SIRIUS PROSPECT (USA)**, 4, b br g Gone West—Stella Blue (FR) **Miss N. I. Yarrow**
13 **SNOW TROOPER**, 4, ch g Iceman—Snow Shoes **Mr K. B. Taylor**
14 **TAGULA NIGHT (IRE)**, 6, b g Tagula—Carpet Lady (IRE) **Hufford & Papworth**
15 **TRIBOULEY**, 4, ch f Bahamian Bounty—Serriera (FR) **Wood Hall Stud Limited**
16 **VALID REASON**, 5, b g Observatory (USA)—Real Trust (USA) **Mr M. J. Yarrow**
17 **ZAFEEN'S PEARL**, 5, ch m Zafeen (FR)—Deep Sea Pearl **Heather Yarrow & Lesley Ivory**

THREE-YEAR-OLDS

18 **APPEASE**, b g Oasis Dream—Penchee **Mr J. J. Reddington**
19 **CIARA BOO (IRE)**, b f Red Clubs (IRE)—National Ballet **Mr J. J. Reddington**
20 **COPP THE LOT (USA)**, gr g Exchange Rate (USA)—Argentum (USA) **Mr G. M. Copp**
21 **ECECHEIRA**, ch f Three Valleys (USA)—Evening Guest (FR) **Mrs A. R. Ruggles**
22 **FINALIST**, b f Avonbridge—High Finale **K. T. Ivory**

MR DEAN IVORY—continued

23 **HILL OF DREAMS (IRE)**, b f Indian Danehill (IRE)—Shaunas Vision (IRE) **Mr I Gethin & Mr R Gethin**
24 **MIDNIGHT BAHIA (IRE)**, b f Refuse To Bend (IRE)—Midnight Partner (IRE) **Mr K. B. Taylor**
25 B f Three Valleys (USA)—Over The Limit (IRE)
26 **PREMATURE**, ch f Needwood Blade—Ivory's Joy **K. T. Ivory**
27 **TOM RED**, gr g Piccolo—Joyful Illusion **John Reddington & K. T. Ivory**

TWO-YEAR-OLDS

28 **DUBAI DELIGHT**, b c 26/3 Dubai Destination (USA)—Gayanula (USA) (Yonaguska (USA)) (10000) **Mr G. M. Copp**
29 B g 11/3 Assertive—Enclave (USA) (Woodman (USA)) (11000) **K. T. Ivory**
30 B f 7/4 Bertolini (USA)—High Finale (Sure Blade (USA)) **K. T. Ivory**
31 B f 5/2 Assertive—Ivory's Joy (Tina's Pet) **K. T. Ivory**
32 **LYNFORYOU**, ch f 14/2 Tumbleweed Ridge—
    Bens Georgie (IRE) (Opening Verse (USA)) **World Freight Consultants Ltd**

Other Owners: Mr R. Bajaj, Mr R. Beadle, Mr P. J. Bennett, Mr J. F. Connolly, Dean Ivory Racing Ltd, Mr I. R. Gethin, Mr R. Gethin, Mr J. Hufford, D. K. Ivory, Mrs L. A. Ivory, G. Papworth, Mrs H. Yarrow.

Assistant Trainer: Chris Scally

---

353   **MISS TINA JACKSON, Loftus**
Postal: **Tick Hill Farm, Liverton, Loftus, Saltburn, Cleveland, TS13 4TG**

1 **ARDESIA (IRE)**, 8, b g Red Sunset—Lowtown **A. Jackson**
2 **BABBLON BROOKE (IRE)**, 7, ch g Bob Back (USA)—Scary Spice (IRE) **H. L. Thompson**
3 **BORIS THE BLADE**, 10, gr g Cloudings (IRE)—Cherry Lane **Mrs P. A. Cowey**
4 **GEORGEDOUBLEYOU (IRE)**, 11, b g Lord Americo—Ballybeg Rose (IRE) **D Tucker, M Styler & H Thompson**
5 **MISS SUNFLOWER**, 10, ch m Keen—Ellfiedick **H. L. Thompson**
6 **MISS TOSCA (IRE)**, 11, b m Oscar (IRE)—Protrial **H. L. Thompson**
7 **NO LADY**, 5, b m Exit To Nowhere (USA)—Bonnie Buttons

Other Owners: Panther Racing Limited, M. J. Styler, Mr D. Tucker.

---

354   **MRS VALERIE JACKSON, Newcastle Upon Tyne**
Postal: **Edge House, Belsay, Newcastle Upon Tyne, Tyne and Wear, NE20 0HH**
Contacts: **PHONE (01830) 530218 MOBILE (07808) 812213**

1 **CAST IRON CASEY (IRE)**, 10, ch g Carroll House—Ashie's Friend (IRE) **Mrs V. S. Jackson**
2 **WAVE POWER (IRE)**, 8, ch g Definite Article—Romany Rose (IRE) **Mrs V. S. Jackson**
3 **WHEYAYE**, 10, ch m Midnight Legend—Sayin Nowt **Mrs V. S. Jackson**

---

355   **MR LEE JAMES, Malton**
Postal: **4 Wayfaring Close, Norton, Malton, North Yorkshire, YO17 9DW**
Contacts: **PHONE (01653) 699466 FAX (01653) 691455 MOBILE (07732) 556322**

1 **ATTACK MINDED**, 11, ch g Timeless Times (USA)—French Ginger **Mrs C. Lloyd-James**
2 **FREEDOM FLYING**, 9, b m Kalanisi (IRE)—Free Spirit (IRE) **Mrs C. Lloyd-James**
3 **REVOLVING WORLD (IRE)**, 9, b g Spinning World (USA)—Mannakea (USA) **L. R. James**
4 5, B g Sugarfoot—She Who Dares Wins **Mrs C. Lloyd-James**
5 **SHE WHO DARES WINS**, 12, b m Atraf—Mirani (IRE) **Mrs C. Lloyd-James**
6 **STRIKEMASTER (IRE)**, 6, b g Xaar—Mas A Fuera (IRE) **Mrs C. Lloyd-James**
7 **TOBY MAC**, 10, b g Presidium—Ski Path **L. R. James**
8 **ZOOM IN**, 4, b g Indesatchel—Korolieva (IRE) **Mrs C. Lloyd-James**

TWO-YEAR-OLDS

9 B c 26/2 Echo of Light—Alisdanza (Namaqualand (USA)) **Mrs C. Lloyd-James**
10 B f 16/4 Dubai Destination (USA)—Palisandra (USA) (Chief's Crown (USA)) **Mrs C. Lloyd-James**

Assistant Trainer: Carol James

Conditional: Kyle James. **Amateur:** Mr A. James.

356 MR IAIN JARDINE, Hawick
Postal: **Paradise Cottage, Gatehousecote, Bonchester Bridge, Hawick, Roxburghshire, TD9 8JD**

1 **CARTERS REST**, 9, gr g Rock City—Yemaail (IRE) **Mr A. Dawson & Mrs K. Campbell**
2 **FIVE BUCKS (IRE)**, 5, b g Luso—Five Rascals (IRE)
3 **LA BACOUETTEUSE (FR)**, 7, b g Miesque's Son (USA)—Toryka **Miss S. A. Booth**
4 **NELSON DU RONCERAY (FR)**, 11, b g Lute Antique (FR)—Trieste (FR) **J. A. Glass**
5 **PROBABLY GEORGE**, 5, gr g Silver Patriarch (IRE)—Java Dawn (IRE)

Other Owners: Mrs K. Campbell, A. Dawson.

357 MR ALAN JARVIS, Twyford
Postal: **Twyford Mill, Mill Lane, Twyford, Buckingham, Buckinghamshire, MK18 4HA**
Contacts: **PHONE (01296) 730707 FAX (01296) 733572 MOBILE (07770) 785551**
E-MAIL **alan@alanjarvis.co.uk** WEBSITE **www.alanjarvis.co.uk**

1 4, Ch g Redback—Annahala (IRE)
2 **ANOTHER TRY (IRE)**, 7, b g Spinning World (USA)—Mad Annie (USA) **The Twyford Partnership**
3 **BOW TO NO ONE (IRE)**, 6, b m Refuse To Bend (IRE)—Deadly Buzz (IRE) **A. L. R. Morton**
4 **DICEY VOWS (USA)**, 4, b g Broken Vow (USA)—Pretty Dicey (USA) **A. L. R. Morton**
5 **ELLIE IN THE PINK (IRE)**, 4, ch f Johannesburg (USA)—Stravinia (USA) **Jakellie**
6 **LIBRETTELA**, 4, b g Librettist (USA)—Ella's Wish (IRE) **Jarvis Associates**
7 **MATAVIA BAY (IRE)**, 4, b g Bahamian Bounty—Rosewater (GER) **Geoffrey Bishop & Jarvis Associates**
8 **NAVAJO CHIEF**, 5, b g King's Best (USA)—Navajo Rainbow **Mr G. S. Bishop**
9 **OETZI**, 4, ch g Iceman—Mad Annie (USA) **Allen B. Pope & Jarvis Associates**
10 **RIGHT STEP**, 5, b g Xaar—Maid To Dance **Allen B. Pope & Jarvis Associates**

THREE-YEAR-OLDS

11 **ELEGANT FLIGHT**, ch f Deportivo—On The Wing **Grant & Bowman Limited**
12 **ITALIAN LADY (USA)**, b br f Medaglia d'oro (USA)—Way Beyond (USA) **Nesbitt Emery**
13 **KING VAHE (IRE)**, b g One Cool Cat (USA)—Tethkar **Cedars Partnership**
14 **LADY VAHE (IRE)**, b f Rock of Gibraltar (IRE)—Lady Adnil (IRE) **Buckingham Flooring**
15 **MULTI BLESSING**, b c Multiplex—Bahamian Belle **Jarvis Associates**
16 **NAVAJO CHARM**, b f Authorized (IRE)—Navajo Love Song (IRE) **Mr G. S. Bishop**
17 B g Aussie Rules (USA)—Silk Law (IRE) **Jarvis Associates**
18 **SUNRISE DANCE**, ch f Monsieur Bond (IRE)—Wachiwi (IRE) **Mr M. Saunders**
19 **TURNED TO GOLD (IRE)**, ch g Teofilo (IRE)—Silver Bracelet **Nesbitt Emery**
20 **VAN DER ART**, ch f Dutch Art—Chase The Lady (USA) **Market Avenue Racing Club Ltd**
21 **WISE VENTURE (IRE)**, b g Kheleyf (USA)—Chia Laguna (IRE) **Allen B Pope - Geoffrey Bishop**

TWO-YEAR-OLDS

22 **ANNIE'S FORTUNE (IRE)**, b f 15/4 Montjeu (IRE)—Semaphore (Zamindar (USA)) **Cedars Partnership**
23 B f 15/2 Excellent Art—Blushing Away (USA) (Blushing Groom (FR)) **Jarvis Associates**
24 B f 29/4 Manduro (GER)—Coveted (Sinndar (IRE)) (7500)
25 B c 9/4 Duke of Marmalade (IRE)—Damson (IRE) (Entrepreneur) (32000)
26 Ch c 29/4 Fracas (IRE)—Dance Fontaine (Danehill Dancer (IRE)) **C. H. Shankland**
27 B f 18/3 Montjeu (IRE)—Edabiya (IRE) (Rainbow Quest (USA)) **Cedars Partnership**
28 B f 26/5 Lemon Drop Kid (USA)—Final Legacy (USA) (Boston Harbor (USA)) (20000)
29 B f 5/3 Johannesburg (USA)—Lerici (USA) (Woodman (USA)) (6567)
30 B f 2/4 Tiger Hill (IRE)—Moon Crystal (Fasliyev) (USA) **Mr G. S. Bishop**
31 B c 30/3 Cape Cross (IRE)—Off Message (IRE) (In The Wings) (21000)
32 B c 6/3 Tiger Hill (IRE)—Sabreon (Caerleon (USA)) **Mr G. S. Bishop**
33 B f 9/3 Byron—Sahariri (IRE) (Red Ransom (USA)) **C. H. Shankland**
34 B f 14/3 Sleeping Indian—Silent Waters (Polish Precedent (USA))
35 **SWIFT CEDAR (IRE)**, ch c 19/4 Excellent Art—Ravish (Efisio) **Cedars Partnership**
36 Ch c 10/5 Cockney Rebel (IRE)—Wachiwi (IRE) (Namid)

Other Owners: Mrs Ann Jarvis, A. P. Jarvis, A. B. Pope, Mr G. J. Reboul, Mrs H. Reboul.

Assistant Trainers: M. A. Jarvis, S. E. Simmons, T. O. Jarvis.

Apprentice: Harry Bentley, Jordan Uys.

358 MR WILLIAM JARVIS, Newmarket
Postal: **Phantom House, Fordham Road, Newmarket, Suffolk, CB8 7AA**
Contacts: **OFFICE (01638) 669873 HOME (01638) 662677 FAX (01638) 667328**
E-MAIL mail@williamjarvis.com WEBSITE www.williamjarvis.com

1 **BRIGADOON**, 5, b g Compton Place—Briggsmaid **Mr J. Bowditch**
2 **CUTHBERT (IRE)**, 5, ch g Bertolini (USA)—Tequise (IRE) **Canisbay Bloodstock**
3 **DIVERTING**, 4, b f Nayef (USA)—Tawny Way **J. A. Reed**
4 **FLOATING MOUNTAIN**, 4, b f Sakhee (USA)—Engulfed (USA) **Mr T. M. Hedin**
5 **KATY'S SECRET**, 5, b m Mind Games—Katy O'hara **Miss S. E. Hall**
6 **LOKI'S REVENGE**, 4, b c Kyllachy—Amira **Dr J. Walker**
7 **ORIENTAL SCOT**, 5, ch g Selkirk (USA)—Robe Chinoise **Dr J. Walker**
8 4, B g Cadeaux Genereux—Orlena (USA) **Mrs S. J. Davis**
9 **PRIVATE EQUITY (IRE)**, 6, b m Haafhd—Profit Alert (IRE) **Mrs S. J. Davis**
10 **QUSHCHI**, 4, b br f Encosta de Lago (AUS)—La Persiana **Dr J. Walker**
11 **ROCK A DOODLE DOO (IRE)**, 5, b h Oratorio (IRE)—Nousaiyra (IRE) **The Doodle Doo Partnership**

THREE-YEAR-OLDS

12 **ASHDOWN LAD**, ch g Sir Percy—Antibes (IRE) **The FOPS**
13 **BEAUFORT TWELVE**, b c Hurricane Run (IRE)—Violette **Tony Foster & John Kelsey-Fry**
14 **BERLUSCA (IRE)**, b c Holy Roman Emperor (IRE)—Shemanikha (FR) **The Berlusca Partnership**
15 **BESITO**, b f Kodiac—Christmas Kiss **A. Foster**
16 **BLACK DOUGLAS**, b g Kyllachy—Penmavne **Dr J. Walker**
17 **CAPPIELOW PARK**, b c Exceed And Excel (AUS)—Barakat **Dr J. Walker**
18 **CHART**, b c Dutch Art—Masandra (IRE) **Rupert Villers & Partners**
19 **CHEVIOT QUEST (IRE)**, ch c Sir Percy—Cushat Law (IRE) **Anthony Reed**
20 **CHORISTER SPORT (IRE)**, b c Diamond Green (FR)—
　　　　Spend A Rubble (USA) **Michael Payton, A Briam & I Robertson**
21 **CONOWEN**, ch c Ishiguro (USA)—Velma Kelly **Darren Brooks & Partners**
22 **LOTHIAN SKY (IRE)**, b c Authorized (IRE)—Golly Gosh (IRE) **Dr J. Walker**
23 **NIP AND TUCK**, b c Green Desert (USA)—Coveted **Mrs M. Bryce**
24 **SALTIRE BLUE**, ch f Compton Place—Seine Bleue (FR) **Dr J. Walker**
25 **SCRIPTURIST**, b c Oratorio (IRE)—Lambroza (IRE) **Lady G. De Walden**
26 **SILKE TOP**, b f Librettist (USA)—Zaza Top (GER) **Mr K. J. Hickman**

TWO-YEAR-OLDS

27 B c 29/1 Oratorio (IRE)—Always Attractive (IRE) (King's Best (USA)) (42857) **Tony Foster & Partners**
28 **ARGENT KNIGHT**, gr c 8/5 Sir Percy—Tussah (Daylami (IRE)) (55000) **Dr J. Walker**
29 **ARTORIUS CASTUS**, ch c 12/3 Dutch Art—
　　　　Miss Madame (IRE) (Cape Cross (IRE)) (17000) **The Round Table Partnership**
30 B f 2/3 Sakhee's Secret—Bolsena (USA) (Red Ransom (USA)) (16000) **A Partnership**
31 B f 16/4 Henrythenavigator (USA)—
　　　　Diamond Necklace (USA) (Unbridled's Song (USA)) (130000) **Mr K. J. Hickman**
32 Br c 15/3 Kheleyf (USA)—First Approval (Royal Applause) (9000)
33 **LAUDATION**, b c 4/4 Royal Applause—Calamanco (Clantime) (30000) **The Laudation Partnership**
34 **NIGHT'S WATCH**, b c 26/3 Authorized (IRE)—Nachtigall (GER) (Danehill (USA)) (16000) **Dr J. Walker**
35 Ch f 25/2 Bahamian Bounty—Persian Lass (IRE) (Grand Lodge (USA)) (3500)
36 B c 20/3 Authorized (IRE)—Umthoulah (IRE) (Unfuwain (USA)) (6000) **Darren Brooks & Friends**

Other Owners: Mr Tony Briam, Mr W. F. Charnley, Mrs Wendy Dio, Mr A. Donald, Mrs M. Ferrier, Mr Anthony Foster, G. B. Turnbull Ltd, Mr & Mrs J. R. B. George, Mr William Jarvis, Mr John Kelsey-Fry, Mr R. F. Kilby, Mr David Marshall, Mr Geoff Meall, Mr Gavin Millar, Mr C. Miller, Mr David Morgan, Mrs Victoria Pakenham, Mr A. E. Pakenham, Mr Michael Payton, Mr Simon Porter, Mr E. Randall, Mr Nigel Rich, Mr Ian Robertson, Mrs J. Slogrove, Mr Bradley St Pierre, Miss Maureen Stopher, Mr R. C. C. Villers, Mr Neil Warnock, Mr Alex Wood, Mr Simon Wyatt.

359 MR MALCOLM JEFFERSON, Malton
Postal: **Newstead Cottage Stables, Norton, Malton, North Yorkshire, YO17 9PJ**
Contacts: **PHONE (01653) 697225 MOBILE (07710) 502044**
E-MAIL newsteadracing@btconnect.com

1 **ACCORDING TO PETE**, 11, b g Accordion—Magic Bloom **P. Nelson**
2 **ALTAN KHAN**, 7, b g Kayf Tara—Anabranch **Mrs J. E. Pallister**
3 4, Ch g Revoque (IRE)—Altogether Now (IRE) **J. M. Jefferson**
4 **ATTAGLANCE**, 6, b g Passing Glance—Our Ethel **H Young, G Eifert, R Snyder**
5 **BEAMAZED**, 8, ch g Silver Patriarch (IRE)—Gotogeton **Mr T. A. Pearcy**

MR MALCOLM JEFFERSON—continued

6 **BROOKLYN BROWNIE (IRE)**, 13, b g Presenting—
In The Brownies (IRE) **Mrs K. S. Gaffney & Mr J. N. Stevenson**
7 **CAPE TRIBULATION**, 8, b g Hernando (FR)—Gay Fantastic **J. D. Abell**
8 **CLASSIC RALLY (IRE)**, 6, b g Zagreb (USA)—Classic Material **T. J. Hemmings**
9 **DREAMERS OF DREAMS (IRE)**, 7, b g Flemensfirth (USA)—
Cushogan (IRE) **Dean Bostock & Raymond Bostock**
10 **ENCHANTED GARDEN**, 4, ch g Sulamani (IRE)—Calachuchi **Mr & Mrs J. M. Davenport**
11 **GREY LIFE**, 6, gr g Terimon—More To Life **D. T. Todd**
12 5, Ch g Accordion—Hannigan's Lodger (IRE) **J. R. Bostock**
13 **HENRY JENKINS**, 5, gr g Fair Mix (IRE)—Altogether Now (IRE) **Mrs K. M. Richardson**
14 **HI GEORGE**, 4, b g Doyen (IRE)—Our Ethel **Mr & Mrs H Young**
15 **KING FONTAINE (IRE)**, 9, b g King's Theatre (IRE)—Kerfontaine **T. J. Hemmings**
16 **KING OF THE WOLDS (IRE)**, 5, b g Presenting—Azaban (IRE) **J. M. Jefferson**
17 **LUA DE ITAPOAN (IRE)**, 7, gr m Silver Patriarch (IRE)—Gotogeton **Mr T. A. Pearcy**
18 **MAC AEDA**, 8, gr g Kayf Tara—Altogether Now (IRE) **Mr & Mrs J. M. Davenport**
19 **MAGIC PRESENT**, 5, b g Presenting—Magic Bloom **P. Nelson**
20 **MCMURROUGH (IRE)**, 8, b g Spectrum (IRE)—Sensitive (IRE) **Mr & Mrs J. M. Davenport**
21 **OVERBRANCH**, 9, br m Overbury (IRE)—Anabranch **Mrs S. Jefferson**
22 **POLAR GUNNER**, 15, b g Gunner B—Polar Belle **Mrs M. E. Dixon**
23 **QUANNAPOWITT (IRE)**, 8, b g Bob's Return—Autumn Sunset (IRE) **R. G. Marshall**
24 **QUITE THE MAN (IRE)**, 7, b g Zagreb (USA)—Ballinard Lizzie (IRE) **Boundary Garage (Bury) Limited**
25 **RUBIPRESENT (IRE)**, 8, b g Presenting—Azaban (IRE) **Mr J. H. Wilson**
26 **SCALES (IRE)**, 6, b g Bob Back (USA)—Mrs Avery (IRE) **T. J. Hemmings**
27 **SCHINKEN OTTO (IRE)**, 11, ch g Shinko Forest (IRE)—Athassel Rose (IRE) **J. Donald**
28 **STICK TOGETHER**, 9, gr m Kayf Tara—Altogether Now (IRE) **Mrs J M Jefferson & N J Taylor**
29 **SUN CLOUD (IRE)**, 5, b g Cloudings (IRE)—Miss Melrose **Boundary Garage (Bury) Limited**
30 **THE MAGIC BISHOP**, 7, b g Bishop of Cashel—Magic Bloom **P. Nelson**
31 **THE PANAMA KID (IRE)**, 8, b g Presenting—Mrs Jodi **Mr & Mrs J. M. Davenport**
32 **TOBETALL**, 5, b m Tobougg (IRE)—Our Ethel **Croftstyle 1867 & Mrs E A Young**
33 **TWIGLET THE PIGLET**, 5, b m Rainbow High—Forum Girl (USA) **Miss C. Bell**
34 **WHITE DIAMOND**, 5, b m Bertolini (USA)—Diamond White **T. R. Pryke**
35 **ZOENICIBEL**, 8, b m Kayf Tara—Romany Hill **Capt M. S. Bagley**

THREE-YEAR-OLDS

36 B f Revoque (IRE)—Anabranch **Mrs S Jefferson**
37 B g Doyen (IRE)—Julatten (IRE) **J. D. Abell**
38 B g Revoque (IRE)—Magic Bloom **P. Nelson**

Other Owners: Mr J. R. Bostock, Mr Dean Graham Bostock, Mr J. M. Davenport, Mrs J. M. Davenport, Mr G. Eifert, Mrs K. S. Gaffney, Mr J. M. Jefferson, Mr R. Synder Jnr, Mr J. N. Stevenson, Mr N. J. Taylor, Mr T. Wharton, Mrs J. Wharton, Mrs E. A. Young, Mr H. Young.

---

360 **MR J. R. JENKINS, Royston**
Postal: Kings Ride, Baldock Road, Royston, Hertfordshire, SG8 9NN
Contacts: PHONE (01763) 241141 HOME (01763) 246611 FAX (01763) 248223
MOBILE Car: (07802) 750855
E-MAIL john@johnjenkinsracing.co.uk WEBSITE www.johnjenkinsracing.co.uk

1 **ABADEJO**, 4, b g Acclamation—Silvereine (FR) **Mrs I. C. Hampson**
2 **AMOSITE**, 6, b m Central Park (IRE)—Waterline Dancer (IRE) **Mrs W. A. Jenkins**
3 **BILLY RED**, 8, ch g Dr Fong (USA)—Liberty Bound **Mrs I. C. Hampson**
4 **BINT ALAKAABER (IRE)**, 4, b f Elusive City (USA)—Lady of Pleasure (IRE) **Mrs W. A. Jenkins**
5 **BOOKIESINDEX BOY**, 8, b br g Piccolo—United Passion **Mr R. Stevens**
6 **CARAMELITA**, 5, b m Deportivo—Apple of My Eye **La Senoritas**
7 **D'URBERVILLE**, 5, b g Auction House (USA)—Laser Crystal (IRE) **Mrs W. A. Jenkins**
8 **DORCEUS**, 5, b g Doyen (IRE)—Jawwala (USA) **P. J. Kirkpatrick**
9 **ENCIRCLED**, 8, b m In The Wings—Ring of Esteem **Mrs W. A. Jenkins**
10 **FIFTH AUNTIE**, 5, ch m Nayef (USA)—Subtle One (IRE) **Michael Ng**
11 **FROLIC ALONG (IRE)**, 5, b m Medecis—High Glider **Mrs W. A. Jenkins**
12 **FROSTY FRIDAY**, 4, b f Storming Home—Seasonal Blossom (IRE) **Mr F. Al Harthi**
13 **GO AMWELL**, 9, b g Kayf Tara—Daarat Alayaam (IRE) **Mr R. Stevens**
14 **GRAYFRIARS**, 4, gr g Proclamation (IRE)—Hilltop **Mr G. H. Noble**
15 **GREAT EXPECTATIONS**, 4, b c Storming Home—Fresh Fruit Daily **The Great Expectations Partnership**
16 **GROUP LEADER (IRE)**, 6, ch g Noverre (USA)—Stem The Tide (USA) **Mr & Mrs J. Sales**

MR J. R. JENKINS—continued

17 **HANDSOME KING**, 5, ch g Lucky Story (USA)—Samar Qand **Mr F. Al Harthi**
18 **HI TIDE (IRE)**, 8, br g Idris (IRE)—High Glider **Mrs W. A. Jenkins**
19 **KARAM ALBAARI (IRE)**, 4, b c King's Best—Lilakiya (IRE) **Mr F. Al Harthi**
20 **LOUPHOLE**, 10, ch g Loup Sauvage (USA)—Goodwood Lass (IRE) **Mrs W. A. Jenkins**
21 **LOVE YOU LOUIS**, 6, b g Mark of Esteem (IRE)—Maddie's A Jem **J. Pepper**
22 **MAWAAKEF (IRE)**, 4, b g Azamour (IRE)—Al Euro (FR) **The Three Honest Men**
23 **MEDITERRANEAN SEA (IRE)**, 6, b m Medecis—High Glider **Mrs W. A. Jenkins**
24 **MISHRIF (USA)**, 6, b br g Arch (USA)—Peppy Priscilla (USA) **Mrs W. A. Jenkins**
25 **MONSIEUR JAMIE**, 4, b c Monsieur Bond (IRE)—Primula Bairn **Mark Goldstein & Stephen Pettman**
26 **MY FLAME**, 7, b g Cool Jazz—Suselja (IRE) **Mr A. J. Turner**
27 **MYBOYALFIE (USA)**, 5, b g Johannesburg (USA)—Scotchbonnetpepper (USA) **D. Badham**
28 **NOT TIL MONDAY (IRE)**, 6, b g Spartacus (IRE)—Halomix **The Three Honest Men**
29 **ONLY TEN PER CENT (IRE)**, 4, b g Kheleyf (USA)—Cory Everson (IRE) **B. Silkman**
30 **PAPAGENO**, 5, b g Piccolo—Fresh Fruit Daily **The Papageno Partnership**
31 **PRIDE OF MINE**, 9, b m Kayf Tara—Triple Zee (USA) **Mr R. Stevens**
32 **RAMBO WILL**, 4, b g Danbird (AUS)—Opera Belle **Mr & Mrs T H Bambridge**
33 **RAY OF JOY**, 6, b m Tobougg—Once Removed **Mr R. Stevens**
34 **SPITFIRE**, 7, b g Mujahid (USA)—Fresh Fruit Daily **The Spitfire Partnership**
35 **SWEET SUGAR (IRE)**, 6, ch g Loup Solitaire (USA)—Violette d'avril (FR) **Sweet Sugar Racing Club**
36 **THANK YOU JOY**, 4, b f Iceman—Once Removed **Mr R. Stevens**
37 **TILSWORTH GLENBOY**, 5, b g Doyen (IRE)—Chara **Michael Ng**
38 **TRACHONITIS (IRE)**, 8, b g Dansili—Hasina (IRE) **Mr & Mrs C. Schwick**
39 **WILLOW THE ROSE**, 5, b m Zamindar (USA)—Lilac Lady **Mr & Mrs T H Bambridge**
40 **ZAGALINIS SPEECH**, 4, b f Bertolini (USA)—Zagala **The Speech Partnership**

THREE-YEAR-OLDS

41 **BOOKIESINDEXDOTNET**, b f Piccolo—United Passion **Bookmakers Index Ltd**
42 Ch g Phoenix Reach (IRE)—Irja **Mrs S. Bambridge**
43 **JERMATT**, b c Kyllachy—Miss Ippolita **D. J. P. Bryans**
44 **LAURA'S BAIRN**, ch c Piccolo—Primula Bairn **Mr M. D. Goldstein**
45 **MINSTRELS GALLERY (IRE)**, ch c Refuse To Bend—Lilakiya (IRE) **The Three Honest Men**
46 **SILENT MISTRESS**, b f Fraam—Once Removed **Mrs W. A. Jenkins**
47 **WILLOW BEAUTY**, br f Val Royal (FR)—Opera Belle **Susan Bambridge & Wendy Jenkins**

TWO-YEAR-OLDS

48 B c 29/4 Sakhee (USA)—Ashwell Rose (Anabaa (USA)) **Mr & Mrs C. Schwick**
49 **OSCARS JOURNEY**, ch g 8/3 Dubai Destination (USA)—Fruit of Glory (Glory of Dancer) **R. B. Hill**

Other Owners: D. Abrey, R. Bradbury, S. J. Brewer, Mr S. M. Bullock, Mr G. J. Burchell, Mr I. J. Callaway, Miss P. Casey, M. A. Francis, Mrs C. A. Hill, Mr T H Bambridge T/As The Willow Stud, G. J. Pascoe, Mr S. P. Pettman, Mr P. Pooley, Mr J. Sales, Mrs K. Sales, Miss C. A. Salmon, Miss K. Salmon, C. Schwick, Mrs C. V. Schwick.

Apprentice: Danny Brock. **Amateur:** Mr Ray Barrett.

MR ALAN JESSOP, Chelmsford
Postal: **Flemings Farm, Warren Road, South Hanningfield, Chelmsford, Essex, CM3 8HU**
Contacts: **PHONE (01268) 710210 MOBILE (07718) 736482**

1 **CORAL POINT (IRE)**, 6, ch g Hawkeye (IRE)—Green Crystal **Mrs G. Jessop**
2 **MAHAB EL SHAMAAL**, 4, b g Motivator—Soliza (IRE) **Mrs G. Jessop**
3 **MAJY D'AUTEUIL (FR)**, 10, b g Discover d'auteuil (FR)—Majestic Dancer (FR) **Mrs G. Jessop**
4 **STEEPLEOFCOPPER (IRE)**, 6, ch g Classic Cliche—Tanya Thyne (IRE) **Mrs G. Jessop**
5 **STICKERS**, 5, b g Generous (IRE)—Dunsfold Duchess (IRE) **Mrs G. Jessop**

362
MRS LINDA JEWELL, Sutton Valence
Postal: **Southfield Stables, South Lane, Sutton Valence, Maidstone, Kent, ME17 3AZ**
Contacts: **PHONE (01622) 842788 FAX (01622) 842943 MOBILE (07856) 686657**
E-MAIL lindajewell@hotmail.com WEBSITE www.lindajewellracing.co.uk

1 **BIRTHDAY STAR (IRE)**, 10, b g Desert King (IRE)—White Paper (IRE) **Dr D. Chapman-Jones**
2 **BYRESTEADS FARM**, 5, b m Beat All (USA)—Kinnahalla (IRE) **Mrs L. C. Jewell**
3 **CALYPSO MAGIC (IRE)**, 4, gr g Aussie Rules (USA)—Calypso Dancer (FR) **K. Johnson, K. Jessup**
4 **CLONUSKER (IRE)**, 4, b g Fasliyev (USA)—Tamburello (IRE) **J. P. Jones**

MRS LINDA JEWELL—continued

5 **DANCE TIL MIDNIGHT,** 5, b m Imperial Dancer—Flinders **Leith Hill Chasers**
6 **DURGAN,** 6, b g Dansili—Peryllys **Mr M. J. Boutcher**
7 **FIFI L'AMOUR (IRE),** 6, ch m Flemensfirth (USA)—Supreme Adventure (IRE) **P. A. Oppenheimer**
8 **HEREDITARY,** 10, ch g Hernando (FR)—Eversince (USA) **P. A. Oppenheimer**
9 **KAYFLIN (FR),** 4, b f Kayf Tara—Flinders **Leith Hill Chasers**
10 **KNOCK BOY (IRE),** 10, b g Pistolet Bleu (IRE)—Past Times (IRE) **Wild Card**
11 **LEITH HILL DANCER,** 5, ch m Imperial Dancer—Leith Hill Star
12 **LUNA LIGHTNING,** 8, b m Rainbow High—Wilomeno **Mr K. E. Hay**
13 **RED ANCHOR (IRE),** 8, ch g Snurge—Clonartic (IRE) **Mrs S. M. Stanier**
14 **ROE VALLEY (IRE),** 5, ch g Arakan (USA)—Waaedah (USA) **Mr R. B. Morton**
15 **ROWE PARK,** 9, b g Dancing Spree (USA)—Magic Legs **Mrs S. M. Ashdown**
16 **SHE'S HUMBLE (IRE),** 10, ch m Humbel (USA)—She's No Tourist (IRE) **Valence Racing Too**
17 **SHE'S JOLLY (IRE),** 7, b m Jolly Jake (NZ)—She's No Tourist (IRE) **Mrs R. V. Watson**
18 **SPIRIT OF XAAR (IRE),** 6, b g Xaar—Jet Cat (IRE) **K. Johnson, K. Jessup**

THREE-YEAR-OLDS

19 **ALMIRAH,** ch f Ishiguru (USA)—Brogue Lanterns (IRE) **Brian Kennard**
20 **FLEETING INDIAN (IRE),** b c Sleeping Indian—Glebe Garden **Mr M. J. Boutcher**
21 **MONESSA (IRE),** ch f Le Vie Dei Colori—Nasaria (IRE)
22 **STRATEGIC ACTION (IRE),** ch c Strategic Prince—Ruby Cairo (IRE) **Mr M. J. Boutcher**
23 **TANGTASTIC (IRE),** b f Elusive City (USA)—Infozoid (IRE)

Other Owners: Mrs Linda Jewell, Mrs A. Emanuel, Mr D. Fisher, Mr K. Jessup, Mr K. Johnson, Mrs N. F. Maltby, Mrs A. May, Mr O. J. C. Shannon, Mr R. I. B. Young.

Assistant Trainer: Karen Jewell

Jockey (flat): Steve Drowne. **Jockey (NH):** Richard Johnson, Jamie Moore, Charlie Studd, Andrew Thornton. **Amateur:** Mr T. Cheesman.

---

363 MR BRETT JOHNSON, Epsom
Postal: **The Durdans Stables, Chalk Lane, Epsom, Surrey, KT18 7AX**
Contacts: **MOBILE** (07768) 697141
E-MAIL thedurdansstables@googlemail.com WEBSITE www.brjohnsonracing.co.uk

1 **ABIGAILS ANGEL,** 5, br m Olden Times—Make Ready **B. R. Johnson**
2 **AMAZON TWILIGHT,** 4, b f Librettist (USA)—My Way (IRE) **Mrs A M Upsdell & Mr J Daniels**
3 **EAGLE NEBULA,** 8, ch g Observatory (USA)—Tarocchi (USA) **Tann Racing**
4 **KING'S COLOUR,** 7, b g King's Best (USA)—Red Garland **Tann Racing**
5 **ONEIRIC,** 4, gr f Act One—Ecstasy **Mr S. Sivagnanam**

THREE-YEAR-OLDS

6 **MR HENDRIX,** b g Librettist (USA)—Sprinkle **G. W. Chambers**
7 **MY SCAT DADDY (USA),** b g Scat Daddy—Will Be A Bates (USA) **J. Daniels**
8 Ch f Zafeen (FR)—Nocturnal Lady **Follow The Flag Partnership**
9 **SANDFRANKSKIPSGO,** ch g Piccolo—Alhufoof (USA) **P. D. Crate**
10 **VALENTINO ROCKS,** b c Arkadian Hero (USA)—Orpen Annie (IRE) **G. W. Chambers**

TWO-YEAR-OLDS

11 Ch f 10/5 Bertolini (USA)—Days of Grace (Wolfhound (USA)) **Omni Colour Presentations Ltd**
12 Br f 28/1 Sakhee's Secret—Point Perfect (Dansili) (9000) **Tann Racing**

Other Owners: Mr D. Popely, Mr R. A. Popely, Mr Gary Tann, Mrs E. Tann, Mrs A. M. Upsdell.

Assistant Trainer: Vanessa Johnson

Apprentice: Accursio Romeo.

364 MISS EVE JOHNSON HOUGHTON, Blewbury
Postal: **Woodway, Blewbury, Didcot, Oxfordshire, OX11 9EZ**
Contacts: PHONE **(01235) 850480 (01235) 850500 (Home)** FAX **(01235) 851045**
MOBILE **(07721) 622700**
E-MAIL **Eve@JohnsonHoughton.com** WEBSITE **www.JohnsonHoughton.com**

1 **AMISTRESS**, 4, b f Kalanisi (IRE)—Atwirl **Mrs R. L. M. Robeson**
2 **BARRISTERS BRIEF**, 4, b g Diktat—Ski Run **Mr T. D. Holland-Martin**
3 **CATCHANOVA (IRE)**, 5, b g Catcher In The Rye (IRE)—
Head For The Stars (IRE) **Andrew Wyer Darrell Blake Hugh Arthur**
4 **ELLEN DEAN**, 4, b f Pursuit of Love—Cressex Katie **Mr M. Young**
5 **FONTLEY**, 5, b m Sadler's Wells (USA)—Horatia (IRE) **Mrs V. D. Neale**
6 **GOLDEN TEMPEST (IRE)**, 4, b f Clodovil (IRE)—Honey Storm (IRE) **Silver Linings**
7 **GOLDEN WATERS**, 5, b m Dubai Destination (USA)—Faraway Waters **Mr R. E. Crutchley**
8 **JUDD STREET**, 10, b g Compton Place—Pudding Lane (IRE) **R. F. Johnson Houghton**
9 **LOVAT LANE**, 4, b f Avonbridge—Pudding Lane (IRE) **R. F. Johnson Houghton**
10 **MIDNIGHT FEAST**, 4, b g Ishiguru (USA)—Prince's Feather (IRE) **P. L. Winkworth**
11 **MRS GREELEY**, 4, b f Mr Greeley (USA)—Swain's Gold (USA) **Mrs R. Arber**
12 **PHLUKE**, 11, b g Most Welcome—Phlirty **Mrs F. M. Johnson Houghton**
13 **ROODLE**, 5, b m Xaar—Roodeye **Mrs F. M. Johnson Houghton**
14 **STRENGTH AND STAY (IRE)**, 4, b g Motivator—Queen's Cape **Mrs V. D. Neale**
15 **THE CHEKA (IRE)**, 6, b g Xaar—Veiled Beauty (USA) **Anthony Pye-Jeary & Mel Smith**
16 **YURITUNI**, 5, b m Bahamian Bounty—Vax Star **The Ascot Colts & Fillies Club**

THREE-YEAR-OLDS
17 B f Dubai Destination (USA)—Alpenrot (IRE) **Mrs V. D. Neale**
18 **LUNAR DEITY**, b c Medicean—Luminda (IRE) **Eden Racing (III) & P. A. Deal**
19 **MORNING CALL**, b g Sleeping Indian—Fanfare
20 **ORDERS FROM ROME (IRE)**, b g Holy Roman Emperor (IRE)—Fatat Alarab (USA) **G. C. Stevens**
21 **RASPBERRY FIZZ**, b f Red Ransom (USA)—Dubai Spirit (USA) **Mrs F. M. Johnson Houghton**
22 **RIVER PAGEANT**, ch f Primo Valentino—Belly Dancer (IRE) **P. L. Winkworth**
23 **RUM PUNCH**, b f Ishiguru (USA)—Cajole (IRE) **Mr & Mrs C. J. Hue Williams**
24 **RUN OF THE DAY**, b f Three Valleys (USA)—Shall We Run **Mrs F. M. Johnson Houghton**
25 **SIMPLY**, b f Nayef (USA)—Polish Lake **Mrs R. Arber**
26 **SOVEREIGN WATERS**, ch f Haafhd—Faraway Waters **Mr R. E. Crutchley**
27 **SPOKE TO CARLO**, b c Halling (USA)—Red Shareef **Anthony Pye-Jeary & Mel Smith**
28 **TRUSTING (IRE)**, b f Red Clubs (IRE)—Tertia (IRE) **Miss S. Von Schilcher**
29 **UNCLE ROGER (IRE)**, b g Camacho—Felin Gruvy (IRE) **Mrs J. E. O'Halloran**
30 **ZINGANA**, b f Zamindar (USA)—Change Partners (IRE) **Lord Astor,Lady Lewinton,R Morgan-Jones**

TWO-YEAR-OLDS
31 **CLEMENT (IRE)**, b c 31/3 Clodovil (IRE)—Winnifred (Green Desert (USA)) (15000) **P. Deal & C. Brown**
32 B gr c 23/3 Red Clubs (IRE)—El Morocco (USA) (El Prado (IRE)) (14000)
33 B f 18/4 Majestic Missile (IRE)—Felin Gruvy (IRE) (Tagula (IRE)) (656) **Mrs J. E. O'Halloran**
34 **IMPERIAL OAK**, b c 18/5 Imperial Dancer—Shalad'or (Golden Heights) (1500)
35 **KNIGHT CHARM**, b c 17/4 Haafhd—Enchanted Princess (Royal Applause) (18000) **Fairweather Friends**
36 Br c 3/2 Shirocco (GER)—Melatonina (IRE) (King Charlemagne (USA)) (16000)
37 **MUST BE ME**, b f 22/3 Trade Fair—Roodeye (Inchinor)
38 **PEACE TREATY**, b c 6/5 Lucky Story (USA)—Peace Lily (Dansili)
39 B c 6/4 Tagula (IRE)—Queeny's Princess (IRE) (Daggers Drawn (USA)) (8209) **Eden Racing IV**
40 **RECTORY LANE**, ch f 21/4 Compton Place—Pudding Lane (IRE) (College Chapel) **R. F. Johnson Houghton**
41 **VESTIBULE**, ch f 28/2 Kheleyf (USA)—Lobby Card (USA) (Saint Ballado (CAN)) (4761)

Other Owners: H. R. F. Arthur, Viscount Astor, Mr D. S. Blake, P. A. Deal, Mrs P. A. Deal, Mr J. C. Edington-Brown, Mrs G. Fullerton, Mrs C. J. Hue Williams, Mr C. J. Hue Williams, Miss E. A. Johnson Houghton, Lady Lewinton, Mrs J. A. McWilliam, R. J. Morgan-Jones, A. J. Pye-Jeary, M. K. Smith, Mr O. A. Wideson, A. P. Wyer.

Assistant Trainer: R. F. Johnson Houghton

365 MR ROBERT JOHNSON, Newcastle Upon Tyne
Postal: **Johnson Racing Ltd, Grange Farm, Newburn, Newcastle Upon Tyne**
Contacts: PHONE **(01912) 674464** MOBILE **(07774) 131133**

1 **A BEAT SO FAR**, 6, b m Beat All (USA)—Only So Far **R. W. Johnson**
2 **BALLYBANKS (IRE)**, 8, b g Exit To Nowhere (USA)—Incharder (IRE) **Mrs A. E. Speke**

MR ROBERT JOHNSON—continued

3 **DECHIPER (IRE)**, 10, b br g Almutawakel—Safiya (USA) **J. L. Armstrong**
4 **EILA WHEELER**, 5, b m Central Park (IRE)—Only So Far **Lister/Andersen In P/ship With R.Johnson**
5 **KALKAN BAY**, 4, b g Pastoral Pursuits—Gibraltar Bay (IRE) **J. S. Kennerley**
6 **LINDSEYFIELD LODGE (IRE)**, 11, br g Presenting—Missusan (IRE) **Toon Racing**
7 **MAINLAND (USA)**, 6, b g Empire Maker (USA)—Imroz (USA)
8 **MEDIA STARS**, 7, gr g Green Desert (USA)—Starine (FR) **R. C. Whitelock**
9 **NAPOLETANO (ITY)**, 6, b g Kyllachy—Nationality **R. W. Johnson**
10 **POLITELYSED**, 6, ch m Courteous—Allegedly Red **Mr Robert Johnson & Mr J. Lund**
11 **TOULOUSE EXPRESS (IRE)**, 13, b g Toulon—Miss Ivy (IRE) **R. W. Johnson**
12 **VODKA RED (IRE)**, 4, b g Ivan Denisovich (IRE)—Begine (IRE) **Do Well Racing & Partners**

THREE-YEAR-OLDS

13 **I'LL BE GOOD**, b c Red Clubs (IRE)—Willisa **Do Well Racing**

Other Owners: Mr I. M. Blacklock, Mr G. D. Brown, Mr N. K. Lister, Mr J. Lund, Mr B. J. Maxted, Mr W. A. Shaw.

Jockey (NH): Kenny Johnson. **Amateur:** Mr P. S. Johnson.

---

366 **MR MARK JOHNSTON, Middleham**
Postal: **Kingsley House Racing Stables, Middleham, Leyburn, North Yorkshire, DL8 4PH**
Contacts: **PHONE (01969) 622237 FAX (01969) 622484**
E-MAIL mark@markjohnstonracing.com WEBSITE www.markjohnstonracing.com

1 **AMPLEFORTH**, 4, ch c Pivotal—Anna Amalia (IRE) **Sheikh Hamdan Bin Mohammed Al Maktoum**
2 **AQUA LAD**, 4, b g Garrison Savannah (NZ)—Caysue **C. H. Greensit**
3 **BECAUSEWECAN (USA)**, 6, b g Giant's Causeway (USA)—Belle Sultane (USA) **D. C. Livingston**
4 **BELLE JOSEPHINE**, 4, b f Dubawi (IRE)—Bella Lambada **Sheikh Hamdan Bin Mohammed Al Maktoum**
5 **BOWDLER'S MAGIC**, 5, b g Hernando (FR)—Slew The Moon (ARG) **P. Dean**
6 **CALYPSO CAY**, 4, b g Tiger Hill (IRE)—Tessa Reef (IRE) **Sheikh Hamdan Bin Mohammed Al Maktoum**
7 **COLOUR GUARD**, 4, b g Shamardal (USA)—Colorvista **Sheikh Hamdan Bin Mohammed Al Maktoum**
8 **CROWN COUNSEL (IRE)**, 4, b c Invincible Spirit (IRE)—
Virgin Hawk (USA) **Sheikh Hamdan Bin Mohammed Al Maktoum**
9 **ECOSSAISE**, 4, ch f Selkirk (USA)—Diablerette **Miss K. Rausing**
10 **ENGLISH SUMMER**, 5, b g Montjeu (IRE)—Hunt The Sun **Dr M. B. Q. S. Koukash**
11 **ETERNAL HEART (IRE)**, 4, b c Alhaarth (IRE)—Lady In Pace **Mrs J. Keaney**
12 **EXEMPLARY**, 5, b g Sulamani (IRE)—Epitome (IRE) **Dr M. B. Q. S. Koukash**
13 **EYEDORO (USA)**, 4, b br g Medaglia d'oro (USA)—
Critical Eye (USA) **Sheikh Hamdan Bin Mohammed Al Maktoum**
14 **FASCINATING (IRE)**, 4, b c Cape Cross (IRE)—Something Exciting **N. Mourad**
15 **GULF OF NAPLES (IRE)**, 4, gr c Dubawi (IRE)—Kapria (FR) **Sheikh Hamdan Bin Mohammed Al Maktoum**
16 **HURRICANE HIGGINS (IRE)**, 4, br g Hurricane Run (IRE)—Mare Aux Fees **A. D. Spence**
17 **ITHOUGHTITWASOVER (IRE)**, 4, b c Hurricane Run (IRE)—Green Castle (IRE) **Crone Stud Farms Ltd**
18 **JEU DE VIVRE**, 4, b f Montjeu (IRE)—In My Life (IRE) **Ms J. F. Bianco**
19 **JOE LE TAXI (IRE)**, 4, ch g Johannesburg (USA)—Attasliyah (IRE) **Mark Johnston Racing Ltd**
20 **JUKEBOX JURY (IRE)**, 6, gr h Montjeu (IRE)—Mare Aux Fees **Mr A D Spence & Bamford/Ryan Partnership**
21 **KINGSCROFT (IRE)**, 4, b g Antonius Pius (USA)—Handsome Anna (IRE) **Dr M. B. Q. S. Koukash**
22 **LANDAMAN (IRE)**, 4, br g Cape Cross (IRE)—Mayoress **Sheikh Hamdan Bin Mohammed Al Maktoum**
23 **LICENCE TO TILL (USA)**, 5, b g War Chant (USA)—With A Wink (USA) **The Vine Accord**
24 **MADRILENE (USA)**, 4, b f El Prado (USA)—Lignify (ARG) **Sheikh Hamdan Bin Mohammed Al Maktoum**
25 **MEDAL OF VALOUR (JPN)**, 4, b c Medaglia d'oro (USA)—
Tres Tres Joli (USA) **Sheikh Hamdan Bin Mohammed Al Maktoum**
26 **MONTPARNASSE (IRE)**, 5, b g Montjeu (IRE)—Capades Dancer (USA) **Dr M. B. Q. S. Koukash**
27 **NEZHENKA**, 5, b m With Approval (CAN)—Ninotchka (USA) **Miss K. Rausing**
28 **OCEANWAY (USA)**, 4, b f Street Cry (IRE)—Sea Gift (USA) **Sheikh Hamdan Bin Mohammed Al Maktoum**
29 **PLATTSBURGH (USA)**, 4, b br c Bernardini (USA)—
Saranac Lake (USA) **Sheikh Hamdan Bin Mohammed Al Maktoum**
30 **QUEEN OF DENMARK (USA)**, 4, b f Kingmambo (USA)—
Danelagh (AUS) **Sheikh Hamdan Bin Mohammed Al Maktoum**
31 **SENNOCKIAN STORM (USA)**, 5, b m Storm Cat (USA)—Winning Season (USA) **The Vine Accord**
32 **SHIELDMAIDEN (USA)**, 4, ch f Smart Strike (CAN)—
Code Book (USA) **Sheikh Hamdan Bin Mohammed Al Maktoum**
33 **SILVER BULLITT**, 4, gr g Proclamation (IRE)—Eurolinka (IRE) **Antoniades Family**
34 **SMART STEP**, 4, b f Montjeu (IRE)—Miss Pinkerton **S. R. Counsell**
35 **SON VIDA (IRE)**, 4, b c Titus Livius (FR)—Sombreffe **Jim McGrath, Roger & Dianne Trevitt**

MR MARK JOHNSTON—continued

36 **SOUTHERN STATE (USA)**, 4, ch c Street Cry (IRE)—Tigi (USA) **Sheikh Hamdan Bin Mohammed Al Maktoum**
37 **SWIFT ALHAARTH (IRE)**, 4, b g Alhaarth (IRE)—Simla Bibi **Dr M. B. Q. S. Koukash**
38 **TARTAN JURA**, 4, b c Green Desert (USA)—On A Soapbox (USA) **Exors of the Late Mrs N. I. Bird**
39 **THE BELLS O PEOVER**, 4, b g Selkirk (USA)—Bay Tree (IRE) **D&G Mercer**
40 **TMAAM (USA)**, 4, b br c Dynaformer (USA)—Thread (USA) **J. Abdullah**

THREE-YEAR-OLDS

41 **ABISHENA (IRE)**, ch f Pivotal—Massomah (USA) **Sheikh Hamdan Bin Mohammed Al Maktoum**
42 B f Oratorio (IRE)—Act of The Pace (IRE) **Mrs J. Keaney**
43 **AL BATTANI (USA)**, ch c Street Cry (IRE)—Sunspangled (IRE) **Sheikh Hamdan Bin Mohammed Al Maktoum**
44 **ALIANTE**, ch f Sir Percy—Alexandrine (IRE) **Miss K. Rausing**
45 **ALKADI (IRE)**, b f Oasis Dream—Vista Bella **Sheikh Hamdan Bin Mohammed Al Maktoum**
46 **ALWAYS EAGER**, b g With Approval (CAN)—Slew The Moon (ARG) **Always Trying Partnership VIII**
47 **ALWAYS ENDS WELL (IRE)**, b f Tiger Hill (IRE)—Awwal Malika (USA) **Always Trying Partnership VIII**
48 **ARCH OF COLOURS**, b f Monsun (GER)—Sunray Superstar **Sheikh Hamdan Bin Mohammed Al Maktoum**
49 **ARIOSO (IRE)**, b c Elusive Quality (USA)—Balletomaine (IRE) **Sheikh Hamdan Bin Mohammed Al Maktoum**
50 **ASSIZES**, b gr c Teofilo (IRE)—Requesting **Sheikh Hamdan Bin Mohammed Al Maktoum**
51 **AUTHENTICATION**, b c Authorized (IRE)—Valley of Gold (FR) **Sheikh Hamdan Bin Mohammed Al Maktoum**
52 **BAILEYS DUTCH**, gr g Dutch Art—Southern Psychic (USA) **G. R. Bailey Ltd**
53 **BAILEYS STRIDER**, b c Aragorn (IRE)—Missisipi Star (IRE) **G. R. Bailey Ltd**
54 **BANNOCK (IRE)**, b c Bertolini (IRE)—Laoub (USA) **Sheikh Hamdan Bin Mohammed Al Maktoum**
55 **BEVIS MARKS (USA)**, b c Street Cry (IRE)—Blue Duster (USA) **Exors of the Late Mrs N. I. Bird**
56 **BISHOP'S CASTLE (USA)**, b br c Distorted Humor (USA)—
Miss Caerleona (FR) **Sheikh Hamdan Bin Mohammed Al Maktoum**
57 **BLUE DUNE**, b f Invincible Spirit (IRE)—Scatina (IRE) **Sheikh Hamdan Bin Mohammed Al Maktoum**
58 **BORDONI (USA)**, b c Bernardini (USA)—Argentina (IRE) **Sheikh Hamdan Bin Mohammed Al Maktoum**
59 **BOUNTY SEEKER (USA)**, b c A P Indy (USA)—Plenty of Light (USA) **A. D. Spence**
60 **BROXBOURNE (IRE)**, b f Refuse To Bend (IRE)—Rafting (IRE) **Racegoers Club Owners Group**
61 **BUTE HALL**, ch c Halling (USA)—Les Hurlants (IRE) **Mark Johnston Racing Ltd**
62 **CAPTIVITY**, b c Echo of Light—Tee Cee **Sheikh Hamdan Bin Mohammed Al Maktoum**
63 **CHATTERATI (USA)**, b f Street Cry (IRE)—Melhor Ainda (USA) **Sheikh Hamdan Bin Mohammed Al Maktoum**
64 **COMICAL**, b g Dubai Destination (USA)—Amusing Time (IRE) **Sheikh Hamdan Bin Mohammed Al Maktoum**
65 **COURTESY CALL (IRE)**, b g Manduro (GER)—Three Wrens (IRE) **A. D. Spence**
66 **CRAVAT**, b c Dubai Destination (USA)—Crinolette (IRE) **Sheikh Hamdan Bin Mohammed Al Maktoum**
67 **CROFTAMIE**, b f Selkirk (USA)—Embraced **Mark Johnston Racing Ltd**
68 **DANUBE RIVER**, ch f Teofilo (IRE)—Last Rhapsody (IRE) **Sheikh Hamdan Bin Mohammed Al Maktoum**
69 **EL LAIL (USA)**, ch f Haafhd—Dufoof (USA) **Hamdan Al Maktoum**
70 **ELKHART (IRE)**, b c Refuse To Bend (IRE)—Princess Taise (USA) **Sheikh Hamdan Bin Mohammed Al Maktoum**
71 **EMILY CARR (IRE)**, b f Teofilo (IRE)—Vimy Ridge (IRE) **Sheikh Hamdan Bin Mohammed Al Maktoum**
72 **ENERY (IRE)**, b c Teofilo (IRE)—Annee Lumiere (IRE) **Sheikh Hamdan Bin Mohammed Al Maktoum**
73 **EQUITY CARD (FR)**, b br f Dubai Destination (USA)—
Snow Ballerina **Sheikh Hamdan Bin Mohammed Al Maktoum**
74 **ERAADA**, ch f Medicean—Elfaslah (IRE) **Hamdan Al Maktoum**
75 **ES QUE LOVE (IRE)**, br c Clodovil (IRE)—Es Que **Crone Stud Farms Ltd**
76 **FALCONINTHEDESERT (IRE)**, gr c Clodovil (IRE)—Mise (IRE) **J. Abdullah**
77 **FENNELL BAY (IRE)**, b c Dubawi (IRE)—Woodrising **Sheikh Hamdan Bin Mohammed Al Maktoum**
78 **FINITY RUN (GER)**, b f Hurricane Run (IRE)—Finity (USA) **Mark Johnston Racing Ltd**
79 **FULBRIGHT**, b c Exceed And Excel (AUS)—Lindfield Belle (USA) **Sheikh Hamdan Bin Mohammed Al Maktoum**
80 **GABRIAL'S HOPE (FR)**, b c Teofilo (IRE)—Wedding Night (FR) **Dr M. B. Q. S. Koukash**
81 **GABRIAL'S LAYLA (IRE)**, b f Dylan Thomas (IRE)—Marlene-D **Dr M. B. Q. S. Koukash**
82 **GALICIAN**, gr f Redoute's Choice (AUS)—Gweneira **Sheikh Hamdan Bin Mohammed Al Maktoum**
83 **GHALAA (IRE)**, b br f Nayef (USA)—Mouwadh (USA) **Hamdan Al Maktoum**
84 **GHOST TRAIN (IRE)**, b g Holy Roman Emperor (IRE)—Adrastea (IRE) **A. D. Spence**
85 **GLEN ELLYN**, gr c Shamardal (USA)—Giorgia Rae (IRE) **Sheikh Hamdan Bin Mohammed Al Maktoum**
86 **GOOD MORNING STAR (IRE)**, b br f Shirocco (GER)—Hollow Ridge **J. Abdullah**
87 **GREEK COLONY**, b g Pivotal—Taranto **Sheikh Hamdan Bin Mohammed Al Maktoum**
88 **HAJRAS (IRE)**, b c Dubai Destination (USA)—Nufoos **Hamdan Al Maktoum**
89 **HAMIS AL BIN (IRE)**, b c Acclamation—Paimpolaise (IRE) **Mr A. Jaber**
90 **HAYMARKET**, b c Singspiel (IRE)—Quickstyx **Sheikh Hamdan Bin Mohammed Al Maktoum**
91 **HENRY CLAY**, b c Dubawi (IRE)—Congressional (USA) **Sheikh Hamdan Bin Mohammed Al Maktoum**
92 **HENRY GEORGE**, b c Zamindar (USA)—Melpomene **Mrs C. E. Budden**
93 **HIKMA (USA)**, b f Street Cry (IRE)—Innuendo **Sheikh Hamdan Bin Mohammed Al Maktoum**
94 **HURRICANE EMERALD (IRE)**, b g Hurricane Run (IRE)—Love Emerald (USA) **Crone Stud Farms Ltd**
95 **HURRIYA**, b f Invincible Spirit (IRE)—Adonita **Sheikh Hamdan Bin Mohammed Al Maktoum**
96 **HYPERLINK (IRE)**, b g Cape Cross (IRE)—Surf The Web (USA) **Sheikh Hamdan Bin Mohammed Al Maktoum**

MR MARK JOHNSTON—continued

97 **ICELANDER (USA)**, b c Stormy Atlantic (USA)—
　　　　　　　　　　　Painted Lady (USA) **Sheikh Hamdan Bin Mohammed Al Maktoum**
98 **IDLER (IRE)**, b c Exceed And Excel (AUS)—Dilly Dally (AUS) **Sheikh Hamdan Bin Mohammed Al Maktoum**
99 **INCESSANT (IRE)**, b f Elusive Quality (USA)—
　　　　　　　　　　　Infinite Spirit (USA) **Sheikh Hamdan Bin Mohammed Al Maktoum**
100 **KEY GOLD**, b f Cape Cross (IRE)—Key Academy **J. Abdullah**
101 **KINLOCH CASTLE**, b c Echo of Light—Sound of Sleat **Sheikh Hamdan Bin Mohammed Al Maktoum**
102 **LADY MACDUFF (IRE)**, b f Iffraaj—Tamora **Sheikh Hamdan Bin Mohammed Al Maktoum**
103 **LEQQAA (USA)**, b c Street Cry (IRE)—Guerre Et Paix (USA) **Hamdan Al Maktoum**
104 **LIONROCK (FR)**, ch c Shamardal (USA)—Genevale (FR) **Sheikh Hamdan Bin Mohammed Al Maktoum**
105 **LITHOGRAPH (USA)**, b f Echo of Light—Forum Floozie (NZ) **Sheikh Hamdan Bin Mohammed Al Maktoum**
106 **LONG LOST LOVE**, b f Langfuhr (CAN)—Heat of The Night **Miss K. Rausing**
107 **MAASTRICHT (IRE)**, b g Tiger Hill (IRE)—
　　　　　　　　　　　Eurolink Raindance (IRE) **Sheikh Hamdan Bin Mohammed Al Maktoum**
108 **MASTER OF AGES (IRE)**, b g Exceed And Excel (AUS)—
　　　　　　　　　　　Historian (IRE) **Sheikh Hamdan Bin Mohammed Al Maktoum**
109 **MOATAZ (USA)**, ch g Elusive Quality (USA)—Ramatuelle (CHI) **Dr M. B. Q. S. Koukash**
110 **MOLL'S GAP**, ch f Street Cry (IRE)—Maids Causeway (IRE) **Sheikh Hamdan Bin Mohammed Al Maktoum**
111 **MONICKER**, b f Manduro (GER)—Guadalajara (GER) **Sheikh Hamdan Bin Mohammed Al Maktoum**
112 **MOON TRIP**, b g Cape Cross (IRE)—Fading Light **Sheikh Hamdan Bin Mohammed Al Maktoum**
113 **NATIONAL HERO (IRE)**, ch c Exceed And Excel (AUS)—Miss Marvellous (USA) **A. Saeed**
114 **NEW DECADE**, ch g Pivotal—Irresistible **Claire Riordan & Kieran Coughlan**
115 **NICE ROSE**, ch f Teofilo (IRE)—Souvenance **Mr A. Jaber**
116 **NIMIETY**, b f Stormy Atlantic (USA)—Nadeszhda **Miss K. Rausing**
117 **OASIS LOVE (IRE)**, b c Oasis Dream—Lunathea (IRE) **Crone Stud Farms Ltd**
118 **PARLEY (USA)**, b br f Elusive Quality (USA)—Tout Charmant (USA) **Sheikh Hamdan Bin Mohammed Al Maktoum**
119 **PARTY LINE**, b f Montjeu (IRE)—Party (IRE) **S. R. Counsell**
120 **PETER ANDERS**, b c Pivotal—Astorg (USA) **Newsells Park Stud Limited**
121 **PRUSSIAN**, b f Dubai Destination (USA)—Russian Snows (IRE) **Sheikh Hamdan Bin Mohammed Al Maktoum**
122 **PUGNACIOUS (IRE)**, b c Street Cry (IRE)—Dignify (USA) **Sheikh Hamdan Bin Mohammed Al Maktoum**
123 **QUEEN'S ESTATE (GER)**, b c Hurricane Run (IRE)—Questabelle **Mr J. C. Daley**
124 **QUIET APPEAL (IRE)**, b f Cape Cross (IRE)—Rise and Fall (USA) **T T Bloodstocks**
125 **RAFEEJ**, b c Iffraaj—Muffled (USA) **Hamdan Al Maktoum**
126 **RAHEEBA**, b f Invincible Spirit (IRE)—Wild Gardenia **Sheikh Hamdan Bin Mohammed Al Maktoum**
127 **RAINBOW GOLD**, ch c Selkirk (USA)—Diablerette **J. Abdullah**
128 **RED ORATOR**, ch c Osorio (GER)—Red Roses Story (FR) **Newsells Park Stud Limited**
129 **ROSBY WAVES (USA)**, b f Distorted Humor (USA)—
　　　　　　　　　　　Windsharp (USA) **Sheikh Hamdan Bin Mohammed Al Maktoum**
130 **RYTHMIC**, ch f Dubai Destination (USA)—Northern Melody (IRE) **Sheikh Hamdan Bin Mohammed Al Maktoum**
131 **SAFE HOUSE (IRE)**, ch f Exceed And Excel (AUS)—Last Resort **Sheikh Hamdan Bin Mohammed Al Maktoum**
132 **SAMEDI**, b f Any Given Saturday (USA)—Hush Money (CHI) **Sheikh Hamdan Bin Mohammed Al Maktoum**
133 **SASLONG**, b c Zamindar (USA)—Cosmodrome (USA) **Around The World Partnership**
134 **SCATTER DICE (IRE)**, ch f Manduro (GER)—Sensation **Sheikh Hamdan Bin Mohammed Al Maktoum**
135 **SIR GRAHAM WADE (IRE)**, gr c Dalakhani (IRE)—Needwood Epic **P. Dean**
136 **SKIRMISH**, b c Teofilo (IRE)—Jessica's Dream (IRE) **Sheikh Hamdan Bin Mohammed Al Maktoum**
137 **SOAPY DELIGHT**, b f Dansili—On A Soapbox (USA) **Newsells Park Stud Limited**
138 **STAR LAHIB (IRE)**, b f Cape Cross (IRE)—Cannikin (IRE) **J. Abdullah**
139 **SWITZERLAND (IRE)**, b c Shamardal (USA)—Sahra Alsalam (USA) **Sheikh M. B. M. Al Maktoum**
140 B gr c Clodovil (IRE)—Tawaafur **Mark Johnston Racing Ltd**
141 **TEIDE PEAK (IRE)**, b c Cape Cross (IRE)—Teide Lady **Sheikh Hamdan Bin Mohammed Al Maktoum**
142 **THREE BARDS (IRE)**, ch c Dubawi (IRE)—Polish Affair (IRE) **Sheikh Hamdan Bin Mohammed Al Maktoum**
143 **TIGRESA (IRE)**, b f Tiger Hill (IRE)—Carakiysa (IRE) **M. W. Graff**
144 **TO THE SEA (USA)**, ch f Giant's Causeway (USA)—Oceans Apart **Elite Racing Club**
145 **UKRAINIAN (IRE)**, b c Teofilo (IRE)—Livadiya (IRE) **Sheikh M. B. M. Al Maktoum**
146 **VAN ELLIS**, b c Shamardal (USA)—Jalousie (USA) **Sheikh Hamdan Bin Mohammed Al Maktoum**
147 **VENA AMORIS (USA)**, b f Dixie Union (USA)—
　　　　　　　　　　　Love Locket (USA) **Sheikh Hamdan Bin Mohammed Al Maktoum**
148 **VOCATIONAL (USA)**, b f Exceed And Excel (AUS)—
　　　　　　　　　　　Carry On Katie (USA) **Sheikh Hamdan Bin Mohammed Al Maktoum**
149 **WILLPOWER (IRE)**, b c Montjeu (IRE)—Noble Pearl (GER) **A. D. Spence**
150 **ZA'LAN (USA)**, b g Street Sense (USA)—Calista **Sheikh Hamdan Bin Mohammed Al Maktoum**
151 **ZAVIER (FR)**, b c Shamardal (USA)—Zarkiyna (FR) **Sheikh Hamdan Bin Mohammed Al Maktoum**

TWO-YEAR-OLDS

152 B f 12/4 Zamindar (USA)—Art Eyes (USA) (Halling (USA)) (50903) **Ms J. F. Bianco**

MR MARK JOHNSTON—continued

153 B c 4/4 Elusive Quality (USA)—Blue Duster (USA) (Danzig (USA)) **Sheikh Hamdan Bin Mohammed Al Maktoum**
154 BRAVO RAGAZZO (IRE), b c 4/4 Pivotal—Kitza (IRE) (Danehill (USA)) (33660) **J. Abdullah**
155 B f 22/2 Street Cry (IRE)—Carry On Katie (USA) (Fasliyev (USA)) **Sheikh Hamdan Bin Mohammed Al Maktoum**
156 B c 2/4 Halling (USA)—Cercle d'amour (USA) (Storm Cat (USA)) **Sheikh Hamdan Bin Mohammed Al Maktoum**
157 Ch c 4/5 Rock of Gibraltar (IRE)—Chorist (Pivotal) (36000) **The Vine Accord**
158 B f 18/4 New Approach (IRE)—
                     Deveron (USA) (Cozzene (USA)) (100000) **Sheikh Hamdan Bin Mohammed Al Maktoum**
159 Ch c 11/3 Shamardal (USA)—
                     Dignify (IRE) (Rainbow Quest (USA)) **Sheikh Hamdan Bin Mohammed Al Maktoum**
160 Ch c 12/3 Raven's Pass (USA)—
                     Discreet Brief (IRE) (Darshaan) (80000) **Sheikh Hamdan Bin Mohammed Al Maktoum**
161 DOUBLE YOUR MONEY (IRE), b c 5/5 Shamardal (USA)—Zeiting (IRE) (Zieten (USA)) **A. D. Spence**
162 Ch c 16/5 Pivotal—Easy Option (IRE) (Prince Sabo) **Sheikh Hamdan Bin Mohammed Al Maktoum**
163 B c 15/3 New Approach (IRE)—Endorsement (Warning) (110000) **Sheikh Hamdan Bin Mohammed Al Maktoum**
164 B c 22/3 Dylan Thomas (IRE)—Eurolink Raindance (IRE) (Alzao (USA)) (20000) **Antoniades Family**
165 EXCELLENT MARINER (IRE), b f 1/2 Henrythenavigator (USA)—
                     Castara Beach (IRE) (Danehill (USA)) (32019) **Ian Harland (Excellence Racing)**
166 FLASHLIGHT (IRE), b c 14/4 Shamardal (USA)—
                     Jazzy Jan (IRE) (Royal Academy (USA)) **Sheikh Hamdan Bin Mohammed Al Maktoum**
167 HEAVY METAL, b c 4/4 Exceed And Excel (AUS)—
                     Rock Opera (SAF) (Lecture (USA)) **Sheikh Hamdan Bin Mohammed Al Maktoum**
168 HOUSE OF ORANGE (IRE), b c 13/5 Kheleyf (USA)—
                     Cox Orange (USA) (Trempolino (USA)) **Sheikh Hamdan Bin Mohammed Al Maktoum**
169 B br f 15/3 New Approach (IRE)—
                     Idilic Calm (IRE) (Indian Ridge) (100000) **Sheikh Hamdan Bin Mohammed Al Maktoum**
170 B f 13/4 Galileo (IRE)—In My Life (IRE) (Rainbow Quest (USA)) (61576) **Ms J. F. Bianco**
171 B f 6/3 Shamardal (USA)—
                     Innclassic (IRE) (Stravinsky (USA)) (12315) **Sheikh Hamdan Bin Mohammed Al Maktoum**
172 B c 10/5 Cape Cross (IRE)—Insijaam (USA) (Secretariat (USA)) **Sheikh Hamdan Bin Mohammed Al Maktoum**
173 B c 6/5 Cape Cross (IRE)—
                     Isla Azul (IRE) (Machiavellian (USA)) (115000) **Sheikh Hamdan Bin Mohammed Al Maktoum**
174 B c 2/6 Lucky Story (USA)—Jerre Jo Glanville (USA) (Skywalker (USA)) **Mark Johnston Racing Ltd**
175 B c 3/3 Dubawi (IRE)—
                     Kalana (FR) (Rainbow Quest (USA)) (65681) **Sheikh Hamdan Bin Mohammed Al Maktoum**
176 KINGSVILLE, b c 22/4 Royal Applause—Kalinova (IRE) (Red Ransom (USA)) **Elite Racing Club**
177 LIGHT ROSE (IRE), b f 14/2 Cape Cross (IRE)—
                     Laureldean Lady (IRE) (Statue of Liberty (USA)) (36945) **J. Abdullah**
178 Ch f 29/4 Elusive Quality (USA)—
                     Louve Mysterieuse (USA) (Seeking The Gold (USA)) (160000) **Sheikh Hamdan Bin Mohammed Al Maktoum**
179 B f 16/3 Danehill Dancer (IRE)—Love Everlasting (Pursuit of Love) (55000) **Greenland Park Stud**
180 B c 23/2 Shamardal (USA)—
                     Love Me Tender (Green Desert (USA)) (78000) **Sheikh Hamdan Bin Mohammed Al Maktoum**
181 B c 8/5 Singspiel (IRE)—
                     Majoune (FR) (Take Risks (FR)) (150000) **Sheikh Hamdan Bin Mohammed Al Maktoum**
182 B c 19/2 Rail Link—Melpomene (Peintre Celebre (USA)) **Mrs C. E. Budden**
183 B f 19/4 Bahamian Bounty—Missisipi Star (IRE) (Mujahid (USA)) (18095) **G. R. Bailey Ltd**
184 MOSCOW CIRCUS (IRE), b c 20/4 Hurricane Run (IRE)—Zalama (FR) (Red Ransom (USA)) (12315) **C. N. Wright**
185 NELLIE BLY, b f 12/4 Exceed And Excel (AUS)—
                     La Presse (USA) (Gone West (USA)) **Sheikh Hamdan Bin Mohammed Al Maktoum**
186 B c 18/2 Kheleyf (USA)—Neptune's Bride (USA) (Bering) **Sheikh Hamdan Bin Mohammed Al Maktoum**
187 B c 19/5 Elusive Quality (USA)—
                     Never Is A Promise (USA) (Capote (USA)) **Sheikh Hamdan Bin Mohammed Al Maktoum**
188 B c 13/2 Shamardal (USA)—
                     Nova Cyngi (USA) (Kris S (USA)) (59047) **Sheikh Hamdan Bin Mohammed Al Maktoum**
189 Ch c 4/4 Street Boss (USA)—
                     Now It Begins (USA) (Two Punch (USA)) (61050) **Sheikh Hamdan Bin Mohammed Al Maktoum**
190 PIPER'S LASS (IRE), b f 2/2 Singspiel (IRE)—
                     Dunloskin (Selkirk (USA)) **Sheikh Hamdan Bin Mohammed Al Maktoum**
191 Ch c 26/2 E Dubai (USA)—
                     Possession (USA) (Belong To Me (USA)) **Sheikh Hamdan Bin Mohammed Al Maktoum**
192 PRIVATE CAPTAIN (IRE), ch c 14/3 Astronomer Royal (USA)—
                     Private Whisper (USA) (Roar (USA)) (26000) **J. Abdullah**
193 PURE EXCELLENCE, b f 8/3 Exceed And Excel (AUS)—Albavilla (Spectrum (IRE)) (20000) **Excellence Racing**
194 RAINESTORM (IRE), b c 26/1 Hurricane Run (IRE)—Love Thirty (Mister Baileys) (20524) **Mr A. R. Harrison**
195 REGGAE STAR, b f 24/2 Cape Cross (IRE)—Caribbean Dancer (USA) (Theatrical) **Sheikh Hamdan Bin Mohammed Al Maktoum**
196 Ch c 7/4 Bahamian Bounty—Roo (Rudimentary (USA)) (40000) **M. J. Pilkington**

MR MARK JOHNSTON—continued

197 B br f 31/3 Oasis Dream—Royal Blue (Machiavellian (USA)) (32840) **Mr Tom Monaghan**
198 SHAGWA (IRE), b f 4/3 Clodovil (IRE)—Hedera (USA) (Woodman (USA)) (16000) **J. Abdullah**
199 B c 1/5 Kheleyf (USA)—Simla Bibi (Indian Ridge) (20000) **Dr M. B. Q. S. Koukash**
200 SKYTRAIN, ch c 23/1 Exceed And Excel (AUS)—Viola da Braccio (IRE) (Vettori (IRE)) (57471) **A. D. Spence**
201 STEER BY THE STARS (IRE), b f 12/2 Pivotal—
Mundus Novus (USA) (Unbridled's Song (USA)) (41050) **Capt Alasdair & Mrs Eliza Ross**
202 B c 19/2 Invincible Spirit (IRE)—
Storm Lily (USA) (Storm Cat (USA)) **Sheikh Hamdan Bin Mohammed Al Maktoum**
203 TORNADO BATTLE, b c 15/3 War Chant (USA)—
Child Bride (USA) (Coronado's Quest (USA)) (40000) **J. Abdullah**
204 B c 1/3 Iffraaj—Totally Yours (IRE) (Desert Sun) **Sheikh Hamdan Bin Mohammed Al Maktoum**
205 TUSSIE MUSSIE, b f 22/2 Royal Applause—
Loveleaves (Polar Falcon (USA)) (60000) **Mark Johnston Racing Ltd**
206 UPPER ECHELON, ch f 6/4 Danehill Dancer (IRE)—
Lady High Havens (IRE) (Bluebird (USA)) (20000) **Mark Johnston Racing Ltd**
207 B c 2/2 Royal Applause—Voliere (Zafonic (USA)) (30000) **Mark Johnston Racing Ltd**
208 WINDHOEK, b c 3/2 Cape Cross (IRE)—
Kahlua Kiss (Mister Baileys) (110000) **Sheikh Hamdan Bin Mohammed Al Maktoum**
209 B c 16/4 Montjeu (IRE)—Woodland Orchid (IRE) (Woodman (USA)) (65680)
210 B c 2/4 Cape Cross (IRE)—Zarara (USA) (Manila (USA)) (50000) **Sheikh Hamdan Bin Mohammed Al Maktoum**
211 Gr c 30/4 Verglas (IRE)—Zut Alors (IRE) (Pivotal) (36945) **A. D. Spence**

Other Owners: Mrs Carolyn Antoniades, Miss Emma Antoniades, Miss Alethea Antoniades, Mr Tony Antoniades, Mrs C. O. Bamford, Mr A. J. Bell, Mr E. Brierley, Mr M. Budden, Mr Matthew Budden, Mr Alan J. Burke, Mr N. K. Coughlan, Mr A. Greenhalgh, Mr Ian Harland, Mr Tony Hill, Mrs Deirdre Johnston, Mr J. R. Kennedy, Mrs Stephen Knight, Mr M. R. Lonsdorfer, Mark Johnston Racing Ltd, Mr Jim McGrath, Mr Grant Mercer, Mr D. C. Mercer, Miss M. Noden, Mr Colin J. Norton, Ms C. M. Riordan, Capt. Alasdair Ross, Mrs Eliza Ross, Mr Gerry Ryan, Mr A. D. Spence, Mr Roger Trevitt, Mrs Dianne Trevitt, Mr C. Wachter, Mr J. Wachter.

Assistant Trainers: Deirdre Johnston & Jock Bennett

Jockey (flat): Silvestre De Sousa, Joe Fanning. **Apprentice:** Daryl Byrne.

367

MR ALAN JONES, Minehead
Postal: **East Harwood Farm, Timberscombe, Minehead, Somerset, TA24 7UE**
Contacts: **FAX 01633 680232 MOBILE (07901) 505064**
E-MAIL heritageracing@btconnect.com WEBSITE www.alanjonesracing.co.uk

1 BOBBITS WAY, 7, b g Overbury (IRE)—Bit of A Chick **Burnham Plastering & Drylining Ltd**
2 BULL MARKET (IRE), 9, b bl g Danehill (USA)—Paper Moon (IRE) **Rupert Dubai Racing**
3 FREDDY'S STAR (IRE), 10, ch g Kris—Kutaisi (IRE) **F. A. Clegg**
4 HUMBEL BEN (IRE), 9, br g Humbel (USA)—Donegans Daughter **Burnham Plastering & Drylining Ltd**
5 KORALSDARLING (IRE), 8, b g Witness Box (USA)—Jenny's Jewel (IRE) **Burnham Plastering & Drylining Ltd**
6 MIX N MATCH, 8, b g Royal Applause—South Wind **F. A. Clegg**
7 MURFREESBORO, 9, b g Bahamian Bounty—Merry Rous **Burnham Plastering & Drylining Ltd**
8 NORISAN, 8, ch g Inchinor—Dream On Deya (IRE) **Burnham Plastering & Drylining Ltd**
9 QUINCY DES PICTONS (FR), 8, b g Kadalko (FR)—Izabel des Pictons (FR) **Burnham Plastering & Drylining Ltd**
10 SECRET DANCER (IRE), 7, b g Sadler's Wells (USA)—Discreet Brief (IRE) **Burnham Plastering & Drylining Ltd**
11 TUSKAR (USA), 6, ch g Mr Greeley (USA)—Maria Donna (USA) **Burnham Plastering & Drylining Ltd**

Other Owners: Mr Stephen Hunt, Mr T. Stayt.

Assistant Trainer: Miss A. Bartelink

Jockey (NH): Christian Williams, Richard Johnson, Paddy Brennan, Tom O' Brien. **Amateur:** Mr O. Greenall.

368

MR GEORGE JONES, Tenbury Wells
Postal: **13 Market Square, Tenbury Wells, Worcestershire, WR15 8BL**

1 ALMOWJ, 9, b g Fasliyev (USA)—Tiriana **Mrs A. M. McCartney**
2 MI MAN SAM (IRE), 7, ch g Exit To Nowhere (USA)—Brinawa (IRE) **Tom Mulkeen, Mick Mifflin & George Jones**

Other Owners: G. H. Jones, T. M. Mifflin, Mr T. G. Mulkeen.

369 **MR GRUFFYDD JONES, Lampeter**
Postal: **Lluestnewydd, Bettws, Lampeter, Dyfed, SA48 8PB**
Contacts: **PHONE (01570) 493261 MOBILE (07817) 885504**

1 **ORREZZO (GER)**, 12, br g Zinaad—Ordessa (GER) **G. Elwyn Jones**
2 **TANCREDI (SWE)**, 10, b g Rossini (USA)—Begine (IRE) **G. Elwyn Jones**

Jockey (NH): Tom O'Brien. **Conditional:** Brian Toomey, Robert Kirk, James Best.

370 **MS LUCY JONES, Kilgetty**
Postal: **2 South Row, Cresselly, Kilgetty, Pembrokeshire, SA68 0SR**

1 **ALL ON JOHN**, 5, b g Hazaaf (USA)—Sand Star **Mr H. D. R. Harrison-Allen**
2 **CALL ME FRANKIE (IRE)**, 6, b g Indian Danehill (IRE)—Violets Wild (IRE) **S. Jones**
3 **CHAMPAGNE JOHNNY**, 5, b g Kier Park (IRE)—Cavvies Niece **S. Jones**
4 **DERAWAR (IRE)**, 13, b g Kahyasi—Denizliya (IRE) **S. Jones**
5 5, B g Beat All (USA)—Florida Fact **Mrs R. E. Mansell**
6 **THE HUMBEL MONK (IRE)**, 10, b g Humbel (USA)—Miss Monks (IRE) **Mr A. G. Davies**

371 **MRS VIOLET M. JORDAN, Moreton Morrell**
Postal: **Far Westfields Farm, Moreton Morrell, Warwick, Warwickshire, CV35 9DB**
Contacts: **MOBILE (07831) 101632**
E-MAIL jordyracer29@hotmail.co.uk

1 **ALACCORDION**, 7, br g Alflora (IRE)—Song For Jess (IRE) **Farmers & Cricketers Partnership**
2 **ALDERLEY STAR (IRE)**, 7, b g Alderbrook—Cherry Avenue **Mrs Violet M. Jordan**
3 **ALL THE FASHION (IRE)**, 8, br m Alflora (IRE)—Fashion Day **Mrs Violet M. Jordan**
4 **FORMEDABLE (IRE)**, 10, ch g Moonax (IRE)—Castle Flame (IRE) **Farmers & Cricketers Partnership**
5 **HIDDEN FOX**, 4, ch g Kadastrof (FR)—Hidden Smile (USA) **Mr T. Powell**
6 **JERRY LEE (IRE)**, 9, b g Orpen (USA)—Vinicky (USA) **Mrs Violet M. Jordan**
7 **KILLFINNAN CASTLE (IRE)**, 9, br g Arctic Lord—Golden Seekers **Mrs Violet M. Jordan**
8 **KING DIAMOND (FR)**, 11, b g Exit To Nowhere (USA)—Diamona (FR) **Mrs Violet M. Jordan**
9 **LIBRE**, 12, b g Bahamian Bounty—Premier Blues (FR) **On The Up Partnership**
10 **MONSIEUR GEORGES (FR)**, 12, b g Kadalko (FR)—Djoumi (FR) **Near & Far Racing**
11 4, Br f Fair Mix (IRE)—Song For Jess (IRE)

Other Owners: R. K. Betts, Mr D. J. Pearson, D. M. Thornton, Mrs J. G. Williams.

Assistant Trainer: Gaye Williams

372 **MR TOM KEDDY, Newmarket**
Postal: **246 Exning Road, Newmarket, Suffolk, CB8 0AN**
Contacts: **PHONE (01638) 561498 FAX (01638) 561498 MOBILE (07542) 036544/(07745) 238018**
E-MAIL tkracing1@hotmail.co.uk

1 **ARCHIE RICE (USA)**, 6, b g Arch (USA)—Gold Bowl (USA) **A. J. Duffield**
2 **CAIRANNE**, 4, b f High Chaparral (IRE)—Celestial Choir **J. H. Fielding**
3 **DINNER DATE**, 10, ch g Groom Dancer (USA)—Misleading Lady **Mrs H. E. Keddy**
4 **PISCEAN (USA)**, 7, b br g Stravinsky (USA)—Navasha (USA) **A. J. Duffield**
5 **RASTEAU (IRE)**, 4, b g Barathea (IRE)—Mistra (IRE) **J. H. Fielding**
6 **ROYAL PREMIER (IRE)**, 9, b g King's Theatre (IRE)—Mystic Shadow (IRE) **Maynard Durrant Partnership I**

THREE-YEAR-OLDS

7 **KARISTAR (IRE)**, b f Montjeu (IRE)—Showcall (USA) **A. J. Duffield**
8 **SASSI SIOUX**, b f Sleeping Indian—Durwah (IRE) **A. J. Duffield**

Other Owners: Mr R. J. Durrant, Mr R. L. Maynard.

Assistant Trainer: Hayley Keddy

373 MRS CAROLINE KEEVIL, Motcombe

Postal: **Larkinglass Farm, Motcombe, Shaftesbury, Dorset, SP7 9HY**
Contacts: PHONE **(07768) 867424** FAX **(01761) 463927** MOBILE **(07768) 867424**
E-MAIL **carolinekeevil@yahoo.co.uk**

1 ARCTIC FLOW, 8, b m Alflora (IRE)—Flow **Mrs H. R. Dunn**
2 BALLY LEGEND, 7, b g Midnight Legend—Bally Lira **B. A. Derrick**
3 BLUE BLOODED, 6, b g Nayef (USA)—Aristocratique **Mrs Angela Yeoman & Mr Peter Hart**
4 BLUE LOVELL (FR), 6, gr m Loup Solitaire (USA)—Wackie (USA) **P. L. Hart**
5 BOBS PRESENT, 5, b m Presenting—Bobs Bay (IRE) **R. J. Croker**
6 CADEAUX CERISE (IRE), 8, b m Cadeaux Genereux—Cerisette (IRE) **The Boot Inn Partnership**
7 CINEVATOR (IRE), 5, b g Dr Massini (IRE)—Hurricane Bella (IRE) **The Optimist & Pessimist Partnership**
8 CIVIL DISOBEDIENCE, 8, b g Roi de Rome (USA)—Biddles **R. C. Mitford-Slade**
9 DEEP POCKETS (IRE), 13, b g Fourstars Allstar—Pocket Price (IRE) **The Deep Pockets Partnership**
10 DOVECOTE WOOD, 7, b g Fleetwood (IRE)—Flakey Dove **K S B Bloodstock**
11 FOREST PENNANT (IRE), 10, b br g Accordion—Prudent View (IRE) **P. L. Hart**
12 GENERAL GIRLING, 5, b g General Gambul—Gold Charm **The Yeovilton Flyers**
13 IDENTIMIN, 8, b m Tamure (IRE)—Minigale **Mr M. R. B. Gregson**
14 INSURED, 7, ch g Intikhab (USA)—Self Assured (IRE) **Mr L. J. Tibbatts**
15 JUDGE DAVIS, 5, b g Alflora (IRE)—Minimum **Gale Force Three**
16 LYNFORD NAKITA, 6, ch m Baryshnikov (AUS)—Lynphord Girl **The Cayford Partnership**
17 MARSHAL ZHUKOV (IRE), 6, b g Morozov (USA)—Artic Brush (IRE) **Mrs Sara Biggins & Mrs Celia Djivanovic**
18 MATAKO (FR), 9, b g Nikos—Verabatim (FR) **P. M. Bryant**
19 MIDNIGHT LIRA, 5, ch m Midnight Legend—Bally Lira **B. A. Derrick**
20 MOORLAND SUNSET, 9, b g Pasternak—Lady Harriet Luis **P. F. Popham**
21 PUSH TO EXIT, 4, b g Exit To Nowhere (USA)—Shiny Thing **Ms J. H. Menzies**
22 REGAL FLOW, 5, b m Erhaab (USA)—Flow **Mrs H. R. Dunn**
23 SHADDAII (FR), 6, gr g April Night (FR)—Gypsie d'artois (FR) **Mrs C. E. Davies**
24 SOUND STAGE, 9, b g Saddlers' Hall (IRE)—Re-Release **K S B Bloodstock**
25 SOUTHFIELD THEATRE (IRE), 4, b g King's Theatre (IRE)—Chamoss Royale (FR) **Mrs A. B. Yeoman**
26 SUPER FORMEN (FR), 8, b g Kizitca (FR)—Daly Turk (FR) **Mr Peter Hart & Mr Bill Bolsover**
27 TASHEBA, 7, ch g Dubai Destination (USA)—Tatanka (IRE) **T. W. Benson**
28 THE OMEN, 6, b g Sir Harry Lewis (USA)—High Sturt **J. Myerscough-Walker**
29 THUNDER ON, 5, ch m Clerkenwell (USA)—Thunder Thighs **Mr A. Gibbs**
30 TIME DO (FR), 5, ch g Grand Tresor (FR)—Demoiselle Do (FR) **Mrs L. R. Lovell**

Other Owners: Mr K. W. Biggins, Mrs S. J. Biggins, Mr G. W. Bolsover, Mr W. R. Bougourd, A. Cayford, Mrs J. A. Cayford, Mrs C. J. Djivanovic, Mr M. Doughty, Mrs L. Fielding-Johnson, Mr A. P. Gale, Mrs A. J. Girling, Mr A. Girling, Mrs C. Keevil, Mr H. F. Morris, J. G. Storey, Mr R. F. Turner, Mrs R. A. Turner.

Jockey (NH): Tom O'Brien, Will Kennedy. **Conditional:** Ian Popham.

374 MR MARTIN KEIGHLEY, Moreton-In-Marsh

Postal: **Condicote Stables, Luckley, Moreton-In-Marsh, Gloucestershire, GL56 0RD**
Contacts: PHONE **(01451) 830209** MOBILE **(07767) 472547**
E-MAIL **info@martinkeighleyracing.com** WEBSITE **www.martinkeighleyracing.com**

1 ALL FOR FREE (IRE), 6, b g Atraf—Milain (IRE) **The Jesters**
2 ALWAYS BOLD (IRE), 7, ch g King's Best (USA)—Tarakana (USA) **Mrs B. J. Keighley**
3 ANY CURRENCY (IRE), 9, b g Moscow Society (USA)—Native Bavard (USA) **Cash Is King**
4 BENBANE HEAD (USA), 8, ch g Giant's Causeway (USA)—Prospectress (USA) **Mrs L. Jones**
5 BOLD TARA, 5, b m Kayf Tara—Bruley **Mrs Anne Lee-Warner**
6 BRIMHAM BOY, 10, ch g Minster Son—Winnie Lorraine **Davids Thorpe & Cowie**
7 CAUGHT BY WITNESS (IRE), 7, b g Witness Box (USA)—Donegans Daughter **Mrs D. Dewbery**
8 CHAMPION COURT (IRE), 7, b g Court Cave (IRE)—Mooneys Hill (IRE) **M. Boothright**
9 5, B g Terimon—Cle de Lune (FR) **Mr Roger Allsop**
10 CONINGTON, 8, gr m Silver Patriarch (IRE)—Child Star (FR) **Mrs B. Keighley**
11 CONSULT, 5, ch g Dr Fong (USA)—Merle **Mrs Ruth Nelmes & Mr Richard Adkins**
12 COURT IN SESSION (IRE), 7, b g Court Cave (IRE)—Dangerous Dolly (IRE) **The Figjam Partnership**
13 DE FORGOTTEN MAN (IRE), 7, b g Commander Collins (IRE)—Jrred Up (IRE) **Mrs P. Andrews**
14 FEDERSTAR (GER), 10, b g In A Tiff (IRE)—Federspeil **C. W. Booth**
15 FITANDPROPERJOB, 8, b g Helissio (FR)—Talkasha **S.E.D Racing Partnership**
16 FLEMENTIME (IRE), 4, ch f Flemensfirth (USA)—Funny Times **Figjam II**
17 HARD TO SWALLOW (IRE), 6, b g Snurge—Nicat's Daughter (USA) **Mrs L. Jones**
18 HAVINGOTASCOOBYDO (IRE), 7, b g Witness Box (USA)—
In Blue (IRE) **D Bishop C Bowkley M Parker M Thornton**

MR MARTIN KEIGHLEY—continued

19 4, B c Oscar (IRE)—Indian Miss **Mr R. T. Crellin**
20 **JACKO'S BOY**, 9, b g Kayf Tara—O My Love **North Park Farm Racing**
21 **JUNIOR JACK**, 7, b g Kayf Tara—O My Love **North Park Farm Racing**
22 **MANOR COURT (IRE)**, 6, b g Court Cave (IRE)—Mooneys Hill (IRE) **Mrs B. J. Keighley**
23 **MARLENO (GER)**, 6, b g Lecroix (GER)—Mondalita (GER) **Pet Necessities Partnership**
24 **MAURICETHEATHLETE (IRE)**, 9, b g Sayarshan (FR)—Ardagh Princess **Mr A. G. Slatter**
25 **MONTY'S REVENGE (IRE)**, 7, b g Bob's Return (IRE)—Native Bavard (IRE) **Partnership**
26 **ONE MORE COOKIE (IRE)**, 6, b m Old Vic—Lady Bellingham (IRE) **Mr R. T. Crellin**
27 **PILGRIMS LANE (IRE)**, 8, b g Dr Massini (IRE)—Miss Mylette (IRE) **Mrs S. E. Brown**
28 **R CRAIG (IRE)**, 7, b g Presenting—Sparkling Buck **Mrs K. J Foster-Smith**
29 **SAFFRON LORD**, 7, b g Alflora (IRE)—Jan's Dream **Mrs J. A. Chenery**
30 **SKY CALLING**, 9, b m Bal Harbour—Curlew Calling (IRE) **Nicholson Racing Syndicates A**
31 **SPRING MOON (IRE)**, 7, b g Anshan—Toasted Oats (IRE) **Mrs L. Jones**
32 **TESHALI (IRE)**, 6, br gr g Anabaa (USA)—Tashiriya (IRE) **Mrs D.J. Brown**
33 **THE WICKED KIPPER**, 4, b f King's Theatre (IRE)—Wicked Crack (IRE) **Mr R. T. Crellin**
34 **TOTAL SUBMISSION**, 7, gr g Kayf Tara—Ardentinny **Mrs L. Jones**
35 **TYPHON DE GUYE (FR)**, 5, ch g Dom Alco (FR)—Mascotte de Guye (FR) **Daydream Believers**
36 **UKRAINIAN STAR (IRE)**, 9, ch g Carrowkeel (IRE)—Gemmasdelemma (IRE) **The Class Act Partnership**
37 **UNE DAME D'OR (FR)**, 4, b f Astarabad (USA)—Une Pomme d'or (FR) **Mr O. Pawle**
38 **WOLF MOON (IRE)**, 9, b g Presenting—Toasted Oats (IRE) **Mrs L. Jones**

Other Owners: Mr M. J. Allen, Mr Robert Aplin, Mr David Cowie (Gloucestershire), Mr Stewart Darvill, Mrs Diane Dewbery, Mr A. Felder, Mr Jonathan Feldman, Mr N. G. Jackson, Mr Robert Kanerick, Mrs D. Nicholson, Mr R. Pullen, Mr A. Saffrin.

Assistant Trainer: Mrs Belinda Keighley

Jockey (NH): Ian Popham, Alain Cawley. **Conditional:** Daniel Hiskett. **Amateur:** Mr Barry Denvir.

---

375 MR CHRISTOPHER KELLETT, Swadlincote
Postal: **Jubilee Racing Stables, Snarestone Road, Appleby Magna, Swadlincote, Derbyshire, DE12 7AJ**
Contacts: **PHONE (01530) 515395 FAX (01530) 515395 MOBILE (07966) 097989**
E-MAIL christopherkellett@btinternet.com WEBSITE www.chriskellettracing.co.uk

1 **A P LING**, 5, b m Antonius Pius—Spain **J. E. Titley**
2 **CELTS ESPERE**, 9, ch g Samraan (USA)—Celtic Dream **Ricochet Management Limited**
3 **ELLIS**, 5, ch g Central Park (IRE)—Precious Island **J. E. Titley**
4 **FEMME D'ESPERE**, 6, b m Celts Espere—Drummer's Dream (IRE) **Ricochet Management Limited**
5 **KNOCKAVARDAGH BOY (IRE)**, 6, ch g Halling (USA)—Forget Me Not (IRE) **G. C. Chipman**
6 **LADY BLYTHE**, 5, b m Slip Anchor—Mayroni **J. E. Titley**
7 **NORTHWOLD**, 8, b g Cloudings (IRE)—Briery Gale **D. H. Muir & Exors of the Late Mrs R. E. Muir**
8 **SPACECRAFT (IRE)**, 5, b g Starcraft (NZ)—Brazilian Samba (IRE) **The Edwardsons**

THREE-YEAR-OLDS

9 B f Deportivo—Whittle Rock

TWO-YEAR-OLDS

10 **BRYTER LAYTER**, b c 29/4 Deportivo—Bahhmirage (IRE) (Bahhare (USA)) (761) **Miss S. L. Walley**

Other Owners: Mr Kevin Edwardson, Mrs Julia Edwardson, Mr Drew Muir, Exors of the late Mrs R. E. Muir.

---

376 MISS GAY KELLEWAY, Newmarket
Postal: **Queen Alexandra Stables, 2 Chapel Street, Exning, Newmarket, Suffolk, CB8 7HA**
Contacts: **PHONE (01638) 577778 MOBILE (07974) 948768**
E-MAIL gaykellewayracing@hotmail.co.uk WEBSITE www.gaykellewayracing.com

1 **AVON SUPREME**, 4, ch f Avonbridge—Fredora **B. C. Oakley**
2 **BASLE**, 5, b m Trade Fair—Gibaltarik (IRE) **Countrywide Classics Ltd**
3 **CLEAR ICE (IRE)**, 5, gr g Verglas (IRE)—Mynu Girl (IRE) **T & Z Racing Club**
4 **CONDUCTING**, 4, b g Oratorio (IRE)—Aiming **Distinctive, Dosanjh & Whatley**
5 **HAWAANA (IRE)**, 7, b g Bahri (USA)—Congress (IRE) **Mr Jagger,Mullin,Clarke & Panther Racing**

MISS GAY KELLEWAY—continued

6 JORDAURA, 6, br g Primo Valentino (IRE)—Christina's Dream **Whispering Winds**
7 KISHANDA, 4, gr f Sleeping Indian—Kali **J Farley & Whispering Winds**
8 LAYLINE (IRE), 5, b g King's Best (USA)—Belle Reine **Whispering Winds & Bob Smith**
9 UPHOLD, 5, b g Oasis Dream—Allegro Viva (USA) **J Ballamy, G Kelleway & T Hawthorne**

THREE-YEAR-OLDS

10 CAT QUEEN, b f One Cool Cat (USA)—Oatey **T & Z Racing Club**
11 JUDAS JO (FR), ch f Muhtathir—Lovna (USA) **Mrs G. Lamprell**
12 ONE MORE ROMAN (IRE), b c Holy Roman Emperor (IRE)—Satulagi (USA) **Miss G. M. Kelleway**
13 PINK EVIE, ch f Dutch Art—Cressida **Mrs Y. E. Foley**
14 SWING ALONE (IRE), b c Celtic Swing—Groupetime (USA) **Whatley,Stanbrook,Bowles & Krolikowski**
15 YOGIC FLYER, b f Phoenix Reach (IRE)—Rainbows Guest (IRE) **Winterbeck Manor Stud Ltd**

Other Owners: Mrs J. A. Ballamy, Mrs D. J. Bond, Miss M. Bowles, N. I. P. Brown, Mr D. J. Clarke, Mr H. Dosanjh, Miss Z. Fakirmohamed, Mr J. W. Farley, Mr T. Hawthorne, E. Jagger, Mr A. Krolikowski, S. Lamprell, D. Metcalfe, Panther Racing Limited, R. W. Smith, Mrs L. C. Stanbrook, M. C. Whatley, Mr T. White, Mr J. Wright.

Head Girl: Liz Mullin

Jockey (NH): Jamie Moore. **Apprentice:** Kylie Manser.

---

377 MR G. P. KELLY, Sheriff Hutton
Postal: **3 Church End Cottages, Sheriff Hutton, North Yorkshire, YO60 6SY**
Contacts: **HOME (01347) 878770/878994 MOBILE (07866) 285187**

1 ABOVE STANDARD (IRE), 4, ch g Shamardal (USA)—Prealpina (IRE) **Mr Ashok Saka**
2 AZYGOUS, 9, ch g Foxhound (USA)—Flag **G. P. Kelly**
3 BIGALO'S LAURA B (IRE), 4, ch f Needwood Blade—Rash **Mr J. R. Swift**
4 BILLY TEAL, 7, ch g Keen—Morcat **C. I. Ratcliffe**
5 5, Gr m Terimon—Derry Ann **Mr C. I. Ratcliffe**
6 HIGH WINDOW (IRE), 12, b g King's Theatre (IRE)—Kayradja (IRE) **G. P. Kelly**
7 KEEN'S TOKEN, 6, b g Keen—Bella Mary **Mr C. I. Ratcliffe**
8 5, B m Gentleman's Deal (IRE)—Morcat **Mr C. I. Ratcliffe**

Assistant Trainer: Ian Ratcliffe

Jockey (flat): Paddy Aspell. **Apprentice:** James Sullivan, David Simmonson. **Amateur:** Miss S. Brotherton, Mr M. Walford.

---

378 MISS LYNSEY KENDALL, Carlisle
Postal: **The Stables, Lambley Bank, Scotby, Carlisle, Cumbria, CA4 8BX**
Contacts: **PHONE (01228) 513069 MOBILE (07818) 487227**
E-MAIL lynseykendall@hotmail.co.uk

1 GRIMWITH, 5, b g Doyen (IRE)—Poyle Caitlin (IRE) **Mr & Mrs R. S. Kendall**
2 WALTHAM ABBEY, 11, b g Relief Pitcher—Flash-By **Mr & Mrs R. S. Kendall**

Other Owners: Mr R. S. Kendall, Mrs M. E. Kendall.

---

379 MR NICK KENT, Brigg
Postal: **Newstead House, Newstead Priory, Cadney Road, Brigg, Lincolnshire, DN20 9HP**

1 AROUND A POUND (IRE), 7, b g Old Vic—Mary Ellen Best (IRE) **Nick Kent Racing Club**
2 CASTLEY LANE, 6, b g Dapper—Holly **Mrs E. M. Horn**
3 CIAN BOY (IRE), 6, b br g Indian Danehill (IRE)—Dotty Dee (IRE) **Newstead Priory Racing Club**
4 FARMER FRANK, 9, b g Cotation—Carly-J **R. J. Jackson**
5 ITS MURPHY AGAIN (IRE), 6, gr g Amilynx (FR)—Alphadel (IRE) **R. J. Jackson**
6 LINCS LAD, 7, ch g Alflora (IRE)—Tiger Paws (IRE) **Mr A. R. P. Parkin**
7 SKYFIRE, 5, ch g Storm Cat (USA)—Sunray Superstar **Miss C. Commons**
8 TOUZ MASTER (FR), 8, ch g Wagon Master (FR)—Tressa (FR) **Mrs W. M. Wesley**

Other Owners: J. N. Kent, Ms V. Mitchell.

380 MR ALAN KING, Wroughton

Postal: **Barbury Castle Stables, Wroughton, Wiltshire, SN4 0QZ**
Contacts: **PHONE (01793) 815009 FAX (01793) 845080 MOBILE (07973) 461233**
E-MAIL alanking.racing@virgin.net WEBSITE www.alankingracing.co.uk

1 **ALI BABA**, 6, ch g Nayef (USA)—Alligram (USA) **Alan King**
2 **ARABIAN HEIGHTS**, 4, gr g Araafa (IRE)—Makhsusah (IRE) **McNeill Family Ltd**
3 **ARALDUR (FR)**, 8, ch g Spadoun (FR)—Aimessa (FR) **Mr D. J. S. Sewell**
4 **ARDLUI (IRE)**, 4, b c Galileo (IRE)—Epping **T. Barr**
5 **AWESOME BELLA**, 5, b m Karinga Bay—Awesome Aunt (IRE) **Mrs G. Meacham**
6 **BAKBENSCHER**, 9, gr g Bob Back (USA)—Jessolle **Three Line Whip**
7 **BALDER SUCCES (FR)**, 4, b g Goldneyev (USA)—Frija Eria (FR) **Masterson Holdings Limited**
8 **BALERINA (FR)**, 5, b m Della Francesca (USA)—Santa Marina (FR) **Tim & Sarah Ingram Hill**
9 **BALZACCIO (FR)**, 7, b g Marchand de Sable (USA)—Baliyna (USA) **King, Roberts, Flintham & MCL**
10 **BATONNIER (FR)**, 6, ch g Spadoun (FR)—La Bazine (FR) **H. R. Mould**
11 **BLAZING BAILEY**, 10, b g Mister Baileys—Wannaplantatree **Three Line Whip**
12 **BLESS THE WINGS (IRE)**, 7, b g Winged Love (IRE)—Silva Venture (IRE) **Mrs L. H. Field**
13 **BYGONES IN BRID (IRE)**, 6, b g Old Vic—St Carol (IRE) **H. Redknapp**
14 **CALL ME A STAR**, 5, b m Midnight Legend—Second Call **Mrs K. Holmes**
15 **CALYPSO PRINCESS**, 5, b m Helissio (FR)—Marathea (FR) **The Wildmoor Racing Partnership**
16 **CHILLI ROSE**, 7, gr m Classic Cliche (IRE)—Solo Rose **Withyslade**
17 **COLD KNIGHT**, 6, b g Sir Harry Lewis (USA)—Arctic Chick **Winter Madness**
18 **COOL STEEL (IRE)**, 6, b g Craigsteel—Coolafinka (IRE) **A. P. Racing**
19 **COSWAY SPIRIT (IRE)**, 5, ch g Shantou (USA)—Annalisa (IRE) **Alan Marsh & Partners**
20 **COUNTERPARTY**, 4, b f Nayef (USA)—Mistress Bankes (IRE) **Nigel Bunter & Tim Leadbeater**
21 **CUSTER OF THE WEST (IRE)**, 7, ch g Shernazar—Karlybelle (FR) **Mrs E. A. Prowting**
22 **DALAVAR (IRE)**, 4, b g Dalakhani (IRE)—Giant's Way (IRE) **N. S. G. Bunter**
23 **DANEHILL DANTE (IRE)**, 4, ch g Danehill Dancer (IRE)—En Garde (USA) **N. S. G. Bunter**
24 **DENALI HIGHWAY (IRE)**, 5, ch g Governor Brown (USA)—Amaretto Flame (IRE) **Ian Payne & Kim Franklin**
25 **DESERT JOE (IRE)**, 6, b g Anshan—Wide Country (IRE) **Mrs E. A. Prowting**
26 **DEVIL TO PAY**, 6, b g Red Ransom (USA)—My Way (IRE) **Horace 5**
27 **DHAAFER**, 5, b g Nayef (USA)—Almurooj **S. E. Munir**
28 **DIAMOND SWEEPER (IRE)**, 6, b g Witness Box (USA)—Vinecroft (IRE) **M. J. P. Fordham**
29 **DINEUR (FR)**, 6, ch g Discover d'auteuil (FR)—Sky Rocket (FR) **H. R. Mould**
30 **DONA**, 8, b g Anabaa Blue—Dominicana (FR) **The Hallowed Turf Partnership**
31 **DUNRAVEN PRINCE (IRE)**, 5, b g Alderbrook—Lost Prairie (IRE) **A. P. Racing**
32 **FIRE FIGHTER (IRE)**, 4, b g Tiger Hill (IRE)—Firecrest (USA) **Masterson Holdings Limited**
33 **FLAMING CHARLIE (IRE)**, 8, ch g Oscar Schindler (IRE)—Castle Flame (IRE) **Mrs P. Andrews**
34 4, Ch g Primo Valentino (IRE)—Flintwood **Withyslade**
35 **FORRESTERS FOLLY**, 6, b g Bollin Eric—Miss Wyandotte **Mr E. T. D. Leadbeater**
36 **FRIZZO (FR)**, 5, ch g Ballingarry (IRE)—Floridene (FR) **Bromley, Minton, Jenks & King**
37 **GENSTONE TRAIL**, 6, b m Generous (USA)—Stoney Path **Mickleton Racing Club**
38 **GODSMEJUDGE (IRE)**, 6, b g Witness Box (USA)—Eliza Everett (IRE) **Favourites Racing IV**
39 **GOLD INGOT**, 5, ch g Best of The Bests (IRE)—Realms of Gold (USA) **Mrs Sue Welch & Ms Caroline Rowland**
40 **GOLDEN FIREBIRD (IRE)**, 5, b m Old Vic—Kinnegads Pride (IRE) **M. J. P. Fordham**
41 **GOSPEL PREACHER**, 7, b g Kayf Tara—Gospel (IRE) **Mrs S C Welch & Mrs A A Shutes**
42 **GRUMETI**, 4, b g Sakhee (USA)—Tetravella (IRE) **McNeill Family Ltd**
43 **HABBIE SIMPSON**, 7, b g Elmaamul (USA)—Hamanaka (USA) **S. Love**
44 **HENRY SAN (IRE)**, 5, ch g Exceed And Excel (AUS)—Esclava (USA) **Mrs M. C. Sweeney**
45 **HINDON ROAD (IRE)**, 5, b g Antonius Pius (USA)—Filoli Gardens **A. J. Viall**
46 **HOLD ON JULIO (IRE)**, 9, br g Blueprint (IRE)—Eileens Native (IRE) **Mr & Mrs F Bell,N Farrell, A Marsh**
47 **HOLLOW PENNY**, 4, b g Beat Hollow—Lomapamar **Mr D. J. S. Sewell**
48 4, B c Desert King (USA)—Hot 'n Saucy **M. R. Brooks**
49 **HURRICANE MILLY (IRE)**, 6, b m Milan—Winnowing (IRE) **John J. Murray & Niall Farrell**
50 **INVICTUS (IRE)**, 6, b g Flemensfirth (USA)—Clashwilliam Girl (IRE) **Mr & Mrs R. G. Kelvin Hughes**
51 **IRON CHANCELLOR (IRE)**, 7, b g Alderbrook—Masriyna (IRE) **Mrs Lesley Field,J Sigler & D Anderson**
52 **ISHIKAWA (IRE)**, 4, b g Chineur (FR)—Nautical Light **ROA Racing Partnership V**
53 **JETNOVA (IRE)**, 7, b g Luso—Yamashina (IRE) **Mr D. J. S. Sewell**
54 **JOJABEAN (IRE)**, 5, b g Milan—Garden City (IRE) **The Dunkley & Reilly Partnership**
55 **JOSHING**, 4, bl g Overbury (IRE)—Roslin **Roger & Yvonne Allsop**
56 **KAUTO THE ROC (IRE)**, 8, ch g With The Flow (USA)—
          Kauto of Realm (FR) **Davies,Horton,King,Lake,Powell & West**
57 **KENAI PENINSULA**, 4, gr g Tikkanen (USA)—Realms of Gold (USA) **Ian Payne & Kim Franklin**
58 **KINGS BAYONET**, 5, ch g Needwood Blade—Retaliator **W. H. Ponsonby**
59 **KUMBESHWAR**, 5, b g Doyen (IRE)—Camp Fire (IRE) **McNeill Family & Mr Nigel Bunter**
60 **LA BELLE DOYENNE**, 4, ch f Doyen (IRE)—Tarabela (CHI) **Mrs C. Skan**
61 **LETSBY AVENUE**, 4, b g Tikkanen (USA)—Peel Me A Grape **Mrs E. A. Prowting**

MR ALAN KING—continued

62 **LIDAR (FR)**, 7, ch g Take Risks (FR)—Light Wave (FR) **High 5**
63 **LIKE A HURRICANE (IRE)**, 9, b g Simply Great (FR)—Legal Challenge (IRE) **M. J. P. Fordham**
64 **LOVCEN (GER)**, 7, b g Tiger Hill (IRE)—Lady Hawk (GER) **The Barbury Apes**
65 **MANAGEMENT (IRE)**, 6, b g True Brave (USA)—Princesse Ira (FR) **Ridgeway Downs Racing**
66 **MEDERMIT (FR)**, 8, gr g Medaaly—Miss d'hermite (FR) **The Dunkley & Reilly Partnership**
67 **MEDINAS (FR)**, 5, b br g Malinas (GER)—Medicis (FR) **Mr & Mrs F. D. Bell**
68 **MIDNIGHT APPEAL**, 7, b g Midnight Legend—Lac Marmot (FR) **Mr D. J. S. Sewell**
69 **MIDNIGHT PRAYER**, 7, b g Midnight Legend—Onawing Andaprayer **The Legends Partnership**
70 **MIDNIGHT SAIL**, 9, b g Midnight Legend—Mayina **M 2 C Racing Partnership**
71 **MISS EXHIBITIONIST**, 4, b f Trade Fair—Miss McGuire **The Trouble Partnership**
72 **MISTER CHANCER (IRE)**, 7, b g Craigsteel—Cluain Chaoin (IRE) **Bensaranat Club**
73 **MISTER STICKLER (IRE)**, 8, b g Alflora (IRE)—Almost Trumps **T. J. Hemmings**
74 **MONTBAZON (FR)**, 5, b br g Alberto Giacometti (IRE)—Duchesse Pierji (FR) **Mr D. J. S. Sewell**
75 **MONTURGEON (FR)**, 5, b g Turgeon (USA)—Bella Eria (FR) **Miss J. M. Bodycote**
76 **MR ROBERTO**, 4, ch g Dubai Destination (USA)—Normandy (CHI) **The Laodiceans**
77 **NEXT MAN IN (IRE)**, 6, b g Trans Island—I'll Be Waiting **Mr D. J. S. Sewell**
78 **NIGHT ROSE**, 6, b m Midnight Legend—Fortunes Course (IRE) **J. E. Garrett**
79 **NO SUBSTITUTE (IRE)**, 7, b g Definite Article—Kindly Light (IRE) **Mr J. R. Hales**
80 **OH CRICK (FR)**, 9, ch g Nikos—Other Crik (FR) **Mr D. J. S. Sewell**
81 **PANTXOA (FR)**, 5, b g Daliapour (IRE)—Palmeria (FR) **The Dunkley & Reilly Partnership**
82 **PATSY FINNEGAN**, 10, b g Sir Harry Lewis (USA)—Bampton Fair **The Wasp Partnership**
83 4, Bl g Fair Mix (IRE)—Pennant Princess **Alan King**
84 4, B f King's Theatre (IRE)—Platinum Leader (IRE) **M. J. P. Fordham**
85 **POUVOIR (FR)**, 9, gr g Verglas (IRE)—Policia (FR) **Mr & Mrs R. Scott**
86 **PRINCE DU SEUIL (FR)**, 9, b g Lucky Dream (FR)—Hermione III (FR) **Mrs E. A. Prowting**
87 **QUOTICA DE POYANS (FR)**, 8, b g Subotica (FR)—Etole II (FR) **McNeill Family & Tim & Sarah Ingram-Hill**
88 **RAYA STAR (IRE)**, 6, b g Milan—Garden City (IRE) **S. E. Munir**
89 **REYAMOUR**, 4, b f Azamour (IRE)—Reynosa (IRE) **D. J. Barry**
90 **RISKAREAS (FR)**, 6, gr g Take Risks (FR)—Dunarea (FR) **The Dunkley & Reilly Partnership**
91 **RIVERMOUTH**, 7, ch g Karinga Bay—Rippling Brook **D Wallace,Mrs M Snook & Fuzzy Logic**
92 **ROMULUS D'ARTAIX (FR)**, 6, b g Sassanian (USA)—Kadisha (FR) **The Remus Partnership**
93 **RULING PARTY**, 7, ch g Fleetwood (IRE)—My Tern (IRE) **Elite Racing Club**
94 **RUSTARIX (FR)**, 11, b g Housamix (FR)—Star of Russia (FR) **Mrs C. Skan**
95 **SALMANAZAR**, 4, b g Classic Cliche (IRE)—Leroy's Sister (FR) **Alan King & Richard Webb**
96 **SAMSONS SON**, 8, b g Primo Valentino (IRE)—Santibuni (IRE) **M. Folan**
97 **SAUDI PEARL (IRE)**, 4, br g Rakti—Cheeky Weeky **D. M. Mason**
98 **SECRET GAGE**, 4, b g Tobougg (IRE)—Burton Ash **Nigel Bunter & David Anderson**
99 **SHADY LANE**, 5, b m Alflora (IRE)—Stoney Path **Ms C Rowland,Mrs Welch & R Fitzgerald**
100 **SIR HARRY ORMESHER**, 9, b g Sir Harry Lewis (USA)—Glamour Game **Mr D. J. S. Sewell**
101 **SMAD PLACE (FR)**, 5, gr g Smadoun (FR)—Bienna Star (FR) **Mrs P. Andrews**
102 **SOIR D'ESTRUVAL (FR)**, 6, b br g Sheyrann—Kob d'estruval (FR) **Masterson Holdings Limited**
103 **SOLEIL D'AVRIL (FR)**, 6, b br g Laveron—Melanie du Chenet (FR) **Let's Get Ready To Rumble Partnership**
104 **STAR HILL**, 5, b br g Starcraft (NZ)—Mistress Bankes (IRE) **Alan King**
105 **STONEY'S TREASURE**, 8, ch g Silver Patriarch (IRE)—Stoney Path **Mrs S. C. Welch**
106 **SUBURBAN BAY**, 7, ch g Karinga Bay—Orchid House **S. Bullimore**
107 **SWEET IRONY (FR)**, 6, b g Laveron—Medicis (FR) **S. M. Smith**
108 **TANTE SISSI (FR)**, 5, b m Lesotho (USA)—Kadjara (FR) **Thurloe 51**
109 **THE MUMPER (IRE)**, 5, br g Craigsteel—Na Moilltear (IRE) **The Weighed In Partnership**
110 **THETWINCAMDRIFT (IRE)**, 10, b g Humbel (USA)—
Air Hostess (IRE) **Bensaranat Club,Sporle Farms & A King**
111 **TICKITY BLEUE**, 4, gr f Tikkanen (USA)—Cerise Bleue (FR) **Let's Live Racing**
112 **TORPHICHEN**, 7, ch g Alhaarth (IRE)—Genoa **Million in Mind Partnership**
113 **TRADE ON**, 5, b g Trade Fair—Mystic Beauty (IRE) **Mr Alan King & Mrs Juliet Minton**
114 **TRIGGER THE LIGHT**, 11, ch g Double Trigger (IRE)—Lamper's Light **Mrs D. Shutes**
115 **TSARINOVA**, 7, b m Alflora (IRE)—Dawn Spinner **Pall Mall Partners (NH)**
116 **TURN OVER SIVOLA (FR)**, 5, b g Assessor (IRE)—Notting Hill (FR) **International Plywood (Importers) Ltd**
117 **TUSCAN GOLD**, 5, ch g Medicean—Louella (USA) **Highclere Thoroughbred Racing-TuscanGold**
118 **ULYS DU CHARMIL (FR)**, 4, b g Malinas (GER)—Jest In Ball (FR) **S. E. Munir**
119 **VALDEZ**, 5, ch g Doyen (IRE)—Skew **Riverdee Stable**
120 **VENDOR (FR)**, 4, gr g Kendor (FR)—Village Rainbow (FR) **Thurloe 52**
121 **VOLCAN SURPRISE (FR)**, 4, b g Dom Alco (FR)—Invitee Surprise (FR) **Lady Bamford & Tim Leadbeater**
122 **WALKON (FR)**, 7, gr g Take Risks (FR)—La Tirana (FR) **McNeill Family Ltd**
123 **WAY BACK WHEN**, 7, b m Phantom Breeze—Makounji (FR) **Pall Mall Partners (NH)**
124 **WEST END ROCKER (IRE)**, 10, b br g Grand Plaisir (IRE)—
Slyguff Lord (IRE) **Mr Barry Winfield & Mr Tim Leadbeater**

MR ALAN KING—continued

125 WILLOUGHBY HEDGE, 5, b g King's Theatre (IRE)—Mini Mandy **J. W. Haydon**
126 YABADABADOO, 4, b g Doyen (IRE)—Kabayil **Elite Racing Club**

Other Owners: R. Allsop, Mrs Y. E. Allsop, Mr D. J. Anderson, Mr R. B. Antell, Mrs V. A. P. Antell, M. Ball, Lady Bamford, Mr P. J. Barrett, Mrs H. L. Bell, Mr F. D. Bell, R. J. Benton, Mrs A. Blackwell, Mr P. A. Bland, Mr David Bond, D. R. Bramhill, A. R. Bromley, Mrs L. M. Bugden, Mrs C. E. Caddick, Mr R. J. Caddick, Mr M. L. Cheesmer, Mr S. Clancy, Exors of the Late Mr G. J. Clark, J. L. Clarke, Mr D. E. Collier, Mrs A. L. Davies, G. F. Davies, Mrs M. C. Diplock, P. J. Dunkley, A. T. Eggleton, Mrs S. Evans, N. Farrell, Mr R. J. N. Fitzgerald, L. R. Frampton, Miss K. M. Franklin, S. G. Friend, G. F. Goode, A. P. Gregory, Mr M. Grier, Mr P. S. Hayward, Mr D. A. Heffer, The Hon H. M. Herbert, Highclere Thoroughbred Racing Ltd, A. J. Hill, Mr R. G. Holbrook, J. Holmes, Mr A. Horne, Mr A. Humphreys, D. Humphreys, Mr T. Ingram-Hill, Mrs S. P. Ingram-Hill, Mr R. A. Jacobs, Mr S. R. Kapoor, R. G. Kelvin-Hughes, Mrs E. A. Kelvin-Hughes, A. S. Kilpatrick, Mrs R. J. King, Mr J. D. King, Ms M. Machin-Jefferies, P. T. Maggs, Mr G. T. Mann, Mr A. R. W. Marsh, J. G. G. Mason, Mrs G. Mason, R. L. Maynard, R. J. McCreery, Mrs J. M. Minton, W. D. C. Minton, Mr J. J. Murray, Mr D. Newton, Mrs D. C. Nicholson, Miss M. Noden, Mr P. J. O'Neill, Mrs L. H. Oakley, O. J. W. Pawle, Mr I. T. Payne, Miss H. Pease, Mr J. R. Peppiatt, Mr R. M. Potter, Mr S. A. Prater, Mrs D. Pye, D. F. Reilly, J. P. L. Reynolds, Mr A. J. Roberts, Ms C. C. Rowland, R. F. Sayer, R. Scott, Mrs P. M. Scott, J. Sigler, Prof D. B. A. Silk, Mrs C. M. Snook, Mr J. A. B. Stafford, Mr J. A. Taylor, A. J. Thompson, Mrs K. J. Tudor, D. A. Wallace, Mr M. Warren, Mrs S. J. Warren, Miss S. M. Waugh, Mr R. A. Webb, B. Winfield.

Assistant Trainers: Noel Williams, Mark Weeks

Jockey (NH): Robert Thornton, Wayne Hutchinson, Gerard Tumelty, Jimmy McCarthy. **Conditional:** Charlie Huxley, Peter Hatton, Emma Clutterbuck, Ciaran McKee. **Amateur:** Mr Dan Horsford, Mr Josh Newman, Mr Robbie Henderson.

---

381 MR NEIL KING, Newmarket

Postal: **St Gatien Racing Ltd, St Gatien Cottage, Vicarage Road, Newmarket, Suffolk, CB8 8HP**
Contacts: **PHONE/FAX (01638) 666150 FAX (01638) 666150 MOBILE (07880) 702325**
E-MAIL neil@neil-king.co.uk WEBSITE www.neil-king.co.uk

1 **A LITTLE SWIFTER (IRE),** 6, ch m Noverre (USA)—Swiftur **Dr Clive Layton,Mr Ken Lawrence & N King**
2 **AFSOUN (FR),** 10, b g Kahyasi—Afragha (IRE) **Mrs H. M. Buckle**
3 **BALLYVONEEN (IRE),** 7, b g Stowaway—Miss Ira Zarad (IRE) **Across The Pond Partnership**
4 **BOLLIN TAHINI,** 6, b m Bollin Eric—Cinnamon Club **A. W. K. Merriam**
5 **CERIUM (FR),** 11, b g Vaguely Pleasant (FR)—Tantatura (FR) **Mr R. N. Bothway**
6 **DELGANY GUNNER,** 8, b g Commanche Run—No Grandad **Charles Wilson & Charles Garside**
7 **EVELLA (IRE),** 8, ch m Beneficial—Drimadrian **Mrs S. M. Richards**
8 **GET READY TO GO (IRE),** 8, b g Turtle Island (IRE)—Buckalong (IRE) **Mr R. N. Bothway**
9 **JOLLY VALENTINE,** 4, b g Sakhee (USA)—Violet (IRE) **Mrs P. I. Veenbaas**
10 **KAYSERSBERG (FR),** 5, b g Khalkevi (IRE)—Alliance Royale (FR) **Mrs Julien Turner & Mr Andrew Merriam**
11 **KEEP TALKING (IRE),** 8, b g Religiously (USA)—Celia Barros (IRE) **Nott, Webb, Smith, Lawrence & King**
12 **QUANAH PARKER (IRE),** 6, b g Namid—Uncertain Affair (IRE) **Mrs H. M. Buckle**
13 **RAIFTEIRI (IRE),** 5, b g Galileo (IRE)—Naziriya (FR) **Across The Pond Partnership**
14 **RASAM ALDAAR,** 4, b g Sakhee (USA)—Recherchee **Sarah & Wayne Dale**
15 **RUSSIAN FLAG (FR),** 9, b g Kingsalsa (USA)—Nousa Nousa (FR) **The Drovers & Drifters**
16 **SHALATINA,** 5, b m Silver Patriarch (IRE)—Shalateeno **The Dyball Partnership**
17 **SILBY,** 5, b m Silver Patriarch (IRE)—Tealby **The Dyball Partnership**
18 **SMALL AND MIGHTY,** 5, ch m Erhaab (USA)—Nearly At Sea **The St Gatien Racing For Fun Partnership**
19 **THE RED LAIRD,** 9, b g Kayf Tara—Sekhmet **The St Gatien Racing For Fun Partnership**

Other Owners: Mr N. J. Catterwell, Miss J. M. Custerson, Mrs S. J. Dale, Mr W. R. Dale, D. J. S. Dyball, C. A. Dyball, Mr C. A. Garside, Mrs S. Hitchcock, N. King, Mr K. Lawrence, Dr C. A. Layton, Mr A. J. Lee, D. F. Nott, R. W. Smith, Mrs N. C. Turner, Mr J. C. Webb, Mr B. M. V. Williams, C. M. Wilson.

Assistant Trainer: Marie Parker

Jockey (flat): Hayley Turner, Eddie Ahern, Adam Kirby. **Jockey (NH):** Alex Merriam, Jamie Moore, Dougie Costello, Richard Johnson. **Conditional:** Giles Hawkins, Trevor Whelan. **Amateur:** Mr J. Owen, Mr Richard Collinson.

---

382 MR RICHARD KING, Tolpuddle

Postal: **The Lanches, East Farm, Tolpuddle, Dorchester, Dorset, DT2 7EP**
Contacts: **PHONE (01305) 848592 FAX (01305) 849134 MOBILE (07779) 991356**
E-MAIL sherilyn.king@yahoo.co.uk

1 **DIFLOCK,** 9, gr g Baryshnikov (AUS)—Cold Feet **Mrs S. King**
2 **LADY THERMAL,** 7, ch m Baryshnikov (AUS)—Cold Feet **Mrs S. King**
3 **MADAM NOSO,** 8, ch m Riverwise (USA)—Lady Noso **Mrs S. King**

383 MR PHILIP KIRBY, Castleton

Postal: **Dibble Bridge Stables, Castleton, North Yorkshire, YO21 2DR**
Contacts: **PHONE (01287) 660444 MOBILE (07984) 403558**
E-MAIL prporley@btinternet.com WEBSITE www.philipkirbyracing.co.uk

1 ACKNOWLEDGEMENT, 10, b g Josr Algarhoud (IRE)—On Request (IRE) **Skip Racing Limited**
2 AMAZING KING (IRE), 8, b g King Charlemagne (USA)—Kraemer (USA) **Amazing Optimists**
3 ANTOELLA (IRE), 5, gr m Antonius Pius (USA)—Bella Estella (GER) **Ramjam and Ownaracehorse**
4 BLACK JACARI (IRE), 7, b g Black Sam Bellamy (IRE)—Amalia (IRE) **C B Construction (Cleveland) Limited**
5 CALL IT ON (IRE), 6, ch g Raise A Grand (IRE)—Birthday Present **The Wiggins Family**
6 COOL OPERATOR, 9, b g Kahyasi—Gardana (FR) **Alderclad Ltd**
7 CRUMBLE, 6, ch m Karinga Bay—Castle Lynch (IRE) **Ownaracehorse Ltd**
8 ELSPETH'S BOY (USA), 5, b br g Tiznow (USA)—Miss Waki Club (USA) **Preesall Garage**
9 HUNTINGFORTREASURE, 5, b g Pastoral Pursuits—Treasure Trove (USA) **P. Kirby**
10 IKTIVIEW, 4, ch g Iktibas—Eastview Princess **Eastview Thoroughbreds**
11 MILLIEJANE, 5, b m Iktibas—Staggering (IRE) **Mr D. J. Phillips**
12 NUMBER ONE GUY, 5, br g Rock of Gibraltar (IRE)—Dubious **Keith Foster & John Lees**
13 PRINCE FREDDIE, 4, b g Red Ransom (USA)—Pitcroy **P. Kirby**
14 RIVERSIDE POPPET, 6, ch m Courteous—Topothenorthracing (IRE) **Tom & Mary Stone**
15 ROYAL ENTOURAGE, 7, b g Royal Applause—Trempkate (USA) **C B Construction (Cleveland) Limited**
16 SKIP THE PRESENT (IRE), 9, br g Presenting—Dante's Skip (IRE) **Skip Racing Limited**
17 STORMY MORNING, 6, ch g Nayef—Sokoa (USA) **Colin Fletcher & Ownaracehorse**
18 TRIPLE EIGHT (IRE), 4, b g Royal Applause—Hidden Charm (IRE) **C B Construction (Cleveland) Limited**

Other Owners: Mr Eddie Coates, Mr C. Fletcher, Mr K. Foster, Mr P. A. Helm, Mr M. P. Helm, Mr John Lees, Mr J. Maguire, Ownaracehorse Ltd, Dr Tom Stone, Mrs Mary Stone, Mr L. C. Wiggins, Mr S. A. Wiggins, Mr M. Wilson.

Assistant Trainer: Simon Olley

Jockey (NH): James Reveley, Richie McGrath. **Conditional:** Kyle James.

384 MR SYLVESTER KIRK, Upper Lambourn

Postal: **Cedar Lodge Stables, Upper Lambourn, Hungerford, Berkshire, RG17 8QT**
Contacts: **PHONE (01488) 73215 FAX (01488) 670012 MOBILE (07768) 855261**
E-MAIL sylvester@sylvesterkirkracing.co.uk WEBSITE www.sylvesterkirkracing.co.uk

1 CHARLES CAMOIN (IRE), 4, b g Peintre Celebre (USA)—
Birthday (IRE) **Mr C. Wright & The Hon Mrs J.M.Corbett**
2 CHASIN' RAINBOWS, 4, b f Piccolo—Tamara **J. B. J. Richards**
3 DELAGOA BAY (IRE), 4, b f Encosta de Lago (AUS)—Amory (GER) **Homebred Racing**
4 GREAT SHOT, 4, b g Marju (IRE)—Highland Shot **J. C. Smith**
5 IRIE UTE, 4, b g Sleeping Indian—Prends Ca (IRE) **I. A. N. Wight**
6 NORSE BLUES, 4, ch g Norse Dancer (IRE)—Indiana Blues **J. C. Smith**
7 O MA LAD (IRE), 4, ch g Redback—Raydaniya (IRE) **J. Duddy**
8 SILLY BILLY (IRE), 4, b g Noverre (USA)—Rock Dove (IRE) **The Only Pub In The World Too**

THREE-YEAR-OLDS

9 ALOYSIA, b f Amadeus Wolf—Anthea **R. E. Pocock**
10 BERWIN (IRE), b f Lawman (FR)—Topiary (IRE) **Mr & Mrs R. G. Kelvin Hughes**
11 DARK CASTLE, b c Dark Angel (IRE)—True Magic **Ms C. Cleary**
12 DON'T TEMPT ME (IRE), b f Moss Vale (IRE)—Banutan (IRE) **The Festival Partnership**
13 ELMORA, ch f Elnadim (USA)—Ringarooma **M. Nicolson, G. Doran, A. Wilson**
14 Ch f Dutch Art—Endear **Ms C. Cleary**
15 FROCK (IRE), b f Excellent Art—Maimana (IRE) **S. A. Kirk**
16 GLENNTEN, b g Ishiguru (USA)—Uplifting **Mr S. H. Glenn**
17 GOODIE GOODIE, b f Shirocco (GER)—Goodie Twosues **Lady Davis**
18 ICE MISSILE, br f One Cool Cat (USA)—Exorcet (FR) **J. C. Smith**
19 L'ARLESIENNE, ch f Dutch Art—Angry Bark (USA) **Wood Street Syndicate III**
20 LET YOUR LOVE FLOW (IRE), b f Iffraaj—Miss Odlum (IRE) **Mrs K. Devlin**
21 LIQUID SUNSHINE, br f Baltic King—Sylvan (IRE) **Mr R. Gander, Mr R. A. Gadd, Mr R. Hannon**
22 LONE FOOT LADDIE (IRE), b g Red Clubs (IRE)—Alexander Phantom (IRE) **Dr J. Wilson**
23 LUCIFERS SHADOW (IRE), gr g Dark Angel (IRE)—Marianne's Dancer (IRE) **Dr J. Wilson**
24 MAKE A FUSS, gr f Proclamation (IRE)—Fustaan (IRE) **Homebred Racing**
25 MARINUS (IRE), b c Holy Roman Emperor (IRE)—Yawl **M. H. Dixon**
26 MRS CASH (IRE), b f Holy Roman Emperor (IRE)—Ring of Fire (USA) **Mr D. O'Loughlin**

MR SYLVESTER KIRK—continued

27 **MY SHARONA**, gr f Dark Angel (IRE)—Tanda Tula (IRE) **Verano Quartet**
28 **OPERA BUFF**, b c Oratorio (IRE)—Opera Glass **J. C. Smith**
29 **ORATORIAN (IRE)**, b g Oratorio (IRE)—Raindancing (IRE) **Miss J .A .Challen & Mr T. Pearson**
30 **PURLEY QUEEN (IRE)**, b f Piccolo—Queenie **D. Boocock & P. D. Merritt**
31 **RAFFINN**, b g Sakhee (USA)—Blue Mistral (IRE) **Mr N. Simpson**
32 **ROCK ON CANDY**, b f Excellent Art—Rock Candy (IRE) **T. M. Hayes**
33 **ROMAN MYST (IRE)**, b g Holy Roman Emperor (IRE)—Mystiara (IRE) **Sapphire Racing Partnership**
34 **STAG HILL (IRE)**, ch g Redback—Counting Blessings **Fanny's Friends II**
35 **THE GIVING TREE (IRE)**, b f Rock of Gibraltar (IRE)—Starry Messenger **Mr Nelius Hayes**
36 **THE NOBLE ORD**, b c Indesatchel (IRE)—Four Legs Good (IRE) **Verano Quartet**
37 **TUNDRIDGE**, b g Authorized (IRE)—Salanka (IRE) **T. M. Hayes**

TWO-YEAR-OLDS

38 **ADMIRALS WALK (IRE)**, b c 6/6 Tagula (IRE)—Very Racy (USA) (Sri Pekan (USA)) (20000) **N. Pickett**
39 B c 22/3 Sakhee's Secret—Anthea (Tobougg (IRE)) (13000) **Mr T. Pearson**
40 **BANOVALLUM**, b c 23/3 Invincible Spirit (IRE)—
                          Sinduda (Anabaa (USA)) (95000) **Mr C. Wright & The Hon Mrs J.M.Corbett**
41 B c 4/3 Medaglia d'oro (USA)—Becky In Pink (USA) (Formal Gold (CAN)) (85000) **Mr H. Balasuriya**
42 B c 23/1 Teofilo (IRE)—Bunditten (IRE) (Soviet Star (USA)) **J. C. Smith**
43 Gr c 21/3 Cape Town (IRE)—Doris Souter (IRE) (Desert Story (IRE)) **Mr P. D. Merritt**
44 B f 24/1 Indesatchel (IRE)—Four Legs Good (IRE) (Be My Guest (USA)) (5500)
45 Ch c 21/2 Sakhee's Secret—Indiana Blues (Indian Ridge) **J. C. Smith**
46 Ch c 29/1 Sakhee's Secret—Intermission (IRE) (Royal Applause) (25000) **Verano Quartet**
47 B c 28/3 Pastoral Pursuits—Lalina (GER) (Trempolino (USA)) (21000) **R. Hannon & I. A. N. Wight**
48 Ch c 12/4 Ad Valorem (USA)—Lapis Lazuli (Rainbow Quest (USA)) (8209)
49 Ch f 4/3 Choisir (AUS)—Miss Kinabalu (Shirley Heights) (13136) **I. A. N. Wight**
50 B c 29/1 Royal Applause—Our Faye (College Chapel) (36190) **Mr H. Balasuriya**
51 B br f 28/2 Excellent Art—Princess Sabaah (IRE) (Desert King (IRE)) (13000) **Mr D. Brocock**
52 B br f 31/3 Mr Greeley (USA)—Victorica (USA) (Exbourne (USA)) (32840) **Ms C. Cleary**
53 Bf f 13/4 Rock of Gibraltar (IRE)—Yaky Romani (IRE) (Victory Note (USA)) (12315)

Other Owners: Mr D. Boocock, Mr R. J. Brennan, Miss J. A. Challen, Mr Tommy Cummins, Ms Gill Doran, Mr Mark East, Mr R. A. Gadd, Mr R. Gander, Mr R. Hannon, Mr M. V. Hill, Mr Sylvester Kirk, Mrs B. J. Lee, Dr Barbara A. Matalon, Mr P. D. Merritt, Mr G. Morrin, Mr David P. Moss, Mr M. Nicolson, Mr D. O'Loughlin, Mr R. X. O'Rahilly, Mr Barry Payne, Mr Timothy Pearson, Miss E. Power, Mr J. P. Repard, Mrs Paul Shanahan, Mr J. S. Threadwell, Mr Chris Wall, Mrs Sarah Wall, Mr P. Wheatley, Mr Patrick Wilmott, Mr Alasdair Wilson.

Assistant Trainer: Fanny Kirk

Jockey (flat): James Doyle, Liam Keniry.

385
MR STUART KITTOW, Cullompton
Postal: **Haynefield Farm, Blackborough, Cullompton, Devon, EX15 2JD**
Contacts: **HOME (01823) 680183 FAX (01823) 680601 MOBILE (07714) 218921**
E-MAIL **stuartkittowracing@hotmail.com** WEBSITE **stuartkittowracing.com**

1 **DOVE COTTAGE (IRE)**, 10, b g Great Commotion (USA)—Pooka **R. S. E. Gifford**
2 **FROZEN OVER**, 4, b g Iceman—Pearly River **P. A. & M. J. Reditt**
3 **HAWRIDGE KING**, 10, b g Erhaab (USA)—Sadaka **E. J. S. Gadsden**
4 **HAWRIDGE STAR (IRE)**, 10, b g Alzao (USA)—Serenity **E. J. S. Gadsden**
5 **KEN'S GIRL**, 8, ch m Ishiguru (USA)—There's Two (IRE) **Midd Shire Racing**
6 **KLEITOMACHOS (IRE)**, 4, b g Barathea—Theben (GER) **E. J. S. Gadsden**
7 **MACDILLON**, 6, b g Acclamation—Dilys **Boswell,Pillans,Harris,Urquhart & Kittow**
8 **MAY BE SOME TIME**, 4, ch g Iceman—Let Alone **Dr G. S. Plastow**
9 **OUR FOLLY**, 4, b g Sakhee (USA)—Regent's Folly (IRE) **Midd Shire Racing**
10 **RASH JUDGEMENT**, 7, b g Mark of Esteem (IRE)—Let Alone **R. S. E. Gifford**
11 **RESURGE (IRE)**, 7, b g Danehill Dancer (IRE)—Resurgence **Chris & David Stam**
12 **SIGNIFICANT MOVE**, 5, b g Motivator—Strike Lightly **Midd Shire Racing**
13 **UPPERCUT**, 4, ch g Needwood Blade—Uplifting **H. A. Cushing**
14 **WEAPON OF CHOICE (IRE)**, 4, b g Iffraaj—Tullawadgeen (IRE) **Chris & David Stam**

THREE-YEAR-OLDS

15 Ch f Act One—In The Stocks **E. J. S. Gadsden**
16 **MIRIAM'S SONG**, b f Royal Applause—Miriam **D. R. Tucker**
17 **ROYAL REYAH**, b c Royal Applause—Dilys **B Hopkins, M Harris & R Perry**

MR STUART KITTOW—continued

TWO-YEAR-OLDS

18 DILGURA, b f 22/4 Ishiguru (USA)—Dilys (Efisio) **S. Kittow, R. Perry, B. Hopkins**
19 B c 29/4 Bertolini (USA)—Feathergrass (IRE) (Fasliyev (USA)) **P. J. Green**
20 GUILDED SPIRIT, b c 3/5 Ishiguru (USA)—Soft Touch (IRE) (Petorius) (13333) **The Racing Guild**
21 B f 22/3 Tobougg (IRE)—Mellifluous (IRE) (Noverre (USA))
22 SAND ORCHID, ch f 24/4 Sandwaki (USA)—Doliouchka (Saumarez)
23 WISHING GATE (IRE), b c 3/5 Kyllachy—Rydal Mount (IRE) (Cape Cross (IRE)) **R. S. E. Gifford**

Other Owners: Mrs S. G. Arnesen, D. W. Arnesen, John Boswell, M. E. Harris, Mr B. S. Hopkins, W. S. Kittow, B. G. Middleton, Mrs R. J. M. Perry, Mr M. D. Pillans, Mrs P. A. Reditt, M. J. Reditt, A. J. Shire, Mr D. B. Stam, Dr C. Stam, Ms W. A. Stoker, R. A. Stoker, Mr J. R. Urquhart.

Assistant Trainer: Mrs Judy Kittow

Jockey (flat): Fergus Sweeney. **Jockey (NH):** Tom Scudamore.

---

386 MISS HENRIETTA KNIGHT, Wantage
Postal: **West Lockinge Farm, Wantage, Oxfordshire, OX12 8QF**
Contacts: PHONE **(01235) 833535** FAX **(01235) 820110** MOBILE **(07860) 110153**
E-MAIL hen@westlockinge.co.uk WEBSITE www.henandterry.com

1 AIRDRIE (IRE), 6, b g Oscar (IRE)—Smokey Began It (IRE) **The Octavians**
2 BALBRIGGAN (IRE), 5, gr g King's Theatre (IRE)—Halfway Home **Mrs C. M. Radford**
3 BALLYGARVEY (IRE), 6, b g Laveron—Vollore (FR) **The Dark Horse Syndicate**
4 BALLYLIFEN (IRE), 5, b g Brian Boru—Line Jade (FR) **Mr W. W. Dennison**
5 BALLYPATRICK (IRE), 6, b br g Presenting—Jewell For A King (IRE) **Martin, Jocelyn & Steve Broughton**
6 5, B h Lord Americo—Bewitch **Mrs C. Bailey**
7 CALGARY BAY (IRE), 9, b g Taipan (IRE)—Dante's Thatch (IRE) **Mrs C. M. Radford**
8 CRAIGNURE (IRE), 6, b g Craigsteel—De Lissa (IRE) **Double Four**
9 GINGERS REFLECTION, 6, ch g Alflora (IRE)—Trassey Bridge **Mrs S. R. Bailey**
10 GLENS BOY (IRE), 8, b g Dushyantor (USA)—Glens Lady (IRE) **Lady Bamford & Alice Bamford**
11 GUNNA SOUND (IRE), 6, b g Old Vic—Naughty Executive (IRE) **Mrs C. M. Radford**
12 HARVEST SONG (IRE), 6, b g Sadler's Wells (USA)—La Mouline (IRE) **Her Majesty The Queen**
13 HIGH KITE (IRE), 6, b br g High-Rise—Sister Rose (IRE) **The High Kites**
14 ISLEOFHOPENDREAMS, 5, b g Flemensfirth (USA)—Cool Island (IRE) **Kilbroney Racing**
15 LOCH BA (IRE), 6, b g Craigsteel—Lenmore Lisa (IRE) **Mrs C. M. Radford**
16 MILLERS GLEN (IRE), 6, b g Accordion—Vul Gale **T. J. Hemmings**
17 MOSCOW RED (IRE), 6, ch g Moscow Society (USA)—
Chirouble (IRE) **H. Stephen Smith, Robin Brazier, H Knight**
18 MY FRIEND RIQUET (FR), 5, b g Laveron—Brave Chartreuse (FR) **Mr W. W. Dennison**
19 PUTIACCA BELLA (FR), 5, b m Corri Piano (FR)—Prima Sinfonia (FR) **Miss H. C. Knight**
20 ROCK OF ALLEN (IRE), 5, b g Chevalier (IRE)—Umlaut **Mrs C. M. Radford**
21 SEVENTH HUSSAR (IRE), 6, b g Alflora (IRE)—Shuil Do (IRE) **M. E. R. Allsopp**
22 SILVER ROQUE (FR), 6, b g Laveron—Bible Gun (FR) **Lord Vestey**
23 SLICK OPERATOR (IRE), 6, b g Flemensfirth (USA)—Glacier Lilly (IRE) **T. J. Hemmings**
24 SOIXANTE (IRE), 9, b g Old Vic—Dantes Serenade (IRE) **Martin, Jocelyn & Steve Broughton**
25 SOMERSBY (IRE), 8, b g Second Empire (IRE)—Back To Roost (IRE) **Mrs C. M. Radford**
26 TICKLE ME (IRE), 6, ch g Definite Article—Coming Home (FR) **T. Cole**
27 TYCOONS REFLECTION (IRE), 7, b g Definite Article—Tudor Thyne (IRE) **Mrs S. R. Bailey**

Other Owners: Lady Bamford, Miss A. C. Bamford, T. W. Biddlecombe, Mr R. W. Brazier, Sir M. F. Broughton, S. W. Broughton, Mr H. W. Cox, Mr M. W. Gregory, Mr K. O'Hare, Miss J. Pimblett, H. S. Smith, Mr S. Sweeney, The Hon A. G. Vestey.

---

387 MR WILLIAM KNIGHT, Angmering
Postal: **Lower Coombe Racing Stables, Angmering Park, Littlehampton, West Sussex, BN16 4EX**
Contacts: PHONE **(01903) 871188** FAX **(01903) 871184** MOBILE **(07770) 720828**
E-MAIL william@wknightracing.co.uk WEBSITE www.wknightracing.co.uk

1 BLOODSWEATANDTEARS, 4, b g Barathea—Celestial Princess **Canisbay Bloodstock**
2 CAPE ROCK, 7, b g Cape Cross (IRE)—Wildwood Flower **Mrs B. Sumner**
3 IZ SHE, 4, b f Ishiguru (USA)—Regal Gallery (IRE) **Mrs B. Sumner**
4 KYLLACHY SPIRIT, 4, b g Kyllachy—Cartuccia (IRE) **Mrs J. R. Jenrick & Mr R. D. Jenrick**

MR WILLIAM KNIGHT—continued

5 **MONSTER MUNCHIE (JPN),** 4, b f Deep Impact (JPN)—Muncie (IRE) **A. W. Black**
6 **PALACE MOON,** 7, b g Fantastic Light (USA)—Palace Street (USA) **Canisbay Bloodstock**
7 **PASSION PLAY,** 4, gr f Act One—Addicted To Love **Mascalls Stud**
8 **PRINCESS LEXI (IRE),** 5, ch m Rock of Gibraltar (IRE)—Etaaq (IRE) **Ecurie Franglaise**
9 **PROPER CHARLIE,** 4, b g Cadeaux Genereux—Ring of Love **Mr Peter Oakley & Mr Charles Whittaker**
10 **TENAVON,** 4, b f Avonbridge—Tender (IRE) **Mrs F. Ashfield**
11 **TITAN TRIUMPH,** 8, b g Zamindar (USA)—Triple Green **Canisbay Bloodstock**
12 **WESTERN PEARL,** 5, b m High Chaparral (IRE)—Pulau Pinang (IRE) **Mrs N. J. Welby**

THREE-YEAR-OLDS

13 **ANY OTHER DAY,** b f Royal Applause—A Days Grace **Mrs N. J. Welby**
14 **CAPHIRA,** ch f Singspiel (IRE)—Dream Quest **Bluehills Racing Limited**
15 **COOL SKY,** b g Millkom—Intersky High (USA) **No Quarter Partnership**
16 **DANCE COMPANY,** b f Aussie Rules (USA)—Corps de Ballet (IRE) **Mrs P. G. M. Jamison**
17 **DARROW (IRE),** b g Lawman (FR)—Azolla **Mr Raymond Tooth & Mr Steve Gilbey**
18 **DUSTY RED,** ch f Teofilo (IRE)—Dust Dancer **Mr & Mrs J. Kelsey-Fry**
19 **FLY HAAF (IRE),** b g Haafhd—Rose Indien (FR) **The Pheasant Rew Partnership**
20 **FRAMED,** ch f Elnadim (USA)—Photo Flash (IRE) **Mrs P. G. M. Jamison**
21 **HOONOSE,** ch g Cadeaux Genereux—Roodeye **Four Men & A Dream Partnership**
22 **JAMBOBO,** b g Acclamation—Hovering (IRE) **Mr J. B. Henderson**
23 **LA PAMPITA (IRE),** b f Intikhab (USA)—Jacaranda Ridge **Mrs Melba Bryce**
24 **NASSAU STORM,** b c Bahamian Bounty—Got To Go **The Oil Men Partnership**
25 **OBLITEREIGHT (IRE),** ch c Bertolini (USA)—Doctrine **The Oil Men Partnership**
26 **ROMAN AROUND,** b f Antonius Pius (USA)—Koniya (USA) **Mr G. Roddick**
27 **SAFARI SUNSEEKER (IRE),** b g Tagula (IRE)—Mooching Along (IRE) **P. L. Winkworth**
28 **STORY WRITER,** b g Sakhee (USA)—Celestial Princess **Mr J. B. Henderson**
29 **TENDERLY PLACE,** ch f Compton Place—Tender (IRE) **Mrs F. Ashfield**
30 **VIOLA DA GAMBA (IRE),** b f Alhaarth (IRE)—Addaya (IRE) **Mrs S. M. Mitchell**
31 **ZAMURAI,** ch g Zamindar (USA)—Indian Mystery (IRE) **Mr I. & M. Tracey, D. & B. Willis**
32 **ZUZU ANGEL (IRE),** gr f Clodovil (IRE)—Zither **Mrs N. J. Welby**

TWO-YEAR-OLDS

33 **AUSSIE REIGNS (IRE),** b c 15/4 Aussie Rules (USA)—Rohain (IRE) (Singspiel (USA)) (29556) **The Old Brokers**
34 Ch f 12/2 Bahamian Bounty—Blue Mistral (IRE) (Spinning World (USA)) (10000) **Mrs S. M. Mitchell**
35 **EXCLUSIVE WATERS (IRE),** b c 11/5 Elusive City (USA)—
                     Pelican Waters (IRE) (Key of Luck (USA)) (41050) **The Old Brokers**
36 Br f 17/3 Superior Premium—Hinton Pearl (Loch Pearl) **Miss S. Bannatyne**
37 Ch f 14/2 Sakhee's Secret—Starfleet (Inchinor) (19000) **Mrs N. J. Welby**
38 B f 6/3 Motivator—Tarneem (USA) (Zilzal (USA)) (16000) **R. C. Tooth**
39 B c 14/4 Whipper (USA)—Topiary (IRE) (Selkirk (USA)) (32000) **The Oil Merchants**

Other Owners: Mr R. G. W. Brown, Mr Matthew Duncan, Mr D. Ellis, Mr Steve Gilbey, Mrs J. R. Jenrick, Mr R. D. Jenrick, Miss K. J. Keir, Mr R. F. Kilby, Mr W. J. Knight, Mr Peter Oakley, Mr Nick Peacock, Mr P Pritchard-Gordon, Mr N. J. Roach, Mr Mike Rudd, Miss Maureen Stopher, Mr Raymond Tooth, Mr Mark Tracey, Mrs I. M. Tracey, Mr Charles Whittaker, Mr B. Willis, Mrs D. A. Willis.

Assistant Trainer: Matthew Darling

---

388 | **MR C. LAFFON-PARIAS, Chantilly**
Postal: **38, Avenue du General Leclerc, 60500 Chantilly, France**
Contacts: **PHONE (0033) 3445 75375 MOBILE (0033) 6801 82909**
E-MAIL claffon@club-internet.fr

1 **AXIONIKI (IRE),** 4, b f Holy Roman Emperor (IRE)—Mahrah (USA) **Stilvi Compania Financiera**
2 **CHINCHON (IRE),** 7, b h Marju (IRE)—Jarama (IRE) **Sarl Darpat France**
3 **ESLES (FR),** 4, b c Motivator—Resquilleuse (USA) **S. L. Bering**
4 **GOOD NEWS (FR),** 4, b f Numerous—Great News (FR) **Haras Du Quesnay**
5 **GREAT MOON (USA),** 4, b f Malibu Moon (USA)—Great Connection (USA) **Ghislaine Head**
6 **MATREAS (FR),** 5, b g Peintre Celebre (USA)—Tritonia (AUS) **Stilvi Compania Financiera**
7 **NYMFIA (IRE),** 4, b f Invincible Spirit (IRE)—Aguinaga (IRE) **Stilvi Compania Financiera**
8 **OLYNTHOS (IRE),** 4, ch c Chineur (FR)—Mistic Sun **Stilvi Compania Financiera**
9 **PRIEGO (USA),** 5, b h Elusive Quality (USA)—Ronda **Sarl Darpat France**
10 **TIA KIA (IRE),** 5, b m Montjeu (IRE)—Antioquia **Stilvi Compania Financiera**
11 **TREVIERES (FR),** 4, ch g Gold Away (IRE)—Castilly **Stilvi Compania Financiera**

MR C. LAFFON-PARIAS—continued

12 **VASIAS (FR)**, 4, b c Motivator—Vivacity **Stilvi Compania Financiera**
13 **VICTORINNA (FR)**, 4, ch f Gentlewave (IRE)—Marcela Howard (IRE) **Stilvi Compania Financiera**

THREE-YEAR-OLDS

14 **ABAYO (USA)**, b c Arch (USA)—Sashimi (USA) **Wertheimer Et Frere**
15 **ACTIVISTE (IRE)**, b c Giant's Causeway (USA)—Occupandiste (IRE) **Wertheimer Et Frere**
16 **AKASTI (IRE)**, b f Holy Roman Emperor (IRE)—Shikasta (IRE) **Stilvi Compania Financiera**
17 **ASAGAYA (FR)**, b c Medicean—Akhla **Stilvi Compania Financiera**
18 **ATARFE (IRE)**, b f Anabaa (USA)—Arazena (USA) **Sarl Darpat France**
19 **AVANTE**, b c Shamardal (USA)—Se Me Va (USA) **Cuadra Africa S.A.**
20 **AXIOPI (FR)**, b f Kavafi—Alfreda **Stilvi Compania Financiera**
21 **BANKRUPTCY (USA)**, b f Arch (USA)—Seeking The Heart (USA) **Wertheimer Et Frere**
22 **BRUYANTE (USA)**, ch f Awesome Again (CAN)—Quiet Royal (USA) **Wertheimer Et Frere**
23 **CHARMEUSE (IRE)**, b f Montjeu (IRE)—Underwater (USA) **Wertheimer Et Frere**
24 **CONFIDENTE (IRE)**, ch f Awesome Again (CAN)—Fidelite (IRE) **Wertheimer Et Frere**
25 **DANCING BELIEF (IRE)**, b c Danehill Dancer (IRE)—Beyond Belief (IRE) **Paul Fudge**
26 **DERKIOS (IRE)**, br c One Cool Cat (USA)—Granadilla **Stilvi Compania Financiera**
27 **ELDANDY (IRE)**, b c Danehill Dancer (IRE)—Spinola (FR) **Felipe Hinojosa**
28 **ELIXOS (FR)**, b c Motivator—Efesos **Stilvi Compania Financiera**
29 **FOREIGN TUNE**, b f Invincible Spirit (IRE)—Gwenseb (FR) **Wertheimer Et Frere**
30 **GRACILIA (FR)**, b f Anabaa—Great News **Haras Du Quesnay**
31 **GRACIOSILLA (SPA)**, b f Caradak (IRE)—Gracious Line (FR) **F. Hinojosa**
32 **GRAFFITO (FR)**, b c Aussie Rules (USA)—Diotima **Stilvi Compania Financiera**
33 **IMRIEL**, b c King's Best (USA)—Kezia (FR) **Stilvi Compania Financiera**
34 **INCROYABLE (USA)**, b f Singspiel—Soft Pleasure **Wertheimer Et Frere**
35 **KREOUSA**, b f Hurricane Run (IRE)—Drosia (IRE) **Stilvi Compania Financiera**
36 **LA ZUBIA**, br f Montjeu (IRE)—Trylko **Sarl Darpat France**
37 **LOUSSIA (FR)**, b f Footstepsinthesand—Obsidianne (FR) **Stilvi Compania Financiera**
38 **MARACENA (FR)**, b f Marju (IRE)—Highphar (FR) **Sarl Darpat France**
39 **MATHEMATICIENNE (IRE)**, ch f Galileo (IRE)—Never Green (IRE) **Wertheimer Et Frere**
40 **MEHITABEL (FR)**, b f Authorized (IRE)—Kresna (FR) **Stilvi Compania Financiera**
41 **MELEAGROS (IRE)**, b c King's Best (USA)—Viola Royale (IRE) **Stilvi Compania Financiera**
42 **MENISKA (FR)**, b f Invincible Spirit (IRE)—Royal Liverpool (USA) **Stilvi Compania Financiera**
43 **MENYLLOS (GR)**, b g Kavafi—Ipeiros **Stilvi Compania Financiera**
44 **MOMBAKA**, b c Monsun (GER)—Trumbaka (IRE) **Wertheimer Et Frere**
45 **NUTELLO (USA)**, b c Lemon Drop Kid (USA)—Nutcase (USA) **Wertheimer Et Frere**
46 **ORFNEA (FR)**, b f Gentlewave (IRE)—Fatale (IRE) **Stilvi Compania Financiera**
47 **PANCORBO (USA)**, b c Arch (USA)—Briviesca **Sarl Darpat France**
48 **SAMYNTHA (FR)**, b f Cape Town (USA)—Cobblestone Road (USA) **Stilvi Compania Financiera**
49 **SMYRNES (FR)**, b f Anabaa (USA)—Silver Fame (USA) **Haras Du Quesnay**
50 **SOFT LIPS**, b f Rahy (USA)—Iron Lips **Wertheimer Et Frere**
51 **SWEET IRON (USA)**, b c Mr Greeley (USA)—Sweet Travel (IRE) **Wertheimer Et Frere**
52 **TEKTEA (FR)**, b f Teofilo (IRE)—Betwixt (IRE) **Stilvi Compania Financiera**
53 **TELETI (FR)**, b f Peintre Celebre (USA)—Tritonia (GR) **Stilvi Compania Financiera**
54 **TORREMOLINOS (FR)**, b c Street Cry (IRE)—Ronda **Sarl Darpat France**
55 **TROPAIOS**, ch g Excellent Art—Light Quest (USA) **Stilvi Compania Financiera**
56 **TROPHY BABY**, ch f Gone West (USA)—Sismix (FR) **Wertheimer Et Frere**
57 **UTRERA (IRE)**, b f Singspiel (IRE)—Benalmadena (FR) **Sarl Darpat France**
58 **ZOGRAFIA (FR)**, b f Rock of Gibraltar (IRE)—Agiel (FR) **Stilvi Compania Financiera**

TWO-YEAR-OLDS

59 **AMARYSIA (FR)**, ch f 1/1 Medicean—Light Quest (USA) (Quest For Fame) **Stilvi Compania Financiera**
60 **ARNOLFINI (IRE)**, b c 26/1 Peintre Celebre (USA)—
                                                  Wandering Spirit (GER) (Dashing Blade) **Wertheimer Et Frere**
61 **BAYAKA (FR)**, b f 1/1 Nayef (USA)—Senkaya (FR) (Valanour (IRE)) **Wertheimer Et Frere**
62 B f 26/3 Montjeu (IRE)—Betilla (IRE) (Bering) **C. Laffon-Parias**
63 B f 1/1 More Than Ready (USA)—Briviesca (Peintre Celebre (USA)) **Sarl Darpat France**
64 B f 1/1 Green Tune—Cerita **Stilvi Compania Financiera**
65 **COALIS**, b c 8/5 Oasis Dream—Gwenseb (FR) (Green Tune (USA)) **Wertheimer Et Frere**
66 **CROSSTOWN**, b c 11/2 Cape Cross (IRE)—Esneh (IRE) (Sadler's Wells (USA)) **Wertheimer Et Frere**
67 **DIVISME (USA)**, b c 4/2 Elusive Quality (USA)—Toppisme (USA) (Saint Ballado (CAN)) **Wertheimer Et Frere**
68 **DROMEOS**, b c 16/4 Zamindar (USA)—Loxandra (Last Tycoon) **Stilvi Compania Financiera**
69 **EFTEOS (FR)**, b c 1/1 Teofilo—Efesos **Stilvi Compania Financiera**
70 **ERASMIOS (FR)**, ch c 1/1 King's Best—Eriza **Stilvi Compania Financiera**
71 **EXAMOS (FR)**, ch c 30/1 Green Tune—Delfinia (Drastikos) **Stilvi Compania Financiera**

MR C. LAFFON-PARIAS—continued

72 **FEREVIA (IRE)**, b f 8/2 Motivator—Frynia (USA) (Cat Thief (USA)) **Stilvi Compania Financiera**
73 **GAIETE (FR)**, ch f 1/1 Kentucky Dynamite—Grenade **Haras du Quesnay**
74 **GOLDATOR (FR)**, b c 1/1 Cape Cross (IRE)—Soft Gold (USA) (Gulch (USA)) **Wertheimer Et Frere**
75 Ch f 13/4 Gold Away (IRE)—Highphar (FR) (Highest Honor (FR)) **Sarl Darpat France**
76 **IKONE (IRE)**, ch c 9/3 Peintre Celebre (USA)—Koed (USA) (Royal Academy (USA)) **Wertheimer Et Frere**
77 **KRYMKA (IRE)**, ch f 6/3 Medicean—La Seine (USA) (Rahy (USA)) **Stilvi Compania Financiera**
78 **LYKASTOS (IRE)**, b c 17/2 Holy Roman Emperor (IRE)—Granadilla (Zafonic (USA)) **Stilvi Compania Financiera**
79 **LYKEA (IRE)**, b f 13/2 Oasis Dream—Alyzea (IRE) (King Charlemagne (USA)) **Stilvi Compania Financiera**
80 **MANIKARAA (FR)**, b f 1/1 Anabaa—Zaragoza Girl (BRZ) **Wertheimer et Frere**
81 **MELODIQUE (FR)**, b f 18/2 Falco (USA)—Elodie des Charmes (FR) (Diesis) (45155) **Wertheimer Et Frere**
82 **MENEAS (FR)**, b c 3/2 American Post—Okalea (IRE) (Dalakhani (IRE)) **Stilvi Compania Financiera**
83 **MODESTIE (FR)**, ch f 1/1 Nayef (USA)—Gold Round (IRE) (Caerleon (USA)) **Wertheimer Et Frere**
84 **SEAHORSE (FR)**, b c 21/3 Falco—Sea Paint (Peintre Celebre) **Wertheimer Et Frere**
85 **SEXY (FR)**, b f 19/3 Sinndar (IRE)—Seacleef (FR) (A P Indy (USA)) **Haras Du Quesnay**
86 **SILASOL (IRE)**, b f 9/2 Monsun (GER)—Stormina (USA) (Gulch (USA)) **Wertheimer Et Frere**
87 **SINGING (FR)**, b c 1/1 Singspiel (IRE)—Ring Beaune (USA) (Bering) **Wertheimer Et Frere**
88 **SINGLE (FR)**, ch f 1/1 Singspiel (IRE)—Tender Morn (Dayjur (USA)) **Wertheimer Et Frere**
89 Ch f 15/2 Halling (USA)—Sleeping Storm (IRE) (Danehill Dancer (IRE)) **C. Laffon-Parias**
90 **SNOWDAY (FR)**, b c 11/2 Falco—Oceanique (USA) (Forest Wildcat) **Wertheimer Et Frere**
91 **SOJO (USA)**, b c 1/1 Smart Strike (CAN)—Arme Ancienne (Sillery (USA))
92 **SPILIADA (FR)**, b f 1/1 Falco (USA)—Vivacity (Trempolino (USA)) **Stilvi Compania Financiera**
93 **TOP CHILL (FR)**, b c 1/1 Falco—Top Order **Wertheimer et Frere**
94 **TOPAZE BLANCHE (IRE)**, b f 23/2 Zamindar (USA)—
                                    Pearl Earrine (FR) (Kaldounevees (FR)) **Stilvi Compania Financiera**
95 Ch c 12/3 Pivotal—Trylko (USA) (Diesis) **Sarl Darpat France**
96 **UTOPIQUE (USA)**, b f 1/1 Falco (USA)—Ydillique (IRE) (Sadler's Wells (USA)) **Wertheimer Et Frere**
97 **VARDARIS (IRE)**, b c 21/3 Beat Hollow—Drosia (IRE) (King's Best (USA)) **Stilvi Compania Financiera**

Assistant Trainer: Charles Peck

---

389 **MR NICK LAMPARD, Marlborough**
Postal: **South Cottage, 2 The Crossroads, Clatford, Marlborough, Wiltshire, SN8 4EA**

1 **GOOCHYPOOCHYPRADER**, 5, ch m Karinga Bay—Mrs Ritchie **Glamourbelles**
2 **LA BELLE AU BOIS (IRE)**, 6, b m Val Royal (FR)—Pomme Pomme (USA) **The Outside Chance Racing Club**
3 **PINNACLE OFPASSION (IRE)**, 4, b f Presenting—Olives Hall (IRE) **Mr H Spooner & Mr M Jonas**
4 **PODIUM DANCER**, 5, b m Revoque (IRE)—Mille Et Une Nuits (FR) **Mr H. Spooner**
5 **PUR DE SIVOLA (FR)**, 9, b g Robin des Champs (FR)—Gamine d'ici (FR) **Howard Spooner & Alison Solomon**

Other Owners: Mr M. Jonas, Miss A. E. A. Solomon, Mrs A. Spooner.

---

390 **MR DAVID LANIGAN, Upper Lambourn**
Postal: **Kingsdown Stables, Upper Lambourn, Hungerford, Berkshire, RG17 8QX**
Contacts: **PHONE (01488) 71786 FAX (01488) 674148**
E-MAIL david@laniganracing.co.uk WEBSITE www.laniganracing.co.uk

1 **DAWN SKY**, 8, b g Fantastic Light (USA)—Zacheta
2 **FOR WHAT (USA)**, 4, ch c Mingun (USA)—Cuanto Es (USA)
3 **PLANETOID (IRE)**, 4, b g Galileo (IRE)—Palmeraie (USA)
4 **SUHAILI**, 4, b g Shirocco (GER)—Mezzogiorno

THREE-YEAR-OLDS

5 **BIOGRAPHER**, b c Montjeu (IRE)—Reflective (USA)
6 **BUZKASHI (IRE)**, b f Nayef (USA)—Min Alhawa (USA)
7 **CHAPELLE DU ROI (USA)**, ch c Danehill Dancer (IRE)—Capilla Bonita (USA)
8 **DUTCH SUPREME**, ch g Dutch Art—Barnacla (IRE)
9 **IMPERIAL WAVE (IRE)**, br f Holy Roman Emperor (IRE)—Jalisco (IRE)
10 **IRONICALLY (IRE)**, b f Refuse To Bend—Dutch Auction (USA)
11 **LEAN ON PETE (IRE)**, b g Oasis Dream—Superfonic (FR)
12 **MAIN LINE**, b c Rail Link—Cooden Beach (IRE)
13 **MAIN SEQUENCE (USA)**, ch c Aldebaran (USA)—Ikat (IRE)
14 **MELODRAMA (IRE)**, b f Oratorio—Lila

MR DAVID LANIGAN—continued

15 **PROTANTO (IRE)**, b g Lawman (FR)—Incoming Call (USA)
16 **SHESTHEMAN**, b f Manduro (GER)—Clear Vision
17 **TIS ROCK 'N' ROLL (USA)**, b br c Rock of Gibraltar (IRE)—Tis Me (USA)
18 **VIRGINIA GALILEI (IRE)**, ch f Galileo (IRE)—Tilbury

TWO-YEAR-OLDS

19 B f 29/1 Assertive—Agent Kensington (Mujahid (USA))
20 B f 22/6 Passing Glance—Ajeebah (IRE) (Mujtahid (USA))
21 B f 25/3 Empire Maker (USA)—Arabian Spell (IRE) (Desert Prince (IRE))
22 Ch f 29/3 Raven's Pass (USA)—Badee'a (IRE) (Marju (IRE)) (160000)
23 B c 24/2 Mujadil (USA)—Bradamante (Sadler's Wells (USA)) (50000)
24 **BRAVESTAR (IRE)**, b c 26/3 Lawman (FR)—High Fidelity (GER) (Peintre Celebre (USA)) (80000)
25 B f 12/2 Authorized (IRE)—Bread of Heaven (Machiavellian (USA)) (10000)
26 B f 24/3 Dansili—Crystal Reef (King's Best (USA)) (45000)
27 B f 29/3 Smart Strike (CAN)—Ebaraya (IRE) (Sadler's Wells (USA))
28 B c 29/1 Galileo (IRE)—Egyptian Queen (USA) (Storm Cat (USA)) (320512)
29 B f 26/1 Duke of Marmalade (IRE)—Fashion Model (Rainbow Quest (USA))
30 Ch f 12/3 Rock of Gibraltar (IRE)—Fig Tree Drive (USA) (Miswaki (USA))
31 Br c 8/5 Monsun (GER)—Geminiani (IRE) (King of Kings (IRE)) (80000)
32 B c 14/2 Compton Place—Guermantes (Distant Relative) (105000)
33 B f 27/1 Selkirk (USA)—Have Faith (USA) (Machiavellian (USA)) (180000)
34 **INDE TIGRESS**, b f 27/2 Indesatchel (IRE)—Ortigueira (BRZ) (Yagli (USA))
35 Ch f 13/2 Exceed And Excel (AUS)—Lighthouse (Warning) (170000)
36 B c 24/1 Monsun (GER)—Melodramatic (IRE) (Sadler's Wells (USA)) (221674)
37 B br f 2/3 Street Cry (IRE)—Meribel (USA) (Peaks and Valleys (USA)) (67155)
38 B c 3/5 Singspiel (IRE)—Monawara (IRE) (Namaqualand (USA))
39 B c 15/5 Singspiel (IRE)—Moonlight Dance (USA) (Alysheba (USA))
40 B f 28/3 Cape Cross (IRE)—Nantyglo (Mark of Esteem (IRE)) (95000)
41 **NO JET LAG (USA)**, b c 24/1 Johar (USA)—Desert Sky (IRE) (Green Desert (USA))
42 Ch c 26/2 Danehill Dancer (IRE)—One So Wonderful (Nashwan (USA)) (210000)
43 B c 15/2 Dansili—Palmeraie (USA) (Lear Fan (USA))
44 B c 22/3 Shamardal (USA)—Prima Luce (Galileo (IRE)) (330000)
45 B c 6/4 Dansili—Private Life (FR) (Bering)
46 Ch f 20/2 Hurricane Run (IRE)—Rose Parade (Machiavellian (USA)) (12315)
47 **TYPHON (USA)**, b c 29/4 Proud Citizen (USA)—Seven Moons (JPN) (Sunday Silence (USA))

Owners: Mr Trevor Benton, Mr Catesby Clay, Mr Bill Farish, Les and Caroline Harlow, Liza Judd, The Kathryn Stud, Mr Bob Lanigan, Mrs David Lanigan, Mr Robert Lapenta, Lord and Lady Lloyd-Webber, Mrs John Magnier, Mick and Janice Mariscotti, Mr and Mrs William McAlpin, Niarchos Family, Mr Bjorn Nielsen, Mr Ben Sangster, Usk Valley Stud, Mr Charles Wentworth, Mr Chris Wright.

Jockey (flat): Ted Durcan.

---

391 MISS EMMA LAVELLE, Andover

Postal: **Cottage Stables, Hatherden, Andover, Hampshire, SP11 0HY**
Contacts: PHONE **(01264) 735509** OFFICE **(01264) 735412** FAX **(01264) 735529**
MOBILE **(07774) 993998**
E-MAIL **emma@elavelle.freeserve.co.uk** WEBSITE **www.emmalavelle.com**

1 **AFRICAN EAGLE (IRE)**, 5, b g Trade Fair—Trushan **Frisky Fillies 6**
2 **BALLYCARNEY (IRE)**, 8, b g Classic Cliche (IRE)—Rhythm Hill (IRE) **Elite Racing Club**
3 **BEAU COLONEL (FR)**, 6, gr g Colonel Collins (USA)—Brave Lola (FR) **Axom XXV**
4 **BENIGN DICTATOR (IRE)**, 5, b g Flemensfirth (USA)—Old Moon (IRE) **N. Mustoe**
5 **BLUES AND TWOS**, 6, b g Presenting—Blue Gallery (IRE) **Mr T. D. J. Syder & Mr N. Mustoe**
6 **BOUGGLER**, 7, b g Tobougg (IRE)—Rush Hour (IRE) **Axom (XXI)**
7 **CAMAS BRIDGE**, 8, ch g Alflora (IRE)—Bobupandown **The High Altitude Partnership**
8 **CAPTAIN SUNSHINE**, 6, b g Oscar—Gaye Fame **Mrs N. C. Turner**
9 **CHARIOT CHARGER (IRE)**, 8, b g Oscar (IRE)—Queen Boadicea (IRE) **The Fox Inn Syndicate**
10 **CHOICE WORDS (USA)**, 4, b g Redoute's Choice (AUS)—Alizes (NZ) **Caloona Racing**
11 **CLARET CLOAK**, 5, b g Vinnie Roe (IRE)—Bewildered (IRE) **Hawksmoor Partnership**
12 **COMPASSION**, 4, b f Tiger Hill (IRE)—Windmill **Mrs S. Metcalfe**
13 **COURT BY SURPRISE (IRE)**, 7, b g Beneficial—Garryduff Princess (IRE) **N. Mustoe**
14 **COURT IN MOTION (IRE)**, 7, br g Fruits of Love (USA)—Peace Time Girl (IRE) **N. Mustoe**
15 **COURT VICTORY (IRE)**, 7, b g Old Vic—Sarah's Smile **N. Mustoe**

MISS EMMA LAVELLE—continued

16 **DANCING TEASEL**, 5, ch m Snurge—Cajole (IRE) **Mrs S. H. West**
17 **DAYMAR BAY (IRE)**, 6, b g Oscar (IRE)—Sunset View (IRE) **The Second Fox Inn Syndicate**
18 **EASTER DANCER**, 5, ch m Karinga Bay—Easter Comet **Mr & Mrs Willes & Mr & Mrs J Brankin-Frisby**
19 **EASTER METEOR**, 6, b g Midnight Legend—Easter Comet **Mr S. C. Willes**
20 **ELEGANT TOUCH (IRE)**, 6, b m Kayf Tara—Faucon **Mr A. Gemmell**
21 4, B g Milan—Elma Joyce (IRE) **The C H F Partnership**
22 **FIRE AND RAIN (FR)**, 9, b g Galileo (IRE)—Quatre Saisons (FR) **Fraser Miller Racing**
23 **FONTANO (FR)**, 6, gr g Astarabad (USA)—Little Bud (FR) **Mrs Julien Turner & Mr Andrew Merriam**
24 **FOX APPEAL (IRE)**, 5, b g Brian Boru—Lady Appeal (IRE) **Fox Inn Syndicate 3**
25 **FURTHER MORE (IRE)**, 5, gr g Hasten To Add (USA)—Cottage Lass (IRE) **Frisky Fillies 4**
26 **GLEANN EAGAS (IRE)**, 5, b g Gold Well—Glen Princess (IRE) **R. J. Lavelle**
27 **GLOBAL WARMING (IRE)**, 8, b g King's Theatre (IRE)—Croi Na Greine (IRE) **The Older But No Wiser Syndicate**
28 **GREY WULFF (IRE)**, 7, gr g Oscar (IRE)—Only A Rose **Mrs S. V. M. Stevens**
29 **GULLINBURSTI (IRE)**, 6, b g Milan—D'ygrande (IRE) **N. Mustoe**
30 **HIGHLAND LODGE (IRE)**, 6, b g Flemensfirth (USA)—Supreme Von Pres (IRE) **The Unusual Suspects**
31 **HURRICANE HENRY (IRE)**, 5, b g Highest Honor (FR)—Make Rings **T. D. J. Syder**
32 **KANGAROO COURT (IRE)**, 8, b g Lahib (USA)—Tombazaan (IRE) **N. Mustoe**
33 **KENTFORD GREY LADY**, 6, gr m Silver Patriarch (IRE)—Kentford Grebe **D. I. Bare**
34 **KIND OF EASY (IRE)**, 6, b g Kalanisi (IRE)—Specifiedrisk (IRE) **N. Mustoe & T. Syder**
35 **KINDLY NOTE**, 5, ch m Generous (IRE)—Vent d'aout (IRE) **Elite Racing Club**
36 **KING OZYMANDIAS**, 5, ch g Generous (IRE)—
                                        Mavourneen (IRE) **James Thorburn-Muirhead & John Kevin Lomax**
37 **KUMASI CLAN (IRE)**, 5, b g Moscow Society (USA)—Ashanti Dancer (IRE) **N. Mustoe**
38 **KUSADIKI (IRE)**, 6, b g Tobougg (IRE)—Mother Molly (USA) **The Optimists**
39 **LE BEC (FR)**, 4, ch g Smadoun (FR)—La Pelode (FR) **T. D. J. Syder**
40 **OCEANA GOLD**, 8, ch g Primo Valentino (IRE)—Silken Dalliance (IRE) **The C H F Partnership**
41 **OFF THE GROUND (IRE)**, 6, b g Oscar (IRE)—Kaysel (IRE) **Axom (XXVI)**
42 **OUZBECK (FR)**, 10, b br g Denham Red (FR)—Volodia (FR) **Axom VII**
43 **PAUSE AND CLAUSE (IRE)**, 8, b g Saddlers' Hall (IRE)—Silver Glen (IRE) **Mr R. D. P. Cohen**
44 **PENNY MAX (IRE)**, 6, b g Flemensfirth (USA)—
                                        Ballymartin Trix (IRE) **Highclere Thoroughbred Racing - Penny Max**
45 **QIANSHAN LEADER (IRE)**, 8, b g Anshan—Gaelic Leader (IRE) **The Pick 'N' Mix Partnership**
46 **QUEEN'S FOREST (IRE)**, 7, b m King's Theatre (IRE)—Glen Princess (IRE) **R. J. Lavelle**
47 **RAVENCLAW (IRE)**, 9, b g Blueprint (IRE)—
                                        Enchanted Heart (IRE) **Chris & Helen Awdry & Graham & Sue Willetts**
48 **RED MILE (FR)**, 7, ch g Kapgarde (FR)—Katespeed (FR) **T. D. J. Syder**
49 **RIDGEWAY POPPY**, 7, b m Alflora (IRE)—Coquelles (FR) **A. P. Holland**
50 **ROYAL COMMISSION (IRE)**, 5, b g Orpen (USA)—Princess of Iona (IRE) **Cakey Bundles**
51 **SHINING EMBERS**, 6, b g High-Rise (IRE)—Ballykea (IRE) **Mrs A. C. Lavelle**
52 **SILVER FOOTNOTE**, 7, gr g Silver Patriarch (IRE)—
                                        Mavourneen (IRE) **James Thorburn-Muirhead & John Kevin Lomax**
53 **STAIGUE FORT**, 4, b g Kirkwall—Mulberry Wine **Lady Bland**
54 **STOLEN THUNDER**, 7, b g Alflora (IRE)—Cullen Bay (IRE) **Colin Bothway & Roger Hetherington**
55 **THE LAST NIGHT (FR)**, 5, ch g April Night (FR)—La Pelode (FR) **T. D. J. Syder**
56 **THYMELESS**, 7, b m Alflora (IRE)—Four Thyme **Miss C. C. R. Jenks**
57 **TIDAL DANCE (IRE)**, 5, b g Craigsteel—Musical Waves (IRE) **Pinks Gym & Leisure Wear Ltd**
58 **TIM THE CHAIR (IRE)**, 7, b g Pierre—Dinah B (IRE) **Frisky Fillies 5**
59 **TOCCA FERRO (FR)**, 7, gr g April Night (FR)—La Pelode (FR) **Mrs Sarah Prior and Mr Tim Syder**
60 **TREVIS**, 9, ch g Tobougg (IRE)—La Piazza (IRE) **Hunter Racing**
61 **VIC AR AGHAIDH (IRE)**, 6, b m Old Vic—Rith Ar Aghaidh (IRE) **George Ward**
62 **WATER WAGTAIL**, 5, b g Kahyasi—Kentford Grebe **D. I. Bare**
63 **WELL REGARDED (IRE)**, 7, b g Dr Massini (IRE)—Glenelly Valley (IRE) **The Unusual Suspects**
64 **ZARRAFAKT (IRE)**, 8, b g Rudimentary (USA)—Carrick Glen (IRE) **Mr G. P. MacIntosh**
65 **ZEBRANO**, 6, br g Storming Home—Ambience Lady **Caloona Racing**

Other Owners: P. R. Attwater, Mr H. R. Attwater, Mr C. V. Awdry, Axom Ltd, Mr R. A. Beach, Mr C. H. Bothway, Mrs J. S. Brankin-Frisby, Mr G. C. Clifford, Mr K. J. Clifford, Mr I. W. Dale, Mr D. Downie, K. H. Fischer, C. H. Fischer, Mrs J. R. Foster, Mr R. J. Fowler, C. G. Hellyer, Mrs S. C. Hepworth, The Hon H. M. Herbert, Mr R. R. Hetherington, Highclere Thoroughbred Racing Ltd, A. J. Hill, J. R. Hulme, Mr R. Hunter, Mrs K. Hunter, J. R. Lavelle, K. J. Lomax, Mr J. P. McNeile, A. W. K. Merriam, P. B. Mitford-Slade, Mr P. Nicholls, Miss M. Noden, G. B. Pomford, Mrs S. K. Prior, Mr H. E. Seymour, Sir David Sieff, B. G. Slade, J. Thorburn-Muirhead, Mr J. W. Turner, Mrs J. C. Verity, Mr P. R. Weston, Mr A. G. Weston, Mr G. J. Willetts.

Assistant Trainer: Barry Fenton

392 MS JOAN L. LE BROCQ, Jersey
Postal: **Greystones, La Rue Coentyn, St Ouens, Jersey, Channel Islands, JE3 2GY**
Contacts: **PHONE/FAX (01534) 481461 MOBILE (07797) 750823**
E-MAIL joanlebrocq@gmail.com

1 BOLLIN FERGUS, 8, br g Vettori (IRE)—Bollin Harriet **Joan Le Brocq & Angie Richardson**
2 FINE THE WORLD, 8, b m Agnes World (USA)—Fine Honor (FR) **N. G. Ahier**
3 HIGH VOLTAGE, 11, ch g Wolfhound (USA)—Real Emotion (USA) **Joan Le Brocq**
4 LANDOLINO (FR), 7, b g Trempolino (USA)—Champagne Sorbet (FR) **Lavender Racing**
5 LORD OF THE WING, 7, b g Daggers Drawn (USA)—Brangane (IRE) **Frank & Annette Brady**
6 RUNAROUND RITA (FR), 4, ch f Protektor (GER)—Wild Rita **Joan Le Brocq**
7 SCULASTIC, 9, b g Galileo (IRE)—Mutual Consent (IRE) **Joan Le Brocq**
8 SECRET ASSASSIN (IRE), 9, b g Daggers Drawn (USA)—Lypharden (IRE) **The Name's Bond Partnership**
9 WILD IN WOOLLY (FR), 5, gr g Al Namix (FR)—Wild Rita **Joan Le Brocq**

Other Owners: D. Barrons, Mr Allan Butler, J. Davies, Seamus Gallagher, Advocate R. Michel, Caroline Michel, Mike Quenault, Joe Quinn, Lesley Norton, David Fish, Mr M. & Mrs J. Chambers, Jannine Davies, Lavender Racing.

Assistant Trainer: Edward Hanmer

Jockey: Mattie Batchelor, Jamie Goldstein.

393 MR BARRY LEAVY, Stoke-on-Trent
Postal: **Cash Heath Farm, Cash Heath, Forsbrook, Stoke-on-Trent, ST11 9DE**
Contacts: **HOME/FAX (01782) 398591 MOBILE (07540) 806915**
E-MAIL lauraleavy@hotmail.co.uk

1 4, b g Deploy—Capricorn Princess **Mr & Mrs Leavy**
2 IRIS'S FLYER, 10, gr g Terimon—Miss Shaw **M. Tucker**
3 JIMBATAI (IRE), 9, ch g Moscow Society (USA)—Kouron **Cops & Robbers**
4 KING ZEAL (IRE), 8, b g King's Best (USA)—Manureva (USA) **Deborah Hart & Alan Jackson**
5 KIRKHAMMERTON (IRE), 10, ch g Grand Lodge (USA)—Nawara **Valentino Racing**
6 LEAN BURN (USA), 6, b g Johannesburg (USA)—Anthelion (USA) **N. Heath**
7 MOHI RAHRERE (IRE), 9, b g New Frontier (IRE)—Collinstown Lady (IRE) **Mrs S. D. Williams-Ashford**
8 QUAHADI (IRE), 6, b g Montjeu (IRE)—Kicking Bird (FR) **N. Heath**
9 QUIAMO MALTA (FR), 8, b g Sassanian (USA)—Dame Au Diamant (FR) **P. J. Lea**

Other Owners: Mrs Deborah Hart, Mr Alan Jackson, Mr Barry Leavy, Mr Chris Nightingale, Mr D. Rowlinson.

Assistant Trainer: Mrs L Leavy

Jockey (NH): Danny Cook.

394 MR RICHARD LEE, Presteigne
Postal: **The Bell House, Byton, Presteigne, LD8 2HS**
Contacts: **PHONE (01544) 267672 FAX (01544) 260247 MOBILE (07836) 537145**
E-MAIL rleeracing@btinternet.com WEBSITE www.rleeracing.com

1 BACKFROMTHECONGO (IRE), 11, b br g Bob Back (USA)—
Market Lass (IRE) **D. Cound, J. Jackson & A. Compton**
2 BACKSTREET BILLY (IRE), 8, br g Presenting—Basically (IRE) **P. A. Bonner**
3 BIG NEWS, 6, ch g Karinga Bay—Welcome News **Mrs C. L. Shaw**
4 BLACK IS BEAUTIFUL (FR), 4, b g Black Sam Bellamy (IRE)—Queen's Theatre (FR) **B Bailey & K Edwards**
5 CADOUDALAS (FR), 9, b g Cadoudal (FR)—Popie D'ecorcei (FR) **Six To Five Against G D Thorp, R L Baker**
6 DARING ORIGYN (FR), 7, ch g Blushing Flame (USA)—Forza Malta (FR) **Gavin MacEchern & Lord Daresbury**
7 FIGHTING CHANCE (IRE), 12, b g Germany—Una Juna (IRE) **P. A. Bonner**
8 GREY GOLD (IRE), 7, gr g Strategic Choice (USA)—Grouse-N-Heather **Mrs M. A. Boden**
9 HEATHCLIFF (IRE), 10, b g Glacial Storm (USA)—Gaye Le Moss **Mrs C. J. Lee**
10 HECTOR'S CHOICE (FR), 8, b br g Grey Risk (FR)—The Voice (FR) **James & Jean Potter**
11 HIGHWAY CODE (USA), 6, b g Street Cry (IRE)—Fairy Heights (IRE) **D. E. Edwards**
12 INCENTIVISE (IRE), 9, ch g Snurge—Festive Isle (IRE) **Ron Bartlett, F J Ayres & Jeff Hulston**
13 KNOCK A HAND (IRE), 7, br g Lend A Hand—Knockcross (IRE) **D. A. Halsall**
14 LE BEAU BAI (FR), 9, b g Cadoudal (FR)—Dame Blonde (FR) **Glass Half Full**
15 MARKED MAN (IRE), 16, b g Grand Plaisir (IRE)—Teazle **Mr & Mrs C. R. Elliott**
16 MIGHTY RIVER (IRE), 5, b g Presenting—Dame de L'oise (USA) **G. D. Thorp - R. L. Baker**

MR RICHARD LEE—continued

17 **MILO MILAN (IRE)**, 7, b g Milan—Simply Divine (IRE) **Mrs C. L. Shaw**
18 **NOBLE CRUSADER (USA)**, 9, b g Giant's Causeway (USA)—
Suitably Discreet (USA) **Nicola Shields Peter Phillips Will Roseff**
19 **PAUL REVERE (IRE)**, 8, b g Exit To Nowhere (USA)—Sharkezan (IRE) **Mr & Mrs A. D. Stewart**
20 **RIFLEMAN (IRE)**, 12, ch g Starborough—En Garde (USA) **J. M. Jackson**
21 **RUSSE BLANC (FR)**, 5, wh g Machiavellian Tsar (FR)—Fleur de Mad (FR) **Mr M. R. H. Jackson**
22 **RYE ROCKET (FR)**, 4, b g Catcher In The Rye (IRE)—Platinum Michelle **Alan Beard & Brian Beard**
23 **SARRACO (IRE)**, 6, ch g Old Vic—Harelda **George Brookes & Family II**
24 **SIMPLY WINGS (IRE)**, 8, b g Winged Love (FR)—
Simply Deep (IRE) **G D Thorp Bevan Bros Edmonds & Sampson**
25 **THE CHAZER (IRE)**, 7, gr g Witness Box (USA)—Saffron Holly (IRE) **Mr & Mrs C. R. Elliott**
26 **TRESOR DE BONTEE (FR)**, 5, b g Grand Seigneur (FR)—Bontee (FR) **R. A. Lee**
27 **VICTORY GUNNER (IRE)**, 14, ch g Old Vic—Gunner B Sharp **Ron Bartlett & F. J. Ayres**
28 **WESTERN WHISKY (FR)**, 10, b g Passing Sale (FR)—Winska Girl (FR) **A Beard B Beard D Lott S Ripley**
29 **YOUNG VICTORIA**, 6, b m Old Vic—Siroyalta (FR) **G. D. Thorp - R. L. Baker**

Other Owners: Mrs S. Archdale, F. J. Ayres, B. J. Bailey, Mr R. L. Baker, R. Bartlett, A. C. Beard, B. M. Beard, M. J. Bevan, G. E. Brookes, A. J. Compton, J. D. Cound, Lord Daresbury, K. Edwards, C. R. Elliott, Mrs J. A. Elliott, R. L. C. Hartley, J. P. Hulston, Dr D. Lott, G. M. MacEchern, Mr P. T. G. Phillips, J. E. Potter, Mrs M. J. Potter, Lady H. S. Ripley, W. Roseff, Mrs N. J. Shields, A. D. Stewart, Mrs V. M. Stewart, G. D. Thorp.

Assistant Trainer: Kerry Lewis

Jockey (NH): Charlie Poste, Richard Johnson, Robert Thornton. **Conditional:** Giles Hawkins.

---

395 MRS SOPHIE LEECH, Newnham
Postal: **Tudor Racing Stables, Elton Road, Elton, Newnham, Gloucestershire, GL14 1JN**
Contacts: **PHONE (01452) 760691 MOBILE (07775) 874630**
E-MAIL info@leechracing.co.uk WEBSITE www.leechracing.co.uk

1 **BANYAN TREE (IRE)**, 5, b g Danehill Dancer (IRE)—User Friendly **C. J. Leech**
2 **BLOWING A HOOLIE (IRE)**, 4, b f Val Royal (FR)—Moly **The Futures Bright Partnership**
3 **CEBONNE (FR)**, 11, b g Pistolet Bleu (IRE)—Northine (FR)
4 **HELIUM (FR)**, 3, b g Dream Well (FR)—Sure Harbour (SWI) **G Thompson, C J Leech, P Stock**
5 **HERON BAY**, 8, b g Hernando (FR)—Wiener Wald (FR) **G. D. Thompson**
6 **IS IT ME (USA)**, 9, ch g Sky Classic (CAN)—Thea (GER) **G Thompson & C J Leech**
7 **KEENES DAY (FR)**, 7, gr g Daylami (IRE)—Key Academy **J. O'Brien & C. J. Leech**
8 **KINGS STORY (IRE)**, 8, b g Royal Applause—Poppy Carew (IRE) **C. J. Leech**
9 **LE GRAND CHENE (FR)**, 6, b g Turgeon (USA)—Faitiche d'aubry (FR) **Mr R. M. Green**
10 **MANSOLIAS (FR)**, 8, b g Mansonnien (FR)—Popie D'ecorcei (FR) **C. J. Leech**
11 **MASTER D'OR (FR)**, 12, b g Cyborg (FR)—Une Pomme d'or (FR) **Cheltenham Racing Club**
12 **OLD MAGIC (FR)**, 7, b g Old Vic—Maeve's Magic (IRE) **C. J. Leech**
13 **OLYMPIAN BOY (IRE)**, 8, b g Flemensfirth (USA)—Notanissue (IRE) **J Cocks, P Stock & CJ Leech**
14 **OUMEYADE (FR)**, 10, b g Smadoun (FR)—Debandade (FR) **C. J. Leech**
15 **PISTOLET DOVE (IRE)**, 10, br g Pistolet Bleu (IRE)—Emerald Dove **C. J. Leech**
16 **RIVER D'OR (FR)**, 7, b g Saint Preuil (FR)—Une Pomme d'or (FR) **G. Doel & C. J. Leech**
17 **SILMI**, 8, gr g Daylami (IRE)—Intimaa (IRE) **J. O'Brien & C. J. Leech**
18 **TAMARILLO GROVE (IRE)**, 5, b g Cape Cross (IRE)—Tamarillo **G Thompson & C J Leech**
19 **VALENTINE BHOY**, 5, b g Beat All (USA)—Deep Line **C. J. Leech**

Other Owners: Mr G. Bryan, S. J. Bryan, Mr J. J. Cocks, G. Doel, Mr C J Hodgson, J. O'Brien, Mr C. Parkin.

Assistant Trainer: Christian Leech (07880) 788464

Jockey (NH): Paul Moloney.

---

396 MR DAVID LEWIS, Tewkesbury
Postal: **Broadfields Farm, Longdon, Tewkesbury, Gloucestershire, GL20 6AN**

1 **ALPHA JULIET (IRE)**, 11, b m Victory Note (USA)—Zara's Birthday (IRE) **Mr M. J. Foley**
2 **CASCO BAY (IRE)**, 8, b g Fath (USA)—Montana Miss (IRE) **Mr D. T. Lewis**
3 **DR ANUBIS (IRE)**, 7, ch g Beneficial—Gaelic (IRE) **Mr D. T. Lewis**
4 **ESTATE**, 10, b g Montjeu (IRE)—Fig Tree Drive (USA) **Mr D. T. Lewis**

MR DAVID LEWIS—continued

5 **GILDED YOUTH,** 8, b g Gorse—Nisha **Mr D. T. Lewis**
6 **OSCAR RAINBOW,** 6, b g Oscar (IRE)—Fionnula's Rainbow (IRE) **Mr D. T. Lewis**
7 **STAR OF GERMANY (IRE),** 12, b g Germany (USA)—Twinkle Bright (USA) **Mr D. T. Lewis**
8 **TOTAL VICTORY (IRE),** 9, br g Titus Livius (FR)—Snipe Victory (IRE) **Mr D. T. Lewis**

---

397 MR ALASTAIR LIDDERDALE, Lambourn

Postal: **Lidderdale Racing LLP, High View Stables, Folly Road, Lambourn, Berkshire, RG17 8QE**
Contacts: **PHONE** (01488) 670443 (01488) 73694 **FAX** (01488) 670443 **MOBILE** (07785) 785375
E-MAIL alastairlidderdale@btinternet.com WEBSITE www.lidderdaleracing.co.uk

1 **AHWAAK (USA),** 8, b g Dynaformer (USA)—Saudia (USA) **Hamilton Hallows Racing**
2 **ALDO,** 5, b h Lucky Owners (NZ)—Chaperone **Entertainments Committee**
3 **AVERTIS,** 7, b g Averti (IRE)—Double Stake (USA) **Mrs S. J. Doyle**
4 **BLACK OR RED (IRE),** 7, b g Cape Cross (IRE)—Gentle Thoughts **Sporting Arbitrage**
5 **DESERT ICON (IRE),** 6, b g Desert Style (IRE)—Gilded Vanity (IRE) **Chris Beek Racing**
6 **DIDDUMS,** 6, b g Royal Applause—Sahara Shade (USA) **Chris Beek Racing**
7 **EVERGREEN FOREST (IRE),** 4, ch g Haafhd—Inaaq **Chris Beek Racing**
8 **FAULT,** 6, b g Bahamian Bounty—Trundley Wood **Chris Beek Racing**
9 **GROSS PROPHET,** 7, b g Lujain (USA)—Done And Dusted (IRE) **Lambourn Valley Racing**
10 **HOBSON,** 7, b g Choisir (AUS)—Educating Rita **Chris Beek Racing**
11 **IT'S DUBAI DOLLY,** 6, ch m Dubai Destination (USA)—Betrothal (IRE) **Mr M. M. Cox**
12 **KIJIVU,** 7, gr m Erhaab (USA)—Alsiba **KMC Partnership Three**
13 **KILBURN,** 8, b g Grand Lodge (USA)—Lady Lahar **Royal Windsor Racing Club**
14 **KNOW NO FEAR,** 7, b g Primo Valentino (IRE)—Alustar **Chris Beek Racing**
15 **LOUGH CORRIB (USA),** 4, b g Tiznow (USA)—Desert Glow (IRE) **Chris Beek Racing**
16 **MEGLIO ANCORA,** 5, ch g Best of The Bests (IRE)—May Fox **Chris Beek Racing**
17 **NESNAAS (USA),** 11, ch g Gulch (USA)—Sedrah (USA) **Chris Beek Racing**
18 **NIBANI (IRE),** 5, ch g Dalakhani (IRE)—Dance of The Sea (IRE) **Chris Beek Racing**
19 **NORTH CAPE (USA),** 6, b g Action This Day (USA)—Cape (USA) **Mr A. McIver**
20 **PEACHEZ,** 4, ch f Observatory (USA)—Streccia **The P And P Partnership**
21 **PHOTO OPPORTUNITY,** 5, b g Zamindar (USA)—Fame At Last (USA) **Chris Beek Racing**
22 **PIPERS PIPING (IRE),** 6, b g Noverre (USA)—Monarchy (IRE) **Chris Beek Racing**
23 **POCKETWOOD,** 10, b g Fleetwood (IRE)—Pocket Venus (IRE) **The Sw1ft Buck Partnership**
24 **POLLY ADLER,** 5, br m Fantastic Light (USA)—Urania **Chris Beek Racing**
25 **PROHIBITION (IRE),** 6, b g Danehill Dancer (USA)—Crumpetsfortea (IRE) **Chris Beek Racing**
26 **REGGAE RHYTHM (IRE),** 18, b g Be My Native (USA)—Invery Lady **Mrs A. Lidderdale**
27 **RESPLENDENT ALPHA,** 8, ch g Best of The Bests (IRE)—Sunley Scent **Chris Beek Racing**
28 **ROYAL ALCOR (IRE),** 5, b g Chevalier (IRE)—Arundhati (IRE) **Royal Windsor Racing Club**
29 **RUBY DOO,** 4, b f Imperial Dancer—On Cloud Nine **Mr T. W. Stubbings**
30 **SPICE RUN,** 9, b g Zafonic (USA)—Palatial **Mrs S. J. Doyle**
31 **STARGAZY,** 8, b g Observatory (USA)—Romantic Myth **Chris Beek Racing**
32 **TAKE IT THERE,** 10, ch m Cadeaux Genereux—Feel Free (IRE) **Entertainments Committee**
33 **TAMINO (IRE),** 9, b g Mozart (IRE)—Stop Out **Chris Beek Racing**
34 **TIMOCRACY,** 7, br g Cape Cross (IRE)—Tithcar **Mr B. S. Hicks**
35 **TWIN BARRELS,** 5, ch g Double Trigger (IRE)—Caballe (USA) **Mr B. S. Hicks**
36 **VANADIUM,** 10, b g Dansili—Musianica **Chris Beek Racing**
37 **VITZNAU (IRE),** 8, b g Val Royal (FR)—Neat Dish (CAN) **Chris Beek Racing**
38 **WHERE'S REILEY (USA),** 6, b br g Doneraile Court (USA)—Plateau (USA) **Mr C. S. J. Beek**
39 **WINDSOR KNIGHTS,** 4, b g Dubai Destination (USA)—Betrothal (IRE) **Royal Windsor Racing Club**

THREE-YEAR-OLDS

40 **ADDAZERO,** b g Putra Sas (IRE)—Poker Queen **Red Hot Partnership**
41 **CLONE DEVIL (IRE),** gr g Clodovil (IRE)—Willy Nilly **Chris Beek Racing**
42 Ch f Iceman—Double Stake (USA) **Mrs S. J. Doyle**
43 **LADY ARABELLA (IRE),** b f Dark Angel (IRE)—Lady Fabiola (USA) **The Arabella Partnership**
44 **MAJESTIC ZAFEEN,** b f Zafeen (FR)—Arasong **Lambourn Valley Racing II**
45 **SALAAHEB (IRE),** b f Tiger Hill (IRE)—Sayedati Eljamilah (USA) **Chris Beek Racing**
46 **TRIPLE SALCHOW,** b f Needwood Blade—Icky Woo **The Pivotal Partnership**

TWO-YEAR-OLDS

47 B f 26/2 Assertive—Birthday Venture (Soviet Star (USA)) **Lidderdale Racing LLP**
48 B c 25/2 Manipulator (IRE)—Claws (Marju (IRE)) **Orbit Performance**
49 Ch f 5/2 Notnowcato—Italian Goddess (Medicean) (1000) **Chris Beek Racing**
50 B g 9/3 What A Caper (IRE)—Zahaadid (FR) (Limpid) **Royal Windsor Racing Club**

MR ALASTAIR LIDDERDALE—continued

Other Owners: Mr C. S. J. Beek, Mr C. C. Capel, Mr Bill Evans, Mr M. J. Foxton-Duffy, Mr A. J. H. Hallows, Mrs A. Lidderdale, A. J. D. Lidderdale, Mr L. Lugg, Ms Joan Major, Mr K. P. McCarthy, Mr David J. Muir, Ms J. M. Smith, Ms L. Stoten.

Assistant Trainer: Clark Judd

Apprentice: Leonna Mayor. **Amateur:** Miss Zoe Lilly.

---

398 MR CLIFFORD LINES, Newmarket
Postal: **Hethersett House, Church House, Exning, Newmarket, Suffolk, CB8 7EH**
Contacts: **PHONE (01638) 608016 FAX (01638) 608016 MOBILE (07980) 120157**
E-MAIL hethersetthouse@gmail.com

1 BALESTEEM, 5, ch g Mark of Esteem (IRE)—Ball Gown **Prima Racing Partnership**
2 PROUD CHIEFTAIN, 4, b g Sleeping Indian—Skimra **Prima Racing Partnership**
3 STRIKE FORCE, 8, b g Dansili—Miswaki Belle (USA) **Miss A. L. Hutchinson**

THREE-YEAR-OLDS

4 CONFLUENCE, ch f Milk It Mick—Skimra **Mr N. Ratnasingham**

Jockey (flat): James Doyle. **Amateur:** Miss A. L. Hutchinson.

---

399 MR NICK LITTMODEN, Newmarket
Postal: **Brook Farm, Dullingham Ley, Newmarket, Suffolk, CB8 9XG**
Contacts: **PHONE (01638) 508491 FAX (01638) 508491 MOBILE (07770) 964865**
E-MAIL nicklittmoden@btinternet.com WEBSITE www.nicklittmoden.com

1 BULL FIVE, 5, b g Intikhab (USA)—Digamist Girl (IRE)
　　　　　　　　　　　　　　　　　Mr T. A. Ringer, Mr Nick Littmoden & Mrs Karen Graham
2 COOKIESHAKE, 4, b g Cadeaux Genereux—Hawait Al Barr **N. P. Littmoden**
3 CUT ACROSS (IRE), 4, b g Cape Cross (IRE)—Incise **Mr Nick Littmoden & Mr Nigel Shields**
4 LORD THEO, 8, b g Averti (IRE)—Love You Too **Mrs K. B. Graham**
5 MUHANDIS (IRE), 4, b g Muhtathir—Ahdaaf (USA) **A. A. Goodman**
6 PENBRYN (USA), 5, b g Pivotal—Brocatelle **Mrs K. Graham, N. Littmoden, A. Highfield**
7 WAVERTREE WARRIOR (IRE), 10, br g Indian Lodge (IRE)—Karamana **N. P. Littmoden**

THREE-YEAR-OLDS

8 BETTY BROOK (IRE), b f Refuse To Bend (IRE)—Ikan (IRE) **Mrs E. P. Littmoden**
9 ECHO OF THUNDER (IRE), b f Echo of Light—Aquatic Warrior (USA) **Mrs E. P. Littmoden**
10 MILLIBAR (IRE), b f Manduro (GER)—Iktidar **Mrs L. M. Francis**
11 POPULAR CHOICE, ch c Medicean—Stella Marine (FR) **Phoenix Bloodstock**

TWO-YEAR-OLDS

12 Gr f 18/3 Aussie Rules (USA)—Grenouillere (USA) (Alysheba (USA)) (10000) **N. P. Littmoden**
13 B c 6/4 Zamindar (USA)—Joshua's Princess (Danehill (USA)) (8000) **Mr G. Gredley**

Other Owners: Mr T. Clarke, T. M. Clarke, Mr R. Hartshorn, Mr A. J. Highfield, Mr D. D. Sutherland.

Amateur: Mrs Emma Littmoden.

---

400 MR BERNARD LLEWELLYN, Bargoed
Postal: **Ffynonau Duon Farm, Pentwyn, Fochriw, Bargoed, Mid-Glamorgan, CF81 9NP**
Contacts: **PHONE (01685) 841259 (08701) 115600 FAX (01685) 843838**
MOBILE (07971) 233473/(07971) 283262
E-MAIL bernard.llewellyn@btopenworld.com

1 AAMAN (IRE), 6, gr g Dubai Destination (USA)—Amellnaa (IRE) **Mr A. James**
2 BAZART, 10, b g Highest Honor (FR)—Summer Exhibition **Mr A. James**
3 BUDVA, 5, b g Kylian (USA)—Danlu (USA) **Mr J. Tucker**
4 CAPTAIN SHARPE, 4, ch g Tobougg (IRE)—Helen Sharp **Bluebirds Racing**
5 DANCEWITHTHEDEVIL (IRE), 11, b br g Dr Massini (IRE)—Hibba (IRE) **T. P. Faulkner**

MR BERNARD LLEWELLYN—continued

6 **DESPERATE TIMES (IRE)**, 7, b g Bishop of Cashel—Midnight Lover **B. J. Llewellyn**
7 **GOLDEN GRAHAM**, 5, b g Grape Tree Road—Star of Love (FR) **T. P. Faulkner**
8 **GREAT SHOW**, 5, ch m Choisir (AUS)—Maple Branch (USA) **P. A. Price**
9 **ILLYSANTACHRISTINA**, 9, b m Parthian Springs—Arian Spirit (IRE) **Mr M. Cohen**
10 **JAMES POLLARD (IRE)**, 7, ch g Indian Ridge—Manuetti (IRE) **B. J. Llewellyn**
11 **KHORUN (GER)**, 7, ch g Lord of Men—Kalata (GER) **Unregistered Partnership**
12 **L FRANK BAUM (IRE)**, 5, b g Sinndar (IRE)—Rainbow City (IRE) **B. J. Llewellyn**
13 **LIGHTENING FIRE (IRE)**, 10, b g Woodborough (USA)—Glowlamp (IRE) **A. J. Williams**
14 **LISSELAN PLEASURE (IRE)**, 5, gr ro m Macho Uno (USA)—Cute Connie (USA) **B. J. Llewellyn**
15 **MR UDAGAWA**, 6, b g Bahamian Bounty—Untold Riches (USA) **B. J. Llewellyn**
16 **PANDORICA**, 4, b f Indesatchel (IRE)—Hope Chest **B. J. Llewellyn**
17 **PENN DA BENN (FR)**, 9, b g Passing Sale (FR)—Gwen Ha Du (FR) **J. T. Warner**
18 **PICOT DE SAY**, 10, b g Largesse—Facsimile **Irish Legend Racing Team**
19 **PIRAN (IRE)**, 10, b g Orpen (USA)—Dancing At Lunasa (IRE) **Welsh Valleys Syndicate No. 2**
20 **RESPLENDENT LIGHT**, 7, b g Fantastic Light (USA)—Bright Halo (IRE) **B. J. Llewellyn**
21 **ROCK PEAK (IRE)**, 7, b g Dalakhani (IRE)—Convenience (IRE) **B. J. Llewellyn**
22 **SALONTYRE (GER)**, 6, b g Pentire—Salonrolle (IRE) **Mr A. James**
23 **SWEET WORLD**, 8, b g Agnes World (USA)—Douce Maison (IRE) **B. J. Llewellyn**
24 **TASTE THE WINE (IRE)**, 6, gr g Verglas (IRE)—Azia (IRE) **A. J. Williams**
25 **TIJORI (IRE)**, 4, b g Kyllachy—Polish Belle **B. J. Llewellyn**
26 **TIMETORING**, 10, ch g Karinga Bay—Little Time **B. J. Llewellyn**
27 **TURBULANCE (IRE)**, 10, gr g Snurge—Full Deck (IRE) **B. J. Llewellyn**
28 **WINE 'N DINE**, 7, b g Rainbow Quest (USA)—Seasonal Splendour (IRE) **Mr A. James**

Other Owners: Dr Simon Clarke, Mr P. M. Evans, Mr S. Harrison, Mr S. W. Hughes, Mr Alex James, Mr B. J. Llewellyn, Mr J. G. Narduzzo.

Assistant Trainer: J L Llewellyn

Jockey (flat): David Probert, Robert Havlin. **Jockey (NH):** Christian Williams. **Amateur:** Mr R. J. Williams.

---

401 **MISS NATALIE LLOYD-BEAVIS, East Garston**
Postal: **2 Parsonage Cottages, Newbury Road, East Garston, Hungerford, Berkshire, RG17 7ER**
Contacts: **PHONE (07768) 117656 MOBILE (07768) 117656**
E-MAIL nlbracing@gmail.com

1 **DUNKELLY CASTLE (IRE)**, 8, ch g Old Vic—Nanna's Joy (IRE) **R. P. Behan**
2 **LET'S BE FAMOUS (IRE)**, 5, b g Indian Danehill (IRE)—Mulligans Fool (IRE) **Mrs M. B. Rowley**
3 **LILY LILY**, 5, b m Efisio—Bel Tempo **Miss N. A. Lloyd-Beavis**
4 **MARCHING ORDERS (IRE)**, 5, b g Rock of Gibraltar (IRE)—Phantom Rain **Mrs Victoria Tett**
5 **MASSAPOAG (IRE)**, 9, b g Bob Back (USA)—Mondeo Rose (IRE) **Mr C. Hetherington**
6 **MEIRIG'S DREAM (IRE)**, 6, b g Golan (IRE)—Women In Love (IRE) **Miss V. Dunn & Mr H. Davies**
7 **MUNICH (IRE)**, 8, b g Noverre (USA)—Mayara (IRE) **Mr S. Lloyd-Beavis**
8 **PEINTRE DU ROI (USA)**, 8, ch g El Prado (IRE)—Peinture Bleue (USA) **Miss N. A. Lloyd-Beavis**

Other Owners: H. J. Davies, Miss V. C. Dunn.

Assistant Trainer: Hywel Davies

Jockey (NH): James Davies. **Apprentice:** Ryan Clark.

---

402 **MR ALAN LOCKWOOD, Malton**
Postal: **Fleet Cross Farm, Brawby, Malton, North Yorkshire, YO17 6QA**
Contacts: **PHONE (01751) 431796 MOBILE (07747) 002535**

1 **BOLLIN FREDDIE**, 8, ch g Golden Snake (USA)—Bollin Roberta **Highgreen Partnership**
2 **PARCHMENT (IRE)**, 10, ch g Singspiel (IRE)—Hannalou (FR) **A. J. Lockwood**
3 **PORT VIEW (IRE)**, 6, b g Classic Cliche (IRE)—Francie's Treble **A. J. Lockwood**
4 **SAXBY (IRE)**, 5, ch g Pastoral Pursuits—Madam Waajib (IRE) **A. J. Lockwood**

Other Owners: J. Richardson, J. Stubbs, D. Wilson.

403   MR JOHN E. LONG, Woldingham

Postal: **Main Yard, Tillingdowns, Woldingham, Caterham, Surrey, CR3 7JA**
Contacts: PHONE **(01883) 340730 MOBILE (07958) 296945/(07815) 186085**
E-MAIL winalot@aol.com

1 AMARONI, 4, b c Sulamani (IRE)—Fortunes Favourite **Advani Family**
2 BRIANNSTA (IRE), 10, b g Bluebird (USA)—Nacote (IRE) **P. R. Saxon**
3 CATIVO CAVALLINO, 9, ch g Bertolini (USA)—Sea Isle **P. R. Saxon**
4 CHANDRAYAAN, 5, ch g Bertolini (USA)—Muffled (USA) **P. R. Saxon**
5 CUSTOM HOUSE (IRE), 4, b g Tale of The Cat (USA)—L'acajou (CAN) **Mr B C Oakley & Mr H Robin Heffer**
6 EFISIO PRINCESS, 9, br m Efisio—Hardiprincess **Miss M. B. Fernandes**
7 ESTEE WILL, 5, ch m Mark of Esteem (IRE)—Irja **Mr T. H. Bambridge**
8 FANTASY FIGHTER (IRE), 7, b g Danetime (IRE)—Lady Montekin **The Fantasy Fellowship F**
9 FOR LIFE (IRE), 10, b g Bachir (IRE)—Zest (USA) **B. C. Oakley**
10 MICROLIGHT, 4, b g Sleeping Indian—Skytrial (USA) **R. D. John**
11 PRINCE BLUE, 5, b g Doyen (IRE)—Dixie d'oats **Downlands Racing**
12 PRINCESS WILLOW, 4, b f Phoenix Reach (IRE)—Highland Hannah (IRE) **Mr & Mrs T H Bambridge**
13 TINKERBELL WILL, 5, ch m Where Or When (IRE)—Highland Hannah (IRE) **Mr & Mrs T H Bambridge**
14 TRUST ME BOY, 4, gr g Avonbridge—Eastern Lyric **R. Pearson & J. Pearson**

TWO-YEAR-OLDS

15 B f 31/3 Ishiguru (USA)—Lefty's Dollbaby (USA) (Brocco (USA)) **Mrs A. M. Sturges**

Other Owners: Mr Vijay Advani, Mr A. Advani, Mrs S. Bambridge, Mr D. Bentley, Mr A. M. Blewitt, Mr Peter Coll, Mr Martin J. Gibbs, Mr H. Robin Heffer, Mr G. G. Margarson, Mr T. H. Bambridge, Mr Brian C. Oakley, Mr R. Pearson, Miss J. Pearson, Mr Mick Robinson, Mrs A. M. Sturges.

Assistant Trainer: Miss S Cassidy

Jockey (flat): Natalia Gemelova, Richard Thomas.

404   MR CHARLIE LONGSDON, Chipping Norton

Postal: **Hull Farm Stables, Stratford Road, Chipping Norton, Oxfordshire, OX7 5QF**
Contacts: PHONE **(08450) 525264 FAX (08450) 525265 MOBILE (07775) 993263**
E-MAIL charlie@charlielongsdonracing.com WEBSITE www.charlielongsdonracing.com

1 ACCORDINTOLAWRENCE (IRE), 6, b g Accordion—Giolldante (IRE) **Soccer AM**
2 AREUWITMENOW (IRE), 7, b g Beneficial—Clonartic (IRE) **Whites of Coventry Limited**
3 BARRISON, 5, gr g Baryshnikov (AUS)—Good Skills **Mrs M. A. Cuff**
4 BASEBALL TED (IRE), 10, b g Beneficial—Lishpower **A. E. Peterson**
5 BE MY LIGHT (IRE), 6, b m Oscar (IRE)—Simply Divine **Foxtrot NH Racing Partnership IV**
6 BROTHER BOB (IRE), 6, b g Robert Emmet—Noon Performance **D. A. Halsall**
7 CASTLETOWN BRIDGE (IRE), 5, ch g Bienamado (USA)—Midnight Orchid (IRE) **Mr T. Hanlon**
8 CHIEF HECKLER (IRE), 6, b g Dushyantor (USA)—Asidewager (IRE) **C. Longsdon**
9 CREDIT FOR LIFE (IRE), 5, b g Zagreb (USA)—Nero's Gem **Hopeful Half Dozen**
10 CROSS OF HONOUR (IRE), 5, ch g Publisher (USA)—Threecrossmammies (IRE) **C. Booth, J. Hughes, C. Longsdon, M. Ogilvy**
11 CRYSTAL PRINCE, 8, b g Marju (IRE)—Crystal Ring (USA) **Bulls & Bears**
12 DAWN COMMANDER (GER), 5, gr g Mamool (IRE)—Dark Lady (GER) **D. A. Halsall**
13 DELAYS EXPECTED (IRE), 10, ch m Presenting—Greavesfind **Killinghurst Park Stud**
14 GETAWAY DRIVER (IRE), 5, br g Zagreb (USA)—Catch The Mouse (IRE) **Catchusifyoucan Partnership**
15 GETMEOUTHEDOLDRUMS, 7, b g Dolpour—Ruby Laser **C. Longsdon**
16 GRANDADS HORSE, 6, b g Bollin Eric—Solid Land (FR) **Whites of Coventry Limited**
17 HAYJACK, 7, b g Karinga Bay—Celtic Native (IRE) **James Hayman-Joyce & HJ Racing**
18 HAZY TOM (IRE), 6, b g Heron Island (IRE)—The Wounded Cook (IRE) **D. A. Halsall**
19 HIDDEN KEEL, 7, gr g Kirkwall—Royal Keel **Mr J. F. Horn & Exors of the Late Mrs M. J. Matthey**
20 HILDISVINI (IRE), 6, b g Milan—Site Mistress (IRE) **J. H. & S. M. Wall**
21 HORACE, 4, b g Hernando (FR)—Ancora (IRE) **Normandie Stud Ltd.**
22 JOLIBOB (IRE), 10, b g Bob's Return (IRE)—Short of A Buck (IRE) **Mrs C. S. Baylis**
23 KINGARRICK, 4, ch g Selkirk (USA)—Rosacara **Miss Y. M. G. Jacques**
24 LADY KARINGA, 7, ch m Karinga Bay—Tachometer (IRE) **Terry Harman & Jan Johnson**
25 LITTLE CHIP (IRE), 5, b g Dushyantor (USA)—Aunt Chris (IRE) **L. Dens (Shipbrokers) Limited**
26 LOOSE CHIPS, 4, b g Sir Harry Lewis (USA)—Worlaby Rose **Barrels Of Courage**
27 MAGNIFIQUE ETOILE, 5, b g Kayf Tara—Star Diva (IRE) **Magnifique Etoile Partnership**
28 MEGZZAMS BOY (IRE), 4, b g Milan—Montanara (IRE) **Nationwide Vehicle Contracts Ltd.**

MR CHARLIE LONGSDON—continued

29 **MINELLA BOYS (IRE)**, 10, br g Bob's Return (IRE)—Ring-Em-All **Miss P. A. Zygmant**
30 **MY MISS LUCY**, 6, b m Alflora (IRE)—Corn Lily **Mrs Susan McDonald**
31 **NEWTON TONIC**, 7, br g Sir Harry Lewis (USA)—Wedidthat (IRE) **J. H. & N. J. Foxon**
32 **NO NO BINGO (IRE)**, 6, b g Craigsteel—Little Anna (IRE) **R. Jenner & J. Green**
33 **OSTLAND (GER)**, 7, b g Lando (GER)—Ost Tycoon (GER) **Mr Richard & Mrs Susan Perkins**
34 **PAINTBALL (IRE)**, 5, b g Le Vie Dei Colori—Camassina (IRE) **D. A. Halsall**
35 **PAMPELONNE (IRE)**, 6, b m Oscar (IRE)—Bondi Storm (IRE) **The Stewkley Shindiggers Partnership**
36 **QHILIMAR (FR)**, 8, b g Ragmar (FR)—Fhilida (FR) **Whites of Coventry & Stephen Dunn**
37 **RAVASTREE (IRE)**, 6, b g Lord Americo—Stonehill Princess (IRE) **Friend Of Greatwood**
38 **RESTEZEN D'ARMOR (FR)**, 7, b g Grand Tresor (FR)—Lafrizen d'armor (FR) **Over Norton**
39 **REY NACARADO (IRE)**, 7, b g Posidonas—Ice Pearl **Runthatbymeagainagain**
40 **ROSSMORE LAD (IRE)**, 7, b br g Beneficial—Celestial Rose (IRE) **T. P. Bostwick**
41 **SPANISH CRUISE (IRE)**, 8, gr g Daylami (USA)—Baldemara (FR) **The Chosen Few**
42 **SPIRIT OF SHANKLY**, 4, ch g Sulamani (IRE)—Lago d'oro **C. Longsdon**
43 **STEALING THE LINE (IRE)**, 5, ch g Presenting—Kilkea (IRE) **The Hunting Partnership**
44 **STRONGBOWS LEGEND**, 7, ch g Midnight Legend—Miss Crabapple **Box A45**
45 **TATISPOUT (FR)**, 5, b m Califet (FR)—Larmonie (FR) **Mrs S. B. Lockhart**
46 **TIME FOR SPRING**, 8, b g Snurge—Burksie (IRE) **MacEchern, Pottinger, Badcock**
47 **TOPAZE COLLONGES (FR)**, 5, gr g Dom Alco (FR)—Flicka Collonges (FR) **No Boys Allowed**
48 **TRAFALGAR ROAD (IRE)**, 8, b g Bob's Return (IRE)—Call Catherine (IRE) **D. A. Halsall**
49 **UP TO SOMETHING (FR)**, 4, b g Brier Creek (USA)—Evane (FR) **E. M. G. Roberts**
50 **VINCITORE (FR)**, 6, b g Starborough—Viva Vodka (FR) **The Veni, Vidi, Vici Partnership**
51 **VULCANITE (IRE)**, 5, b g Dubawi (IRE)—Daraliya (IRE) **Pearl Bloodstock Limited**
52 **WEST BRIT (IRE)**, 4, b g High Chaparral (IRE)—Aldburgh **Mr T. Hanlon**
53 **WIDE RECEIVER (IRE)**, 9, b g Taipan (IRE)—The Plud (IRE) **Girls Allowed**
54 **WILD DESERT (FR)**, 7, b br g Desert Prince (IRE)—Sallivera (IRE) **Whites of Coventry & Stephen Dunn**
55 **WILLOW'S SAVIOUR**, 5, ch g Septieme Ciel (USA)—Willow Gale **Triple F Partnership**

Other Owners: Mr D. Abraham, Mr N. B. Attenborough, Mr Clive Badcock, Mr Oliver Battersby, Mr C. J. Booth, Mr G. A. Bosley, Mr R. T. Burns, Mrs P. M. Colson, Mr A. E. Connor, Mrs Margaret Cuff, Mr S. W. Dunn, Mr H. Fentum, Mr J. H. Foxon, Mrs N. J. Foxon, Mr Mark Goodall, Mrs J. Green, Mrs L. I. Greenlees, Mr J. N. Greenley, Mr M. W. Gregory, Mr J. E. Hall, Mr Terry Harman, Mr R. D. Hawkins, Mr James Hayman-Joyce, Mrs Lottie Hayman-Joyce, Mr W. John Henderson, Mrs H. J. Hoffman, Mr John F. Horn, Mr Jon Hughes, Mr Rob Jackson, Ms R. Jenner, Mrs Jan Johnson, Mrs Louise King, Mrs K. Knott, Mrs Sarah Jane Lavan, Mr Charlie Longsdon, Mrs S Longsdon, Mr Gavin MacEchern, Mr C. Marriott, Exors of the Late Mrs M. J. Matthey, Mr C. McFadden, Mr R. D. Nicholas, Dr M. M. Ogilvy, Mrs H. Pauling, Mrs Penny Perriss, Mr P. J. D. Pottinger, Mr Adam Signy, Mr S. Spencer-Jones, Mrs S. Spencer-Jones, Mr R. Stainer, Mr John Studd, Exors of the Late Mrs B. M. Studd, Mr Christopher Vine, Mr J. S. Wall, Mrs S. M. Wall, Whites of Coventry Limited, Mr Richard Wilkin.

405 MR DANIEL MARK LOUGHNANE, Butterton
Postal: **10 Appleton Drive, Whitmore, Newcastle-Under-Lyme, Staffordshire, ST5 5BT**

1 **ARDERIN (IRE)**, 7, b g Accordion—Killoughy Fairy (IRE) **Mr M. P. Lambe**
2 **FIRST IN COMMAND (IRE)**, 7, b g Captain Rio—Queen Sigi (IRE) **Mrs C. M. Loughnane**
3 **HEAD OF THE RIVER (IRE)**, 8, b g Galileo (IRE)—Vignelaure (IRE)
4 **HONEST STRIKE (USA)**, 5, b g Smart Strike (CAN)—Honest Lady (USA) **M. V. Kirby**
5 **LISCAHILL KARELLA (IRE)**, 10, ch g Pistolet Bleu (IRE)—Liscahill Breeze (IRE) **Mrs C. M. Loughnane**
6 **MONADREEN DANCER**, 4, b f Kheleyf (USA)—Volitant **Mrs C. M. Loughnane**
7 **YOURINTHEWILL**, 4, ch g Aragorn (IRE)—Lenarue (USA) **Mrs C. M. Loughnane**

THREE-YEAR-OLDS

8 **FOR SHIA AND LULA (IRE)**, b g Majestic Missile (IRE)—Jack-N-Jilly (IRE) **M. V. Kirby**
9 **SOURCE OF LIGHT (IRE)**, b f Diamond Green (FR)—Alycus (USA)
10 **SPEEDY YAKI (IRE)**, b c Refuse To Bend (IRE)—Love In The Mist (USA) **Mrs C. M. Loughnane**

406 MR SHAUN LYCETT, Bourton-On-The-Water
Postal: **3 Broadmoor Cottage, Nr Clapton-On-The-Hill, Bourton-On-The-Water, Gloucestershire, GL54 2LQ**
Contacts: PHONE (01451) 824143 MOBILE (07788) 100894
E-MAIL trainer@bourtonhillracing.co.uk WEBSITE www.bourtonhillracing.co.uk

1 **ALL THE WINDS (GER)**, 7, ch g Samum (GER)—All Our Luck (GER) **Nicholls Family**
2 **DIXIE CASE (IRE)**, 7, b g Close Conflict (USA)—Rashaga (IRE) **R. Nicholls**

MR SHAUN LYCETT—continued

3 **FADE TO GREY (IRE)**, 8, gr g Aljabr (USA)—Aly McBear (USA) **Worcester Racing Club**
4 **HACKETT (IRE)**, 4, b c Hawk Wing (USA)—Khudud **M. Quinn**
5 **HALDIBARI (IRE)**, 8, b g Kahyasi—Haladiya (IRE) **Nicholls Family**
6 **IRONICAL (IRE)**, 8, b g Bob's Return (IRE)—Cheryls Pet (IRE) **Lady Blyth**
7 **LADY HANNAH**, 7, b m Muhtarram (USA)—Piracy **Mr C. D. Rogers**
8 **THE WINGED ASSASIN (USA)**, 6, b g Fusaichi Pegasus (USA)—Gran Dama (USA) **Mr A. R. James**
9 **TINELYRA (IRE)**, 6, b g Mr Combustible (IRE)—Ladyogan (IRE) **Mr M. Costello**
10 **VINOMORE**, 6, b m Grape Tree Road—Sillymore **Rupert Dubai Racing**
11 **WEAPON OF WAR (IRE)**, 8, ro g Alderbrook—Nagillah (IRE)

Other Owners: M. P. Hill, S. Hunt, Mr R. Nicholls, Mrs E. Nicholls, T. C. Stayt.

Amateur: Mr Jonathan England.

407
MR G. M. LYONS, Dunsany
Postal: **Glenburnie Stables, Kiltale, Dunsany, Co. Meath, Ireland**
Contacts: **PHONE (00353) 46 9025666 FAX (00353) 46 9026364 MOBILE (00353) 86 8502439
E-MAIL ger@gerlyons.ie or office@gerlyons.ie WEBSITE www.gerlyons.ie**

1 **BOOM TO BUST (IRE)**, 4, br g Big Bad Bob (IRE)—Forever Phoenix **Anamoine Ltd**
2 **BUCCANEER BOB (IRE)**, 4, b g Big Bad Bob (IRE)—Cosmic Speed Queen (USA) **Anamoine Ltd**
3 **JOE EILE (IRE)**, 4, b g Iffraaj—Encouragement **H B Syndicate**
4 **PRESCIENT (IRE)**, 4, b f Invincible Spirit (IRE)—Littlefeather **Miss A. H. Marshall**
5 **RED ARMY BLUES (IRE)**, 4, b g Soviet Star (USA)—Liscoa (IRE) **Mr S. Jones**
6 **SHISHA THREESIXTY (IRE)**, 4, b g High Chaparral (IRE)—Nicene (USA) **Mr D. Nolan**
7 **SOLENT RIDGE**, 7, br g Namid—Carrozzina **Mr C. Dineen**
8 **SUPERCHARGED (IRE)**, 4, b f Iffraaj—Glympse (IRE) **Mr D. Maher**
9 **TARRSILLE (IRE)**, 6, b g Dansili—Tara Gold (IRE) **Eugene Blaney**
10 **THE REAPER (IRE)**, 4, b g Footstepsinthesand—Lady Gregory (IRE) **Mr S. Jones**
11 **THE RESISTANCE (IRE)**, 4, b g Encosta de Lago (AUS)—Cordelia **Mr S. Jones**
12 **UNION CITY BLUES (IRE)**, 4, ch f Encosta de Lago (AUS)—Child Prodigy (IRE) **Mr S. Jones**

THREE-YEAR-OLDS

13 B g Sleeping Indian—Berkeley Note (IRE)
14 **BIBLE BLACK (IRE)**, br g Big Bad Bob (IRE)—Convent Girl (IRE) **Anamoine Ltd**
15 **BRENDAN BRACKAN (IRE)**, b g Big Bad Bob (IRE)—Abeyr **Anamoine Ltd**
16 **BURN THE BOATS (IRE)**, br g Big Bad Bob (IRE)—Forever Phoenix **Anamoine Ltd**
17 **BURNIE BRAES (IRE)**, b c Moss Vale (IRE)—Etica (IRE) **Mr S. Jones**
18 **CHOCOLATE HILLS (FR)**, b f Exceed And Excel (AUS)—Rawabi **H.H. Sheikh Mohammed Al Maktoum**
19 **CHOICE PEARL (USA)**, b br f Any Given Saturday (USA)—Horns Gray (USA) **Pearl Bloodstock**
20 **FLUIDITY**, ch g Pastoral Pursuits—Pips Way (IRE) **Mr V. Gaul**
21 **GREEK CANYON (IRE)**, b g Moss Vale (IRE)—Lazaretta (IRE) **Mr S. Jones**
22 **HURRICANE HUGO (IRE)**, b g Hurricane Run (IRE)—All Time Great **Mr S. Jones**
23 **JAMMING (IRE)**, b g Jeremy (USA)—Perfect Sound (FR) **Mrs L. Lyons**
24 **KASHMIR PEAK (IRE)**, b g Tiger Hill (GER)—Elhareer (USA) **Mr S. Jones**
25 **KING'S WARRANT (IRE)**, b c King's Best (USA)—Ask Annie (IRE) **Miss A. H. Marshall**
26 **LIGHTENING PEARL (IRE)**, b f Marju (IRE)—Jioconda (IRE) **Pearl Bloodstock**
27 **MOUNT MERU**, b g Red Clubs (IRE)—Shangazi (USA) **Mr S. Jones**
28 **OH SO LUCY (IRE)**, b f Galileo (IRE)—Miss Beatrix (IRE) **Durkan Bloodstock Ltd**
29 **PC HENRY**, b g Ishiguru (USA)—Elhida (IRE) **Mr R. Pegum**
30 **PIRI WANGO (IRE)**, ch g Choisir (AUS)—Zoldan **Mr D. Spratt**
31 **SHUKHOV (IRE)**, b g Ivan Denisovich (IRE)—Just One Smile (USA) **Mr S. Jones**
32 **STRADA COLORATO (IRE)**, b g Le Vie Dei Colori—Goodwood March **Mr S. Jones**
33 **THE KERNIGAL (IRE)**, b g Red Clubs (IRE)—Ellens Princess (IRE) **Mr S. Jones**
34 **THUNDER MOON (IRE)**, b g Authorized (IRE)—Calico Moon (USA) **Mr S. Jones**
35 **ZERMATT (IRE)**, ch g Strategic Prince—Await (IRE) **Mr S. Jones**

TWO-YEAR-OLDS

36 B c 4/4 Captain Marvelous (IRE)—Answer Do (Groom Dancer (USA)) **Mr C. Dineen**
37 B f 20/2 Oasis Dream—Athlumney Lady (Lycius (USA)) **Miss A. H. Marshall**
38 B c 16/3 Oratorio (IRE)—Balamiyda (IRE) (Ashkalani (IRE)) (34481) **Pearl Bloodstock**
39 B f 7/4 Cape Cross (IRE)—Barring Order (IRE) (Barathea (IRE)) **Miss A. H. Marshall**
40 B c 4/4 Kodiac—Bundle of Joy (IRE) (Golan (IRE)) (20000) **Mr S. Jones**
41 B c 2/4 Kodiac—Catch A Smile (USA) (Silver Hawk (USA)) (14778) **Mr S. Jones**

MR G. M. LYONS—continued

42 B c 2/5 Excellent Art—Chameleon (Green Desert (USA)) (13136) **Mr C. Dineen**
43 B c 20/4 Moss Vale (IRE)—Cloonkeary (In The Wings) (14285) **Mr V. Gaul**
44 Ch c 15/2 Sakhee's Secret—First Fantasy (Be My Chief) (32840)
45 B c 30/1 King's Best (USA)—Gamma (FR) (Sadler's Wells (USA)) (20000) **Mr S. Jones**
46 B c 9/3 Moss Vale (IRE)—Jersey Lillie (IRE) (Hector Protector (USA)) (14285) **Mr D. Nolan**
47 Gr ro c 29/3 Verglas (IRE)—Jinxy Jill (Royal Applause) (9851) **Mr D. Nolan**
48 B c 19/5 Zamindar (USA)—Kythia (IRE) (Kahyasi) (15000) **Mr S. Jones**
49 B c 14/3 Street Sense (USA)—
　　　　　　　　　Make My Heart Sing (USA) (King of Kings (IRE)) **H.H. Sheikh Mohammed Al Maktoum**
50 B c 11/3 Notnowcato—Marias Magic (Mtoto) (18000) **Mr S. Jones**
51 B c 22/3 Sir Percy—Mrs Brown (Royal Applause) (22000) **Mr S. Jones**
52 B f 22/3 Teofilo (IRE)—My (King's Best (USA)) (50000) **H.H. Sheikh Mohammed Al Maktoum**
53 B c 5/4 Henrythenavigator (USA)—Mythical Echo (Stravinsky (USA)) (46000) **Mr S. Jones**
54 Ch c 7/3 Giant's Causeway (USA)—Northern Mischief (USA) (Yankee Victor (USA)) (80000) **Pearl Bloodstock**
55 B br c 29/1 Curlin (USA)—Peak Maria's Way (USA) (Pyramid Peak) (33577) **Pearl Bloodstock**
56 Ch c 22/4 Bertolini (USA)—Questama (Rainbow Quest (USA)) (9440) **Mr S. Jones**
57 Ch c 8/5 Danehill Dancer (IRE)—Rain Flower (IRE) (Indian Ridge) (30377) **Mr S. Jones**
58 Ch c 7/5 Pastoral Pursuits—Raindrop (Primo Dominie) (30000) **Mr V. Gaul**
59 B f 28/2 Cape Cross (IRE)—Recite (JPN) (Forty Niner (USA)) **Miss A. H. Marshall**
60 B c 17/3 Lawman (FR)—Requested Pleasure (Rainbow Quest (USA)) (31198) **Mr S. Jones**
61 Ch c 25/4 Excellent Art—Romancing (Dr Devious (IRE)) (18882) **Mr S. Jones**
62 B f 19/3 Bernardini (USA)—Turn Me Loose (Kris S (USA)) (137362) **Pearl Bloodstock**
63 B c 3/2 Kheleyf (USA)—Windbeneathmywings (IRE) (In The Wings) (33597) **Mr S. Jones**
64 B c 30/3 Cape Cross (IRE)—Yaria (IRE) (Danehill (USA)) (40000) **Pearl Bloodstock**
65 B br c 16/3 Footstepsinthesand—Zawariq (IRE) (Marju (IRE)) (37766) **Mr S. Jones**

Jockey (flat): Niall McCullagh, Johnny Murtagh. **Apprentice:** Gary Philips, Megan Carberry, Samantha Wynne. **Amateur:** Mr Andrew Duff.

408　MR GUILLAUME MACAIRE, Les Mathes
Postal: Hippodrome de la Palmyre, 17570 Les Mathes, France
Contacts: PHONE (0033) 5462 36254 FAX (0033) 5462 25438 MOBILE (0033) 6076 54992
E-MAIL entrainement-g.macaire@wanadoo.fr WEBSITE www.guillaume-macaire.com

1 **BALKAN HERO**, 4, b g Turgeon—Aubane **Mrs P. Papot**
2 **BLONDE VIRGINIA (FR)**, 4, b f Kapgarde (FR)—Sweet Jaune (FR) **Mr. G. Le Baron**
3 **COEUR DES AS**, 4, b g Kahyasi—Valbonne **Mr E. Van Haaren**
4 **D'ARTAGNAN (GER)**, 4, b c Doyen (IRE)—Dawn Dane (FR) **Mr S. Swarc**
5 **DAME DE GUERRE**, 4, b f Balko—Kamailya **SCEA Ecurie Sagara**
6 **FAGO (FR)**, 4, b g Balko—Merciki **Mr G. Blain**
7 **FAISSI FAISSI**, 4, gr g Saint des Saints—Jolie Lili **Mr J. Detre**
8 **INTO VINCERES (GER)**, 4, b g Sholokhov (IRE)—Iaskre (GER) **Mr P. Moinier**
9 **INVINCIBLE DANCER**, 4, b g Invincible Spirit—Smala Tica **Mr G. Gilles**
10 **KALIPSIS (FR)**, 4, b g Apsis—Kaldona (FR) **Mr S. Munir**
11 **LADY PASCALINE (FR)**, 4, b f Poliglotte—Lady Dancer **Mr G. Morosini**
12 **LE GRAND BABU**, 4, b g Balko—Maelis **Mr J-M. Reillier**
13 **LE SHOCK (GER)**, 5, b g Sholokhov (IRE)—La Blue (GER) **Mrs M. Bryant**
14 **LUNATORIO (FR)**, 4, b g Oratorio (IRE)—Lunaba (FR) **Mrs M. Bryant**
15 **MICHTO**, 4, b g Balko—Elenou **Mr J. Detre**
16 **MONPILOU (FR)**, 5, b g Saint Des Saints—Gavotte De Brejoux **Mr J. Detre**
17 **PRINCE DES GABIERS (FR)**, 5, ch g Ballingarry (IRE)—Belle Maison (FR) **Ecurie Jaeckin**
18 **RIO ATHENAS (FR)**, 5, b m Kaldou Star—Rio Amata (GER) **Mrs E. Van Haaren**
19 **ROI DE TREVE**, 4, gr g Martaline—Dame de Treve **Mr S. Munir**
20 **SOLEIL VERT (FR)**, 4, b g Green Tune (USA)—Mensa Sonne (FR) **Ecurie Sagara**
21 **TADZIO (FR)**, 5, b g Dom Alco (FR)—Formosa (FR) **Mr S. Munir**
22 **TOUT ROUGE**, 5, b g Dom Alco—Loi Du Plus Fort **Mr S. Munir**
23 **UCELLO CONTI (FR)**, 4, b g Martaline—Gazelle Lulu (FR) **Mr P. Joubert**
24 **UMIRO (FR)**, 5, b g Doyen (IRE)—Ulanowa (GER) **Mr P. Blazy**
25 **UNATOU D'ESTRUVAL**, 4, b g Discover D'auteuil—Heure D'estruval **Mrs B. Le Gentil**
26 **UNE DE CIERGUES (FR)**, 4, gr f Dom Alco (FR)—Java de Ciergues (FR) **Mr D. Galt**
27 **UNIONISTE (FR)**, 4, gr g Alberto Giacometti (IRE)—Gleep Will (FR) **Haras de Saint Voir**
28 **UNITED PARK**, 4, b g Antarctique—Goldoulyssa **Mr T. Amos**
29 **UNO D'ESTRUVAL**, 4, b g Nononito—Dune D'estruval **Mrs B. Le Gentil**
30 **UPSILON BLEU (FR)**, 4, b g Panoramic—Glycine Bleue (FR) **Mr S. Munir**
31 **URAK**, 4, b g Protektor—Galvanie **Mr J. Robin**

MR GUILLAUME MACAIRE—continued

32 **URBI D'ESTRUVAL**, 4, b g Martaline—Onde D'estruval **Mrs B. Le Gentil**
33 **URFE D'ESTRUVAL (FR)**, 4, b f Martaline—Mome d'estruval (FR) **Mrs B. Le Gentil**
34 **URGENCE D'ESTRUVAL**, 4, b f Enrique—Perle d'estruval **Mme B. Le Gentil**
35 **URSULO DU RIB**, 4, ch g Kapgarde—Petite Shabby **Ecurie Rib**
36 **URVE BRUERE (FR)**, 4, b g Kapgarde (FR)—Hervine Bruere (FR) **Mrs M. Bryant**
37 **USER ET ABUSER (FR)**, 4, ch f Trempolino (USA)—Flower des Champs (FR) **Haras de Saint Voir**
38 **UTO**, 4, b g Bering—Nouvelle Zelande **Mr J. Detre**
39 **UZES D'ESTRUVAL (FR)**, 4, b f Forestier (FR)—Kermesse d'estruval (FR) **Mrs B. Le Gentil**

THREE-YEAR-OLDS

40 **A CUERPO LIMPIO**, b g Sholokhov—Al Shuura **Mr J. Bisson**
41 **ABAKAHN**, b g Sholokhov—Albula **Ecurie Sagara**
42 **ALEXANDRA SIX**, b g Robin Des Champs—Karmiva **Mr R. Fougedoire**
43 **ALOARA (FR)**, b c Great Pretender (IRE)—Sainte Lea (FR) **Mr T. Amos**
44 **AMOUR DU PUY NOIR**, b g Ballingary—Virosa **Mr J. Detre**
45 **ANNAKOV (GER)**, b g Sholokhov (IRE)—Anna Diana (GER) **Ecurie Jaeckin**
46 **CAPITEUX**, b g Kapgarde—Rouge Folie **Mr R. Fougedoire**
47 **CHUTIQUETTA (FR)**, b f Gold Away (IRE)—Vitrolles (USA) **Mrs P. Papot**
48 **CLASSIC DIVA (GER)**, b f Sholokhov (IRE)—Classic Cara (GER) **Ecurie Jaeckin**
49 **DECURION**, b g Sholokhov—Deborah **Mr R. Fougedoire**
50 **ELOGIEUX**, b g Kapgarde—Visite Princiere **Mr R. Fougedoire**
51 **FATALITE (FR)**, b f Victory Note (USA)—Incorrigible (FR) **Ecure de L'Hexagone**
52 **FINORO (GER)**, b g Sholokhov (IRE)—Finora (GER) **Mrs P. Papot**
53 **FLOGAROSE**, ch f Bonbon Rose—Rosala **Mr F. Fernandes**
54 **GET YOUR WAY**, b f Kapgarde—Bibelle **Mrs P. Papot**
55 **GORVELLO**, b g Poliglote—Rolandale **Mrs P. Papot**
56 **HOTAL CALIFORNIA (FR)**, b f Loup Solitaire (USA)—Madame Extra (FR) **Eurl du Chene**
57 **IRISH BOY**, b g Irish Wells—Savita **Mr J. Detre**
58 **JAVIRCO (FR)**, b g Lavirco (GER)—Junta (FR) **Mrs P. Papot**
59 **KAPTAINE (FR)**, b c Turgeon (USA)—Kaprika (FR) **Mr F. Picoulet**
60 **KAYAGUA**, b f Kahyasi—Acancagua **Mr F. Picoulet**
61 **LOFTE PLACE**, b f Poliglote—Queen Place **Mrs M-C. Tyssandier**
62 **LOTTIE BELLE**, b g Kapgarde—Hunorisk **Mr J. Cotton**
63 **MANJANO**, b g Sholokhov—Maja **Ecurie Sagara**
64 **MEGALYPOS (FR)**, b g Limnos (JPN)—Bourbonnaise (FR) **Mr J. Bisson**
65 **MY FAIR LADY**, b f Poliglote—Royale The Best **Mrs M-C. Tyssandier**
66 **NOTARIO HAS (FR)**, b g Turgeon (USA)—Noria des Bordes (FR) **Mr S. Munir**
67 **OTTOSTAR**, b g Sholokhov (IRE)—Omicenta (IRE) **Ecurie Jaeckin**
68 **PISTOLET JAUNE**, ch g Maille Pistol—Sweet Jaune **Mr R. Fougedoire**
69 **QUEL PLAISIR**, b g Act One—Pleasuring **Mr S. Munir**
70 **ROCKBURN**, b f Saint Des Saints—Segre **Mrs P. Papot**
71 **SAHYAP**, b g Kahyasi—Tulipe Boire **Ecurie Sagara**
72 **SAINT DE GARDE (FR)**, b g Saint des Saints (FR)—Balgarde (FR) **Mr S. Munir**
73 **SAINTE ECALINE**, b f Saint Des Saints—Ecaline **Mr J. Andt**
74 **SAINTE ROQUE**, b f Saint Des Saints—Bible Gun **Mrs R. Mongin**
75 **SAMETEGAL**, b g Saints Des Saints—Loya Lescribaa **Mr P. de Maleisssye**
76 **SANTALINE**, ch f Fragrant Mix—Stenoree **Mr J. Andt**
77 **SIRENE JO**, b f Irish Wells—Une Sainte **Mrs P. Papot**
78 **STORM OF SAINTLY**, b g Saint Des Saints—The Storm **Mr J. Andt**
79 **SUERTE PARA TODOS**, ch g Kapgarde—Hever Rose **Mr P. de Maleisssye**
80 **SUITE A COEUR**, b f Great Pretender—Nouvelle Donne **Mr R. Fougedoire**
81 **TARQUINO (FR)**, ch c Kapgarde (FR)—Osmose (FR) **Mrs P. Papot**
82 **TIBERIUS (GER)**, b g Sholokhov (IRE)—Trinidad (GER) **Mr R. Fougedoire**
83 **TRAPRAIN**, gr g Turgeon—Paola Pierji **Mr R. A. Green**
84 **UNTIL PASS (FR)**, ch g Until Sundown (USA)—Fuela Pass (FR) **Ecurie de L'Hexagone**
85 **VAILLANCE**, b f Epalo—Bertruge **Mr R. Fougedoire**
86 **VANIKA PLACE**, ch f Kapgarde—Okawanga Royale **Mrs B. Gabeur**
87 **VANILLA CRUSH (FR)**, b g Martaline—Latitude (FR) **Mrs P. Papot**
88 **VATULELE**, b g Lavirco—Nouvelle Zelande **Mr J. Detre**
89 **VAUDAIRE**, b f Astarabad (USA)—Miss Academy (FR) **Mrs J. Shalam**
90 **VAUTOUR**, b g Robin Des Champs—Gazelle de Mai **Haras de St Voir**
91 **VEILLE AU GRAIN**, ch f Dom Alco—Flower Des Champs **Haras de Saint Voir**
92 **VELEHA (FR)**, b f Saint des Saints (FR)—Ellapampa (FR) **Mrs M. Bryant**
93 **VERTIGE DE COTTE (FR)**, ch g Epalo (GER)—Pensee de Cotte (FR) **Mrs J-M. Robin**
94 **VICE ROI GEORGES**, b g Assessor—Jack Line **Ecurie de L'Hexagone**

MR GUILLAUME MACAIRE—continued

95 **VINGT DIEUX (FR)**, b g Robin des Champs (FR)—Ribalina (FR) **Mr J-P. Moutafian**
96 **VISION DES CHAMPS**, b g Saint Des Saints—Manita Des Champs **Mr J. Detre**
97 **VIVALKO**, ch g Balko—Magenta **Mr R. Fougedoire**
98 **VOLCAN D'AINAY**, ch g Epalo—Etoile D'ainay **Mrs P. Papot**
99 **VOSTOK (FR)**, b g Lavirco (GER)—Falkland III (FR) **Mr J. Detre**
100 **VOTEZ POUR MOI**, b g Sacro Saint—Biblique **Haras de St Voir**
101 **VUELTA DE CAMPANA**, b f Kapgarde—Kountrissime **Mrs J-M. Robin**
102 **VULPIO**, b g Assessor—Oblia **Palmyr Racing**

Jockey (NH): Jacques Ricou, Bertrand Lestrade, Hector De Lageneste, Steven Le Vot. **Conditional:** Derek McCormack.

409
MR R. MACDONALD, Hawick
Postal: **Midburn Farm Cottage, Hawick, Roxburghshire, TD9 9SD**
Contacts: **PHONE (01450) 860724 MOBILE (07921) 317692**
E-MAIL **midburnracingstables@hotmail.co.uk**

1 **GOLDEN EMPEROR (IRE)**, 5, ro gr g Antonius Pius (USA)—Lily Shing Shang **R. MacDonald**
2 **KIT CARSON (IRE)**, 12, b g Dr Massini (IRE)—Roses Niece (IRE) **Mrs M. A. MacDonald**
3 **STEADYS BREEZE**, 8, b m Nomadic Way (USA)—Willies Witch **R. MacDonald**
4 **THE DUNION**, 9, br g Beckett (IRE)—Dacian (USA) **Mrs M. A. MacDonald**
5 **WOR LASS**, 4, br f And Beyond (IRE)—Patience Please **Mrs M. A. MacDonald**

Assistant Trainer: Les Dodds

Jockey (NH): Campbell Gillies, Brian Hughes. **Conditional:** Gary Rutherford.

410
MR JOHN MACKIE, Church Broughton
Postal: **The Bungalow, Barton Blount, Church Broughton, Derby, Derbyshire, DE65 5AN**
Contacts: **PHONE (01283) 585604/585603 FAX (01283) 585603 MOBILE (07799) 145283**
E-MAIL **jmackie@bartonblount.freeserve.co.uk** WEBSITE **www.johnmackieracing.co.uk**

1 **AEGEAN DESTINY**, 5, b m Beat Hollow—Starlist **Derbyshire Racing III**
2 **ARIZONA JOHN (IRE)**, 7, b g Rahy (USA)—Preseli (IRE) **Derbyshire Racing**
3 **CORAL COVE**, 7, b g Karinga Bay—Herself **Mrs S. P. Adams**
4 **DART**, 8, br m Diktat—Eilean Shona **The Caroline Lawson and Sarah Underwood**
5 **GUGA (IRE)**, 6, b g Rock of Gibraltar (IRE)—Attitre (FR) **Mrs E. M. Mackie**
6 **HALLSTATT (IRE)**, 6, ch g Halling (USA)—Last Resort **Mr A. B. Hill**
7 **ILLUSTRIOUS FOREST**, 4, ch g Shinko Forest (IRE)—Illustre Inconnue (USA) **Derbyshire Racing VII**
8 **KNIGHT IN PURPLE**, 8, b g Sir Harry Lewis (USA)—Cerise Bleue (FR) **A J Wall, G Hicks & N Hooper**
9 **LAYLA'S BOY**, 5, ch g Sakhee (USA)—Gay Romance **RJM Racing**
10 **MILL MICK**, 5, b g Karinga Bay—Step On Degas **Mr M. T. Bloore & Mrs J. E. Lockwood**
11 **NEUTRAFA (IRE)**, 4, ch f Araafa (IRE)—Neutrina (IRE) **Mr J. A. Ashley**
12 **RIVER PURPLE**, 5, b g Bollin Eric—Cerise Bleue (FR) **Sotby Farming Company Limited**
13 **SAINT THOMAS (IRE)**, 5, b g Alhaarth (IRE)—Aguilas Perla (IRE) **P. Riley**
14 **SCOURIE BAY**, 5, b g Needwood Blade—Impish Jude **J. W. H. Fryer**
15 **SHEMP**, 6, b g Mtoto—Shearwater **G. B. Maher**
16 **SKY DIAMOND (IRE)**, 4, b g Diamond Green (FR)—Jewell In The Sky (IRE) **W. I. Bloomfield**
17 **THE BANANA MAN**, 7, b g Classic Cliche (IRE)—Marlands **Mrs D. E. Watson**
18 **VANILLA RUM**, 5, b g Reset (AUS)—Snoozy **Derbyshire Racing VI**
19 **VIZEAN (IRE)**, 4, b f Medicean—Viz (IRE) **Mr J. A. Ashley**

THREE-YEAR-OLDS

20 **BRIDAL MEDIC**, ch g Medicean—Bridal Path **Mr J. A. Ashley**
21 **CHELSEA MEDIC**, b c Hawk Wing (USA)—Chelsey Jayne (IRE) **Mr J. A. Ashley**
22 **MIGHTY MOTIVE**, ch c Motivator—Mitraillette (USA) **Mr J. A. Ashley**

Other Owners: S. P. Adams, M. A. Bates, M. T. Bloore, Mr G. B. Hicks, Mr N. P. Hooper, Mrs J. E. L. Lockwood, Mr R. E. Milner, NSU Leisure Ltd, Mr D. R. Penman, A. J. Wall.

411 MR ALAN MACTAGGART, Hawick
Postal: **Wells, Denholm, Hawick, Roxburghshire, TD9 8TD**
Contacts: **PHONE (01450) 870060 MOBILE (07711) 200445**

1 **HARD TO NAME,** 9, b g Beat All (USA)—Hobbs Choice **Mrs A. H. Mactaggart**
2 **ROYAL MACKINTOSH,** 11, b g Sovereign Water (FR)—Quick Quote **A. H. Mactaggart**

Assistant Trainer: Mrs M A Mactaggart

412 MR BRUCE MACTAGGART, Hawick
Postal: **Greendale, Hawick, Roxburghshire, TD9 7LH**
Contacts: **PHONE/FAX (01450) 372086 MOBILE (07764) 159852/(07718) 920072**
E-MAIL brucemct@btinternet.co.uk

1 **CASSIUS (IRE),** 10, b g Pistolet Bleu (IRE)—L'enfant Unique (IRE) **Mrs Hilary Mactaggart & John R Elgin**
2 7, B g Winged Love (IRE)—Cavalry **B. MacTaggart**
3 **CRAICNEASY (IRE),** 9, br g Anshan—Craic Go Leor **Harlequin Racing**
4 **HANSOMIS (IRE),** 8, b m Titus Livius (FR)—Handsome Anna (IRE) **Corsby Racing**
5 **LADIES PRIDE (IRE),** 7, ch m Anshan—Craic Go Leor **W. B. MacTaggart**
6 **RED TANBER (IRE),** 9, ch g Karinga Bay—Dreamy Desire **Hugh T. Redhead**
7 **STEEL MAN (IRE),** 10, b g Anshan—One Edge (IRE) **B. MacTaggart**

THREE-YEAR-OLDS

8 B f King's Theatre (IRE)—Friendly Craic (IRE) **W. B. MacTaggart**

TWO-YEAR-OLDS

9 B f 11/5 Flemensfirth (USA)—Water Stratford (IRE) (Jurado (USA)) **W. B. MacTaggart**

Other Owners: Mr J. R. Elgin, Mrs Frances Godson, Mr R. N. Ker-Ramsay, Mrs Hilary Mactaggart, Mr J. R. Williams.

Assistant Trainer: Mrs H Mactaggart

Jockey (NH): Graham Lee.

413 MR PETER MADDISON, Skewsby
Postal: **5 West End Cottages, Skewsby, York, YO61 4SG**
Contacts: **PHONE (01347) 888385**

1 **BATTLEDANCER,** 6, b g Baryshnikov (AUS)—Cede Nullis **P. Maddison**
2 **MINDEN MARCH,** 7, b m Baryshnikov (AUS)—Minden Rose **P. Maddison**

Jockey (NH): Robert Walford.

414 MR MICHAEL MADGWICK, Denmead
Postal: **Forest Farm, Forest Road, Denmead, Waterlooville, Hampshire, PO7 6UA**
Contacts: **PHONE/FAX (02392) 258313 MOBILE (07835) 964969**

1 **BEAUBRAV,** 6, b g Falbrav (IRE)—Wavy Up (IRE) **The B B Partnership**
2 **COMEDY HOUSE,** 4, b g Auction House (USA)—Kyle Akin **M. J. Madgwick**
3 **DICHOH,** 9, b g Diktat—Hoh Dancer **M. J. Madgwick**
4 **RAY DIAMOND,** 7, ch g Medicean—Musical Twist (USA) **Mrs L. N. Harmes**
5 **SHANTOU BREEZE (IRE),** 5, b m Shantou (USA)—Homersmare (IRE) **M. J. Madgwick**
6 **WARBOND,** 4, ch g Monsieur Bond (IRE)—Pick A Nice Name **I. M. McGready**
7 **WHERE'S SUSIE,** 7, ch m Where Or When (IRE)—Linda's Schoolgirl (IRE) **Recycled Products Limited**

THREE-YEAR-OLDS

8 **HERE COMES JEANIE,** b f Act One—Full English **Recycled Products Limited**
9 **LEADING STAR,** b f Motivator—Movie Mogul **Recycled Products Limited**
10 B g Act One—Linda's Schoolgirl (IRE) **Recycled Products Limited**
11 Gr f Cape Town (IRE)—Think It Over (IRE) **Recycled Products Limited**

MR MICHAEL MADGWICK—continued

TWO-YEAR-OLDS

12 B c 12/3 Multiplex—Attlongglast (Groom Dancer (USA)) **Mrs L. N. Harmes**
13 Ch c 1/6 Denounce—Jewel (IRE) (Cyrano de Bergerac) **Mrs L. N. Harmes**
14 Ch c 25/5 Needwood Blade—Quiz Time (Efisio) **Mrs L.N. Harmes**

Other Owners: Mr Nikolai Askaroff, Mr D. R. Lodge, Mr Oli Lodge, Mr M. Madgwick, Mr G. F. Peacock.

Assistant Trainer: David Madgwick

Jockey (flat): Jimmy Quinn. **Jockey (NH):** Jamie Moore. **Conditional:** Marc Goldstein.

---

415 **MR MIKAEL MAGNUSSON, Upper Lambourn**
Postal: **The Old Manor, Upper Lambourn, Hungerford, Berkshire, RG17 8RG**
Contacts: **FAX (01488) 71702 MOBILE (07775) 556306**
E-MAIL mikael.magnusson@virgin.net

1 ALWAYS A WAY, 4, ch f Danehill Dancer (IRE)—Waypoint **Eastwind Racing Ltd & Martha Trussell**
2 BRIDGE OF GOLD (USA), 6, b h Giant's Causeway (USA)—
Lady Doc (USA) **Eastwind Racing Ltd & Martha Trussell**
3 ESCAPE TO GLORY (USA), 4, b c Bernstein (USA)—Escape To Victory **Eastwind Racing Ltd & Martha Trussell**
4 KING OF CADEAUX (IRE), 7, br g Cadeaux Genereux—Purple Haze (IRE) **East Wind Racing Ltd**
5 PROUD SCHOLAR (USA), 10, br m Royal Academy (USA)—Proud Fact (USA) **East Wind Racing Ltd**
6 STAND TO REASON (IRE), 4, ch c Danehill Dancer (IRE)—
Ho Hi The Moon (IRE) **B Nielsen & Eastwind Racing & M Trussell**

THREE-YEAR-OLDS

7 OXFORD CHARLEY (USA), b c Lemon Drop Kid (USA)—
La Sarto (USA) **Eastwind Racing Ltd & Martha Trussell**
8 PARADISE SEA (USA), b f Stormy Atlantic (USA)—
Paradise River (USA) **Eastwind Racing Ltd & Martha Trussell**
9 STAR FOR LIFE (USA), b br c Giant's Causeway (USA)—
Clerical Etoile (ARG) **Eastwind Racing Ltd & Martha Trussell**
10 TIGER CUB, b f Dr Fong (USA)—Clouded Leopard (USA) **Miss Helena Halling**
11 USER NAME (USA), b f Mr Greeley (USA)—User Cat (USA) **EastWind Racing Martha Trussell Antony Beck**

TWO-YEAR-OLDS

12 Gr c 17/4 Dalakhani (IRE)—Lucky (IRE) (Sadler's Wells (USA)) (35000) **Eastwind Racing Ltd & Martha Trussell**

Other Owners: Mr A. R. Beck, B. E. Nielsen, Mrs M. Trussell.

Assistant Trainer: Mr Paul O'Neill

---

416 **MRS HEATHER MAIN, Wantage**
Postal: **Kingston Common Farm, Kingston Lisle, Wantage, Oxfordshire, OX12 9QT**

1 BEAUTIFUL LANDO (FR), 4, b br g Lando (GER)—Beautiful Baroness (USA) **Les Chevaliers**
2 CODY WYOMING, 6, b g Passing Glance—Tenderfoot **Highnote Thoroughbreds**
3 IRON GREEN (FR), 4, b g Iron Mask (USA)—Love For Ever (FR) **Les Chevaliers**
4 ISLESMAN, 4, b g Oratorio (IRE)—Purple Vision **Ormonde Racing & Les Chevaliers**
5 PADRE ETERNO, 7, b g Luso—Right On Target (IRE) **Highnote Thoroughbreds**
6 PEPELINA (IRE), 4, b f Vinnie Roe (IRE)—Vallee Doree (FR) **Mrs M. Campbell-Andenaes**

THREE-YEAR-OLDS

7 PRINCESS STEPH (IRE), b f Oratorio (IRE)—Eurostorm (USA) **Les Chevaliers**
8 SOUTH KENTER (USA), ch c Silver Deputy (CAN)—Crystal Downs (USA) **Mr M. Kurt**

TWO-YEAR-OLDS

9 B f 8/3 Henny Hughes (USA)—Heart Lake (CAN) (Unbridled (USA)) (13431) **Mrs H. S. Main**
10 B f 20/1 Haafhd—Solva (Singspiel (IRE)) (7500)

Other Owners: K. A. Ingram, Mr A. Kosari, J. P. M. Main.

417 MR PETER MAKIN, Marlborough
Postal: **Bonita Racing Stables, Ogbourne Maisey, Marlborough, Wiltshire, SN8 1RY**
Contacts: **PHONE (01672) 512973 FAX (01672) 514166**
E-MAIL hq@petermakin-racing.com WEBSITE www.petermakin-racing.com

1 FABREZE, 7, ch g Choisir (AUS)—Impulsive Decision (IRE) **Weldspec Glasgow Limited**
2 FLEETWOODMAXI (USA), 5, b br g Afleet Alex (USA)—Swain's Gold (USA) **Weldspec Glasgow Limited**
3 GOOSEBERRY BUSH, 5, b m Tobougg (IRE)—Away To Me **Mrs P. J. Makin**
4 HOLLIE, 4, ch f Bertolini (USA)—Musical Refrain (IRE) **Mr T. J. Sainty**
5 KUANYAO (IRE), 6, b g American Post—Nullarbor **D. M. Ahier**
6 LUNAR LIMELIGHT, 7, b g Royal Applause—Moon Magic **Mrs P. J. Makin**
7 MORACHE MUSIC, 4, b g Sleeping Indian—Enchanted Princess **R P Marchant D M Ahier Mrs E Lee**
8 PEPONI, 6, ch h Kris Kin (USA)—Polmara (IRE) **Mrs P. J. Makin**
9 QUEEN OF HEAVEN (USA), 4, b br f Mr Greeley (USA)—Be My Queen (IRE) **Wedgewood Estates**

THREE-YEAR-OLDS
10 BLANC DE CHINE (IRE), gr f Dark Angel (IRE)—Nullarbor **R. P. Marchant & Mrs E. Lee**
11 KISS MY HEART, br f Byron—Kisses **Wedgewood Estates**
12 KNAVE OF CLUBS (IRE), b c Red Clubs (IRE)—Royal Bounty (IRE) **Mr J. P. Carrington**
13 MARAH MUSIC, b g Royal Applause—Marah **Mrs E Lee, R P Marchant, D M Ahier**
14 MULTIPLY, b c Multiplex—Scarlett Ribbon **Mrs P. J. Makin**
15 RODE TWO DESTINY (IRE), b f Dark Angel (IRE)—
Dear Catch (IRE) **M Holland H Davies D Allen S Woods F Everleigh**
16 SAINT BONIFACE, ch g Bahamian Bounty—Nursling (IRE) **Mrs P. J. Makin**
17 WORDISMYBOND, b c Monsieur Bond (IRE)—La Gessa **T. W. Wellard & Partners**

TWO-YEAR-OLDS
18 B c 22/2 Jeremy (USA)—Easter Song (USA) (Rubiano (USA)) (10000) **Mrs P. J. Makin**
19 B f 9/3 Echo of Light—Highland Cascade (Tipsy Creek (USA)) (1200) **P. J. Makin**
20 B f 8/3 Bahamian Bounty—Maysarah (IRE) (Green Desert (USA)) (5000) **P. J. Makin**
21 Ch c 11/3 Kheleyf (USA)—Pearl Trader (IRE) (Dubai Destination (USA)) (13000) **Unregistered Partnership**
22 B gr f 17/3 Ishiguru (USA)—Vellena (Lucky Story (USA)) (40000) **Unregistered Partnership**
23 WHISTLING BUDDY, b c 27/1 Piccolo—Sahara Silk (IRE) (Desert Style (IRE)) (20000) **Four Seasons Racing Ltd**

Other Owners: Mr K. A. Carter, H. J. W. Davies, M. H. Holland, Mr P. A. Lee, The Countess Of Lonsdale, R. P. Marchant, T. W. Wellard.

418 MRS ALYSON MALZARD, Jersey
Postal: **Les Etabl'yes, Grosnez Farm, St Ouen, Jersey, JE3 2AD**
Contacts: **PHONE (01534) 483773 MOBILE (07797) 738128**
E-MAIL themalzards@localdial.com

1 AZARIA (FR), 6, b m Miesque's Son (USA)—Polar Return (FR) **Macwin Racing**
2 GRENANE (IRE), 9, b g Princely Heir (IRE)—Another Rainbow (IRE) **Trevor & Pat Gallienne**
3 KERSIVAY, 6, b g Royal Applause—Lochmaddy **Malzard Racing**
4 KOKA FAST (FR), 10, ch g Start Fast (FR)—Kaly Flight (FR) **Miss Joan Lowery**
5 LA VERTE RUE (USA), 6, b m Johannesburg (USA)—Settling In (USA) **Mr A. Taylor**
6 LANG SHINING (IRE), 8, ch g Dr Fong (USA)—Dragnet (IRE) **Mr A. Taylor & Mr T. Busher**
7 LES LANDES (IRE), 4, b g Aussie Rules (USA)—Splendid (IRE) **Mr A. Taylor & Mr T. Busher**
8 NEUILLY, 5, b m Nayef (USA)—Narasimha (USA) **Bob & Helene Bonney**
9 NORDIC LIGHT, 8, b br g Belong To Me (USA)—Midriff (USA) **Phil Banfield & John Hackett**
10 PALANOUR (FR), 4, ch g Valanour (IRE)—Palala River **Jane Edgar & John Mercier**
11 REACH OUT, 4, ch g Phoenix Reach (IRE)—Cocorica (IRE) **Malzard Racing**
12 RIVER DU NORD (FR), 5, b m Voix du Nord (FR)—Palala River **Jane Edgar & John Mercier**
13 SANS SA DAME (FR), 9, ch g Wathik (USA)—Danemara (FR) **P. A. Guiton & Y. Stead**
14 SHIP'S HILL (IRE), 11, b g Oscar (IRE)—Ballykea (IRE) **Mr A. Taylor**
15 SISSI GUIHEN (FR), 6, ch m Lord of Men—Assermara (FR) **P. A. Guiton & Y. Stead**
16 SPANISH BOUNTY, 7, b g Bahamian Bounty—Spanish Gold **Malzard Racing**
17 SUPERDUPER, 7, b m Erhaab (USA)—I'm Magic **Gold Dolphin Racing**
18 UNIFORM RUBY, 4, b f Iceman—Winter Moon **The Unwin Family**
19 VAMOS (IRE), 6, b g Royal Applause—Feather Boa (IRE) **Bob & Helene Bonney**

Other Owners: Godfray Amy, Jim Jamouneaux.

Jockey (flat): Kylie Manser, Jemma Marshall. **Jockey (NH):** Mattie Batchelor, Rob Kirk, Tony Proctor. **Apprentice:** Tim Clarke. **Amateur:** Miss Caroline Hurley.

419 MR JAMES JOSEPH MANGAN, Mallow
Postal: **Curraheen, Conna, Mallow, Co. Cork, Ireland**
Contacts: PHONE **(00353) 585 9116** FAX **(00353) 585 9116** MOBILE **(00353) 8726 84611**

1 CARRIES DARLING, 5, b m Flemensfirth (USA)—Knock Down (IRE) **Mr W. M. Mangan**
2 CASTLE WINGS (IRE), 7, b g Winged Love (IRE)—Mrs Hegarty **The Kings Syndicate**
3 CYPRUSORMILAN, 5, b g Milan—Persrolla **Handford Chemists Ltd.**
4 DONT TELL PA (IRE), 5, b g Oscar (IRE)—Glacial Snowboard (IRE) **Mr J. G. O'Flaherty**
5 FORJOETHEPLUMBER (IRE), 8, b g Corrouge (USA)—Lady Conchita (USA) **Mr Paul Bradford**
6 GREAT SPAN (IRE), 6, b g Brian Boru—Web of Gold **Handford Chemists Ltd.**
7 KILCREA (IRE), 5, b g Definite Article—Lightly Dreaming (FR) **Mr M. I. O'Driscoll**
8 KNOCKRAHA LAD (IRE), 8, b g Oscar (IRE)—Queenofclubs (IRE) **Mr M. I. O'Donoghue**
9 NORAS FANCY (IRE), 6, b m Brian Boru—Verney Bird (IRE) **Mr M. I. Dixon**
10 QUARRYVALE (IRE), 8, b m Beneficial—Miss McCormick (IRE) **Mr Tom O'Flynn**

Assistant Trainer: Mary Mangan

Conditional: P. F. Mangan. **Amateur:** Mr Damien Murphy, Miss Jane Mangan.

420 MR CHARLIE MANN, Upper Lambourn
Postal: **Whitcoombe House Stables, Maddle Road, Upper Lambourn, Hungerford, Berkshire, RG17 8RA**
Contacts: PHONE **(01488) 71717 / 73118** FAX **(01488) 73223** MOBILE **(07721) 888333**
E-MAIL **charlie@charliemann.com** WEBSITE **www.charliemann.com**

1 AIR FORCE ONE (GER), 10, ch g Lando (GER)—Ame Soeur (FR) **B. Walsh**
2 AIRMEN'S FRIEND (IRE), 6, b g Craigsteel—High Academy (IRE) **Prolinx Limited**
3 BALLYMURRY (IRE), 6, b g Publisher (USA)—Little Nibbler (IRE) **C. J. Mann**
4 BENCH WARRENT (IRE), 9, b g Witness Box—Tee Aitch Kay (IRE) **Mrs J. M. Mayo**
5 CARRIGLEA WOOD (IRE), 6, br g Sunshine Street (USA)—Lady Sallyanna (IRE) **The Mini Partnership**
6 CAST CADA (IRE), 9, b g Exit To Nowhere (USA)—Inch Rose (IRE) **R. E. Good**
7 CHARMING LAD (IRE), 7, b g Dushyantor (USA)—Glens Lady (IRE) **Tom & Charlotte-Anne Swerling**
8 DE WAITING GAME (IRE), 6, b g Sesaro (USA)—Tansey Yearwood (IRE) **Safest Syndicate 3**
9 DUKE OF MONMOUTH (IRE), 5, b g Presenting—Hayley Cometh (IRE) **Bryan & Philippa Burrough**
10 DUN SEE DEE (IRE), 8, b m Flemensfirth (USA)—Crafty Classy (IRE) **The Icy Fire Partnership**
11 EBONY DIAMOND (IRE), 8, b g Marignan (USA)—Mrs Quigley (USA) **C. J. Mann**
12 FAIR POINT (IRE), 10, ch g Moonax (IRE)—Pampered Molly (IRE) **Mrs Rollo Duckworth & Mr Charlie Mann**
13 FIN VIN DE LEU (GER), 6, b g Dr Fong (USA)—Fairy Queen (IRE) **R Curry, Cathy Leuchars & R P Michaelson**
14 FINE PARCHMENT (IRE), 9, b g Presenting—Run For Cover (IRE) **N. W. A. Bannister**
15 GREYFRIARS DRUMMER, 4, ch c Where Or When (IRE)—Loveleaves **Charlie Mann**
16 HEAD HUNTED, 5, b g Dubai Destination (USA)—Tropical Breeze (IRE) **Tony Hayward & Sue Head**
17 HOW'S BUSINESS, 8, b m Jost Algarhoud (IRE)—Love And Kisses **Group Clean Ltd**
18 KATIES TUITOR, 9, b g Kayf Tara—Penny Gold (IRE) **Mr W. Adams**
19 KING BREX (DEN), 9, b g Primatico (USA)—Moon Shine (DEN) **Nigel Kempner & Lady Hart**
20 LORD OF HOUSE (GER), 4, b c Lord of England (GER)—Lake House (IRE) **C. J. Mann**
21 LOW GALES (IRE), 6, b g Dr Massini (IRE)—Glorious Gale (IRE) **The Low Gales Partnership**
22 MAGIC PROSPECT (IRE), 5, b g Miesque's Son (USA)—Clarissa Dalloway (FR) **Taylor & Frosell**
23 MAHAYOGIN (USA), 4, b br g Dixie Union—Shiva (JPN) **Red Letter Syndicate**
24 MARINGO BAY (IRE), 7, b g Old Vic—Waterland Lady **John & Peter Heron**
25 MASKED MAN, 9, ch g Alhaarth (IRE)—Misbegotten (IRE) **Major J. G. Thorneloe**
26 MOON OVER MIAMI (GER), 11, b g Dashing Blade—Miss Esther (GER) **Safest Syndicate 3**
27 NEXT HIGHT (IRE), 5, b g High Chaparral (IRE)—
Night Petticoat (GER) **W Brindle, B Fulton, T Hayward & P Merritt**
28 NOSECOND CHANCE (IRE), 6, b g Classic Cliche (IRE)—Mandy's Treasure (IRE) **H. E. C. Villiers**
29 PROLINX (IRE), 7, b g Oscar (IRE)—Winter Break (IRE) **Prolinx Limited**
30 REBEL MELODY (IRE), 11, b g Houmayoun (FR)—Queenford Melody (IRE) **Mrs J. F. Maynard**
31 RED ADMIRAL (USA), 10, b g Red Ransom (USA)—Ausherra (USA) **Tom & Charlotte-Anne Swerling**
32 SCHUMPTERS LAD (IRE), 7, gr g Beneficial—Stepfaster **Mrs J Maynard,Mrs J Weaver,Mr P Docherty**
33 SEVENTH SKY (GER), 5, b g King's Best (USA)—Sacarina **John & Peter Heron**
34 SHOCKINGTIMES (IRE), 5, b g Wareed (IRE)—Jolly Lady (IRE) **S.Beccle, J.Maynard, Lady Hart, Boscobel EL**
35 SIMPLY STRONG (IRE), 8, ch g Simply Great (FR)—Sheltered (IRE) **Bill Booth & Charlie Mann**
36 SPACE MISSION (IRE), 10, b g Kayf Tara—Jupiter's Message **Mrs L. C. Taylor**
37 SPEAR THISTLE, 10, ch g Selkirk (USA)—Ardisia (USA) **Tony Hayward & Sue Head**
38 SUM LAFF (IRE), 8, ch g Publisher (USA)—Tiergarten (USA) **Bryan & Philippa Burrough**
39 TARQUINIUS (FR), 9, gr g Turgeon (USA)—Shannon Bells (FR) **H. E. C. Villiers**
40 TRAFFIC CHAOS (IRE), 7, b g Zagreb (USA)—Classic Material **C Hunter, D Batten, S Beccle, T Stapleton**

MR CHARLIE MANN—continued

41 **VICTOR LEUDORUM (IRE)**, 5, b g Wareed (IRE)—Rock Garden (IRE) **Richard Curry & Cathy Leuchars**
42 **VOLTIGGER HILL (GER)**, 7, b g Tiger Hill (IRE)—Village (GER) **Group Clean Ltd**
43 **WESTERN KING (IRE)**, 5, b g Definite Article—Western Road (GER) **The Western King Partnership**
44 **WHISPERING JACK**, 7, b g Beat All (USA)—Ski Shot **Mr Roger Bender & Mrs Sarah Bender**
45 **WHO OWNS ME (IRE)**, 6, b g Milan—Top Lassie **Fromthestables.com Racing**

Other Owners: Mr David Batten, Mr S. Beccle, Mr R. J. Bender, Mrs S. L. Bender, Mr C. W. Booth, Boscobel Estates Limited, Mr W. Brindle, Mr B. R. H. Burrough, Mrs Philippa Burrough, Mr N. A. Coster, Mr R. M. F. Curry, Mr P. Docherty, Mrs Rollo Duckworth, Mr Rollo Duckworth, Mr Robert Frosell, Mr B. N. Fulton, Lady Hart, Mr Tony Hayward, Mrs Sue Head, Mr John Heron, Mr Peter Heron, Mrs Caroline Hunter, Miss D. Jones, Mr N. J. Kempner, Mr Charlie Mann, Mr I. G. Martin, Mrs Judy Maynard, Miss S. McDougall, Miss K. McDougall, Mr P. D. Merritt, Mr R. P. B. Michaelson, Mrs Dorothy Mosley, Mr C. R. Nugent, Mr Tony Stapleton, Mr T. A. Swerling, Mrs Charlotte-Anne Swerling, Mrs L. C. Taylor, Mrs Julie Weaver, Mrs Penny Zarbafi.

Assistant Trainer: D J Jeffreys

Jockey (NH): Noel Fehily. **Conditional:** Gavin Sheehan.

---

421 **MRS AUDREY MANNERS, Minehead**
Postal: **Oaktrow Farm, Timberscombe, Minehead, Somerset, TA24 7UF**
Contacts: **PHONE (01793) 762232 FAX (01793) 861781 MOBILE (07753) 638858**
E-MAIL commonfarm@btconnect.com

1 **LADFROMHIGHWORTH**, 7, b g Kier Park (IRE)—Cavisoir **Mrs A. M. Manners**

Amateur: Mr Sam Painting, Miss Lucy Barry.

---

422 **MR GEORGE MARGARSON, Newmarket**
Postal: **Graham Lodge, Birdcage Walk, Newmarket, Suffolk, CB8 0NE**
Contacts: **HOME/FAX (01638) 668043 MOBILE (07860) 198303**
E-MAIL george@georgemargarson.co.uk WEBSITE www.georgemargason.co.uk

1 **DANAHER**, 5, ch g Where Or When (IRE)—Quirkie **Mr S. Quirk**
2 **DOUBLE DICE**, 4, ro f Verglas (IRE)—Fiddle-Dee-Dee (IRE) **Mr M. B. Jenner**
3 **ENCHANTED DREAM**, 4, b f Halling (USA)—Enchanted **Norcroft Park Stud**
4 **EXCELLENT AIM**, 5, b g Exceed And Excel (AUS)—Snugfit Annie **Norcroft Park Stud**
5 **EXCELLENT GUEST**, 5, b g Exceed And Excel (AUS)—Princess Speedfit (FR) **John Guest Racing Ltd**
6 **IMAGINARY DIVA**, 6, b m Lend A Hand—Distant Diva **Graham Lodge Partnership**
7 **IMPERIAL GUEST**, 6, ch g Imperial Dancer—Princess Speedfit (FR) **John Guest Racing Ltd**
8 **LAYLA'S KING**, 4, b c Dubawi (IRE)—Top Jem **Norcroft Park Stud**
9 **MAGICAL SPEEDFIT (IRE)**, 7, ch g Bold Fact (USA)—Magical Peace (IRE) **Graham Lodge Partnership**
10 **SPEEDFIT GIRL (IRE)**, 4, b f Kodiac—Staylily (IRE) **John Guest Racing Ltd**
11 **STAR REBEL**, 4, b g Doyen (IRE)—Star of Normandie (USA) **Norcroft Park Stud**
12 **STORM RUNNER (IRE)**, 4, b g Rakti—Saibhreas (IRE) **Pitfield Partnership**
13 **SUPREME SPIRIT (IRE)**, 5, b m Invincible Spirit (IRE)—Asseverate (USA) **Mrs C. C. Regalado-Gonzalez**
14 **TAKE COVER**, 5, b g Singspiel (IRE)—Enchanted **Norcroft Park Stud**
15 **TIBERIUS CLAUDIUS (IRE)**, 4, br g Clodovil (IRE)—Final Favour (IRE) **The Hook / Morrison Partnership**
16 **WOOLFALL SOVEREIGN (IRE)**, 6, b g Noverre (USA)—Mandragore (USA) **Graham Lodge Partnership**
17 **YOUNG JACKIE**, 4, b f Doyen (IRE)—Just Warning **M. F. Kentish**
18 **YOUNG SIMON**, 5, ch g Piccolo—Fragrant Cloud **M. F. Kentish**

THREE-YEAR-OLDS

19 **ARTFUL LADY (IRE)**, br f Excellent Art—Fear And Greed (IRE) **Mrs E. L. Hook**
20 B c Byron—Assertive Dancer (USA) **Paul Rodgers**
21 **BROTHER TIGER**, b c Singspiel (IRE)—Three Secrets (IRE) **Norcroft Park Stud**
22 **EXCELLENT JEM**, b c Exceed And Excel (AUS)—Polar Jem **Norcroft Park Stud**
23 **I SEE YOU**, ch f Sleeping Indian—Pikaboo **Mrs C. C. Regalado-Gonzalez**
24 **INDIANA GUEST (IRE)**, b g Indian Haven—Princess Speedfit (FR) **John Guest Racing Ltd**
25 **REBELLIOUS GUEST**, b c Cockney Rebel (IRE)—Marisa (GER) **John Guest Racing Ltd**
26 **STORM KING**, b c Shamardal (USA)—Tarandot (IRE) **Norcroft Park Stud**
27 **YOUNG LISA**, b f Echo of Light—Just Warning **M. F. Kentish**

MR GEORGE MARGARSON—continued

TWO-YEAR-OLDS

28 B c 3/4 Duke of Marmalade (IRE)—Ardbrae Lady (Overbury (IRE)) (68000) **John Guest Racing Ltd**
29 Ch f 2/4 Zafeen (FR)—Limegreen Bow (Efisio) **M V S & Mrs Aram**
30 Ch c 2/3 Bahamian Bounty—Mamoura (IRE) (Lomond (USA)) (67000) **John Guest Racing Ltd**
31 Ch f 21/4 Zafeen (FR)—Nihal (IRE) (Singspiel (IRE)) **Stableside Racing Partnership**
32 B c 9/3 Red Clubs (IRE)—Princess Speedfit (FR) (Desert Prince (IRE)) (24630) **John Guest Racing Ltd**
33 RED CATKIN, b f 5/2 Notnowcato—Red Salvia (Selkirk (USA)) (22000) **Mrs E. L. Hook**

Assistant Trainer: Katie Margarson

Jockey (flat): Ian Mongan, Tom Queally. **Amateur:** Miss Katie Margarson.

423
MR STEPHEN MARSHALL, Morpeth
Postal: **West Moneylaws Farm, Cornhill-On-Tweed, Northumberland, TD12 4QD**
Contacts: **PHONE (01890) 850673 MOBILE (07833) 493500**
E-MAIL lizannett@hotmail.com

1 FLAMING CLINT, 6, b m Milieu—Croaghnacree (IRE) **Mrs E. Annett**
2 MONEY DIEU (IRE), 7, b m Turtle Island (IRE)—Aon Suil Amhain (IRE) **Mrs E. Annett**
3 PURPLE MONEY (IRE), 7, b m Milan—The Purple Penguin **Mrs E. Annett**

Other Owners: S. J. Marshall.

Assistant Trainer: Liz Annett

424
MR A. J. MARTIN, Summerhill
Postal: **Arodstown, Moynalvey, Summerhill, Co. Meath, Ireland**
Contacts: **PHONE (00353) 46 955 8633 FAX (00353) 46 955 8632 MOBILE (00353) 86 276 0835**
E-MAIL arodstown@eircom.net

1 ASKMEROE (IRE), 9, b g Rudimentary (USA)—Mill Lady (IRE) **Mr A. F. Shiels & Niall Reilly**
2 ASYMMETRICAL (IRE), 6, b g Exit To Nowhere (USA)—Incharder (IRE) **We Must Be Mad Syndicate**
3 BENEFFICIENT (IRE), 6, ch g Beneficial—Supreme Breda (IRE) **Aidan Shiels**
4 BOG WARRIOR (IRE), 8, b g Strategic Choice (USA)—Kilmac Princess (IRE) **Gigginstown House Stud**
5 DARA TANGO (FR), 5, b g Lando (GER)—Dara Dancer **Daniel Hartnett/Mrs E. A. Lawlor/A. Sheils**
6 DEDIGOUT (IRE), 6, b g Bob Back (USA)—Dainty Daisy (IRE) **Gigginstown House Stud**
7 EDEYMI (IRE), 4, b g Barathea (IRE)—Edabiya (IRE) **Gigginstown House Stud**
8 GIFT OF DGAB (IRE), 8, b g Winged Love (IRE)—Creative Princess (IRE) **Gigginstown House Stud**
9 GOD'S COUNTY (FR), 7, gr g Verglas (IRE)—Toujours Elle (IRE) **Gigginstown House Stud**
10 KING OF THE REFS (IRE), 7, b g Zagreb (USA)—Regal Pursuit (IRE) **Eamon Waters**
11 LISDALEEN (IRE), 7, b m Saddlers' Hall (IRE)—Ballymaguirelass (IRE) **Mr S. Campion**
12 LOCHAN LACHA (IRE), 11, b g Taipan (IRE)—Hopeful Memory (IRE) **Mrs E. A. Lawlor**
13 MADE IN TAIPAN (IRE), 10, br g Taipan (IRE)—No Easy Way (IRE) **Mrs M. Martin**
14 MILITARY BOWL (USA), 4, b g Mr Greeley—Turtle Bow (FR) **Bowled Over Syndicate**
15 MIRIAM'S DREAM (IRE), 6, b g Lord Americo—Butlers Meadow (IRE) **Ultimate Dreams Syndicate**
16 MONTAN (FR), 8, b g Trempolino (USA)—Mandchoue (FR) **William Moffett/Margan Cassidy**
17 MULLEADY (IRE), 4, ch f Definite Article—Brief Sentiment (IRE) **Hard Hat Syndicate**
18 NEAREST THE PIN (IRE), 7, br g Court Cave (IRE)—Carnbelle (IRE) **Sox Syndicate**
19 OSCAR DAN DAN (IRE), 10, b g Oscar (IRE)—Warmley's Gem (IRE) **Mrs M. Martin**
20 OSIRIXAMIX (IRE), 9, b g Desert Prince (IRE)—Osirixa (FR) **Timothy Fitzgerald**
21 PIRES, 8, br g Generous (USA)—Kaydee Queen (IRE) **Mrs E. A. Lawlor**
22 PSYCHO (IRE), 11, b g Dr Massini (IRE)—Tiverton Castle (IRE) **Exors of the Late Cecil McClure**
23 REDERA (IRE), 6, b g Chevalier (IRE)—Lady Redera (IRE) **Peter William Partnership**
24 SADDLERS STORM (IRE), 10, b g Saddlers' Hall (IRE)—
                                        Lisa's Storm (IRE) **William Moffett/R. T. McLoughlin/J. R. McLoughlin**
25 SAVELLO (IRE), 6, ch g Anshan—Fontaine Frances (IRE) **Gigginstown House Stud**
26 SENSATIONAL SEMA (IRE), 8, br g Witness Box (USA)—Shuil Ar Spraoi (IRE) **Pats Bar Syndicate**
27 SOBER SAILOR (IRE), 5, b g Hawkeye (IRE)—Ronni Pancake **Sean Dalton**
28 SUGHERA (IRE), 5, b m Alhaarth (IRE)—Gold Bar (IRE) **Mrs Mac Partnership**
29 TED VEALE (IRE), 5, b g Revoque (IRE)—Rose Tanner (IRE) **John Breslin**
30 THOMAS EDISON (IRE), 5, b g Danehill Dancer (USA)—Bright Bank (IRE) **Promising Silver Syndicate**
31 TRAZAR (FR), 5, b g Kahyasi—No Exit (FR) **Mrs Kay Devlin**
32 VICTRIX GALE (IRE), 6, b m Presenting—Ballyclough Gale **Badgers Syndicate**
33 WINGTIPS (FR), 4, gr g High Chaparral (IRE)—Without Shoes (FR) **Mrs Sheila Moffett**

425 MRS JENNIFER MASON, Cirencester
Postal: 2 Manor Farm Cottages, Ablington, Bibury, Cirencester, Gloucestershire, GL7 5NY

1 **HACKPENTHOMAS,** 4, b g Grape Tree Road—Kentford Duchess **Mr N. A. Thomas**
2 **LOVE OF TARA,** 10, b m Kayf Tara—O My Love **North Park Farm Racing**
3 **PRETTY PENNY,** 8, b m Alflora (IRE)—Mrs Moneypenny **Mr C. C. B. Mathew**
4 **TOMMY TIGER,** 4, b g Tiger Hill (IRE)—Special Green (FR) **The If At First Partnership**

Other Owners: Mrs R. D. Greenwood, Mr N. G. Jackson, Mr R. E. Pullen, Mrs M. E. Slocock.

426 MR ROBIN MATHEW, Burford
Postal: Church Farm, Little Barrington, Burford, Oxfordshire, OX18 4TE
Contacts: PHONE (01451) 844311

1 **BALLY SANDS (IRE),** 8, b g Luso—Sandwell Old Rose (IRE) **R. Mathew**
2 **BEHEST,** 7, b m Rainbow Quest (USA)—Keyboogie (USA) **R. Mathew**
3 **BRAVO RIQUET (FR),** 6, br g Laveron—Jeroline (FR) **R. Mathew**
4 **EMPEROR COMMODOS,** 5, b g Midnight Legend—Theme Arena **R. Mathew**
5 **LOST ARCA (FR),** 6, b g Lost World (IRE)—Luarca **R. Mathew**
6 **SUPRALUNARY,** 6, b g Midnight Legend—Heresy (IRE) **R. Mathew**

Jockey (NH): Sean Quinlan, Dave Crosse.

427 MISS JANE MATHIAS, Llancarfan
Postal: Crosstown, Llancarfan, Vale of Glamorgan, CF62 3AD

1 **SOHAPPYHARRY,** 6, ch g Sir Harry Lewis (USA)—Sohapara **Mrs S. E. Mathias**

428 MR G. C. MAUNDRELL, Marlborough
Postal: Ogbourne Down, Ogbourne St Andrew, Marlborough, Wilts
Contacts: PHONE (01672) 841202

1 **DREAM PERFORMANCE (IRE),** 7, b m Oscar (IRE)—Pharlen's Dream (IRE) **G. C. Maundrell**
2 **DROPPY'S (IRE),** 11, br g Houmayoun (FR)—Whizaway (IRE) **G. C. Maundrell**
3 **MINOR CHORD,** 6, b m Alflora (IRE)—Minimum **G. C. Maundrell**

Jockey (NH): G. Tumelty.

429 MISS OLIVIA MAYLAM, Epsom
Postal: Chalk Pit Stables, Headley Road, Epsom, Surrey, KT18 6BW

1 **BEAR FOX BEN,** 5, ch g Sulamani (IRE)—Lady Birgitta **Alan Shaw & Paul Sweeting**
2 **COULD IT BE MAGIC,** 5, b g Dubai Destination (USA)—Lomapamar **Miss O. Maylam**
3 **DASHO,** 4, ch g Dubawi (IRE)—New Choice (IRE) **Mrs P. A. Clark**
4 **FEDORA (IRE),** 6, b m Cape Cross (IRE)—Mahamuni (IRE) **Mrs V. A. Ward**
5 **JACKIE LOVE (IRE),** 4, b f Tobougg (IRE)—Gutter Press (IRE) **Miss O. Maylam**
6 **LADY MORGANNA (IRE),** 4, b f Diamond Green (FR)—Lucky Flirt (USA) **Ms T. Keane**
7 **LADY ROYAL OAK (IRE),** 5, b m Exceed And Excel (AUS)—Enclave (USA) **A. C. Maylam**
8 **MAD GINGER ALICE,** 4, ch f Beat Hollow—Peryllys **A. C. Maylam**
9 **MANDY'S HERO,** 4, b g Compton Place—Bandanna **Mr A. C. D. Main**
10 **ZIP LOCK (IRE),** 6, b g Invincible Spirit (IRE)—Buckle (IRE) **B. Neaves**

THREE-YEAR-OLDS

11 **KYLIN,** ch f Kyllachy—Descriptive (IRE) **R. C. Tooth**

Other Owners: Mr A. L. Shaw, P. Sweeting.

430 **MR JAMES MCAULEY, Gormanston**
Postal: Cois Farraige, Silverbeach, Gormanston, Co. Meath, Ireland
Contacts: PHONE (00353) 1 6903065 FAX (00353) 1 6903065 MOBILE (00353) 86 8399713
E-MAIL hilltop.stables@hotmail.com

1 DESERT MOONLIGHT, 5, ch g Halling (USA)—Time Changes (USA) **James Gough**
2 FAILED THE TEST (IRE), 6, b m Dushyantor (USA)—Room To Room Magic (IRE) **Mr S. F. Gallagher**
3 GASPAR (IRE), 12, br g Desert King (IRE)—Exponent (USA) **James Gough**
4 HANG UP MY BOOTS (IRE), 6, gr g Great Palm (USA)—Carmenta (USA) **James Gough**
5 SERIOUS BREACH, 4, b g Intikhab (USA)—Double Crossed **James Gough**
6 WARRANTS A NAME (IRE), 6, b g Muroto—Ballinard Sarah (IRE) **Mr S. F. Gallagher**

Assistant Trainer: James Gough

Jockey (NH): Ian McCarthy. Jockey (flat): Joseph O'Brien. Amateur: Mr Jamie Codd.

431 **MR KEVIN MCAULIFFE, Faringdon**
Postal: Fernham Farm, Fernham, Faringdon, Oxfordshire, SN7 7NX

THREE-YEAR-OLDS

1 HILLWALK, b g Pastoral Pursuits—Glory Oatway (IRE) **K. McAuliffe**
2 Ch c Medecean—Just Wood (FR)
3 Ch c Motivator—Lalina (GER) **K. McAuliffe**

432 **MR CHARLIE MCBRIDE, Newmarket**
Postal: Exeter House Stables, 33 Exeter Road, Newmarket, Suffolk,
Contacts: PHONE/FAX (01638) 667841 MOBILE (07929) 265711

1 EXTREMELY SO, 6, ch m Kyllachy—Antigua
2 FIRE CHIEF, 4, b g Firebreak—Compton Amber **P. J. McBride**
3 ICE COLD BEX, 4, ch g Iceman—Musica
4 INPURSUITOFFREEDOM, 5, b m Pastoral Pursuits—Quilt **P. J. McBride**
5 JOHN LOUIS, 4, ch g Bertolini (USA)—Native Ring (FR) **Four Winds Racing**

THREE-YEAR-OLDS

6 CASA BEX, b g Auction House (USA)—Feather Game
7 MALLT (IRE), b f Kheleyf (USA)—Titania **Mr J. V. Egan**
8 SPEEDI MOUSE, b f Alhaarth (IRE)—Meredith
9 WORDS COME EASY, ch f Byron—Aliena (IRE) **Four Winds Racing**

Other Owners: Mr S. C. C. Skey, Mrs C. E. Skey.

433 **MR ALAN MCCABE, Averham**
Postal: Cheveral Barn, Averham, Newark, Nottinghamshire, NG23 5RU
Contacts: PHONE (01636) 701668 FAX (01636) 706579 MOBILE (07766) 302092
E-MAIL ajmacc@tiscali.co.uk

1 AJDAAD (USA), 5, b g Horse Chestnut (SAF)—Hasene (FR) **Mrs Z. Wentworth**
2 BEAT OF THE BLUES, 4, b g Beat Hollow—Skies Are Blue **T. R. Pearson**
3 BEDOUIN BAY, 4, b g Dubai Destination (USA)—Sahara Sonnet (USA) **Mrs Z. Wentworth**
4 BRIO, 4, b g Araafa (IRE)—Salsa Brava (IRE) **Sale Of The Century**
5 CALICO BAY (IRE), 4, b g Whipper (USA)—Caribbean Escape **Mr A. J. McCabe**
6 CARNAC (IRE), 6, gr g Dalakhani (IRE)—Traou Mad (IRE) **Mr A. J. McCabe & Mr Charles Wentworth**
7 CITY LEGEND, 4, b g Lucky Story (USA)—Urban Calm **Contango Syndicate**
8 CLOSE TO THE EDGE (IRE), 4, b f Iffraaj—Iktidar **C. V. Wentworth**
9 CORNUS, 10, ch g Inchinor—Demerger (USA) **Triple A Partnership**
10 DARUBAND, 4, ch g Singspiel (IRE)—Gagajulu **Mrs J. Bownes**
11 DESERT ICON (IRE), 6, b g Desert Style (IRE)—Gilded Vanity (IRE) **Mrs M. J. McCabe**
12 DESERT STRIKE, 6, b g Bertolini (USA)—Mary Jane **Mrs M. J. McCabe**
13 EASTERN HILLS, 7, b g Dubai Destination (USA)—Rainbow Mountain **C. V. Wentworth**

MR ALAN MCCABE—continued

14 **ELUSIVE WARRIOR (USA)**, 9, b g Elusive Quality (USA)—Love To Fight (CAN) **Mrs M. J. McCabe**
15 **FOLLOW THE FLAG (IRE)**, 8, ch g Traditionally (USA)—Iktidar **Mr S. Gillen**
16 **FORTY PROOF (IRE)**, 4, b g Invincible Spirit (IRE)—Cefira (USA) **Mr A. J. McCabe**
17 **FRATELLINO**, 5, ch h Auction House (USA)—Vida (IRE) **Sale Of The Century**
18 **IL BATTISTA**, 4, b g Medicean—Peace **Alotincommon Partnership**
19 **LEVITATE**, 4, ch g Pivotal—Soar **C. V. Wentworth**
20 **NEAT SWEEP (IRE)**, 4, b f Tiger Hill (GER)—Flagship **Mr A. J. McCabe**
21 **OPEN COUNTRY (IRE)**, 6, b br g Flemensfirth (USA)—Tricky Tina (IRE) **Mr A. J. McCabe**
22 **PHOENIX FLAME**, 4, ch f Phoenix Reach (IRE)—Generosia **Winterbeck Manor Stud Ltd**
23 **REVE DE NUIT (USA)**, 4, ch g Giant's Causeway—My Dream Castles (USA) **Mrs Z. Wentworth**
24 **SHOWBOATING (IRE)**, 4, b g Shamardal (USA)—
                                                              Sadinga (IRE) **Mr M. & Mrs L. Cooke, Mr A. Pierce, Mr A. McCabe**
25 **SILVER WIND**, 7, b g Ishiguru (USA)—My Bonus **D. J. Buckley**
26 **SPIRIT OF GRACE**, 4, b f Invincible Spirit (IRE)—Scottish Heights (IRE) **Placida Racing**
27 **TISLAAM (IRE)**, 5, gr g With Approval (CAN)—Lady Angola (USA) **Mrs Z. Wentworth**
28 **WATCH CHAIN (IRE)**, 5, b g Traditionally (USA)—Dangle (IRE) **Lucky Heather**
29 **ZACYNTHUS (IRE)**, 4, ch c Iffraaj—Ziria (IRE) **Mrs J. Bownes**

THREE-YEAR-OLDS

30 **BELLS OF BERLIN**, ch c Pivotal—Choirgirl **C. V. Wentworth**
31 **BOSONIC**, b g Phoenix Reach (IRE)—Antigoni (IRE) **Winterbeck Manor Stud Ltd**
32 **CASPAR NETSCHER**, b c Dutch Art—Bella Cantata **C. V. Wentworth**
33 **CLEAN BOWLED (IRE)**, b g Footstepsinthesand—Miznapp **Mrs M. J. McCabe**
34 **DAWN LIGHTNING**, gr f Dark Angel (IRE)—River Crossing **Mr A. J. Wittering**
35 **EVANESCENT (IRE)**, b c Elusive City (USA)—Itsanothergirl **C. V. Wentworth**
36 **FLYING PICKETS (IRE)**, b g Piccolo—Burn **Mrs M. J. McCabe**
37 B c Zamindar (USA)—Jath
38 **KUWAIT MOON**, br g Resplendent Glory (IRE)—Tapsalteerie **Mr A. J. McCabe**
39 **KUWAIT STAR**, ch c Resplendent Glory (IRE)—Mofeyda (IRE) **Mr A. J. McCabe**
40 **LADY NICKANDY (IRE)**, b f Kheleyf (USA)—Tanzie (IRE) **Mr K. N. Lane**
41 **MOUNT MCLEOD (IRE)**, b f Holy Roman Emperor (IRE)—Northern Gulch (USA) **Mrs M. J. McCabe**
42 **MOUSIE**, b f Auction House (USA)—Goes A Treat (IRE) **Lucky Heather**
43 **PINK BELINI**, ch f Phoenix Reach (IRE)—Pink Supreme **Winterbeck Manor Stud Ltd**
44 **REVE DU JOUR (IRE)**, b f Iffraaj—Melaaya (USA) **Mrs Z. Wentworth**
45 **SYMPHONY OF SPACE**, b f Primo Valentino—Flying Lion **T. R. Pearson**
46 **VERBEECK**, b c Dutch Art—Tesary **Mr F. Al Dabbous**

TWO-YEAR-OLDS

47 B c 11/4 Tobougg (IRE)—Benjarong (Sharpo) (5714)
48 B f 3/4 Dubai Destination (USA)—Blinding Mission (IRE) (Marju (IRE)) (800)
49 B f 27/3 Sleeping Indian—Cape Dancer (IRE) (Cape Cross (IRE)) (761) **C. V. Wentworth**
50 B c 30/4 Antonius Pius (USA)—Consultant Stylist (IRE) (Desert Style) (19047) **Mrs Z. Wentworth**
51 **DARAKTI (IRE)**, b c 27/3 Rakti—Mitawa (IRE) (Alhaarth (IRE)) (4761) **Mrs D. E. Sharp**
52 **DOLLY BANTRY**, ch f 17/4 Pastoral Pursuits—Seeker (Rainbow Quest (USA)) (800) **Lucky Heather**
53 Ch c 7/3 Refuse To Bend (IRE)—Zuniga's Date (USA) (Diesis) (18095) **Mrs Z. Wentworth**

Other Owners: Mr A. D. Baker, Miss H. P. Chellingworth, Mr M. Cooke, Mrs M. J. McCabe, Mr A. J. McCabe, Mr Fran McCabe, Mr John McCabe, Mr C. J. Shelton, Mr D. A. Thompson, Mr A. C. Timms, Mr Charles Wentworth, Mr Alan Wilson.

Assistant Trainers: Alex Bevan, Ivan Furtado

Jockey (flat): Natalia Gemelova, Seb Sanders, Robert Winston, Shane Kelly. **Apprentice:** Declan Cannon.

---

434   **MR DONALD MCCAIN, Cholmondeley**
Postal: **Bankhouse, Cholmondeley, Malpas, Cheshire, SY14 8AL**
Contacts: **PHONE** (01829) 720351/720352 **FAX** (01829) 720475 **MOBILE** (07903) 066194
E-MAIL bankhouse.racing@virgin.net **WEBSITE** www.donaldmccain.co.uk

1 **A BRIDGE TOO FAR (IRE)**, 6, b g Oscar (IRE)—Private Rose **Glen's Fools**
2 **ABSINTHE (IRE)**, 6, b g King's Best (USA)—Triple Try (IRE) **Mr & Mrs Paul Rooney**
3 **ACROSS THE BAY (IRE)**, 8, b g Bob's Return (IRE)—The Southern (IRE) **Scotch Piper Syndicate**
4 **AGENT ARCHIE (USA)**, 5, b g Smart Strike (CAN)—Dans La Ville (CHI) **D. M. Gorton**
5 **AL QEDDAAF (IRE)**, 6, b g Alhaarth (IRE)—Just Special **T. G. Leslie**
6 **ALDERLEY ROVER (IRE)**, 8, gr g Beneficial—St Anne's Lady (IRE) **A. Craig & A. Dick**

MR DONALD McCAIN—continued

7 **ALEXANDER ROAD (IRE)**, 7, b m Kaldounevees (FR)—Trinity Belle (FR) **Mr B. J. Richardson**
8 **AMRON LAD (IRE)**, 5, b g Zagreb (USA)—Pear Tart (IRE) **Mr D. Hanafin**
9 **AN CAPALL MOR (IRE)**, 6, b g Flemensfirth (USA)—Corravilla (IRE) **Boretech & Glen Sadler**
10 **ANOTHER MIRACLE**, 7, ch g Nikos—Orchid **C. E. R. Greenway**
11 **ANY GIVEN DAY (IRE)**, 7, gr g Clodovil (IRE)—Five of Wands **T. G. Leslie**
12 **ARAUCARIA (IRE)**, 8, b m Accordion—Native Artist (IRE) **Miss L. J. Hales**
13 **ART SCHOOL (IRE)**, 4, b g Byron—Intrepidity
14 **AVENGING ACE (IRE)**, 6, b g Heron Island (IRE)—How Provincial (IRE) **T. G. Leslie**
15 **BALLABRIGGS (IRE)**, 11, b g Presenting—Papoose (IRE) **T. J. Hemmings**
16 **BARAATHEN (USA)**, 5, b g Sakhee (USA)—Attaared (USA) **Mr & Mrs P. J. Douglas**
17 **BARDELI (IRE)**, 5, br g Overbury (IRE)—Miss Denman (IRE) **T. G. Leslie**
18 **BEER AND SKITTLES (IRE)**, 5, b g Oscar (IRE)—Katie Quinn (IRE) **Andrew Dick & Philip Holden**
19 **BENJAMIN BITTERN (IRE)**, 5, b g Heron Island (IRE)—Reasoning **D. Passant & H. Williams**
20 **BEST POLICY (USA)**, 4, b g Giant's Causeway (USA)—Honest Lady (USA) **Crow Partnership**
21 **BHALTAIR (IRE)**, 6, gr g Great Palm (USA)—Gypsy Kelly (IRE) **Boretech Limited**
22 **BILLIE HALE (IRE)**, 5, b g Vinnie Roe (IRE)—Charnwood Song **Mr J. M. Glews**
23 **BORULER (IRE)**, 6, b g Brian Boru—Lulus Ride (IRE) **Deva Racing Boruler Partnership**
24 **BOUND FOR GLORY (IRE)**, 6, b g Witness Box (USA)—Musical View (IRE) **T. Meehan & D. J. Burke**
25 **BOURNE**, 6, gr g Linamix (FR)—L'affaire Monique **Timeform Betfair Racing Club Ltd**
26 **BUNCLODY (IRE)**, 7, b g Overbury (IRE)—Wahiba Reason (IRE) **Allan Stennett & Brian Williams**
27 **CALL BACK**, 4, b g Beat Hollow—Payphone **Mr D. Hanafin**
28 **CHAMIREY (FR)**, 9, b g Cadoudal (FR)—Guigone (FR) **D. McCain Jnr**
29 **CHARMINSTER (IRE)**, 6, b g Broadway Flyer (USA)—Monteleena (IRE) **T. G. Leslie**
30 **CHESTER LAD**, 7, ch g Fraam—Our Krissie **J. Henderson**
31 **CINDERS AND ASHES**, 5, b g Beat Hollow—Moon Search **Dermot Hanafin & Phil Cunningham**
32 **CODE BLUE**, 9, b g Sir Harry Lewis (USA)—Nevermind Hey **Peter & Richard Foden & D. McCain Jnr**
33 **CONSTANT CONTACT**, 5, b g Passing Glance—Floriana **Delboy & Rodney**
34 **COOL MISSION (IRE)**, 8, ch g Definite Article—Mettlesome **T. G. Leslie**
35 **CORDILLERA**, 4, ch f Araafa (IRE)—Alexander Celebre (IRE) **Mrs B. McCain**
36 **CUBAN PIECE (IRE)**, 4, b g Azamour (IRE)—Naazeq **The Cuban Partnership**
37 **CYGNET**, 6, b g Dansili—Ballet Princess **Mr & Mrs John & Sue Douglas**
38 **DANNANCEYS HILL (IRE)**, 5, b g Revoque (IRE)—Some Orchestra (IRE) **T. G. Leslie**
39 **DESERT CRY (IRE)**, 6, b g Desert Prince (IRE)—Hataana (USA) **N.Y.P.D Racing**
40 **DILIGENT**, 4, b f Generous (IRE)—Diletia **Chasing Gold Limited**
41 **DIOCLES (IRE)**, 6, b g Bob Back (USA)—Ardrina **L. G. M. Racing**
42 **DJ MILAN (IRE)**, 6, b g Milan—Cafe Matisse (IRE) **Boretech Ltd**
43 **DORABELLE (IRE)**, 7, b m King's Theatre (IRE)—Stateable Case (IRE) **Mr B. J. Richardson**
44 **DOYLY CARTE**, 4, b f Doyen (IRE)—Generous Diana **Elite Racing Club**
45 **DRILL SERGEANT**, 7, br g Rock of Gibraltar (IRE)—Dolydille (IRE) **T. G. Leslie**
46 **DUNOWEN POINT (IRE)**, 6, b g Old Vic—Esbeggi **T. G. Leslie**
47 **EBANOUR (IRE)**, 5, ch g Indian Ridge—Ebadiyla (IRE) **T. G. Leslie**
48 **EIGHTEEN CARAT (IRE)**, 8, b g Luso—Jemma's Gold (IRE) **Halewood International Ltd**
49 **EMPRESS ORCHID**, 7, b m Sir Harry Lewis (USA)—Empress of China (IRE) **Mr W. Bromley & Mrs L. King**
50 **EMRANI (USA)**, 5, b g Rahy (USA)—Ebaza (IRE) **T. G. Leslie**
51 **FABALU (IRE)**, 10, b g Oscar (IRE)—Lizes Birthday (IRE) **T. G. Leslie**
52 **FINLAY**, 9, gr g Parthian Springs—Grey Scally **D. Lockwood**
53 **FLICKA WILLIAMS (IRE)**, 5, b g Broadway Flyer (USA)—
Millies Girl (IRE) **Twenty Four Seven Recruitment Services Ltd**
54 **FRECKLETON (IRE)**, 4, b g Milan—Chancy Lass (IRE) **David Barlow & John A. Raybone**
55 **GHAABESH (IRE)**, 5, b g Alhaarth (IRE)—Alyakkh (IRE) **D. McCain Jnr**
56 **GLENWOOD KNIGHT (IRE)**, 9, ch g Presenting—Glens Lady (IRE) **Peter Knight & Jon Glews**
57 **GOLDEN CALL (IRE)**, 8, b g Goldmark (USA)—Call Me Countess (IRE) **Mr M. M. Allen**
58 **GOTTANY O'S**, 4, b g Storming Home—Miletrian Cares (IRE) **Mr F. McAleavy**
59 **GREAT BOSS (IRE)**, 6, b g Great Palm (USA)—Rezoned (IRE) **Mr J. M. Glews**
60 **GROUSE LODGE (IRE)**, 6, b g Well Chosen—Arctic Jane (IRE) **Mr R. O'Byrne**
61 **GULF PUNCH**, 5, b m Dubawi (IRE)—Fruit Punch (IRE) **Mr R. J. Gwynne**
62 **HIGH ON A HILL (IRE)**, 5, b g Val Royal (FR)—Blue Kestrel (IRE) **Fred Basset's Scratch & Sniff Club**
63 4, b g Old Vic—Hirayna **T. G. Leslie**
64 **HOLLOW TREE**, 4, b g Beat Hollow—Hesperia **Brannon Dennis Dick Holden**
65 **HOWABOUTNOW (IRE)**, 5, ch g Shantou (USA)—Sarah's Cottage (IRE) **Brannon, Dick, Hernon & Holden**
66 **HURRABORU (IRE)**, 5, b g Brian Boru—Fastlass **Deva Racing Brian Boru Partnership**
67 **I'M A GANGSTER (IRE)**, 5, b g Flemensfirth (USA)—Pataya (IRE) **D. McCain Jnr**
68 **ISOBAR (GER)**, 6, b g Monsun (GER)—Ice Dream (GER) **D. McCain Jnr**
69 **IT'S OSCAR (IRE)**, 5, b g Oscar (IRE)—Lady Bramble (IRE) **Mr J. R. Hales**
70 **JACKSON CAGE (IRE)**, 7, b g Oscar (IRE)—Phenics Allstar (IRE) **Penketh & Sankey Jech Racing Club**
71 **JUBAIL (IRE)**, 5, ch g Redback—Daneville (IRE) **C. E. R. Greenway**

MR DONALD MCCAIN—continued

72 **KARINGA DREAM**, 6, b m Karinga Bay—Function Dreamer **R. Kent**
73 **KARINGA HEY**, 7, b g Karinga Bay—Nevermind Hey **D. McCain Jnr**
74 **KARRICAL**, 7, b g Barathea (IRE)—Analogical **Four Fogeys**
75 **KEENELAND (IRE)**, 5, b g Westerner—Delphinium (IRE) **Mr & Mrs Paul Rooney**
76 **KIE (IRE)**, 4, b g Old Vic—Asura (GER) **A. Stennett**
77 **KING'S GRACE**, 6, b g King's Theatre (IRE)—Beauchamp Grace **T. G. Leslie**
78 **KOUP DE KANON (FR)**, 6, b g Robin des Pres (FR)—
　　　　　　　　　　Coup de Sabre (FR) **Timeform Betfair Racing Club & M. Taylor**
79 **LEXI'S BOY (IRE)**, 4, gr g Verglas (IRE)—Jazan (IRE) **T. G. Leslie**
80 **LITTLE GEORGE (IRE)**, 9, b g Heron Island (IRE)—Kyle Eile (IRE) **R. A. George**
81 **LIVELY BARON (IRE)**, 7, b g Presenting—Greavesfind **T. J. Hemmings**
82 **LODEN**, 5, b g Barathea (IRE)—Tentpole (USA) **Mr D. Hanafin**
83 5, B h Oscar (IRE)—Mariaetta (IRE) **Miss A. Lindsell**
84 **MISTOFFELEES**, 6, b g Tiger Hill (IRE)—Auenlust (GER) **Mr & Mrs P. J. Douglas**
85 **MOSCOW PRESENTS (IRE)**, 4, b g Presenting—Moscow Madame (IRE) **Mr J. Duggan**
86 **MOUNTAIN HIKER (IRE)**, 5, b g Azamour (IRE)—Sagamartha **Mr J. M. Glews**
87 **MR CHIPPY (IRE)**, 8, b g Laveron—Lady Denel (IRE) **Mr P. Holden**
88 4, B g Darsi (FR)—Mrs McClintock (IRE) **Mr P. Williams**
89 **MWALESHI**, 7, b g Oscar (IRE)—Roxy River **D. McCain Jnr**
90 **NODFORM RICHARD**, 6, b g Groom Dancer (USA)—Shayzara (IRE) **D. M. Gorton**
91 **NOWURHURLIN (IRE)**, 5, b g Saddlers' Hall (IRE)—Pint Taken (IRE) **The Ground Hurlers**
92 **OMOKOROA (IRE)**, 6, b g Hawkeye (IRE)—Alycus (USA) **Brendan Richardson & Jon Glews**
93 **ONE FOR LOU (IRE)**, 6, b g Presenting—One Last Chance **Andrew & Louise Dick**
94 **ORLITTLEBYLITTLE**, 6, b g Bollin Eric—Davana Blue (FR) **Deva Racing Bollin Eric Partnership**
95 **OUR MICK**, 6, gr g Karinga Bay—Dawn's Della **K. Benson & Mrs E. Benson**
96 **OVERAFRICA (IRE)**, 6, b g Overbury (IRE)—Siberiansdaughter (IRE) **T. J. Hemmings**
97 **OVERTURN (IRE)**, 8, b g Barathea (IRE)—Kristal Bridge **T. G. Leslie**
98 **PAINTED SKY**, 9, ch g Rainbow Quest (USA)—Emplane (USA) **Mr R. Drye**
99 **PAMPANITO**, 6, b g Bollin Eric—Seamill (IRE) **Tim & Miranda Johnson Partnership**
100 **PEDDLERS CROSS (IRE)**, 7, b g Oscar (IRE)—Patscilla **T. G. Leslie**
101 **PHILANDER**, 5, b g Red Ransom (USA)—Fidelio's Miracle (USA) **D. Hanafin & P. Cunningham**
102 **RAILWAY DILLON (IRE)**, 7, b g Witness Box (USA)—Laura's Native (IRE) **Johnson, Maxwell & Purcell**
103 **RAIN MAC**, 4, b c Beat Hollow—Quenched **Mr T. Bloom**
104 **RAWAAJ**, 6, ro g Linamix (FR)—Inaaq **Tim & Miranda Johnson Partnership**
105 **REAL MILAN (IRE)**, 7, b g Milan—The Real Athlete (IRE) **Mrs D. L. Whateley**
106 **REALIGNMENT (IRE)**, 7, b g Celtic Swing—Sharera (IRE) **Mr Patrick McKeon**
107 **REALMONT (IRE)**, 7, b g Khalkevi (IRE)—Christina (FR) **T. G. Leslie**
108 **RECORD BREAKER (IRE)**, 8, b g In The Wings—Overruled (IRE) **The Generals Men Racing Club I**
109 **RED MERLIN (IRE)**, 7, ch g Soviet Star (USA)—
　　　　　　　　　　Truly Bewitched (USA) **Timeform Betfair Racing Club & M. Taylor**
110 **RED ROCCO (IRE)**, 5, ch g Croco Rouge (IRE)—Youbetido (IRE) **Glen's Fools 2**
111 **REINDEER DIPPIN**, 10, b g Sir Harry Lewis (USA)—Analogical **Sandgrounders**
112 **SAGA DE TERCEY (FR)**, 7, b g Sagacity (FR)—Fanciulla Del West (FR) **Mr P. Holden**
113 **SAN BELLINO**, 4, ch g Galileo (IRE)—Canda (USA) **Crow Partnership**
114 5, B g Cloudings (IRE)—Santavino (IRE) **Halewood International Ltd**
115 **SEEDLESS**, 7, br m Mtoto—Unseeded **R. Kent**
116 **SHORT TAKES (USA)**, 4, ch g Lemon Drop Kid (USA)—Gabriellina Giof **Mr T. P. McMahon & Mr D. McMahon**
117 **SILVER GYPSY (IRE)**, 7, b m Luso—Your Life **Mrs T. D. Yeomans**
118 **SMADYNIUM (IRE)**, 4, gr g Smadoun (FR)—Sea Music (FR) **Mr C. R. B. Hunt**
119 **SMART ACT (IRE)**, 6, b g Oscar (IRE)—La Luna (IRE) **T. J. Hemmings**
120 **SMITHY THE HORSE (IRE)**, 6, ch g Kris Kin (USA)—Priyanka **John Smith's Racing Limited**
121 **SON OF FLICKA**, 8, b g Groom Dancer (USA)—Calendula **Twenty Four Seven Recruitment Services Ltd**
122 **SPIDER PALM (IRE)**, 6, ch g Great Palm (USA)—Incy Wincy Spider **Racegoers Club Owners Group**
123 **SPORTS LINE (IRE)**, 9, b g Norwich—Hot Line (IRE) **Mr T. A. Killoran**
124 **STAR IN FLIGHT**, 5, b g Mtoto—Star Entry **Lucky Bin Racing**
125 **STORMING GALE (IRE)**, 6, b g Revoque (IRE)—Dikler Gale (IRE) **T. G. Leslie**
126 **SUD PACIFIQUE (IRE)**, 4, b g Montjeu—Anestasia (IRE) **Mr T. Bloom**
127 **SUPER DUTY (IRE)**, 6, b g Shantou (USA)—Sarah's Cottage (IRE) **Brannon, Dick, Hernon & Holden**
128 **SWIFT ARROW (IRE)**, 6, b g Overbury (IRE)—Clover Run (IRE) **Mr & Mrs C. Strang Steel**
129 **SYDNEY PAGET (IRE)**, 5, b g Flemensfirth (USA)—Shuil Aoibhinn (IRE) **Roger O'Byrne**
130 **TARA ROYAL**, 7, b g Kayf Tara—Poussetiere Deux (FR) **T. G. Leslie**
131 **TARLAN (IRE)**, 6, b g Milan—Nethertara **T. G. Leslie**
132 **TC SPITFIRE (IRE)**, 5, b g Garuda (IRE)—Stamford Lady (IRE) **T. J. Crehan**
133 **THE WEATHERMAN (IRE)**, 5, b g Definite Article—Stateable Case (IRE) **Clwydian Connections**
134 **THUNDERCRACK (IRE)**, 7, b g Oscar (IRE)—Champagne Warrior (IRE) **The Bassington Gilroy Partnership**
135 **TIGER MAGUIRE (IRE)**, 7, b g Flemensfirth (USA)—De La Renta (IRE) **The MerseyClyde Partnership**

MR DONALD MCCAIN—continued

136 **TONVADOSA**, 4, b f Flemensfirth (USA)—Sleepless Eye **T. Meehan & D. J. Burke**
137 **TORNADO BOB (IRE)**, 7, b br g Bob Back (USA)—Double Glazed (IRE) **Mrs D. L. Whateley**
138 **TOTAL REBELLION (IRE)**, 6, b g Craigsteel—Hil Rhapsody **James & Jean Potter**
139 **VFORVICTORY (GER)**, 9, b g Poliglote—Valentine Rose (GER) **T. G. Leslie**
140 **WALK LIKE A MAN (IRE)**, 6, b g Milan—Hushlet **D. McCain Jnr**
141 **WEIRD AL (IRE)**, 9, b g Accordion—Bucks Gift (IRE) **Brannon Dennis Dick Holden**
142 **WOODPOLE ACADEMY (IRE)**, 5, b g Beneficial—Midday Caller (IRE) **Boretech Limited**
143 **WYMOTT (IRE)**, 8, b g Witness Box (USA)—Tanya Thyne (IRE) **T. J. Hemmings**

Other Owners: Mr D. Albert, Mr N. P. Armstrong, Mr Dave Barlow, Mrs Anita Bassington, Mr K. Benson, Mrs E. Benson, Boretech, Mr W. A. Bromley, Mr Andrew Brown, Mr D. J. Burke, Mr Mick Burrowes, Mr N. Caddy, Mr G. Caine, Mr Anthony Coyne, Mr K. Coyne, Mr Alec Craig, Mr Phil Cunningham, Mr M. N. Dennis, Mr Andrew Dick, Mrs Louise Dick, Mr Peter J. Douglas, Mrs Sue Douglas, Mr John Douglas, Mrs L. Douglas, Mr Rob Drye, Mr Malcolm Drye, Mr Andrew Duckworth, Mr W. A. Eastup, Mr E. P. Foden, Mr R. P. Foden, Mr M. Foster, Mrs J. Foster, Mr Jon Glews, Miss L. Hales, Mr J. Hales, Mr D. Hanafin, Mr Tony Hill, Mr Philip Holden, Mr Tim Johnson, Mrs Miranda Johnson, Mr G. L. Joynson, Mr S. A. Kaznowski, Mrs Kay Kent, Mr Steve Kent, Mrs Linda King, Mr P. A. Knight, Mr George Maxwell, Mr D. McCain Jnr, Mrs B. McCain, Mr D. McMahon, Mr T. P McMahon, Mr Tom Meagher, Mr Tony Meehan, Mr R. Mentha, Mr D. Moyes, Mr Kevin Mulville, Miss M. McMahon, Mr T. P McMahon, Mr Tom Meagher, Mr Tony Meehan, Mr R. Mentha, Mr D. Moyes, Mr Kevin Mulville, Miss M. Noden, Mr Michael Owen, Mr Ray Pattison, Mr Dave Pearson, Mr J. E. Potter, Mrs J. E. Potter, Mr Richard Purcell, Ms C. Ralls, Mr John A. Raybone, Mr P. Ryan, Mr Tony Sadler, Mrs Glen Sadler, Mr P. Scholes, Mr Allan Stennett, Mr Matthew Taylor, Timeform Betfair Racing Club Ltd, Mr E. C. Watson, Mr Neil Watt, Miss H. L. Webster, Mr Brian S. Williams, Mr Graham Worsley.

Jockey (NH): Jason Maguire, Adrian Lane. **Conditional:** Callum Whillans, Conor Flanelly, Henry Brooke, John Kington.
Amateur: Mr N. Slatter.

435
MR TIM MCCARTHY, Godstone
Postal: **Nags Hall Farm, Oxted Road, Godstone, Surrey, RH9 8DB**
Contacts: PHONE **(01883) 740379** FAX **(01883) 740381** MOBILE **(07887) 763062**

1 **CAVALRY GUARD (USA)**, 8, ch g Officer (USA)—Leeward City (USA) **Surrey Racing Club**
2 **CRAICAJACK (IRE)**, 5, ch g Avonbridge—Rash Gift **Cavendish Star Racing**
3 **GOODISON PARK**, 5, ch m Big Shuffle (USA)—Perfect Dream **A & J Racing, Alex Semel & Nick Horsfall**
4 **JIMMY RYAN (IRE)**, 11, b g Orpen (USA)—Kaysama (FR) **Mrs C. V. McCarthy**
5 **MA FILLE SAUVAGE**, 4, ch f Loup Sauvage (USA)—Ma Barnicle (IRE) **Mrs C. V. McCarthy**
6 **TAQAAT (USA)**, 4, b c Forestry (USA)—Alrayihah (IRE) **Mr K. J. P. Gundlach**
7 **UNDERSTORY (USA)**, 5, b h Forestry (USA)—Sha Tha (USA) **The Bordeaux Fine Wines Racing Club**
8 **VINCES**, 8, gr g Lomitas—Vadinaxa (FR) **T. D. McCarthy**

THREE-YEAR-OLDS
9 **PERIWINKLE WAY**, b f Acclamation—Millsini **Mrs G. Scudder**

Other Owners: A & J Racing Ltd, R. Frost, Mr N. P. Horsfall, S. J. Piper, Mrs A. J. Semel.

Assistant Trainer: Mrs C.V. McCarthy

436
MR WILLIE MCCREERY, Kildare
Postal: **Rathbride Stables, Kildare, Co. Kildare, Ireland**
Contacts: PHONE **(00 353) 455 22444** FAX **(00 353) 455 22455** MOBILE **(00 353) 876 783303**
E-MAIL **info@willie-mccreery.com** WEBSITE **www.willie-mccreery.com**

1 **BANK ON BLACK (IRE)**, 5, b m Big Bad Bob (IRE)—Lady Belzoni (IRE) **Mrs Amanda McCreery**
2 **COLOUR OF LOVE (IRE)**, 4, ch f Le Vie Dei Colori—Priceoflove (IRE) **GAA Legends Syndicate**
3 **DOLLIES CHILD (IRE)**, 5, ch m Naheez (USA)—Pharlucy (IRE) **Mrs Lucy Lynch**
4 **GERALDINES LASS (IRE)**, 4, ch f Titus Livius (FR)—Nullarbor **Mrs Amanda McCreery**
5 **IONISPHERE**, 7, b g Vettori (IRE)—Liska's Dance (USA) **Mrs Amanda McCreery**
6 **JUDIES CHILD (IRE)**, 4, b f Majestic Missile (IRE)—Belle Child (USA) **Mrs Lucy Lynch**
7 **MCMONAGLE (USA)**, 4, ch g Mizzen Mast (USA)—Dippers (USA) **Mr Christopher Grosso**
8 **NOBLE FOUR (IRE)**, 4, b br g Kheleyf (USA)—Buttons Galore (IRE) **Noeleen Slattery**
9 **NUTAKOVA (IRE)**, 4, b g Ad Valorem (USA)—Nutley Dancer (IRE) **Thomas Jones**
10 **OVERNOVA (IRE)**, 4, br f Diamond Green (FR)—Over Rating **Thomas Jones**
11 **ROBYN RUA (IRE)**, 6, b g King's Theatre (IRE)—Keep Hunting (IRE) **John McDonald**
12 5, B g Snurge—Strong Heather (IRE) **Liam McGee**
13 **SURE THYNE (IRE)**, 6, b br m Definite Article—Proverbial Thyne (IRE) **John O'Dwyer**

MR WILLIE MCCREERY—continued

14 VALBUCCA (IRE), 5, b m Val Royal (FR)—Nambucca **Pat Cosgrave**
15 WHISPER COOL (IRE), 5, b g One Cool Cat (USA)—Whispering (IRE) **Bernard Phelan, Joe Kirwan**

THREE-YEAR-OLDS

16 BEFOREIT'STOOLATE (IRE), b f Alhaarth (IRE)—Namoos (USA) **Shane Doyle**
17 BROTHER RABBIT (IRE), b g Modigliani (USA)—Son Chou **Mrs Amanda McCreery**
18 DIABOLITO (IRE), b c Lend A Hand—Spirit of Hope (IRE) **Nicola Cullen**
19 ELEGANT SISI (IRE), b f Elnadim (USA)—Elba (IRE) **Damien McElroy, Stan Glynn**
20 KANES PASS (IRE), br f Clodovil (IRE)—Pagan Game (IRE) **Pat Cosgrove**
21 SOPHIES ECHO (IRE), b f Footstepsinthesand—Lapis Lazuli **David Kennedy**
22 SUSIESCOT (IRE), gr f Verglas (IRE)—Princess Susie **Paul Newman**
23 TAKING CHANCES (IRE), b f Strategic Prince—Phantom Act (USA) **Mrs Amanda McCreery**

TWO-YEAR-OLDS

24 Ch c 5/3 Haafet (USA)—Asfurah's Dream (IRE) (Nayef (USA)) (18061) **GAA Legends Syndicate**
25 B f 28/3 Red Clubs (IRE)—Beat The Rain (Beat Hollow) (8209) **David O'Rourke, Joe Kirwan, Noeleen McCreevy**
26 B f 5/4 Street Sense (USA)—Crown of Jewels (USA) (Half a Year (USA)) (18315) **Thomas Jones**
27 Ch f 22/2 Choisir (AUS)—Spinaimanwin (IRE) (Spinning World (USA)) **Brendan Cullinane**

---

437 **MR PHIL MCENTEE, Newmarket**
Postal: Racefield Stables, Carriageway, Hamilton Road, Newmarket, Suffolk, CB8 7JQ
Contacts: **PHONE** (01638) 662092 **FAX** (01638) 662092 **MOBILE** (07802) 663256

1 BIRD DOG, 6, ch g Compton Place—Form At Last **S. P. Shore**
2 BLACK BACCARA, 5, b m Superior Premium—Areish (IRE) **Eventmaker Racehorses**
3 BON ROYALE, 4, b f Val Royal (FR)—Bonella (IRE) **The Wayfarers**
4 COMMUNITY (USA), 4, b f Proud Citizen (USA)—Rimini Road (USA) **Mr S. Jakes**
5 JONNIE SKULL (IRE), 6, b g Pyrus (USA)—Sovereign Touch (IRE) **Eventmaker Racehorses**
6 LADY ELLICE, 4, b f Iceman—Optimise (IRE) **Mrs Y. Calder**
7 MI REGALO, 4, b g Cadeaux Genereux—Lloc **Mr S. Jakes**
8 PUTIN (IRE), 4, b g Fasliyev (USA)—Consignia (IRE) **Mr S. Jakes**
9 TIME FOR HARRY, 5, b g Doyen (IRE)—Corn Circle (IRE) **Eagle Bloodstock & Racing**

THREE-YEAR-OLDS

10 ANGEL CAKE (IRE), b f Dark Angel (IRE)—Royal Jelly **Mr W. J. Sewell**
11 CORN MAIDEN, b f Refuse To Bend (IRE)—Namat (IRE) **Ms J. McHugh**
12 ISHIAMIRACLE, ch f Ishiguru (USA)—Sukuma (IRE) **Mr S. Jakes**

Other Owners: Mr A. P. Bendelow, Mrs D. C. Cooper, C. J. Cooper, Mr I. Hancock, Miss R. M. Hatley, Mr M. A. Humphris, T. D. Johnson, Mrs R. L. McEntee.

Jockey (NH): Jimmy McCarthy.

---

438 **MR MURTY MCGRATH, Maidstone**
Postal: Spicketts House, Kiln Barn Road, East Malling, Kent, ME19 6BJ
Contacts: **PHONE** (01732) 840173 **FAX** (01732) 873774 **MOBILE** (07818) 098073
E-MAIL mjmcgrath@hotmail.com

1 FINLODEX, 5, ch g Pastoral Pursuits—Ela Aphrodite **Mr R. P. Gallagher**
2 REZWAAN, 5, b g Alhaarth (IRE)—Nasij (USA) **Gallagher Equine Ltd**
3 WHATS YOUR STORY, 4, b g Bertolini (USA)—Legal Belle **Mr R. P. Gallagher**

THREE-YEAR-OLDS

4 AMERICAN BLING (USA), b g Johannesburg (USA)—American Jewel (USA) **Gallagher Equine Ltd**
5 BEN CROY, b g Nayef (USA)—Chrysalis **Gallagher Equine Ltd**
6 B g Tiger Hill (IRE)—Klaribel (IRE) **Gallagher Equine Ltd**
7 Ch c Stonesider (USA)—Sweet Charity (USA) **Gallagher Equine Ltd**

TWO-YEAR-OLDS

8 B c 8/4 Royal Applause—Spanish Springs (IRE) (Xaar) (50000) **Gallagher Equine Ltd**

Assistant Trainer: Heidi Harris (07795) 178178

Jockey (flat): Shane Kelly. **Jockey (NH):** Timmy Murphy.

439 MRS JEAN MCGREGOR, Milnathort
Postal: Tillyrie House, Milnathort, Kinross, KY13 0RW
Contacts: PHONE (01577) 865071 (01577) 863418 MOBILE (07764) 464299
E-MAIL john-lawrie@btconnect.com

1 ASKALOTT (IRE), 7, b g Ashkalani (IRE)—Alottalady (IRE) **Miss A. L. McGregor**
2 CIGALAS, 7, ch g Selkirk (USA)—Langoustine (AUS) **Tillyrie Racing Club**
3 JACKOFHEARTS, 4, b g Beat Hollow—Boutique **Mr S. Taylor**
4 KING'S ENVOY (USA), 13, b g Royal Academy (USA)—Island of Silver (USA) **Miss A. L. McGregor**
5 MORE SHENNANIGANS, 11, ch g Rock City—Blooming Spring (IRE) **J. Thomson**
6 SNOOZE N YOU LOSE, 7, b g Helissio (FR)—Utmost (IRE) **Miss A. L. McGregor**
7 5, B g Fraam—Trilby
8 WATERSKI, 11, b g Petoski—Celtic Waters **The Good To Soft Firm**

Other Owners: Mr J. A. S. Burnett, Mrs J. C. McGregor, Mrs D. Thomson.

Jockey (flat): Andrew Mullen. Jockey (NH): Keith Mercer. Conditional: Ryan Mania. Apprentice: Shane B. Kelly. Amateur: Miss A.L. McGregor.

440 MR IAN MCINNES, Catwick
Postal: Ivy House, Main Street, Catwick, Beverley, North Humberside, HU17 5PJ
Contacts: HOME/FAX (01964) 542115 FAX (01964) 542115 MOBILE (07720) 451233

1 BERTBRAND, 7, b g Bertolini (USA)—Mi Amor (IRE) **B. Kirby**
2 BONNIE PRINCE BLUE, 9, ch g Tipsy Creek (USA)—Heart So Blue **Mr M. Hardcastle**
3 DOCTOR ZHIVAGO, 5, b g Shamardal (USA)—Balalaika **T. Elsey**
4 FORBIDDEN (IRE), 9, b g Singspiel (IRE)—Fragrant Oasis **J. Morris**
5 INGLEBY STAR (IRE), 7, b g Fath (USA)—Rosy Scintilla (IRE) **S. P. Hackney**
6 MORAL ISSUE, 4, b g Ishiguru (USA)—Morale **B. Valentine**
7 MORERMALOKE, 4, ch g Bahamian Bounty—Rainbow End **C. G. R. Booth**
8 PAPARAAZI (IRE), 10, b g Victory Note (USA)—Raazi **J. Morris**
9 POWERFUL PIERRE, 5, ch g Compton Place—Alzianah **R. J. Mustill**
10 SHARP SOVEREIGN (USA), 6, b g Cactus Ridge (USA)—Queen of Humor (USA) **S. P. Hackney**
11 SLEIGHTS BOY (IRE), 4, b g Kyllachy—Fanny Bay (IRE) **T Elsey, S A Elsey, R Mustill, J Agar**
12 TAGULA BREEZE (IRE), 6, b g Tagula (IRE)—Pearl Egg (IRE) **T. Elsey**

TWO-YEAR-OLDS

13 Ch g 11/4 Thousand Words—Elite Hope (USA) (Moment of Hope (USA)) (2462)
14 B g 5/4 Soviet Star—Inourthoughts (IRE) (Desert Style (IRE)) (6978) **I. D. Woolfitt**
15 B f 10/4 Compton Place—Mrs Snaffles (IRE) (Indian Danehill (IRE)) (6666) **B. Valentine**
16 B f 9/2 Baltic King—Rosy Scintilla (IRE) (Thatching) (4515)
17 Ch f 11/4 Choisir (AUS)—Valley of The Moon (IRE) (Monashee Mountain (USA)) (2095) **T. Elsey**

Other Owners: Mr J. Agar, Mrs S. A. Elsey, I. W. McInnes.

Assistant Trainer: Mr Ian McInnes (Senior)

441 MS KAREN MCLINTOCK, Newcastle Upon Tyne
Postal: The Byerley Stud, Ingoe, Newcastle-Upon-Tyne, NE20 0SZ
Contacts: PHONE (01661) 886356 FAX (01661) 886356 MOBILE (07966) 776710
E-MAIL karen.mclintock@equiname.co.uk WEBSITE www.karenmclintock.co.uk

1 ABSOLUTELY BYGONES (IRE), 4, b g Alderbrook—Majella (IRE) **Mr G. R. Stockdale**
2 BRIDLINGTONBYGONES (IRE), 7, br g Bob's Return (IRE)—Slaney Athlete (USA) **Mr A. C. Lamont**
3 BYGONES OF BRID (IRE), 9, b g Alderbrook—Glenadore **J. R. Callow**
4 CADDELLS ROW, 4, b g Lahib (USA)—Tartan Belle **Mr A. C. Lamont**
5 4, B g Milan—Letterwoman **Mr C. A. Kerr**
6 MADAME BLAVATSKY (FR), 4, gr f Super Celebre (FR)—Lovarisk (FR) **Ms D. E. Young**
7 MASON DAVID BROWN (IRE), 5, b g Luso—Hindi (FR) **Mr A. C. Lamont**
8 MASON HINDMARSH, 5, ch g Dr Fong (USA)—Sierra Virgen (USA) **Mr J. R. Adams**
9 NODFORMS VIOLET (IRE), 8, ch g Rashar (USA)—Whose Yer Wan (IRE) **Mr A. C. Lamont**
10 OMANI REBEL, 4, b g Runyon (IRE)—Forgotten Flowers (IRE) **Mr A. C. Lamont**
11 SECRET PAST (IRE), 7, b g Rudimentary (USA)—Lucifer's Way **Mr A. C. Lamont**
12 SIGN PRO (IRE), 4, b g Noverre (USA)—Sadalsud (IRE) **Equiname Ltd**

MS KAREN MCLINTOCK—continued

13 **SUGAR SANDS**, 7, b g Beat All (USA)—Beanley Brook **Mrs S. A. Sutton**
14 **ULTIEP (FR)**, 4, gr g Ragmar (FR)—Naltiepy (FR) **Mr A. C. Lamont**

Assistant Trainer: Donald Eddy

---

442   **MR ED McMAHON, Lichfield**
Postal: **Horsley Brook Farm, Tamworth Road, Lichfield, Staffordshire, WS14 9PT**
Contacts: **PHONE** (01543) 481224 **FAX** (01543) 651100 **MOBILE** (07787) 951630
E-MAIL comeracing@horsleybrook.fsnet.co.uk **WEBSITE** www.edmcmahonracing.co.uk

1 **ASTROPHYSICAL JET**, 5, b m Dubawi (IRE)—Common Knowledge **Ladas**
2 **BEAUTY PAGEANT (IRE)**, 5, ch m Bahamian Bounty—My American Beauty **J. C. Fretwell**
3 **EASY OVER (IRE)**, 4, ch g Dr Fong (USA)—Desert Alchemy (IRE) **D. J. Allen. S. E. Allen/ G. A. Weetman**
4 **KENYAN CAT**, 5, br m One Cool Cat (USA)—Nairobi (FR) **David Botterill & John Guest**
5 **NOBLE STORM (USA)**, 6, b h Yankee Gentleman (USA)—Changed Tune (USA) **R. L. Bedding**
6 **OMEGA CENTAURI**, 4, ch f Needwood Blade—Distant Stars (IRE) **Mrs J. McMahon**
7 **PIDDIE'S POWER**, 5, ch m Starcraft (NZ)—Telori **The Brookfield Stud & Partners**
8 **SHALUCA**, 5, br m Shamardal (USA)—Noushkey **Mr M. W. Crane**
9 **TAMASOU (IRE)**, 7, b g Tamarisk (IRE)—Soubresaut (IRE) **Brooklands Racing**
10 **TEMPLE MEADS**, 4, ch c Avonbridge—Harryana **J. C. Fretwell**
11 **VENUTIUS**, 5, b g Doyen—Boadicea's Chariot **Dr H. Jones**

THREE-YEAR-OLDS

12 **ARTISTIC JEWEL (IRE)**, ch f Excellent Art—Danish Gem **R. L. Bedding**
13 **KODIAC ISLAND**, b f Kodiac—Inveraray **David Botterill & John Guest**
14 **RADIO GAGA**, b f Multiplex—Gagajulu **Multiplex Racing**
15 **SMALL STEPS (IRE)**, b f Acclamation—Last Tango (IRE) **J. C. Fretwell**
16 **TARTIFLETTE**, b f Dr Fong (USA)—Bright Moll **A. R. F. Buxton**
17 **VESPASIA**, b f Medicean—Agrippina **Mrs F. S. Williams**
18 **WAYWARD WIND**, b g Needwood Blade—Yabint El Sham **Mrs J. McMahon**

TWO-YEAR-OLDS

19 B f 31/3 Compton Place—Ashover Amber (Green Desert (USA)) (7142)
20 B f 20/3 Kodiac—Berenica (IRE) (College Chapel) (24761)
21 B c 20/3 Oratorio (IRE)—Blue Reema (IRE) (Bluebird (USA)) (26666)
22 B c 29/4 Royal Applause—Cherokee Stream (IRE) (Indian Ridge) (50000)
23 **COLOUR MY WORLD**, gr c 14/3 With Approval (CAN)—Nadeszhda (Nashwan (USA)) (30000) **Mr P. A. Wilkins**
24 Ch c 30/4 Iffraaj—Dance On (Caerleon (USA)) (32000)
25 **DUSTY STORM**, ch f 8/4 Kyllachy—Halliwell House (Selkirk (USA)) (30000) **R. L. Bedding**
26 B c 8/4 Haafet (USA)—Fantastic Account (Fantastic Light (USA)) (25000)
27 **FLIRTINASKIRT**, b f 11/1 Avonbridge—Talampaya (IRE) (Elusive Quality (USA)) (10476) **Mr P. A. Wilkins**
28 Ch c 25/3 Sakhee's Secret—Lark In The Park (IRE) (Grand Lodge (USA)) **Unregistered Partnership**
29 **LOOK ON BY**, gr c 28/2 Byron—Where's Carol (Anfield) **S. L. Edwards**
30 **MISS METICULOUS**, ch f 26/2 Bahamian Bounty—Umniya (IRE) (Bluebird (USA)) (27619) **The LAM Partnership**
31 **SECRET LOOK**, ch c 23/3 Sakhee's Secret—Look Here's Carol (IRE) (Safawan) **S. L. Edwards**
32 Ch c 21/3 Choisir (AUS)—Selique (Selkirk (USA)) (31000)
33 B f 12/2 Royal Applause—Smooch (Inchinor) (28571)
34 B c 19/3 Hernando (FR)—Trullitti (Bahri (USA)) (62000) **The LAM Partnership**
35 Br c 29/3 Cockney Rebel (IRE)—Vino Veritas (USA) (Chief's Crown (USA)) (33333)

Other Owners: D. J. Allen, Mrs S. E. Allen, M. Ball, M. H. Bates, D. R. Botterill, Dr M. F. Ford, Mr J. J. Guest, Miss L. Lawler, D. S. Lovatt, Mrs A. M. Mercs, Ms L. M. Mulcahy, Mr C. Mullin, Mrs M. T. Mullin, A. Stennett, Mrs G. A. Weetman, N. Willmott.

Assistant Trainer: Bryan Arthur McMahon

Jockey (flat): Graham Gibbons.

---

443   **MR BRIAN McMATH, Newmarket**
Postal: **Marlborough House Stables, Old Station Road, Newmarket, Suffolk, CB8 8DW**
Contacts: **PHONE** (01638) 660706 **FAX** (01638) 660706 **MOBILE** (07734) 564923
E-MAIL brian.mcmath@tesco.net

1 **FIRST COMING**, 8, ch g Best of The Bests (IRE)—Arriving **Mr S. Jakes**
2 **I AM THE MAN**, 7, b g Auction House (USA)—Sally Gardens **Mr R. C. Ames**

444 MR GRAEME MCPHERSON, Stow-On-The-Wold
Postal: **Martins Hill, Bledington Road, Stow-on-the-Wold, Gloucestershire, GL54 1JH**
Contacts: PHONE **(01451) 830769** MOBILE **(07815) 887360**
WEBSITE www.mcphersonracing.co.uk

1 COCACOBANA (IRE), 7, ch g Snurge—Dun Dun (IRE) **Mr D. Rodney**
2 CONSTANT CUPID (IRE), 8, b g Winged Love (IRE)—Eva Ross (IRE) **Mr D. R. Du Croz**
3 DANCING EMILY (IRE), 6, ch m Anshan—Goodthyne Lady (IRE) **Burnham Plastering & Drylining Ltd**
4 FAIRVIEW SUE, 8, gr m Alflora (IRE)—Tall Story **Mr A. D. Davis**
5 HARRY HUNT, 5, b g Bertolini (USA)—Qasirah (IRE) **Arion Racing**
6 HURRICANE ELECTRIC (IRE), 7, b g Dansili—Heaven's Echo (USA) **Mr R. W. Orr**
7 JE NE SAIS PLUS (FR), 8, gr m Spadoun (FR)—Sheer Drop (FR) **Mrs L. Day**
8 KILCREA ASLA (IRE), 11, b g Oscar (IRE)—Alottalady (IRE) **Mrs L. Day**
9 LANEGUY (FR), 7, b g Nikos—Aykoku Saky (FR) **Mrs L. Day**
10 MISS BROWNES FANCY (IRE), 4, b f Encosta de Lago (AUS)—
Be Dignified (IRE) **The Martins Hill Racing Partnership**
11 MOULIN TOUR (FR), 6, ch g Majorien—Queen of Kenda (FR)
12 PRESENTED (IRE), 5, ch g Presenting—Rustic Court (IRE) **The Presented Out Of Court Partnership**
13 QUEL BRUERE (FR), 8, gr g Sassanian—Housseliere (FR) **The Reserved Judgment Partnership**
14 QUIZWORK (FR), 8, b g Network (GER)—Galene de Saisy (FR) **Quizzy Rascals**
15 RORY BOY (USA), 7, b g Aldebaran (USA)—Purr Pleasure (USA) **Mr P. A. Randall**
16 SOCIETY SHARES (IRE), 7, ch g Moscow Society (USA)—Presenting Shares (IRE) **Arion Racing**
17 TICKATACK (IRE), 7, gr g Tikkanen (USA)—Theflyingcannister (IRE) **The Martins Hill Racing Partnership**
18 TRADITIONAL BOB (IRE), 7, b g Saddlers' Hall (IRE)—Portia's Delight (IRE) **M. D. Jones**
19 WESTLIN' WINDS (IRE), 6, b g Montjeu (IRE)—Uliana (USA) **Mr P. A. Randall**
20 5, B g Great Palm (USA)—Woodside
21 WYCHWOODS DANCER, 5, b m Carnival Dancer—Miss Gratis (IRE) **Kevin & Anne Glastonbury**
22 WYCHWOODS MIST, 5, b m Umistim—Blackchurch Lass (IRE) **Kevin & Anne Glastonbury**
23 YOUNG JIM (IRE), 6, b g Winged Love (IRE)—Sitoco (USA) **The Gaining Ground Partnership**
24 ZANIR (FR), 8, b g Munir—Shahmy (USA) **Mrs L. Day**

Other Owners: Mr S. Barnes, Mr H. Burdett, K. J. Glastonbury, Mrs A. J. Glastonbury, Mr A. N. Green, Mrs S. Hartley, Mr S. E. Holah, Mr S. P. Lamberton, G. McPherson, Mrs S. M. McPherson, Ms P. A. Smith.

Assistant Trainer: Mick Finn

Jockey (NH): Jodie Mogford, Paddy Brennan. **Conditional:** Tom Molloy, Killian Moore. **Amateur:** Mr Oliver Garner.

445 MR HUGH MCWILLIAMS, Pilling
Postal: **Moss Side Farm, Lancaster Road, Pilling, Preston, Lancashire, PR3 6SR**

1 CARNIVAL DREAM, 7, b m Carnival Dancer—Reach The Wind (USA) **J. D. Riches**
2 COLAMANDIS, 5, b m Lucky Story (USA)—Merry May **J. D. Riches**
3 FORZARZI (IRE), 8, b g Forzando—Zarzi (IRE) **J. D. Riches**
4 GOUGANE (IRE), 9, b g Luso—Gill's Honey (IRE) **Mrs L. Wohlers**
5 ILLAWALLA, 4, b g Indesatchel (IRE)—Adorable Cherub (USA) **Mr S. Kellett**
6 RUNNING WATER, 4, ch f Blue Dakota (IRE)—Floral Spark **Mr S. Kellett**
7 SNOW DANCER (IRE), 8, b m Desert Style (IRE)—Bella Vie (IRE) **Mrs L. Wohlers**

THREE-YEAR-OLDS

8 IDAROSE (IRE), b f Scorpion (IRE)—Garra Princess (IRE) **J. D. Riches**

Other Owners: Mr D. Peach.

446 MR NOEL MEADE, Navan
Postal: **Tu Va Stables, Castletown-Kilpatrick, Navan, Co. Meath, Ireland**
Contacts: PHONE **(00 353) 46 905 4197** FAX **(00 353) 46 905 4459** MOBILE **(00 353) 87 256 6039**
E-MAIL tuvastables@eircom.net

1 AITMATOV (GER), 11, b g Lomitas—Atoka (GER)
2 ANGE BLANC (FR), 4, gr g Keltos (FR)—Trasimene
3 ANOTHER PALM (IRE), 7, gr g Great Palm (USA)—Park Rose (IRE)
4 APACHE STRONGHOLD (IRE), 4, b g Milan—First Battle (IRE)

MR NOEL MEADE—continued

5 **BAT MASTERSON (IRE)**, 4, b g Alhaarth (IRE)—Desert Grouse (USA)
6 **BENEMEADE (IRE)**, 4, b g Beneficial—Millicent Bridge (IRE)
7 **BENEVOLENT (IRE)**, 5, ch g Beneficial—Bobs Lass (IRE)
8 **BLISSFUL MOMENT (USA)**, 5, b br g Dynaformer (USA)—Arabian Spell (IRE)
9 **BLUE CANNON (IRE)**, 4, B G High Chaparral (IRE)—Blushing Barada (USA)
10 **BOSE IKARD (IRE)**, 4, br g Brian Boru—Dolldyedee (IRE)
11 **BRIARY GAP (IRE)**, 5, b g Westerner—Fu's Legend (IRE)
12 **CAMLIN FLOW (IRE)**, 5, b g Oscar (IRE)—Shannon Foam
13 **CLOUDGAZER (IRE)**, 4, b g Dalakhani (IRE)—City Zone (IRE)
14 **COPS AND ROBBERS**, 4, ch g Pivotal—Threefold (USA)
15 **CORBALLY GHOST (IRE)**, 5, gr g Central Park (IRE)—Classic Lin (FR)
16 **CORSKEAGH ROYALE (IRE)**, 9, ch g Beneficial—Rubys Shadow (IRE)
17 **COULEUR FRANCE (IRE)**, 4, b g Flemensfirth (USA)—Gaye Mercy
18 **CROSS APPEAL (IRE)**, 6, b g Cape Cross (IRE)—Hadeb
19 **CURLEY BILL (IRE)**, 4, b g Heron Island (IRE)—In Excelsis (GER)
20 **DARK PROSPECT (IRE)**, 5, b g Nayef (USA)—Miss Mirasol
21 **DERRYVALE ROSE (IRE)**, 6, b m Flemensfirth (USA)—Derry Vale (IRE)
22 **DEVILS PAINTBRUSH (IRE)**, 4, b g Shantou (USA)—Back Log (IRE)
23 **DONNAS PALM (IRE)**, 8, gr g Great Palm (USA)—Donna's Tarquin (IRE)
24 **DUNMOE (IRE)**, 6, b br g Presenting—Regal Holly
25 **DYLAN ROSS (IRE)**, 6, b g Shantou (USA)—Quit The Noise (IRE)
26 **FICKLE FORTUNE (IRE)**, 4, b f Heron Island (IRE)—That's The Bonus (IRE)
27 **FISHER BRIDGE (IRE)**, 9, ch g Singspiel (IRE)—Kristal Bridge
28 5, B g Stardan (IRE)—Forever Silver (IRE)
29 **FORMIDABLEOPPONENT (IRE)**, 5, b g Arakan (USA)—Sliding
30 **FOUNTAIN OF HONOUR (IRE)**, 4, b f Sadler's Wells (USA)—Belle of Honour (USA)
31 **FULLY FUNDED (USA)**, 7, b g Aptitude (USA)—Fully Invested (USA)
32 **GAIUS MARIUS (IRE)**, 4, b g Tiger Hill (IRE)—Russian Muse (FR)
33 **GO NATIVE (IRE)**, 9, br g Double Eclipse (IRE)—Native Idea (IRE)
34 **GRAN TORINO (IRE)**, 7, b g Milan—Miss Greinton (GER)
35 **GRANGE HOUSE (IRE)**, 6, b g Great Palm (USA)—Abadila (IRE)
36 **GRIESENAU (IRE)**, 6, b g Luso—Persian Wonder (IRE)
37 **HARCHIE (IRE)**, 4, gr g Oscar (IRE)—Dame d'harvard (USA)
38 **HECK THOMAS (IRE)**, 4, b g Oscar (IRE)—Good Heighway (IRE)
39 **IL FENOMENO (ITY)**, 6, b g Denon (USA)—Fabulous Charm (ITY)
40 **IPSOS DU BERLAIS (FR)**, 6, gr g Poliglote—Isis Du Berlais (FR)
41 **JAKROS (IRE)**, 7, b g Beneficial—Parkdota (IRE)
42 **JAZZ CONCERTO (IRE)**, 5, b g Ransom O'war (USA)—In The Saltmine (FR)
43 **JIM BOWIE (IRE)**, 7, b g Dushyantor (USA)—Delibonne (IRE)
44 **JOHANNISBERGER (IRE)**, 5, b g Arakan (USA)—Housekeeping
45 **KNOCKGRAFFON KING (IRE)**, 7, ch g Beneficial—Kilternan Gale (IRE)
46 **LEAN TIMES (IRE)**, 7, ch g Marignan (USA)—Renewed Spirit (IRE)
47 **LECEILE (USA)**, 6, b br m Forest Camp (USA)—Summerwood (USA)
48 **LEROY PARKER (IRE)**, 4, ch g Titus Livius (FR)—Jameela (IRE)
49 **LONDON BRIDGE**, 6, br g Beat Hollow—Cantanta
50 **LOUP DU SAUBOUAS (FR)**, 9, b g Loup Solitaire (USA)—Minaudeuse (CAN)
51 **MEDICAL CARD (IRE)**, 8, b g Flemensfirth (USA)—Me Grannys Endoors (IRE)
52 **MICKELSON (IRE)**, 6, b g Old Vic—Life Support (IRE)
53 **MONASTRELL**, 7, b g Terimon—In Memoriam (IRE)
54 **MONKSLAND (IRE)**, 5, b g Beneficial—Cush Jewel (IRE)
55 **MUIRHEAD (IRE)**, 9, b g Flemensfirth (USA)—Silaoce (FR)
56 **NED BUNTLINE**, 4, b g Refuse To Bend (IRE)—Intrum Morshaan (IRE)
57 **NEWS CARVER (IRE)**, 4, b g Alhaarth (IRE)—Advancing (IRE)
58 **ON YOUR EOIN (IRE)**, 5, b g Brian Boru—Spring Lake (IRE)
59 **ORIGINAL OPTION (IRE)**, 7, br g Anshan—Deepest Thoughts (IRE)
60 **PANDORAMA (IRE)**, 9, b g Flemensfirth (USA)—Gretchen's Castle (IRE)
61 **PARSONS PISTOL (IRE)**, 10, b g Pistolet Bleu (IRE)—Parsons Honour (IRE)
62 **PAT GARRETT (IRE)**, 5, b g Fruits of Love (USA)—Junga Connection
63 **PERFECT SMILE (IRE)**, 7, b br g Anshan—Mambo Music (IRE)
64 **PLEASE TALK (IRE)**, 6, b g Beneficial—Fresh Partner (IRE)
65 **PRIMA VISTA**, 7, b g Singspiel (IRE)—Papering (IRE)
66 **PROTARAS (USA)**, 5, b br g Lemon Drop Kid (USA)—Seven Moons (JPN)
67 **REALT DUBH (IRE)**, 8, b g Beneficial—Suez Canal (FR)
68 **SILVER TASSIE (IRE)**, 4, b g Shantou (USA)—Silver Castor (IRE)
69 **SILVERHAND (IRE)**, 8, gr g Lend A Hand—Karmisymixa (FR)
70 **SINE METU (IRE)**, 4, b g Alhaarth (IRE)—Polish Odyssey (IRE)

MR NOEL MEADE—continued

71 **SIX STONE NED (IRE)**, 6, gr g Great Palm (USA)—Ashfield Rosie (IRE)
72 **SMITHFIELD (IRE)**, 4, b g Cape Cross (IRE)—Daraliya (IRE)
73 **SWORD OF DESTINY (IRE)**, 6, gr g Shantou (USA)—Sparkling Sword
74 **TELLEGIO**, 5, b g Milan—Cash 'n' Credit
75 **TEXAS JACK (IRE)**, 6, b g Curtain Time (IRE)—Sailors Run (IRE)
76 **THEGREATJOHNBROWNE (IRE)**, 8, ch g Beneficial—Alltoplayfor (IRE)
77 **THOUVA (FR)**, 5, ro g Ragmar (FR)—Lady Thou (FR)
78 **TOM HORN (IRE)**, 6, ch g Beneficial—Lady Shackleton (IRE)
79 5, B g Beneficial—Torus Or You (IRE)
80 **VELESGO (IRE)**, 4, gr g Dansili—Cassandra Go (IRE)
81 **WATERLOO CHATEAU (IRE)**, 9, br g Presenting—Be My Flower (IRE)
82 **WESLEY HARDIN (IRE)**, 4, ch g Kris Kin (USA)—Old Society (IRE)
83 **WESTHAVEN (IRE)**, 4, b g Alhaarth (IRE)—Dashiba

THREE-YEAR-OLDS

84 **DAN BOGAN (IRE)**, b g Windsor Knot (IRE)—Housekeeping
85 **DUTCH HENRY (IRE)**, b g Barathea (IRE)—Unlock (IRE)
86 **ELIJAH GARDNER (IRE)**, b g Refuse To Bend (IRE)—Anna Kareena (IRE)
87 **HONOURABLE EMPEROR (IRE)**, b c Holy Roman Emperor (IRE)—Belle of Honour (USA)
88 **MILT YARBERRY**, b g Librettist (USA)—Polar Storm (USA)
89 B f Hurricane Run (IRE)—Showering
90 **TOP MAN MICHAEL (IRE)**, b c Antonius Pius (USA)—Top Brex (FR)
91 **TUCKER CASEY (IRE)**, b g Ivan Denisovich (IRE)—Alhaadh (USA)

Assistant Trainer: Damien McGillick

Jockey (NH): Davy Condon, Paul Carberry. **Conditional:** Tim Carroll. **Amateur:** Miss Nina Carberry.

---

447 **MR BRIAN MEEHAN, Manton**
Postal: **The Racing Office, Manton House Estate, Marlborough SN8 1PN**
Contacts: **PHONE (01672) 517191 FAX (01672) 517192 MOBILE (07836) 754254**
E-MAIL info@brianmeehan.com WEBSITE www.brianmeehan.com

 1 **AAIM TO PROSPER (IRE)**, 8, br g Val Royal (FR)—Bint Al Balad (IRE) **CGA Racing Partnership 2**
 2 **CATFISH (IRE)**, 4, b br f One Cool Cat (USA)—Castellane (FR) **R. C. Tooth**
 3 **COCKNEY CLASS (USA)**, 5, gr ro g Speightstown (USA)—Snappy Little Cat (USA) **Roldvale Ltd**
 4 **DANGEROUS MIDGE (USA)**, 6, b h Lion Heart (USA)—Adored Slew (USA) **I. Parvizi**
 5 **ELUSIVITY (IRE)**, 4, b g Elusive City (USA)—Tough Chic (IRE) **Mrs P. Good**
 6 **MANTOBA**, 4, b c Noverre (USA)—Coming Home **J. Paul Reddam**
 7 **MIA MADONNA**, 4, b f Motivator—Musique Magique (USA) **Mr J. R. Hobby**
 8 **MISS ELEGANCE**, 4, b f Mind Games—Mania (IRE) **Mr & Mrs B Buckley & Mr T G & Mrs M E Holdcroft**
 9 **MORTITIA**, 4, b f Dansili—Simianna **Mr T. G. & Mrs M. E. Holdcroft**
10 **TITUS MILLS**, 4, ch c Dubawi (IRE)—Anayid **Titus Mills Partnership**

THREE-YEAR-OLDS

11 **ALL NIGHTER (IRE)**, b g Bertolini (USA)—Symbol of Peace (IRE) **Decadent Racing**
12 **ANGELIC NOTE (IRE)**, b f Excellent Art—Evangeline **Mrs B. V. Sangster**
13 **ARCHBISHOP (USA)**, b c Arch (USA)—Avaricity (USA) **Mr C. W. Clay**
14 B g Rock of Gibraltar (IRE)—Autumnal (IRE) **Paul & Jenny Green**
15 **BALATON**, br f Singspiel (IRE)—Traverse City (USA) **Mr & Mrs G. Middlebrook**
16 **BALLESTEROS**, ch g Tomba—Flamenco Dancer **Mrs P. Good**
17 **BALLYHEIGUE (IRE)**, b g High Chaparral (IRE)—Lypharden (IRE) **A. Bengough, P. O'Sullivan, KWB Bloodstock**
18 **BAYAN (IRE)**, b c Danehill Dancer (IRE)—Kindling **I. Parvizi**
19 **BEN CRÓY (IRE)**, b g Nayef (USA)—Chrysalis **Gallagher Equine Ltd**
20 **BERENGAR (IRE)**, b g Holy Roman Emperor (IRE)—Double Fantasy (GER) **Astor Syndicate**
21 **BULLDOG BEASLEY (USA)**, b g Van Nistelrooy (USA)—Dixie Eyes Blazing (USA) **Orwell Partnership**
22 **BURANO (IRE)**, ch c Dalakhani (IRE)—Kalimanta (IRE) **Mr J. R. Harvey**
23 **CAPITOL GAIN (IRE)**, b g Bahamian Bounty—
                                    Emmas Princess (IRE) **N.Attenborough, Mrs L Mann, M.Wilmshurst**
24 **CATHEDRAL**, b c Invincible Spirit (IRE)—Capades Dancer (USA) **Lady Rothschild**
25 **CHAPELLERIE (IRE)**, b f Acclamation—Castellane (FR) **Smoke & Mirrors**
26 **COGITO (USA)**, b c Giant's Causeway (USA)—Ladies Cruise (USA) **J. Paul Reddam**
27 **CRIMSON CHEER (USA)**, b f Van Nistelrooy (USA)—Yousefia (USA) **Highbury Terrace Owners Club**
28 **DIAMONDHEAD (IRE)**, b c Kyllachy—Hammrah **Sir R. Ogden C.B.E., LLD**

MR BRIAN MEEHAN—continued

29 **EDRAAQ**, b g Dubai Destination (USA)—Shatarah **Hamdan Al Maktoum**
30 **JUNIOR DIARY (USA)**, ch f Mr Greeley (USA)—Cross Channel (USA) **Mrs L. J. Freedman**
31 **KELNER'S CROSS**, b g Cape Cross (IRE)—Gretna **R. P. Foden**
32 **MADAME ST CLAIR (IRE)**, b f High Chaparral (IRE)—Numbers Game **Astor Syndicate**
33 **MEHDI (IRE)**, b c Holy Roman Emperor (IRE)—College Fund Girl (IRE) **I. Parvizi**
34 **MISS COMPLEX**, b f Compton Place—Extremely Rare (IRE) **Miss E. J. Tanner**
35 **MISSISSIPPI**, b c Exceed And Excel (AUS)—Ruby Rocket (IRE) **Sir Robert Ogden C.B.E. LLB**
36 **MOST IMPROVED (IRE)**, b c Lawman (FR)—Tonnara (IRE) **I. Parvizi**
37 **MUHDIQ (USA)**, b c Hard Spun (USA)—Enfiraaj (USA) **Hamdan Al Maktoum**
38 **NELSON'S BAY**, b g Needwood Blade—In Good Faith (USA) **Raymond Tooth**
39 **ORWELLIAN**, b g Bahamian Bounty—Trinny **Orwell Partnership**
40 Ch f Giant's Causeway (USA)—Quiero Ganar (USA) **Mrs John Magnier & Mrs Lucy Sangster**
41 **RAWAAFED (IRE)**, b br c Invasor (ARG)—Holly's Kid (USA) **Hamdan Al Maktoum**
42 **RIGHT DIVINE (IRE)**, ro g Verglas (IRE)—Yellow Trumpet **Right Tack Partnership**
43 **RIGHT TO DREAM (IRE)**, b c Oasis Dream—Granny Kelly (USA) **Right Tack Partnership**
44 **RUBY GLASS (IRE)**, b g Red Clubs (IRE)—Gold Bar (IRE) **Ballymacoll Stud Farm Ltd**
45 **SAMOAN (IRE)**, b c Danehill Dancer (IRE)—Rain Flower (IRE) **Sangster Family & Mrs J. Magnier**
46 **SANDBETWEENOURTOES (IRE)**, b g Footstepsinthesand—Callanish **Trelawny II**
47 **SIR BEDIVERE (IRE)**, b c Dansili—Miss Ivanhoe (IRE) **Trelawny II**
48 **STRAIGHT SHOT (IRE)**, ch g Manduro (GER)—Forest Express (AUS) **Orwell Partnership**
49 **SUJET BELLAGIO**, b g Acclamation—Markova's Dance **Lanesborough**
50 **SYMPHONY TIME (IRE)**, b f Cape Cross (IRE)—Gems of Araby **Mr P. McCutcheon**
51 **TOPPLED (IRE)**, ch f Pivotal—Pietra Dura **Mr A. Rosen**
52 **WOODLAND SCENE (IRE)**, gr f Act One—Wiener Wald (USA) **Car Colston Hall Stud**
53 **WORTH**, b f Indesatchel (IRE)—Woore Lass (IRE) **Miss P. A. Zygmant**
54 **YAZDI (IRE)**, b c Galileo (IRE)—Lucky Spin **I. Parvizi**

TWO-YEAR-OLDS

55 B f 6/4 Dalakhani (IRE)—Almatinka (IRE) (Indian Ridge) (10000) **Mr D. J. Burke**
56 Ch c 12/2 Jazil (USA)—Alsabaqa (USA) (Sakhee (USA)) **Hamdan Al Maktoum**
57 Ch c 15/3 Sakhee's Secret—Barboukh (Night Shift (USA)) (23000)
58 **BATASH**, b c 6/5 Royal Applause—Regal Asset (USA) (Regal Classic (CAN)) (30000) **Mr Sultan Ali**
59 **BIX (IRE)**, b c 22/3 Holy Roman Emperor (IRE)—Belle Rebelle (IRE) (In The Wings) (20000) **I. Parvizi**
60 B c 23/3 Amadeus Wolf—Cantaloupe (Priolo (USA)) (22857)
61 **CARD HIGH (IRE)**, b c 13/3 Red Clubs (IRE)—Think (FR) (Marchand de Sable (USA)) (24761)
62 B c 6/2 Kheleyf (USA)—Catching Stars (IRE) (Halling (USA)) (52380)
63 B c 16/3 Excellent Art—China Pink (Oasis Dream) (26000)
64 B c 16/2 Dynaformer (USA)—Enfiraaj (USA) (Kingmambo (USA)) **Hamdan Al Maktoum**
65 B c 24/2 Teofilo (IRE)—Eyrecourt (IRE) (Efisio)
66 **FANTACISE**, ch f 27/3 Pivotal—My First Romance (Danehill (USA)) (70000) **Mr T. G. & Mrs M. E. Holdcroft**
67 B c 30/4 Royal Applause—Fantastic Santanyi (Fantastic Light (USA)) (38000)
68 Ch c 10/2 Redback—Feet of Flame (USA) (Theatrical) (8000)
69 B c 10/4 Kyllachy—Fen Guest (Woodborough (USA)) (74285)
70 B f 15/3 Tamayuz—Frond (Alzao (USA)) **Hamdan Al Maktoum**
71 B f 9/2 Mount Nelson—Give A Whistle (IRE) (Mujadil (USA)) (34481) **Newsells Park Stud**
72 Ch c 27/3 Excellent Art—Granny Kelly (USA) (Irish River (FR)) (45155)
73 **HASAAD (USA)**, b c 23/3 Kheleyf (USA)—Maha Dubai (USA) (Kingmambo (USA)) **Hamdan Al Maktoum**
74 B c 12/3 Daaher (CAN)—Hasheema (IRE) (Darshaan) **Hamdan Al Maktoum**
75 B f 1/2 Papal Bull—Humble Fifteen (USA) (Feather Ridge (USA)) (21345)
76 Ch c 28/2 Exceed And Excel (AUS)—Indian Love Bird (Efisio) **Mrs P. Good**
77 Gr c 8/2 Haatef (USA)—Intishaar (IRE) (Dubai Millennium) **Hamdan Al Maktoum**
78 B c 6/4 Royal Applause—Just Julie (USA) (Gulch (USA)) (45155)
79 B c 23/4 Halling (USA)—L'affaire Monique (Machiavellian) (65000)
80 Ch f 14/4 Shamardal (USA)—La Vita E Bella (IRE) (Definite Article) (80000)
81 **LOOKS CAN KILL**, b f 14/4 Dylan Thomas (IRE)—Looker (Barathea (IRE)) (3000) **Invictus**
82 B br c 25/2 Elnadim (USA)—Mawaared (Machiavellian (USA)) **Hamdan Al Maktoum**
83 **MEETING IN PARIS (IRE)**, b f 23/3 Dutch Art—Sharplaw Star (Xaar) **Sir R. Ogden C.B.E., LLD**
84 B f 6/2 Danehill Dancer (IRE)—Myth And Magic (IRE) (Namid) (150000) **Mr A. Rosen**
85 B f 5/2 Indesatchel (IRE)—New Havens (Indian Ridge) (476) **Mr & Mrs B. Buckley**
86 Ch c 9/2 Exceed And Excel (AUS)—Our Sheila (Bahamian Bounty) (31000)
87 **PEARL BELL (IRE)**, b f 12/2 Camacho—Magnificent Bell (IRE) (Octagonal (NZ)) (23809) **Pearl Bloodstock**
88 B c 25/1 Bahamian Bounty—Perdicula (IRE) (Persian Heights) (50000)
89 B c 8/4 Acclamation—Perils of Joy (IRE) (Rainbow Quest (USA)) (41050)
90 B c 30/4 Lawman (FR)—Pink Sovietstaia (FR) (Soviet Star (USA)) (65000)
91 Ch c 21/3 Exceed And Excel (AUS)—Psychic (IRE) (Alhaarth (IRE)) (80000)

MR BRIAN MEEHAN—continued

92 Ch f 23/1 Stormy Atlantic (USA)—Rebuke (USA) (Carson City (USA)) **Mr A. Rosen**
93 Br c 18/3 Shamardal (USA)—Red Bandanna (IRE) (Montjeu (IRE)) (41050) **F. Nass**
94 B c 22/4 Iffraaj—Reign of Fire (IRE) (Perugino (USA)) (65680)
95 B c 30/1 Invincible Spirit (IRE)—Riotous Applause (Royal Applause) **Car Colston Hall Stud**
96 **RUN IT TWICE (IRE),** b c 18/2 Dark Angel (IRE)—Alinda (IRE) (Revoque (IRE)) (75000) **I. Parvizi**
97 Gr c 29/3 Duke of Marmalade (IRE)—Santa Sophia (IRE) (Linamix (FR)) (62000)
98 Ch f 24/3 Teofilo (IRE)—Scarlett Rose (Royal Applause) (147782) **Mr A. Rosen**
99 B f 2/3 Zamindar (USA)—Sea Chorus (Singspiel (IRE)) **Car Colston Hall Stud**
100 B c 18/4 Royal Applause—Shatarah (Gulch (USA)) (27914) **Clipper Holdings**
101 B c 16/2 Arch (USA)—Siyadah (USA) (Mr Prospector (USA)) **Hamdan Al Maktoum**
102 **SMOOTHTALKINRASCAL (IRE),** b c 14/4 Kodiac—Cool Tarifa (IRE) (One Cool Cat (USA)) (20000) **Invictus**
103 Ch c 26/1 Bahamian Bounty—Snake's Head (Golden Snake (USA)) (36190)
104 Ch c 27/3 Exceed And Excel (AUS)—Snowy Indian (Indian Ridge) (40000)
105 B c 3/3 Moss Vale (IRE)—Street Style (IRE) (Rock of Gibraltar (IRE)) (28571)
106 B c 13/4 Duke of Marmalade (IRE)—Stylist (IRE) (Sadler's Wells (USA)) (55000)
107 **SUPERNOVA HEIGHTS (IRE),** b f 16/4 Oasis Dream—Athene (IRE) (Rousillon (USA)) **Ballymacoll Stud**
108 B c 7/5 Lawman (FR)—Surf The Web (IRE) (Ela-Mana-Mou) (26272)
109 **THANKSGIVING DAY (USA),** b c 20/3 Harlan's Holiday (USA)—Frappay (USA) (Deputy Minister (CAN)) (42000)
110 B c 10/2 Invincible Spirit (IRE)—Three Wrens (IRE) (Second Empire (IRE)) (80000)
111 B c 10/4 Moss Vale (IRE)—Trader Secret (IRE) (Montjeu (IRE))
112 B f 27/2 Speightstown (USA)—Unrestrained (USA) (Unbridled (USA)) (65000)
113 Br c 5/5 Kheleyf (USA)—Upskittled (Diktat) (26666)
114 B c 3/3 Invincible Spirit (IRE)—Vadorga (Grand Lodge (USA)) (53365)
115 B c 13/3 Iron Roman Emperor (IRE)—Web of Intrigue (Machiavellian (USA)) (38000)
116 **WHIPPER'S BOY (IRE),** b c 19/5 Whipper (USA)—Glympse (IRE) (Spectrum (IRE)) (42692)
117 B f 5/5 Montjeu (IRE)—Wiener Wald (USA) (Woodman (USA)) **Car Colston Hall Stud**

Other Owners: Mr Sultan Ali, Mr Ahmad Alkuallafi, Mr N. B. Attenborough, Mr James Barber, Mr A. N. C. Bengough, Mr K. W. Biggins, Mrs S. J. Biggins, Mrs Jonathan Blacklock, Mr Tim Bostwick, Mr D. J. Burke, Clipper Logistics, Mr R. P Foden, Mrs M. J. Forman Hardy, Mrs N. J. Forman Hardy, Mr Paul Green, Mrs Jenny Green, Mr Hung Yat Fai, Invictus, Mr Stewart Jones, Mr Benson Lo, Mrs John Magnier, Mr Ranjan Mahtani, Mrs Lyndsey Mann, Mrs Johnny McKeever, Mr P. S. McNally, Mr D. McCormick, Mr B. J. Meehan, Mrs Kim Meehan, Mr P. O'Sullivan, Mrs R. Philipps, Mr Peter Sands, Mr G. E. Sangster, Mr N. E. Sangster, Mr B. V. Sangster, Mr S. E. Sangster, Mr Raymond Tooth, Lord Vestey, Mrs L. Way, Mr Michael Wilmshurst.

Assistant Trainers: R. O'Dowd, P. Macewan

Apprentice: Jade Muggeridge.

448
MR ANTHONY MIDDLETON, Granborough
Postal: Hogshaw Road Farm, Hogshaw Road, Granborough, Buckingham, Buckinghamshire, MK18 3NL
Contacts: **PHONE (01844) 292463 FAX (01844) 292463 MOBILE (07894) 909542**
E-MAIL tony@granboroughracing.co.uk WEBSITE www.granboroughracing.co.uk

1 **FILUN,** 7, b g Montjeu (IRE)—Sispre (FR) **R. J. Matthews**
2 **HAND PAINTED,** 6, b g Lend A Hand—Scarlett Holly **The Wacky Racing Club**
3 **MAC'S GREY (IRE),** 5, gr g Great Palm—Gypsy Kelly (IRE) **Macable Partnership**
4 **MOSSMANN GORGE,** 10, b g Lujain (USA)—North Pine **The Wacky Racing Club**
5 **MY FAITHFUL ANNIE (IRE),** 11, b m Arctic Lord—Laugh Away **Mrs F. Thomas**
6 **PORTHGWIDDEN BEACH (USA),** 4, b f Street Cry (IRE)—Suaviter (USA) **Macable Partnership**
7 **TOOKA,** 11, b g Sure Blade (USA)—Parsons Lass (IRE) **Mr A. Middleton**

THREE-YEAR-OLDS

8 **GADREEL (IRE),** b g Dark Angel (IRE)—Borsalino (USA) **Mrs C. J. Middleton**

Other Owners: Mr S. Mackintosh, Mr F. W. Mackintosh.

Assistant Trainer: Mrs C. Middleton

Jockey (NH): Charlie Poste. **Conditional:** Tom Molloy.

449 **MR PHILIP MIDDLETON, Aylesbury**
Postal: **The Stables, Dorton Park Farm, Dorton, Aylesbury, Buckinghamshire, HP18 9NR**
Contacts: **PHONE (01844) 237503 FAX (01844) 237503 MOBILE (07860) 426607**

1 **LIKE ICE**, 7, b g Beat All (USA)—Susie's Money **P. W. Middleton**
2 **MARJU KING (IRE)**, 6, b g Marju (IRE)—Blue Reema (IRE) **P. W. Middleton**
3 **OLYMPIAN (FR)**, 10, b g Video Rock (FR)—Attualita (FR) **P. W. Middleton**
4 **TRIP THE LIGHT**, 7, b g Fantastic Light (USA)—Jumaireyah **P. W. Middleton**

Assistant Trainer: Helen Day

450 **MR PAUL MIDGLEY, Westow**
Postal: **Sandfield Farm, Westow, York, YO60 7LS**
Contacts: **Office (01653) 658790 FAX (01653) 658790 MOBILE (07976) 965220**
E-MAIL ptmidgley@aol.com WEBSITE www.ptmidgley.com

1 **ALWAYS GUNNER**, 6, b g Mujahid (USA)—Westcourt Ruby **Mrs M. P. Walker**
2 **ANOTHER WISE KID (IRE)**, 4, b g Whipper (USA)—Romancing **M. Ng**
3 **BERTIE SOUTHSTREET**, 9, b br g Bertolini (USA)—Salvezza (IRE) **J. D. Walker**
4 **BESTY**, 5, ch g Compton Place—Petrovna (IRE) **Mr A. Turton & Mr P. Langford**
5 **CELTIC SULTAN (IRE)**, 8, b g Celtic Swing—Farjah (IRE) **Mr A. M. Taylor**
6 **CHOC'A'MOCA (IRE)**, 5, b g Camacho—Dear Catch (IRE) **John Milburn - Andrew Stephenson**
7 **COOL IN THE SHADE**, 4, b f Pastoral Pursuits—Captain Margaret **The Rumpole Partnership**
8 **CROWN CHOICE**, 7, b g King's Best (USA)—Belle Allemande (CAN) **Mr A. M. Taylor**
9 **DIMASHQ**, 10, b m Mtoto—Agwaas (IRE) **A. Bell**
10 **DISPOL GRAND (IRE)**, 6, b g Raise A Grand (IRE)—Hever Rosina **Mr T. W. Midgley**
11 **DUBAI BAY (FR)**, 4, b f Zafeen (FR)—Yemen Desert (IRE) **D. I. Perry**
12 **EVER ROSES**, 4, br f Pastoral Pursuits—Eljariha **R. K. L. Man**
13 **GOODMANYOURSELF**, 4, b g Dubawi (IRE)—Frazzled (USA) **D. Mann**
14 **HAAJES**, 8, ch g Indian Ridge—Imelda (USA) **N Lomas, A Taylor Snr, A Taylor Jnr**
15 **HIGHLAND WARRIOR**, 13, b g Makbul—Highland Rowena **P. T. Midgley**
16 **HOPPY'S FLYER (FR)**, 4, b f Country Reel (USA)—Madeleine's Blush (USA) **Gap Personnel Franchises Limited**
17 **INTERNATIONALDEBUT (IRE)**, 7, b g High Chaparral (IRE)—Whisper Light (IRE) **Mr A. M. Taylor**
18 **IRISH BOY (IRE)**, 4, b g Desert Millennium (IRE)—Shone Island (IRE) **Annwell Inn Syndicate**
19 **JAY JAYS JOY**, 4, b g Diktat—Agrippina **Sandfield Racing**
20 **LADY SLEDMERE (IRE)**, 4, b f Barathea (IRE)—Helena's Paris (IRE) **J. A. Milburn**
21 **LIVER BIRD**, 4, b g Tiger Hill (IRE)—Oiseau Rare (FR) **D. Mann**
22 **MAGGIE MEY (IRE)**, 4, b f Kodiac—Christmas Kiss **The Ten Commandments**
23 **MUFTARRES (IRE)**, 7, b g Green Desert (USA)—Ghazal (USA) **Mr T. W. Midgley**
24 **NEZAMI (IRE)**, 7, b g Elnadim (USA)—Stands To Reason (USA) **R. Wardlaw**
25 **NO MEAN TRICK (USA)**, 6, b g Grand Slam—Ruby's Reception (USA) **J. A. Milburn**
26 **NOMOREBLONDES**, 8, ch m Ishiguru (USA)—Statuette **A. D. Copley**
27 **QUAROMA**, 7, ch m Pivotal—Quiz Time **The Legend's Syndicate II**
28 **RA JUNIOR (USA)**, 6, b g Rahy (USA)—Fantasia Girl (IRE) **P. T. Midgley**
29 **SILVANUS (IRE)**, 7, b g Danehill Dancer (IRE)—Mala Mala (IRE) **C. Alton**
30 **SPIRIT OF CONISTON**, 9, b g Lake Coniston (IRE)—Kigema (IRE) **Sandfield Racing**
31 **SUNRAIDER (IRE)**, 5, b g Namid—Doctrine **Gap Personnel Franchises Limited**
32 **TANCRED SPIRIT**, 4, b f Mind Games—Tancred Times **D. W. Barker**
33 **TOBY TYLER**, 6, b g Best of The Bests (IRE)—Pain Perdu (IRE) **A. D. Copley**
34 **WISEMAN'S DIAMOND**, 7, b m Wiseman's Ferry (USA)—Aswhatilldois (IRE) **D. I. Perry**

THREE-YEAR-OLDS

35 **BRUNSWICK VALE (IRE)**, b f Moss Vale (IRE)—Brunswick **Sandfield Racing**
36 **HEADSTIGHT (IRE)**, b f Holy Roman Emperor (IRE)—Regal Star **A. Bell**
37 **MAD FOR FUN (IRE)**, b f Ivan Denisovich (IRE)—Franny **Mad 4 Fun Syndicate**
38 **MADE IN THE SHADE**, b f Ishiguru (USA)—Dispol Katie **The Rumpole Partnership**
39 **MIDDLETON FLYER (IRE)**, ch f Titus Livius (FR)—Autumn Star (IRE) **Gap Personnel Franchises Limited**
40 **PHOENIX CLUBS (IRE)**, b f Red Clubs (IRE)—Hollow Haze (USA) **Williams, Lindley, Turton, Bate**
41 **WHIP IT IN (IRE)**, b f Whipper (USA)—Viami (IRE) **Sandfield Racing**

TWO-YEAR-OLDS

42 B f 7/4 Sakhee's Secret—Accusation (IRE) (Barathea (IRE)) (4104) **D. Mann**
43 B g 12/2 Red Clubs (IRE)—In The Fashion (IRE) (In The Wings) (1148) **R. Wardlaw**
44 B g 2/4 Moss Vale (IRE)—Lady of Bilston (IRE) (Bin Ajwaad (IRE)) (3047) **21st Century Racing**
45 Br f 12/2 Diamond Green (FR)—Magdalene (FR) (College Chapel) (656) **Unregistered Partnership**

MR PAUL MIDGLEY—continued
46 B f 14/3 Ad Valorem (USA)—Noctilucent (JPN) (Lammtarra (USA)) (800) **P. T. Midgley**
47 Ch f 12/3 Sleeping Indian—Rainbow Treasure (IRE) (Rainbow Quest (USA)) **F. Brady**

Other Owners: Mr G. Bate, G. Bromley, A. W. Catterall, Mrs B. Catterall, M. J. Dyas, Miss C. Foster, E. Jagger, Mr P. M. Langford, Mr P. N. Lindley, Mr N. G. Lomas, M. A. Scaife, C. G. Simpson, Mr M. Skellett, Mr P. Smith, T. A. Stephenson, Mr J. A. Taylor, Mr A. Turton, A. Williams.

Assistant Trainer: Miss W. Gibson

Jockey (flat): Micky Fenton. **Amateur:** Miss H. Dukes, Miss W. Gibson.

451
MR ROD MILLMAN, Cullompton
Postal: The Paddocks, Kentisbeare, Cullompton, Devon, EX15 2DX
Contacts: **PHONE/FAX** (01884) 266620 **MOBILE** (07885) 168447
E-MAIL rod.millman@ic24.net

1 ALSHAZAH, 4, b g Haafhd—Mountain Law (USA) **The Links Partnership**
2 EIGHT KEYS, 4, b g Sakhee (USA)—Summertime Parkes **Seasons Holidays**
3 GALATIAN, 5, ch g Traditionally (USA)—Easy To Imagine (USA) **Tarka Racing**
4 GEORGE THISBY, 6, b g Royal Applause—Warning Belle **Mr R. G. Thisby**
5 HAWRIDGE SONG, 4, ch g Singspiel (IRE)—Clear Vision **E. J. S. Gadsden**
6 ICEBUSTER, 4, ch g Iceman—Radiate **The Links Partnership**
7 INTO THE WIND, 5, ch m Piccolo—In The Stocks **E. J. S. Gadsden**
8 IRISH JUGGER (USA), 5, ch g Johannesburg (USA)—Jinny's Gold (USA) **Rod Millman Racing Club**
9 MADAME KINTYRE, 4, b f Trade Fair—Chorus **Rod Millman Racing Club**
10 MASAI MOON, 8, b g Lujain (USA)—Easy To Imagine (USA) **Rod Millman Racing Club**
11 MOBAASHER (USA), 9, ch g Rahy (USA)—Balistroika (USA) **Seasons Holidays**
12 MONEY MONEY MONEY, 6, b m Generous (IRE)—Shi Shi **Mrs J. A. M. Willment**
13 MUSTAJED, 11, b g Alhaarth (IRE)—Jasarah (IRE) **Rod Millman Racing Club**
14 NOW, 6, br m Where Or When (IRE)—Tup Tim **Mrs J. A. M. Willment**
15 NUMIDE (FR), 9, b g Highest Honor (FR)—Numidie (FR) **Midd Shire Racing**
16 ON THE FEATHER, 6, br m Josr Algarhoud (IRE)—Fotheringhay **Mrs J. A. M. Willment**
17 SHAVANSKY, 8, b g Rock of Gibraltar (IRE)—Limelighting (USA) **The Links Partnership**
18 SHERMAN MCCOY, 6, ch g Reset (AUS)—Naomi Wildman (USA) **Mustajed Partnership**
19 SHY, 7, ch m Erhaab (USA)—Shi Shi **Mrs J. A. M. Willment**
20 SOUTHERNESS, 8, ch g Halling (USA)—Teresa Balbi **G. D. Thompson**
21 STARVING MARVIN, 4, b g Hawk Wing (USA)—Oleana (IRE) **Seasons Holidays**
22 STRIKING WILLOW, 4, b g Striking Ambition—Willows World **Rod Millman Racing Club**
23 SUNSHINE BUDDY, 5, b m Reel Buddy (USA)—Bullion **No Illusions Partnership**
24 TONY HOLLIS, 4, b g Antonius Pius (USA)—Seasons Parks **Seasons Holidays**
25 WAKE UP GIRL, 4, b f Sleeping Indian—Mighty Magic
26 YES CHEF, 5, ch g Best of The Bests (IRE)—Lady Chef **Coombeshead Racing**

THREE-YEAR-OLDS

27 BLACKDOWN FAIR, b f Trade Fair—Shielaligh **Mr R. Brooke**
28 CLOWANCE KEYS, b g High Chaparral (IRE)—Seasons Parks **Seasons Holidays**
29 DANCE, b f Erhaab (USA)—Shi Shi **Mrs J. A. M. Willment**
30 DOVILS DATE, gr g Clodovil (IRE)—Lucky Date (IRE) **Always Hopeful Partnership**
31 GAELIC ICE, b f Iceman—Gaelic Lime **The Jack High Racing Partnership**
32 ICE TRES, br f Iceman—Tup Tim **Mrs J. A. M. Willment**
33 ISHI, b f Ishiguro (USA)—Chorus **Kintyre Racing**
34 JACASA TOO, b f Arkadian Hero (USA)—Lucky Jacasa **Mrs J. B. Chesters**
35 KATHRYN'S GLORY, br f Striking Ambition—Songbook **P. Webb**
36 MACCABEES, b g Motivator—Takarna (IRE) **Mr C. Roper**
37 MISTER MUSICMASTER, b g Amadeus Wolf—Misty Eyed (IRE) **Mrs J. Fuller**
38 MY BOY GINGER, ch c Byron—Lady Chef **Coombeshead Racing**
39 PRINCESS ANNABELLE, ch f Sworn In (USA)—Marybelle
40 SMART AFFAIR, b f Trade Fair—Che Chic (IRE) **Rod Millman Racing Club**
41 STUDIOUS MICHAEL, b g Striking Ambition—Dream Rose (IRE) **P. Webb**
42 TWEET LADY, b f Royal Applause—Fuschia **D. J. Deer**
43 WYNDHAM WAVE, gr g Dr Fong (USA)—Atlantic Light **Kentisbeare Racing**

MR ROD MILLMAN—continued

TWO-YEAR-OLDS

44 **ASTRUM**, gr c 16/3 Haafhd—Vax Star (Petong) (30000) **The Links Partnership**
45 **BURNT FINGERS (IRE)**, b f 9/4 Kheleyf (USA)—Play With Fire (FR) (Priolo (USA)) (1904) **Miss G. J. Abbey**
46 **ISIS BLUE**, b c 7/2 Cockney Rebel (IRE)—Bramaputra (IRE) (Choisir (AUS))
47 B c 21/4 Auction House (USA)—Lady of Limerick (IRE) (Thatching) (5000)
48 **POETIC VERSE**, ch f 21/3 Byron—Nina Fontenail (FR) (Kaldounevees (FR)) (952) **The Links Partnership**
49 **SHAHDAROBA (IRE)**, br c 18/3 Haatef (USA)—
                                              Gold Script (FR) (Script Ohio (USA)) (23809) **The Links Partnership**
50 B c 26/3 Ishiguru (USA)—Shielaligh (Aragon) (14285) **Mr R. Brooke**
51 **SWEET ALABAMA**, gr f 3/3 Johannesburg (USA)—
                                              Alybgood (CAN) (Alydeed (CAN)) (22000) **The Links Partnership**
52 **YES TWO**, b c 3/3 Indesatchel (IRE)—Charlie Girl (Puissance) (10476) **Mustajed Partnership**

Other Owners: P. Bartlam, Mr A. Bricknell-Webb, Mrs C. T. Bricknell-Webb, A. J. Conway, Mrs A. C. Dominy, Mrs J. Elliott, Mr N. D. Elliott, Mr D. J. Hornby, Mrs C. Knowles, V. B. Lewer, D. A. Little, B. G. Middleton, Mrs L. S. Millman, B. R. Millman, S. M. Perry, Mrs D. M. Philpott, Mr M. J. Philpott, A. J. Shire.

Assistant Trainer: Louise Millman

Jockey (flat): James Millman. **Amateur:** Mr P. Millman.

---

452 MR ROBERT MILLS, Epsom
Postal: Loretta Lodge Racing Stables, Tilley Lane, Headley, Epsom, Surrey, KT18 6EP
Contacts: PHONE (01372) 377209 FAX (01372) 386578
E-MAIL lorettalodge@aol.com

1 **BUXFIZZ (USA)**, 4, b g Elusive Quality (USA)—Argentina (USA) **Buxted Partnership**
2 **CHARLTON**, 9, b g Inchinor—Sabina **Mrs B. B. Mills**
3 **GREYLAMI (IRE)**, 7, gr g Daylami (IRE)—Silent Crystal (USA) **Mr J. Humphreys & Mr B. Ecclestone**
4 **JACOBS SON**, 4, ch g Refuse To Bend (IRE)—Woodwin (IRE) **Jacobs Construction (Holdings) Limited**
5 **KELTBRAY (IRE)**, 4, b g Galileo (IRE)—Mill Guineas (USA) **Keltbray Limited**
6 **MONTEREY (IRE)**, 5, b g Montjeu (IRE)—
                                      Magnificient Style (USA) **Mrs B. B. Mills, J. Humphreys, B. Ecclestone**
7 **PAPERETTO**, 4, b g Selkirk (USA)—Song of Hope **Mrs B. B. Mills**
8 **PETARA BAY (IRE)**, 8, b g Peintre Celebre (USA)—
                                      Magnificient Style (USA) **Mrs B. Ecclestone, J. Humphreys, Mrs B. Mills**
9 **STANDING STRONG (IRE)**, 4, b g Green Desert (USA)—Alexander Three D (IRE) **Mrs B. B. Mills**

THREE-YEAR-OLDS

10 **AUTHENTIC SWING (IRE)**, ch c Pivotal—Woodland Orchid (IRE) **Mrs B. B. Mills**
11 **EWELL PLACE (IRE)**, br g Namid—Miss Gibraltar **Mr Brendan Kerr, Mrs B. B. Mills**
12 **HE'S NO ANGEL (IRE)**, ch c Excellent Art—Gentle Night **B. Ecclestone, J. Humphreys, Mrs B. Mills**
13 **JASIE JAC (IRE)**, b c Namid—Dynah Mo Hum (IRE) **Portish Holdings, Mrs B. B. Mills**
14 **LA PASSIONATA**, ch f Proclamation (IRE)—Miss Madame (IRE) **Mrs K. M. Young**
15 **MACY ANNE (IRE)**, b f King's Best (USA)—Gilah (IRE) **Portish Holdings, Mrs B. B. Mills**
16 **STAR KINGDOM (IRE)**, b c Marju (IRE)—Appetina **Mrs B. B. Mills**
17 **YOUNG PRINCE (IRE)**, b g Strategic Prince—Aspasias Tizzy (USA) **Mrs B. B. Mills**

TWO-YEAR-OLDS

18 **CLOSE TOGETHER (IRE)**, b f 11/4 Dylan Thomas (IRE)—
                                      Maritana (USA) (Rahy (USA)) (6978) **Miss J. A. Leighs & Mrs B. B. Mills**
19 B c 31/1 Piccolo—Emouna (Cadeaux Genereux) (17142)
20 B c 4/3 Marju (IRE)—Idesia (IRE) (Green Desert (USA)) (36000) **Mr Trevor Jacobs & Mrs B. B. Mills**
21 **MOSSTANG**, b c 30/1 Moss Vale—Lovely Dream (IRE) (Elnadim (USA)) (4925) **Pinehurst Racing**
22 Br f 4/3 Amadeus Wolf—Peshawar (Persian Bold) (8209)
23 B c 29/1 Zamindar (USA)—Shahmina (IRE) (Danehill (USA)) (21000) **Mrs B. B. Mills**
24 Ch c 14/4 Kyllachy—Sheila's Secret (IRE) (Bluebird (USA)) (428) **Sherwoods Transport Ltd**
25 Ch c 24/4 Hurricane Run (IRE)—Vale View (FR) (Anabaa (USA)) (38587) **Mr B. Kerr**

Other Owners: Mr B. Ecclestone, Mr Jim Hanifin, Mr John Humphreys, Mr T. Jacobs, Mr Brendan Kerr, Miss J. A. Leighs, Mrs B. B. Mills, Portish Holdings Limited, Mrs J. Ruthven.

Assistant Trainer: Richard Ryan

453 **MR COLIN MITCHELL, Dorchester**
Postal: White House, Buckland Newton, Dorchester, Dorset, DT2 7DE
Contacts: PHONE (01300) 345276

1 LITTLE FEE, 7, b m Emperor Fountain—Passing Fair C. W. Mitchell

454 **MR NICK MITCHELL, Dorchester**
Postal: Brick House, Piddletrenthide, Dorchester, Dorset, DT2 7QP

1 BAND OF THUNDER, 4, ch g Shirocco (GER)—Black Opal J. R. Boughey
2 BETABOB (IRE), 9, b g Bob's Return (IRE)—Cellatica (USA) Guy and Sophie Henderson
3 COACH LANE, 11, b g Barathea (IRE)—Emplane (USA) B. Moore & E. C. Stephens
4 COLIN'S DESIRE, 6, gr g Pasternak—Sarah's Destiny C. W. Mitchell
5 DRYBROOK BEDOUIN, 5, b g Nomadic Way (USA)—Biddles Fourpay
6 ELECTRIC MAYHEM, 5, b g Alflora (IRE)—She's No Muppet Mr & Mrs Andrew May
7 FLYING WHALE, 8, b m Kayf Tara—Baby Whale (IRE) F. D. A. Snowden
8 JUST TOOTSIE, 8, ch g Emperor Fountain—Thamesdown Tootsie A. J. M. Trowbridge
9 KAYFROU, 7, b g Kayf Tara—Roufontaine Mr N. R. Mitchell
10 MISS FLEUR, 9, b m Bandmaster (USA)—Floral Park Milcombe Racing
11 MISSTREE DANCER, 8, b m Bandmaster (USA)—Miss Match Mrs S. J. Faulks
12 OVER THE RUBICON (IRE), 5, gr g Overbury (IRE)—Brasya (FR) Mr N. R. Mitchell
13 POINT WEST (IRE), 8, b g Tamayaz (CAN)—Coming Home (FR) The Point West Partnership
14 SIMPLY BEN (IRE), 6, b g Pilsudski (IRE)—Peace Time Girl (IRE) Guy and Sophie Henderson

Other Owners: Mr S. Browne-Wilkinson, Mr G. Henderson, Mrs S. J. Henderson, Ms K. J. Holmes, Mr D. Loveys, Mrs S. H. May, A. J. May, B. Moore, Mr L. R. Pinkawa, E. C. Stephens, Mr A. Willmington.

455 **MR RICHARD MITCHELL, Dorchester**
Postal: East Hill Stables, Piddletrenthide, Dorchester, Dorset, DT2 7QY
Contacts: PHONE/FAX (01300) 348739 MOBILE (07775) 843136

1 APATURA DIK, 11, b g Deltic (USA)—Apatura Hati N. R. Mitchell
2 BEDIBYES, 4, b f Sleeping Indian—Aunt Sadie J. R. Boughey
3 BETHEHOLYGOBBS (IRE), 10, ch g Insan (USA)—Parverb (IRE) Mrs E. Mitchell
4 BUCK BUNNIE, 7, b g Wared (USA)—Apatura Cherry N. R. Mitchell
5 DONT WORRY, 6, b g Bertolini (USA)—Persian Dream (IRE) Mr & Mrs Andrew May
6 KNOCKVICAR (IRE), 10, b m Anshan—It Time To Run (IRE) N. R. Mitchell
7 MASSINI SUNSET, 12, b g Dr Massini (IRE)—Burgundy Sunset (IRE) Mr & Mrs Andrew May
8 PADDY THE YANK (IRE), 9, b g Sassanian (USA)—
                                          Celias Fancy (IRE) Piddle Valley Racing Club & N R Mitchell

Other Owners: Mrs S. H. May, A. J. May.

Assistant Trainer: Mrs E Mitchell

456 **MR JAMES MOFFATT, Grange-Over-Sands**
Postal: Pit Farm Racing Stables, Cartmel, Grange-Over-Sands, Cumbria, LA11 6PJ
Contacts: PHONE (01539) 536689 FAX (01539) 536236 MOBILE (07767) 367282
E-MAIL james@jamesmoffatt.co.uk WEBSITE www.jamesmoffatt.co.uk

1 ALMUTAHAM (USA), 5, b br h Dynaformer (USA)—Forest Lady (USA) David & Nicky Robinson
2 ARISEA (IRE), 9, b m Cape Cross (USA)—Castelfranca (IRE) P. Bushell, B. Walton & P. Bartlett
3 BLAZING BAY (IRE), 7, b m Luso—Blazing Missile (IRE) Coachmans Cottagers
4 BORDER TALE, 12, b g Selkirk (USA)—Likely Story (IRE) Mr D. J. Moffatt
5 BROWNEYES BLUE (IRE), 14, b g Satco (FR)—Bawnard Lady Mr M. W. Chapman
6 CABBYL DOO, 9, b h Killer Instinct—Chipewyas (FR) Mrs A. Stamper
7 CHIEF DAN GEORGE (IRE), 12, b g Lord Americo—Colleen Donn Mr M. W. Chapman
8 DAR ES SALAAM, 8, ch g King's Best (USA)—Place de L'opera Mr A. Macleod
9 DIVINATORE, 6, b g Sakhee (USA)—Divina Mia Mrs E. M. Milligan
10 DOLLAR MICK (IRE), 7, b g Presenting—Bula Beag (IRE) Mr M. W. Chapman
11 ERGO (FR), 8, b h Grand Lodge (USA)—Erhawah Mrs E. M. Milligan
12 HAMPSFELL, 4, gr g Distant Music (USA)—Schatzi Mrs J. A. Moffatt

MR JAMES MOFFATT—continued

13 **ITSTOOEARLY,** 9, br m Overbury (IRE)—Deb's Ball **Kernow Bloodstock**
14 **MOGHAAYER,** 7, b g Sinndar (IRE)—Guest of Anchor **Coachmans Cottagers**
15 **QUEL ELITE (FR),** 8, b g Subotica (FR)—Jeenly (FR) **Mr M. W. Chapman**
16 **RISK RUNNER (IRE),** 9, b g Mull of Kintyre (USA)—Fizzygig **Mr V. R. Vyner-Brooks**
17 **SAM LORD,** 8, ch g Observatory (USA)—My Mariam **Coachmans Cottagers**
18 **SEIZE,** 10, gr g Silver Patriarch (IRE)—Sleepline Princess **Mr V. R. Vyner-Brooks**
19 **SPIRIT OF A NATION (IRE),** 7, b g Invincible Spirit (IRE)—Fabulous Pet **Mr & Mrs Gordon Grant**
20 **STOLEN MOMENTS (FR),** 11, gr g Villez (USA)—Brave Lola (FR) **Neil Headdock & Murray B. Johnston**
21 **TONGALOOMA,** 6, ch m Shinko Forest (IRE)—Schatzi **Mrs J. A. Moffatt**
22 **TROPENFEUER (FR),** 5, b m Banyumanik (IRE)—Tropensonne (GER) **JSB Racing Partnership**

TWO-YEAR-OLDS

23 **OH BOY OH BOY,** b g 23/3 Misu Bond (IRE)—Mitchelland (Namaqualand (USA)) **Mr R. R. Whitton**

Other Owners: Mr P. Bartlett, Mr K. Bowron, Mr S. Brookfield, Ms S. Brookfield, Mr P. E. Bushell, Mr Gordon Grant, Mrs C. H. Grant, Mr N. Headdock, Mrs A. L. Heayns, Mr Trevor Heayns, Mr M. B. Johnston, Mr A. R. Mills, Mr D. J. Moffatt, Mr David Robinson (Little Langdale), Mrs N. G. Robinson, Mr B. Walton, Mr Simon Wilson, Mrs J. C. Wilson.

Assistant Trainer: Jennie Moffatt

Jockey (flat): Paddy Aspell, P. J. McDonald, Royston Ffrench, Darren Moffatt. **Jockey (NH):** Brian Hughes, Wilson Renwick.
Conditional: Joel Belbin. **Amateur:** Miss Rebecca Sparkes.

---

457 MRS LAURA MONGAN, Epsom
Postal: **Condover Stables, Langley Vale Road, Epsom, Surrey, KT18 6AP**
Contacts: **PHONE (01372) 271494 FAX (01372) 271494 MOBILE (07788) 122942**
E-MAIL **ljmongan@hotmail.co.uk** WEBSITE **www.lauramongan.co.uk**

1 **CAPTAIN HERO (IRE),** 5, b g Captain Rio—Fairy Free **Mrs P. J. Sheen**
2 **DIVINE RULE (IRE),** 4, br g Cacique (IRE)—Island Destiny **Mrs L. J. Mongan**
3 **FIRST AVENUE,** 7, b g Montjeu (IRE)—Marciala (IRE) **Mrs L. J. Mongan**
4 **MASTER DARCY,** 10, b br g Cloudings (IRE)—Swift Conveyance (IRE) **Mrs P. J. Sheen**
5 **MORAR,** 6, b m Kalanisi (IRE)—Moidart **Mrs P. J. Sheen**
6 **MUSASHI (IRE),** 7, ch g Hawk Wing (USA)—Soubrette (USA) **Mrs P. J. Sheen**
7 **ORSM,** 5, b g Erhaab (USA)—Royal Roulette **Mrs P. J. Sheen**
8 **PEPITO COLLONGES (FR),** 9, b g Brier Creek (USA)—Berceuse Collonges (FR) **Mrs P. J. Sheen**
9 **ROBBY BOBBY,** 7, ch g Selkirk (USA)—Dancing Mirage (IRE) **Mrs L. J. Mongan**
10 **ROSOFF (IRE),** 10, b g New Frontier (USA)—Annida (IRE) **Mrs P. J. Sheen**
11 **SAHARA SUNSHINE,** 7, b m Hernando (FR)—Sahara Sunrise (USA) **Mrs P. J. Sheen**
12 **SHINE IN TIME (IRE),** 4, b f Definite Article—Time To Shine **Mrs P. J. Sheen**
13 **SYNTHE DAVIS (FR),** 7, b m Saint des Saints (FR)—Trumpet Davis (FR) **Mrs P. J. Sheen**

---

458 MR ARTHUR MOORE, Naas
Postal: **Dereens, Naas, Co. Kildare, Ireland**
Contacts: **PHONE (00353) 4587 6292 FAX (00353) 4589 9247 MOBILE (00353) 8725 52535**
E-MAIL **arthurlmoore@eircom.net**

1 **AUTHINGER (IRE),** 4, b g Sadler's Wells (USA)—Ange Bleu (USA) **Michael D. Ryan**
2 **BACK OFF MATE (IRE),** 4, b g Old Vic—Flyhalf (IRE) **M. Beresford**
3 **BACK ON THE ROAD (IRE),** 10, br g Broken Hearted—Special Trix (IRE) **C. Jones**
4 **CLARAGH NATIVE (IRE),** 7, ch g Beneficial—Susy In The Summer (IRE) **Not For Friend Partnership**
5 **DART QUEEN (GER),** 5, b m King's Best (USA)—Dream Play (IRE) **Lyreen Syndicate**
6 **DRUMLISTER (IRE),** 6, b g Luso—Murrurundi (IRE) **P. Hale**
7 **DUOMO DI MILANO (IRE),** 7, b g Milan—Parsons Alert (IRE) **Duomo Syndicate**
8 **EL SORO (FR),** 4, b g Malinas (GER)—La Esplendida (FR) **P. McCarthy**
9 **FEVER PITCH (IRE),** 6, b g Dushyantor (USA)—Stormey Tune (IRE) **J. P. McManus**
10 **FREE WORLD (FR),** 8, b g Lost World (IRE)—Fautine (FR) **C. D. Smith**
11 **GENTLEMAN DUKE (IRE),** 4, b g Bachelor Duke (USA)—Housekeeping **J. P. McManus**
12 **HIGH DESERT (GER),** 7, b g Next Desert (IRE)—Helsinki (GER) **G. B. Turkington**
13 **HOME FARM (IRE),** 5, b g Presenting—Tynelucy (IRE) **C. Jones**
14 **HOP IN (IRE),** 5, b g Flemensfirth (USA)—Prowler (IRE) **C. Hanbury**
15 **LASTOFTHELEADERS (IRE),** 9, b g Supreme Leader—Heather Breeze (IRE) **Desmond Doherty/Declan Gannon**
16 **LINNEL (IRE),** 7, b g Moscow Society (USA)—The Last Bank (IRE) **R. A. Bartlett**

MR ARTHUR MOORE—continued

17 **ORGANISEDCONFUSION (IRE)**, 7, b g Laveron—Histologie (FR) **Mrs A. Dunlop**
18 **PASS THE HAT**, 5, ch g Karinga Bay—Moor Spring **M. Beresford**
19 **SHENZHOU**, 5, ch m Starcraft (NZ)—River Saint (USA) **C. Beihan**
20 **SORCEROR (FR)**, 8, b g Sleeping Car (FR)—Coyote Davis (IRE) **Gigginstown House Stud**
21 **TALBOT ROAD (IRE)**, 4, b g Old Vic—Over The Glen (IRE) **J. P. Byrne**
22 **TREAT YOURSELF (IRE)**, 5, b g Beat Hollow—Cartesian **L. Breslin**
23 **WHAT A CHARM (IRE)**, 5, b m Key of Luck (USA)—Atalina (FR) **C. Jones**

THREE-YEAR-OLDS

24 **ANOTHER DUCHESS**, b f Nayef (USA)—River Cara (USA) **Mr A. L. T. Moore**
25 **OH SO QUAINT (IRE)**, b f Iffraaj—Papaha (IRE) **Mrs S Barrett**
26 **POSITIVE VIBES**, ch g Nayef (USA)—Steeple **F. Jones**
27 **REGAL TIE (IRE)**, ch f Windsor Knot (IRE)—Tawala (IRE) **L. Flood**

TWO-YEAR-OLDS

28 B f 24/4 Dark Angel (IRE)—Quadri (Polish Precedent (USA)) (7000) **L. Flood & Lady Legard**
29 B f 2/4 Cockney Rebel (IRE)—Signella (Selkirk (USA)) (13000) **L. Flood**

Jockey (flat): F. Berry. **Jockey (NH):** D. J. Casey, A. McNamara, P. Townend. **Conditional:** G. Malone. **Amateur:** Mr N. M. Kelly.

---

459 **MR BILL MOORE, Ledsham**
Postal: **Badgers Rake Farm and Castle Quarter Stud, Chester High Road, Ledsham, Ellesmere Port, South Wirral, CH66 8PH**
Contacts: **PHONE (0151) 3391026 FAX (0151) 3391026 MOBILE (07834) 884060**

1 **ACCUMULATE**, 9, b g Second Empire (IRE)—Bee-Bee-Gee (IRE) **C. W. Moore**
2 4, B f Desert King (IRE)—Bee-Bee-Gee (IRE) **C. W. Moore**
3 **COPSEHILL GIRL (IRE)**, 7, b br m Carroll House—Merapi **Denis Gallagher**
4 **DIDDLEY DEE**, 8, b g Riverhead (USA)—Ballydiddle **Mrs I. M. Moore**
5 **FLYING PHOEBE**, 6, b m Sakhee (USA)—Altaweelah (IRE) **C. W. Moore**
6 **REDHOTDOC**, 8, ch m Dr Fong (USA)—Gecko Rouge **C. W. Moore**

Assistant Trainer: Miss Jane Fargher

Conditional: Derek Smith.

---

460 **MR GARY MOORE, Horsham**
Postal: **Cisswood Racing Stables, Sandygate Lane, Lower Beeding, Horsham, West Sussex, RH13 6LR**
Contacts: **HOME (01403) 891997 YARD (01403) 891912 FAX (01403) 891924 MOBILE (07753) 863123**
E-MAIL garyjayne.moore@virgin.net WEBSITE www.garymooreracing.com

1 **ACTION IMPACT (ARG)**, 8, b g Bernstein (USA)—Valeur (ARG) **Mr T. Bowley**
2 **AL AMAAN**, 7, b g Nayef (USA)—Siobhan **Mr M. L. Waters**
3 **ALLTERRAIN (IRE)**, 9, b g Almutawakel—Queen of Art (IRE) **Mr Raymond Petchey & Mr & Mrs David Newland**
4 **AMAURY DE LUSIGNAN (IRE)**, 6, b g Dushyantor (USA)—Celtic Sails (IRE) **Mr A. E. Dean**
5 **ANCESTRAL DREAM**, 5, ch g Dubai Destination (USA)—B Beautiful (IRE) **Mrs D. Rodway**
6 **ANNESBROOK (IRE)**, 6, b g Needle Gun (IRE)—Stepfonic (IRE) **Lady Forwood & Mr Michael Tibbatts**
7 4, B g Old Vic—Baliya (USA)
8 **BALLYFOY (IRE)**, 11, b br g Alderbrook—Okanagan Valley (IRE) **M. K. George**
9 **BEAU FIGHTER**, 7, b g Tobougg (IRE)—Belle de Jour **The Hillians**
10 **BERGO (GER)**, 9, b g Silvano (GER)—Bella Figura (GER) **Mrs A. Burrows**
11 **BERT THE ALERT**, 4, b g Proclamation (IRE)—Megalex **Mr Jerry Hinds**
12 **BILLY BONKERS (IRE)**, 6, b g Hubbly Bubbly (USA)—Pass Date (IRE) **R. A. Gadd**
13 **BOBBYSCOT (IRE)**, 5, b g Alhaarth (IRE)—Sogno Verde (IRE) **Mr R. Kadyrov**
14 **BRONZE CANNON (USA)**, 7, b br h Lemon Drop Kid (USA)—Victoria Cross (IRE) **Mr R. Kadyrov**
15 **CHAMPS DE BLEU (FR)**, 9, b g Shambo—Flashing Silks **A. G. C. Russell**
16 **CHARLIE CHEESECAKE (IRE)**, 6, br g Kayf Tara—Darabaka (IRE) **Mr G. Gillespie**
17 **CLEARWATER BAY (IRE)**, 5, b h Sadler's Wells (USA)—Shouk **Mr C. Bird**
18 **COIN OF THE REALM (IRE)**, 7, b g Galileo (IRE)—Common Knowledge **B. Siddle & B. D. Haynes**
19 **CRETE (IRE)**, 10, b g Montjeu (IRE)—Paesanella **Chegwidden Systems Limited**

MR GARY MOORE—continued

20 DALAYIR (FR), 5, gr g Tiger Hill (IRE)—Dalataya (IRE) C. E. Stedman
21 DEUX ETOILES (IRE), 5, b g Montjeu (IRE)—Onereuse Heart Of The South Racing
22 DOROTHY'S DANCING (IRE), 4, b f Acclamation—Segoria (IRE) Mr T. Glynn
23 DR THISTLE (IRE), 5, b g Dr Massini (IRE)—Thistle Thyne (IRE) D. Leon
24 DRAGON'S ROOST (IRE), 7, b g Craigsteel—Nancy's First (IRE) Ms J. A. Lambert
25 DYNAMIC IDOL (USA), 5, b br g Dynaformer (USA)—El Nafis (USA) Heart of the South Racing
26 EBONY BOOM (IRE), 5, b g Boreal (GER)—Elegant As Well (IRE) PKD Partnership
27 EDDIE G (IRE), 9, b g Insan (USA)—Dusty Lane (IRE) G. L. Moore
28 FATHOM FIVE (IRE), 8, b g Fath (USA)—Ambria (ITY) B. Siddle & B. D. Haynes
29 FINCH FLYER (IRE), 5, ch g Indian Ridge—Imelda (USA) Prix Mature Racing
30 FIX THE RIB (IRE), 9, b g Dr Massini (IRE)—Hot Curry (IRE) Mr A. E. Dean
31 FORGET IT, 7, b g Galileo (IRE)—Queens Way (FR) The Cockpit Crew (Mr Bill Gibson)
32 FRUITY O'ROONEY, 9, b g Kahyasi—Recipe Heart Of The South Racing
33 GAELIC SILVER (FR), 6, b g Lando (GER)—Galatza (FR) The Winning Hand
34 GALIOTTO (IRE), 6, b g Galileo (IRE)—Welsh Motto (USA) Mr A. D. Bradmore
35 GEE DEE NEN, 9, b g Mister Baileys—Special Beat Mr C. Duggan & Mr B. Gilligan
36 GITANO HERNANDO, 6, ch h Hernando (FR)—Gino's Spirits President Ramzan Kadyrov
37 GRABTHEGLORY (IRE), 6, b g Accordion—Full of Surprises (FR) Mr S. J. Cohen
38 GREEN WADI, 7, b g Dansili—Peryllys Mr A. D. Bradmore
39 GUARDS CHAPEL, 4, b g Motivator—Intaaj (IRE) Mr A. D. Bradmore
40 HARRY TRICKER, 8, b g Hernando (FR)—Katy Nowaitee R. Green
41 HEATHCOTE, 10, b g Unfuwain (USA)—Chere Amie (USA) B. Siddle & B. D. Haynes
42 HERSCHEL (IRE), 6, br g Dr Fong (USA)—Rafting (IRE) Mr S. E. Sangster
43 IL PORTICO, 5, b g Zafeen (FR)—Diddymu (IRE) Heart Of The South Racing
44 JODAWES (USA), 5, b br g Burning Roma (USA)—Venetian Peach (USA) Stephen Fisher & John Ball
45 KAHFRE, 5, ch g Peintre Celebre (USA)—Minerva (IRE) SelectRacingClub.co.uk & Dr C. A. Barnett
46 KAMBIS, 4, b g Tobougg (IRE)—Queen Tomyra (IRE) Mr & Mrs Leslie Vine
47 KAVALOTI (IRE), 8, b g Kahyasi—Just As Good (FR) G. Gillespie
48 KINGSFOLD FLARE, 5, ch m Central Park (IRE)—Kingsfold Blaze 8 Wealth Management (Ian Riggs)
49 LAJIDAAL (USA), 5, b g Dynaformer (USA)—Tayibah (IRE) Dedman Properties Limited
50 LAUGHTON PARK, 7, ch g Karinga Bay—Brass Castle (IRE) A. G. C. Russell
51 LIGHT WELL (IRE), 4, b g Sadler's Wells (USA)—L'ancresse (IRE) Mr B. D. Siddle, Mr B. D. Haynes
52 LIGHTNING SPIRIT, 4, b f Storming Home—Lucky Dice Heart Of The South Racing
53 LOCH FLEET (IRE), 4, br g Celtic Swing—Share The Feeling (IRE) G. L. Moore
54 LOMBOK, 6, b g Hernando (FR)—Miss Rinjani Pink Punters & Partners
55 LORD SINGER (FR), 7, b g Secret Singer (FR)—Cricale (FR) The Winning Hand
56 LUPANAR (IRE), 8, ch g Galileo (IRE)—Louve Sacree (USA) Mrs E. A. Kiernan
57 5, B g Kahyasi—Madame Stella (FR)
58 MADE IN ITALY (IRE), 6, b g Milan—Handmade (IRE) D. J. Coles
59 MEGASTAR, 7, b g Kayf Tara—Megalex Hinds, Waddingham, Arthur, Herbert, Day
60 MIKHAIL GLINKA (IRE), 5, b h Galileo (IRE)—Lady Karr Mr R. Kadyrov
61 MINISTRY, 4, b c Iceman—Choirgirl Phil Collins
62 MORESWEETS 'N LACE, 5, b m Zafeen (FR)—Another Secret Mr D. P. Hinds
63 MOSSINI (IRE), 7, b g Dr Massini (IRE)—Ballylooby Moss (IRE) J. A. Gent
64 MOUNTAINEER (IRE), 7, b g Saint des Saints (FR)—Mistica (FR) Mr C. E. Stedman
65 MOUNTRATH, 5, b g Dubai Destination (USA)—Eurolink Sundance Mr D. Phelan
66 NETHERBY, 6, b g Fair Mix (IRE)—Lissadell (IRE) R. Green
67 NEW CODE, 5, ch g Reset (AUS)—Illeana (GER) Mr Paul Chapman, Mrs R. Kiernan
68 ORZARE (IRE), 6, b g Montjeu (IRE)—Contare B. Fry
69 PANJO BERE (FR), 9, b g Robin des Pres (FR)—Honeymoon Suite (FR) Paul Chapman, Mrs Elizabeth Kiernan
70 PEPLUM (FR), 9, b g Subotica (FR)—Great Filly (FR) P. J. Wilmott
71 PETIT ECUYER (FR), 6, b g Equerry (USA)—Petite Majeste (FR) A. Jee, F. Ledger, J. Bateman
72 POPPY COME RUNNING (IRE), 8, b m Definite Article—Haakool A. G. C. Russell
73 PORTRAIT EMOTION (IRE), 5, ch g Portrait Gallery (IRE)—Gleann Present (IRE)
74 PSI (USA), 7, b g Hernando (FR)—Visions of Clarity (IRE) Mr N. J. Peacock
75 RAJAMAND (FR), 6, gr g Linamix (FR)—Ridafa (FR) GDM Partnership
76 RAPID WATER, 6, b g Anabaa (USA)—Lochsong G. A. Jackman
77 REBLIS (FR), 7, b g Assessor (IRE)—Silbere (FR) Kingsley, Avery, Farr, Glover, Humphreys
78 REGAL PARK (IRE), 5, b g Montjeu (IRE)—Classic Park
79 REZWAAN, 5, b g Alhaarth (IRE)—Nasij (USA) Gallagher Equine Limited
80 RIGHT STUFF (IRE), 9, b br g Dansili—Specificity (USA) The Ashden Partnership & Partners
81 SAWAGO (FR), 6, b br g Gold Away (FR)—Maikawa (FR) GDM Partnership
82 SILENT SAM, 4, b c Elusive City (USA)—Luisa Miller (FR) Mr M. Park
83 SIRCOZY (IRE), 6, b g Celtic Swing—Furnish Mr A. E. Dean
84 SIRE DE GRUGY (FR), 6, ch g My Risk (FR)—Hirlish (FR) The Preston Family & Friends
85 SOME SLAM (IRE), 7, B G Orpen (USA)—Diva Aldante (IRE)

MR GARY MOORE—continued

86 **SOUTH CAPE,** 9, b g Cape Cross (IRE)—Aunt Ruby (USA) **Heart Of The South Racing**
87 **STENTORIAN (IRE),** 4, ch c Street Cry (IRE)—Nomistakeaboutit (CAN) **Mrs M. J. George**
88 **SUNLEY PEACE,** 8, ch g Lomitas—Messila Rose **Davies, Sunley and Cox**
89 **SUNNY SPELLS,** 7, b g Zamindar (USA)—Bright Spells **P. J. Wilmott**
90 **SWIFT LORD (IRE),** 7, b g Spectrum (IRE)—Ediyrna (IRE) **R. Green**
91 **TOBAGO BAY,** 7, b g Tobougg (IRE)—Perfect Dream **Heart Of The South Racing**
92 **VIA GALILEI (IRE),** 7, b g Galileo (IRE)—Manger Square (USA) **C. E. Stedman**
93 **VINO GRIEGO (FR),** 7, b g Kahyasi—Vie de Reine (FR) **C. E. Stedman**
94 **WELL REFRESHED,** 8, b g Nikos—Cool Spring (IRE) **P. J. Wilmott**
95 **WHITBY JACK,** 5, b g Bering—Sablonne (USA) **C. E. Stedman**
96 **WINNING SPARK (USA),** 5, b g Theatrical—Spark Sept (FR) **Mrs Elizabeth Kiernan, Paul Chapman**
97 **WOOLFALL TREASURE,** 7, gr g Daylami (IRE)—Treasure Trove (USA) **Mr A. D. Bradmore**
98 **ZELOS DIKTATOR,** 6, br g Diktat—Chanterelle (IRE) **G. A. Jackman**
99 **ZOUTI (FR),** 4, b g Kahyasi—Reine de Sabot (FR) **Mr David Miles & Mr M. G. Rogers**

THREE-YEAR-OLDS

100 B g Avonbridge—Amazing Dream (IRE) **Mr D. J. Deer**
101 **AMERICAN BLING (USA),** b g Johannesburg (USA)—American Jewel (USA) **Gallagher Equine Limited**
102 **ART NEWS (IRE),** b g Dansili—Lucky (IRE) **R. Green**
103 **CHRIS PEA GREEN,** b g Proclamation (IRE)—Another Secret **Mr J. Hinds**
104 **DALMO,** b c Dalakhani (IRE)—Morina (USA) **Sir Eric Parker**
105 **DUTCH OLD MASTER,** b g Jeremy (USA)—Wicken Wonder (IRE) **R. Green**
106 **FINE PAINTING (IRE),** ch f Iffraaj—Just One Look **R. Green**
107 **GIGONDAS,** ch g Grape Tree Road—Queen's Dancer **C. E. Stedman**
108 **GOOD LUCK CHARM,** b g Doyen (IRE)—Lucky Dice **Heart Of The South Racing**
109 **JOLLY'S CRACKED IT (FR),** b g Astarabad (USA)—Jolly Harbour **GDM Partnership**
110 **JUPITER STORM,** ch c Galileo (IRE)—Exciting Times (FR) **Heart Of The South Racing**
111 **KAYLEE,** b f Selkirk (USA)—Mrs Brown **Visionary Bloodstock Ltd**
112 B f Multiplex—Kingsfold Blaze **8 Wealth Management (Mr Ian Ross)**
113 B g Tiger Hill (IRE)—Klaribel (IRE) **Mr Pat Gallagher**
114 **MODERATOR,** b g Motivator—Alessandra **D. J. Deer**
115 **MR FICKLE (IRE),** b c Jeremy (USA)—Mamara Reef **A. J. Perkins**
116 **OUR COOL CAT (IRE),** b c One Cool Cat (USA)—Beautiful Dancer (IRE) **Mr David Phelan**
117 **PICTURE DEALER,** b c Royal Applause—Tychy **R. Green**
118 Ch f Avonbridge—Prowse (USA) **Mr D. J. Deer**
119 **SANTADELACRUZE,** b c Pastoral Pursuits—Jupiters Princess **Mr D. M. & Mrs M. A. Newland, Mr R. Petchey**
120 **SHAMAHAN,** b c Shamardal (USA)—Hanella (IRE) **Heart Of The South Racing**
121 **SILVER MARIZAH (IRE),** b f Manduro (GER)—Maharani (USA) **Mr Z. Malik**
122 **VENETIAN VIEW (IRE),** b g Amadeus Wolf—Twilight Tango **R. Green**
123 **VICGERNIC,** b g Indesatchel (IRE)—Maysie (IRE) **A. Head**
124 **WHINGING WILLIE (IRE),** b g Cape Cross (IRE)—Pacific Grove **Mr P. B. Moorhead**

TWO-YEAR-OLDS

125 B f 8/3 Acclamation—Expectation (IRE) (Night Shift (USA)) (55000) **Mr C. Bird**
126 Ch f 14/3 Tamayuz—Jazz Up (Cadeaux Genereux) (30000) **Mr C. Bird**
127 B c 9/2 Acclamation—Kondakova (IRE) (Soviet Star (USA)) (100000) **Mr R. Green**
128 B c 26/3 Exceed And Excel (AUS)—Stormy Weather (Nashwan (USA)) (14000)
129 B f 11/1 Galileo (IRE)—Tingling (USA) (Storm Cat (USA)) **Mr C. Bird**
130 B f 23/1 Red Clubs (IRE)—Villa Nova (IRE) (Petardia) (19000)

Other Owners: Mr J. Ball, Dr C. A. Barnett, Mr Wayne Barr, Mr J. Bateman, Mr M. J. Blogg, Mr R. Brown, Rev L. M. Brown, Mr Paul Chapman, Mr Gregory Charlesworth, Mr Daniel Charlesworth, Mrs Cynthia Connolly, Mr Chris Duggan, Mr S. Fisher, Lady Forwood, Mr Brendan Gilligan, Mr B. D. Haynes, Mr R. Henderson, Mr Philip Herbert, Mr Darrell Hinds, Mrs Jill Ho, Mrs L. Jenkins, Mrs Elizabeth Kiernan, Mr F. Ledger, Mrs J. Mellon, Mr D. Miles, Mr G. L. Moore, Mr D. Newland, Mrs M. A. Newland, Mr John Penny, Mrs Caroline Penny, Mr S. Preston, Mr John Ripley, Mr M. G. Rogers, www.Select-Racing-Club.co.uk, Mr R. M. Siddle, Mr Michael Smith, Mr Michael Tibbatts, Mr L. R. Vine, Mrs S. J. Vine, Mr M. C. Waddingham.

Assistant Trainer: David Wilson, Philip Hide

Jockey (flat): George Baker, Ryan Moore, Fergus Sweeney. **Jockey (NH):** Andrew Glassonbury, Jamie Moore.
Conditional: Joshua Moore, Joseph Akehurst, Lee Oswin. **Apprentice:** Ryan Duthie. **Amateur:** Miss Hayley Moore.

461 MR GEORGE MOORE, Middleham

Postal: **Warwick Lodge Stables, Middleham, Leyburn, North Yorkshire, DL8 4PB**
Contacts: **PHONE** (01969) 623823 **FAX** (01969) 623823 **MOBILE** (07711) 321117
E-MAIL georgeandcarolmoore@hotmail.co.uk **WEBSITE** www.george-moore-racing.co.uk

1 **ANNIE'S PRIDE**, 5, ch m Loup Sauvage (USA)—Whatagale **Mr G R Orchard & Mr B Rhodes**
2 **ANOTHER ALFIE**, 4, b g King's Theatre (IRE)—Memsahib Ofesteem **J. B. Wallwin**
3 **ARIZONA RIVER**, 6, b m Fair Mix (IRE)—Halo Flora **Miss S. R. Robertson**
4 **BIJOU DAN**, 11, ch g Bijou d'inde—Cal Norma's Lady (IRE) **Mrs I. I. Plumb**
5 **BRASINGAMAN ERIC**, 5, b g Bollin Eric—Serene Pearl (IRE) **Mr R. J. Morgan**
6 **CHARLES DE MILLE**, 4, b g Tiger Hill (IRE)—Apple Town **Mrs M. E. Ingham**
7 **DANBROOK (IRE)**, 4, ch g Danroad (AUS)—Pip'n Judy **A Crute & Partners**
8 **EASBY PARK**, 9, b g Tamure (IRE)—Mossfield **G. R. Orchard**
9 **FINELLAS FORTUNE**, 7, b m Elmaamul (USA)—Fortune's Filly **Mrs G. A. Kendall**
10 5, Ch m Central Park (IRE)—Function Dreamer **Mrs A. M. O'Sullivan**
11 **JACK THE GENT (IRE)**, 8, b g Anshan—Asidewager (IRE) **J. B. Wallwin**
12 **KEALSHORE**, 5, ch g Alflora (IRE)—Top of The Dee **J. Pickavance**
13 **KING OF THORNS (IRE)**, 5, b g Close Conflict (USA)—Rolled Thistle (IRE) **Mrs M. Hatfield & Mrs S. Kramer**
14 **LADY AMAKHALA**, 4, b f Val Royal (FR)—Isla Negra (IRE) **Mrs D. N. B. Pearson**
15 **MAJESTIC MAYHEM (IRE)**, 9, b g Luso—Florida Bay (IRE) **J. B. Wallwin**
16 **PETELLA**, 6, b m Tamure (IRE)—Miss Petronella **A Crute & Partners**
17 **PRESQUE PERDRE**, 8, ch g Desert Prince (IRE)—Kindle **G. R. Orchard**
18 **PUY D'ARNAC (FR)**, 9, b g Acteur Francais (USA)—Chaumeil (FR) **Barrow Brook Racing**
19 **SILVER TIGRESS**, 4, gr f Tiger Hill (IRE)—Cinnamon Tree (IRE) **A Crute & Partners**
20 **TARANTELLA LADY**, 4, b f Noverre (USA)—Shortfall **D. Parker**
21 **THE SHY MAN (IRE)**, 9, b g Grand Plaisir (IRE)—Black Betty **S. P. Graham**
22 **TOURTIERE**, 4, b g Act One—Kindle **J. W. Andrews**
23 **TURF TRIVIA**, 5, gr g Alhaarth (IRE)—Exclusive Approval (USA) **Mrs M. Hatfield & Mrs S. Kramer**
24 **WOLF SHIELD (IRE)**, 5, b g King's Theatre (IRE)—Garlucy (IRE) **Mr J. M. Gray & Mr G. R. Orchard**

THREE-YEAR-OLDS

25 **BRASINGAMAN ESPEE**, b g Silver Patriarch (IRE)—Serene Pearl (IRE) **Mr R. J. Morgan**
26 **DYLAN GEORGE**, b g Sakhee (USA)—Movie Star (IRE) **Mrs S. C. Moore**
27 **EXCLUSIVE DANCER**, ch f Notnowcato—Exclusive Approval (USA) **D. Parker**
28 **ISOLDE'S RETURN**, b f Avonbridge—Up And About **Mrs M. E. Ingham**
29 **JUST FABULOUS**, b f Sakhee (USA)—Tipsy Me **S. P. Graham**
30 B g Milan—Samarinnda (IRE) **S. P. Graham**
31 **STARS LEGACY**, b f Presidium—Pagan Star **Richard J. Phizacklea**
32 **WILLY MCBAY**, b g Multiplex—Meandering Rose (USA) **J. B. Stead**

TWO-YEAR-OLDS

33 **BELLA CINDERELLA**, b f 15/4 Tiger Hill (IRE)—Design Perfection (USA) (Diesis) **A. Crute & Partners**
34 Ch g 28/3 Proclamation (IRE)—Blushing Heart (Observatory) (USA)) **Mrs D. N. B. Pearson**
35 **ERICA STARPRINCESS**, b f 18/2 Bollin Eric—Presidium Star (Presidium) **Richard J. Phizacklea**
36 **LADY POPPY**, b f 12/2 Kyllachy—Poppets Sweetlove (Foxhound (USA)) (24761) **Ingham Racing Syndicate**
37 **RED KOKO (IRE)**, ch f 20/3 Sleeping Indian—Aunt Sadie (Pursuit of Love) **A Crute & Partners**
38 Ch f 12/4 Hernando (FR)—Succinct (Hector Protector (USA)) (17000) **S. P. Graham**

Other Owners: Mr D. G. Colledge, Mr A. Crute, Mrs C. A. Crute, Mrs Mary Hatfield, Mr T. S. Ingham, Mrs Susan Kramer, Mr G. R. Orchard, Mr M. D. Parker, Mr Barry Rhodes.

Assistant Trainer: Mrs Susan Moore

Jockey (flat): P. J. McDonald, Andrew Mullen. **Jockey (NH):** Barry Keniry. **Conditional:** Joseph Palmowski. **Amateur:** Mr Mathew Garnett.

462 MR J. S. MOORE, Upper Lambourn

Postal: **Berkeley House Stables, Upper Lambourn, Hungerford, Berkshire, RG17 8QP**
Contacts: **PHONE** (01488) 73887 **FAX** (01488) 73997 **MOBILE** (07860) 811127 / (07900) 402856
E-MAIL jsmoore.racing@btopenworld.com **WEBSITE** www.stanmooreracing.co.uk

1 **COPPER CANYON**, 4, ch g Haafhd—Deep Ravine **J. S. Moore**
2 **DUSTY BLUEBELLS (IRE)**, 4, ch f Le Vie Dei Colori—Flying Ridge (IRE) **Mr S A Belton & J S Moore**
3 **QUINSMAN**, 6, b g Singspiel (IRE)—Penny Cross **J. S. Moore**
4 **ROSEWOOD LAD**, 5, ch g Needwood Blade—Meandering Rose (USA) **Miss D L Wisbey & Mr R J Viney**

MR J. S. MOORE—continued

5 TRAFFIC SISTER (USA), 4, b br f More Than Ready (USA)—Street Scene (IRE) Mrs F. H. Hay
6 WISECRAIC, 5, ch g Kheleyf (USA)—Belle Genius (USA) Mrs L Mann & Mr N Attenborough
7 WISHFORMORE (IRE), 5, b m Chevalier (IRE)—Terra Nova J. S. Moore

THREE-YEAR-OLDS

8 CROWNING STAR (IRE), b g Royal Applause—Dossier Mr Ray Styles & J. S. Moore
9 B f Multiplex—Diamond Vanessa (IRE) D L Wisbey, R J Viney & J S Moore
10 EVERVESCENT (IRE), b g Elnadim (USA)—Purepleasureseeker (IRE) Ever Equine
11 GINGER MONKEY (IRE), ch g Cockney Rebel (IRE)—Miss Interpret (IRE) Phil Cunningham & J. S. Moore
12 IDYLLIC STAR (IRE), ch f Choisir (AUS)—Idolize Mr Ray Styles & J. S. Moore
13 IMELDA MAYHEM, ch f Byron—Halland Park Girl (IRE) Mrs E O'Leary & J S Moore
14 ISLAND MELODY (IRE), b g Oratorio (IRE)—Pout Mr D Kerr & J S Moore
15 LYRICAL GANGSTER (IRE), ch c Redback—Feet of Flame (USA) Phil Cunningham & J. S. Moore
16 MARY FILDES (IRE), b f Chineur (FR)—Scarlet Empress Norton Common Farm Racing & J S Moore
17 NOTNOWSTANLEY, ch g Notnowcato—Denice Mr T Wilkinson & J S Moore
18 ONE MORE ROMAN (IRE), b c Holy Roman Emperor (IRE)—Satulagi (USA) Mrs F. H. Hay
19 PINK DELIGHT (IRE), ch f Rock of Gibraltar (IRE)—Turkana Girl Mrs F. H. Hay
20 PURPLE AFFAIR (IRE), gr ro g Clodovil (IRE)—Akariyda (IRE)
21 B c One Cool Cat (USA)—Ribald J Keapocks & J. S. Moore
22 SHEILA'S BUDDY, ch g Reel Buddy—Loreto Rose R. J. Styles
23 SWEETEST FRIEND (IRE), b f Holy Roman Emperor (IRE)—Royal Devotion (IRE) J. S. Moore
24 TITUS STAR (IRE), ch g Titus Livius (FR)—The Oldladysays No (IRE) Mr Ray Styles & J. S. Moore
25 B f Needwood Blade—Wizby Mr R. J. Viney & Miss D. Wisbey

TWO-YEAR-OLDS

26 B f 28/4 Papal Bull—Caipirinia (IRE) (Desert Prince (IRE)) (4925)
27 B f 5/5 Jeremy (USA)—Champoluc (IRE) (Indian Ridge) (1066)
28 DON EDUARDO, b c 31/5 Byron—
    Angie And Liz (IRE) (Spectrum (IRE)) (1714) Mrs Evelyn Yates, Mr T Yates and J S Moore
29 EVERREADYNEDDY, ch g 24/4 Ad Valorem (USA)—
    Maugwenna (Danehill (USA)) (6731) Ever Equine & J. S. Moore
30 B f 19/3 Amadeus Wolf—Fortress (Generous (IRE)) (9523) Mrs E O'Leary & J S Moore
31 B c 3/2 Piccolo—Greenfly (Green Desert (USA)) Norton Common Farm Racing Ltd
32 B f 9/4 Redback—Gypsy Royal (IRE) (Desert Prince (IRE)) (1025)
33 B f 19/2 Azamour (IRE)—Lady Ragazza (IRE) (Bering) (1231)
34 B c 14/3 Elnadim (USA)—Nesaah's Princess (Sinndar (IRE)) (1428)
35 B c 2/4 Cape Cross (IRE)—Paris Glory (USA) (Honour And Glory (USA))
36 RAKTICATE (IRE), b f 16/4 Rakti—Authenticate (Dansili) (6157) Mr G V March & J S Moore
37 B c 31/3 Assertive—Reeli Silli (Dansili) (6666) Marchwood Aggregates Ltd
38 Ch f 16/4 Arakan—Riskie Things (Risk Me (FR)) (476) J. S. Moore
39 Ch f 25/1 Shamardal (USA)—Shakti (Indian Ridge) (9523) Norton Common Farm Racing & J S Moore
40 B c 2/4 Redback—Shall We Tell (Intikhab (USA)) (4925) Wall To Wall Partnership
41 B f 6/3 Amadeus Wolf—Story (Observatory (USA)) (9030) Norton Common Farm Racing & J S Moore
42 TIGER SUNSET (IRE), b c 18/2 Balmont (USA)—
    Zuccini Business (IRE) (Entrepreneur) (820) Mr G V March & J S Moore
43 B f 29/3 Duke of Marmalade (IRE)—Vingt Et Une (FR) (Sadler's Wells (USA)) (28571)

Other Owners: Mr R. Ambrose, Mr N. B. Attenborough, Mr S. A. Belton, Mr Phil Cunningham, Mr Donald M. Kerr, Mrs Lyndsey Mann, Mr J. S. Moore, Mrs E. O'Leary, Mr W. J. Reilly, Mr Ray Styles, Mr R. J. Viney, Mr T. Wilkinson, Miss D. L. Wisbey.

Assistant Trainer: Mrs S. Moore

Jockey (flat): Liam Keniry, Luke Morris. Apprentice: Ryan Powell.

---

463 MR KEVIN MORGAN, Newmarket
Postal: Gazeley Park Stables, 13 - 15 Moulton Road, Gazeley, Newmarket, Suffolk, CB8 8RA
Contacts: PHONE (01638) 551888 FAX (01638) 551888 MOBILE (07768) 996103
E-MAIL morgan.k@btconnect.com

1 CAMERA SHY (IRE), 8, ch g Pivotal—Shy Danceuse (FR) Mr M. D. Ogburn
2 EZDIYAAD (IRE), 8, b g Galileo (IRE)—Wijdan (USA) Roemex Ltd

MR KEVIN MORGAN—continued

3 ISDAAL, 5, ch m Dubawi (IRE)—Faydah (USA) **Roemex Ltd**
4 LATARADUD (IRE), 5, br g Marju (IRE)—Abington Angel **Mrs Marie Twomey**
5 MADAME TAVELURE, 4, b f Librettist (USA)—Plumeria **Miss C. Y. Wootten**
6 MY FARMER GIRL, 6, b m Karinga Bay—See My Girl **Mr J. Duckworth**
7 NUMEROLOGY, 5, gr g Numerous (USA)—Kaldounya **Mr M. D. Ogburn**
8 RAAMZ (IRE), 5, ch m Haafhd—Tarbiyah **Roemex Ltd**
9 TAARESH (IRE), 7, b g Sakhee (USA)—Tanaghum **Roemex Ltd**

Head Lad: S. Rathore

Jockey (flat): Jimmy Quinn. **Jockey (NH):** Leighton Aspell. **Amateur:** Miss Kelly Morgan, Mr Chris Watson.

464
MR DAVE MORRIS, Newmarket
Postal: **Mokefield, Baxters Green, Wickhambrook, Newmarket, Suffolk, CB8 8UY**

1 CHEZ VRONY, 6, b g Lujain (USA)—Polish Abbey **Stag & Huntsman**
2 CRAGGANMORE CREEK, 9, b g Tipsy Creek (USA)—Polish Abbey **Stag & Huntsman**
3 ZAHEEB, 4, b g Haafhd—Gay Music (FR) **Mr S. C. Wood**

Other Owners: Ms C. C. Fagerstrom, The Hon W. H. Smith.

Jockey (flat): Franny Norton.

465
MR M. F. MORRIS, Fethard
Postal: **Everardsgrange, Fethard, Co. Tipperary, Ireland**
Contacts: PHONE (00353) 52 6131474 (00353) 52 6131654 FAX (00353) 52 6131654
E-MAIL mouse@eircom.net

1 BAILY BEAU, 6, b g Kayf Tara—Coolvawn Lady (IRE) **R. A. Scott**
2 BAILY DUSK (IRE), 6, br g Dushyantor (USA)—Gentle Lady (IRE) **R. A. Scott**
3 BAILY GREEN (IRE), 6, b g King's Theatre (IRE)—Dream On Boys (IRE) **R. A. Scott**
4 BAILY ROCK (IRE), 9, b br g Supreme Leader—Knapping Princess (IRE) **M. O'Flynn**
5 BECKETT ROCK (IRE), 8, b br g Presenting—Juresse (IRE) **M. O'Flynn**
6 BIG GAME HUNTER (IRE), 6, b g Sadler's Wells (USA)—Hill of Snow **M. O'Flynn**
7 BRUFF (IRE), 5, b g Presenting—Aniston (IRE) **J. P. McManus**
8 CARRY EACH OTHER (IRE), 6, b g Milan—Jennys Supreme (IRE) **Gigginstown Stud**
9 CASPIAN PIPER (IRE), 5, b g Millenary—Pepsi Starlet (IRE) **The Rubber Bandit Syndicate**
10 CHINA ROCK (IRE), 9, ch g Presenting—Kigali (IRE) **M. O'Flynn**
11 COPSIANO (IRE), 9, b g Flemensfirth (USA)—Tanya Thyne (IRE) **M. O'Flynn & J. O'Flynn**
12 ELYSIAN ROCK, 8, b g King's Theatre (IRE)—Elaine Tully (IRE) **M. O'Flynn**
13 FIRST LIEUTENANT (IRE), 7, ch g Presenting—Fourstargale (IRE) **Gigginstown Stud**
14 FOUR COMMANDERS (IRE), 6, b g Old Vic—Fairy Blaze (IRE) **Gigginstown Stud**
15 GROOMED (IRE), 4, b g Acclamation—Enamoured **Gigginstown Stud**
16 MIRADANE, 5, b g Kayf Tara—Coolvawn Lady (IRE) **B. Maloney**
17 PRESENT POTENTIAL (IRE), 5, b g Presenting—Calbrooke (IRE) **B. Maloney**
18 RATHLIN, 7, b g Kayf Tara—Princess Timon **Gigginstown Stud**
19 ROCKFIELD ABBEY, 8, b g Kayf Tara—Louise Moillon **M. O'Flynn**
20 SHANE ROCK, 7, b g King's Theatre (IRE)—Elaine Tully (IRE) **M. O'Flynn**
21 SPOT FINE, 6, b g Kayf Tara—Lily The Lark **M. & J. O'Flynn**
22 THE HURL (IRE), 9, b g Supreme Leader—No Dunce (IRE) **J. P. McManus**
23 TILLAHOW (IRE), 5, b g Tillerman—Ale' Ale' (USA) **Gigginstown Stud**
24 TINAKELLYLAD (IRE), 8, b g Witness Box (USA)—Iora (IRE) **Mrs B. Twomey**

Jockey (NH): M. Ferris, D. Russell.

466
MR HUGHIE MORRISON, East Ilsley
Postal: **Summerdown, East Ilsley, Newbury, Berkshire, RG20 7LB**
Contacts: PHONE (01635) 281678 FAX (01635) 281746 MOBILE (07836) 687799
E-MAIL hughie@hughiemorrison.co.uk WEBSITE www.hughiemorrison.co.uk

1 CAPTAIN BELLAMY (USA), 4, ch g Bellamy Road (USA)—Thesky'sthelimit (USA) **Mr H. Morrison**
2 CASTERNOVA, 4, ch f Avonbridge—Casterossa **Mr D. P. Barrie**

MR HUGHIE MORRISON—continued

3 CECILY PARSLEY, 6, b m Fantastic Light (USA)—Salim Toto **Mr L. A. Garfield**
4 CILL RIALAIG, 7, gr m Environment Friend—Pang Valley Girl **Pangfield Partners**
5 COSIMO DE MEDICI, 5, b g Medicean—Wish Bevan, Doyle & Lawrence
6 COUSIN KHEE, 5, b g Sakhee (USA)—Cugina **Mr R. C. Tooth**
7 DAFFYDOWNDILLY, 4, b f Oasis Dream—Art Eyes (USA) **Lady Blyth**
8 DAWN GALE (IRE), 4, b f Hurricane Run (IRE)—Latest Chapter (IRE) **Mrs Lucy Birley & Mr Robin Birley**
9 DECANA, 4, ch f Doyen (IRE)—Sahara Belle (USA) **R. M., S. R. & P. J. Payne**
10 DUSTER, 5, b g Pastoral Pursuits—Spring Clean (FR) **Mr M. T. Bevan**
11 FAIR TRADE, 5, ch g Trade Fair—Ballet **Mr R. C. Tooth**
12 GENTLEMAN JIMMY, 12, br g Alderbrook—Irish Orchid **Burridge & Rutland**
13 GOLDEN DELICIOUS, 4, ch f Cadeaux Genereux—Playgirl (IRE) **Mr N. M. H. Jones**
14 ICE NELLY (IRE), 4, b f Iceman—Dancing Nelly **Lady Hardy**
15 LITTLE CURTSEY, 4, b f Royal Applause—Tychy **Lady Faringdon**
16 MILLERS PUDSEY, 6, b g Pasternak—Gables Girl **Mr P. J. Cave**
17 MUCH WANTS MORE (IRE), 4, b g Exit To Nowhere (USA)—Raichu (IRE) **Mr J. C. Harley**
18 NAZREEF, 5, b g Zafeen (FR)—Roofer (IRE) **Deborah Collett & M. J. Watson**
19 NON DOM (IRE), 6, br g Hawk Wing (USA)—Kafayet (USA) **Mr R. C. Tooth**
20 PASTORAL PLAYER, 5, b g Pastoral Pursuits—Copy-Cat **The Pursuits Partnership**
21 PETE THE PASTOR, 4, b g Pastoral Pursuits—Franciscaine (USA) **Mrs M. D. W. Morrison**
22 PICK A LITTLE, 4, b g Piccolo—Little Caroline (IRE) **Mr K. B. Hodges**
23 QUIZ MISTRESS, 4, ch f Doyen (IRE)—Seren Quest **The Fairy Story Partnership**
24 SAGRAMOR, 4, ch c Pastoral Pursuits—Jasmick (IRE) **Melksham Craic**
25 SLEEPY HOLLOW, 7, b g Beat Hollow—Crackling **Lady Blyth**
26 SOHRAAB, 8, b g Erhaab (USA)—Riverine **Pangfield Racing**
27 SPARTAN SPIRIT (IRE), 4, b g Invincible Spirit (IRE)—Kylemore (IRE) **Thurloe Thoroughbred XXVIII**
28 TAIKOO, 7, b g Dr Fong (USA)—So True **Mrs M. D. W. Morrison**
29 VALENCHA, 5, ch m Domedriver (IRE)—Riverine **Pangfield Partners**

THREE-YEAR-OLDS

30 ABI SCARLET (IRE), b f Baltic King—Petarga **H. Morrison**
31 ABUNDANTLY, b f Sakhee (USA)—Composing (IRE) **J. Repard & S. Dibb**
32 ACROSS THE GALAXY, b f Cape Cross (IRE)—Galaxy Highflyer **Helena Springfield Ltd**
33 BELLA OPHELIA (IRE), b f Baltic King—Banco Solo **Mrs Belinda Scott & Partners**
34 BLISSAMORE, b f Kyllachy—Tremiere (FR) **Lady Bland**
35 BURNHAM, b c Nayef (USA)—Salim Toto **The Hill Stud**
36 CALEDONIAN LAD, ch g Pastoral Pursuits—Jasmick (IRE) **The Caledonian Racing Society**
37 CHIL THE KITE, b c Notnowcato—Copy-Cat **Hazel Lawrence & Graham Doyle**
38 COQUET, b f Sir Percy—One So Marvellous **Hon Mary Morrison & Partners**
39 DANGEROUS TO KNOW, b f Byron—Bogus Mix (IRE) **Sherin Lloyd & Friends**
40 DORA'S GIFT, b f Cadeaux Genereux—Conquestadora **The Fairy Story Partnership**
41 EGRETTA (IRE), b f Motivator—Firecrest (IRE) **Sir Thomas Pilkington & Mrs S. Rogers**
42 FLEXIBLE FLYER, b c Exceed And Excel (AUS)—Windermere Island **A. J. Struthers, J. F. Dean & Mrs J. Scott**
43 FREDERICKTHEGREAT, b g Exceed And Excel (AUS)—Torgau (IRE) **Wood Street Syndicate II**
44 GLAZE, ch f Kyllachy—Raindrop **Lady Margadale, Fiona Trenchard, Anne Usher**
45 HALLING'S QUEST, b g Halling (USA)—Capriolla **The Fairy Story Partnership**
46 ISOBELLA, b f Royal Applause—Gwyneth **The End-R-Ways Partnership**
47 MAE ROSE COTTAGE (IRE), ch f Dylan Thomas (IRE)—Maskaya (IRE) **P. A. Byrne**
48 NO COMPROMISE, b f Avonbridge—Highly Liquid **Mrs A. J. Hamilton-Fairley**
49 PARISIAN PRINCESS (IRE), b f Teofilo (IRE)—Night Sphere (IRE) **Simply Racing Limited**
50 PHANTOM RANCH, b g Act One—Highbrook (USA) **Mrs S. Rowley-Williams**
51 PLACE THAT FACE, b f Compton Place—Notjustaprettyface (USA) **Mr R. J. Cornelius**
52 PORT CHARLOTTE, b f Oasis Dream—Maria Theresa **The Caledonian Racing Society**
53 PRIMACY (IRE), br f Primary (USA)—Seaborne **Prime Of Life 2**
54 RESPONSIVE, b f Dutch Art—Xtrasensory **Thurloe Thoroughbreds XXIX**
55 SEA FRET, b f Nayef (USA)—Shifting Mist **Mrs C. R. Philipson**
56 SHIROCCO STAR, b f Shirocco (GER)—Spectral Star **Helena Springfield Ltd**
57 SOLFILIA, ch f Teofilo (IRE)—Suntory (IRE) **Swire, Scott, Margadale**
58 SUN SEAL, b f Cape Cross (IRE)—Soliza (IRE) **Mr Michael Kerr-Dineen & Partners**
59 SUPAHEART, b f Lion Heart (USA)—Supamova (USA) **M. Arbib**
60 SWIFT WINGED, b f Motivator—Swift Spring (FR) **Ben & Sir Martyn Arbib, Mr C. Budgett**
61 TUNNAGER GROVE, b g Piccolo—Violet's Walk **M. E. Wates**

MR HUGHIE MORRISON—continued

TWO-YEAR-OLDS

62 **ANOTHER COCKTAIL**, b c 20/2 Dalakhani (IRE)—Yummy Mummy (Montjeu (IRE)) (85000) **Mr M. Kerr-Dineen**
63 **BANOFFEE (IRE)**, b f 12/4 Hurricane Run (IRE)—
　　　　　Nanabanana (IRE) (Anabaa (USA)) (49261) **M. Kerr-Dineen, Hon W. H. Smith & Partners**
64 B c 8/2 Observatory (USA)—Capriolla (In The Wings) **The Fairy Story Partnership**
65 **CHURCH OF ENGLAND**, bl c 13/3 Pastoral Pursuits—Lawyers Choice (Namid) **Mr R. C. Tooth**
66 **COUNTRYMAN**, b c 15/2 Pastoral Pursuits—
　　　　　Baileys Silver (Marlin (USA)) (22000) **H. Scott-Barrett, S. de Zoete & A. Pickford**
67 Ch f 21/4 Indian Haven—Coventina (IRE) (Daylami (IRE)) (3000) **The Lavington Stud & Partners**
68 Ch f 30/3 Medicean—Dash To The Front (Diktat) (45000) **Helena Springfield Ltd**
69 B c 18/4 Pastoral Pursuits—Fealeview Lady (USA) (Red Ransom (USA)) **Pangfield Pursuits**
70 **FELIX FABULA**, b c 15/4 Lucky Story (USA)—Laser Crystal (IRE) (King's Theatre (IRE)) (10000) **Mrs I. Eavis**
71 Ch c 28/2 Sakhee's Secret—Folly Lodge (Grand Lodge (USA)) (47000) **Thurloe Thoroughbreds XXX**
72 Ch f 24/1 Sakhee's Secret—Glencal (Compton Place) (952) **G. Doyle & Lord Margadale**
73 B g 26/4 Motivator—Good Girl (IRE) (College Chapel) **Mr L. A. Garfield**
74 **JUBILANTE**, b f 6/3 Royal Applause—Lavinia's Grace (USA) (Green Desert (USA)) (14000)
　　　　　Mr S. De Zoete, Mr A. Pickford & Mr R. C. A. Hammond
75 B f 13/3 Sakhee's Secret—Maria Theresa (Primo Dominie) (1523) **Lord Margadale**
76 B c 20/3 Officer (USA)—Married for Money (USA) (Not For Love (USA)) (35000)
　　　　　Lord Margadale, Mr M. Kerr-Dineen, Mr H. Scott-Barrett & The Hon W. Henry Smith
77 **MIDAZ**, br c 19/4 Zamindar (USA)—Schlague (FR) (Pulpit (USA)) (20525) **Mr M. Bevan, Mr S. De Zeote**
78 Gr f 30/3 Dalakhani (IRE)—Peppermint Green (Green Desert (USA)) (20000) **Helena Springfield Ltd**
79 **REALIZE**, b c 18/1 Zafeen (FR)—Relkida (Bertolini (USA)) **Deborah Collett & M. J. Watson**
80 B c 25/3 Beat Hollow—Riverine (Risk Me (FR)) **Pangfield Racing III**
81 Ch f 22/2 Raven's Pass (USA)—Rosinka (IRE) (Soviet Star (USA)) **Capt J. Macdonald-Buchanan**
82 Ch f 30/1 Dalakhani (IRE)—Salsa Steps (USA) (Giant's Causeway (USA)) **Ben & Sir Martyn Arbib**
83 **SECRET TALENT**, b g 28/2 Sakhee's Secret—Aqaba (Lake Coniston (IRE)) (6000) **Mr J. Repard**
84 B f 27/2 Avonbridge—Summertime Parkes (Silver Patriarch (IRE)) (4761) **Mr Simon Malcolm**
85 **TOWN MOUSE**, ch c 22/4 Sakhee (USA)—
　　　　　Megdale (IRE) (Waajib) (15000) **Justin Dowley & Mouse Hamilton-Fairley**
86 Ch f 5/3 Sakhee's Secret—Up At Dawn (Inchinor) (28000) **Mr C. Harper & Mr N. Poole**
87 B f 30/3 Manduro (GER)—Wild Gardenia (Alhaarth (IRE)) **Lofts Hall Stud & Mrs C. R. Philipson**
88 **ZIEKHANI**, ch gr c 22/3 Dalakhani (IRE)—Zietory (Zieten (USA)) **The Fairy Story Partnership**

Other Owners: Mr Michael Kerr-Dineen, Mr E. R. Goodwin, Mrs M. D. W. Morrison, Mr H. Morrison, Sir Martyn Arbib, Mr Ben Arbib, Mr C. Benson, Mr T. M. Bird, Mr J. G. St P. Burridge, Miss D. Collett, Mr J. F. Dean, Mr Sam Dibb, Mr Graham Doyle, Mrs H. S. Ellingsen, Lady Andrew Hay, Miss Hazel Lawrence, Mrs Sherin Lloyd, Mr Rodney Lloyd, Lord Margadale, Lady Margadale, Hon. Miss Mary Morrison, Mr B. G. W. Parker, Mr O. J. W. Pawle, Mrs P Payne, Mr R. M. Payne, Mr S. R. Payne, Mr J. P. Repard, Mrs Sonia Rogers, Mrs Belinda Scott, Mrs Julia Scott, Miss C. S. Scott-Balls, Mr Hugh Scott-Barrett, Hon W. H. Smith, Mr J. A. B. Stafford, Mr A. J. Struthers, Mr M. Taylor, Viscountess Trenchard, Mr M. J. Watson, Mr M. Weinfeld, Mr S. West, Mr A. W. Wood.

Assistant Trainer: Susannah Procter

Amateur: Miss Nicola Dumelow, Mr Robert Pooles.

---

467 | **MR WILLIAM MUIR, Lambourn**
Postal: Linkslade, Wantage Road, Lambourn, Hungerford, Berkshire, RG17 8UG
Contacts: OFFICE (01488) 73098 HOME (01488) 73748 FAX (01488) 73490
MOBILE (07831) 457074
E-MAIL william@williammuir.com WEBSITE www.williammuir.com

1 **COURT APPLAUSE (IRE)**, 4, b g Royal Applause—Forever Blue **John H. W. Finch Ian Knightley David Ross**
2 **CRUISER**, 4, b g Oasis Dream—Good Girl (IRE) **C. L. A. Edginton**
3 **ENROLLER (IRE)**, 7, b g Marju (IRE)—Walk On Quest (FR) **D. G. Clarke & C. L. A. Edginton**
4 **FANCOURT**, 4, b f Diktat—Santorini (USA) **Fancourt Partnership**
5 **GRIFFIN POINT (IRE)**, 5, b m Tagula (IRE)—Lady Corduff (IRE) **F. P. Hope**
6 **MIDAS MOMENT**, 4, b f Danehill Dancer (IRE)—Special Moment (IRE) **Foursome Thoroughbreds**
7 **PERSIAN HERALD**, 4, gr g Proclamation (IRE)—Persian Fortune **Inside Track Racing Club**
8 **SECRET ERA**, 5, b m Cape Cross (IRE)—Secret History (USA) **Carmel Stud**

MR WILLIAM MUIR—continued

9 **TALBOT GREEN,** 4, b g Green Desert (USA)—One of The Family **Claridge, Quaintance, Egan & Mercer**
10 **TELLMETHINGS,** 4, b f Distant Music (USA)—Faraude **Mr J. M. O'Mulloy**
11 **THE GURU OF GLOOM (IRE),** 4, b g Dubai Destination (USA)—Gabriella **R. Haim**
12 **WE HAVE A DREAM,** 7, b br g Oasis Dream—Final Shot **The Dreaming Squires**

THREE-YEAR-OLDS

13 **ALICE'S DANCER (IRE),** br f Clodovil (IRE)—Islandagore (IRE) **Perspicacious Punters Racing Club**
14 **ARMIGER,** b g Araafa (IRE)—Welsh Valley (USA) **Muir Racing Partnership - London**
15 **BREAKING THE BANK,** ch c Medicean—Russian Queen (USA) **R. W. Devlin**
16 **CHARITABLE ACT (FR),** b c Cadeaux Genereux—Acatama (USA) **Muir Racing Partnership - Chester**
17 **FUZZY LOGIC (IRE),** b g Dylan Thomas (IRE)—
　　　　　　　　　　　　　　　　Gates of Eden (USA) **Builder, Baker & Candlestick Maker Partnership**
18 **HOLLYWOOD ALL STAR (IRE),** b g Kheleyf (USA)—Camassina (IRE) **The Lavelle Family**
19 **INNISCASTLE BOY,** b c Sir Percy—Galapagar (USA) **The Lavelle Family**
20 **KITTENS,** b f Marju (IRE)—Purring (USA) **Muir Racing Partnership - Chester**
21 **LAST SHADOW,** b c Notnowcato—Fairy Queen (IRE) **M. J. Caddy**
22 **LITTLE CHINA,** b f Kyllachy—China Beads **S. Lamb**
23 **LONDON WELSH,** b c Cape Cross (IRE)—Croesi Cariad **M. Graham & Mr K. Mercer**
24 **MOMENT IN THE SUN,** ch f Dubai Destination (USA)—Special Moment (IRE) **Foursome Thoroughbreds**
25 **MOODY DANCER,** b f Cape Cross (IRE)—
　　　　　　　　　　　　　　　　Bluebelle Dancer (IRE) **Builder, Baker & Candlestick Maker Partnership**
26 **REGISTER (IRE),** b g Lawman (FR)—Paldouna (IRE) **Mrs D. L. Edginton**
27 **SAINT HILARY,** b f Authorized (USA)—Bright Halo (IRE) **Usk Valley Stud**
28 **SANGRAIL,** b f Singspiel (IRE)—Wars (IRE) **Muir Racing Partnership - London**
29 **SILENCE IS EASY,** b f Cape Cross (IRE)—African Queen (IRE) **Builder, Baker & Candlestick Maker Partnership**
30 **SIOUXPERHERO (IRE),** b g Sleeping Indian—Tintern **Muir Racing Partnership - Bath**
31 **ST ATHAN,** b f Authorized (USA)—Nantyglo **M. Graham & Mr K. Mercer**
32 **STEPPER POINT,** b c Kyllachy—Sacre Coeur **C. L. A. Edginton**
33 **SUEDEHEAD,** b f Cape Cross (IRE)—Oshiponga **Frontier Racing Group**
34 **SUGAR LOAF,** b f Singspiel (IRE)—Annapurna (IRE) **Usk Valley Stud**
35 **TYPOGRAPHY,** br g Byron—Bold Byzantium **North Farm Partnership**
36 **VILLENEUVE,** ch f Zamindar (USA)—Emilion **Mr & Mrs G. Middlebrook**
37 **WELSH ROYALE,** b g Royal Applause—Brecon **Muir Racing Partnership - London**

TWO-YEAR-OLDS

38 **FOIE GRAS,** b c 8/3 Kyllachy—Bint Zamayem (IRE) (Rainbow Quest (USA)) (28000) **Mrs G. E. Rowland-Clark**
39 **GRAYSWOOD,** gr c 4/5 Dalakhani (IRE)—Argent du Bois (USA) (Silver Hawk (USA)) (75000) **C. L. A. Edginton**
40 **KENNY'S GIRL (IRE),** b f 18/3 Manduro (GER)—Tanz (IRE) (Sadler's Wells (USA)) (8000) **D. F. White**
41 B c 9/3 Sakhee's Secret—Malelane (IRE) (Prince Sabo) (42857)
42 B f 28/1 Singspiel (IRE)—Portmeirion (Polish Precedent (USA))
43 B f 5/4 Mount Nelson—Purring (USA) (Mountain Cat (USA)) (11500)
44 B f 19/4 Jeremy (USA)—Staceymac (IRE) (Elnadim (USA)) (9523)
45 B f 7/2 Clodovil (IRE)—Tintern (Diktat)
46 B f 13/4 Haafhd—Welsh Valley (USA) (Irish River (FR))

Other Owners: Mr Joseph Barton, Mr A. Baverstock, Mr R. J. Burden, Mr M. J. Caddy, Mr P. T. Claridge, Mr N. Clark, Mr D. G. Clarke, Mr J. D. Clements, Mr R. Cooper, Mr G. Cox, Mr Mike Dawson, Mr Roger Devlin, Mr R. Dix, Mr Adam John Driver, Mr C. L. A. Edginton, Mr D. Egan, Mr John H. W. Finch, Mr P. W. Goodfellow, Mr Martin P. Graham, Mr R. Haim, Mr John Hobson, Mrs J. Hubbard, Mrs L. Humphries, Inside Track Racing Club, Mr Stewart Jones, Mr Tony Jones, Mr I. G. Knightley, Mr D. P. Knox, Mr R. Kolien, Mr S. Lamb, Mr E. Lavelle, Mr M. J. C. Lavelle, Mr K. J. Mercer, Mrs S. Mercer, Mr G. Middlebrook, Mrs L. Middlebrook, Mr W. R. Muir, Mrs J. M. Muir, Mr David J. Muir, Mrs A. Muir, Mr J. O'Mulloy, Miss C. O'Neill, Quaintance Partnership, Mr David Ross, Mrs G. Rowland-Clark, Mr B. Sancto, Mr N. J. Sillett, Mr L. Slater, Mr & Mrs G. Stacey, Mr M. Wass, Mr G. Weir, Mr P. J. Wheatley, Mr & Mrs G. Wood.

Jockey (flat): Martin Dwyer. **Apprentice:** James Rogers.

---

468 **MR CLIVE MULHALL, Scarcroft**
Postal: **Scarcroft Hall Farm, Thorner Lane, Scarcroft, Leeds, LS14 3AQ**
Contacts: **PHONE (0113) 2893095 FAX (0113) 2896815 MOBILE (07979) 527675**
E-MAIL clive@scarcrofthallracing.co.uk WEBSITE www.clivemulhallracing.co.uk

1 **ALIMURE,** 6, b m Tamure (IRE)—Auntie Alice **Mr K. H. Rainbow**
2 **PRINCE SAMOS (IRE),** 10, b g Mujadil (USA)—Sabaniya (FR) **Mrs C. M. Mulhall**
3 **SHARADIYN,** 9, b g Generous (IRE)—Sharadiya (IRE) **Simon Ballance & Mrs C M Mulhall**

MR CLIVE MULHALL—continued

4 **SIMHAL**, 8, b g Minster Son—Busky Girl **Josttigo Racing**
5 **THINK**, 5, ch g Sulamani (IRE)—Natalie Jay **Mrs C M Mulhall & Over The Rainbow**
6 **TUKITINYASOK (IRE)**, 5, b g Fath (USA)—Mevlana (IRE) **Mrs C. M. Mulhall**

Other Owners: Mr S. T. Ballance, Mr M. Bisogno, G. Halsall, Hugh T. Redhead, Mr C. Sim, S. M. Taylor, Mr T. D. Wooldridge.

Assistant Trainer: Mrs Martina Mulhall

Amateur: Mr C. Mulhall, Mr O. Churton.

---

469 **MR NEIL MULHOLLAND, Tiverton**
Postal: Sunnyside Stables, Burlescombe, Tiverton, Devon, EX16 7JZ
Contacts: **MOBILE (07739) 258607**
E-MAIL neil@neilmulhollandracing.com WEBSITE www.neilmulhollandracing.com

1 **ASHCOTT BOY**, 4, ch g Lahib (USA)—Last Ambition (IRE) **Mr J. Hobbs**
2 4, B g Midnight Legend—Ballad Opera
3 **BAN UISCE (IRE)**, 7, b g Lahib (USA)—Scolboa Gold (IRE) **The Don't Tell Daddy Racing Partnership**
4 **BAROQUE MAN**, 5, b g Revoque (IRE)—Barton May **Mr P. G. Gray & Mrs J. M. Abbott**
5 4, Ch g Midnight Legend—Barton Dante **Lady H. J. Clarke**
6 **BARTON FELIX**, 5, gr g Fair Mix (USA)—Home From The Hill (IRE) **Lady H. J. Clarke**
7 4, B c First Trump—Bay of Plenty
8 **BENEATH**, 5, b g Dansili—Neath **Wellcroomed Ltd**
9 **BIG KNICKERS**, 7, b m Bob Back (USA)—Island Hopper **Matrow Properties Limited**
10 **CAROLE'S DESTRIER**, 4, b g Kayf Tara—Barton May **Mrs C. Skipworth**
11 **CAUNAY**, 5, ch g Generous (IRE)—Chantilly Lady **Mr R. Moore**
12 **CHICHARITO (IRE)**, 5, ch m Croco Rouge—Mama Jaffa (IRE) **D. J. Bridger**
13 **COLONIAL HARRY**, 5, b g Sir Harry Lewis (USA)—Shaadin (USA) **The Colony Stable LLC**
14 **COURT GAMBLE (IRE)**, 8, b m King's Theatre (IRE)—Black Queen (IRE) **Mr S. Noyce**
15 **FRAN'S FOLLY**, 6, b m Baryshnikov (AUS)—Lansdowne Park **Neil Mulholland Racing Club**
16 **GALLIMAUFRY**, 6, b m Sir Harry Lewis (USA)—Hinemoa (IRE) **Mr H. R. Cross**
17 **HOBB'S DREAM (IRE)**, 8, br m Winged Love (IRE)—La-Greine **Mr John & Jeanette Hobbs & Mr P J Proudley**
18 4, Ch g Midnight Legend—Home From The Hill (IRE) **Lady H. J. Clarke**
19 **HOPATINA (IRE)**, 6, b m Flemensfirth (USA)—Bonny Lass **J. & S. Baigent**
20 **IHEARDU**, 6, b g Overbury (IRE)—Tina Gee **Wellcroomed Ltd**
21 **JUST THE JOB (IRE)**, 8, b g Religiously (USA)—Fashions Side **Mr B. F. Mulholland**
22 **KIERANN (IRE)**, 5, b g Samraan (USA)—Kiera's Gale (IRE) **Mr B. F. Mulholland**
23 **KILRUSH (IRE)**, 6, gr g Dilshaan—Pride of Passion (IRE) **J & S Baigent**
24 **MABEL TASMAN**, 6, ch m Midnight Legend—West Coast **Mabels Ladies Partnership**
25 **MAD MAX (IRE)**, 10, b g Kayf Tara—Carole's Crusader **Mrs C. Skipworth**
26 **MATROW'S LADY (IRE)**, 5, b m Cloudings (IRE)—I'm Maggy (NZ) **Matrow Properties Limited**
27 **MEET ME AT DAWN**, 8, ch m Afflora (IRE)—Quiet Dawn **Dajam Ltd**
28 **MIDNIGHT CHASE**, 10, b g Midnight Legend—Yamrah **Lady H. J. Clarke**
29 **MIDNIGHT OPERA**, 6, b g Midnight Legend—Ballad Opera **D. J. Bridger**
30 **NEWMANS BOY**, 5, ch g Loup Sauvage (USA)—Newman's Conquest **P. C. Tory**
31 **NOVABRIDGE**, 4, ch g Avonbridge—Petrovna (IRE) **Dajam Ltd**
32 4, B g Reel Buddy (USA)—Party Charmer
33 **POINT OF REFERENCE**, 5, b m Exit To Nowhere (USA)—Pointlet (USA) **Neil Mulholland Racing Club**
34 **RUN ALONG BOY**, 7, b g Beat All (USA)—Gunner Be Good **Mr J. Hobbs**
35 **SILSULA**, 6, gr ro m Silver Patriarch (USA)—Sulapuff **Dajam Ltd**
36 **WAIT NO MORE (IRE)**, 7, ch g Strategic Choice (USA)—Tearaway Lady (IRE) **Mr J. Hobbs**
37 **YOU CAN OF COURSE (IRE)**, 9, b g Saddlers' Hall (IRE)—O'dalaigh (IRE) **Mr I. S. Woodward**

THREE-YEAR-OLDS

38 **JIMMY THE LOLLIPOP (IRE)**, b g Amadeus Wolf—
Royal Consort (IRE) **eyewearoutlet.co.uk/woodward/mulholland**
39 **THE YOUNG MASTER**, b g Echo of Light—Fine Frenzy (IRE) **Dajam Ltd**

Other Owners: Mrs J. M. Abbott, Mrs J. A. V. Allen, Mr J. R. Baigent, Mrs S. J. Baigent, Mrs H. R. Cross, Mr P. G. J. Devlin, Mr P. G. Gray, Mr John Hobbs, Mr Billy Kenneally, Mr Brian D. Makepeace, Mr Neil Mulholland, Mrs Melanie Poole, Mr P. J. Proudley, Mrs A. G. L. Walker, Wellcroomed T/A eyewearoutlet.co.uk, Mr I. S. Woodward.

Conditional: Andrias Guerin.

470 MR LAWRENCE MULLANEY, Malton
Postal: 5 Blacksmiths Row, Great Habton, Malton, North Yorkshire, YO17 6TU

1 FILE AND PAINT (IRE), 4, b f Chevalier (IRE)—Have A Heart (IRE) **L. A. Mullaney**
2 LOGANS LEGEND (IRE), 4, b g Johannesburg (USA)—Almost Blue (USA) **L. A. Mullaney**

THREE-YEAR-OLDS

3 LOLITA LEBRON (IRE), b f Royal Applause—Alsharq (IRE) **Ian Buckley**

471 MR MICHAEL MULLINEAUX, Tarporley
Postal: Southley Farm, Alpraham, Tarporley, Cheshire, CW6 9JD
Contacts: PHONE (01829) 261440 FAX (01829) 261440 MOBILE (07753) 650263
E-MAIL southlearacing@btinternet.com WEBSITE www.cheshiretrainer.co.uk

1 ABSA LUTTE (IRE), 9, b m Darnay—Zenana (IRE) **D & D Coatings Ltd**
2 4, B c Needwood Blade—Beechy Bank (IRE) **Miss L. S. Young**
3 BOLLISTICK, 6, b g Bollin Eric—Slip Killick **P. Currey**
4 BOXER SHORTS, 6, b g Puissance—Lady Boxer **P. Clacher**
5 CARYS'S LAD, 9, b g Exit To Nowhere (USA)—Dawn Spinner **M. Mullineaux**
6 DANZIG FOX, 7, b g Foxhound (USA)—Via Dolorosa **Southley Racing Partnership**
7 FAST RUBY, 5, ch m Fleetwood (IRE)—Tinoforty (FR) **Mr A. Johnstone**
8 FRANCIS ALBERT, 6, b g Mind Games—Via Dolorosa **M. Mullineaux**
9 HE'S A HAWKER (IRE), 7, ch g Fourstars Allstar (USA)—Dromin Deel (IRE) **Mr I. S. Ross**
10 KIRSTYS LAD, 10, b g Lake Coniston (IRE)—Killick **S. A. Pritchard**
11 LULU'S GIFT (IRE), 6, gr m Lahib (USA)—She's A Gift **M. Mullineaux**
12 LYON'S HILL, 8, ch g Generous (IRE)—New Abbey **D. Ashbrook**
13 METHAALY (IRE), 9, b g Red Ransom (USA)—Santorini (USA) **Noel Racing**
14 MOLKO JACK (FR), 8, b br g Lavirco (GER)—Line As (FR) **D & D Coatings Ltd**
15 MUZEY'S PRINCESS, 6, b m Grape Tree Road—Premier Princess **D. M. Drury**
16 NAFA (IRE), 4, br f Shamardal (USA)—Champs Elysees (USA) **M. Mullineaux**
17 OLYNARD (IRE), 6, b g Exceed And Excel (AUS)—Reddening **D & D Coatings Ltd**
18 ORPEN BID (IRE), 7, b m Orpen (USA)—Glorious Bid (IRE) **Miss L. S. Young**
19 SACCO D'ORO, 6, b m Rainbow High—Speedy Native (IRE) **Mr P. R. D'Amato**
20 SIR BOSS (IRE), 7, b g Tagula (IRE)—Good Thought (IRE) **Miss M Mullineaux,Mr P Lawton,Mr I Ross**
21 SMIRFY'S SILVER, 8, b g Desert Prince (IRE)—Goodwood Blizzard **Mrs D. Plant**
22 TACKSWOP (IRE), 8, b m Revoque (IRE)—Fainne Oir (IRE) **M. Mullineaux**
23 TWO TURTLE DOVES (IRE), 6, b m Night Shift (USA)—Purple Rain (IRE) **Mr G. Cornes**

THREE-YEAR-OLDS

24 B f Gulch (USA)—Hypoxia (USA)
25 MY TIME, b c Mind Games—Tick Tock **M. Mullineaux**

TWO-YEAR-OLDS

26 B f 13/2 Halling (USA)—Jazz Baby (IRE) (Fasliyev (USA)) (32840)

Other Owners: Mr N. R. Garner, Miss J. Hogg, P. J. Lawton, Miss M. Mullineaux, Mr F. Noel.

Assistant Trainers: Stuart Ross & Susan Mullineaux

Conditional: Peter Hatton. **Amateur:** Miss M. J. L. Mullineaux, Mr S. Ross.

472 MR SEAMUS MULLINS, Amesbury
Postal: Wilsford Stables, Wilsford-Cum-Lake, Amesbury, Salisbury, Wiltshire, SP4 7BL
Contacts: PHONE/FAX (01980) 626344 MOBILE (07702) 559634
E-MAIL info@jwmullins.co.uk WEBSITE www.seamusmullins.co.uk

1 ALDER MAIRI (IRE), 5, ch m Alderbrook—Amari Queen **F. G. Matthews**
2 ALLDUNNANDUSTED (IRE), 8, b g Rudimentary (USA)—Megans Dreamer (IRE) **Mr C. R. Dunning**
3 ANNIMATION (IRE), 8, b m Accordion—Euro Breeze (IRE) **Dr R. Jowett**
4 BACK TO MY PLACE (IRE), 6, ch m Bob Back (USA)—Homebird (IRE) **J. W. Mullins**
5 BENOZZO GOZZOLI, 6, ch g Medicean—Star Precision **J. W. Mullins**
6 BOSS IN BOOTS (IRE), 4, gr g King's Theatre (IRE)—Grey Mo (IRE) **Mr M. Adams**

MR SEAMUS MULLINS—continued

7 **BRUNETTE'SONLY (IRE)**, 7, ch m Flemensfirth (USA)—Pride of St Gallen (IRE) **Mrs M. M. Rayner**
8 **CATCH THE RASCAL (IRE)**, 6, b m Presenting—
Eneeymeenymineeymo (IRE) **Mr & Mrs Chris and Stella Watson and Jock Cullen**
9 **CHAMBRAY DANCER (IRE)**, 4, b f Darsi (FR)—Cotton Gale **First Impressions Racing Group**
10 **COMBUSTIBLE LADY (IRE)**, 7, b m Mr Combustible (IRE)—Ladyogan (IRE) **J. W. Mullins**
11 **FERGALL (IRE)**, 5, br g Norwich—Gaybrook Girl (IRE) **Andrew Cocks & Tara Johnson**
12 **FITOBUST (IRE)**, 6, b g Classic Cliche (IRE)—Noan Rose (IRE) **Wilsford Racing Partnership**
13 **FOREST RHYTHM (IRE)**, 8, b g Great Palm (IRE)—Eurythmic **New Forest Racing Partnership**
14 **GENEROUS BOB**, 5, ch g Generous (IRE)—Bob's Finesse **Miss C. A. James**
15 **HEAD SPIN (IRE)**, 4, b g Beneficial—Who Tells Jan **Mr M. Adams**
16 **HIGH SAMANA**, 4, b g High Chaparral (IRE)—Kirkby Belle **Chimera Racing**
17 **HILL FORTS GLORIA (IRE)**, 7, b m King's Theatre (IRE)—Ad Gloria (IRE) **Mrs J. C. Scorgie**
18 **HOMER RUN (IRE)**, 5, b g Classic Cliche (IRE)—Suir Native (IRE) **Seamus Mullins Racing**
19 **JOIN THE NAVY**, 7, b g Sea Freedom—Join The Parade **G. B. Balding**
20 **KUCHAROVA (IRE)**, 4, b f Danehill Dancer (IRE)—Gates of Eden (USA) **J. W. Mullins**
21 **LANDERBEE (IRE)**, 5, b g Exit To Nowhere (USA)—Ithastobedone (IRE) **Mr C. J. Baldwin**
22 **MIGHT AS WELL**, 9, gr g Terimon—Might Be **Dr & Mrs John Millar**
23 **OR SING ABOUT (FR)**, 10, b g Le Balafre (FR)—Grande Folie (FR) **A. M. Day**
24 **RUBY GLOW**, 4, b f Septieme Ciel (USA)—Ruby Too **Dr R. Jowett**
25 **RUSSIAN CONQUEST**, 6, gr g Baryshnikov (AUS)—Kellys Conquest **F. G. Matthews**
26 **SAPPHIRE ROUGE (IRE)**, 6, ch m Alderbrook—Emerald Express **Lake Racing**
27 **THERE AND THEN**, 6, b g Where Or When (IRE)—Cugina **G. B. Balding**
28 **TIME TO THINK**, 7, b m Alflora (IRE)—Shuil Do (IRE) **Mrs V. F. Hewett**
29 **TOP SMART**, 6, b g Karinga Bay—Clover Dove **The Calvera Partnership No. 2**
30 **UP YOUR GAME (IRE)**, 4, b g Milan—Katie Snurge (IRE) **Mr M. Adams**
31 **WELL GREEN (IRE)**, 8, b g Quws—Coca's Well (IRE) **Seamus Mullins Racing**
32 **WILDE RUBY (IRE)**, 5, b m Oscar (IRE)—Ruby Thewes **J. W. Mullins**

Other Owners: Miss C. L. Brown, Mr A. P. Cocks, Mr W. G. Cullen, Exors of the Late Mr P. Everard, R. Hatchard, P. Hickey, Mr A. K. Horsman, Mrs E. M. J. James, Mr A. C. James, Mr S. E. James, Miss T. Johnson, D. A. Lucie-Smith, Dr J. W. Millar, Mrs J. D. Millar, J. D. Oakey, C. R. Watson, Mrs S. Watson, Miss L. J. Whitehorn, C. Wilson, J. H. Young.

Assistant Trainer: Miss Charlotte Brown

Jockey (NH): Jimmy Derham, Wayne Kavanagh, Andrew Thornton. **Conditional:** Darren O'Keeffe. **Amateur:** Miss C. L. Brown, Mr K. Jones.

---

473 MR WILLIAM P. MULLINS, Carlow
Postal: **Closutton, Bagenalstown, Co. Carlow, Ireland**
Contacts: **PHONE (00353) 5997 21786 FAX (00353) 5997 21786 MOBILE (00353) 8725 64940**
E-MAIL wpmullins@eircom.net WEBSITE www.wpmullins.com

1 **A FINE YOUNG MAN (IRE)**, 7, b g Snurge—Miss Platinum (IRE) **T. J. Doran**
2 **ALFRED JAMES**, 6, b g Old Vic—Jupiter's Message **Mrs Rose Boyd**
3 **ALLEE GARDE (FR)**, 7, b g Kapgarde (FR)—Allee Du Port (FR) **Mr T. J. Doran**
4 **ALLURE OF ILLUSION (IRE)**, 6, ch g Captain Rio—Sixhills (FR) **Mrs S. Ricci**
5 **APT APPROACH (IRE)**, 9, ch g Bob Back (USA)—Imminent Approach (IRE) **Greenstar Syndicate**
6 **ARE YA RIGHT CHIEF (IRE)**, 7, b g Flemensfirth (USA)—River Clyde (IRE) **Mrs M McMahon**
7 **AUPCHARLIE (IRE)**, 6, b g Daliapour (IRE)—Lirfa (USA) **Ann & Alan Potts Partnership**
8 **BACK IN FOCUS (IRE)**, 7, ch g Bob Back (USA)—Dun Belle (IRE) **Andrea & Graham Wylie**
9 **BAGBER**, 6, b g Diktat—Torcross **Mr Allan McLuckie**
10 **BALLYCASEY (IRE)**, 5, gr g Presenting—Pink Mist (IRE) **Mrs S. Ricci**
11 **BALLYHAUNIS (IRE)**, 7, b g Daylami (IRE)—Ballet **Mrs S. Ricci**
12 **BISHOPSFURZE (IRE)**, 7, b g Broadway Flyer (USA)—Supreme Dipper (IRE) **Mrs C. M. Hurley**
13 **BLACKSTAIRMOUNTAIN (IRE)**, 7, b g Imperial Ballet (IRE)—Sixhills (FR) **Mrs S. Ricci**
14 **BLAZING TEMPO (IRE)**, 8, b m Accordion—Leading Duke **Mrs S. Ricci**
15 **BOLD BANKS (IRE)**, 9, b g Taipan (IRE)—A Womans Heart (IRE) **Mrs J. M. Mullins**
16 **BOSTON BOB (IRE)**, 7, b g Bob Back (USA)—Bavaway **Andrea & Graham Wylie**
17 **BOWFINGER (IRE)**, 9, ch g Anshan—Galley Flash (IRE) **Mrs J. M. Mullins**
18 **BOXER GEORG (IRE)**, 10, b g Taipan (IRE)—Country Course (IRE) **Mr W. Murray**
19 **BUNDLE OF FUN (IRE)**, 9, ch g Topanoora—Leaden Sky (IRE) **Shanakiel Racing Syndicate**
20 **CADSPEED (FR)**, 9, b g Vertical Speed (FR)—Cadmina (FR) **Carra Ethos Syndicate**
21 **CALL THE POLICE (IRE)**, 9, b g Accordion—Evangelica (USA) **DD Racing Syndicate**
22 **CEOL RUA (IRE)**, 7, ch m Bob Back (USA)—Glens Music (IRE) **Ms F. McStay**
23 **CHAMPAGNE AGENT (IRE)**, 6, b g Smadoun (FR)—Madame Jean (FR) **John J. Fallon**

MR WILLIAM P. MULLINS—continued

24 **COOLDINE (IRE)**, 10, b g Beneficial—Shean Alainn (IRE) **Mrs V. O'Leary**
25 **COUSIN VINNY (IRE)**, 9, b g Bob Back (USA)—Trixskin (IRE) **Festival Syndicate**
26 **DANI CATALONIA (IRE)**, 6, b m Daggers Drawn (USA)—Tryphaena (FR) **W. K. McCarthy**
27 **DARE TO DOUBT**, 8, b m King's Theatre (IRE)—Karawa **J. T. Ennis**
28 **DARROUN (IRE)**, 4, gr g Dalakhani (IRE)—Darayka (FR) **Mrs S. Ricci**
29 **DEUTSCHLAND (USA)**, 9, b g Red Ransom (USA)—Rhine Valley (USA) **A. McLuckie**
30 **DIGENTA (IRE)**, 5, b g Helissio (FR)—
                  Scolboa Gold (IRE) **Dr I. M. P. Moran, Colland Sand & Gravel Syndicate**
31 **DRIVE ON REGARDLES (IRE)**, 9, ch g Shernazar—Wayward Queen **S. Ahern**
32 **DRIVE TIME (USA)**, 7, b g King Cugat (USA)—Arbusha (USA) **Andrea & Graham Wylie**
33 **EARLS QUARTER (IRE)**, 6, b g Shantou (USA)—Par Street (IRE) **B. Doyle**
34 **EQUUS MAXIMUS (IRE)**, 12, b g Flemensfirth (USA)—Sambara (IRE) **Andrea & Graham Wylie**
35 **FELIX YONGER (IRE)**, 6, b g Oscar (IRE)—Marble Sound (IRE) **Mr D. Taylor**
36 **FINAL APPROACH**, 6, b g Pivotal—College Fund Girl **Mr D. Taylor**
37 **FIVEFORTHREE (IRE)**, 10, gr g Arzanni—What A Queen **Olde Crowbars Syndicate**
38 **FLASH OF GENIUS**, 6, b g Definite Article—Fortune's Girl **Gigginstown House Stud**
39 **FLAT OUT (FR)**, 7, gr g Sagamix (FR)—Divine Rodney (FR) **M. O'Riordan**
40 **GIGANTA (IRE)**, 5, b g Helissio (FR)
41 **GORGEOUS SIXTY (FR)**, 4, b f Touch of The Blues (FR)—Sixty Six (FR) **Mrs S. Ricci**
42 **HAMMERSMITH (IRE)**, 9, b g Turtle Island (IRE)—Park Belle (IRE) **George Creighton**
43 **HATS AND HEELS (IRE)**, 5, b m Flemensfirth (USA)—Great Cullen (IRE) **Supreme Horse Racing Club**
44 **HURRICANE FLY (IRE)**, 8, b g Montjeu (IRE)—Scandisk (IRE) **George Creighton**
45 **INSPECTOR CLOUSEAU (IRE)**, 7, gr g Daylami (IRE)—Claustra (FR) **Allan McLuckie**
46 **JAYO (FR)**, 9, ch g Grape Tree Road—Joie de Nuit (USA) **Mr P. Garvey**
47 **KERB APPEAL (IRE)**, 7, b g Needle Gun (IRE)—Great Days (IRE) **Olde Crowbars Syndicate**
48 **LAGANBANK (IRE)**, 6, b g Norwich—Listen Up **Mrs Rose Boyd**
49 **LAMBRO (IRE)**, 7, b g Milan—Beautiful Tune (FR) **Byerly Thoroughbred Racing**
50 **LIDAKAN (FR)**, 4, gr g Intikhab (USA)—Laxlova (FR) **Gigginstown House Stud**
51 **LIOS A CHOILL (IRE)**, 8, b g Saddlers' Hall (IRE)—Shuil Liss **J. P. McManus**
52 **LOCH ARD (IRE)**, 4, b g Pivotal—My Giddy Aunt (IRE) **Wicklow Bloodstock Ltd**
53 **LORD GALE (IRE)**, 6, ch g Bach (IRE)—Wire Lady (IRE) **Mrs Robin Birley**
54 **LUC JORDAN**, 6, b g Intikhab (USA)—Saphila (IRE) **Bertie Hourihan**
55 **MAGGIE CONNOLLY (IRE)**, 7, ch m Definite Article—Catch The Breeze (IRE) **Hugh Curtis**
56 **MAID FROM MILAN (IRE)**, 7, b m Milan—Raishah (GER) **Brian Keenan**
57 **MAKE YOUR MARK (IRE)**, 5, b g Beneficial—Bell Star (IRE) **Gigginstown House Stud**
58 **MARASONNIEN (FR)**, 6, b g Mansonnien (FR)—Maracay (FR) **Mrs S. Ricci**
59 **MARITO (GER)**, 5, b g Alkalde (GER)—Maratea (USA) **Mrs S. Ricci**
60 **MIDNIGHT GAME**, 5, b g Montjeu (IRE)—Midnight Angel (GER) **Gigginstown House Stud**
61 **MIDNIGHT OIL**, 4, b g Motivator—One So Marvellous **Gigginstown House Stud**
62 **MIKAEL D'HAGUENET (FR)**, 8, b g Lavirco (GER)—Fleur d'haguenet (FR) **Mrs S. Ricci**
63 **MOON OVER MANDALAY (GER)**, 6, b g Dashing Blade—Miss Esther (GER) **Dermot Owens**
64 **MOURAD (IRE)**, 7, ch g Sinndar (IRE)—Mouramara (IRE) **Teahon Consulting Limited**
65 **MOZOLTOV**, 6, b g Kayf Tara—Fairmead Princess **Martin Lynch**
66 **ON HIS OWN (IRE)**, 8, b g Presenting—Shuil Na Mhuire (IRE) **Andrea & Graham Wylie**
67 **OUR MONTY (IRE)**, 9, b g Montjeu (IRE)—She's Our Mare (IRE) **Colland Sand & Gravel Ltd**
68 **PASSAGE VENDOME (FR)**, 6, b g Polish Summer—Herodiade (FR) **Mr G. Mullins**
69 **PEKING TO PARIS (IRE)**, 7, ch g Flemensfirth (USA)—Castlehaven (IRE) **Joe O'Keefe**
70 **PERFECT GENTLEMAN (IRE)**, 7, b g King's Theatre (IRE)—Millennium Lilly (IRE) **Mrs J. M. Mullins**
71 **PICKAPOCKETORTWO (IRE)**, 8, b g Fruits of Love (USA)—Lamp of Phoebus (USA) **YITBA Racing Club**
72 **PIQUE SOUS (FR)**, 5, gr g Martaline—Six Fois Sept (FR) **Not Just Any Racing Club**
73 **POMME TIEPY (FR)**, 9, b m Apple Tree (FR)—Unetiepy (FR) **Mrs S. Ricci**
74 **POPCORN (FR)**, 9, b g Roakarad—Baie de Chalamont (FR) **Mrs J. M. Mullins**
75 **PRIDE OFTHE PARISH (IRE)**, 8, b g Flemensfirth (USA)—Rose Island **Mrs V. O'Leary**
76 **PRIMROSEANDBLUE (IRE)**, 8, b g Shernazar—Karlybelle (FR)
77 **PRINCE DE BEAUCHENE (FR)**, 9, b g French Glory—Chipie d'angron (FR) **Andrea & Graham Wylie**
78 **QUADRILLON (FR)**, 8, b br g Dounba (FR)—Gastibelza (FR) **Mrs M. McMahon**
79 **QUAQUO DE FLOTTE (FR)**, 8, b g Comte du Bourg (FR)—Isati's (FR) **The Three D Syndicate**
80 **QUEL ESPRIT (FR)**, 8, gr g Saint des Saints (FR)—Jeune d'esprit (FR) **Red Barn Syndicate**
81 **QUEVEGA (FR)**, 8, b m Robin des Champs (FR)—Vega IV (FR) **Hammer & Trowel Syndicate**
82 **QUISCOVER FONTAINE (FR)**, 8, b g Antarctique (FR)—Blanche Fontaine (FR) **J. P. McManus**
83 **RAISE HELL (IRE)**, 5, b g Presenting—Markiza (IRE) **Gigginstown House Stud**
84 **RAPTOR (FR)**, 7, gr g Caballo Raptor (CAN)—Tiwa (FR) **Aiden Devawey**
85 **RATTAN (USA)**, 7, ch g Royal Anthem—Rouwaki (USA) **J. A. Coleman**
86 **ROBIN ANGEVIN (FR)**, 7, b g Saint Cyrien (FR)—Gypsie d'artois (FR) **Mr B. Cunningham**
87 **ROCKYABOYA (IRE)**, 8, ch g Rock Hopper—Motility **Flip A Coin Syndicate**
88 **ROLLY BABY (FR)**, 7, b g Funny Baby (FR)—Vancia (FR) **Teahon Consulting**

MR WILLIAM P. MULLINS—continued

89 SAMAIN (GER), 6, b g Black Sam Bellamy (IRE)—Selva (IRE) **Gigginstown House Stud**
90 SARABAD (FR), 4, b g Astarabad (USA)—Saraphine (FR) **Mrs S. Ricci**
91 SCHOLARS MATE (IRE), 11, ch g Shernazar—Hazel Honey (IRE) **Glassdrummond Racing Syndicate**
92 SCOTSIRISH (IRE), 11, b g Zaffaran (USA)—Serjitak **Double R Stables LLP Syndicate**
93 SHAKERVILZ (FR), 9, b g Villez (USA)—Zamsara (FR) **Mrs J. M. Mullins**
94 SHAMAR (FR), 4, b c Dr Fong (USA)—Shamalana (IRE) **Mrs S. Ricci**
95 SHIFA (FR), 6, b m Lost World (IRE)—Infancy (FR) **Alain Couetil**
96 SICILIAN SECRET (IRE), 9, b g Flemensfirth (USA)—Kala Supreme (IRE) **Mrs S. Ricci**
97 SIMENON (IRE), 5, b g Marju (IRE)—Epistoliere (IRE) **Wicklow Bloodstock Ltd**
98 SIN PALO (IRE), 8, b g Dushyantor (USA)—Platinum Gold **Downthehatch Syndicate**
99 SIR DES CHAMPS (FR), 6, b br g Robin des Champs (FR)—Liste En Tete (FR) **Gigginstown House Stud**
100 SIZING SAHARA, 4, gr g Shirocco (GER)—Aristocratique **Ann & Alan Potts Partnership**
101 SKORCHER (IRE), 8, b g Flemensfirth (USA)—River Clyde (IRE) **Sean O'Driscoll**
102 SO YOUNG (FR), 6, b g Lavirco (GER)—Honey (FR) **Mrs McMahon**
103 SOLL, 7, ch g Presenting—Montelfolene (IRE) **Derrick Mossop**
104 SOME TARGET (IRE), 8, b g Witness Box (USA)—Bayloughbess (IRE) **Captain Conflict Syndicate**
105 SOUS LES CIEUX (FR), 6, ch g Robin des Champs (FR)—Joie de La Vie (FR) **Mrs S. Ricci**
106 STRAIN OF FAME (IRE), 6, b br g King's Theatre (IRE)—Carolina (FR) **T. I. Naughton**
107 SUPER SONIC BOOM (IRE), 5, b g Azamour (IRE)—Spirit of Age (IRE) **Mrs J. M. Mullins**
108 SUPREME CAROLINA (IRE), 5, b m Traditionally (USA)—Carolina (FR) **Supreme Horse Racing Club**
109 SWEET MY LORD (FR), 6, b g Johann Quatz (FR)—Hasta Manana (FR) **Mr A. Devaney**
110 TARLA (FR), 6, b m Lavirco (GER)—Targerine (FR) **Mrs S. Ricci**
111 TAWAAGG, 9, b g Kyllachy—Ascendancy **E. Duignan**
112 TEMPO DU CAMP (FR), 5, b g Charming Groom (FR)—Floriane du Camp (FR) **Gigginstown Stud**
113 TENNIS CAP (FR), 5, b g Snow Cap (FR)—Jijie (FR) **Mrs Violet O'Leary**
114 TERMINAL (FR), 5, b g Passing Sale (FR)—Durendal (FR) **Favourites Racing Syndicate**
115 THE BOSSES COUSIN (IRE), 7, b g King's Theatre (IRE)—Seductive Dance **Mrs J. M. Mullins**
116 THE MIDNIGHT CLUB (IRE), 11, ch g Flemensfirth (USA)—Larry's Peach **Mrs S. Ricci**
117 THE PAPARRAZI KID (IRE), 5, b g Milan—Banbury Cross (IRE) **Byerley Thoroughbred Racing**
118 THELEZE (FR), 5, b m Lavirco (GER)—Divette (FR) **Ann & Alan Potts Partnership**
119 THOUSAND STARS (FR), 8, gr g Grey Risk (FR)—Livaniana (FR) **Hammer & Trowel Syndicate**
120 TOOSTRONG (FR), 5, ch g Network (GER)—Fleurissa (FR) **Gigginstown House Stud**
121 TURBAN (FR), 5, b g Dom Alco (FR)—Indianabelle (FR) **Edward O'Connell**
122 TWIGLINE (FR), 5, gr m Martaline—Natty Twigy (FR) **Hammer & Trowel Syndicate**
123 TWINLIGHT (FR), 5, b g Muhtathir—Fairlight (GER) **M L Bloodstock Limited**
124 UN ATOUT (IRE), 4, b g Robin des Champs (FR)—Badrapette (FR) **Gigginstown House Stud**
125 UNCLE JUNIOR (IRE), 11, b g Saddlers' Hall (IRE)—Caslain Nua **Mrs M. McMahon**
126 UP OU THAT (IRE), 7, b g Alderbrook—Delnac **E. O'Connell**
127 UP THE BEAT, 7, b br g Beat All (USA)—Everything's Rosy **Mrs A. M. Varmen**
128 UT DE SIVOLA (FR), 4, b g Robin des Champs (FR)—Kerrana (FR) **Philip J. Reynolds**
129 VAST CONSUMPTION (IRE), 9, b m Rudimentary (USA)—Castalino
130 VESPER BELL (IRE), 6, b g Beneficial—Fair Choice (IRE) **George Mullins**
131 ZADARSKA (IRE), 7, b g Zagreb (USA)—Betterbebob (IRE) **Festival Syndicate**
132 ZAIDPOUR (FR), 6, b g Red Ransom (USA)—Zainta (IRE) **Mrs S. Ricci**

---

474 **MRS ANABEL MURPHY, Stratford-Upon-Avon**
Postal: Ridgeway House, Moor Farm, Wilmcote, Stratford-upon-Avon, Warwickshire, CV37 9XG
Contacts: **OFFICE** (01789) 205087 **HOME** (01789) 298346 **FAX** (01789) 263260
MOBILE (07774) 117777
E-MAIL anabelking.racing@virgin.net

1 AMALRIC (FR), 5, b g Laveron—Aimessa du Berlais (FR) **Touchwood Racing**
2 ASTON CANTLOW, 4, b g Hurricane Run (IRE)—Princess Caraboo (IRE) **H. A. Murphy**
3 BLACK CACHE (IRE), 6, b g Cachet Noir (USA)—Hindi (FR) **Mrs A. L. M. Murphy**
4 BOYCHUK (IRE), 11, b g Insan (USA)—Golden Flower (GER) **H. A. Murphy**
5 CAP FALCO (IRE), 7, gr g Beneficial—Banderole (IRE) **Mrs D. L. Whateley**
6 DORMOUSE, 7, b g Medicean—Black Fighter (USA) **H. A. Murphy**
7 HIMRAYN, 9, b g Generous (IRE)—Himaya (IRE) **Touchwood Racing**
8 KAKAPUKA, 5, br g Shinko Forest (IRE)—No Rehearsal (FR) **Mrs E Mills & Mr A Murphy**
9 KING'S ROAD, 7, ch g King's Best (USA)—Saphire **Mrs A. L. M. Murphy**
10 KORNATI KID, 10, b g Kayf Tara—Hiltonstown Lass **H. A. Murphy**
11 LIFE LONG (IRE), 8, b g Old Vic—Be My Rainbow (IRE) **Mrs Roz Wyles & Mr Aiden Murphy**
12 PREFERRED LIES (IRE), 7, ch g Definite Article—Knocktartan (IRE) **Mrs L Field & Mr A Murphy**
13 PRINCE OF DENIAL (IRE), 8, b g Old Vic—Lerichi (IRE) **The Nino's Partnership**
14 PRINCE TAIME (FR), 9, b g Astarabad (USA)—Maite (FR) **Mrs D. L. Whateley**

MRS ANABEL MURPHY—continued

15 **QUEEN'S CHOICE (IRE)**, 4, b f Choisir (AUS)—Queen of Fibres (IRE) **All The Kings Horses**
16 **RHYTHM SEEKER**, 9, b g Alflora (IRE)—Pearlossa **H. A. Murphy**
17 **TOTAL EFFECTS (IRE)**, 8, b g Alderbrook—Bounty (IRE) **Touchwood Racing**
18 **UP WITH THE LARK**, 7, b g Kayf Tara—Lily The Lark **Mrs S. P. Allen**
19 **VOLITO**, 6, ch g Bertolini (USA)—Vax Rapide **All The Kings Horses**
20 **WARREN CHASE (IRE)**, 7, b g Oscar (IRE)—Kilcash Cross **Touchwood Racing**

THREE-YEAR-OLDS

21 **BEAUMONT COOPER**, b c Invincible Spirit (IRE)—Atlantide (USA) **Touchwood Racing**

Other Owners: Mrs L. H. Field, Mrs A. J. Forde, Mrs E. A. Mills, Mrs R. J. Wyles.

Assistant Trainer: Aiden Murphy

Amateur: Mr O. J. Murphy.

---

475 MR COLM MURPHY, Gorey
Postal: Ballinadrummin, Killena, Gorey, Co. Wexford, Ireland
Contacts: PHONE (00353) 53 9482690 FAX (00353) 53 9482690 MOBILE (00353) 862 629538
E-MAIL murphycolma@hotmail.com WEBSITE www.colmmurphyracing.ie

1 **ALADDINS CAVE**, 8, b g Rainbow Quest (USA)—Flight of Fancy **Treasure Hunters Syndicate**
2 **BELLA MANA MOU (IRE)**, 10, b m Snurge—How Provincial (IRE) **Basement Syndicate**
3 **BIG ZEB (IRE)**, 11, b g Oscar (IRE)—Our Siveen **Mr Patrick J. Redmond**
4 **BIRZALI (FR)**, 5, gr g Kalanisi (IRE)—Bernimixa (FR) **Gigginstown House Stud**
5 **BOUILLABAISSE (IRE)**, 6, b m Beat Hollow—Cattermole (USA) **Barry Connell**
6 **CENTURIAN (IRE)**, 6, b g Oscar (IRE)—Diklers Dante **T. J. Fletcher**
7 **DANGAN DAYLIGHT (IRE)**, 6, ch m Old Vic—Nobull (IRE) **Michael Hoare**
8 **EMPIRE OF DIRT (IRE)**, 5, b g Westerner—Rose of Inchiquin (IRE) **Gigginstown House Stud**
9 **GATES OF ROME (IRE)**, 8, b g Luso—Express Mail (IRE) **Gigginstown House Stud**
10 **GLAM GERRY (IRE)**, 8, b g Dr Massini (IRE)—Daraheen Diamond (IRE) **Barry Connell**
11 **GROVE FIELD (IRE)**, 5, ch g Moscow Society (USA)—Wall-Nut Grove (IRE) **E. Nolan**
12 **HOLY SMOKES (IRE)**, 5, b g Oscar (IRE)—Can't Buy Me Love **Eamon J. Kelly**
13 **HUME TOWER (IRE)**, 6, ch g Old Vic—Camlin Rose **Castlehume Syndicate**
14 **JEWEL STAR (IRE)**, 5, b m Flemensfirth (USA)—Thetravellinglady (IRE) **John P. McManus**
15 **MAGIC SPEAR (IRE)**, 6, b g Dr Massini (IRE)—Charming Present (USA) **Mrs Teresa Murphy**
16 **PIPE LADY (IRE)**, 5, b m Flemensfirth (USA)—Native Sparkle (IRE) **J. Condron**
17 **QUITO DE LA ROQUE (FR)**, 8, b g Saint des Saints (FR)—Moody Cloud (FR) **Gigginstown House Stud**
18 **SHARIYAN (IRE)**, 6, b g Kahyasi—Sharesha (IRE) **Mrs Teresa Murphy**
19 **SHOOTIN THE BREEZE (IRE)**, 7, b g Alderbrook—Maghereareagh Lady (IRE) **Old Moss Farm Syndicate**
20 **SLATE LADY (IRE)**, 5, b m Shantou (USA)—Statim **J. Condron**
21 **TEN BOB (IRE)**, 6, b g Oscar (IRE)—Ariann's Pride (IRE) **John P. McManus**
22 **THE HARD HAT (IRE)**, 8, b g Beneficial—Three Hats (IRE) **Shane J. Harrington**
23 **TILE LADY (IRE)**, 5, b m Milan—Orwell Gaye (IRE) **J. Condron**
24 **TOP SPIN (IRE)**, 5, b br g Cape Cross (IRE)—Beguine (USA) **John P. McManus**
25 **TRUPENNY BIT (IRE)**, 6, b g Accordion—Royal Thimble (IRE) **John P. McManus**
26 **VOLER LA VEDETTE (IRE)**, 8, b m King's Theatre—Steel Grey Lady (IRE) **Mrs M. Brophy**
27 **ZAARITO (IRE)**, 10, b g Tiraaz (USA)—Coppenagh Girl **Victoria Syndicate**

---

476 MR FERDY MURPHY, West Witton
Postal: Wynbury Stables, West Witton, Leyburn, North Yorkshire, DL8 4LR
Contacts: PHONE (01969) 622289 FAX (01969) 625278
MOBILE (07703) 444398 & (07747) 017960
E-MAIL office@wynburystables.fsnet.co.uk WEBSITE www.ferdymurphyracing.co.uk

1 **ALMADAN (IRE)**, 4, b g Azamour (IRE)—Alamouna (IRE) **A & S Enterprises Ltd**
2 **ANGEL SUN (FR)**, 6, b g Astarabad (USA)—Five Rivers (FR) **Outhart, Trembath, Hyde, Fletcher, Hill**
3 **BADGERS RETREAT (IRE)**, 6, b g Elusive City (USA)—Heuston Station (IRE) **F. Murphy**
4 **BIG FELLA THANKS**, 10, b g Primitive Rising (USA)—Nunsdream **Crossed Fingers Partnership**
5 **BLUE SHARK (FR)**, 10, b br g Cadoudal (FR)—Sweet Beauty (FR) **Premier Racing Partnerships**
6 **BORDERHOPPER**, 8, ch g Zaha (CAN)—Tom's Influence **Mr P. Cranney**
7 **BRANDON THOMAS**, 6, br g Norwich—Last Sunrise (IRE) **S. L. Rodwell**
8 **CAPRICORNUS (USA)**, 5, ch h Rahy (USA)—Silent Partner (USA) **Let's Live Racing**

MR FERDY MURPHY—continued

9 CAUGHTONTHERIVER (IRE), 10, b m Charente River (IRE)—Blasgan (IRE) **F. Murphy**
10 CHARINGWORTH (IRE), 9, b g Supreme Leader—
          Quinnsboro Guest (IRE) **Mr Simon Roberts & A & S Enterprises**
11 CRYSTAL CHILD, 4, b f Keltos (FR)—Aliuska (IRE) **Miss V. Cartmel**
12 CYBORA (FR), 10, ch m Cyborg (FR)—Jolie Rapide (FR) **D. Clinton, S. Gale, F. Murphy**
13 DE BOITRON (FR), 8, b g Sassanian (USA)—Pondiki **Mrs J. Morgan & Mrs Lindsey J. Shaw**
14 DEN OF INIQUITY, 11, b g Supreme Leader—Divine Comedy (IRE) **M. C. Denmark**
15 DESPERATE DEX (IRE), 12, b g Un Desperado (FR)—Too Sharp **Crossed Fingers Partnership**
16 DIVERS (FR), 8, gr g Highest Honor (FR)—Divination (FR) **Let's Live Racing**
17 DOMOLY (FR), 9, b g Varese (FR)—Queen d'ouilly (FR) **F. Murphy**
18 ELIADES RUN (IRE), 6, b g Turtle Island (IRE)—Chancy Gal **Mr C. T. Eliades**
19 ELZAHANN (IRE), 10, b m Saddlers' Hall (IRE)—Serpentine Artiste **Mr I. A. Todd**
20 EMPEROR CHARLIE, 8, b g Emperor Fountain—State Lady **Universal Recycling Company**
21 ERIN DANCER (FR), 7, b g Chevalier (FR)—Negria (FR) **J. & A. Millar**
22 EWE ARE JOKING, 4, b g Midnight Legend—Ewe Beauty (FR) **Mrs J. E. Iveson**
23 FORMULATION (IRE), 5, b g Danehill Dancer (IRE)—
          Formal Approval (USA) **Poppies Europe Ltd, Clinton, Gale, Rosser**
24 FROSTY LAD (IRE), 8, b g Moscow Society (USA)—Johnston's Crest (IRE) **C. W. Cooper**
25 GALANT NUIT (FR), 8, b g Comte du Bourg (FR)—Little Blue (FR) **D. Parry**
26 GAVROCHE GAUGAIN (FR), 8, b g Varese (FR)—Jobereine (FR) **Universal Recycling Company**
27 GLASSON LAD (IRE), 5, b g Quws—Glasson House (IRE) **M. F. Bourke**
28 GOING WRONG, 9, b g Bob Back (USA)—Lucy Glitters **Universal Recycling Company**
29 GUESS AGAIN (IRE), 7, b g Milan—Guess Twice **M. C. Denmark**
30 HENNESSY (IRE), 11, b g Presenting—Steel Grey Lady (IRE) **M. C. Denmark**
31 HOLLO LADIES (IRE), 7, ch g Captain Rio—Lace Flower
32 IBN HIYYAN (USA), 5, gr ro g El Prado (IRE)—Lovely Later (USA) **Mr C. Eliades & Mr C. McHugh**
33 JAWS, 8, ch g Karinga Bay—Material Girl **M. C. Denmark**
34 KALAHARI KING (FR), 11, b br g Kahyasi—Queen of Warsaw (FR) **Mrs J. Morgan**
35 KELLYSTOWN LAD (IRE), 9, b g Old Vic—Kissangel (IRE) **Crossed Fingers Partnership**
36 LAP OF HONOUR (IRE), 8, b g Danehill Dancer (IRE)—Kingsridge (IRE) **D. Clinton, S. Gale, M. Milns**
37 LE ROI ROUGE (FR), 10, ch g Bateau Rouge—Reine de Lutece (FR) **G. T. W. Fenwicke-Clennell**
38 LE VERT GALANT (FR), 9, b g Vertical Speed (FR)—Marie Prends Garde (FR) **Mr C. McHugh & Mr C. Eliades**
39 LEADER OF THE GANG, 6, b g Karinga Bay—Material Girl **M. C. Denmark**
40 LONGWAYTOTIPPERARY, 4, b f Midnight Legend—Cudder Or Shudder (IRE) **F. Murphy**
41 LORD VILLEZ (FR), 8, b g Villez (USA)—Samina (FR) **A. G. Chappell**
42 4, Ch g Tobougg (IRE)—Lumpini Park **F. Murphy**
43 MACS ISLAND (IRE), 11, br g Heron Island (IRE)—Lady Clara (IRE) **F. Murphy**
44 MANSONIEN L'AS (FR), 6, b g Mansonnien (FR)—Star des As (FR) **Let's Live Racing**
45 MASTERFUL ACT (USA), 5, ch g Pleasantly Perfect (USA)—Catnip (USA) **Universal Recycling Company**
46 MISTER WALL STREET (FR), 7, b br g Take Risks (FR)—Miss Breezy (FR) **Gay & Peter Hartley**
47 NAIAD DU MISSELOT (FR), 11, b g Dom Alco (FR)—Une Nuit (FR)
48 NEGUS DE BEAUMONT (FR), 11, b g Blushing Flame (USA)—Givry (FR) **Mr J. Tierney & F. Murphy**
49 NINE DE SIVOLA (FR), 11, b g Video Rock (FR)—Quine de Chalamont (FR) **Let's Live Racing**
50 OCKEY DE NEULLIAC (FR), 10, ch g Cyborg (FR)—Graine de Neulliac (FR) **F. Murphy**
51 ON GOSSAMER WINGS (IRE), 8, b g Winged Love (IRE)—Katie Parson **F. Murphy**
52 ON THE RIGHT PATH, 5, b g Pursuit of Love—Glen Falls **F. Murphy**
53 ONLY THE BEST, 9, b g Flemensfirth (USA)—Celtic Remorse **Let's Live Racing**
54 OR D'OUDAIRIES (FR), 10, b g April Night (FR)—Belle Truval (FR) **Gay & Peter Hartley**
55 OUEST ECLAIR (FR), 7, b g Sagacity (FR)—Kalistina (FR) **C. W. Cooper**
56 PILLAR OF HERCULES (IRE), 8, b g Rock of Gibraltar (IRE)—Sabreon **Miss J. E. Moore**
57 PISTOL BASC (FR), 8, ch g Maille Pistol (FR)—Moldane (FR) **Let's Live Racing**
58 POKER DE SIVOLA (FR), 9, b g Discover d'auteuil (FR)—Legal Union **D. A. Johnson**
59 RICH LORD, 8, b g Zamindar (USA)—Al Corniche (IRE) **Let's Live Racing**
60 RIGUEZ DANCER, 8, b g Dansili—Tricoteuse **Let's Live Racing**
61 ROCKING AND REELIN, 5, b g Supreme Sound—Cudder Or Shudder (IRE) **The Melanoma Charity Partnership**
62 ROLLWITHTHEPUNCHES, 7, b g Hernando (FR)—Zarma (FR) **Four Winds Racing**
63 ROYAL MILE (IRE), 8, br g Bob's Return (IRE)—Country Style **M. C. Denmark**
64 SAMSON COLLONGES (FR), 6, gr g Fragrant Mix (IRE)—Idole Collonges (FR) **F. Murphy**
65 SAN CASSIANO (IRE), 5, b g Bertolini—Celtic Silhouette **F. Murphy**
66 SECRET DESERT, 6, b g Dubai Destination (USA)—Lady Bankes (IRE) **The Extra Time Partnership**
67 SEIGNEUR DES BOIS (FR), 6, b g Ballingarry (IRE)—Studieuse (FR) **Crossed Fingers Partnership**
68 SENDIYM (FR), 5, b g Rainbow Quest (USA)—Seraya (FR) **Mr A. S. Ambler**
69 SMART MISTRESS, 10, b gr m Silver Patriarch (IRE)—Smart Rhythm **Helen Harvey Robert Woodward**
70 SOPHONIE (FR), 6, b m Kapgarde (FR)—Kore des Obeaux (FR) **Crossed Fingers Partnership**
71 STAND CLEAR, 7, b m Sir Harry Lewis (USA)—Clair Valley **Beautifully Bred Partnership**
72 STUFF OF DREAMS, 7, b m Groom Dancer (USA)—Best of The Best (FR) **F. Murphy**

MR FERDY MURPHY—continued

73 **SUMAK (FR)**, 8, b g Kahyasi—Lady Slave (IRE) **Tony Pye & Masoud Khadem**
74 **THE HOLLINWELL**, 9, b g Classic Cliche (IRE)—Action de Balle (FR) **Mr & Mrs N. Iveson**
75 **VUVUZELA**, 6, ch g Sir Harry Lewis (USA)—Clair Valley **Premier Racing Partnerships**
76 **WADNAAN**, 5, ch g Shamardal (USA)—Australian Dreams **Mrs J. Morgan**
77 **ZACANA (FR)**, 4, b f Robin des Champs (FR)—Cohiba (FR) **F. Murphy**

Other Owners: A & S Enterprises Ltd, Mr M. Ball, Miss Dorothy M. Clinton, Mr C. Eliades, Mr J. M. Fawbert, Mr Neil Fletcher, Mr L. R. Frampton, Mrs Sandra V. Gale, Mr P A. H. Hartley, Mrs P A. H. Hartley, Mrs Helen Harvey, Mr D. N. Iveson, Mrs J. E. Iveson, Mr D. A. Johnson, Mr Masoud Khadem, Mr Chris McHugh, Miss R. E. A. Menzies, Mr A. Millar, Mrs J. Millar, Mrs M. Milns, Mrs J. Morgan, Mr Ferdy Murphy, Mr Tony Outhart, Mr Gary Peacock, Poppies Europe Limited, Mr Tony Pye, Mr Simon N. Roberts, Mr Jon Rosser, Mrs Lindsey J. Shaw, Mr S. C. C. Skey, Mrs Caroline Skey, Ms J. Storrow, Ms Clare B Storrow, Mr J. Tierney, Mr Nicholas Williamson, Mr R. H. Woodward.

Assistant Trainer: Victoria Hayter

Jockey (NH): Graham Lee, Keith Mercer. **Conditional:** Tony Kelly, Robert McCarth, John Winston. **Amateur:** Mr John Roche, Miss Catherine Walton.

MR MIKE MURPHY, Westoning
Postal: **Broadlands, Manor Park Stud, Westoning, Bedfordshire, MK45 5LA**
Contacts: PHONE (01525) 717305 FAX (01525) 717305 MOBILE (07770) 496103
E-MAIL mmurphy@globalnet.co.uk WEBSITE www.mikemurphyracing.co.uk

1 **BENANDONNER (USA)**, 9, ch g Giant's Causeway (USA)—Cape Verdi (IRE) **M. Murphy**
2 **CHAPTER AND VERSE (IRE)**, 6, gr g One Cool Cat (USA)—Beautiful Hill (IRE) **Mr D. J. Ellis**
3 **DUCAL**, 4, b g Iceman—Noble Lady **M. Murphy**
4 **GREENSWARD**, 6, b g Green Desert (USA)—Frizzante **The Furlong Friends**
5 **IF YOU WHISPER (IRE)**, 4, b g Iffraaj—Little Whisper (IRE) **Mr P. J. A. Woods**
6 **LOVE YOUR LOOKS**, 4, b f Iffraaj—Play Around (IRE) **M. Murphy**
7 **LUTINE BELL**, 5, ch g Starcraft (NZ)—Satin Bell **Rogerson, Carr & Murphy**
8 **RED SOMERSET (USA)**, 9, b g Red Ransom (USA)—Bielska (USA) **M. Murphy**
9 **ROCK ANTHEM (IRE)**, 8, ch g Rock of Gibraltar (IRE)—Regal Portrait (IRE) **R. Bright**
10 **SUNSET KITTY (USA)**, 5, b br m Gone West (USA)—Honorable Cat (USA) **Cool Cats**

THREE-YEAR-OLDS

11 **IL PAZZO**, b g Multiplex—Nut (IRE) **Borgatti Moir and Murphy**
12 **MITIE MOUSE**, b c Exceed And Excel (AUS)—Mimi Mouse **Mr B. Rogerson**
13 **SILVER NATIVE (IRE)**, b g Elusive City (USA)—Love of Silver (USA) **Mrs J. Thompson**

Other Owners: Mr M. Borgatti, Mrs M. Bright, J. B. Jessop, Mr S. Moir, Mrs C. Rogerson.

Assistant Trainer: J.P Cullinan

MR PAT MURPHY, Hungerford
Postal: **Glebe House Stables, School Lane, East Garston, Nr Hungerford, Berkshire, RG17 7HR**
Contacts: OFFICE (01488) 648473 FAX (01488) 649775 MOBILE (07831) 410409
E-MAIL pat@mabberleys.freeserve.co.uk WEBSITE www.patmurphyracing.com

1 **CATALINAS DIAMOND (IRE)**, 4, b f One Cool Cat (USA)—Diamondiferous (USA) **Briton International**
2 **CLOUDY BOB (IRE)**, 5, gr g Cloudings (IRE)—Keen Supreme (IRE) **P. G. Murphy**
3 **FANTINO**, 6, b g Shinko Forest (IRE)—Illustre Inconnue (USA) **N. A. Blyth**
4 **GOWITHDFLO (IRE)**, 5, b m Flemensfirth (USA)—Lady Zephyr (IRE) **Mr M. Jonas**
5 **MOSCOW IN APRIL (IRE)**, 5, ch m Moscow Society (USA)—Muharib Lady (IRE) **P. G. Murphy**
6 **TARATEENO**, 9, b g Kayf Tara—Shalateeno **The Golden Anorak Partnership & D Murphy**
7 **TEMLETT (IRE)**, 8, b g Desert Prince (IRE)—Bering Down (USA) **Mr J. Chambers**

Other Owners: B. H. Goldswain, Mrs J. B. H. Goldswain, Mrs K. M. Graham, Mrs D. E. Murphy, A. D. Potts.

Assistant Trainer: Mrs Dianne Murphy

Jockey (flat): Robert Havlin, Steve Drowne. **Jockey (NH):** Leighton Aspell, Colin Bolger.

479 MR BARRY MURTAGH, Carlisle
Postal: **Hurst Farm, Ivegill, Carlisle, Cumbria, CA4 0NL**
Contacts: PHONE **(01768) 484649** FAX **(01768) 484744** MOBILE **(07714) 026741**
E-MAIL **sue@suemurtagh.wanadoo.co.uk**

1 CARRIETAU, 9, b g Key of Luck (USA)—Carreamia **A. R. White**
2 CLOUSEAU (NZ), 8, ch g Riviera (FR)—Miss Marple (NZ) **Mrs S. Murtagh**
3 DANNY JOHN BOY, 9, b g Classic Cliche (IRE)—Tactix **D. J. Teasdale**
4 DEFERTO DELPHI, 5, ch g Mark of Esteem (IRE)—Delphic Way **N. M. Wright**
5 DYNAMIC DRIVE (IRE), 5, b g Motivator—Biriyani (IRE) **Ring Of Fire**
6 EMOTIVE, 9, b g Pursuit of Love—Ruby Julie **Hurst Farm Racing**
7 FLY BY WHITE (IRE), 4, ch f Hawk Wing (USA)—Le Montrachet **Mrs S. Murtagh**
8 ILLUSTRATION (IRE), 4, b c Pivotal—In Anticipation (IRE) **R & K Carter**
9 KEALIGOLANE (IRE), 8, gr g Beneficial—Leone Des Pres (FR) **J. R. Callow**
10 KING PUC, 7, gr g Karinga Bay—Squirrellsdaughter **Woodgate Partnership**
11 KING'S CHORISTER, 6, ch g King's Best (USA)—Chorist **Woodgate Partnership**
12 LUCKY MELLOR, 5, b g Lucky Story (USA)—Lady Natilda **Mr Don O'Connor & Mr Derek Wilson**
13 PENTON HOOK, 6, gr g Lucky Owners (NZ)—Cosmic Star **Lucky Owners**
14 PETE, 9, b g Overbury (IRE)—Fen Terrier **Mrs S. Murtagh**
15 RAGGIOS BOY, 6, ch g Karinga Bay—Fen Terrier **Mrs S. Murtagh**
16 STANLEY BRIDGE, 5, b g Avonbridge—Antonia's Folly **The Early Doors Partnership**
17 TOY GUN (IRE), 10, b g Pistolet Bleu (IRE)—Di's Wag **Ellenvalley Optimists**

Other Owners: Mr James Bowers, Exors of the Late Mr Jim Buchanan, Mrs F. Buchanan, Mr Robert Carter, Mrs F. K. Carter, Mr Stevan Houliston, Mrs M. Hutt, Mr B. M. Johnson, Mr J. H. B. Metcalf, Mr James Murtagh, Mr F. P. Murtagh, Mr Nigel North, Mr D. O'Connor, Mr Michael A. Proudfoot, Mr Derek Wilson, Mr N. M. Wright.

Assistant Trainer: S A Murtagh

480 MR WILLIE MUSSON, Newmarket
Postal: **Saville House, St Mary's Square, Newmarket, Suffolk, CB8 0HZ**
Contacts: PHONE **(01638) 663371** FAX **(01638) 667979**
E-MAIL **willie@williemusson.co.uk** WEBSITE **www.williemusson.co.uk**

1 AKARANA (IRE), 5, b g Danehill Dancer (IRE)—Castle Quest (IRE) **The City Boys**
2 ASTERALES, 5, b m Royal Applause—Shalimar (IRE) **W. J. Musson**
3 BASSETT ROAD (IRE), 4, ch g Byron—Topiary (IRE) **The Poets**
4 BOLD ADVENTURE, 8, ch g Arkadian Hero (USA)—Impatiente (USA) **The Adventurers**
5 BROUGHTON PLACE, 4, b f Compton Place—Classic Millennium **Broughton Thermal Insulations**
6 BROUGHTON SANDS, 4, b f Nayef (USA)—Pachanga **Broughton Thermal Insulations**
7 BROUGHTONS BANDIT, 5, b g Kyllachy—Broughton Bounty **Broughton Thermal Insulations**
8 BROUGHTONS CLASSIC, 6, b g Medicean—Classic Millennium **Broughton Thermal Insulations**
9 BROUGHTONS PARADIS (IRE), 6, b m Royal Applause—Amankila (IRE) **Broughton Thermal Insulations**
10 BROUGHTONS STAR, 5, ch g Starcraft (NZ)—Marrakech (IRE) **Broughton Thermal Insulations**
11 BROUGHTONS SWINGER, 5, b m Celtic Swing—Pachanga **Broughton Thermal Insulations**
12 COZY TIGER (USA), 7, gr g Hold That Tiger (USA)—Cozelia (USA) **McHugh & Partners**
13 EMEEBEE, 6, b g Medicean—Broughtons Motto **Broughton Thermal Insulations**
14 FIBS AND FLANNEL, 5, ch g Tobougg (IRE)—Queens Jubilee **Paul Prince & Partners**
15 FOOTSTEPSOFSPRING (FR), 5, b g Footstepsinthesand—Moon West (USA) **Le Printemps Partnership**
16 HURRICANE HYMNBOOK (USA), 7, b g Pulpit (USA)—April Squall (USA) **Python Partners**
17 KHUN JOHN (IRE), 9, b g Marju (IRE)—Kathy Caerleon (IRE) **The Strawberries To A Donkey Partnership**
18 LIFE OF LAUGHTER (USA), 4, b g Elusive Quality (USA)—Country Garden **Mr P. Twomey**
19 MADAME ALLSORTS, 7, b m Double Trigger (IRE)—Always A Pleasure **R. D. Musson**
20 MAGICALMYSTERYTOUR (IRE), 9, b g Sadler's Wells (USA)—Jude **Broughton Thermal Insulations**
21 MARAJAA (IRE), 10, b g Green Desert (USA)—Ghyraan (USA) **Willie Musson Racing Club**
22 MONSIEUR BROUGHTON, 4, ch g Monsieur Bond (IRE)—Rainy Day Song **Broughton Thermal Insulations**
23 NOVELLEN LAD (IRE), 7, b g Noverre (USA)—Lady Ellen **Johnson & Broughton**
24 REDINESSENCE (IRE), 4, b f Oratorio (IRE)—Red Liason (IRE) **E. E. A. Buddle**
25 ROCKET ROB (IRE), 6, b g Danetime (IRE)—Queen of Fibres (IRE) **Bill Hinge & John Searchfield**
26 RUSTIC DEACON, 5, ch g Pastoral Pursuits—Anne-Lise **Mrs R. H. Brown**
27 SAFWAAN, 5, b g Selkirk (USA)—Kawn **Libertys**

THREE-YEAR-OLDS

28 ABSENT AMY (IRE), b f Redback—Twitcher's Delight **Gone Away Partnership**
29 CAPRISKA, b f Bahri (USA)—Guignol (IRE) **W. J. Musson**

MR WILLIE MUSSON—continued

30 **OH FOR SURE (IRE)**, ch c Bahamian Bounty—Anne-Lise **Paul V Jackson & Janet P Jackson**
31 **YARRA VALLEY**, b f Aussie Rules (USA)—Frambroise **W. J. Musson**

TWO-YEAR-OLDS

32 B f 12/4 Ishiguru (USA)—Mistress Cooper (Kyllachy) **Mrs Rita Brown**
33 B f 15/4 Bahri (USA)—Yaqootah (USA) (Gone West (USA)) (19000)

Other Owners: Miss A. Abdullah, Mr J. Babbs, Mr E. K. Baker, Mr R. S. Brook, Broughton Thermal Insulation, Mrs Rita Brown, Mr E. Buddle, Mr K. D. Clarke, Mr K. A. Cosby, Mr A. Duke, Mr C. Eliades, Mr Fergus Falk, Mr B. N. Fulton, Mrs M. Graham-Campbell, Mr J Gunnell, Mr Bill Hinge, Mr Paul V. Jackson, Mr John D. Jacques, Mr I. Johnson, Mr I. K. Johnson, Mr Chris McHugh, Mr R. D. Musson, Mr John Scrider, Mr John Searchfield.

Jockey (flat): Stevie Donohoe, Jamie Mackay. **Jockey (NH):** Leighton Aspell, Timmy Murphy. **Apprentice:** Shannon Edmondson.

481

DR JEREMY NAYLOR, Shrewton
Postal: The Cleeve, Elston Lane, Shrewton, Wiltshire, SP3 4HL
Contacts: PHONE (01980) 620804 FAX (01980) 621999 MOBILE (07771) 740126
E-MAIL info@jeremynaylor.com WEBSITE www.jeremynaylor.com

1 **ACOSTA**, 8, b g Foxhound (USA)—Dancing Heights (IRE) **The Acosta Partnership**
2 **DOLORES ORTIZ (IRE)**, 6, b m High Chaparral (IRE)—Ma N'ieme Biche (USA) **The Acosta Partnership**
3 **INDIAN CHASE**, 15, b g Terimon—Icy Gunner **Dr J. R. J. Naylor**
4 **PADOVA**, 6, b g Shahrastani (USA)—My Song of Songs **Mr A. Brown**
5 **PITTON RIVERS**, 8, ch m Riverwise (USA)—Blind Justice **Martin Blandford**
6 **POPPY GREGG**, 7, b m Tamure (IRE)—Opalette **The Acosta Partnership**
7 **PRINCE CHARLEMAGNE (IRE)**, 9, br g King Charlemagne (USA)—
Ciubanga (IRE) **Cleeve Stables Racing Partnership**
8 **TOUS LES DEUX**, 9, b g Efisio—Caerosa **Dr J. R. J. Naylor**

THREE-YEAR-OLDS

9 B f Striking Ambition—Daphne's Doll (IRE)

Other Owners: Mrs S. P. Elphick.

Apprentice: Matthew Cosham.

482

MR JOHN NEEDHAM, Ludlow
Postal: Gorsty Farm, Mary Knoll, Ludlow, Shropshire, SY8 2HD
Contacts: PHONE (01584) 872112/874826 FAX (01584) 873256 MOBILE (07811) 451137

1 **BRINGEWOOD BELLE**, 9, b m Kayf Tara—Carlingford Belle **J. L. Needham**
2 **BRINGEWOOD BUNNY**, 8, b m King's Theatre (IRE)—Native Fox **Miss J. C. L. Needham**
3 **BRINGEWOOD FOX**, 10, gr g Cloudings (IRE)—Leinthall Fox **Miss J. C. L. Needham**
4 **ELTON FOX**, 7, br g Bob Back (USA)—Leinthall Fox **Miss J. C. L. Needham**
5 **ITALIAN LEGACE (IRE)**, 7, b g Milan—Honeybunch (IRE) **J. L. Needham**
6 **JUST ANOTHER JOKER**, 10, gr g Cloudings (IRE)—Just For A Laugh **Miss J. C. L. Needham**
7 **MISS HARRIET LEWIS**, 7, b m Sir Harry Lewis (USA)—Forest Heights **J. L. Needham**
8 **MORTIMERS CROSS**, 11, b g Cloudings (IRE)—Leinthall Doe **J. L. Needham**

Assistant Trainer: P. Hanly

Jockey (NH): Jason Maguire, Tommy Phelan. **Amateur:** Mr Robert Cooper.

483

MRS HELEN NELMES, Dorchester
Postal: Warmwell Stables, 2 Church Cottages, Warmwell, Dorchester, Dorset, DT2 8HQ
Contacts: PHONE/FAX (01305) 852254 MOBILE (07977) 510318
E-MAIL warmwellstud@tiscali.co.uk WEBSITE www.warmwellracing.co.uk

1 **BESTWOOD LODGE**, 6, ch m Dubai Destination (USA)—Three Green Leaves (IRE) **Warmwellcome Partnership**
2 **GALANTOS (GER)**, 11, b g Winged Love (IRE)—Grey Metal (GER) **Mrs C. Knowles**
3 **KALMBEFORETHESTORM**, 4, ch g Storming Home—Miss Honeypenny (IRE) **K. A. Nelmes**

MRS HELEN NELMES—continued

4 **KRISTOFFERSEN**, 12, ch g Kris—Towaahi (IRE) **T M W Partnership**
5 **MANICS MAN**, 7, ch g Double Trigger (IRE)—No Near Miss **Mrs K. M. House**
6 **MAYBEESWAY**, 6, gr m Nomadic Way (USA)—Maenad **K. A. Nelmes**
7 **MEGAGRACE**, 5, ch m Kirkwall—Megalex **Trickle Treat Partnership**
8 **ORVITA (FR)**, 10, b g Lute Antique (FR)—Ulvita (FR) **K. A. Nelmes**
9 **PRINCE OF KING**, 7, b g King O' The Mana (IRE)—Bogus Ballet **Miss S. J. Hartley**
10 **RIVIERE RUBY**, 5, b m King O' The Mana (IRE)—Madonna da Rossi **Miss S. J. Hartley**
11 **SWAINSON (USA)**, 11, br g Swain (IRE)—Lyphard's Delta (USA) **T M W Partnership**
12 **THE CLYDA ROVER (IRE)**, 8, ch g Moonax (IRE)—Pampered Molly (IRE) **K. A. Nelmes**
13 **WEST BAY HOOLIE**, 6, b g Nomadic Way (USA)—West Bay Breeze **C. T. & A. Samways**

Other Owners: Mr Richard Bance, Joe Cox, Mr R. Howsam, Mr A. Johnson, Miss Victoria O. Kardas, Mrs C. Knowles, Mr D. McKinnon, Mr P. Mears, Mr M. Miller, Mr C. Mundy, Mr K. A. Nelmes, Anne Neville, Mrs M. Pengelly, Mr D. Price, Mr C. T. Samways, Mrs A. Samways, Mr S. Scott, Mr D. Thompson.

Assistant Trainer: K Nelmes

Jockey (NH): Jamie Moore. **Amateur:** Mr Dean J. Nelmes, Mr James Legg.

484

MR CHRIS NENADICH, Sutton
Postal: **Lakes Farm, Sutton, Herefordshire, HR1 3NS**
Contacts: **PHONE (01432) 880278 MOBILE (07860) 484400**

1 **ANNIE CONFIDENTIAL (IRE)**, 9, b m Turtle Island (IRE)—Black Ivor (USA) **C. Nenadich**
2 **PRIEST FIELD (IRE)**, 8, ch g Daggers Drawn (USA)—Masakira (IRE) **Chris & Nick Nenadich**

Other Owners: Mr N. Nenadich.

Assistant Trainer: Marion Collins

485

MR TONY NEWCOMBE, Barnstaple
Postal: **Lower Delworthy, Yarnscombe, Barnstaple, Devon, EX31 3LT**
Contacts: **PHONE/FAX (01271) 858554 MOBILE (07785) 297210**
E-MAIL huntshawequineforest@talktalk.net

1 **ACTODOS (IRE)**, 8, ro g Act One—Really Gifted (IRE) **Mr G. D. C. Jewell**
2 **BABY DRIVER**, 4, gr g Proclamation (IRE)—Renee **A. G. Newcombe**
3 **BRANNOC (IRE)**, 7, b g Pilsudski (IRE)—Ned's Choice (IRE) **D. G. Staddon**
4 **CAPE KIMBERLEY**, 5, b g Arakan (USA)—Etoile Volant (USA) **J. R. Salter**
5 **DUNHOY (IRE)**, 4, ch c Goodricke—Belle of The Blues (IRE) **D. M. J. Gilbert**
6 **EVER THE OPTIMIST (IRE)**, 4, b g Cape Cross (IRE)—Have Faith (IRE) **D. M. J. Gilbert**
7 **HANOVERIAN BARON**, 7, b g Green Desert (USA)—Josh's Pearl (IRE) **P. Moulton**
8 **HOLDEN EAGLE**, 7, b g Catcher In The Rye (IRE)—Bird of Prey (IRE) **The About A Fortnight Partnership**
9 **JOLLY RANCH**, 6, gr m Compton Place—How Do I Know **Joli Racing**
10 **LUNDY BAY**, 5, b g Tobougg (IRE)—Nazaaha (USA) **The Devonian Partnership**
11 **LUNDY SKY**, 7, b g Zaha (CAN)—Rosina Mae **The Devonian Partnership**
12 **MAMBO SPIRIT (IRE)**, 8, b g Invincible Spirit (IRE)—Mambodorga (USA) **N. P. Hardy**
13 **MY METEOR**, 5, b g Bahamian Bounty—Emerald Peace (IRE) **A. G. Newcombe**
14 **PROFAB BOY**, 4, b c Zafeen (FR)—Three Strikes (IRE) **Mrs V. L. Nicholas**
15 **RED AVALANCHE (IRE)**, 5, gr g Verglas (IRE)—Maura's Guest (IRE) **R. J. Turton**
16 **SIGNORA FRASI (IRE)**, 7, b m Indian Ridge—Sheba (IRE) **Mr K. Eastup**
17 **VICTORIAN BOUNTY**, 7, b g Bahamian Bounty—Baby Bunting **D. M. J. Gilbert**
18 **WITCHRY**, 10, gr g Green Desert (USA)—Indian Skimmer (USA) **White Swan Racing & A. G. Newcombe**

THREE-YEAR-OLDS

19 **BITTER LEMON**, b f Indesatchel (IRE)—Citron **Joli Racing**
20 **I B A GEE GEE**, b c Proclamation (IRE)—Elvina **Capel Madison McCarthy & Easterling**
21 **SPELLMAKER**, b c Kheleyf (USA)—Midnight Spell **Joli Racing**

TWO-YEAR-OLDS

22 B c 17/2 King's Theatre (IRE)—Talinas Rose (IRE) (Definite Article) (24630) **Reefer Distribution Services Ltd**

MR TONY NEWCOMBE—continued

Other Owners: Mr J. Babb, Mr S. R. Baker, M. Blagg, C. J. Buckerfield, C. C. Capel, Miss K. E. Caryle, Mrs A. Cook, A. G. Craig, Mr J. W. Heal, K. P. McCarthy, Mr G. Milsom, Mr C. S. Pike.

Assistant Trainer: John Lovejoy

Jockey (flat): Dane O'Neill, Fergus Sweeney, Tom Queally. **Jockey (NH):** Liam Treadwell, Andrew Thornton.

---

486 DR RICHARD NEWLAND, Claines
Postal: **Newland Associates Ltd, Linacres Farm, Egg Lane, Claines, Worcester, WR3 7SB**
Contacts: **PHONE (07956) 196535**
E-MAIL **richard.newland1@btopenworld.com**

1 **ACT OF KALANISI (IRE)**, 6, b g Kalanisi (IRE)—Act of The Pace (IRE) **C E Stedman & Dr R D P Newland**
2 **BELLFLOWER BOY (IRE)**, 9, b g Old Vic—Dante's Arrow (IRE) **The Five Nations Partnership**
3 **BOBOWEN (IRE)**, 6, b g Bob Back (USA)—Opus One **D. P. Constable**
4 **CARRICKMINES (IRE)**, 10, b g Saddlers' Hall (IRE)—Orlas Castle (IRE) **Dr R. D. P. & Mrs L. J. Newland**
5 **CHANGING THE GUARD**, 6, b g King's Best (USA)—Our Queen of Kings **BetterTipster.co.uk**
6 **DENTON (NZ)**, 9, b g Montjeu (IRE)—Melora (NZ) **G. N. Carstairs**
7 **HERNELLO (IRE)**, 4, b f Hernando (FR)—Consuelo **P. Murphy**
8 **NIGHT ALLIANCE (IRE)**, 7, ch g Pierre—Next Venture (IRE) **Dr R. D. P. Newland**
9 **ROWAN TIGER**, 6, b g Tiger Hill (IRE)—Lemon Tree (USA) **Mr P. Jenkins**
10 **SCHINDLER'S GOLD (IRE)**, 10, ch g Oscar Schindler (IRE)—Saraemma **Dr R. D. P. & Mrs L. J. Newland**
11 **SILVER ADONIS (IRE)**, 11, gr g Portrait Gallery (IRE)—Fair Fontaine (IRE) **C. E. Stedman & R. J. Corsan**
12 **THEOLOGIST (IRE)**, 6, b g Galileo (IRE)—Medina (IRE) **C. E. Stedman**
13 **WAR PARTY**, 8, b g Fantastic Light (USA)—War Game (FR) **J A Provan,C E Stedman,Prof D E Newland**

Other Owners: Mr T. J. Baynham, Mr J. R. Couldwell, Mr D. Crampsie, Mrs L. J. Newland, Prof D. E. Newland, J. A. Provan, S. R. Trow.

Assistant Trainer: S. R. Trow

Amateur: Mr T. Weston.

---

487 MISS ANNA NEWTON-SMITH, Polegate
Postal: **Bull Pen Cottage, Jevington, Polegate, East Sussex, BN26 5QB**
Contacts: **PHONE (01323) 488354 FAX (01323) 488354 MOBILE (07970) 914124**
E-MAIL **anna_newtonsmith@o2.co.uk WEBSITE www.annanewtonsmith.co.uk**

1 **BIG BERTIE (IRE)**, 8, b g Luso—Next Venture (IRE) **D. O. Moon**
2 **BUDSSON**, 6, b g Alflora (IRE)—Little Bud **Mrs S. B. S. Grist**
3 **CLOUDY WAGER**, 7, b m Cloudings (IRE)—Gemma's Wager (IRE) **Mr B. Noakes & Baroness S. Noakes**
4 **GORING ONE (IRE)**, 7, b g Broadway Flyer (USA)—Brigette's Secret **Mr G. E. Goring**
5 **GORING TWO (IRE)**, 7, br g Needle Gun (IRE)—Kam Slave **Mr G. E. Goring**
6 **KNIGHT FLIGHT**, 7, b m Sir Harry Lewis (USA)—Punnett's Town **Mrs B. Day**
7 **LIBERATION BELLE (IRE)**, 5, b m Exit To Nowhere (USA)—Mistletoeandwine (IRE) **D. O. Moon**
8 **LITTLE ROXY (IRE)**, 7, b m Dilshaan—Brunswick **The Ash Tree Inn Racing Club**
9 **PETE THE FEAT (IRE)**, 8, b g King's Theatre (IRE)—Tourist Attraction (IRE) **Mr G. J. Larby & Mr P. J. Smith**
10 **PHILIPEDEFROXFIELD**, 4, b g Fair Mix (IRE)—Kansas City (FR) **D. O. Moon**
11 **PORTRAIT ROYALE (IRE)**, 10, b m Portrait Gallery (IRE)—Crows Cross (IRE) **PPS Racing**
12 **QUARTZ DU MONTCEAU (FR)**, 8, b g Robin des Champs (FR)—Emeraude (FR) **Mr E. S. Hicks**
13 **THE HARDY BOY**, 12, br g Overbury (IRE)—Miss Nero **Mrs S. B. S. Grist**
14 **TWIN BUD**, 7, b m Double Trigger (IRE)—Little Bud **Mrs S. B. S. Grist**

Other Owners: Mr M. K. Baker, G. J. Larby, Baroness S. Noakes, C. B. Noakes, His Honour Judge A. Patience, His Honour Judge J. R. Peppitt, P. J. Smith, A. K. Walker.

Assistant Trainer: Sally Harler

Jockey (flat): Hayley Turner. **Jockey (NH):** Mattie Batchelor, Aidan Coleman, Felix De Giles, Jimmy Derham, Nick Schofield, Andrew Thornton. **Conditional:** Marc Goldstein, Tom Cannon.

488 **MR DAVID NICHOLLS, Thirsk**
Postal: Tall Trees Racing Ltd, Tall Trees, Sessay, Thirsk, North Yorkshire, YO7 3ND
Contacts: **PHONE (01845) 501470 FAX (01845) 501666 MOBILE (07971) 555105**
E-MAIL david.nicholls@btconnect.com WEBSITE www.davidnichollsracing.com

1 **ADDICTIVE DREAM (IRE)**, 5, ch g Kheleyf (USA)—Nottambula (IRE) **B. Morton**
2 **AMENABLE (IRE)**, 5, b g Bertolini (USA)—Graceful Air (IRE) **Turton Brown Williams Lindley**
3 **ARRY'S ORSE**, 5, b g Exceed And Excel (AUS)—Georgianna (IRE) **H. Redknapp**
4 **BEACON LODGE (IRE)**, 7, b h Clodovil (IRE)—Royal House (FR) **D. Nicholls**
5 **BONNIE CHARLIE**, 6, ch g Intikhab (USA)—Scottish Exile (IRE) **Mrs A. M. Mcmanus**
6 **CRIMEA (IRE)**, 6, b g Kheleyf (USA)—Russian Countess (USA) **Middleham Park Racing XVI**
7 **DOCTOR CRANE (USA)**, 6, b g Doneraile Court (USA)—Sharons Song (USA) **D. Nicholls**
8 **DON'T CALL ME (IRE)**, 5, ch g Haafhd—Just Call Me (NZ) **Matt Morgan & Lauren Morgan**
9 **DUNN'O (IRE)**, 7, b g Cape Cross (IRE)—Indian Express **Mr S. Hussey**
10 **ESPRIT DE MIDAS**, 6, b g Namid—Spritzeria **Mr G. M. Copp**
11 **FITZ FLYER (IRE)**, 6, b g Acclamation—Starry Night
12 **FOL HOLLOW (IRE)**, 7, b g Monashee Mountain (USA)—Constance Do **Middleham Park Racing III**
13 **FORMIDABLE GIRL (USA)**, 4, b br f Roman Ruler (USA)—Gracility (USA) **Mike & Caroline McGeever**
14 **FREMEN (USA)**, 12, ch g Rahy (USA)—Northern Trick (USA) **Middleham Park Racing XXXV C King A Seed**
15 **GEORGE BENJAMIN**, 5, b g Trade Fair—Unchain My Heart **C. M. & M. A. Scaife**
16 **GREENHEAD HIGH**, 4, b g Statue of Liberty (USA)—Artistry **Mr C. Castle**
17 **HAMOODY (USA)**, 8, ch g Johannesburg (USA)—Northern Gulch (USA) **Hart Inn I**
18 **INDIAN TRAIL**, 12, ch g Indian Ridge—Take Heart **M. P. Love**
19 **INXILE (IRE)**, 7, b g Fayruz—Grandel **Mr D. Nicholls & Mrs J. Love**
20 **JACK DAWKINS (USA)**, 7, b g Fantastic Light (USA)—Do The Mambo (USA) **The Three K's**
21 **JARROW (IRE)**, 5, ch g Shamardal—Wolf Cleugh (IRE) **Dab Hand Racing**
22 **KARAKA JACK**, 5, ch g Pivotal—Mauri Moon **M. Mackay & S. Bruce**
23 **KEYS OF CYPRUS**, 10, ch g Deploy—Krisia **The Beasley Gees**
24 **LOWTHER**, 7, b g Beat All (USA)—Ever So Lonely **D. Nicholls**
25 **MISTER MANANNAN (IRE)**, 5, b g Desert Style (IRE)—Cover Girl (IRE) **Mrs M. C. Schofield**
26 **MUJAADEL (USA)**, 7, ch g Street Cry (IRE)—Quiet Rumour (USA) **W R B Racing 49**
27 **MY GACHO (IRE)**, 10, b g Shinko Forest (IRE)—Floralia **G. Mercer**
28 **NASRI**, 6, b g Kyllachy—Triple Sharp **Dab Hand Racing**
29 **NOSEDIVE**, 5, ch g Observatory (USA)—Resistance Heroine **EERC**
30 **ONE PURSUIT (IRE)**, 4, br g Pastoral Pursuits—Karinski (USA) **Mr E. F. Maher**
31 **RAIN DELAYED (IRE)**, 6, b g Oasis Dream—Forever Phoenix **Lady C. J. O'Reilly**
32 **RASSELAS (IRE)**, 5, b g Danehill Dancer (IRE)—Regal Darcey (IRE) **J. P. Honeyman**
33 **REGAL PARADE**, 8, ch g Pivotal—Model Queen (USA) **Dab Hand Racing**
34 **RIO COBOLO (IRE)**, 6, b g Captain Rio—Sofistication (IRE) **The Grech Family & The Quinn Family**
35 **SALIK TAG (USA)**, 4, ch g Hennessy (USA)—Clever Empress **Malih L. Al Basti**
36 **SAUCY BROWN (IRE)**, 6, b g Fasliyev (USA)—Danseuse du Bois (USA) **Matt Morgan & Lauren Shipley**
37 **SILAAH**, 8, b g Mind Games—Ocean Grove (IRE) **Mrs Jackie Love & Mr David Nicholls**
38 **SNOW BAY**, 6, ch g Bahamian Bounty—Goodwood Blizzard **Pinnacle Bahamian Bounty Partnership**
39 **ST MORITZ (IRE)**, 6, b g Medicean—Statua (IRE) **Mr R. W. Hughes**
40 **SWILLY FERRY (USA)**, 5, b g Wiseman's Ferry (USA)—Keepers Hill (IRE) **Mr J. A. Law**
41 **TAX FREE (IRE)**, 10, b g Tagula (IRE)—Grandel **I. Hewitson**
42 **VICTOIRE DE LYPHAR (IRE)**, 5, b g Bertolini (USA)—Victory Peak **Middleham Park Racing XVIII**
43 **WILDCAT WIZARD (USA)**, 6, b g Forest Wildcat (USA)—
Tip the Scale (USA) **The Rock & A Hard Place Partnership**
44 **XILERATOR (IRE)**, 5, b g Arakan (USA)—Grandel **Mr J. A. Law**

THREE-YEAR-OLDS

45 **ANNIE WALKER (IRE)**, b f Bertolini (USA)—Pantoufle **D. Nicholls**
46 B g Acclamation—Appleblossom Pearl (IRE) **D. Nicholls**
47 **BRAVE ONE (IRE)**, b f Moss Vale (IRE)—Smart Pet **D. Nicholls**
48 **COME ON DAVE (IRE)**, b g Red Clubs (IRE)—Desert Sprite (IRE) **Middleham Park Racing XLIV**
49 **DADDY WARBUCKS (IRE)**, b g Multiplex—Skerries (IRE) **M. P. Love**
50 B g Distant Music (USA)—Desert Sceptre **M. P. Love**
51 B g Antonius Pius (USA)—Double Precedent **Mr D. Nicholls**
52 **DUKE LIAM (IRE)**, b g Bachelor Duke (USA)—Petite Arvine (USA) **M. F. Browne**
53 **FIFTEENTWO**, b g Piccolo—Turkish Delight **Mr C A Mills,Mr A Fallon,Mr G Purchase**
54 **IMPERIAL LEGEND (IRE)**, b g Mujadil (USA)—Titian Saga (USA) **Pinnacle Mujadil Partnership**
55 **INDEGO BLUES**, b g Indesatchel (IRE)—Yanomami (USA) **Pinnacle Indesatchel Partnership**
56 **KID DYNAMITE**, b g Avonbridge—Zephrina **Mr D. L. Dixon**
57 **KNIGHT VISION**, b g Haafhd—Enford Princess **Pinnacle Haafhd Partnership**
58 **LORD GAGA (IRE)**, b g Moss Vale (IRE)—Agouti **Gaga Syndicate**

MR DAVID NICHOLLS—continued

59 **MAJESTIC MANANNAN (IRE)**, b g Majestic Missile (IRE)—Miraculous (IRE) **Mark & Maureen Schofield**
60 **POINT AT ISSUE (IRE)**, b g One Cool Cat (USA)—Atishoo (IRE) **D. T. Fish**
61 **RELEASE THE FUNDS (IRE)**, ch g Kheleyf (USA)—Indian Imp **David L Dixon & James R F Stunt**
62 Ch g Orientor—Swindling **Middleham Park Racing LIII**
63 **TAKEALOOKATMENOW (IRE)**, b f Moss Vale (IRE)—Batool (USA) **Mr D Nicholls & Mrs S J Barker**
64 **THREE DARLINGS (IRE)**, gr f Elusive City (USA)—Tibouchina (IRE) **B. Morton**
65 **WISH AGAIN (IRE)**, b g Moss Vale (IRE)—Wildwish (IRE) **Pinnacle Moss Vale Partnership**

TWO-YEAR-OLDS

66 B c 1/2 Multiplex—Park's Girl (Averti (IRE)) (19047) **D. Nicholls**
67 B f 13/4 Royal Applause—Peryllys (Warning) (19000) **D. Nicholls**

Other Owners: Mr A. D. Baker, Mr R. Banks, Mrs S. J. Barker, Mr Andrew Bates, Mr M. H. Bates, Mr S. Baynes, Mrs S. Beasley, Mr A. Black, Mr S. W. Brown, Mr S. Bruce, Mrs Rebecca Byrne, Mr Justin Byrne, Mr P.G. Dawson, Ms Finola Devaney, Mr Paul J. Dixon, Mrs Yvette Dixon, Mr David L. Dixon, Mr Andrew Fallon, Mr S. Frobisher, Mr Claudio Michael Grech, Mr M. L. Howarth, General Sir Geoffrey Howlett, Mr James S. Kennerley, Miss C. King, Mr Paul Langford, Mr J. Law, Mr Paul Lindley, Mr D. S. Lovatt, Mrs Jackie Love, Mr Michael Mackay, Mr Mike McGeever, Mrs Caroline McGeever, Mrs A. M. Mercs, Mr Carl Mills, Mr Matthew Morgan, Mr Brian Morton, Mr T. Murray, Mr K. J. Newsome, Mr D. Nicholls, Mrs Alex Nicholls, Mr T. S. Palin, Mr D. Pearson, Mr Alan Pirie, Mr M. Prince, Mr Gavin Purchase, Mr Sean Quinn, Mr K. Robinson, Mr A. L. Roche, Mr S. W. Rowbotham, Mrs Susan Roy, Mrs J. Ryan, Mr C. M. A. Scaife, Mr M. A. Scaife, Mr A. Scaife, Mrs M. Schofield, Mr Mark Schofield, Mrs Angela C. Seed, Miss Lauren Stapley, Mr J. R. F. Stunt, Mrs S. Thomson, Mr A. C. Timms, Mr Andrew Turton, Wetherby Racing Bureau Ltd, Mr A. Williams.

Assistant Trainers: Ben Beasley, Ernie Greaves

Jockey (flat): Andrew Mullen, Adrian Nicholls, Paul Quinn. **Apprentice:** Billy Cray, Michael O'Connell, Shirley Teasdale.

---

489 MR PAUL NICHOLLS, Shepton Mallet

Postal: **Manor Farm Stables, Ditcheat, Shepton Mallet, Somerset, BA4 6RD**
Contacts: **PHONE** (01749) 860656 **FAX** (01749) 860523 **MOBILE** (07977) 270706
E-MAIL info@paulnichollsracing.com **WEBSITE** www.paulnichollsracing.com

1 **AERIAL (FR)**, 6, b g Turgeon (USA)—Fille Formidable (USA) **Tony Hayward & Barry Fulton**
2 **AITEEN THIRTYTHREE (IRE)**, 8, b g Old Vic—Prudent View (IRE) **Mr Paul K Barber & The Stewart Family**
3 **AL FEROF (FR)**, 7, gr g Dom Alco (FR)—Maralta (FR) **Mr J. R. Hales**
4 **ALDERTUNE (IRE)**, 8, ch g Alderbrook—Frankies Tune (IRE) **Mrs A. M. Millard**
5 **AMERICAN TRILOGY (IRE)**, 8, gr g Sendawar (IRE)—
Affaire Classee (FR) **Fulton,Donlon,Kilduff & Scott-MacDonald**
6 **ATLANTIC ROLLER (IRE)**, 5, b g Old Vic—Tourist Attraction (IRE) **C. G. Roach**
7 **BALDING BANKER (IRE)**, 6, b g Accordion—What A Breeze (IRE) **Potensis Limited & Mr Ian Axe**
8 **BIG BUCK'S (FR)**, 9, b br g Cadoudal (FR)—Buck's (FR) **The Stewart Family**
9 **BILLY MERRIOTT (IRE)**, 6, b g Dr Massini (IRE)—Hurricane Bella (IRE) **G. D. Taylor**
10 **BLACK THUNDER (FR)**, 5, bl g Malinas (GER)—Blackmika (GER) **Donlon, Macdonald, Fulton & Webb**
11 **BOLD CHIEF (IRE)**, 7, br g Oscar (IRE)—Cottage Girl (IRE) **The Eyre Family**
12 **BRAMPOUR (IRE)**, 5, b g Daylami (USA)—Brusca (USA) **Banks, Blackshaw & Gannon**
13 **CAPTAIN KELLY (IRE)**, 5, b g Oscar (IRE)—Tri Folene (FR) **Donlon, Doyle, MacDonald & Webb**
14 **CARLICUE (IRE)**, 7, b g King's Theatre (IRE)—Woodville Star (IRE) **Potensis Limited**
15 **CASTLETOWNSEND (IRE)**, 6, b g Presenting—Friendly Flick (IRE) **The Stewart Family**
16 **CEDRE BLEU (FR)**, 5, b g Le Fou (IRE)—Arvoire (IRE) **Mr Paul K. Barber & Mr D. A. Johnson**
17 **CELESTIAL HALO (IRE)**, 8, b g Galileo (IRE)—Pay The Bank **The Stewart Family**
18 **CRACK AWAY JACK (IRE)**, 8, ch g Gold Away (IRE)—Jolly Harbour **GDM Partnership**
19 **CRIQTONIC (IRE)**, 5, ch g Green Tune (USA)—Criquetot (FR) **Axom XXXIII**
20 **CRISTAL BONUS (FR)**, 6, b g Della Francesca (USA)—Cristal Springs (FR) **Mr R. J. H. Geffen**
21 **CURRENT EVENT (FR)**, 5, b g Muhtathir—La Curamalai (IRE) **Mrs A. M. Millard**
22 **CURTAIN RAZER (IRE)**, 6, b g Old Vic—Echo Creek (IRE) **C. G. Roach**
23 **DEIREADH RE (IRE)**, 6, b g Old Vic—Donaghmore Lady (IRE) **Mr I. J. Fogg**
24 **DILDAR (IRE)**, 4, b g Red Ransom (USA)—Diamond Tango (FR) **Mrs S. De La Hey**
25 **DODGING BULLETS (IRE)**, 4, b g Dubawi (IRE)—Nova Cyngi (USA) **Martin Broughton & Friends**
26 **DOESLESSTHANME (IRE)**, 8, ch g Definite Article—Damemill (IRE) **Andrea & Graham Wylie**
27 **DOMTALINE (FR)**, 5, gr g Martaline—Domna Noune (FR) **Mr & Mrs J. D. Cotton**
28 **DUALLA LORD (IRE)**, 7, gr g Lord Americo—Marthas Prayer (IRE) **Mrs M. G. Barber**
29 **EARTH PLANET (IRE)**, 10, b g Kayf Tara—Arctic Rose (IRE) **R. M. Penny**
30 **EASTER DAY (FR)**, 4, b g Malinas (GER)—Sainte Lea (FR) **Nicholls & Webb**
31 **EDGARDO SOL (FR)**, 5, ch g Kapgarde (FR)—Tikiti Dancer (FR) **Axom XXXII**

MR PAUL NICHOLLS—continued

32 **EGYPT MILL SPIRIT (IRE)**, 6, b g Overbury (IRE)—Miss Tickill (IRE) **Mr S. R. Webb**
33 **EMPIRE LEVANT (USA)**, 5, gr ro g Empire Maker (USA)—
Orellana (USA) **Sir A Ferguson,G Mason,R Wood & P Done**
34 **ESCORT'MEN (FR)**, 6, ch g Robin des Champs (FR)—Escortee (FR) **Donlon, Doyle & MacDonald**
35 **ESCUDERO (IRE)**, 7, ch g Snurge—What A Breeze (IRE) **Michael & Niall Earls**
36 **EXPRESS LEADER**, 9, b g Supreme Leader—Karawa **R Metherell & J George & Mrs L Squire**
37 **FAIR DREAMER**, 4, gr g Fair Mix (IRE)—Emma's Dream **J. P. Blakeney**
38 **FINAL GIFT (IRE)**, 6, b g Old Vic—Lost Prairie (IRE) **Mr Ian J. Fogg & Mr Paul K. Barber**
39 **FISTRAL BEACH (IRE)**, 9, b g Definite Article—Empress of Light **C. G. Roach**
40 **FIVE DREAM (FR)**, 8, b g Take Risks (FR)—Jenny Pous (FR) **Scott-MacDonald, Kilduff, Donlon & Doyle**
41 **FLAMING GORGE (IRE)**, 7, ch g Alderbrook—Solmus (IRE) **Hilton & Lyn Ramseyer**
42 **FOGGY'S WALL (IRE)**, 4, b g Golan (IRE)—Mrs Masters (IRE) **Mr Ian Fogg & Mr Paul Nicholls**
43 **FRANKIE FIGG (IRE)**, 10, b g Portrait Gallery (IRE)—Ardnataggle (IRE) **Andrea & Graham Wylie**
44 **GHIZAO (GER)**, 8, b g Tiger Hill (IRE)—Glorosia (FR) **The Johnson & Stewart Families**
45 **GRANDIOSO (IRE)**, 5, b g Westerner—Champagne Warrior (IRE) **Andrea & Graham Wylie**
46 **GULLIBLE GORDON (IRE)**, 9, ch g Anshan—Cronohill (IRE) **Mrs A. M. Millard**
47 **HARRY THE VIKING**, 7, ch g Sir Harry Lewis (USA)—Viking Flame **Sir A Ferguson,G Mason,R Wood & P Done**
48 **HAWKES POINT**, 7, b g Kayf Tara—Mandys Native (IRE) **C. G. Roach**
49 **HEEZ A CRACKER (IRE)**, 6, b g Goldneyev (USA)—Jolly Harbour **GDM Partnership**
50 **HINTERLAND (FR)**, 4, b g Poliglote—Queen Place (FR) **Potensis Limited & Mr Chris Giles**
51 **HOLD FAST (IRE)**, 8, ch g Flemensfirth (USA)—Delko **Andrea & Graham Wylie**
52 **HOO LA BALOO (FR)**, 11, b g Unfuwain (USA)—Via Saleria (IRE) **The Stewart Family**
53 **INDIAN DAUDAIE (FR)**, 5, ch g Nicobar—Aldounia (FR) **TimeformBetfairRacingClub & Clive Smith**
54 **ITALIAN MASTER (IRE)**, 6, b br g Milan—Augusta Brook (IRE) **Mr J. R. Hales**
55 **JOIN TOGETHER (IRE)**, 7, b g Old Vic—Open Cry (IRE) **Mr Paul K Barber & Mr Ian J Fogg**
56 **JUMP CITY (FR)**, 6, b g Muhtathir—Just Fizzy **Mrs Angela Tincknell & Mr W. Tincknell**
57 **JUST AMAZING (IRE)**, 9, b g Presenting—Just Precious **Mrs C. E. Penny**
58 **KAUTO STAR (FR)**, 12, b g Village Star (FR)—Kauto Relka (FR) **C. D. Smith**
59 **KAUTO STONE (FR)**, 6, ch g With The Flow (USA)—Kauto Relka (FR) **Mr R. J. H. Geffen**
60 **KING OF THE NIGHT (GER)**, 8, b g Lomitas—Kaiserlerche (GER) **Mr & Mrs G. Calder**
61 **LANDSCAPE (FR)**, 4, b g Lando (GER)—Universelle (USA) **Betfair & Ambassadors Dixon Greenwood Vaughan**
62 **LIKE MINDED**, 8, b g Kayf Tara—Sun Dante (IRE) **Jim Lewis, Derek Holder & Terry Warner**
63 **LIKEABLE ROGUE (IRE)**, 6, b g Old Vic—Grangeclare Rose (IRE) **Potensis Limited & Mr Chris Giles**
64 **MARTYS MISSION (IRE)**, 10, b g Zaffaran (USA)—Parson's Lodge (IRE) **The Stewart Family**
65 **MERRION SQUARE (IRE)**, 6, b g Kotashaan (FR)—Parverb (IRE) **The Stewart Family**
66 **MICHEL LE BON (FR)**, 9, b g Villez (USA)—Rosacotte (FR) **C. G. Roach**
67 **MINELLA STARS (IRE)**, 7, b g Accordion—V'soske Gale (IRE) **Mrs S. De La Hey**
68 **MON PARRAIN (FR)**, 6, b g Trempolino (USA)—Kadaina (FR) **Mr & Mrs J. D. Cotton**
69 **MR HUDSON (IRE)**, 7, b g Old Vic—Esbeggi **Mrs Angela Tincknell & Mr W. Tincknell**
70 **MR MOLE (IRE)**, 4, br g Great Pretender (IRE)—Emmylou du Berlais (FR) **P. F. Nicholls**
71 **NEPTUNE COLLONGES (FR)**, 11, gr g Dom Alco (FR)—Castille Collonges (FR) **Mr J. R. Hales**
72 **NICHE MARKET (IRE)**, 10, b g Presenting—Juresse (IRE) **G. J. P. Regan**
73 **NO LOOSE CHANGE (IRE)**, 7, b g Bob Back (USA)—Quit The Noise (IRE) **Donlon, Doyle, MacDonald & Webb**
74 **NOLAND**, 11, b g Exit To Nowhere (USA)—Molakai (USA) **Mr J. R. Hales**
75 **OPENING BATSMAN (IRE)**, 6, b g Morozov (USA)—Jolly Signal (IRE) **The Twelfth Man Partnership**
76 **OSCARGO (IRE)**, 8, b g Oscar (IRE)—Broken Rein (IRE) **Hordle, Evans & Nicholls**
77 **OSCARSLAD (IRE)**, 6, b g Oscar (IRE)—Velvet Huxley (IRE) **Mr J. M. Dare**
78 **PACHA DU POLDER (FR)**, 5, b g Muhtathir—Ambri Piotta (FR) **The Stewart & Wylie Families**
79 **PASCO (SWI)**, 9, ro g Selkirk (USA)—Palena **J. T. Warner**
80 **PEARL SWAN (FR)**, 4, b g Gentlewave (IRE)—Swanson (USA) **Giles, Nicholls & Potensis**
81 **PICTURE THIS (IRE)**, 9, ch g Old Vic—Below The Wind **Sir Alex Ferguson, Ged Mason & Ron Wood**
82 **PLENTY POCKET (FR)**, 5, ch g Super Celebre (FR)—Almadina (FR) **TimeformBetfairRacingClub & Clive Smith**
83 **POLISKY (FR)**, 5, b g Poliglote—Dusky Royale (FR) **Mrs S. De La Hey**
84 **POQUELIN (FR)**, 9, bl g Lahint (USA)—Babolna (FR) **The Stewart Family**
85 **POUNGACH (FR)**, 6, b g Daliapour (IRE)—Shalaine (FR) **Donlon, Doyle, MacDonald & Webb**
86 **PRESENTING ARMS (IRE)**, 5, b g Presenting—Banningham Blaze **Mr J. M. Dare**
87 **PRINCE TOM**, 8, b g King's Theatre (IRE)—Cresswell Native (IRE) **Mrs Angela Tincknell & Mr W. Tincknell**
88 **PROMISING ANSHAN (IRE)**, 7, ch g Anshan—Old Promises (IRE) **Jared Sullivan & Simon Brown**
89 **PROSPECT WELLS (FR)**, 7, b g Sadler's Wells—Brooklyn's Dance (FR) **Andrea & Graham Wylie**
90 **RAMSES DE MARCIGNY (FR)**, 7, b br g Subotica (FR)—Isca de Thaix (FR) **The Festival Goers**
91 **RANGITOTO (IRE)**, 7, b g Old Vic—Kendos Dream (IRE) **Mr Paul K. Barber & Mr Charles Whittaker**
92 **RANJAAN (FR)**, 4, b g Dubai Destination (USA)—Ridafa (IRE) **Highclere Thoroughbred Racing - Ranjaan**
93 **REBEL DU MAQUIS (FR)**, 7, b g Brier Creek (USA)—Jade de Chalamont (FR) **Mrs K. A. Stuart**
94 **REBEL REBELLION (IRE)**, 7, b g Lord Americo—Tourmaline Girl (IRE) **Mr Chris Giles & Mr Jared Sullivan**
95 **REDLYNCH ROCK (IRE)**, 4, b g Brian Boru—College Ground (IRE) **The Subtle Partnership**
96 **ROBINSON COLLONGES (FR)**, 7, gr g Dom Alco (FR)—Grace Collonges (FR) **Mr & Mrs G. Calder**

MR PAUL NICHOLLS—continued

97 **ROCK ON RUBY (IRE)**, 7, b g Oscar (IRE)—Stony View (IRE) **The Festival Goers**
98 **ROCKY CREEK (IRE)**, 6, b g Dr Massini (IRE)—Kissantell (IRE) **The Johnson & Stewart Families**
99 **ROGER BEANTOWN (IRE)**, 7, b g Indian Danehill (IRE)—Best Wait (IRE) **Andrea & Graham Wylie**
100 **ROLLING ACES (IRE)**, 6, b g Whitmore's Conn (USA)—Pay Roll (IRE) **David Martin,Ian Fogg & Paul Barber**
101 **ROUND TOM (IRE)**, 7, br g Sleeping Car (FR)—
                    Mamie Bleue (FR) **The Hon Mrs Townshend & Mr J.R.Townshend**
102 **ROWDY RAMPAGE (IRE)**, 8, b g Lahib (USA)—Rowdy Nights (IRE) **The Rowdy Boys**
103 **ROYAL CHARM (FR)**, 7, bl g Cadoudal (FR)—Victoria Royale (FR) **Mrs Angela Tincknell & Mr W. Tincknell**
104 **RUBEN COTTER (IRE)**, 6, b g Beneficial—Bonnie Thynes (IRE) **C. G. Roach**
105 **SAINT ROQUE (FR)**, 6, b g Lavirco (GER)—Moody Cloud (FR) **Mr Chris Giles & Potensis Limited**
106 **SALUBRIOUS (IRE)**, 5, b g Beneficial—Who Tells Jan **The Johnson & Stewart Families**
107 **SANCTUAIRE (FR)**, 6, b br g Kendor (FR)—Biblique (FR) **Mr J. J. Sullivan**
108 **SILVINIACO CONTI (FR)**, 6, ch g Dom Alco (FR)—Gazelle Lulu (FR) **Potensis Limited & Mr Chris Giles**
109 **SIN BIN (IRE)**, 6, b g Presenting—Navaro (IRE) **T. J. Hemmings**
110 **SIR DU BEARN (FR)**, 6, b br g Passing Sale (FR)—Girl du Bearn (FR) **Potensis Limited**
111 **SIRE COLLONGES (FR)**, 6, gr g Dom Alco (FR)—Idylle Collonges (FR) **Mr Chris Giles & Mr & Mrs W Tincknell**
112 **SKY WATCH (IRE)**, 5, b g Flemensfirth (USA)—The Shining Force (IRE) **Mr Ian Axe & Potensis Limited**
113 **SLIGHTLY TANNED (IRE)**, 6, b g Brian Boru—Connells Cross (IRE) **Mr Chris Giles & Potensis Limited**
114 **SONOFVIC (IRE)**, 7, ch g Old Vic—Prudent View (IRE) **Mrs A. R. Hart**
115 **SPOCK (FR)**, 7, b g Lost World (IRE)—Quark Top (FR) **J. G. Hordle**
116 **SUBTLE SOVEREIGN (IRE)**, 5, gr g Subtle Power (IRE)—Katonka **The Subtle Partnership**
117 **SUERTE AL SALTO (IRE)**, 5, b g Old Vic—The Great O'malley (IRE) **Mr Chris Giles & Mr Paul K. Barber**
118 **TAKE THE BREEZE (FR)**, 9, gr g Take Risks (FR)—Reine Breeze (FR) **Mr & Mrs G. Calder**
119 **TAKEROC (FR)**, 9, gr g Take Risks (FR)—Rochambelle (FR) **Chris Giles,Paul Nicholls & Julie Derham**
120 **TAOUFICK DU SEUIL (FR)**, 5, b g Truth Or Dare—Marie du Seuil (FR) **Sam McVie & Gordon Law**
121 **TED SPREAD**, 5, b g Beat Hollow—Highbrook (USA) **False Nose 'n Glasses Partnership**
122 **THAT'LL DO**, 7, b g Beat All (USA)—Forever Shineing **Mr Paul Barber & Mr & Mrs Mark Woodhouse**
123 **THAT'LLDOBOY (FR)**, 6, b g Turgeon (USA)—A Womans Heart (USA) **The Sparkes Family**
124 **THE GOSSMOOR YANK (IRE)**, 9, b g Shernazar—Nightngale Express (IRE) **The Sparkes Family**
125 **THE KNOXS (IRE)**, 9, b g Close Conflict (USA)—Nicola Marie (IRE) **Andrea & Graham Wylie**
126 **THE MINACK (IRE)**, 8, b g King's Theatre (IRE)—Ebony Jane **C. G. Roach**
127 **THE NIGHTINGALE (FR)**, 9, b br g Cadoudal (FR)—Double Spring (FR) **C. G. Roach**
128 **THE PRETENDER (FR)**, 5, b g Great Pretender (IRE)—La Fleur du Roy (FR) **Million in Mind Partnership**
129 **THE REFORMER (FR)**, 7, b g Pilsudski (IRE)—Tinogloria (FR) **C. G. Roach**
130 **THEMILANHORSE (IRE)**, 6, b g Milan—Sports Leader (IRE) **Arron & Katya Banks**
131 **TIDAL BAY (IRE)**, 11, b g Flemensfirth (USA)—June's Bride (IRE) **Andrea & Graham Wylie**
132 **TIGRE D'ARON (FR)**, 5, gr g Dom Alco (FR)—Fleche Noir II (FR) **Andrea & Graham Wylie**
133 **TONIC MELLYSSE (FR)**, 5, b g Smadoun (FR)—Mellyssa (FR) **S. E. Munir**
134 **TOUBAB (FR)**, 6, gr g Martaline—Tabachines (FR) **Hills of Ledbury Ltd**
135 **ULCK DU LIN (FR)**, 4, b g Sassanian (USA)—Miss Fast (FR) **Mrs S. De La Hey**
136 **UNPARTOU (FR)**, 4, b g Shaanmer (IRE)—Mamithou (FR) **Timeform Betfair Racing Club Ltd**
137 **VIOLIN DAVIS (FR)**, 6, b m Turgeon (USA)—Trumpet Davis (FR) **Mr A. D. Polson**
138 **VRAI VERT (IRE)**, 5, b g Westerner—Roses Dreams (FR) **S. E. Munir**
139 **WHAT A FRIEND**, 9, b g Alflora (IRE)—Friendly Lady **Mr Ged Mason & Sir Alex Ferguson**
140 **WHISKY YANKEE (IRE)**, 5, br g Presenting—Southcoat Gale (FR) **Walters Plant Hire Ltd**
141 **WIFFY CHATSBY (IRE)**, 5, br g Presenting—Star Child (GER) **Inch Bloodstock**
142 **WOOLCOMBE FOLLY (IRE)**, 9, b br g Presenting—Strong Gara (IRE) **The Hon Mrs C. A. Townshend**
143 **WORKBENCH (FR)**, 4, b g Network (GER)—Danhelis (FR) **Nicholls, Fry, Skelton & Whittaker**
144 **ZARKANDAR (IRE)**, 5, b g Azamour (IRE)—Zarkasha (FR) **Potensis Limited & Mr Chris Giles**

Other Owners: Mr S. A. Ashley, Mr I. Axe, Axom Ltd, Mr A. F. A. Banks, Mrs E. Banks, P. K. Barber, J. R. Barber, Mr C. L. Barber, Mr G. Barrett, Mrs J. M. Blackshaw, P. H. Boss, A. R. Bromley, Sir M. F. Broughton, S. W. Broughton, S. J. Brown, Mr A. P. Brown, G. Calder, Mrs J. Calder, G. Charlesworth, D. Charlesworth, D. J. Coles, J. D. Cotton, Mrs B. Cotton, Mrs J. E. Derham, Mr P. E. Done, Mr C. A. Donlon, Mr D. Downie, Mr A. Doyle, Mr M. Earls, Mr N. Earls, Mr C. W. Evans, Mrs C. A. Eyre, Mr C. G. S. Eyre, Mr H. Eyre, Miss R. E. Eyre, Sir A. Ferguson, R. A. Fry, B. N. Fulton, Mr J. Gannon, Mr J. W. George, Mr C. M. Giles, G. F. Goode, Miss L. J. Hales, A. A. Hayward, The Hon H. M. Herbert, Highclere Thoroughbred Racing Ltd, A. J. Hill, D. C. Holder, Mr M. J. Holman, Mrs L. Hunt, Mr P. J. Inch, Mrs L. Inch, D. A. Johnson, T. Kilduff, Mr G. Law, F. E. J. Lewis, Mr D. J. Martin, G. A. Mason, S. McVie, R. J. Metherell, W. D. C. Minton, Mrs D. C. Nicholson, Mr G. Pettit, Mr M. Powell, Mr H. Ramseyer, Mrs L. Ramseyer, Mr L. Scott-MacDonald, A. G. Sim, Miss Claire Simmonds, Mr D. N. Skelton, Mr M. Smith, Mr K. Sparkes, Mrs K. M. Sparkes, Mrs L. J. Squire, Mr A. Stewart, Mrs J. A. Stewart, Mrs A. Tincknell, W. C. Tincknell, J. R. Townshend, S. L. Walker, Mr R. A. Webb, C. R. Whittaker, Mr R. J. Wood, M. J. M. Woodhouse, Mrs T. A. Woodhouse, A. W. G. Wylie, Mrs A. Wylie.

Assistant Trainers: Daniel Skelton, Richard Barber, Harry Fry, Tom Jonason

Jockey (NH): Ruby Walsh, Daryl Jacob, Nick Scholfield, Harry Skelton. **Conditional:** David Prichard, Harry Derham, Ryan Mahon. **Amateur:** Mr Jack Barber, Mr Dan Collins, Mr James Cowley.

490 MR PETER NIVEN, Malton
Postal: **Clovafield, Barton-Le-Street, Malton, North Yorkshire, YO17 6PN**
Contacts: **PHONE (01653) 628176 FAX (01653) 627295 MOBILE (07860) 260999**
E-MAIL pruniven@btinternet.com

1 BARTON BOUNTY, 5, b g Bahamian Bounty—Tenebrae (IRE) **Francis Green Racing Ltd**
2 BEAT THE SHOWER, 6, b g Beat Hollow—Crimson Shower **Mrs K. J. Young**
3 CELTIC STEP, 8, br g Selkirk (USA)—Inchiri **Mrs Muriel Ward**
4 DE VINE MEMORY, 5, b m Grape Tree Road—Mystic Memory **Mrs J. A. Niven**
5 GALA SPIRIT (IRE), 5, b m Invincible Spirit (IRE)—Luggala (IRE) **J. Cullinan**
6 GOLDEN FUTURE, 9, b g Muhtarram (USA)—Nazca **The Little Ice Club**
7 INDIAN EMPEROR (IRE), 4, b g Araafa (IRE)—Soft (USA) **Francis Green Racing Ltd**
8 MEADOW MIX, 5, gr m Fair Mix (IRE)—Clova **Mrs K. J. Young**
9 MIDDLEBROOK (IRE), 7, ch g Ashkalani (IRE)—
Accordeon Royale (IRE) **Sandy Lodge Racing Club & Mr P.D.Niven**
10 PINOTAGE, 4, br g Danbird (AUS)—Keen Melody (USA) **Mr S. Bowett**
11 POSH BIRD (IRE), 9, b m Winged Love (IRE)—Lady Oakwell (IRE) **David Bamber**
12 RENDL BEACH (IRE), 5, b g Milan—Erins Emblem (IRE) **Mr S. Knowles**
13 UNCUT STONE (IRE), 4, b g Awesome Again (CAN)—Suitably Discreet (USA) **Francis Green Racing Ltd**

Other Owners: Mr C. Bracher, Mrs Joanne Iceton, Mr Ken Little, Mr Andrew Needham, Mr P.D. Niven, Mrs J. A. Niven, Ms Lynn Tomkins, Mr R. M. Whitaker, Mrs R. M. Whitaker.

491 MR GEORGE NIXON, Selkirk
Postal: **Oakwood Farm, Ettrickbridge, Selkirk, Selkirkshire, TD7 5HJ**
Contacts: **PHONE (01750) 52245 FAX (01750) 52313**

1 GYMDOLI, 5, br g Endoli (USA)—Split The Wind **Rayson & Susan Nixon**
2 HOLLYROCK, 6, b m Rock City—Delightfool **Rayson & Susan Nixon**
3 JUST MADDIE, 8, gr m Supreme Sound—Delightfool **Rayson & Susan Nixon**
4 JUST STRIPE, 5, br m Supreme Sound—Delightfool **Rayson & Susan Nixon**
5 KEMPSKI, 12, b g Petoski—Little Katrina **Rayson & Susan Nixon**
6 NORMINSTER, 11, ch g Minster Son—Delightfool **Rayson & Susan Nixon**
7 POLITICAL PADDY, 10, b g Vitus—Political Mill **Rayson & Susan Nixon**

Other Owners: Mr G. R. S. Nixon, Mrs S. Nixon.

Assistant Trainer: Mrs S. Nixon

Jockey (NH): Ryan Mania, Fearghal Davis.

492 MRS SUSAN NOCK, Stow-on-the-Wold
Postal: **Smenham Farm, Icomb, Stow-On-The-Wold, Cheltenham, Gloucestershire, GL54 1JQ**
Contacts: **PHONE (01451) 831688 FAX (01451) 831404 MOBILE (07816) 889500**

1 HATTERS RIVER (IRE), 5, b g Milan—Curzon Ridge (IRE) **G. Nock**
2 MASTER ALFREDO, 8, b g Alflora (IRE)—Frosty Mistress **Camilla & Rosie Nock**
3 MYLORD COLLONGES (FR), 12, bl g Video Rock (FR)—Diane Collonges (FR) **Camilla & Rosie Nock**
4 PICTURE IN THE SKY (IRE), 11, ch g Portrait Gallery (IRE)—Little Bloom **G. Nock**

Other Owners: Miss R. C. Nock, Miss C. D. Nock.

493 MR DONAL NOLAN, Wishaw
Postal: **Deer Park Farm, Mill Road, Morningside, Newmains, Wishaw**
Contacts: **PHONE (01698) 383850 FAX (01698) 383850 MOBILE (07900) 918471**

1 ARDENT NUMBER, 12, b g Alderbrook—Pretty Average **Mr M. J. Russell**
2 5, B m Rambling Bear—Avesa
3 BLUE TOMATO, 11, b g Orpen (USA)—Ocean Grove (IRE) **Miss M. F. Mcfadyen-Murray**
4 COMPTON LAD, 9, b g Compton Place—Kintara **Miss M. F. Mcfadyen-Murray**
5 CRICKET BOY, 8, b g Alflora (IRE)—Lady Cricket (FR) **Mrs D. M. Monteith**
6 DEER PARK LORD, 8, b g Compton Admiral—Pretty Average **Miss M. F. Mcfadyen-Murray**
7 DEFI (IRE), 10, b g Rainbow Quest (USA)—Danse Classique (IRE) **Miss M. F. Mcfadyen-Murray**

MR DONAL NOLAN—continued

8 5, B g Rambling Bear—Gladys Aylward **Miss M. F. Mcfadyen-Murray**
9 HOWARDS WAY, 7, b g Bertolini (USA)—Love Quest **Miss M. F. Mcfadyen-Murray**
10 JIM MARTIN, 7, b g Auction House (USA)—Folly Finnesse **Miss M. F. Mcfadyen-Murray**
11 PRIMO WAY, 11, b c g Primo Dominie—Waypoint **Miss M. F. Mcfadyen-Murray**
12 4, Ch c Boogie Street—Woolfe

Assistant Trainer: Miss M McFadyen-Murray

---

494 MRS LUCY NORMILE, Glenfarg
Postal: Duncrievie, Glenfarg, Perthshire, PH2 9PD
Contacts: PHONE (01577) 830330 FAX (01577) 830658 MOBILE (07721) 454818
E-MAIL lucy@normileracing.co.uk WEBSITE www.normileracing.co.uk

1 AGRICULTURAL, 6, b g Daylami (IRE)—Rustic (IRE) **Mrs J. Carnaby**
2 BALLYCARBERY, 6, b g Bollin Eric—Carbery Spirit (IRE) **Mrs F. M. Whitaker**
3 BARR HEAD (IRE), 8, b g Anshan—Doolin Lake (IRE) **Mrs P. Sinclair**
4 4, B f Revoque—Carbery Spirit (IRE) **Mrs F. M. Whitaker**
5 CARNELIAN (IRE), 5, b g Singspiel (IRE)—Red Zinger (USA) **Oatridge Ltd**
6 DICKIE HENDERHOOP (IRE), 7, b g Milan—Merry Breeze **L B N Racing Club**
7 EDINBURGH GIN TIME, 6, b g Bollin Terry—Good Job **Sheep Dip Racing**
8 ENGLISH CITY (IRE), 9, ch h City On A Hill (USA)—Toledana (IRE) **Mr P. Carnaby**
9 FRITH (IRE), 10, b g Benny The Dip (USA)—Melodist (USA) **L B N Racing Club**
10 KARINGO, 5, ch g Karinga Bay—Wild Happening (GER) **Douglas Black, P. A. & P. J. Carnaby**
11 LOCAL QUINE (IRE), 6, b br m Great Palm (USA)—Soul Lady (IRE) **Douglas Black & Peter Carnaby**
12 MISS DEEFIANT, 6, b m Muhtarram (USA)—Hiding Place **Mrs L. B. Normile**
13 MR MANSSON (IRE), 5, b g Millenary—Supreme Dare (IRE) **Mr K. N. R. MacNicol**
14 PARSON'S PUNCH, 7, b g Beat Hollow—Ordained **Mr K. N. R. MacNicol**
15 PRIMROSE TIME, 9, gr m Alflora (IRE)—The Whirlie Weevil **The Explorers**
16 RINNAGREE ROSIE, 6, gr m Silver Patriarch (IRE)—Gretton **The Silver Tops**
17 SPORTED AND PLAYED (IRE), 9, b m Saddlers' Hall (IRE)—Alice Freyne (IRE) **L B N Racing Club**
18 STROBE, 8, ch g Fantastic Light (USA)—Sadaka (USA) **Miss P. A. & Mr P. J. Carnaby**

Other Owners: Mr D. Black, Miss P. A. Carnaby, Mr P. J. Carnaby, Mr Peter Carnaby, Miss F. M. Fletcher, Mr A. G. Nicol, Mrs J. C. M. Nicol, Mrs L. Normile, Mr A. C. Rodger, Mrs D. A. Whitaker.

Assistant Trainer: Libby Brodie (07947) 592438

Jockey (NH): Jimmy McCarthy, Dougie Costello. **Conditional:** Lucy Alexander, Alexander Voy. **Amateur:** Mr R. Wilson.

---

495 MR JOHN NORTON, Barnsley
Postal: Globe Farm, High Hoyland, Barnsley, South Yorkshire, S75 4BE
Contacts: PHONE/FAX (01226) 387633 MOBILE (07970) 212707
E-MAIL johnrnorton@hotmail.com

1 BAHRI BEAT (IRE), 4, b g Bahri (USA)—Optimal Quest (IRE) **J. R. Norton Ltd**
2 BARTERED BRIDE, 4, b f Gentleman's Deal (IRE)—Stolen Glance **J. R. Norton Ltd**
3 6, B m Almaty (IRE)—Captive Heart **J. R. Norton Ltd**
4 DEPORTATION, 5, b g Deportivo—Kyle Rhea **J. R. Norton Ltd**
5 GOREY LANE (IRE), 6, b g Oscar (IRE)—Supremely Deep (IRE) **Jaffa Racing Syndicate**
6 MANAGER MICK (IRE), 4, b g Clodovil—Nashua Song (IRE) **Mrs H. Tattersall**
7 NIPPY NIKKI, 4, b f Needwood Blade—Spielbound **J. Norton**
8 QUAY MEADOW (IRE), 10, b br g Alderbrook—Harp Song **Jaffa Racing Syndicate**
9 RISK IT, 7, b g Beat All (USA)—Cranborne (IRE) **J. R. Norton Ltd**
10 SNOW ALERT, 6, ch g Where Or When (IRE)—Ela Aphrodite **J. R. Norton Ltd**

THREE-YEAR-OLDS

11 B f Danbird (AUS)—Rapturous **J. R. Norton Ltd**
12 Ch f Three Valleys (USA)—Spielbound **J. Norton**

TWO-YEAR-OLDS

13 FINN MAC, ch g 10/2 Norse Dancer (IRE)—Strictly Elsie (IRE) (No Excuse Needed) **M. R. & T. Simcox**
14 B f 28/4 Passing Glance—True Melody (IRE) (Grand Lodge (USA)) **A. R. Middleton**

Other Owners: Udo J. Eppinger, Mr R. M. Firth, Mr P. J. Marshall.

Amateur: Mr P. Hardy.

496 MR JEREMY NOSEDA, Newmarket

Postal: Shalfleet, 17 Bury Road, Newmarket, Suffolk, CB8 7BX
Contacts: PHONE (01638) 664010 FAX (01638) 664100 MOBILE (07710) 294093
E-MAIL jeremy@jeremynoseda.com WEBSITE www.jeremynoseda.com

1 BIG CREEK (IRE), 5, b h Galileo (IRE)—Baranja (USA)
2 ELAS DIAMOND, 4, b gr f Danehill Dancer (IRE)—Ela Athena
3 GARDE COTIERE (USA), 4, b c Giant's Causeway (USA)—Amonita
4 INSTANCE, 4, b f Invincible Spirit (IRE)—Hannda (IRE)
5 LEAHURST (IRE), 6, gr g Verglas (IRE)—Badee'a (IRE)
6 NOGUCHI (IRE), 7, ch g Pivotal—Tuscania (USA)
7 PETER MARTINS (USA), 4, ch c Johannesburg (USA)—Pretty Meadow (USA)
8 SANS FRONTIERES (IRE), 6, ch h Galileo (IRE)—Llia
9 TORNADO FORCE (IRE), 4, ch g Shamardal (USA)—Pharma West (USA)
10 TRIPLE CHARM, 4, ch f Pivotal—Triple Joy
11 WESTERN ARISTOCRAT (USA), 4, b c Mr Greeley (USA)—Aristocratic Lady (USA)

THREE-YEAR-OLDS

12 ATTENBOROUGH (USA), b c Medaglia d'oro (USA)—Julie's Prospect (USA)
13 BARBERTON (USA), ch c Johannesburg (USA)—Mythical Echo (USA)
14 BIBA DIVA (IRE), b f Danehill Dancer (IRE)—Mowaadah (IRE)
15 BURKE'S ROCK, b f Cape Cross (IRE)—Miss Lacey (IRE)
16 CUTTING IT FINE (IRE), b c Iffraaj—Limit (IRE)
17 DELFT, b f Dutch Art—Plucky
18 FAIREST (IRE), ch f Elusive Quality (USA)—Joan Joan Joan (USA)
19 FALCON IN FLIGHT, b f Shamardal (USA)—Marine City (JPN)
20 FALCON'S REIGN (FR), ch c Haafhd (IRE)—Al Badeya (IRE)
21 FURBELOW, b f Pivotal—Red Tiara (USA)
22 GAME TAKEN, ch f Shamardal (USA)—Midpoint (USA)
23 GOLD EDITION, ch c Mr Greeley (USA)—Triple Edition (USA)
24 GRANDEUR (IRE), gr c Verglas (IRE)—Misskinta (IRE)
25 HANNIBAL HAYES (USA), ch c Elusive Quality (USA)—Top Ten List (CAN)
26 HARVARD N YALE (USA), ch c Smart Strike (CAN)—Compete (USA)
27 HIGH MISWAKI (FR), b c High Chaparral (IRE)—Driving Miswaki (USA)
28 ILLAUNGLASS (IRE), b f Red Clubs (IRE)—Esterlina (IRE)
29 INITIATOR, b c Motivator—Dawnus (IRE)
30 KAYLENA, b f Teofilo (IRE)—Kootenay (IRE)
31 LIFE IS GOLDEN (USA), ch f Giant's Causeway (USA)—Lizzy Cool (USA)
32 MAORI DANCER (USA), b br c Dynaformer (USA)—Juke (USA)
33 NET WHIZZ (USA), b br c Mr Greeley (USA)—Reboot (USA)
34 NIGER (IRE), ch c Pivotal—Tithcar
35 NOCTURN, b c Oasis Dream—Pizzicato
36 RECKONING (IRE), b f Danehill Dancer (IRE)—Great Hope (IRE)
37 REFLECTED GLORY (AUS), b f Starcraft (NZ)—No Fear No Favour (AUS)
38 REGAL REALM, b f Medicean—Regal Riband
39 ROCK OF AGES, ch c Pivotal—Magic Peak (IRE)
40 ROSA CLARA (IRE), b f Peintre Celebre (USA)—Blushing Barada (USA)
41 ROXELANA (IRE), b f Oasis Dream—Macadamia (IRE)
42 TALWAR (IRE), b c Acclamation—Moore's Melody (IRE)
43 THREE SUGARS (AUS), b f Starcraft (NZ)—Hoh Dear (IRE)
44 VALBCHEK (IRE), b c Acclamation—Spectacular Show (USA)
45 VOLDEMORT (BRZ), ch c Vettori (IRE)—Femme Fatale (BRZ)
46 WHISPERING WARRIOR (IRE), b c Oasis Dream—Varenka (IRE)
47 WILDOMAR, b c Kyllachy—Murrieta
48 WINNER'S WISH, b f Clodovil (IRE)—Alla Prima (IRE)

TWO-YEAR-OLDS

49 B f 7/2 More Than Ready (USA)—Baffled (USA) (Distorted Humor (USA)) (76312)
50 BEAMING STAR (USA), b f 26/4 Giant's Causeway (USA)—Wandering Star (USA) (Red Ransom (USA)) (79365)
51 B f 9/2 Kheleyf (USA)—Blinking (Marju (IRE)) (50000)
52 B f 9/2 Nayef (USA)—Blue Rhapsody (Cape Cross (IRE)) (41050)
53 B f 1/2 Medaglia d'oro (USA)—Chandelle No Five (USA) (Yes It's True (USA)) (42735)
54 CONSIGN, b c 19/2 Dutch Art—Maid To Dance (Pyramus (USA)) (68000)
55 Ch gr c 3/4 Verglas (IRE)—Dazzling Dancer (Nashwan (USA)) (41050)
56 DUTIFUL SON (IRE), b c 14/3 Invincible Spirit (IRE)—Grecian Dancer (Dansili) (123152)
57 Gr f 11/3 Lawman (FR)—Ela Athena (Ezzoud (IRE))

MR JEREMY NOSEDA—continued

58 B f 14/2 Sixties Icon—Endless Love (IRE) (Dubai Destination (USA))
59 **ENVIABLE (IRE)**, b c 10/3 Kyllachy—Eternal Beauty (IRE) (Zafonic (USA)) (75000)
60 Br c 27/2 Holy Roman Emperor (IRE)—Epiphany (Zafonic (USA))
61 **EVIDENT (IRE)**, b c 7/4 Excellent Art—Vestavia (IRE) (Alhaarth (IRE)) (77996)
62 **EVOKE (IRE)**, gr f 6/4 Dark Angel (IRE)—Happy Talk (IRE) (Hamas (IRE)) (24630)
63 B f 7/5 Medicean—Fabulously Fast (USA) (Deputy Minister (CAN)) (32000)
64 Ch f 29/3 Halling (USA)—Flying Finish (FR) (Priolo (USA))
65 B f 25/1 Red Clubs (IRE)—Fuerta Ventura (IRE) (Desert Sun) (70000)
66 **GIDDY HEIGHTS**, b c 12/2 Pivotal—Light Hearted (Green Desert (USA))
67 **HENRIETTA ROSE (USA)**, b f 7/3 Henrythenavigator (USA)—Shermeen (IRE) (Desert Style (IRE))
68 **HI FILWAH (USA)**, b c 29/1 Medaglia d'oro (USA)—Star Landing (USA) (Caller I D (USA)) (131362)
69 **HOMAGE (IRE)**, b c 23/4 Acclamation—Night Sphere (IRE) (Night Shift (USA)) (65680)
70 **HORNBOY**, b c 26/3 Medicean—Soar (Danzero (AUS)) (115000)
71 B c 5/3 Invincible Spirit (IRE)—Imiloa (USA) (Kingmambo (USA)) (90311)
72 **INTIMIDATE**, b c 7/3 Royal Applause—Crystal Power (USA) (Pleasant Colony (USA)) (88000)
73 **INVESTMENT EXPERT (IRE)**, b c 21/3 Tamayuz—Kindling (Dr Fong (USA)) (125000)
74 **IRIDESCENCE**, b f 23/2 Dutch Art—Radiate (Sadler's Wells (USA))
75 Ch c 2/3 Pivotal—Jamboretta (IRE) (Danehill (USA)) (215000)
76 **JOE PALOOKA (IRE)**, b c 20/2 Galileo (IRE)—Glinting Dancer (IRE) (Desert Prince (IRE)) (155000)
77 Ch c 2/3 Giant's Causeway (USA)—La Reina (USA) (A P Indy (USA)) (198412)
78 B c 8/3 Mr Greeley—Lafirma (USA) (Giant's Causeway (USA)) (61050)
79 **MAGIQUE (IRE)**, b f 21/4 Jeremy (USA)—Misskinta (IRE) (Desert Sun) (31198)
80 **MARCIANO (IRE)**, b c 15/1 Pivotal—Kitty Matcham (IRE) (Rock of Gibraltar (IRE)) (360000)
81 B f 2/5 Rock of Gibraltar (IRE)—Marula (USA) (Sadler's Wells (USA)) (40000)
82 Ch f 8/2 Exceed And Excel (AUS)—Miss University (USA) (Beau Genius (CAN)) (55000)
83 **RED BATON**, b f 9/3 Exceed And Excel (AUS)—Ruby Rocket (IRE) (Indian Rocket) (200000)
84 **RED TURBAN**, b c 20/3 Kyllachy—Red Tiara (USA) (Mr Prospector (USA))
85 **REGAL SILK**, b f 16/2 Pivotal—Regal Velvet (Halling (USA))
86 Ch c 8/3 Dalakhani (IRE)—Rhadegunda (Pivotal) (210000)
87 B c 9/2 Mr Greeley—Sand Pirate (CAN) (Desert Wine (USA)) (91575)
88 Ch c 25/2 Speightstown (USA)—She's Loaded (USA) (Deputy Minister (CAN))
89 Ch c 24/1 Shirocco (GER)—Shell Garland (USA) (Sadler's Wells (USA))
90 Ch c 11/2 Refuse To Bend (IRE)—Sovereign's Honour (USA) (Kingmambo (USA))
91 Ch c 17/4 Dutch Art—Speech (Red Ransom (USA)) (55000)
92 **THE BEST DOCTOR (IRE)**, ch c 3/3 Pivotal—Strawberry Fledge (USA) (Kingmambo (USA)) (110000)
93 **WARRIGAL (IRE)**, ch c 24/4 Mount Nelson—Waldblume (GER) (Halling (USA)) (34481)
94 **WHY AREEB (IRE)**, b c 29/1 Galileo (IRE)—Piquetnol (USA) (Private Account (USA)) (164203)
95 **WILD OCEAN**, b f 18/3 Pivotal—Mystery Ocean (Dr Fong (USA))
96 B c 18/2 Sakhee (USA)—Winner's Call (Indian Ridge)

Owners: Mr S. Al Homaizi, Mr Al Mansoori, Sheikh Khaled Duaij Al Sabah, Mr I. Al Sagar, Mr A. Ali, Mr F. M. Alsheikh, Mr A. Beck, Bluehills Racing Limited, Mrs M. Bryce, Mrs P. Burns, Cheveley Park Stud, Mr C. Fox, Franconson Partners, Highclere Thoroughbred Racing Limited, Miss Y. Jacques, Mr Richard Keen, Mr G. Kent, Mr V. Khosla, Mr Tom Ludt, Captain J. Macdonald-Buchanan, The Hon Earle Mack, Mrs J. Magnier, Mr P. Makin, Newsells Park Stud, Alexander Nezhenets, Miss K. Nikkel, Mr N. O'Sullivan, Sir R. Ogden, Mr D. Pittack, Mrs S. Roy, SE Construction Limited, Mr D. Smith, Mr P. Smith, Mr G. C. Stevens, Mrs S. Suhail, Mr M. Tabor, The Quarrymen, The Hon A. Vestey, The Hon W. Vestey.

Assistant Trainer: Dave Bradley

---

497 **MR DANIEL O'BRIEN, Tonbridge**
Postal: Knowles Bank, Capel, Tonbridge, Kent, TN11 0PU
Contacts: PHONE (01892) 824072

1 **BERNIE'S WEAPON**, 6, b g Winged Love (IRE)—On The Game **Mr C. Attrell**
2 **DOCTORED**, 11, ch g Dr Devious (IRE)—Polygueza (FR) **Mr A. Achilleous**
3 **INTHEJUNGLE (IRE)**, 9, ch g Bob Back (USA)—Whizz **A Achilleous, C Attrell, D C O'Brien**
4 **NEMO SPIRIT (IRE)**, 7, gr g Daylami (IRE)—La Bayadere **A Achilleous, C Attrell, D C O'Brien**
5 **SACRILEGE**, 7, ch g Sakhee (USA)—Idolize **Mr C Attrell, A Achilleous & D O'Brien**
6 **THE SAUCY SNIPE**, 6, b m Josr Algarhoud (IRE)—The Dark Eider **Mr C Attrell, A Achilleous & D O'Brien**

Other Owners: D. C. O'Brien.

Assistant Trainer: Christopher O'Bryan

Jockey (NH): M. Batchelor, Sam Twiston-Davies.

498 MR FERGAL O'BRIEN, Cheltenham
Postal: Cilldara Stud, Coln St. Dennis, Cheltenham, Gloucestershire, GL54 3AR

1 **ACCORDINGTOEILEEN (IRE)**, 7, ch m Accordion—Hannigan's Lodger (IRE) **Mrs M. Curran**
2 **AKIEM (IRE)**, 7, b g Kutub (IRE)—Anacapri (FR) **Masterson Holdings Limited**
3 **ALLERTON (IRE)**, 5, b g Flemensfirth (USA)—Bonny Hall (IRE) **T. M. Evans**
4 **BAGSY'S BRIDGE (IRE)**, 8, b g Great Palm (USA)—Princess Megan (IRE) **The Marvellous Partnership**
5 **BEACON BRIGHT**, 7, b g Alflora (IRE)—Shining Beacon **Mr F. M. O'Brien**
6 **BEGGAR'S VELVET (IRE)**, 6, b g Dr Massini (IRE)—Lakelough (IRE) **Mrs V. J. R. Ramm**
7 **BUBBLY BRUCE (IRE)**, 8, br g Quws—Oakleaf Express (IRE) **Masterson Holdings Limited**
8 **CHECKERBOARD (IRE)**, 9, b g Alderbrook—Jamie's Lady **P. J. Wilmott**
9 **COOPERS HILL**, 6, gr g Silver Patriarch (IRE)—Mimizan (IRE) **Mrs C. E. M. R. Mackness**
10 **DOUBLE SILVER**, 5, gr m Silver Patriarch (IRE)—Shadows of Silver **Mr R. C. Mayall**
11 **FAITH KEEPER (IRE)**, 7, ch g Beneficial—Witney Girl **North And South Racing Partnership**
12 **FATHER PROBUS**, 6, ch h Fleetwood (IRE)—Nearly At Sea **Mr E. G. M. Beard**
13 **GUD DAY (IRE)**, 4, gr g Aussie Rules (USA)—Queen Al Andalous (IRE) **The Yes No Wait Sorries**
14 **HORSHAM LAD (IRE)**, 8, b g Muroto—Comeragh Queen **Mr & Mrs William Rucker**
15 **HOUROFTIME (IRE)**, 5, b g Dr Massini (IRE)—Lucky Hour (IRE) **Mr F. M. O'Brien**
16 **KILMACOWEN (IRE)**, 6, b g Flemensfirth (USA)—Baunfaun Run (IRE) **The Kilmacowens**
17 **LOUXOR DES MOTTES (FR)**, 4, ch g High Yield (USA)—
Thebes Eria (FR) **Jilly Scott Jane Tufnell Scilla Phillips**
18 **MR ONE TOO (IRE)**, 7, b g Mr Combustible (IRE)—Too Back (IRE) **The H & H Partnership**
19 **QUEEN OF MANTUA (IRE)**, 6, b m Old Vic—Papoose (IRE) **Mr R. J. Rexton**
20 **REPOSE DE PAILLE (IRE)**, 10, b g Supreme Leader—Wondermac (IRE) **T. M. Evans**
21 **THUNDER SHEIK (IRE)**, 4, b c Green Tune (USA)—Realy Queen (USA) **Mr R. J. Rexton**
22 **YOUNG MAGS (IRE)**, 5, ch m Presenting—Mags Benefit (IRE) **Masterson Holdings Limited**

Other Owners: J. Baldwin, J. R. Bayer, N. J. Chamberlain, C. S. J. Coley, J. S. Dale, P. A. Deal, G. K. Duncan, R. A. Green, Mrs L. Hall, Mr P. Hall, S. Hurst, D. M. Hussey, Mr C. Levan, Mrs P. M. Phillips, I. Robinson, Mrs G. C. Robinson, W. J. Rucker, Mrs A. Rucker, Ms C. A. Sawer, Mrs J. Scott, M. J. Silver, Mrs R. J. Tufnell, I. F. White.

499 MR EDWARD J. O'GRADY, Thurles
Postal: Killeens, Ballynonty, Thurles, Co. Tipperary, Ireland
Contacts: PHONE (00353) 529 156 156 FAX (00353) 529 156 466 MOBILE (00353) 86 2590764
E-MAIL edward@edwardogrady.com

1 **ACAPULCO (IRE)**, 8, b g Galileo (IRE)—Harasava (FR) **Mr J. Higgins**
2 **BANANA FLAMBE (IRE)**, 4, b g Darsi (FR)—Roupolino (IRE) **Arthur Quinlan**
3 **BIG EARED FRAN (IRE)**, 9, gr g Danehill (USA)—Zarawa (IRE) **T. Barr**
4 **CAPELLANUS (IRE)**, 6, b g Montjeu (IRE)—Secret Dream (IRE) **P. J. Wilmott**
5 **CASH AND GO (IRE)**, 5, b g Sulamani (IRE)—Calcida (GER) **D. Monaghan**
6 **CASH IS GOOD (IRE)**, 4, b g Kalanisi (IRE)—Gift Token **J. J. Power**
7 **CELTIC CUB (IRE)**, 7, b g Milan—Erins Elect (IRE) **Mrs John Magnier**
8 **CLICKSNMORTAR (IRE)**, 8, ch g Presenting—Nick's Jule (IRE) **Mrs C. McCabe**
9 **CORBALLY CROSS (IRE)**, 5, b g Brian Boru—Colleen Easpick (IRE) **J. P. McManus**
10 **CROCUS BAY (IRE)**, 6, b g Overbury (IRE)—Midnight Pond (IRE) **Simon J. H. Davis**
11 **DEFINITE RIDGE (IRE)**, 5, ch g Definite Article—Do The Right Thing **D. O'Connor**
12 **DO BRAZIL (IRE)**, 6, ch g Flemensfirth (USA)—Ballybeg Rose (IRE) **M. V. Magnier**
13 **FLAMING DAWN (IRE)**, 4, ch g Flemensfirth (USA)—Saddlers Dawn (IRE) **Mrs E. J. O'Grady**
14 **JUDGE ROY BEAN (IRE)**, 9, b g Sadler's Wells (USA)—Be My Hope (IRE) **J. P. McManus**
15 **KICKHAMSTOWN (IRE)**, 6, ch g Flemensfirth (USA)—Dr Sandra (IRE) **Simon J. H. Davis**
16 **MISS CONCEPTION (IRE)**, 4, b f Dr Massini (IRE)—Miss Information (IRE) **Blues Brothers Syndicate**
17 **MISS NOMER (IRE)**, 5, b m Overbury (IRE)—Miss Information (IRE) **Star Racing Syndicate**
18 **MUBROOK (USA)**, 7, b g Alhaarth (IRE)—Zomaradah **P. J. Wilmott**
19 **OSANA (FR)**, 10, b g Video Rock (FR)—Voilette (FR) **J. P. McManus**
20 **OUT NOW (IRE)**, 8, br g Muroto—Raven Night (IRE) **Dermot Cox**
21 **PARTHIAN EMPIRE**, 6, b g Parthian Springs—Dudeen (IRE) **Thefourofus Partnership**
22 **PESOTO (FR)**, 9, gr g Lesotho (USA)—Istoire (FR) **M. Lowry**
23 **PUR STYLE (FR)**, 4, ch f Turgeon (USA)—Cayras Style (FR) **Mrs Olivia Cox Hoare**
24 **ROCCO'S HALL (IRE)**, 10, b g Saddlers' Hall (IRE)—Miss San Siro (IRE) **G. Terrinoni**
25 **SAILORS WARN (IRE)**, 5, b g Redback—Coral Dawn (IRE) **P. J. Wilmott**
26 **SEATTLE DRIVE (IRE)**, 4, b c Motivator—Seattle Ribbon (USA) **P. J. Wilmott**
27 **SHOT FROM THE HIP (GER)**, 8, b g Monsun (GER)—Sopran Biro (IRE) **J. P. McManus**
28 **SLIEVEARDAGH (IRE)**, 8, b g King's Theatre (IRE)—Gayephar **Simon J. H. Davis**
29 **SPORTSMASTER (IRE)**, 4, b g Ad Valorem (USA)—Boston Ivy (USA) **J. P. McManus**

MR EDWARD J. O'GRADY—continued

30 **ST MAXIME (IRE)**, 4, ch f Alhaarth (IRE)—Estivua (USA) **J. Higgins**
31 **STAR OF MASSINI (IRE)**, 5, b g Dr Massini (IRE)—Star of The Orient (IRE) **Mrs E. J. O'Grady**
32 **STAYING ARTICLE (IRE)**, 7, b g Definite Article—Sejour (IRE) **T. Barr**
33 **SUN FISHER (IRE)**, 6, b g Dr Massini (IRE)—Native Nancy (IRE) **Simon J. H. Davis**
34 **TANJUNG AGAS (IRE)**, 4, b g Montjeu (IRE)—Najmati **Peter Deal**
35 **THE LEGAL ARTICLE (IRE)**, 4, ch g Definite Article—Soul Mate (IRE) **Mrs E. J. O'Grady**
36 **THE REAL ARTICLE (IRE)**, 7, b g Definite Article—Soul Mate (IRE) **Mrs Patricia Wallace**
37 **THE REAL TYSON (IRE)**, 9, b g Turtle Island (IRE)—Cailin Chuinne (IRE) **N. Murphy**
38 **THE WAY WE WERE (IRE)**, 6, br g Definite Article—Shuil Oilean (IRE) **J. P. McManus**
39 **TOBAR NA GAOISE (IRE)**, 4, b c Whipper (USA)—Starchy **J. P. McManus**
40 **TRANQUIL SEA (IRE)**, 10, b g Sea Raven (IRE)—Silver Valley (IRE) **Nelius Hayes**
41 **TRAVIS MCGEE (FR)**, 4, b g Kahyasi—Detonante (FR) **Piers Pottinger**
42 **TUGBOAT (IRE)**, 4, b g Galileo (IRE)—Alleluia **T. Barr**
43 **VENTO DI PONENTE (IRE)**, 4, b f Westerner—Storm Front (IRE) **N. Hayes**

THREE-YEAR-OLDS

44 **AMIENS STREET (IRE)**, b g Rail Link—Broken Spectre **Mrs E. J. O'Grady**
45 **GARDE FREINET (IRE)**, br f High Chaparral (IRE)—Cradle of Love (USA) **Mrs E. J. O'Grady**

Other Owners: P. O'Connell, M. Cahill.

MR JEDD O'KEEFFE, Leyburn

Postal: **Highbeck, Brecongill, Coverham, Leyburn, North Yorkshire, DL8 4TJ**
Contacts: PHONE **(01969) 640330** FAX **(01969) 640397** MOBILE **(07710) 476705**
E-MAIL **jedd@jeddokeefferacing.co.uk** WEBSITE **www.jeddokeefferacing.co.uk**

1 **BID FOR GOLD**, 8, b g Auction House (USA)—Gold And Blue (IRE) **J. E. D. O'Keeffe**
2 **GEMINUS (IRE)**, 4, b g Choisir (AUS)—Macca Luna (IRE) **W R B Racing 54**
3 **HIGHLAND LOVE**, 7, b g Fruits of Love (USA)—Diabaig **John & Susan Robertson**
4 **LADY KILDARE (IRE)**, 4, br f Bachelor Duke (USA)—Teodora (IRE) **The Fatalists**
5 **SECRET VENUE**, 6, ch g Where Or When (IRE)—Sheila's Secret (IRE) **Ken & Delia Shaw Racing**

THREE-YEAR-OLDS

6 **BYRONIC HERO**, b g Byron—Starbeck (IRE) **Highbeck Racing**
7 Gr f Norse Dancer (IRE)—Charlotte Lamb **Miss S. E. Hall**
8 **KIAN'S JOY**, b g Mind Games—Lunasa (IRE) **Jenny & Ray Butler**
9 **KIERON'S ROCK (IRE)**, ch g Rock of Gibraltar (IRE)—Princess Killeen (IRE) **Jenny & Ray Butler**
10 **SATANIC BEAT (IRE)**, br g Dark Angel (IRE)—Slow Jazz (USA) **Caron & Paul Chapman**

TWO-YEAR-OLDS

11 B c 15/2 Oasis Dream—Alexander Alliance (IRE) (Danetime (IRE)) (61904) **Caron & Paul Chapman**
12 **CAPTAIN'S DREAM (IRE)**, b c 18/2 Kheleyf (USA)—
                                     Somaggia (IRE) (Desert King (IRE)) (28000) **Mr & Mrs Bruce McAllister**
13 **DARK OCEAN**, b c 11/2 Dylan Thomas (IRE)—Neutral (Beat Hollow) (13500) **Miss S. Long**
14 B c 23/4 Byron—Fresher (Fabulous Dancer (USA)) (2857) **Highbeck Racing**
15 Ch c 29/5 Paris House—Hula Ballew (Weldnaas (USA)) (9523) **Highbeck Racing**
16 B f 29/4 Avonbridge—Jade Pet (Petong) (7619) **Ken & Delia Shaw Racing**
17 B f 22/3 Pastoral Pursuits—Katy O'hara (Komaite (USA)) (19047) **Caron & Paul Chapman**
18 Ch c 18/3 Rock of Gibraltar (IRE)—Landela (Alhaarth (IRE)) (14285) **Highbeck Racing**
19 **ROYAL JENRAY**, gr c 26/3 Royal Applause—In The Highlands (Petong) (15238) **Jenny & Ray Butler**
20 Ch g 15/5 Pastoral Pursuits—Turn Back (Pivotal) **Miss S. E. Hall**

Other Owners: Mr R. Berry, Mr & Mrs P. Griffiths, Mr A. Henderson, Mr E. R. D. Johnson, David & Louise Louden, Mr & Mrs J. McGhee, Colin & Melanie Moore, Mr & Mrs J. Murphy, Mr R. Ord, Mr & Mrs E. Rider, Mr & Mrs H. M. Sadler, Mr & Mrs A. Shaw, Mr & Mrs G. Shaw, Mr A. Walker.

Assistant Trainer: Andrea O'Keeffe

Jockey (NH): Fearghal Davis.

501 MR DAVID O'MEARA, Nawton

Postal: **Arthington Barn, Highfield Lane, Nawton, York, North Yorkshire, YO62 7TU**
Contacts: **PHONE (01439) 770437 FAX (01439) 770437**
WEBSITE www.davidomeara.co.uk

1 **ANDERIEGO (IRE)**, 4, b c Invincible Spirit (IRE)—Anna Frid (GER)
2 **APACHE WARRIOR**, 5, b g Westerner—Aldevonie **Mr & Mrs G. Turnbull**
3 **BAY OF FIRES (IRE)**, 4, b f Iffraaj—No Tippling (IRE) **P Bamford J M Binns R G Fell & K Everitt**
4 **BOGSIDE THEATRE (IRE)**, 8, b m Fruits of Love (USA)—Royal Jubilee (IRE) **Mr & Mrs G. Turnbull**
5 **CHANCERY (USA)**, 4, b br g Street Cry (IRE)—Follow That Dream **Hollowdean**
6 **CLASSIC COLORI (IRE)**, 5, b g Le Vie Dei Colori—Beryl **The Classic Strollers Partnership**
7 **CLASSICAL MIST**, 8, ch m Classic Cliche—Mademist Jaz **The Cuckoo Partnership**
8 **COMEDY ACT**, 5, b g Motivator—Comic (IRE) **Middleham Park Racing XXII & P Drury**
9 **COUNT BERTONI (IRE)**, 5, b g Bertolini (USA)—Queen Sceptre (IRE) **Equality Racing**
10 **DANCE FOR JULIE (IRE)**, 5, b m Redback—Dancing Steps **Mersey Racing, Bolingbroke Racing**
11 **DESCARO (USA)**, 6, gr g Dr Fong (USA)—Miarixa (FR) **Mr R. Fell & Mr K. Everitt**
12 **EDMAAJ (IRE)**, 4, ch g Intikhab (USA)—Lady Angola (USA) **K. Nicholson**
13 **EL TORBELLINO (IRE)**, 4, b f Chineur (FR)—Deeday Bay (IRE) **Crowther, Fell & Everitt**
14 **GINGER GREY (IRE)**, 5, gr g Bertolini—Just In Love (FR) **Liam, Johnny & Mecca Too**
15 **GOODNESS**, 4, ch g Cadeaux Genereux—Dayrose **The Goodness Project**
16 **HAL OF A LOVER**, 4, b g Halling (USA)—Latent Lover (IRE) **Glenn Briers & The Dreamers**
17 **HEROSTATUS**, 5, ch g Dalakhani (IRE)—Desired **R. Naylor**
18 **HORATIO CARTER**, 7, b g Bahamian Bounty—Jitterbug (IRE) **Mr R. G. Fell**
19 **IFANDBUTWHYNOT (IRE)**, 6, b g Raise A Grand (IRE)—Cockney Ground (IRE) **C. Hollowood and H. Dean**
20 **KING IN WAITING (IRE)**, 9, b g Sadler's Wells (USA)—Ballerina (IRE) **AKV Cladding Fabrications Ltd**
21 **KING'S COUNSEL (IRE)**, 6, ch g Refuse To Bend (IRE)—Nesaah's Princess **W R B Racing 44**
22 **MADAM MACIE (IRE)**, 5, ch m Bertolini (USA)—Dictatrice (FR) **Mr R. Fell & Mr K. Everitt**
23 **MAGIC MILLIE (IRE)**, 5, b br m Marju (IRE)—Fille de La Terre (IRE) **Mr C Varley,Mr K Everitt & Mr R Fell**
24 **MAYOMAN (IRE)**, 7, b g Namid—America Lontana (FR) **Mr T. J. Tuohy**
25 **PEEDEEQUE**, 6, b g Kayf Tara—Sister Kit (USA) **Mrs C. Hollowood**
26 **PENITENT**, 6, b g Kyllachy—Pious **Cheveley Park Stud Limited**
27 **PLAYING THE FIELD (IRE)**, 7, b g Deploy—Gaelic Buccaneer (IRE) **R. Collins**
28 **POWERFUL PRESENCE (IRE)**, 6, ch g Refuse To Bend (IRE)—
    Miss a Note (USA) **The Lawton Bamforth Partnership**
29 **SIMPLE JIM (FR)**, 8, b g Jimble (FR)—Stop The Wedding (USA) **Mr R. G. Fell**
30 **SKENAKILLA CROSS (IRE)**, 7, ch m Flemensfirth (USA)—Dun Ar Aill (IRE) **Mr D. J. G. O'Keeffe**
31 **SMARTY SOCKS (IRE)**, 8, ch g Elnadim (USA)—Unicamp **Mr R. Fell & Mr K. Everitt**
32 **SONG OF THE SIREN**, 4, ch f With Approval (CAN)—Sulitelma (USA)
33 **SPAHI (FR)**, 6, b g Dubai Destination (USA)—Lusitanie (IRE) **Mr R. G. Fell**
34 **SPIEKEROOG**, 6, ch g Lomitas—Special **Mr G. Schoeningh**
35 **ST OSWALD**, 4, b g Royal Applause—Susun Kelapa (USA) **R. Jefferies**
36 **SYMBOLISM (IRE)**, 4, b c Tiger Hill (IRE)—Silver Bracelet **Claire Hollowood & Henry Dean**
37 **TAZAAMUN (IRE)**, 4, b g Shirocco (GER)—Glorious **Patterns & Profiles 1**
38 **TEMPLEFIRE (GER)**, 5, gr g Sternkoenig—Temple Esprit **Mr G. Schoeningh**
39 **THE BUSKA (IRE)**, 4, ch g Haafhd—Play That Tune **Tom Tuohy & Tony Jafrate**
40 **TRANS SONIC**, 9, ch g Trans Island—Sankaty Light (USA) **Mrs L. Lumley**
41 **VIVA COLONIA (IRE)**, 7, ch g Traditionally (USA)—Ansariya (USA) **Bolingbroke Racing, Mersey Racing**
42 **WAR POET**, 5, b g Singspiel (IRE)—Summer Sonnet **Mr M. Kirby**
43 **YAS MARINA (USA)**, 4, ch c Bernardini (USA)—Silvery Swan (USA) **Middleham Park**

THREE-YEAR-OLDS

44 **KOALITION (IRE)**, b g Kodiac—Arbitration (IRE) **Mrs S. K. O'Meara**

TWO-YEAR-OLDS

45 Ch c 9/5 Sakhee's Secret—Al Euro (FR) (Mujtahid (USA)) (22000)
46 B c 21/4 Red Clubs (IRE)—Dianella (IRE) (Gold Away (IRE)) (4515)
47 B c 28/4 Baltic King—Dorn Hill (Lujain (USA)) (3447)
48 B br c 27/2 Arch (USA)—Dot C C (USA) (Cozzene (USA)) (38000)
49 B f 4/3 Chineur (FR)—Flower Bowl (Noverre (USA)) (6157)
50 B g 7/3 Moss Vale (IRE)—Gold Majesty (Josr Algarhoud (IRE)) (6666)
51 B br g 11/3 Araafa (IRE)—Golden Flyer (FR) (Machiavellian (USA)) (3047)
52 B g 27/1 Oratorio (IRE)—Grand Splendour (Shirley Heights) (14285)
53 Ch f 2/4 Compton Place—Gulf Stream Lady (IRE) (Cadeaux Genereux) (3000)
54 B g 14/2 Bertolini (USA)—Jasmine Breeze (Saddlers' Hall (IRE)) (3809)
55 B f 12/4 Byron—Knowing Look (Daylami (IRE))
56 B f 31/1 Misu Bond (IRE)—Lawless Bridget (Alnasr Alwasheek) (3809)

MR DAVID O'MEARA—continued

57 B c 28/4 Mujadil (USA)—Maddie's Pearl (IRE) (Clodovil (IRE)) (9030)
58 Ch c 18/4 Sleeping Indian—Remedy (Pivotal) (13546)
59 B f 18/2 Redback—Storm Lady (IRE) (Alhaarth (IRE)) (9440)
60 B c 4/5 Pivotal—Triple Edition (USA) (Lear Fan (USA)) (14000)
61 B f 11/2 Redback—Zafaraya (IRE) (Ashkalani (IRE)) (5910)

Other Owners: Mr T. Alderson, Mr P. Bamford, Mr S. H. Bamforth, Mr Andrew Bates, Mr J. M. Binns, Mr Lee Bolingbroke, Mr Glenn Briers, Mr Steve Cannon, Mr A. Crowther, Mr H. T. H. Dean, Mr Paul Drury, Mr K. M. Everitt, Mr R. G. Fell, Mr Andy Franks, Ms R. Galbraith, Mr A. Gibson, Mr D. P. Grundy, Mr M. J. Hill, Mrs Claire Hollowood, Dr John Hollowood, Mr Tony Jafrate, Mr M. F. Lawton, Mr David T. J. Metcalfe, Mrs S. O'Meara, Mr A. Owen, Mr T. S. Palin, Mr M. Prince, Mr J. P. Rider, Mr Evan M. Sutherland, Mr Tom Tuohy, Mr Geoffrey Turnbull, Mrs S. E. Turnbull, Mr S. R. H. Turner, Mr C. Varley, Wetherby Racing Bureau Ltd, Mr Ian White.

Assistant Trainer: R. G. Fell

Jockey (flat): Daniel Tudhope, Silvestre De Sousa. **Jockey (NH):** Denis O'Regan, Keith Mercer.

---

502 MR JOHN O'NEILL, Bicester
Postal: **Hall Farm, Stratton Audley, Nr Bicester, Oxfordshire, OX27 9BT**
Contacts: **PHONE (01869) 277202 MOBILE (07785) 394128**
E-MAIL jgoneill@lineone.net

1 CABARET GIRL, 5, ch m Karinga Bay—Little Miss Prim **Ms D. Keane**
2 IRISH GUARD, 11, b g Infantry—Sharp Practice **J. G. O'Neill**
3 OVERLAY, 8, br m Overbury (IRE)—Lay It Off (IRE) **J. G. O'Neill**

---

503 MR JONJO O'NEILL, Cheltenham
Postal: **Jackdaws Castle, Temple Guiting, Cheltenham, Gloucestershire, GL54 5XU**
Contacts: **PHONE (01386) 584209 FAX (01386) 584219**
E-MAIL reception@jonjooneillracing.com WEBSITE www.jonjooneillracing.com

1 ABNAKI (IRE), 7, b g Milan—Laboc **Masterson Holdings Limited**
2 ACCORDION EXHIBIT (IRE), 6, ch g Accordion—Curraghmeela (IRE) **Masterson Holdings Limited**
3 ALBERTAS RUN (IRE), 11, b g Accordion—Holly Grove Lass **T. J. Hemmings**
4 AMBER CLOUD, 5, ch m Lomitas—Diamant Noir **Mr D. J. Burke**
5 BABYSITTER (IRE), 9, b g Rashar (USA)—Piel Eagle (FR) **The Magnificent Six**
6 BALINROAB (IRE), 5, b g Milan—Gentle Eyre (IRE) **T. J. Hemmings**
7 BALLYCLOUGH (IRE), 5, b g Heron Island (IRE)—That's The Bonus (IRE) **J. P. McManus**
8 BARRIE BURN (IRE), 6, ch g Flemensfirth (USA)—Phardester (IRE) **J. P. McManus**
9 CARDINAL ROSE, 5, ch g Karinga Bay—Miniature Rose **Broughtons Jones Weaver Wilson**
10 CASTLEROCK, 8, gr g Kayf Tara—Jessolle **Michael & John O'Flynn**
11 CATCH THAT (IRE), 5, ch g Presenting—Beenaround **Mrs J. S. T. O'Neill**
12 CHIT CHAT, 7, b m Bob Back (USA)—Consuelo **Mrs Felicity Loudon**
13 CROSS THE FLAGS (IRE), 5, b m Flemensfirth (USA)—Mayasta (IRE) **J. P. McManus**
14 DEED OF GIFT (IRE), 5, b g Beneficial—Ardlow (IRE) **Mrs R. D. Hodgson**
15 DEPUTY DOG (IRE), 6, b g Kahyasi—Hirayna **Mrs G. K. Smith**
16 DRAMATIC DUKE, 6, b g Old Vic—Dramatic Dame (IRE) **Favourites Racing VIII**
17 DREAM AGAIN BOYS (IRE), 5, ch g Presenting—The Silver Dyer (IRE) **Crutched Flyers**
18 DREAM CATCHER (SWE), 9, b g Songline (SWE)—Queen Ida (SWE) **Ms M. Miles**
19 EASTLAKE (IRE), 6, b g Beneficial—Guigone (FR) **J. P. McManus**
20 EDDIE THE EAGLE (IRE), 6, gr g Great Palm (USA)—Becca's Rose (IRE) **W. J. Gott**
21 FAVOURED NATION (IRE), 5, b g Milan—Bless of Honour (IRE) **J. P. McManus**
22 FIDDLEDEDEE (IRE), 7, b m Beneficial—Betty Balfour **Mrs A. F. Bond**
23 FILIPPO LIPPI (IRE), 7, b g Oscar (IRE)—Marhabtain **Mrs A. F. Bond**
24 FOUNDATION MAN (IRE), 5, b g Presenting—Function Dream (IRE) **P. Hickey**
25 FULL OF JOY (IRE), 7, b g King's Theatre (IRE)—Penny Brae (IRE) **J. P. McManus**
26 GALAXY ROCK (IRE), 8, b g Heron Island (IRE)—Blue Pool **Michael & John O'Flynn**
27 GET ME OUT OF HERE (IRE), 8, b g Accordion—Home At Last (IRE) **J. P. McManus**
28 GILBARRY (IRE), 7, b g Bahri—Starry Night **Mrs A. F. Bond**
29 HAWK RUN, 6, ch g Central Park (IRE)—Bobbie Black (IRE) **Mrs B. B. Grainger**
30 HEAR MY SONG (IRE), 7, ch g Snurge—Siberiansdaughter (IRE) **J. C. & S. R. Hitchins**
31 HOGAN'S BRIDGE (IRE), 5, b g Perugino—Mrs Mustard (IRE) **J. P. McManus**
32 HOLYWELL (IRE), 5, b g Gold Well—Hillcrest (IRE) **Mrs Gay Smith**
33 HOPEFUL START (IRE), 8, b g Flemensfirth (USA)—Calishee (IRE) **J. P. McManus**

MR JONJO O'NEILL—continued

34 **I CAN RUN CAN YOU (IRE)**, 6, ch g Old Vic—Merry Batim (IRE) **Mrs G. K. Smith**
35 **IT'S A GIMME (IRE)**, 5, b g Beneficial—Sorcera (GER) **J. P. McManus**
36 **JOHNS SPIRIT (IRE)**, 5, b g Gold Well—Gilt Ridden (IRE) **Mr C. Johnston**
37 **KEEP KICKING (IRE)**, 5, b g Tiger Hill (IRE)—Dalannda (IRE) **P. McCarthy**
38 **LITTLE MISS FLORA**, 6, ch m Alflora (IRE)—Mistletoe (IRE) **Mrs Felicity Loudon**
39 **LOUGH INCH (IRE)**, 5, b g Jimble (FR)—Ballerina Gold (USA) **Mr John Power & Mrs Sheena Mcelroy**
40 **MASTER MILAN (IRE)**, 6, b g Milan—English Clover **J. P. McManus**
41 **MAURITINO (GER)**, 8, b g Dashing Blade—Miss Page **P. A. Byrne**
42 **MERRY KING (IRE)**, 5, ch g Old Vic—Merry Queen (IRE) **F. Gillespie**
43 **MINELLA FOR STEAK (IRE)**, 5, b g King's Theatre (IRE)—
                                     Preview Days (IRE) **Mrs Gay Smith & Mrs John Magnier**
44 **MISSION COMPLETE (IRE)**, 6, b g Milan—Kilmington Breeze (IRE) **J. P. McManus**
45 **MISTER HYDE (IRE)**, 7, b g Beneficial—Solar Quest (IRE) **Bensaranat Club & Mr W McLuskey**
46 **MOHAYER (IRE)**, 10, gr g Giant's Causeway (USA)—Karlafsha **G. & P. Barker Ltd**
47 **MY MATE VINNIE (IRE)**, 5, ch g Vinnie Roe (IRE)—A Rare One (IRE) **G. & P. Barker Ltd**
48 **PALACE JESTER**, 7, b g King's Theatre (IRE)—Jessolle **T. J. Hemmings**
49 **QUAZY DE JOIE (FR)**, 8, b g Fado (FR)—Gerboise II (FR) **J. P. McManus**
50 **RAPID INCREASE (IRE)**, 9, br g Sonus (IRE)—Lady Margaretta **Mrs G. K. Smith**
51 **RATE OF KNOTS (IRE)**, 9, b m Saddlers' Hall (IRE)—Fast Time (IRE) **J. P. McManus**
52 **ROCKY RACCOON (IRE)**, 5, b g Presenting—My Native Gesture (IRE) **Mr J. C. & S. R. Hitchins & P. J. Bond**
53 **ROPER (IRE)**, 7, b g Beneficial—Lady Fancy (IRE) **T. J. Hemmings**
54 **ROYAL DIAMOND (IRE)**, 6, b g King's Best (USA)—Irresistible Jewel (IRE) **Mr W. A. Tinkler**
55 **SALPIERRE (IRE)**, 7, b g Pierre—Promalady (IRE) **F. Gillespie**
56 **SAVES TIME (IRE)**, 5, b g Presenting—Coole Eile (IRE) **J. P. McManus**
57 **SCHISM**, 4, ch f Shirocco (GER)—Alla Prima (IRE) **The Dirty Dozen**
58 **SENTIMENTALJOURNEY (IRE)**, 5, ch g Portrait Gallery (IRE)—Hazy Rose (IRE) **J. P. McManus**
59 **SHARPSHOOTER (IRE)**, 5, br g Accordion—Full of Surprises (IRE) **Mrs J. S. T. O'Neill**
60 **SHUTTHEFRONTDOOR (IRE)**, 5, b br g Accordion—Hurricane Girl (IRE) **J. P. McManus**
61 **SILVER STIRRUP (IRE)**, 5, b g High Chaparral (IRE)—Meseta **Mr D Smith, Mrs J Magnier & Mr M Tabor**
62 **SIR ROGER (IRE)**, 6, ch g Flemensfirth (USA)—Balreask Lady (IRE) **Mrs V. F. Burke**
63 **SOCIAL REALISM**, 4, b f Pivotal—Russian Revolution **Trinity Racing**
64 **SPOIL ME (IRE)**, 5, b g Presenting—Akayid **Mrs A. F. Bond**
65 **SPOT THE BALL (IRE)**, 7, b g Oscar (IRE)—Sudden Inspiration (IRE) **J. P. McManus**
66 **STORM SURVIVOR (IRE)**, 6, b g Milan—Lindas Present (IRE) **J. P. McManus**
67 **STRONGLY SUGGESTED**, 5, b g Kayf Tara—Branston Lily **J. P. McManus**
68 **SUNNYHILLBOY (IRE)**, 9, b g Old Vic—Sizzle **J. P. McManus**
69 **SURF AND TURF (IRE)**, 6, ch g Beneficial—Clear Top Waltz (IRE) **J. P. McManus**
70 **SWEET PRINCE (IRE)**, 5, b g Court Cave—Simply Sweep (IRE) **Mrs S. M. Farmer**
71 **SYNCHRONISED (IRE)**, 9, b g Sadler's Wells (USA)—Mayasta (IRE) **J. P. McManus**
72 **TAQUIN DU SEUIL (FR)**, 5, b br g Voix du Nord (FR)—Sweet Laly (FR) **Martin Broughton & Friends**
73 **TARVINI (IRE)**, 7, b g Kalanisi (IRE)—Tarwila (IRE) **J. P. McManus**
74 **TELL ME Y (IRE)**, 5, ch g Kris Kin (USA)—Ebony Jane **Mr Trevor Hemmings**
75 **TEMPLE LORD (FR)**, 6, gr g Califet (FR)—Temple Queen (GER) **J. P. McManus**
76 **THEHILLOFUISNEACH (IRE)**, 8, b g Flemensfirth (USA)—Miniconjou (IRE) **Walters Plant Hire Ltd**
77 **TIGRESSE BLEUE**, 4, b f Bachelor Duke (USA)—Tigresse Africaine (FR) **Mr John Loudon**
78 **TWIRLING MAGNET (IRE)**, 6, b g Imperial Ballet (IRE)—Molly Maguire (IRE) **Mrs G. K. Smith**
79 **VALLEY VIEW (IRE)**, 6, b g Anshan—Sweet Valley High (IRE) **J. P. McManus**
80 **VERY STYLISH (IRE)**, 8, b g Winged Love (IRE)—Native Craft (IRE) **Mrs G. K. Smith**
81 **VIMIERO (USA)**, 5, b br g Dynaformer (USA)—Merrymaker (ARG) **Trinity Racing**
82 **WASHINGTON ROAD (IRE)**, 5, b g Heron Island (IRE)—Lady Tarka (IRE) **J. P. McManus**
83 **WELL HELLO THERE (IRE)**, 6, b g Oscar (IRE)—Bird of Passage **J. P. McManus**
84 **WHERES THE HARE (IRE)**, 5, b g Flemensfirth (USA)—Knocknabrogue (IRE) **Mrs A. F. Bond**
85 **WHISTLING SENATOR (IRE)**, 5, b g Presenting—Merry Batim (IRE) **J. P. McManus**
86 **YOU'RE SO SPECIAL (FR)**, 5, b g Highest Honor (FR)—Bric Mamaille (FR) **Mrs A. F. Bond**

Other Owners: Mr Mark Atkinson, Mrs Jocelyn Broughton, Mr Stephen Broughton, Mr D. J. Burke, Mr Mick Coulson, Mr J. C. Hitchins, Mr S. R. Hitchins, Mrs Nicholas Jones, Mrs John Magnier, Mrs Sheena McElroy, Mr W. McLuskey, Mr Michael O'Flynn, Mr John O'Flynn, Mr J. J. Powell, Mr John Power, Mr S. Prater, Mr Toby Roberts, Mrs Karen Salters, Mr Graham Skeats, Mr Derrick Smith, Mrs Gay Smith, Mr M. Tabor, Mr M. Warren, Mrs S. J. Warren, Mrs Giles Weaver, Mrs Jane Wilson.

504 **MR JOHN O'SHEA, Newnham**
Postal: **The Stables, Bell House, Lumbars Lane, Newnham, Gloucestershire, GL14 1LH**
Contacts: **(01452) 760835 FAX (01452) 760233 MOBILE (07917) 124717**
WEBSITE www.johnoshearacing.co.uk

1 CHEVY TO THE LEVY (IRE), 10, b g Saddlers' Hall (IRE)—Be The One (IRE) **K. W. Bell**
2 CITYAR (FR), 8, b g Sagacity (FR)—Starry Dust (FR) **Quality Pipe Supports (Q.P.S.) Ltd**
3 LADY RUMBA, 4, b f Ishiguru (USA)—Costa Packet (IRE) **Mr B. R. Harris**
4 LITTLEDEAN JIMMY (IRE), 7, b g Indian Danehill (IRE)—Gold Stamp **K. W. Bell**
5 MY VIKING BAY (IRE), 8, b m Saddlers' Hall (IRE)—So Supreme (IRE) **Mrs R. E. Neimes**
6 NICKY NUTJOB (GER), 6, b g Fasliyev (USA)—Natalie Too (USA) **Quality Pipe Supports (Q.P.S.) Ltd**
7 RADMORES OSCAR, 6, ch g Karinga Bay—Harvey's Sister **J. R. Salter**
8 RADMORES REVENGE, 9, b g Overbury (IRE)—Harvey's Sister **J. R. Salter**
9 STAFFORD CHARLIE, 6, ch g Silver Patriarch (IRE)—Miss Roberto (IRE) **N. G. H. Ayliffe**
10 SWENDAB (IRE), 4, b g Trans Island—Lavish Spirit (USA) **The Cross Racing Club & Patrick Brady**
11 THE JAILER, 9, b m Mujahid (USA)—Once Removed **Quality Pipe Supports (Q.P.S.) Ltd**
12 THOMAS BELL (IRE), 8, b g Moscow Society (USA)—Cottage Girl (IRE) **K. W. Bell**
13 VIVARINI, 8, b g Hernando (FR)—Venetian Red (USA) **Pete Smith Car Sales**

THREE-YEAR-OLDS

14 EL MCGLYNN (IRE), b f Elnadim (USA)—Evelyn One **Mr M. G. Mcglynn**
15 TAKE TWO, b c Act One—Lac Marmot (FR) **S. P. Bloodstock**

Other Owners: P. Brady, C. L. Dubois, P. Smith, Mrs S. Smith, Mr S. T. Wallace, Mrs P. S. Wallace.

Jockey (flat): Robert Havlin, Luke Morris, Fergus Sweeney. Jockey (NH): Charlie Wallis. Amateur: Miss S. Randell, Mr S. Juckes.

505 **MR JIM OLD, Wroughton**
Postal: **Upper Herdswick Farm, Hackpen, Burderop, Wroughton, Swindon, Wiltshire, SN4 0QH**
Contacts: PHONE (01793) 845200 CAR (07836) 721459 OFFICE (01793) 845200
FAX (01793) 845201 MOBILE (07836) 721459
E-MAIL racing@jimold.co.uk WEBSITE www.jimoldracing.co.uk

1 4, Gr g Terimon—Bessie Blues
2 COUNTING HOUSE (IRE), 9, ch g King's Best (USA)—Inforapenny **W. E. Sturt**
3 EURHYTHMIC (IRE), 5, b g Danehill Dancer (IRE)—Russian Ballet (USA) **W. E. Sturt**
4 MY FRIEND SANDY, 11, ch g Anshan—Gaye Fame **W. E. Sturt**
5 OKAFRANCA (IRE), 7, b g Okawango (USA)—Villafranca (IRE) **W. E. Sturt**
6 ROUND THE HORN (IRE), 12, ch g Master Willie—Gaye Fame **Old Fools Partnership**
7 THE HUDNALLS (IRE), 11, ch g Shernazar—Toposki (FR) **C. J. Jenkins**
8 THEDREAMSTILLALIVE (IRE), 12, ch g Houmayoun (FR)—State of Dream (IRE) **J. A. B. Old**
9 TODAREISTODO, 6, gr g Fair Mix (IRE)—Its Meant To Be **Mrs J. A. Fowler**
10 VALID POINT (IRE), 6, b g Val Royal (FR)—Ricadonna **W. E. Sturt**
11 WITCH'S HAT (IRE), 9, br g Hubbly Bubbly (USA)—Bold Shilling (IRE) **Old Fools Partnership**

Other Owners: Mrs P. V. Antrobus, C. C. Walker.

Assistant Trainer: Emma Grierson

Jockey (NH): Jason Maguire, Rhys Flint.

506 **MR GEOFFREY OLDROYD, Malton**
Postal: **Flint Hall Farm, Morr Lane, Brawby, Malton, North Yorkshire, YO17 6PZ**
Contacts: PHONE (01653) 668279 MOBILE (07730) 642620

1 ALFRED HUTCHINSON, 4, ch g Monsieur Bond (IRE)—Chez Cherie **R. C. Bond**
2 BOND BLADE, 4, ch g Needwood Blade—Bond Cat (IRE) **R. C. Bond**
3 BOND FASTRAC, 5, b g Monsieur Bond (IRE)—Kanisfluh (IRE) **R. C. Bond**
4 CHOSEN FOREVER, 7, b g Choisir (AUS)—Forever Bond **R. C. Bond**
5 FOREVER'S GIRL, 6, b m Monsieur Bond (IRE)—Forever Bond **R. C. Bond**
6 JUST BOND (IRE), 10, b g Namid—Give Warning (IRE) **R. C. Bond**
7 LADIES ARE FOREVER, 4, b f Monsieur Bond (IRE)—Forever Bond **R. C. Bond**
8 LADIES IN CHICAGO, 4, b f Monsieur Bond (IRE)—Chicago Bond (USA) **R. C. Bond**

MR GEOFFREY OLDROYD—continued

9 **LADY GAR GAR**, 4, ch f Monsieur Bond (IRE)—Triple Tricks (IRE) **R. C. Bond**
10 **LADY PLATINUM CLUB**, 4, ch f Monsieur Bond (IRE)—Bond Platinum Club **M. Keegan**
11 **LADY ROYALE**, 4, ch f Monsieur Bond (IRE)—Bond Royale **R. C. Bond**
12 **MAJOR MUSCARI (IRE)**, 4, ch g Exceed And Excel (AUS)—Muscari **South Yorkshire Racing**
13 **STRIKER TORRES (IRE)**, 6, ch g Danehill Dancer (IRE)—Silver Skates (IRE) **R. C. Bond**

THREE-YEAR-OLDS

14 **BOND ARTIST (IRE)**, b f Excellent Art—Pitrizza (IRE) **R. C. Bond**
15 **CATRAMIS**, b g Misu Bond (IRE)—Bond Cat (IRE) **R. C. Bond**
16 **CHARMEL'S DELIGHT**, b f Monsieur Bond (IRE)—Jane's Delight (IRE) **Mrs M. J. Marshall & R. C. Bond**
17 **CROSSLEY**, ch g Monsieur Bond (IRE)—Dispol Diamond **P. Drewery**
18 **PRINCESS KHELEYF**, b f Kheleyf (USA)—Jugendliebe (IRE) **Pamela Morris**
19 B g Misu Bond (IRE)—Triple Tricks (IRE) **R. C. Bond**
20 **TRUE BOND**, ch f Monsieur Bond (IRE)—Splicing **Only Tyres & Horses**
21 **TYRE GIANT DOT COM**, b g Misu Bond (IRE)—Villa Del Sol **R. C. Bond**

TWO-YEAR-OLDS

22 B g 6/2 Misu Bond (IRE)—At Amal (IRE) (Astronef) **R. C. Bond**
23 B f 5/2 Misu Bond (IRE)—Bond Babe (Forzando) **R. C. Bond**
24 B c 29/4 Misu Bond (IRE)—Bond Platinum Club (Pivotal) **R. C. Bond**
25 Ch c 17/4 Monsieur Bond (IRE)—Bond Royale (Piccolo) **R. C. Bond**
26 Ch f 20/4 Monsieur Bond (IRE)—Bond Shakira (Daggers Drawn (USA)) (19047) **R. C. Bond**
27 B f 14/3 Monsieur Bond (IRE)—Kanisfluh (Pivotal) (37142) **South Yorkshire Racing**
28 Ch c 7/5 Monsieur Bond (IRE)—Triple Tricks (IRE) (Royal Academy (USA)) **R. C. Bond**

Other Owners: Mr C. S. Bond, Mr R. C. Bond, Mr G. Daniels, Mr W. Standeven.

Assistant Trainer: Marie Keegan

---

507 **MR JAMIE OSBORNE, Upper Lambourn**
Postal: **The Old Malthouse**, Upper Lambourn, Hungerford, Berkshire, RG17 8RG
Contacts: **PHONE (01488) 73139 FAX (01488) 73084 MOBILE (07860) 533422**
E-MAIL info@jamieosborne.com WEBSITE www.jamieosborne.com

1 **ALMAIL (USA)**, 6, b g Swain (IRE)—Khassah **A. Taylor**
2 **CLOUDY START**, 6, b g Oasis Dream—Set Fair (USA) **Martin St Quinton & Giles Wilson**
3 **COMMERCIAL (IRE)**, 4, br g Kodiac—Call Collect (USA) **Mrs F. Walwyn**
4 **CORPORAL MADDOX**, 5, b g Royal Applause—Noble View (USA) **Dr Marwan Koukash**
5 **DRAWNFROMTHEPAST (IRE)**, 7, ch g Tagula (IRE)—Ball Cat (FR) **Dr Marwan Koukash**
6 **EASTBURY**, 4, ch gr g Pivotal—Sita (IRE) **Mrs F. Walwyn**
7 **FACE THE PROBLEM (IRE)**, 4, b g Johannesburg (USA)—Foofaraw (USA) **Dr Marwan Koukash**
8 **FIELD OF DREAM**, 5, b g Oasis Dream—Field of Hope (IRE) **Mr K. J. P. Gundlach**
9 **MR DAVID (USA)**, 5, b g Sky Mesa (USA)—Dancewiththebride (USA) **Mr K. J. P. Gundlach**
10 **NEVER CAN TELL (IRE)**, 5, b m Montjeu (IRE)—Shaanara (IRE) **Dr Marwan Koukash**
11 **RAKAAN (IRE)**, 5, ch g Bahamian Bounty—Petite Spectre **Dr Marwan Koukash**
12 **TREADWELL (IRE)**, 5, b h Footstepsinthesand—Lady Wells (IRE) **Mrs F Walwyn & A Taylor**

THREE-YEAR-OLDS

13 **AMADEUS WOLFE TONE (IRE)**, b g Amadeus Wolf—Slieve **Dr Brendan McDonald & Mr John Duddy**
14 **APPLAUDERE**, b f Royal Applause—Let Alone **Mrs S. Griffiths**
15 **BYRON BLUE (IRE)**, br c Dylan Thomas—High Society (IRE) **Mr & Mrs I. H. Bendelow**
16 **CLARKSON (IRE)**, b g Jeremy (USA)—Gold Marie (IRE) **A. Taylor**
17 **CLODHOPPER (IRE)**, gr f Clodovil (IRE)—Clochette (IRE) **A. Taylor**
18 **CUORE (IRE)**, b g Singspiel (IRE)—Miss Trish (IRE) **P. J. D. Pottinger**
19 **FISTFUL OF DOLLARS (IRE)**, b g Holy Roman Emperor (IRE)—
                                      Taking Liberties (IRE) **J. Stunt, D. Dixon, S. Bukhari**
20 **FOUR BETTER**, b f Holy Roman Emperor (IRE)—Moonshadow **C Woollett P Hearn & Mr & Mrs J Wilson**
21 **FOUR RICHER**, b c Ishiguru (USA)—To The Woods (IRE) **Mr & Mrs J Wilson C Woollett & P Hearn**
22 **GREATEST DANCER (IRE)**, b f Iffraaj—Seasonal Style (IRE) **Mr David L. Dixon**
23 **JERICHO (IRE)**, br g Manduro (GER)—Jinsiyah (USA) **Morsethehorse Syndicate**
24 B f Shirocco (GER)—Last Dream (IRE) **Mrs E. White, W. Harris, P. Blows**
25 **NO TIME TO LOSE**, b g Authorized (IRE)—Ballymore Celebre (IRE) **Michael Buckley**
26 **ROEDEAN (IRE)**, b f Oratorio (IRE)—Exotic Mix (FR) **Dr Marwan Koukash**

MR JAMIE OSBORNE—continued

27 **RUSSIAN BULLET**, b g Royal Applause—Gandini **Martyn & Elaine Booth**
28 **SONDEDURO**, br c Manduro (GER)—Madame Cerito (USA) **Lady Blyth**

TWO-YEAR-OLDS

29 B c 18/4 Cape Cross (IRE)—Amarice (Suave Dancer (USA)) **Lady Blyth**
30 Br f 19/4 Byron—Bella Beguine (Komaite (USA)) **Michael Turner**
31 B f 6/5 Footstepsinthesand—Colour And Spice (IRE) (Machiavellian (USA)) (7388) **Simon Christian Racing**
32 Ch c 7/3 Assertive—Dahshah (Mujtahid (USA)) (28571)
33 **DARKEST NIGHT (IRE)**, b c 28/4 Dark Angel (IRE)—
Vadarousse (GER) (Numerous (USA)) (32840) **Miss E. Asprey & Christopher Wright**
34 B f 1/1 Dutch Art—Ellcon (IRE) (Royal Applause) **Michael Turner**
35 B f 9/3 Lucky Story—Ellway Queen (USA) (Bahri (USA)) (9047) **Hearn / Margolis / Pennick**
36 **HARDY BLUE (IRE)**, b f 11/3 Red Clubs (IRE)—
Alexander Wonder (IRE) (Redback) (28735) **Patrick Gage & Tony Taylor**
37 **HARDY RED (IRE)**, b c 5/4 Mujadil (USA)—
Salonga (IRE) (Shinko Forest (IRE)) (27000) **Tony Taylor & Patrick Gage**
38 B c 8/4 Pivotal—Kahina (GER) (Warning) (9851) **Hearn / Margolis / Pennick**
39 B c 11/4 Haafhd—Last Dream (IRE) (Alzao (USA)) **Mrs E. White, W. Harris, P. Blows**
40 Ch c 3/4 Kheleyf (USA)—Leenane (IRE) (Grand Lodge (USA)) (21345)
41 B f 7/3 Bertolini (USA)—Lighted Way (Kris) (8571) **Brightwalton Stud & Partners**
42 **LORAINE**, b f 13/2 Sir Percy—
Emirates First (IRE) (In The Wings) (27000) **Mrs F. Walwyn, Mr & Mrs A. Pakenham, A. Taylor**
43 B c 21/2 Sakhee's Secret—Midnight Sky (Desert Prince (IRE)) (40000) **Mr & Mrs I. H. Bendelow**
44 **POOR DUKE (IRE)**, b c 13/2 Bachelor Duke (USA)—
Graze On Too (IRE) (Rainbow Quest (USA)) (9851) **The Duke's Partnership**
45 B c 21/4 Excellent Art—Puck's Castle (Shirley Heights) (31198) **Mr K. J. P. Gundlach**
46 B f 3/3 Holy Roman Emperor (IRE)—Raphimix (FR) (Linamix (FR)) (11428) **Hearn / Margolis / Pennick**
47 B 21/3 Oratorio (IRE)—Seeking The Fun (Alhaarth (IRE)) (20952) **Mr D. Christian**
48 B f 2/2 Dalakhani (IRE)—Shesasmartlady (IRE) (Dolphin Street (FR)) (75000) **Hearn / Margolis / Pennick**
49 Gr f 26/2 Dark Angel (IRE)—Showmesomething (Mujadil (USA)) (13957) **Simon Christian Partnership**
50 Ch f 4/3 Auction House (USA)—Thicket (Wolfhound (USA)) **Llety Stud**
51 B c 21/4 Amadeus Wolf—Yasmin Satine (IRE) (Key of Luck (USA)) (42000) **Dr B. McDonald**

Other Owners: Lady Aitken, Mr I. H. Bendelow, Mrs P. Bendelow, Mr P. Blows, Mr Martyn Booth, Mrs Elaine Booth, Mr John Duddy, Mr Rob E. L. Frost, Mr W. Harris, Mr P. J. Hearn, Mr Duncan Heath, Mr Les Marshall, Mr A. F. O'Callaghan, Brigadier Andrew Parker Bowles, Mr S. J. Piper, Mr M. G. St Quinton, Mr M. A. Stone, Mr J. R. F. Stunt, Mr A. Taylor, Mrs E. White, Mr Giles Wilson, Mr James Wilson, Mrs Celia Woollett, Mr Christopher Wright.

Apprentice: Caroline Kelly.

---

508 **MR JOHN M. OXX, Kildare**
Postal: **Creeve, Curragbeg, Kildare, Co. Kildare, Ireland**
Contacts: **PHONE (00353) 455 21310 FAX (00353) 455 22236**

1 **ALANZA (IRE)**, 4, ch f Dubai Destination (USA)—Alasha (IRE) **H. H. Aga Khan**
2 **DUBAWI STAR**, 4, b g Dubawi (IRE)—Cloud Hill **Sultan Ali**
3 **KALABAYA (IRE)**, 4, b f Sinndar (IRE)—Kalandara (IRE) **H. H. Aga Khan**
4 **LONG JOURNEY HOME (IRE)**, 4, b c Dansili—Quest For Eternity (IRE) **Mr N. Jones**
5 **MANIEREE (IRE)**, 4, br f Medicean—Sheer Spirit (IRE) **Mr M. Morris**
6 **NATIVE KHAN (FR)**, 4, gr c Azamour (IRE)—Viva Maria (FR) **Mr V. I. Araci**
7 **SADDLER'S ROCK (IRE)**, 4, b c Sadler's Wells (USA)—Grecian Bride (IRE) **Mr M. O'Flynn**
8 **SHARESTAN (IRE)**, 4, b c Shamardal (USA)—Sharesha (IRE) **H. H. Aga Khan**
9 **ZABARAJAD (IRE)**, 4, b g Invincible Spirit (IRE)—Zalaiyma (FR) **H. H. Aga Khan**
10 **ZAFARQAND (IRE)**, 4, gr c Halling (USA)—Zafaraniya (IRE) **H. H. Aga Khan**

THREE-YEAR-OLDS

11 **AKEED MOFEED**, b c Dubawi (IRE)—Wonder Why (GER) **Jaber Abdullah**
12 **AKEED WAFI (IRE)**, b c Street Cry (IRE)—Shy Lady (FR) **Jaber Abdullah**
13 **AKLAN (IRE)**, gr c Dalakhani (IRE)—Akdara (IRE) **H. H. Aga Khan**
14 **ALINDJAR (IRE)**, ch c Nayef (USA)—Alasha (IRE) **H. H. Aga Khan**
15 **ALIZARI (IRE)**, b c Oratorio (IRE)—Alaya (IRE) **H. H. Aga Khan**
16 **ALLOWED**, b c Authorized (IRE)—Japanese Whisper (UAE) **Sheikh Mohammed**
17 **AZANARA (IRE)**, b f Hurricane Run (IRE)—Anaza **Mr M. Taylor**
18 **BADGED**, b g High Chaparral (IRE)—Meshhed **Mr L. J. Williams**
19 **BEHANA (IRE)**, b f Halling (USA)—Behra (IRE) **H. H. Aga Khan**

MR JOHN M. OXX—continued

20 **BORN TO SEA (IRE)**, b c Invincible Spirit (IRE)—Urban Sea (USA) **Mr C. Tsui**
21 **CALL TO BATTLE (IRE)**, b c King's Best (USA)—Dance The Classics (IRE) **Mr N. Jones**
22 **CHOLESKY (IRE)**, b c Galileo (IRE)—Funsie (FR) **Paulyn Ltd**
23 **CLESSIDRA (IRE)**, b f Desert King (IRE)—Caeribland (IRE) **Mr M. Valade**
24 **CROPLEY (IRE)**, gr c Galileo (IRE)—Niyla (IRE) **Mr L. J. Williams**
25 **DARING QUEEN (IRE)**, ch f Refuse To Bend (IRE)—Lorraine's Secret (IRE) **Mrs H. Keaveney**
26 **EBALVIYRA (IRE)**, b f Anabaa (USA)—Ebareva (IRE) **H. H. Aga Khan**
27 **EBAZAN (USA)**, ch c Lemon Drop Kid (USA)—Ebaza (IRE) **H. H. Aga Khan**
28 **ECHOES IN THE WIND (IRE)**, b f Montjeu (IRE)—Preseli (IRE) **Mr N. Jones**
29 **ENGLISH NIGHT (IRE)**, gr c Dalakhani (IRE)—Sassenach (IRE) **Mr C. Tsui**
30 **HANDAZAN (IRE)**, b c Nayef (USA)—Handaza (IRE) **H. H. Aga Khan**
31 **HARTANI (IRE)**, gr c Shirocco (GER)—Harsiya (IRE) **H. H. Aga Khan**
32 **HAY POINT (IRE)**, b f Authorized (IRE)—Genova (IRE) **Sheikh Mohammed**
33 **KALAJAR (USA)**, b c Smart Strike (CAN)—Kaloura (IRE) **H. H. Aga Khan**
34 **KARATASH (IRE)**, ch c Halling (USA)—Karawana (IRE) **H. H. Aga Khan**
35 **KASTOVIA (USA)**, ch f Giant's Causeway (USA)—Kastoria (IRE) **H. H. Aga Khan**
36 **KATIOLA (IRE)**, b f Oratorio (IRE)—Katiykha (IRE) **H. H. Aga Khan**
37 **LA BARACCA (IRE)**, b f Hurricane Run (IRE)—Hoity Toity **Mrs C. McStay**
38 **ROYAL SEA (IRE)**, b g Refuse To Bend (IRE)—Janayen (USA) **Jaber Abdullah**
39 **ROYAL VISIT (IRE)**, b f King's Best (USA)—Catch The Blues (IRE) **Mrs H. Keaveney**
40 **RUBINA (IRE)**, b f Invincible Spirit (IRE)—Riyafa (IRE) **H. H. Aga Khan**
41 **SECRET SEA (IRE)**, b f Galileo (IRE)—Epping **Mr C. Tsui**
42 **SHAIYZAR (IRE)**, b c Azamour (IRE)—Shaiyzima (IRE) **H. H. Aga Khan**
43 **SHALAMAN (IRE)**, b c Oratorio (IRE)—Shalama (IRE) **H. H. Aga Khan**
44 **SHAMOODA (IRE)**, b f Azamour (IRE)—Shemaka (IRE) **H. H. Aga Khan**
45 **SHEBELLA (IRE)**, b f Dubai Destination (USA)—Shibina (IRE) **H. H. Aga Khan**
46 **SHELFORD (IRE)**, b g Galileo (IRE)—Lyrical **Mr L. J. Williams**
47 **SINDJARA (USA)**, br f Include (USA)—Sindirana (IRE) **H. H. Aga Khan**
48 **SOMEWHERE (IRE)**, gr f Dalakhani (IRE)—Quest For Eternity (IRE) **Mr N. Jones**
49 **TAKAR (IRE)**, b c Oratorio (IRE)—Takarouna (USA) **H. H. Aga Khan**
50 **TIMAROUN (USA)**, ch c Giant's Causeway (USA)—Timarwa (IRE) **H. H. Aga Khan**
51 **URBAN BALL (IRE)**, b f Galileo (IRE)—Ball Chairman (USA) **Mr C. Fipke**
52 **VEDANI (IRE)**, b c Dalakhani (IRE)—Velandia (IRE) **H. H. Aga Khan**
53 **WASABI'S HOUSE (IRE)**, br f Dark Angel (IRE)—Pent House (IRE) **Mrs A. O'Neill**
54 **WAVING (IRE)**, b c High Chaparral (IRE)—Pretty Davis (USA) **Mr L. J. Williams**
55 **ZALANTOUN (IRE)**, ch c Dalakhani (IRE)—Zalaiyma (FR) **H. H. Aga Khan**

TWO-YEAR-OLDS

56 **ABU NAYEF (IRE)**, ch c 27/3 Nayef (USA)—Queen's Logic (IRE) (Grand Lodge (USA)) **Jaber Abdullah**
57 **AL HILALY (IRE)**, ch c 2/4 Teofilo (IRE)—In A Silent Way (IRE) (Desert Prince (IRE)) (80000) **Sultan Ali**
58 B f 8/4 Shirocco (GER)—Alasha (IRE) (Barathea (IRE)) **H. H. Aga Khan**
59 B f 18/3 Medaglia d'oro (USA)—Always Awesome (USA) (Awesome Again (CAN)) **Mr C. Fipke**
60 **AZMIYNA (IRE)**, b f 31/1 Galileo (IRE)—Asmara (USA) (Lear Fan (USA)) **H. H. Aga Khan**
61 **BRECCBENNACH**, b c 19/2 Oasis Dream—Next (In The Wings) (190000) **Mr T. Barr**
62 B c 11/3 Bazamour (IRE)—Cadence (Cadeaux Genereux) **CDA Bloodstock**
63 B c 28/4 Singspiel (IRE)—Crystal House (CHI) (Golden Voyager (USA)) **Sheikh Mohammed**
64 **DALUKA (IRE)**, b f 3/4 Dylan Thomas (IRE)—Daliya (IRE) (Giant's Causeway (USA)) **H. H. Aga Khan**
65 B f 24/2 Sinndar (IRE)—Ebadiyla (IRE) (Sadler's Wells (USA)) **H. H. Aga Khan**
66 **EMAZAR (USA)**, b c 22/4 Elusive Quality (USA)—Ebaza (Sinndar (IRE)) **H. H. Aga Khan**
67 B f 16/4 Montjeu (IRE)—Fashion Statement (Rainbow Quest (USA)) (35000) **Mrs C. McStay**
68 **FLASHY APPROACH**, ch c 20/2 New Approach (IRE)—Flashy Wings (Zafonic (USA)) **Jaber Abdullah**
69 **HARASIYA (IRE)**, br f 20/2 Pivotal—Hazariya (IRE) (Xaar) **H. H. Aga Khan**
70 B c 23/2 Giant's Causeway (USA)—Hasanka (IRE) (Kalanisi (IRE)) **H. H. Aga Khan**
71 **HERMIA (IRE)**, b f 17/3 Cape Cross (IRE)—Twinkling (NZ) (Star Way) **Mr J. R. Ancell**
72 B f 18/4 Rock Hard Ten (USA)—High Maintenance (Danehill (USA)) (42735) **Mr P. Garvey**
73 **JUMAIRA TOWER (IRE)**, b c 3/5 Dubawi (IRE)—
    Jumaireyah (Fairy King (USA)) **Sheikh Mohammed Obaid Al Maktoum**
74 B f 6/2 Invincible Spirit (IRE)—Karawana (IRE) (King's Best (USA)) **H. H. Aga Khan**
75 **KARLIDI (USA)**, ch c 18/3 Smart Strike (CAN)—Kastoria (IRE) (Selkirk (USA)) **H. H. Aga Khan**
76 B f 2/3 Azamour (IRE)—Kerania (IRE) (Daylami (USA)) **H. H. Aga Khan**
77 **MAJESTIC JASMINE (IRE)**, ch f 4/3 New Approach (IRE)—Majestic Roi (USA) (Street Cry (IRE)) **Jaber Abdullah**
78 B c 19/2 Dalakhani (IRE)—Mouramara (IRE) (Kahyasi) **H. H. Aga Khan**
79 **NOOR AL WATAN**, b c 8/5 Raven's Pass (USA)—Shy Lady (FR) (Kaldoun (FR)) **Jaber Abdullah**
80 Ch f 5/4 Teofilo (IRE)—Out of Time (IRE) (Anabaa (USA)) (55828) **Mr C. Jones**
81 **PALACE OF WINDS (IRE)**, b f 25/3 Monsun (GER)—Exciting Times (FR) (Jeune Homme (USA)) **Mrs B. Keller**

MR JOHN M. OXX—continued

82 **PAPAYA (IRE)**, ch f 8/4 Teofilo (IRE)—Janaat (Kris) **Sheikh Mohammed**
83 **QEWY (IRE)**, b c 3/3 Street Cry (IRE)—Princess Nada (Barathea (IRE)) **Sheikh Mohammed Obaid Al Maktoum**
84 **RAYOUNABAD (IRE)**, b c 12/2 Nayef (USA)—Raydiya (IRE) (Marju (IRE)) **H. H. Aga Khan**
85 **RAZIA (IRE)**, b f 1/4 Marju (IRE)—Ramzia (IRE) (Soviet Star (USA)) **H. H. Aga Khan**
86 **RIYABA (IRE)**, b f 19/4 Dalakhani (IRE)—Riyafa (IRE) (Kahyasi) **H. H. Aga Khan**
87 B f 25/4 Acclamation—Saik (USA) (Riverman (USA)) (19703) **Mr M. Morris**
88 B c 3/5 Lawman (FR)—Sharesha (IRE) (Ashkalani (IRE)) **H. H. Aga Khan**
89 B f 4/2 Zamindar (USA)—Sharleez (IRE) (Marju (IRE)) **H. H. Aga Khan**
90 B f 17/4 Marju (IRE)—Sheer Bliss (IRE) (Sadler's Wells (USA)) **Mr M. Morris**
91 B f 29/4 Dalakhani (IRE)—Shemaka (IRE) (Nishapour (FR)) **H. H. Aga Khan**
92 B br f 5/5 More Than Ready (USA)—Sindirana (IRE) (Kalanisi (IRE)) **H. H. Aga Khan**
93 B f 29/1 Cape Cross (IRE)—Tarakala (IRE) (Dr Fong (USA)) **H. H. Aga Khan**
94 **TIMIKAR (USA)**, b c 1/5 Dynaformer (USA)—Timarwa (IRE) (Daylami (IRE)) **H. H. Aga Khan**
95 **WAAHY (IRE)**, b c 14/3 Manduro (GER)—Wonder Why (GER) (Tiger Hill (IRE)) **Jaber Abdullah**
96 **WINTER LION (IRE)**, ch c 16/5 Galileo (IRE)—Hill of Snow (Reference Point) **Mr N. Jones**
97 B br c 8/3 Arch (USA)—Xinji (IRE) (Xaar) **Mr F. Fabre**
98 **ZANDIA (IRE)**, b f 2/3 Dr Fong (USA)—Zafayra (IRE) (Nayef (USA)) **H. H. Aga Khan**
99 **ZAND (IRE)**, b c 11/5 Zamindar (USA)—Zanara (IRE) (Kahyasi) **H. H. Aga Khan**

Jockey (flat): J. P. Murtagh, N. G. McCullagh, B. A. Curtis.

---

509   MR BRYN PALLING, Cowbridge
Postal: Ty-Wyth-Newydd, Tredodridge, Cowbridge, South Glamorgan CF71 7UL
Contacts: PHONE (01446) 760122 FAX (01446) 760067 MOBILE (07831) 422492

1 **AARANYOW (IRE)**, 4, ch g Compton Place—Cutpurse Moll **The Bill & Ben Partnership**
2 **BIDABLE**, 8, b m Auction House (USA)—Dubitable **Flying Eight Partnership**
3 **CALLIE'S ANGEL**, 4, b g Piccolo—Oriel Girl **W. Devine**
4 **CHERREGO (USA)**, 4, ch f Borrego (USA)—My Cherie (USA) **Maywood Racing**
5 **CORRIB (IRE)**, 9, b m Lahib (USA)—Montana Miss (IRE) **Bryn Palling**
6 **CWMNI**, 6, b m Auction House (USA)—Sontime **Flying Eight Partnership**
7 **ELLEPHIL (IRE)**, 4, b f Elusive City (USA)—Carna (IRE) **Bryn Palling**
8 **FORWARD FELINE (IRE)**, 6, b m One Cool Cat (USA)—Ymlaen (IRE) **Mr & Mrs D. D. Clee**
9 **IFAN (IRE)**, 4, b g Ivan Denisovich (IRE)—Montana Miss (IRE) **Bryn Palling**
10 **LADY DEANIE (IRE)**, 4, ch f Noverre (USA)—Darling Deanie (IRE) **H. Perkins**
11 **MADAM TESSA (IRE)**, 4, br f Hawk Wing (USA)—Anita's Contessa (IRE) **H. Perkins**
12 **MELROSE GOLD**, 4, br g Goodricke—Deep Sea Pearl **Bryn Palling**
13 **MOSA MINE**, 5, b m Exceed And Excel (AUS)—Baldemosa (FR) **Maywood Racing**
14 **PELHAM CRESCENT (IRE)**, 9, ch g Giant's Causeway (USA)—Sweet Times **W. Devine**
15 **QUADRA HOP (IRE)**, 4, ch g Compton Place—Yding (IRE) **Mr & Mrs D. D. Clee**
16 **SIR BRUNO**, 5, ch g Hernando (FR)—Moon Tree (FR) **H. Perkins**
17 **SPRING SECRET**, 6, b g Reset (AUS)—Miss Brooks **Flying Eight Partnership**

THREE-YEAR-OLDS

18 **CWM CAT**, b g One Cool Cat (USA)—Calonnog (IRE) **Mr & Mrs D. D. Clee**
19 B br f Asian Heights—Dolphin Stamp (IRE) **Bryn Palling**
20 **EWENNY STAR**, b f Indesatchel (IRE)—My Bonus **W. Devine**
21 **GYPSY RIDER**, b g Ishiguru (USA)—Spaniola (IRE) **Bryn Palling**
22 **JANDEE**, br f Needwood Blade—Deep Sea Pearl **Bryn Palling**

TWO-YEAR-OLDS

23 Ch c 1/5 Vita Rosa (JPN)—Calonnog (IRE) (Peintre Celebre (USA)) (8000) **Mr & Mrs D. D. Clee**
24 B f 15/3 Piccolo—Edge of Light (Xaar) **C. J. Mason**
25 B f 24/2 Byron—Sofia Royale (Royal Applause) **Unregistered Partnership**

Other Owners: Mr P.G. Amos, D. D. Clee, Mrs J. P. Clee, Mr A. D. Matthews, Mr P. Ragan, B. Reynolds, S. Salimeni, Mrs B. E. Strong, Mrs K. Thomas.

Assistant Trainer: Miss Jennifer Thomas

510 MR HUGO PALMER, Newmarket
Postal: **Kremlin Cottage Stables, Snailwell Road, Newmarket, Suffolk, CB8 7DP**
Contacts: **PHONE (01638) 669880 FAX (01638) 666383 MOBILE (07824) 887886**
E-MAIL info@hugopalmer.com WEBSITE www.hugopalmer.com

1 **FREMONT (IRE)**, 5, b g Marju (IRE)—Snow Peak **Orr-Ewing, Malins & Barby**
2 **MAKING EYES (IRE)**, 4, b f Dansili—Lady's View **Starter For Ten Partnership**
3 **MAROON MACHINE (IRE)**, 5, ch g Muhtathir—Mediaeval (FR) **Mr H. Palmer**
4 **SOAP WARS**, 7, b g Acclamation—Gooseberry Pie **Orr-Ewing, Malins & Barby**

THREE-YEAR-OLDS

5 **AUNT GER (IRE)**, gr f Bertolini (USA)—Nuit Chaud (USA) **Max Morris**
6 **GAME ALL (IRE)**, b f Acclamation—Love Thirty **Astor,Brudenell,Deal,Fellowes,Palmer&2JC**
7 **INCENDIARY (IRE)**, b c Excellent Art—Clytha **D. G. Iceton**
8 **MALINGERING**, ch c Bahamian Bounty—Orange Lily **Jo Malins & Roger Barby**
9 **NOTHING'S SIMPLE**, ch g Avonbridge—Suzie Fong **Mr H. Palmer**
10 **PRINCESS PALMER**, b f Iceman—Tapas En Bal (FR) **Rothmere Racing Ltd**
11 **QUICK BITE (IRE)**, b f Redback—Park Haven (IRE) **Chisholm, Vestey, Warrender, Kerr-Dineen**
12 **TALK OF THE NORTH**, b f Haafhd—Ammo (IRE) **Northern Folly**

TWO-YEAR-OLDS

13 **B BARDOT (IRE)**, b f 17/4 Sixties Icon—Indiannie Moon (Fraam) (26666) **Coriolan Links Partnership III**
14 **BORN TO RUN**, b f 28/3 Ishiguru (USA)—Maid For Running (Namaqualand (USA)) (19047) **Born To Run Racing**
15 B f 18/3 High Chaparral (IRE)—Dane Thyme (IRE) (Danetime (IRE)) (9030) **Mrs Tom Magnier**
16 B f 18/3 Excellent Art—Desert Classic (Green Desert (USA)) **Mr N E Sangster**
17 **EARLY ONE MORNING**, b f 24/2 Medicean—Still Small Voice (Polish Precedent (USA)) (28000) **Mrs M. Bryce**
18 B f 3/3 Strategic Prince—Ellanova (Kyllachy) (22987) **Chisholm, Vestey, Kerr-Dineen & Gibbs**
19 B f 2/3 Black Sam Bellamy (IRE)—Exexel (Dansili) (5000)
20 **RED RED WINE**, b c 14/3 Dutch Art—Atnab (Riverman (USA)) (62000) **Mr K. J. P. Gundlach**
21 B f 2/4 Medicean—Sleave Silk (IRE) (Unfuwain (USA)) (1000)
22 B f 29/1 Tagula (IRE)—Sonic Night (IRE) (Night Shift (USA)) (13809) **Mr H. Palmer**
23 **TIPPING OVER (IRE)**, b f 27/2 Aussie Rules (USA)—
Precipice (Observatory (USA)) (6978) **Anglia Bloodstock Syndicate**
24 **TWO IN THE PINK (IRE)**, b f 21/4 Clodovil (IRE)—Secret Circle (Magic Ring (IRE)) (30476) **Mr K. J. P. Gundlach**

Other Owners: Lyn Alexander, Emma Anderson, Jake Astor, Roger Barby, Sue Bates, Nicky Bell, Clare Blewitt, Charlotte Bowmont, Amanda Brudenell, Thomas Brudenell, Melba Bryce, John Carson, Iona Carsons, Edwina Charlton, Colin Chisholm, Caroline Church, Peter Darlington, Peter Deal, Nik Elmer, Alexander Fellowes, Henry St George, James St George, Philip Gibbs, Anthea Gibson Fleming, Richard Griffiths, Kate Grimwade, Mr & Mrs Grimwade, Kenneth G P Gundlach, Derek Iceton, Angus Keate, Michael Kerr-Dinneen, Angus Maclay, Sophie Magnier, Jo Malins, Derrick McIntyre, Paul Mcbride, Jill Notley, John Oakes, Colin Orr-Ewing, Laura Palmer, Lady Cornelia Palmer, Lady Charlotte Peel, Angela Perkins, General Ramsay, Julie Sampson, Sam Sangster, Ned Sangster, Pete Shemilt, Lady Henrietta Spencer Churchill, Becky Steel, Kevin & Katie Still, Calie Stone, Julie Stone, Colin Strang Steel, Sal Strang Steel, Michael Strang Steel, Lady Tidbury, Mrs Tweedie, Mr D K Tweedie, Arthur Vestey, Lord Vestey, Keith Walpole, Anthony Warrender.

511 MR H. A. PANTALL, Beaupreau
Postal: **Le Bois du Coin, Beaupreau 49600, France**
Contacts: **PHONE (0033) 241 636715 FAX (0033) 241 636503 MOBILE (0033) 607 450647**
E-MAIL hapantall@wanadoo.fr

1 **ARDHA (USA)**, 5, b m Elusive Quality (USA)—Dance Trick (USA)
2 **BASSEL (FR)**, 7, b br h Daliapour (IRE)—Bint El Hawa (FR)
3 **CALIPATRIA**, 5, ch m Shamardal (USA)—Golden Silca
4 **CHARMSTONE (USA)**, 4, b f Dynaformer (USA)—Pure Charm (USA)
5 **DISMAY**, 4, ch f Dubawi (IRE)—Desired
6 **DOUCEUR NOCTURNE (FR)**, 7, b m Zieten (USA)—Dentelle (FR)
7 **EMBOSS (IRE)**, 4, b f Cape Cross (IRE)—Eilean Ban (USA)
8 **FEMME FATALE (SWI)**, 4, b f Feliciano (SWI)—Formida (FR)
9 **GAMMARTH (FR)**, 4, ch c Layman (USA)—Emouna Queen (IRE)
10 **GIULIO CESARE (IRE)**, 4, b g Montjeu (IRE)—Gone To The Moon (USA)
11 **HAPPY WEDDING (IRE)**, 6, b m Green Tune (USA)—Diamond White
12 **HIGH SPEED (SWI)**, 4, b c Blue Canari (FR)—High Mare (FR)
13 **JACK MALONE (FR)**, 4, b g Sagacity (FR)—Saryshnikova (FR)
14 **JAG WAR (FR)**, 4, b c Meshaheer (USA)—Just Fizzy
15 **KARLINHA (IRE)**, 4, gr f Desert Style (IRE)—Karlinaxa

MR H. A. PANTALL—continued

16 **KEPRESH (FR)**, 5, b h Bahhare (USA)—Miss Balines (FR)
17 **LA PELEGRINA (USA)**, 4, b f Redoute's Choice (AUS)—Forest Pearl (USA)
18 **LAW BLADE (FR)**, 7, b g Dashing Blade—Lonia (GER)
19 **LIBRE TEMPS (FR)**, 4, b c Cadeaux Genereux—Nellie Gwyn
20 **MEZZOTINTO (FR)**, 5, gr g Fairly Ransom (USA)—Montgarri (FR)
21 **MI AMOR (SWI)**, 4, b g Feliciano (SWI)—Mescalina (IRE)
22 **MISS CATSY (IRE)**, 4, b br f Hurricane Cat (USA)—Miss Sissy (FR)
23 **NICOLE (FR)**, 4, ch f Dashing Blade—Nicol's Girl
24 **NIGHT SERENADE (IRE)**, 5, b m Golan (IRE)—Night Teeny
25 **NUIT D'ETE (FR)**, 5, b m Dashing Blade—Nachtigall (GER)
26 **PAGERA (FR)**, 4, ch f Gentlewave (IRE)—Panthesilea (FR)
27 **PIANO SHOW (USA)**, 4, ch f Kingmambo (USA)—Mannington (AUS)
28 **PLUTARQUE (FR)**, 5, ch g Sinndar (IRE)—Peony Girl (FR)
29 **POINCON DE FRANCE (IRE)**, 8, b g Peintre Celebre (USA)—Poughkeepsie (IRE)
30 **POLARIX**, 6, gr ro h Linamix (FR)—Freezing (USA)
31 **PRIVATE JET (FR)**, 4, gr c Aussie Rules (USA)—Norwegian Princess (IRE)
32 **RIWAN (FR)**, 4, ch g Numerous (USA)—Belle Suisse (FR)
33 **SABRATAH**, 4, b f Oasis Dream—Marika
34 **SERENITY STAR**, 4, b f Monsun (GER)—Nalani (IRE)
35 **SINGAPORE JOY (FR)**, 4, b f Sagacity (FR)—Doliouchka
36 **SNAPE MALTINGS (IRE)**, 5, b h Sadler's Wells (USA)—Hanami
37 **TIDESPRING (IRE)**, 4, b f Monsun (GER)—Sweet Stream (ITY)
38 **VALIDOR (FR)**, 6, ch h American Post—Panthesilea (FR)
39 **VIOLANTE (USA)**, 4, b f Kingmambo (USA)—Allez Les Trois (USA)
40 **WAITRESS (USA)**, 4, b f Kingmambo (USA)—Do The Honours (IRE)
41 **YORKSHIRE LASS (IRE)**, 4, b br f Pivotal—White Rose (GER)

THREE-YEAR-OLDS

42 **AFFECTIONATE**, b f Distorted Humor (USA)—Loving Kindness (USA)
43 **ANA NOVA (FR)**, b f Anabaa (USA)—Tambura (FR)
44 **AUSONE (FR)**, b c Muhtathir—Scalotta (GER)
45 **BALLROOM BELLE (IRE)**, ch f Choisir (AUS)—Beriosova (FR)
46 **BIG DUFFY (FR)**, b f Black Sam Bellamy (IRE)—Big Bunny (GER)
47 **BOULBA D'ALBEN (FR)**, b f Dark Angel (IRE)—Wixon (FR)
48 **BRICTESSE (FR)**, b f Desert Prince (IRE)—Brictop (USA)
49 **BYRON SON (IRE)**, ch g Byron—Carinamix (FR)
50 **CHACHA HEELS (FR)**, b f Meshaheer (USA)—Just Fizzy
51 **CIGALON (FR)**, b f Verglas (IRE)—Paintbox
52 **DANSKER (FR)**, ch c Way of Light (USA)—Individual (USA)
53 **DYCTYNNA (FR)**, b f Stormy River (FR)—Dentelle (FR)
54 **EXCELLENTE ARTISTE (IRE)**, ch f Excellent Art—Glenarff (USA)
55 **FRENCH RULES (FR)**, gr c Aussie Rules (USA)—Ouarzazate (IRE)
56 **GLASSIK (FR)**, ch f Gold Away (IRE)—Hersana (FR)
57 **HEAVEN GREY (USA)**, gr ro f Eddington (USA)—Pahlmuhree (USA)
58 **HOLLY POLLY (GER)**, b f Dylan Thomas (IRE)—Hanami
59 **IRISH TIGER (FR)**, b c Speedmaster (GER)—Intention (GER)
60 **J'N KA AVENUE (FR)**, b f Hurricane Cat (USA)—Glinka Des Aigles (FR)
61 **KING OF SONG (FR)**, b c Sinndar (IRE)—Karsawina (GER)
62 **LA ULTIMA COPA (FR)**, b f Early March—Dalmara (FR)
63 **LAGUNA SUN (FR)**, b f Speedmaster (GER)—Loving Away (FR)
64 **LIVING WELL**, b f Zamindar (USA)—Tobermory (IRE)
65 **LONELY TIGER (IRE)**, ch c Layman (USA)—La Victoria (IRE)
66 **LUISA MILLER (GER)**, b f High Chaparral (USA)—Lycette
67 **MAND CHICK**, b f Manduro (GER)—Rock Chick
68 **MISS BESTSY (IRE)**, b f King's Best (USA)—Miss Sissy (FR)
69 **MISTER RYAN (FR)**, b c Acclamation—Irish Flower (IRE)
70 **MONDAY NIGHT (SWI)**, b f Feliciano (SWI)—Mescalina (IRE)
71 **NAXXOS (FR)**, b c Generous (IRE)—Nijenrode (GER)
72 **NIGHT WAVE (FR)**, b c Rock of Gibraltar (IRE)—Aldeburgh Music (IRE)
73 **NINNARELLA (FR)**, b f Vespone (IRE)—Narcose (FR)
74 **NORWEGIAN LADY (FR)**, ch f Hold That Tiger (USA)—Norwegian Princess (IRE)
75 **NOTTINGHAM ROAD (FR)**, b f American Post—Galgarina (FR)
76 **OMANA (FR)**, b f Speedmaster (GER)—Orion Girl (GER)
77 **ORION MOON (FR)**, ch f Manduro (GER)—Okocha (GER)
78 **PANTHEDOR (FR)**, b c Gentlewave (IRE)—Panthesilea (FR)

MR H. A. PANTALL—continued

79 **PASSARINHO (IRE)**, ch c Ad Valorem (USA)—Semiramide (IRE)
80 **PASSIOR (FR)**, b c Vatori (FR)—Abedissa (FR)
81 **PRAIRIE BELLA (FR)**, b f Konigstiger (GER)—Prairie Scilla (GER)
82 **PRINCE OF SOFIA (FR)**, b c Rock of Gibraltar (IRE)—Princess Sofia (UAE)
83 **READ OVER (FR)**, ch c Osorio (GER)—Reading Habit (USA)
84 **SANSIWA (IRE)**, b f Dansili—Sanwa (GER)
85 **SCHNAPS (FR)**, ch c Shirocco (GER)—Serandine (IRE)
86 **SECRET MARKS (FR)**, b f Echo of Light—Secret Music (USA)
87 **SOHO ROSE (IRE)**, b f Hernando (FR)—Russian Rose (IRE)
88 **SPECIAL FAVOUR**, b f Royal Applause—Nellie Gwyn
89 **SPEEDY MARTIN (FR)**, b c Rail Link—Speed Lass (FR)
90 **SPIRO**, ch c Avonbridge—Singing Lark (FR)
91 **TANGATCHEK (IRE)**, ch c Mr Greeley (USA)—Tivadare (FR)
92 **TETH**, br f Dansili—Beta
93 **TIFONGO (FR)**, b c Dr Fong (USA)—Tishkara (FR)
94 **TOUJOURS (GER)**, b br f Bertolini (USA)—Tonight (GER)
95 **TRES DANCE (FR)**, b f Sinndar (IRE)—Tres Ravi (GER)
96 **VALSE BLEUE**, ch f Barathea (IRE)—Valse Mystique (IRE)
97 **VILLERAMBERT (FR)**, b c Meshaheer (USA)—Round Sister (FR)
98 **VOLVORETAS CAPE**, b f Cape Cross (IRE)—Volvoreta

TWO-YEAR-OLDS

99 **BEATRICE**, b f 23/2 Dr Fong (USA)—Brangane (IRE) (Anita's Prince) (11494)
100 **BONTO (FR)**, b f 16/3 Tiger Hill (IRE)—Bedara (Barathea (IRE)) (8210)
101 **BONTONI (FR)**, ro c 10/2 Silvano (GER)—Brictop (USA) (Mizzen Mast (USA)) (30377)
102 B f 8/4 Hurricane Run (IRE)—Cloudy Bay (GER) (Zilzal (USA)) (9852)
103 **ENCYIA (FR)**, b f 1/1 Gold Away (FR)—Eloisa (GER) (Black Sam Bellamy (IRE))
104 **GOLDY MOON (FR)**, gr f 1/1 Smaldoun—Goldy Honor
105 B f 1/1 Monsun (GER)—Hanami (Hernando (FR))
106 **KARADARGENT (FR)**, b c 1/1 Kendargent—Tishkara
107 **LAGUNA QUEEN (GER)**, b f 1/1 Speedmaster—Loving Away
108 **LIBR'ARTTIST (FR)**, b c 1/1 Librettist—Tejaara
109 B f 22/2 Anabaa Blue—Lily Bolero (King's Best (USA))
110 **LOCAL LOVER (FR)**, ch c 1/1 Choisir—La Victoria
111 **MAY DANCE (FR)**, b c 24/4 Early March—Dalmara (FR) (Halling (USA)) (5747)
112 B f 13/4 Anabaa (USA)—Miss Emma May (IRE) (Hawk Wing (USA))
113 **MISTER BAWI (FR)**, ch c 1/1 Dubawi (IRE)—Miss Sissy (FR) (Sicyos (USA))
114 Ch f 1/1 Motivator—Nanty
115 B f 26/4 Bahamian Bounty—Nellie Gwyn (King's Best (USA))
116 B c 1/1 Royal Applause—Nice Matin (USA) (Tiznow (USA))
117 B f 16/2 Desert Style (IRE)—Nightdance Sun (GER) (Monsun (GER)) (49261)
118 B f 16/2 Medicean—Nolas Lolly (IRE) (Lomitas) (37766)
119 B f 19/3 Kentucky Dynamite (USA)—Noor Forever (FR) (Highest Honor (FR)) (2463)
120 **ORION LOVE**, ch f 10/3 Zamindar (USA)—Okocha (GER) (Platini (GER)) (32840)
121 **PASSAGE DU CAIRE (FR)**, b f 28/5 Linngari (IRE)—Festive Style (SAF) (Fort Wood (USA)) (7389)
122 B f 19/5 Linngari (IRE)—Peaceful Love (GER) (Dashing Blade) (14778)
123 **PRAIRIE SUNSET (FR)**, b f 1/1 Silvano—Prairie Scilla
124 Ch c 11/3 Pivotal—Precocious Star (FR) (Bold Fact (USA))
125 **RED SHOT (FR)**, b f 22/1 Gentlewave (IRE)—Red Kiss (IRE) (Fasliyev (USA)) (9031)
126 **ROCCARINA (FR)**, gr f 1/1 Shirocco (GER)—Carinamix (FR) (Linamix (FR))
127 Ch c 1/2 Osorio (GER)—Serpina (IRE) (Grand Lodge (USA))
128 **SINGAPORE ZEN (FR)**, ch f 15/4 Sandwaki (USA)—Castlevania (USA) (Slew City Slew (USA)) (4926)
129 **SORRY WOMAN (FR)**, b f 29/3 Ivan Denisovich (IRE)—Oppamattox (FR) (Munir) (5747)
130 **SPEED OF ANABAA (IRE)**, b f 4/3 Anabaa (USA)—Speedgirl (FR) (Monsun (GER))
131 B c 19/2 Meshaheer (USA)—Starks (FR) (Daylami (IRE)) (4926)
132 B c 5/3 Zamindar (USA)—Tobermory (IRE) (Green Desert (USA))
133 B c 1/1 One Cool Cat (USA)—Top Sauce (Hector Protector (USA)) (6568)
134 **TREASURE ROCK (FR)**, b f 1/1 Rock of Gibraltar (IRE)—Tiara (Risk Me (FR))
135 **TRES BLUE (IRE)**, b c 3/5 Anabaa Blue—Tres Ravi (GER) (Monsun (GER))
136 **TURFBLUTE (GER)**, b f 1/2 Big Shuffle—Turfblume (GER) (Lando (GER)) (15599)
137 **VARING (FR)**, b c 1/1 Vadasin—Noverings

Assistant Trainer: Ludovic Gadbin (0033) 685 070620

Jockey (flat): M. Guyon, F. Veron.

512 MR JOHN PANVERT, Tiverton
Postal: **Steart Farm Racing Stables, Stoodleigh, Tiverton, Devon, EX16 9QA**
Contacts: **MOBILE (07590) 120314/(07732) 273837**
E-MAIL **jpanvert@btinternet.com**

1 SOVEREIGNS LEGACY, 5, b g Helissio (FR)—Sovereign **J. F. Panvert**
2 TITCH STRIDER (IRE), 7, b m Milan—Just Little **J. F. Panvert**

Assistant Trainer: Miss J Clark

513 MR ANDREW PARKER, Lockerbie
Postal: **The Orchard, Ecclefechan, Lockerbie, Dumfriesshire, DG11 3JH**
Contacts: **PHONE (01576) 300238 FAX (01576) 300238 MOBILE (07968) 325650**
E-MAIL **ap.parkerracing@btinternet.com**

1 ARC WARRIOR (FR), 8, b g Even Top (IRE)—What The Hell (IRE) **J. J. Paterson**
2 BIGGAR (IRE), 4, b g Court Cave (IRE)—Native Success (IRE) **Mr A. McAllister**
3 CAPTAIN WOODHOUSE, 5, b g Tamayaz (CAN)—Woodhouse Bay (IRE) **Mr A. W. Miller**
4 CORKY DANCER, 7, b g Groom Dancer (USA)—Cita Verda (FR) **Mr & Mrs Raymond Anderson Green**
5 GALWAY GEM (IRE), 4, b f Golan (IRE)—Hasty Native (IRE) **Mr M. & Mrs D. E. Andrews**
6 HEART O ANNANDALE (IRE), 5, b g Winged Love (IRE)—She's All Heart **K. Milligan Partnership**
7 MERIGO (FR), 11, ch g Pistolet Bleu (IRE)—Muleta (FR) **Mr & Mrs Raymond Anderson Green**
8 RUDEMEISTER (IRE), 6, b g Rudimentary (USA)—Boardroom Belle (IRE) **Mr A. McAllister**
9 SETTLEDOUTOFCOURT (IRE), 6, b g Court Cave (IRE)—Ardagh Princess **Mr A. McAllister**
10 SHOOTING TIMES, 7, b g Commanche Run—Rainbow Times (IRE) **Mrs J. M. R. Lancaster**
11 SUPER ALLY (IRE), 7, b g Flemensfirth (USA)—Strong Tide **Mr & Mrs Raymond Anderson Green**

Other Owners: Mr Raymond Anderson Green, Mrs Anita Green, Mr T. D. Griffiths, Mr Kenneth J. Milligan, Mr Andrew Parker.

514 MR JAMES PAYNE, Dulverton
Postal: **Lower Holworthy Farm, Brompton Regis, Dulverton, Somerset, TA22 9NY**
Contacts: **HOME/FAX (01398) 371244**
E-MAIL **holworthyfarm@aol.co.uk** WEBSITE **www.holworthyfarm.com**

1 DOWN THE STRETCH, 12, b g Rakaposhi King—Si-Gaoith **J. R. Payne**
2 KNAPP BRIDGE BOY, 12, b g Wimbleball—Toll Bridge **R. J. Payne**

515 MR RAY PEACOCK, Tenbury Wells
Postal: **Elliott House Farm, Vine Lane, Kyre, Tenbury Wells, Worcestershire, WR15 8RL**
Contacts: **PHONE (01885) 410772 MOBILE (07748) 565574/ 07881440135**

1 GIFTED HEIR (IRE), 8, b g Princely Heir (IRE)—Inzar Lady (IRE) **R. E. Peacock**
2 INTERCHOICE STAR, 7, b g Josr Algarhoud (IRE)—Blakeshall Girl **Mr J. P. Evitt**
3 KOMREYEV STAR, 10, b g Komaite (USA)—L'ancressaan **Mr G. Whittaker**
4 PORTRUSH STORM, 7, ch m Observatory (USA)—Overcast (IRE) **Mr J. P. Evitt**
5 RICH HARVEST (USA), 7, b br g High Yield (USA)—Mangano (USA) **R. E. Peacock**
6 SWORDS, 10, b g Vettori (IRE)—Pomorie (IRE) **R. E. Peacock**

Assistant Trainer: Mrs C Peacock

Jockey (flat): C. Catlin, T. Eaves. **Jockey (NH):** Christian Williams. **Amateur:** Miss S. Peacock.

516 MRS LYDIA PEARCE, Newmarket
Postal: **Wroughton House, 37 Old Station Road, Newmarket, Suffolk, CB8 8DT**
Contacts: **PHONE (01638) 664669 (01638) 669891 FAX (01638) 669891 MOBILE (07787) 517864**
E-MAIL **lsp_8@live.com**

1 AGILETE, 10, b g Piccolo—Ingerence (FR) **S & M Supplies (Aylsham) Ltd**
2 BEGINNINGS (USA), 4, b f Aptitude (USA)—Birthplace (USA) **Lady Green**
3 BLACK ICEMAN, 4, bl gr g Iceman—Slite **Mr P. J. Stephenson**

MRS LYDIA PEARCE—continued

4 **COUNT CEPRANO (IRE)**, 8, b g Desert Prince (IRE)—Camerlata **Mrs L. J. Marsh**
5 **DR FINLEY (IRE)**, 5, ch g Dr Fong (USA)—Farrfesheena (USA) **Killarney Glen**
6 **GHUFA (IRE)**, 8, b g Sakhee (USA)—Hawriyah (USA) **S & M Supplies (Aylsham) Ltd**
7 **HATTA STREAM (IRE)**, 6, b g Oasis Dream—Rubies From Burma (USA) **Macniler Racing Partnership**
8 **HITS ONLY CASH**, 10, b g Inchinor—Persian Blue **Oceana Racing**
9 **LAND HAWK (IRE)**, 6, br g Trans Island—Heike **S & M Supplies (Aylsham) Ltd**
10 **MATAALEB**, 5, b h Dalakhani (IRE)—Elfaslah (IRE) **Killarney Glen**
11 **MOTIRANI**, 5, br g Motivator—Maharani (USA) **Mr R. C. Ames**
12 **OLIMAMU (IRE)**, 5, b m Barathea (IRE)—La Galeisa (IRE) **Mrs L. S. Pearce**

THREE-YEAR-OLDS

13 B c Byron—Molly Pitcher (IRE) **A Partnership**
14 **NEWINGTON**, b f Iceman—Almunia (IRE) **Mr Arthur Old**
15 **NOBODY LOVES ME**, b f Piccolo—Samadilla (IRE) **Orlagh Doyle**
16 **PULL THE PIN (IRE)**, b c Kheleyf (USA)—Inscribed (IRE) **Mr C. J. Harding**
17 **THERESNONEEDFORDAT (IRE)**, b c Holy Roman Emperor (IRE)—Manuscript **R. Morris**

TWO-YEAR-OLDS

18 B f 7/4 Tobougg (IRE)—Bowled Out (GER) (Dansili) (800) **A Partnership**
19 B f 13/3 Oratorio (IRE)—Quiet Counsel (IRE) (Law Society (USA)) (800) **A Partnership**
20 B c 27/1 Shamardal (USA)—Steam Cuisine (Mark of Esteem (IRE)) (70000) **Killarney Glen Partnership**
21 B c 26/1 Oratorio (IRE)—Sweet Namibia (IRE) (Namid) (18000) **Killarney Glen Partnership**

Other Owners: Mr Jeff Jewitt, Mr Eric Jones, Mr Nigel Hanger, Mr Stuart Andrews, Mr Dick Devereux, Mr John Harrison, Mr Keith F. J. Loads, Mrs Jennifer Marsh, Mr & Mrs K. Mullins, Mrs Pam O'Shea, Mr Puddick, Mr T. H. Rossiter, Mr R. G. Thurston.

Assistant Trainer: Gavin Cosgrave

Apprentice: Simon Pearce.

---

517 **MR OLLIE PEARS, Malton**
Postal: **The Old Farmhouse, Beverley Road, Norton, Malton, North Yorkshire, YO17 9PJ**
Contacts: **PHONE (01653) 690746 MOBILE (07760) 197103**
E-MAIL info@olliepearsracing.co.uk WEBSITE www.olliepearsracing.co.uk

1 **BOY THE BELL**, 5, b g Choisir (AUS)—Bella Beguine **K. C. West**
2 **LAST SOVEREIGN**, 8, b g Pivotal—Zayala **R. Walker**
3 **MYKIA**, 4, b c Iktibas—My Desire **Mr J. D. Spensley & Mrs M. A. Spensley**
4 **OUR MATE JOE (IRE)**, 4, b g Ivan Denisovich (IRE)—Westwood (FR) **An Englishman, Irishman & Scotsman**
5 **PASS MUSTER**, 5, b g Theatrical—Morning Pride (IRE) **An Englishman, Irishman & Scotsman**
6 **PETSAS PLEASURE**, 6, b g Observatory (USA)—Swynford Pleasure **Mr P. Bottomley**
7 **ROWAN LODGE (IRE)**, 10, ch g Indian Lodge (IRE)—Tirol Hope (IRE) **O. J. Pears**
8 **SIR GEORGE (IRE)**, 7, b g Mujadil (USA)—Torrmana (IRE) **Venture Racing & Partners**
9 **SOUND AMIGO (IRE)**, 4, b g Iceman—Holly Hayes (IRE) **Mr T. J. McManus**
10 **TOMBI (USA)**, 8, b g Johannesburg (USA)—Tune in to the Cat (USA) **An Englishman, Irishman & Scotsman**
11 **WHAT'S THE POINT**, 4, ch g Bertolini (USA)—Point of Balance (IRE) **J. J. Maguire**

THREE-YEAR-OLDS

12 **PARDOVEN (IRE)**, b f Clodovil (IRE)—Dancing Prize (IRE) **J. Harrison**

Other Owners: Mr A. R. Findlay, Mr J. D. Hawley, Mrs H. E. Hawley, Mrs P. M. Lowndes, Mr A. J. Macari, K. Meynell, Mrs M. A. Spensley, Mr J. D. Spensley.

Assistant Trainer: Vicky Pears

Jockey (NH): Brian Hughes.

518 MR DAVID PEARSON, High Peak
Postal: **Lower Fold Farm, Rowarth, High Peak, Derbyshire, SK22 1ED**
Contacts: **PHONE (01663) 741471 MOBILE (07775) 842009**

1 BALLYCRACKEN (IRE), 8, b g Flemensfirth (USA)—Cons Dual Sale (IRE) **D. Pearson**
2 HEVER ROAD (IRE), 13, ch g Anshan—The Little Bag **D. Pearson**

Assistant Trainer: Eileen Pearson

519 MISS LINDA PERRATT, East Kilbride
Postal: **North Allerton Farm, East Kilbride, Glasgow, Lanarkshire, G75 8RR**
Contacts: **PHONE (01355) 303425 MOBILE (07931) 306147**
E-MAIL linda.perratt@btinternet.com

1 ABERNETHY (IRE), 4, b g Hernando (FR)—Marsh Harrier (USA) **J. K. McGarrity**
2 ANITOPIA, 7, gr g Alflora (IRE)—The Whirlie Weevil **Mrs A. Hay**
3 ARRIVA LA DIVA, 6, ch m Needwood Blade—Hillside Girl (IRE) **J. K. McGarrity**
4 BERBICE (IRE), 7, gr g Acclamation—Pearl Bright (FR) **J. K. McGarrity**
5 CAYMAN FOX, 7, ch m Cayman Kai (IRE)—Kalarram **Mr R. R. Whitton**
6 DISTANT SUN, 8, b g Distant View (USA)—The Great Flora (USA) **Jackton Racing Club**
7 HIGH RESOLUTION, 5, ch g Haafhd—Individual Talents (USA) **Mrs H. F. Perratt**
8 JINKY, 4, b g Noverre (USA)—Aries (GER) **Mr J. Murphy**
9 MAID OF MEFT, 5, b m Auction House (USA)—Lady Margaret **Lease Terminated**
10 RETREAT CONTENT (IRE), 4, b g Dubai Destination (USA)—Sharp Point (IRE) **Jackton Racing Club**
11 ROYAL STRAIGHT, 7, ch g Halling (USA)—High Straits **J. K. McGarrity**
12 SABRATHA (IRE), 4, b f Hawk Wing (USA)—Aitch (IRE) **Shatin Racing Group**
13 SANTIAGO BOY, 6, b g Silver Patriarch (IRE)—Gunner Marc **Mrs H. F. Perratt**
14 SAXONETTE, 4, b f Piccolo—Solmorin **Mr J. Murphy**
15 SHUNKAWAKHAN (IRE), 9, b g Indian Danehill (IRE)—Special Park (USA) **Mrs H. F. Perratt**
16 SILVER RIME (FR), 7, gr g Verglas (IRE)—Severina **J. K. McGarrity**
17 TABIET, 5, ch m Danroad (AUS)—Frabrofen **Mr R. R. Whitton**
18 TADALAVIL, 7, gr g Clodovil (IRE)—Blandish **Ayrshire Racing**

THREE-YEAR-OLDS

19 CAFE EXPRESS (IRE), ch f Bertolini (USA)—Cafe Creme (IRE) **Mrs S. Burns**
20 LOLLYPOP LADY, b f Misu Bond (IRE)—Frabrofen **Mr R. R. Whitton**
21 ROCK CANYON (IRE), b g Rock of Gibraltar (IRE)—Tuesday Morning **Mr Brendan Kerr, Mrs B B Mills**
22 SCHMOOZE (IRE), b f One Cool Cat (USA)—If Dubai (USA) **Jackton Racing Club**

TWO-YEAR-OLDS

23 B c 31/1 Red Clubs (IRE)—Baltic Belle (IRE) (Redback) (26000) **Mr Stewart Anderson**
24 B c 28/2 Notnowcato—Mystical Ayr (IRE) (Namid) (19047)
25 B f 14/4 Kodiac—Silk Point (IRE) (BaratIrea (IRE)) (9440)

Other Owners: I. Burns, Mr B. Kerr, Mr D. W. McIntyre, Mrs B. B. Mills, Miss L. A. Perratt, P. Tsim.

Jockey (flat): Tony Hamilton, Tom Eaves, Phillip Makin, Paul Hanagan. **Jockey (NH):** Graham Lee, Campbell Gillies, Brian Hughes, Wilson Renwick. **Conditional:** Callum Whillans. **Apprentice:** Ross Smith. **Amateur:** Mr Stephen Feeney.

520 MRS AMANDA PERRETT, Pulborough
Postal: **Coombelands Racing Stables, Pulborough, West Sussex, RH20 1BP**
Contacts: **OFFICE (01798) 873011 HOME (01798) 874894 FAX (01798) 875163**
MOBILE (07803) 088713
E-MAIL aperrett@coombelands-stables.com WEBSITE www.amandaperrett.com

1 BRAMSHAW (USA), 5, gr ro g Langfuhr (CAN)—Milagra (USA) **Paul & Clare Cuttill, Brenda Karn-Smith**
2 CLASSIC VINTAGE (USA), 6, b g El Prado (IRE)—
                                      Cellars Shiraz (USA) **R & P Scott A & J Powell Gallagher Stud**
3 CURACAO, 6, br g Sakhee (USA)—Bourbonella **Mrs S Conway, Coombelands Racing Stables**
4 FOUR NATIONS (USA), 4, ch g Langfuhr (CAN)—Kiswahili **G. D. P. Materna**
5 HEAD OF STEAM (USA), 5, ch g Mizzen Mast (USA)—Summer Mist (USA) **G. D. P. Materna**
6 HUFF AND PUFF, 5, b g Azamour (IRE)—Coyote **A. D. Spence**
7 JOHNNY CASTLE, 4, b g Shamardal (USA)—Photogenic **George Materna & John McInerney**

MRS AMANDA PERRETT—continued

8 **LADY BARASTAR (IRE)**, 4, b f Barathea (IRE)—Stariya (IRE) **Mrs K. J. L. Hancock**
9 **LIFE AND SOUL (IRE)**, 5, b g Azamour (IRE)—Way For Life (GER) **A. D. Spence**
10 **PIVOTMAN**, 4, ch g Pivotal—Grandalea **J. P. Connolly**
11 **RIO ROYALE (IRE)**, 6, b g Captain Rio—Lady Nasrana (FR) **Mrs A. J. Perrett**
12 **ROXY FLYER (IRE)**, 5, b m Rock of Gibraltar (IRE)—Dyna Flyer (USA) **Mr & Mrs F. Cotton Mrs S. Conway**
13 **SABORIDO (USA)**, 6, gr g Dixie Union—Alexine (ARG) **Tracey, Cotton, James, Slade**
14 **TROVARE (USA)**, 5, b g Smart Strike (CAN)—Abita (USA) **J. P. Connolly**
15 **VIVIANI (IRE)**, 5, ch g Galileo (IRE)—Bintalreef (USA) **J. P. Connolly**

THREE-YEAR-OLDS

16 **ALLEGRO STAR (IRE)**, b c Oratorio (IRE)—Delphini (IRE) **K. Quinn/ C. Benham/ I. Saunders**
17 **ALTARIA**, b f Rail Link—Costa Rica (IRE) **K. Abdulla**
18 **ARCH VILLAIN (IRE)**, b g Arch (USA)—Barzah (IRE) **Mr & Mrs F Cotton,Mr & Mrs P Conway**
19 **AUTARCH**, ch g Gone West (USA)—Vargas Girl (USA) **John Connolly & Odile Griffith**
20 **BLACK MINSTREL (IRE)**, b c Dylan Thomas (IRE)—Overlook **A. D. Spence**
21 **BLANK CZECH (IRE)**, b g Clodovil (IRE)—Shambodia (IRE) **G. D. P. Materna**
22 **BLUE SURF**, ch g Excellent Art—Wavy Up (IRE) **The Green Dot Partnership**
23 **BRAMSHILL LASS**, ch f Notnowcato—Disco Ball **Mrs K. J. L. Hancock**
24 **BRIEF CHAT (USA)**, b br f Pleasant Tap (USA)—Sambac (USA) **K. Abdulla**
25 **CAPE PRIDE**, b c Cape Cross (IRE)—Princess Ellen **Mrs Y. E. Perry**
26 **CATO MINOR**, b g Notnowcato—Violet (IRE) **Matthew & Alison Swayne & Partners**
27 **COUP DE GRACE (IRE)**, b g Elusive City (USA)—No Way (IRE) **J. E. Bodie**
28 **DR HOUSEMAN**, b g Motivator—Photogenic **Normandie Stud Ltd**
29 **EASTER DIVA (IRE)**, b f Dansili—Easter Fairy (USA) **K. J. Quinn**
30 **EMBANKMENT**, b c Zamindar (USA)—Esplanade **K. Abdulla**
31 **GREEN LEGACY (USA)**, ch c Discreet Cat (USA)—Mira Costa (USA) **The Green Dot Partnership**
32 **HIDDEN JUSTICE (IRE)**, b g Lawman (FR)—Uncharted Haven **G. D. P. Materna**
33 **ISTHMUS**, b c Oasis Dream—Krisia **K. Abdulla**
34 **KNOYDART (USA)**, b br g Forest Wildcat (USA)—
                                   Chasenthebluesaway (USA) **John Fleming, Paul Cuttill & Guy Harwood**
35 **LANCASTER GATE**, b c Zamindar (USA)—Bayswater **K. Abdulla**
36 **MULTILATERAL (USA)**, gr ro g Mizzen Mast (USA)—Single Market (USA) **K. Abdulla**
37 **OPUS (IRE)**, b c Danehill Dancer (IRE)—Mixed Blessing **Odile Griffith & John Connolly**
38 **PENTAMETER**, br c Dansili—Tuning **K. Abdulla**
39 **PLUS FOURS**, gr ro g Mizzen Mast (USA)—Quick To Please (USA) **K. Abdulla**
40 **POMARINE (USA)**, b f Aptitude (USA)—Diese (USA) **K. Abdulla**
41 **ROCK SONG**, b c Rock of Gibraltar (IRE)—Jackie's Opera (FR) **Harwoods Racing Club Limited**
42 **SELFSAME (USA)**, b f Dansili—Reflections **K. Abdulla**
43 **SIGNED UP**, b c Rail Link—Sing For Fame (USA) **K. Abdulla**
44 **SIR GLANTON (IRE)**, ch g Choisir (AUS)—Ctesiphon (USA) **Slade, Clouting, Ross, Wells**
45 **SIR MIKE**, ch g Haafhd—Tara Moon **M. H. and Mrs G. Tourle**
46 **TREASURED DREAM**, b f Oasis Dream—Maid To Treasure (IRE) **Normandie Stud Ltd**
47 **TREND IS MY FRIEND (USA)**, b br c Lemon Drop Kid (USA)—Silva (FR) **D. M. Gorton**
48 **TRUE PRINCE (USA)**, ch c Yes It's True (USA)—Whenthedoveflies (USA) **Harwoods Racing Club Limited**
49 **VINTAAJ WAY (IRE)**, b f Hurricane Run (IRE)—Intaaj (IRE) **Mrs A. J. Chandris**
50 **WELSH NAYBER**, ch g Nayef (USA)—Aberdovey **Coombelands Racing Syndicate**
51 **WYE VALLEY**, b f Three Valleys (USA)—Welsh Autumn **K. Abdulla**

TWO-YEAR-OLDS

52 Gr ro f 30/1 Mizzen Mast (USA)—Complex (USA) (Unbridled's Song (USA)) **K. Abdulla**
53 **CZECH IT OUT (IRE)**, b c 8/3 Oratorio (IRE)—Naval Affair (IRE) (Last Tycoon) (58000) **G. D. P. Materna**
54 B c 10/4 Tiger Hill (IRE)—Dimakya (USA) (Dayjur (USA)) **Sir Eric Parker**
55 **EBONY ROC (IRE)**, br c 2/3 Shirocco (GER)—
                         Chia Laguna (IRE) (Ela-Mana-Mou) (38000) **The To-Agori-Mou Partnership**
56 **EMPIRICIST (IRE)**, b c 10/3 Holy Roman Emperor (IRE)—
                         Charaig (Rainbow Quest) (67000) **John Connolly & Odile Griffith**
57 **EXTRASOLAR**, b c 5/3 Exceed And Excel (AUS)—
                         Amicable Terms (Royal Applause) (73891) **Odile Griffith & John Connolly**
58 **FORMERLY HOT**, b c 20/4 Sakhee—Photogenic (Midyan (USA)) **Normandie Stud Ltd**
59 **HERO'S STORY**, b c 30/4 Mount Nelson—Red Roses Story (FR) (Pink (FR)) **The Recitation Partnership**
60 **KNIGHT'S PARADE (IRE)**, b c 25/4 Dark Angel (IRE)—
                         Toy Show (FR) (Danehill (USA)) (36000) **The Recitation Partnership**
61 B f 11/3 Beat Hollow—New Order (Singspiel (IRE)) **K. Abdulla**
62 **OVATORY**, b c 13/2 Acclamation—Millsini (Rossini (USA)) (220000) **John Connolly & Odile Griffith**
63 Br c 24/5 Rock of Gibraltar (IRE)—Petite Nymphe (Golan (IRE)) (31000) **Woodcote Stud Ltd**

MRS AMANDA PERRETT—continued

64 **PIVOTAL SILENCE,** ch f 28/4 Vita Rosa (JPN)—Tara Moon (Pivotal) **M. H. and Mrs G. Tourle**
65 **SAUCY MINX (IRE),** b f 9/4 Dylan Thomas (IRE)—
 Market Day (Tobougg (IRE)) (42000) **Mr & Mrs F Cotton,Mr & Mrs P Conway**
66 Ch c 20/4 Beat Hollow—Second of May (Lion Cavern (USA)) **Mrs A. J. Chandris**
67 B c 12/4 E Dubai (USA)—Shoogle (USA) (A P Indy (USA)) **K. Abdulla**
68 B c 3/5 Danehill Dancer (IRE)—Showbiz (IRE) (Sadler's Wells (USA)) (85000) **Guy Harwood**
69 Ch f 6/2 Three Valleys (USA)—Tentative (USA) (Distant View (USA)) **K. Abdulla**
70 B c 28/1 Rail Link—Tricked (Beat Hollow) **K. Abdulla**
71 B br c 22/5 Arch (USA)—Valentine Band (USA) (Dixieland Band (USA)) **K. Abdulla**

Other Owners: Mr G. D. Bailey, Mr C. F. Benham, Mrs M. Brody, Mrs J. S. Clouting, Mrs S. M. Conway, F. G. Cotton, Mrs S. H. Cotton, S. R. Counsell, Mr P. A. Cuttill, Mr J. M. D. Fleming, Mrs J. M. V. Freeman, Ms O. L. Griffith, D. M. James, Mrs B. A. Karn-Smith, Dr J. P. McInerney, Mr A. E. Powell, Mrs J. Powell, Mr D. G. Ross, Mr I. N. Saunders, R. Scott, Mrs P. M. Scott, D. M. Slade, Mrs V. J. M. Slade, Mr M. B. Swayne, arrs A. J. Swayne, Mr M. H. Tourle, Mrs G. O. Tourle, Mr M. J. Tracey, J. R. L. Wells.

Assistant Trainer: Mark Perrett

---

521 **MR PAT PHELAN, Epsom**
Postal: Ermyn Lodge, Shepherds Walk, Epsom, Surrey, KT18 6DF
Contacts: PHONE (01372) 229014 FAX (01372) 229001 MOBILE (07917) 762781
E-MAIL pat.phelan@ermynlodge.com WEBSITE www.ermynlodge.com

1 **BABY DOTTIE,** 5, ch m Dr Fong (USA)—Auntie Dot Com **Mr A. J. Smith**
2 **BUBBLY BRAVEHEART (IRE),** 5, b g Cape Cross (IRE)—Infinity (FR) **The Only Pub In The World**
3 **CELTIC CHARLIE (FR),** 7, ch h Until Sundown (USA)—India Regalona (USA) **Celtic Contractors Limited**
4 **COCOHATCHEE,** 4, b c Avonbridge—Chilly Cracker **J. James**
5 **DELLS BREEZER,** 4, ch g Kheleyf (USA)—Here To Me **G. D. Newton**
6 **DO MORE BUSINESS (IRE),** 5, b g Dubai Destination (USA)—Tokyo Song (USA) **Mr C. N. Fisher**
7 **EDE'SAJOLYGOODFELO,** 4, b g Exceed And Excel (AUS)—For Love (USA) **Ede's (UK) Ltd**
8 **EPSOM SALTS,** 7, b g Josr Algarhoud (IRE)—Captive Heart **Epsom Racegoers**
9 **ERMYNTRUDE,** 5, b br m Rock of Gibraltar (IRE)—Ruthie **Epsom Racegoers No.2**
10 **GALLOPING MINISTER (IRE),** 4, b g Ad Valorem (USA)—Gladstone Street (IRE) **G. D. Newton**
11 **GREEN EARTH (IRE),** 5, b g Cape Cross (IRE)—Inchyre **Mr P. J. Wheatley**
12 **POW R JACK,** 4, br g Diktat—How Do I Know **Mr C. N. Fisher**
13 **SUPER DUPLEX,** 5, b g Footstepsinthesand—Penelope Tree (IRE) **Special Piping Materials Ltd**
14 **SWANINSTOCKWELL (IRE),** 4, b g Footstepsinthesand—Dan's Delight **Mr & Mrs D. Dowling**
15 **TECKTAL (FR),** 9, ch m Pivotal—Wenge (USA) **Celtic Contractors Limited**
16 **YOUNG DOTTIE,** 6, b m Desert Sun—Auntie Dot Com **Mr A. J. Smith**

THREE-YEAR-OLDS

17 **DELLBUOY,** b c Acclamation—Ruthie **Mr A. J. Smith**

Other Owners: D. J. Dowling, Mrs E. C. Dowling, Ermyn Lodge Stud Limited, Mr R. G. Mappley, T. Zachariades.

Assistant Trainer: Mr Gareth Thomas

Jockey (flat): Ian Mongan. **Jockey (NH):** Colin Bolger, Gareth Thomas. **Amateur:** Mr. Freddie Mitchell.

---

522 **MR RICHARD PHILLIPS, Moreton-in-Marsh**
Postal: Adlestrop Stables, Adlestrop, Moreton-in-Marsh, Gloucestershire, GL56 0YN
Contacts: PHONE (01608) 658710 FAX (01608) 658713 MOBILE (07774) 832715
E-MAIL info@richardphillipsracing.com WEBSITE www.richardphillipsracing.com

1 **ATA BOY (IRE),** 6, b g Key of Luck (USA)—Atalina (FR) **Mrs E. C. Roberts**
2 **BLUEGRASS BID (USA),** 6, b g During (USA)—Call Cleta (USA) **The Someday's Here Racing Partnership**
3 **BOLD IDENTITY (IRE),** 6, b g Tagula (IRE)—Identify (IRE) **Nut Club Partnership**
4 **BRIGHT LIGHT,** 5, ch m Exit To Nowhere (USA)—Lamp's Return **Mrs S. C. Welch**
5 **CAPTAIN TIDDS (IRE),** 11, b g Presenting—Kilmana (IRE) **C. Pocock**
6 **CRYSTAL SWING,** 5, b g Trade Fair—Due West **Enjoy The Journey**
7 **DRUSSELL (IRE),** 6, b g Orpen (USA)—Cahermee Queen (USA) **Walid & Paula Marzouk**
8 **EXCELSIOR ACADEMY,** 6, b g Montjeu (IRE)—Birthday Suit (IRE) **Upthorpe Racing**
9 **FAIR BREEZE,** 5, b m Trade Fair—Soft Touch (IRE) **Ellangowan Racing Partners**

MR RICHARD PHILLIPS—continued

10 GREAT HERO, 7, ch g Arkadian Hero (USA)—Great Tern **Mr J & Mrs P Cantrill**
11 JUST BENNY (IRE), 7, b g Beneficial—Artic Squaw (IRE) **Glass Holdings Ltd**
12 KING JACK, 10, b g Classic Cliche (IRE)—Hack On **Gryffindor I (www.vendeeevents.com)**
13 MICK'S DANCER, 7, b g Pivotal—La Piaf (FR) **P M T Partnership**
14 MISTER NEWBY (IRE), 6, b g Oscar (IRE)—Sallie's Girl (IRE) **C. Pocock**
15 MOTOU (FR), 7, b g Astarabad (USA)—Picoletta (FR) **G. Lansbury**
16 MR TINGLE, 8, br g Beat All (USA)—Dianthus (IRE) **Mr & Mrs W. Brogan-Higgins & Gryffindor**
17 PAK JACK (FR), 12, ch g Pitchounet (FR)—Miss Noir Et Or (FR) **The Pak Jack Partnership**
18 PHARDESSA, 11, b m Pharly (FR)—Mardessa **Robert Brown & Partners**
19 RICH BUDDY, 6, b g Kayf Tara—Silver Gyre (IRE) **Mrs E. A. Prowting**
20 SALTO D'ALBAIN (FR), 6, b g Dark Moondancer—Emeraude du Moulin (FR) **The Squashed Club**
21 SATICON, 7, b g Act One—Saumareine (FR) **S. M. Smith**
22 STOP THE SHOW (IRE), 11, b g King's Theatre (IRE)—Rathsallagh Tartan **The Adlestrop Club**
23 THORNTON ALICE, 7, b m Kayf Tara—Lindrick Lady (IRE) **The Listeners**
24 UPPER DECK (IRE), 7, b g Beckett (IRE)—Princess Accord (USA) **Mr C. A. J. Allan**
25 WHENEVER, 8, ch g Medicean—Alessandra **Dozen Dreamers Partnership**
26 WHICHEVER, 6, ch m Where Or When (IRE)—Pips Way (IRE) **Upthorpe Racing**

Other Owners: Ms K. M. Anderson, J. E. Barnes, Mr J. R. Brown, R. Brown, Mr E. G. Brown, J. S. Cantrill, Mrs P. J. Cantrill, Mrs E. J. Clarke, Mr J. E. S. Colling, B. J. Duckett, Mr D. E. Ford, Mrs S. J. Harvey, M. B. Hawtin, Mr W. Marzouk, Mrs P. Marzouk, R. J. Meaney, W. D. S. Murdoch, Mrs H. M. Nixseaman, J. S. Palfreyman, R. T. Phillips, M. T. Phillips, Dr E. D. Theodore, Mrs L. A. Wright, A. W. D. Wright.

Jockey (NH): Sean Quinlan, Richard Johnson, Sam Twiston-Davies.

---

523 | **MR JOHN PICKERING, Hinckley**
Postal: **Cottage Farm, Wigston Parva, Hinckley, Leicestershire, LE10 3AP**
Contacts: **PHONE (01455) 220535**

1 DEPORTISTA, 6, ch m Deportivo—Wadenhoe (IRE) **J. A. Pickering**
2 DUCHESS OF MALFI, 6, ch m Falbrav (IRE)—Play That Tune **J. A. Pickering**
3 5, B m Superior Premium—Princeable Lady (IRE)

---

524 | **MR DAVID PINDER, Wantage**
Postal: **Little Farm, Fawler Road, Kingston Lisle, Wantage, Oxfordshire, OX12 9QH**
Contacts: **PHONE (01367) 820280 FAX (01367) 820280 MOBILE (07711) 396191**
E-MAIL david@davidpinderracing.com WEBSITE www.davidpinderracing.com

1 AMBER HEIGHTS, 4, b f Kyllachy—Jumairah Sun (IRE) **Ms L. Burns**
2 DREAM CATCHER (FR), 4, gr g Della Francesca (USA)—Gallopade (FR) **Miss N. M. Haine**
3 GAZBOOLOU, 8, b g Royal Applause—Warning Star **Mrs A. M. Pinder**
4 WOOLSTON FERRY (IRE), 6, b g Fath (USA)—Cathy Garcia (IRE) **Ms L. Burns**

---

525 | **MR DAVID PIPE, Wellington**
Postal: **Pond House, Nicholashayne, Wellington, Somerset, TA21 9QY**
Contacts: **PHONE (01884) 840715 FAX (01884) 841343**
E-MAIL david@davidpipe.com WEBSITE www.davidpipe.com

1 AFRICAN BROADWAY (IRE), 6, b g Broadway Flyer (USA)—African Lily (IRE) **A. E. Frost**
2 ALDERLUCK (IRE), 9, ch g Alderbrook—Cecelia's Charm (IRE) **Mrs C. J. Rayner**
3 ARAB LEAGUE (IRE), 7, b g Dubai Destination (USA)—Johnny And Clyde (USA) **S. M. Mercer**
4 ARRAYAN, 7, b g Catcher In The Rye (IRE)—Ganga (IRE) **Mrs Angela Tincknell & Mr W. Tincknell**
5 ASHBRITTLE, 5, b g Rainbow Quest (USA)—Caesarea (GER) **Mr P. A. Deal & J. L. Rowsell**
6 ASHKAZAR (FR), 8, b g Sadler's Wells (USA)—Asharna (IRE) **D. A. Johnson**
7 BALGARRY (FR), 5, ch g Ballingarry (IRE)—Marie de Motreff (FR) **Brocade Racing**
8 BAMBOLEO (IRE), 5, b g Old Vic—Sorivera **M. C. Denmark**
9 BARNEY COOL, 5, b g Bollin Eric—Laurel Diver **N. G. Mills**
10 BATHWICK BRAVE (IRE), 5, b g Westerner—Dorans Grove **H. M. W. Clifford**
11 BATHWICK QUEST (IRE), 8, b m Barathea (IRE)—Ninth Quest (USA) **H. M. W. Clifford**
12 BATTLE GROUP (IRE), 7, b g Beat Hollow—Cantanta **Jolly Boys Outing**
13 BEATTIE GREEN, 5, b m Beat Hollow—Shades of Green **Mr J A Gent, Mr R Wilkin, Prof C Tisdall**
14 BEYOND (IRE), 5, ch g Galileo (IRE)—Run To Jane (IRE) **Mr R. J. H. Geffen**
15 BIG OCCASION (IRE), 5, b g Sadler's Wells (USA)—Asnieres (USA) **The Old Betfairians**

MR DAVID PIPE—continued

16 **BLADOUN (FR)**, 4, gr g Smadoun (FR)—Blabliramic (FR) **H. M. W. Clifford**
17 **BOBBY EWING (IRE)**, 7, b g Bob's Return (IRE)—Jacqueline's Glen **Just Good Friends**
18 **BUDDY BOLERO (IRE)**, 6, b g Accordion—Quinnsboro Ice (IRE) **M. C. Denmark**
19 **BUENA VISTA (IRE)**, 11, b g In The Wings—Park Special **Matt Archer & The Late Miss Jean Broadhurst**
20 **BYGONES SOVEREIGN (IRE)**, 6, b g Old Vic—Miss Hollygrove (IRE) **Arnie & Alan Kaplan**
21 **CATCH TAMMY (IRE)**, 6, br g Tamayaz (CAN)—Bramble Orchard (IRE) **R. S. Brookhouse**
22 **CHARTREUX (FR)**, 7, ro g Colonel Collins (USA)—Ruaha River (FR) **R. S. Brookhouse**
23 **CLEVER DICK (IRE)**, 6, b g Presenting—Amitge (FR) **M. C. Denmark**
24 **CLOSE HOUSE**, 5, b g Generous (IRE)—Not Now Nellie **R. S. Brookhouse**
25 **CONSIGLIERE (FR)**, 9, ch g Trempolino (USA)—Gianna Nannini (ITY) **Mr E. A. P. Scouller**
26 **DAN BREEN (IRE)**, 7, b g Mull of Kintyre (USA)—Kunuz **Mr Stuart & Simon Mercer**
27 **DECOY (FR)**, 6, b g Della Francesca (USA)—Vagualame (FR) **Stefanos Stefanou**
28 **DIAMOND'S RETURN (IRE)**, 8, b g Bob's Return (IRE)—Mitsubishi Diamond **Mr S. J. P. O'Farrell**
29 **DREAM ESTEEM**, 7, b m Mark of Esteem (IRE)—City of Angels **R. S. Brookhouse**
30 **DUKES ART**, 6, b g Bachelor Duke (USA)—Creme Caramel (USA) **Mr J. Diver**
31 **DYNASTE (FR)**, 6, gr g Martaline—Bellissima de Mai (FR) **A. J. White**
32 **EFFERVESCE (IRE)**, 5, ch m Galileo (IRE)—Royal Fizz (IRE) **Mrs J Magnier, Mr M Tabor & Mr D Smith**
33 **EL LOBO (FR)**, 5, b g Loup Solitaire (USA)—Mirage du Simbeu (FR) **James & Jean Potter**
34 **ENFANT DE LUNE (FR)**, 8, ch g Inchinor—Ombre de Lune (IRE) **Ashton Racing Club**
35 **FAASEL (IRE)**, 11, b g Unfuwain (USA)—Waqood (USA) **J. T. Ennis**
36 **FIULIN**, 7, ch g Galileo (IRE)—Fafinta (IRE) **Mr R. J. H. Geffen**
37 **FROSTED GRAPE (IRE)**, 6, b m Kheleyf (USA)—Two Shonas (IRE) **The Wise Partners**
38 **GASPARA (FR)**, 9, b m Astarabad (USA)—Gaspaisie (FR) **P. McMahon**
39 **GEVREY CHAMBERTIN (FR)**, 4, gr g Dom Alco (FR)—Fee Magic (FR) **Roger Stanley & Yvonne Reynolds III**
40 **GLASSAWINE**, 5, gr g Verglas (IRE)—Persian Ruby (IRE) **R. S. Brookhouse**
41 **GOULANES (IRE)**, 6, b g Mr Combustible (IRE)—Reboglane (IRE) **R. S. Brookhouse**
42 **GRANDS CRUS (FR)**, 7, gr g Dom Alco (FR)—Fee Magic (FR) **Roger Stanley & Yvonne Reynolds III**
43 **GREAT ENDEAVOUR (IRE)**, 8, gr g Great Palm (USA)—Strong Irish (IRE) **D. A. Johnson**
44 **HOME RUN (GER)**, 4, ch g Motivator—Hold Off (IRE) **Mr M. K. Williams**
45 **HUGO DRAX (IRE)**, 5, b g Bienamado (USA)—Young Love (USA) **M. C. Denmark**
46 **I'M SO LUCKY**, 10, b g Zilzal (USA)—City of Angels **Mrs S. J. Brookhouse**
47 **I'MSINGINGTHEBLUES (IRE)**, 10, b g Pistolet Bleu (IRE)—Nova Rose **Mrs J. Tracey**
48 **JUNIOR**, 9, ch g Singspiel (IRE)—For More (FR) **Middleham Park Racing LI**
49 **KAZLIAN (FR)**, 4, b g Sinndar (IRE)—Quiet Splendor (USA) **Twelve Pipers Piping**
50 **KILRYE (IRE)**, 5, b g Catcher In The Rye (IRE)—Kiladante (IRE) **A. J. White & Mrs A. Underhill**
51 **LADYVIE (FR)**, 5, b m Vic Toto (FR)—Ladykish (FR) **Pond House Racing**
52 **LAFLAMMEDEGLORIE**, 6, b g Fair Mix (IRE)—Swazi Princess (IRE) **D. R. Mead**
53 **LE CHASSE SPLEEN (FR)**, 6, b g Caballo Raptor (CAN)—Joon (FR) **Mr J. T. Chalmers**
54 **LOVES A BRAZILIAN (IRE)**, 5, b g Bach (USA)—Croom River (IRE) **George, Ives, Johnson Partnership**
55 **LUCY'S PERFECT**, 6, ch m Systematic—Water Flower **Avalon Surfacing & Construction Co Ltd**
56 **MARTIAL LAW (IRE)**, 6, ch g Galileo (IRE)—Tree Tops **Mr R. J. H. Geffen**
57 **MASSINI'S MAGUIRE (IRE)**, 11, b g Dr Massini (IRE)—Molly Maguire (IRE) **A. E. Peterson**
58 **MASTER OF ARTS (USA)**, 7, b br g Swain (IRE)—Grazia **R. S. Brookhouse**
59 **MASTER OVERSEER (IRE)**, 9, b g Old Vic—Crogeen Lass **Brocade Racing**
60 **MATUHI**, 9, b g Dansili—Montserrat **Willsford Racing Ltd**
61 **MIDNIGHT TUESDAY (FR)**, 7, b g Kapgarde (FR)—Deat Heat (FR) **A. C. Eaves**
62 **MOOSE MORAN (USA)**, 5, gr ro g Lemon Drop Kid (USA)—After All (IRE) **R. C. Tooth**
63 **MR CHOW (IRE)**, 8, b g King's Theatre (IRE)—Della Wee (IRE) **M. C. Denmark**
64 **MS CORDELIA (USA)**, 4, b f Anabaa (USA)—Gingivere (USA) **R. C. Tooth**
65 **MY BROTHER SYLVEST**, 6, b g Bach (IRE)—Senna da Silva **Teddington Racing Club**
66 **NO SECRETS (IRE)**, 8, b g King's Theatre (IRE)—Happy Native (IRE) **M. C. Denmark**
67 **NORTHERN JEM**, 8, b g Mark of Esteem (IRE)—Top Jem **Lady H. J. Clarke**
68 **NOTUS DE LA TOUR (FR)**, 6, b g Kutub (IRE)—Ridiyla (IRE) **D Bradshaw,J Dale,P Deal,J Smee,W Walsh**
69 **ON KHEE**, 5, b m Sakhee (USA)—Star Precision **Palatinate Thoroughbred Racing Limited**
70 **OUR FATHER (IRE)**, 6, gr g Shantou (USA)—Rosepan (IRE) **The Ives & Johnson Families**
71 **PAINTER MAN (FR)**, 10, b g Double Bed (FR)—Diana La Belle (FR) **David & Elaine Long**
72 **PIRAYA (FR)**, 9, gr g Lost World (IRE)—Ella Royale (FR) **T. Neill**
73 **POOLE MASTER**, 7, ch g Fleetwood (IRE)—Juste Belle (IRE) **G. D. Thompson**
74 **PRASINA RUSSATA (IRE)**, 5, b g Accordion—Henrietta (IRE) **B. A. Kilpatrick**
75 **PRESENTING ACE (IRE)**, 6, b g Presenting—Sesame Squeeze **Walters Plant Hire Ltd**
76 **QALINAS (FR)**, 5, gr g Malinas (GER)—Tabletiere (FR) **Middleham Park Racing XX**
77 **QUINTE DU CHATELET (FR)**, 8, b g Lavirco (GER)—Grandeur Royale (GER) **Brocade Racing**
78 **QUOCOTIEP (FR)**, 8, b g Network (GER)—Unetiepy (FR) **Taylor & Frosell**
79 **ROI DE ROSE (FR)**, 8, b g Insatiable (USA)—Couture Rose (IRE) **Mr A. Wichser**
80 **ROSE OF THE MOON (IRE)**, 7, gr g Moonax (IRE)—
Little Rose (IRE) **Middleham Park Racing XXXIII & Partners**

MR DAVID PIPE—continued

81 **SALUT FLO (FR)**, 7, b g Saint des Saints (FR)—Royale Marie (FR) **A. Stennett**
82 **SHAKING HANDS (IRE)**, 8, b g Bach (IRE)—Picton Lass **Brocade Racing**
83 **SHALLOW BAY**, 5, b g Shamardal (USA)—Yawl **Mr P. J. McGee**
84 **SHOEGAZER (IRE)**, 7, b g Bach (IRE)—American Native (IRE) **H. M. W. Clifford**
85 **SHOTAVODKA (IRE)**, 6, ch g Alderbrook—Another Vodka (IRE) **Mrs J. Gerard-Pearse**
86 **SONA SASTA (IRE)**, 9, b g Sonus (IRE)—Derry Lark (IRE) **R. S. Brookhouse**
87 **SPIRIT OF BARBADOS (IRE)**, 6, b g Oscar (IRE)—Finnisk Dream (IRE) **A. E. Peterson**
88 **STAR OF ANGELS**, 8, b g Diktat—City of Angels **R. S. Brookhouse**
89 **STREET ENTERTAINER (IRE)**, 5, br g Danehill Dancer (USA)—Opera Ridge (FR) **Barnett, Manasseh & Partners**
90 **SURE JOSIE SURE (FR)**, 7, gr m Kalanisi (IRE)—Aerdee (FR) **Mrs J. Tracey**
91 **SWING BILL (FR)**, 11, gr g Grey Risk (FR)—Melodie Royale (FR) **D. A. Johnson**
92 **SWING BOWLER**, 5, b m Galileo (IRE)—Lady Cricket (FR) **D. A. Johnson**
93 **TAKE OVER SIVOLA (FR)**, 5, b g Assessor—Maya Rock (FR) **G. D. Thompson**
94 **TAMARINBLEU (FR)**, 12, b g Epervier Bleu—Tamainia (FR) **The Arthur White Partnership**
95 **TARATATA SIVOLA (FR)**, 5, b g Assessor—Jolie Fabi (FR) **Palatinate Thoroughbred Racing Limited**
96 **TERFEL'S TOSCAR (IRE)**, 7, b g Oscar (IRE)—Jill's Girl (IRE) **A. E. Peterson**
97 **THE LITTLE MINX**, 6, ch m Central Park (IRE)—Philatelic Lady (IRE) **D. R. Mead**
98 **THE PACKAGE**, 9, br g Kayf Tara—Ardent Bride **D. A. Johnson**
99 **THE PIER (IRE)**, 6, ch g Alhaarth (IRE)—Cois Cuain (IRE) **A. Stennett**
100 **THE PRIME VIPER (IRE)**, 5, b m Traditionally (USA)—Accordeon Royale (IRE) **Foxtrot NH Racing Partnership V**
101 **THE TATKIN (IRE)**, 6, b m Tikkanen (USA)—Miss Bobby Bennett **B. A. Kilpatrick**
102 **THE TRACEY SHUFFLE**, 6, br g Kapgarde (FR)—Gaspaisie (FR) **Mrs J. Tracey**
103 **TOP WOOD (FR)**, 5, ch g Kotky Bleu (FR)—Heure Bleu (FR) **Lady H. J. Clarke**
104 **TROP FORT (FR)**, 5, b g Bernebeau (FR)—Violeta (FR) **A. E. Peterson**
105 **UNEX DEGAS (IRE)**, 4, b g High Chaparral (IRE)—Alaynia (IRE) **W. J. Gredley**
106 **WAR SINGER (USA)**, 5, b g War Chant (USA)—Sister Marilyn (USA) **The War Cabinet**
107 **WATER GARDEN (FR)**, 6, gr g Turgeon (USA)—Queenstown (FR) **D. A. Johnson**
108 **WATERUNDER (IRE)**, 5, br g Vinnie Roe (IRE)—Be My Katie (IRE) **Mrs S. Clifford**
109 **WINGS OF ICARUS (IRE)**, 5, ch g Cut Quartz (FR)—Moody Cloud (FR) **Shirl & The Girls**
110 **WOODLARK ISLAND (IRE)**, 6, b g Tagula (IRE)—Be My Lover **Eminence Grise Partnership**

Other Owners: Mr D. Abraham, J. Apiafi, M. Archer, Mr S. P. Bamber, Mr J. Barnett, Mr D. M. Bradshaw, Exors of the Late Miss E. V. Broadhurst, Mr G. R. Broom, Mrs A. E. M. Broom, Mr A. Cole, Mr M. J. Cruddace, J. S. Dale, Lord Daresbury, P. A. Deal, Mrs C. M. Du Pon, Mrs L. A. Farquhar, Mr M. J. Fitzpatrick, W. F. Frewen, R. N. Froseill, J. A. Gent, Mr P. George, R. B. Gray, P. J. Green, Mr J. Gwyther, Mrs L. B. Hart, T. W. Hosier, Mr K. R. Ives, Mr D. L. Ives, Mrs D. A. Johnson, Mrs C. Johnson, M. B. Jones, Alan Kaplan, Mr L. King, Mrs S. J. Ling, D. J. Long, Mrs E. Long, Mrs S. Magnier, Mr D. C. Manasseh, Mr S. S. Mercer, Mr C. G. Paletta, T. S. Palin, M. C. Pipe, J. E. Potter, Mrs M. J. Potter, Mr M. Prince, Mrs Y. J. Reynolds, D. G. Robinson, J. L. Rowsell, Mr J. Smee, D. Smith, R. K. Stanley, M. Tabor, Mrs L. C. Taylor, Mrs A. Tincknell, W. C. Tincknell, Prof C. Tisdall, Mrs A. Underhill, W D Lewis Holdings Ltd, W. T. Walsh, Mr J. Webb, J. B. Webb, Mr R. C. Wilkin.

Assistant Trainer: Mr M. C. Pipe C.B.E.

Jockey (NH): Tom Scudamore, Timmy Murphy, Gerry Supple, Johnny Farrelly, Hadden Frost. **Conditional:** Conor O'Farrell, Francis Hayes. **Amateur:** Mr Kieron Edgar, Mr Tom Bellamy, Mr Michael Ennis.

526 MR TIM PITT, Newmarket
Postal: **Frankland Lodge, Hamilton Road, Newmarket, Suffolk, CB8 7JQ**
Contacts: PHONE (01653) 666344 FAX (01638) 666344 MOBILE (07917) 541341
E-MAIL timjoelpitt@aol.com WEBSITE www.timpittracing.com

1 **BRINK**, 5, b m Powerscourt—Fonage **Ferrybank Properties Limited**
2 **CRUNCHED**, 5, b g Dubai Destination (USA)—Amica **Decadent Racing**
3 **DARK RANGER**, 6, br g Where Or When (IRE)—Dark Raider (IRE) **Recycled Products Limited**
4 **JORDANS CHRISSY (IRE)**, 4, gr f Iffraaj—Gentilesse **B. A. Jordan, J. Burke & Mrs A. Pitt**
5 **NOTHINGBUTTHETRUTH (IRE)**, 8, b g Witness Box (USA)—
　　Named And Shamed (IRE) **Ferrybank Properties Limited**
6 **PALOS CONTI (FR)**, 9, ch g Robin des Champs (FR)—Dona Mirande (FR) **C. N. Barnes**
7 **PORGY**, 7, b g Dansili—Light Ballet **A. Barnes & C. N. Barnes**

THREE-YEAR-OLDS

8 **DARK CELT (IRE)**, b c Lawman (FR)—Dark Raider (IRE) **Recycled Products Limited**
9 **GEANIE MAC (IRE)**, ch f Needwood Blade—Dixie Evans **Drinkmore Stud**
10 **MOROCCO MOON**, b f Rock of Gibraltar (IRE)—One Giant Leap (IRE) **N. E. Sangster**
11 **PACIFIC HEIGHTS (IRE)**, b c Galileo (IRE)—Song to Remember (USA) **A. Barnes & C. N. Barnes**

MR TIM PITT—continued
12 **SONKO (IRE)**, b f Red Clubs (IRE)—Baltic Belle (IRE) **Saintly Racing**
13 **SUGAR PRINCE (IRE)**, b c Strategic Prince—Security Tiger (IRE) **Burrage, Ward, Sangster**

TWO-YEAR-OLDS
14 **DARK JUSTICE (IRE)**, b f 15/4 Lawman (FR)—Dark Raider (IRE) (Definite Article) **Recycled Products Limited**
15 **EMPEROR'S DAUGHTER**, b f 19/4 Bahamian Bounty—Hatun Suyay (USA) (Strong Hope (USA)) (2200) **Invictus**
16 **KATIE GALE**, b f 6/2 Shirocco (GER)—Karla June (Unfuwain (USA)) (26000) **Ferrybank Properties Limited**
17 **LAVENDER BAY**, b f 14/4 Needwood Blade—In Good Faith (USA) (Dynaformer (USA)) **Invictus**
18 B g 3/4 Zamindar (USA)—Mail Express (USA) (Cape Cross) **For Sale**
19 Ch f 16/2 Iffraaj—Radiancy (IRE) (Mujtahid (USA)) (32000) **Ferrybank Properties Limited**

Jockey (flat): Shane Kelly. **Jockey (NH):** Dougie Costello.

---

527 | ## MR CHARLES POGSON, Farnsfield
Postal: Allamoor Farm, Mansfield Road, Farnsfield, Nottinghamshire, NG22 8HZ
Contacts: **PHONE (01623) 882275 MOBILE (07977) 016155**

1 **ALFLORAMOOR**, 10, b g Alflora (IRE)—Diamond Wind (USA) **C. T. Pogson**
2 **AUSSIE BLUE (IRE)**, 8, b g Bahamian Bounty—Luanshya **C. T. Pogson**
3 **HOPEAND**, 7, b m King's Theatre (IRE)—Land of Glory **C. T. Pogson**
4 **IRON CROSS (IRE)**, 7, b g Cape Cross (IRE)—Alithini (IRE) **Wordingham Plant Hire**
5 **MOONSTREAKER**, 9, b g Foxhound (USA)—Ling Lane **Wordingham Plant Hire**
6 **MOROCCHIUS (USA)**, 7, b g Black Minnaloushe (USA)—Shakespearean (USA) **C. T. Pogson**
7 **NOBLE WITNESS (IRE)**, 9, b g Witness Box (USA)—Jennas Pride (IRE) **Wordingham Plant Hire & Partner**
8 **WORDY'S BOY**, 7, b g Kayf Tara—Wordy's Wonder **Wordingham Plant Hire**

Other Owners: P. L. Wordingham, Mrs P. A. Wordingham.

Assistant Trainer: Adam Pogson

Jockey (NH): Adam Pogson.

---

528 | ## MR NICHOLAS POMFRET, Tilton-on-the-Hill
Postal: Red Lodge Farm, Marefield Lane, Tilton-on-the-Hill, Leicester, Leicestershire, LE7 9LJ
Contacts: **PHONE (01162) 597537 MOBILE (07885) 598810**

1 **ARROWMINT**, 6, b m Executive Perk—Araminta **R. P. Brett**
2 **FIRST LAD**, 5, ch g First Trump—Intrepid Gal **J. N. Cheatle**

---

529 | ## MR JONATHAN PORTMAN, Compton
Postal: Hamilton Stables, Hockham Road, Compton, Newbury, Berkshire, RG20 6QJ
Contacts: **OFFICE (01635) 578031 FAX (01635) 579323 MOBILE (07798) 824513**
E-MAIL portman.hamiltonstables@virgin.net WEBSITE www.jonathanportmanracing.co.uk

1 **ADAEZE (IRE)**, 4, b f Footstepsinthesand—Ringmoor Down **Prof C. D. Green**
2 **CHEAP STREET**, 8, ch g Compton Place—Anneliina **J. G. B. Portman**
3 **CLYFFE TOP**, 5, b m Turgeon (USA)—Chandni (IRE) **Mrs C. F. E. Hall**
4 **CUCKOO ROCK (IRE)**, 5, b g Refuse To Bend (IRE)—Ringmoor Down **Prof C. D. Green**
5 **CUNNING ACT**, 4, ch g Act One—Saffron Fox **M. J. Vandenberghe**
6 **HAVING A BALL**, 8, b g Mark of Esteem (IRE)—All Smiles **P. D. Cundell**
7 **INDIAN SHUFFLE (IRE)**, 4, b g Sleeping Indian—Hufflepuff (IRE) **Out To Grass Partnership**
8 **JODY BEAR**, 4, b f Joe Bear (IRE)—Colins Lady (FR) **Joe Bear Racing**
9 **JOE PACKET**, 5, ch g Joe Bear (IRE)—Costa Packet (IRE) **Paul Moulton**
10 **LILY IN PINK**, 4, b f Sakhee (USA)—In Luck **Miss Sarah Lloyd**
11 **MASSANNIE (IRE)**, 4, b f Dr Massini (IRE)—Bathwick Annie **H. M. W. Clifford**
12 **MINDER**, 6, b g Mind Games—Exotic Forest **M. J. Vandenberghe & Portlee Bloodstock**
13 **MR PYRAMUS**, 4, b g Act One—Eiszeit (GER) **Mr J. T. Habershon-Butcher**
14 **NOW WHAT**, 5, ch m Where Or When (IRE)—Vallauris **Mrs S. J. Portman**
15 **OBSCURITY (IRE)**, 4, ch g Exit To Nowhere (USA)—Lady Cadia (FR) **M. J. Vandenberghe**
16 **QUITE A CATCH (IRE)**, 4, b g Camacho—Dear Catch (IRE) **J. G. B. Portman**
17 **RUSSIAN RAVE**, 6, ch m Danehill Dancer (IRE)—Russian Ruby (FR) **The Traditionalists**
18 **SHESHA BEAR**, 7, b m Tobougg (IRE)—Sunny Davis (USA) **RWH Partnership**

MR JONATHAN PORTMAN—continued

19 **UNCLE PETTIT (IRE)**, 4, b br g Heron Island (IRE)—Special Ballot (IRE) **A. R. Boswood**
20 **VAN DOESBURG (IRE)**, 4, gr g Westerner—Winter Daydream (IRE) **Prof C. D. Green**
21 **WEATHER BABE**, 4, b f Storming Home—Bathwick Babe (IRE) **H. M. W. Clifford**
22 **WILDE AT HEART (IRE)**, 5, b m Oscar (IRE)—Back To Bavaria (IRE) **Peter Wales**
23 **ZEN FACTOR**, 7, b g Josr Algarhoud (IRE)—Zabelina (USA) **Mr J. T. Habershon-Butcher**

THREE-YEAR-OLDS

24 **ALLEGRA BYRON**, ch f Byron—Colourflash (IRE) **Portlee Bloodstock**
25 **BONDI MIST (IRE)**, gr f Aussie Rules (USA)—Akoya (IRE) **Looks A Bright Prospect Racing**
26 **COURTLAND AVENUE (IRE)**, b g Kodiac—Chingford (IRE) **Prof C. D. Green**
27 **IDA INKLEY (IRE)**, b f One Cool Cat (USA)—Tara Too (IRE) **Prof C. D. Green**
28 **ISOLA BELLA**, ch f Sleeping Indian—Tetravella (IRE) **Berkeley Racing**
29 **KOZMINA BAY**, b f Notnowcato—Kozmina (IRE) **Peter Deal**
30 **LADRAM BAY (IRE)**, b f Oratorio (IRE)—Ringmoor Down **Prof C. D. Green**
31 **OCEAN MYTH**, b f Acclamation—Mystery Ocean **Mrs R. Knipe**
32 **PLAY STREET**, ch f Tobougg (IRE)—Zoena **Anthony Boswood**
33 **RUSSIAN RUMBA (IRE)**, b f Whipper (USA)—Pink Sovietstaia (FR) **More Money Than Sense Partnership**
34 **SILENT LAUGHTER**, b f Shamardal (USA)—Tease (IRE) **Mrs D. O. Joly**
35 **SINGLE GIRL (IRE)**, ch f Singspiel (IRE)—Bumble **W. Clifford**
36 B f Hawk Wing (USA)—Sokoa (USA)
37 **STRICTLY MINE**, ch f Piccolo—My Dancer (IRE) **Lady Whent**
38 **WHITE FLIGHT**, gr f Doyen (IRE)—Reason To Dance **Mrs D. O. Joly**

TWO-YEAR-OLDS

39 B gr f 27/4 Ishiguru (USA)—Demolition Jo (Petong) (9000) **Prof C. D. Green**
40 **DOUBLE STAR**, b f 18/4 Elusive City (USA)—Tease (IRE) (Green Desert (USA)) (15238) **Mrs D. O. Joly**
41 B c 12/5 Astronomer Royal (USA)—Happy Clapper (Royal Applause)
42 B f 14/3 Lucky Story (USA)—May Fox (Zilzal (USA)) (952)
43 **MONSIEUR RIEUSSEC**, bl c 20/3 Halling (USA)—
    Muscovado (USA) (Mr Greeley (USA)) (45000) **Mr J. T. Habershon-Butcher**
44 **PASAKA BOY**, ch c 2/4 Haafhd—Shesha Bear (Tobougg (IRE)) (952) **RWH Partnership**
45 B f 8/5 Footstepsinthesand—Ringmoor Down (Pivotal) **Prof C. D. Green**
46 B c 2/2 Sleeping Indian—Tri Pac (IRE) (Fairy King (USA)) (800) **Jaliza Partnership**

Other Owners: Mr M. Baker, Mr G. Bishop, Mr Jeremy Brownlee, Mr G. F. Clark, Mr S. E. Dawes, Mr A. Edwards, Mr T. Edwards, Mr P. Hibbard, Mr Jonathan Homan, Miss J. Kempsey, Mr Stuart McPhee, Mr J. Morley, Miss D. Powell, Mr S. Ransom, Mr M. Reditt, Mrs P. Reditt, Mr P. Sandy, Mrs H. Stalder, Mr G. C. Wickens.

Assistant Trainer: Sophie Portman

---

530 **MR JAMIE POULTON, Lewes**
Postal: **White Cottage, Telscombe, Lewes, East Sussex, BN7 3HZ**
Contacts: **YARD (01273) 300515 HOME (01273) 300127 FAX (01273) 300915 MOBILE (07980) 596952**
E-MAIL jamie@poulton8.orangehome.co.uk

1 **CORRIB DRIFT (USA)**, 12, ch g Sandpit (BRZ)—Bygones (USA) **Mr L. C. Best**
2 **DOUBLE WHAMMY**, 6, b g Systematic—Honor Rouge (IRE) **Alex & Janet Card**
3 **FARBREAGA (IRE)**, 6, b g Shernazar—Gleann Alainn **Miss V. Markowiak**
4 **FORMIDABLE GUEST**, 8, b m Dilshaan—Fizzy Treat **Oceana Racing**
5 **HIGHLAND HARVEST**, 8, b g Averti (IRE)—Bee One (IRE) **Mr J. Wotherspoon**
6 4, B c Double Trigger (IRE)—Linden Grace (USA) **Mr I. C. Cusselle**
7 **PERSIAN BUDDY**, 5, gr g Reel Buddy (USA)—Breeze Again (USA) **Ormonde Racing**
8 **PUSH ME (IRE)**, 5, gr m Verglas (IRE)—Gilda Lilly (USA) **Alex & Janet Card**
9 **SAUCY BUCK (IRE)**, 4, b g Mujadil (USA)—Phantom Ring **Surrey Elite**
10 **WHERES JOHNNY**, 11, gr g Touch of Grey—Lady Poly **Oceana Racing**
11 **WHITCOMBE SPIRIT**, 7, b g Diktat—L'evangile **Telscombe Racing**

Other Owners: Mr A. Baker, Mr A. M. Card, Mrs J. A. Card, J. Harrison, K. A. Ingram, Mr A. Kosari, Mr S. Lang, Mr G. Mercer, Mr B. Pearce, Mr A. Stocker.

Assistant Trainer: Mrs C D Poulton

Jockey (flat): Robert Havlin, Franny Norton. **Jockey (NH):** Mattie Batchelor.

531 MR BRENDAN POWELL, Upper Lambourn
Postal: Newlands Stables, Upper Lambourn, Hungerford, Berkshire, RG17 8QX
Contacts: PHONE (01488) 73650 FAX (01488) 73650 MOBILE (07785) 390737
E-MAIL brendan.powell@btconnect.com WEBSITE www.brendanpowellracing.com

1 **ACIANO (IRE)**, 4, b g Kheleyf (USA)—Blue Crystal (IRE) **Mrs S. M. Tucker**
2 **ARCTIC REACH**, 4, b g Phoenix Reach (IRE)—Arctic Queen **Holistic Racing Ltd**
3 **ARDENT GREEN GRAPE**, 6, b m Grape Tree Road—Bee-A-Scally **Church Racing Partnership**
4 **AWARD WINNER**, 9, b g Alflora (IRE)—Blackwater Bay (IRE) **J. P. McManus**
5 **BENNYS WELL (IRE)**, 6, b g Beneficial—Alure (IRE) **Mrs A. Ellis**
6 **BRING IT ON HOME**, 8, b g Beat Hollow—Dernier Cri **Ms S. L. Kerswell**
7 **CODA AGENCY**, 9, b g Agnes World (USA)—The Frog Lady (IRE) **P. Banfield**
8 **DARK AND DANGEROUS (IRE)**, 4, b g Cacique (IRE)—Gilah (IRE) **North South Alliance**
9 **GEMINI JIM (IRE)**, 7, b g Luso—River Grove (IRE) **Mrs H. A. Tinkler**
10 **GRAFITE**, 7, gr g Act One—Silver Gyre (IRE) **Dr Jeff Dalton & Mr C Shankland**
11 **IBIZA SUNSET (IRE)**, 4, b g Chineur (FR)—Romanylei (IRE) **R. H. Kerswell**
12 **JAYA BELLA (IRE)**, 7, gr m Tikkanen (USA)—Maxis Girl (IRE) **Mr R. J. Aplin**
13 **KING SPIRIT (IRE)**, 4, b g Fruits of Love (USA)—Tariana (IRE) **Mr J. J. King**
14 **MEET THE CRITICS (IRE)**, 9, b g Rashar (USA)—Rose Basket (IRE) **The Roysun Syndicate**
15 **MILANS WELL (IRE)**, 6, b g Milan—Panoora Queen (IRE) **A. Head**
16 **MORESTEAD (IRE)**, 7, ch g Traditionally (USA)—Itsy Bitsy Betsy (USA) **L. Gilbert**
17 **NUMBERCRUNCHER (IRE)**, 6, b g Beneficial—Josie's Turn (IRE) **Walters Plant Hire Ltd**
18 **OFFBEAT SAFARIS (IRE)**, 4, b g Le Vie Dei Colori—Baywood **P. L. Winkworth**
19 **ONLY WITNESS (IRE)**, 7, b g Witness Box (USA)—Shiny Button **Arkle Bar Partnership & Mr R Stanley**
20 **OPHELIA'S KISS**, 5, b m Karinga Bay—Baileys Baby **J. S. Warner**
21 **PIPE BANNER**, 8, b g Silver Patriarch (IRE)—Bella Macrae **Miss C. Elks**
22 **SAM HALL (FR)**, 7, ch g Kapgarde (FR)—Salsigne (FR) **B. G. Powell**
23 **SHOREACRES (IRE)**, 9, b g Turtle Island (IRE)—Call Me Dara (IRE) **D. P. Nash**
24 **SONORAN SANDS (IRE)**, 4, b g Footstepsinthesand—Atishoo **C. F. Harrington**
25 **SPEEDY DIRECTA (IRE)**, 9, b g Areion (GER)—Sourour (IRE) **Mr R. J. Aplin**
26 **SWANSBROOK (IRE)**, 9, b g Alderbrook—Bobsyourdad (IRE) **The Jesters**
27 **TERRA BLEU (IRE)**, 5, b g Azamour (IRE)—Pinaflore (FR) **Mr P. F. Barry**
28 **THE LEMONPIE (GER)**, 7, b h Next Desert (GER)—Terra Novalis (GER) **B. G. Powell**
29 **UNCLE DERMOT (IRE)**, 4, b g Arakan (USA)—Cappadoce (IRE) **Mr K. R. E. Rhatigan**
30 **WARNE'S WAY (IRE)**, 9, ch g Spinning World (USA)—Kafayef (USA) **N. J. Stafford**
31 **XENOPHON**, 4, b g Phoenix Reach (IRE)—Comtesse Noire (CAN) **Holistic Racing Ltd**
32 **YACHT LONDON LADY**, 6, b m Beat All (USA)—Country Choice (IRE) **Yacht London Racing**

THREE-YEAR-OLDS

33 **COPPER FALLS**, b f Trade Fair—Strat's Quest **P. Banfield**
34 **LADY ROMANZA (IRE)**, b f Holy Roman Emperor (IRE)—Sharakawa (IRE) **Mr P. Morris**

TWO-YEAR-OLDS

35 **STARLIGHT SYMPHONY (IRE)**, b f 11/4 Oratorio (IRE)—Phillippa (IRE) (Galileo (IRE)) (13136) **B. P. McNamee**

Other Owners: J. E. Bone, Mr L. H. Brewin, Mr A. P. Brown, Mr C. Chislett, Mr S. J. Corcoran, Dr J. D. Dalton, G. M. Flood, J. Kavanagh, D. Leon, Mr J. K. Llewellyn, C. H. Shankland, R. K. Stanley.

Jockey (flat): George Baker, Michael Hills. **Conditional:** Brendan Powell.

532 MR TED POWELL, Reigate
Postal: Nutwood Farm, Gatton Park Road, Reigate, Surrey, RH2 0SX

1 **AJJAADD (USA)**, 6, b g Elusive Quality (USA)—Millstream (USA) **Katy & Lol Pratt**
2 **CORMORANT WHARF (IRE)**, 12, b g Alzao (USA)—Mercy Bien (IRE) **Miss J. Powell**

Other Owners: Mrs K. J. Pratt, L. C. Pratt.

533 MR KEVIN M. PRENDERGAST, Malton
Postal: **Valley View, Pockley, York, North Yorkshire, YO62 7TE**
Contacts: **PHONE (01439) 770906 MOBILE (07795) 363992**
E-MAIL Kevin@prendergastracing.com WEBSITE www.prendergastracing.com

1 **CHARGEN (IRE)**, 9, b g Charente River (IRE)—Blasgan (IRE) **Mrs E. Madden**
2 **IT'S A MANS WORLD**, 6, b g Kyllachy—Exhibitor (USA) **K. M. Prendergast**
3 **LINDORO**, 7, b g Marju (IRE)—Floppie (FR) **Alchemy Bloodstock**
4 **RUBI DIA**, 5, ch g Hernando (FR)—Oblique (IRE) **Mrs B. Hardiman**
5 **SUGARLOAF SARAH**, 5, b m Grape Tree Road—Noreen Bawn (IRE) **R. J. Parsons**

THREE-YEAR-OLDS
6 **HIGHWAY WARRIOR**, b f Ishiguru (USA)—Blue Topaz (USA) **Mr P. M. Mannion**

TWO-YEAR-OLDS
7 B f 6/2 Holy Roman Emperor (IRE)—Coquette Rouge (IRE) (Croco Rouge (IRE)) **Lady C. J. O'Reilly**
8 B f 29/3 Montjeu (IRE)—Madeira Mist (IRE) (Grand Lodge (USA)) (120000) **Lady C. J. O'Reilly**

Other Owners: Mr P. J. Raybould, Mrs H. A. Raybould.

Assistant Trainer: M. G. Prendergast

Jockey (flat): Andrew Heffernan. **Jockey (NH):** Brian Toomey.

534 SIR MARK PRESCOTT BT, Newmarket
Postal: **Heath House, Newmarket, Suffolk, CB8 8DU**
Contacts: **PHONE (01638) 662117 FAX (01638) 666572**

1 **ALBARAKA**, 4, gr f Selkirk (USA)—Alborada **Miss K. Rausing**
2 **ALL MY HEART**, 4, gr f Sadler's Wells (USA)—Alba Stella **Miss K. Rausing**
3 **APPEAL (IRE)**, 4, gr f Selkirk (USA)—Amenixa (FR) **Denford Stud**
4 **CLINICAL**, 4, gr f Motivator—Doctor's Glory (USA) **Cheveley Park Stud**
5 **DANCE TO THE STARS (IRE)**, 4, b g Montjeu (IRE)—Dancingintheclouds (IRE) **W. E. Sturt - Osborne House**
6 **KEPLER'S LAW**, 4, b g Galileo (IRE)—Tina Heights **Rectory Racing**
7 **MOTIVADO**, 4, b g Motivator—Tamise (USA) **Syndicate 2009**
8 **SAMARKAND (IRE)**, 4, b g Sadler's Wells (USA)—Romantic Venture (IRE) **Moyglare Stud Farms Ltd**
9 **WORTHADD (IRE)**, 5, b b Dubawi (IRE)—Wigman (IRE) **Scuderia Incolinx**

THREE-YEAR-OLDS
10 **ALBAMARA**, b f Galileo (IRE)—Albanova **Miss K. Rausing**
11 **ALBASPINA (IRE)**, gr f Selkirk (USA)—Alabastrine **Miss K. Rausing**
12 **ATHENIAN (IRE)**, b f Acclamation—Ziria (IRE) **Axom (XXXI)**
13 **AWESOME PEARL (USA)**, b c Awesome Again (CAN)—Gottcha Last (USA) **Pearl Bloodstock Ltd**
14 **BETWEEN US**, b f Galileo (IRE)—Confidante (USA) **Cheveley Park Stud**
15 **BOLD CUFFS**, b g Dutch Art—Chambray (IRE) **Fawzi Abdulla Nass**
16 **BRISTOL FASHION**, b f Dansili—Approach **Denford Stud**
17 **CELESTIAL RAY**, ch c Pivotal—Heavenly Ray (USA) **Cheveley Park Stud**
18 **CRITICAL POINT**, ch g Pivotal—Finlaggan **G. Moore - Osborne House**
19 **FRESA**, b f Selkirk (USA)—Flor Y Nata (USA) **Miss K. Rausing**
20 **GARZONI**, ch f Medicean—Rainbow Queen **Cheveley Park Stud**
21 **GASSIN GOLF**, b g Montjeu (IRE)—Miss Riviera Golf **J. L. C. Pearce**
23 **GOOSEBERRY FOOL**, b f Danehill Dancer (IRE)—Last Second (IRE) **Mt. Brilliant Farm & Ranch**
24 **HOLISTIC**, gr f Pivotal—Doctor's Glory (USA) **Cheveley Park Stud**
25 **ITALIAN RIVIERA**, b g Galileo (IRE)—Miss Corniche **J. L. C. Pearce**
26 **KINETICA**, b f Stormy Atlantic (USA)—Kiswahili **Miss K. Rausing**
27 **LATE NIGHT MOVIE (IRE)**, b f Holy Roman Emperor (IRE)—Gifts Galore (IRE) **Moyglare Stud Farms Ltd**
28 **LUCKY MONEY**, ch g Selkirk (USA)—Autumn Wealth (IRE) **J. M. Brown**
29 **MUTUAL REGARD (IRE)**, b g Hernando (FR)—Hidden Charm (IRE) **Moyglare Stud Farms Ltd**
30 **NEIGE D'ANTAN**, gr f Aussie Rules (USA)—Ninotchka (USA) **Miss K. Rausing**
31 **PALLASATOR**, b g Motivator—Ela Athena **Baxter, Gregson, Jenkins & Warman**
32 **PONCHO**, b f Cape Cross (IRE)—Pixie Ring **Nicholas Jones**
33 **POSITION**, b g Medicean—Poise (USA) **Cheveley Park Stud**
34 **REPEATER**, b g Montjeu (IRE)—Time Over **Cheveley Park Stud**
35 **SEVEN VEILS (IRE)**, b f Danehill Dancer (IRE)—Ahdaab (USA) **Mrs Olivia Hoare**
36 **SOLAR VIEW (IRE)**, ch g Galileo (IRE)—Ellen (IRE) **Neil Greig - Osborne House**

SIR MARK PRESCOTT BT—continued

37 **THE BARONET**, b g Sir Percy—Windmill **Charles C. Walker - Osborne House**
38 **WELSH BARD (IRE)**, ch g Dylan Thomas (IRE)—Delphinium (IRE) **Eclipse Thoroughbreds - Osborne House**
39 **YOURS EVER**, b f Dansili—Love Everlasting **Cheveley Park Stud**

TWO-YEAR-OLDS

40 **ALCAEUS**, b c 23/2 Hernando (FR)—Alvarita (Selkirk (USA) (43000) **Ne'er Do Wells IV**
41 **ALWILDA**, gr f 12/2 Hernando (FR)—Albanova (Alzao (USA)) **Miss K. Rausing**
42 **ALZAVOLA**, gr f 14/2 With Approval (CAN)—Alizadora (Zilzal (USA)) **Miss K. Rausing**
43 **ARABIAN STORM (IRE)**, ch c 21/2 Hurricane Run (IRE)—
  Fatwa (IRE) (Lahib (USA)) (27093) **The Green Door Partnership**
44 **BIG THUNDER**, gr c 14/3 Dalakhani (IRE)—
  Charlotte O Fraise (IRE) (Beat Hollow) (80000) **John Brown & Megan Dennis**
45 **CURIOUS MIND**, b f 17/2 Dansili—Intrigued (Darshaan) **Denford Stud**
46 **HELICONIA**, b f 28/2 Hernando (FR)—Flor Y Nata (USA) (Fusaichi Pegasus (USA)) **Miss K. Rausing**
47 **HIDDEN LINK**, b c 10/3 Rail Link—Gloved Hand (Royal Applause) (32840) **W. E. Sturt - Osborne House III**
48 **HYPNOTISM**, ch c 21/3 Pivotal—Hypnotize (Machiavellian (USA)) **Cheveley Park Stud**
49 **ICY REPLY**, gr f 28/4 Hernando (FR)—Frosty Welcome (USA) (With Approval (CAN)) **Miss K. Rausing**
50 **INHERITED**, b c 10/2 Selkirk (USA)—Akdariya (IRE) (Shirley Heights) (24630) **P. J. McSwiney - Osborne House**
51 **JULY WAITS (USA)**, b f 2/4 Mr Greeley (USA)—
  Unique Pose (IRE) (Sadler's Wells) **Moyglare Stud Farms Ltd**
52 **LIBER**, b c 12/2 Ishiguru (USA)—Startori (Vettori (IRE)) (26666) **William Charnley & Richard Pegum**
53 **LYRIC PIECE**, ch f 16/2 Dutch Art—Humouresque (Pivotal) **Cheveley Park Stud**
54 **MAN FROM SEVILLE**, ch c 25/1 Duke of Marmalade (IRE)—
  Basanti (USA) (Galileo (IRE)) (120000) **Mr & Mrs William Rucker**
55 **MEDICOE**, ch g 28/1 Medicean—Blue Dream (IRE) (Cadeaux Genereux) **J. B. Haggas**
56 **MISS VISTAERO**, b f 25/2 Montjeu (IRE)—Miss Corniche (Hernando (FR)) **J. L. C. Pearce**
57 **NORTH POLE**, b c 17/3 Compton Place—
  Cool Question (Polar Falcon (USA)) **Lady Fairhaven & The Hon. C & H Broughton**
58 **OASIS CANNES**, b c 27/2 Oasis Dream—Miss Provence (Hernando (FR)) **J. L. C. Pearce**
59 **PEARL ANGEL (IRE)**, b f 12/2 Dark Angel (IRE)—Serious Delight (Lomond (USA)) (69785) **Pearl Bloodstock Ltd**
60 **PEARL SPICE (IRE)**, ch c 22/2 Dalakhani (IRE)—
  Cinnamon Rose (USA) (Trempolino (USA)) (135467) **Pearl Bloodstock Ltd**
61 **PIGEON POWER**, b f 5/3 Byron—Making Waves (IRE) (Danehill (USA)) (13333) **P. Bamford**
62 **PORTRAIT**, ch f 15/2 Peintre Celebre (USA)—Annalina (USA) (Cozzene (USA)) **Denford Stud**
63 **PRIVACY ORDER**, b f 31/1 Azamour (IRE)—Confidential Lady (Singspiel (IRE)) **Cheveley Park Stud**
64 **SAGESSE**, ch f 23/1 Smart Strike (CAN)—Summer Night (Nashwan (USA)) **Miss K. Rausing**
65 **SAVANNA LA MAR (USA)**, ch f 12/3 Curlin (USA)—Soft Morning (Pivotal) **Miss K. Rausing**
66 **SECRET SONG**, b c 7/3 Singspiel (USA)—
  Confidante (USA) (Dayjur (USA)) (85000) **W. E. Sturt - Osborne House II**
67 **SLIP OF THE TONGUE**, ch c 10/3 Zamindar (USA)—
  Kiswahili (Selkirk (USA)) (34481) **J. E. Fishpool - Osborne House**
68 **SZABO'S ART**, br f 1/4 Excellent Art—Violette (Observatory (USA)) (10000) **C. G. Rowles-Nicholson**
69 **WILD DIAMOND (IRE)**, b f 16/4 Hernando (FR)—
  Step With Style (USA) (Gulch (USA)) **Moyglare Stud Farms Ltd**

Other Owners: Mr E. A. Baxter, Mr & Mrs Timothy Bunting, Mr B. D. Burnet, Mr Terry Corden, Mr J. Donnelly, Mr Darren Ellis, Mr Phil Fry, Mr Greg Goodman, The Hon. Mrs G. Greenwood, Mrs Caroline Gregson, Mr Chris Jenkins, Mr L. A. Larratt, Mr David Lowrey, Mr E. B. Rimmer, Mrs Sonia Rogers, Mr Mike Rudd, Mr & Mrs Dennis Russell, Prince Faisal Salman, Mr Ian Spearing, Mr Barry Taylor, Mrs J. Taylor, Mr Mark Tracey, The Hon. Lady Troubridge, Mrs S. L. Warman, Mr E. J. Williams.

Assistant Trainer: William Butler, **Pupil Assistant:** James Horton

Jockey (flat): S. Sanders, S. Donohoe. **Apprentice:** R. Jessop, T. Clark.

---

535 MR ANDREW PRICE, Leominster
Postal: Eaton Hall Farm, Leominster, Herefordshire, HR6 0NA
Contacts: **PHONE** (01568) 611137 **FAX** (01568) 611137 **MOBILE** (07729) 838660
E-MAIL helen@aepriceracing.plus.com

1 **BOBBY DOVE**, 5, b g Fraam—Flakey Dove **Mrs G. M. Price**
2 5, B m Alflora (IRE)—Castanet **Mrs C. Davis**
3 **FRAAM LEA**, 6, b m Fraam—Castanet **Mrs C. Davis**
4 **JOHN'S OSCAR (IRE)**, 5, b g Oscar (IRE)—Vigna Maggio (FR) **Mrs H. L. Price**
5 **MIDNIGHT DOVE**, 7, ch g Karinga Bay—Flighty Dove **M. G. Racing**

MR ANDREW PRICE—continued

6 MISTER FIZZ, 4, b g Sulamani (IRE)—Court Champagne Mrs M. J. Wilson
7 SPENCER LEA, 4, b g Overbury (IRE)—Castanet Mrs C. Davis

Other Owners: A. G. Bathurst, Mr M. Jones, Mrs E. R. Kitt.

Assistant Trainer: Mrs H L Price

---

536 MRS ANN PRICE, Presteigne
Postal: The Meeting House, Norton, Presteigne, Powys, LD8 2HA
Contacts: PHONE (01544) 267221

1 BRIMLEY, 9, b g Bandmaster (USA)—Tinkers Night Mrs A. Price
2 GRASSCUTTER (IRE), 8, b g Presenting—Cherry Black (IRE) Mrs A. Price
3 GUNNADOIT (USA), 7, b br g Almutawakel—Gharam (USA) Mrs A. Price
4 HOH NELSON, 11, b g Halling (USA)—Birsay Mrs A. Price
5 MISTER TWIRLEY (IRE), 8, b g Zagreb (USA)—Dotties Rose (IRE) Mrs A. Price
6 TYUP POMPEY (IRE), 11, ch g Docksider (USA)—Cindy's Baby Mrs A. Price

Jockey (NH): Lee Stephens. Amateur: Mr R. Hodges.

---

537 MR JOHN PRICE, Ebbw Vale
Postal: 41 Beaufort Terrace, Ebbw Vale, Gwent, NP23 5NW
Contacts: PHONE (01495) 306113 MOBILE (07870) 475156

1 BOLD PERK (IRE), 10, ch g Executive Perk—Mugazine J. K. Price

Assistant Trainer: A J Price

---

538 MR RICHARD PRICE, Hereford
Postal: Criftage Farm, Ullingswick, Hereford, Herefordshire, HR1 3JG
Contacts: PHONE (01432) 820263 FAX (01432) 820785 MOBILE (07929) 200598

1 BARONS SPY (IRE), 11, b g Danzero (AUS)—Princess Accord (USA) B. Veasey
2 CHEVETON, 8, ch g Most Welcome—Attribute Mrs K. E. Oseman
3 COURT WING (IRE), 6, b m Hawk Wing (USA)—Nicely (IRE) Court Reclamation & Salvage Ltd
4 CRUISE CONTROL, 6, b g Piccolo—Urban Dancer (IRE) Cruise Control Partnership
5 DEPDEN (IRE), 4, ch g Captain Rio—Attribute Mrs K. E. Oseman
6 FARMERS DREAM (IRE), 5, b m Antonius Pius (USA)—Beucaire (IRE) D. J. Oseman
7 GALLEGO, 10, br g Danzero (AUS)—Shafir (IRE) My Left Foot Racing Syndicate
8 GRACIE'S GAMES, 6, b m Mind Games—Little Kenny Mr D. Prosser & Mr K. Warrington
9 GREYEMKAY, 4, gr g Fair Mix (IRE)—Magic Orb Mr R. J. Price & Maria Slade
10 K ISLAND (IRE), 4, b f Fruits of Love (USA)—Indiana Princess H. B. McGahon
11 KING KIEREN (IRE), 7, ch g King's Best (USA)—Across The Ice (USA) Mrs V. J. Morse
12 NALEDI, 8, b g Indian Ridge—Red Carnation (IRE) Mrs J. Thompson
13 PRINCE GOLAN (IRE), 8, b g Golan (IRE)—Mohican Princess R. J. Price
14 SEPTOS, 8, b g Nikos—Tres Chic (IRE) Mr P. D. Jefferies
15 TAURUS TWINS, 6, b g Deportivo—Intellibet One G. E. Amey & G. D. Bailey
16 TRANSFER, 7, br g Trans Island—Sankaty Light (USA) G. Ivall & R. J. Price
17 WESTERN PRIDE, 9, b m Classic Cliche (IRE)—Llanfihangel Lass G. E. Amey
18 YOU'VE BEEN MOWED, 6, ch m Ishiguru (USA)—Sandblaster Mrs K. E. Oseman

Other Owners: Mr A. J. Chance, Mr P. J. Hoare, Mr G. Ivall, Mr G. J. Meredith, Mr P. Packman, Mr R. J. Price, Mrs Helen R. Davies, Mr A. Wright.

Assistant Trainer: Jane Price

Amateur: Mr M. Price.

539 MR PETER PRITCHARD, Shipston-on-Stour
Postal: **The Gate House, Whatcote, Shipston-On-Stour, Warwickshire, CV36 5EF**
Contacts: **PHONE (01295) 680689**

1 **COWBRIDGE (IRE)**, 6, b g Pilsudski (IRE)—Clyde Goddess (IRE) **Trustmark**
2 **EARCOMESTHEDREAM (IRE)**, 9, b g Marignan (USA)—
            Play It By Ear (IRE) **Woodland Generators & Mr D R Pritchard**
3 **OVERTON LAD**, 11, gr g Overbury (IRE)—Safe Arrival (USA) **D. R. Pritchard**
4 **ROMAN LANDING**, 8, ch g Roi de Rome (USA)—Safe Arrival (USA) **D. R. Pritchard**
5 **SAM'S PRIDE**, 7, b g Needle Gun (IRE)—Bromley Supreme (IRE) **P. A. Pritchard**
6 **SHADESOFNAVY**, 6, ch g Fleetwood (IRE)—Safe Arrival (USA) **Whittington Racing Club**
7 **TISFREETDREAM (IRE)**, 11, b g Oscar (IRE)—Gayley Gale (IRE) **Woodland Generators & Mr D R Pritchard**

Other Owners: Mr W. R. Evans, Mr R. A. Evans, Mrs V. L. Pryor, Mr C. S. White, Woodlands (Worcestershire) Ltd.

Assistant Trainer: Mrs. E. Gardner

Jockey (NH): J. Doyle, Jamie Moore.

540 MR GEORGE PRODROMOU, East Harling
Postal: **Georges Farm, Bryants Bridge, East Harling, Norfolk, NR16 2JR**
Contacts: **OFFICE (01953) 717224 FAX (01953) 717317 MOBILE (07899) 071001**
E-MAIL georgeprodromouracing@hotmail.co.uk

1 **CALLISTO LIGHT**, 5, ch m Medicean—Luminda (IRE) **G. Prodromou**
2 **CHILLIE PEPPAR**, 4, b g Araafa (IRE)—Obsessive (USA) **Mr M. Bartram**
3 **MISTER FROSTY (IRE)**, 6, gr g Verglas (IRE)—La Chinampina (FR) **Mr M. Bartram**
4 **NAHEELL**, 6, ch h Lomitas—Seyooll (IRE) **Mr F. Al Dabbous**
5 **RAUCOUS BEHAVIOUR (USA)**, 4, b g Street Cry (IRE)—Caffe Latte (IRE) **Mr M. Bartram**
6 **TRIP SWITCH**, 5, b g Reset (AUS)—Caribbean Star **G. Prodromou**
7 **TROJAN ROCKET (IRE)**, 4, b g Elusive City (USA)—Tagula Bay (IRE) **G. D. J. Linder**

THREE-YEAR-OLDS

8 **ENGLISHGREEK (IRE)**, b g Desert Style (IRE)—Hot Dish (USA) **Mr P. Hajipiery**
9 **GREEK MUSIC**, gr f Librettist (USA)—Silver Spell **Mr A. Prodromou**

Assistant Trainer: Paul Ferguson

Jockey (NH): Robert Thornton. **Amateur:** Mr Matthew Smith.

541 MR PETER PURDY, Bridgwater
Postal: **Fyne Court Farm, Broomfield, Bridgwater, Somerset, TA5 2EQ**
Contacts: **PHONE (01823) 451632 FAX (01823) 451632 MOBILE (07860) 392786**
E-MAIL purdy844@btinternet.com

1 **BOWMANS WELL (IRE)**, 7, b m Cadeaux Genereux—Guignol (IRE) **P. D. Purdy**
2 **COURT FINALE**, 11, ch g One Voice (USA)—Tudor Sunset **P. D. Purdy**
3 **COURT HUMOUR**, 9, b g Joligeneration—Tudor Sunset **P. D. Purdy**
4 **JOLI'S DAUGHTER**, 7, b m Joligeneration—Tudor Sunset **P. D. Purdy**
5 **MAY COURT**, 5, b g Groomsbridge May I—Tudor Sunset **P. D. Purdy**
6 **SUNRISE COURT**, 13, ch g One Voice (USA)—Tudor Sunset **P. D. Purdy**
7 **THE BLONDE EMPEROR**, 7, ch g Emperor Fountain—Tudor Blonde **P. D. Purdy**

Assistant Trainer: Alison J Purdy

Jockey (flat): Neil Chambers. **Jockey (NH):** Harry Challoner. **Apprentice:** Charles Bishop. **Amateur:** Miss A. Purdy.

542 MR NOEL QUINLAN, Newmarket
Postal: **Grange House Stables, Hamilton Road, Newmarket, Suffolk, CB8 0TE**
Contacts: **PHONE (01638) 660464 FAX (01638) 663282 MOBILE (07815) 072946**
E-MAIL noelquinlanracing@hotmail.com

1 **ABRIACHAN**, 5, b g Celtic Swing—Cape Finisterre (IRE) **Mr T. Mann**
2 4, Ch c Danroad (AUS)—Alpathar (IRE) **Miss M. Quinlan**
3 **ARIYFA (IRE)**, 4, br f Cape Cross (IRE)—Arameen (IRE) **Mr Tommy Cummins**

MR NOEL QUINLAN—continued

4 **BILIDN**, 4, b f Tiger Hill (IRE)—Brightest Star **P. J. Wilmott**
5 **BLANCHE DUBAWI (IRE)**, 4, b f Dubawi (IRE)—Dixie Belle **Burns Farm Racing**
6 **CELTIC SIXPENCE (IRE)**, 4, b f Celtic Swing—Penny Ha'penny **Burns Farm Racing**
7 **CRAFTY ROBERTO**, 4, ch g Intikhab (USA)—Mowazana (IRE) **The Twice Shy Partnership**
8 **ENRICHING (USA)**, 4, ch c Lemon Drop Kid (USA)—Popozinha (USA) **Miss J. E. Moore**
9 **OUR GAL**, 4, b f Kyllachy—Moxby **Mr G. Wilding**
10 **PEADAR MIGUEL**, 5, b g Danroad (AUS)—La Corujera **Mr P. Moran**
11 **RAYNELL**, 4, b g Araafa (IRE)—Milly-M **Mr R. O. Simpson**
12 **REPOSER (IRE)**, 4, br g Kheleyf (USA)—Tragic Point (IRE) **Miss J. E. Moore**
13 **TIGER GIRL**, 5, b m Tiger Hill (IRE)—Girl of My Dreams (IRE) **A. Parker**

THREE-YEAR-OLDS

14 **AMOURE MEDICI**, b g Medicean—Lifetime Romance (IRE) **Mrs D. Jeromson**
15 **ARROW LAKE (FR)**, b f Refuse To Bend (IRE)—Lake Nipigon **Burns Farm Racing**
16 **DIAMOND BELLE**, b f Rock of Gibraltar (IRE)—Dixie Belle **Burns Farm Racing**
17 **HARMONIE (IRE)**, b f Teofilo (IRE)—Harmonist (USA) **Newtown Anner Stud Farm**
18 **LESOTHO (IRE)**, gr f Excellent Art—Limpopo **Swordlestown Stud**
19 **NO PLAN B (IRE)**, b f Le Vie Dei Colori—Heres The Plan (IRE) **Mrs Jeanette Johnson & Mr Paul Crowley**
20 **STORMIN GORDON (IRE)**, b f Tagula (IRE)—Karashino (IRE) **Phil Mills, J. Farrell, A. & C. Smith**
21 B f Footstepsinthesand—Sweet Times **Swordlestown Stud**
22 **TWEEDLE DEE (IRE)**, b f Araafa (IRE)—Sismique **Mr G. Wilding**

TWO-YEAR-OLDS

23 B f 8/3 Cockney Rebel (IRE)—Groom Landing (PR) (Runaway Groom (CAN)) **Mr T. Elliot**
24 B f 26/4 Rock of Gibraltar (IRE)—Marie de Blois (IRE) (Barathea (IRE)) (8000) **Mr Tommy Cummins**
25 B c 12/3 Lucky Story (USA)—Penny Ha'penny (Bishop of Cashel) (9523)
26 B c 1/4 Oasis Dream—Pinacotheque (IRE) (In The Wings) **R. G. & T. E. Levin**
27 B c 24/4 Three Valleys (USA)—Query (USA) (Distant View) (2666) **Burns Farm Racing**
28 B f 19/4 Moss Vale (IRE)—Toldya (Beveled (USA)) (820) **Mr Tommy Cummins**

---

543 MR JOHN QUINN, Malton

Postal: Bellwood Cottage Stables, Settrington, Malton, North Yorkshire, YO17 8NR
Contacts: PHONE (01944) 768370 FAX (01944) 768261 MOBILE (07899) 873304
E-MAIL johnquinnracing@btconnect.com WEBSITE www.johnquinnracing.co.uk

1 **ABIDHABIDUBAI**, 4, b f Dubai Destination (USA)—Madamoiselle Jones **N. S. Cooper**
2 **BALLYBRIGGAN (IRE)**, 8, b g Flemensfirth (USA)—Shean Hill (IRE) **Stewart Andrew & Jim Shaw**
3 **BLUE DESTINATION**, 4, b g Dubai Destination (USA)—Bluebelle **Maxilead Limited**
4 **COUNTRYWIDE FLAME**, 4, b g Haafhd—Third Party **Estio Pinnacle Racing**
5 **DISTIME (IRE)**, 6, b g Flemensfirth (USA)—Technohead (IRE) **Maxilead Limited**
6 **DUCHESS DORA (IRE)**, 5, b m Tagula (IRE)—Teodora (IRE) **The Clay Family**
7 **FOLK TUNE (IRE)**, 9, b g Danehill (USA)—Musk Lime (USA) **J. N. Blackburn**
8 **HAWK MOUNTAIN (UAE)**, 7, b g Halling (USA)—Friendly (USA) **P. Morrison & N. Luck**
9 **INDIAN ARROW**, 4, b c Sleeping Indian—Hillside Girl (IRE) **A. Stennett**
10 **IULUS**, 4, ch g Kheleyf (USA)—Miri (IRE) **Mrs S. Quinn**
11 **KIAMA BAY (IRE)**, 6, b g Fraam—La Panthere (USA) **Dr M. B. Q. S. Koukash**
12 **KING FINGAL (IRE)**, 7, b g King's Best (USA)—Llia **William (Bill) Hobson**
13 **LAYLA'S HERO (IRE)**, 5, b g One Cool Cat (USA)—Capua (USA) **Dr M. B. Q. S. Koukash**
14 **LIGHT FROM MARS**, 7, gr g Fantastic Light (USA)—Hylandra (USA) **Dr M. B. Q. S. Koukash**
15 **LUCCOMBE CHINE**, 7, ch m Karinga Bay—Sounds Familiar (IRE) **Mrs M. L. Luck**
16 **MADAMLILY (IRE)**, 6, b m Refuse To Bend (IRE)—Rainbow Dream **R. N. McMillan**
17 **MARSTER PARKES**, 4, b g Nayef (USA)—Lucky Parkes **J. Heler**
18 **MASSINI LOTTO (IRE)**, 5, b g Dr Massini (IRE)—Our Lot (IRE) **Mr P. Taylor & Mr J. Stone**
19 **MOONLIGHT DRIVE (IRE)**, 6, b g Oscar (IRE)—Perspex Queen (IRE) **Maxilead Limited**
20 **NEW PLANET (IRE)**, 4, ch g Majestic Missile (IRE)—Xena (IRE) **Mr R. Harmon**
21 **NEWPORT ARCH**, 4, b c Pastoral Pursuits—Mashmoun **A. Mann**
22 **PALAWI (IRE)**, 5, ch g Dubawi (IRE)—Palwina (FR) **R. N. McMillan**
23 **ROYAL BONSAI**, 4, b g Val Royal (FR)—Bonsai (IRE) **R. Kent**
24 **SELECT COMMITTEE**, 7, b g Fayruz—Demolition Jo **Which Bits Mine Syndicate**
25 **TARTAN TIGER (IRE)**, 6, ch g Flemensfirth (USA)—River Clyde (IRE) **Distillery Racing Club**
26 **UNCLE BRYN**, 4, b g Royal Applause—Happy Omen **Mrs E. Wright**
27 **VEILED APPLAUSE**, 9, b g Royal Applause—Scarlet Veil **Far 2 Many Sues**
28 **VIOLENT VELOCITY (IRE)**, 9, b g Namid—Lear's Crown (USA) **Mrs S. Quinn**

MR JOHN QUINN—continued

29 **ZAPLAMATION (IRE)**, 7, b g Acclamation—Zapatista **Mr Andrew Turton & Mr David Barker**
30 **ZOMERLUST**, 10, b g Josr Algarhoud (IRE)—Passiflora **Dawson & Quinn**

THREE-YEAR-OLDS

31 **ALL OR NOTHIN (IRE)**, b g Majestic Missile (IRE)—Lady Peculiar (CAN) **Mr R. Harmon**
32 **BALTIC BOMBER (IRE)**, b g Baltic King—Dieci Anno (IRE) **The New Century Partnership**
33 **CMONBABYLITEMYFIRE (IRE)**, b f Piccolo—Danetime Out (IRE) **Dawson & Quinn**
34 **DORA'S SISTER (IRE)**, b f Dark Angel (IRE)—Teodora (IRE) **The Clay Family**
35 **KYLLACHY DANCER**, b f Kyllachy—Aunt Susan **Bellwood Cottage Syndicate I**
36 **MARSHALL ART**, b c Lawman (FR)—Portrait of A Lady (IRE) **A. Stennett**
37 **PLANETEX (IRE)**, b c Majestic Missile (IRE)—Xena (IRE) **Mr R. Harmon**
38 **RED DUKE (USA)**, ch c Hard Spun (USA)—Saudia (USA) **Maxilead Limited**
39 **RED TYKE (IRE)**, b g Red Clubs (IRE)—Teutonic (IRE) **Mr T. G. S. Wood**
40 **ROLL OF THUNDER**, b g Antonius Pius (USA)—Ischia **A. W. Robson & Mrs M. H. Robson**
41 **SIR WINDSORLOT (IRE)**, b g Windsor Knot (IRE)—Hever Rosina **Which Bits Mine Syndicate 2**
42 **SUPERPLEX**, b c Multiplex—Hillside Girl (IRE) **A. Stennett**
43 **UNCLE TIMMY**, b g Multiplex—Park's Girl **Mrs A. M. O'Sullivan**

TWO-YEAR-OLDS

44 Ch c 1/3 Sakhee's Secret—Angry Bark (USA) (Woodman (USA)) (20000) **Mrs S. Quinn**
45 B f 23/4 Smart Strike (CAN)—Asuncion (USA) (Powerscourt) (15262) **Mr R. Harmon**
46 B br c 7/3 Gone West (USA)—Katherine Seymour (Green Desert (USA)) (73260) **Maxilead Limited**
47 **MAJOR PARKES**, gr c 19/2 Fair Mix (IRE)—My Melody Parkes (Teenoso (USA)) **J. Heler**
48 **PACQUIAO (IRE)**, b c 2/3 Teofilo (IRE)—Woodland Chant (USA) (War Chant (USA)) (24630) **Mr R. Harmon**
49 B g 7/3 Duke of Marmalade (IRE)—Rambler (Selkirk (USA)) (23809) **J. R. Rowbottom**
50 **THARAWAL LADY (IRE)**, b f 8/3 Moss Vale—Notley Park (Wolfhound (USA)) (10476) **Highfield Racing**

Other Owners: Mr D. W. Barker, Mr H. J. Cook, Mrs S. E. Cook, Mr Elliot Graham, Mr Fergus J. Grimes, Mr R. Kent, Mr Les Lawson, Mr N. E. F. Luck, Mr P. R. C. Morrison, Mrs S. Quinn, Mr Robert Robinson, Mr Robert Turner, Mr Andrew Turton.

Assistant Trainer: Paul Dalton

Jockey (NH): Dougie Costello. **Conditional:** Dean Pratt.

 MR MICHAEL QUINN, Newmarket
Postal: **Southgate Barn, Hamilton Road, Newmarket, Suffolk, CB8 0WY**
Contacts: **PHONE (01638) 660017 FAX (01638) 660017 MOBILE (07973) 260054**
E-MAIL mick@quinn2562.fsnet.co.uk

1 **AUDACIOUS**, 4, b g Motivator—Flash of Gold **A & J Racing Ltd**
2 **GAY GALLIVANTER**, 4, b f Iceman—Gallivant **A. Viner**
3 **MIAKORA**, 4, ch f Compton Place—Hickleton Lady (IRE) **M. Quinn**
4 **ROMAN FLAME**, 4, ch f Bertolini (USA)—Dakhla Oasis (IRE) **The Ten Fools & A Horse Partnership**
5 **TOUCAN TANGO (IRE)**, 4, b g Mujadil (USA)—Walk On Quest (FR) **A & J Racing Ltd**
6 **WATERLOO DOCK**, 7, b g Hunting Lion (IRE)—Scenic Air **Mr M. J. Quinn**

THREE-YEAR-OLDS

7 **KASHMIRI STAR**, b f Barathea (IRE)—Biriyani (IRE) **A & J Racing Ltd**

Other Owners: Mr J. W. Blake, Mr G. P. Chapman, Mr J. G. Henry, Mr A. Newby, J. E. Quorn.

Assistant Trainer: Miss Karen Davies

Jockey (flat): Franny Norton.

---

545 **MR C. I. RATCLIFFE, York**
Postal: **Creets House Farm, Teal Cottage Stud, Welburn, York, YO6 7EP**

1 **TEALS STAR**, 8, b g Gods Solution—Morcat **C. I. Ratcliffe**

546 **MR WILLIAM REED, Umberleigh**
Postal: Stowford Farm, East Stowford, Chittlehampton, Umberleigh, Devon, EX37 9RU
Contacts: PHONE (01769) 540292 MOBILE (07967) 130991

1 ALMOST HERE (IRE), 9, b g Lear Spear (USA)—Second Violin (IRE) W. J. Reed
2 LISSELAN GALAXY (IRE), 6, b g Galileo (IRE)—Amazonian (CAN) W. J. Reed
3 LITTLE WADHAM, 7, b m Bandmaster (USA)—Sport of Fools (IRE) W. J. Reed
4 QARAARAT (IRE), 9, ch g In The Wings—Filfilah W. J. Reed
5 WADHAM HILL, 10, b m Bandmaster (USA)—Sport of Fools (IRE) W. J. Reed

547 **MR DAVID REES, Haverfordwest**
Postal: The Grove Yard, Clarbeston Road, Haverfordwest, Pembrokeshire, SA63 4SP
Contacts: PHONE (01437) 731308 FAX (01437) 731551 MOBILE (07775) 662463
E-MAIL davidreesfencing@lineone.net

1 CHANGING LANES, 9, b g Overbury (IRE)—Snowdon Lily Mrs J. Mathias
2 COMEHOMEQUIETLY (IRE), 8, b g King's Theatre (IRE)—Windswept Lady (IRE) IWEC International Ltd
3 FISHING BRIDGE (IRE), 7, ch g Definite Article—Rith Ar Aghaidh (IRE) D. A. Rees
4 MACARTHUR, 8, b g Montjeu (IRE)—Out West (USA) Mr Dai Rees & Mr Billy Evans
5 MACRA NA FEIRME (IRE), 9, br g Exit To Nowhere (USA)—De Derri (IRE) IWEC International Ltd
6 MAJOR DECISION (IRE), 10, b br g Saddlers' Hall (IRE)—Real Prospect (IRE) D. A. Rees
7 RIME AVEC GENTIL (FR), 7, b g Kapgarde (FR)—Quenice (FR) D. A. Rees
8 RIMINI (FR), 7, b g Bedawin (FR)—Ma'am (FR) D. A. Rees
9 TREV TARA, 5, b g Kayf Tara—Scarlet Dawn (IRE) D. A. Rees
10 TWO SHOOK MEN (IRE), 8, b g Posidonas—Birthday Honours (IRE) D. A. Rees
11 WARWICKSHIRE (IRE), 5, b g Westerner—Emeranna (IRE) Mr R. J. C. Lewis / Mr P.A.T. Rice

Other Owners: Mr N. Adams, Mrs Denise Cross, Mrs Siobhan Devonald, Mr W. J. Evans, Miss Emma Noremac, Mr D. Rees.

Assistant Trainer: Mr John Mathias

Amateur: Mr John Mathias.

548 **MRS HELEN REES, Dorchester**
Postal: Distant Hills, Chalmington, Dorchester, Dorset, DT2 0HB
Contacts: PHONE (01300) 320683 MOBILE (07715) 558289
E-MAIL helen-rees@live.co.uk

1 CNOC MOY (IRE), 8, b g Mull of Kintyre (USA)—Ewar Sunrise Mrs H. E. Rees

Assistant Trainer: Mr Rupert Rees

549 **MR SEAN REGAN, Middleham**
Postal: Alma House Farm, West Witton, Leyburn, North Yorkshire, DL8 4UG

1 FLOAT MY BOAT, 6, b g Beat All (USA)—Bit of A Chick F. Butler
2 MERIDIEM, 8, b g Tamure—Anatomic Mr M. S. U. Hustler
3 PTOLOMEOS, 9, b g Kayf Tara—Lucy Tufty Mrs C. D. Taylor
4 RENEGE THE JOKER, 9, b g Alflora (IRE)—Bunty S. Regan
5 SHEILA'S CASTLE, 8, b m Karinga Bay—Candarela Ms J. M. Carrington

550 **MR ANDREW REID, Mill Hill, London**
Postal: Highwood Lodge, Highwood Hill, Mill Hill, London, NW7 4HB
Contacts: PHONE (07836) 214617 FAX (02089) 061255 MOBILE (07747) 751603

1 AMETHYST DAWN (IRE), 6, gr m Act One—A L'aube (IRE) A. S. Reid
2 DAVIDS DILEMMA, 4, ch g Teofilo (IRE)—Prairie Oyster Dr D. S. Myers & Mr A. S. Reid
3 DECIMATE, 4, br g Teofilo (IRE)—Kirriemuir A. S. Reid
4 MOSQUETA, 5, b m Doyen—Arantxa A. S. Reid
5 MR PLOD, 7, ch g Silver Patriarch (IRE)—Emily-Mou (IRE) A. S. Reid
6 OVERWHELM, 4, ch f Bahamian Bounty—Depressed A. S. Reid

MR ANDREW REID—continued

7 **PULLMEN**, 4, gr g Silver Patriarch (IRE)—Moon Spinner **A. S. Reid**

THREE-YEAR-OLDS

8 **ATHLETIC**, b g Doyen (IRE)—Gentle Irony **A. S. Reid**
9 **CHAMBLES**, b f Shamardal (USA)—Pants **A. S. Reid**
10 **CRISTAL GEM**, ch f Cadeaux Genereux—Desert Cristal (IRE) **A. S. Reid**
11 **MALTEASE AH**, br f Librettist (USA)—Manic **A. S. Reid**

TWO-YEAR-OLDS

12 Ch f 3/4 Bahamian Bounty—Depressed (Most Welcome) **A. S. Reid**
13 B f 1/4 Act One—Pants (Pivotal)

Other Owners: Dr D. S. Myers, Mr A. S. Reid.

Assistant Trainer: Ricardo Lanfranco

Jockey (flat): Jim Crowley.

---

551 MRS JACQUELINE RETTER, Cullompton
Postal: **Dulford Cottage, Dulford, Cullompton, Devon, EX15 2DX**
Contacts: **PHONE/FAX** (01884) 266078 **MOBILE** (07912) 889655

1 **ALFIE BROWN**, 9, b g Alflora (IRE)—Broughton Manor **Mrs J. G. Retter**
2 **EXILES RETURN (IRE)**, 10, b g Needle Gun (IRE)—Moores Girl (IRE) **Mrs J. G. Retter**
3 **ON THE RAZ**, 5, b m Rakaposhi King—Trillow **Mrs J. G. Retter**

---

552 MR KEITH REVELEY, Saltburn
Postal: **Groundhill Farm, Lingdale, Saltburn-by-the-Sea, Cleveland, TS12 3HD**
Contacts: **OFFICE** (01287) 650456 **FAX** (01287) 653095 **MOBILE** (07971) 784539
E-MAIL reveleyracing@yahoo.co.uk

1 **ALORA MONEY**, 9, b m Alflora (IRE)—Mrs Moneypenny **Shade Oak Stud**
2 **BARDOLET (IRE)**, 9, b g Snurge—Bonne Atthenagh (IRE) **Mrs S. A. Smith**
3 **BENNY BE GOOD**, 9, b g Benny The Dip (USA)—Hembane (FR) **J. Wade**
4 **BOLD RANSOM (IRE)**, 10, b g Lord of Appeal—Bodalmore Rose (IRE) **Mrs G. P. Furness**
5 **BROCTUNE PAPA GIO**, 5, b g Tobougg (IRE)—Fairlie **Broctune Partners I**
6 **CATEGORICAL**, 9, b g Diktat—Zibet **Rug, Grub & Pub Partnership**
7 **COLUMBUS SECRET (IRE)**, 7, b g Luso—Bid For Fun (IRE) **R. Collins**
8 **CORKAGE (IRE)**, 9, b g Second Empire (IRE)—Maslam (IRE) **The Scarth Racing Partnership**
9 **CROWNING JEWEL**, 6, b g Sulamani (IRE)—Pennys Pride (IRE) **Sir Ian Good**
10 **CUE TO CUE**, 6, b m King's Theatre (IRE)—Marello **Mr & Mrs W. J. Williams**
11 **D'GIGI**, 6, ch m Beat Hollow—Strictly Cool (USA) **Sunking Partnership**
12 **DANCE OF TIME**, 5, b g Presenting—Northern Native (IRE) **Mrs S. A. Smith**
13 **DANCING ART (IRE)**, 6, b g Definite Article—Seductive Dance **R. Collins**
14 **DELTA FORTY**, 4, b f Alflora (IRE)—Northern Native (IRE) **Mrs S. Smith**
15 **EYRE SQUARE (IRE)**, 9, b g Publisher (USA)—Eyre Eile (IRE) **J. Wade**
16 **FLORA'S PRIDE**, 8, b m Alflora (IRE)—Pennys Pride (IRE) **The Eleven O'Clock Club II**
17 **FLORAROSSA**, 8, b m Alflora (IRE)—Bayrouge (IRE) **Mrs A. Fulton**
18 **HARVEY'S HOPE**, 6, b g Sinndar (IRE)—Ancara **The Home & Away Partnership**
19 **HEAVENLY CHORUS**, 10, b m Key of Luck (USA)—Celestial Choir **Rug, Grub & Pub Partnership**
20 **I GOT MUSIC**, 5, gr m Silver Patriarch (IRE)—I Got Rhythm **Mrs M. B. Thwaites**
21 **IRISH CHAPERONE (IRE)**, 5, b g High Chaparral (IRE)—Harry's Irish Rose (USA) **R. Collins**
22 **JESSICA VALENTINE (IRE)**, 5, b m King's Theatre (IRE)—Jessica One (IRE) **Mr I. Valentine**
23 **JUKEBOX MELODY (IRE)**, 6, b g Brian Boru—Carmels Cottage (IRE) **J. Wade**
24 **KARINGREASON**, 9, b m Karinga Bay—Noreasonatall **Mr A G Knowles & Mr & Mrs Darren Allick**
25 **KINGS GREY (IRE)**, 8, gr g King's Theatre—Grey Mo (IRE) **J. Wade**
26 **LA CALINDA**, 5, b m Presenting—Bayrouge (IRE) **Mac & Lingdale Optimists Partnership**
27 **MADRASA (IRE)**, 4, b g High Chaparral (IRE)—Shir Dar (FR) **Mr M. W. Joyce**
28 **MR PUCK (IRE)**, 5, gr g Tikkanen (USA)—Vicky's Music (IRE) **Major P. & Mrs S. Arkwright, Mrs I. C. Sellars**
29 **NIGHT IN MILAN (IRE)**, 6, b g Milan—Chione (IRE) **R. Collins**
30 **OAKLANDS ELISE**, 5, ch m Prince Daniel (USA)—Out of The Shadows **Mrs V. Munro**
31 **PEGASUS PRINCE (USA)**, 8, b g Fusaichi Pegasus (USA)—Avian Eden (USA) **J. Wade**
32 4, B f Flemensfirth (USA)—Pennys Pride (IRE) **Reveley Farms**

MR KEITH REVELEY—continued

33 **REASONABLE FORCE**, 6, b g Forzando—Noreasonatall **Cristiana's Crew & A. G. Knowles**
34 **ROBBIE**, 8, b g Robellino (USA)—Corn Lily **Mrs S. McDonald**
35 **SAM D'OC (FR)**, 6, b g Chef de Clan (FR)—Samarie (FR) **The Supreme Alliance**
36 **SAMBELUCKY (IRE)**, 7, b g Barathea (IRE)—Kalimar (IRE) **Maurice Foxton, JBP & DAG Partnership**
37 **SEREN GRIS**, 6, gr m Fair Mix (IRE)—Bayrouge (IRE) **Phoenix Racing & Mr Jeremy Mitchell**
38 **SEREN ROUGE**, 7, b g Old Vic—Bayrouge (IRE) **Phoenix Racing & Mr Jeremy Mitchell**
39 **SPECIAL CATCH (IRE)**, 5, b g Catcher In The Rye (IRE)—Top Quality **Mr Mike Browne & Mr William McKeown**
40 **SWINGING SULTAN**, 5, b g Sulamani (IRE)—Nobratinetta (FR) **Reveley Racing 1**
41 **THURNHAM**, 6, b g Tobougg (IRE)—Nobratinetta (FR) **J. M. & Mrs M. R. Edwardson**
42 **VICTOR HEWGO**, 7, b g Old Vic—Pennys Pride (IRE) **Sir Ian Good & MAC Partnership**
43 **VINETTA**, 4, b f Grape Tree Road—Nobratinetta (FR) **The Thoughtful Partnership**

THREE-YEAR-OLDS

44 **GIVEITAGO**, b g Tobougg (IRE)—Trevorsninepoints **Mrs M. Child**

Other Owners: Mr. R. J. Ainscough, Mrs Sally Allick, Mr Darren Allick, Mr C. Anderson, Mrs Marilyn Bauckham, Mr D. E. Baxter, Mrs C. M. Baxter, Mr J. P Bladen, Mr D. Bowen, Mr M. Bradley, Mr A. E. Brown, Mr Mike Browne, Mr Hugh Chatterton, Mrs M. Clark-Wright, Ms J. Clarson, Exors of the Late Mr D. C. Clewer, Mr J. W. Coates, Mr E. Coll, Mr A. E. Corbett, Mrs P.E. Drinkall, Mr J. M. Edwardson, Mrs M. R. Edwardson, Mr M. E. Foxton, Mr Ian Fraser, Sir Ian Good, Mr Brian W. Goodall, Mr Jeff Goodall, Mr George Gray, Mr David A. Green, Mrs D. Greenhalgh, Mr Roger Hart, Mr Anthony Iceton, Mr R. F. Johnson, Mr Ernest Johnson, Mr A. G. Knowles, Mrs Christine Lally, Mr P Longstaff, Mr D. Lovell, Mr Ken Matthews, Mr W. McKeown, Mr T. M. McKain, Miss J. Mitchell, Mrs Lynn Morrison, Mrs D. A. Oliver, Mr Douglas Renton, Mr Graeme Renton, Mrs M. A. Renton, Reveley Farms, Mr J. Rodgers, Mrs A. Rodgers, Mr J. Scarth, Mr Richard V. Smith, Mrs Elizabeth Stephens, Mr Richard Stephens, Mr V. P Stevens, Mr Jim Struth, Mr J. Thoroughgood, Mr Michael Walsh, Mr Ron Whitehead, Mr David Wild, Mr W. J. Williams, Mrs M. Williams, Mr M. Wood, Mrs C. M. Yates, Lord Zetland.

Assistant Trainer: Fiona Reveley

Jockey (NH): James Reveley. **Amateur:** Mr Colm McCormack, Mr Russell Lindsay.

---

553 MR PAUL RICH, Newport
Postal: Cwrt-y-Mwnws Farmhouse, Allt-yr-Yn, Newport, Gwent, NP20 5EL

1 **AIM**, 7, b g Weetman's Weigh (IRE)—Ballet On Ice (FR) **Miss R. Martin & Mrs J. M. Martin**
2 **EDGWARE ROAD**, 4, ch g Selkirk (USA)—Bayswater **L. M. Power**
3 **EPIC STORM (IRE)**, 4, b c Montjeu (IRE)—Jaya (USA) **L. M. Power**
4 **FIRST BATTALION (IRE)**, 4, b g Sadler's Wells (USA)—Mubkera (IRE) **Mrs E. Johansen-Wooder**
5 **HOW NICE (IRE)**, 6, b g Indian Danehill (IRE)—Native Baby (IRE) **Mr A. Wells**
6 **LESLEY'S CHOICE**, 6, b g Lucky Story (USA)—Wathbat Mtoto **L. M. Power**
7 **MINORTRANSGRESSION (USA)**, 5, ch g Yes It's True (USA)—Casting Pearls (USA) **Mr G. A. Morgan**
8 **NATURAL HIGH (IRE)**, 7, b g Sadler's Wells (USA)—Cool Clarity (IRE) **L. M. Power**
9 **OFFICER IN COMMAND (USA)**, 6, b br h Officer (USA)—Luv to Stay n Chat (USA) **P. M. Rich**
10 **RAILWAY RICO (IRE)**, 7, b g Beneficial—Lester's Perk (IRE) **Connect Eight**
11 **RICH KAYF**, 8, b g Kayf Tara—Granny Rich **P. M. Rich**
12 **SAINGLEND**, 7, b g Galileo (IRE)—Verbal Intrigue (USA) **Mr W. J. Byrne**
13 **SIZING AMERICA (IRE)**, 11, b g Lord America—Annfield Lady (IRE) **The Good, The Bad & The Handsome**
14 **WALDSEE (GER)**, 7, b g Xaar—Wurftaube (GER) **L M Power & Global Self Drive**
15 **WHODATHOUGHT (IRE)**, 4, b c Choisir (AUS)—Consultant Stylist (IRE) **L. M. Power**

Other Owners: Mr C. E. Barnes, Mr W. H. R. Grindle, Mr J. P. Hampson, Mr M. Hampson, Mr N. D. Harrison, Miss R. M. Martin, Mrs J. M. Martin, Mrs J. C. Murray, Mr D. J. Murrell, Mr R. S. Parker, Mr C. Webb, Mr H. P. Whittaker.

---

554 MR DAVID RICHARDS, Abergavenny
Postal: White House, Llantilio Crossenny, Abergavenny, Gwent, NP7 8SU

1 **ANOTHER KATE (IRE)**, 8, gr m Norwich—Cracking Kate (IRE) **D. M. Richards**
2 **SILVER KATE (IRE)**, 9, gr m Insan (USA)—Cracking Kate (IRE) **D. M. Richards**

555   MRS LYDIA RICHARDS, Chichester

Postal: Lynch Farm, Hares Lane, Funtington, Chichester, West Sussex, PO18 9LW
Contacts: YARD (01243) 574379 HOME (01243) 574882 MOBILE (07803) 199061
E-MAIL lydia.richards@sky.com

1 AALY, 5, b g Milan—Leyaaly M. P. Merwood
2 DEMOISELLE BOND, 4, ch f Monsieur Bond (IRE)—Baytown Flyer The Demoiselle Bond Partnership
3 4, Gr ro f Silver Patriarch (IRE)—Henrietta Holmes (IRE) Mrs Lydia Richards
4 HENRY HOLMES, 9, b g Josr Algarhoud (IRE)—Henrietta Holmes (IRE) Mrs E. F. J. Seal
5 INNER STEEL (IRE), 7, b g Zagreb (USA)—Mrs McClintock (IRE) The Inner Steel Partnership
6 KING ALFRED, 12, b g Doubletour (USA)—Society Girl L. Howard
7 NOVEL DANCER, 4, b g Dansili—Fictitious Mrs Lydia Richards
8 OUR PLAY (IRE), 4, b g Oratorio (IRE)—Red Shoe Mrs Lydia Richards
9 TROOPER KIT, 13, b g Petoski—Rolling Dice Mrs Lydia Richards
10 VENETIAN LAD, 7, ro g Midnight Legend—Henrietta Holmes (IRE) The Venetian Lad Partnership
11 ZIGZAGA (IRE), 6, b g Zagreb (USA)—Mrs McClintock (IRE) Mrs Lydia Richards

Other Owners: Mr H. B. Kinmond, Mr G. H. R. Musker, E. T. Wright.

556   MR NICKY RICHARDS, Greystoke

Postal: Rectory Farm, Greystoke, Penrith, Cumbria, CA11 0UJ
Contacts: OFFICE (01768) 483392 HOME (01768) 483160 FAX (01768) 483933
MOBILE (07771) 906609
E-MAIL n.g.richards@virgin.net

1 ABBEY GARTH (IRE), 5, b g Dr Massini (IRE)—Elegant Gale (IRE) Mrs S. Johnson
2 AND THE MAN, 6, ch g Generous (IRE)—Retro's Lady The Little Green Syndicate
3 ARTIC NIGHT (FR), 6, gr g Take Risks (FR)—Just Win (FR) Mrs Pat Sloan
4 BENMADIGAN (IRE), 10, ch g Presenting—Dont Tell Nell (IRE) Charlie & Nick Fortescue
5 BERNAEDELLI (IRE), 4, b g Golan (IRE)—Beautiful Blue (IRE) Mark Barnard & Richard Helliwell
6 BRIJOMI QUEEN (IRE), 5, b m King's Theatre (IRE)—Tempest Belle (IRE) Syndicate
7 COVERHOLDER (IRE), 5, b g Oscar (IRE)—Lasado (IRE) Mr R. A. B. Duff
8 4, B g Morozov (USA)—Dinny Kenn (IRE) Mr E. Melville
9 DOWD'S DESTINY (IRE), 9, b g Flemensfirth (USA)—Windy Run C. Bennett
10 DUKE OF NAVAN (IRE), 4, b br g Presenting—Greenfieldflyer (IRE) David & Nicky Robinson
11 FIND A KEY (IRE), 5, b g Definite Article—Jims Leader (IRE) Mrs S. Johnson
12 FLINTY BAY (IRE), 7, b g King's Theatre (IRE)—
 Autumn Vixen (IRE) Miss A. Condon, Mrs J. Magnier & M. Tabor
13 GETTING READY (IRE), 5, b g Westerner—Last Campaign (IRE) D. Wesley-Yates
14 GLINGERBANK (IRE), 12, b g Supreme Leader—Mauradante (IRE) James Westoll
15 GLINGERBURN (IRE), 4, b g King's Theatre (IRE)—Wychnor Dawn (IRE) James Westoll
16 HANNAH JACQUES (IRE), 7, b m Flemensfirth (USA)—
 Richs Mermaid (IRE) M S Borders Racing Club & Partners
17 HOUSTON DYNIMO (IRE), 7, b g Rock of Gibraltar (IRE)—
 Quiet Mouse (IRE) Mark Barnard & Richard Helliwell
18 ISABELLE B (IRE), 5, b m High Chaparral (IRE)—Isabella R (IRE) J. A. Dugdeon
19 ITZACLICHE (IRE), 12, b g Classic Cliche (IRE)—Ower (IRE) Miss J. R. Richards
20 KINGS CANYON (IRE), 6, ch g Stowaway—Hurricane Debbie (IRE) Mrs S. Johnson
21 LAHIB THE FIFTH (IRE), 12, br g Lahib (USA)—Bob's Girl (IRE) Mr Jim Ennis
22 MALIN BAY (IRE), 7, b g Milan—Mirror of Flowers David & Nicky Robinson
23 MERRYDOWN (IRE), 9, b g Oscar (IRE)—Euro Coin Lady (IRE) Mrs Pat Sloan
24 MISTER MARKER (IRE), 8, ch g Beneficial—Bavards Girl (IRE) Mr Jimmy Dugdeon
25 MOUFATANGO (IRE), 6, b br g Sagacity (FR)—Bold-E-Be Mr Jimmy Dugdeon
26 NEXT TO NOWHERE (IRE), 7, ch g Exit To Nowhere (USA)—Zarote (IRE) Miss Lisa Hales
27 NOBLE ALAN (GER), 9, gr g King's Theatre (IRE)—Nirvavita (FR) C. Bennett
28 ONE FOR HARRY (IRE), 4, b br g Generous—Strawberry Fool (FR) The Fife Boys + 1
29 ONE FOR HOCKY (IRE), 4, b g Brian Boru—Wire Lady (IRE) Kingdom Taverns Ltd
30 PARC DES PRINCES (USA), 6, b br g Ten Most Wanted (USA)—Miss Orah Bob Bennett & Bill Graham
31 PEACHEY MOMENT (USA), 7, b br g Stormin Fever (USA)—Given Moment (USA) Greystoke Stables
32 POINTLESS, 6, ch g Courteous—Rainbow Times (IRE) Mrs J. M. R. Lancaster
33 PREMIER DANE (IRE), 10, b g Indian Danehill (IRE)—Crystal Blue (IRE) Jim Ennis Construction Ltd
34 PREMIER SAGAS (FR), 8, b g Sagacity (FR)—Estampe (FR) D. Wesley-Yates
35 RAIN STOPS PLAY (IRE), 10, b g Desert Prince—Pinta (IRE) P. Montgomery
36 REALT MOR (IRE), 7, b g Beneficial—Suez Canal (FR) Mrs Pat Sloan
37 RESTORATION (FR), 10, gr g Zafonic (USA)—Restless Mixa (IRE) Mrs Pat Sloan
38 SCARLET FIRE (IRE), 5, b g Helissio (FR)—Ross Dana (IRE) Mrs T. H. Barclay/Mrs F. D. McInnes Skinner

MR NICKY RICHARDS—continued

39 **SHAMOUR (IRE)**, 4, b g Fruits of Love (USA)—
Shamaiyla (FR) **Mrs J. Fortescue, Mrs E. Gifford, Mrs D. McGawn**
40 **SIMPLY NED (IRE)**, 5, ch g Fruits of Love (USA)—Bishops Lass (IRE) **David & Nicky Robinson**
41 **SKIPPERS BRIG (IRE)**, 11, b g Zaffaran (USA)—Mathewsrose (IRE) **Ashleybank Investments Limited**
42 **SUNDOWN TRAIL (IRE)**, 7, ch g Old Vic—Mary's View (IRE) **J. P. McManus**
43 **TALKIN THOMAS (IRE)**, 6, b g Talkin Man (CAN)—Keerou Lady (IRE) **Henriques & Lloyd-Bakers**
44 5, B g Equerry (USA)—Tchatchacoya (FR) **Mr Peter Norbury**
45 **THAT'LL DO NICELY (IRE)**, 9, b g Bahhare (USA)—Return Again (IRE) **Syndicate**
46 **TUTCHEC (FR)**, 5, gr g Turgeon (USA)—Pocahontas (FR) **Club 4 Racing**
47 **WALDVOGEL (IRE)**, 8, ch g Polish Precedent (USA)—Wurftaube (GER) **C. Bennett**
48 **WINTER ALCHEMY (IRE)**, 7, b g Fruits of Love (USA)—Native Land **The Alchemy Partnership**

Other Owners: Mr A. Clark, Mr G. Dowd, Mr G. Dowling, Mrs R. L. Elliot, Mr Andrew Hamilton, Mr M. Henriques, Mr P. Laverty, Mr C. G. M. Lloyd-Baker, Mr H. M. A. Lloyd-Baker, Mr Walter Morris, Miss J. R. Richards.

Assistant Trainer: Miss Joey Richards

Jockey (NH): Fearghal Davis, Brian Harding, Dougie Costello. **Conditional:** Brian Treanor. **Amateur:** Miss J. R. Richards.

---

557 MR MARK RIMELL, Witney
Postal: **Fairspear Racing Stables, Fairspear Road, Leafield, Witney, Oxfordshire, OX29 9NT**
Contacts: **PHONE (01993) 878551 FAX (01993) 878823 MOBILE (07778) 648303/(07973) 627054**
E-MAIL rimell@rimellracing.com WEBSITE www.rimellracing.com

1 **AZULADA BAY (IRE)**, 8, ch g Karinga Bay—Azulada (FR) **M. G. Rimell**
2 **BENEFIT CUT (IRE)**, 6, b g Beneficial—I'm Maggy (NZ) **M. G. Rimell**
3 **BHAKTI (IRE)**, 5, b g Rakti—Royal Bossi (IRE) **M. G. Rimell**
4 **CAPTAIN JOHN SMITH**, 7, b g Hernando (FR)—Lady Rebecca **M. G. Rimell**
5 **CAPTAIN WILSON**, 5, b g Olden Times—Competa **Mr P. Balding**
6 **DEFINITE LADY (IRE)**, 6, b m Definite Article—Phillis Hill **M. G. Rimell**
7 **JUST BLUE**, 6, gr g Silver Patriarch (IRE)—Miss Millie **W. W. Stroud**
8 **JUST PLAYFULL**, 10, b g Sure Blade (USA)—Miss Millie **W. W. Stroud**
9 **KINCORA COURT (IRE)**, 5, b g Brian Boru—Dawn Court **M. G. Rimell**
10 **MON HOMME**, 5, br g Loup Sauvage (USA)—Mistinguish (IRE) **Kevin Wright, Mark Rimell**
11 **OURS (FR)**, 10, b g Discover d'auteuil (FR)—Geographie (FR) **David Pratt & Paul Porter**
12 **PERKIN WARBECK**, 10, ch g Karinga Bay—Supreme Lady (IRE) **M. G. Rimell**

THREE-YEAR-OLDS

13 **LOVE TALE**, ch f Lucky Story (USA)—Bold Love **M. G. Rimell**

Other Owners: P. Porter, Mr D. J. Pratt, Mr K. T. H. Wright.

Assistant Trainer: Anne Rimell

---

558 MR MARK RIMMER, Newmarket
Postal: **Chesnut Tree Stables, Newmarket, Suffolk, CB8 0NY**
Contacts: **PHONE (01638) 577498 MOBILE (07913) 111205**

1 **BLACK DRAGON**, 4, b g Iceman—My Valentina **C. Dennett**
2 **DIRECTOR'S DREAM (IRE)**, 4, gr f Act One—Najayeb (USA) **C. Dennett**
3 **SATWA BALLERINA**, 4, b f Barathea (IRE)—Ballerina Rosa (FR) **M. E. Rimmer**
4 **TUMBLED AGAIN**, 5, br g Tumbleweed Ridge—Amber Brown **M. E. Rimmer**

THREE-YEAR-OLDS

5 **THORPE BAY**, b g Piccolo—My Valentina **Mr C. G. Donovan**

TWO-YEAR-OLDS

6 **GRAPES HILL**, b f 11/3 Kingsalsa (USA)—Red Blossom (Green Desert (USA)) (6500) **C. Dennett**

Amateur: Mr J. Pearce.

559 MR DAVE ROBERTS, Kenley
Postal: Leasowes Farm, Kenley, Shrewsbury, Shropshire, SY5 6NY

1 BELLABOOSH (IRE), 6, b m Dushyantor (USA)—Ara Blend (IRE) D. B. Roberts
2 BIG BAD BOO, 6, b g Almutawakel—Forever Loved D. B. Roberts
3 CHICAGO ALLEY, 11, br m Bob Back (USA)—Winnetka Gal (IRE) D. B. Roberts
4 INDEFINITE HOPE (ITY), 5, b m Ekraar (USA)—Ricredes (IRE) D. B. Roberts
5 4, B f Revoque (IRE)—Prideway (IRE) D. B. Roberts
6 SCOGLIO, 4, b g Monsieur Bond (IRE)—Ex Mill Lady D. B. Roberts

THREE-YEAR-OLDS

7 B g Revoque (IRE)—Cool Spring (IRE) D. B. Roberts

560 MR MICHAEL ROBERTS, Hailsham
Postal: Summertree Farm, Bodle Street Green, Hailsham, East Sussex, BN27 4QT
Contacts: PHONE (01435) 830231 FAX (01435) 830887
E-MAIL mike@summertree-racing.com

1 ALFLORABUNDA, 6, b m Alflora (IRE)—Appley Dapply M. J. Roberts
2 CANAZTA, 7, b g Zaha (CAN)—Canal Street M. J. Roberts
3 HAZY BAY, 7, b g Zaha (CAN)—Barton Bay (IRE) M. J. Roberts

561 MRS RENEE ROBESON, Newport Pagnell
Postal: Fences Farm, Tyringham, Newport Pagnell, Buckinghamshire, MK16 9EN
Contacts: PHONE/FAX (01908) 611255 MOBILE (07831) 579898
E-MAIL robesons@attglobal.net

1 AESCHYLUS, 5, b gr g Act One—Circe A D G Oldrey, G C Hartigan & S F Oldrey
2 COLEBROOKE, 4, b g Shamardal (USA)—Shimna TMT Grand
3 E MAJOR, 7, ch g Singspiel (IRE)—Crystal Cavern (USA) Sir E. de Rothschild
4 GRASSFINCH, 6, ch m Generous (IRE)—Stock Dove Mrs R. L. M. Robeson
5 HONEYCREEPER, 5, ch m Sir Harry Lewis (USA)—Hazel Grouse Mrs R. L. M. Robeson
6 JUSTAZIPPY, 5, b m Where Or When (IRE)—Theatre Lady (IRE) M. W. Lawrence
7 KIKOS (FR), 10, ch g Nikos—Balgarde (FR) Nick Brown Racing
8 OGEE, 9, ch g Generous (IRE)—Aethra (USA) Sir E. de Rothschild
9 OMARURU (IRE), 5, b g Cape Cross (IRE)—Monturani (IRE) Nick Brown Racing
10 REYNO, 4, b g Sleeping Indian—Tereyna Mrs R. L. M. Robeson
11 SAN TELM (IRE), 7, b g Oscar (IRE)—Magical Mist (IRE) The Tyringham Partnership
12 SILVER WREN, 5, gr m Silver Patriarch (IRE)—Wren Warbler Mrs R. L. M. Robeson
13 SMART EXIT (IRE), 5, b g Exit To Nowhere (USA)—Navaro (IRE) The Ravenstone Partnership

Other Owners: Mr N. J. Brown, G. C. Hartigan, A. D. G. Oldrey, S. F. Oldrey, Mr B. H. Turner, D. Yates.

562 MISS SARAH ROBINSON, Bridgwater
Postal: Newnham Farm, Shurton, Stogursey, Bridgwater, Somerset, TA5 1QG
Contacts: PHONE (01278) 732357 FAX (01278) 732357 MOBILE (07866) 435197
E-MAIL info@sarahrobinsonracing.co.uk WEBSITE www.sarahrobinsonracing.co.uk

1 FLAMING SPIRT, 13, b m Blushing Flame (USA)—Fair Test Mr B. Robinson
2 MOLLYCARRS TOPCLIF, 4, b f General Gambul—Eugenie Mrs J. A. Carr-Evans
3 MOLLYCARRSBREKFAST, 17, b g Presidium—Imperial Flame Mr B. Robinson
4 NEWNHAM FLYER (IRE), 10, gr m Exit To Nowhere (USA)—Paper Flight Mr B. Robinson

Assistant Trainer: Mr B. Robinson

Jockey (NH): Lee Stephens, Chris Honour. **Amateur:** Miss Sarah Robinson.

563 MISS PAULINE ROBSON, Capheaton
Postal: **Kidlaw Farm, Capheaton, Newcastle Upon Tyne, NE19 2AW**
Contacts: **PHONE (01830) 530241 MOBILE (07721) 887489 or (07814) 708725 (David)**
E-MAIL pauline.robson@virgin.net

1 **BUBBLY BREEZE (IRE)**, 7, br g Hubbly Bubbly (USA)—
Belon Breeze (IRE) **Major & Mrs P Arkwright & Mrs IC Sellars**
2 **HUMBIE (IRE)**, 8, b g Karinga Bay—South Queen Lady (IRE) **Mr & Mrs Raymond Anderson Green**
3 **JUMBY BAY (IRE)**, 7, b g Great Palm (USA)—Welsh Rhapsody (IRE) **Mr & Mrs Raymond Anderson Green**
4 **LOCKED INTHEPOCKET (IRE)**, 8, b g Beneficial—Ruby Rubenstein (IRE) **Mr & Mrs Raymond Anderson Green**
5 **RIVAL D'ESTRUVAL (FR)**, 7, b g Khalkevi (IRE)—
Kermesse d'estruval (FR) **Mr & Mrs Raymond Anderson Green**

Other Owners: Major P. W. F. Arkwright, Mrs Sandra G. E. Arkwright, R. A. Green, Mrs A. Green, Mrs N. P. Sellars.

Assistant Trainer: David Parker

Jockey (NH): Timmy Murphy, Richie McGrath.

564 MR FRANCOIS ROHAUT, Sauvagnon
Postal: **26, Rue Du Bearn, 64230 Sauvagnon, France**
Contacts: **PHONE (0033) 5593 32486 FAX (0033) 5596 24652 MOBILE (0033) 6727 75619**
E-MAIL ecurie.rohaut@wanadoo.fr

1 **AGENT SECRET (IRE)**, 6, br h Pyrus (USA)—Ron's Secret **Mr R. Tema**
2 **AKTAR LOTOIS (FR)**, 6, b h Akbar (FR)—Larissa Lotoise (FR) **Hamdan Al Maktoum**
3 **BORGO**, 4, b g Poliglote—Bengalie (FR) **Mr F. Rohaut**
4 **CINDY SHERMAN (FR)**, 4, b f Shamardal (USA)—O' Keefe (IRE) **Mr B. Bargues**
5 **CINTA**, 4, b f Monsun (GER)—Night Year (IRE) **Mrs M. Campbell-Andenaes**
6 **DIVINE CREATION (FR)**, 4, b f Lando (GER)—Danse Polonaise (USA) **Mr J. M. Cledat**
7 **FIRST RAINS**, 4, b f Green Desert (USA)—Nanty (IRE) **Khalifa Dasmal**
8 **KALAHARI GOLD (IRE)**, 7, ch g Trans Island—Neat Shilling (IRE) **Hamdan Al Maktoum**
9 **MARONI (FR)**, 7, b g Oasis Dream—Miss Chryss (IRE) **Mr M. Perret**
10 **NOVA KEDIET (USA)**, 4, b c Speightstown—Dynamous (USA) **Mr A. Mouknass**
11 **NOVA VALOREM (IRE)**, 4, ch c Ad Valorem (USA)—Utr (USA) **Mr A. Mouknass**
12 **RADAMES (FR)**, 4, b c Kerbella (FR)—Mlaika (FR) **Hamdan Al Maktoum**
13 **SANDY'S CHARM (FR)**, 4, b f Footstepsinthesand—First Charm (FR) **Mrs M. Bryant**
14 **SILVER GREEN (FR)**, 5, gr g Slickly (FR)—Love Green (FR) **Mr J. Strauss**
15 **THE SHACK (FR)**, 4, ch g Muhtathir—Jane Eria (IRE) **F. Courturier**
16 **ULTIME BERE (FR)**, 4, b g High Yield (USA)—Poet's Studio (USA) **Mr J. Gispert**

THREE-YEAR-OLDS

17 **A HOT DREAM (FR)**, b f Stormy River (FR)—Garota da Ipanema (FR) **Mr A. Mouknass**
18 **A HUGE DREAM (IRE)**, b f Refuse To Bend (IRE)—Great Joy (IRE) **Mr A. Mouknass**
19 **A MOI (FR)**, b f Elusive Quality (USA)—Amorama (FR) **Haras de Saint Pair**
20 **ALLY BLACK (FR)**, b f Black Sam Bellamy (IRE)—Avera (GER) **Roger Marot**
21 **ASYL (IRE)**, b f Peintre Celebre (USA)—Coup d'eclat (IRE) **Mr Saeed Nasser Al Romaithi**
22 **AVODALE (FR)**, b f Lawman (FR)—Aldovea **Khalifa Dasmal**
23 **AZEVILLE**, gr f Shamardal (USA)—At Once (GER) **Mr G. Augustin-Normand**
24 **BASSAMBA (FR)**, b f American Post—Benzolina (IRE) **Mr F. Rohaut**
25 **BORODINO**, ch g Turtle Bowl—Baie **Mr F. Rohaut**
26 **BRAVIA**, ch f Shamardal (USA)—Albahaca (USA) **Mme A. Cuadra-Lores**
27 **BROOKLYN THOMAS (IRE)**, b c Dylan Thomas (IRE)—Brooklyn Academy (USA) **S. Boucheron**
28 **BUNOOK**, b c Sakhee (USA)—Amanah (USA) **Hamdan Al Maktoum**
29 **CASHMERE ROSE**, b f Cape Cross (IRE)—Roslea Lady (IRE) **Khalifa Dasmal**
30 **CHICHI KING (FR)**, b c Chichicastenango (FR)—Acqualina Beauty (IRE) **Mr A. Mouknass**
31 **COMMON DENOMINATOR**, b c Royal Applause—Lalectra **J. Calva**
32 **DANCE TOUPIE (FR)**, b c Dansili—Toupie **R. Verspieren**
33 **DARNETAL (IRE)**, b c Invincible Spirit (IRE)—Larme (IRE) **Mr G. Augustin-Normand**
34 **EDEN STAR (FR)**, b g Keltos (FR)—Magistar (FR) **P. Catala**
35 **ELUSIVE STORM (FR)**, b f Elusive City (USA)—Queen of Fairies (IRE) **Mr J. J. Taieb**
36 **FORTUNE HUNTER (FR)**, b f High Chaparral (IRE)—King's Folly (FR) **Skymarc Farm**
37 **GAANYA (FR)**, b f Oasis Dream—Saba (ITY) **Hamdan Al Maktoum**
38 **GREYVENTURE (FR)**, b f Smadoun—Nouvelle Aventure **Mr J. J. Taieb**
39 **HARD DREAM (IRE)**, br c Oasis Dream—Rose Melody (IRE) **Pandora Stud LLC**

MR FRANCOIS ROHAUT—continued

40 **HEURTEVENT**, b g Hold That Tiger (USA)—Sybilia (GER) **Mr G. Augustin-Normand**
41 **INDRIYA (FR)**, b f Stormy River (FR)—Killgra (IRE) **Mr A. Mouknass**
42 **IVORY ROSE**, b f Green Desert (USA)—Bal de La Rose (IRE) **Mr B. Van Dalfsen**
43 **KAMATE (FR)**, b f Early March—Solitudine **Mr G. Augustin-Normand**
44 **KENTUCKY BILL (FR)**, b g Kentucky Dynamite (USA)—Mahelia (FR) **R. Temam**
45 **KINGSTON**, br c Dylan Thomas (IRE)—Katy Carr **Mr G. Augustin-Normand**
46 **KITTLE (IRE)**, b f Jeremy (USA)—Kindle **J. Wigan**
47 **LA NOE**, b f Nayef (USA)—Snow Gretel (IRE) **Mr G. Augustin-Normand**
48 **LADY LYNCH (FR)**, b f Rashbag—Kiritsou (FR) **Mme M. Bryant**
49 **LANDELLES (FR)**, b f High Chaparral (IRE)—Crimson Glory **Mr G. Austin-Normand**
50 **LHENY (FR)**, b g Le Triton (USA)—Besca Nueva (FR) **M. Cordero**
51 **LILY AMERICA (FR)**, b f American Post—Miller's Lily (FR) **Pandora Stud LLC**
52 **LUCAYAN (FR)**, b c Turtle Bowl (IRE)—La Vltava (IRE) **Mr A. Mouknass**
53 **LUCRECE**, ch f Pivotal—Sun Bittern (USA) **SARL Ecurie Tagada**
54 **MAZAYYEN**, ch f American Post—Tropical Barth (IRE) **Hamdan Al Maktoum**
55 **MILLION (FR)**, b g Motivator—Miss Alabama (FR) **Mr G. Laboureau**
56 **MISFAAT (USA)**, ch f Haafhd—Kaseema (USA) **Hamdan Al Maktoum**
57 **MISS POST OFFICE (FR)**, b f American Post—Miss Prism (USA) **Mr J. J. Taieb**
58 **MUSTAHEEL (IRE)**, b c Lawman (FR)—Lidanski (IRE) **Hamdan Al Maktoum**
59 **OMINOUS**, b c Oasis Dream—Merle **J. Wigan**
60 **ORMEL**, b g Observatory (USA)—Eiszeit (GER) **Mr G. Augustin-Normand**
61 **PATH OF HOPE (USA)**, gr ro g Bernstein (USA)—Kenbu (FR) **Mr A. Mouknass**
62 **PATH OF JUSTICE (USA)**, br g Pleasant Tap (USA)—Millie's Quest (USA) **Mr A. Mouknass**
63 **PATH OF LIFE (USA)**, b f Vindication (USA)—Winter's Day (USA) **Mr A. Mouknass**
64 **PEARLS OR PASSION**, b f Monsun (GER)—Pearly Shells **Haras de Saint Pair**
65 **PEAU DOUCE (IRE)**, b f Royal Assault (USA)—Princesse Jasmine (FR) **P. Sabban**
66 **QAMARYA (USA)**, gr ro f Nayef (USA)—Wid (USA) **Hamdan Al Maktoum**
67 **RJWA (IRE)**, ch f Muhtathir—Minallon (ARG) **Mr Saeed Nasser Al Romaithi**
68 **ROERO (FR)**, b g Acclamation—Ricine (USA) **Haras de Saint Pair**
69 **ROSEBERY AVENUE (FR)**, b f Choisir (AUS)—Olvera (IRE) **Mr M. Perret**
70 **SALAMANSA (FR)**, f Dalakhani (IRE)—Sasanuma (USA) **Mr G. Laboureau**
71 **SALISBURY BLUE (FR)**, b g Irish Wells (FR)—Fasliyeva (USA) **Mr B. Van Dalfsen**
72 **SAMBA CHRYSS (IRE)**, b f Galileo (IRE)—Brazilian Bride (IRE) **Haras de Saint Pair**
73 **SAN PEDRO**, b c Hernando (FR)—Spring Stroll (USA) **M. Lagasse**
74 **SEBIA**, b f American Post—Silver Silence (FR) **Mr F. Rohaut**
75 **SILOE (FR)**, b f Domedriver (IRE)—Starks (FR) **P. Chedeville**
76 **SINGERSIDE (IRE)**, b c Nayef (USA)—Light Step (USA) **Pandora Stud LLC**
77 **SINNKOSAKO**, b c Anabaa—Reinamixa **Mme L. Samoun**
78 **SPIRITUS HIT**, b f Dubai Destination (USA)—Broadway Hit **Pandora Stud LLC**
79 **SPIRITUS QUEEN**, b f Dubai Destination (USA)—Bandit Queen **Pandora Stud LLC**
80 **STRATEGIE**, b f Muhtathir—Seelland **Lady O'Reilly**
81 **TROIS LUNES (FR)**, b f Manduro (GER)—Trip To The Moon **Haras de Saint Pair**
82 **TURTLE GREEN (FR)**, b g Turtle Bowl (IRE)—Love Green (FR) **Mr J. Strauss**
83 **VERONA**, b f Iffraaj—Blackberry Pie (USA) **Mr J. Gispert**

TWO-YEAR-OLDS

84 B c 11/4 Cape Cross (IRE)—Anbella (FR) (Common Grounds) (105000) **Hamdan Al Maktoum**
85 B c 17/1 Observatory (USA)—Anna Pavlova (Danehill Dancer (IRE)) (36945) **Mr A. Mouknass**
86 **AUBREE (FR)**, b f 30/3 Kingsalsa (USA)—Individual (Gulch (USA)) (13957) **G. Augustin-Normand**
87 **BAKI (FR)**, b f 4/5 Turtle Bowl—Benzolina (Second Empire) **Mr F. Rohaut**
88 B f 8/4 Oasis Dream—Cattiva Generosa (Cadeaux Genereux) **Haras de Saint Pair**
89 **HELOISE (FR)**, b f 7/2 American Post—Hijaziyah (Testa Rossa (AUS)) (41050) **P. Chedeville**
90 B f 17/5 Invincible Spirit (IRE)—Moon's Whisper (Storm Cat (USA)) **Hamdan Al Maktoum**
91 B br c 18/2 Muhtathir—Nasheed (USA) (Riverman (USA)) **Hamdan Al Maktoum**
92 **NORMAN STORM (FR)**, b c 9/4 Stormy River (FR)—Touch of Pink (FR) (Pink (FR)) (14778) **Mr A. Mouknass**
93 **PEARLY AVENUE (FR)**, b f 7/4 Anabaa (USA)—Pearly Shells (Efisio) **Haras de Saint Pair**
94 **PRETTY PANTHER (FR)**, ch f 18/1 Hurricane Run—Princesse Jasmine (Gold Away) **P. Sabban**
95 **PRIME WINNER (FR)**, b c 23/3 Orpen—Perle Rare (Dansili) **P. Sabban**
96 B c 28/2 Elusive City (USA)—Queseraisjesanstoi (FR) (Rainbow Quest (USA)) **Haras D'Etreham**
97 **SEL DE PROVENCE (FR)**, b f 12/3 Great Journey—Sel et Poivre (Lyphards Wish) **Mrs L. Samoun**
98 B c 3/5 Dansili—Squaw Dance (Indian Ridge) (98522) **Hamdan Al Maktoum**
99 **STAR OF SUNDAY (FR)**, b c 20/2 Sunday Break (JPN)—Lilli Star (FR) (Fly To The Stars) (9031) **G. Juppe**
100 Ch f 3/3 Danehill Dancer (USA)—Thanks Again (IRE) (Anabaa Blue) (139573) **Haras de Saint Pair**
101 B f 16/4 Sakhee (USA)—Tomoohat (Danzig (USA)) **Hamdan Al Maktoum**
102 B c 2/3 Daaher (CAN)—Torrestrella (IRE) (Orpen (USA)) **Hamdan Al Maktoum**

MR FRANCOIS ROHAUT—continued

103 B c 27/2 Muhtathir—Tuiga (FR) (Commands (AUS)) (31198) **Hamdan Al Maktoum**
104 B c 11/4 Henrythenavigator (USA)—Turtle Bow (FR) (Turtle Island (IRE)) **B. Van Dalfsen**
105 VERNITA GREEN (FR), b f 7/4 Turtle Bowl (IRE)—Loving Smile (FR) (Sillery (USA)) (11494) **Mr A. Mouknass**

Jockey (flat): F. X. Bertras, C. Brechon, R. Marchelli, F. Billieres. **Apprentice:** C. Cadel.

---

565 **MR W. M. ROPER, Curragh**
Postal: **French Furze, Maddenstown, The Curragh, Co. Kildare, Ireland**
Contacts: **PHONE (00353) 45 441821 MOBILE (00353) 86 823 4279**
E-MAIL markroper1@eircom.net

1 CLARIOR EX OBSCURO (IRE), 6, br g Morozov (USA)—Achates (IRE) **Mr W. M. Roper**
2 COURTLY CONDUCT (IRE), 7, b g Court Cave (IRE)—Regency Charm (IRE) **Mr P. E. I. Newell**
3 GINOLAD (AUS), 12, br g Perugino (USA)—High Royale (AUS) **A. MacAuley**
4 5, B g Pilsudski (IRE)—Lady Mayday (IRE) **R. T. MacAuley**
5 LARSEN BEE (IRE), 6, ch m Frenchmans Bay (FR)—Surabaya (FR) **Mr W. M. Roper**
6 VAALWATER (IRE), 7, b g Danehill Dancer (IRE)—Amaranthus (USA) **Mr W. M. Roper**

---

566 **MR BRIAN ROTHWELL, Malton**
Postal: **3 St Nicholas Street, Norton, Malton, North Yorkshire, YO17 9AQ**
Contacts: **PHONE (01653) 694475 OFFICE (01439) 770437 HOME (01439) 770168**
FAX (01439) 770437 MOBILE (07969) 968241
E-MAIL brian.rothwell1@googlemail.com

1 4, B f Majestic Missile (IRE)—Blue Velvet
2 BONNIE BURNETT (IRE), 5, b br m Hawk Wing (USA)—Chameleon **Mrs G. Sparks**
3 5, B g Bienamado (USA)—Buck On **B. S. Rothwell**
4 CAT O' NINE TAILS, 5, b m Motivator—Purring (USA) **Mrs G. Sparks**
5 COMMANDER VEEJAY, 4, ch g Piccolo—Poly Blue (IRE) **B. S. Rothwell**
6 FAIRY MIST (IRE), 5, b g Oratorio (IRE)—Prealpina (IRE) **B. S. Rothwell**
7 INDIAN OCEAN (IRE), 6, b g Montjeu (IRE)—Dance Desire (IRE) **Mr C. R. Howell**
8 KARMAROUGE (IRE), 4, b f Croco Rouge (IRE)—Karmafair (IRE) **B. S. Rothwell**
9 KATA ROCK (USA), 5, ch g Giant's Causeway (USA)—Harpia (USA) **P. Moorhouse**
10 LADY NORLELA, 6, b m Reset (AUS)—Lady Netbetsports (IRE) **Mrs G. Sparks**
11 SRIMENANTI, 4, b f Diktat—Lady Netbetsports (IRE) **P. Moorhouse**
12 TINSELTOWN, 6, b g Sadler's Wells (USA)—Peony **Mr A. F. Arnott**
13 5, B m Gold Well—Vulcan Belle **B. S. Rothwell**

THREE-YEAR-OLDS

14 B f Majestic Missile (IRE)—Free Angel (USA)
15 MISS FORTYWINKS, gr f Act One—Andromache **Mr J. T. Brown**

TWO-YEAR-OLDS

16 Ch f 1/4 Sakhee (USA)—Fu Wa (USA) (Distant View (USA)) (800) **Mr J. T. Brown**
17 B f 20/3 Diamond Green (FR)—Mackem Beat (Aragon) **Mike Whitehead**

Other Owners: Mr Tony Appelbe, Mr Steve Clasper, Mr Brian Rothwell, Mr Andrew Sparks, Mr Brian Valentine.

---

567 **MR RICHARD ROWE, Pulborough**
Postal: **Ashleigh House Stables, Sullington Lane, Storrington, Pulborough, West Sussex, RH20 4AE**
Contacts: **PHONE (01903) 742871 MOBILE (07831) 345636**
E-MAIL r.rowe.racing@virgin.net WEBSITE www.richardrowe-racing.co.uk

1 AIKIDEAU (FR), 5, b g Le Balafre (FR)—Kizitso (FR) **The Stewart Family**
2 ALTERANTHELA (IRE), 8, br g Alderbrook—Anthela (GER) **T. L. Clowes**
3 AMIRICO (IRE), 7, b g Lord Americo—Maori's Delight **Mr A. D. Didlick**
4 BENNELONG, 6, b g Bahamian Bounty—Bundle Up (USA) **Miss V. J. Baalham**
5 CURRENT CLIMATE (IRE), 8, b g Luso—Kambaya (IRE) **The Encore Partnership IV**
6 GRACE AND FORTUNE, 5, b m Grape Tree Road—Nouveau Cheval **Fortune Racing**
7 HIGH OSCAR, 11, b g Oscar (IRE)—Highfrith **Richard Rowe Racing Partnership**
8 I NO UNDERSTAND (IRE), 6, b g Overbury (IRE)—Falika (FR) **Richard Rowe Racing Partnership**

MR RICHARD ROWE—continued

9 **IT WASN'T US (IRE)**, 5, gr m Astarabad (USA)—Agladora (FR) **Crew Bourgeois**
10 **IT'S A KILLER**, 7, b g Killer Instinct—Lykoa **The Reality Partnership**
11 **KECKERROCKERNIXES (IRE)**, 6, ch g Tomba—Dromhall Lady (IRE) **R. Rowe**
12 **KNOCKNAREEN BOY (IRE)**, 4, b g Winged Love—Princess Roxanne **R. Rowe**
13 **LITTLEMISSPERFECT**, 4, b f Pastoral Pursuits—Dancing Flame **Mr A. J. Taylor**
14 **MANELE BAY**, 9, ch m Karinga Bay—Lacounsel (FR) **Capt Adrian Pratt & Friends**
15 **MARBLE WALK (IRE)**, 7, b g Oscar (IRE)—Clowater Lassie (IRE) **Winterfields Farm Ltd**
16 **MINELLA MISTAKE (IRE)**, 8, b m Witness Box (USA)—Minella Madam **Richard Rowe Racing Partnership**
17 **NEAR THE WATER (IRE)**, 8, b g Oscar (IRE)—The Dark One (IRE) **Ms E. J. Southall**
18 **PASTORAL JET**, 4, b br c Pastoral Pursuits—Genteel (IRE) **Mr A. J. Taylor**
19 **POCKET ACES (IRE)**, 10, b g Dr Massini (IRE)—Mrs Mustard (IRE) **The Encore Partnership III**
20 **STEADY GAZE**, 7, b g Zamindar (USA)—Krisia **Miss V. J. Baalham**
21 **TATENEN (FR)**, 8, b g Lost World (IRE)—Tamaziya (IRE) **The Stewart Family**
22 **THE BISHOPS BABY (IRE)**, 9, b m Bishop of Cashel—Mystical Treat (IRE) **Richard Rowe Racing Partnership**
23 **WATERGATE (IRE)**, 6, gr g Verglas (IRE)—Moy Water (IRE) **The Stewart Family**
24 **WHATAGOA (IRE)**, 5, b m Bishop of Cashel—Gotta Goa (IRE) **Richard Rowe Racing Partnership**

Other Owners: M. W. Barber, A. Blades, Mr D. M. Bradshaw, Mrs H. C. G. Butcher, Mr N. S. Campbell, Mrs J. Case, Mrs J. E. Debenham, M. D. P Fortune, Miss L. Gemmell, Mrs F. M. Gordon, Mr T. L. J. Mills, P. A. Naret-Barnes, Lady B. M. P Neville, Capt A. Pratt, Mr A. Stewart, Mrs J. A. Stewart, Mr T. E. Stimson, J. S. Tackley, T. W. Wellard, Mr J. M. Wilson.

Assistant Trainer: Mr Paul Hacking

Apprentice: Richard Rowe.

---

568 **MISS MANDY ROWLAND, Lower Blidworth**
Postal: **Kirkfields, Calverton Road, Lower Blidworth, Nottingham, Nottinghamshire, NG21 0NW**
Contacts: **PHONE (01623) 794831 MOBILE (07768) 224666**

1 **BALLYCROY BOY (IRE)**, 7, b g Captain Rio—Royal Baldini (USA) **Miss M. E. Rowland**
2 **FINAL TUNE (IRE)**, 9, ch g Grand Lodge (USA)—Jackie's Opera (FR) **Miss M. E. Rowland**
3 **HI SPEC (IRE)**, 9, b m Spectrum (IRE)—Queen of Fibres (IRE) **Miss M. E. Rowland**
4 **HIGHLAND BRAVE (IRE)**, 6, b g High Chaparral (IRE)—Princessa (GER) **Miss M. E. Rowland**
5 **MADAM ISSHE**, 5, b m Ishiguru (USA)—Lucky Dip **Miss M. E. Rowland**
6 **MR CHOCOLATE DROP (IRE)**, 8, b g Danetime (IRE)—Forest Blade (IRE) **Miss M. E. Rowland**
7 **SWEET MIRASOL (IRE)**, 5, b m Celtic Swing—Sallwa (IRE) **Miss M. E. Rowland**
8 4, Br f Lahib (USA)—Up The Creek (IRE) **Miss M. E. Rowland**

THREE-YEAR-OLDS

9 Ch f Yoshka—Danum Diva (IRE)

Assistant Trainer: Sarah Mitchel

Jockey (flat): Adam Kirby, Jimmy Quinn. **Jockey (NH):** Jodie Mogford, Adam Pogson. **Apprentice:** Nathan Alison.

---

569 **MR A. DE ROYER-DUPRE, Chantilly**
Postal: **3 Chemin des Aigles, 60500 Chantilly, France**
Contacts: **PHONE (0033) 34458 0303 MOBILE (0033) 6702 32901**
E-MAIL de-royer-dupre@wanadoo.fr

1 **DIRAMA (FR)**, 9, b m Dormane (FR)—Diyala (FR) **H. H. Aga Khan**
2 **GIOFRA (FR)**, 4, b f Dansili—Gracefully (IRE) **Haras de la Perelle**
3 **IVORY LAND (FR)**, 5, ch h Lando (GER)—Ivory Coast (FR) **Eduardo Fierro**
4 **JEHANNEDARC (IRE)**, 4, b f Montjeu (IRE)—Lucky Rainbow (USA) **Zaro Srl**
5 **LONE RANGER (FR)**, 4, b c Muhtathir—L'etoile de Mer (FR) **Ecurie Wildenstein**
6 **MONBLUE**, 5, b m Monsun (GER)—Salonbride (IRE) **SCEA Haras de Saint Pair**
7 **MUNK (IRE)**, 4, ch c Dalakhani (IRE)—Memoire (FR) **Ecurie Wildenstein**
8 **PACIFIQUE (IRE)**, 4, b f Montjeu (IRE)—Platonic **Ecurie Skymarc Farm**
9 **PAREO (FR)**, 4, b c Galileo (IRE)—Pearly Shells **P. A. Putsch**
10 **PEINTURE ABSTRAITE**, 4, b f Holy Roman Emperor (IRE)—Peinture Bleue (USA) **Ecurie Wildenstein**

MR A. DE ROYER-DUPRE—continued

11 **RELIABLE MAN**, 4, gr c Dalakhani (IRE)—On Fair Stage (IRE) **Pride Racing Club**
12 **SHARETA (IRE)**, 4, b f Sinndar (IRE)—Shawara (IRE) **S. A. Aga Khan**
13 **SINDAJAN (IRE)**, 7, b h Medicean—Sinndiya (IRE) **S. A. Aga Khan**
14 **SUPREME WISDOM**, 4, b c Oratorio (IRE)—Happy At Last **Pride Racing Club**
15 **TOSS THE DICE (FR)**, 4, b c Medicean—Seltitude (IRE) **Pride Racing Club**
16 **VADAMAR (FR)**, 4, gr c Dalakhani (IRE)—Vadawina (IRE) **H. H. Aga Khan**
17 **VALIYR (IRE)**, 4, b c Alhaarth (IRE)—Valima (FR) **H. H. Aga Khan**

THREE-YEAR-OLDS

18 **ADECA (IRE)**, b f Oasis Dream—Alloway **Haras de la Perelle**
19 **AKOYAMA**, b gr f Peintre Celebre (USA)—Aerdee (USA) **Mlle M. Bliard**
20 **ALBERT D'ANABAA (FR)**, b c Anabaa (USA)—Anna Victoria (GER) **Mme M. Bryant**
21 **ALLEZ HONGKONG (GER)**, b f Sakhee (USA)—Autriche (IRE) **W. Engelbrecht-Bresges**
22 **AMERICAN BEAUTY (IRE)**, ch f Galileo (IRE)—Airline (USA) **Ecurie Wildenstein**
23 **AMSHAD (FR)**, b c Sinndar—Amen Desert **H. H. Aga Khan**
24 **ANDUCAS (FR)**, b c Rock of Gibraltar (IRE)—Anna Mona (GER) **SCEA Haras de Saint Pair**
25 **APOLLO ELEVEN (IRE)**, b c Manduro (GER)—Arlesienne (IRE) **Ecurie Wildenstein**
26 **ASHKIYR (FR)**, c Rock of Gibraltar (IRE)—Asharna (IRE) **S. A. Aga Khan**
27 **BAYRIR (FR)**, b c Medicean—Balankiya **S. A. Aga Khan**
28 **BRICMATE (IRE)**, b c Montjeu (IRE)—Spirit of South (AUS) **Finn Blichfeldt**
29 **BUGIE D'AMORE**, b f Rail Link—Asmita **SCEA Haras de Saint Pair**
30 **CATERINA DE MEDICI (FR)**, b f Redoute's Choice (AUS)—Night Dhu **Peter Maher**
31 **CHENDIYR (FR)**, gr c Red Ransom (USA)—Cherryxma (FR) **H. H. Aga Khan**
32 **CLAQUE (FR)**, b f Green Tune—Soviet Lights **Umberto Saini-Fasanotti**
33 **CLARIYN (FR)**, b f Acclamation—Clodovina **H. H. Aga Khan**
34 **DALKALA (USA)**, b br f Giant's Causeway—Daltaya (USA) **S. A. Aga Khan**
35 **DALTIANA (FR)**, ch f Selkirk (USA)—Daltaiyma (IRE) **S. A. Aga Khan**
36 **DARIEN (FR)**, c Galileo (IRE)—Darinska (IRE) **Princess Z. P. Aga Khan**
37 **DARVAZA (USA)**, b br f Smart Strike (CAN)—Darkara (IRE) **Princesse Z. Aga Khan**
38 **DARYLA (USA)**, ch f Mr Greeley (USA)—Daryaba (IRE) **S. A. Aga Khan**
39 **DAYITA (FR)**, b f Dansili—Daltawa (IRE) **S. A. Aga Khan**
40 **DIAKALI (FR)**, b c Sinndar—Diasilixa **H. H. Aga Khan**
41 **DINAFOR (FR)**, ch c Gold Away (IRE)—Dissertation (FR) **William J. Preston**
42 **EARTH AMBER**, ch f Hurricane Run (IRE)—Too Marvelous (FR) **Mise de Moratalla**
43 **FAIRLY FAIR (FR)**, gr f Sinndar (IRE)—Fairly Grey (USA) **SCEA Haras de Saint Pair**
44 **FANTANELLA (IRE)**, b f Montjeu (IRE)—Floating Away (USA) **Ecurie des Monceaux**
45 **FARIDPOUR (FR)**, ch c Dubai Destination (USA)—Fraloga (IRE) **H. H. Aga Khan**
46 **FATE (FR)**, b f Teofilo (USA)—Specificity (USA) **Salinity Stables**
47 **FOL AMI (FR)**, b c Archange d'or (USA)—Vodka (FR) **E. Fierro**
48 **GANDALAK (FR)**, b c Oasis Dream—Grand Vadla (FR) **H. H. Aga Khan**
49 **GUYAPI**, b c Dansili—Gracefully (IRE) **Haras de la Perelle**
50 **ITASCA (FR)**, f Dylan Thomas (IRE)—Lune Rouge (IRE) **Mise de Moratalla**
51 **KALIK (FR)**, b c Dalakhani (IRE)—Kadiana (IRE) **H. H. Aga Khan**
52 **KASIGAR (FR)**, b c Dalakhani (IRE)—Kasakiya (IRE) **S. A. Aga Khan**
53 **KIZIL (FR)**, b c Sinndar (IRE)—King Luna (IRE) **H. H. Aga Khan**
54 **LAGO MINTO**, ch c Galileo (IRE)—Maroussie (FR) **Marquise De Moratalla**
55 **LICORNE BLEUE (USA)**, b f War Chant (USA)—Louveterie (USA) **Ecurie Wildenstein**
56 **MAKANA (FR)**, gr f Dalakhani (IRE)—Marasima (IRE) **S. A. Aga Khan**
57 **MANDISTANA (FR)**, gr f Azamour (IRE)—Minatlya (FR) **H. H. Aga Khan**
58 **MANDOUR (USA)**, ch c Smart Strike (USA)—Mandesha (FR) **Princess Z. P. Aga Khan**
59 **MANSERA (FR)**, b f Manduro (GER)—Mintly Fresh (USA) **H. H. Aga Khan**
60 **MARADINI (FR)**, b c Galileo (IRE)—Marque Royale **H. H. Aga Khan**
61 **MOON QUADRILLE (FR)**, ch f Kentucky Dynamite—Bits Of Paradise **Viktor Timoshenko**
62 **OH LADY BE GOOD (FR)**, b f Oasis Dream—On Fair Stage (IRE) **Salinity Stables**
63 **OSCEOLA (FR)**, b f Layman (USA)—Olympic Skater (IRE) **Ecurie Wildenstein**
64 **PAZARI (FR)**, b c Tiger Hill (IRE)—Posadas (USA) **H. H. Aga Khan**
65 **PIRACICABA (IRE)**, b f Dansili—Montaria (GER) **J. G. A. Camargo**
66 **QUANZHOU (FR)**, b f Dubawi—Quezon Sun **Haras de la Perelle**
67 **RAINBOW QUARTZ (FR)**, b c Pulpit (USA)—Rolly Polly (IRE) **Ecurie Wildenstein**
68 **RELIZANE**, b f Zamindar (USA)—Reine Zao (FR) **Haras de la Perelle**
69 **ROXELANA (IRE)**, b f Oasis Dream—Macadamia (IRE) **H. H. Aga Khan**
70 **SAGARIYA (FR)**, b f Shamardal (USA)—Saga d'ouilly (USA) **H. H. Aga Khan**
71 **SAGAWARA**, b gr f Shamardal (USA)—Sagalina (IRE) **H. H. Aga Khan**
72 **SARKIYLA (FR)**, b f Oasis Dream—Sarlisa (FR) **S. A. Aga Khan**
73 **SECRET NIGHT (USA)**, b f Giant's Causeway (USA)—Famously (IRE) **Ecurie Victoria Dreams**

MR A. DE ROYER-DUPRE—continued

74 **SEVEN SUMMITS (GER)**, c Manduro (GER)—Sacarina **Finn Blichfeldt**
75 **SHADARPOUR (IRE)**, b c Dr Fong (USA)—Shamadara (IRE) **S. A. Aga Khan**
76 **SHAMIYRA (FR)**, b f Medicean—Shemala (IRE) **S. A. Aga Khan**
77 **SHAMSIKHAN (IRE)**, ch c Dr Fong (USA)—Shamdala (IRE) **S. A. Aga Khan**
78 **SHEMBARA (FR)**, b f Dylan Thomas (IRE)—Shemaya (IRE) **S. A. Aga Khan**
79 **SHENDAMA (FR)**, b f Dr Fong—Shendaya **S. A. Aga Khan**
80 **SHUTTERFLY (IRE)**, b c Dalakhani (IRE)—Elle Galante (GER) **F. Sauque**
81 **SNOW SIGN (FR)**, b c Anabaa (USA)—Snow Lady **Mme Salmon**
82 **STARLET'S SISTER (IRE)**, ch f Galileo (IRE)—Premiere Creation (FR) **W. J. Preston**
83 **SUAMA (FR)**, b f Monsun (GER)—Suave (IRE) **J. Koellmann**
84 **SVIATOPOLK (USA)**, b c Johannesburg (USA)—Theater R N (USA) **Viktor Timoshenko**
85 **TROON (FR)**, b c Red Ransom (USA)—Tigresse Africaine (FR) **Ecurie Wildenstein**
86 **VADERANA (FR)**, b f Monsun (GER)—Vadawina (IRE) **H. H. Aga Khan**
87 **VEREMA (FR)**, b f Barathea (IRE)—Vermentina (IRE) **S. A. Aga Khan**
88 **VISALIA (IRE)**, b f Dansili—Virginia Waters (USA) **Ecurie Wildenstein**
89 **VISINOVA (FR)**, b f Anabaa (USA)—Visor (USA) **H. H. Aga Khan**
90 **VIVACITE (FR)**, b f Kentucky Dynamite (USA)—Villadolide (FR) **Viktor Timoshenko**
91 **ZARKALAN (FR)**, b c Dalakhani (IRE)—Zarkasha (IRE) **S. A. Aga Khan**
92 **ZELAMAR (FR)**, b c Zamindar (USA)—Zewara (IRE) **H. H. Aga Khan**

TWO-YEAR-OLDS

93 **AIDEN SEA (IRE)**, b f 30/4 Danehill Dancer (IRE)—Airline (USA) (Woodman (USA)) **Ecurie Wildenstein**
94 B c 17/5 Oasis Dream—Alamouna (IRE) (Indian Ridge) **S. A. Aga Khan**
95 B f 6/2 Dansili—Alexandrova (IRE) (Sadler's Wells (USA)) **Sheik Mohammed Bin Kalifa Al T**
96 **ALLOWAY BLUE (FR)**, b f 1/1 Lando—American Adventure (Miswaki) **Ecurie Wildenstein**
97 **ALMALYK (FR)**, b f 1/1 Dalakhani (IRE)—Alnamara (FR) (Linamix (FR)) **H. H. Aga Khan**
98 B c 1/1 Montjeu (IRE)—Artistique (IRE) (Linamix (FR)) **H. H. Aga Khan**
99 c 1/1 Oasis Dream—Asharna (IRE) (Darshaan) **S. A. Aga Khan**
100 Ch f 12/2 New Approach (IRE)—Bal de La Rose (IRE) (Cadeaux Genereux) (229885) **Viktor Timoshenko**
101 B f 1/1 Montjeu—Balankiya (Darshaan) **S. A. Aga Khan**
102 B f 1/1 Sinndar—Cherryxma (Linamix) **H. H. Aga Khan**
103 c 1/1 Azamour (IRE)—Daltawa (IRE) (Miswaki (USA)) **S. A. Aga Khan**
104 B br c 22/4 Dynaformer (USA)—Daltaya (FR) (Anabaa (USA)) **S. A. Aga Khan**
105 **DOUTZEN (IRE)**, b f 4/2 Shirocco (GER)—Dacca (Deploy) **Mme S. Debernardi**
106 **EDMONTON**, ch c 21/4 Exceed And Excel (AUS)—Ela Merici (FR) (Beaudelaire (USA)) **Ecurie Wildenstein**
107 **ELLE SAME**, b f 1/1 Samum (GER)—Elle Danzig (GER) (Roi Danzig (USA)) **Viktor Timoshenko**
108 B f 6/4 Galileo (IRE)—Evita (Selkirk (USA)) (430000) **Sheik Mohammed Bin Kalifa Al Thani**
109 Gr c 8/2 Verglas (FR)—Fontaine Guerard (FR) (Homme de Loi (IRE)) (41050) **Mise de Moratalla**
110 B c 6/4 Dansili—Fraloga (IRE) (Grand Lodge (USA)) **H. H. Aga Khan**
111 Ch c 20/4 Dalakhani (IRE)—Grand Vadla (FR) (Grand Lodge (USA)) **H. H. Aga Khan**
112 **HANDANA (IRE)**, b f 14/2 Desert Style (IRE)—Handaza (IRE) (Be My Guest (USA)) **S. A. Aga Khan**
113 **IPSWICH (IRE)**, ch f 24/4 Danehill Dancer (IRE)—
Imperial Beauty (USA) (Imperial Ballet (IRE)) **Ecurie Wildenstein**
114 B f 2/4 Arch—Jacira (FR) (Sillery (USA)) (53366) **Mme M. Bryant**
115 f 1/1 Azamour (IRE)—Kadiana (IRE) (Grand Lodge (USA)) **S. A. Aga Khan**
116 **KARKYIN (IRE)**, b f 21/2 Cape Cross (IRE)—Karkiyla (IRE) (Darshaan) **S. A. Aga Khan**
117 **KING OF ENGLAND**, ch c 28/3 Galileo (IRE)—
Royal Highness (Monsun (GER)) (410509) **Waratah Thoroughbreds Pty Ltd**
118 B f 10/4 Dalakhani (IRE)—Lune d'or (FR) (Green Tune (USA)) (127257) **Ecurie Wildenstein**
119 B m 1/1 Anabaa—Marasima (Barathea) **S. A. Aga Khan**
120 c 1/1 Medicean—Marque Royale (Royal Academy (USA)) **H. H. Aga Khan**
121 B f 1/1 Cape Cross—Minatlya (Linamix) **H. H. Aga Khan**
122 c 1/1 Dalakhani (IRE)—Mintly Fresh (USA) (Rubiano (USA)) **H. H. Aga Khan**
123 **MODERN EAGLE (GER)**, b f 1/1 Montjeu—Millionaia (Peintre Celebre) **Ecurie Wildenstein**
124 B f 5/4 Dubawi (IRE)—Narmina (GER) (Alhaarth (IRE)) **S. A. Aga Khan**
125 **PARKER RIDGE (FR)**, ch c 24/4 Green Tune (USA)—Peinture Bleue (USA) (Alydar (USA)) **Ecurie Wildenstein**
126 **PIONEER GIRL (IRE)**, b f 25/4 Anabaa (USA)—Porlezza (FR) (Sicyos (USA)) **Ecurie Wildenstein**
127 B c 31/3 Invincible Spirit (IRE)—Rayyana (FR) (Rainbow Quest (USA)) **S. A. Aga Khan**
128 Ch c 16/4 Dylan Thomas (IRE)—Rosawa (FR) (Linamix (FR)) **H. H. Aga Khan**
129 **ROSENSAUM**, b f 30/3 Samum (GER)—Rosenreihe (IRE) (Catcher In The Rye (IRE)) **Viktor Timoshenko**
130 B f 18/3 Anabaa (USA)—Sanariya (IRE) (Darshaan) **S. A. Aga Khan**
131 c 1/1 Manduro (GER)—Shamdara (IRE) (Dr Devious (IRE)) **S. A. Aga Khan**
132 **SHEHILA (IRE)**, b f 18/3 Zamindar (USA)—Shehira (FR) (Sendawar (IRE)) **S. A. Aga Khan**
133 **SHIKARPOUR (IRE)**, ch c 5/3 Dr Fong (USA)—Shibina (IRE) (Kalanisi (IRE)) **S. A. Aga Khan**
134 **SIYENICA (FR)**, b f 1/1 Azamour (IRE)—Sichilla (IRE) (Danehill (USA)) **H. H. Aga Khan**

MR A. DE ROYER-DUPRE—continued

135 **SLEEPING GIANT (GER)**, c 1/1 Dalakhani (IRE)—Special Delivery (IRE) (Danehill (USA)) **Ecurie Wildenstein**
136   c 1/1 Dalakhani (IRE)—Vadaza (FR) (Zafonic (USA)) **H. H. Aga Khan**
137 **VALAMAR (FR)**, b c 13/3 Cape Cross (IRE)—Vadapolina (FR) (Trempolino (USA)) **H. H. Aga Khan**
138   c 1/1 Nayef (USA)—Valima (FR) (Linamix (FR)) **H. H. Aga Khan**
139   c 1/1 Rock of Gibraltar (IRE)—Visionnaire (FR) (Linamix (FR)) **H. H. Aga Khan**
140 B c 16/4 Lawman (FR)—Wenge (USA) (Housebuster (USA)) (57471) **Finn Blichfeldt**
141 B f 19/4 Oasis Dream—Ysoldina (FR) (Kendor (FR)) **Mme G. Forien**
142 **ZAFERI (IRE)**, b c 13/2 Raven's Pass (USA)—Zafaraniya (IRE) (Doyoun) **S. A. Aga Khan**
143 **ZARDAKA (IRE)**, b f 22/4 Zamindar (USA)—Zarafsha (IRE) (Alzao (USA)) **S. A. Aga Khan**
144   c 1/1 Shamardal (USA)—Zayanida (IRE) (King's Best (USA)) **S. A. Aga Khan**
145 B c 1/1 Tiger Hill—Zewara (Alhaarth) **S. A. Aga Khan**

---

570 MRS LUCINDA RUSSELL, Kinross

Postal: **Arlary House Stables, Milnathort, Kinross, Tayside, KY13 9SJ**
Contacts: **PHONE (01577) 862482 YARD (01577) 865512 OFFICE (01577) 865512**
FAX (01577) 861171 MOBILE (07970) 645261
E-MAIL lucinda@arlary.fsnet.co.uk WEBSITE www.lucindarussell.com

1 **ARRAN LAW (IRE)**, 8, ch g Flemensfirth (USA)—Windy Run **Mr I. D. Miller**
2 **BADGER FOOT (IRE)**, 7, b br g Beneficial—Droim Alton Gale (IRE) **P. J. S. Russell**
3 **BALLYBEN (IRE)**, 4, ch g Beneficial—I'm Maggy (NZ) **Drew & Ailsa Russell**
4 **BARELLO ROAD**, 6, b m Grape Tree Road—Haudello (FR) **Drew & Ailsa Russell**
5 **BARLIFFEY (IRE)**, 7, b g Bahri—Kildare Lady (IRE) **Brahms & Liszt**
6 **BEAR DANCING (IRE)**, 8, b g Dancing High—Sandholes (IRE) **P. J. S. Russell**
7 **BEAT THE BAND**, 7, br m Beat All (USA)—Blue Gallery (IRE) **Mr G. Truscott**
8 **BEIDH TINE ANSEO (IRE)**, 6, b g Rock of Gibraltar (IRE)—Siamsa (USA) **Mr I. D. Miller**
9 **BESCOT SPRINGS (IRE)**, 7, b g Saddlers' Hall (IRE)—Silver Glen (IRE) **Mrs J. Tracey**
10 **BLAZIN WHITE FACE (IRE)**, 5, b m Noverre (USA)—Watch The Clock **Mr I. D. Miller**
11 **BLENHEIM BROOK (IRE)**, 7, br g Alderbrook—Blenheim Blinder (IRE) **The County Set Three**
12 **BOLD SIR BRIAN (IRE)**, 6, b g Brian Boru—Black Queen (IRE) **A. R. Trotter**
13 **BRINDISI BREEZE (IRE)**, 6, b g King's Theatre—Miss Poutine (IRE) **Mr Sandy Seymour**
14 **CADORE (IRE)**, 4, b g Hurricane Run (IRE)—Mansiya **Mr S. Townshend**
15 **COPPER'S GOLD (IRE)**, 8, b g Presenting—West Hill Rose (IRE) **J. R. Adam**
16 **CRACKERJACK LAD (IRE)**, 9, br g Exit To Nowhere (USA)—Crowther Homes **Mr I. D. Miller**
17 **DEGAS ART (IRE)**, 9, b g Danehill Dancer (USA)—Answer **Barber Bruce Fleming Levein Russell**
18 **DELIGHTFULLY (FR)**, 8, br m Sagacity (FR)—Green House (FR) **Mr R. M. Boyd**
19 **DEVOTION TO DUTY (IRE)**, 6, b g Montjeu—Charmante (USA) **Racing Management & Training Ltd**
20 **DO IT FOR DALKEY**, 10, b g Silver Patriarch (IRE)—Dalkey Sound **G. S. Brown**
21 **DRAMATIC JEWEL (USA)**, 6, b g Diesis—Seeking the Jewel (USA) **Racing Management & Training Ltd**
22 **ET MAINTENANT (FR)**, 10, ch g Johann Quatz (FR)—Dunlora **Mr K. Alexander**
23 **ETXALAR (FR)**, 9, b g Kingsalsa (USA)—Tender To Love **Mrs E. B. Ferguson**
24 **EYRE APPARENT (IRE)**, 7, ch g Turgeon (USA)—Miss Poutine (IRE) **Mr Sandy Seymour**
25 **FOG PATCHES (IRE)**, 6, br g Oscar (IRE)—Flash Parade **Sunny Days**
26 **GEORGES STREET (IRE)**, 6, b g King's Theatre (IRE)—Georges Girl (IRE) **P. J. S. Russell**
27 **GLENORA GALE (IRE)**, 7, br m Milan—Avra Gale (IRE) **Distillery Racing Club**
28 **GOLFER'S CROSSING (IRE)**, 9, b g City Honours (USA)—Queens Rook (IRE) **Lord Leigh**
29 **GREAT WISDOM (IRE)**, 6, b g Rock of Gibraltar (IRE)—Sudden Hope (IRE) **Kelso Members Lowflyers Club**
30 **HOLE IN ONE (IRE)**, 6, b m Saddlers' Hall (IRE)—Shuildante (IRE) **Mrs L. A. Stevenson**
31 **HURRICANE JACK**, 9, gr g Silver Patriarch (IRE)—Gale **G. S. Brown**
32 **KAI BROON (IRE)**, 5, b g Marju—Restiv Star (FR) **Mrs E. B. Ferguson**
33 **KNOCKANDO**, 7, b g Milan—Cherry Lane **Distillery Racing Club**
34 **LAUREATE DES LOGES (FR)**, 8, b m Marathon (USA)—The Paradis (FR) **M. D. McMillan**
35 **LEGBEFOREWICKET (IRE)**, 9, gr m Silver Patriarch (IRE)—Shazana **Mrs V. M. Stewart**
36 **LIVVY INN (USA)**, 7, ch g Woodman (USA)—London Be Good (USA) **Mrs E. B. Ferguson**
37 **LONG DISTANCE (IRE)**, 7, b br g Storming Home—Lovers Luck (IRE) **Mr & Mrs T. P. Winnell**
38 **LUCIA BAY**, 7, ch m Karinga Bay—Lucia Forte **Drew & Ailsa Russell**
39 **MOMKINZAIN (USA)**, 5, b g Rahy (USA)—Fait Accompli (USA) **John R. Adam & Sons Ltd**
40 **MOSCOW MISCHIEF**, 8, ch m Moscow Society (USA)—Desperate Measures **A. D. Stewart**
41 **MUMGOS DEBUT (IRE)**, 4, b g Royal Anthem (USA)—Black Queen (IRE) **Mrs Suzy Brown & Mr Peter R Brown**
42 **MY ZEAL**, 4, ch g Presenting—Innovate (IRE) **P. K. Dale**
43 **NAVY LIST (FR)**, 5, b g Nayef (USA)—Fasliyeva (FR) **Mutual Friends**
44 **NELLIEDONETHAT (IRE)**, 12, b g Warcraft (USA)—Kilmana (USA) **Kelso Members Lowflyers Club**
45 **NUTS N BOLTS**, 6, b g Marju—Anniversary **The County Set**
46 **OH SO BEAUTIFUL (IRE)**, 5, b m Montjeu (IRE)—Dart Board (IRE) **Mr G. Truscott**
47 **OUTLAW TOM (IRE)**, 8, b g Luso—Timely Approach (IRE) **Milnathort Racing Club**

MRS LUCINDA RUSSELL—continued

48 **PENA DORADA (IRE)**, 5, b g Key of Luck (USA)—Uluwatu (IRE) **Mr J. J. Murray**
49 **PORRIDGE**, 5, b g Pilsudski (USA)—Sandholes (IRE) **Dig In Racing**
50 **PROSECCO (IRE)**, 10, b g Perpendicular—Bay Gale (IRE) **Tay Valley Chasers Racing Club**
51 **QUACITY (FR)**, 8, b g Sagacity (FR)—Desert Show (IRE) **J. R. Adam**
52 **QUINDER SPRING (FR)**, 8, gr g Chef de Clan (FR)—Virginia Spring (FR) **P. J. S. Russell**
53 **QUITO DU TRESOR (FR)**, 8, b g Jeune Homme (USA)—Itiga (FR) **Mrs J. Tracey**
54 **RAYSROCK (IRE)**, 10, br g Anshan—Sovereign Leader (IRE) **A. Irvine**
55 **RHYMERS HA'**, 5, br g Kasakov—Salu **Mr G. F. Adam**
56 **ROWDY ROCHER (IRE)**, 6, br g Winged Love (IRE)—Madam Rocher (IRE) **Michelle And Dan Macdonald**
57 **RYTON RUNNER (IRE)**, 4, b g Sadler's Wells (USA)—Love For Ever (IRE) **G. Godsman**
58 **SAFARI ADVENTURES (IRE)**, 10, b g King's Theatre (IRE)—
                                Persian Walk (FR) **Mrs PK Clark, Mr PG Stephen & Mr H McCaig**
59 **SANTA'S SON (IRE)**, 12, ch g Basanta (IRE)—Rivers Town Rosie (IRE) **Douglas Pryde Jim Beaumont**
60 **STORMION (IRE)**, 7, b g Flemensfirth (USA)—El Moss (IRE) **Peter J S Russell & Bill Fraser**
61 **TANZANITE BAY**, 7, b m Karinga Bay—Diamond Wind (USA) **Lord Leigh & Mrs Bettine Evans**
62 **TAP NIGHT (USA)**, 5, ch g Pleasant Tap (USA)—Day Mate (USA) **Miss J. A. Buchanan**
63 **TCHICO POLOS (FR)**, 8, b g Sassanian (USA)—Miss Saint Germain (FR) **Mrs Sandra Giles**
64 5, B g Exit To Nowhere (USA)—Temple Leader **J. T. Pate**
65 **THE STARBOARD BOW**, 5, b g Observatory (USA)—Overboard (IRE) **John R. Adam & Sons Ltd**
66 **TITO BUSTILLO (FR)**, 7, b g Kahyasi—Litani Queen **Mrs A. Yeoman & Mrs S. Larson**
67 **URBAN KODE (IRE)**, 4, b c Kodiac—Urbanize (USA) **Suzy Brown, John Baird, Tony Evans**
68 **VALLANI (IRE)**, 7, ch m Vettori (IRE)—Hecuba **Mr A. Barclay**
69 **VAMIZI (IRE)**, 9, b g Supreme Leader—Cuilin Bui **Remenham Racing**
70 **VIA ARCHIMEDE (USA)**, 7, ch g Hussonet (USA)—Azarina (IRE) **K C Partnership**

Other Owners: Mr J. Apiafi, Mr John Baird, Mr R. H. T. Barber, Mr Jim Beaumont, Mrs Suzy Brown, Mr Peter R. Brown, Mr Geoff Bruce, Mr A. Cadger, Mr James Dawson, Mrs Bettine Evans, Mr Tony Evans, Mr Mark Fleming, Mr Bill Fraser, Mr George Godsman, Mr Elliot Graham, Mrs Ishbel Grant, Mr P N. Gray, Mrs S. Larson, Lord Leigh, Mr James S. Lessells, Mr C. W. Levein, Mrs Michelle Macdonald, Mr Dan Macdonald, Mr K. J. Mackie, Mr John J. Murray, Mr D. G. Pryde, Mr G. G. Ritchie, Mr Robert Robinson, Mr Peter J. S. Russell, Mr Drew Russell, Mrs Ailsa Russell, Miss Lucinda V. Russell, Mr S. Townshend, Mr T. P. Winnell, Mrs M. Winnell, Mrs Angela Yeoman.

Assistant Trainers: Jaimie Duff, Peter Scudamore.

Jockey (NH): Peter Buchanan, Campbell Gillies. **Conditional:** Grant Cockburn, Adam Nicol. **Amateur:** Mr Dan Ockenden, Mr Steven Fox, Mr Craig Nichol.

---

571 **MR JOHN RYALL, Yeovil**
Postal: **Higher Farm, Rimpton, Yeovil, Somerset, BA22 8AD**
Contacts: **PHONE/FAX (01935) 850222 MOBILE (07592) 738848**
E-MAIL bjmryall@btconnect.com

1 **CYPRESS GROVE (IRE)**, 9, b g Windsor Castle—Grecian Queen **Mr P. J. O'Donovan**
2 **MICHIGAN D'ISOP (FR)**, 12, b g Cadoudal (FR)—Julie Du Berlais (FR) **B. J. M. Ryall**
3 **SPRING BAY**, 7, b m Karinga Bay—Spring Grass **B. J. M. Ryall**
4 **THE GRIFTER**, 10, b g Thowra (FR)—Spring Grass **The Chocoholics**
5 **THIS WAY (IRE)**, 10, b g Exit To Nowhere (USA)—Hawthorn's Way (IRE) **Mrs G. C. Pritchard & Mrs D. Tucker**
6 5, B g Emperor Fountain—Win A Hand **B. J. M. Ryall**

Other Owners: Mrs G. C. Pritchard, Mrs R. C. Ryall, Mr B. J. M. Ryall.

Assistant Trainer: Mrs R C Ryall

---

572 **MR JOHN RYAN, Newmarket**
Postal: **Cadland Stables, Moulton Road, Newmarket, Suffolk, CB8 8DU**
Contacts: **PHONE (01638) 664172 MOBILE (07739) 801235**
E-MAIL john.ryan@jryanracing.com WEBSITE www.jryanracing.com

1 **BLUEBERRY FIZZ (IRE)**, 4, b f Kheleyf (USA)—Miss Poppets **Dr R A & Mrs J L Dixon**
2 **CLEARING HOUSE**, 7, ch g Zamindar (USA)—Easy Option (IRE) **J. Ryan Racing**
3 **FOCAIL EILE**, 7, b g Noverre (USA)—Glittering Image **Mr C. Fegan**
4 **FOCAIL MAITH**, 4, b g Oratorio (IRE)—Glittering Image **Mr C. Fegan**
5 **GRECIAN GODDESS (IRE)**, 4, b f Kris Kin (USA)—Grecian Air (FR) **Mr C Letcher & Mr J. Ryan**
6 **IF WHAT AND MAYBE**, 4, ch g Needwood Blade—Pink Champagne **If What And Maybe**

MR JOHN RYAN—continued

7 **IVER BRIDGE LAD,** 5, b h Avonbridge—Fittonia (FR) **The Iver Lads**
8 **OCEAN BAY,** 4, b c Dubai Destination (USA)—Aldora **Mr W. McLuskey**
9 **OCEAN'S MINSTREL,** 6, b g Pivotal—Minstrel's Dance (USA) **Mr W. McLuskey**
10 **OCEANS DESTINATION,** 4, b g Dubai Destination (USA)—Notable Lady (IRE) **Mr W. McLuskey**
11 **SIMPLE RHYTHM,** 6, b m Piccolo—Easy Beat (IRE) **John Ryan Racing Partnership**
12 4, Ch f Shamardal (USA)—Tarbela (IRE)

THREE-YEAR-OLDS

13 **BIT A CRAIC,** ch f Avonbridge—Twenty Seven (IRE) **Mr G. R. McGladery**
14 Ch f Medecis—Coulisse (IRE)
15 **MASTERS BLAZING,** ch c Iceman—Loquacity **Masters Stud**
16 **MASTERS CLUB,** b g Red Clubs (IRE)—Waaedah (USA) **Masters Stud**
17 B f Diamond Green (FR)—Mrs Kanning
18 **OCEAN TEMPEST,** gr c Act One—Ipsa Loquitur **Mr W McLuskey & Mr C Little**
19 **ORINOCCO,** b c Shirocco (GER)—Norcroft Joy **Norcroft Park Stud**
20 **SOMEMOTHERSDOHAVEM,** ch g Avonbridge—Show Off **Mr J. B. Ryan**
21 **THECORNISHCOCKNEY,** bl g Cockney Rebel (IRE)—Glittering Image (IRE) **Mr C Letcher & Mr J Ryan**
22 **THECORNISHCOWBOY,** b c Haafhd—Oriental Dance **Mr C Letcher & Mr J Ryan**
23 **TUMBLEOWTASHOES,** ch g Tumbleweed Ridge—Darling Belinda **Mr & Mrs Priestley**

TWO-YEAR-OLDS

24 B c 1/4 Royal Applause—Aldora (Magic Ring (IRE)) (48000) **Mr W. McLuskey**
25 B c 18/4 Royal Applause—Ukraine (Cape Cross (IRE)) (50000) **Mr G. R. McGladery**

Other Owners: Mr M. Byron, Miss L. M. Collins, Dr R. A. Dixon, Mrs J. L. Dixon, Mr Neil Hooper, Mr Christopher Letcher, Mr C. W. Little, Mr W. McLuskey, Mr J. Ryan, Mrs J. Williams.

Apprentice: Bradley Bosley.

---

573 **MR KEVIN RYAN, Hambleton**
Postal: **Hambleton Lodge, Hambleton, Thirsk, North Yorkshire, YO7 2HA**
Contacts: **PHONE Office (01845) 597010 / (01845)597622 FAX (01845) 597622**
MOBILE (07768) 016930
E-MAIL kevin.hambleton@virgin.net WEBSITE www.kevinryanracing.com

1 **ACTIVATE,** 5, b g Motivator—Princess Manila (CAN)
2 **BRAVE DREAM,** 4, b g Sleeping Indian—Aimee's Delight **Hokey Cokey Partnership**
3 **BREATHLESS KISS (USA),** 5, b m Roman Ruler (USA)—Crusading Miss Cox (USA) **Mrs A. Bailey**
4 **CAPAILL LIATH (IRE),** 4, gr g Iffraaj—Bethesda **Mr T. R. B. T. A. Shah**
5 **CAPTAIN RAMIUS (IRE),** 6, b g Kheleyf (USA)—Princess Mood (GER) **Mrs C. McStay**
6 **COURAGEOUS (IRE),** 6, ch g Refuse to Bend (IRE)—Bella Bella (IRE) **Dab Hand Racing**
7 **DASHING EDDIE (IRE),** 4, b c Dubawi (IRE)—Step Too Far (USA) **Mr T. R. B. T. A. Shah**
8 **EXCUSE ME,** 4, b g Diktat—After You **G. Reed**
9 **FALASTEEN (IRE),** 5, ch g Titus Livius (FR)—Law Review (IRE) **Dr M. B. Q. S. Koukash**
10 **FLAMING ARROW (IRE),** 4, b g Sadler's Wells (USA)—Pescia (IRE) **Mrs R. G. Hillen**
11 **GEORGE FERNBECK,** 4, ch g Java Gold (USA)—Burmese Days **S. C. B. Limited**
12 **GOOD BOY JACKSON,** 4, b g Firebreak—Fisher Island (IRE) **The C H F Partnership**
13 **GRAMERCY (IRE),** 5, b g Whipper (USA)—Topiary (IRE) **Dr M. B. Q. S. Koukash**
14 **KING KURT (IRE),** 4, b g Holy Roman Emperor (IRE)—Rutledge (IRE) **M. J. Taylor**
15 **LEXI'S HERO (IRE),** 4, b g Invincible Spirit (IRE)—Christel Flame **Dr M. B. Q. S. Koukash**
16 **LIGHTNING CLOUD (IRE),** 4, gr g Sleeping Indian—Spree (IRE) **Hambleton Racing Ltd XVIII**
17 **LOUIS THE PIOUS,** 4, b br g Holy Roman Emperor (IRE)—Whole Grain **F. Gillespie**
18 **MASAMAH (IRE),** 6, gr g Exceed And Excel (AUS)—Bethesda **Dr M. B. Q. S. Koukash**
19 **MISERE,** 4, b f Val Royal (FR)—Card Games **G. Reed**
20 **NASHARRA (IRE),** 4, ch g Iffraaj—There With Me (USA) **Mr & Mrs Julian & Rosie Richer**
21 **OUR JONATHAN,** 5, b g Invincible Spirit (IRE)—Sheik'n Swing **Dr M. B. Q. S. Koukash**
22 **PARISIAN PYRAMID (IRE),** 6, gr g Verglas—Sharadja (IRE) **Dr M. B. Q. S. Koukash**
23 **PARTNER (IRE),** 6, b g Indian Ridge—Oregon Trail (USA)
24 **RACY,** 5, b g Medicean—Soar **The C H F Partnership**
25 **SHIFTING GOLD (IRE),** 6, b g Night Shift (USA)—Gold Bust **Hambleton Racing Ltd VIII**
26 **SHOSHONI WIND,** 4, b f Sleeping Indian—Cadeau Speciale **Hambleton Racing Ltd XVI**
27 **TIDDLIWINKS,** 6, b g Piccolo—Card Games **G. Reed**
28 **UNKNOWN REBEL (IRE),** 4, b g Night Shift (USA)—Crystalline Stream (FR) **D. Reilly & Mrs C. Reilly**
29 **WAKING WARRIOR,** 4, b g Sleeping Indian—Scented Garden **Hambleton Racing Ltd XVII**

MR KEVIN RYAN—continued

30 YORK GLORY (USA), 4, gr ro c Five Star Day (USA)—Minicolony (USA) **Salman Rashed & Mohamed Khalifa**
31 YOURS, 4, b f Piccolo—Uno **G. Reed**

THREE-YEAR-OLDS

32 B f Piccolo—Ailsa **G. Reed**
33 AL DAIN (IRE), b f Diamond Green (FR)—Mitchella (IRE) **Mr A. N. Mubarak**
34 AL DOHA, ch f Iffraaj—Lobby Card (USA) **Mr A. N. Mubarak**
35 AL SHAQAB (IRE), b g Amadeus Wolf—Common Rumpus (IRE) **Mr A. N. Mubarak**
36 ARDMAY (IRE), b g Strategic Prince—Right After Moyne (IRE) **A. C. Henson**
37 BAPAK CHINTA (USA), gr ro c Speightstown (USA)—Suena Cay (USA) **Mr T. R. B. T. A. Shah**
38 BAPAK PINTAR, gr c Royal Applause—Victory Spirit (USA) **Mr T. R. B. T. A. Shah**
39 B g Peintre Celebre (USA)—Blossom **G. Reed**
40 BOGART, ch c Bahamian Bounty—Lauren Louise **Mrs A. Bailey**
41 BROCKLEBANK (IRE), b g Diamond Green (FR)—La Stellina (IRE) **Highclere T'Bred Racing & Mrs M Forsyth**
42 BU SAMRA (IRE), b g Lawman (FR)—Distant Drama (USA) **Mr A. N. Mubarak**
43 CHOOSEDAY (IRE), b g Choisir (AUS)—Break of Day (USA) **Mrs S. J. Barker**
44 DAM BEAUTIFUL, b f Sleeping Indian—Nellie Melba **Mrs L. Dartnell**
45 DESERT PHILOSOPHER, b c Pastoral Pursuits—Tembladora (IRE) **A. Al Shaikh**
46 DISCRESSION, b c Indesatchel (IRE)—Night Gypsy **Mr TG & Mrs ME Holdcroft,Mr K MacPherson**
47 B c Bahamian Bounty—Enchanted Princess **Hambleton Racing Ltd XXI**
48 END OF DREAMS (USA), ch f Horse Chestnut (SAF)—Folk Tale (USA) **Mr A. N. Mubarak**
49 B g Soviet Star (USA)—Fluffy **G. Reed**
50 FORGET ME NOT LANE (IRE), b g Holy Roman Emperor (IRE)—Mrs Arkada (FR) **J. Hanson**
51 GABRIAL THE KING (USA), b g Speightstown (USA)—Dynamous (USA) **Dr M. B. Q. S. Koukash**
52 HAMZA (IRE), b g Amadeus Wolf—Lady Shanghai (IRE) **Mr A. N. Mubarak**
53 HOT SUGAR (USA), b g Lemon Drop Kid (USA)—Plaisir Des Yeux (FR) **The C H F Partnership**
54 INDEPUB, b g Indesatchel (IRE)—Champenoise **D. W. Barker**
55 INETROBIL (IRE), ch f Bertolini (USA)—Tigava (USA) **Highclere T'Bred Racing & Mr P Beirne**
56 KYLESKU (IRE), b f Moss Vale (IRE)—Gisela (IRE) **Mrs J. H. Ryan**
57 LAFFAN (IRE), b g Dark Angel (IRE)—Lady Corduff (IRE) **Mr A. N. Mubarak**
58 LET'S FALL IN LOVE, b f Piccolo—Takes Two To Tango **G. Reed**
59 LOLLINA PAULINA, b f Holy Roman Emperor (IRE)—Alexia Reveuse (IRE) **The Paulina Partnership**
60 MALIHA (IRE), b f Amadeus Wolf—Folcara (IRE) **Mr A. N. Mubarak**
61 MY PEARL (IRE), b g Sleeping Indian—My-Lorraine (IRE) **Mrs M. Forsyth**
62 NAGHAM (IRE), b f Camacho—Happy Talk (IRE) **Mr A. N. Mubarak**
63 PEA SHOOTER, b g Piccolo—Sparkling Eyes **Mrs M. Forsyth**
64 B f Royal Applause—Polo **G. Reed**
65 PRINCE GABRIAL (IRE), b g Moss Vale (IRE)—Baileys Cream **Dr M. B. Q. S. Koukash**
66 ROUGHLYN, ch g Haafhd—Dime Bag **Chester Racing Club Ltd**
67 SARDANAPALUS, b g Byron—Crinkle (IRE) **J. Nixon**
68 B c Peintre Celebre (USA)—Shall We Dance **G. Reed**
69 STOP FLIRTING, b f Piccolo—Chasing A Dream **G. Reed**
70 SUPREME LUXURY (IRE), b f Iffraaj—Stay Hernanda **Mr A. N. Mubarak**
71 TAHNEE MARA (IRE), b f Sleeping Indian—Totally Yours (IRE) **Hambleton Racing XX**
72 TORERO, b g Hernando (FR)—After You **G. Reed**
73 TORTONI (IRE), b g Teofilo (IRE)—Nipping (IRE) **B. P. Hayes**
74 TRAIL BLAZE (IRE), b c Tagula (IRE)—Kingpin Delight **Mr & Mrs Julian & Rosie Richer**
75 UNTOLD MELODY, b f Oratorio (IRE)—Different Story (USA) **Hambleton Racing XIX**
76 WHAT'S UP (IRE), b f Dylan Thomas (IRE)—Ridotto **A & A**
77 ZAKREET, ch c Cadeaux Genereux—Chili Dip **Mr A. N. Mubarak**

TWO-YEAR-OLDS

78 B c 16/3 Red Clubs (IRE)—Alexander Goldmine (Dansili) (19047) **Hambleton Racing Ltd XXII**
79 ANGILINA, b f 22/2 Teofilo (IRE)—Finnmark (Halling (USA)) **S. Ali**
80 BAIN'S PASS (IRE), ch c 18/4 Johannesburg (USA)—
    Rose Bourbon (USA) (Woodman (USA)) (30377) **Mrs M. Forsyth**
81 B f 9/2 Oratorio (IRE)—Blue Indigo (FR) (Pistolet Bleu (IRE)) (11428) **Mrs J. H. Ryan**
82 Ch c 1/4 Dubai Destination (USA)—Bukhoor (IRE) (Danehill (USA)) (20952) **Mrs J. H. Ryan**
83 DELORES ROCKET, b f 22/3 Firebreak—Artistic (IRE) (Noverre (USA)) (18095) **J. Nixon**
84 DEWI CHINTA (IRE), b f 9/4 Tagula (IRE)—
    Damjanich (IRE) (Mull of Kintyre (USA)) (15238) **Mr T. R. B. T. A. Shah**
85 B f 15/3 Tagula (IRE)—Erne Project (IRE) (Project Manager) (14285) **Mrs A. Bailey**
86 FENWICK GALE (IRE), ch f 2/2 Kyllachy—
    Carranza (IRE) (Lead On Time (USA)) (13333) **Mr Allan Kerr Mr Peter McGivney**
87 B c 19/2 Sleeping Indian—Flora Burn (UAE) (Jade Robbery (USA)) (12380) **Mrs J. H. Ryan**

MR KEVIN RYAN—continued

88 B f 2/2 Bertolini (USA)—Flying Highest (Spectrum (IRE)) (15714) **Mr P. Beirne**
89 GARMELOW GIRL, b f 22/1 Piccolo—Juncea (Elnadim (USA)) (9523) **Mrs M. Forsyth**
90 Ch c 17/4 Verglas (IRE)—Gold Strike (IRE) (Rainbow Quest (USA)) (12315) **Mr A. N. Mubarak**
91 B g 11/2 Diamond Green (FR)—Golden (FR) (Sanglamore (USA)) (5714) **Mr A. N. Mubarak**
92 GREAT PHILOSOPHER (IRE), ch c 20/2 Choisir (AUS)—Sandbox Two (IRE) (Foxhound (USA)) (31428) **A & A**
93 Ch c 9/3 Sleeping Indian—Harlem Dancer (Dr Devious (IRE)) (20952) **Kenneth MacPherson**
94 IRREPLACABLE, b f 2/5 Indesatchel (IRE)—
                                   Razzle (IRE) (Green Desert (USA)) (6567) **Mr T. G. & Mrs M. E. Holdcroft**
95 JORDANSTOWN, ch c 16/3 Piccolo—Pigment (Zamindar (USA)) (12380) **Countrywide Racing**
96 MARHABA MALAYEEN (IRE), b c 14/3 Dutch Art—Poyle Caitlin (IRE) (Bachir (IRE)) (62000) **A. Al Shaikh**
97 B f 8/2 Holy Roman Emperor (IRE)—Miss Delila (IRE) (Malibu Moon (USA)) (18000)
98 B f 13/2 Muhtathir—Miss Mission (IRE) (Second Empire (IRE)) (38587) **Highbank Stud**
99 Ch c 18/3 Byron—Muja Farewell (Mujtahid (USA)) (7142) **Mrs A. Bailey**
100 B c 6/5 Pastoral Pursuits—Nsx (Roi Danzig (USA))
101 PEARL RANSOM (IRE), b c 15/2 Intikhab (USA)—Massada (Most Welcome) (62000) **Pearl Bloodstock Limited**
102 B f 11/4 Diamond Green (FR)—Rectify (IRE) (Mujadil (USA)) (11082) **Mr A. N. Mubarak**
103 RUN FAT LASS RUN, b f 10/4 Sakhee (USA)—Feolin (Dr Fong (USA)) **S. C. B. Limited**
104 B c 6/3 Elnadim (USA)—Shulammite Woman (IRE) (Desert Sun) (24630) **C. G. J. Chua**
105 SOMETHINGBOUTMARY, ch f 14/1 Sleeping Indian—Lochleven (Selkirk (USA))
106 B f 13/3 Holy Roman Emperor (IRE)—Star Profile (IRE) (Sadler's Wells (USA)) (28000) **Dr M. B. Q. S. Koukash**
107 B f 12/2 Byron—Tanwir (Unfuwain (USA)) (10000) **Mr A. N. Mubarak**
108 Ch c 24/1 Compton Place—Tembladora (IRE) (Docksider (USA)) (20000) **Mrs A. Bailey**
109 UNASSAILABLE, ch c 30/4 Bahamian Bounty—Reeling N' Rocking (IRE) (Mr Greeley (USA)) (22000) **J. Nixon**
110 B f 12/1 Sleeping Indian—Vale of Belvoir (IRE) (Mull of Kintyre (USA)) (33333) **A. Al Shaikh**
111 Ch c 25/4 Speightstown—Valid Move (USA) (Valid Expectations (USA)) (112942) **Mr T. R. B. T. A. Shah**
112 B f 14/2 Cadeaux Genereux—Venoge (IRE) (Green Desert (USA)) (11428) **Middleham Park Racing XLV**
113 B f 31/3 Authorized (USA)—Vyatka (Lion Cavern (USA)) (20000) **S. Ali**

Other Owners: Sheikh S. R. Al Khalifa, Mr A. A. Al Shaikh, Mr S. M. Alkhalifa, Mrs E. A. Dale, K. H. Fischer, C. H. Fischer, J. A. Forsyth, B. Gaunt, D. M. Gibbons, Hambleton Racing Ltd, The Hon H. M. Herbert, Highclere Thoroughbred Racing Ltd, Mr A. Kerr, D. McAllister, Mr P. McGivney, T. S. Palin, D. Pearson, A. D. Pirie, M. Prince, D. P. Reilly, Mrs C. J. Reilly, Mrs R. L. Richer, J. Richer, Mr S. R. H. Turner, Mrs I. M. Wainwright, Mr M. A. Wainwright, Mrs L. Whitehead.

Assistant Trainers: Joe O'Gorman, Adam Ryan.

Jockey (flat): Philip Makin. **Conditional:** Brian Toomey. **Apprentice:** Amy Ryan, Julie Burke, Paul McGiff.

---

574 MR AYTACH SADIK, Kidderminster
Postal: Wolverley Court Coach House, Wolverley, Kidderminster, Worcestershire, DY10 3RP
Contacts: **PHONE (01562) 852362 MOBILE (07803) 040344**

1 APACHE DAWN, 8, ch g Pursuit of Love—Taza **A. M. Sadik**
2 BLIZZARD BLUES (USA), 6, ch g Mr Greeley (USA)—Blush Damask (USA) **A. M. Sadik**
3 HOW'S D STRAWBOSS (IRE), 7, gr g Environment Friend—Taken For A Ride (IRE) **A. M. Sadik**
4 INDIAN PIPE DREAM (IRE), 10, br g Indian Danehill (IRE)—Build A Dream (USA) **A. M. Sadik**
5 RINGSEND ROSE (IRE), 9, b m Beneficial—Charwin (IRE) **A. M. Sadik**

---

575 MR PETER SALMON, Wetherby
Postal: Ingmanthorpe Racing Stables, Loshpot Lane, Kirk Deighton, Wetherby, West Yorkshire, LS22 5HL
Contacts: **PHONE (01937) 587552 FAX (01937) 587552 MOBILE (07828) 958820**
E-MAIL psalmon@ingmanthorperacing.co.uk

1 ADARE PRINCE (IRE), 11, b g Supreme Leader—Legal Challenge (IRE) **Ann & Eric Lumley**
2 ALASKAN PRINCE (IRE), 7, b g Exit To Nowhere (USA)—Alaskan Princess (IRE) **Mrs W. M. Crump**
3 HALF A CROWN (IRE), 7, b g Compton Place—Penny Ha'penny **Viscount Environmental**
4 HYDRANT, 6, b g Haafhd—Spring **Mr C. Hatch**
5 OPTION MONEY (IRE), 10, b g Kotashaan (FR)—Be My Bargain (IRE) **Ann & Eric Lumley**
6 WHY SO SERIOUS, 6, ch g Falbrav (IRE)—Marrakech (IRE) **Mrs A. L. Lumley**

THREE-YEAR-OLDS

7 B g Pursuit of Love—Star Sign **Mr G. N. Parker**

MR PETER SALMON—continued

Other Owners: Mr Graham Davies, Mr Eric Lumley, Mrs Ann Lumley.

Jockey (flat): Frankie Dettori, Billy Cray, Paul Hanagan, Andrew Mullen. **Jockey (NH):** Andrew Thornton, Jan Faltejsek.
Conditional: Daryl Millar. **Apprentice:** Hannah Nunn. **Amateur:** Mr Jack Salmon.

---

576 **MRS DEBORAH SANDERSON, Tickhill**
Postal: **Moorhouse Farm, Tickhill Spital, Doncaster, South Yorkshire, DN11 9EY**
Contacts: **PHONE (01777) 818751 (01427) 884692 FAX (01777) 818751 MOBILE (07968) 821074**
E-MAIL debbie.sanderson@btconnect.com WEBSITE www.wisetonstables.co.uk

1 LENNY BEE, 6, gr ro g Kyllachy—Smart Hostess **Mr R. Hull**
2 MOTHER JONES, 4, b f Sleeping Indian—Bella Chica (IRE) **Mr R. Hull**

THREE-YEAR-OLDS

3 BITAPHON (IRE), br g Acclamation—Pitrizzia **Mrs C. J. Walsh**
4 GOLD DEAL (IRE), b g Chineur (FR)—Alexander Express (IRE) **Mr R. Hull**
5 KEY AMBITION, ch g Auction House (USA)—Love Thing **Mr R. Hull**

TWO-YEAR-OLDS

6 BERTIE ROYALE, b c 15/2 Bertolini (USA)—Riva Royale (Royal Applause) **Mr R. Hull**
7 GRACE HULL, gr f 17/2 Piccolo—Smart Hostess (Most Welcome) (20952) **Mr R. Hull**
8 READY (IRE), ch g 3/2 Elnadim (USA)—Fusili (IRE) (Silvano (GER)) (16190) **Mr R. Hull**

Other Owners: Mrs P. C. Murch.

Jockey (flat): Edward Creighton, Silvestre De Sousa. **Amateur:** Miss Dora Lenge.

---

577 **MRS KATHLEEN SANDERSON, Tiverton**
Postal: **New Cottage, Rackenford Road, Calverleigh, Tiverton, Devon, EX16 8BE**
Contacts: **PHONE (01884) 254217**

1 BLINDING LIGHTS (IRE), 7, b g Snurge—Tender Return (IRE) **Mrs K. M. Sanderson**
2 ECLIPSE AWARD (IRE), 6, br g Definite Article—Aries Girl **Mrs K. M. Sanderson**
3 POWERFULLBEAT, 8, b g Beat All (USA)—Lacounsel (FR) **Mrs H. D. Power**

Jockey (NH): Danny Cook. **Amateur:** Mr Will Biddick.

---

578 **MR MALCOLM SAUNDERS, Wells**
Postal: **Blue Mountain Farm, Wells Hill Bottom, Haydon, Wells, Somerset, BA5 3EZ**
Contacts: **OFFICE/FAX (01749) 841011 MOBILE (07771) 601035**
E-MAIL malcolm@malcolmsaunders.co.uk WEBSITE www.malcolmsaunders.co.uk

1 SARANGOO, 4, b f Piccolo—Craic Sa Ceili (IRE) **B. C. Scott**
2 WOODEN KING (IRE), 7, b g Danetime (IRE)—Olympic Rock (IRE) **Mr P. K. Hancock**

THREE-YEAR-OLDS

3 TRIO OF TRIX, b f Act One—Dictatrix **A. P. Holland**

TWO-YEAR-OLDS

4 B f 19/3 Antonius Pius (USA)—Await (IRE) (Peintre Celebre (USA)) (24630) **T. P. Bostwick**
5 BALTIC GIN (IRE), b f 24/4 Baltic King—Deeday Bay (IRE) (Brave Act) (5746) **Mr P. S. G. Nicholas**
6 B f 20/3 Piccolo—Craic Sa Ceili (IRE) (Danehill Dancer (IRE))
7 Ch f 2/2 Sleeping Indian—Easy Mover (IRE) (Bluebird (USA)) **M. S. Saunders**
8 B f 3/3 Red Clubs (IRE)—Majestic Eviction (IRE) (King's Theatre (IRE)) (6567) **M. S. Saunders**
9 SILVERRICA (IRE), gr f 30/4 Ad Valorem (USA)—Allegorica (IRE) (Alzao (USA)) (10672) **Mrs V. L. Nicholas**

579 MRS DIANNE SAYER, Penrith
Postal: **Town End Farm, Hackthorpe, Penrith, Cumbria, CA10 2HX**
Contacts: **PHONE (01931) 712245 MOBILE (07980) 295316**

1 **ALLORO**, 8, ch g Auction House (USA)—Minette **A. Slack**
2 **AUBERGE (IRE)**, 8, ch m Blueprint (IRE)—Castlegrace (IRE) **R. H. Affleck**
3 **COOL BARANCA (GER)**, 6, b m Beat Hollow—Cool Storm (IRE) **Mr D. J. Coppola**
4 **ENDEAVOR**, 7, ch g Selkirk (USA)—Midnight Mambo (USA) **Mrs M. Coppola**
5 **LONG RANGE**, 6, b g Pivotal—Flight of Fancy **Mrs F. C. Rayson**
6 **MARKADAM**, 6, b g Mark of Esteem (IRE)—Elucidate **Mr R. A. Harrison**
7 **MISS ABBEY**, 8, ch m Missed Flight—Little Brockwell (IRE) **Craig's Gold**
8 **MORE EQUITY**, 10, b m Classic Cliche (IRE)—Sillymore **Mrs M. Coppola**
9 **OH RIGHT (IRE)**, 8, b g Zagreb (USA)—Conna Bride Lady (IRE) **J. A. Sayer**
10 **RED KINGDOM (IRE)**, 8, b g Red Ransom (USA)—Eucalyptus Hill (USA) **Mrs F. C. Rayson**
11 **SERGEANT PINK (IRE)**, 6, b g Fasliyev (USA)—Ring Pink (USA) **J. A. Sayer**
12 **SHOAL BAY DREAMER**, 6, b m Central Park (IRE)—Ninfa (IRE) **The Transatlantics**
13 **SILK DRUM (IRE)**, 7, gr g Intikhab (USA)—Aneydia (IRE) **A. R. White**
14 **WORTH A KING'S**, 6, b g Red Ransom (USA)—Top Romance (IRE) **Mr D. A. Price**

Other Owners: Mr A. Craig, Mr J. Goldie, Mrs J. D. Howard, R. Kent, Mrs H. D. Sayer.

Assistant Trainer: Miss Joanna Sayer

Amateur: Miss Emma Sayer, Miss Natalie Sayer, Miss Robyn Gray.

580 DR JON SCARGILL, Newmarket
Postal: **Red House Stables, Hamilton Road, Newmarket, Suffolk, CB8 0TE**
Contacts: **PHONE (01638) 663254 MOBILE (07785) 350705**
E-MAIL scargill@redhousestables.freeserve.co.uk WEBSITE www.drjonscargill.co.uk

1 **CARPENTRAS**, 4, b f Val Royal (FR)—Molly Brown **Mr D. J. Meilton**
2 **JUNKET**, 5, b m Medicean—Gallivant **Silent Partners**

TWO-YEAR-OLDS

3 B c 7/3 Tobougg (IRE)—Four-Legged Friend (Aragon) (5714) **J P T Partnership**

Other Owners: A. Millar, G. F. L. Robinson, Mrs S. M. Scargill, Mr P. J. Scargill.

581 MR DERRICK SCOTT, Minehead
Postal: **East Lynch, Minehead, Somerset, TA24 8SS**
Contacts: **PHONE (01643) 702430 FAX (01643) 702430**

1 **LUPITA (IRE)**, 8, ch m Intikhab (USA)—Sarah (IRE) **Mrs R. Scott**

582 MRS ELIZABETH SCOTT, Axbridge
Postal: **Moorland Farm, Axbridge, Somerset, BS26 2BA**

1 **PORTMEADE**, 10, b g Thowra (FR)—Oneninefive **Mrs E. B. Scott**

583 MR JEREMY SCOTT, Dulverton
Postal: **Higher Holworthy Farm, Brompton Regis, Dulverton, Somerset, TA22 9NY**
Contacts: **PHONE (01398) 371414 MOBILE (07709) 279483**
E-MAIL holworthyfarm@yahoo.com

1 **AZIONE**, 9, b m Exit To Nowhere (USA)—Little Feat **Mr P. A. Brend**
2 **BOWNTOBEBAD (IRE)**, 7, b g Alderbrook—Angels Flame (IRE) **G. S. Brown**
3 **CLASH DUFF (IRE)**, 7, gr g Great Palm (USA)—Evnelu (IRE) **Gale Force Four**
4 **COOL FRIEND (IRE)**, 9, b m Anshan—Glacial Friend (IRE) **Mrs Messer-Bennetts Mrs Clarke-Hall**
5 **DECIMUS (IRE)**, 5, b g Bienamado (USA)—Catch Me Dreaming (IRE) **The Ten 2 One Gang**
6 **DREAMBROOK LADY (IRE)**, 6, b m Alderbrook—Easter Day (IRE) **Ms M. Miles**
7 **FIVE STAR WILSHAM (IRE)**, 8, b g Bob's Return (IRE)—Riverpauper (IRE) **Mr & Mrs Richard Organ**

MR JEREMY SCOTT—continued

8 **GOLDEN GAEL**, 6, ch m Generous (IRE)—Gaelic Gold (IRE) **The Wild Bunch**
9 **IFYOULETMEFINISH (IRE)**, 5, b g Bonbon Rose (FR)—Surfing France (FR) **Bradley Partnership**
10 **JOSH'S DREAMWAY (IRE)**, 6, b m Deploy—Midway (IRE) **Ms M. Miles**
11 **LYRICAL CHANT (IRE)**, 8, ch m Deploy—Vic Melody (FR) **Mrs N. A. Ward & Mrs N. Welby**
12 **MARIAS ROCK**, 10, b m I'm Supposin (IRE)—Our Lottie **G. T. Lever**
13 **MASTER FLIGHT**, 8, ch g Alflora (IRE)—Morning Flight (IRE) **Master Partners 1**
14 **MYSTIC APPEAL**, 6, br g Alderbrook—Piseog (IRE) **Gale Force Two**
15 **NOTARFBAD (IRE)**, 6, b g Alderbrook—Angels Flame (IRE) **Govier & Brown**
16 **OTTER MIST**, 7, gr g Karinga Bay—Absolutley Foxed **A. E. Ford**
17 **PERICOLOSO (IRE)**, 8, b g Heron Island (IRE)—Phills Serenade (IRE) **Mrs C. C. Scott**
18 **PYLEIGH LASS**, 6, gr m Silver Patriarch (IRE)—Lady Callernish **F. D. Popham**
19 **SIR KEZBAAH (IRE)**, 8, b g Oscar (IRE)—Madam Chloe **Andrew & Vanessa Maddox**
20 **THE BOSS (IRE)**, 7, ch g Accordion—Danjo's Lady (IRE) **Mrs Messer-Bennetts,Clarke Hall & Gilbert**
21 **ULTRAVOX (USA)**, 5, b g Lemon Drop Kid (USA)—Lynnwood Chase (USA) **G. T. Lever**
22 **WEBBERYS DREAM**, 9, b g Bandmaster (USA)—Sheilas Dream **S. G. Searle**
23 **WHAT ER SAY**, 7, b g Karinga Bay—Spread The Word **Mrs P. J. Pengelly**

Other Owners: J. Bagwell-Purefoy, Mr P. W. Brockman, Mrs C. Clarke-Hall, R. Coates, Mr A. P. Gale, Mrs A. G. Gale, Mrs K. Gilbert, Mrs G. D. Giles, Mr P. Govier, Mr P. F. Govier, M. D. Greatorex, R. W. S. Jevon, Mr A. P. Maddox, Mrs V. Maddox, Miss N. Martin, Mrs S. D. Messer-Bennetts, Dr M. M. Ogilvy, Mr R. H. Organ, Mrs J. Organ, Mrs S. M. Ragg, Mr J. Simpson, J. G. Storey, Mrs C. W. Ward, Mrs N. J. Welby.

Assistant Trainer: Camilla Scott

MR BERNARD SCRIVEN, Taunton
Postal: **Cogload Farm, Durston, Taunton, Somerset, TA3 5AW**
Contacts: **PHONE (01823) 490208**

1 **DRUMBEATER (IRE)**, 12, b g Supreme Leader—Ballydrummund (IRE) **B. Scriven**
2 **PUERTO AZUL (IRE)**, 8, ch g Beneficial—Droichidin **B. Scriven**

Assistant Trainer: Miss Kay Scriven

MR MICHAEL SCUDAMORE, Bromsash
Postal: **Eccleswall Court, Bromsash, Nr. Ross-on-Wye, Herefordshire, HR9 7PP**
Contacts: **PHONE (01989) 750844 FAX (01989) 750281 MOBILE (07901) 853520**
E-MAIL michael.scu@btconnect.com WEBSITE www.scudamoreracing.co.uk

1 **ADDIKT (IRE)**, 7, b h Diktat—Frond **Good Breed Limited**
2 **AMBROSE PRINCESS (IRE)**, 7, b m Chevalier (IRE)—Mark One **The Yes No Wait Sorries**
3 **APERITIF**, 11, ch g Pivotal—Art Deco Lady **M. Scudamore**
4 **ARUMUN (IRE)**, 11, b g Posidonas—Adwoa (IRE) **Mr M. R. Blandford**
5 **BOUNDS AND LEAPS**, 7, b m Laveron—Geisha **Mason Scudamore Racing**
6 **DA PONTE**, 4, b g Librettist (USA)—Naharnook **Mrs B. V. Evans**
7 **DARK ENERGY**, 8, br g Observatory (USA)—Waterfowl Creek (IRE) **The Yes No Wait Sorries**
8 **EUROQUIP BOY (IRE)**, 5, b g Antonius Pius (USA)—La Shalak (IRE) **Mr Ted Bennett**
9 **EUROQUIP SUSIE**, 4, b f Monsieur Bond (IRE)—Fizzy Lady **Mr Ted Bennett**
10 **GLOUCESTER**, 9, b g Montjeu (IRE)—Birdlip (USA) **Mr S. M. Smith & Keith Hunter**
11 **GUEST BOOK (IRE)**, 5, b g Green Desert (USA)—Your Welcome **M. Scudamore**
12 **GUNNER ROSE**, 9, ch g Gunner B—Fortria Rosie Dawn **M. J. & W. J. Fenn**
13 **GUNSLINGER (FR)**, 7, b g High Chaparral (IRE)—Gamine (IRE) **Mr S. M. Smith & Keith Hunter**
14 **HAZY DAWN**, 7, b m Cloudings (IRE)—Quiet Dawn **The King's Men**
15 **I'LLDOIT**, 5, br g Tamayaz (CAN)—Club Oasis **Good Breed Limited**
16 **KAPRICORNE (FR)**, 5, b g Kapgarde (FR)—Colombe Royale (FR) **Mr M. R. Blandford**
17 **KAYEF (GER)**, 5, ch h Nayef (USA)—Kassna (IRE) **Chua, Katriya, Hunter & Ong**
18 **LUCAS PITT**, 5, b g Kyllachy—Bardot **Mr Ted Bennett**
19 **MONBEG DUDE (IRE)**, 7, b g Witness Box (USA)—Ten Dollar Bill (IRE) **Oydunow**
20 **NO THROUGH ROAD**, 5, b g Grape Tree Road—Pendil's Delight **A. P. Barwell**
21 **PRINCESSE FLEUR**, 4, b f Grape Tree Road—Princesse Grec (FR) **The Honfleur Syndicate**
22 **RED CURRENT**, 8, b m Soviet Star (USA)—Fleet Amour (USA) **M. Scudamore**
23 **RIPTIDE**, 6, b g Val Royal (FR)—Glittering Image (IRE) **Middletons**
24 **ROYAL ACCLAMATION (IRE)**, 7, b g Acclamation—Lady Abigail (IRE) **M. Scudamore**
25 **SAPHIR RIVER (FR)**, 6, gr g Slickly (FR)—Miss Bio (FR) **Fat Gary Sports**
26 **SEYMOUR ALFIE**, 6, b g Alflora (IRE)—Seymour Chance **Mrs C. J. Black**

MR MICHAEL SCUDAMORE—continued

27 **SEYMOUR ERIC**, 7, b g Bollin Eric—Seymour Chance **Mrs C. J. Black & Ten Out Of Ten Racing**
28 **SOCIETY VENUE**, 7, b g Where Or When (IRE)—Society Rose **Mr & Mrs T. P. Winnell**
29 4, B c Golan (IRE)—Special Case (IRE) **Mr M. R. Blandford**
30 **TEN POLE TUDOR**, 7, b g Royal Applause—Amaniy (USA) **The Yes No Wait Sorries**
31 **UNE DES BIEFFES (FR)**, 4, b f Le Fou (IRE)—Belle D'ecajeul (FR) **Michael Fitzpatrick & Mark Blandford**
32 **UNNECESSARY XPENSE**, 5, b g Grape Tree Road—
Manque Pas d'air (FR) **Simpson-Daniel & Scudamore Racing**
33 **VON GALEN (IRE)**, 11, b g Germany (USA)—Castle Carrig (IRE) **Mrs B. V. Evans**
34 **WITH HINDSIGHT (IRE)**, 4, ch g Ad Valorem (USA)—Lady From Limerick (IRE)

THREE-YEAR-OLDS

35 **CHURCH MUSIC (IRE)**, b c Amadeus Wolf—Cappella (IRE) **C. G. J. Chua**
36 **EUROQUIP ROSE**, b f Orientor—Madrasee **Mr Ted Bennett**

Other Owners: Mr Sydney Baker, Mr Neil Bannister, Mr Shaun Bannister, Mr Mark Blandford, Mr J. C. G. Chua, Mr Chris Coley, Mr R. B. Denny, Mr Stephen Evans, Mr M. J. Fenn, Mr W. J. Fenn, Mr Michael Fitzpatrick, Ms Carolyn Harding, Mr Keith Hunter, Mr David Hussey, Mr A. Mason, Mr G. D. Middleton, Mr A. D. Middleton, Dr S. M. Readings, Mr N. J. Robinson, Mr E. J. Saunders, Mrs Marilyn Scudamore, Mr. M. Scudamore, Mr J. D. Simpson-Daniel, Mr S. M. Smith, Mr M. Tindall.

---

586 MR IAN SEMPLE, Carluke
Postal: **61 Kirk Road, Carluke, Lanarkshire, ML8 5BP**
Contacts: PHONE **(01357) 300911** FAX **(01357) 300911** MOBILE **(07950) 175207**

1 **AMNO DANCER (IRE)**, 5, b g Namid—Special Dancer **R. Reid**
2 **ARGENTINE (IRE)**, 8, b g Fasliyev (USA)—Teller (ARG) **R. Reid**
3 **BLUES JAZZ**, 6, b g Josr Algarhoud (IRE)—Belle of The Blues (IRE) **R. Reid**
4 **BURNWYND BOY**, 7, b g Tobougg (IRE)—Cadeau Speciale **R. Reid**
5 **DESERT AUCTION (IRE)**, 5, b g Desert Style (IRE)—Double Gamble **R. Reid**
6 **HARDROCK DIAMOND**, 4, b g Avonbridge—Clansinge **Patersons of Greenoakhill Limited**
7 **HERE NOW AND WHY (IRE)**, 5, br g Pastoral Pursuits—Why Now **Kenman Properties**
8 **LIBERTY ISLAND (IRE)**, 7, b g Statue of Liberty (USA)—Birthday (IRE) **R. Reid**
9 **MISSILE ATTACK (IRE)**, 4, b g Majestic Missile (IRE)—Aquatint **D. Irvine**
10 **SKYSTREAM (IRE)**, 4, b br f Captain Rio—Nuit des Temps **R. Reid**
11 **THE FIERY CROSS**, 5, b g Acclamation—Miriam **R. Reid**

THREE-YEAR-OLDS

12 **BURNWYND SPIRIT (IRE)**, b g Kodiac—Bluebird Spirit **R. Reid**
13 **GRAN CANARIA QUEEN**, b br f Compton Place—Ex Mill Lady **Mr M. Gillies**
14 **GREAT NICANOR (IRE)**, b g Bertolini (USA)—No More Maybes (IRE) **Exchange Court Properties Ltd**
15 Gr c Verglas (IRE)—Hetty (IRE)

TWO-YEAR-OLDS

16 B g 21/4 Whipper (USA)—Freya Tricks (Noverre (USA)) **Mr Ian Wilson**

Other Owners: Mr R. Hyndman, Ms Maureen Kennedy.

Assistant Trainer: Paul Semple

Jockey (flat): Robert Winston, Tom Eaves. Apprentice: Daniel Morgan.

---

587 MR PHILIP SHARP, Whatlington
Postal: **Swallows Oast Farm, Whatlington, Battle, East Sussex, TN33 0NR**

1 **GIULIETTA DA VINCI**, 5, b m Mujahid (USA)—Gennie Bond **P. J. Sharp**
2 **IDRIS (GER)**, 11, ch g Generous (IRE)—Idraak **P. J. Sharp**
3 **SOITSAKAI**, 5, ch h Cayman Kai (IRE)—Itsinthepost **P. J. Sharp**
4 **WHATLINGTON (IRE)**, 5, b g Oscar (IRE)—Gli Gli (IRE) **P. J. Sharp**
5 **WINGMAN (IRE)**, 10, b g In The Wings—Precedence (IRE) **T. G. Gillespie**

MR PHILIP SHARP—continued

THREE-YEAR-OLDS

  6 B c Prince Daniel (USA)—Gymcrak Cyrano (IRE)
  7 Ch c Prince Daniel (USA)—Riverain
  8 Ch c Grand Finale (IRE)—Welcome Lu

---

588 | **MR DEREK SHAW, Sproxton**
Postal: **The Sidings, Saltby Road, Sproxton, Melton Mowbray, Leicestershire, LE14 4RA**
Contacts: PHONE (01476) 860578 FAX (01476) 860578 MOBILE (07721) 039645
E-MAIL mail@derekshawracing.com WEBSITE www.derekshawracing.com

  1 ACTION FRONT (USA), 4, b br c Aptitude (USA)—Palisade (USA) **Mr D. Shaw**
  2 AEGEAN MEMORIES, 4, b f Haafhd—Perdicula (IRE) **Theobalds Stud**
  3 AVONROSE, 5, b m Avonbridge—Loveleaves **Moorland Racing**
  4 BABY STRANGE, 8, gr g Superior Premium—The Manx Touch (IRE) **Market Avenue Racing Club Ltd**
  5 BILKO PAK (IRE), 4, b g Barathea (IRE)—Vale View (FR) **Mr P. F. Barry**
  6 BINT ELNADIM (IRE), 4, b f Elnadim (USA)—Redrightreturning **Mr D. G. Morris**
  7 BLACKSTONE VEGAS, 6, ch g Nayef (USA)—Waqood (USA) **Shakespeare Racing**
  8 FAIR PASSION, 5, b m Trade Fair—United Passion **The Whiteman Partnership**
  9 FENELLA FUDGE, 4, b f Rock Hard Ten—Rahcak (IRE) **Mr Brian Johnson**
10 INVIGILATOR, 4, b c Motivator—Midpoint (USA) **Shawthing Racing Partnership**
11 LOYALTY, 5, b g Medicean—Ecoutila (USA) **Mr B. Johnson**
12 MATAAJIR (USA), 4, b g Redoute's Choice (AUS)—Hamasah (USA) **Mr D. Shaw**
13 MONEY BRIDGE, 5, ch g Doyen (USA)—Crochet (IRE) **The Whiteman Partnership**
14 NIALLY NOO, 4, b g Oasis Dream—Millyant **Market Avenue Racing Club**
15 OUR PRINCESS ELLIE (USA), 4, ch f Borrego (USA)—Dear Abigail (USA) **Mrs L. J. Shaw**
16 PATCH PATCH, 5, b g Avonbridge—Sandgate Cygnet **Mr C. B. Hamilton**
17 PRICKLES, 7, ch m Karinga Bay—Squeaky **Mr D. Shaw**
18 PRINCE OF PASSION (CAN), 4, ch g Roman Ruler—Rare Passion (CAN) **Mr C. B. Hamilton**
19 RAIMOND RIDGE (IRE), 6, b br g Namid—Jinsiyah (USA) **D. P. Fremel**
20 REAPING, 4, b f Dansili—Cut Corn **Mr D. Shaw**
21 REMMYNISS, 8, b m Sea Freedom—Royal Lark **Mr Chris Lee**
22 SAKTOON (USA), 4, b f El Prado (IRE)—Galore (USA) **Mr D. Shaw**
23 SHAWKANTANGO, 5, b g Piccolo—Kitty Kitty Cancan **Shawthing Racing Partnership**
24 SHAWS DIAMOND (USA), 6, ch m Ecton Park (USA)—
                                                 Dear Abigail (USA) **Ownaracehorse Diamond Partnership**
25 SKYLLA, 5, b m Kyllachy—Day Star **Facts & Figures**
26 TEENAGE DREAM (IRE), 4, b g Antonius Pius (USA)—Lucayan Star (IRE) **Market Avenue Racing Club**
27 THORNCLIFFER, 8, ch g Generous (IRE)—Recipe **Moorland Racing & Mr P. R. Whilock**
28 TWICE RED, 4, b g Intikhab—Red Shareef **M. C. Shirley**

THREE-YEAR-OLDS

29 AZAMARA STAR, ch f Three Valleys (USA)—Sunrise Girl **Unity Farm Holiday Centre Ltd**
30 CHATEAU LOLA, b f Byron—Glensara **Basingstoke Commercials**
31 CLASSY LASS, b f Trade Fair—Kythia (IRE) **Ownaracehorse.co.uk (Shaw)**
32 COLORI D'AMORE, b f Le Vie Dei Colori—Muscida (USA) **Mr D. Shaw**
33 CONAS ATA TU, b f Medicean—Sociable **Mr D. Shaw**
34 DANCING ELLIE MAE, b f Proclamation (IRE)—Park Star **Ownaracehorse.co.uk (Shaw)**
35 GHAZEER (IRE), b c Intikhab—Genial Jenny (IRE) **Mr D. Shaw**
36 HAWKINO (IRE), b g Hawk Wing (USA)—Halicardia **G. Horsford**
37 MIDNITE MOTIVATION, b f Motivator—Tamise (USA) **The Whiteman Partnership**

TWO-YEAR-OLDS

38 Ch f 21/5 Compton Place—Blushing Sunrise (USA) (Cox's Ridge (USA)) (2857) **Mrs L. J. Shaw**
39 B f 24/4 Firebreak—Charolles (Ajdal (USA)) **Mr D. Shaw**
40 Gr ch f 14/2 Shamardal (USA)—Elitista (FR) (Linamix (FR)) (45000) **Mr Brian Johnson**
41 B f 31/5 Byron—Florentine Lady (Medicean) **Mrs L. J. Shaw**
42 B c 2/2 Exceed And Excel (AUS)—Injaaz (Sheikh Albadou) (42000) **Mr Brian Johnson**
43 B f 21/2 Authorized (IRE)—Nice Tune (Diktat) (800) **Mrs L. J. Shaw**
44 B c 11/4 Manduro (GER)—Rakata (USA) (Quiet American (USA)) (20000) **Mr D. Shaw**
45 B f 29/3 Cockney Rebel (IRE)—Silent Miracle (IRE) (Night Shift (USA)) (800) **Mr D. Shaw**
46 B f 10/2 Sakhee (USA)—Sociable (Danehill (USA)) **Mr D. Shaw**
47 B f 4/5 Manduro (GER)—Trick of Ace (USA) (Clever Trick (USA)) (25000) **Mr Brian Johnson**

MR DEREK SHAW—continued

Other Owners: Exors of the Late Mr T. H. Blackman, Mr J. P. Hames, Mr Nick Higginson, Mr Tim Lively, Mr S. A. Mace, Mrs A. M. Mace, Mr D. N. McLiesh, Ownaracehorse Ltd (ownaracehorse.co.uk), Mr G. Pickering, Mr P. A. Saxton, Mr Derek Shaw, Mrs Lyndsey Shaw, Mr P. R. Whilock, Mr S. A. Whiteman.

---

589 | **MRS FIONA SHAW, Dorchester**
Postal: **Skippet Cottage, Bradford Peverell, Dorchester, Dorset, DT2 9SE**

1 BUSY ISIT, 12, br g Busy Flight—Eatons **P. B. Shaw**
2 KARSHAAN (FR), 9, b g Kahyasi—Mon Petitnamour (IRE) **Mrs F. M. Shaw**
3 MY SPACE, 6, b m Pasternak—Eatons **P. B. Shaw**
4 PIMBURY (IRE), 10, b g Pistolet Bleu (IRE)—Duchess of Kinsale (IRE) **Mrs F. M. Shaw**

---

590 | **MR JAMES SHEPPARD, Faringdon**
Postal: **1 Leamington Drive, Faringdon, Oxfordshire, SN7 7JZ**

1 CAPTAIN HASTINGS (IRE), 8, b br g Tamayaz (CAN)—Ard Tia (IRE) **Mr J. Sheppard**

---

591 | **MR MATT SHEPPARD, Ledbury**
Postal: **Home Farm Cottage, Eastnor, Ledbury, Herefordshire, HR8 1RD**
Contacts: **FAX (01531) 634846 MOBILE (07770) 625061**
E-MAIL **matthew.sheppard@cmail.co.uk** WEBSITE **www.mattsheppardracing.co.uk**

1 ACHIMOTA (IRE), 6, b g Double Eclipse (IRE)—Tullyfoyle (IRE) **W. J. Odell**
2 BELLEAU (IRE), 4, b f Big Bad Bob (IRE)—Fantasy Wood (IRE) **Mrs H. M. West**
3 DAWNS GREY LIGHT, 4, gr g Proclamation (IRE)—Reaf **K. Arrowsmith**
4 IKORODU ROAD, 9, b g Double Trigger (IRE)—Cerisier (IRE) **W. J. Odell**
5 KILDARE KITTEN (USA), 4, ch f Kitten's Joy (USA)—Philanthropy Lady (USA) **Mrs N. Sheppard**
6 LOUGHALDER (IRE), 6, ch g Alderbrook—Lough Lein Leader (IRE) **S. J. D. Gegg**
7 MUNLOCHY BAY, 8, b m Karinga Bay—Meghdoot **The Blues Partnership**
8 PIN D'ESTRUVAL (FR), 9, ch g Lute Antique (FR)—Haie d'estruval (FR) **Lost In The Summer Wine**

Other Owners: M. R. Bown, R. A. Kujawa, Mr A. J. Scrivin, Mr P. R. W. Smith.

Amateur: Mr L. Payter.

---

592 | **MR FRANK SHERIDAN, Wolverhampton**
Postal: **3 The Mews, Gorsebrook Road, Dunstall Park, Wolverhampton, West Midlands, WV6 0PE**
Contacts: **MOBILE (07889) 962218**
E-MAIL **sheridanfrank@libero.it**

1 AHLAWY (IRE), 9, gr g Green Desert (USA)—On Call **Mr F. Sheridan**
2 DUBONNY, 5, b m Dubawi (IRE)—Ravishing (IRE) **Sport Of Gentleman Ltd**
3 EXEPTIONAL GIRL, 6, b m Medicean—Crimson Rosella **Sport Of Gentleman Ltd**
4 EYES ON, 4, b f Diktat—Almost Amber (USA) **Four Winds Racing**
5 FORTUNELINI, 7, b m Bertolini (USA)—River of Fortune (IRE) **Sport Of Gentleman Ltd**
6 GREENMEETIC (IRE), 5, b m Black Sam Bellamy (IRE)—Asura (GER)
7 HIMAYNA, 8, b m Generous (IRE)—Himaya (IRE) **The Futures Bright Partnership**
8 MYSTIC HALO, 9, ch m Medicean—Aglow **Sport Of Gentleman Ltd**
9 NEEDWOOD RIDGE, 5, ch g Needwood Blade—Aspen Ridge (IRE) **Mr F. Sheridan**
10 PHLORIAN, 6, b g Falbrav (IRE)—Ravishing (IRE) **Sport Of Gentleman Ltd**
11 POLEMICA (IRE), 6, b m Rock of Gibraltar (IRE)—Lady Scarlett **Mr F. Sheridan**
12 RAVANCHI, 8, br m Indian Danehill (IRE)—Ravishing (IRE) **Sport Of Gentleman Ltd**
13 5, Br m Generous (IRE)—Sharadiya (IRE)
14 SOPRAN NAD (ITY), 8, b h Masad (IRE)—Sopran Newar **Mr F. Sheridan**

THREE-YEAR-OLDS

15 AGLAJA, b f Tiger Cafe (JPN)—Undovica **Mr B. Vitale Brovarone**
16 Ch g Sleeping Indian—Cashel Kiss
17 DANAFISIAK (IRE), b c Stardan (IRE)—Afisiak **Sport Of Gentleman Ltd**

MR FRANK SHERIDAN—continued

18 **DR ALBERT,** b c Son And Heir (IRE)—Tyne Goddess **Sport Of Gentleman Ltd**
19 B f Multiplex—Ellen Mooney
20 **GREEN MITAS (ITY),** ch c Denon (USA)—Sequita (GER)
21 **GREEN WAVE (ITY),** b f Sulamani (IRE)—Sopran Danys (IRE)
22 **GUAVA,** b f Kyllachy—Spunger **R. Naylor**
23 **HOMEWARD STRUT,** ch g Needwood Blade—Piccante **Mersey Racing, Bolingbroke Racing**
24 **LONE STAR STATE (IRE),** b c Stardan (IRE)—Rachelsfriend (IRE) **Sport Of Gentleman Ltd**
25 Gr f Aussie Rules (USA)—Spicey **Mr F. Sheridan**

Other Owners: L. A. Bolingbroke, Mr G. Bryan, S. J. Bryan, S. Cannon, Mr D. P. Grundy, Mr S. C. C. Skey, Mrs C. E. Skey.

---

593 **MR OLIVER SHERWOOD, Upper Lambourn**
Postal: **Rhonehurst House, Upper Lambourn, Hungerford, Berkshire, RG17 8RG**
Contacts: **PHONE** (01488) 71411 **FAX** (01488) 72786 **MOBILE** (07979) 591867
E-MAIL oliver.sherwood@virgin.net **WEBSITE** www.oliversherwood.com

1 **ACE SERVE,** 4, b f King's Best (USA)—Match Point **Mr Ian O'Connor**
2 **ADDICTION,** 7, b m Alflora (IRE)—Premier Princess **Fawley House Stud**
3 **BEETUNA (IRE),** 7, b g Statue of Liberty (USA)—High Atlas **Mr Ian O'Connor**
4 **BERTIE'S DESIRE,** 4, b g King's Theatre (IRE)—Temptation (FR) **T. D. J. Syder**
5 **BUXOM (IRE),** 5, b m Milan—Bermuda Bay (IRE) **Mr D. Redvers**
6 **CAMDEN (IRE),** 6, b g Old Vic—Electric View (IRE) **T. D. J. Syder**
7 5, B m Presenting—Cent Prime
8 **CHEERS,** 4, b f Haafhd—Ziggy Zaggy **J. Duddy**
9 **CLERK'S CHOICE (IRE),** 6, b g Bachelor Duke—Credit Crunch (IRE) **M. C. Banks**
10 **D'ARGENT CLOUD,** 4, gr g Tikkanen (USA)—Sounds Familiar (IRE) **CPM Group Limited**
11 **DARTFORD WARBLER (IRE),** 5, b g Overbury (IRE)—Stony View (IRE) **Stony Broke Partners**
12 **DEPUTY DAN (IRE),** 4, b g Westerner—Louisas Dream (IRE) **T. D. J. Syder**
13 4, Ch f Sulamani (IRE)—Dissolve **P. K. Gardner T/A Springcombe Park Stud**
14 **DOWNTOWN MANHATTAN (IRE),** 5, b br g Presenting—La Speziana (IRE) **Club 40 - 60**
15 **DRUM VALLEY,** 4, b g Beat Hollow—Euippe **Mr D J Burke & Mr T Meehan**
16 **DUNE SHINE,** 7, b g Karinga Bay—Caipirinha (IRE) **Mobile Distribution Solutions Ltd**
17 **FINANCIAL CLIMATE (IRE),** 5, b g Exit To Nowhere (USA)—Claudia's Pearl **Mrs S. C. Fillery**
18 **FLORAFERN,** 7, b m Alflora (IRE)—Mossy Fern **G. R. Waters**
19 **FURROWS,** 7, b g Alflora (IRE)—See More Furrows **Furrows Ltd**
20 **GLOBAL POWER (IRE),** 6, b g Subtle Power (IRE)—Bartelko (IRE) **It Wasn't Us**
21 **GREENLAW,** 6, b g Helissio (FR)—Juris Prudence (IRE) **Mr & Mrs Simon and June Cadzow**
22 **HARD HOUSE,** 5, ch g Trade Fair—Tuppenny Blue
23 **IMPINELLA,** 8, b m Alflora (IRE)—See More Furrows **Furrows Ltd**
24 **JEANO DE TOULOUSE (FR),** 5, b g Lavirco (GER)—Indecidable (FR) **O. M. C. Sherwood**
25 **KARACAS (IRE),** 6, ch m Karinga Bay—Suntas (IRE) **Fawley House Stud**
26 **KASBADALI (IRE),** 7, b g Kahyasi—Nikalie (FR) **T. D. J. Syder**
27 **KITCHEN LOAN (IRE),** 9, b m Presenting—
                                  Greenfield Noora (IRE) **Mr Michael Opperman and Mr Guy Opperman**
28 **KNOCKALONGI,** 6, b g Fair Mix (IRE)—Understudy **The St Joseph Partnership**
29 **KRISTIANO (IRE),** 5, b g Kris Kin (USA)—Moy Valley (IRE) **Mrs S. C. Fillery**
30 **LADY SINATRA,** 4, b f Where Or When (IRE)—Kythia (IRE) **The Pretty Hopeful Syndicate**
31 **MAJORICA KING (FR),** 6, b g Kahyasi—Majorica Queen (FR) **Mrs S. Griffiths**
32 **MANY CLOUDS (IRE),** 5, b g Cloudings (IRE)—Bobbing Back (IRE) **T. J. Hemmings**
33 **MILGEN BAY,** 6, br g Generous (IRE)—Lemon's Mill (USA) **G. R. Waters**
34 **MILLY MALONE (IRE),** 6, b m Milan—Sharp Single (IRE) **T. Syder & J. Ratcliffe**
35 **MISCHIEVOUS MILLY (IRE),** 4, b f Old Vic—Jennifers Diary (IRE) **A. Stewart & A. Taylor**
36 **PACCO (FR),** 9, b g Assessor (IRE)—Uguette IV (FR) **Ray & Marian Elbro**
37 **POKERHUNTRESS (IRE),** 5, b m Indian Danehill (IRE)—Chanson Indienne (FR) **A. Taylor**
38 **PUFFIN BILLY (IRE),** 4, b g Heron Island (IRE)—Downtown Train (USA) **T. D. J. Syder**
39 **ROCK ME GENTLY,** 5, b m Sulamani (IRE)—Disallowed (IRE)
40 **SILVER ACCORD (IRE),** 9, b brg g Accordion—Mazza **Mrs S. Griffiths**

Other Owners: Mr B. E. Alder, D. J. Burke, Mr S. R. Cadzow, Mrs J. Cadzow, J. Dwyer, Mrs M. Elbro, Mr R. J. Elbro, Mr R. O. J. Jenkins, Mrs S. D. McGrath, Mr R. H. Mcgrath, Mr A. E. Meehan, Mr M. E. O'Hara, J. M. Opperman, Mr G. T. Opperman, J. S. Palfreyman, H. M. J. Pope, J. Ratcliffe, W. L. Smith, Mr A. R. Stewart, V. J. Walsh, D. P. Walsh.

Assistant Trainer: Tom Fillery **Head Lad:** Stefan Namesansky

Jockey (NH): Sam Jones, Leighton Aspell, Dominic Elsworth. **Conditional:** Chris Timmons. **Amateur:** Mr J. Sherwood.

594 MR RAYMOND SHIELS, Jedburgh
Postal: **Thickside Farm, Jedburgh, Roxburghshire, TD8 6QY**
Contacts: **PHONE (01835) 864060 MOBILE (07790) 295645**

1 MOSCOW SUMFINN (IRE), 6, b g Moscow Society (USA)—Royal Broderick (IRE) **R. Shiels**
2 TOMZATACKMAN (IRE), 7, b g Saddlers' Hall (IRE)—Zafilly **R. Shiels**

595 MR SIMON SHIRLEY-BEAVAN, Hawick
Postal: **Gatehousecote, Bonchester Bridge, Hawick, Roxburghshire, TD9 8JD**
Contacts: **PHONE (01450) 860210**

1 HEART DANCER (FR), 6, b g Dark Moondancer—Petite Emilie (FR) **Mrs P. M. Shirley-Beavan**
2 RAMATUEL (FR), 7, b g Video Rock (FR)—Jade des Sacarts (FR) **Mrs P. M. Shirley-Beavan**
3 SHOW PUBLIC (FR), 6, b g Network (GER)—Grageline (FR) **Mrs P. M. Shirley-Beavan**
4 TAMBOUR MAJOR (FR), 5, b g Myrakalu (FR)—Joaillere (FR) **Mrs P. M. Shirley-Beavan**
5 TRACKANAIS (FR), 5, b g Milford Track (IRE)—Havanaise (FR) **Mrs P. M. Shirley-Beavan**

Amateur: Miss Kelly Bryson.

596 MISS LYNN SIDDALL, Tadcaster
Postal: **Stonebridge Farm, Colton, Tadcaster, North Yorkshire, LS24 8EP**
Contacts: **PHONE (01904) 744291 FAX (01904) 744291 MOBILE (07778) 216692/4**

1 AZEBRA, 7, b m Picea—Bonita Joana (IRE) **Miss J. M. Slater**
2 BACH STREET GIRL (IRE), 8, ch m Bach (IRE)—Millmount (IRE) **G. Kennington**
3 DIRECT APPROACH (IRE), 8, b g Tel Quel (FR)—Miss Telimar (IRE) **G. Kennington**
4 GREY LOCKER, 9, gr m Silver Patriarch (IRE)—Not So Prim **Mrs D. Ibbotson**
5 LISDONAGH HOUSE (IRE), 10, b g Little Bighorn—Lifinsa Barina (IRE) **J. P. G. Cooke**
6 MUKTARA (IRE), 6, b g Mukhalif (IRE)—Millmounts Tara (IRE) **Lynn Siddall Racing II**
7 PRIZE FIGHTER (IRE), 10, b g Desert Sun—Papal **Pennine Racing Associates**
8 WESTWIRE TOBY (IRE), 10, ch g Anshan—Ware It Well (IRE) **Stonebridge Racing II**

Other Owners: Mr C. W. Abbott, Mrs V. Ellison, Mrs K. M. Kennington, Miss L. C. Siddall, Miss S. E. Vinden.

Assistant Trainer: Stephen Hackney

Jockey (NH): Tom Siddall.

597 MR DAVID SIMCOCK, Newmarket
Postal: **The Office, Trillium Place, Birdcage Walk, Newmarket, Suffolk, CB8 0NE**
Contacts: **PHONE (01638) 662968 FAX (01638) 663888 MOBILE (07808) 954109**
E-MAIL david@davidsimcock.co.uk WEBSITE www.davidsimcock.co.uk

1 AJEEB (USA), 4, b g Harlan's Holiday (USA)—Fair Settlement (USA)
2 AL KHAWANEEJ, 4, br c Arch (USA)—Fraulein
3 AL MAYASAH (IRE), 4, b f Shamardal (USA)—Mia Mambo (USA)
4 ASHIRI (IRE), 4, ch c Hurricane Run (IRE)—Gorband (USA)
5 BUSHMAN, 8, gr g Maria's Mon (USA)—Housa Dancer (FR)
6 DESERT PHANTOM (USA), 6, b g Arch (USA)—Junkinthetrunk (USA)
7 FATHSTA (IRE), 7, b g Fath (USA)—Kilbride Lass (IRE)
8 HAYLAMAN (IRE), 4, b g Diamond Green (FR)—Schonbein (IRE)
9 I'M A DREAMER (IRE), 5, b m Noverre (USA)—Summer Dreams (IRE)
10 LOOK LEFT, 4, ch g Observatory (USA)—Stage Left
11 MARHABA MALYOON (IRE), 4, b g Tiger Hill (GER)—Mamonta
12 MUBTADI, 4, br c Dr Fong (USA)—Noble Peregrine
13 NAVE (USA), 5, br g Pulpit (USA)—Lakabi (USA)
14 NAVIGATION TRACK, 4, b g King's Best (USA)—Tegwen (USA)
15 NO HERETIC, 4, b c Galileo (IRE)—Intrigued
16 NOBLE CITIZEN (USA), 7, b h Proud Citizen (USA)—Serene Nobility (USA)
17 PINTURA, 5, ch g Efisio—Picolette
18 SAMMY ALEXANDER, 4, br g Storming Home—Sweet Angeline
19 STRATEGIC BID, 4, b g Selkirk (USA)—Eminencia
20 TRADE STORM, 4, b c Trade Fair—Frisson

MR DAVID SIMCOCK—continued

THREE-YEAR-OLDS

21 **AL FAYLASOOF (USA),** b c Lemon Drop Kid (USA)—Mahhdooda (USA)
22 **AL MAMZAR (IRE),** b c Teofilo (IRE)—Avila
23 **ANDALIEB,** b c Zamindar (USA)—Sakhya (IRE)
24 **ANY GIVEN DREAM (IRE),** br g Bahri (USA)—Anazara (USA)
25 **ATTRACTION TICKET,** b c Selkirk (USA)—Trick (IRE)
26 **CAPE SAVANNAH,** b c Cape Cross (IRE)—Lady High Havens (IRE)
27 **CARDINAL WALTER (IRE),** br c Cape Cross (IRE)—Sheer Spirit (IRE)
28 **CASTILO DEL DIABLO (IRE),** br c Teofilo (IRE)—Hundred Year Flood (USA)
29 **COFFEE KING (IRE),** b g King's Best (USA)—Passarelle (USA)
30 **CRAZY TOO (IRE),** b f Invincible Spirit (IRE)—Reform Act (USA)
31 **EMIRATES ECHO,** b c Sir Percy—Ann Veronica (IRE)
32 **GABRIAL THE HERO (USA),** b c War Front (USA)—Ball Gown (USA)
33 **GABRIAL'S GIFT (IRE),** gr c Verglas (IRE)—Sahara Lady (IRE)
34 **GHOST PROTOCOL (IRE),** b g Cockney Rebel (IRE)—Stroke of Six (IRE)
35 **GLORIAM (USA),** b c War Chant (USA)—Amandas Bandit (USA)
36 **GOLD FALCON (IRE),** b c Iffraaj (USA)—Pretty Majestic (IRE)
37 **GREAT SOPRANO (USA),** br c Arch (USA)—Insan Mala (USA)
38 **GREY FALCON (FR),** gr g Clodovil (IRE)—Sugar (FR)
39 **GUCCI D'ORO (USA),** br c Medaglia d'oro (USA)—Ninette (USA)
40 **HELLO DUBAI,** ch f Teofilo (IRE)—Bush Cat (USA)
41 **HELLO GLORY,** b f Zamindar (USA)—Affair of State (IRE)
42 **IT'S MY TIME,** b f Green Desert (USA)—Soviet Terms
43 **MALEKAT JAMAL (IRE),** br f Dutch Art—Haretha (IRE)
44 **MISS AZEZA,** br f Dutch Art—Miss Respect
45 **MONTASER (IRE),** b c Rail Link—For Example (USA)
46 **MR FONG,** ch g Dr Fong (USA)—Selkirk Sky
47 **MY OWN EYES,** br f Sakhee (USA)—Seed Al Maha (USA)
48 **PLAY TIGER (FR),** b c Tiger Hill (IRE)—Shagadellic (USA)
49 **PRIME RUN,** br f Dansili—Silca-Cisa
50 **SALOOMY,** ch c Shamardal (USA)—Oystermouth
51 **SAUNTA,** b f Invincible Spirit (IRE)—Baize
52 **SHEIKHZAYEDROAD,** b g Dubawi (IRE)—Royal Secrets (IRE)
53 **STAR BONITA (IRE),** b f Invincible Spirit (IRE)—Honour Bright (IRE)
54 **STILL I'M A STAR (IRE),** b f Lawman (FR)—Aminata
55 **WAVEGUIDE (IRE),** b f Dubawi (IRE)—Million Waves (IRE)
56 **WHITE NILE (IRE),** B C Galileo (IRE)—Super Gift (IRE)

TWO-YEAR-OLDS

57 **AL BANDAR,** ch c 8/4 Pivotal—Kotsi (IRE) (Nayef (USA)) (26000)
58 **AL EMIRATI (IRE),** b c 12/3 Tamayuz—Corrine (IRE) (Spectrum (IRE)) (18095)
59 **AL MEEZAN,** ch c 3/3 Nayef (USA)—Festivale (IRE) (Invincible Spirit (IRE)) (16000)
60 Ch f 6/2 Kheleyf (USA)—Areyaam (USA) (Elusive Quality (USA))
61 Ch c 10/4 Street Boss (USA)—Bacinella (USA) (El Gran Senor (USA)) (29000)
62 **BRETON ROCK (IRE),** b c 12/2 Bahamian Bounty—Anna's Rock (IRE) (Rock of Gibraltar (IRE)) (19047)
63 B c 23/4 Exceed And Excel (AUS)—Broadway Hit (Sadler's Wells (USA)) (145000)
64 B c 20/4 Sakhee (USA)—Catch Us (FR) (Selkirk (USA))
65 **DEIRA PHANTOM (IRE),** b c 8/3 Cape Cross (IRE)—Ammo (IRE) (Sadler's Wells (USA)) (35000)
66 B f 17/5 Kheleyf (USA)—Dora Carrington (IRE) (Sri Pekan (USA)) (18000)
67 **DREAM CAST (IRE),** b c 9/3 Refuse To Bend—Star Studded (Cadeaux Genereux) (73891)
68 **EMIRATI SPIRIT,** b f 7/4 Dutch Art—Pintle (Pivotal) (40000)
69 **EVERLASTING DREAM,** b f 27/2 Oasis Dream—Magdalene (Act One) (80000)
70 **GLASS OFFICE,** br gr c 16/3 Verglas (IRE)—Oval Office (Pursuit of Love) (49260)
71 B f 12/2 Refuse To Bend—Grecian Air (FR) (King's Best)
72 B f 12/4 Dalakhani (IRE)—Heavenly Whisper (Halling (USA)) (60000)
73 Ch c 14/5 Indian Haven—Hidden Charm (IRE) (Big Shuffle (USA)) (13957)
74 B f 7/2 Dixie Union—Keladora (USA) (Crafty Prospector (USA)) (30000)
75 Ch c 27/3 Galileo (USA)—Kentucky Warbler (IRE) (Spinning World (USA)) (168308)
76 Ch f 26/3 Galileo (IRE)—La Vida Loca (IRE) (Caerleon (USA))
77 **MAJEED,** b c 19/2 Mount Nelson—Clever Millie (Cape Canaveral (USA))
78 B f 21/3 Zamindar (USA)—Mennetou (IRE) (Entrepreneur) (180000)
79 B c 25/3 Kyllachy—Molly Brown (Rudimentary (USA)) (76190)
80 B f 14/4 Footstepsinthesand—My Heart's Deelite (USA) (Afternoon Deelites (USA))
81 B c 14/3 Zamindar (USA)—Paint The Town (IRE) (Sadler's Wells (USA)) (21000)

MR DAVID SIMCOCK—continued

82 B g 6/4 Kheleyf (USA)—Pelican Key (IRE) (Mujadil (USA)) (14285)
83 **POSTE RESTANTE**, b f 27/1 Halling (USA)—Postage Stampe (Singspiel (IRE))
84 B c 23/3 Iffraaj—Pretty Majestic (IRE) (Invincible Spirit (IRE))
85 B f 7/4 Authorized (IRE)—Princess Danah (IRE) (Danehill (USA))
86 B c 7/3 Kyllachy—Taghreed (IRE) (Zamindar (USA))
87 B f 15/2 Haafhd—Takawiri (IRE) (Danehill (USA))
88 B f 31/3 Jeremy (USA)—Valandraud (IRE) (College Chapel) (20000)
89 **WE'RE IN THE RED (IRE)**, br c 7/4 Daaher (CAN)—Elaflaak (USA) (Gulch (USA)) (4761)

Owners: Saleh Al Homaizi, Abdulla Al Mansoori, H.E. Sheikh Sultan Bin Khalifa Al Nahyan, Imad Al Sagar, Abdulla Al Shaikh, Ahmad Al Shaikh, Simon Bamber, Jonathan Barnett, Andrew Black, Oliver Brendon, R.G.W. Brown, Malcolm Caine, John Cook, Khalifa Dasmal, Dunchurch Lodge Stud Co, Mrs T. A. Foreman, Zaid A. Galadari, Gee Ceffyl Bach Club, Brian Harris, Mrs Fitri Hay, Anthony Hogarth, Dr Marwan Koukash, Graham Lucas, Mike McKeon, Bob Michaelson, David Myers, Sir Robert Ogden, Daniel Pittack, Rabbah Bloodstock Ltd, Ann Simcock, St Albans Bloodstock, Michael Swinburn, Raymond Tooth, Universal Racing, Michael Wates, Dennis Whitfield, Major Wyatt.

Assistant Trainer: Tom Clover

Jockey (flat): Martin Lane, Laura Pike, William Buick, Jamie Spencer. **Apprentice:** Alice Haynes, Siobhan Miller. **Amateur:** Mr Jack Salmon.

---

598 MRS EVELYN SLACK, Appleby
Postal: **Stoneriggs, Hilton, Appleby, Cumbria, CA16 6LS**
Contacts: **PHONE (01768) 351354 MOBILE (07503) 161240**

1 **ANOTHER MYSTERY**, 7, b m Beat All (USA)—Mariner's Air **Mrs D. E. Slack**
2 **BUNRATTY (IRE)**, 6, b g Rudimentary (USA)—Miss Huff N Puff (IRE) **A. Slack**
3 **HATHAMORE**, 8, b m Classic Cliche (IRE)—Sillymore **A. Slack**
4 **SCRIPTWRITER (IRE)**, 10, b g Sadler's Wells (USA)—Dayanata **A. Slack**
5 **TEENAGE IDOL (IRE)**, 8, b br g Sadler's Wells (USA)—Kaaba **A. Slack**

Assistant Trainer: K. A. A. Slack (01768) 351922 Or (07931) 137413

Amateur: Miss Natalie Sayer.

---

599 MRS PAM SLY, Peterborough
Postal: **Singlecote, Thorney, Peterborough, Cambridgeshire, PE6 0PB**
Contacts: **PHONE (01733) 270212 FAX (01733) 270212 MOBILE (07850) 511267**

1 **ARKAIM**, 4, b g Oasis Dream—Habariya (IRE) **G.A.Libson D.L.Bayliss G.Taylor P.M.Sly**
2 **BARNACK**, 6, b g Karinga Bay—Ima Delight **Mrs P. M. Sly**
3 **BODIE**, 4, ch g Iceman—Saida Lenasera (FR) **Mrs P. M. Sly**
4 **CHICKLEMIX**, 6, gr m Fair Mix (IRE)—Chichell's Hurst **M. H. Sly, Dr T. Davies & Mrs P. Sly**
5 **CIRCUS STAR (USA)**, 4, b g Borrego (USA)—Picadilly Circus (USA) **G.A.Libson D.L.Bayliss G.Taylor P.M.Sly**
6 **HELPSTON**, 8, b g Sir Harry Lewis (USA)—Chichell's Hurst **Mrs P. M. Sly**
7 **KAYAAN**, 5, br g Marju (IRE)—Raheefa (USA) **D. L. Bayliss**
8 **PHEIDIAS (IRE)**, 8, ch g Spectrum (IRE)—Danse Grecque (IRE) **G.A.Libson D.L.Bayliss G.Taylor P.M.Sly**
9 **SAN ANTONIO**, 12, b g Efisio—Winnebago **Mrs P. M. Sly**
10 **TRICKY TREE (IRE)**, 6, b g Montjeu (IRE)—Ruissec (USA) **Mrs V. M. Edmonson**
11 **VIABLE**, 10, b g Vettori (IRE)—Danseuse Davis (FR) **Thorney Racing Club**
12 **WISTOW**, 8, b m Sir Harry Lewis (USA)—River Bay (IRE) **Mrs P. M. Sly**
13 **WOM**, 4, b g Tiger Hill (IRE)—Vayavaig **Mr M. Harrod**

THREE-YEAR-OLDS

14 **BOUNTIFUL CATCH**, ch c Bahamian Bounty—Saida Lenasera (FR) **Team Speciosa**
15 **SCARLET WHISPERS**, b f Sir Percy—Hieroglyph **Mr G. A. Libson**
16 **VERMUYDEN**, b c Oasis Dream—Speciosa (IRE) **M. H. Sly, Dr T. Davies & Mrs P. Sly**

Other Owners: Mr David L. Bayliss, Dr T. J. W. Davies, Mark Harrod, Mr John Hitchin, Mr G. A. Libson, Mrs P. M. Sly, Mr Michael H. Sly, Mr Derek Sly, Mr G. Taylor.

Jockey (flat): Micky Fenton. **Jockey (NH):** David England, Sean Quinlan. **Apprentice:** Christy Mews. **Amateur:** Miss Gina Andrews.

600 MR DAVID SMAGA, Lamorlaye

Postal: **17 Voie de la Grange des Pres, 60260 Lamorlaye, France**
Contacts: **PHONE (0033) 3442 15005 FAX (0033) 3442 15356**

1 **BOOKEND**, 8, b g Dansili—Roupala (USA) **Mr David Smaga**
2 **DON BOSCO (FR)**, 5, ch h Barathea (IRE)—Perfidie (IRE) **Omar El Sharif**
3 **DORADE ROSE (FR)**, 4, b f Marchand de Sable (USA)—Shadai Stone (JPN) **Robert Bellaiche**
4 **FRED LALLOUPET**, 5, b h Elusive City (USA)—Firm Friend (IRE) **Maurice Lagasse**
5 **GOLDEN DREAMS (FR)**, 4, b g Take Risks (FR)—Faintly (FR) **Gerard Augustin-Normand**
6 **GYPSY HIGHWAY (IRE)**, 4, b f High Chaparral (IRE)—Rose Gypsy **T. Yoshida**
7 **HIDDEN RAINBOW (IRE)**, 9, ch g Spectrum (IRE)—Grecian Urn **Mr David Smaga**
8 **ILHABELA (IRE)**, 4, b f Azamour (IRE)—Vadsa Honor (FR) **Robert Nahas**
9 **ILLUSIO (FR)**, 5, b m Voix du Nord (FR)—Celere (FR) **Mr David Smaga**
10 **KASLIK (FR)**, 11, b g Desert Prince (IRE)—Mrs Ting (USA) **Mr David Smaga**
11 **LUMIERE DU SOIR (FR)**, 5, b m Anabaa (USA)—Dame Edith (FR) **Robert Nahas**
12 **MR DOYEN**, 4, b br c Doyen (IRE)—Masrora (USA) **Gerard Augustin-Normand**
13 **PATAGONIA (FR)**, 4, b f Layman (USA)—Gorgonzola (ARG) **Alain Louis-Dreyfus**
14 **SHARGA (IRE)**, 7, gr g Highest Honor (FR)—Glebe Place (FR) **Omar El Sharif**
15 **STAY COOL (FR)**, 6, b h One Cool Cat (USA)—A La Longue (GER) **Mr David Smaga**

THREE-YEAR-OLDS

16 **AURELIO AURELI (FR)**, b c Green Tune (USA)—Anna Airy (IRE) **Mme Louise Calamari**
17 **BIT BY BIT**, b gr f Rail Link—Lixian **K. Abdulla**
18 **BROWN TIGER (IRE)**, b c Galileo (IRE)—Guarded **Robert Nahas**
19 **CANTICUM**, b c Cacique (IRE)—Allegro Viva (USA) **K. Abdulla**
20 **CAROLINGIAN (USA)**, b c Empire Maker (USA)—Shoogle (USA) **K. Abdulla**
21 **CHEAM KSAH (IRE)**, b f Hurricane Run (IRE)—Mawhiba (USA) **Mr David Smaga**
22 **COULEUVRE (USA)**, b f Mizzen Mast (USA)—Velvet Morning (USA) **K. Abdulla**
23 **DONT TEUTCH (FR)**, b f Country Reel (USA)—Simonkikou (FR) **Gerard Augustin-Normand**
24 **HAREM LADY (FR)**, b f Teofilo (IRE)—Luminosity **Robert Nahas**
25 **KATCHAGUA (FR)**, b f Anabaa (USA)—Pats Martini (USA) **Alain Louis-Dreyfus**
26 **MANUKA (USA)**, ch f Mr Greeley (USA)—Chaibia (IRE) **Malcolm Parrish**
27 **MOONDAY SUN (USA)**, gr ro c Mizzen Mast (USA)—Storm Dove (USA) **K. Abdulla**
28 **NILSON (GER)**, b c Big Shuffle (USA)—Nouvelle Fortune (IRE) **Mr Malcolm Parrish**
29 **REDIAL (GB)**, ch f Three Valleys (USA)—Dialing Tone (USA) **K. Abdulla**
30 **SAINT ELIER (FR)**, b c Stormy River (FR)—Basse Besogne (IRE) **Gerard Augustin-Normand**
31 **SEGUIDA (USA)**, b f Vindication (USA)—Sur Ma Vie (USA) **Haras D'Etreham**
32 **SIMPLON**, b f Rail Link—Neath **K. Abdulla**
33 **SUNSEEK (GB)**, b f Rail Link—Hunt The Sun **K. Abdulla**
34 **WEST COUNTRY (USA)**, ch c Latent Heat (USA)—Devon Heights (USA) **K. Abdulla**

TWO-YEAR-OLDS

35 B f 16/4 First Defence (USA)—Birthplace (USA) (King of Kings (IRE)) **K. Abdulla**
36 **DELANTERA (FR)**, b f 3/4 Lawman (FR)—Dirigeante (FR) (Lead On Time (USA)) **Haras D'Etreham**
37 **EGADE (FR)**, ch f 18/5 Royal Assault (USA)—Flavignana (FR) (Anabaa Blue) **Mme Kathleen Bokobsa**
38 B c 14/3 Zamindar (USA)—Galipette (Green Desert (USA)) (36945) **Omar El Sharif**
39 B f 12/2 Mizzen Mast (USA)—Gateway (USA) (A P Indy (USA)) **K. Abdulla**
40 **GONAWIN (FR)**, b f 30/4 Anabaa (USA)—Funny Feerie (FR) (Sillery (USA)) (164203) **Wafic Said**
41 B c 17/4 Hannouma (IRE)—Japan (GER) (Key Royal (GER)) **Malcolm Parrish**
42 **MILEDOUSHE (FR)**, b f 22/3 Dylan Thomas (IRE)—Khamsin (USA) (Mr Prospector (USA)) **Alain Louis-Dreyfus**
43 **MISTER TEE (FR)**, b c 21/2 Manduro (FR)—Floride (IRE) (Sadler's Wells (USA)) **Franck Amar**
44 B f 2/4 Muhtathir—Perfidie (IRE) (Monsun (GER)) (45155) **Omar El Sharif**
45 B c 26/2 Rail Link—Plum Fairy (Sadler's Wells (USA)) **K. Abdulla**
46 B c 2/4 Hannouma (IRE)—Poltava (FR) (Victory Note (USA)) (28735) **Mr David Smaga**
47 **SANIMA (IRE)**, b f 18/3 Galileo (IRE)—Sophisticat (Storm Cat (USA)) **Haras D'Etreham**
48 B f 11/1 Elusive Quality (USA)—Sur Ma Vie (Fusaichi Pegasus (USA)) (106732) **Robert Nahas**
49 B br c 31/1 Mizzen Mast (USA)—Tinge (USA) (Kingmambo (USA)) **K. Abdulla**
50 **VAL DE SAANE (IRE)**, b c 2/3 Rock of Gibraltar (IRE)—
                                    Mahendra (GER) (Next Desert (IRE)) (42692) **Gerard Augustin-Normand**
51 B f 27/2 Teofilo (IRE)—Victoria College (FR) (Rock of Gibraltar (IRE)) **Omar El Sharif**
52 B c 3/4 First Defence (USA)—Wandesta (Nashwan (USA)) **K. Abdulla**

601 **MR BRYAN SMART, Thirsk**
Postal: Hambleton House, Sutton Bank, Thirsk, North Yorkshire, YO7 2HA
Contacts: **PHONE (01845) 597481 FAX (01845) 597480 MOBILE (07748) 634797**
E-MAIL office@bryansmart.plus.com WEBSITE www.bryansmart-racing.com

1 **ANGARIC (IRE)**, 9, ch g Pivotal—Grannys Reluctance (IRE) **B. Smart**
2 **APASSIONFORFASHION**, 4, b f Beat Hollow—Trinny **Just For Girls Partnership**
3 **AVERTUOSO**, 8, b g Averti (IRE)—First Musical **Crossfields Racing**
4 **BANDSTAND**, 6, b g Royal Applause—Incise **Crossfields Racing**
5 **DA'QUONDE (IRE)**, 4, br f Pivotal—Bobcat Greeley (USA) **The Barber Girls**
6 **DUBAI HILLS**, 6, b g Dubai Destination (USA)—Hill Welcome **Mrs F. Denniff**
7 **ENDERBY SPIRIT (GR)**, 6, gr g Invincible Spirit (IRE)—Arctic Ice (IRE) **Mrs P. M. Brown**
8 **EXCEL BOLT**, 4, ch c Exceed And Excel (AUS)—Dearest Daisy **Elders, Turton, Brown & Rhodes**
9 **FEARLESS POET (IRE)**, 4, b g Byron—Fear Not (IRE) **The Smart Fear Not Partnership**
10 **FEEL THE HEAT**, 5, ch g Firebreak—Spindara (IRE) **B. Smart**
11 **FLASH CITY (ITY)**, 4, b g Elusive City (USA)—Furnish **Ceffyl Racing**
12 **HAMBLETON**, 5, b g Monsieur Bond (IRE)—Only Yours **B. Smart**
13 **J R HARTLEY**, 4, b g Refuse To Bend (IRE)—Flyfisher (USA) **The Smart Flyfisher Partnership**
14 **MASTER LEON**, 5, b g Monsieur Bond (IRE)—Bollin Rita **Mr A. H. L. Zheng**
15 **MASTER ROONEY (IRE)**, 6, b br g Cape Cross (IRE)—Wimple (USA) **A. Turton, P. Langford & S. Brown**
16 **MONTE CASSINO (IRE)**, 7, ch g Choisir (AUS)—Saucy Maid (IRE) **Woodcock Electrical Limited**
17 **NICKEL SILVER**, 7, gr g Choisir (AUS)—Negligee **M. Barber**
18 **PULSATILLA**, 4, b f Monsieur Bond (IRE)—Resemblance **Mrs V. Smart**
19 **RONINSKI (IRE)**, 4, b c Cadeaux Genereux—Ruby Affair (IRE) **Mr R. Hull**
20 **ROSA LUXEMBURG**, 4, ch f Needwood Blade—Colonel's Daughter **B. Smart**
21 **SMALLJOHN**, 6, ch g Needwood Blade—My Bonus **B. Smart**
22 **TANGERINE TREES**, 7, b g Mind Games—Easy To Imagine (USA) **Tangerine Trees Partnership**
23 **VERINCO**, 6, b g Bahamian Bounty—Dark Eyed Lady **B. Smart**
24 **WELLS LYRICAL (IRE)**, 7, b g Sadler's Wells (USA)—Lyrical **M. Barber**

THREE-YEAR-OLDS

25 **BARTLEY**, ch g Monsieur Bond (IRE)—Annie Harvey **Mrs V. Smart**
26 **BOND STYLE**, ch c Monsieur Bond (IRE)—In Some Style (IRE) **Mrs M. J. Marshall & Mr R. C. Bond**
27 **BOP IT**, b c Misu Bond (IRE)—Forever Bond **A. Turton, J. Blackburn & R. Bond**
28 **CODE SIX (IRE)**, gr f Kodiac—Grey Pursuit (IRE) **Woodcock Electrical Limited**
29 **COMMANCHE**, ch c Sleeping Indian—Happy Memories (IRE) **Mr W. A. Tinkler**
30 **CONE DONKEY (IRE)**, b f Medicean—Nan Scurry (FR) **Mr D. O'Brien**
31 **DANCE THE RAIN**, b f Rock of Gibraltar—Antediluvian **Ceffyl Racing**
32 **DIVA DONKEY (IRE)**, b f Acclamation—Lupulina (CAN) **Mr D. O'Brien**
33 B f Iceman—Double Fantasy **P. A. Darling**
34 **DOYOUKNOWWHOIAM**, ch g Monsieur Bond (IRE)—Tibesti **A. Turton, J. Blackburn & R. Bond**
35 **EXCEEDANCE**, ch c Exceed And Excel (AUS)—Hill Welcome **Mr W. A. Tinkler**
36 **EXCELETTE (IRE)**, b f Exceed And Excel (AUS)—Madam Ninette **Crossfields Racing**
37 **FOXTROT ROMEO (IRE)**, b c Danehill Dancer (IRE)—Hawala (IRE) **Mr W. A. Tinkler**
38 **FREE ZONE**, b g Kyllachy—Aldora **Fromthestables.Com Racing**
39 **GABRIAL'S PRINCESS (IRE)**, b f Royal Applause—Happy Go Lily **Dr M. B. Q. S. Koukash**
40 **GABRIAL'S STAR**, b c Hernando (FR)—Grain Only **Dr M. B. Q. S. Koukash**
41 **GULF STORM (IRE)**, b c Pivotal—Beyrouth (USA) **Mr P. J. Shaw**
42 **IRRATIONAL**, b f Kyllachy—Belladera (IRE) **Crossfields Racing**
43 **ITALIAN ICE**, b f Milk It Mick—Segretezza (IRE) **Mrs B. A. Matthews**
44 **LADY LAYLA**, b f Excellent Art—Tartouche **Dr M. B. Q. S. Koukash**
45 **LEGAL BOND**, b g Misu Bond (IRE)—Lawless Bridget **Mr W. A. Tinkler**
46 **LOWTHERWOOD**, b c Green Desert (USA)—
Imperial Bailiwick (IRE) **Mr & Mrs Middlebrook/Mr & Mrs Nicholson**
47 **MASTER BOND**, b c Misu Bond (IRE)—Bond Royale **Bonded Twentyten Partnership**
48 **PTOLEMAIC**, b c Excellent Art—Pompey Girl **Mrs F. Denniff**
49 **STEPHARLIE**, ch f Dutch Art—Lady Agnes **Fromthestables.Com Racing**
50 **STUNNING ICON**, b f Dr Fong (USA)—Karminskey Park **Mr S. Tolley**
51 **VITE (IRE)**, b c Acclamation—Assafiyah (IRE) **Mr R. Hull**
52 **WELL WISHES**, ch f Piccolo—Muja Farewell **Mr W. A. Tinkler**
53 **WILD SAUCE**, b f Exceed And Excel (AUS)—Salsa Brava (IRE) **R. A. Page**
54 **YOUNG FREDDIE (IRE)**, gr g Clodovil (IRE)—Quecha (IRE) **Sir Alex Ferguson & Jack Hanson**

TWO-YEAR-OLDS

55 Ch f 5/3 Exceed And Excel (AUS)—Aberdovey (Mister Baileys) (18000) **Ceffyl Racing**
56 **ABSOLUTE DIAMOND**, ch f 30/3 Monsieur Bond (IRE)—
Tibesti (Machiavellian (USA)) (38095) **A. Turton, J. Blackburn, R. Bond & C. Bond**

MR BRYAN SMART—continued

57 **ANGEL GRIGIO**, gr f 18/3 Dark Angel (IRE)—
Owdbetts (IRE) (High Estate) (36190) **A. Turton, J. Blackburn, R. Bond & C. Bond**
58 Ch c 8/3 Byron—Annie Harvey (Fleetwood (IRE)) (3619) **Mrs V. Smart**
59 **AYASHA**, b f 3/3 Indesatchel (IRE)—Nizhoni (USA) (Mineshaft (USA)) **Crossfields Racing**
60 B c 23/4 Captain Marvelous (IRE)—
Dame Laura (IRE) (Royal Academy (USA)) (20000) **The Smart Dame Laura Partnership**
61 Ch c 3/5 Sleeping Indian—Distant Music (Darshaan) (4571)
62 B f 20/3 Exceed And Excel (AUS)—Durrah Green (Green Desert (USA)) (6190) **Mr D. H. Francis**
63 **ELUSIVE HEIR (IRE)**, b c 11/4 Elusive City (USA)—Princess Nala (IRE) (In The Wings) (13333) **Mr W. A. Tinkler**
64 B f 22/2 Sakhee's Secret—Empress Jain (Lujain (USA)) (5714) **The Smart Empress Jain Partnership**
65 **EQUINOX**, b f 11/3 Medicean—Plucky (Kyllachy) (15714) **Crossfields Racing**
66 **FINALIZE**, b f 11/3 Firebreak—Choisette (Choisir (AUS)) **Crossfields Racing**
67 B f 9/5 Monsieur Bond (IRE)—Forever Bond (Danetime (IRE)) (140000) **Mr R. C. Bond**
68 **HAKURAA (IRE)**, b f 10/4 Elnadim (USA)—Miss Donovan (Royal Applause) (656) **Crossfields Racing**
69 **ICHIMOKU**, b c 20/4 Indesatchel (IRE)—Mythicism (Oasis Dream) **Crossfields Racing**
70 B f 29/3 Dylan Thomas (IRE)—Keyaki (IRE) (Shinko Forest (IRE)) (9000) **Mr M. Barber**
71 **NAVAJO NIGHTS**, b c 13/4 Sleeping Indian—Nuit Sans Fin (FR) (Lead On Time (USA)) (21904) **Mr W. A. Tinkler**
72 Ch c 15/4 Choisir (AUS)—Oriane (Nashwan (USA)) (21000) **Mr F. Nass**
73 **ROSIE HALL (IRE)**, ch f 20/2 Lion Heart (USA)—
Baltic Dip (IRE) (Benny The Dip (USA)) (7619) **R. & E. Hall & Son**

Other Owners: Mr M. Barber, Mrs Patricia Barrell, Mr J. N. Blackburn, Mr R. C. Bond, Mr C. S. Bond, Mr S. W. Brown, Mr M. G. Bullock, Mrs Tina Bullock, Mr N. A. Coster, Mrs F. Denniff, Mr Dave Elders, Sir Alex Ferguson, Mr J. Hanson, Mrs A. C. Hudson, Mr Paul Langford, Mrs M. J. Marshall, Mr I. G. Martin, Mrs B. A. Matthews, Mr G. Middlebrook, Mrs L. Middlebrook, Mr D. Nicholson, Mr Richard Page, Mr A. Rhodes, Mr B. Smart, Mrs V. R. Smart, Mr Andrew Turton, Mrs Lesley Winn, Mr Thomas Winn.

Assistant Trainers: Mrs V. R. Smart, Mr K. Edmunds

Jockey (flat): Tom Eaves. **Apprentice:** Justin Newman.

---

602 | **MR CHARLES SMITH, Wellingore**
Postal: **Thompsons Bottom Farm, Temple Bruer, Wellingore, Lincoln LN5 0DE**
Contacts: **PHONE/FAX (01526) 833245 MOBILE (0378) 149188**

1 **FATHEY (IRE)**, 6, ch g Fath (USA)—Christoph's Girl **R. J. Lewin**
2 **GENERAL TUFTO**, 7, b g Fantastic Light (USA)—Miss Pinkerton **Mr J. R. Theaker**
3 **LA DANSE CHAMPETRE**, 4, ch f Pastoral Pursuits—Dancing Spirit (IRE) **Mr N. J. Baines**
4 **PENDERYN**, 5, b m Sakhee (USA)—Brecon **Mr N. J. Baines**
5 **ROSIE RAYMOND**, 7, b m Kris Kin (USA)—Iota **C. Smith**
6 **SAIRAAM (IRE)**, 6, b m Marju (IRE)—Sayedati Eljamilah (USA) **Mr Phil Martin & Trev Sleath**

Other Owners: Mr P. E. Martin, T. Sleath.

---

603 | **MR JULIAN SMITH, Tirley**
Postal: **Tirley Court, Tirley, Gloucester**
Contacts: PHONE **(01452) 780461** FAX **(01452) 780461** MOBILE **(07880) 732337**
E-MAIL nicola.smith9156@o2.co.uk

1 **CRYSTAL CLICHE**, 7, b m Classic Cliche (IRE)—Tirley Pop Eye **Exors of the Late Mr D. E. S. Smith**
2 **FORTUNA ROSE**, 6, b m Sir Harry Lewis (USA)—Swiss Rose **Grand Jury Partnership**
3 **HERO'S CALL**, 7, b m Arkadian Hero (USA)—Sense of Value **Exors of the Late Mr D. E. S. Smith**
4 **IONA DAYS (IRE)**, 7, br g Epistolaire (IRE)—Miss Best (FR) **Mrs J.A. Benson & Miss S.N. Benson**
5 **NO PRINCIPLES**, 9, b g Overbury (IRE)—Selective Rose **Exors of the Late Mr D. E. S. Smith**
6 **PETIT FLEUR**, 10, b m Nomadic Way (USA)—Sense of Value **Exors of the Late Mr D. E. S. Smith**
7 **SAILOR'S SOVEREIGN**, 11, b g Sovereign Water (FR)—Tirley Pop Eye **Exors of the Late Mr D. E. S. Smith**
8 5, B m Sir Harry Lewis (USA)—Swiss Rose **Grand Jury Partnership**
9 **THE LAST SELECTION**, 7, b g Sir Harry Lewis (USA)—Deep Selection (IRE) **Exors of the Late Mr D. E. S. Smith**

Other Owners: Mrs J. A. Benson, Miss S. N. Benson, Mr A. W. Brookes, Mr R. Brookes.

Assistant Trainer: Mrs Nicky Smith

Jockey (NH): Timmy Murphy, Sam Twiston-Davies. **Conditional:** Charles Greene. **Amateur:** Mr J. M. Ridley.

604 MR MICHAEL SMITH, Kirkheaton
Postal: **Toft Hall Farm, Kirkheaton, Newcastle Upon Tyne, Tyne and Wear, NE19 2DH**
Contacts: **PHONE (01830) 530044 MOBILE (07976) 903233**
E-MAIL sandy.smith01@btinternet.com

1 ANDIAMO VIA, 5, b g Mujahid (USA)—Efizia **Mrs H. I. S. Calzini**
2 MAKBULLET, 5, gr g Makbul—Gold Belt (IRE) **Mr D. Armstrong**
3 NADEEN (IRE), 5, b g Bahamian Bounty—Janayen (USA) **Miss R. J. Smith**
4 ORSIPPUS (USA), 6, b br g Sunday Break (JPN)—Mirror Dancing (USA) **Mrs S. Smith**
5 PRINCE OF VASA (IRE), 5, b g Kheleyf (USA)—Suzy Street (IRE) **Mrs S. Smith**
6 SOMERSET ISLAND (IRE), 4, b g Barathea (IRE)—Art Work **Un-named Partnership**
7 TEXAS HOLDEM (IRE), 13, b g Topanoora—Lough N Uisce **Mrs S. Smith**
8 UNEX GOYA (IRE), 4, b g Medicean—Arabica (USA) **Mrs S. Smith**
9 VITO VOLTERRA (IRE), 5, b g Antonius Pius (USA)—River Abouali **Ace Racing**

THREE-YEAR-OLDS
10 JOSIE LENNON, ch f Royal Anthem (USA)—Lorna Lennon (IRE) **Carvin Wilson Smailes**

Other Owners: Mrs Jean Carvin, Mr John Smailes, Mrs Sandra Smith, Mr Michael Smith, Mr Patrick Wilson.

Assistant Trainer: Sandra Smith

605 MR ROBERT SMITH, Galston
Postal: **West Loudoun Farm, Galston, Ayrshire, KA4 8PB**

1 DESERTMORE STAR (IRE), 11, b g Dr Massini (IRE)—Very Very Sweet (IRE) **R. M. Smith**
2 ITS BOBKAT (IRE), 6, b g Bob Back (USA)—Katieella (IRE) **R. M. Smith**
3 KENNELMAN (IRE), 9, b g Flemensfirth (USA)—Celtic Fox (IRE) **R. M. Smith**
4 MACK MILAN (IRE), 5, b g Milan—Luisa di Camerata (IRE) **R. M. Smith**
5 MISTY CLOUD, 9, gr m Cloudings (IRE)—Tibbi Blues **R. M. Smith**

606 MRS SUE SMITH, Bingley
Postal: **Craiglands Farm, High Eldwick, Bingley, West Yorkshire, BD16 3BE**
Contacts: **PHONE (01274) 564930 FAX (01274) 560626**
E-MAIL craiglandsracing@yahoo.co.uk

1 ALBA KING (IRE), 6, b g Beauchamp King—Alba Dancer **Mrs S. J. Smith**
2 ALF THE AUDACIOUS, 6, gr g Alflora (IRE)—Rua Ros (IRE) **Mr R. Preston**
3 AURORAS ENCORE (IRE), 10, b g Second Empire (IRE)—Sama Veda (IRE) **Mrs Alicia Skene & W. S. Skene**
4 BALTIC PATHFINDER (IRE), 8, b g Alflora (IRE)—Boro Bow (IRE) **John Regan & John Conroy**
5 BELMORE BARON, 10, ch g Double Trigger (IRE)—Belmore Cloud **Mrs S. J. Smith**
6 BROTHER SCOTT, 5, b g Kirkwall—Crimson Shower **Mrs S. J. Smith**
7 CHINA EXCELS, 5, b g Exceed And Excel (AUS)—China Beauty **Mrs S. J. Smith**
8 CLOUDY DAWN, 7, gr g Cloudings (IRE)—Persistent Gunner **Mrs S. J. Smith**
9 CLOUDY TOO (IRE), 6, b g Cloudings (IRE)—Curra Citizen (IRE) **Formulated Polymer Products Ltd**
10 CRAFTI BOOKIE (IRE), 6, b g Winged Love (IRE)—Cerise de Totes (FR) **Mrs S. J. Smith**
11 DALDINI, 10, b g Josr Algarhoud (IRE)—Arianna Aldini **P. J. Dixon**
12 DOUGLAS JULIAN, 10, b g Overbury (IRE)—Swing Quartet (IRE) **Mrs S. J. Smith**
13 FILL THE POWER (IRE), 6, b g Subtle Power (IRE)—Our Alma (IRE) **The McGoldrick Partnership**
14 FORWARD FLIGHT (IRE), 6, b g Dilshaan—Too Advanced (USA) **J. P. McManus**
15 FURIUS, 6, b g Montjeu—Frottola **Mrs S. J. Smith**
16 GANSEY (IRE), 10, br g Anshan—Ebony Jane **T. J. Hemmings**
17 GUN AND MORE, 7, ch g Double Trigger (IRE)—Snowmore **Mrs S. J. Smith**
18 HEATHER GLEN (IRE), 6, b m Luso—Kadara (IRE) **Mrs S. J. Smith**
19 HELENA OF TROY, 6, b m Largesse—Just Julia **Mrs S. J. Smith**
20 HIGH HOYLANDER, 6, b g Aljabr (USA)—Ma-Arif (IRE) **The McGoldrick Partnership**
21 HIGHRATE (IRE), 6, b g Presenting—Hollygrove Cliche **T. J. Hemmings**
22 KARMADICE, 10, b g Minster Son—Manettia (IRE) **K. Nicholson**
23 KENT STREET (IRE), 7, ch g Flemensfirth (USA)—Fernhill (IRE) **K. Nicholson**
24 KILKENNY ALL STAR (IRE), 11, b g Alderbrook—Borris Bounty (IRE) **Mrs S. J. Smith**
25 LACKAMON, 7, b g Fleetwood (IRE)—Pearlossa **Mrs S. J. Smith**
26 MANAHEJ (USA), 6, b g Mr Greeley (USA)—Indemnify (USA) **Mrs S. J. Smith**
27 MELUA MAID (IRE), 10, b m Flemensfirth (USA)—Chatty Lookalike (IRE) **Mrs S. J. Smith**

MRS SUE SMITH—continued

28 **MR MOONSHINE (IRE)**, 8, b g Double Eclipse (IRE)—Kinross **Mrs S. J. Smith**
29 **NO PLANNING**, 5, b g Kayf Tara—Poor Celt **Mr A. W. Muir**
30 **PAPA CARUSO**, 8, b g Kayf Tara—Madonna da Rossi **Mrs S. J. Smith**
31 **PINEROLO**, 6, b g Milan—Hollybush (IRE) **Mrs S. J. Smith**
32 **PLENMELLER (IRE)**, 6, ch g Moscow Society (USA)—Lantys Luck (IRE) **R. H. Scholey & M. B. Scholey**
33 **RATTLIN**, 4, b f Bollin Eric—Parslin **Broadband Partnership**
34 **REBEL SWING**, 6, b g Robellino (USA)—Ninia (USA) **Broadway Racing Club 15**
35 **SHADRACK (IRE)**, 8, gr g Tamayaz (CAN)—Alba Dancer **Mrs S. P. Granger**
36 **SIR TAMBURLANE (IRE)**, 7, b g Tamayaz (CAN)—Lady Lupin **Mrs S. J. Smith**
37 **SMUDGER**, 7, b g Alflora (IRE)—Debutante Days **Mrs S. J. Smith**
38 **SPARKLING TARA**, 7, b g Kayf Tara—Sparkling Yasmin **Mrs S. J. Smith**
39 **STAGECOACH JASPER**, 6, b g Sir Harry Lewis (USA)—Flintwood **Mrs J. Conroy**
40 **STAGECOACH PEARL**, 8, gr g Classic Cliche (IRE)—Linwood **John Conroy Jacqueline Conroy**
41 **TAHITI PEARL (IRE)**, 8, b g Winged Love (IRE)—Clara's Dream (IRE) **M. B. Scholey & R. H. Scholey**
42 **TEENANDO (IRE)**, 12, b g Teenoso (USA)—Ananda **Mrs S. J. Smith**
43 **TIPPERING (IRE)**, 7, b g Flemensfirth (USA)—Tart of Tipp (IRE) **T. J. Hemmings**
44 **TIPSY INDIAN**, 9, ch g Commanche Run—Dubelle **Mrs S. J. Smith**
45 **TWICE LUCKY**, 8, b g Mtoto—Foehn Gale (IRE) **Mrs S. J. Smith**
46 **VINTAGE STAR (IRE)**, 6, b g Presenting—Rare Vintage (IRE) **T. J. Hemmings**
47 **WHISKEY RIDGE (IRE)**, 6, b g High-Rise (IRE)—Little Chartridge **Widdop Wanderers**
48 **WILLY C**, 6, b g Zamindar (USA)—Rosa Canina **M. F. Spence**
49 **YOU KNOW YOURSELF (IRE)**, 9, b g Dr Massini (IRE)—Gift of The Gab (IRE) **Mrs S. J. Smith**

Other Owners: Mr R. S. Bebb, R. F. Broad, J. J. Brummitt, J. Conroy, A. D. Hollinrake, R. J. Longley, C. C. S. MacMillan, Mr A. M. Phillips, J. Regan, Mrs M. B. Scholey, R. H. Scholey, Mrs J. C. Short, W. S. Skene, Mrs A. Skene.

Assistant Trainer: Henry Oliver

Jockey (NH): Henry Oliver. **Conditional:** Shane Byrne, Zachery-James Gaughan, Jonathan England.

---

607 **MISS SUZY SMITH, Lewes**
Postal: **County Stables, The Old Racecourse, Lewes, East Sussex, BN7 1UR**
Contacts: **PHONE (01273) 477173 FAX (01273) 477173 MOBILE (07970) 550828**
E-MAIL **suzy@suzysmithracing.co.uk** WEBSITE **www.suzysmithracing.co.uk**

1 **AIMIGAYLE**, 9, b m Midnight Legend—Cherrygayle (IRE) **P. J. Mercer**
2 **BEAU LAKE (IRE)**, 8, b br g Heron Island (IRE)—Brennan For Audits (IRE) **P. J. Mercer**
3 **EMMASLEGEND**, 7, b m Midnight Legend—Cherrygayle (IRE) **P. J. Mercer**
4 **GEORGIAN KING**, 9, b g Overbury (IRE)—Roslin **R. Allsop**
5 **INVICTA LAKE (IRE)**, 5, b g Dr Massini (IRE)—Classic Material **Bernard & Jan Wolford**
6 **JORDAN**, 9, b m Golden Snake (USA)—Formula One Affair **Mr D Forster Mrs SJ Somner & Mr EW Dale**
7 **MADAME JASMINE**, 7, gr m Karinga Bay—Roslin **Mrs Y. E. Allsop**
8 **NATURAL SPRING**, 7, b m Generous (IRE)—Highbrook (USA) **The Natural Spring Partnership**
9 **O MALLEY'S OSCAR (IRE)**, 7, b g Oscar (IRE)—Notre Dame (IRE) **Exors of the Late Mr M. J. Weaver**
10 **PASS ME BY**, 13, b g Balinbarbi—Errol Emerald **Passers By**
11 **QUIPE ME POSTED (FR)**, 8, b g Discover d'auteuil (FR)—Harlem (FR) **Mrs V. Palmer**
12 **ROYAL KICKS (FR)**, 11, b g Garde Royale—Al Kicks (FR)
13 **SEA FURY (IRE)**, 5, b m Hawk Wing (USA)—Scruple (IRE) **Miss S. Smith**

Other Owners: Mrs D. J. Arstall, E. W. Dale, Mr D. E. Forster, Mr D. J. Harrison, Mr A. J. McDonald, R. F. Smith, Mrs S. J. Somner, C. P Thompkins, B. Wolford, Mrs J. Wolford.

Assistant Trainer: Mr S E Gordon-Watson

Jockey (flat): Sam Hitchcott. **Jockey (NH):** Colin Bolger.

---

608 **MR GILES SMYLY, Broadway**
Postal: **Garden Cottage, Wormington Grange, Broadway, Worcestershire, WR12 7NJ**
Contacts: PHONE **(01386) 584085 FAX (01386) 584085 MOBILE (07747) 035169**
E-MAIL **gilessmiler@aol.com** WEBSITE **www.smylyracing.co.uk**

1 **FERGAL MAEL DUIN**, 4, gr g Tikkanen (USA)—Fad Amach (IRE) **J. M. Messenger**
2 **GENERAL MELCHETT (IRE)**, 5, b g Broadway Flyer (USA)—Kept In The Dark **D. Maxwell**
3 **LE BURF (FR)**, 11, b g Lute Antique (FR)—Fripperie (FR) **M. Burford**

MR GILES SMYLY—continued

4 **LIEUTENANT GEORGE (IRE)**, 4, b g Broadway Flyer (USA)—Kept In The Dark
5 **NOAKARAD DE VERZEE (FR)**, 11, b g Roakarad—Taratata (FR) **D. Maxwell**
6 **PINGARO DE LA VIRE (FR)**, 9, br g Ungaro (GER)—Kina de La Vire (FR) **D. Maxwell**
7 **PLUM PUDDING (FR)**, 9, b g Fado (FR)—Tale (FR) **J. M. Messenger**
8 **TAIGAN (FR)**, 5, b g Panoramic—Lazary (FR) **M. Burford**
9 **TIHUI SEPT**, 4, ch f Septieme Ciel (USA)—Tihui Two (IRE) **Ms Gillian Metherell**

Other Owners: D. J. Keyte, C. M. Clarke, N. R. Sutton, G. Dowty, J. Lees, W. Rucker, G. Swire, A. Ward Thomas.

Assistant Trainer: Kim Smyly

Jockey (NH): David England, Liam Treadwell. **Conditional:** Ed Cookson.

---

609 **MR HARRY SMYTH, Ballyclare**
Postal: 'Fields Of Dreams', 26 Legaloy Road, Ballyclare, Co. Antrim, BT39 9PS
Contacts: **PHONE (02893) 352299 MOBILE (07802) 604411**

1 **BALLYNAMONABONANZA**, 6, b g Sonus (IRE)—Sight'n Sound **Harry Smyth**
2 **CANTRELL (IRE)**, 9, b g High Roller (IRE)—Executive Seat (IRE) **Harry Smyth**
3 **IF U BELIEVE (IRE)**, 5, b g Oscar (IRE)—Arctic Rose (IRE) **Harry Smyth**
4 **MY BROTHERS WILL (IRE)**, 5, b g Sayadaw (FR)—Zaffaran Express (IRE) **Harry Smyth**
5 **NEVER ROAM (IRE)**, 5, br m Milan—Night Class (IRE) **Coleman Rooney**

---

610 **MR JAMIE SNOWDEN, Lambourn**
Postal: Folly House, Upper Lambourn Road, Lambourn, Hungerford, Berkshire, RG17 8QG
Contacts: **PHONE (01488) 72800 (office) Twitter: @jamiesnowden MOBILE (07779) 497563**
E-MAIL info@jamiesnowdenracing.co.uk WEBSITE www.jamiesnowdenracing.co.uk

1 **AMERICAN LADIE**, 6, b m Monashee Mountain (USA)—Dounine **Mrs K. Gunn**
2 **BALLYBOKER BOY (IRE)**, 8, b g Snurge—Ballyboker Lady (IRE) **The Ballyboker Boy Partnership**
3 **BALLYSPELLAN STORM (IRE)**, 7, b g Glacial Storm (USA)—Coolbawn Rose (IRE) **J. H. W. Finch**
4 **CAMINERO (IRE)**, 5, b g Cloudings (IRE)—Sounds Confident (IRE) **Jamie Snowden**
5 **EL DIEGO (IRE)**, 8, b g Sadler's Wells—
                                                    Goncharova (USA) **T. P. & D. M. Lambert & R. C. & C. R. Keightley**
6 **GRADUATION NIGHT**, 6, br g Kayf Tara—Jadidh **Martin Broughton Racing Partners**
7 **IXORA (IRE)**, 6, gr m Milan—Tucacas (FR) **The Ixora Racing Partnership**
8 **JAMESSON (IRE)**, 7, b g Bishop of Cashel—Native Belle (IRE) **The Sandylini Racing Partnership**
9 **KNIGHTON COMBE**, 12, b g Midnight Legend—Cindercombe **I. R. Snowden**
10 **LOUGH DERG WAY (IRE)**, 6, b g Dushyantor (USA)—Lotschberg Express **The Folly Partnership**
11 **MARODIMA (FR)**, 9, b g Robin des Pres (FR)—Balbeyssac (FR) **The Mista Rossa Racing Partnership**
12 **MILLERS REEF (IRE)**, 6, b g Bob Back (USA)—Silent Supreme (IRE) **Jamie Snowden Racing Club**
13 **MISS MILBORNE**, 6, b m Tamure (IRE)—Motown Melody (IRE) **Adrian Brown and Friends**
14 **MISTA ROSSA**, 7, b g Red Ransom (USA)—Cloud Hill **The Mista Rossa Racing Partnership**
15 **MOUNTAIN RETREAT (IRE)**, 5, b g Sadler's Wells (USA)—Fig Tree Drive (USA) **J. H. W. Finch**
16 **SANDY'S DOUBLE**, 6, ch g Double Trigger (IRE)—Skipcarl (IRE) **Ms L. V. Agran**
17 **SHINKO MOON**, 5, b g Shinko Forest (IRE)—Silver Moon **Mr C. Roberts**
18 **SUTTON WHO (FR)**, 6, b g Dark Moondancer—Magik (FR) **The Franks Family**
19 **TEA CADDY**, 6, b m Kadastrof (FR)—Little Tern (IRE) **R. T. S. Matthews**
20 **TOM SANG (FR)**, 5, b g Dom Alco (FR)—Idee (FR) **Mr A. C. T. Bath**
21 **ZAVA RIVER (IRE)**, 5, b g Zagreb (USA)—Great Accord (USA) **Chalke Valley Racing Partnership**

Other Owners: Mr Tony Bath, Sir Martin Broughton, Mr Stephen Broughton, Mr A. P. Brown, Mr D. J. Coles, Mr Paul Donaldson, Mr M. Holman, Miss L. Horner, Mr Jon Hughes, Mr Andrew J. Huntly, Mrs C. Keightley, Mr R. J. Kilford, Mr Peter Lambert, Mr C. Ricketts, Mr Martin Shenfield, Mr J. E. Snowden, Mrs Ian Snowden, Mrs L. Snowden, Mr Alan Watson.

Assistant Trainer: Kate Robinson

Jockey (NH): Daryl Jacob, Tom O'Brien, Noel Fehily, Sam Twiston-Davies. **Conditional:** Ryan Mahon.

611 **MR MIKE SOWERSBY, York**
Postal: **Southwold Farm, Goodmanham Wold, Market Weighton, York, East Yorkshire, YO43 3NA**
Contacts: **PHONE (01430) 810534 MOBILE (07855) 551056**

1 BOLD INDIAN (IRE), 8, b g Indian Danehill (IRE)—Desert Gift **Racing Ladies 1**
2 CARMELA MARIA, 7, b m Medicean—Carmela Owen **Mrs Janet Cooper & Mr M. E. Sowersby**
3 CONVITEZZA, 6, b m Domedriver (IRE)—Condoleezza (USA) **I. L. Westwood**
4 FRENCH APPLAUSE (IRE), 6, b g Royal Applause—A Ma Guise (USA) **I. L. Westwood**
5 HAMMER, 7, b g Beat Hollow—Tranquil Moon **J. Payne**
6 ICING SUGAR, 4, ch f Doyen (IRE)—Cryptogam **R. D. Seldon**
7 MOON MELODY (GER), 9, b g Montjeu (IRE)—Midnight Fever (IRE) **Mrs J. H. Cooper**
8 OCEAN BLUFF (IRE), 4, b br f Dalakhani (IRE)—Karaliyfa (IRE) **M. E. Sowersby**
9 QUITE SPARKY, 5, b g Lucky Story (USA)—Imperialistic (IRE) **R. D. Seldon**
10 SEVEN STARS, 7, b g Dubai Destination—Galette **The Southwold Set**
11 SILVERS SPIRIT, 6, b m Makbul—Shadows of Silver **R. N. Forman**
12 STARBIRD, 5, br g Danbird (AUS)—Tennessee Star **Queens Head Racing Club**
13 SYCHO FRED (IRE), 11, b g Buster King—Rebecca Steel (IRE) **Mrs E. A. Verity**
14 TREGARO (FR), 6, b g Phantom Breeze—Touques (FR) **A. Lyons**

Other Owners: Mr Paul Clifton, Mrs Janet Cooper, Mr J. Deno, Mrs Jean W. Robinson, Mr M. E. Sowersby, Mrs J. Wiltschinsky.

Assistant Trainer: Mary Sowersby

Jockey (flat): Tom Eaves. **Jockey (NH):** Keith Mercer. **Conditional:** Campbell Gillies, Edmond Linehan.

612 **MR JOHN SPEARING, Kinnersley**
Postal: **John Spearing Racing Ltd, Kinnersley Racing Stables, Kinnersley, Severn Stoke, Worcestershire, WR8 9JR**
Contacts: **PHONE (01905) 371054 FAX (01905) 371054 MOBILE (07801) 552922**
E-MAIL jlspearing@aol.com

1 BARTON GIFT, 5, b g Alflora (IRE)—Marina Bird **Mercy Rimell & Kate Ive**
2 BERMONDSEY BOB (IRE), 6, b g Trans Island—Tread Softly (IRE) **A. A. Campbell**
3 CLEAR SPRING (IRE), 4, b c Chineur (FR)—Holly Springs **Mr H. James**
4 CROESO MAWR, 6, ch m Bertolini (USA)—Croeso-I-Cymru **Mrs S. A. Evans**
5 EQUULEUS PICTOR, 8, br g Piccolo—Vax Rapide **Masonaires**
6 FULL SHILLING (IRE), 4, b f Intikhab (USA)—Full Cream (USA) **Not The Full Shilling Syndicate**
7 HAWK MOTH (IRE), 4, b g Hawk Wing (USA)—Sasimoto (USA) **Kinnersley Partnership**
8 KAYF PARADIS, 7, b m Kayf Tara—Paris Fashion (FR) **P. Kelsall**
9 ROSENBLATT (GER), 10, b g Dashing Blade—Roseraie (GER) **J. L. Spearing**
10 SPARKLING AIR, 6, ch m Central Park (IRE)—Moonlight Air **Mrs W. M. Badger**
11 WHITECREST, 4, ch f Ishiguru (USA)—Risky Valentine **G. M. Eales**

THREE-YEAR-OLDS

12 ASHPAN SAM, b c Firebreak—Sweet Patoopie **Advantage Chemicals Holdings Ltd**
13 IMPERIAL WEAPON (IRE), ch f Majestic Missile (IRE)—Regal Lustre **Kinnersley Partnership II**
14 LA SONADORA, gr f Proclamation (IRE)—Evening Falls **Mrs C. J. Welch**
15 MISS CONDUCT, b f Overbury (IRE)—Risky Valentine **Miss C. J. Ive**

Other Owners: S. J. Court, G. J. Daly, Mr E. Devereaux, Mr J. M. Eccleson, W. J. Goddard, Mr A. O'Brien, Mrs M. Rimell.

Assistant Trainer: Miss C Ive

Jockey (flat): Steve Drowne.

613 **MR MICHAEL SQUANCE, Newmarket**
Postal: **36 Golden Miller Close, Newmarket, Suffolk, CB8 7RT**
Contacts: **PHONE (01638) 661824 MOBILE (07532) 372557**
WEBSITE www.michaelsquanceracing.co.uk

1 DIPLOMATIC (IRE), 7, b g Cape Cross (IRE)—Embassy **K Squance & R Favarulo**
2 ESTONIA, 5, b m Exceed And Excel (AUS)—Global Trend **Miss K. L. Squance**
3 EXCEEDINGTHESTARS, 5, b m Exceed And Excel (AUS)—Starbeck (IRE) **Miss K. L. Squance**

MR MICHAEL SQUANCE—continued

4 **LADY BRICKHOUSE,** 5, b m Choisir (AUS)—Music Maid (IRE) **K. D. Crabb**
5 **ONCEAPONATIME (IRE),** 7, b g Invincible Spirit (IRE)—Lake Nyasa (IRE) **Miss K. L. Squance**

THREE-YEAR-OLDS

6 B f Motivator—Dumnoni **C. R. Withers**
7 B c Royal Applause—Ticki Tori (IRE) **C. R. Withers**

TWO-YEAR-OLDS

8 B c 24/2 Trade Fair—Starbeck (IRE) (Spectrum (IRE)) **K. D. Crabb**
9 B f 2/3 Pastoral Pursuits—Tilly's Dream (Arkadian Hero (USA)) (3000) **C. R. Withers**

Other Owners: Mr R. Favarulo.

MR TOMMY STACK, Cashel
Postal: **Thomastown Castle, Golden, Cashel, Co. Tipperary, Ireland**

1 **CELERINA (IRE),** 5, ch m Choisir (AUS)—Chantarella (IRE)
2 **CNOCAN DIVA (IRE),** 4, b f Danehill Dancer (IRE)—Dancing Diva (FR)
3 **GREAT HUZZAR (IRE),** 4, b g Danehill Dancer (IRE)—Labrusca
4 **MISTER CARTER (IRE),** 5, b g Antonius Pius (USA)—Kotdiji
5 **PARKERS MILL (IRE),** 4, b g High Chaparral (IRE)—Celtic Wing
6 **PIPER HILL (IRE),** 4, b g Hawk Wing (USA)—Mini Dane (IRE)
7 **PIVOTAL ROCK (IRE),** 5, b g Pivotal—Kitza (IRE)
8 **SIKARA (IRE),** 4, b f Aussie Rules (USA)—Beucaire (IRE)
9 **WINDSOCKS,** 4, b f Hurricane Run (IRE)—Shall We Tell
10 **ZVONAREAVE (IRE),** 4, ch f Choisir (AUS)—Chantarella (IRE)

THREE-YEAR-OLDS

11 **ATACX (IRE),** b c Elusive City (USA)—Lure of The Moon (USA)
12 **BIRD'S EYE VIEW,** b f Royal Applause—Opopmil (IRE)
13 **CAPE OF APPROVAL (IRE),** b g Cape Cross (IRE)—Wyola (USA)
14 B c Dylan Thomas (IRE)—Chanterelle (IRE)
15 **COIN OF COURAGE (IRE),** b c Dylan Thomas (IRE)—Daralaka (USA)
16 **CROI AN OR (IRE),** b c Windsor Knot (IRE)—Exponent (USA)
17 **DIAVOLEZZA,** b f Iceman—Danehurst
18 **EQUITY SWAP (IRE),** ch c Strategic Prince—Medicean Star (IRE)
19 **FURTHER PROOF,** b g Royal Applause—Fabine
20 **KEDLESTON (IRE),** b c Oratorio (IRE)—Bluebell Wood (IRE)
21 **MOLDOWNEY,** ch c Dalakhani (IRE)—Danehill's Dream (IRE)
22 **NERO EMPEROR (IRE),** b c Holy Roman Emperor (IRE)—Blue Iris
23 **PENNISTON LINE (IRE),** b g Holy Roman Emperor (IRE)—Willowbridge (IRE)
24 **QUEENS VISIT,** b f Authorized (IRE)—Royale Rose (FR)
25 **ROMANTIC STROLL (IRE),** b f Oratorio (IRE)—Home You Stroll (IRE)
26 Ch f Excellent Art—Shaanara (IRE)
27 **SPARKLING ROCK (IRE),** b f Rock of Gibraltar (IRE)—Urgele (FR)
28 **SPIDER ZAGATO (IRE),** b c High Chaparral (IRE)—Mille Miglia (IRE)
29 Ch f Dylan Thomas (IRE)—State Crystal (IRE)
30 **THE TALLY HO KID (IRE),** b g Oratorio (IRE)—Edetana (USA)
31 **TIME OF MY LIFE (IRE),** b c Galileo (IRE)—In My Life (IRE)

TWO-YEAR-OLDS

32 **ADDICTEDTOPROGRESS (IRE),** b f 27/3 Holy Roman Emperor (IRE)—Farthingale (IRE) (Nashwan (USA)) (65680)
33 Br c 9/5 Rock of Gibraltar (IRE)—Almaaseh (IRE) (Dancing Brave (USA)) (53365)
34 **ASTER CASS (IRE),** b f 25/3 Duke of Marmalade (IRE)—Mayfair Lane (IRE) (Sadler's Wells (USA))
35 B f 2/4 Galileo (IRE)—Banquise (IRE) (Last Tycoon)
36 **BECK CASS (IRE),** b c 9/2 Baratmea (IRE)—Rafine (Peintre Celebre (USA))
37 B c 12/4 Jeremy (USA)—Birdsong (IRE) (Dolphin Street (FR)) (28735)
38 Ch f 8/3 Dubawi (IRE)—Blond Moment (Affirmed (USA)) (9523)
39 Br c 10/4 Choisir (AUS)—Family Focus (IRE) (Alzao (USA))
40 B c 3/2 Montjeu (IRE)—Gamra (IRE) (Green Desert (USA)) (90000)
41 B f 19/4 Duke of Marmalade (IRE)—Higher Love (IRE) (Sadler's Wells (USA)) (125000)
42 B f 17/4 Oratorio (IRE)—Holly Blue (Bluebird (USA)) (24630)

MR TOMMY STACK—continued

43 Br c 28/3 Rock of Gibraltar (IRE)—Jalisco (IRE) (Machiavellian (USA)) (23809)
44 B br c 27/4 Excellent Art—Kafayef (USA) (Secreto (USA)) (19000)
45 **LIGHT STORM CASS (IRE),** b f 11/3 Dylan Thomas (IRE)—Fand (USA) (Kingmambo (USA))
46 **MISCHIEF N MAYHEM,** b f 6/4 Nayef (USA)—Mail The Desert (IRE) (Desert Prince (IRE)) (66666)
47 B f 16/4 Shamardal (USA)—Nassma (IRE) (Sadler's Wells (USA)) (39408)
48 B f 19/4 Dylan Thomas (IRE)—No Way (IRE) (Rainbows For Life (CAN)) (65680)
49 B c 20/3 Footstepsinthesand—Nubar Lady (IRE) (Danetime (IRE))
50 B f 8/3 Holy Roman Emperor (IRE)—On The Nile (IRE) (Sadler's Wells (USA)) (5714)
51 B c 26/2 Haatef (USA)—Openness (Grand Lodge (USA)) (38095)
52 **PECTIN (IRE),** b f 15/4 Duke of Marmalade (IRE)—On Air (FR) (Chief Singer)
53 Ch c 2/2 Bahamian Bounty—Raja (IRE) (Pivotal) (54080)
54 B c 20/2 Henrythenavigator (USA)—Saintly Speech (USA) (Southern Halo (USA)) (100000)
55 **SPEEDWAY CASS (IRE),** ch c 18/3 Shamardal (USA)—Golden Mask (USA) (Seeking The Gold (USA))
56 **YOUR PAL TAL,** b c 24/2 Dark Angel (IRE)—Good Health (Magic Ring (IRE)) (45000)

Owners: Mr Michael Begley, Mr John Byrne, Mr Justin Caffney, Mr John Connaughton, Mr Terry Corden, Mr Dean Harrod, Mr T. Hyde Jnr, JSC Kasandros Grupe, Mr D. Keoghan, Mrs J. Magnier, Mr Casey McKliney, Mr J. P.McManus, Eimear Mulhearne, Newtownanner Stud, Mr Gerard O'Brien, Michael O'Flynn, Mr Peter Piller, Mr David Slater, Mr Derrick Smith, Mr Alfred Sweetnam, Mr Michael Tabor, The Bucketlist Syndicate, The Pension Fund Syndicate, The Tallyho Kiddo Syndicate, Ms Kinvara Vaughan, Wilgerbosdrift.

Jockey (flat): Wayne Lordan. **Jockey (NH):** W. J. Lee. **Apprentice:** S. A. Gray, Patrick O'Donnell.

---

615 MR JOHN STIMPSON, Newcastle-under-Lyme
Postal: **Trainers Lodge, Butterton Racing Stables, Off Park Road, Butterton, Newcastle-Under-Lyme, Staffordshire, ST5 4DZ**
Contacts: **PHONE (01782) 636020 FAX (01782) 633533 MOBILE (07768) 213531**
E-MAIL info@jtsintltd.co.uk

1 APACHE GLORY (IRE), 4, b br f Cherokee Run (USA)—Jumeirah Glory (USA) **J. Stimpson**
2 JAWBREAKER (IRE), 7, b g Catcher In The Rye (IRE)—Alpine Lady (IRE) **J. T. S. (International) Ltd**
3 LION COURT (IRE), 4, ch g Iffraaj—Spanish Falls **J. Stimpson**
4 SILENT DECISION (USA), 6, ch m Mr Greeley (USA)—Aly Sangue (USA) **J. T. S. (International) Ltd**
5 WONDERWINDER (IRE), 10, b g Kayf Tara—Girlie Set (IRE) **J. T. S. (International) Ltd**
6 ZED CANDY (FR), 9, b g Medicean—Intrum Morshaan (IRE) **J. T. S. (International) Ltd**

THREE-YEAR-OLDS

7 FLUMPS, ch f Auction House (USA)—Demolition Jo **Marshmallows International S. L.**
8 HAWAIIAN FREEZE, b f Avonbridge—Autumn Affair **J. T. S. (International) Ltd**
9 JAWBREAKERONASTICK, b g Striking Ambition—Danalia (IRE) **J. T. S. (International) Ltd**
10 MR MALLO, b g Bertolini (USA)—Londonnet (IRE) **Marshmallows International S. L.**

Assistant Trainer: Mandy Bradley (07850) 775349

---

616 MR WILLIAM STONE, West Wickham
Postal: **The Meadow, Streetly End, West Wickham, Cambridge, Cambridgeshire, CB21 4RP**
Contacts: **PHONE (01223) 894617 MOBILE (07788) 971094**

1 BARBIROLLI, 10, b g Machiavellian (USA)—Blushing Barada (USA) **Miss C. M. Scott**
2 DELORAIN (IRE), 9, b g Kalanisi (IRE)—Lady Nasrana (FR) **Miss C. M. Scott**
3 IMJIN RIVER (IRE), 5, b g Namid—Lady Nasrana (FR) **Miss C. M. Scott**
4 LACONICOS (IRE), 10, ch g Foxhound (USA)—Thermopylae **Miss C. M. Scott**
5 MY MATE MAL, 8, b g Daawe (USA)—Kandymal (IRE) **Miss C. M. Scott**
6 SUFFOLINI, 4, b f Bertolini (USA)—Hotel California (IRE) **Shane Fairweather & Jack Pearce**
7 WARDEN BOND, 4, ch g Monsieur Bond (IRE)—Warden Rose **Mr J. A. Ross & Miss C. M. Scott**

THREE-YEAR-OLDS

8 STORMS RANSOM (IRE), b g Antonius Pius (USA)—Walt Mc Don (IRE) **Mr S. A. Fairweather**

Other Owners: Mr Shane Fairweather, Mr Jack Pearce, Mr J. A. Ross, Miss Caroline Scott.

617 MR BRIAN STOREY, Kirklinton
Postal: **Low Dubwath, Kirklinton, Carlisle, Cumbria, CA6 6EF**
Contacts: **PHONE (01228) 675376 FAX (01228) 675977 MOBILE (07950) 925576**
E-MAIL jackie@brianstoreyracing.co.uk WEBSITE www.brianstoreyracing.co.uk

1 **ANNIE ANSHAN (IRE)**, 6, b m Anshan—Lotta Talk (IRE) **Suzanne & Nigel Williams**
2 **BIRNIES BOY**, 8, b g Thowra (FR)—Drumkilly Lilly (IRE) **Mrs V. Birnie**
3 **BOLT FROM THE BLUE**, 7, gr g Terimon—Den Is Over (IRE) **J. Wade**
4 **CASHEL ROSE (IRE)**, 5, b m Flemensfirth—Always Present (IRE) **Suzanne & Nigel Williams**
5 **DAY OF DESTINY (IRE)**, 7, gr g Clodovil (IRE)—El Corazon (IRE) **Suzanne & Nigel Williams**
6 5, B m And Beyond (IRE)—Dusky Dame **F. S. Storey**
7 **FANNYTHEWUNDAHORSE (IRE)**, 5, b m Alderbrook—Woodford Beauty (IRE) **Suzanne & Nigel Williams**
8 **HUMOUROUS (IRE)**, 10, b g Darshaan—Amusing Time (IRE) **Graham, Storey, Campbell**
9 **HURRYONHARRY**, 6, b g Erhaab (USA)—Gypsy Race (IRE) **Mr J. Hutchinson**
10 **JIM TANGO (FR)**, 8, b br g Jimble (FR)—Fitanga (FR) **Mrs C. J. Todd**
11 4, B gr f Overbury (IRE)—Ladylliat (FR) **Mrs V. A. Birnie**
12 **LANGTOON LASS**, 4, b f Captain Rio—Mindanao **Mr J. Campbell**
13 **LORIENT EXPRESS (FR)**, 13, b g Sleeping Car (FR)—Envie de Chalamont (FR) **Suzanne & Nigel Williams**
14 **LOW REACTOR (IRE)**, 11, b g Taipan (IRE)—Strong Opinion **Suzanne & Nigel Williams**
15 **LUCKY SUNNY (IRE)**, 9, b g Pasternak—Flying Fur (IRE) **Suzanne & Nigel Williams**
16 **NAJLAA**, 5, b br m Nayef (USA)—Perfect Plum (IRE) **Suzanne & Nigel Williams**
17 **NO WAY HOZAY**, 6, b g Nomadic Way (USA)—Sweet Sensation **J. Wade**
18 **PARKY (IRE)**, 8, b g Saddlers' Hall (IRE)—Parskint (IRE) **Mr & Mrs Raymond Anderson Green**
19 **PRIDEUS (IRE)**, 8, gr g Atticus (USA)—Pride Of Baino (USA) **Fraser McClung & Belinda Wares**
20 **QUO VISTA (IRE)**, 5, b g Anshan—Miss Cooline (IRE) **Mr J. Hutchinson & Mr J. Storey**
21 **RHYTON (IRE)**, 5, b g Rainbow Quest (USA)—Sea Picture (IRE) **Mrs J. M. Fraser**
22 **SMACK DOWN**, 6, ch g Karinga Bay—Lambrini (IRE) **Mr G. Wilkinson**
23 **THEBOYFROMBRAZIL (IRE)**, 5, b br g Dr Massini (IRE)—Rapid Dawn (IRE) **Suzanne & Nigel Williams**
24 **WOODYS BROTHER (IRE)**, 9, b g Flemensfirth (USA)—Woodram Delight **Mr J. T. Hutchinson**
25 **YOUNG SPARKY (IRE)**, 5, b br g Oscar (IRE)—Our Dream (IRE) **Mr & Mrs Raymond Anderson Green**

Other Owners: Mr J. Campbell, Mr W. Graham, Mr Raymond Anderson Green, Mrs Anita Green, Mr B. Storey, Mr F. S. Storey, Mrs Suzanne Williams, Mr N. Williams.

Assistant Trainer: Mrs Jackie Storey

Jockey (flat): P. J. McDonald. **Jockey (NH):** Brian Hughes, Richie McGrath. **Conditional:** James Halliday. **Amateur:** Miss Jackie Coward.

618 MR WILF STOREY, Consett
Postal: **Grange Farm & Stud, Muggleswick, Consett, Co. Durham, DH8 9DW**
Contacts: **PHONE (01207) 255259 FAX (01207) 255259 MOBILE (07860) 510441**
E-MAIL wlstorey@metronet.co.uk WEBSITE www.wilfstorey.com

1 **BOSTON COURT (IRE)**, 4, b g Tomba—Chiffon **W. L. Storey**
2 **DAN'S HEIR**, 10, b g Dansili—Million Heiress **P. Tomlinson**
3 **JAN SMUTS (IRE)**, 4, b g Johannesburg (USA)—Choice House (USA) **H. S. Hutchinson**
4 **MONTHLY MEDAL**, 9, b g Danehill Dancer (IRE)—Sovereign Abbey (IRE) **W. L. Storey**
5 **PETROCELLI**, 5, b g Piccolo—Sarcita **W. L. Storey**
6 **RED LITE (IRE)**, 4, b f Red Ransom (USA)—Cloudy Bay (GER) **The Durham Company Limited**
7 **TRISKAIDEKAPHOBIA**, 9, b g Bertolini (USA)—Seren Teg **W. L. Storey**

Other Owners: Mr S. P. Gilbey.

Assistant Trainer: Miss S. Storey

619 SIR MICHAEL STOUTE, Newmarket
Postal: Freemason Lodge, Bury Road, Newmarket, Suffolk, CB8 7BY
Contacts: **PHONE (01638) 663801 FAX (01638) 667276**

1 **CARLTON HOUSE (USA)**, 4, b c Street Cry (IRE)—Talented
2 **FIORENTE (IRE)**, 4, br c Monsun (GER)—Desert Bloom (IRE)
3 **LABARINTO**, 4, b c Dansili—Tarocchi (USA)
4 **PURSUITOEXCELLENCE (IRE)**, 4, b c Galileo (IRE)—Lila
5 **SEA MOON**, 4, b c Beat Hollow—Eva Luna (USA)

SIR MICHAEL STOUTE—continued

6 **TAZAHUM (USA)**, 4, b c Redoute's Choice (AUS)—Huja (IRE)
7 **TOP DIKTAT**, 4, b g Diktat—Top Romance (IRE)

THREE-YEAR-OLDS

8 Ch c Galileo (IRE)—Adoration (USA)
9 **AFFECTIONATELY**, ch f Galileo (IRE)—Rafha
10 **ALBANKA (USA)**, b f Giant's Causeway (USA)—Alidiva
11 **AUGUSTUS SNODGRASS (USA)**, b br c Medaglia d'oro (USA)—Greeley Appealing (USA)
12 **BETWEEN THE LINES (IRE)**, gr c Dalakhani (IRE)—Stage Struck (IRE)
13 **CANTAL**, ch f Pivotal—Canda (USA)
14 **CAPTION**, b f Motivator—Razzle (USA)
15 **CASKELENA (IRE)**, b f Galileo (IRE)—Clara Bow (FR)
16 **CAYUGA**, b c Montjeu—Ithaca (USA)
17 **CECCHETTI METHOD (IRE)**, b c Danehill Dancer (IRE)—Desert Bloom (IRE)
18 **CLASS WIN**, ch c Notnowcato—Prithee
19 **COMMEND**, ch c Pivotal—Reputable
20 **COUNSEL (IRE)**, b g Dansili—Kitty O'shea
21 **COURAGE (IRE)**, b g Invincible Spirit (IRE)—Mamonta
22 **DANK**, b f Dansili—Masskana (IRE)
23 **DEBATING SOCIETY (IRE)**, b c Invincible Spirit (IRE)—Drama Class (IRE)
24 **DIAMOND DAME (IRE)**, b f King's Best (USA)—Arabian Treasure (USA)
25 **DREAMS OF FIRE (USA)**, b f Dynaformer (USA)—Angel In My Heart (FR)
26 **DUKE OF FIRENZE**, ch c Pivotal—Nannina
27 **EL GRECO (IRE)**, ch c Monsun (GER)—Olympienne (IRE)
28 **ELTIFAAT (IRE)**, ch c Medicean—Dhelaal
29 **ELYSIAN**, b f Galileo (IRE)—Echelon
30 **ENROL**, b f Pivotal—Constitute (USA)
31 **ESTIMATE (IRE)**, b f Monsun (GER)—Ebaziya (IRE)
32 **FLEUR DE CACTUS (IRE)**, b f Montjeu (GER)—Desert Beauty (IRE)
33 **GALLEON**, b c Galileo (IRE)—Tempting Prospect
34 **GLITTERBALL (IRE)**, b f Smart Strike (CAN)—Crystal Music (USA)
35 **GLITTERING GOLD**, b c Galileo (IRE)—Phantom Gold
36 **GOSPEL CHOIR**, ch c Galileo (IRE)—Chorist
37 **GRANDILOQUENT**, b c Rail Link—High Praise (USA)
38 **GREATEST (FR)**, b c Anabaa (USA)—Golden Life (USA)
39 **HONOUR**, b f Dansili—Virtuous
40 **KEENE DANCER**, ch f Danehill Dancer (IRE)—Kinnaird (IRE)
41 **LADYSHIP**, b f Oasis Dream—Peeress
42 **LASHYN (USA)**, ch f Mr Greeley (USA)—Sleepytime (IRE)
43 **LEO LUNA**, b c Galileo (IRE)—Eva Luna (USA)
44 **LUCANIN**, b c Galileo (IRE)—Teggiano (IRE)
45 **MANUKA (IRE)**, ch c Galileo (IRE)—Honey Gold (IRE)
46 **MARIA'S CHOICE (IRE)**, b c Oratorio (IRE)—Amathusia
47 **MARTIN CHUZZLEWIT (IRE)**, ch c Galileo (IRE)—Alta Anna (FR)
48 **MAWAQEET (USA)**, b g Dynaformer (USA)—Lady Ilsley (USA)
49 **MAWASEM**, b c Street Cry (IRE)—Saree
50 **MEDEA (IRE)**, ch f Danehill Dancer (IRE)—Scoop of Gold (USA)
51 **MINOAN DANCER (IRE)**, b f Galileo (IRE)—Grecian Dancer
52 **MINORITY INTEREST**, ch c Galileo (IRE)—Minority
53 **MODERN TUTOR**, b c Selkirk (USA)—Magical Romance (IRE)
54 **MONSHAK (IRE)**, b f Monsun (GER)—Woman Secret (IRE)
55 **MOONSHIP**, b c Halling (USA)—Soviet Moon (IRE)
56 **MR MAYNARD**, ch c Notnowcato—Crystal Cavern (USA)
57 **MUQANTARA (USA)**, b f First Samurai (USA)—Adventure (USA)
58 **NEVER FOREVER**, ch c Sir Percy—Codename
59 **OPINION (IRE)**, b c Oasis Dream—Kiltubber (IRE)
60 **PISTOL (IRE)**, b g High Chaparral (USA)—Alinea (USA)
61 **PLASTIKI**, b g Oasis Dream—Dayrose
62 **POSITIVELY**, b f Oasis Dream—Be Glad
63 **PRESUME**, b f Galileo (IRE)—Summer Breeze
64 **PROXIMITY**, b f Nayef (USA)—Contiguous (USA)
65 **PULVERIZE (USA)**, ch c Pulpit (USA)—Critical Eye (USA)
66 **RED HALO (IRE)**, gr f Galileo (IRE)- -St Roch (IRE)
67 **RELINQUISH**, ch c Pivotal—Abandon (USA)
68 **REVERED CITIZEN (USA)**, b c Proud Citizen (USA)—Well Revered (USA)

SIR MICHAEL STOUTE—continued

69 **RUSSELLIANA**, ch f Medicean—Rosacara
70 **RYE HOUSE (IRE)**, b c Dansili—Threefold (USA)
71 **SABRE TOOTH (IRE)**, b c Medicean—Desert Tigress (USA)
72 **SAMAAH (IRE)**, br f Cape Cross (IRE)—Native Force (IRE)
73 **SANDS OF FORTUNE (IRE)**, ch c Shamardal (USA)—Shell Garland (USA)
74 **SAVIDA (IRE)**, b f King's Best (USA)—Sadima (IRE)
75 **SCOTTISH VESPERS (IRE)**, ch c Dylan Thomas (IRE)—Scottish Stage (IRE)
76 **SEQUENCE (IRE)**, b f Selkirk (USA)—Sinntara (IRE)
77 **SHADA (IRE)**, ch f Galileo (IRE)—Banquise (IRE)
78 **SIR JOHN HAWKWOOD (IRE)**, b c Sir Percy—Athene (IRE)
79 **SKY BOAT (IRE)**, b f Dansili—Angara
80 **STAR RATING (IRE)**, b f Dansili—Islington (IRE)
81 **STRIDENT FORCE**, b c Refuse To Bend (IRE)—Takawiri (IRE)
82 **TALES OF GRIMM (USA)**, b c Distorted Humor (USA)—Stupendous Miss (USA)
83 **TENURE**, b c Dansili—Alumni
84 **TINLEY LODGE**, b c Montjeu (IRE)—Shining Bright
85 **ULTRASONIC (USA)**, b f Mizzen Mast (USA)—Quickfire
86 **UPRISE**, b c Pivotal—Soar
87 **URIAH HEEP (FR)**, b c Danehill Dancer (IRE)—Canasita
88 **YANABEEAA (USA)**, gr ro f Street Cry (IRE)—Queen (IRE)
89 **ZENAAT**, b f Galileo (IRE)—Janet
90 **ZUMBI (IRE)**, b c Dubawi (IRE)—Star Studded

TWO-YEAR-OLDS

91 B c 8/4 Nayef (USA)—Allegretto (IRE) (Galileo (IRE)) (210000)
92 B c 12/4 Galileo (IRE)—Approach (Darshaan) (320000)
93 **ARAB SPRING (IRE)**, b c 8/2 Monsun (GER)—Spring Symphony (IRE) (Darshaan)
94 B c 27/2 Oasis Dream—Arrive (Kahyasi)
95 **ASTONISHING (IRE)**, b f 16/4 Galileo (IRE)—Amazing Krisken (USA) (Kris S (USA))
96 B f 25/3 Galileo (IRE)—Astorg (USA) (Lear Fan (USA)) (123152)
97 **AULD ALLIANCE (IRE)**, b f 5/4 Montjeu (IRE)—Highland Gift (IRE) (Generous (USA))
98 **AVIETTA (IRE)**, gr f 21/4 Dalakhani (IRE)—Alabastrine (Green Desert (USA)) (340000)
99 **BOHEMIAN DANCE (IRE)**, br f 24/1 Dansili—Islington (IRE) (Sadler's Wells (USA))
100 B f 19/4 Galileo (IRE)—Butterfly Cove (USA) (Storm Cat (USA))
101 **CENTRED (IRE)**, gr f 16/3 Dalakhani (IRE)—Drama Class (IRE) (Caerleon (USA))
102 B c 3/2 Oasis Dream—Change Course (Sadler's Wells (USA))
103 **CONTRADICT**, b f 16/4 Raven's Pass (USA)—Acts of Grace (USA) (Bahri (USA)) (130000)
104 **DAMBUSTER (IRE)**, b c 8/5 Dalakhani (IRE)—Threefold (USA) (Gulch (USA))
105 B c 31/3 Teofilo (IRE)—Dhelaal (Green Desert (USA))
106 B f 15/4 Green Desert (USA)—Dorothea Brooke (IRE) (Dancing Brave (USA)) (75000)
107 B c 19/1 Street Cry (IRE)—Dream Ticket (USA) (Danzig (USA))
108 **DUBDAY**, ch c 21/3 Dubawi (IRE)—Dayrose (Daylami (IRE))
109 **DUKE COSIMO**, ch c 31/3 Pivotal—Nannina (Medicean) (130000)
110 **EL CORDOBES (IRE)**, b c 30/3 Montjeu (IRE)—Mayano Sophia (IRE) (Rock of Gibraltar (IRE)) (246304)
111 **ELIK (IRE)**, b f 1/2 Dalakhani (IRE)—Elopa (GER) (Tiger Hill (IRE)) (240000)
112 **ENDLESS LIGHT**, ch f 7/2 Pivotal—Celeste (Green Desert (IRE))
113 **ENOBLED**, b c 2/5 Dansili—Peeress (Pivotal)
114 **EVANGELIST**, b c 3/3 Oasis Dream—Hi Calypso (IRE) (In The Wings)
115 **FANTASY IN BLUE**, b f 17/4 Galileo (IRE)—Blue Symphony (Darshaan) (410000)
116 B c 12/2 Pivotal—Hathrah (IRE) (Linamix (FR))
117 **HILLSTAR**, b c 22/2 Danehill Dancer (IRE)—Crystal Star (Mark of Esteem (IRE))
118 B c 16/3 Oasis Dream—Hovering (IRE) (In The Wings) (164202)
119 **INFATUATE**, ch f 15/2 Dalakhani (IRE)—Fantasize (Groom Dancer (USA))
120 **INTEGRAL**, b f 13/3 Dalakhani (IRE)—Echelon (Danehill (USA))
121 B c 10/2 First Defence (USA)—Intercontinental (Danehill (USA))
122 **INTRINSIC**, b c 2/4 Oasis Dream—Infallible (Pivotal)
123 B f 20/1 Danehill Dancer (IRE)—Jane Austen (IRE) (Galileo (IRE)) (175000)
124 B c 2/5 Galileo (IRE)—Kasora (IRE) (Darshaan)
125 **LEGENDS (IRE)**, b c 14/4 Medaglia d'oro (USA)—Elusive Legend (USA) (Elusive Quality (USA))
126 **LIBER NAUTICUS (IRE)**, b f 22/3 Azamour (IRE)—Serres (IRE) (Daylami (IRE))
127 **LOVE MAGIC**, b f 24/2 Dansili—Magical Romance (IRE) (Barathea (IRE))
128 **MADAME VESTRIS (IRE)**, ch f 26/2 Galileo (IRE)—Mrs Lindsay (USA) (Theatrical) (350000)
129 B f 2/2 First Samurai (USA)—Manaal (USA) (Bahri (USA))
130 **MEDDLING**, ch f 13/4 Halling (USA)—Piffling (Pivotal) (16000)
131 Ch c 17/4 Singspiel (IRE)—Misleading Lady (Warning)

SIR MICHAEL STOUTE—continued

132 B c 7/3 Dansili—Moon Search (Rainbow Quest (USA))
133 B f 3/3 Oasis Dream—Mumayeza (Indian Ridge)
134 NAZYM (IRE), ch f 1/2 Galileo (IRE)—Brigid (USA) (Irish River (FR)) (1700000)
135 B c 20/4 Galileo (IRE)—Necklace (Darshaan)
136 NORTHERN MEETING (IRE), b f 11/2 Dylan Thomas (IRE)—Scottish Stage (IRE) (Selkirk (USA))
137 Ch c 5/2 New Approach (IRE)—Palace Weekend (USA) (Seattle Dancer (USA)) (73891)
138 Ch f 4/4 Three Valleys (USA)—Payphone (Anabaa (USA))
139 PERSEPOLIS (IRE), b c 23/4 Marju (IRE)—La Persiana (Daylami (IRE)) (55000)
140 PLAYBILL, b f 18/4 Medicean—Set The Scene (IRE) (Sadler's Wells (USA))
141 B f 5/2 Arch (USA)—Princess Kris (Kris) (279145)
142 B c 12/2 Empire Maker (USA)—Promising Lead (Danehill (USA))
143 RAUSHAN (IRE), gr f 20/2 Dalakhani (IRE)—Chiang Mai (IRE) (Sadler's Wells (USA)) (400000)
144 B c 28/2 Medicean—Razzle (USA) (Danzig (USA))
145 RUSSIAN REALM, b c 9/2 Dansili—Russian Rhythm (USA) (Kingmambo (USA))
146 SHIMMERING SAL, b f 4/5 Oasis Dream—Salydora (FR) (Peintre Celebre (USA))
147 B f 28/1 Oasis Dream—Short Dance (USA) (Hennessy (USA))
148 B c 19/2 Street Cry (IRE)—Showlady (USA) (Theatrical)
149 B c 18/2 Dansili—Silver Pivotal (IRE) (Pivotal)
150 STOMACHION (IRE), b c 2/4 Duke of Marmalade (IRE)—Insight (FR) (Sadler's Wells (USA))
151 STRING THEORY (IRE), b c 20/3 Medicean—Shebelia (GER) (Black Sam Bellamy (IRE)) (73891)
152 TAFAASEEL (USA), b f 11/2 Mr Greeley (USA)—Wasseema (USA) (Danzig (USA))
153 B f 7/3 Acclamation—Takrice (Cadeaux Genereux) (90311)
154 B c 6/3 Sakhee (USA)—Thamara (USA) (Street Cry (USA))
155 THEODORE GERICAULT (IRE), b c 6/2 Sir Percy—Tableau Vivant (IRE) (Pivotal)
156 B f 21/2 Arch (USA)—Tsar's Pride (Sadler's Wells (USA))
157 B c 25/1 Galileo (IRE)—Velouette (Darshaan)
158 VODNIK (IRE), b c 13/2 Zamindar (USA)—Dance of The Sea (IRE) (Sinndar (IRE))
159 WAILA, ch f 5/2 Notnowcato—Crystal Cavern (USA) (Be My Guest (USA))
160 WATCHABLE, ch c 2/3 Pivotal—Irresistible (Cadeaux Genereux)
161 WEST OF THE MOON, ch f 19/3 Pivotal—Canda (USA) (Storm Cat (USA))
162 B f 6/5 Oasis Dream—Wince (Selkirk (USA))
163 B f 18/2 King's Best (USA)—Winners Chant (IRE) (Dalakhani (IRE))
164 B c 14/5 Invincible Spirit (IRE)—Zibilene (Rainbow Quest (USA)) (200000)

Owners: HM The Queen, Mr K. Abdulla, Sheikh Mohammed bin Khalifa Al Thani, Mr Malih al Basti, Ballymacoll Stud, Mr Nurlan Bizakov, Cheveley Park Stud, Mr Athos Christodoulou, Cornerstone Thoroughbreds, Sir Evelyn de Rothschild, Prince A. A. Faisal, Mr John Greetham, Mr Hamdan Al Maktoum, Mr & Mrs Denis Haynes, Highclere Thoroughbred Racing, Mrs John Magnier, Miss A. H. Marshall, Mr Fawzi Abdullah Nass, Newsells Park Stud, Mr Philip Newton, Niarchos Family, Sir Robert Ogden, Lady Rothschild, Mr Derrick Smith, Mr George Strawbridge, Mr Saeed Suhail, Mr Michael Tabor, Mr Andrew Tinkler, Mr & Mrs James Wigan.

MRS LINDA STUBBS, Malton
Postal: **Beverley House Stables, Beverley Road, Malton, North Yorkshire, YO17 9PJ**
Phone: **PHONE (01653) 698731 FAX (01653) 698724 MOBILE (07747) 613962 / (07801) 167707**
E-MAIL **l.stubbs@btconnect.com** WEBSITE **www.lindastubbsracing.com**

1 BRONZE BEAU, 5, ch g Compton Place—Bella Cantata **D. G. Arundale**
2 DESLAYA (IRE), 4, b f Green Desert (USA)—Behlaya (USA) **P & L Partners**
3 FIVE STAR JUNIOR (USA), 6, b g Five Star Day (USA)—Sir Harriett (USA) **Moyns Park Estate and Stud Ltd**
4 FORTUNATE BID (IRE), 6, ch g Modigliani (USA)—Mystery Bid **Mrs L. Stubbs**
5 ICE TROOPER, 4, b g Iceman—Out Like Magic **J. P. Hames**
6 QUBUH (IRE), 4, b g Invincible Spirit (USA)—Chica Roca **D. M. Smith**
7 RESUSCITATOR (USA), 5, b g Bernstein (USA)—Lac du Printemps (USA) **O. J. Williams**

THREE-YEAR-OLDS

8 LATTE, b g Multiplex—Coffee To Go **Tyme Partnership**
9 B g Namid—Silly Mid-On **Mervyn Williams**
10 TARQUIN (IRE), b g Excellent Art—Umlani (IRE) **D. G. Arundale**

TWO-YEAR-OLDS

11 ANTONIUS, b g 25/4 Antonius Pius (USA)—
Queen of Poland (FR) (Polish Precedent (USA)) (9852) **The B.P.J. Partnership**
12 BOGSNOG (IRE), b g 5/4 Moss Vale (IRE)—Lovers Kiss (Night Shift (USA)) (9851) **Facts & Figures**
13 MASTER MOON (IRE), b g 6/3 Excellent Art—Moon On A Spoon (Dansili) (5746) **P & L Bloodstock**

MRS LINDA STUBBS—continued

14 MEGAMUNCH (IRE), b g 29/4 Camacho—Liscoa (IRE) (Foxhound (USA)) (15000) **P & L Bloodstock**
15 MIDNIGHT DREAM (FR), b br g 20/3 Country Reel (USA)—
　　　　　　Tatante (IRE) (Highest Honor (FR)) (7389) **P. G. Shorrock & O. J. Williams**
16 POLAR CHIEF, b g 24/4 Motivator—Polar Storm (IRE) (Law Society (USA)) (7500) **P & L Bloodstock**
17 B g 19/3 Gold Away (IRE)—Theorie (FR) (Anabaa (USA)) (6568) **D. G. Arundale**

Other Owners: Mr R. A. Graves, Mr Eric Hemming, Mr A. Larkin, Mr M. S. Martin, Mr T. Osborne, Mr G. Pickering, Mrs Valerie Pittman, Mr P. G. Shorrock, Mrs L. Stubbs.

Assistant Trainer: Kristin Stubbs

Jockey (flat): Tony Hamilton, Tom Eaves. **Apprentice:** James Sullivan. **Amateur:** Miss Sarah Watson.

622　**MR ROB SUMMERS, Solihull**
Postal: **Hill Farm, Pigtrot Lane, Tanworth-In-Arden, Solihull, West Midlands, B94 5BJ**
Contacts: **PHONE (01564) 742667 MOBILE (07775) 898327**

1 ANYAULDIRON (IRE), 9, b g Lord Americo—Bodalmore Rose (IRE) **Whites of Coventry & Stephen Dunn**
2 ESPRIT DE FER (FR), 8, b g Esprit du Nord (USA)—Fernie (FR) **Solihull Racing Club**
3 FINTAN, 9, ch g Generous (IRE)—Seeker **Mr S. W. Dunn**
4 MONTJUIC (FR), 8, b h Montjeu (IRE)—Apparentee (USA) **K. W. Bradley**
5 PHOTOGENIQUE (FR), 9, b m Cyborg (FR)—Colombia (FR) **Solihull Racing Club**
6 RED WHISPER, 8, ch g Midnight Legend—Secret Whisper **Solihull Racing Club**
7 7, Ch h Executive Perk—Secret Whisper **Mrs G. M. Summers**
8 5, Ch m Weld—Secret Whisper **Mrs G. M. Summers**

Other Owners: Whites of Coventry Limited, Mr S. J. Wood.

Assistant Trainer: Mrs G. M. Summers

623　**MRS S. SUNTER, Ferryhill**
Postal: **Low Copelaw Farm, Rushyford, Ferryhill, Co. Durham, DL17 0NP**

1 BRADDOCK ISLAND, 9, b g Rock City—Bally Small **Mrs S. Sunter**

624　**MR JOHN A. SUPPLE, Abbeyfeale**
Postal: **Feale View Stud, Coolaneelig, Abbeyfeale P.O., Co. Limerick, Ireland**
Contacts: **PHONE (00353) 68 45890 FAX (00353) 68 45890 MOBILE (00353) 86 7390841**
E-MAIL j.supple@fealeviewstud.com

1 BLACKWELL SYNERGY (FR), 6, b g Antarctique (IRE)—Pyu (GER) **Mr Johnny Byrne**
2 BURNSWOOD (IRE), 8, b g Monsun (GER)—Banaja (IRE) **Mr William Byrne**
3 4, B g Kalanisi (IRE)—Fairy Dawn (IRE) **Mr Johnny Byrne**
4 4, B g Shirocco (GER)—Highland Ceilidh (IRE) **Mr Johnny Byrne**
5 KILLCARA BOY, 7, b g Tobougg (IRE)—Barakat **Miss Julianna Byrne**
6 LIKEAROLLINGSTONE (IRE), 7, ch g Definite Article—Bannow Girl (IRE) **Mr Johnny Byrne**
7 MASTEROFTHEBREE (IRE), 8, ch g Definite Article—Bannow Girl (IRE) **Mr Johnny Byrne**
8 THELIFEOF (IRE), 6, b g Brian Boru—Dream Adventure (IRE) **Mr Johnny Byrne**

Other Owners: Mr Nolan Byrne.

Assistant Trainer: Lorna Preston

Conditional: J. P. Holly.

625　**MR ALAN SWINBANK, Richmond**
Postal: **Western House Stables, East Road, Melsonby, Richmond, North Yorkshire, DL10 5NF**
Contacts: **PHONE (01325) 339964 MOBILE (07860) 368365 / (07711) 488341**
E-MAIL info@alanswinbank.com WEBSITE www.alanswinbank.com

1 AD VALUE (IRE), 4, b g Ad Valorem (USA)—Sopran Marida (IRE) **Mrs V. McGee**
2 ANNA'S ARCH (IRE), 5, b g Arch (USA)—Lady Angharad (IRE) **C. Tremewan**

MR ALAN SWINBANK—continued

3 ANYCHANCEDAVE (IRE), 5, ro g Act One—Nabadhaat (USA) **David Manasseh,Titus Bramble, Lee Cattermole**
4 BANDANAMAN (IRE), 6, b g Danehill Dancer (IRE)—Band of Angels (IRE) **Miss J. S. Peat**
5 BARSEVENTYTWO (IRE), 7, b g Dernier Empereur (USA)—Woodram Delight **Mrs J. Perratt**
6 BE DEVIOUS (IRE), 4, b g Barathea (IRE)—Almansa (IRE) **Mr G. H. Bell**
7 BIG WATER (IRE), 4, ch g Saffron Walden (FR)—Magic Feeling (IRE) **T. B. Tarn**
8 BIVOUAC (UAE), 8, b g Jade Robbery (USA)—Tentpole (USA) **Mrs J. M. Penney**
9 BOB'S LADY TARA, 4, b f Kayf Tara—Bob Back's Lady (IRE) **J. R. Wills**
10 BORN TO SHINE (USA), 4, b g Suave (USA)—Sentimental Keep (USA) **Mrs J. Perratt**
11 CAPE RISING (IRE), 5, b m Cape Cross (IRE)—Woodrising **J. R. Wills**
12 CHERRY TREE HILL (IRE), 4, b g Ivan Denisovich (IRE)—Ring Pink (USA) **N. Shutts**
13 CORAL SANDS (IRE), 4, b g Footstepsinthesand—Daziyra (IRE) **Mrs J. M. Penney**
14 ENTIHAA, 4, b g Tiger Hill (IRE)—Magic Tree (UAE) **Elsa Crankshaw & G. Allan**
15 FIRST ROCK (IRE), 6, b g Rock of Gibraltar (IRE)—Sakkara (IRE) **United Five Racing**
16 FOURTH GENERATION (IRE), 5, ch g Kris Kin (USA)—Merewood Lodge (IRE) **B. Boanson & M. Wane**
17 GEORGE ADAMSON (IRE), 6, b g Where Or When (IRE)—Tactile **Mrs S. L. Sanbrook**
18 GEORGEY GIRL, 4, b f Doyen (IRE)—Thrasher **Viv McGee, Joy Forrest & Joyce Porter**
19 GOGEO (IRE), 5, b g Val Royal (FR)—Steal 'em **Mrs J. Porter**
20 I'M SUPER TOO (IRE), 5, b g Fasliyev (USA)—Congress (IRE) **D. C. Young**
21 LAW TO HIMSELF (IRE), 5, b g Rakti—Samhat Mtoto **A. Mallen**
22 LINE OF DUTY (IRE), 5, b g Arakan (USA)—Zibaline (FR) **R. A. Pegum**
23 LINROYALE BOY (USA), 4, ch g Giant's Causeway (USA)—Welcometotheworld (USA) **Mr I. J. Clark**
24 LUCKY WINDMILL (IRE), 5, b g Lucky Story (USA)—Windmill Princess **Mrs J. Porter**
25 MITCHELL'S WAY, 5, ch g Needwood Blade—Ghana (GER) **Ontoawinner 2**
26 MR SINGLETON (IRE), 4, b g Motivator—Tanzania (USA) **Mr A. Wright**
27 NOBLE SCHOLAR (IRE), 7, b g Anabaa—Lisieux Rose (IRE) **Pam & Richard Ellis**
28 NORTHSIDE PRINCE (IRE), 6, b g Desert Prince (IRE)—Spartan Girl (IRE) **Mr S. S. Anderson**
29 ONEOFAPEAR (IRE), 6, b g Pyrus (USA)—Whitegate Way **Mrs I. Gibson & Dr C. Emmerson**
30 PAINTED TAIL (IRE), 5, b m Mark of Esteem (IRE)—Bronwen (IRE) **M. R. Green**
31 PHOENIX RETURNS (IRE), 4, br g Phoenix Reach (IRE)—Oscar's Lady **Mrs J. Porter**
32 PRICELESS ART (IRE), 7, b g Anabaa (USA)—My Ballerina (USA) **Matthew Green & David Manasseh**
33 PROUD TIMES (USA), 6, b g Proud Citizen (USA)—Laura's Pistolette (USA) **Mrs H. E. Aitkin**
34 REGAL SWAIN (IRE), 4, b g Ivan Denisovich (IRE)—Targhyb **Mr A. J. Sparks**
35 ROYAL SWAIN (IRE), 6, b g Val Royal (FR)—Targhyb (IRE) **Mr A. J. Sparks**
36 4, Ch f Hurricane Run (IRE)—Salvinia (USA) **The Twopin Partnership**
37 SARTINGO (IRE), 5, b g Encosta de Lago (AUS)—Alicia (IRE) **Mr M. Robson**
38 SAVEIRO (FR), 8, b g Raintrap—Branceilles (FR) **Solway Stayers**
39 SIR BOREAS HAWK, 10, b g Overbury (IRE)—Fringe Benefit (IRE) **C. Tremewan**
40 SIR TANTALLUS HAWK, 8, b g Overbury (IRE)—Mobile Miss (IRE) **Highland Racing 4 & Mrs E. Melrose**
41 SKY HIGH DIVER (IRE), 4, b f Celtic Swing—Limit (IRE) **Mrs M. C. Keogh**
42 STANSONNIT, 4, b g Shirocco—Twilight Sonnet **The Twopin Partnership**
43 THE FERICK (IRE), 6, b g Kris Kin (USA)—Minaun Heights **J. P. Jones**
44 TRICKSOFTHETRADE (IRE), 6, b g Mull of Kintyre (USA)—Soden (IRE) **A. Butler**
45 WILLIAM HAIGH (IRE), 4, b g Refuse To Bend (IRE)—Ivowen **Shropshire Wolves II**

THREE-YEAR-OLDS

46 BIGGINS BOY (IRE), b g Motivator—Optimal (IRE) **Mr G. H. Bell**
47 DARK RULER (IRE), b g Dark Angel (IRE)—Gino Lady (IRE) **Mrs E. Walters**
48 LADY KASHAAN (IRE), b f Manduro (GER)—Lady's Secret (IRE) **G. McCann**
49 PIONEER BOY (USA), ch g Pioneering (USA)—Vieille Rose (IRE) **Solway Stayers**
50 SILVER BLAZE, ch g Haafhd—Antigua **Mrs I. Gibson**
51 URBONITE (IRE), b g Proud Citizen (USA)—Bronze Baby (USA) **Mr A. J. Sparks**

TWO-YEAR-OLDS

52 Br gr c 19/2 Verglas (IRE)—Danzelline (Danzero (AUS)) (24630) **John Babb**
53 Ch f 10/2 Excellent Art—Elauyun (IRE) (Muhtarram (USA)) (20524) **Matthew Green**
54 B c 9/3 Manduro (GER)—Felucca (Green Desert (USA)) (13333) **S. P. C. Woods**
55 B c 20/4 Elnadim (USA)—Freedom (GER) (Second Empire (IRE)) (28000) **J. C. Parsons**
56 Ch g 25/4 Dr Fong (USA)—Garra Molly (IRE) (Nayef (USA)) (7388) **D. Cosgrove**
57 Br c 7/4 Red Clubs (IRE)—Lady Singspiel (IRE) (Singspiel (IRE)) (12725) **Iris Gibson**
58 B g 6/3 Kheleyf (USA)—Miss Lacey (IRE) (Diktat) (40952) **S. P. C. Woods**
59 Gr ro g 17/2 Aussie Rules (USA)—Mistic Sun (Dashing Blade) (24000) **G. H. Bell**
60 B g 31/1 Roman Ruler (USA)—Richen (USA) (Well Decorated (USA)) (25451) **Mrs J. Porter**

MR ALAN SWINBANK—continued

Other Owners: Mr G. Allan, Mr J. Babb, Mr T. Bramble, Mr K. J. Burrow, Mr A. J. Burrow, Mr Lee Cattermole, Miss Elsa Crankshaw, Mr Mac Creedon, Mr Richard Ellis, Mrs Pam Ellis, Mr Matthew Green, Mr Tim Hawkins, Miss Sally R. Haynes, Mr D. Hunter, Mr S. E. Kennedy, Mr David Manasseh, Mrs Eleanor Melrose, Mr P. Moorby, Mr K. E. Moorby, Mr N. J. O'Brien, Dr Roy Palmer, Mr William A. Powrie, Mr Richard Simpson, Miss M. Swinbank, Mr I. Tweddall, Mr M. Wane.

Assistant Trainers: Mr W.W. Haigh & Miss Sally Haynes

Jockey (flat): P. J. McDonald, Robert Winston. **Jockey (NH):** Barry Keniry, Fearghal Davis, Rhys Flint. **Conditional:** Lucy Alexander, Jake Greenall, Gary Whillans.

---

626 MR TOM SYMONDS, Ross-On-Wye
Postal: **Dason Court Cottage, Hentland, Ross-On-Wye, Herefordshire, HR9 6LW**
Contacts: PHONE **(01989) 730869** MOBILE **(07823) 324649**
E-MAIL **dasoncourt@gmail.com** WEBSITE **www.thomassymonds.co.uk**

1 **BOSTON GLOBE (IRE)**, 8, b g Oscar (IRE)—Mills Moss (IRE) **Brendan, Sue Foster**
2 5, B m Midnight Legend—Cherry Alley (IRE) **Patricia Holtrop**
3 **DUC DE REGNIERE (FR)**, 10, b g Rajpoute (FR)—Gladys de Richerie (FR) **Sir Peter & Lady Gibbings**
4 **FIRST ACT**, 6, b m King's Theatre (IRE)—Darbela (IRE) **P. Murphy**
5 **FLEUR DE VASSY**, 8, ch m Alflora (IRE)—Royale De Vassy (FR) **L. J. Jakeman**
6 **HAROUET (FR)**, 7, ch g Vertical Speed (FR)—Lairna (FR) **Walters Plant Hire Ltd**
7 **HARRYS BOY**, 7, ch g Karinga Bay—Scottish Dance **Scottish Dance Syndicate**
8 **LIQUEUR ROSE**, 5, b m Alflora (IRE)—Teenero **The Mumbo Jumbos**
9 **MARICO (FR)**, 4, b br g Lavirco (GER)—Mary Bay (FR) **Mr T. R. Symonds**
10 **MIRIFIC (FR)**, 6, gr g Linamix (FR)—Matanilla (FR) **M. A. C. Buckley**
11 5, B g Beneficial—Mrs Paddy Jack (IRE)
12 **NUISANCE**, 4, b f Overbury (IRE)—Mothers Help
13 **PRINCE BUSTER**, 9, b g Sinjar (FR)—Eliflo (FR) **The Unusual Racegoers Partnership**
14 **SCHOLASTICA**, 5, b m Old Vic—La Perrotine (FR) **Mr D. Redvers**
15 **SCOTSBROOK LEGEND**, 4, b f Midnight Legend—Scots Brook Terror **A. E. J. Price**
16 4, B g Milan—Shannon Native (IRE) **G & M Roberts, Churchward, Frost, Green, Whittal-Williams**
17 **STRATHCAL**, 6, b g Beat Hollow—Shall We Run **Shenkman, Foster, Tinsley, Coe, Stagg**
18 **THE FLAMING MATRON (IRE)**, 6, b m Flemensfirth (USA)—The Mighty Matron (IRE) **Mark Molloy**
19 **TROJAN SUN**, 6, b g Kayf Tara—Sun Dante (IRE) **I. A. Low**
20 **TWEEDLEDRUM**, 5, b m Beat Hollow—Tweed Mill **Wainwright, Hill, Atkin, Cheshire**
21 **VALMARI (IRE)**, 9, b m Kalanisi (IRE)—Penza **Leonard Jay Ltd**
22 **WOGAN**, 12, b g Presenting—Fall About **P. A. Deal & Mrs H. Plumbly**
23 **ZENNOR**, 5, b m Doyen (IRE)—Salanka (IRE) **Miss A. L. Murphy**
24 **ALPHA WAY (GER)**, 8, b g Kendor (FR)—Alpha City **Lady Susan Brooke**

THREE-YEAR-OLDS

25 **KINGS APOLLO**, b g King's Theatre (IRE)—
Temple Dancer **G & M Roberts Churchward Frost Green Whittal-Williams**

Jockey (NH): Denis O'Regan. **Conditional:** Nathan Cook.

---

627 MR PATRICK TALLIS, Freshford
Postal: **Clontubrid, Freshford, Co. Kilkenny, Ireland**
Contacts: PHONE **(00353) 56 883 2216** FAX **(00353) 56 883 2350** MOBILE **(00353) 86 256 0968**
E-MAIL **tallis@esatclear.ie**

1 **ACUSHLADEAR (IRE)**, 6, b m Tagula (IRE)—Darling Smile (IRE) **P. Tallis**
2 **BATTLE FOR GLORY (IRE)**, 4, b g Ivan Denisovich (IRE)—Hever Golf Lover (IRE) **C. Holohan**
3 **CANNOT GIVE (USA)**, 7, b m Proud Citizen (USA)—September Kaper (USA) **P. Tallis**
4 **MAITH GALORE (IRE)**, 5, b g Barathea (USA)—Bois de Citron (USA) **C. Holohan**

TWO-YEAR-OLDS

5 B f 27/4 Cape Cross (IRE)—Begin The Beguine (IRE) (Peintre Celebre (USA)) **C. Holohan**
6 B g 22/2 Bachelor Duke (USA)—Trendy Celt (IRE) (Celtic Swing) **P. Tallis**

Assistant Trainer: D. Bergin

628 MR JAMES TATE, Newmarket
Postal: **Jamesfield Place, Hamilton Road, Newmarket, Suffolk, CB8 7JQ**

1 **BORUG (USA)**, 4, b c Kingmambo (USA)—Marienbad (FR) **S. Ali**
2 **FLYING POWER**, 4, b g Dubai Destination (USA)—Rah Wa (FR) **S. Ali**
3 **HAWAWI**, 4, b g Motivator—Abide (FR) **Saif Ali & Saeed H. Altayer**

THREE-YEAR-OLDS

4 **AIAAM AL NAMOOS**, b c Teofilo (IRE)—Deveron (USA) **S. Ali**
5 **AIAAM AL WAFA (IRE)**, b f Authorized (IRE)—State Secret **S. Ali**
6 **CAPE SAFARI**, b f Cape Cross (IRE)—Finnmark **S. Ali**
7 **DARK FALCON (IRE)**, b br c Dark Angel (IRE)—Absolute Pleasure **S. Manana**
8 **DREAM PROSPECTOR**, b g Oasis Dream—Prospectress (USA) **S. Ali**
9 B c Cape Cross (IRE)—Eve **S. Ali**
10 **IMTITHAL (IRE)**, b f Invincible Spirit (IRE)—Dream Time **S. Manana**
11 **KHALEEJIYA (IRE)**, b f Jeremy (USA)—Certainly Brave **S. Manana**
12 B f Dubai Destination (USA)—Purple Tiger (IRE) **S. Ali**
13 **SAABOOG**, b f Teofilo (IRE)—Saabiq (USA) **S. Ali**
14 **SHAMARDELIAH (IRE)**, b f Shamardal (USA)—Sunsetter (USA) **S. Ali**
15 **STRAWBERRY FLAVOUR (GER)**, gr f Motivator—Strawberry Morn (CAN) **S. Ali**

TWO-YEAR-OLDS

16 B f 25/3 Exceed And Excel (AUS)—Al Cobra (IRE) (Sadler's Wells (USA)) **S. Ali**
17 B f 21/2 Royal Applause—Ask Carol (IRE) (Foxhound (USA)) (29556) **S. Ali**
18 B f 17/3 Dynaformer (USA)—Cloud Castle (In The Wings) **S. Manana**
19 B c 30/3 Exceed And Excel (AUS)—Darrfonah (IRE) (Singspiel (IRE)) **S. Ali**
20 B c 17/3 Manduro (GER)—Dust Dancer (Suave Dancer (USA)) (38000) **S. Ali**
21 B f 30/1 Exceed And Excel (AUS)—Fanny's Fancy (Groom Dancer (USA)) (38000) **S. Manana**
22 B c 7/3 Tiger Hill (IRE)—Fly Me To The Moon (GER) (Galileo (IRE)) **S. Ali**
23 B f 29/3 Compton Place—Glimpse (Night Shift (USA)) (24000) **S. Manana**
24 B c 12/3 Authorized (IRE)—Jabbara (IRE) (Kingmambo (USA)) (30000) **S. Manana**
25 B c 8/4 Elusive City (USA)—Laheen (IRE) (Bluebird (USA)) (20000) **S. Ali**
26 Br c 8/4 Manduro (GER)—Masandra (IRE) (Desert Prince (IRE)) (26000) **S. Manana**
27 B f 6/3 A P Indy (USA)—Maskunah (IRE) (Sadler's Wells (USA)) **S. Ali**
28 B c 19/4 Teofilo (IRE)—Mauri Moon (Green Desert (USA)) (30000) **S. Ali**
29 B f 26/2 Teofilo (IRE)—Mazaaya (USA) (Cozzene (USA)) **S. Ali**
30 Br c 3/3 Singspiel (IRE)—Mexican Hawk (USA) (Silver Hawk (USA)) (30000) **S. Ali**
31 B f 23/4 Authorized (IRE)—Nasij (USA) (Elusive Quality (USA)) (30000) **S. Ali**
32 B f 22/4 Hernando (FR)—Odabella's Charm (Cadeaux Genereux) (17000) **S. Ali**
33 B c 25/1 Royal Applause—Persian Sea (UAE) (Dubai Destination (USA)) (31000) **S. Manana**
34 B f 14/3 Exceed And Excel (AUS)—Purple Tiger (IRE) (Rainbow Quest (USA)) (28000) **S. Ali**
35 B c 28/2 Cape Cross (IRE)—Queen's Best (King's Best (USA)) (34000) **S. Ali**
36 B f 4/3 Street Cry (IRE)—Rajeem (Diktat) **S. Manana**
37 B c 25/3 Exceed And Excel (AUS)—Saabiq (USA) (Grand Slam (USA)) (70000) **S. Ali**
38 Ch f 16/4 Teofilo (IRE)—Shimna (Mr Prospector (USA)) **S. Manana**
39 Ch c 9/2 Sir Percy—String Quartet (IRE) (Sadler's Wells (USA)) (50000) **S. Ali**
40 B c 13/2 Hard Spun (USA)—Tamdiid (USA) (Horse Chestnut (SAF)) **S. Manana**
41 B f 3/5 Bernardini (USA)—Transition Time (USA) (Dynaformer (USA)) (40000) **S. Ali**
42 B c 3/2 Shamardal (USA)—Tullynally (Dansili) (20000) **S. Ali**
43 B f 6/3 New Approach (USA)—Wimple (USA) (Kingmambo (USA)) **S. Manana**

Other Owners: S. H. Altayer.

629 MR TOM TATE, Tadcaster
Postal: **Castle Farm, Hazelwood, Tadcaster, North Yorkshire, LS24 9NJ**
Contacts: **PHONE (01937) 836036 FAX (01937) 530011 MOBILE (07970) 122818**
E-MAIL **tomtate@castlefarmstables.fsnet.co.uk** WEBSITE **www.tomtate.co.uk**

1 **EAGLE ROCK (IRE)**, 4, b g High Chaparral (IRE)—Silk Fan (IRE) **The Ivy Syndicate**
2 **ELAND ALLY**, 4, b g Striking Ambition—Dream Rose (IRE) **The Ivy Syndicate**
3 **FLAMINGO CAY**, 4, b g Tiger Hill (IRE)—Woodbeck **The Ivy Syndicate**
4 **KINGS GAMBIT (SAF)**, 8, ch g Silvano (GER)—Lady Brompton (SAF) **Mrs F. H. Hay**
5 **KOOL SHUFFLE (GER)**, 4, ch g Big Shuffle (USA)—Kedah (GER) **T T Racing**
6 **KUDU COUNTRY (IRE)**, 6, gr g Captain Rio—Nirvavita (FR) **The Flat Cap Syndicate**

MR TOM TATE—continued

7 **OPERA NORTH**, 5, ch g Nayef (USA)—Reveuse de Jour (IRE) **T T Racing**
8 **PRINCE OF JOHANNE (IRE)**, 6, gr g Johannesburg (USA)—Paiute Princess (FR) **Mr D. Storey**

THREE-YEAR-OLDS

9 **BEYOND CONCEIT (IRE)**, b c Galileo (IRE)—Baraka (IRE) **Mrs F. H. Hay**
10 **DUBAI KISS**, b g Dubai Destination (USA)—Smooch **T T Racing**
11 **JOYFUL MOTIVE**, ch g Motivator—Triple Joy **T T Racing**
12 **KEY APPOINTMENT**, b g Pivotal—Appointed One (USA) **Mrs F. H. Hay**
13 **MEAN IT (IRE)**, b g Danehill Dancer (IRE)—Lilissa (IRE) **Mrs F. H. Hay**
14 **MORE BOTTLE (IRE)**, b f Barathea (IRE)—More Respect (IRE) **Ms M. F. Cassidy**
15 **NEVER PERFECT (IRE)**, b g Galileo (IRE)—Dapprima (GER) **Mrs F. H. Hay**
16 **PARC DE LAUNAY**, ch g Monsieur Bond (IRE)—Franglais (GER) **Mrs F. H. Hay**
17 **RED SEAL**, ch g Haafhd—Seal Indigo (IRE) **T T Racing**
18 **THANE OF CAWDOR (IRE)**, b g Danehill Dancer (IRE)—Holy Nola (USA) **Mrs F. H. Hay**

TWO-YEAR-OLDS

19 B f 30/4 Mount Nelson—Ares Vallis (IRE) (Caerleon (USA)) (17142) **T T Racing**
20 Br ro f 14/2 Dark Angel (IRE)—Nonsense (IRE) (Soviet Star (USA)) (8571) **T T Racing**
21 Ch f 6/4 Haatef (USA)—Privileged Speech (USA) (General Assembly (USA)) (9030) **T T Racing**
22 B f 14/2 Duke of Marmalade (IRE)—Promise of Love (Royal Applause) (16420) **T T Racing**
23 B f 15/2 Sakhee's Secret—Sabrina Brown (Polar Falcon (USA)) (17142) **T T Racing**

Other Owners: Mr D. M. W. Hodgkiss, Mrs S. Hodgkiss, Mr T. P. Tate, Mrs Hazel Tate.

Assistant Trainer: Hazel Tate

Jockey (flat): Micky Fenton, Jamie Spencer. **Jockey (NH):** Graham Lee.

---

630 **MRS SUSAN TAYLOR, Alnwick**
Postal: **The Lookout, Lesbury, Alnwick, Northumberland, NE66 3PQ**

1 **CHAMPERTY (IRE)**, 6, b m Saffron Walden (FR)—Nashville Skyline **Mrs S. Taylor**
2 **CHESTER LEGEND**, 5, ch g Pasternak—Sally Smith **Mrs S. Taylor**
3 **HIGH INTEREST**, 6, b g Milieu—Witness of Truth **Mrs S. Taylor**
4 **RAKERIN LAD (IRE)**, 9, b g New Frontier (IRE)—Lotta (IRE) **Mrs S. Taylor**

---

631 **MR COLIN TEAGUE, Wingate**
Postal: **Bridgefield Farm, Trimdon Lane, Station Town, Wingate, Co. Durham, TS28 5NE**
Contacts: **PHONE (01429) 837087 MOBILE (07967) 330929**
E-MAIL colin.teague@btopenworld.com

1 **DAVANA**, 6, b m Primo Valentino (IRE)—Bombay Sapphire **T. B. Tarn**
2 **JALDARSHAAN (IRE)**, 5, b m Fath—Jaldini (IRE) **T. B. Tarn**
3 **LEES ANTHEM**, 5, b g Mujahid (USA)—Lady Rock **A. Rice**
4 **MAGICAL DANCERS**, 5, ch h Tobougg (IRE)—Passing Fancy **Collins Chauffeur Driven Executive Cars**
5 **MICKY MAC (IRE)**, 8, b g Lend A Hand—Gazette It Tonight **A. M. McArdle**
6 **MONTE PATTINO (USA)**, 8, ch g Rahy (USA)—Jood (USA) **Collins Chauffeur Driven Executive Cars**
7 **MUJAHOPE**, 7, b g Mujahid (USA)—Speak **Collins Chauffeur Driven Executive Cars**
8 **RUBICON BAY (IRE)**, 5, b m One Cool Cat (USA)—Mrs Moonlight **Collins Chauffeur Driven Executive Cars**
9 **SHANAVAZ**, 6, gr m Golden Snake (USA)—Safinaz **Mr N. A. Old**
10 **SPOSALIZIO (IRE)**, 5, ch g Dr Fong (USA)—Wedding Cake (IRE) **Mr J. G. Armstrong**

---

632 **MR ROGER TEAL, Epsom**
Postal: **Thirty Acre Barn Stables, Shepherds Walk, Epsom, Surrey, KT18 6BX**
Contacts: **PHONE (01372) 279535 FAX (01372) 271981 MOBILE (07710) 325521**
E-MAIL rteal@thirtyacre.co.uk WEBSITE www.thirtyacrestables.co.uk

1 **BARATHEA DANCER (IRE)**, 4, b f Barathea (IRE)—Showering **Lord Helpus Partnership**
2 **CAHALA DANCER (IRE)**, 4, ch f Elnadim (USA)—Ranma **Corkers Racing Club**
3 **CHARTPLAN (IRE)**, 6, ch g Marignan (USA)—Classic Moments (IRE) **B. Kitcherside**
4 **COCHABAMBA (IRE)**, 4, ch f Hurricane Run (IRE)—Bolivia (USA) **The Rat Racers**

MR ROGER TEAL—continued

5 **OSTENTATION**, 5, ch g Dubawi (IRE)—Oshiponga **A. J. Morton**
6 **ROSCO FLYER (IRE)**, 6, b g Val Royal (FR)—Palace Soy (IRE) **Mr Chris Simpson, Miss Elizabeth Ross**
7 **STEELE TANGO (USA)**, 7, ch h Okawango (USA)—Waltzing Around (IRE) **The Thirty Acre Racing Partnership**
8 **THE TICHBORNE (IRE)**, 4, b g Shinko Forest (IRE)—Brunswick **Mr Chris Simpson & Mick Waghorn**

THREE-YEAR-OLDS

9 **CHARLOTTE ROSINA**, b f Choisir (AUS)—Intriguing Glimpse **E. Hyde**
10 **CHRISSYCROSS (IRE)**, b f Cape Cross (IRE)—Penang (IRE) **A. J. Morton**
11 **JACK OF DIAMONDS (IRE)**, b g Red Clubs (IRE)—Sakkara Star (IRE) **Inside Track Racing Club**
12 **JOHNNY SPLASH (IRE)**, b c Dark Angel (IRE)—Ja Ganhou **Epping Racing**
13 **LANGLEY VALE**, b g Piccolo—Running Glimpse (IRE) **Dr G C Forward & Robert Allen**
14 **PUCON**, b f Kyllachy—The Fugative **Mr J. A. Redmond**
15 **RED LARKSPUR (IRE)**, b f Red Clubs (IRE)—Holda (IRE) **The Gracenote Partnership**
16 **SURREY DREAM (IRE)**, b g Oasis Dream—Trois Graces (USA) **Mr M. Vickers**
17 **TIGERS TALE (IRE)**, b c Tiger Hill (IRE)—Vayenga (FR) **B. Kitcherside**
18 **TOSS A COIN (IRE)**, b g Antonius Pius—Irish Verse (IRE) **Corkers Racing Club**
19 **WINTER DRESS**, ch f Haafhd—Ermine (IRE) **The Young Professionals**

TWO-YEAR-OLDS

20 Ch c 4/3 Excellent Art—Sensibility (Halling (USA)) (12000)

Other Owners: Mr D. D. Filtness, Mr Stephen Fisher, Miss B. C. Greener, Mr Barry Kitcherside, Mr John Morton, Mr C. Roase, Miss Elizabeth Ross, Mr Chris Simpson, Mrs Toni Steele, Mr Darren Waterer, Mr S. Wylde.

---

633 | **MRS D. THOMAS, Bridgend**
Postal: **Pen-Y-Lan Farm, Aberkenfig, Bridgend, Mid Glamorgan, CF32 9AN**
Contacts: **PHONE (01656) 720254 FAX (01656) 720254 MOBILE (07989) 462130**
E-MAIL beccania@hotmail.com

1 **AM I BLUE**, 6, b m Dubai Destination (USA)—Seal Indigo (IRE) **Mrs D. Thomas**

Assistant Trainer: Brett Norris

Jockey (NH): Richard Johnson. **Amateur:** Mr M. T. Stanley, Mr Simon Walker.

---

634 | **MR DAVID THOMPSON, Darlington**
Postal: **South View Racing, Ashley Cottage, South View, Bolam, Darlington, Co. Durham, DL2 2UP**
Contacts: **PHONE (01388) 835806 (01388) 832658 FAX (01325) 835806 MOBILE (07795) 161657**
E-MAIL dwthompson61@hotmail.co.uk WEBSITE www.dwthompson.co.uk

1 **ANTIHERO**, 5, b g Motivator—Damsel **Mr N. Park**
2 **BILLYTHESHIP (IRE)**, 9, b g Naheez (USA)—Let'shaveaparty (IRE) **Mr R. G. Owens**
3 **CORTINAS (GER)**, 10, b g Lomitas—Cocorna **Mr R. G. Owens**
4 **CRACKERJAC BOY (USA)**, 7, b g Catienus (USA)—Julie Apple (USA) **J. A. Moore**
5 **HOT 'N' HOLY**, 13, b g Supreme Leader—Clonmello **A. J. Duffield**
6 **LADY BY RED (IRE)**, 4, ch f Redback—Antonia's Dream
7 **LEOPOLD (SLO)**, 11, b g Solarstern (FR)—Lucera (GER) **A. J. Duffield**
8 **LOGICAL APPROACH (IRE)**, 5, b g Tikkanen (USA)—Anntella (IRE) **Mr I. Fox**
9 **MASRA**, 9, b g Silver Patriarch (IRE)—Go Sally Go (IRE) **C P M Racing**
10 **ROYAL AND ANCIENT (IRE)**, 5, b g Danehill Dancer (IRE)—Champaka (IRE) **A. J. Duffield**
11 **RUFF DIAMOND (USA)**, 7, b br g Stormin Fever (USA)—Whalah (USA) **A. J. Duffield**
12 **SILVER SPEECH**, 4, gr f Proclamation (IRE)—Sophies Symphony **A. J. Duffield**
13 **THE DIAL HOUSE**, 6, b g Tagula (IRE)—Marliana (IRE) **A. J. Duffield**
14 **THE THIRSTY BRICKY (IRE)**, 10, b g Saddlers' Hall (IRE)—Splendid Choice (IRE) **Mr T. J. A. Thompson**
15 4, B g Byron—Titania **South View Racing**
16 **TOUCH TONE**, 5, b m Selkirk (USA)—Payphone **Mr & Mrs Garnet**

THREE-YEAR-OLDS

17 **NAKURU BREEZE (IRE)**, b f King's Best (USA)—Tropical Breeze (IRE) **Mr I. Fox**

TWO-YEAR-OLDS

18 B c 20/5 Rob Roy (USA)—One Rose (Roi de Rome (USA)) **Mr J. A. Moore**

MR DAVID THOMPSON—continued

Other Owners: Mr & Mrs W. Garnet.

Assistant Trainer: A Dickman

Jockey (flat): Andrew Elliott, Tony Hamilton. **Jockey (NH):** Campbell Gillies. **Amateur:** Mr G. R. Smith.

---

635 **MR VICTOR THOMPSON, Alnwick**
Postal: **Link House Farm, Newton By The Sea, Embleton, Alnwick, Northumberland, NE66 3ED**
Contacts: **PHONE (01665) 576272**

1 **ANNS BENEFIT (IRE)**, 11, br m Beneficial—Katie Dick (IRE) **V. Thompson**
2 **CHOSEN KEYS (IRE)**, 6, b m Well Chosen—Lost Keys (IRE) **V. Thompson**
3 **GIN COBBLER**, 6, b g Beneficial—Cassia **V. Thompson**
4 **GREY WHISPER (IRE)**, 9, gr g Luso—Minature Miss **V. Thompson**
5 **KILLEANEY PRINCESS (IRE)**, 9, b m Flemensfirth (USA)—Niamh's Song (IRE) **V. Thompson**
6 **LASTING MEMORYS (IRE)**, 7, b g Sonus (IRE)—Collinstown Queen (IRE) **V. Thompson**
7 **LINK HOUSE APPEAL (IRE)**, 8, b g Lord of Appeal—Marbleade (IRE) **V. Thompson**
8 **MANDARIN SUNSET (IRE)**, 5, ch g Presenting—Danatello (FR) **V. Thompson**
9 **MISSING YOU (IRE)**, 6, b g Witness Box (USA)—Mega Drama (IRE) **V. Thompson**
10 **MONOGRAM**, 8, ch g Karinga Bay—Dusky Dante (IRE) **V. Thompson**
11 **MOOR RED**, 11, b g Classic Cliche (IRE)—Navos **V. Thompson**
12 **MR SHAHADY (IRE)**, 7, b g Xaar—Shunaire (USA) **V. Thompson**
13 **RED MYST (IRE)**, 7, ch g Beneficial—That's Not Fair (IRE) **V. Thompson**
14 **SENOR ALCO (FR)**, 6, gr g Dom Alco (FR)—Alconea (FR) **V. Thompson**
15 **SHARIVARRY (FR)**, 6, ch g Ballingarry (IRE)—Sharsala (IRE) **V. Thompson**
16 **TOMMYSTEEL (IRE)**, 7, br g Craigsteel—Sarahs Music (IRE) **V. Thompson**
17 **VANNIN (IRE)**, 6, b g Golan (IRE)—Khalsheva **Mr Mark Thompson**
18 **VICTORY SURGE (IRE)**, 8, b g Old Vic—Quinnsboro Guest (IRE) **Mr Mark Thompson**

Assistant Trainer: M Thompson

---

636 **MR SANDY THOMSON, Greenlaw**
Postal: **Lambden, Greenlaw, Duns, Berwickshire, TD10 6UN**
Contacts: **PHONE (01361) 810211 MOBILE (07876) 142787**
E-MAIL sandy@lambdenfarm.co.uk WEBSITE www.lambdenracing.co.uk

1 **ANY GIVEN MOMENT (IRE)**, 6, b g Alhaarth (IRE)—Shastri (USA) **Mr & Mrs A. M. Thomson**
2 **BLAZING DIVA (IRE)**, 9, gr m Blueprint (IRE)—Irene's Call (IRE) **Mr & Mrs A. M. Thomson**
3 **HIGGY'S BOY (IRE)**, 7, b g Choisir (AUS)—Pagan Rhythm (USA) **Mr & Mrs A. M. Thomson**
4 **JUST AWAKE**, 5, b g Prince Daniel (USA)—Katinka **Mr & Mrs A. M. Thomson**
5 **LITTLE FIFI**, 7, ch m Karinga Bay—Festival Fancy **Mr & Mrs A. M. Thomson**
6 **MINI BECK**, 13, ch g Meadowbrook—Minibrig **Mr & Mrs A. M. Thomson**
7 **NETMINDER (IRE)**, 6, b g Insatiable (IRE)—Princess Douglas **Mr & Mrs A. M. Thomson**

Other Owners: Mrs A. M. Thomson, Mr A. M. Thomson.

Assistant Trainer: Mrs A M Thomson

---

637 **MRS ALISON THORPE, Carmarthen**
Postal: **Felinfach, Bronwydd, Carmarthen, Carmarthenshire, SA33 6BE**
Contacts: **PHONE (01267) 253030 FAX (01267) 253030 MOBILE (07795) 832004**
E-MAIL info@alisonthorperacing.co.uk WEBSITE www.alisonthorperacing.co.uk

1 **ABBI JICARO**, 5, b m Passing Glance—Makeover **G. D. Kendrick**
2 **AL SHABABIYA (IRE)**, 5, b m Dubawi (IRE)—Multaka (USA) **Richard Abbott & Mario Stavrou**
3 **BETA BLOCKER**, 7, b g Beat All (USA)—Majestic Golfe **Hanford's Chemist Ltd**
4 5, B m Putra Sandhurst (IRE)—Butterflier
5 **DOUBLE FORTUNE**, 5, b m Singspiel (IRE)—Four-Legged Friend **R. W. Huggins**
6 **DROMORE HILL**, 8, b g Flemensfirth (USA)—Tree Oaks (IRE) **Mr Tim Wixted & Mr Tony Anderson**
7 **DRUMMERS DRUMMING (USA)**, 6, b g Stroll (USA)—Afleet Summer (USA) **Alison Thorpe & Don Jones**
8 **HOLD THE FORT (IRE)**, 5, b g Brian Boru—Go Katie **Alison Thorpe & Don Jones**
9 **KING'S REALM (IRE)**, 5, ch g King's Best (USA)—Sweet Home Alabama (IRE) **Alison Thorpe & Don Jones**

MRS ALISON THORPE—continued

10 **LEOPARD HILLS (IRE)**, 5, b g Acclamation—Sadler's Park (USA) **Alison Thorpe & Don Jones**
11 **MARIE DES ANGES (FR)**, 4, b f Ballingarry (IRE)—No Coincidence (IRE) **Atlantic Racing & R. W. Huggins**
12 **OENOLOGUE (FR)**, 10, b g Ragmar (FR)—Cabira des Saccart (FR) **Hanford's Chemist Ltd**
13 **ROMANESCO (FR)**, 7, b g Epistolaire (IRE)—Kadrige (FR) **Happy Go Racing Faces**
14 **THISTLE STIKK**, 5, b g Selkirk (USA)—Tamso (USA) **Palms Landscaping Limited**

Other Owners: Mr Richard Abbott, Mr Tony Anderson, Atlantic Racing Limited, Mr R. W. Huggins, Mr Don Jones, Mr J. Rees, Mr M. Stavrou, Mrs A. M. Thorpe, Mr Tim Wixted.

---

638 **MR RUAIDHRI J. TIERNEY, Kinsale**
Postal: Ardkilly Stables, Sandycove, Kinsale, Co. Cork, Ireland
Contacts: PHONE (00353) 86 0424763 FAX (00353) 21 4773445 MOBILE (00353) 86 0424763
E-MAIL r.j.tierney@hotmail.com WEBSITE www.rjtierneyracing.com

1 **BESTSELLER (GER)**, 7, b g Tiger Hill (IRE)—Book of Love **R. Tierney**
2 **BOLAND'S CORNER (GER)**, 7, br g Fraam—Bravo Gorl (GER) **De Courcey Syndicate**

---

639 **MR COLIN TIZZARD, Sherborne**
Postal: Venn Farm, Milborne Port, Sherborne, Dorset, DT9 5RA
Contacts: PHONE (01963) 250598 FAX (01963) 250598 MOBILE (07976) 778656
E-MAIL info@colintizzard.co.uk WEBSITE www.colintizzard.co.uk

1 **ABRA ABRA CADABRA**, 6, b g Pasternak—Dame Fonteyn **Mr & Mrs R. Tizzard**
2 **ALPHABETICAL ORDER**, 4, b g Alflora (IRE)—Lady Turk (FR) **Mr & Mrs R. Tizzard**
3 **BESIDE THE FIRE**, 7, b g Cois Na Tine (IRE)—Champagne N Dreams **The Con Club**
4 **BILLY NO NAME (IRE)**, 4, b g Westerner—Just Little **Mrs J. R. Bishop**
5 **CANNINGTON BROOK (IRE)**, 8, b g Winged Love (IRE)—
Rosie Brook (IRE) **Mrs Sara Biggins & Mrs Celia Djivanovic**
6 **CEEPEEGEE (IRE)**, 7, b g Karinga Bay—That's Holly **Mrs W. M. Hezel**
7 **COUP ROYALE (FR)**, 8, b g Balleroy (USA)—Coup de Rouge (FR) **Mrs J. R. Bishop**
8 **CUE CARD**, 6, b g King's Theatre (IRE)—Wicked Crack (IRE) **Mrs J. R. Bishop**
9 **DEAN'S GRANGE**, 7, br g Alflora (IRE)—Bobupandown **Gale Force Six**
10 **DIMPSY TIME**, 6, b m Kayf Tara—Cool Shuil (IRE) **Mrs J. E. Purdie**
11 **DOURYNA**, 9, b m Generous (IRE)—Dounya (USA) **Chasing Gold Limited**
12 **DRAWN FREE (IRE)**, 4, b g Tagula (IRE)—Mayfair **The Jazz Club**
13 **FALCON ISLAND**, 7, b g Turtle Island (IRE)—Dolly Sparks (IRE) **The Butterwick Syndicate**
14 **FLAMING CHARMER (IRE)**, 4, ch g Flemensfirth (USA)—Kates Charm (IRE) **T. H. Chadney**
15 **GOLDEN CHIEFTAIN (IRE)**, 7, b g Tikkanen (USA)—Golden Flower (GER) **Brocade Racing**
16 **GRAND VISION (IRE)**, 6, gr g Old Vic—West Hill Rose (IRE) **J. T. Warner**
17 **HANDY ANDY (IRE)**, 6, b g Beneficial—Maslam (IRE) **Brocade Racing**
18 **HEALTH IS WEALTH (IRE)**, 7, br g Anshan—Cherry Black (IRE) **Gale Force Five**
19 **HEARTY ROYALE (IRE)**, 7, ch g Right Win (IRE)—Killeeva (IRE) **Gerry Taylor, MJ O'Hara**
20 **HELL'S BAY (FR)**, 10, b g Supreme Leader—Queen's Flagship (IRE) **A. G. Fear & A. J. Norman**
21 **HEY BIG SPENDER (IRE)**, 9, b g Rudimentary (USA)—Jim's Monkey **Brocade Racing**
22 **HOT CHOICE**, 5, br m Zafeen (FR)—Mammy's Choice (IRE) **D. E. M. Young**
23 **INSIDE DEALER (IRE)**, 8, b g Presenting—Sea Gale (IRE) **J. M. Dare, T. Hamlin, J. W. Snook**
24 **INTAC (IRE)**, 10, b g Dr Massini (IRE)—Nlcat **P Stranger & Mrs J Mogridge**
25 **IVOR'S KING (IRE)**, 5, b g King's Theatre (IRE)—Christelle (IRE) **W. I. M. Perry**
26 **JACKERS**, 7, ch g Carnival Dancer—Welcome Home **J. T. Warner**
27 **JUMPS ROAD**, 5, b g Clerkenwell (USA)—Diletia **Chasing Gold Limited**
28 **JUSTABOUT**, 9, br g Classic Cliche—Dubacilla **Brocade Racing**
29 **KALA PATTHAR**, 5, b g Tobougg (IRE)—Lady Emily **P. M. Warren**
30 **KINGS LAD (IRE)**, 5, b g King's Theatre (IRE)—Festival Leader (IRE) **G. F. Gingell**
31 **LANHYDROCK**, 8, gr g Slip Anchor—Absalom's Lady **Mr & Mrs R. Tizzard**
32 **LORD OF THE DUNES (IRE)**, 4, b g Desert King (USA)—Dame Fonteyn **Mr & Mrs R. Tizzard**
33 **LOST TWO STARS (IRE)**, 7, gr m Fourstars Allstar (USA)—Beagan Rose (IRE) **Mrs K. Harvey**
34 **MIBLEU (FR)**, 12, b g Agent Bleu (FR)—Eauseille (FR) **Chasing Gold Limited**
35 **MILARROW (IRE)**, 5, b g Milan—Fleeting Arrow (IRE) **P. M. Warren**
36 **MOUNT OSCAR (IRE)**, 13, b g Oscar (IRE)—Sweet Mount (IRE) **Mrs J. R. Bishop**
37 **MR BINGLEY**, 4, b g Generous—Fiancee (IRE) **K S B Bloodstock**
38 **NAMPOUR (FR)**, 7, gr g Daylami (IRE)—Nadira (FR) **J. T. Warner**
39 **OHIO GOLD (IRE)**, 6, b g Flemensfirth (USA)—Kiniohio (FR) **P. M. Warren**
40 **OISEAU DE NUIT (FR)**, 10, b g Evening World (FR)—Idylle du Marais (FR) **J. T. Warner**
41 **OLD TRICKS (IRE)**, 5, br g Flemensfirth (USA)—Cabin Glory **C. L. Tizzard**

MR COLIN TIZZARD—continued

42 **QUEEN'S BAY**, 6, b m Karinga Bay—Minibelle **Mr M Fear & Mrs R R Dickinson**
43 **RATEABLE VALUE**, 8, ch g Classic Cliche (IRE)—Dame Fonteyn **R. G. Tizzard**
44 **ROYAL GUARDSMAN (IRE)**, 5, b g King's Theatre (IRE)—Lisa du Chenet (FR) **Camilla & Rosie Nock**
45 **SEW ON TARGET (IRE)**, 7, b g Needle Gun (IRE)—Ballykea (IRE) **A. G. Selway**
46 **SONG SUNG BLUE (IRE)**, 9, b g Supreme Leader—Greenflag Princess (IRE) **Singing & Dancing Racing**
47 **THEATRE GUIDE (IRE)**, 5, b g King's Theatre (IRE)—Erintante (IRE) **Mrs J. R. Bishop**
48 **THEATRICAL STAR**, 6, b g King's Theatre (IRE)—Lucy Glitters **Brocade Racing**
49 **THIRD INTENTION (IRE)**, 5, b g Azamour (IRE)—Third Dimension (FR) **Mr & Mrs R. Tizzard**
50 **TIME BOOK (IRE)**, 6, b g Galileo (IRE)—Pocket Book (IRE) **D. V. Stevens**
51 **VIRGINIA ASH (IRE)**, 4, ch g Definite Article—Peace Time Girl (IRE) **Mr J. P. Romans**
52 **WOSAYU**, 6, b g Central Park (IRE)—Waltz On Air **J K Farms**
53 **XAARCET**, 5, b g Xaar—Anoukit **T. H. Chadney**

Other Owners: Mrs S. J. Biggins, Mr K. W. Biggins, Mr G. R. Broom, Mrs A. E. M. Broom, Mr C. Cole, Mr J. M. Dare, Mrs R. L. J. Dickinson, Mrs C. J. Djivanovic, A. G. Fear, Mr R. M. Fear, Mr A. P. Gale, T. Hamlin, Mr K. F. Honeybun, Mrs J. Honeybun, Mrs J. Mogridge, Miss R. C. Nock, Miss C. D. Nock, A. J. Norman, Mr M. J. O'Hara, J. W. Snook, J. G. Storey, P. A. Stranger, Mr G. P. Taylor, Mrs S. L. Tizzard, Mr E. R. Vickery.

Assistant Trainer: Mrs K. Gingell

Jockey (NH): Joe Tizzard. **Conditional:** Steven Clements, Brendan Powell.

---

640 **MR MARTIN TODHUNTER, Penrith**
Postal: **The Park, Orton, Penrith, Cumbria, CA10 3SD**
Contacts: **PHONE (01539) 624314 FAX (01539) 624811 MOBILE (07976) 440082**
WEBSITE www.martintodhunter.co.uk

1 **ACORDINGTOSCRIPT (IRE)**, 6, ch g Accordion—Jane Jones (IRE) **The Surf & Turf Partnership**
2 **ALLANARD (IRE)**, 8, b g Oscar (IRE)—Allatrim (IRE) **Mr E. R. Madden**
3 **AUTHENTIC ACT (IRE)**, 8, ch g Pivotal—All In All **Mr & Mrs Ian Hall**
4 **BEHINDCLOSEDDOORS (IRE)**, 6, b g Tillerman—Vivacious Lass (IRE) **Mr N. Haughan & Mr D. Graves**
5 **CAILIN NA RI (IRE)**, 9, b m King's Theatre (IRE)—Kings Gap (IRE) **B. Brown**
6 **CATCH THE CASH**, 5, b m Law Society (USA)—Casiana (GER) **P. G. Airey**
7 **CAVITE ETA (IRE)**, 5, br g Spadoun (FR)—Samarinnda (IRE) **Don't Tell Henry**
8 **CELIAN (FR)**, 9, b g Indian River (FR)—Celinda (FR) **Park Farms Racing Syndicate 1**
9 **DOUBLE DEFAULT (IRE)**, 11, ch g Beneficial—Over The Risc (IRE) **Gill & Bill Hazeldean**
10 **EXIT TO ANYWHERE**, 7, b g Exit To Nowhere (USA)—Ground Game **Mr A. Bell**
11 **JUST TYN (IRE)**, 5, b g Westerner—Christian Cullen (USA) **Mr E. R. Madden**
12 **LISBON LION (IRE)**, 7, br gr g Mull of Kintyre (USA)—Ludovica **David & Nicky Robinson**
13 **MIGHTY MAGNUS (IRE)**, 9, ch g Night Shift (USA)—Arbaletta (GER) **Charles Broome & Partners**
14 **QUETZAL (IRE)**, 7, b g Mr Combustible (IRE)—Auction Piece (IRE) **The Centaur Group Partnership III**
15 **SEE WHAT HAPPENS (IRE)**, 6, b g Tikkanen (USA)—Fontanalia **J. D. Gordon**
16 **SHAKER STYLE (USA)**, 6, ch g Gulch (USA)—Carr Shaker (USA) **K. Fitzsimons**
17 **STORM SURGE (IRE)**, 9, gr g Great Palm (USA)—Ashfield Rosie (IRE) **Javas Charvers**
18 **THE LODGE ROAD (IRE)**, 4, b g Holy Roman Emperor (IRE)—Golden Coral (USA) **Mr & Mrs Ian Hall**
19 **THE MONGOLIAN (IRE)**, 4, b f Presenting—Elegant City **Murphy's Law Partnership**
20 **TRANSACT (IRE)**, 7, ch g Trans Island—Khrisma **J D Racing**
21 **WITHOUT EQUAL**, 6, ch m Tobougg (IRE)—Sans Egale (FR) **Mr K. Fitzsimons & Mr G. Fell**

Other Owners: Mr C. M. Broome, Mrs J. M. Broome, J. R. Callow, P. W. Clement, Mr A. J. Cork, Mr P. M. Croan, W. Downs, Mr G. Fell, Mr J. W. Fryer-Spedding, Mr J. D. Graves, Mr N. Haughan, J. W. Hazeldean, Ms G. Hazeldean, Mr J. D. Hornsby, Mr J. B. Pattinson, Mr D. Robinson, Mrs N. G. Robinson, K. Sobey, Mr J. I. A. Spedding, D. M. Todhunter, S. T. Uprichard.

Jockey (NH): James Reveley, Denis O'Regan, Graham Lee.

---

641 **MR JAMES TOLLER, Newmarket**
Postal: **Eve Lodge Stables, Hamilton Road, Newmarket, Suffolk, CB8 0NY**
Contacts: **PHONE (01638) 668918 FAX (01638) 669384 MOBILE (07887) 942234**
E-MAIL james.toller@btconnect.com

1 **LOVING SPIRIT**, 4, b g Azamour (IRE)—Lolla's Spirit (IRE) **P. C. J. Dalby & R. D. Schuster**
2 **SOHAR**, 4, b f Iceman—Desert Joy **G. B. Partnership**
3 **TWICE BITTEN**, 4, ch g Beat Hollow—Duena **The Cobra Partnership**

MR JAMES TOLLER—continued

THREE-YEAR-OLDS

4 **GLAISDALE**, b f Hurricane Run (IRE)—Picacho (IRE) **J. A. Gibson**
5 **REWARDED**, b c Motivator—Granted (FR) **P. C. J. Dalby & R. D. Schuster**
6 **SAIGON**, b c Royal Applause—Luanshya **P. C. J. Dalby & R. D. Schuster**
7 **SOHO ROCKS**, b f Rock of Gibraltar (IRE)—Millisecond **G. B. Partnership**
8 **SOHO SPIRIT**, ch f Nayef (USA)—Cruinn A Bhord **G. B. Partnership**
9 **SOHO SUSIE (IRE)**, br f Montjeu (IRE)—Lucina **G. B. Partnership**
10 **SPARK OF GENIUS**, b f Oratorio (IRE)—Lolla's Spirit (IRE) **N. J. Charrington**

TWO-YEAR-OLDS

11 **CHERRY TIGER**, b c 31/3 Tiger Hill (IRE)—
Lolla's Spirit (IRE) (Montjeu (IRE)) (5500) **Buckingham Thoroughbreds I**
12 **CHESTER ROW**, ch c 21/1 Compton Place—Sophie's Girl (Bahamian Bounty) (28000)
13 Ch f 9/4 Nayef (USA)—Dusty Answer (Zafonic (USA)) (21000) **Partnership**
14 B f 16/3 Motivator—Ela's Giant (Giant's Causeway (USA)) (1000) **G. Wates**
15 **LIVING DESERT**, gr c 12/2 Oasis Dream—Sell Out (Act One) (100000) **G. B. Partnership**
16 **SMOKETHATTHUNDERS (IRE)**, gr c 29/3 Elusive City (USA)—Zinstar (IRE) (Sinndar (IRE)) (30000) **M. E. Wates**
17 **SOHO DANCER**, b f 10/4 Galileo (IRE)—River Belle (Lahib (USA)) (310000) **G. B. Partnership**
18 **SUNNY HOLLOW**, b f 3/5 Beat Hollow—Corndavon (USA) (Sheikh Albadou) (7000) **Mr S. A. Herbert**

Other Owners: Mr P. C. J. Dalby, Mr M. G. H. Heald, Mr Andrew Heald, Mrs J. E. Lee-Smith, Mrs Asha Narang, Mr G. E. Sangster, Mr Richard Schuster, Mr L. Straszewski, Mr R. A. C. Toller, Mr J. A. R. Toller.

Jockey (flat): Robert Havlin.

---

642 **MR MARK TOMPKINS, Newmarket**
Postal: **Flint Cottage Stables, Rayes Lane, Newmarket, Suffolk, CB8 7AB**
Contacts: **PHONE (01638) 661434 FAX (01638) 668107 MOBILE (07799) 663339**
E-MAIL mht@marktompkins.co.uk WEBSITE www.marktompkins.co.uk

1 **AKULA (IRE)**, 5, ch g Soviet Star—Danielli (IRE) **Jay Three Racing**
2 **ASTROLEO**, 6, ch g Groom Dancer (USA)—Astrolove (IRE) **Mystic Meg Limited**
3 **ASTROLIBRA**, 8, b m Sakhee (USA)—Optimistic **Mystic Meg Limited**
4 **ASTROMAGICK**, 4, b f Rainbow Quest (USA)—Astrocharm (IRE) **Mystic Meg Limited**
5 **BARWICK**, 4, b g Beat Hollow—Tenpence **Mr S. Ashley**
6 **BATTERY POWER**, 4, b f Royal Applause—Missouri **H-Squared Electronics Limited**
7 **BLIMEY O'RILEY (IRE)**, 7, b g Kalanisi (IRE)—Kafayef (USA) **Mr T. J. Benton**
8 **BRUSHING**, 6, ch m Medicean—Seasonal Blossom (IRE) **J. Brenchley**
9 **CAT ISLAND**, 4, b f Bahamian Bounty—Dolls House **Dullingham Park Stud**
10 **COMRADE BOND**, 4, ch g Monsieur Bond (IRE)—Eurolink Cafe **Raceworld**
11 **COTTON GRASS**, 4, b f Medicean—Astromancer (USA) **Kingsville Promotions Limited**
12 **DAZINSKI**, 6, ch g Sulamani (IRE)—Shuheb **Mrs B. M. Lockey**
13 **FIVE HEARTS**, 4, b f Bertolini (USA)—Light Hand **TCWS Ltd**
14 **KATHLEEN FRANCES**, 5, b m Sakhee (USA)—Trew Class **Russell Trew Ltd**
15 **LOCUM**, 7, ch g Dr Fong (USA)—Exhibitor **Ray Smith & Partners**
16 **MARVO**, 8, b g Bahamian Bounty—Mega (IRE) **M. P. Bowring**
17 **MYSTERY STAR (IRE)**, 7, ch g Kris Kin (USA)—Mystery Hill (USA) **J. Brenchley**
18 **NO RULES**, 7, b g Fraam—Golden Daring (IRE) **M. P. Bowring**
19 **OLD BOY TED**, 4, b g Tobougg (IRE)—Grove Dancer **H-Squared Electronics Limited**
20 **RON**, 4, ch g Dubai Destination (USA)—Trew Class **Russell Trew Ltd**
21 **SMOKEY OAKEY (IRE)**, 8, b g Tendulkar (USA)—Veronica **Judi Dench & Bryan Agar**
22 **STAR COMMANDER**, 4, b g Desert Style (IRE)—Barakat **J. Brenchley**
23 **ZENARINDA**, b m Zamindar (USA)—Tenpence **Judi Dench & Partners**

THREE-YEAR-OLDS

24 **ASTROGOLD**, ch f Motivator—Mega (IRE) **Mystic Meg Limited**
25 **ASTROSCARLET**, ch f Carnival Dancer—Astrolove (IRE) **Mystic Meg Limited**
26 **CHANKILLO**, ch c Observatory—Seasonal Blossom (IRE) **Sarabex**
27 **DINE OUT**, b f Piccolo—Sosumi **The Fat Boys**
28 **EANANS BAY (IRE)**, b g Tiger Hill (IRE)—Gold Hush (USA) **Mr D. Sinclair**
29 **JENNIFER J**, ch f Motivator—Trew Class **Russell Trew Ltd**
30 **JOE THE COAT**, ch g Act One—Torcross **Roalco Ltd**
31 **LADY BELLATRIX**, br f Singspiel (IRE)—Humility **J. Brenchley**

MR MARK TOMPKINS—continued

32 **LIKE CLOCKWORK**, b g Rail Link—Tenpence **Dullingham Park Stud**
33 **MY GUARDIAN ANGEL**, b g Araafa (IRE)—Angels Guard You **Sarabex**
34 **ON THE ROCKS**, b g Iceman—Fiddle-Dee-Dee (IRE) **Raceworld**
35 **RAYVIN BLACK**, b c Halling (USA)—Optimistic **Mr R. White & Mr V. J. Walsh**
36 **RED HERMES (IRE)**, ch f Windsor Knot (IRE)—Imposition (UAE) **Dullingham Park Stud**
37 **SHOMBERG**, b g Bahamian Bounty—Qilin (IRE) **Kenneth MacPherson**
38 **SLEIGH BELLS**, b f Three Valleys (USA)—Dolls House **Dullingham Park Stud**
39 **TOPTEMPO**, ch f Halling (USA)—Topatoo **Roalco Ltd**

TWO-YEAR-OLDS

40 **ASTRODREAMS**, b f 24/3 Rail Link—Nutmeg (IRE) (Lake Coniston (IRE)) **Mystic Meg Limited**
41 **ASTROSAPPHIRE**, b f 12/2 Manduro (GER)—Astromancer (USA) (Silver Hawk (USA)) **Mystic Meg Limited**
42 **BARBSIZ (IRE)**, ch f 26/4 Elnadim (USA)—Bianca Cappello (IRE) (Glenstal (USA)) (8000) **Mr G. J. Megson**
43 **FREDERICK ALFRED**, ch c 8/4 Halling (USA)—Trew Class (Inchinor) **Russell Trew Ltd**
44 **LIKELIKELIKEIT**, b f 13/2 Avonbridge—Rutland Water (IRE) (Hawk Wing (USA)) (2000) **M. H. Tompkins**
45 **MARSH DRAGON**, b f 11/4 Beat Hollow—Qilin (IRE) (Second Set (IRE)) **M. H. Tompkins**
46 Ch f 6/3 Haafhd—Sosumi (Be My Chief (USA))
47 **STAR OF MISSOURI**, ch c 28/3 Namid—Missouri (Charnwood Forest (IRE)) **J. Brenchley**
48 **TOPAMICHI**, b c 13/3 Beat Hollow—Topatori (IRE) (Topanoora) **Roalco Ltd**

Other Owners: Mr Bryan Agar, Mr N. M. Hanger, Mr Eric Jones, Mr K. Lawrence, Mr Conrad Lockey, Mr R. D. E. Marriott, Mr B. Platts, Mrs P. M. Rickett, Mr P. A. Sakal, Mr R. J. Thornalley, Mr David Tompkins, Mr K. D. Waller, Mr M. Winter.

Assistant Trainers: Steven Avery & Iain Williams

Jockey (NH): Colin Bolger.

---

643 MR MARCUS TREGONING, Lambourn
Postal: **Kingwood House Stables, Lambourn, Berkshire, RG17 7RS**
Contacts: **PHONE** (01488) 73300 **FAX** (01488) 71728 **MOBILE** (07767) 888100
E-MAIL info@marcustregoningracing.co.uk **WEBSITE** www.marcustregoningracing.co.uk

1 **ARCHELAO (IRE)**, 4, br g Cape Cross (IRE)—Brindisi **Mark & Emma Dixon**
2 **ASKAR TAU (FR)**, 7, b g Montjeu (IRE)—Autriche (IRE) **N. Bizakov**
3 **ASKER (IRE)**, 4, b g High Chaparral (IRE)—Pay The Bank **N. Bizakov**
4 **BOOM AND BUST (IRE)**, 5, b g Footstepsinthesand—Forest Call **Mr J. Singh**
5 **BOWSERS BRAVE (USA)**, 6, ch g Dixieland Band (USA)—Hazimah (USA) **Mrs J. R. A. Aldridge**
6 **CHATTERER (IRE)**, 4, b f Alhaarth (IRE)—Miss Bellbird (IRE) **Horne, Hoare, Gaskell & Partners**
7 **HARTING HILL**, 7, b g Mujahid (USA)—Mossy Rose **Miss S. M. Sharp**
8 **HAWAAFEZ**, 4, b f Nayef (USA)—Merayaat (IRE) **Hamdan Al Maktoum**
9 **HEDDWYN (IRE)**, 5, b g Bahri (USA)—Penny Rouge (IRE) **Mr J. A. Tabet**
10 **HOMEBOY (IRE)**, 4, b g Camacho—Berenica (IRE) **Home Marketing**
11 **KONSTANTIN (IRE)**, 4, br g Balmont (USA)—Manuka Magic (IRE) **Lady Tennant**
12 **LADY ROSAMUNDE**, 4, gr f Maria's Mon (USA)—String Quartet (IRE) **Mr & Mrs A. E. Pakenham**
13 **MISS DARLEY**, 4, b f Doyen (IRE)—Forum Finale (USA) **Mr M. West**
14 **MISS KINGWOOD**, 5, b m Reset (AUS)—Forum Finale (USA) **Mr M. West**
15 **MULAQEN**, 4, ch c Haafhd—Burqa **Hamdan Al Maktoum**
16 **OPERA BOX**, 4, b f Singspiel (IRE)—Annex **Efemera Stud**
17 **ROSE AURORA**, 5, gr m Pastoral Pursuits—Khaladja (IRE) **Kingwood House Racing**
18 **SEA THE FLAMES (IRE)**, 4, b g Chineur (FR)—Flames **David & Gwyn Joseph**
19 **VERTIBES**, 4, gr g Verglas (IRE)—Antibes (IRE) **Mr & Mrs A. E. Pakenham**
20 **WATERED SILK**, 4, gr g Encosta de Lago (AUS)—Tussah **Mr & Mrs A. E. Pakenham**
21 **ZAHRAAN (IRE)**, 4, b c Elusive City (USA)—Rihana (IRE) **Sheikh Ahmed Al Maktoum**

THREE-YEAR-OLDS

22 **ALWAFFAA (USA)**, b f Discreet Cat (USA)—Elaflaak (USA) **Hamdan Al Maktoum**
23 **ANQOODA (USA)**, b f Oasis Dream—Atayeb (USA) **Hamdan Al Maktoum**
24 **ARABEYA (USA)**, b f Mr Greeley (USA)—Awtaan (USA) **Hamdan Al Maktoum**
25 **BRONZE ANGEL (IRE)**, b c Dark Angel (IRE)—Rihana (IRE) **Lady Tennant**
26 **CAVALEIRO (IRE)**, ch c Sir Percy—Khibraat **Mr G. C. B. Brook**
27 **CHRONIC FLAME (TUR)**, b f Dubai Destination (USA)—All Grain **Mr Mehmet Kurt**
28 **EBTISAMA (USA)**, b f Kingmambo—Misterah **Hamdan Al Maktoum**
29 **ESTEDAAMA (IRE)**, b f Marju (IRE)—Mohafazaat (IRE) **Hamdan Al Maktoum**
30 **ESTEMAALA (IRE)**, b f Cape Cross (IRE)—Elutrah **Hamdan Al Maktoum**

MR MARCUS TREGONING—continued

31 JOURNALISTIC (USA), b c Street Sense (USA)—Cajun Two Step (USA) F. Nass
32 KOGERSHIN (USA), ch f Giant's Causeway (USA)—Kokadrie (USA) N. Bizakov
33 LULLA, b f Oasis Dream—Dominica Mrs R. B. Kennard
34 MARMAS, ch c Sir Percy—Kitabaat (IRE) Hamdan Al Maktoum
35 MISS BLAKENEY, b f Sir Percy—Misplace (IRE) Mr & Mrs A. E. Pakenham
36 MORINDA, b f Selkirk (USA)—Morning Queen (GER) Mrs M. Campbell-Andenaes
37 MUHARRER, b c Shamardal (USA)—Shawahid (USA) Hamdan Al Maktoum
38 MUJANNAD (IRE), b c Red Ransom (USA)—Hureya (USA) Hamdan Al Maktoum
39 MUTANAWWER, br c Red Ransom (USA)—Nasheed (USA) Hamdan Al Maktoum
40 OLD TIMES SAKE (TUR), b f Singspiel (IRE)—Moldova (USA) Mr Mehmet Kurt
41 ON MY OWN (TUR), b c Rock of Gibraltar (IRE)—Dancingintheclouds (IRE) Mr Mehmet Kurt
42 ROYAL TRIX, b f Royal Applause—Apple Town Mrs Lynn Turner & Mr Guy Brook
43 SCARLET BELLE, ch f Sir Percy—Nicola Bella (IRE) The FOPS
44 SCARLETT FEVER, b f Haafhd—Scarlet Buttons (IRE) The O.D's
45 SHY ROSA (USA), b br f Dixie Union (USA)—Lethal Temper (USA) Mr G. C. B. Brook
46 SPINNING SILK (IRE), ch f Redback—Silk Point (IRE) Park Walk Racing
47 THAWABEL (IRE), b f Nayef (USA)—Shohrah (IRE) Hamdan Al Maktoum
48 WAAFID (USA), b c Hard Spun (USA)—Hazimah (USA) Hamdan Al Maktoum
49 WEAAM (IRE), b c Shamardal (USA)—Merayaat (IRE) Hamdan Al Maktoum

TWO-YEAR-OLDS

50 B f 28/3 Invincible Spirit (IRE)—Alshamatry (USA) (Seeking The Gold (USA)) Hamdan Al Maktoum
51 ATALANTA BAY (IRE), b f 5/2 Strategic Prince—Wood Sprite (Mister Baileys) (8209) Miss S. M. Sharp
52 CAERWYN, ch c 15/2 Pastoral Pursuits—Preference (Efisio) (29523) Mr J. A. Tabet
53 DELWYN, b f 18/3 Bahamian Bounty—Acquifer (Oasis Dream) (9523) Mr J. A. Tabet
54 EASY LIFE, b f 20/4 Sir Percy—Eternelle (Green Desert (USA)) Miss K. Rausing
55 B f 13/5 Holy Roman Emperor (IRE)—Ellen (IRE) (Machiavellian (USA)) (80000) Mr G. C. B. Brook
56 B c 30/1 Elnadim (USA)—Elutrah (Darshaan) Hamdan Al Maktoum
57 B c 9/2 Nayef (USA)—Emerald Peace (IRE) (Green Desert (USA)) (100000) Mr G. C. B. Brook
58 B c 12/4 I Was Framed (USA)—Glint (Pivotal) (1904) Mrs M. Campbell-Andenaes
59 B c 18/2 Muhtathir—Itqaan (USA) (Danzig (USA)) Hamdan Al Maktoum
60 B c 17/3 Oasis Dream—Katayeb (USA) (Machiavellian (USA)) Hamdan Al Maktoum
61 B f 3/3 Shamardal (USA)—Merayaat (IRE) (Darshaan) Hamdan Al Maktoum
62 PERDU, b c 10/5 Sir Percy—Misplace (IRE) (Green Desert (USA)) (25000) Mr & Mrs A. E. Pakenham
63 B c 7/2 Sir Percy—Sahara Belle (USA) (Sanglamore (USA)) (25000) R. C. C. Villers
64 SAINT JEROME (IRE), b c 6/3 Jeremy—Eminence Gift (Cadeaux Genereux) (52380) Lady Tennant
65 B c 1/1 Street Sense (USA)—Sayedah (IRE) (Darshaan) Hamdan Al Maktoum
66 Br f 16/3 Cape Cross (IRE)—Shohrah (IRE) (Giant's Causeway (USA)) Hamdan Al Maktoum
67 Ch f 2/4 Sir Percy—Sirena (GER) (Tejano (USA)) (2462)
68 B c 26/3 Jeremy (USA)—Special Park (USA) (Trempolino (USA)) (4285)
69 B c 29/4 Rock of Gibraltar (USA)—Sweeping Story (USA) (End Sweep (USA)) (18882) Mr J. Singh
70 B f 8/2 Marju (IRE)—Tadris (USA) (Red Ransom (USA)) Hamdan Al Maktoum
71 B f 25/2 Jazil (USA)—Taleef (Sakhee (USA)) Hamdan Al Maktoum
72 B f 1/1 Lemon Drop Kid (USA)—Tayibah (IRE) (Sadler's Wells (USA)) Hamdan Al Maktoum

Other Owners: Viscountess Allendale, Mrs Charles Baker, Mr A. A. Bamboye, Mr Giles Blomfeild, Mr Guy Brook, Mr Charles Curtis, Mrs Hugh Dalgety, Mr M. H. Dixon, Miss E. J. Dixon, Mrs Louise Ferrand, Mr R. F. U. Gaskell, Mr Michael Gatehouse, Captain Victor Hoare, Mrs Mark Horne, Mr N. M. Jackson, Mr D. M. Joseph, Mr D. G. Joseph, Mr Alvaro Maccioni, Mr A. E. Pakenham, Mrs Victoria Pakenham, Mr N. A. Penston, Mr R. J. Penston, Mr John Raw, Mr D. Sewards, Mr Graham V. Sherren, Mr Jas Singh, Mr Julian Tregoning, Mrs Lynn Turner, Mr J. R. Wallis, Mrs Bruce Willis.

Jockey (flat): Tadhg O'Shea, Richard Hills, Hayley Turner. Apprentice: Katia Scallan.

---

644 MR EDWIN TUER, Northallerton
Postal: Granary Barn, Birkby, Northallerton, North Yorkshire, DL7 0EF
Contacts: PHONE (01609) 881798 FAX (01609) 881798 MOBILE (07808) 330306

1 AILSA CRAIG (IRE), 6, b m Chevalier (IRE)—Sharplaw Destiny (IRE) E. Tuer
2 BIG BENJIE, 4, ch g Lahib (USA)—Bula Rose (IRE) E. Tuer
3 DONNA ELVIRA, 5, b m Doyen (IRE)—Impatiente (USA) Far Distant Partnership
4 EASY TERMS, 5, b m Trade Fair—Effie E. Tuer
5 FAZZA, 5, ch g Sulamani (IRE)—Markievicz (IRE) E. Tuer
6 LEAVING ALONE (USA), 5, ch m Mr Greeley (USA)—Spankin' (USA) E. Tuer
7 PATAVIUM (IRE), 9, b g Titus Livius (FR)—Arcevia (IRE) Mr J. A. Nixon

MR EDWIN TUER—continued

8 SALLY FRIDAY (IRE), 4, b f Footstepsinthesand—Salee (IRE) **E. Tuer**
9 SPHINX (FR), 14, b g Snurge—Egyptale **Ontoawinner**

THREE-YEAR-OLDS

10 THE BLUE BANANA (IRE), b g Red Clubs (IRE)—Rinneen (IRE) **E. Tuer**

Other Owners: E. Carr, Mr C. Holcroft, N. J. O'Brien, A. C. Tompkins, Mrs A. R. Tompkins.

---

645 **MR JOSEPH TUITE, Hungerford**
Postal: Tuite Racing Ltd, Shefford Valley Stables, Great Shefford, Hungerford, Berks, RG17 7EF
Contacts: PHONE (01488) 649641 MOBILE (07769) 977351
E-MAIL joe.tuite@tuiteracing.com WEBSITE www.tuiteracing.com

1 ADVERTISE, 6, br g Passing Glance—Averami **The Outta Lunch Partnership**
2 COME ON SAFARI (IRE), 5, b g Antonius Pius (USA)—Calypso Dancer (FR) **Montagu Racing**
3 INTERAKT, 5, b m Rakti—Amelie Pouliche (FR) **Heart Of The South Racing**
4 KYNCRAIGHE (IRE), 4, b g Kyllachy—Brighella **Mr C. S. J. Beek**
5 PREMIUM COFFEE, 4, b g Superior Premium—Coffee Ice **The Outta Lunch Partnership**
6 RED YARN, 5, b m Lucky Story (USA)—Aunt Ruby (USA) **Heart Of The South Racing**
7 RYEDALE LASS, 4, b f Val Royal (FR)—First Dawn **J. A. Dewhurst**
8 SPIN CAST, 4, b g Marju (IRE)—Some Diva **Dr M. B. Q. S. Koukash**
9 WHITSTABLE NATIVE, 4, b g Bertolini (USA)—Break of Dawn (USA) **Mr B. Woodward**

THREE-YEAR-OLDS

10 ANGINOLA (IRE), b f Kodiac—Lady Montekin **Mr A. Liddiard**
11 LADY SYLVIA, ch f Haafhd—Abide (FR) **Mr D. J. Keast**
12 ONERTOTHER, b g Nomadic Way (USA)—Ceilidh Band **Penny & Adrian Burton, Bob & Angela Lampard**
13 PRESBURG (IRE), b g Balmont (USA)—Eschasse (USA) **Ise Language**
14 TIME TO DANCE, b c Silent Times (IRE)—Bravo Dancer **Mr J. M. Tuite**

TWO-YEAR-OLDS

15 B f 23/2 Kheleyf (USA)—Carraigoona (IRE) (Rock of Gibraltar (IRE)) (7388) **Heart Of The South Racing**
16 Ch c 3/4 Indian Haven—Emerald Storm (USA) (Diesis) (14000) **P. Gleeson**
17 Ch c 10/3 Kyllachy—Resistance Heroine (Dr Fong (USA)) (11428)
18 B f 20/4 Piccolo—Rosein (Komaite (USA)) (20952) **The Outta Lunch Partnership**
19 B f 4/3 Oratorio (IRE)—Saphila (IRE) (Sadler's Wells (USA)) (11000) **D. Keast**
20 B f 19/4 Pastoral Pursuits—Tuppenny (Salse (USA)) (800)
21 B f 9/3 Azamour (IRE)—Uva Fragola (Nashwan (USA)) (16420)

---

646 **MR ANDY TURNELL, Swindon**
Postal: Elmcross House, Broad Hinton, Swindon, Wiltshire, SN4 9PF
Contacts: PHONE (01793) 731481 FAX (01793) 739001 MOBILE (07973) 933450
E-MAIL a.turnell@virgin.net WEBSITE andyturnellracing.com

1 BLACK PHANTOM (IRE), 6, br g Alderbrook—Blenheim Blinder (IRE) **T. L. Morshead**
2 CAULFIELDS VENTURE (IRE), 6, b g Catcher In The Rye—Saddlers' Venture (IRE) **C. F. Colquhoun**
3 CHANDOS (IRE), 4, b g Heron Island (IRE)—Park Belle (IRE) **Mr J. R. Adam**
4 DOUBLE THE TROUBLE, 11, b g Double Trigger (IRE)—Upton Lass (IRE) **Mrs M. R. Taylor**
5 FAHA (IRE), 6, b m Catcher In The Rye (IRE)—Tarayib **Andrew Turnell**
6 GOTOYOURPLAY (IRE), 8, ch g Definite Article—Johnston's Flyer (IRE) **Miss S. Douglas-Pennant**
7 HAAR, 8, ch g Selkirk (USA)—Chilly Start (IRE) **Mrs R. M. Hill**
8 MICHEAL FLIPS (IRE), 8, b g Kayf Tara—Pianissimo (IRE) **Mr M. J. Tedham**
9 ORCHARD ROAD (USA), 5, b g Street Cry (IRE)—Aunt Mottz (USA) **P. A. Deal**
10 5, B g Muhtarram (USA)—Peacefull River (IRE)
11 PIANO CONCERTO (USA), 5, b g Red Ransom (USA)—
Storm Song (USA) **C Buckle, P Deal, R Garner & G Thorner**
12 QUALYPSO D'ALLIER (FR), 8, b g Dark Moondancer—Miss Akarad (FR) **Mr M. J. Tedham**
13 SABLAZO (FR), 6, b g Ragmar (FR)—Daytona II (FR) **Miss S. Douglas-Pennant**
14 THE DRUIDS NEPHEW (IRE), 5, b g King's Theatre (IRE)—Gifted **The Stonehenge Druids**
15 VEHEMENT, 6, b m Refuse To Bend (IRE)—Velvet Lady **Thorner, Goodman, Hix & Batts**

MR ANDY TURNELL—continued

TWO-YEAR-OLDS

16 **OLIVIA'S LAD,** b g 4/5 Sir Percy—Hazel Bank Lass (IRE) (Insan (USA)) **Mr M. J. Tedham**

Other Owners: Mrs L. S. Atwell, Mr D. Batts, C. R. Buckle, Mrs A. C. Crofts, Mr R. F. Garner, Mrs D. Goodman, M. P. Hill, Mrs K. E. Hix, L. G. Kimber, Mr G. E. Thorner, Mr G. J. Villis.

Jockey (NH): Nick Scholfield.

---

647 **MR BILL TURNER, Sherborne**
Postal: **Sigwells Farm, Sigwells, Corton Denham, Sherborne, Dorset, DT9 4LN**
Contacts: **PHONE (01963) 220523 FAX (01963) 220046 MOBILE (07932) 100173**

1 **A LITTLE BIT DUSTY,** 4, ch g Needwood Blade—Dusty Dazzler (IRE) **Trowbridge Office Cleaning Services Ltd**
2 **BUFFALOSPRINGFIELD,** 4, b g Tobougg (IRE)—Three Gifts **Mrs S. Read**
3 **CIDER LOLLY,** 6, ch m Loup Sauvage (USA)—Lady Turk (FR) **Mr & Mrs R. Tizzard**
4 **DEW REWARD (IRE),** 4, b g Aussie Rules (USA)—Shariyfa (USA) **Mrs D. Tucker**
5 **DREAM EXPRESS (IRE),** 7, b g Fasliyev (USA)—Lothlorien (USA) **Mrs A. Nash**
6 **DUSTY DANE (IRE),** 10, b g Indian Danehill (USA)—Teer On Eer (IRE) **Mrs P. A. Turner**
7 **EDLOMOND (IRE),** 6, gr g Great Palm (USA)—Samardana (IRE) **E. A. Brook**
8 **FIVE COOL KATS (IRE),** 4, b g One Cool Cat (USA)—Katavi (USA) **Five Cool Kats Racing**
9 **FRECKLE FACE,** 5, br g Septieme Ciel (USA)—Wavet **Mrs C. M. Goldsmith**
10 **GWENS BOY,** 5, b g Helissio (FR)—Needwood Truffle (IRE) **R. A. Bracken**
11 **LADY PRODEE,** 4, b f Proclamation (IRE)—Dee-Lady **Mrs M. S. Teversham**
12 **LAMBLORD (IRE),** 5, b g Brian Boru—Princess Symphony (IRE) **The Lamb Inn - Pethy**
13 **LATIN SCHOLAR (IRE),** 7, ch g Titus Livius (FR)—Crimada (IRE) **Michael Potter**
14 **LIKE A BOY,** 4, b c Medicean—Like A Dame **Sparsholt Stud**
15 **LORD OF THE STORM,** 4, b g Avonbridge—Just Run (IRE) **Mrs M. S. Teversham**
16 **LUCKY DIVA,** 5, ch m Lucky Story (USA)—Cosmic Countess (IRE) **D. Coombes**
17 **MENEUR (FR),** 10, gr g Septieme Ciel (USA)—Mamamia (FR) **The New Foursome Partnership**
18 **SIX OF CLUBS,** 6, ch g Bertolini (USA)—Windmill Princess **Gongolfin**
19 **SUTTON STORM,** 7, b g Emperor Fountain—Rock Rose **Mrs A. Davis**
20 **VIVRE LA SECRET,** 4, b f Ishiguru (USA)—Vivre Sa Vie **Sparsholt Stud**

THREE-YEAR-OLDS

21 **I'M STILL THE MAN (IRE),** b c Acclamation—Kapera (FR) **Mr J. Tucker**
22 **THE DANCING LORD,** br g Imperial Dancer—Miss Brookie **Mrs M. S. Teversham**

TWO-YEAR-OLDS

23 B c 3/5 Captain Marvelous (IRE)—Amoras (IRE) (Hamas (IRE)) **Miss Karen Theobald**
24 B f 6/4 Notnowcato— Apple Sauce (Prince Sabo) **Tracy Turner**
25 B f 23/2 Sakhee's Secret—Calypso Charms (Dansili) **P. Thorman**
26 B c 28/3 Tiger Hill (IRE)—Emerald Fire (Pivotal) **Mr Richard Jeffries**
27 B c 23/2 Haathd—Erreur (IRE) (Desert King (IRE)) (14285) **Mr Eric Brook**
28 B c 4/4 Amadeus Wolf—Fancy Feathers (IRE) (Redback) (9047) **Mr J. J. O'Hara**
29 **IT'S ONLY BUSINESS,** ch c 17/3 Haathd—Noble Plum (IRE) (King's Best (USA)) (10000) **Mr B. Ansell**
30 **MISTERAY,** ch c 15/4 Singspiel (IRE)—Hannda (IRE) (Dr Devious (IRE)) (10000) **Mr B. Ansell**
31 B f 5/4 Diamond Green (FR)—Oh So Rosie (IRE) (Danehill Dancer (IRE)) **Miss Karen Theobald**
32 Ch f 24/4 Bahamian Bounty—Royal Mistress (Fasliyev (USA)) **Tracy Turner**
33 B c 19/4 Sleeping Indian—Seagreen (IRE) (Green Desert (USA)) (1428) **Mr Eric Brook**
34 B c 11/4 Majestic Missile (IRE)—Secret Combe (IRE) (Mujadil (USA)) **Miss Karen Theobald**
35 B f 31/1 Elusive City (USA)—Tomorrow's World (IRE) (Machiavellian (USA)) **Tracy Turner**

Other Owners: Mr Mark Barrett, Mr Nick Conduit, Mr Gregory Cowell, Mr James Doyle, Mr J. A. Gent, Mr Peter Hunt, Mrs Sally Hunt, Mr A. Morrish, Mr R. Sherwood, Mr R. L. Squire, Mr R. G. Tizzard, Mrs Sarah Tizzard.

Jockey (NH): Tom O'Connor. **Apprentice:** Jake Payne, Ryan While.

648 **MR JAMES TURNER, Helperby**
Postal: **Mayfield Farm, Norton-le-Clay, Helperby, York, North Yorkshire, YO61 2RS**
Contacts: **PHONE (01423) 322239 FAX (01423) 322239**

1 NEEDY MCCREDIE, 6, ch m Needwood Blade—Vocation (IRE) **J. R. Turner**
2 SHELOMOH (IRE), 11, b g Zaffaran (USA)—Parson's Run **Mr A. J. Ward**

Other Owners: Miss S. J. Turner, G. W. Turner, Mr J. R. Turner, Mrs Janet Ward.

Assistant Trainer: Oliver J. Turner

Jockey (flat): Paddy Aspell, Paul Hanagan.

649 **MRS KAREN TUTTY, Northallerton**
Postal: **Trenholme House Farm, Osmotherley, Northallerton, North Yorkshire, DL6 3QA**
Contacts: **PHONE (01609) 883624 FAX 01609 883624 MOBILE (07967) 837406**
E-MAIL karentutty@btinternet.com WEBSITE www.karentuttyracing.co.uk

1 GRACEFUL DESCENT (FR), 7, b m Hawk Wing (USA)—Itab (USA) **Thoroughbred Homes Ltd**
2 KILCASKIN STAR (IRE), 6, b g Zagreb (USA)—Kentucky Key (IRE) **Thoroughbred Homes Ltd**

Amateur: Miss G. Tutty, Miss P. Tutty.

650 **MR NIGEL TWISTON-DAVIES, Cheltenham**
Postal: **T/a Grange Hill Farm Limited, Grange Hill Farm, Naunton, Cheltenham, Gloucestershire, GL54 3AY**
Contacts: **PHONE (01451) 850278 FAX (01451) 850101 MOBILE (07836) 664440**
E-MAIL nigel@nigeltwistondavies.com WEBSITE www.nigeltwistondavies.co.uk

1 ACKERTAC (IRE), 7, ch g Anshan—Clonsingle Native (IRE) **Mark Aspey & Steve Catton**
2 ALBERT STROLLER, 5, b g Fair Mix (IRE)—Persistent Gunner **Geoffrey & Donna Keeys**
3 ASTRACAD (FR), 6, br g Cadoudal (FR)—Astre Eria (FR) **H. R. Mould**
4 BALLYFITZ, 12, b g Overbury (IRE)—Running For Gold **Mr F. J. Mills & Mr W. Mills**
5 BATTLECRY, 11, b br g Accordion—Miss Orchestra (IRE) **N. A. Twiston-Davies**
6 BENBENS (IRE), 7, ch g Beneficial—Millicent Bridge (IRE) **Mrs S. E. Such**
7 BILLIE MAGERN, 8, b g Alderbrook—Outfield **R. Nicholls**
8 BOBBIE MAGERN, 7, b g Alderbrook—Outfield **R. Nicholls**
9 BRING ON THE JUDGE (IRE), 9, b g Witness Box (USA)—Turnpike Junction **Mrs S. Bauer**
10 BROUSSE EN FEUX (FR), 9, ch m April Night (FR)—Antoniola (FR) **N. A. Twiston-Davies**
11 C'MONTHEHAMMERS (IRE), 9, ch g Snurge—Mounthenry Lady (IRE) **Mr F. J. Mills & Mr W. Mills**
12 CANADIAN DREAMER (IRE), 5, b g Westerner—Ride The Tide (IRE) **Mr R. Bauer**
13 CAUSING CHAOS (IRE), 6, b g Alderbrook—Sue's Song **Mr R. J. Rexton**
14 CHAMPAGNE FLORA, 5, b m Alflora (IRE)—Champagne Lil **Mrs J. M. M. Mordaunt**
15 CIVIL SERVANT, 7, gr g Diktat—Zafadola (IRE) **N. A. Twiston-Davies**
16 COOTEHILL (IRE), 8, b g Alflora (IRE)—Dancing Dove (IRE) **Mrs F. E. Griffin**
17 CRESCENT ISLAND (IRE), 9, b g Presenting—Island Crest **Sarah Bays, Jill Scott, Sarah MacEchern**
18 DOUBLE ROSS (IRE), 6, ch g Double Eclipse (IRE)—Kinross **Options O Syndicate**
19 EDUCATED EVANS (IRE), 7, b g Bishop of Cashel—Pavlova (IRE) **Mrs C. S. C. Beresford-Wylie**
20 EMILY'S FLYER (IRE), 5, b m Oscar (IRE)—Lady Rolfe (IRE) **Mr C. Cornes**
21 EPEE CELESTE (FR), 6, ch m Spadoun (FR)—Juste Ciel (USA) **N. A. Twiston-Davies**
22 FIORENZA, 6, b m Kayf Tara—Priests Bridge (IRE) **Geoffrey & Donna Keeys**
23 FLEMISH INVADER (IRE), 9, b g Flemensfirth (USA)—Lite 'n Easy (IRE) **A. M. Armitage**
24 FRASCATI PARK (IRE), 8, b g Bach (IRE)—Hot Curry (IRE) **B. Connell**
25 FRONTIER SPIRIT (IRE), 8, b g New Frontier (IRE)—Psalmist **Jump For Fun Racing**
26 GO ON ARCH (IRE), 6, b g Oscar (IRE)—Good Aim (IRE) **Walters Plant Hire P T Civil Engineering**
27 GOAT CASTLE (IRE), 8, b g Goldmark (USA)—Rolands Girl (IRE) **Ford Associated Racing Team**
28 HELLO BUD (IRE), 14, b g Jurado (USA)—Orchestral Sport (IRE) **Mr S. Murphy**
29 HENOK (FR), 6, ch g Kapgarde (FR)—Harkosa (FR) **Walters Plant Hire**
30 HERECOMESTHEHOLLOW (IRE), 6, ch g Flemensfirth (USA)—Drumcay Polly (IRE) **The Hollow Partnership**
31 HOLLOW BLUE SKY (FR), 5, gr g Turgeon (USA)—Run For Laborie (FR) **The Hollow Partnership**
32 HOLLOW HEARTBEAT (IRE), 5, b g Flemensfirth (USA)—Polly's Joy (IRE) **The Hollow Partnership**
33 HUNTERS LODGE (IRE), 6, ch g Subtle Power (IRE)—Native Orchid (IRE) **R. Nicholls**
34 JAUNTY JOURNEY, 9, ch g Karinga Bay—Jaunty June **Mr C. Roberts**
35 KAYBEEW, 7, b g Alflora (IRE)—Lunareva (USA) **Roberts Green Whittall-Williams Savidge**
36 KAYF ARAMIS, 10, b g Kayf Tara—Ara **Mr J. Goodman**

MR NIGEL TWISTON-DAVIES—continued

37 **KHYBER KIM**, 10, b g Mujahid (USA)—Jungle Rose **Mrs C. M. Mould**
38 **KILVERGAN BOY (IRE)**, 8, br g Zagreb (USA)—Brigante (IRE) **The Yes No Wait Sorries**
39 **LISTEN BOY (IRE)**, 6, ch g Presenting—Buckalong (IRE) **Bryan & Philippa Burrough**
40 **LODGICIAN (IRE)**, 10, b g Grand Lodge (USA)—Dundel (IRE) **The Yes No Wait Sorries**
41 **MAD MOOSE (IRE)**, 8, ch g Presenting—Sheshollystar (IRE) **Middleham Park Racing XXXV & Partner**
42 **MASTER OF THE SEA (IRE)**, 5, b g Misternando—Sea Gale (IRE) **N. A. Twiston-Davies**
43 **MAVALENTA (IRE)**, 5, b m Montjeu (IRE)—Velouette **The Yes No Wait Sorries**
44 **MOUNTAINOUS (IRE)**, 7, b g Milan—Mullaghcloga (IRE) **Walters Plant Hire & James & Jean Potter**
45 **NIKOLA (FR)**, 11, b g Roi de Rome (USA)—Envie de Chalamont (FR) **Graham & Alison Jelley**
46 **NUDGE AND NURDLE (IRE)**, 11, b g Shernazar—Firey Comet (IRE) **The Yes No Wait Sorries**
47 **ORIGINAL PRANKSTER (IRE)**, 7, ch g Carroll House—Kinallen Lady (IRE) **Graham & Alison Jelley**
48 **PAPRADON**, 8, b g Tobougg (IRE)—Salvezza (IRE) **A. J. Cresser**
49 **PEG LEG**, 5, b g Alflora (IRE)—The Lyme Volunteer (IRE) **N. A. Twiston-Davies**
50 **PETTIFOUR (IRE)**, 10, b g Supreme Leader—Queen of Natives (IRE) **Mr J. B. Pettifer**
51 **PIGEON ISLAND**, 9, gr g Daylami (IRE)—Morina (USA) **H. R. Mould**
52 **POWER PACK JACK (IRE)**, 9, b g Rudimentary (USA)—Monas Jem (IRE) **Mr S. Murphy**
53 **QUELQU'UN COMME TOI (FR)**, 8, b g Evening World (FR)—Urta (FR) **RobRoy Racing**
54 **RED RIVERMAN**, 4, b g Haafhd—Mocca (IRE) **Options O Syndicate**
55 **RED ROUBLE (IRE)**, 7, ch g Moscow Society (USA)—Chirouble (IRE) **P. A. Bancroft**
56 **RHUM (FR)**, 7, ch g Dark Moondancer—Ireland (IRE) **H. R. Mould**
57 **ROCKABILLY (FR)**, 7, ch g Robin des Champs (FR)—Massada (FR) **Mrs C. M. Mould**
58 **ROYAL RIVIERA**, 6, b g Nayef (USA)—Miss Cap Ferrat **Mr A. G. Bloom**
59 **SAME DIFFERENCE (IRE)**, 6, b g Mr Combustible (IRE)—Sarahs Reprive (IRE) **Mrs R. I. Vaughan**
60 **SHANNONS BOY (IRE)**, 10, b g Anshan—Dusky Lady **Walters Plant Hire Ltd**
61 **SHERWANI WOLF (IRE)**, 8, b g Loup Sauvage (USA)—Sherwani (IRE) **Mr C. S. Davies**
62 **STORMHOEK (IRE)**, 7, ch g Alderbrook—Auntie Honnie (IRE) **The New Club Partnership**
63 **SWINCOMBE ROCK**, 7, ch g Double Trigger (IRE)—Soloism **Mills & Mason Partnership**
64 **SYBARITE (FR)**, 6, b br g Dark Moondancer—Haida III (FR) **H. R. Mould**
65 **TARA ROSE**, 7, br m Kayf Tara—True Rose (IRE) **Mr B. J. Mould**
66 **THE COCKNEY MACKEM (IRE)**, 6, b g Milan—Divine Prospect (IRE) **Mills & Mason Partnership**
67 **THE GREAT ALFIE**, 9, b g Alflora (IRE)—Like Manner **N. A. Twiston-Davies**
68 **THE MUSICAL GUY (IRE)**, 6, b g Lahib (USA)—Orchestral Sport (IRE) **The Musical Guy's Girls**
69 **THE NEW ONE (IRE)**, 4, b g King's Theatre (IRE)—Thuringe (FR) **Mrs S. E. Such**
70 **TOREADOR (FR)**, 5, b g Epalo (GER)—Etoile d'or II (FR) **Mrs C. M. Mould**
71 **TOUR DES CHAMPS (FR)**, 5, b br g Robin des Champs (FR)—Massada (FR) **H. R. Mould**
72 **TRAFALGAR (FR)**, 5, b g Laveron—Dzaoudzie (FR) **Mr & Mrs Gordon Pink**
73 **VIKING BLOND (FR)**, 7, ch g Varese (FR)—Sweet Jaune (FR) **Mrs C. M. Mould**
74 **WHAT A GOOD NIGHT (IRE)**, 4, br g Westerner—Southern Skies (IRE) **Mr & Mrs Gordon Pink**
75 **WHAT A WARRIOR (IRE)**, 5, b g Westerner—Be Right (IRE) **Mr & Mrs Gordon Pink**
76 **WHAT AN OSCAR (IRE)**, 7, b g Oscar (IRE)—Katie Buckers (IRE) **Mr & Mrs Gordon Pink**
77 **WOOD YER (IRE)**, 6, ch g Anshan—Glenasheen (IRE) **Miss K. J. Holland**
78 **LITTLE JOSH (IRE)**, 10, ch g Pasternak—Miss Top (IRE) **Mr Tony Bloom**

Other Owners: Mr F. J. Allen, Mrs Fanny Armitage, Mr Mark Aspey, Mrs Celia Baker, Mr Michael Baker, Mrs Pam Bates, Mrs E. M. Bathurst, Mrs John Bays, Mr B. R. H. Burrough, Mrs Philippa Burrough, Mr John Cantrill, Mr Steve Catton, Mr Rob Clilverd, Mr Chris Coley, Mr Ian Dunbar, Mr J. Flannery, Mr F. M. Green, Mrs Fiona Gregory, Mr David Hussey, Mr Graham Jelley, Mrs Alison Jelley, Mr Geoffrey Keeys, Mrs Donna Keeys, Mr H. J. Kelly, Mrs S. A. MacEchern, Mr David Mason, Mr F. J. Mills, Mr W. R. Mills, P T Civil Engineering (UK) Ltd, Mr T. S. Palin, Mr C. Pettigrew, Mrs Scilla Phillips, Mr G. K. G. Pink, Mrs K. M. Pink, Mr J. E. Potter, Mrs J. E. Potter, Mr G. M. Powell, Mrs V. J. Powell, Mr M. Prince, Mr R. M. Richards, Mr G. A. Roberts, Mr Ian A. Robinson, Mrs Gillian Robinson, Mr Mark Savidge, Mrs C. M. Scott, Mr R. I. Sims, Mr N. A. Twiston-Davies, Walters Plant Hire Ltd, Mr E. B. Whittal-Williams, Mr S. Wignall.

Assistant Trainer: Carl Llewellyn

Jockey (NH): Sam Twiston-Davies, David England. **Conditional:** Tom Molloy, William Twiston-Davies. **Amateur:** Mr Ryan Hatch, Mr Ally Rawlinson.

---

651 **MR JAMES UNETT, Oswestry**
Postal: **Garden Cottage, Tedsmore, West Felton, Oswestry, Shropshire, SY11 4HD**
Contacts: PHONE **(01743) 709529** FAX **(01743) 709529** MOBILE **(07887) 534753**

1 **CHILLIANWALLAH**, 4, ch g Primo Valentino (IRE)—Spark Up **Miss C. H. Jones**
2 **HERBERT**, 4, gr g Erhaab (USA)—Ruby Vision (IRE) **G. J. G. Roberts**
3 **KNOWE HEAD (NZ)**, 5, b g High Chaparral (IRE)—Royal Errant (NZ) **Lord S. J. Stone**
4 **MCCOOL BANNANAS**, 4, b g Firebreak—Dances With Angels (IRE) **Mr M. A. Sheehy**

MR JAMES UNETT—continued

THREE-YEAR-OLDS

5 **BONNIE BLADE**, b f Needwood Blade—Kyrhena **Shirley Downes & Neil Rowlands**
6 Br f Clodovil (IRE)—Casual Remark (IRE) **Miss C. Doyle**
7 **MONUMENTAL MAN**, b g Vital Equine (IRE)—Spark Up **C. Chell**

TWO-YEAR-OLDS

8 B f 23/4 Firebreak—Amber Mill (Doulab (USA)) (1000)
9 B f 13/4 Mujadil (USA)—Ambria (ITY) (Final Straw) (15000)
10 B f 12/3 Holy Roman Emperor (IRE)—Aurelia (Rainbow Quest (USA)) (17000)
11 B f 4/3 Clodovil (IRE)—Kibarague (Barathea) (5746)
12 B f 12/4 Indesatchel (IRE)—Miss Mirasol (Sheikh Albadou) (7500)

Other Owners: Mrs S. A. Downes, Mr N. Rowlands.

Assistant Trainer: Miss C. H. Jones

---

652 **MR JOHN UPSON, Towcester**
Postal: **Glebe Stables, Blakesley Heath, Maidford, Towcester, Northamptonshire, NN12 8HN**
Contacts: **PHONE (01327) 860043 FAX (01327) 860238**

1 **BEN TROVATO (IRE)**, 6, b g Subtle Power (IRE)—Dawn Eile (IRE) **Lord Nicholas Wilson**
2 **CURSUM PERFICIO**, 10, b g Tagula (IRE)—Simply Sooty **The Nap Hand Partnership**
3 **DRAMATIC VICTORY (IRE)**, 5, b g Old Vic—Pinky The Nose (IRE) **The Nap Hand Partnership**
4 **GRITTI PALACE (IRE)**, 12, b g Duky—Glittering Grit (IRE) **The Nap Hand Partnership**
5 4, B g Vinnie Roe (IRE)—Queens Fantasy **The Nap Hand Partnership**
6 **SAMIZDAT (FR)**, 9, b g Soviet Star (USA)—Secret Account (FR) **Honorvell Partnership**
7 5, B g Dilshaan—Sunset Park (IRE)
8 5, B g Fruits of Love (USA)—Tanti's Storm (IRE)
9 **WISHES OR WATCHES (IRE)**, 12, br g Bravefoot—Shadya's Amal **The Peter Partnership**

Other Owners: M. H. Beesley, D. Deveney, G. G. Fowler, Mr R. W. George, Mrs K. Hopewell, M. E. White.

---

653 **MR MARK USHER, Upper Lambourn**
Postal: **Saxon House Stables, Upper Lambourn, Hungerford, Berkshire, RG17 8QH**
Contacts: **PHONE (01488) 72598 FAX (01488) 73630 MOBILE (07831) 873531**
E-MAIL markusherracing@btconnect.com WEBSITE www.markusherracing.co.uk

1 **BEST BE CAREFUL (IRE)**, 4, b f Exceed And Excel (AUS)—Precautionary **Mrs J. F. Pellett**
2 **BLUE COSSACK (IRE)**, 4, b g Ivan Denisovich (IRE)—Biasca **Reg Brookes & Richard Jurd**
3 **DIAMOND DEE**, 6, ch m Deploy—Diamond Swan **M. D. I. Usher**
4 **FOUR STEPS BACK**, 5, ch g Royal Academy (USA)—Runaway Queen (USA) **Mrs D. J. Hughes**
5 **HONOURABLE KNIGHT (IRE)**, 4, b c Celtic Swing—Deemeh (IRE) **B. Fry**
6 **HOPE POINT**, 4, b f Overbury (IRE)—East Rose **The Ridgeway Partnership**
7 **IDOL DEPUTY (FR)**, 6, gr g Silver Deputy (CAN)—Runaway Venus (USA) **Miss J. C. Blackwell**
8 **KATMAI RIVER (IRE)**, 5, b g Choisir (AUS)—Katavi (USA) **M. D. I. Usher**
9 **LADY OF BURGUNDY**, 6, b m Montjeu—Helena's Paris (IRE) **Mr B.C.Rogan**
10 **LENNOXWOOD (IRE)**, 4, gr ro g Verglas (IRE)—Sigonella (IRE) **Midweek Racing**
11 **MAY'S BOY**, 4, gr c Proclamation (IRE)—Sweet Portia **M. D. I. Usher**
12 4, Ch g Choisir (AUS)—Missish **M. D. I. Usher**
13 **MY SISTER**, 5, b m Royal Applause—Mysistra (FR) **Itchen Valley Stud & Partners**
14 **OUR GOLDEN BOY (IRE)**, 6, b g Milan—Just Little **The Golden Boys**
15 **RIDGEWAY HAWK**, 4, ch g Monsieur Bond (IRE)—Barefooted Flyer (USA) **Goodracing Partnership**
16 **RIDGEWAY SAPPHIRE**, 5, b m Zafeen (FR)—Barefooted Flyer (USA) **Goodracing Partnership**
17 **SAXON HOUSE (IRE)**, 6, b g Flemensfirth (USA)—Suka (IRE) **Mrs Fulke Walwyn**
18 **SPICE FAIR**, 5, ch g Trade Fair—Focosa (ITY) **Saxon House Racing**
19 **TITAN DIAMOND (IRE)**, 4, b g Diamond Green (FR)—Ditton Dancer **I.J.Sheward**

THREE-YEAR-OLDS

20 **CAPE RAINBOW**, b c Cape Cross (IRE)—Mambo Halo (USA) **M. D. I. Usher**
21 **HIGH FIVE PRINCE (IRE)**, br g Strategic Prince—Lady Georgina **Miss D. G. Kerr**
22 **LADY PERCY (IRE)**, b f Sir Percy—Genuinely (IRE) **Ushers Court**
23 **LITTLECOTE LADY**, b f Byron—Barefooted Flyer (USA) **Littlecote House Racing**

MR MARK USHER—continued

24 **SONGBIRD BLUES**, b f Beat All (USA)—Billie Holiday **Goodracing Partnership**
25 **SWEET OVATION**, b f Royal Applause—Sweetest Revenge (IRE) **The Ridgeway Bloodstock Company Ltd**
26 **VALLEY QUEEN**, b f Three Valleys (USA)—Queen of Havana (USA) **Itchen Valley Stud**

TWO-YEAR-OLDS

27 Ch f 5/4 Trade Fair—Bold Love (Bold Edge) **Saxon House Racing**
28 B f 12/4 Haatef (USA)—Felona (Caerleon (USA)) (7142) **Ushers Court**
29 B f 15/1 Ishiguru (USA)—Honesty Pays (Dr Fong (USA)) (6500) **High Five Racing**
30 **IT'S TABOO**, b f 20/3 Tobougg (IRE)—Faraway Moon (Distant Relative) **Mrs T. J. Channing-Williams**
31 **JINKS AND CO**, ch f 20/3 Ishiguru (USA)—Crofters Ceilidh (Scottish Reel) (11904) **The High Jinks Partnership**
32 **LITTLECOTE LAD**, b c 23/3 Multiplex—Divine Love (IRE) (Barathea (IRE)) **Littlecote House Racing**
33 Ch f 29/4 Notnowcato—Mary Sea (FR) (Selkirk (USA)) (2000) **M. D. I. Usher**
34 Ch f 8/3 Dutch Art—Nemorosa (Pivotal) **The Golden Boys**
35 B c 12/5 Byron—Sweetest Revenge (IRE) (Daggers Drawn (USA)) **The Ridgeway Alchemist's**
36 Ch f 4/4 Three Valleys (USA)—Twitch Hill (Piccolo) (1000) **Ushers Court**

---

654 **MR ROGER VARIAN**, Newmarket
Postal: **Kremlin House Stables, Fordham Road, Newmarket, Suffolk, CB8 7AQ**
Contacts: PHONE (01638) 661702 FAX (01638) 667018 MOBILE (07879) 414664
E-MAIL roger@varianstable.com

1 **ALAINMAAR (FR)**, 6, b g Johar (USA)—Lady Elgar (IRE) **Hamdan Al Maktoum**
2 **BEYOND DESIRE**, 5, b m Invincible Spirit (IRE)—Compradore **Clipper Group Holdings Ltd**
3 **BOOGIE SHOES**, 4, b g Bertolini (USA)—Space Time (FR) **A. D. Spence**
4 **DARK PROMISE**, 5, b m Shamardal (USA)—La Sky (IRE) **Lordship Stud**
5 **DUBAWI SOUND**, 4, b c Dubawi (IRE)—Hannah's Music **Pearl Bloodstock Limited**
6 **ELZAAM (AUS)**, 4, b c Redoute's Choice (AUS)—Mambo In Freeport (USA) **Hamdan Al Maktoum**
7 **EMKANAAT**, 4, b g Green Desert (USA)—Miss Anabaa **Michael Hill**
8 **ETON FOREVER (IRE)**, 5, b g Oratorio (IRE)—True Joy (IRE) **H.R.H. Sultan Ahmad Shah**
9 **GLADYS' GAL**, 4, b f Tobougg (IRE)—Charming Lotte **Fishlake Commercial Motors Ltd**
10 **HARRY PATCH**, 6, b g Lujain (USA)—Hoh Dancer **Mrs G. A. S. Jarvis**
11 **ITTIRAD (USA)**, 4, b g Dubai Destination (USA)—Noushkey **Sheikh Ahmed Al Maktoum**
12 **JAARYAH (IRE)**, 4, ch f Halling (USA)—Albahja **Sheikh Ahmed Al Maktoum**
13 **JIWEN (CAN)**, 4, b br f Singspiel (IRE)—Love Medicine (USA) **Hamdan Al Maktoum**
14 **KOTA SAS (IRE)**, 4, b g Cape Cross (IRE)—Harda Arda (USA) **H.R.H. Sultan Ahmad Shah**
15 **KUDA HURAA (IRE)**, 4, b g Montjeu (IRE)—Healing Music (FR) **Mrs F. H. Hay**
16 **LAAHEB**, 6, b g Cape Cross (IRE)—Maskunah (IRE) **Hamdan Al Maktoum**
17 **MIJHAAR (IRE)**, 4, b c Shirocco (GER)—Jathaabeh **Sheikh Ahmed Al Maktoum**
18 **NAHRAIN**, 4, ch f Selkirk (USA)—Bahr **Sheikh Ahmed Al Maktoum**
19 **NATIVE COLONY**, 4, b g St Jovite (USA)—Self Esteem **Native Colony Partnership**
20 **PEKAN STAR**, 5, b g Montjeu (IRE)—Delicieuse Lady **H.R.H. Sultan Ahmad Shah**
21 **SHAHZAN (IRE)**, 4, br c Dansili—Femme Fatale **H.R.H. Sultan Ahmad Shah**
22 **SHIMMERING SURF (IRE)**, 5, b m Danehill Dancer (IRE)—Sun On The Sea (IRE) **P. L. Winkworth**
23 **SHUBAT**, 5, ch g Monsun (GER)—Zaynaat **Sheikh Ahmed Al Maktoum**
24 **SRI PUTRA**, 6, b h Oasis Dream—Wendylina (IRE) **H.R.H. Sultan Ahmad Shah**
25 **STEPS (IRE)**, 4, br c Verglas (IRE)—Killinallan **Michael Hill**
26 **ZAFARANA**, 4, b f Tiger Hill (IRE)—Miss Meltemi **Mr M. Al Suboosi**

THREE-YEAR-OLDS

27 **AFRAAH (USA)**, b f Hard Spun (USA)—Sarayir (USA) **Hamdan Al Maktoum**
28 **AL BAIDAA**, b f Exceed And Excel (AUS)—Intrum Morshaan (IRE) **S. Ali**
29 **AL FREEJ (IRE)**, b f Iffraaj—Why Now **S. Ali**
30 **ALJAMAAHEER (IRE)**, ch c Dubawi (IRE)—Kelly Nicole (IRE) **Hamdan Al Maktoum**
31 **ALMOST GEMINI (IRE)**, gr c Dylan Thomas (IRE)—Streetcar (IRE) **Mrs F. H. Hay**
32 **ALWARGA (USA)**, b f Street Sense (USA)—Sheroog (USA) **Sheikh Ahmed Al Maktoum**
33 **ALZAHRA**, b f Exceed And Excel (AUS)—Aunty Mary **Sheikh Ahmed Al Maktoum**
34 **AMBIVALENT (IRE)**, b f Authorized (IRE)—Darrery **A. S. Belhab**
35 **ATTWAAL (IRE)**, b g Teofilo (IRE)—Qasirah (IRE) **Sheikh Ahmed Al Maktoum**
36 **BAHEEJA**, b f Dubawi (IRE)—Hasty Words (IRE) **Sheikh Ahmed Al Maktoum**
37 **CAMERON HIGHLAND (IRE)**, b c Galileo (IRE)—Landmark (USA) **H.R.H. Sultan Ahmad Shah**
38 Br f Oasis Dream—Celtic Fling **P. D. Savill**
39 **EAMAADD**, b c Medicean—Emanant **Sheikh Ahmed Al Maktoum**
40 **EKTIHAAM (IRE)**, b c Invincible Spirit (IRE)—Liscune (IRE) **Hamdan Al Maktoum**
41 **ELYASSAAT**, b c Nayef (USA)—Blue Symphony **Hamdan Al Maktoum**

MR ROGER VARIAN—continued

42 **FARRAAJ (IRE)**, b c Dubai Destination (USA)—Pastorale **Sheikh Ahmed Al Maktoum**
43 **FIRDAWS (USA)**, b f Mr Greeley (USA)—Eswarah **Hamdan Al Maktoum**
44 **FRASERS HILL**, ch c Selkirk (USA)—Shemriyna (IRE) **H.R.H. Sultan Ahmad Shah**
45 **FULL SWING**, br c Manduro (GER)—Gloriosia (FR) **A. D. Spence**
46 **GO DUTCH (IRE)**, ch c Dutch Art—Paix Royale **K Allen, R Marchant, G Moss & G Jarvis**
47 **HAVIN' A GOOD TIME (IRE)**, b f Jeremy (USA)—Flanders (IRE) **A. D. Spence**
48 **HENRY ALLINGHAM**, ch g Three Valleys (USA)—Hoh Dancer **R Baines, J Collins & N Horsfall**
49 **KEYAADI**, b g Iffraaj—Arabescato (UAE) **Sheikh Ahmed Al Maktoum**
50 **KHAJOOL (IRE)**, ch f Haafhd—Khulood (USA) **Hamdan Al Maktoum**
51 **MAAKIRR (IRE)**, b c Street Cry (IRE)—Zayn Zen **Sheikh Ahmed Al Maktoum**
52 **MAZEYDD**, b c Motivator—Jathaabeh **Sheikh Ahmed Al Maktoum**
53 **MIN BANAT ALREEH (IRE)**, b f Oasis Dream—Tariysha (IRE) **Hamdan Al Maktoum**
54 **MOKBIL (IRE)**, b g Dansili—Chatifa (IRE) **Hamdan Al Maktoum**
55 **MONROE**, b f Tomba—Princess Zara **Mrs P. Good**
56 **MORATAB (IRE)**, b g Dubai Destination (USA)—Bahr **Sheikh Ahmed Al Maktoum**
57 **MOSSBRAE**, ch g Selkirk (USA)—Frosty Welcome (USA) **Highclere Thoroughbred Racing -Spearmint**
58 **MUTAALEQ (IRE)**, b c Oasis Dream—Siringas (IRE) **Hamdan Al Maktoum**
59 **MUTASADDER (USA)**, b c Distorted Humor (USA)—Dessert (USA) **Hamdan Al Maktoum**
60 **MUZDAAN (IRE)**, ch f Exceed And Excel (AUS)—Belle Genius (USA) **Sheikh Ahmed Al Maktoum**
61 **MYLINGTON MAID**, b f Dubai Destination (USA)—Urania **Ketton Ashwell Ltd**
62 B c Notnowcato—Nsx **H.R.H. Sultan Ahmad Shah**
63 **OBBOORR**, b c Cape Cross (IRE)—Felawnah (USA) **Sheikh Ahmed Al Maktoum**
64 **OOJOOBA**, b f Monsun (GER)—Ameerat **Sheikh Ahmed Al Maktoum**
65 **OSUS (USA)**, b g Street Sense—Aurelia (USA) **Hamdan Al Maktoum**
66 **PANETTONE (IRE)**, b f Montjeu (IRE)—Tea Break **Mr Duncan Jones & Dr Sosie Kassab**
67 **PERFECT STEP (IRE)**, b f Iffraaj—Spiritual Air **Clipper Group Holdings Ltd**
68 **PINK DAMSEL (IRE)**, b f Galileo (IRE)—Riskaverse (USA) **Mrs F. H. Hay**
69 **RIOJA RESERVA**, b f Haafhd—High Reserve **Helena Springfield Ltd**
70 **ROSCOE**, b g Oasis Dream—Hydro Calido (USA) **Lordship Stud**
71 **ROSE SEASON**, b f Cape Cross (IRE)—Endorsement **S. Ali**
72 **SABAWEEYA**, b f Street Cry (IRE)—Marienbad (FR) **S. Ali**
73 **SHABORA (IRE)**, b f Cape Cross (IRE)—Wardat Allayl (IRE) **Sheikh Ahmed Al Maktoum**
74 **SHALEEK**, ch f Pivotal—Dorrati (USA) **Sheikh Ahmed Al Maktoum**
75 **SIGNOR SASSI**, b c Acclamation—Fairy Contessa (IRE) **Mr P. D. Smith**
76 **SOUND HEARTS (USA)**, b f Sir Percy—Crystal Seas **Mr Y. Masuda**
77 **SPORTING GOLD (IRE)**, b c Shirocco (GER)—Pink Stone (FR) **A. D. Spence**
78 **TAFAWUK (USA)**, b g Nayef (USA)—Yaqeen **Hamdan Al Maktoum**
79 **TAZWEED (IRE)**, b g Dubawi (IRE)—Albahja **Sheikh Ahmed Al Maktoum**
80 **TIOMAN PEARL**, b c Royal Applause—Mazarine Blue **H.R.H. Sultan Ahmad Shah**
81 **WATHEEQ (USA)**, b g Street Cry (IRE)—Mehthaaf (USA) **Hamdan Al Maktoum**
82 **WHATSOFUNNY (IRE)**, ch f Rock of Gibraltar (IRE)—Celtic Heroine (IRE) **P. D. Savill**
83 **YOU DON'T LOVE ME (IRE)**, b f Teofilo (IRE)—Alleluia **P. Makin**
84 **ZANOTTI**, b c Authorized (IRE)—Majestic Sakeena (IRE) **Saleh Al Homaizi & Imad Al Sagar**
85 **ZOWAINA**, b f Manduro (GER)—Zaynaat **Sheikh Ahmed Al Maktoum**

TWO-YEAR-OLDS

86 **AGLAOPHONOS**, ch c 7/3 Dutch Art—
Lasting Image (Zilzal (USA)) (60000) **Sir Alex Ferguson & Sotirios Hassiakos**
87 B f 29/3 Dalakhani (IRE)—Albahja (Sinndar (IRE)) **Sheikh Ahmed Al Maktoum**
88 Br f 30/1 New Approach (IRE)—Almoutezah (USA (Storm Cat (USA)) **Hamdan Al Maktoum**
89 **ALOHA**, b f 28/2 With Approval (CAN)—Almamia (Hernando (FR)) **Miss K. Rausing**
90 B f 20/3 New Approach (IRE)—Ameerat (Mark of Esteem (IRE)) **Sheikh Ahmed Al Maktoum**
91 B f 23/3 Teofilo (IRE)—Anaamil (IRE) (Darshaan) **Sheikh Ahmed Al Maktoum**
92 B c 18/3 Danehill Dancer (IRE)—Anna Pallida (Sadler's Wells (USA)) (400000) **H.R.H. Sultan Ahmad Shah**
93 **ARDINGLY (IRE)**, b f 8/4 Danehill Dancer (IRE)—Asnieres (Spend A Buck (USA)) (300000) **Mrs F. H. Hay**
94 B c 2/3 Cape Cross (IRE)—Aryaamm (IRE) (Galileo (IRE)) **Sheikh Ahmed Al Maktoum**
95 B c 28/2 Cape Cross (IRE)—Atamana (IRE) (Lahib (USA)) **Sheikh Ahmed Al Maktoum**
96 Ch f 5/4 Mount Nelson—Atlantic Light (Linamix (FR)) (16000) **Ketton Ashwell Ltd**
97 **BALLOOR (USA)**, b f 20/4 Pivotal—Nasmatt (Danehill (USA)) **Sheikh Ahmed Al Maktoum**
98 B c 7/4 Exceed And Excel (AUS)—Blue Parade (Singspiel (IRE)) (100000)
99 Ch c 3/5 Sir Percy—Bombazine (IRE) (Generous (IRE)) (260000) **Saleh Al Homaizi & Imad Al Sagar**
100 Ch f 24/1 Tale of The Cat (USA)—Breathtaking (USA) (Mineshaft (USA)) (73260)
101 Ch f 25/1 Zamindar (USA)—Bunood (IRE) (Sadler's Wells (USA)) **Hamdan Al Maktoum**
102 **CHELWOOD GATE (IRE)**, b grc 8/2 Aussie Rules—Jusoor (USA) (El Prado (IRE)) (45714) **Mrs F. H. Hay**
103 Bl c 2/2 New Approach (IRE)—Comic (IRE) (Be My Chief (USA)) (220000) **Hamdan Al Maktoum**

MR ROGER VARIAN—continued

104 Ch c 23/4 Giant's Causeway (USA)—Danzig's Humor (USA) (Lemon Drop Kid (USA)) (61050)
105 B f 19/2 Danehill Dancer (IRE)—Dashing (IRE) (Sadler's Wells (USA)) **Saleh Al Homaizi & Imad Al Sagar**
106 B c 29/1 Raven's Pass (USA)—Delphinus (Soviet Star (USA)) (150000) **A. D. Spence**
107 B c 16/3 Dark Angel (IRE)—Dilag (IRE) (Almutawakel) (98522) **S. Suhail**
108 Gr f 26/3 Excellent Art—Divine Grace (IRE) (Definite Article) (125000) **A. D. Spence**
109 Ch c 24/3 Pivotal—Dorrati (USA) (Dubai Millennium) **Sheikh Ahmed Al Maktoum**
110 DUCAB (IRE), b c 4/4 Dansili—Twyla Tharp (IRE) (Sadler's Wells (USA)) (33000) **S. Ali**
111 B c 29/3 Invincible Spirit (IRE)—Fonda (USA) (Quiet American (USA)) (280000) **Hamdan Al Maktoum**
112 B c 14/1 Raven's Pass (USA)—Ghaidaa (IRE) (Cape Cross (IRE)) **Hamdan Al Maktoum**
113 B c 9/4 Azamour (IRE)—Glenmara (USA) (Known Fact (USA)) (70000) **A. D. Spence**
114 Ch c 4/3 Distorted Humor (USA)—Habibti (USA) (Tabasco Cat (USA)) **Hamdan Al Maktoum**
115 B f 10/2 Refuse To Bend (IRE)—Hall Hee (IRE) (Invincible Spirit (IRE)) **Sheikh Ahmed Al Maktoum**
116 B br c 28/3 Authorized (IRE)—Henties Bay (IRE) (Cape Cross (IRE)) (120000) **H.R.H. Sultan Ahmad Shah**
117 HORSTED KEYNES (FR), ch c 22/2 Giant's Causeway (USA)—
Viking's Cove (USA) (Miswaki (USA)) (145000) **Mrs F. H. Hay**
118 Ch c 10/4 Iffraaj—Hurricane Irene (IRE) (Green Desert (USA)) (110000) **Sheikh Ahmed Al Maktoum**
119 B c 25/4 Manduro (GER)—Jalousie (USA) (Barathea (IRE)) **Mr D. A. Yardy**
120 B c 17/3 Green Tune (USA)—Janistra (USA) (Grand Slam (USA)) (106732) **S. Suhail**
121 B f 28/3 Singspiel (IRE)—Jathaabeh (Nashwan (USA)) **Sheikh Ahmed Al Maktoum**
122 B c 20/4 Authorized (IRE)—Kartuzy (JPN) (Polish Precedent (USA)) (20000) **S. Ali**
123 B c 30/1 Acclamation—Keriyka (IRE) (Indian Ridge) (100000) **Clipper Group Holdings Ltd**
124 B c 15/2 Shamardal (USA)—Lanzana (IRE) (Kalanisi (IRE)) (100000) **Sheikh Ahmed Al Maktoum**
125 B f 9/2 Tapit (USA)—Lexi Star (USA) (Crypto Star (USA)) (91575) **Pearl Bloodstock Limited**
126 B c 11/2 Dubawi (IRE)—Makaaseb (USA) (Pulpit (USA)) **Hamdan Al Maktoum**
127 B g 24/2 Dubai Destination (USA)—Malaaq (Green Desert (USA)) **Mrs G. A. S. Jarvis**
128 Ch c 17/2 New Approach (IRE)—Masaafat (Act One) **Hamdan Al Maktoum**
129 Ch f 19/2 Nayef—Millistar (Galileo (IRE)) **Helena Springfield Ltd**
130 B f 10/4 Marju (IRE)—Much Faster (IRE) (Fasliyev (USA)) (180000) **Saleh Al Homaizi & Imad Al Sagar**
131 Ch c 12/4 Kheleyf (USA)—My Dubai (IRE) (Dubai Millennium) **Sheikh Ahmed Al Maktoum**
132 NADMAH, ch f 12/4 Sakhee (USA)—Hamsat Elqamar (Nayef (USA)) **Sheikh Hamdan Bin Maktoum Al Maktoum**
133 B f 21/4 Invincible Spirit (IRE)—Qasirah (IRE) (Machiavellian (USA)) **Sheikh Ahmed Al Maktoum**
134 B f 7/4 Iffraaj—Red Vale (IRE) (Halling (USA)) (145000) **Mrs F. H. Hay**
135 B c 16/4 Elusive City (USA)—Rock Salt (Selkirk (USA)) (105000) **Sheikh Ahmed Al Maktoum**
136 B f 11/1 Shirocco (GER)—Sahara Lady (IRE) (Lomitas) (9523) **P. L. Winkworth**
137 SEVERIANO (USA), b c 19/1 Danehill Dancer (USA)—
Time Control (Sadler's Wells (USA)) **Merry Fox Stud Limited**
138 SINISTER (IRE), b c 8/4 Sinndar (IRE)—Shamsada (IRE) (Kahyasi)
139 Ch c 22/2 Exceed And Excel (AUS)—Sister Moonshine (FR) (Tycoon) (120000) **Sheikh Ahmed Al Maktoum**
140 B c 18/2 Motivator—Small Fortune (Anabaa (USA)) **Fishlake Commercial Motors Ltd**
141 SOARING SPIRITS (IRE), ch c 18/3 Tamayuz—Follow My Lead (Night Shift (USA)) (32840) **Mrs G. O'Driscoll**
142 B c 22/1 Raven's Pass (USA)—Sortita (GER) (Monsun (GER)) **Hamdan Al Maktoum**
143 Br c 17/3 Singspiel (IRE)—Street Fire (IRE) (Street Cry (IRE)) **A. D. Spence**
144 B c 2/3 Refuse To Bend (IRE)—Summerstrand (IRE) (Cape Cross (IRE)) **Sheikh Ahmed Al Maktoum**
145 B f 29/1 Elusive City (USA)—Sweetsformysweet (USA) (Forest Wildcat (USA))
146 Br f 29/4 Cape Cross (IRE)—Tarfishi (Mtoto) **Sheikh Ahmed Al Maktoum**
147 TENOR (IRE), b c 18/2 Oratorio (IRE)—
Cedar Sea (IRE) (Persian Bold) (36945) **Highclere Thoroughbred Racing-John Porter**
148 B c 25/2 Green Desert (USA)—Thornton Piccolo (Groom Dancer (USA)) (150000) **Mr P. D. Smith**
149 Br f 19/2 Exceed And Excel (AUS)—Turning Leaf (IRE) (Last Tycoon) (85000) **Thurloe Thoroughbreds XXX**
150 TUSCAN FUN, ch c 25/3 Medicean—Elfin Laughter (Alzao (USA)) (22000) **K Allen, R Marchant & G Jarvis**
151 B c 5/4 Dansili—Vital Statistics (Indian Ridge) (110000) **Sheikh Ahmed Al Maktoum**
152 B c 1/3 Monsun (GER)—Zahrat Dubai (Unfuwain (USA)) **Sheikh Ahmed Al Maktoum**

Other Owners: I. J. Al-Sagar, Mr K. Allen, R. J. Baines, Mr J. A. Collins, Mrs H. S. Ellingsen, Sir A. Ferguson, T. F. Harris, Mrs E. A. Harris, S. Hassiakos, The Hon H. M. Herbert, Highclere Thoroughbred Racing Ltd, Saleh Al Homaizi, Mr N. P. Horsfall, Mr D. Jones, Dr S. C. Kassab, Mr D. R. Mann, R. P. Marchant, Mr G. Moss, Mr N. P. Nunn, O. J. W. Pawle, Mr J. A. B. Stafford, M. Weinfeld.

Assistant Trainers: Gay Jarvis, David Eustace

Jockey (flat): Neil Callan. **Apprentice:** Simon De Donato, Malin Holmberg, Jean Van Overmeire.

655 MR EDWARD VAUGHAN, Newmarket
Postal: **Machell Place Stables, Old Station Road, Newmarket, Suffolk, CB8 8DW**
Contacts: PHONE **(01638) 667411** FAX **(01638) 667452** MOBILE **(07799) 144901**
E-MAIL **ed@efvaughan.com** WEBSITE **www.efvaughan.com**

1 **DANCE AND DANCE (IRE)**, 6, b g Royal Applause—Caldy Dancer (IRE) **Mr M. Rashid**
2 **GOOGLETTE (IRE)**, 4, b f Exceed And Excel (AUS)—Jayzdoll (IRE) **Pearl Bloodstock Limited**
3 **REDVERS (IRE)**, 4, br g Ishiguru (USA)—Cradle Brief (IRE) **M. J. C. Hawkes & E. J. C. Hawkes**
4 **ROBIN HOODS BAY**, 4, b g Motivator—Bijou A Moi **A. M. Pickering**
5 **SCARBOROUGH LILY**, 4, b f Dansili—Queen Isabella **A. M. Pickering**
6 **WHITBY JET (IRE)**, 4, b g Mujadil (USA)—Anazah (USA) **A. M. Pickering**

THREE-YEAR-OLDS

7 **ADELINDUS**, b f King's Best (USA)—Possessive Artiste **Mr & Mrs W R Swinburn**
8 **AUBRIETIA**, b f Dutch Art—Petong's Pet **C. J. Murfitt**
9 **CLAPPED**, b g Royal Applause—Susun Kelapa (USA) **Hamer & Hawkes**
10 **COMPLACENT (IRE)**, b f Kheleyf (USA)—Mambodorga (USA) **E. F. Vaughan**
11 **DIAMONDSINHEREYES (IRE)**, b f Diamond Green (FR)—Glencoagh Order (IRE) **E. F. Vaughan**
12 **FLAMBOROUGH BREEZE**, ro f Ad Valorem (USA)—Lothian Lass (IRE) **A. M. Pickering**
13 **LEGENDARY**, b g Exceed And Excel (AUS)—Red Carnation (IRE) **Mrs D. M. Swinburn**
14 **NETTIE**, b f Nayef (USA)—Bakhtawar (IRE) **Mrs D. M. Swinburn**
15 **QUIZZED**, b f Oratorio (IRE)—Tree Peony **Mr O. G. Glenn**
16 **SHREDDING (IRE)**, b g Tiger Hill (IRE)—In The Ribbons **Hamer & Hawkes**
17 **SOLEMN OATH (USA)**, b c Elusive Quality (USA)—Bathsheba (USA) **Gold Rush Thoroughbreds**
18 **VERGE (IRE)**, b f Acclamation—Marliana (IRE) **Hungerford Park Limited**

TWO-YEAR-OLDS

19 Ch c 14/2 Byron—Caldy Dancer (IRE) (Soviet Star (USA)) (15000) **Mr M. Rashid**
20 Ch f 14/2 Giant's Causeway (USA)—Clear In The West (USA) (Gone West (USA)) (48840) **Pearl Bloodstock**
21 B f 20/2 Singspiel (IRE)—Mureefa (USA) (Bahri (USA)) (27000) **Mr M. Rashid**
22 Ch c 5/3 Mount Nelson—Phoebe Woodstock (IRE) (Grand Lodge (USA)) (29000) **S. Ali**
23 B c 24/2 Shamardal (USA)—Shraayet (Nayef (USA)) (55000) **Mr S. Misfer**
24 Ch c 26/2 Starcraft (NZ)—Shuaily (PER) (Shuailaan (USA)) (65000)
25 B f 23/3 Nayef (USA)—Tahirah (Green Desert (USA)) (3523) **C. J. Murfitt**

Other Owners: Mr John Fleming, Mr C. M. Hamer, Mr M. Hawkes, Mr E. J. C. Hawkes, Mr Thomas Whitehead.

656 MR NICKY VAUGHAN, Market Drayton
Postal: **Helshaw Grange, Warrant Road, Stoke Heath, Market Drayton, Shropshire, TF9 2JP**
Contacts: PHONE **(01630) 637146** FAX **(01630) 637147** MOBILE **(07771) 700183**
E-MAIL **nicky@nickyvaughanracing.com** WEBSITE **www.nickyvaughanracing.com**

1 **CAVENDISH ROAD (IRE)**, 6, b g Bachelor Duke (USA)—Gronchi Rosa (IRE) **Mrs L. J. Vaughan**
2 **CHES JICARO (IRE)**, 4, ch g Majestic Missile (IRE)—Kelso Magic (USA) **G. D. Kendrick**
3 **GEE MAJOR**, 5, b g Reset (AUS)—Polly Golightly **D. Sykes**
4 **HIGH BALL ROLLER**, 4, ch g Selkirk (USA)—Minerva (IRE) **Mr W. A. Tinkler**
5 **INDE COUNTRY**, 4, b f Indesatchel (IRE)—Countrywide Girl (IRE) **Swanlow Stud**
6 **IRON STEP**, 4, gr g Dubawi (IRE)—Giorgia Rae (IRE) **Mr W. A. Tinkler**
7 **OMID**, 4, b g Dubawi (IRE)—Mille Couleurs (FR) **Mr W. A. Tinkler**
8 **POLLY MCGINTY**, 4, ch f Avonbridge—Polly Golightly **D. Sykes**
9 **QUESTIONNAIRE (IRE)**, 4, b f Iffraaj—Kobalt Sea (FR) **G. D. Kendrick**
10 **SUPERCAST (IRE)**, 9, b g Alhaarth (IRE)—Al Euro (FR) **Mrs L. J. Vaughan**
11 **TIGERBILL**, 4, ch g Hold That Tiger (USA)—Regal Asset (USA) **Mr P. Styth**

THREE-YEAR-OLDS

12 B c Primo Valentino (IRE)—Countrywide Girl (IRE) **Swanlow Stud**
13 B f Cockney Rebel (IRE)—Dipple **G. D. Kendrick**
14 **DUTCH MISTRESS**, b f Dutch Art—Royal Mistress **G. D. Kendrick**
15 **VITAL MERLIN**, b g Vital Equine (IRE)—Claradotnet **G. D. Kendrick**

Other Owners: R. Jinks, Mrs A. G. Jinks.

Assistant Trainer: Lynn Vaughan

657 MR TIM VAUGHAN, Bridgend

Postal: **Pant Wilkin Stables, Llanquian Road, Aberthin, Cowbridge, South Glamorgan, CF71 7HE**
Contacts: **PHONE (01446) 771626 FAX (01446) 774371 MOBILE (07841) 800081**
E-MAIL tim@timvaughanracing.com WEBSITE www.timvaughanracing.com

1 **AFFAIR CHEVAL (IRE)**, b g Chevalier (IRE)—Hayley's Affair (IRE) **Mr P. M. Cooper**
2 **ALAND ISLANDS (IRE)**, 6, b g Stowaway—Champagne Lady (IRE) **J. P. McManus**
3 **AMOK (IRE)**, 4, b c Shirocco (GER)—Alharmina **Mr D. R. Passant**
4 **AND HE'S DREAMING (IRE)**, 6, b g Oscar (IRE)—Have At It (IRE) **Middleham Park Racing LX**
5 **ASHES HOUSE (IRE)**, 6, b g Dushyantor (USA)—Cailinclover **Diamond Racing Ltd**
6 **AUGUSTUS GIBBONS (IRE)**, 6, b g Oscar (IRE)—Derravarra Breeze (IRE)
7 **AZELMA**, 5, b m Kayf Tara—Eponine **P. Murphy**
8 **BAHR NOTHING (IRE)**, 6, b g Bahri (USA)—Glen Innes (IRE) **Diamond Racing Ltd**
9 **BALLYMOAT**, 5, b g Grape Tree Road—Frosty Mistress **Cleeve Hill Racing**
10 **BALLYROCK (IRE)**, 6, b g Milan—Ardent Love (IRE) **Pearn's Pharmacies Ltd**
11 **BEN'S FOLLY (IRE)**, 7, ch g Beneficial—Daddy's Folly **Mr D. E. Lovell**
12 **BENEFIT OF YOUTH (IRE)**, 5, b g Beneficial—Persian Avenue (IRE) **Middleham Park Racing LXIV**
13 **BIZNESS ACCOUNT**, 5, b g Muhtarram (USA)—Blazing Connie **Mr G. Perkins**
14 **BOTTMAN (IRE)**, 7, gr g Milan—Dipped In Silver (IRE) **The Oxymorons**
15 **CAPTAIN MOONMAN (IRE)**, 7, b g Milan—Bridgeofallen (IRE) **Diamond Racing Ltd**
16 **CARAVEL (IRE)**, 8, ch g Medicean—Caraiyma (IRE) **Oceans Racing**
17 **CAVALIER SPIRIT**, 5, b g Generous (IRE)—Shayraz **The Oxymorons**
18 **DEFINITE DAWN (IRE)**, 8, br g Definite Article—Good Dawn (IRE) **R. M. Kirkland**
19 **DESTROYER DEPLOYED**, 6, b g Deploy—Supreme Cove **The Craftsmen**
20 **DINGAT (IRE)**, 7, b g Exit To Nowhere (USA)—Dianeme **Mr G. Handley**
21 **ELSAFEER (IRE)**, 7, b g Sakhee (USA)—Nabadhaat (USA) **Delamere Cottage Racing Partners (1996)**
22 **EXPLAINED (IRE)**, 7, b g Exit To Nowhere (USA)—All Told (IRE) **The oceans-racing.com**
23 **FENNIS BOY (IRE)**, 8, ch g Scribano—Beeches Princess (IRE) **Mr C. F. White**
24 **FINNEGAN PADDY (IRE)**, 6, ch g Moscow Society (USA)—Holy Easter (IRE) **Mr J. P. M. Bowtell**
25 **FIRST FANDANGO**, 5, b g Hernando—First Fantasy **WRB Racing 40 & Premier Chance Racing**
26 **FLYING VIC (IRE)**, 5, b g Old Vic—Iona Flyer (IRE) **Armitage, Butt, Rodosthenous, Whitaker**
27 **GALLOX BRIDGE**, 7, b g Kayf Tara—Explorer **Mr D. W. Fox**
28 **GEORGE WOOLF**, 4, b g Iceman—Beading **Pearn's Pharmacies Ltd**
29 **GOT THE URGE (IRE)**, 10, ch g Snurge—Kyle Lamp (IRE) **Mrs J. Lambert**
30 **GRAND LAHOU (FR)**, 9, ch g Cyborg (USA)—Yota (FR) **Oceans Racing**
31 **GREY CRUZENE (USA)**, 6, gr ro g Cozzene (USA)—Cruise Line **The oceans-racing.com**
32 **HAWKHILL (IRE)**, 6, b g Hawk Wing (USA)—Crimphill (IRE) **Mr R. H. D. Smith**
33 **HAZELDENE**, 10, ch g Dancing High—Gaelic Charm (IRE) **Diamond Racing Ltd**
34 **IN THE DOCK (IRE)**, 6, b g Witness Box (USA)—Company Credit (IRE) **R. M. Kirkland**
35 **IVAN VASILEVICH (IRE)**, 4, b c Ivan Denisovich (IRE)—Delisha **Mr C. J. Fahy**
36 **J'ADHERE (FR)**, 7, b g Nikos—Lettre de Lune (FR) **David & Susan Luke**
37 **JAFFONNIEN (FR)**, 9, b g Mansonnien (FR)—Ostenne (FR) **M & S Clarke**
38 **JIMBILL (IRE)**, 6, br g Flying Legend (USA)—Ah Gowan (IRE) **Mr M. E. Moore & Mr B. Ead**
39 **JIVE MASTER (IRE)**, 7, b g Marignan (USA)—Ardkilly Jive **Mrs M. A. O'Sullivan**
40 **JUDICIARY (IRE)**, 5, b g Invincible Spirit (IRE)—Theory of Law **Diamond Racing Ltd**
41 **KENALECK (GER)**, 8, ch g Urban Ocean (FR)—Kengar (FR) **Mr J. M. Duggan & Mr T. P. Duggan**
42 **KIMBERLITE KING**, 10, b g Good Thyne (USA)—Daraheen Diamond (IRE) **Oceans Racing**
43 **KING'S SUNSET (IRE)**, 7, br g Old Vic—Dysart Lady **Brook Farm Bloodstock**
44 **KOULTAS KING (IRE)**, 5, b g Exit To Nowhere (USA)—Carrigmoorna Style (IRE) **Pearn's Pharmacies Ltd**
45 **LANGLEY**, 5, b g Trempolino (USA)—Late Night (GER) **Mr C. Davies**
46 **MAKHZOON (USA)**, 8, b br g Dynaformer (USA)—Boubskaia **Middleham Park Racing I, S Morris & C Davies**
47 **MIGHTY SNAZY**, 8, b g Overbury (IRE)—Come To Tea (IRE) **D N V Churton & Mrs C Wilson**
48 **MIRACLE HOUSE (IRE)**, 8, b g Carroll House—Mum's Miracle (IRE) **Cleeve Hill Racing**
49 **MISS MAYFAIR (IRE)**, 5, b m Indian Danehill (IRE)—Cocktail Party (USA) **T. E. Vaughan**
50 **MIST THE BOAT**, 4, b g Generous (USA)—Baily Mist (IRE) **Craftsmen2**
51 **MON DESIR (FR)**, 4, b g Le Fou (IRE)—Tribal Art (IRE) **Pearn's Pharmacies Ltd**
52 **MRS PEACOCK (IRE)**, 7, b m Dushyantor (USA)—Peacock Feather **select-racing-club.co.uk & Mr C Davies**
53 **OSCAR SIERRA (IRE)**, 6, b g Oscar (IRE)—Einaun (IRE) **Mrs M. A. O'Sullivan**
54 **OUR ISLAND (IRE)**, 7, b g Turtle Island (IRE)—Linda's Leader (IRE) **Mr D. W. Fox**
55 **PADDY PARTRIDGE**, 6, b g Pivotal—Treble Heights (IRE) **Owen Promotions Limited**
56 **PARADISE EXPECTED**, 9, ch m North Briton—Phenomenon **Messrs M. E. & A. D. I. Harris**
57 **PEAKS OF FIRE (IRE)**, 5, b g High Chaparral (IRE)—Crimson Glory **Mr C. Davies**
58 **POSTMASTER**, 10, b g Dansili—Post Modern (USA) **The Bill & Ben Partnership**
59 **PRIVATE STORY (USA)**, 5, b g Yes It's True (USA)—Said Privately (USA) **Middleham Park Racing XXXII**
60 **PURE GENIUS**, 9, gr m Exit To Nowhere (USA)—Lady of Gortmerron **The Folly Of Molly**
61 **QOUBILAI (FR)**, 8, b g Passing Sale (FR)—Varcady (FR) **Mr J. H. Frost**
62 **QUADRATO (GER)**, 5, br g Sholokhov (IRE)—Quadrata (GER) **Pearn's Pharmacies Ltd**

MR TIM VAUGHAN—continued

63 **RATHNAROUGHY (IRE)**, 8, b g Bach (IRE)—Lee Valley Lady (IRE) **Mr M. L. Harvey**
64 **REV IT UP (IRE)**, 6, b g Revoque (IRE)—Von Carty (IRE) **The Bill & Ben Partnership**
65 **RIGIDITY**, 5, b g Indian Ridge—Alakananda **Pearn's Pharmacies Ltd**
66 **ROUGH TIMES (IRE)**, 7, br g Bishop of Cashel—Lady Arpel (IRE) **The Runthatbymeagain Partnership**
67 **ROYALE PERFORMANCE**, 5, b m King's Theatre (IRE)—Coralisse Royale (FR) **T. E. Vaughan**
68 **RUBY BAY (IRE)**, 7, ch g Beneficial—Ruby Supreme (IRE) **Chasing Gold Limited**
69 **RULER OF ALL (IRE)**, 6, b g Sadler's Wells (USA)—
Shabby Chic (USA) **Johnson, Weston, Whitaker, Rodosthenous**
70 **SAINT ARE (FR)**, 6, b br g Network (GER)—Fortanea (FR) **Mr D. W. Fox**
71 **SAUTE**, 6, br g Hawk Wing (USA)—Lifting (IRE) **Mrs A. Burrows**
72 **SCORCHED SON (IRE)**, 9, b g Norwich—Scorched Air **Diamond Racing Ltd**
73 **SEAN OG KATY (IRE)**, 8, b m Commander Collins (USA)—Valentine Gale (IRE) **Butler Family Syndicate**
74 **SIEGLINDE (IRE)**, 6, b m Canyon Creek (IRE)—Heliette (FR) **Diamond Racing Ltd**
75 **SILICIUM (FR)**, 6, b g Shaanmer (IRE)—Kalgary (FR) **Pearn's Pharmacies Ltd**
76 **SILKY BOB (IRE)**, 6, b br g Bob Back (USA)—Harir **Mr R. I. Clay**
77 **SKI SUNDAY**, 7, b g King's Best (USA)—Lille Hammer **Scarlet Pimpernel**
78 **SOLARAS EXHIBITION (IRE)**, 4, b g Great Exhibition (USA)—Solara (GER) **Mr C. Davies**
79 **SPANISH OPTIMIST (IRE)**, 6, b g Indian Danehill (USA)—La Traviata
80 **SPECIAL MATE**, 6, br g Generous (IRE)—Flying Iris (IRE) **Walters Plant Hire Ltd**
81 **SPEED STEED**, 5, b g One Cool Cat (USA)—Dhakhirah (IRE) **Mr J. H. Frost**
82 **SPIRIT OF ADJISA (IRE)**, 8, br g Invincible Spirit (IRE)—Adjisa (IRE) **Darr, Johnson, Weston & Whitaker**
83 **STEWARTS HOUSE (IRE)**, 10, b g Overbury (IRE)—Osocool **Double Trouble Partnership**
84 **STONETHROWER (IRE)**, 7, b g Dushyantor (USA)—Ciaras Charm (IRE) **M & S Clarke**
85 **SWIFT ESCAPE**, 5, b g Exit To Nowhere (USA)—Vivre Aimer Rire (FR) **The oceans-racing.com**
86 **SWISS GUARD**, 6, b g Montjeu (IRE)—Millennium Dash **Middleham Park Racing LII & J McCarthy**
87 **TANERKO EMERY (FR)**, 6, b g Lavirco (GER)—Frequence (FR) **Walters Plant Hire Ltd Egan Waste Ltd**
88 **TARA WARRIOR (IRE)**, 6, b g Dilshaan—Dungeon Princess (IRE) **Notalotterry**
89 **THE BIG FREEZE (IRE)**, 6, b g Beneficial—Kilfane (IRE) **Pearn's Pharmacies Ltd**
90 **THELOBSTERCATCHER (IRE)**, 8, gr g Silver Patriarch (IRE)—Everything's Rosy **G. A. Moore**
91 **TOTO CORDE MEO (IRE)**, 5, b m Galileo (IRE)—Christel Flame **Mrs A. Burrows**
92 **TOUT REGULIER (IRE)**, 5, b g Beat All (USA)—Winnow **G. A. Moore**
93 **TRUCKERS BENEFIT (IRE)**, 7, b g Beneficial—Lady Jurado (IRE) **Prince, Reuter, Wadley, Williams**
94 **TRUE BLUE (IRE)**, 5, ch g Blueprint (IRE)—Fontaine Frances (IRE) **Middleham Park Racing LVII**
95 **VALLEY LAD (IRE)**, 6, b g Flemensfirth (USA)—Old Moon (USA) **Walters Plant Hire Ltd**
96 **WHATSHALLWEDO**, 7, b g Zindabad (FR)—Key West (FR) **Mr C. Davies**
97 **WINDS OF WAR (IRE)**, 8, ch g Presenting—Shining Willow **Amos, Devonald, Johns, Ragan**
98 **WINGS OF SMOKE (IRE)**, 7, gr g King's Theatre (IRE)—Grey Mo (IRE) **Pearn's Pharmacies Ltd**
99 **ZAMINA (IRE)**, 4, b f Hawk Wing (USA)—Termania (IRE) **M Khan X2**
100 **ZARAZAR**, 4, b g Statue of Liberty (USA)—Babaraja **Diamond Racing Ltd**

Other Owners: Mr P. G. Amos, Dr M. G. Armitage, A. W. A. Bates, Mr A. Bott, Mr G. W. T. Butt, Mr D. N. V. Churton, Mr S. A. Clarke, Mr M. S. Clarke, Mr P. Coates, Mr P. G. Connolly, Mr R. Denness, Mr J. D. Devonald, Mr J. M. Duggan, Mr T. P. Duggan, Mr B. Ead, Mr S. H. Easterby, Mr N. Edwards, Egan Waste Services Ltd, K. H. Foster, Mr I. S. Gallacher, Mr J. Goodrick, Mr J. A. Goodrick, Mr M. E. Harris, A. D. I. Harris, Mr R. Jackson, Mr B. Jagger, D. M. Jenkins, Mr R. T. Johns, Ms S. J. Johnson, T. E. Kerfoot, Mr Khan, Mr. Khan, Mr G. T. Lever, Mrs S. Luke, Mr D. A. Luke, Mr F. M. McGuinness, Mr R. Middleton, Mr S. Middleton, Mr M. E. Moore, Mr J. M. Mordecai, Mrs K. J. Morgan, S. T. Morris, T. H. Northwood, T. S. Palin, Mr J. T. Phillips, D. Prince, M. Prince, Mr N. S. C. Proctor, Mr P. Ragan, Mr J. W. Reuter, A. Robinson, Mr J. Rodosthenous, Mr J. Sanders, The Select Racing Club Limited, D. A. Shinton, Mr J. J. R. Wadley, D. J. Wallis, Mr K. H. Weston, Wetherby Racing Bureau Ltd, Mrs C. S. Whitaker, Mr N. D. Whitham, Mrs P. H. Williams, Mrs C. S. Wilson.

Assistant Trainer: Rhys Hughes

Jockey (flat): Fergus Sweeney. **Jockey (NH):** Richard Johnson. **Conditional:** Michael Byrne. **Amateur:** Mr Matthew Barber, Mr Evan David, Mr Tom David, Mr Bradley Gibbs.

---

658 **MR CHRISTIAN VON DER RECKE, Weilerswist**
Postal: Rennstall Recke, Hovener Hof, D-53919, Weilerswist, Germany
Contacts: PHONE (0049) 2254 84 53 14 FAX (0049) 2254 845315 MOBILE (0049) 171 542 50 50
E-MAIL recke@t-online.de WEBSITE www.rennstall-recke.de

1 **ADITA (GER)**, 4, ch f Mamool—Api Sa **Stall Seeheim**
2 **AMERICAN LIFE (FR)**, 5, b g American Post—Poplite (FR) **Stall Aron**
3 **ANDEX (IRE)**, 4, b c Spartacus (IRE)—Alte Rose (GER) **Stall Nizza**
4 **ANNAKRISTA (GER)**, 4, b f Kallisto (GER)—Annabelle (GER) **Roland Muller**
5 **ASPANTAU (IRE)**, 4, b g Encosta de Lago (AUS)—Jabali (FR) **C. von der Recke**

MR CHRISTIAN VON DER RECKE—continued

6 **AUENDANCER (GER)**, 5, b h Seattle Dancer (USA)—Auenburg (GER) **Stall Hasfeld**
7 **BOUND BY HONOUR (SAF)**, 9, b g Rambo Dancer (CAN)—Child of Grace (SAF) **Stall Saarbrucken**
8 **BUCKED OFF (SAF)**, 8, b g Casey Tibbs (IRE)—See Me Fly (SAF) **Stall Chevalex**
9 **CESARE (GER)**, 6, b g Pentire—Chaguaramas (IRE) **Stall Aron**
10 **CLOCCA SAM**, 4, b c Samum—Cioccolata **Stall Blankenese**
11 **COME AND FIGHT (IRE)**, 4, b f Kris Kin (USA)—Calcida (GER) **Stall Karlshorst**
12 **DARING RUDOLPH (GER)**, 5, b g Soviet Star (USA)—Delightful Sofie (GER) **Frau R. A. Hacker**
13 **DAWARIYA (IRE)**, 4, ch f Selkirk (USA)—Dawera (IRE) **Stall Seeheim**
14 **DE RIGUEUR**, 4, b c Montjeu (IRE)—Exclusive **Frau U. Alck**
15 **DERAPOUR (IRE)**, 5, b g Tiger Hill (IRE)—Dararita (IRE) **Stall Fly Baby Fly**
16 **DISTINCTIVE IMAGE (USA)**, 7, b g Mineshaft (USA)—Dock Leaf (USA) **BMK Racing**
17 **DUBBURG (USA)**, 7, ch g Johannesburg (USA)—Plaisir Des Yeux (FR) **Stall Karlshorst**
18 **EARLSALSA (GER)**, 8, b g Kingsalsa (USA)—Earthly Paradise (GER) **Stall Blankenese**
19 **FAIR STORM (GER)**, 5, b h Konigstiger (GER)—Fairwind (GER) **C. von der Recke**
20 **FAITH THE BID (GER)**, 5, b h Paolini (GER)—Fiery Faith **Frau Sonja Auer**
21 **FIRST STREAM (GER)**, 8, ch g Lomitas—First Class (GER) **Stall Saarbrucken**
22 **FLASH FOX (GER)**, 5, ch g Pentire—Fleurie (GER) **Stall Manon**
23 **FLEURO (GER)**, 4, ch c Desert Prince (IRE)—Fleurie (GER) **Stall Manon**
24 **GHAAYER (GER)**, 6, ch g Nayef (USA)—Valthea (FR) **Galopp Club Deutschland**
25 **GLOW STAR (SAF)**, 8, ch g Muhtafal (USA)—Arctic Glow (SAF) **Stall Burg Muggenhausen**
26 **ISHAN (GER)**, 6, b g Sholokhov (IRE)—Ishika (GER) **Frau R A. Hacker**
27 **LA NEXT (GER)**, 4, b f Next Desert (IRE)—La Constancia **Gestut Elsetal**
28 **MAGDA LENA (GER)**, 4, b f Paolini (GER)—Maria Magdalena (GER) **P. Vogt**
29 **NUGGET (GER)**, 4, b f Gold Away (IRE)—Narcose (FR) **E. Albert**
30 **ORDENSRITTER (GER)**, 4, ch c Samum (GER)—Dramraire Mist **P. Vogt**
31 **OSORIOS TRIAL**, 5, ch g Osorio (GER)—Skytrial (USA) **R. Turton**
32 **TARKHEENA PRINCE (USA)**, 7, b g Aldebaran (USA)—Tarkheena (USA) **BMK Racing**
33 **TOUGHNESS DANON**, 6, b g Tiger Hill (IRE)—Templerin (GER) **Stall Chevalex**
34 **TOWN REBEL (IRE)**, 7, br g Darnay—Alleged Beauty (IRE) **Stall Karlshorst**
35 **TRANQUIL WATERS (IRE)**, 5, b g Sadler's Wells (USA)—Belle of Honour (USA) **C. von der Recke**
36 **VIOLET'S GIFT (IRE)**, 4, b f Cadeaux Genereux—Violet Ballerina (IRE) **C. von der Recke**
37 **WAKY LI (GER)**, 6, b m Royal Dragon (USA)—Waky Su (IRE) **Stall Allez les bleus**
38 **WINNIESTAR (GER)**, 4, b f Dashing Blade—Westafrika (GER) **Stall Mimmi and friends**

THREE-YEAR-OLDS

39 **ACHT (GER)**, b f Big Shuffle (USA)—Avanti Adda (GER) **Gestut Katharinenhof**
40 **ANTONELLO (IRE)**, b c Refuse To Bend (IRE)—Asterita **C. von der Recke**
41 **APISATA (GER)**, b f Mamool—Api Sa **Stall Seeheim**
42 **ARQUES (GER)**, b c Toylsome—Annabelle (GER) **Roland Muller**
43 **ATALEI (GER)**, b c Mamool (IRE)—Avada (GER) **Frau Sonja Auer**
44 **CARIERO (GER)**, b g Nicaron (GER)—Cariera (GER) **Stall Nizza**
45 **CASCADA (GER)**, ch f Kallisto (GER)—Charlott (GER) **Frau Beate Schmitz**
46 **CIOCCOMIA (GER)**, bl f Samum (GER)—Cioccolata (GER) **Stall Blankenese**
47 **ELLE BELLE (GER)**, b f Nicaron (GER)—Excellent Princess (GER) **Stall Nizza**
48 **HELGA (GER)**, ch f Lateral—Helgalill (IRE) **Stall Klosters-Serneus**
49 **JAMAICA SUN (GER)**, b f Nicaron—Juvena **Stall Nizza**
50 **ODIT (GER)**, br c Kallisto (GER)—Ordura (GER) **Stall Seeheim**
51 **ONE DAY SHADOW (GER)**, b c Dai Jin—One Day Star (GER) **Stall Vier Pfoten**
52 **PICCOLA (GER)**, b f Mamool (GER)—Pawella (GER) **Stall Seeheim**
53 **SPARK (GER)**, b c Nicaron (GER)—Song of Night (GER) **Stall Nizza**
54 **THE TIPSY TANGERINE**, b f Soviet Star (USA)—The Spring Flower (GER) **Stall Tommy**
55 **TREVOSE (IRE)**, b g Barathea (GER)—Cape Jasmine (IRE) **C. von der Recke**

TWO-YEAR-OLDS

56 Ch f 30/4 Mamool (USA)—Api Sa (IRE) (Zinaad) **M. Buchner**
57 **CAFE AU LAIT (GER)**, b c 27/3 Nicaron (GER)—Cariera (GER) (Macanal (USA)) **Stall Nizza**
58 **FEUERFUCHS (GER)**, b c 3/5 Lord of England (GER)—
    Flair Sensation (GER) (Platini (GER)) (9031) **Stall Blau-Weiss**
59 **FIERY'S LEGACY (GER)**, ch f 28/2 Lateral—Fiery Faith (Spectacular Bid (USA)) **Frau P. Neumuller**
60 **I'M ON FIRE (GER)**, b f 24/1 Shirocco (GER)—In My Heart (GER) (Tiger Hill (IRE)) **Stall Nizza**
61 **PANESIDORA (GER)**, b f 17/3 Soviet Star (USA)—
    Paradise Search (IRE) (Rainbow Quest (USA)) (5747) **M. E. Veeck**
62 B f 15/1 Mamool (IRE)—Pawella (GER) (Second Set (IRE)) **M. Buchner**
63 **RIBBERY (GER)**, b c 8/4 Areion (GER)—Rosaly (GER) (Kallisto (GER)) **H. Lohmann**

659 MR JOHN WADE, Sedgefield

Postal: Howe Hills, Mordon, Sedgefield, Cleveland, TS21 2HG
Contacts: PHONE (01740) 630310 FAX (01740) 630310 MOBILE (07831) 686968

1 **ALWAYS RIGHT (IRE)**, 10, ch g Right Win (IRE)—Kemal Brave (IRE) **J. Wade**
2 **APACHE BLUE (IRE)**, 8, b g Presenting—La Eile (IRE) **J. Wade**
3 **ARROW BARROW (IRE)**, 7, b g Moscow Society (USA)—Miss Nee (IRE) **J. Wade**
4 **BEANEY TUNES**, 6, b g Central Park (IRE)—Fun While It Lasts **J. Wade**
5 **BEAU DANDY (IRE)**, 7, b br g Exit To Nowhere (USA)—Northern Dandy **J. Wade**
6 **BLAZING BULL (IRE)**, 8, b g Winged Love (IRE)—Our Buttons (IRE) **J. Wade**
7 **BOW BADGER**, 6, b g Sadler's Wells (USA)—Biloxi **J. Wade**
8 **CALL ME MULLIGAN (IRE)**, 8, ch g Bach (IRE)—They Call Me Molly (CAN) **J. Wade**
9 **CARIBBEAN RULES**, 5, b g Milan—Siroyalta (FR) **J. Wade**
10 **CHICAGO OUTFIT (IRE)**, 7, b g Old Vic—Lambourne Lace (IRE) **J. Wade**
11 **COLLEGE GREEN**, 5, b g Beat All (USA)—Velvet Leaf **J. Wade**
12 **COLORADO KID (IRE)**, 6, b g Presenting—Silent Orders (IRE) **J. Wade**
13 **COUNTY COLOURS (IRE)**, 7, ch g Lord of Appeal—Silk Style **J. Wade**
14 **CRANBERRY ICE (IRE)**, 6, b g Tikkanen (USA)—Strawberry Fool (FR) **J. Wade**
15 **DESPERANTO (IRE)**, 6, b g Dushyantor (USA)—Desperado Dawn (IRE) **J. Wade**
16 **DEUTERONOMY (IRE)**, 11, b g Beneficial—Good Heavens (IRE) **J. Wade**
17 **DIAMOND FRONTIER (IRE)**, 9, gr g Sadler's Wells (USA)—Diamond Line (FR) **J. Wade**
18 **DIGG WHITAKER**, 7, b g Mounting Spendent—Function Dreamer **J. Wade**
19 **DOOR BOY (IRE)**, 9, b br g Dr Massini (IRE)—Door Stopper (IRE) **J. Wade**
20 **DREVER ROUTE (IRE)**, 9, b g Flemensfirth (USA)—I Remember It Well (IRE) **J. Wade**
21 **FUSHE JO**, 8, gr g Act One—Aristocratique **J. Wade**
22 **GLENCREE (IRE)**, 8, b g Presenting—Hidden Ability (IRE) **J. Wade**
23 **HARRIS HAWK**, 7, b g Karinga Bay—Harristown Lady **J. Wade**
24 **INDIAN GROOM (IRE)**, 7, gr g High Chaparral (IRE)—Taatof (IRE) **J. Wade**
25 **KING O'THE GYPSIES (IRE)**, 7, b g Sadler's Wells (USA)—Love For Ever (IRE) **J. Wade**
26 **KNOCKAVILLA (IRE)**, 9, b g Saddlers' Hall (IRE)—Native Singer (IRE) **J. Wade**
27 **LITTLE HERCULES (IRE)**, 6, b g King's Theatre (IRE)—Johnston's Crest (IRE) **J. Wade**
28 **MANNERED (IRE)**, 7, b g Afflora (IRE)—Manettia (IRE) **J. Wade**
29 **MERIDIAN CITY (IRE)**, 8, b g Presenting—Talk To The Missus (IRE) **J. Wade**
30 **MOMOTARO (IRE)**, 7, ch g Alderbrook—Gaye Diane **J. Wade**
31 **MOON INDIGO**, 6, b g Sadler's Wells (USA)—Solo de Lune (IRE) **J. Wade**
32 **NAHNEH (IRE)**, 6, b g Beneficial—Arusha Rose (IRE) **J. Wade**
33 **NEWSPAGE (IRE)**, 6, b g Blueprint (IRE)—Newlineview (IRE) **J. Wade**
34 **NOIR ANGELIS**, 5, b g Needle Gun—Bubbling **J. Wade**
35 **OTTO QUERCUS (FR)**, 7, b g Saint Cyrien (FR)—La Haie Blanche (FR) **J. Wade**
36 **PUDSEY HOUSE**, 5, b g Double Trigger (IRE)—Dara's Pride (IRE) **J. Wade**
37 **QUEL BALLISTIC**, 8, b g Kayf Tara—Herballistic **J. Wade**
38 **RAVENS SECRET**, 7, br g Overbury (IRE)—Secret Pearl (IRE) **J. Wade**
39 **RISKIER**, 7, gr g Kier Park (IRE)—Risky Girl **J. Wade**
40 **ROMANY RYME**, 6, ch g Nomadic Way (USA)—Rakaposhi Ryme (IRE) **J. Wade**
41 **RUNSWICK RELAX**, 6, ch g Generous (IRE)—Zany Lady **J. Wade**
42 **SAGLIERE**, 7, gr g Sagamix (FR)—D'egliere (FR) **J. Wade**
43 **SIRMUHTA (FR)**, 8, ch g Muhtathir—Sirkeela (FR) **J. Wade**
44 **SITTING TENNANT**, 9, b g Erhaab (USA)—Aeolina (FR) **J. Wade**
45 **SKIRLAW (IRE)**, 5, b g Gold Well—Lady Boufant (IRE) **J. Wade**
46 **TARAS JOY (IRE)**, 7, b g Kayf Tara—Native Sylph (IRE) **J. Wade**
47 **TYRONE HOUSE (IRE)**, 8, b g Strategic Choice (USA)—Naughty Marietta (IRE) **J. Wade**
48 **VICTORY ROCK (IRE)**, 6, b g Old Vic—Dantes Serenade (IRE) **J. Wade**
49 **VIKING CHIEF (IRE)**, 5, b g Westerner—Diamond Sal (IRE) **J. Wade**
50 **WALSER (IRE)**, 5, b g Milan—Brass Neck (IRE) **J. Wade**
51 **WHATS UP WOODY (IRE)**, 7, b g Beneficial—Lady Noellel (IRE) **J. Wade**
52 **WOODY WALLER**, 7, ch g Lomitas—Reamzafonic **J. Wade**

Assistant Trainer: Miss Maria Myco (07798) 775932

Jockey (NH): Brian Hughes, James Reveley, Wilson Renwick. **Conditional:** Daryl Millar. **Amateur:** Mr John Dawson.

660 MRS LUCY WADHAM, Newmarket

Postal: **The Trainer's House, Moulton Paddocks, Newmarket, Suffolk, CB8 7PJ**
Contacts: **PHONE (01638) 662411 FAX (01638) 668821 MOBILE (07980) 545776**
E-MAIL **lucy.wadham@virgin.net** WEBSITE **www.lucywadhamracing.co.uk**

1 ALARAZI (IRE), 8, b g Spectrum (IRE)—Alaya (IRE) **J. L. Eddis**
2 ALL ANNALENA (IRE), 6, b m Dubai Destination (USA)—Alla Prima (IRE) **Mr & Mrs A. E. Pakenham**
3 AVIADOR (GER), 6, b g Paolini (GER)—Albarana (GER) **Mr R. S. Keeley**
4 BABY SHINE (IRE), 6, b m King's Theatre (IRE)—
Brambleshine (IRE) **P.A.Philipps,T.S.Redman & Mrs L. Redman**
5 BEVNOTT (IRE), 6, b g Shantou (USA)—Grove Juliet (IRE) **P. H. Betts**
6 BOLIVIA (GER), 6, ch m Monsun (GER)—Be My Lady (GER) **Mr & Mrs A. E. Pakenham**
7 CANUSPOTIT, 5, b g Nomadic Way (USA)—Play Alone (IRE) **D. A. Wales & Mr S. J. Wood**
8 CRYSTAL GAL (IRE), 5, b m Galileo (IRE)—Park Crystal (IRE) **Mr & Mrs A. E. Pakenham**
9 DAWN TWISTER (GER), 5, br g Monsun (GER)—Dawn Side (CAN) **Mr R. Davies**
10 EL DANCER (GER), 8, b g Seattle Dancer (USA)—Elea (GER) **Mr R. Davies**
11 ELEAZAR (GER), 11, b br g Alkalde (GER)—Eicidora (GER) **J. J. W. Wadham**
12 EMPEROR CONCERTO, 9, ch g Emperor Fountain—Busy Mittens **J. J. W. Wadham**
13 GENERAL TING (IRE), 7, b g Daylami (IRE)—Luana **The A. T. Partnership**
14 HERON REEF (IRE), 6, b g Heron Island (IRE)—Catherinestown **J. J. W. Wadham**
15 LAVERRE (IRE), 5, b m Noverre (USA)—Ladood **Mr & Mrs A. E. Pakenham**
16 LE REVE (IRE), 4, br g Milan—Open Cry (IRE) **P. H. Betts**
17 MANSHOOR (IRE), 7, gr g Linamix (FR)—Lady Wells (IRE) **Mr T. R. Wood**
18 MIDNIGHT MACARENA, 7, ch m Midnight Legend—Royal Tango **The Bees**
19 MISS THEA, 4, ch f Barathea (IRE)—Misplace (IRE) **Mr & Mrs A. E. Pakenham**
20 MR JAY DEE (IRE), 7, b g Lord Americo—Emmas Flyer (IRE) **Ms K. J. Austin, J. J. W. Wadham**
21 SONGSMITH, 4, b g Librettist (USA)—Venus Rising **Team Supreme**
22 SUPER DIRECTA (GER), 8, b g Protektor (GER)—Summernight Dream (GER) **Mr R. S. Keeley**
23 TEALISSIO, 6, b g Helissio (FR)—Tealby **The Dyball Partnership**
24 THE BLACK BARON (IRE), 10, br g Lord Americo—Royal Nora (IRE) **The Bees**
25 WELL METT (IRE), 5, b g Gold Well—Beit Millat (USA) **R. B. Holt**
26 WIESENTRAUM (GER), 6, ch g Next Desert (IRE)—Wiesenblute (GER) **G. Pascoe & S. Brewer**

THREE-YEAR-OLDS

27 ALL OF A QUIVER, b g Big Bad Bob (IRE)—Brandina (IRE) **The Ranworth Partnership**
28 NOBLE SILK, gr g Sir Percy—Tussah **The FOPS**
29 PERFORCE, b g Sir Percy—Enforce (USA) **Mr & Mrs A. E. Pakenham**

TWO-YEAR-OLDS

30 B f 29/4 Sir Percy—Nicola Bella (IRE) (Sadler's Wells (USA)) **Mr & Mrs A. E. Pakenham**
31 B f 25/4 Sakhee's Secret—Ziggy Zaggy (Diktat) (32000) **Mr & Mrs A. E. Pakenham**

Other Owners: Ms K. J. Austin, Mr S. J. Brewer, D. J. S. Dyball, C. A. Dyball, Mrs L. M. Kemble, Mr Jeff O'Leary, Mrs S. F. O'Leary, Mr A. E. Pakenham, Mrs Victoria Pakenham, Mr G. J. Pascoe, Mr P. A. Philipps, Mr T. S. Redman, Mrs L. E. Redman, Mr Chris Smith, Mrs Lucy Wadham, Mr J. J. W. Wadham.

Jockey (NH): Dominic Elsworth, Leighton Aspell. **Conditional:** Matt Crawley, Rosie McKee.

661 MISS TRACY WAGGOTT, Spennymoor

Postal: **Awakening Stables, Merrington Lane, Spennymoor, Co. Durham, DL16 7HB**
Contacts: **PHONE (01388) 819012 MOBILE (07979) 434498**

1 BORDER BANDIT (USA), 4, b g Selkirk (USA)—Coretta (IRE) **Elsa Crankshaw Gordon Allan**
2 BRIGHT APPLAUSE, 4, b g Royal Applause—Sadaka (USA) **Littlethorpe Park Racing**
3 CAPTAIN ROYALE (IRE), 7, ch g Captain Rio—Paix Royale **H. Conlon**
4 KING PIN, 7, b g Pivotal—Danehurst **H. Conlon**
5 MISSION IMPOSSIBLE, 7, gr g Kyllachy—Eastern Lyric **H. Conlon**
6 NORTON GIRL, 4, b f Diktat—Opening Ceremony (USA) **Mrs J. Waggott**
7 PIVOTAL PROSPECT, 4, b f Nayef (USA)—Buon Amici **Mr C. J. Allan**
8 RIVER ARDECHE, 7, b g Elnadim—Overcome **Littlethorpe Park Racing**
9 SINATRAMANIA, 5, b g Dansili—Come Fly With Me **Miss T. Waggott**
10 VALANTINO OYSTER (IRE), 5, b g Pearl of Love (IRE)—Mishor **Mrs J. Waggott**

MISS TRACY WAGGOTT—continued

THREE-YEAR-OLDS

11 HULWA (USA), b br f Swain (IRE)—Nadawat (USA) **Mr C. J. Allan**

Other Owners: G. Allan, Miss E. Crankshaw, J. M. Hughes, Mr A. Stainton.

---

662 **MR JOHN WAINWRIGHT, Malton**
Postal: Hanging Hill Farm, Kennythorpe, Malton, North Yorkshire, YO17 9LA
Contacts: PHONE (01653) 658537 FAX (01653) 658658 MOBILE (07798) 778070
E-MAIL jswainwright@googlemail.com

1 AMERICAN LOVER (FR), 5, b m American Post—Lovarisk (FR) **P. W. Cooper**
2 BENIDORM, 4, b g Bahamian Bounty—Famcred **Mr W Bavill & Mr D. Bavill**
3 BLUE NOODLES, 6, b g Reset (AUS)—Gleam of Light (IRE) **drawn2win.co.uk Partnership**
4 EXIT TO FREEDOM, 6, ch g Exit To Nowhere (USA)—Bobanvi **Mrs F. J. Wainwright**
5 MEDIA JURY, 5, b g Lucky Owners (NZ)—Landofheartsdesire (IRE) **S. Enwright**
6 MERRJANAH, 4, b f Diktat—Aberdovey **Ms J. A. French**
7 MY FAIR LILY (IRE), 6, b m Sayarshan (IRE)—Golden Mist (IRE) **Mr A. J. Ross**
8 ONIZ TIPTOES (IRE), 11, ch g Russian Revival (USA)—Edionda (IRE) **drawn2win.co.uk Partnership**
9 QUEEN'S PRINCESS, 4, b f Danbird (AUS)—Queen's Lodge (IRE) **Mr W Bavill & Mr D. Bavill**
10 WING N PRAYER (IRE), 5, b m Xaar—Jazmeer **Mrs F. J. Wainwright**

THREE-YEAR-OLDS

11 NANT SAESON (IRE), b g Elusive City (USA)—Lady Power (IRE) **Mrs F. J. Wainwright**

Other Owners: Mr W. C. Bavill, Mr D. Bavill, J. S. Wainwright, Mr P. R. Walker.

Assistant Trainer: Mrs Fiona Wainwright

Jockey (flat): Tom Eaves, T. Hamilton, P. Aspell. Amateur: Mrs F. Wainwright.

---

663 **MR R. B. WALEY-COHEN, Banbury**
Postal: Upton Viva, Banbury, Oxfordshire, OX15 6HT
Contacts: PHONE (02072) 446022 MOBILE (07831) 888778
E-MAIL rwc@uptonviva.co.uk WEBSITE www.uptonestate.co.uk

1 ANY THE WISER, 8, br g Kahyasi—Best of The Best (FR) **R. B. Waley-Cohen**
2 ASHTOWN BOY (IRE), 6, ch g Trans Island—Provacatrice (USA) **R. B. Waley-Cohen**
3 LOOK WHO'S TALKING, 5, b m King's Theatre (IRE)—Makounji (FR) **R. B. Waley-Cohen**
4 MANTON, 5, b br g Milan—Rachel C (IRE) **R. B. Waley-Cohen**
5 OTAGE DE BRION (FR), 10, b g Rajpoute (FR)—Gesse Parade (FR) **R. B. Waley-Cohen**
6 RECIF DE THAIX (FR), 7, br g Fragrant Mix (IRE)—Louisiane de Thaix (FR) **R. B. Waley-Cohen**
7 ROULEZ COOL, 9, b g Classic Cliche (IRE)—Makounji (FR) **R. B. Waley-Cohen**
8 RUMBAVU (IRE), 6, br g Overbury (IRE)—Strong Swimmer (IRE) **R. B. Waley-Cohen**

Assistant Trainer: Kate Mawle

Amateur: Mr S. Waley-Cohen.

---

664 **MR TIM WALFORD, Sheriff Hutton**
Postal: Cornborough Manor, Sheriff Hutton, York, YO60 6QN
Contacts: PHONE (01347) 878382 FAX (01347) 878547 MOBILE (07904) 237676
E-MAIL g_walford@hotmail.com WEBSITE www.timwalford.co.uk

1 CHADFORD, 4, b g Trade Fair—Quiz Time **Chasing Gold Limited**
2 DIABLO DANCER, 4, b f Zafeen (FR)—Faithful Beauty (IRE) **Mr A. Hulme & Partners**
3 FRENCH SEVENTYFIVE, 5, b g Pursuit of Love—Miss Tun **G. Mett Racing & Paul Drury**
4 GRANWOOD, 6, ch m Midnight Legend—Half Each **Mrs C. A. Watson**
5 HAIL TIBERIUS, 5, b g Iktibas—Untidy Daughter **Mr G. Bonson, I. Townsend & B. Bodek**
6 HARRY THE HAWK, 8, b g Pursuit of Love—Elora Gorge (IRE) **D. J. Dickson**
7 HONEYPOT LANE, 5, b g Slip Anchor—Lyra **Richard Adcock Joe Grindal & Nigel Skinner**
8 KING PENDA (IRE), 9, br g Presenting—Peacock Feather **Mr & Mrs K. J. Hickey & Partner**

MR TIM WALFORD—continued

9 **KODICIL (IRE)**, 4, b g Kodiac—Miss Caoimhe (IRE) **Mr D. & Mr S. Woodall**
10 **RIGHT ENOUGH**, 7, gr g Bollin William—Miss Accounts (IRE) **Mr G. Penrose & Partners**
11 **SHORT SUPPLY (USA)**, 6, b m Point Given (USA)—Introducing (USA) **Mr K. Hanson**
12 **SILVER CAROUSEL**, 5, gr m Silver Patriarch (IRE)—Karolina (FR) **Mr M. C. Thuey**
13 **STRONG KNIGHT**, 5, ch g Observatory (USA)—Erudite **A. Quirke & C. Backhouse**
14 **TALENT SCOUT (IRE)**, 6, b g Exceed And Excel (AUS)—Taalluf (USA) **Mr J. Stacey**
15 **TAMANACO (IRE)**, 5, b g Catcher In The Rye (IRE)—Right After Moyne (IRE) **Mr A. J. Hulme**
16 **UBI ACE**, 6, b g First Trump—Faithful Beauty (IRE) **Mr N. J. Maher**
17 **UNO VALOROSO (FR)**, 4, b g Voix du Nord (FR)—Danse d'avril (FR) **Mr C. N. Herman**
18 **ZEFOOHA (FR)**, 8, ch m Lomitas—Bezzaaf **Mr S. Conway**

THREE-YEAR-OLDS

19 **BLUE TOP**, b g Millkom—Pompey Blue **Mr M. Brown & Mr C. Evans**
20 **KEYHOLE KATE**, b f Kheleyf (USA)—Striking Pose (IRE) **Mr F. Ellis & Partners**
21 **MEDIEVAL BISHOP (IRE)**, b g Bachelor Duke (USA)—On The Backfoot (IRE) **Mr & Mrs K. Hamilton**
22 **MR SNOOZY**, b g Pursuit of Love—Hard To Follow **T. W. Heseltine**

TWO-YEAR-OLDS

23 B g 24/4 Motivator—Habla Me (IRE) (Fairy King (USA)) (2000)
24 B g 21/4 Mujadil (USA)—Messina (IRE) (Sadler's Wells (USA)) (761) **Mr A. Hulme & Partners**
25 B f 30/4 Avonbridge—Nefeli (First Trump) (761)

Other Owners: Mr Richard Adcock, Mr C. Backhouse, Mr Michael Blades, Mr B. H. Bodek, Mr Geoff Bonson, Mr David Dickson, Mr Paul Drury, Mrs Catherine Feeney-Hickey, Mr C. J. Grindal, Mr K. J. Hickey, Mr David Longstaff, Mr P. McMahon, Mr A. Quirke, Mr P. Scholes, Mr N. D. Skinner, Mr Ian Townsend, Mrs G. B. Walford.

Assistant Trainer: Mark Walford

Jockey (flat): Graham Gibbons. **Jockey (NH):** Robert Walford. **Apprentice:** Luke Strong. **Amateur:** Mr M. King, Mr M. Walford.

665
MR ED WALKER, Newmarket
Postal: **The Authorized Yard, St Gatien Stables, Newmarket, Suffolk, CB8 9AA**
Contacts: **PHONE (01638) 661106 MOBILE (07787) 534145**
E-MAIL ed@edwalkerracing.com WEBSITE www.edwalkerracing.com

1 **AXIOM**, 8, ch g Pivotal—Exhibitor (USA) **S. Al Ansari**
2 **DANNIOS**, 6, b g Tobougg (IRE)—Fleuve d'or (IRE) **Mrs G. Walker**
3 **NEW LEYF (IRE)**, 6, b br g Kheleyf (USA)—Society Fair (FR) **Mr J. W. Burdett**
4 **RIGGINS (IRE)**, 8, b g Cape Cross (IRE)—Rentless **Dubai Thoroughbred Racing**
5 **THE HIGH MAN**, 4, ch c Medicean—Excellent **Dubai Thoroughbred Racing**

THREE-YEAR-OLDS

6 **DUKE OF DESTINY (IRE)**, br c Bachelor Duke (USA)—Marghelan (FR) **Dubai Thoroughbred Racing**
7 **NICHOLASCOPERNICUS (IRE)**, ch c Medicean—Ascendancy **Greenwood, Halsall and Pegum**
8 **RUSCELLO (IRE)**, b c Cape Cross (IRE)—Sea Picture (IRE) **L. A. Bellman**
9 **SPARKS MIGHT FLY**, ch c Sakhee (USA)—Angel Rays **The Leg Men**
10 **WILLIE WAG TAIL (USA)**, b c Theatrical—Night Risk (USA) **One Carat Partnership**
11 **YES IT'S THE BOY (USA)**, b g Yes It's True (USA)—Storminthegarden (USA) **Mr W. W. W. Tung**

TWO-YEAR-OLDS

12 B c 2/4 Royal Applause—Diksie Dancer (Diktat) (30000)
13 B f 28/3 Acclamation—Eastern Lily (USA) (Eastern Echo (USA)) (20000)
14 **FAITHFILLY (IRE)**, b f 2/3 Red Clubs (IRE)—Bauci (IRE) (Desert King (IRE)) (25000) **L. A. Bellman**
15 **GLORIOUS PROTECTOR (IRE)**, b c 22/2 Azamour (IRE)—
                  Hasaiyda (IRE) (Hector Protector (USA)) (55000) **Mrs A. A. Lau Yap**
16 **GLORIOUS STAR (IRE)**, ch c 20/2 Soviet Star (USA)—
                  Caerlonore (IRE) (Traditionally (USA)) (21000) **Mrs A. A. Lau Yap**
17 **HARD RUN (USA)**, b c 17/4 Cherokee Run (USA)—Meniatarra (USA) (Zilzal (USA)) (65000)
18 B c 8/1 Exceed And Excel (AUS)—Ivy League Star (IRE) (Sadler's Wells (USA)) (15000) **S. Manana**
19 **MEMORIZE (IRE)**, b c 23/3 Dark Angel (IRE)—Cape Cod (IRE) (Unfuwain (USA)) (10000) **L. A. Bellman**
20 B c 31/1 Soviet Star (USA)—Rancho Cucamonga (IRE) (Raphane (USA)) (20000) **S. Manana**
21 Gr c 25/4 Intikhab (USA)—The Manx Touch (IRE) (Petardia) (90000) **Mrs A. A. Lau Yap**

MR ED WALKER—continued

22 B c 6/2 Lawman (FR)—Then 'n Now (Dansili) (30000)
23 URBICUS, b c 20/4 Holy Roman Emperor (IRE)—Scottish Heights (IRE) (Selkirk (USA)) (22000) **Mr S. A. Stuckey**
24 YOU'RE THE BOSS, b c 6/4 Royal Applause—Trinny (Rainbow Quest (USA)) (20952) **L. A. Bellman**

Other Owners: B. J. R. Greenwood, D. A. Halsall, L. Lillingston, Mr J. G. Moore, Mr D. Y. Ohler, E. C. D. Walker, T. J. D. Walker.

Jockey (flat): Jean-Pierre Guillambert. **Apprentice:** Michael J. Murphy.

---

666 MR CHRIS WALL, Newmarket

Postal: **Induna Stables, Fordham Road, Newmarket, Suffolk, CB8 7AQ**
Contacts: **OFFICE (01638) 661999 HOME (01638) 668896 FAX (01638) 667279**
MOBILE (07764) 940255
E-MAIL christianwall@btconnect.com WEBSITE www.chriswallracing.co.uk

1 AMBALA, 4, b f Intikhab (USA)—Mighty Splash **Mrs C. Lilley**
2 CITRUS STAR (USA), 5, b g Broken Vow (USA)—Twist a Lime (USA) **Induna Racing Partners (Two)**
3 DARSAN (IRE), 4, ch f Iffraaj—Coolrain Lady (IRE) **Ne'er Do Wells III**
4 DRIFT AND DREAM, 5, b m Exceed And Excel (AUS)—Sea Drift (FR) **Lady Juliet Tadgell**
5 GREELEY HOUSE, 4, b g Mr Greeley (USA)—Sauvage (FR) **Ms A. Fustoq**
6 HEIGHT OF SUMMER (IRE), 4, b f Alhaarth (IRE)—Summer Dreams (IRE) **Hughes, Gibson & Scott**
7 LES VERGUETTES (IRE), 4, b f Iffraaj—Mitsina **D. M. J. Gilbert**
8 MEIA NOITE, 5, b m Tobougg (IRE)—Executive Lady **M. L. Ayers**
9 MIDNIGHT RIDER (IRE), 4, b g Red Ransom (USA)—Foreplay (IRE) **The Leap Year Partnership**
10 MON VISAGE, 4, ch f Ishiguru (USA)—Pikaboo **Mr D. S. Lee**
11 NO JUSTICE, 4, b g Authorized (USA)—Regrette Rien (USA) **Ms A. Fustoq**
12 OH SO SPICY, 5, ch m Pastoral Pursuits—Almasi (IRE) **The Eight of Diamonds**
13 PEARL BLUE (IRE), 4, b f Exceed And Excel (AUS)—Sanfrancullinan (IRE) **Archangels 2**
14 PREMIO LOCO (USA), 8, ch g Prized (USA)—Crazee Mental **B. R. Westley**
15 ROYAL ROCK, 8, b g Sakhee (USA)—Vanishing Point (USA) **Ms A. Fustoq**
16 SNOW HILL, 4, gr g Halling (USA)—Swift Dispersal **Mollers Racing**

THREE-YEAR-OLDS

17 ALECO, b c Sakhee (USA)—Vanishing Point (USA) **Ms A. Fustoq**
18 BASSARA (IRE), b f Oasis Dream—Sauvage (FR) **Ms A. Fustoq**
19 CHARITY BOX, b f Haafhd—Bible Box (IRE) **J. Sims & M. Sinclair**
20 CURLY COME HOME, b f Notnowcato—Cuyamaca (IRE) **Mrs J. Sinclair**
21 FLAG IS UP, b g Dr Fong (USA)—Rainbow Sky **Follow The Flag Partnership**
22 FOOT TAPPER, b c Invincible Spirit (IRE)—Jazz Princess (IRE) **Howlett, Norden & Westley**
23 B f Green Desert (USA)—Foreign Language (USA) **Strawberry Fields Stud**
24 HARD ROAD, b g Cape Cross (IRE)—Ivy League Star (IRE) **Ms A. Fustoq**
25 INTENSE PINK, b f Pivotal—Clincher Club **Mr D. S. Lee**
26 KEEPAX, b g Dubai Destination (USA)—Stellar Brilliant (USA) **Follow The Flag Partnership**
27 LANGHAM LILY, b br f Badge of Silver (USA)—Silver Frau (USA) **P. J. W. Botham**
28 LIGURIAN SEA, b f Medicean—Shamara (IRE) **Doreen Swinburn & Pierpont Scott**
29 MELLOR, b g Echo of Light—Lumiere d'espoir (FR) **David Andrews Plastering**
30 NORFOLK SKY, ch f Haafhd—Cayman Sound **FarandWide Partners**
31 SILVER LACE (IRE), br gr f Clodovil (IRE)—Rockahoolababy (IRE) **The Equema Partnership**
32 WORLD CLASS, ch f Galileo (IRE)—Out West (USA) **Ms A. Fustoq**
33 ZE KING, b g Manduro (GER)—Top Flight Queen **Ms A. Fustoq**

TWO-YEAR-OLDS

34 B f 24/2 Soviet Star (USA)—Ailincala (IRE) (Pursuit of Love) (10000) **Racingeight Partners**
35 BALLYSHONAGH, b f 25/2 Tiger Hill (IRE)—Shamara (IRE) (Spectrum (IRE)) (27000) **Lady Juliet Tadgell**
36 BLESSING BOX, b f 1/2 Bahamian Bounty—Bible Box (IRE) (Bin Ajwaad (IRE)) **Mr M. Sinclair & Mr J. Sims**
37 EMERALD SEA, b f 18/2 Green Desert (USA)—
                                                  Wind Surf (USA) (Lil's Lad (USA)) **Lady Juliet Tadgell & Major M. G. Wyatt**
38 FIRST PENINSULAR, ch c 16/2 Excellent Art—Sarah's First (Cadeaux Genereux) (52000) **Mollers Racing**
39 B f 16/2 Rock of Gibraltar (IRE)—Hope Island (IRE) (Titus Livius (FR)) **Moyns Park Stud**
40 B br f 21/1 Street Sense (USA)—Island Queen (USA) (Ogygian (USA)) (76312) **Pearl Bloodstock Ltd**
41 B f 20/3 Mount Nelson—Jalissa (Mister Baileys) **Dolly's Dream Syndicate**
42 B c 21/1 Shirocco (GER)—Maryqueenofscots (IRE) (Fantastic Light (USA)) (25000) **Mr D. S. Lee**
43 MEET ME HALFWAY, b f 26/2 Exceed And Excel (AUS)—Pivotal Drive (IRE) (Pivotal) (60000) **Mr D. M. Thurlby**
44 B c 20/4 Iffraaj—Mrs Kanning (Distant View (USA)) (20000) **Mr D. S. Lee**

MR CHRIS WALL—continued

45 B c 1/3 Johannesburg (USA)—Muskoka Dawn (USA) (Miswaki (USA)) (46000) **Mr D. S. Lee**
46 OH SO SASSY, b f 16/1 Pastoral Pursuits—Almasi (IRE) (Petorius) (5200) **The Eight Of Diamonds**
47 RAVENSBURG, ch f 7/3 Raven's Pass (USA)—Generous Lady (Generous (IRE)) **Ms A. Fustoq**
48 RUNNINGLIKETHEWIND (IRE), b c 18/4 Hurricane Run (IRE)—
  Virgin Hawk (USA) (Silver Hawk (USA)) (12000) **Mr D. M. Thurlby**
49 SWITCH ON, b c 5/3 Oasis Dream—Noodle Soup (Alphabet Soup (USA)) (65000) **Ms A. Fustoq**
50 B f 12/2 Authorized (IRE)—Trinkila (USA) (Cat Thief (USA)) (15000) **Mr D. S. Lee**

Other Owners: Mrs E. Botham, Mrs J. Carnegie, Mr T. Carroll, Mr N. Cobby, Mrs Sue Davis, Mr Stuart Feast, Mr R. Fraiser, Mr Don Howlett, Mrs Jill Kerr-Smiley, Mr Richard Norden, Mr D. Popely, Mr R. A. Popely, Mr I. Radford, Mr Ray Rice, Mrs M. Shawsmith, Mrs C. A. Wall, Mr R. J. Wayman, Mr Bernard Westley, Mr E. J. Williams.

Assistant Trainer: Richard Freeman

Jockey (flat): George Baker, Ted Durcan. **Apprentice:** Danny Brock. **Amateur:** Mr Frazier Williams.

---

667 MRS SARAH WALL, Dallington
Postal: Little Pines, Bakers Lane, Dallington, nr Heathfield, East Sussex, TN21 9JS
Contacts: **PHONE/FAX** (01435) 831048 **MOBILE** (07783) 370856
E-MAIL sarah55french@btinternet.com

1 BACH TO FRONT (IRE), 7, b m Bach (IRE)—Celtic Leader (IRE) **J. P. C. Wall**
2 BALLINHASSIG (IRE), 7, ch g Beneficial—Dear Polly (IRE) **Mrs S. Wall**
3 5, Br m Brian Boru—Indian Legend (IRE) **Mrs S. Wall**

Assistant Trainer: Jeremy Wall

---

668 MR TREVOR WALL, Church Stretton
Postal: Harton Manor, Harton, Church Stretton, Shropshire, SY6 7DL
Contacts: **PHONE** (01694) 724144 **FAX** (01694) 724144 **MOBILE** (07972) 732080

1 ECHO DANCER, 6, br g Danehill Dancer (IRE)—Entail (USA) **The Wenlock Edge Optimists**
2 FAIRY ALISHA, 4, ch f Doyen (IRE)—Regal Fairy (IRE) **A. H. Bennett**
3 5, Ch m Karinga Bay—First Bee **D. Pugh**
4 4, B g Sulamani (IRE)—Margarets Wish

THREE-YEAR-OLDS

5 Ch f Needwood Blade—Lola Lola (IRE) **T. R. Wall**

TWO-YEAR-OLDS

6 Gr f 21/4 Fair Mix (IRE)—Margarets Wish (Cloudings (IRE)) **Mrs Jen Wall & Mr A. H. Bennett**

Other Owners: Mr J. D. Evans, Mr T. Wall.

Assistant Trainer: Mrs J. A. Wall

Conditional: Josh Wall.

---

669 MR JAMES WALTON, Morpeth
Postal: Flotterton Hall, Thropton, Morpeth, Northumberland, NE65 7LF

1 COQUET HEAD, 6, br g Alflora (IRE)—Coquet Gold **Messrs F. T. Walton**
2 HIGHLAND CATHEDRAL, 8, ch g Minster Son—Celtic Waters **Messrs F. T. Walton**
3 MERRY MINSTER, 5, b m Minster Son—Merry Tina **Messrs F. T. Walton**
4 RUPERT BEAR, 6, b g Rambling Bear—Glittering Stone **Messrs F. T. Walton**
5 SACRED MOUNTAIN, 11, b g Primitive Rising (USA)—Gone Astray **Messrs F. T. Walton**
6 SADDLE PACK (IRE), 9, b g Saddlers' Hall (IRE)—Zuhal **Messrs F. T. Walton**

Other Owners: J. B. Walton, F. A. Walton.

670 **MRS JANE WALTON, Otterburn**
Postal: Dunns Houses, Otterburn, Newcastle Upon Tyne, Northumberland, NE19 1LB
Contacts: PHONE (01830) 520677 FAX (01830) 520677 MOBILE (07808) 592701
E-MAIL dunnshouses@hotmail.com WEBSITE www.janewaltonhorseracing.co.uk

1 **CHARMING KNIGHT (IRE)**, 11, b g Mohaajir (USA)—Arctic Laura **Mrs J. M. Walton**
2 **HAVE YOU HAD YOURS (IRE)**, 6, br g Whitmore's Conn (USA)—
Mandys Moynavely (IRE) **The Highly Recommended Partnership**
3 **I WITNESS (IRE)**, 10, br g Witness Box (USA)—Challenging Times (IRE) **Mrs J. M. Walton**
4 **MASTER MURPHY (IRE)**, 7, b g Flemensfirth (USA)—Awbeg Beauty (IRE) **Mrs J. M. Walton**
5 **REBECCAS ROSE (IRE)**, 7, gr m Tikkanen (USA)—Debonair Rose (IRE) **Mr F. W. W. Chapman**
6 **SUN LADY (FR)**, 6, b m Rifapour (IRE)—Vousseliere (FR) **T. L. A. Robson**
7 **SUNARRI (IRE)**, 8, b g Sonus (IRE)—Rosearro (IRE) **Fresh Start Partnership**

Other Owners: Mr N. Cruikshank, Mr J. Murray, Mrs M. R. Ridley, Miss J. Rutherford.

Assistant Trainer: Mrs Patricia Robson

Jockey (NH): Alistair Findlay.

671 **MRS KATE WALTON, Middleham**
Postal: Sharp Hill Farm, Middleham, Leyburn, North Yorkshire, DL8 4QY
Contacts: PHONE (01969) 622250 MOBILE (07718) 909356
E-MAIL Katewaltonracing@hotmail.com WEBSITE www.katewaltonracing.co.uk

1 **CROP WALKER (IRE)**, 10, b br g Kotashaan (FR)—Miss Mutley **I. M. Lynch**
2 **DARNBOROUGH (IRE)**, 6, b g Darnay—Princesse Sharpo (USA) **Mrs J. A. Brooke**
3 **EMBSAY CRAG**, 6, b g Elmaamul (USA)—Wigman Lady (IRE) **Keep The Faith Partnership**
4 **EVERAARD (USA)**, 6, ch g Lion Heart (USA)—Via Gras (USA) **Tennant, Sharpe & Boston**
5 **FAIRYNUFF**, 8, gr g Terimon—Hand Inn Glove **New Roc**
6 **MORGAN BE**, 12, b g Alderbrook—Vicie **Mr S. Breakspeare**
7 **PEN GWEN (FR)**, 9, b g Le Balafre (FR)—Dans Dro (FR) **Mrs K. Walton**
8 **RUMBLE OF THUNDER (IRE)**, 6, b g Fath (USA)—Honey Storm (IRE) **The Well Oiled Partnership**
9 4, B g Oscar (IRE)—Shining Lights (IRE) **G. R. Orchard**
10 **STAR BEAT**, 9, b g Beat All (USA)—Autumn Leaf **Blyth, Buttery, Tanfield & Wilson**
11 **STOPPED OUT**, 7, gr g Montjoy (USA)—Kiomi **The Well Oiled Partnership**
12 **TAXI DES OBEAUX (FR)**, 5, b br g Maresca Sorrento (FR)—Madrilene (FR) **Mrs K. Walton**
13 **TURBOLINAS (FR)**, 5, b g Malinas (GER)—L'orchidee (FR) **Yarm Racing Partnership**

Other Owners: Mr J. K. Bell, D. J. Blyth, R. A. Brown, J. H. Madden, C. M. Sharpe, Mr J. G. R. Stent, J. M. Swinglehurst, Mrs G. M. Swinglehurst, J. E. Tennant, O. W. Wilson.

Jockey (NH): Denis O'Regan.

672 **MRS SHEENA WALTON, Hexham**
Postal: Linacres, Wark, Hexham, Northumberland, NE48 3DP
Contacts: PHONE (01434) 230656 MOBILE (07752) 755184
E-MAIL rchrdwltn@aol.com

1 **DOVE HILL (IRE)**, 9, b g Old Vic—Commanchey's Pet (IRE) **Linacres Racing Partnership**
2 **DYSTONIA'S REVENGE (IRE)**, 7, b g Woods of Windsor (USA)—Lady Isaac (USA) **Mr J. L. Blacklock**
3 **FORGE HOUSE (IRE)**, 6, b m Moscow Society (USA)—Divebomb **Mr J. L. Blacklock**
4 **HOBSONS BAY (IRE)**, 7, b g Flemensfirth (USA)—Ou La La (IRE) **R. H. Walton**
5 **ITSBEYONDAJOKE**, 6, b m And Beyond (IRE)—Little Monkside (IRE) **R. H. Walton**
6 **NATIVE OPTIMIST (IRE)**, 5, b g Broadway Flyer (USA)—Native Orchid (IRE) **Rede Tyne Steads Racing**
7 **THE BOOZY BISHOP (IRE)**, 7, b g Bishop of Cashel—Ann's River (IRE) **R. H. Walton**

Assistant Trainer: Mr R. H. Walton

673 **MR JASON WARD, Leyburn**
Postal: **The Dante Yard, Manor House Stables, West End, Middleham, Leyburn, North Yorkshire, DL8 4QL**
Contacts: **PHONE (01969) 622730 MOBILE (07967) 357595**
E-MAIL info@jasonwardracing.co.uk WEBSITE www.jasonwardracing.co.uk

1 APPLAUDE, 7, b g Royal Applause—Flossy **Mrs J. Ward**
2 BRIDGE VALLEY, 5, ch g Avonbridge—Go Between **Mrs J. Ward**
3 4, B f Resplendent Glory (IRE)—Christening (IRE) **Miss V. Pratt**
4 EASTWARD HO, 4, ch g Resplendent Glory (IRE)—Mofeyda (IRE) **Miss V. Pratt**
5 ROMANTICIZE, 6, b m Kyllachy—Romancing **Miss V. Pratt**

THREE-YEAR-OLDS

6 CLOUDS OF GLORY, b f Resplendent Glory (IRE)—Rosewings **Miss V. Pratt**
7 KUWAIT STAR, ch c Resplendent Glory (IRE)—Mofeyda (IRE) **Miss V. Pratt**
8 MORNA'S GLORY, b f Resplendent Glory (IRE)—Tipsy Cake **Miss V. Pratt**
9 ROMANY SPIRIT (IRE), b f Invincible Spirit (IRE)—Attachment (USA) **Mr L. Draycott**
10 SWEETNESSANDLIGHT, b f Aussie Rules (USA)—Taschlynn (IRE) **Mrs J. Ward**
11 YPRES, b g Byron—Esligier (IRE) **Mr R. Popplewell**

Other Owners: Miss Fran Harper, Mr & Mrs McDonald, Mr Charles Tateson.

Assistant Trainer: Tim Ward

674 **MR GEORGE WAREHAM, Findon**
Postal: **1 New Cottages, Gallops Farm, Findon, Worthing, West Sussex, BN14 0RP**

1 NEWSDAY (IRE), 9, b m Shernazar—Streamstownsally (IRE) **G. A. Wareham**

675 **MISS TRACY WATKINS, Kington**
Postal: **Rose Villa, Holmes Marsh, Lyonshall, Kington, Herefordshire, HR5 3JS**

1 BLUE BELL HOUSE (IRE), 6, b g Great Palm (USA)—Copper Cailin (IRE) **K. M. Parry**
2 COLWYN BAY (IRE), 10, b g Sadler's Wells (USA)—Stolen Tear (FR) **K. M. Parry**
3 KING GABRIEL (IRE), 10, b g Desert King (IRE)—Broken Spirit (IRE) **K. M. Parry**

676 **MR FREDERICK WATSON, Sedgefield**
Postal: **Beacon Hill, Sedgefield, Stockton-On-Tees, Cleveland, TS21 3HN**
Contacts: **PHONE (01740) 620582 MOBILE (07773) 321472**
E-MAIL fredwatson@talktalk.net

1 BALLYDAY (IRE), 10, b g Oscar (IRE)—Malbay Sunrise (IRE) **F. Watson**
2 CARA'S DELIGHT (AUS), 5, b m Fusaichi Pegasus (USA)—Carahill (AUS) **F. Watson**
3 CONJUROR'S BLUFF, 4, b c Tiger Hill (IRE)—Portmeirion **F. Watson**
4 DESTINATION AIM, 5, b g Dubai Destination (USA)—Tessa Reef (IRE) **F. Watson**
5 FREDDIE BOLT, 6, b h Diktat—Birjand **F. Watson**
6 REGY FROM SEDGY, 5, ch h Beckett (IRE)—Deekazz (IRE) **F. Watson**
7 REGYTHELION, 6, b g Hunting Lion (IRE)—Deekazz (IRE) **F. Watson**
8 SPOKESPERSON (USA), 4, b c Henny Hughes (USA)—Verbal (USA) **F. Watson**

677 **MRS SHARON WATT, Richmond**
Postal: **Rosey Hill Farm, Scorton Road, Brompton on Swale, Richmond, North Yorkshire, DL10 7EQ**
Contacts: **PHONE (01748) 812064 FAX (01748) 812064 MOBILE (07970) 826046**
E-MAIL wattfences@aol.com

1 ALLORA FLORA, 4, b f Alflora (IRE)—Pequenita
2 LERIDA, 10, ch g Groom Dancer (USA)—Catalonia (IRE) **Famous Five Racing**
3 NOW THEN SAM, 6, b g Presidium—Callace **Mrs P. A. Lemon**

MRS SHARON WATT—continued

THREE-YEAR-OLDS

4 Gr g Beat All (USA)—Auntie Kathleen
5 **CHAMPAGNE VALLEY**, ch f Three Valleys (USA)—Volitant **Famous Five Racing & Major E J Watt**
6 **MADAM LILIBET (IRE)**, b f Authorized (IRE)—Foxilla (IRE) **D. H. Montgomerie**

TWO-YEAR-OLDS

7 B f 28/2 Rail Link—Swynford Pleasure (Reprimand) (5714)

Other Owners: Mr R. Allen, Mr A. J. Markley, Mr D. H. Montgomerie, Mr F. Previtali, Major E. J. Watt.

Assistant Trainer: S. Hole

Jockey (NH): Keith Mercer.

---

678 **MR SIMON WAUGH, Morpeth**
Postal: **Molesden House, Mitford, Morpeth, Northumberland, NE61 3QF**
Contacts: **MOBILE (07860) 561445**
E-MAIL swaugh@dircon.co.uk

1 **BENNY BOY (IRE)**, 12, b g Beneficial—Seefin Lass (IRE) **A. R. G. Waugh**
2 **DIX VILLEZ (FR)**, 13, b g Villez (USA)—Dix Huit Brumaire (FR) **A. R. G. Waugh**
3 **EARTH CRYSTAL (IRE)**, 10, b g Bob's Return (IRE)—Crystal Mover (IRE) **S & A Waugh**
4 **GEORGE MY FRIEND**, 6, b g River Falls—Mystical Madam **Mrs L. C. Balmer**
5 **GRANDE MONSIEUR (IRE)**, 9, b g Houmayoun (FR)—Lady Suntan **A. R. G. Waugh**
6 4, B f Alflora (IRE)—Maid Equal **S. G. Waugh**
7 **NEWYEARSRESOLUTION (IRE)**, 8, b g Mr Combustible (IRE)—That's Magic (IRE) **S. G. Waugh**

---

679 **MISS AMY WEAVER, Newmarket**
Postal: **C/o Green Lodge, The Severals, Newmarket, Suffolk, CB8 7BS**
Contacts: **MOBILE (07947) 442083**
E-MAIL amy@amyweaverracing.com WEBSITE www.amyweaverracing.com

1 **CARINYA (IRE)**, 4, br f Iffraaj—Ma N'ieme Biche (USA) **Mr R. M. Boyd**
2 **SMOKY CLOUD (IRE)**, 5, ch g Refuse To Bend (IRE)—Pirie (USA) **Miss A. K. Weaver**

THREE-YEAR-OLDS

3 **ART OF GOLD**, br f Excellent Art—Siena Gold **C. G. Rowles Nicholson**

TWO-YEAR-OLDS

4 B f 7/3 Moss Vale (IRE)—Flying Ridge (IRE) (Indian Ridge) (2052)

---

680 **MR ROBERT WEBB-BOWEN, Wincanton**
Postal: **Sycamore Farm, Stoke Trister, Wincanton, Somerset, BA9 9PE**
Contacts: **PHONE (01963) 31647 FAX (01963) 31647 MOBILE (07919) 884895**
E-MAIL robert@webb-bowen.co.uk WEBSITE www.camrosestud.org.uk

1 **DEEP KING (IRE)**, 17, b br g King's Ride—Splendid Run **Mr R. I. Webb-Bowen**
2 **WITH SPEED (GER)**, 9, br g Spectrum (IRE)—Well Known (GER) **Mrs D. J. Webb-Bowen**

Assistant Trainer: Mrs Dinah Webb-Bowen

---

681 **MR PAUL WEBBER, Banbury**
Postal: **Cropredy Lawn, Mollington, Banbury, Oxfordshire, OX17 1DR**
Contacts: **PHONE (01295) 750226 FAX (01295) 758482 MOBILE (07836) 232465**
E-MAIL paul@paulwebberracing.com WEBSITE www.paulwebberracing.com

1 **ALASI**, 8, b m Alflora (IRE)—Anamasi **Mr S. Liebermann**
2 4, B g Royal Anthem (USA)—Allaracket (IRE) **Paul Webber Racing**
3 **ALLEANDOE**, 4, ch g Quick Move—Villian **John Nicholls Ltd/Mobley Homes**
4 **AMAAL (USA)**, 4, ch f First Samurai (USA)—Awtaan (USA) **Bordeaux Bandits**
5 **APPLEADAY (IRE)**, 11, gr g Beneficial—Hello Aris (IRE) **D. C. R. Allen**

MR PAUL WEBBER—continued

6 **AUSTRALIA DAY (IRE)**, 9, gr g Key of Luck (USA)—Atalina (FR) **Skippy & The Partners**
7 **BRASS MONKEY (IRE)**, 5, b g Craigsteel—Saltee Great (IRE) **S. C. B. Limited & Kevin Bailey**
8 **CANTLOW (IRE)**, 7, b g Kayf Tara—Winnowing (IRE) **R. V. Shaw**
9 **CITRUS MARK**, 7, b g Mark of Esteem (IRE)—Lemon's Mill (USA) **Economic Security**
10 **COCOA MINNIE (IRE)**, 6, ch m Presenting—Native Lucy (IRE) **Jolly Wolf Racing**
11 **COIS FARRAIG (IRE)**, 7, b g Karinga Bay—Oriel Dream **R. V. Shaw**
12 **COLONEL ALF**, 7, b g Alflora (IRE)—Re-Spin **D. R. Stoddart**
13 **CRIME DONT PAY (IRE)**, 8, b g Saddlers' Hall (IRE)—Maddy's Supreme (IRE) **R. W. Barnett**
14 **DANVILLA**, 5, b m Dansili—Newtown Villa **Shully Liebermann /W. Carson**
15 **DECEPTIVE**, 4, b f Red Ransom (USA)—Fleeting Memory **Paul Webber Racing**
16 **DEFINITELY GLAD (IRE)**, 5, b m Definite Article—Gladys May (IRE) **Mr S. Liebermann**
17 **DEVON DRUM**, 4, b g Beat Hollow—West Devon (USA) **Mr D. Carrington**
18 **EDGBRIAR (FR)**, 10, br g Brier Creek (USA)—Harmonie de Valtat (FR) **D. C. R. Allen**
19 **EDGEBURY**, 9, br g Overbury (IRE)—Dusky Dante (IRE) **D. C. R. Allen**
20 **EDGEOVER**, 10, br g Overbury (IRE)—Dusky Dante (IRE) **D. C. R. Allen**
21 **ENDOFDISCUSION (IRE)**, 5, b g Flemensfirth (USA)—Fake Tan (IRE) **D. C. R. Allen**
22 **FIRM ORDER (IRE)**, 7, b g Winged Love (IRE)—Fairylodge Scarlet (IRE) **The Syndicators**
23 **GUEST OF HONOUR (FR)**, 4, b g Hurricane Run (IRE)—Pats Martini (USA) **M. Tabor**
24 **GUMBALL**, 7, ch g Karinga Bay—Little Dasi (IRE) **Mr D. Carrington**
25 **HALUCHA (IRE)**, 7, b g Luso—Rose Basket (IRE) **R. W. Barnett**
26 **HARRIS GARDEN (IRE)**, 5, b g Pilsudski (IRE)—Bay Pearl (FR)
27 **ICY COLT (ARG)**, 6, br g Colonial Affair (USA)—Icy Desert (USA) **R. M. Kirkland**
28 **KEY CUTTER (IRE)**, 8, b g Alderbrook—Two Roads **Mrs A. W. Timpson**
29 **KING OF KEYS (IRE)**, 4, br g Royal Anthem (USA)—Rosealainn (IRE) **Mrs A. W. Timpson**
30 **KOOLALA (IRE)**, 4, b f Kayf Tara—Squaw Talk (USA) **Lady Wellesley**
31 **LADY DEDDINGTON**, 7, ch m Kirkwall—Carleen Gold **The Deddington Four**
32 **LADY KATHLEEN**, 5, b m Hernando (FR)—Lady of Fortune (IRE) **Mr S. Liebermann**
33 **LASTOFTHEMOHICANS (FR)**, 5, b g Galileo (IRE)—Peace Time (GER) **A. J. Duke**
34 **LEMON DROP RED (USA)**, 4, b g Lemon Drop Kid (USA)—Skipper's Mate (USA) **John Nicholls Ltd**
35 **LEMON'S GENT**, 5, br g Generous (IRE)—Lemon's Mill (USA) **G. R. Waters**
36 **MARLEY ROCA (IRE)**, 8, b br g Tamayaz (CAN)—Gaye Gordon **Mr D. Carrington**
37 4, B g Flemensfirth (USA)—Midnight Lover **Mrs John Magnier**
38 5, B g Zagreb (USA)—Minnie O'grady (IRE) **Fawley House Stud**
39 **MISS HOLBECK GHYLL**, 8, b m Alflora (IRE)—Dominie Breeze **Miss A. M. Dobie**
40 **MONEYMIX**, 5, gr g Fair Mix (IRE)—Sticky Money **D. C. R. Allen**
41 **MONKEY MILAN (IRE)**, 6, b g Milan—Beech Lodge (IRE) **S. C. B. Limited & Kevin Bailey**
42 **MURPHY'S CHOICE**, 5, b g Sakhee (USA)—Ballet Princess **The Large G & T Partnership**
43 4, B g Indian Danehill (IRE)—Persian Avenue (IRE) **Paul Webber Racing**
44 **RAJNAGAN (IRE)**, 8, ch g Muhtarram (USA)—Rajnagara (IRE) **Mrs P. V. E. Morrell**
45 **REPEAT BUSINESS (IRE)**, 4, b g Croco Rouge (IRE)—Bay Pearl (FR) **R. M. Kirkland**
46 **ROUBILIAC (USA)**, 5, ch h Rahy (USA)—Super Tassa (IRE) **C. Humphris**
47 **RYSBRACK (USA)**, 6, ch g Selkirk (USA)—Super Tassa (IRE) **C. Humphris**
48 **SARANDO**, 7, b g Hernando (FR)—Dansara **Eight Men & A Hoss**
49 **SCAMPI BOY (IRE)**, 8, b g Flemensfirth (USA)—Loch Lomond (IRE) **Mr D. Carrington**
50 **SEPTEMBER BLAZE**, 5, b m Exit To Nowhere (USA)—Mid Day Chaser (IRE) **The Blaze Partnership**
51 **SIXTY SOMETHING (IRE)**, 6, gr g Dom Alco (FR)—Jaunas (FR) **Mrs A. W. Timpson**
52 **SOLE SURVIVOR (FR)**, 5, gr g Smadoun (FR)—Sellaginella **Mrs A. W. Timpson**
53 **SOMEWHATINEVITABLE (IRE)**, 7, b g Oscar (IRE)—Maspaloma (IRE) **Dunton Racing Partnership**
54 4, B g Presenting—Star Council (IRE) **David Higgins & Partners**
55 **STRUANMORE**, 5, ch g Doyen (IRE)—Burghmuir (IRE) **Mr I. R. Watters**
56 **SUSSEX SUNSET**, 6, b m Milan—Deep Sunset (IRE) **Neil Grover, Family & Friends**
57 **TAFIKA**, 8, b g Kayf Tara—Shiwa **The Tafika Partnership**
58 **THEODORE LAMB**, 7, b g Lahib (USA)—Our Leader (IRE) **P. F. Charter/Mobley Homes**
59 **THOM THUMB (IRE)**, 6, ch g Flemensfirth (USA)—Ardlea Dawn **Simon & Liz Packer 1**
60 **TIAGRA**, 5, b g Tiger Hill (IRE)—Shifting Mist **The Old Lags Partnership**
61 **TIME FOR RUPERT (IRE)**, 8, ch g Flemensfirth (USA)—Bell Walks Run (IRE) **Littlecote Racing Partnership**
62 **TINDARO (FR)**, 5, gr g Kingsalsa (USA)—Star's Mixa (FR) **The Tindaro Partnership**
63 **UNIVOQUE (FR)**, 5, gr g Turgeon (USA)—Us Et Coutumes (FR) **Mrs M. Campbell-Andenaes**

Other Owners: Mr K. B. Bailey, Mr Nigel Birch, Mr D. G. Carrington, W. Carson, Mr Nigel Chamberlain, Mr P. A. Deal, Mrs Sarah Drysdale, Mr Robert Frosell, Mrs Margaret Gardiner, Mr Raymond Anderson Green, Mr N. A. Grover, Mr Peter Hewett, Mr D. W. Higgins, Mr M. Ince, Mr P. S. Lewis, Sir I. Magee, Mr A. J. Massey, Professor David Metcalf, Mobley Homes, Mrs Liz Packer, Mr Simon Packer, M. Pepper, Mr John Phelan, Mr Tony Roche, Mr Philip Rocher, S. C. B. Limited, Mr Nicholas Sercombe, Mr M. J. Silver, Mr John D. Spence, Mr Paul Webber, Mrs John Webber.

Jockey (flat): Jimmy Fortune, Dane O'Neill. **Jockey (NH):** Dominic Elsworth, Denis O'Regan. **Amateur:** Mr D. Hannig.

682 MR D. K. WELD, The Curragh

Postal: **Rosewell House, The Curragh, Co. Kildare, Irish Republic**
Contacts: **PHONE (00353) 4544 1273 / 441 476 FAX (00353) 4544 1119**
E-MAIL dkweld@eircom.net

1 CELEBRITY SEVI (IRE), 4, b g Peintre Celebre (USA)—Sevi's Choice (USA) **J. P. McManus**
2 DAFFERN SEAL (IRE), 8, b g Fruits of Love (USA)—Miss Tickill (IRE) **Dr R. Lambe**
3 EMULOUS, 5, b m Dansili—Aspiring Diva (USA) **K. Abdulla**
4 FAMOUS NAME, 7, b h Dansili—Fame At Last (IRE) **K. Abdulla**
5 FONT OF WISDOM (IRE), 4, b c Marju (IRE)—Fernanda (IRE) **Dr R. Lambe**
6 GALILEO'S CHOICE (IRE), 6, b g Galileo (IRE)—Sevi's Choice (USA) **Dr R. Lambe**
7 HISAABAAT (IRE), 4, b g Dubawi (IRE)—Phariseek (IRE) **Dr R. Lambe**
8 MAJESTIC CONCORDE (IRE), 9, b g Definite Article—Talina's Law (IRE) **Dr R. Lambe**
9 MALAYAN MIST (IRE), 4, b f Dansili—Misty Heights **Lady O'Reilly**
10 MERCHANT ROYAL (IRE), 8, b g Kayf Tara—Country Store **Mr K. Weld**
11 MIDNIGHT MUSIC (IRE), 4, ch f Dubawi (IRE)—Midnight Mist (IRE) **Lady O'Reilly**
12 NEW PHASE (IRE), 8, b g Spectrum (IRE)—South of Heaven (IRE) **Mr Kris Weld**
13 NOTABLE GRADUATE (IRE), 4, b g Galileo (IRE)—Market Slide (USA) **Moyglare Stud Farms Ltd**
14 OLYMPIAD (IRE), 4, b c Galileo (IRE)—Caumshinaun (IRE) **Sir R. Ogden C.B.E., LLD**
15 PRINCE ERIK, 8, gr g Indian Ridge—Miracle **Dr R. Lambe**
16 RITE OF PASSAGE, 8, ch g Giant's Causeway (USA)—Dahlia's Krissy (USA) **Dr R. Lambe**
17 ROCK CRITIC (IRE), 7, b g Pivotal—Diamond Trim (IRE) **Moyglare Stud Farms Ltd**
18 SAPPHIRE (IRE), 4, b f Medicean—Polished Gem (IRE) **Moyglare Stud Farms Ltd**
19 SENSE OF PURPOSE (IRE), 5, ch m Galileo (IRE)—Super Gift (IRE) **Moyglare Stud Farms Ltd**
20 SILVER CONCORDE, 4, b g Dansili—Sacred Pearl (IRE) **Dr. R. Lambe**
21 TRAIN OF THOUGHT (IRE), 4, b g Sadler's Wells (USA)—Cool Clarity (IRE) **Dr R. Lambe**
22 TROON (USA), 4, b g Kitten's Joy (USA)—Sunday Sport (USA) **Mr Kris Weld**
23 UNACCOMPANIED (IRE), 5, b m Danehill Dancer (USA)—Legend Has It (IRE) **Moyglare Stud Farms Ltd**
24 WAAHEB (USA), 5, b br g Elusive Quality (USA)—Nafisah (USA) **J. P. McManus**
25 ZAMINAST, 4, b f Zamindar (USA)—Fame At Last (IRE) **K. Abdulla**

THREE-YEAR-OLDS

26 ACORN VALLEY (USA), ch g Kitten's Joy (USA)—Mambo With G (USA) **Dr R. Lambe**
27 ANGEL BRIGHT (IRE), b f Dark Angel (IRE)—Cover Girl (IRE) **Mrs C. L. Weld**
28 AQUA REGIA (IRE), ch g Pivotal—Aquarist **Sheikh Mohammed**
29 CAPONATA (USA), b f Selkirk (USA)—Daring Diva **K. Abdulla**
30 CELTIC CUTIE (IRE), b f Teofilo (IRE)—Tropical Lake (IRE) **Deus Bros Racing Syndicate**
31 CLOUDRACER (IRE), b f Rail Link—Catching Stars (IRE) **Lady O'Reilly**
32 CRIMSON SUNRISE (IRE), b f Holy Roman Emperor (IRE)—Zanida (IRE) **Mrs A. Lambe**
33 DAZZLING PEARL (IRE), b g Amadeus Wolf—Fabuco (IRE) **Dr R. Lambe**
34 DIPLOMAT (USA), b c Kitten's Joy (USA)—Waki Affair (USA) **Mr Kenneth Ramsey**
35 DUBAI KITTEN (USA), b br c Kitten's Joy (USA)—Crimson Ore (USA) **Mr Kenneth Ramsey**
36 ENCRYPTED MESSAGE (IRE), b c Dansili—Where We Left Off **Moyglare Stud Farms Ltd**
37 EXHORTATION, b c Zamindar (USA)—Winter Silence **K. Abdulla**
38 FASTIDIOUS, b g Exceed And Excel (AUS)—Felicitous **Sheikh Mohammed**
39 FIERY AMBITION, b c Shamardal (USA)—Xaluna Bay (IRE) **Dr R. Lambe**
40 FIXED GAZE (USA), b f Speightstown (USA)—Unique Pose (IRE) **Moyglare Stud Farms Ltd**
41 FRENCH HEN (USA), b f English Channel (USA)—Miarixa (FR) **Mr B. Kelley**
42 HARBOUR SIDE, b f Dansili—Mooring **K. Abdulla**
43 HIGHLAND MISS (USA), b f Theatrical—Cyrillic (USA) **Mr B. Kelley**
44 HIT THE JACKPOT (IRE), ch c Pivotal—Token Gesture (IRE) **Moyglare Stud Farms Ltd**
45 KAASEB (USA), b c Jazil (USA)—Thawakib (IRE) **Hamdan Al Maktoum**
46 MADHMOONAH (IRE), b f Invincible Spirit (IRE)—Laywaan (USA) **Hamdan Al Maktoum**
47 MAHAAZEN (IRE), b f Cape Cross (IRE)—Innclassic (IRE) **Hamdan Al Maktoum**
48 MODERN ROMANCE (IRE), ch f Muhtathir—Khulan (USA) **Mr Chris McHale**
49 MOONSHED (USA), b c Arch (USA)—Rose of Zollern (IRE) **Hamdan Al Maktoum**
50 MUNTASAF (IRE), b g Acclamation—Tasha's Dream (USA) **Hamdan Al Maktoum**
51 NILE VENTURE, b c Oasis Dream—Strike Lightly **K. Abdulla**
52 PACELLI ROAD (IRE), b c Oratorio—Lexy May (USA) **Mrs N. McCreevy**
53 PALE MIMOSA (IRE), b f Singspiel (IRE)—Katch Me Katie **Dr R. Lambe**
54 PRINCESS HIGHWAY (USA), b f Street Cry (IRE)—Irresistible Jewel (IRE) **Moyglare Stud Farms Ltd**
55 QUICK GLIMPSE, b f Galileo (IRE)—Half Glance **K. Abdulla**
56 RADIO CALL, b c Rail Link—Aspiring Diva (USA) **K. Abdulla**
57 RANSOMED ROSE, b f Oasis Dream—Rapid Ransom (USA) **Lady O'Reilly**
58 SHOW COURT (IRE), b g Vinnie Roe (IRE)—Sparkling Gem (IRE) **Mr Kris Weld**
59 SILK KIMONO, b f Danehill Dancer (IRE)—First Breeze (USA) **Dr R. Lambe**

MR D. K. WELD—continued

60 **SPEAKING OF WHICH (IRE),** b c Invincible Spirit (IRE)—Suitably Discreet (USA) **Moyglare Stud Farms Ltd**
61 **SPIRIT OF CONCORDE,** gr c Authorized (IRE)—Lucky Token (IRE) **Dr R. Lambe**
62 **STARSTRUCK (IRE),** ch f Galileo (IRE)—Agnetha (GER) **Mrs C. L. Weld**
63 **STORM LIGHTNING,** b c Exceed And Excel (AUS)—All For Laura **Mrs A. Lambe**
64 **STUNNED SILENCE (USA),** b f Officer (USA)—Offbeat Fashion (IRE) **Moyglare Stud Farms Ltd**
65 **SUNDRENCHED COAST (USA),** b g Van Nistelrooy (USA)—Harve de Grace (USA) **Dr R. Lambe**
66 **SUPERNOVAE (IRE),** b f Dalakhani (IRE)—Dress To Thrill (IRE) **Moyglare Stud Farms Ltd**
67 **SWEET MYSTERY (IRE),** b g Dark Angel (IRE)—Hartstown House (IRE) **Dr R. Lambe**
68 **SWERVE,** b f Oasis Dream—Avoidance (USA) **K. Abdulla**
69 **TALWEEN,** b f Nayef (USA)—Zaqrah (USA) **Hamdan Al Maktoum**
70 **THREE KINGDOMS (IRE),** ch c Street Cry (IRE)—Chan Tong (BRZ) **Sheikh Mohammed**
71 **TREASURE THE RIDGE (IRE),** b c Galileo (IRE)—Treasure The Lady (IRE) **Mrs A. M. Coughlan**
72 **UNREACHABLE (USA),** ch f Giant's Causeway (USA)—Harpia (USA) **Mr B. Kelley**
73 **VOLEUSE DE COEURS (IRE),** b f Teofilo (IRE)—Vadorga **Lady O'Reilly**
74 **WALNUT HILL,** b f Dansili—Tates Creek (USA) **K. Abdulla**
75 **WILLOW ISLAND (IRE),** b g Dark Angel (IRE)—Cidaris (IRE) **Dr R. Lambe**
76 **YELLOW ROSEBUD (IRE),** b f Jeremy (USA)—Nebraas **Dr R. Lambe**

TWO-YEAR-OLDS

77 **ACTING TALENT (USA),** b f 4/3 Bernstein (USA)—
Soaring Emotions (USA) (Kingmambo (USA)) **Moyglare Stud Farms Ltd**
78 B f 25/4 Teofilo (IRE)—Agnetha (GER) (Big Shuffle (USA)) (36000) **Mr Pat Fleming**
79 Gr f 20/2 Dalakhani (IRE)—Alambic (Cozzene (USA)) **Lady O'Reilly**
80 B f 29/4 Nayef (USA)—Alshakr (Bahri (USA)) **Hamdan Al Maktoum**
81 **AMBER ROMANCE (IRE),** ch f 27/4 Bahamian Bounty—
Polished Gem (IRE) (Danehill (USA)) **Moyglare Stud Farms Ltd**
82 B f 19/2 Three Valleys (USA)—Avoidance (USA) (Cryptoclearance (USA)) **K. Abdulla**
83 B c 10/2 Beat Hollow—Blend (Zafonic (USA)) **K. Abdulla**
84 **BLUE BLUE SONG (IRE),** ch f 25/3 Manduro (GER)—
Dress To Thrill (IRE) (Danehill (USA)) **Moyglare Stud Farms Ltd**
85 B c 22/4 Invincible Spirit (IRE)—Bluebell Park (USA) (Gulch (USA)) (90311) **Mr Joseph Higgins**
86 B f 8/2 Medicean—Bright And Clear (Danehill (USA)) **K. Abdulla**
87 Gr c 20/5 Teofilo (IRE)—Cassandra Go (IRE) (Indian Ridge) (147782) **Hamdan Al Maktoum**
88 **COCKTAIL HOUR (IRE),** b f 20/2 Notnowcato—
Out of Thanks (IRE) (Sadler's Wells (USA)) **Moyglare Stud Farms Ltd**
89 **COOL METALLIC (IRE),** b c 21/4 Medicean—Polite Reply (IRE) (Be My Guest (USA)) **Moyglare Stud Farms Ltd**
90 Ch c 15/3 Elnadim (USA)—Dance Clear (IRE) (Marju (IRE)) (41050) **Dr R. Lambe**
91 Ch c 22/2 Pivotal—Embassy (Cadeaux Genereux) **Sheikh Mohammed**
92 B f 16/2 Marju (IRE)—Esterlina (IRE) (Highest Honor (FR)) **Hamdan Al Maktoum**
93 B f 6/4 Dansili—Fame At Last (USA) (Quest For Fame) **K. Abdulla**
94 B c 7/4 Lawman (FR)—Fernanda (Be My Chief (USA)) (65680) **Dr R. Lambe**
95 **FORGOTTEN RULES (IRE),** b c 9/3 Nayef (USA)—
Utterly Heaven (IRE) (Danehill (USA)) **Moyglare Stud Farms Ltd**
96 Ch c 12/2 Sakhee's Secret—Fudge (Polar Falcon (USA)) (75533) **Dr R. Lambe**
97 **HAMMERED SILVER (IRE),** gr c 20/5 Dalakhani (IRE)—
Desert Ease (IRE) (Green Desert (USA)) **Moyglare Stud Farms Ltd**
98 **HAZY GLOW (IRE),** b f 11/4 Invincible Spirit (IRE)—
Genuine Charm (IRE) (Sadler's Wells (USA)) **Moyglare Stud Farms Ltd**
99 **INSTANT UPDATE (IRE),** b c 17/1 Pivotal—Instant Sparkle (IRE) (Danehill (USA)) **Moyglare Stud Farms Ltd**
100 B c 28/1 High Chaparral (IRE)—Irish Style (IRE) (Mujadil (USA)) (90311) **Dr R. Lambe**
101 Gr c 15/3 Empire Maker (USA)—Jibboom (IRE) (Mizzen Mast (USA)) **K. Abdulla**
102 Ch c 1/4 Tamayuz—Just Special (Cadeaux Genereux) (45155) **Dr R. Lambe**
103 B c 31/1 Marju (IRE)—Katoom (IRE) (Soviet Star (USA)) **Hamdan Al Maktoum**
104 B c 16/4 Oasis Dream—La Coruna (Deploy) **K. Abdulla**
105 **LAPIS BLUE (IRE),** b f 16/3 Invincible Spirit (IRE)—
Triple Try (IRE) (Sadler's Wells (USA)) **Moyglare Stud Farms Ltd**
106 B f 8/3 Haafet—Laywaan (USA) (Fantastic Light (USA)) **Hamdan Al Maktoum**
107 **MAGNOLIA RIDGE (IRE),** b c 14/4 Galileo (IRE)—Treasure The Lady (IRE) (Indian Ridge) **Mrs A. M. Coughlan**
108 **MIDNIGHT THOUGHTS (USA),** b f 27/4 Henrythenavigator (USA)—
Irresistible Jewel (IRE) (Danehill (USA)) **Moyglare Stud Farms Ltd**
109 B f 5/4 Invincible Spirit (IRE)—Moy Water (IRE) (Tirol) (71428) **Dr R. Lambe**
110 B f 13/5 Jeremy (USA)—Nebraas (Green Desert (USA)) (69785) **Lady O'Reilly**
111 B f 8/4 Dansili—Nebraska Tornado (USA) (Storm Cat (USA)) **K. Abdulla**
112 B c 20/2 Arch (USA)—Out of Reach (Warning) **K. Abdulla**
113 Ch f 24/1 New Approach (IRE)—Posterity (IRE) (Indian Ridge) (287356) **Hamdan Al Maktoum**

MR D. K. WELD—continued

114 Gr ro f 28/2 Exchange Rate (USA)—Private Line (USA) (Private Account (USA)) **K. Abdulla**
115 B f 2/2 Oasis Dream—Rapid Ransom (USA) (Red Ransom (USA)) **Lady O'Reilly**
116 **RESOLUTE RESPONSE (IRE),** b c 5/4 Dansili—Lady Luck (IRE) (Kris) **Moyglare Stud Farms Ltd**
117 **RICH DARK INK (USA),** b br c 22/3 Arch (USA)—
        Society Hostess (Seeking The Gold (USA)) **Moyglare Stud Farms Ltd**
118 Ch c 17/3 Kheleyf (USA)—Rifqah (USA) (Elusive Quality (USA)) **Hamdan Al Maktoum**
119 B c 6/5 Rail Link—Shamana (USA) (Woodman (USA)) **K. Abdulla**
120 **SHARP CRISP AIR (IRE),** ch f 2/2 Danehill Dancer (IRE)—
        Token Gesture (IRE) (Alzao (USA)) **Moyglare Stud Farms Ltd**
121 B c 10/5 Shirocco (GER)—Sharp Point (IRE) (Royal Academy (USA)) (86206) **Mr Steven Lo**
122 **SIERRA RED (IRE),** ch c 6/4 Proud Citizen (USA)—
        Burren Rose (USA) (Storm Cat (USA)) **Moyglare Stud Farms Ltd**
123 **SLEEPING BEAUTY (IRE),** b f 17/2 Oasis Dream—Nighttime (IRE) (Galileo (IRE)) **Mrs C. L. Weld**
124 B c 21/4 Hard Spun (USA)—Teeba (USA) (Seeking The Gold (USA)) **Hamdan Al Maktoum**
125 Ch f 9/3 Duke of Marmalade (IRE)—Upperville (IRE) (Selkirk (USA)) **Mr B. R. Firestone**
126 **VIOLET HOUR (USA),** b f 5/3 Elusive Quality (USA)—
        Luminous Beauty (USA) (A P Indy (USA)) **Moyglare Stud Farms Ltd**
127 B c 25/2 Raven's Pass (USA)—Vista Bella (Diktat) **Sheikh Mohammed**
128 B f 2/2 Acclamation—Yarastar (Cape Cross (IRE)) (135467) **Lady O'Reilly**
129 B f 25/3 Invincible Spirit (IRE)—Zaqrah (USA) (Silver Hawk (USA)) **Hamdan Al Maktoum**

Jockey (flat): P. J. Smullen. **Apprentice:** S. M. Gorey, L. F. Roche.

---

683 **MR MARK WELLINGS, Bridgnorth**
Postal: **Broad Acre Stables, Broadlanes, Quatt, Bridgnorth, Shropshire, WV15 6EG**
Contacts: **PHONE (01746) 781019 MOBILE (07973) 763469**
E-MAIL mark@broadacre.fsnet.co.uk

1 **CUT AND THRUST (IRE),** 6, b g Haafhd—Ego **Nicholls Family**
2 **KING OF CONNACHT,** 9, b g Polish Precedent (USA)—
        Lady Melbourne (IRE) **Ann Lindsay,Francis Lindsay,Jim O'Connor**
3 **LITTLE RICHARD (IRE),** 13, b g Alhaarth (IRE)—Intricacy **Mark Wellings Racing**
4 **SPIN AGAIN (IRE),** 7, b g Intikhab (USA)—Queen of The May (IRE) **Mr D. W. Dacosta**

Other Owners: Mr F. Lindsay, Mrs A. V. Lindsay, Mr R. Nicholls, Mrs E. Nicholls, Mr J. O'Connor, A. Tranter, Mark Wellings.

Assistant Trainer: Mrs L A Wellings

---

684 **MISS SHEENA WEST, Lewes**
Postal: **5 Balmer Farm Cottages, Brighton Road, Lewes, East Sussex, BN7 3JN**
Contacts: **PHONE (01273) 621303 FAX (01273) 622189 MOBILE (07748) 181804**
E-MAIL sheenawest11@aol.com WEBSITE www.sheenawest.com

1 **ALFRAAMSEY,** 4, b g Fraam—Evanesce **Tapestry Partnership**
2 **BE ALL MAN (IRE),** 5, b g Dubawi (IRE)—Belle Allemande (CAN) **Mr A. Head, Mr R. Lockwood & Mr M. Burne**
3 **BLAZING BOLTE,** 7, b m Karinga Bay—Tis Gromit **The Odd Partnership**
4 **BRILLIANT BARCA,** 4, b g Imperial Dancer—Fading Away **The Affordable Partnership**
5 **CHILWORTH LASS,** 4, b f Imperial Dancer—Inching **White Diamond Racing Partnership**
6 **COOLAGAD STAR (IRE),** 4, b f Dr Massini—Trinity Flyer (IRE) **Stephen Monks & Niall Coakley**
7 **FREE FALLING,** 6, ch m Selkirk (USA)—Free Flying **A.C. Entertainment Technologies Limited**
8 **GALLOPING QUEEN (IRE),** 4, b f Refuse To Bend (IRE)—Rouge Noir (USA) **Mr A. J. Head**
9 **GOLAN WAY,** 8, b g Golan (IRE)—Silk Daisy **W R B Racing 58**
10 **HI NOTE,** 4, b f Acclamation—Top Tune **G. West**
11 **JUST JOSIE,** 6, b m Josr Algarhoud (IRE)—Spatham Rose **Saloop**
12 **LEG IRON (IRE),** 7, b g Snurge—Southern Skies (IRE) **M. Moriarty**
13 **MAC FEDERAL (IRE),** 10, b g In The Wings—Tocade (IRE) **G. L. Flight**
14 **MOHANAD (IRE),** 6, b g Invincible Spirit (IRE)—Irish Design (IRE) **Heart Of The South Racing**
15 **MR MUDDLE,** 5, gr g Imperial Dancer—Spatham Rose **Saloop**
16 **QUAILS HOLLOW (IRE),** 4, b g Beat Hollow—Bloemfontain (IRE) **Mr A. Head, Mr R. Lockwood & Mr M. Burne**
17 **WHIPPERWAY (IRE),** 5, b m Whipper (USA)—Prince's Passion **The Affordable Partnership**
18 **YA HAFED,** 4, ch g Haafhd—Rule Britannia **Mr A. J. Head**

MISS SHEENA WEST—continued

THREE-YEAR-OLDS

19 FEB THIRTYFIRST, ch c Shirocco (GER)—My Mariam **M. Moriarty**
20 GEORDIE BOY, b br c Araafa (IRE)—Entail (USA) **The Affordable (3) Partnership**
21 SILVER SIX, gr g Aussie Rules (USA)—Bahara **Lord Ilsley Racing (Ashes Syndicate)**

Other Owners: Mr J. A. Barnes, A. W. A. Bates, Mr M. Burne, Mr T. Castle, M. R. Channon, Mr S. Clegg, Mr N. Coakley, Mr R. C. G. Dodds, Mr P. H. Dussek, Mr S. M. Fellows, Ms G. H. Hedley, Mr D. L. Lacey, Mr R. A. Lockwood, Mr S. Monks, Mrs C. S. Muddle, R. A. Muddle, Mr M. J. O'Leary, J. R. Penny, Mrs C. Penny, Miss S. West, Wetherby Racing Bureau Ltd, D. M. Woodward.

Assistant Trainer: Jamie Goldstein

Jockey (flat): J. Goldstein. **Jockey (NH):** J. Goldstein. **Conditional:** M. Goldstein.

---

685 MR SIMON WEST, Middleham
Postal: 14A St Alkeldas Road, Middleham, Leyburn, North Yorkshire, DL8 4PW
Contacts: MOBILE (07855) 924529
E-MAIL simonwest21@hotmail.co.uk WEBSITE www.mkmracing.co.uk

1 AMJAD, 15, ch g Cadeaux Genereux—Babita **Miss M. K. Milligan**
2 CAPTAIN CLAYTON (IRE), 5, b g Subtle Power (IRE)—Dont Hurry (IRE) **Mr S. G. West**
3 DRUMPELLIER (IRE), 5, ch m Rakti—Early Memory (USA) **Red Squares**
4 6, B g Bollin Eric—Frosty Light **Mrs J. M. L. Milligan**
5 B m Flemensfirth (USA)—Jeruflo (IRE) **Mr S. G. West**
6 LOVEY DOVEY (IRE), 8, b m Winged Love (IRE)—Dansana (IRE) **J. D. Gordon**
7 MY MUM MO, 4, b f Statue of Liberty (USA)—Come To The Point **The Red Connection Syndicate**
8 TARUMA (FR), 4, gr g Martaline—Vie de Reine (FR) **J. D. Gordon**
9 THE TIDDLY TADPOLE, 7, b g Tipsy Creek (USA)—Froglet **The Frog Chorus**
10 WOODMORE (IRE), 8, b g Luso—Supreme Stream (IRE) **Mr P. Hothersall**

THREE-YEAR-OLDS

11 MURAAFIQ (USA), b br g Jazil (USA)—Reem Al Barari (USA) **Mr C. R. Hirst**

Other Owners: Mr K. Flint, Mr S. Flint, Mr J. Grayson, Mrs B. Hothersall, D. J. Weston.

Apprentice: Paul Pickard.

---

686 MR JOHN WEYMES, Middleham
Postal: Ashgill, Coverham, Leyburn, North Yorkshire, DL8 4TJ
Contacts: PHONE (01969) 640420 FAX (01969) 640505 MOBILE (07753) 792516
E-MAIL johnweymes@johnweymes.co.uk WEBSITE www.johnweymesracing.co.uk

1 ALMATY EXPRESS, 10, b g Almaty (IRE)—Express Girl **Highmoor Racing 4 & Tag Racing**
2 ARCH WALKER (IRE), 5, ch g Choisir (AUS)—Clunie **Ontoawinner & Mr A Mikhail**
3 BRIAN SPROUT, 4, ch g Zafeen (FR)—Ducal Diva **Thoroughbred Partners**
4 EMERALDS SPIRIT (IRE), 5, b m Rock of Gibraltar (IRE)—Spiritual Air **T. A. Scothern**
5 FINN'S RAINBOW, 4, ch g Iffraaj—Aptina (USA) **Miss K. Buckle**
6 HARRYS WHIM, 7, b m Sir Harry Lewis (USA)—Whimbrel **J. R. Wills**
7 JUST FIVE (IRE), 6, b g Olmodavor (USA)—Wildsplash (USA) **Grange Park Racing & Partner**
8 5, B m Fair Mix (IRE)—Sing And Dance **Highmoor Racing**
9 SKIDDAW SECRET, 5, ch m Tobougg (IRE)—Stealthy **J. R. Wills**
10 WELCOME APPROACH, 9, b g Most Welcome—Lucky Thing **Mr T. A. Scothern & Tag Racing**

THREE-YEAR-OLDS

11 BRACKENDALE, gr g Three Valleys (USA)—Heather Mix **T. A. Scothern**
12 DIRECT, b f Doyen (IRE)—Illustre Inconnue (USA) **N. A. Blyth**
13 FIREFLY, b g Firebreak—Quick Flight **High Moor Racing 2**
14 SELECTIVE SPIRIT, ch f Exceed And Excel (AUS)—Our Sheila **T. A. Scothern**
15 SERENDIPITY BLUE, b f Cadeaux Genereux—Sister Bluebird **Thoroughbred Partners**
16 Gr g Fair Mix (IRE)—Sing And Dance
17 TOMASINI, b g Misu Bond (IRE)—Bond Stasia (IRE) **Mr P. Bowland**
18 VILLA REIGNS, gr g Clodovil (IRE)—Moon Empress (FR) **T. A. Scothern**

MR JOHN WEYMES—continued

TWO-YEAR-OLDS

19 B c 24/4 Camacho—Alkifaf (USA) (Mtoto) (7500) **T. A. Scothern**
20 B f 10/4 Moss Vale (IRE)—Bonkers (Efisio) (4925) **High Moor Racing 2**
21 Ch f 21/3 Haafhd—Bonny Rose (Zaha (CAN)) (3333) **Grange Park Racing**
22 B f 8/3 Multiplex—Cumbrian Concerto (Petong) (3238) **Mr A. J. Jackson**
23 B f 8/4 Camacho—Dark Albatross (USA) (Sheikh Albadou) (4104) **T. A. Scothern**
24 Ch c 7/4 Indian Haven—Graceful Air (IRE) (Danzero (AUS)) **Thoroughbred Partners**
25 B f 2/5 Avonbridge—Linden's Lady (Compton Place) **Rosemary's Racing**
26 B c 28/2 Moss Vale (IRE)—Page (Elmaamul (USA)) (761) **Rosemary's Racing**
27 B f 2/4 Amadeus Wolf—Summer Crush (USA) (Summer Squall (USA)) (5746) **T. A. Scothern**
28 B f 19/2 Oratorio (IRE)—Sun Seasons (IRE) (Salse (USA)) **Rosemary's Racing**
29 Ch f 13/2 Haatef (USA)—Tawaajud (USA) (Dixieland Band (USA)) (6978) **T. A. Scothern**
30 Gr c 7/3 Clodovil (IRE)—Tinareena (IRE) (Barathea (IRE)) (4761) **Thoroughbred Partners**

Other Owners: Mr P. D. Bickley, Miss K. Buckle, Mr Alan D. Crombie, Mr Richard Gayton, Mr Edward Kingsley, Mr Andrew Mikhail, Mrs R. Morley, Mr J. J. Morley, Mr N. J. O'Brien, Mr E. Surr, Mr J. Weymes.

Assistant Trainer: Kirsty Buckle (kirsty@johnweymes.co.uk)

Jockey (flat): Darryll Holland, Philip Makin. **Jockey (NH):** Keith Mercer, Dougie Costello.

---

687 MR ERIC WHEELER, Pangbourne
Postal: **15 St Michaels Close, Lambourn, Hungerford, Berkshire, RG17 8FA**
Contacts: **PHONE (07795) 844185 FAX (01189) 841924 MOBILE (07795) 844185**

1 BATCHWORTH BLAISE, 9, b g Little Jim—Batchworth Dancer **Astrod Limited TA Austin Stroud & Co**
2 4, Ch f Reel Buddy (USA)—Batchworth Breeze **Mr G. W. Witheford**
3 BATCHWORTH FIREFLY, 4, b f Piccolo—Batchworth Belle **Mr D. Price**
4 BEGGERS BELIEF, 4, ch g Bertolini (USA)—Dropitlikeit's Hot (IRE) **Mr G. W. Witheford**
5 BOLD RING, 6, ch m Bold Edge—Floppie Disk **Mr D. Creighton**
6 CLIFFORDS REPRIEVE, 4, b g Kheleyf (USA)—Bijan (IRE) **Mr G. W. Witheford**
7 EL LIBERTADOR (USA), 6, b br g Giant's Causeway (USA)—Istikbal (USA) **Mr J. L. Day**
8 EMERALD ROYAL, 4, b g Royal Applause—Bakhtawar (IRE) **Four Provinces Partnership**
9 EVEN BOLDER, 9, ch g Bold Edge—Level Pegging (IRE) **Astrod Limited TA Austin Stroud & Co**

TWO-YEAR-OLDS

10 BEGGERS LUCK, b f 12/4 Lucky Story (USA)—Dropitlikeit's Hot (IRE) (Tagula (IRE)) **Mr G. W. Witheford**

Assistant Trainer: Miss C Nosworthy

Amateur: Miss C. Nosworthy.

---

688 MR ALISTAIR WHILLANS, Hawick
Postal: **Esker House, Newmill-On-Slitrig, Hawick, Roxburghshire, TD9 9UQ**
Contacts: **PHONE (01450) 376642 FAX (01450) 376082 MOBILE (07771) 550555**
E-MAIL acwracing@hotmail.com

1 AHHDEHKEN, 7, b g Cloudings (IRE)—Swazi Princess (IRE) **A. C. Whillans**
2 BENLUNA (IRE), 8, b g Bob's Return (IRE)—Roseland (IRE) **Mr A C Whillans Mr K Creighton**
3 CLAUDE CARTER, 8, b g Elmaamul (USA)—Cruz Santa **C. N. Whillans**
4 DANCING GIZMO, 7, b g Where Or When (IRE)—Tactile **A. C. Whillans**
5 DUNDOCK, 11, gr g Cloudings (IRE)—Rakajack **A. C. Whillans**
6 EUSTON SQUARE, 6, b g Oasis Dream—Krisia **Granite City Racing & Mr John Waugh**
7 FUNKY MUNKY, 7, b g Talaash (IRE)—Chilibang Bang **The Twelve Munkys**
8 GLEANN NA NDOCHAIS (IRE), 6, b g Zagreb (USA)—Nissereen (USA) **Mr W J E Scott & Mrs M A Scott**
9 ITS TOUGH (IRE), 9, b g Dushyantor (USA)—Parsons Brush (IRE) **Burns Partnership**
10 KIRKAIG, 7, b g Best of The Bests (IRE)—Screen Idol (IRE) **A. C. Whillans**
11 LADY BLUESKY, 9, ch M L Nady **Mrs S. Harrow Mrs L. M. Whillans**
12 MASTER ACT (IRE), 7, br gr g Act One—Celtic Fling **Border Thistle Racing**
13 NORTH BROOK (IRE), 7, b g Alderbrook—Nicola's News (IRE) **Distillery Racing Club**
14 RAVI RIVER (IRE), 8, ch g Barathea (IRE)—Echo River (USA) **Gold Tooth Racing**
15 SAMMY SPIDERMAN, 9, b g Karinga Bay—Thorterdykes Lass (IRE) **John & Liz Elliot, A Brunton, P Copeland**

MR ALISTAIR WHILLANS—continued

16 **SCRAPPER SMITH (IRE)**, 6, b g Choisir (AUS)—Lady Ounavarra (IRE) **A. C. Whillans**
17 **SOTOVIK (IRE)**, 11, gr g Aahsaylad—Moenzi (IRE) **Jethart Justice**
18 **TALESOFRIVERBANK**, 9, b m Minster Son—The White Lion **W. Mckie**
19 **THE GALLOPING SHOE**, 7, b g Observatory (USA)—My Way (IRE) **Mr W. Orr**
20 **VITTACHI**, 5, b g Bertolini (USA)—Miss Lorilaw (FR) **Sutherland Five**
21 **WHAT A STEEL (IRE)**, 8, b g Craigsteel—Sonya's Pearl (IRE) **J. D. Wright**
22 **WILD CHILD LUCY**, 6, b m Karinga Bay—Thorterdykes Lass (IRE) **J&L Elliot P&K Ash A Brunton I Copeland**

Other Owners: Miss Frances Baker, W. M. Ballantyne, C. Bird, C. K. Byers, Mr R. Carter, K. Creighton, J. J. Elliot, Mrs E. J. Elliot, Mr S. R. Fraser, Mr R. J. Goodfellow, E. Graham, Mr J. S. B. Harrold, Mrs S. Harrow, Mr T. McNicholas, Mr B. Melrose, R. Robinson, Mr J. E. Scott, Mrs M. A. Scott, Mr G. J. Valley, Mr J. Waugh, Mr R. E. Wharton, Mrs L. M. Whillans, Mrs S. L. Wright, Mr N. Yeoman.

689
MR DONALD WHILLANS, Hawick
Postal: **Dodlands Steading, Hawick, Roxburghshire, TD9 8LG**
Contacts: BUSINESS (01450) 373128 HOME (01450) 379810 FAX (01450) 376082
MOBILE (07771) 550556
E-MAIL donaldwhillans@aol.com WEBSITE www.donaldwhillansracing.com

1 **BOLLIN FIONA**, 8, ch m Silver Patriarch (IRE)—Bollin Nellie **C. N. Whillans**
2 **BOLLIN JULIE**, 5, b m Bollin Eric—Bollin Nellie **C. N. Whillans**
3 **BOLLIN RUTH**, 10, gr m Silver Patriarch (IRE)—Bollin Roberta **C. N. Whillans**
4 **CHARLIE BUCKET**, 9, ch g Sugarfoot—Stoproveritate **Milsey Bay Racing**
5 **HARRY FLASHMAN**, 11, ch g Minster Son—Youandi **A. Gilchrist, M. Kent, P. Wylie**
6 **HAWAII KLASS**, 7, ch g Classic Cliche (IRE)—Youandi **Allan Gilchrist & Scott Taylor**
7 **JAPP**, 6, b g Trans Island—Patricia Philomena (IRE) **D. W. Whillans**
8 **KING KALIÚM (IRE)**, 6, b g Kayf Tara—Hannah Park (IRE) **The Potassium Partnership**
9 **LEITH (IRE)**, 9, ch m Posidonas—Gothic Shadow (IRE) **D. McComb**
10 **MIA MATRIARCH**, 6, ch m Silver Patriarch (IRE)—Youandi **Allan Gilchrist & Peter Wylie**
11 **MINI THE MINX (IRE)**, 6, br m Accordion—Gypsy Run **D. W. Whillans**
12 **NODDA HIGH KID**, 6, ch g Sir Harry Lewis (USA)—Lindajane (IRE) **D. W. Whillans**
13 4, Br g Indian Danehill (IRE)—Polyanthus Jones **Mr A.J.M. Duncan**
14 **SAM PATCH**, 9, ch g Weldnaas (USA)—Youandi **Allan Gilchrist & Scott Taylor**
15 **SHADOW BOXER**, 7, gr g Makbul—Shadows of Silver **The Peeskie Partnership**
16 **SNAPPING TURTLE (IRE)**, 7, b g Turtle Island—Rachael's Dawn **D. W. Whillans**
17 5, B br g Classic Cliche (IRE)—Strong Edition (IRE) **Mr A.J.M.Duncan**
18 **THIRTY DAYS OUT (IRE)**, 7, b m Beneficial—Executive Move (IRE) **Mr A. J. M. Duncan**
19 6, B m Meadowbrook—Wee Willow
20 **YINFORTHEROAD (IRE)**, 5, b g Cloudings (IRE)—Another Whiskey (IRE) **Mr D. M. Beattie**

Other Owners: Mr John Anderson, Mr Rory Bannerman, Mr D.M. Beattie, Mr H. G. Beeby, Mr G. P. Fairgrieve, Mr Allan Gilchrist, Mr S. A. Taylor, Mr Peter Wylie.

690
MR RICHARD WHITAKER, Scarcroft
Postal: **Hellwood Racing Stables, Hellwood Lane, Scarcroft, Leeds, West Yorkshire, LS14 3BP**
Contacts: PHONE (01132) 892265 FAX (01132) 893680 MOBILE (07831) 870454
E-MAIL rmwhitaker@btconnect.com WEBSITE www.richardwhitaker.org

1 **BAVARIAN NORDIC (USA)**, 7, b g Barathea (IRE)—Dubai Diamond **Six Iron Partnership**
2 **DIAMOND BLUE**, 4, ch f Namid—Petra Nova **Mrs J. E. Newett**
3 **ICY BLUE**, 4, b g Iceman—Bridal Path **Country Lane Partnership**
4 **MEY BLOSSOM**, 7, ch m Captain Rio—Petra Nova **Waz Developments Ltd**
5 **RIO SANDS**, 7, b g Captain Rio—Sally Traffic **The Barflys**
6 **RIO'S ROSANNA (IRE)**, 5, b m Captain Rio—Ling Lane **Mr James Marshall & Mrs Susan Marshall**
7 **SAM NOMBULIST**, 4, ch g Sleeping Indian—Owdbetts (IRE) **Robert Macgregor**
8 **SHALOO DIAMOND**, 7, b g Captain Rio—Alacrity **The Barflys**
9 **SPIN A WISH**, 4, b f Captain Rio—Be My Wish **R. M. Whitaker**
10 **TABARET**, 9, ch g Bertolini (USA)—Luanshya **T. L. Adams**
11 **WOODACRE**, 5, b g Pyrus (USA)—Fairy Ring (IRE) **Mrs R. M. Whitaker**
12 **WOTATOMBOY**, 6, ch m Captain Rio—Keen Melody (USA) **Mrs J. M. Willows**

THREE-YEAR-OLDS

13 B f Avonbridge—African Breeze **R. M. Whitaker**

MR RICHARD WHITAKER—continued

14 **ENDLESS APPLAUSE,** b f Royal Applause—Petra Nova **Mrs J. E. Newett**
15 **LOVE ISLAND,** b f Acclamation—Sally Traffic **J. B. Pemberton**
16 **MISS ELLA JADE,** b f Danbird (AUS)—Keen Melody (USA) **Mr M. Preston**

TWO-YEAR-OLDS

17 Ch g 9/2 Haafhd—Abundant (Zafonic (USA)) (4952)
18 **LICHEN ANGEL,** gr f 12/2 Dark Angel (IRE)—Moss Likely (IRE) (Clodovil (IRE)) **David Horner & David Walker**
19 Ch g 8/4 Piccolo—Madam Valentine (Primo Valentino (IRE))
20 **THREEPENCE,** b c 18/4 Three Valleys (USA)—The Jotter (Night Shift (USA)) (7619) **Nice Day Out Partnership**
21 **TUMBLEWIND,** ch f 11/4 Captain Rio—African Breeze (Atraf) (4761) **Nice Day Out Partnership**
22 **WOTALAD,** b c 16/3 Bertolini (USA)—Cosmic Song (Cosmonaut) (19047) **Mrs J. M. Willows**

Other Owners: Mr M. Allen, K. M. Brown, Mrs M. Clayton, Mr J. C. Holmes, Mr D. A. Horner, J. R. Marshall, Mrs S. Marshall, G. F. Pemberton, G. Sanderson, Mr D. A. Walker, Mrs L. Ziegler.

Assistant Trainer: Simon R Whitaker

Amateur: Mr Adam Howling.

---

691 **MR ARTHUR WHITEHEAD, Craven Arms**
Postal: **Lawn Farm, Beambridge, Aston on Clun, Craven Arms, Shropshire, SY7 0HA**
Contacts: **PHONE (01588) 660424**

1 **DELLA SUN (FR),** 6, b g Della Francesca (USA)—Algarve Sunrise (IRE) **A. J. Whitehead**
2 **JAWAHAL DU MATHAN (FR),** 4, b g Smadoun (FR)—Stone's Glow (USA) **A. J. Whitehead**
3 **JEANRY (FR),** 9, b g Marathon (USA)—Envergure **A. J. Whitehead**
4 **LONESOME BOATMAN (IRE),** 12, b g Old Vic—Midnight Miss (NZ) **A. J. Whitehead**
5 **TON-CHEE,** 13, b g Vettori (IRE)—Najariya **A. J. Whitehead**

Conditional: Chris Timmons, Josh Wall.

---

692 **MR ARTHUR WHITING, Dursley**
Postal: **38 Barrs Lane, North Nibley, Dursley, Gloucestershire, GL11 6DT**
Contacts: **PHONE (01453) 546375 MOBILE (07786) 152539**

1 **BOO BOO BOOYAKASHA,** 8, b g Forzando—Miss Roberto (IRE) **A. J. Whiting**
2 **INDIAN CITIZEN (IRE),** 5, ch m Indian River (FR)—Curra Citizen (IRE) **A. J. Whiting**
3 **ME JULIE,** 9, b m Kayf Tara—Miss Roberto (IRE) **A. J. Whiting**
4 **QUE VIVO (FR),** 8, b g April Night (FR)—Kalynne (FR) **A. J. Whiting**
5 **THE WEE MIDGET,** 7, b g Mtoto—Fragrant Rose **A. J. Whiting**
6 **WILL SCARLET (IRE),** 9, b g Deploy—Wind Scarlet (IRE) **A. J. Whiting**

---

693 **MR MICHAEL WIGHAM, Newmarket**
Postal: **Hamilton Stables, Hamilton Road, Newmarket, Suffolk, CB8 7JQ**
Contacts: **PHONE (01638) 668806 FAX (01638) 668806 MOBILE (07831) 456426**
E-MAIL michaelwigham@hotmail.co.uk

1 **AEGEAN KING,** 6, b g Falbrav (IRE)—Aegean Dream (IRE) **D. Hassan**
2 **FIRE IN BABYLON (IRE),** 4, b g Montjeu (IRE)—Three Owls (IRE) **Palatinate Thoroughbred Racing Limited**
3 **MAGICAL STAR,** 4, b f Arkadian Hero (USA)—Aastral Magic **Mr R. W. Carson**
4 **SABYS GEM (IRE),** 4, b g Diamond Green (FR)—Dust Flicker **S Osman & D Hassan**
5 **YANKEE STORM,** 7, b g Yankee Gentleman (USA)—Yes Virginia (USA) **R. L. Maynard**

THREE-YEAR-OLDS

6 **FAIRWAY TO HEAVEN (IRE),** b c Jeremy (USA)—Luggala (IRE) **Palatinate Thoroughbred Racing Limited**
7 **ORWELLIAN,** b g Bahamian Bounty—Trinny **M. Wigham**
8 **ZAMMY,** ch g Zamindar (USA)—Barbs Pink Diamond (USA) **J Williams & D Hassan**

Other Owners: H. J. Collingridge, Mr S. Osman, Mr J. B. Williams.

Assistant Trainer: Sharon Kenyon

694 **MR MARTIN WILESMITH, Dymock**
Postal: Bellamys Farm, Dymock, Gloucestershire, GL18 2DX
Contacts: PHONE (01531) 890410 (01684) 561238 FAX (01684) 893428 MOBILE (07970) 411638
E-MAIL martin@mswilesmith.co.uk

1 AT YOUR PERIL, 10, b g Alflora (IRE)—Teenero M. S. Wilesmith
2 CRACK OF DAWN, 8, b g Alflora (IRE)—Dawn Breaker M. S. Wilesmith
3 LORD BELLAMY (IRE), 10, b g Lord Americo—Paean Express (IRE) M. S. Wilesmith
4 SHE'SOLOVELY, 8, b m Alflora (IRE)—Cashmere Lady M. S. Wilesmith
5 6, Ch m Alflora (IRE)—Silk Oats M. S. Wilesmith
6 SILK ROSE, 8, gr m Terimon—Silk Oats M. S. Wilesmith
7 THE HUMBEL BUTLER (IRE), 11, b g Humbel—Butler's Lady M. S. Wilesmith

Assistant Trainer: Ms E. C. Wilesmith (07976 926906)

Amateur: Mr M. C. Wilesmith.

695 **MR EVAN WILLIAMS, Llancarfan**
Postal: Aberogwrn Farm, Llancarfan, Nr Barry, Vale of Glamorgan
Contacts: PHONE (01446) 754069 (01446) 754045 FAX (01446) 754069 MOBILE (07950) 381227
E-MAIL evanwilliamsracing@hotmail.co.uk

1 AGREE TO DIFFER (IRE), 6, b g Orpen (USA)—Compton Fair Mr E. O'Sullivan
2 AJMAN (IRE), 7, b g Orpen (USA)—Grand Madam Mr R. P. O'Neil
3 AKARSHAN (IRE), 7, b g Intikhab (USA)—Akdara (IRE) Mr A. Turton & Mr P. Langford
4 ALARMING ALACRITY (IRE), 6, b g Bach (IRE)—More Dash (IRE) I. C. Brice
5 ALAYIR (IRE), 4, b g Azamour (IRE)—Alaya (IRE) Mrs C. A. Williams
6 ALVARADO (IRE), 7, ch g Goldmark (USA)—Mrs Jones (IRE) Mr & Mrs William Rucker
7 AMERICAN CRICKET (IRE), 11, b g Lord Americo—Dixons Dutchess (IRE) R. E. R. Williams
8 ARGAUM (IRE), 5, ch g Medicean—Poppy Carew (IRE) G. Houghton
9 ASHFIELD'S DREAM, 5, b g Alflora (IRE)—Colonial Princess Mr & Mrs William Rucker
10 BARRAKILLA (IRE), 5, b g Milan—Kigali (IRE) Mr & Mrs William Rucker
11 BATTLECAT, 5, b g Tiger Hill (IRE)—Applecross Twyi Syndicate
12 BAY CENTRAL (IRE), 8, b g Exit To Nowhere (USA)—Pretty Beau (IRE) R. E. R. Williams
13 BEAT THE REF, 4, b g Beat Hollow—Bel T. Reffell
14 BEHTARINI (IRE), 5, b g Dalakhani (IRE)—Behkiyra (IRE) Ms S. A. Howell
15 BILLY BLADE, 5, b g Generous (IRE)—Lady Blade (IRE) R. E. R. Williams
16 BIT OF A MADAM, 4, b f Loup Sauvage (USA)—Miss Gratis (IRE) P. C. Green
17 BLACKTOFT (USA), 9, b br g Theatrical—Black Truffle (USA) Mr Chris Watkins & Mr David N. Reynolds
18 BRUSLINI (FR), 7, gr g Linamix (FR)—Brusca (USA) J. T. Warner
19 CANNON FIRE (FR), 11, ch g Grand Lodge—Muirfield (FR) R. E. R. Williams
20 CAPPA BLEU (IRE), 10, b g Pistolet Bleu (IRE)—Cappagale (IRE) Mr & Mrs William Rucker
21 CAPTAIN BROWN, 4, b g Lomitas—Nicola Bella (IRE) Mr & Mrs William Rucker
22 4, B g Kayf Tara—Catherine's Run (IRE)
23 CHARM SCHOOL, 7, b g Dubai Destination (USA)—Eve T. H. Jones
24 CLARION CALL, 4, b g Beat Hollow—Fanfare Mrs C. A. Williams
25 COLD HARBOUR, 8, b g Classic Cliche (IRE)—Anchorage (IRE) Fox & Hounds Racing
26 COURT MINSTREL (IRE), 5, b g Court Cave (IRE)—Theatral Mrs J. Davies
27 DANTARI (IRE), 7, b g Alhaarth (IRE)—Daniysha (IRE) I. C. Brice
28 DARCEYS DANCER (IRE), 9, b g Lear Spear (USA)—Dun Oengus (IRE) Shervington-Jones & Western
29 DE FAOITHESDREAM (IRE), 6, br g Balakheri (IRE)—Cutteen Lass (IRE) Mr R Abbott & Mr M Stavrou
30 DEEP PURPLE, 11, b g Halling (USA)—Seal Indigo (IRE) P. C. Green
31 DI KAPRIO (FR), 6, b g Kapgarde (FR)—Miss Nousha (FR) Mr & Mrs William Rucker
32 DRUMBALOO (IRE), 8, b br g Flemensfirth (USA)—Supreme Baloo (IRE) ARC
33 EXTREME IMPACT, 6, b g Rock of Gibraltar (IRE)—
                    Soviet Moon (IRE) Gareth Morse, Iwan Thomas, Charles Footman
34 FAHRISEE (IRE), 9, b g Fahris (IRE)—Vesper Time Mr Hugh Williams & Mr R Lewis
35 FINISK ROSE (IRE), 8, gr m Goldmark (USA)—Rosealainn (IRE) Mrs C. A. Williams
36 FIVE OUT OF FIVE (IRE), 8, b g Saddlers' Hall (IRE)—Grangemills Mr D. J. Burchell
37 FLY TOWN (IRE), 7, b m Turtle Island (IRE)—Palmrock Donna R. E. R. Williams
38 GAMBOO (IRE), 6, b g Oscar (IRE)—River Thyne (IRE) Mr R. J. Gambarini
39 GAP OF DUNLOE (IRE), 4, b g Hurricane Run (IRE)—Karri Valley (USA) Mrs C. A. Williams
40 GET IT ON (IRE), 7, b g King's Theatre (IRE)—Keshia Mr J. L. Jones
41 GILWEN GLORY (IRE), 9, b m Saddlers' Hall (IRE)—Clowns Glory Keith & Sue Lowry
42 GRINDY (IRE), 6, b g Alderbrook—Blake's Fable (IRE) Paul Bailey & Roger Gambarini
43 GURTACRUE (IRE), 7, ch g Deploy—Biddy Early (IRE) Mr & Mrs William Rucker

MR EVAN WILLIAMS—continued

44 **HIDDEN**, 6, b g Hernando (FR)—For More (FR) **P. C. Green**
45 **HOLD COURT (IRE)**, 5, br g Court Cave (IRE)—Tipsy Miss (IRE) **Edwards & Howell**
46 **ISLANDMAGEE (IRE)**, 5, b g Heron Island (IRE)—Sakanda (IRE) **Mr & Mrs William Rucker**
47 **KAYALAR (IRE)**, 4, b g Noverre (USA)—Katiykha (IRE) **R. E. R. Williams**
48 4, B g Sulamani (IRE)—Lady Blade (IRE)
49 **LANCETTO (FR)**, 7, b g Dubai Destination (USA)—Lanciana (IRE) **Mr R. J. Gambarini**
50 **LAUBERHORN**, 5, b g Dubai Destination (USA)—Ski Run **Border Pointers**
51 **LAVA LAMP (GER)**, 5, b g Shamardal (USA)—La Felicita **Mrs J. Davies**
52 **LUCAINDUBAI (IRE)**, 6, b br g Orpen (USA)—Singhana (IRE) **Mr R. J. Gambarini**
53 **MAC BEATTIE**, 6, b g Beat All (USA)—Macnance (IRE) **Keith & Sue Lowry**
54 **MAC HALEN (IRE)**, 9, b g Lord Americo—Colleen Donn **Keith & Sue Lowry**
55 **MAHER (USA)**, 4, b g Medaglia d'oro (USA)—Bourbon Blues (USA) **T. H. Jones**
56 **MAKETHE MOSTOFNOW (IRE)**, 7, b g Milan—Pass The Leader (IRE) **Mrs J. Davies**
57 **MEGABILL (IRE)**, 8, b g King's Theatre (IRE)—Dawn Bid (IRE) **Mrs J. Davies**
58 **MICKMACMAGOOLE (IRE)**, 10, b g Sadler's Wells (USA)—Musk Lime (USA) **Mr A. Turton & Mr P. Langford**
59 **OSCAR GOGO (IRE)**, 10, b g Oscar (IRE)—Ceolbridgequeen (IRE) **Mrs D. Mccabe**
60 **OSCAR SUNSET (IRE)**, 5, b g Oscar (IRE)—Derravarra Sunset (IRE) **Geoff & Anne Price**
61 **OURSININLAW (IRE)**, 8, gr g Turgeon (USA)—Fontanalia (FR) **Mr J. L. Jones**
62 **PENELOPE PIPS**, 5, ch m Presenting—Chartridge Hill **Mr & Mrs William Rucker**
63 **PHIDIPPIDES (IRE)**, 8, ch g Presenting—Sarah Blue (IRE) **P. C. Green**
64 **PLUNKETT (IRE)**, 9, b g Fourstars Allstar (USA)—Miss Moppit (IRE) **T. H. Jones**
65 **PRIMA PORTA**, 6, b m American Post—Porta Marzia (CHI) **D. P. Barrie**
66 **REALISATION**, 5, b g Alhaarth (IRE)—Live Your Dreams (USA) **Mr R. J. Gambarini**
67 **RIVER RHAPSODY (IRE)**, 6, ch g Alderbrook—Double Symphony (IRE) **Mr & Mrs Vasicek**
68 **RIVIERA STARS**, 4, b g Galileo (IRE)—Miss Riviera Golf **Mrs C. A. Williams**
69 **SILVERBURN (IRE)**, 11, b g Presenting—Polly Puttens **Miss G. L. Green**
70 **STATE OF PLAY**, 12, b g Hernando (FR)—Kaprice (GER) **Mr & Mrs William Rucker**
71 **STEPHEN'S GREEN (USA)**, 4, ch g North Light (IRE)—Grand Natalie Rose (USA) **Mr T. Harris**
72 **STORMYISLAND AHEAD**, 7, b g Turtle Island (IRE)—Queen's Banquet **Mr D. M. Williams**
73 **SUBLIME TALENT (IRE)**, 6, b g Sadler's Wells (USA)—Summer Trysting (USA) **Itsfuninit**
74 **TARKARI (IRE)**, 7, ch g Fantastic Light (USA)—Taraza (IRE) **Clive Cook & Irving Struel**
75 **TEMPTING PARADISE (IRE)**, 9, ch g Grand Lodge (USA)—Summer Trysting (USA) **Norwester Racing Club**
76 **THATS BEN (IRE)**, 7, b g Beneficial—Classy Dancer (IRE) **Mr & Mrs William Rucker**
77 **THE ROCKIES (IRE)**, 5, b g Oscar (IRE)—Calling Classy (IRE) **Mr D. M. Williams**
78 **TIGER O'TOOLE (IRE)**, 7, gr g King's Theatre (IRE)—Memsahib Ofesteem **Ms S. A. Howell**
79 **TIGER RAG (FR)**, 4, ch g Dano-Mast—New Illusion (FR) **R. E. R. Williams**
80 **TIMESAWASTIN (IRE)**, 6, b g Curtain Time (IRE)—Innocent Approach (IRE) **Mrs C. A. Waters**
81 **TIN POT MAN (IRE)**, 6, br g Tillerman—White-Wash **Oaks**
82 **TORNADE DE GUYE (FR)**, 5, b m Ragmar (FR)—Kasibelle de Guye (FR) **Mrs C. A. Williams**
83 **TORNADO IN MILAN (IRE)**, 6, b g Milan—Julika (GER) **Mr & Mrs William Rucker**
84 **TRAITOR**, 4, b g Dansili—Tokyo Rose (UAE) **Mrs J. Davies**
85 **TRIPTICO (FR)**, 6, gr g Turgeon (USA)—Al Kicks (FR) **Mr & Mrs William Rucker**
86 **TROOPER CLARENCE**, 8, b g Trempolino—Ten To Six **Mrs S. De Wilde**
87 **UGO (USA)**, 4, b g Street Cry (IRE)—Min Elreeh (USA) **Mrs C. A. Williams**
88 **WESTER ROSS (IRE)**, 8, b g Fruits of Love (USA)—Diabaig **T. H. Jones**
89 **WHERES WAL (IRE)**, 7, b g City Honours (USA)—Loch Phar (IRE) **T. H. Jones**
90 **WILLIAM'S WISHES (IRE)**, 7, b g Oscar (IRE)—Strong Wishes (IRE) **Mrs D. E. Cheshire**

Other Owners: R. J. Abbott, Mr P. E. Bailey, Mr R. Beynon, Mr C. Cook, J. R. Edwards, Mr D. C. Footman, Mr P. Griffiths, Mr P. M. Langford, Mr R. Lewis, Mrs N. P. Lloyd, D. G. Long, Mrs S. B. Lowry, K. R. Lowry, Mr J. R. Millard, Mrs S. M. Millard, W. J. G. Morse, Mr G. Price, Mrs C. A. Price, Mr P. Pyatt, Mr D. N. Reynolds, W. J. Rucker, Mrs A. Rucker, Mr P. Sevenoaks, Mr D. G. Sevenoaks, Mrs V. Shervington-Jones, Mr A. Smallman, M. Stavrou, I. Struel, D. I. Thomas, Mr A. Turton, J. Vasicek, C. D. Watkins, Mr R. W. Western, Mr H. F. Williams, Mr S. Williams.

Assistant Trainers: James Tudor, Cath Williams

Jockey (NH): Paul Moloney, Christian Williams. **Amateur:** Mr James Tudor.

---

696 **MR IAN WILLIAMS, Alvechurch**
Postal: **Dominion Racing Stables, Seafield Lane, Alvechurch, Birmingham, B48 7HL**
Contacts: **PHONE (01564) 822392 FAX (01564) 829475 MOBILE (07976) 645384**
E-MAIL info@ianwilliamsracing.com WEBSITE www.ianwilliamsracing.com

1 **ADDRESS UNKNOWN**, 5, b g Oasis Dream—Return (USA) **Dr M. B. Q. S. Koukash**
2 **BAILE ANRAI (IRE)**, 8, b g Norwich—Rose Ana (IRE) **Massive**

MR IAN WILLIAMS—continued

   3 **BALLYALTON (IRE)**, 5, b g Pierre—Almilto (IRE) **Mr J. Westwood**
   4 **BARBATOS (FR)**, 6, gr g Martaline—Peace Bay (FR) **Power Panels Electrical Systems Ltd**
   5 **BOBCATBILY (IRE)**, 6, b g Overbury (IRE)—Cush Jewel (IRE) **P. J. Vogt**
   6 **BOND KATHLEEN**, 6, b g Kayf Tara—Con's Nurse (IRE) **I. P. Williams**
   7 **CALL TO REASON (IRE)**, 5, ch m Pivotal—Venturi **Dr M. B. Q. S. Koukash**
   8 **CHABADA (JPN)**, 4, b f Bago (FR)—Taygete (USA) **Dr M. B. Q. S. Koukash**
   9 **COTILLION**, 6, b g Sadler's Wells (USA)—Riberac **P. J. Vogt**
  10 **CRAIGLANDS (IRE)**, 10, b g Dushyantor (USA)—Fernhill (IRE) **J. Tredwell**
  11 **CROAN ROCK (IRE)**, 7, b g Milan—Fiddlers Bar (IRE) **P. J. Vogt**
  12 **DARING INDIAN**, 4, ch g Zamindar (USA)—Anasazi (IRE) **Denarius Consulting Ltd**
  13 **DOBLE VE (IRE)**, 6, b m Deploy—City Times (IRE) **Miss M. L. Peterson**
  14 **DOT OR FEATHER (IRE)**, 7, b g Indian Danehill (IRE)—Gentian Blue (IRE) **Denarius Consulting Ltd**
  15 **DRUMLANG (IRE)**, 6, b g Soviet Star (USA)—Sherekiya (IRE) **M Roberts J O'Shea S Hunt R Stearman**
  16 **FELIX DA HOUSECAT (IRE)**, 9, br g Accordion—Collinstown Queen (IRE) **Miss M. L. Peterson**
  17 **FLUCTUATION (IRE)**, 4, b g Street Cry (IRE)—Rise and Fall (USA) **J. Tredwell**
  18 **FREDO (IRE)**, 8, ch g Lomitas—Felina (GER) **Mrs J. S. Allen**
  19 **GHOST OF A SMILE (IRE)**, 4, b g Oscar (IRE)—Dix Huit Brumaire (FR) **Mr S. Cox**
  20 **GIFTED LEADER (USA)**, 7, b g Diesis—Zaghruta (USA) **Gifted Leader Partners**
  21 **HAWKESHEAD**, 5, b h Rainbow Quest (USA)—Ciboure **Mr & Mrs G. Middlebrook**
  22 **ILE DE RE (FR)**, 6, gr g Linamix (FR)—Ile Mamou (IRE) **Mr D. Mead**
  23 **JOSHUA**, 7, b g Jour Algarhoud (IRE)—Magic Flute **Macable Partnership**
  24 **JUNE FRENCH (FR)**, 4, b f Jimble (FR)—Sunbelt Broker **Brigadier Racing**
  25 **KICKAHEAD (USA)**, 10, b g Danzig (USA)—Krissante (USA) **I. P. Williams**
  26 **LEATH ACRA MOR (IRE)**, 6, b g King's Theatre (IRE)—Happy Native (IRE) **I. P. Williams**
  27 **LEXI'S PRINCESS (IRE)**, 4, gr f Verglas (IRE)—Night Fairy (IRE) **The Ferandlin Peaches**
  28 **MANADAM (FR)**, 9, b g Mansonnien (FR)—Cadoudame (FR) **Macable Partnership**
  29 **MISS LUCKY PENNY**, 6, ch m Karinga Bay—Singing Cottage **S. G. Adams**
  30 **MOUNT ABORA (IRE)**, 5, br m Rock of Gibraltar (IRE)—Ragtime Blues (IRE) **Dr M. B. Q. S. Koukash**
  31 **MY KINGDOM (IRE)**, 6, b g King's Best (USA)—Nebraas **Dr M. B. Q. S. Koukash**
  32 **OH NO NOT HARRY (FR)**, 7, b g Astarabad (USA)—La Pitchoun (FR) **A. C. Eaves**
  33 **PIRATE'S GOLD (IRE)**, 5, b g Gamut (IRE)—Glint of Baron **Pitman Gold Syndicate III**
  34 **POSTSCRIPT (IRE)**, 4, ch g Pivotal—Persian Secret (FR) **Dr M. B. Q. S. Koukash**
  35 **REBEL DANCER (IRE)**, 7, b g Dark Moondancer—Poupee d'ancyre (IRE) **Boston R. S. Ian Bennett**
  36 **RICHMOND (FR)**, 7, b g Assessor (IRE)—Hirondel de Serley (FR) **Hills of Ledbury Ltd**
  37 **ROBOBAR (FR)**, 7, b g Passing Sale (FR)—Carvine d'or (FR) **Mr D. W. Fox**
  38 **SONOFAGUN (FR)**, 6, b g Turgeon (USA)—Detonante (FR) **The Piranha Partnership**
  39 **SPAGETTI WESTERN (IRE)**, 5, b g Luso—Shes Sharp (IRE) **The Ferandlin Peaches**
  40 **SPARTAN KING (IRE)**, 4, ch g King's Best (USA)—Thermopylae **Mr J. Roberts**
  41 **STEVIE GEE (IRE)**, 8, b g Invincible Spirit (IRE)—Margaree Mary (CAN) **S. L. Gray**
  42 **SWINGING HAWK (GER)**, 6, ch h Hawk Wing (USA)—Saldenschwinge (GER) **Mr L. J. Westwood**
  43 **SWITCHED OFF**, 7, b g Catcher In The Rye (IRE)—Button Hole Flower (IRE) **Mr P Nicholls & Mr D Mead**
  44 **TADABEER**, 4, b g Green Desert (USA)—Perfect Plum (IRE) **Sir Alex Ferguson & Sotirios Hassiakos**
  45 **TEDDY'S REFLECTION (IRE)**, 9, b g Beneficial—Regal Pursuit (IRE) **P. J. Vogt**
  46 **TEUTONIC KNIGHT (IRE)**, 5, ch g Daggers Drawn (USA)—Azyaa **R. J. Turton**
  47 **THAT'S SOME MILAN (IRE)**, 7, b g Milan—Ballinapierce Lady (IRE) **Mr D. W. Fox**
  48 **THE GOLDMEISTER (IRE)**, 5, b g Craigsteel—M C A River **Jenny & Mark Pitman Gold Syndicate II**
  49 **TOUCH OF IRISH**, 10, b g Kayf Tara—Portland Row (IRE) **W. A. Walker**
  50 **TOURIST**, 7, b g Oasis Dream—West Devon (USA) **Stratford Bards Racing No 2**
  51 **TWENTYFOURCARAT (IRE)**, 7, b g Craigsteel—Romany River **Jenny & Mark Pitman Gold Club No.1**
  52 **TYRANA (GER)**, 9, ch m Acatenango (GER)—Tascalina (GER) **The Piranha Partnership**
  53 **UNEX PICASSO**, 4, b g Galileo (IRE)—Ruff Shod (USA) **Mrs A. J. Forde & Mr D. Nicholls**
  54 **UPTHEMSTEPS (IRE)**, 7, br g Beneficial—Carrigloss (IRE) **The Ferandlin Peaches**
  55 **VELOCE (IRE)**, 4, b g Hurricane Run (IRE)—Kiftsgate Rose (FR) **Dr M. B. Q. S. Koukash**
  56 **WAYWARD PRINCE**, 8, b g Alflora (IRE)—Bellino Spirit (IRE) **Mr T. J. & Mrs H. Parrott**
  57 **WHISPERING BOB (IRE)**, 5, b g Presenting—Baden's Queen (IRE) **Mr G. P. Bone**
  58 **WONMORENOMORE (IRE)**, 6, br g Bob's Return (IRE)—Marine Leader (IRE) **Macable Partnership**
  59 **WOOP WOOP (IRE)**, 4, b f Oratorio (IRE)—Nihonpillow Mirai (IRE) **Lee Westwood & Chubby Chandler**

THREE-YEAR-OLDS

  60 **ANGEL GABRIAL (IRE)**, b g Hurricane Run (IRE)—Causeway Song (USA) **Dr M. B. Q. S. Koukash**
  61 **GABRIAL'S KING (IRE)**, b g Hurricane Run (IRE)—Danella (IRE) **Dr M. B. Q. S. Koukash**
  62 **J J LEARY (IRE)**, b g Amadeus Wolf—Nautical Design (USA) **Dr M. B. Q. S. Koukash**
  63 B c Excellent Art—Sandtime (IRE)
  64 **WATT BRODERICK (IRE)**, ch c Hawk Wing (USA)—Kingsridge (IRE) **P. Kelly**
  65 **ZAFONIC STAR**, b g Cockney Rebel (IRE)—Enthralled **Shaw Greaves Gamble Fox**

MR IAN WILLIAMS—continued

Other Owners: Mr S. Allardyce, S. Bell, I. M. Bennett, Mrs K. F. Bourdon, P. Brown, M. Burford, D. J. Bussell, A. Chandler, Mr P. J. Duffen, Sir A. Ferguson, Mr D. J. Flynn, Mrs A. J. Forde, Mr D. Greaves, P. V. Harris, Ms R. J. Harris, T. Hart, S. Hassiakos, Mr S. Hunt, Mr S. Mackintosh, Mr F. W. Mackintosh, G. Middlebrook, Mrs L. A. Middlebrook, Mr A. Miles, Mr R. J. Moore, Mr D. T. Nicholls, Mr P. R. Nicholls, P. R. Nodder, Mr J. O'Shea, T. J. Parrott, Mrs H. Parrott, Mr S. Petty, Mr M. J. Petty, M. A. Pitman, Mr M. G. Roberts, Mr P. J. Shaw, Mr T. Spragget, Mr R. Stearman, Mr R. J. Swinbourne, Mrs L. G. Thomas, J. Tyrrell.

Assistant Trainer: Kevin Frost

Jockey (NH): Dougie Costello, Harry Skelton. **Conditional:** Paul Bohan, Shane Shortall. **Amateur:** Mr Jake Hodson.

---

697 **MR NICK WILLIAMS, South Molton**
Postal: Culverhill Farm, George Nympton, South Molton, Devon, EX36 4JE
Contacts: HOME (01769) 574174 FAX (01769) 573661 MOBILE (07855) 450379

1 ALFIE SPINNER (IRE), 7, b g Alflora (IRE)—Little Red Spider **Alan Beard & Brian Beard**
2 DIAMOND BROOK (IRE), 7, b g Alderbrook—Hilda Howard (IRE) **Paul Duffy Diamond Partnership**
3 DIAMOND ECLIPSE (IRE), 6, b g Double Eclipse (IRE)—Glory-Glory (IRE) **Larkhills Racing Partnership**
4 DIAMOND HARRY, 9, b g Sir Harry Lewis (USA)—Swift Conveyance (IRE) **Paul Duffy Diamond Partnership**
5 DOM D'ORGEVAL (FR), 12, b g Belmez (USA)—Marie D'orgeval (FR) **A. J. White & Mrs A. Underhill**
6 ERE ALFIE (IRE), 8, b g High Roller (IRE)—Quench The Lamp (IRE) **Mrs Sally & Miss Isobel Noott**
7 FOR NON STOP (FR), 7, b g Alderbrook—Lost Link (IRE) **Mr J. J. Sullivan**
8 GAUVAIN (GER), 10, b g Sternkoenig (IRE)—Gamina (GER) **Jared Sullivan & Simon Brown**
9 GEORGE NYMPTON (IRE), 6, br g Alderbrook—Countess Camilla **The Bacchanalians**
10 HORATIO HORNBLOWER (IRE), 4, b br g Presenting—Countess Camilla **Huw & Richard Davies**
11 HURRICANE HERBIE (IRE), 4, b g Erhaab (USA)—Rocheflamme (FR) **Mrs J. R. Williams**
12 JAMES DE VASSY (FR), 7, b g Lavirco (GER)—Provenchere (FR) **Jakeman, Barrett, Booth & Ferrand**
13 KATEAL, 9, b m Supreme Leader—Quiet City **Yeo Racing Partnership**
14 LADY EVERYWHERE, 7, br m Exit To Nowhere (USA)—Lady Felix **Yeo Racing Partnership**
15 MATERIAL BOY, 5, b g Karinga Bay—Material Girl **You Can Be Sure**
16 POLITEO (FR), 6, ch g Lando (GER)—Italienne (USA) **Mr M. F. Stenning**
17 PRESENT M'LORD (IRE), 12, b g Presenting—The Red Side (IRE) **Chasing Gold Limited**
18 REVE DE SIVOLA (FR), 7, b g Assessor (IRE)—Eva de Chalamont (FR) **Paul Duffy Diamond Partnership**
19 ROYALE'S CHARTER, 6, ch g Karinga Bay—
Royale De Vassy (FR) **Jakeman, Davies, Downes, Booth & Birchenough**
20 SARIKA (FR), 6, b g Grand Tresor (FR)—Arika (FR) **Mrs J. R. Williams**
21 SHALIMAR FROMENTRO (FR), 6, gr g Martaline—Miss des Ormeaux (FR) **Mrs J. R. Williams**
22 SWINCOMBE FLAME, 6, b m Exit To Nowhere (USA)—Lady Felix **Yeo Racing Partnership**
23 THE ITALIAN YOB (IRE), 4, b g Milan—The Rebel Lady (IRE) **The Macaroni Beach Society**
24 ULIS DE VASSY (FR), 4, b g Voix du Nord (FR)—Helathou (FR) **Len&White,Hewlett,Robinson,Ferrand&Booth**
25 UN AMI (FR), 4, gr g Dom Alco (FR)—Immage (FR) **Mrs J. R. Williams**
26 UN BON P'TIT GARS (FR), 4, b g Robin des Champs (FR)—Nee A Saint Voir (FR) **K Alexander/ R Watts**
27 URBAIN DE SIVOLA (FR), 4, ch g Le Fou (FR)—Neva de Sivola (FR) **Potensis Limited**
28 ZAYNAR (FR), 7, gr g Daylami (IRE)—Zainta (IRE) **Men In Our Position**

THREE-YEAR-OLDS

29 VEAUCE DE SIVOLA (FR), b g Assessor (IRE)—Eva de Chalamont (FR) **D. P. Duffy**

Other Owners: Mr K. Alexander, B. M. Barrett, A. C. Beard, B. M. Beard, Dr M. Booth, S. J. Brown, Mr M. Caine, V. W. Chandler, Dr C. Cowell, H. G. Davies, Mr R. L. Davies, Mr N. Ferrand, Mr A. P. Gale, Mrs E. Hutton, L. J. Jakeman, D. Morgan, Mrs S. A. Noott, P. R. Noott, K. B. W. Parkhouse, G. C. Pratt, Ms A. M. Simmons, Mrs A. Underhill, Mr R. C. Watts, A. J. White, Mrs K. D. Yeo.

Assistant Trainer: Miss Jenny Congdon

Jockey (NH): James Reveley. **Amateur:** Miss Lizzie Kelly.

---

698 **MR STUART WILLIAMS, Newmarket**
Postal: Diomed Stables, Hamilton Road, Newmarket, Suffolk, CB8 0PD
Contacts: STABLES/OFFICE (01638) 663984 HOME (01638) 560143
FAX (01638) 663984 (01638) 560143 MOBILE (07730) 314102
E-MAIL stuart@stuartwilliamsracing.co.uk WEBSITE www.stuartwilliamsracing.co.uk

1 ALDERMOOR (USA), 6, b g Tale of The Cat (USA)—Notting Hill (BRZ) **Mr D. Hudson-Wood**
2 BERTOLIVER, 8, b g Bertolini (USA)—Calcavella **Mrs M. Shone**

MR STUART WILLIAMS—continued

3 **CARA CARMELA**, 4, gr f Compton Place—Carmela Owen **O. Pointing**
4 **CHEYLESMORE (IRE)**, 4, b g Kodiac—Hemaca **Keith & Meta Pryce**
5 **EARLSMEDIC**, 7, ch g Dr Fong (USA)—Area Girl **Hamill, Ostlere & George**
6 **ETON RIFLES (IRE)**, 7, b g Pivotal—Maritsa (IRE) **The Eton Riflemen**
7 **GINGER TED (IRE)**, 5, ch g Fath (USA)—Estertide (IRE) **Maze Rattan Limited**
8 **MICKY P**, 5, gr g Dr Fong (USA)—Carmela Owen **O. Pointing**
9 **PAPHOS**, 5, b g Oasis Dream—Tychy **S. C. Williams**
10 **SIM SALA BIM**, 4, gr ro c Act One—Francia **Mr A. Atkins**
11 **THE STRIG**, 5, b g Mujahid (USA)—Pretty Kool **Brian Piper & David Cobill**

THREE-YEAR-OLDS

12 **AUNTIE KATHRYN (IRE)**, b f Acclamation—Congress (IRE) **Mr J. W. Parry**
13 **BECKFIELD POINT**, b c Shirocco (GER)—Platinum Princess **Mrs M. Shone**
14 **BELLA CARMELA**, gr f Halling (USA)—Carmela Owen **O. Pointing**
15 **CAMBRIDGE DUCHESS**, br f Singspiel (IRE)—Roseum **Mr J. W. Parry**
16 **CHALK AND CHEESE (USA)**, ch g Rahy (USA)—Escoltada (ARG) **S. C. Williams**
17 **CINCINNATI KIT**, br f Cape Cross (IRE)—Princess Georgina **Mr J. W. Parry**
18 **JANE LACHATTE (IRE)**, b f Doyen (IRE)—Simonda **S. P. Tindall**
19 **MOUNT MAYDAY (IRE)**, b c Rock of Gibraltar (IRE)—Fille de Joie (IRE) **P. W. Stevens**
20 **PEARL REBEL**, b c Cockney Rebel (IRE)—Lilli Marlane **Pearl Bloodstock Limited**
21 **PETTOCHSIDE**, b g Refuse To Bend (IRE)—Clear Impression (IRE) **J. G. Thom**
22 **PRINCELY SUM (IRE)**, b c Refuse To Bend (IRE)—Green Dollar (IRE) **Essex Racing Club et al**
23 **ROGUE REPORTER (IRE)**, b c Sir Percy—Princess Nala (IRE) **S. C. Williams**
24 **TIGERTOO (IRE)**, ch g Heliostatic (IRE)—Brightling (IRE) **John Godfrey & Robert Haag**
25 **VENETIAS DREAM (IRE)**, b f Librettist (USA)—Machaera **Essex Racing Club**
26 **WELEASE BWIAN (IRE)**, b g Kheleyf (USA)—Urbanize (USA) **W. E. Enticknap**

TWO-YEAR-OLDS

27 B f 6/3 Pivotal—Birdie (Alhaarth (IRE)) (40000) **Mr J. W. Parry**
28 Ch gr f 8/3 Act One—Francia (Legend of France (USA)) **Mr B. Piper**
29 **PEARL REWARD (USA)**, b br c 23/3 Medaglia d'oro (USA)—
  With Patience (USA) (With Approval (CAN)) (48840) **Pearl Bloodstock Limited**
30 Ch f 11/3 Bahamian Bounty—Persario (Bishop of Cashel) (40000) **Mr J. W. Parry**
31 B f 16/4 Haafhd—Platinum Princess (Diktat) **Mrs M. Shone**
32 **PRINCE OF PROPHETS (IRE)**, b c 14/2 Antonius Pius (USA)—
  Chifney Rush (IRE) (Grand Lodge (USA)) (666) **Miss E. Stevens**
33 B f 12/4 Malibu Moon (USA)—Real Cat (USA) (Storm Cat (USA)) **Gillian S. Ryan**
34 B c 25/3 Tiger Hill (IRE)—Special Green (FR) (Sadler's Wells (USA)) (5000) **Mr J. W. Parry**
35 **TYCHAIOS**, b c 19/3 Green Desert (USA)—Tychy (Suave Dancer (USA)) (12000) **Mr P. Ellinas**

Other Owners: Mr David Cobill, Mrs L. Kerr, Mr B. Piper, Mr Barry Root, Mrs Joan Root, Mr D. A. Shekells, Mr Stuart C. Williams.

Assistant Trainer: Michael Hammond

Jockey (flat): William Carson. **Apprentice:** Ryan Clark.

699 MISS VENETIA WILLIAMS, Hereford
Postal: Aramstone, Kings Caple, Hereford, Herefordshire, HR1 4TU
Contacts: PHONE (01432) 840646 MOBILE (07770) 627108
E-MAIL venetia.williams@virgin.net WEBSITE www.venetiawilliams.com

1 **AACHEN**, 8, b g Rainbow Quest (USA)—Anna of Saxony **Mr A. G. Bloom**
2 **ALBERTUS PICTOR**, 5, gr g Selkirk (USA)—Albanova **P. J. D. Pottinger**
3 **ART PROFESSOR (IRE)**, 8, b g In The Wings—Itab (USA) **J. P. Hancock**
4 **ATOUCHBETWEENACARA (IRE)**, 11, b br g Lord Americo—Rosie Lil (IRE) **P. W. Beck**
5 **BAILEYS CONCERTO (IRE)**, 6, b g Bach (IRE)—None The Wiser (IRE) **G. R. Bailey Ltd**
6 **BALLINTUBBER CROSS (IRE)**, 7, b g Heron Island (IRE)—Snowtan (IRE) **Mrs M. Devine**
7 **BALLYOLIVER**, 8, b g Kayf Tara—Macklette (IRE) **Mr R. M. Britten-Long**
8 **BENNYS MIST (IRE)**, 6, b g Beneficial—Dark Mist (IRE) **Mr G. G. Mezzone**
9 **BOLD JACK (IRE)**, 6, b g Oscar (IRE)—Deep Estee (IRE) **M Graham, L Dalby, P Dixon**
10 **BRICK RED**, 5, ch g Dubawi (IRE)—Duchcov **Julian Taylor & Andrew Brooks**
11 **BROWNS BROOK (IRE)**, 6, b g Bob Back (USA)—All Over Now (IRE) **Mrs V. A. Bingham**
12 **CARRICKBOY (IRE)**, 8, b g Silver Patriarch (IRE)—Alaskan Princess (IRE) **T. J. Hemmings**

MISS VENETIA WILLIAMS—continued

13 **CEANNLINE (IRE)**, 6, b m Lil's Boy (USA)—Scarpetta (USA) **Mr E. P. K. Weatherall**
14 **CICERON (IRE)**, 6, b g Pivotal—Aiglonne (USA) **Verrier, Bowditch, Secretan**
15 **CLOWANCE HOUSE**, 6, ch g Galileo (IRE)—Corsican Sunset (USA) **Seasons Holidays**
16 **COOL CASCADE**, 6, b m Alderbrook—Miss Pout **Mr John Southwell & Miss Frances Molle**
17 **CREDIT SWAP**, 7, b g Diktat—Locharia **M. J. Pilkington**
18 **DEFINITE MEMORIES (IRE)**, 5, b m Definite Article—Memories (FR) **Mr D. A. Hunt**
19 **DRUMSHAMBO (USA)**, 6, b g Dynaformer (USA)—Gossamer (USA) **The Grouse Partnership**
20 **DUNGENESS**, 4, b g Beat All (USA)—Maydoo (IRE) **The Bellamy Partnership**
21 **EMPEROR'S CHOICE (IRE)**, 5, b g Flemensfirth (USA)—House-of-Hearts (IRE) **The Bellamy Partnership**
22 **GORGEHOUS LLIEGE (FR)**, 6, b g Lavirco (GER)—Charme d'estruval (FR) **Mr A. L. Brooks**
23 **GREAT'S AUTRECHENE (FR)**, 5, b g Great Pretender—Daynag Royale (FR) **Mr D. Sutherland**
24 **GUYDUS (IRE)**, 8, b m Old Vic—Lady Mayday (IRE) **Zara & John Johnstone, & Nicky Coe**
25 **HELIOPSIS (IRE)**, 7, b g Beneficial—Bright Note **Mrs R. Godsman & Mr Richard Cadoret**
26 **HOHLETHELONELY**, 8, ch g Medicean—Now And Forever (IRE) **B. Moore & E. C. Stephens**
27 **HOUBLON DES OBEAUX (FR)**, 5, b g Panoramic—Harkosa (FR) **Mrs Julian Blackwell**
28 **HOWARD'S LEGACY (IRE)**, 6, b g Generous (IRE)—Ismene (FR) **A. G. Parker**
29 **KAPGA DE CERISY (FR)**, 4, ch g Kapgarde (FR)—Non Liquet **Mr A. L. Brooks**
30 **KING OF GLORY**, 4, b g Kayf Tara—Glory Be **Mrs B. M. Willcocks**
31 **LA BELLE SAUVAGE**, 5, ch m Old Vic—Lady Rebecca **Kinnersley Optimists**
32 **LAST SHOT (FR)**, 5, b g Le Fou (FR)—Lucky Shot (FR) **Last Shot Partnership**
33 **LATANIER (FR)**, 9, b g Cadoudal (FR)—Lattaquie (FR) **F. M. P. Mahon**
34 **LENA'S BLUEBELL (IRE)**, 6, b m Orpen—Lucayan Star (IRE) **D. A. Hunt**
35 **LIGHTNING STRIKE (GER)**, 9, ch g Danehill Dancer (IRE)—La Capilla **John Nicholls (Trading) Ltd**
36 **LOWER HOPE DANDY**, 5, ch g Karinga Bay—Cheeky Mare **Mr W. S. C. Richards**
37 **MANNLICHEN**, 6, ch g Selkirk (USA)—Robe Chinoise **Mr G. G. Mezzone**
38 **MARAAFEQ (USA)**, 8, b br g Bahri (USA)—Tabrir (IRE) **John & Zara Johnstone**
39 **MARESCSOU (FR)**, 7, b g Maresca Sorrento (FR)—Tugend (GER) **Marescsou partnership**
40 **MASSENA (IRE)**, 5, b g Marju (IRE)—Mayara (IRE) **Mr W. S. C. Richards**
41 **MENTALIST (FR)**, 4, b g Westerner—Lady Carole (FR) **Brooks, Burke & Cunningham**
42 **MIKO DE BEAUCHENE (FR)**, 12, b g Nashamaa—Chipie d'angron (FR) **Mr A. O. Wiles**
43 **MISS TIQUE (FR)**, 4, b f Network (GER)—Berthevine (FR) **Mrs A. W. Timpson**
44 **MON MOME (FR)**, 12, b g Passing Sale (FR)—Etoile du Lion (FR) **Mrs V. A. Bingham**
45 **MORE BALLET MONEY**, 4, b f Old Vic—No More Money **Falcons Line Ltd**
46 **MOUJIK BORGET (FR)**, 4, ch g Layman (USA)—Fancy Tune (FR) **Sunday Lunch Partnership**
47 **NAGPUR (FR)**, 6, b g Byzantium (FR)—Bel'cris (FR) **Miss S. Douglas-Pennant**
48 **NICEONEFRANKIE**, 6, b g Ishiguru (USA)—Chesnut Ripple **The Gambling Cousins**
49 **NOBUNAGA**, 7, ch g Beat Hollow—Absolute Precision (USA) **The Risky Partnership**
50 **OLD WAY (IRE)**, 6, b g Gold Away (IRE)—Brooklyn's Dance (IRE) **B. C. Dice**
51 **ON MY LIVING LIFE (IRE)**, 7, b g Alderbrook—Clever Cherry **The Hon J. R. Drummond**
52 **OPERA OG (IRE)**, 6, b g Oscar (IRE)—Maspaloma (IRE) **Craig, Dick, Duckworth & Matthewman**
53 **ORANGE GIZMO (IRE)**, 8, ch m Exit To Nowhere (USA)—Dark Princess (IRE) **Miss V. M. Williams**
54 **ORIENTAL CAT**, 5, b g Tiger Hill (IRE)—Sentimental Value (USA) **Mr A. L. Brooks**
55 **PANAMA PETRUS (IRE)**, 4, b g Alflora (IRE)—Pride 'n' Joy (IRE) **Andrew Brooks & Julian Taylor**
56 **PENTIFFIC (NZ)**, 9, br g Pentire—Sailing High (NZ) **P Sinn, P Lawrence, L Sutcliffe & M Smith**
57 **PEPITE ROSE (FR)**, 5, b br m Bonbon Rose (FR)—Sambre (FR) **Falcons Line Ltd**
58 **PLEIN POUVOIR (FR)**, 9, b g Maresca Sorrento (FR)—Dellerie (FR) **Dr M. A. Hamlin**
59 **QUARTZ DE THAIX (FR)**, 8, b g Ragmar (FR)—Une Amie (FR) **ROA Arkle Partnership**
60 **RADICAL IMPACT (IRE)**, 4, ch g Beneficial—Shean Alainn (IRE) **Mr C. A. J. Drury**
61 **RAJEEVA (IRE)**, 6, b g Rock of Gibraltar (IRE)—Balade Russe (USA) **A. Krishnan**
62 **RANJOBAIE (FR)**, 7, b g Crillon (FR)—Ilari du Missellot (FR) **Seasons Holidays**
63 **REGINALDINHO (UAE)**, 6, b g Galileo (IRE)—River Patrol **The Neighbours Partnership**
64 **RELAX (FR)**, 7, b g Fragrant Mix (IRE)—Magik (FR) **The Bellamy Partnership**
65 **RENARD (FR)**, 7, b br g Discover d'auteuil (FR)—Kirmelia (FR) **ROA Arkle Partnership**
66 **RIGADIN DE BEAUCHENE (FR)**, 7, b br g Visionary (FR)—Chipie d'angron (FR) **Mr A. O. Wiles**
67 **RILEYEV (FR)**, 7, b g Goldneyev (USA)—Jiletta (FR) **J. H. Mayne**
68 **ROZOLENN (FR)**, 7, gr g Kaktoz d'armor (FR)—Belle Indifference (FR) **Falcons Line Ltd**
69 **RUNAWAY GREEN (FR)**, 6, gr g Balleroy (USA)—Dora Dante (IRE) **The Runaway Green Partnership**
70 **RYDALIS (FR)**, 7, b m Kapgarde (FR)—Fleurissa (FR) **Mrs V. A. Bingham**
71 **SAMURAI WAY**, 10, b g Darshaan—Truly Special **Mrs M. L. Shone**
72 **SANTO THOMAS (FR)**, 6, gr g Chichicastenango (FR)—European Style (FR) **Mrs B. B. Grainger**
73 **SAROQUE (FR)**, 5, b g Revoque (FR)—Sarakin (IRE) **Connect Racing**
74 **SAWPIT SAMBA (IRE)**, 7, b g Orpen—Kymin (FR) **D. A. Hunt**
75 **SAWPIT SUPREME**, 10, b m Cloudings (IRE)—Dara's Course (IRE) **D. A. Hunt**
76 **SENDINPOST**, 9, b m Dansili—Colleville **Miss V. M. Williams**
77 **SHANGANI (USA)**, 6, b g Giant's Causeway (USA)—Tanzania (IRE) **The Bellamy Partnership**
78 **SPECIAL ROBON (FR)**, 4, b g Robin des Champs (FR)—Spinage (FR) **Dr M. A. Hamlin**

MISS VENETIA WILLIAMS—continued

79 **SPIRIT D'ARMOR (FR)**, 6, b g Port Lyautey (FR)—For The Glen (FR) **A. J. Pye-Jeary**
80 **STARS DU GRANITS (FR)**, 6, bl g Robin des Champs (FR)—Ile d'or (FR) **Mr I. R. P. Josephs**
81 **STOW**, 7, ch g Selkirk (USA)—Spry **GSM Properties Ltd**
82 **SUMMERY JUSTICE (IRE)**, 8, b g Witness Box (USA)—Kinsellas Rose (IRE) **Mrs P. Brown**
83 **SUSTAINABILITY (IRE)**, 7, ch g Old Vic—Over The Glen (IRE) **The Silver Cod Partnership**
84 **SYNDICATION (IRE)**, 5, b g Accordion—Huit de Coeur (IRE) **Brooks, Dimsey, James & Keyes**
85 **TANGO DE JUILLEY (FR)**, 4, b g Lesotho (USA)—Lasalsa de Juilley (FR) **Mr M. N. Khan**
86 **TENOR NIVERNAIS (FR)**, 5, b g Shaanmer (IRE)—Hosanna II (FR) **Mr M. N. Khan**
87 **TORGAMAH LAD (IRE)**, 4, b g High-Rise (IRE)—Brook Forte **Miss Mandy D Coughlan & Mr T. B. James**
88 **TUSKAR ROCK (FR)**, 9, gr g Turgeon (USA)—Shannondore (FR) **Anthony Pye-Jeary & Mel Smith**
89 **VAL MONDO (GER)**, 5, b h Lando (GER)—Valleria (GER) **M. J. Pilkington**
90 **VAN MIRA (IRE)**, 4, b g Winged Love (IRE)—Miraflores (IRE) **You Can Be Sure**

THREE-YEAR-OLDS

91 **ZAMDY MAN**, b c Authorized (IRE)—Lauderdale (GER) **Mr M. N. Khan**

Other Owners: Sir John Becher, Mrs C. Belloc Lowndes, Dr Martin Booth, Mr M. Checketts, Mr Bob Clarke, Mr T. H. G. Cooper, Mr Danny Coughlan, Dr Chris Cowell, Mr O. P. Dakin, Mr J. S. Dale, Mr P. A. Davies, Mr P. Davies, Mr Michael J. Davies, Mr P. A. Deal, Mr T. Fawcett, Mr Alexander Frost, Mrs J. E. Gorton, Mr James Hall, Mrs Jeremy Hancock, Mrs P. A. H. Hartley, Mr P. A. H. Hartley, Mr Christopher James, Miss S. Magee, Mr T. D. Rose, Mr M. Secretan, Mr Mel Smith, Mr Howard Spooner, Mrs L. P. Vaughan.

Jockey (NH): Aidan Coleman, Liam Treadwell, Robert Dunne, Sam Thomas. **Conditional:** Harry Challoner, George Bartlett.

700

MRS LISA WILLIAMSON, Chester
Postal: **Saighton Hall, Saighton, Chester, Cheshire, CH3 6EE**
Contacts: **PHONE (01244) 314254 FAX (01244) 314254 (please ring before sending)**
MOBILE **(07970) 437679**
E-MAIL info@lisawilliamson.co.uk WEBSITE www.lisawilliamson.co.uk

1 **BEE STING**, 8, b g Selkirk (USA)—Desert Lynx (IRE) **D. J. Goulding**
2 **BY POPULAR DEMAND (IRE)**, 4, b g Indian Haven—Green Belt (FR) **Chester Racing Club Ltd**
3 **CHESTER DEELYTE (IRE)**, 4, b f Desert Style (IRE)—Bakewell Tart (IRE) **Hindford Oak Racing**
4 **CHINA HOUSE (IRE)**, 9, ch g Flemensfirth (USA)—Chancy Gal **Halewood International Ltd**
5 **COLLIERS CASTLE (IRE)**, 6, b m Karinga Bay—Aneeza (IRE) **Heath House Racing**
6 **CRABBIES GINGER**, 4, ch g Needwood Blade—Dazzling Quintet **Halewood International Ltd**
7 **CRABBIES GOLD (IRE)**, 4, ch g Sleeping Indian—Sharpe's Lady **Halewood International Ltd**
8 **DIAMOND TWISTER (USA)**, 6, b g Omega Code (USA)—King's Pact (USA) **D. J. Goulding**
9 **DIGGERS DAYDREAM (IRE)**, 4, b g Refuse To Bend (IRE)—Enlightened Way (FR) **Chester Racing Club Ltd**
10 **GOLDEN KING (IRE)**, 7, gr g King's Theatre (IRE)—One Swoop (IRE) **D. J. Goulding**
11 **HINDFORD OAK GOLD**, 4, ch g Grape Tree Road—Sharp Susy **Hindford Oak**
12 **JOBEKANI (IRE)**, 6, b g Tagula (IRE)—Lyca Ballerina **Mr A. T Sykes**
13 **JOHN CRABBIES (FR)**, 5, b g Super Celebre (FR)—Clelia La Belle (FR) **Halewood International Ltd**
14 **LAMBRINI LACE (IRE)**, 7, b m Namid—Feather 'n Lace (IRE) **Mrs J. M. Halewood**
15 4, B g Grape Tree Road—Lambrini Queen **Halewood International Ltd**
16 **LORD WHEATHILL**, 5, b g Tobougg (IRE)—Classic Quartet **K C Hire & Sales Ltd**
17 **MUSICAL BRIDGE**, 6, b g Night Shift (USA)—Carrie Pooter **T. Conway**
18 **ODD BALL (IRE)**, 5, b g Redback—Luceball (IRE) **Mrs S Morris**
19 **PINBALL (IRE)**, 6, b m Namid—Luceball (IRE) **Mr M. L. Rush**
20 **POWERBALL (IRE)**, 4, b f Redback—Luceball (IRE) **Mr J. Levenson**
21 **PUYOL (IRE)**, 10, b br g Zaffaran (USA)—Star Mover **Halewood International Ltd**
22 **ROCKETBALL (IRE)**, 7, b g Namid—Luceball (IRE) **Mr J. Levenson**
23 **RODDEE GIANT (IRE)**, 4, b f Footstepsinthesand—Rushing **Chester Racing Club Ltd**
24 **RYAN STYLE (IRE)**, 6, b g Desert Style (IRE)—Westlife **Bluegrass Racing Ltd**
25 **SANTINHO (IRE)**, 9, b g Double Eclipse (IRE)—Gina's Love **Mr K. W. Peach**
26 **SEE THE STORM**, 4, b br g Statue of Liberty (USA)—Khafayif (USA) **M Keating**

THREE-YEAR-OLDS

27 **ALL GOOD NEWS (IRE)**, gr g Moss Vale (IRE)—Blanche Neige (USA) **Bluegrass Racing Ltd**
28 **BABUSHKA'S GIRL**, b f Central Park (IRE)—Shaymee's Girl **B & B Hygiene**
29 B f Fraam—Classic Quartet **Lisa Williamson**
30 **ELAMMATO (IRE)**, b g Strategic Prince—Boadicea **Mr A. T Sykes**
31 **ESPECIALLY RED (IRE)**, b f Red Clubs (IRE)—Midnight Special (IRE) **D. J. Goulding**
32 B g Grape Tree Road—Miss Lambrini **Halewood International Ltd**

MRS LISA WILLIAMSON—continued

TWO-YEAR-OLDS

33 Br gr c 17/4 Auction House (USA)—Amwell Star (USA) (Silver Buck (USA)) (1904) **D. J. Goulding**
34 B f 8/4 Multiplex—Classic Quartet (Classic Cliche (IRE)) **Lisa Williamson**
35 B c 3/4 Vitus—Danehill Princess (IRE) (Danehill (USA)) (761) **Mr J. Levenson**
36 B c 4/4 Kheleyf (USA)—Danehill's Dream (IRE) (Danehill (USA)) (14285) **D. J. Goulding**
37 Ch c 22/3 Auction House (USA)—Dazzling Quintet (Superlative) (6666) **D. J. Goulding**
38 B f 7/5 Proclamation (IRE)—Miss Lambrini (Henbit (USA)) **Halewood International Ltd**
39 B c 10/5 Assertive—Not So Generous (IRE) (Fayruz) (7619) **D. J. Goulding**
40 Ch c 26/4 Cockney Rebel (IRE)—Para Siempre (Mujahid (USA)) (761) **D. J. Goulding**
41 B f 7/3 Amadeus Wolf—Princess Madaen (IRE) (Elusive Quality (USA)) (3694) **D. J. Goulding**
42 TAMBRINI LAD, b g 20/4 Fair Mix (IRE)—Lady Lambrini (Overbury) (Overbury) **M Rush**
43 B f 9/4 Amadeus Wolf—Valencia (FR) (Croco Rouge (IRE)) (2285) **D. J. Goulding**
44 B c 20/4 Moss Vale (IRE)—Westlife (IRE) (Mind Games) (14285) **D. J. Goulding**

Assistant Trainer: Mark Williamson

Jockey (flat): Tom Eaves. **Jockey (NH):** Brian Hughes. **Conditional:** Harry Challoner. **Amateur:** Mr C. Ellingham.

---

701 MR ANDREW WILSON, Penrith
Postal: **Silver Howe, Orton, Penrith, Cumbria, CA10 3RQ**
Contacts: **PHONE (01539) 624071 MOBILE (07813) 846768**

1 REXMEHEAD (IRE), 11, b g Fort Morgan (USA)—Moon Rose (IRE) **Mrs H. J. Wilson**
2 SO BAZAAR (IRE), 5, b g Xaar (USA)—Nature Girl (USA) **Mrs H. J. Wilson**

---

702 MR CHRISTOPHER WILSON, Darlington
Postal: **Manor Farm, Manfield, Darlington, Co. Durham, DL2 2RW**
Contacts: **PHONE (01325) 374595 FAX (01325) 374595 MOBILE (07815) 952306/(07721) 379277**
E-MAIL wilsonracing@aol.com

1 ESME RIDES A GAINE, 10, gr m Doubletour (USA)—Silver Penny **Mrs J. Wilson**
2 INGENTI, 4, ch f Blue Dakota (IRE)—Kungfu Kerry **D. A. J. Bartlett**
3 LATEST FASHION (IRE), 6, ch m Ashkalani (IRE)—Musical Bramble (IRE) **Mrs J. Wilson**
4 STELLA MARRIS, 5, br m Danroad (AUS)—Riyoom (USA) **D. A. J. Bartlett**
5 VALSESIA (IRE), 5, b m Milan—Ballinapierce Lady (IRE) **Mrs J. Wilson**

THREE-YEAR-OLDS

6 NICEONEMYSON, b g Misu Bond (IRE)—Kungfu Kerry **D. A. J. Bartlett**

Assistant Trainer: Julie Wilson

Jockey (flat): Silvestre De Sousa. **Jockey (NH):** Keith Mercer.

---

703 MR JIM WILSON, Cheltenham
Postal: **Glenfall Stables, Ham, Charlton Kings, Cheltenham, Gloucestershire, GL52 6NH**
Contacts: **PHONE (01242) 244713 FAX (01242) 226319 MOBILE (07932) 157243**
E-MAIL ajwglenfall@aol.com

1 BITTA DASH, 12, ch g Bandmaster (USA)—Letitica **Mrs M. J. Wilson**
2 CAPTAIN SULLY (IRE), 7, b g Pairumani Star (IRE)—Ginger Lily (IRE) **The Cotswold Partnership**
3 RUBY VALENTINE (FR), 9, b m Kayf Tara—A Ma Valentine (FR) **The Winbledon Partnership**
4 SEYMOUR LEGEND, 6, b g Midnight Legend—Rosehall **Mrs T. D. Pilkington**

Other Owners: Mr R. S. Alexander, I. R. Anderson, J. W. Griffin, B. J. Hughes, D. B. O'Beirne.

704 MISS MAIRI WILSON, Bawtry
Postal: **Martin Common Farm, Bawtry, Doncaster, South Yorkshire, DN10 6DB**

1 BUSTANINCH, 8, ch g Arkadian Hero (USA)—Inchmore **Mrs M. F. and Miss M. C. Wilson**
2 EASY LED, 7, b g Killer Instinct—Harmony Royal **Mrs M. F. and Miss M. C. Wilson**
3 5, Ch m Lucky Story (USA)—Inchmore **Mrs M. F. and Miss M. C. Wilson**

Other Owners: Mrs M. F. Wilson, Miss M. C. Wilson.

705 MR NOEL WILSON, Thirsk
Postal: **Breckenbrough House (2nd Yard), Sandhutton, Thirsk, North Yorkshire, YO7 4EL**
Contacts: **PHONE (01845) 525969 FAX (01845) 525969 MOBILE (07808) 162631**
E-MAIL nicolawilson@orange.net WEBSITE www.noelwilsonracing.co.uk

1 DEMOLITION, 8, ch g Starborough—Movie Star (IRE) **M. Wormald**
2 DIAMOND SUNRISE (IRE), 4, b f Diamond Green (FR)—Sunrise (IRE) **Noel Wilson & Lauren Stapley**
3 DORBACK, 5, ch g Kyllachy—Pink Supreme **Ms S. V. Hattersley**
4 5, B g King's Theatre (IRE)—Dream Lass (IRE) **Matt Morgan**
5 DRIVE HOME (USA), 5, b br g Mr Greeley (USA)—Unique Pose (IRE) **Wilson Downes Kennedy Tobin**
6 ERYCINA (IRE), 4, gr f Aussie Rules (USA)—Golden (FR) **P. J. Sweeney**
7 GOBAMA, 5, br m Dr Fong (USA)—Chine **Mr W. Y. Chen**
8 GRAND ART (IRE), 8, b g Raise A Grand (IRE)—Mulberry River (IRE) **P. Tsim**
9 GREAT ROAR (USA), 4, b c Thunder Gulch (USA)—Boasting (USA) **Matt Morgan**
10 4, B g Golan (IRE)—Hollygrove Samba (IRE) **Matt Morgan**
11 HOTHAM, 9, b g Komaite (USA)—Malcesine (IRE) **Far 2 Many Sues**
12 HUNTERS BELT (IRE), 8, b g Intikhab (USA)—Three Stars **Mr R. A. Fisher & Mr John Blair**
13 HYPNOSIS, 9, b m Mind Games—Salacious **R. W. Snowden**
14 JOVIAL (IRE), 5, b g Sakhee (USA)—Baalbek **C. T. Van Hoorn**
15 MAKARI, 5, b g Makbul—Seraphim (FR) **Matt & Lauren Morgan**
16 MERCERS ROW, 5, b g Bahamian Bounty—Invincible **Mrs J. A. Smith**
17 MONKTON VALE (IRE), 5, b g Catcher In The Rye (IRE)—Byproxy (IRE) **B. Plows P.M. Watson J. Owen**
18 MYJESTIC MELODY (IRE), 4, b f Majestic Missile (IRE)—Bucaramanga (IRE) **Hurn Racing Club & Partners**
19 NEDRICO, 4, b g Tagula (IRE)—Deserted Island (IRE) **Paul & Linda Dixon**
20 4, B g Oratorio (IRE)—Poule de Luxe (IRE) **Ms S. V. Hattersley**
21 PRAXIOS, 4, b g Val Royal (FR)—Forest Fire (SWE) **Simon Twiggs Matt Morgan Noel Wilson**
22 RED SKIPPER (IRE), 7, ch g Captain Rio—Speed To Lead (IRE) **CW Racing Club & Partner**
23 6, B g Lahib (USA)—Takeyourtime **Miss K. Watson**
24 TOMBELLINI (IRE), 5, ch g Tomba—La Scala (USA) **WRB Racing 52**
25 VELOSO (FR), 10, gr g Kaldounevees (FR)—Miss Recif (IRE) **B. Morton**

THREE-YEAR-OLDS

26 KOOLGREYCAT (IRE), gr f One Cool Cat (USA)—Brooks Masquerade **J. R. Owen & M. Wormald**
27 MAKE UP, b f Kyllachy—Christmas Tart (IRE) **Ms S. V. Hattersley**
28 PAVERS STAR, ch g Pastoral Pursuits—Pride of Kinloch **Mrs C. K. Paver**
29 B c Whipper (USA)—Rustic Princess (IRE) **P. Tsim**
30 SHATIN SPIRIT (IRE), b br g Rock of Gibraltar (IRE)—Forest Walk (IRE)
31 SIMPSON MILLAR, b g Librettist (USA)—Scented Garden **CW Racing Club**

Other Owners: Mr T. Alderson, Mr John Blair, Mr P. A. Burgess, Mr P. A. P. Clays, Mr Paul W. H. Dixon, Mrs L. J. Dixon, Mr Steven Downes, Mr R. A. Fisher, Mr G. P. Henderson, Mrs I. M. Jessop, Mr Gary Kennedy, Mr Matthew Morgan, Mr John R. Owen, Mr G. J. Paver, Mr David Percival, Mr Brian Plows, Miss Lauren Stapley, Mr F. Tobin, Mr Simon Twiggs, Mr P. M. Watson, Mr N. Wilson, Mr M. Wormald.

Assistant Trainer: Mrs N. C. Wilson

Jockey (flat): Jimmy Quinn, Gary Bartley, Barry McHugh, Daniel Tudhope. Jockey (NH): Wilson Renwick. Conditional: Brian Toomey. Apprentice: Paul Pickard, Shirley Teasdale. Amateur: Miss K. Bannon.

706 MR KEN WINGROVE, Bridgnorth
Postal: **6 Netherton Farm Barns, Netherton Lane, Highley, Bridgnorth, Shropshire, WV16 6NJ**
Contacts: **HOME (01746) 861534 MOBILE (07974) 411267**

1 6, B g Superior Premium—Acorn Catcher
2 CLASSICAL LAND, 7, b g Classic Cliche (IRE)—Solid Land (FR)

MR KEN WINGROVE—continued

3 **CONDARIAN (IRE)**, 8, b g Deploy—Makpela (FR)
4 **FARMER GUNNER**, 10, ch g Gunner B—M C A River **L. T. Woodhouse**
5 **GRAND FELLA (IRE)**, 7, ch g Raise A Grand (IRE)—Mummys Best **L. T. Woodhouse**
6 **HARRY OSCAR (IRE)**, 11, b g Oscar (IRE)—Kilcrea Breeze (IRE)
7 4, B f Lake Street Envoy VII—Lake Street Jane VII
8 **LEAHNESS (IRE)**, 5, br m Arakan (USA)—En Retard (IRE) **L. T. Woodhouse**
9 **LERUBIS (FR)**, 13, b g Ragmar (FR)—Perle de Saisy (FR)
10 **LILLY DE ROME**, 9, ch m Roi de Rome (USA)—Bishop's Folly
11 **LOUISE SAUVAGE**, 6, b m Loup Sauvage (USA)—Breezy Louise **F. L. Matthews**
12 **MASTER COSPECTOR**, 7, b g Helissio (FR)—Trinity Reef **F. L. Matthews**
13 6, B g Umistim—Naval Dispatch
14 4, B f Rock City—Princess Diva
15 **WEET IN NERJA**, 6, b g Captain Rio—Persian Fortune **L. T. Woodhouse**
16 **WINROB**, 6, b g Exceed And Excel (AUS)—High Standard
17 **YEAH**, 5, b g Gentleman's Deal (IRE)—Snugfit Dubarry
18 **YELLOWSHRUBMARINE**, 8, ch g Gorse—Naval Dispatch

Assistant Trainer: Isobel Willer

MR ADRIAN WINTLE, Westbury-On-Severn
Postal: 29 Colchester Close, Westbury-On-Severn, Gloucestershire, GL14 1PU

1 **FLETCH AND LENNY (IRE)**, 8, b g Bach (IRE)—Jennylee (IRE) **A. A. Wintle**
2 **GENERAL ROSS (IRE)**, 5, b g Generous (USA)—Rossmore Girl (IRE) **A. A. Wintle**
3 **NOBLE PERK**, 7, ch g Executive Perk—Far From Perfect (IRE) **A. A. Wintle**

MR IAN WOOD, Upper Lambourn
Postal: Neardown Stables, Upper Lambourn, Hungerford, Berkshire, RG17 8QP
Contacts: PHONE (01488) 72324 FAX (01488) 72877 MOBILE (07775) 508111
E-MAIL ianwood@chase3c.com WEBSITE www.neardownracing.com

1 **ADELLE**, 4, ch f Hawk Wing (USA)—Nanette **Mr D. H. L. Jones**
2 **BUTTON MOON (IRE)**, 4, ch f Compton Place—Portelet **P. E. Barrett**
3 **CARDI CRYSTAL (IRE)**, 5, b m Fasliyev (USA)—Tinsel **Mr D. H. L. Jones**
4 **CARDI KING**, 4, b g Fasliyev (USA)—Tinsel **Mr D. H. L. Jones**
5 **DOZY JOE**, 4, b c Sleeping Indian—Surrey Down (USA) **P. E. Barrett**
6 **FASTNETTE (IRE)**, 5, b m Fasliyev (USA)—Nanette **Mr D. H. L. Jones**
7 **HIMALAYAN MOON**, 5, gr m Tiger Hill (IRE)—Sita (IRE) **P. E. Barrett**
8 **PERFECT CH'I (IRE)**, 5, b m Choisir (AUS)—Agouti **P. E. Barrett**
9 **POINT DU JOUR (FR)**, 4, b br g Indian Rocket—Alaiz **P. E. Barrett**
10 **PROFESSOR JOHN (IRE)**, 5, b g Haafhd—Dancing Flower (IRE) **P. E. Barrett**
11 **QUASI CONGAREE (GER)**, 6, ch g Congaree (USA)—Queens Wild (USA) **Mr M. Forbes & Mr C. R. Lamborne**
12 **REQUISITE**, 7, ch m Pivotal—Chicarica (USA) **P. E. Barrett**
13 **RIVAS RHAPSODY**, 4, b f Hawk Wing (USA)—Riva Royale **Mr D. H. L. Jones**
14 **TOWY BOY (IRE)**, 7, b g King Charlemagne (USA)—Solar Flare (IRE) **Mr C. R. Lambourne**
15 **WILLIAM'S WAY**, 10, b g Fraam—Silk Daisy **Neardown Stables**

THREE-YEAR-OLDS

16 **ITSONLYMAKEBELIEVE (IRE)**, b f Amadeus Wolf—Alexander Ridge (IRE) **P. E. Barrett**
17 **KYLEAKIN LASS**, b f Kyllachy—Local Fancy **C.R. Lambourne, M. Forbes, D. Losse**
18 B f Val Royal (FR)—Meditation **P. E. Barrett**
19 **ROYAL AWARD**, b f Cadeaux Genereux—Red Sovereign **Miss Jacqueline Goodearl**
20 **SAMASANA (IRE)**, b f Redback—Singitta **P. E. Barrett**
21 **TATTY**, b f Dylan Thomas (IRE)—Faslen (USA) **P. E. Barrett**

TWO-YEAR-OLDS

22 B c 3/2 Bertolini (USA)—Bonnie Belle (Imperial Ballet (IRE)) **Mr D. H. L. Jones**
23 **MISS MOCCA**, b f 27/2 Bahamian Bounty—
Mocca (IRE) (Sri Pekan (USA)) (11500) **C.R. Lambourne, M. Forbes, D. Losse**
24 B f 25/2 Sleeping Indian—Spree (IRE) (Dansili) (16000) **P. E. Barrett**
25 **THREE CROWNS**, b f 26/3 Three Valleys (USA)—
Red Sovereign (Danzig Connection (USA)) **Miss Jacqueline Goodearl**

MR IAN WOOD—continued

Other Owners: Mr M. I. Forbes, Mr C. R. Lambourne, Mr D. R. Losse, Mrs L. J. Losse.

Jockey (flat): James Doyle. **Amateur:** Mr C. Martin.

---

709 MR STEVE WOODMAN, Chichester
Postal: **Parkers Barn Stables, 8 Pook Lane, East Lavant, Chichester, West Sussex, PO18 0AU**
Contacts: **OFFICE** (01243) 527136 **FAX** (01243) 527136 **MOBILE** (07889) 188519
E-MAIL stevewoodman83@msn.com

1 CHEVISE (IRE), 4, b f Holy Roman Emperor (IRE)—Lipica (IRE) **The Chevise Partnership**
2 GOING TWICE, 7, b g Josr Algarhoud (IRE)—Its Your Bid **Mrs S. B. Woodman**
3 LORD ALDERVALE (IRE), 5, br g Alderbrook—Monavale (IRE) **R. Jenner & J. Green**

Other Owners: Mrs A. J. Green, Ms R. A. Jenner, Mrs P. M. Tyler.

---

710 MRS A. M. WOODROW, High Wycombe
Postal: **Crookswood Stud Farm, Horsleys Green, High Wycombe, Buckinghamshire, HP14 3XB**
Contacts: **PHONE** (01494) 482557 **MOBILE** (07901) 858874
E-MAIL john@woodrow.com

1 LESCER'S LAD, 15, b g Perpendicular—Grange Gracie **Mrs A. M. Woodrow**

Other Owners: J. G. Woodrow.

Assistant Trainer: John Woodrow

Jockey (NH): Felix De Giles, Jimmy McCarthy.

---

711 MR GARRY WOODWARD, Retford
Postal: **Moorgate House Stables, Tiln Lane, Retford, Nottinghamshire, DN22 9JF**
Contacts: **HOME** (01709) 813431 **MOBILE** (07739) 382052
E-MAIL gwoodwardracing@aol.com **WEBSITE** www.garrywoodward.co.uk

1 AMY THORPE, 5, b m Danbird (AUS)—Nunthorpe **J. M. Lacey**
2 BAZGUY, 7, ro g Josr Algarhoud (IRE)—Ewenny **J. M. Lacey**
3 DARCY MAY, 4, b f Danbird (AUS)—Oakwell Ace **Mr K Sayles**
4 DOUBLE CARPET, 9, b g Lahib (USA)—Cupid Miss **G. Woodward**
5 ERRIGAL LAD, 7, ch g Bertolini (USA)—La Belle Vie **Mrs E. Cash**
6 INSIDE KNOWLEDGE (USA), 6, gr ro g Mizzen Mast (USA)—Kithira **Mr & Mrs J. N. Bloom**
7 JUST ZAK, 7, b g Superior Premium—Goodbye Millie **J. M. Lacey**
8 KINGAROO (IRE), 6, b g King Charlemagne (USA)—Lady Naomi (USA) **J. Pownall**
9 MOORGATE LASS, 4, b f Danbird (AUS)—Bolham Lady **J. M. Lacey**
10 MRS MEDLEY, 6, b m Rambling Bear—Animal Cracker **Mr J. Medley**
11 PRINCEOFTHEDESERT, 6, b g Nayef (USA)—Twilight Sonnet **Mr G. Woodward**
12 REVEAL THE LIGHT, 5, b m Fantastic Light (USA)—Paper Chase (FR) **G. Woodward**
13 SECRET LODGE, 4, ch f Needwood Blade—Obsessive Secret (IRE) **G. Woodward**
14 SELF EMPLOYED, 5, b g Sakhee (USA)—Twilight Sonnet **G. Woodward**
15 STEEL CITY BOY (IRE), 9, b g Bold Fact (USA)—Balgren (IRE) **Mr J. Medley**
16 TOOTHACHE, 4, gr f Proclamation (IRE)—Zilkha **Mr G. Woodward**

THREE-YEAR-OLDS

17 MISS BLOOM, ch f Byron—Demolition Molly **Mr & Mrs J. N. Bloom**

Other Owners: Mr J. N. Bloom, Mrs C. S. Bloom, Mr G. D. Brumby, Mrs M. Brumby, Mr K. Sayles, Mr M Wilson.

---

712 MR ROBERT WYLIE, Westhead
Postal: **Brookfields Stables, Charity Lane, Westhead, Lancashire, L40 6LG**
Contacts: **MOBILE** (07900) 880807
E-MAIL wylie_rob@yahoo.co.uk

1 BALLINARGH BOY, 4, b g Royal Applause—Can Can Lady **M. R. Johnson & J. Kenny**
2 BALLINARGH GIRL (IRE), 4, b f Footstepsinthesand—Rack And Ruin (IRE) **M. R. Johnson & J. Kenny**

MR ROBERT WYLIE—continued

3 **JAQUES VERT (FR)**, 6, ch g Dr Fong (USA)—Sayuri (USA) **Mr M. R. Johnson & Mr A. Draper**
4 **JUST CALL ME DAVE (USA)**, 6, b g Gneiss (USA)—Proud Future (USA) **Bluegrass Racing Ltd**
5 **MIND SHOWER (IRE)**, 6, b g Bach (IRE)—Knockacool Breeze **M. R. Johnson & J. Kenny**
6 **SPLENDID SENORITA (IRE)**, 5, b m Helissio (FR)—Friendly Craic (IRE) **M. R. Johnson**

THREE-YEAR-OLDS

7 B g Bach (IRE)—Dawning Day (IRE) **M. R. Johnson**
8 **JAY KAY**, b g Librettist (USA)—Turn Back **Mr J. Kenny**

TWO-YEAR-OLDS

9 B f 9/5 Multiplex—Hillside Girl (IRE) (Tagula (IRE)) (3809)
10 B f 5/4 Avonbridge—Rainbow Spectrum (FR) (Spectrum (IRE)) (1904) **M. R. Johnson**

Other Owners: A. Draper.

---

713   MR RAYMOND YORK, Cobham
Postal: **Newmarsh Farm, Horsley Road, Cobham, Surrey, KT11 3JX**
Contacts: **PHONE (01932) 863594 FAX (01932) 860703 MOBILE (07808) 344131**
E-MAIL ray.york@virgin.net

1 **CHARLOTTE'S BALL (IRE)**, 6, b m Presenting—Thats The Girl (IRE) **R. H. York**
2 **CRIMSON MITRE**, 7, b g Bishop of Cashel—Pink Champagne **D. P. Fremel**
3 **ENCANTADORA**, 5, ch m Generous (USA)—Sninfia (IRE) **R. H. York**
4 **FLAT CAP THURSDAY**, 5, ch m Erhaab (USA)—Zaffre Bleu (IRE) **Mrs D. A. T. Salmon**
5 **JENNY'S GOLD**, 7, b m Dolpour—Zaffre Bleu (IRE) **Mrs D. A. T. Salmon**
6 **MEKONG MISS**, 6, ch m Mark of Esteem (IRE)—Missouri **D. P. Fremel**
7 6, B g Morozov (USA)—Pharbar (IRE) **R. H. York**
8 **QUEEN'S PAWN (IRE)**, 5, br g Strategic Choice (USA)—Curragh Queen (IRE) **F. D. Camis**
9 5, B m Moscow Society (USA)—See More Tricks **R. H. York**
10 5, B m Beat All (USA)—Snowdon Lily **R. H. York**
11 **SORSE**, 6, b g Central Park (IRE)—Tachelle (IRE) **R. H. York**

THREE-YEAR-OLDS

12 **ASPARELLA**, b f Equerry (USA)—Aspra (FR) **Mrs N Carter & Mrs D Salmon**

Other Owners: Mrs N. Carter.

Amateur: Mr P. York.

---

714   MRS LAURA YOUNG, Bridgwater
Postal: **Rooks Castle Stables, Broomfield, Bridgwater, Somerset, TA5 2EW**
Contacts: **PHONE (01278) 661555 FAX (01278) 661555 MOBILE (07766) 514414**
E-MAIL ljyracing@hotmail.com

1 **ADMIRAL BLAKE**, 5, b g Witness Box (USA)—Brenda Bella (FR) **Mrs L. J. Young**
2 6, B m Lyphento (USA)—Capricious Lady (IRE) **Mrs L. J. Young**
3 **DANISH REBEL (IRE)**, 8, b g Danetime (IRE)—Wheatsheaf Lady (IRE) **Total Plumbing Supporters Club**
4 **HEEZMINE (IRE)**, 6, ch g Oscar Schindler (IRE)—It'snicetobenice (IRE) **Mrs L. J. Young**
5 **KAP WEST (FR)**, 7, b g Kapgarde (FR)—Themis Eria (FR) **Mrs S. A. White**
6 **MY GRUNTER (IRE)**, 7, b g Winged Love (USA)—Lady Padivor (IRE) **Total Plumbing Supporters Club**
7 **PARTICIPATION**, 9, b g Dansili—Andaleeb (USA) **Mrs L. J. Young**
8 **TAVALU (USA)**, 10, b g Kingmambo (USA)—Larrocha (IRE) **Total Plumbing Supporters Club**

THREE-YEAR-OLDS

9 Ch f Compton Place—Felona **D. R. Tucker**

Other Owners: C. E. Handford, Mr I. D. Moses.

Assistant Trainer: James Young

715 **MR WILLIAM YOUNG, Carluke**
Postal: **Overton Farm, Crossford, Carluke, Lanarkshire, ML8 5QF**
Contacts: PHONE **(01555) 860226** FAX **(01555) 860137** MOBILE **(07900) 408210**
E-MAIL **peppersyoung@aol.com**

1 **ELLANDSHE (IRE),** 12, b br g Topanoora—Fox Glen **W. G. Young**
2 **FIELD ELECT,** 5, b g Zafeen (FR)—Princess Carranita (IRE) **W. G. Young**
3 **IF EVER (IRE),** 7, ch m Horse Chestnut (SAF)—Lolita's Gold (USA) **W. G. Young**
4 **LUCKY BELLE (IRE),** 5, ch m Barathea (IRE)—Borders Belle (IRE) **W. G. Young**
5 **OVER THE CLYDE,** 7, b g Overbury (IRE)—La Dama (USA) **W. G. Young**
6 **SIXTIES ROCK,** 5, ch g Rock of Gibraltar (IRE)—Scene (IRE) **W. G. Young**

Assistant Trainer: W G Young Jnr

INDEX TO HORSES

The Figure before the name of the horse refers to the number of the team in which it appears and **The Figure after** the horse supplies a ready reference to each animal. Horses are indexed strictly alphabetically, e.g. THE OMEN appears in the T's, MR SNOOZY in the MR's, ST ATHAN in the ST's etc.

71 **A B CELEBRATION** (GB) 1
365 **A BEAT SO FAR** (GB) 1
213 **A BOY NAMED SUZI** (GB) 1
434 **A BRIDGE TOO FAR** (IRE) 1
408 **A CUERPO LIMPIO** 40
473 **A FINE YOUNG MAN** (IRE) 1
169 **A HEART BEATS ON** (IRE) 1
564 **A HOT DREAM** (FR) 17
564 **A HUGE DREAM** (IRE) 18
27 **A J COOK** (IRE) 46
299 **A LADIES MAN** (IRE) 120
647 **A LITTLE BIT DUSTY** (GB) 1
381 **A LITTLE SWIFTER** (IRE) 1
564 **A MOI** (FR) 19
311 **A NEW DAWN** (IRE) 1
340 **A NEW STORY** (IRE) 1
375 **A P LING** (GB) 1
123 **A PARTY FOR TWO** (USA) F 52
342 **A POCKETFUL OF RYE** (IRE) 1
74 **A'FAAL** (GB) 1
49 **A'JUBA** (GB) 68
699 **AACHEN** (GB) 1
447 **AAIM TO PROSPER** (IRE) 1
555 **AALY** (GB) 1
400 **AAMAN** (IRE) 1
509 **AARANYOW** (IRE) 1
285 **AARTI** (IRE) 12
10 **AATHER** (IRE) 1
193 **AAZIF** (IRE) 21
360 **ABADEJO** (IRE) 1
408 **ABAKAHN** 41
238 **ABAYAAN** (GB) 1
388 **ABAYO** (USA) 14
206 **ABBEVILLIAN** (IRE) 1
556 **ABBEY GARTH** (IRE) 1
637 **ABBI JICARO** (GB) 1
223 **ABBRACCIO** (IRE) 1
328 **ABBY ROAD** (IRE) C 72
601 **ABERDOVEY** (GB) F 55
207 **ABERGAVENNY** (IRE) 1
519 **ABERNETHY** (IRE) 1
466 **ABI SCARLET** (IRE) 30
543 **ABIDHABIDUBAI** (GB) 1
363 **ABIGAILS ANGEL** (GB) 1
366 **ABISHENA** (IRE) 41
16 **ABLE DEPUTY** (GB) 1
503 **ABNAKI** (IRE) 1
24 **ABOUT THYNE** (IRE) 1
377 **ABOVE STANDARD** (IRE) 1
220 **ABOVE THE STARS** (GB) 1
639 **ABRA ABRA CADABRA** (GB) 1
191 **ABRAQ** (GB) 44
542 **ABRIACHAN** (GB) 1
471 **ABSA LUTTE** (IRE) 1
480 **ABSENT AMY** (IRE) 28
29 **ABSENT MINDED** (GB) 16
74 **ABSHIR ZAIN** (IRE) 24
434 **ABSINTHE** (IRE) 2

212 **ABSOLUTE BEARING** (IRE) 7
304 **ABSOLUTE CRACKERS** (IRE) 77
601 **ABSOLUTE DIAMOND** (GB) 56
176 **ABSOLUTE PRINCESS** (GB) 1
254 **ABSOLUTE RETURN** (GB) 58
441 **ABSOLUTELY BYGONES** (IRE) 1
228 **ABSOLUTELY ME** (IRE) 10
19 **ABSOLUTELY SO** (IRE) 106
332 **ABSTRACT ART** (USA) 1
508 **ABU NAYEF** (IRE) 56
690 **ABUNDANT** (GB) G 17
466 **ABUNDANTLY** (GB) 31
226 **ACADEMY JANE** (IRE) G 1
499 **ACAPULCO** (IRE) 1
89 **ACAPULCO BAY** (GB) 1
141 **ACCESSION** (IRE) 25
359 **ACCORDING TO PETE** (IRE) 1
256 **ACCORDING TO THEM** (IRE) 1
498 **ACCORDINGTOEILEEN** (IRE) 1
404 **ACCORDINTOLAWRENCE** (IRE) 1
503 **ACCORDION EXHIBIT** (IRE) 2
3 **ACCREDIT** (GB) 45
459 **ACCUMULATE** (GB) 1
172 **ACCUMULUS** (GB) 1
450 **ACCUSATION** (IRE) F 42
42 **ACE FIGHTER PILOT** (GB) 1
160 **ACE HIGH** (GB) 1
60 **ACE MASTER** (IRE) 1
182 **ACE OF SPIES** (IRE) 1
111 **ACE OF VALHALLA** (GB) 23
593 **ACE SERVE** (GB) 1
225 **ACER DIAMONDS** (IRE) 18
299 **ACES DANCING** (GER) C 121
29 **ACHERNAR** (USA) 67
591 **ACHIMOTA** (IRE) 1
658 **ACHT** (GER) 39
531 **ACIANO** (GB) 1
299 **ACIDANTHERA** (GB) C 122
650 **ACKERTAC** (IRE) 1
383 **ACKNOWLEDGEMENT** (GB) 1
241 **ACOL** (GB) 1
640 **ACORDINGTOSCRIPT** (IRE) 1
706 **ACORN CATCHER** (GB) G 1
682 **ACORN VALLEY** (USA) 26
481 **ACOSTA** (GB) 1
231 **ACRAI RUA** (IRE) 1
39 **ACRIVEEN** (IRE) 1
434 **ACROSS THE BAY** (IRE) 3
466 **ACROSS THE GALAXY** (GB) 32
252 **ACROSS THE STRAITS** (FR) 1
24 **ACROSS THE TWEED** (IRE) 2
304 **ACT OF ATTRITION** (GB) 78
486 **ACT OF KALANISI** (GB) 1
171 **ACT OF KINDNESS** (IRE) 1
366 **ACT OF THE PACE** (IRE) F 42
155 **ACT YOUR SHOE SIZE** (GB) 14
682 **ACTING TALENT** (USA) 77
588 **ACTION FRONT** (USA) 1

460 **ACTION IMPACT** (ARG) 1
343 **ACTION MASTER** (GB) 1
313 **ACTION STEEL** (IRE) 1
573 **ACTIVATE** (GB) 1
388 **ACTIVISTE** (IRE) 15
485 **ACTODOS** (IRE) 1
627 **ACUSHLADEAR** (IRE) 1
625 **AD VALUE** (IRE) 1
296 **AD VITAM** (GB) 1
529 **ADAEZE** (IRE) 1
310 **ADAM DE BEAULIEU** (USA) 1
326 **ADAMO** (GER) 1
340 **ADAMS WOOD** (IRE) 2
575 **ADARE PRINCE** (GB) 1
397 **ADDAZERO** (GB) 40
614 **ADDICTEDTOPROGRESS** (IRE) 32
593 **ADDICTION** (GB) 2
488 **ADDICTIVE DREAM** (IRE) 1
585 **ADDIKT** (IRE) 1
696 **ADDRESS UNKNOWN** (GB) 1
569 **ADECA** (IRE) 18
287 **ADELA** (IRE) 57
655 **ADELINDUS** (GB) 7
708 **ADELLE** (GB) 1
207 **ADILI** (IRE) 49
250 **ADIOS ALONSO** (IRE) 1
658 **ADITA** (GER) 1
29 **ADJUDICATE** (GB) 17
58 **ADMIRABLE ART** (IRE) 54
228 **ADMIRABLE DUCHESS** (GB) 1
228 **ADMIRABLE DUQUE** (IRE) 2
714 **ADMIRAL BLAKE** (GB) 1
322 **ADMIRAL BOOM** (IRE) 1
298 **ADMIRAL HAWKE** (IRE) 1
384 **ADMIRALS WALK** (IRE) 38
161 **ADORABLE CHOICE** (IRE) 1
619 **ADORATION** (USA) C 8
276 **ADRANIAN** (IRE) 10
98 **ADROPAUPEP** (IRE) 1
35 **ADVERSE** (IRE) 15
645 **ADVERTISE** (GB) 1
191 **AEGAEUS** (GB) 13
410 **AEGEAN DESTINY** (GB) 1
693 **AEGEAN KING** (IRE) 1
588 **AEGEAN MEMORIES** (GB) 2
107 **AENEID** (GB) 1
489 **AERIAL** (FR) 1
200 **AERODYNAMIC** (GB) 1
621 **AERONAUTICA** (IRE) 1
180 **AERONWYN BRYN** (IRE) 42
561 **AESCHYLUS** (GB) 1
219 **AESOP'S FABLES** (USA) 27
285 **AFAAL** (USA) 13
657 **AFFAIR CHEVAL** (IRE) 1
511 **AFFECTIONATE** (GB) 42
619 **AFFECTIONATELY** (GB) 9
172 **AFFILIATE** (GB) 2
74 **AFKAR** (IRE) 2

193 **AFNOON** (USA) 22
123 **AFRA TSITSI** (FR) C 53
654 **AFRAAH** (USA) 27
690 **AFRICAN BREEZE** (GB) F 13
525 **AFRICAN BROADWAY** (IRE) 1
391 **AFRICAN EAGLE** (IRE) 1
49 **AFRICAN STORY** (GB) 1
147 **AFSARE** (GB) 1
381 **AFSOUN** (FR) 2
149 **AGAPANTHUS** (GER) 1
434 **AGENT ARCHIE** (USA) 4
390 **AGENT KENSINGTON** (GB) F 19
564 **AGENT SECRET** (IRE) 1
145 **AGESILAS** (FR) 1
9 **AGGBAG** (GB) 1
293 **AGGIE'S LAD** (IRE) 1
516 **AGILETE** (GB) 1
335 **AGITATION** (GB) 1
592 **AGLAJA** (GB) 1
654 **AGLAOPHONOS** (GB) 86
682 **AGNETHA** (GB) F 78
695 **AGREE TO DIFFER** (IRE) 1
494 **AGRICULTURAL** (GB) 1
688 **AHHDEHKEN** (GB) 1
592 **AHLAWY** (IRE) 1
4 **AHTOUG** (GB) 1
74 **AHUQD** (IRE) 25
397 **AHWAAK** (USA) 1
49 **AHZEEMAH** (IRE) 69
628 **AIAAM AL NAMOOS** (GB) 4
628 **AIAAM AL WAFA** (IRE) 5
3 **AICHI** (AUS) 2
569 **AIDEN SEA** (IRE) 93
321 **AIGLE D'OR** (GB) 1
29 **AIGLONNE** (USA) C 68
123 **AIGUE MARINE** (GB) 15
180 **AIKATERINE** (GB) G 1
266 **AIKEN** (GB) 1
567 **AIKIDEAU** (FR) 1
218 **AIKMAN** (IRE) 1
329 **AILEEN'S GIFT** (IRE) C 23
666 **AILINCALA** (IRE) F 34
573 **AILSA** (GB) F 32
644 **AILSA CRAIG** (IRE) 1
553 **AIM** (GB) 1
203 **AIMEE'S DELIGHT** (GB) C 13
607 **AIMIGAYLE** (GB) 1
191 **AIMING** (GB) F 45
5 **AIN'T TALKIN'** (GB) 1
183 **AIR BLOND** (GB) 1
420 **AIR FORCE ONE** (GER) 1
111 **AIR TRAFFIC** (GB) 1
192 **AIRBORNE AGAIN** (IRE) 5
386 **AIRDRIE** (IRE) 1
218 **AIREY SCAREY** (GB) 2
420 **AIRMEN'S FRIEND** (IRE) 2
489 **AITEEN THIRTYTHREE** (IRE) 2
446 **AITMATOV** (GER) 1
111 **AJAAN** (GB) 2
49 **AJAWEED** (IRE) 70
433 **AJDAAD** (USA) 1
597 **AJEEB** (USA) 1
390 **AJEEBAH** (IRE) F 20
193 **AJEEL** (IRE) 1
532 **AJJAADD** (USA) 1
695 **AJMAN** (IRE) 2
147 **AJMAN BRIDGE** (GB) 70
147 **AJMANY** (IRE) 71

166 **AJOOL** (USA) 1
169 **AJZAL** (IRE) 2
480 **AKARANA** (IRE) 1
123 **AKARLINA** (IRE) 1
695 **AKARSHAN** (IRE) 3
388 **AKASTI** (IRE) 16
508 **AKEED MOFEED** (GB) 11
508 **AKEED WAFI** (IRE) 12
498 **AKIEM** (IRE) 2
508 **AKLAN** (IRE) 13
569 **AKOYAMA** (GB) 19
53 **AKSOUN** (IRE) 1
564 **AKTAR LOTOIS** (FR) 2
642 **AKULA** (IRE) 1
49 **AL AASIFH** (IRE) 2
331 **AL ALFA** (GB) 1
460 **AL AMAAN** (GB) 2
281 **AL AQABAH** (IRE) 1
654 **AL BAIDAA** (GB) 28
597 **AL BANDAR** (GB) 57
366 **AL BATTANI** (USA) 43
59 **AL CO** (FR) 1
628 **AL COBRA** (IRE) F 16
573 **AL DAIN** (IRE) 33
573 **AL DOHA** (GB) 34
597 **AL EMIRATI** (IRE) 58
501 **AL EURO** (FR) C 45
597 **AL FAYLASOOF** (USA) 21
489 **AL FEROF** (FR) 3
654 **AL FREEJ** (IRE) 29
26 **AL FURAT** (USA) 1
74 **AL HAWA** (USA) C 56
508 **AL HILALY** (GB) 57
285 **AL JABREIAH** (GB) 14
74 **AL KARLOVYYH** (IRE) 26
74 **AL KARTUZYYH** (IRE) 27
119 **AL KAZEEM** (GB) 1
117 **AL KHAN** (IRE) 6
597 **AL KHAWANEEJ** (GB) 2
299 **AL MAHMEYAH** (GB) 20
597 **AL MAMZAR** (IRE) 22
597 **AL MAYASAH** (IRE) 3
597 **AL MEEZAN** (GB) 59
285 **AL QATARI** (USA) 15
434 **AL QEDDAAF** (IRE) 5
49 **AL SAHAM** (GB) 71
58 **AL SAQIYA** (USA) C 55
637 **AL SHABABIYA** (IRE) 2
573 **AL SHAQAB** (IRE) 35
9 **AL SIRAT** (GB) 2
285 **AL WAJBA** (USA) 16
214 **AL'S MEMORY** (IRE) 36
201 **ALABANDA** (IRE) 65
191 **ALABAQ** (USA) F 46
371 **ALACCORDION** (GB) 1
475 **ALADDINS CAVE** (USA) 1
237 **ALAGHIRAAR** (IRE) 1
654 **ALAINMAAR** (FR) 1
29 **ALAMARIE** (FR) 18
682 **ALAMBIC** (GB) F 79
569 **ALAMOUNA** (IRE) C 94
657 **ALAND ISLANDS** (IRE) 2
508 **ALARANA** (IRE) 1
660 **ALARAZI** (IRE) 1
695 **ALARMING ALACRITY** (IRE) 4
508 **ALASHA** (IRE) F 58
681 **ALASI** (GB) 1
35 **ALASKAN BULLET** (IRE) 16

575 **ALASKAN PRINCE** (IRE) 2
695 **ALAYIR** (IRE) 5
606 **ALBA KING** (GB) 1
654 **ALBAHJA** (GB) F 87
534 **ALBAMARA** (GB) 1
619 **ALBANKA** (GB) 10
534 **ALBARAKA** (GB) 1
534 **ALBASPINA** (IRE) 11
219 **ALBEMARLE** (GB) 119
569 **ALBERT D'ANABAA** (IRE) 20
650 **ALBERT STROLLER** (GB) 2
503 **ALBERTAS RUN** (IRE) 3
699 **ALBERTUS PICTOR** (GB) 2
219 **ALBION** (GB) 28
534 **ALCAEUS** (GB) 40
40 **ALCALDE** (GB) 1
127 **ALCANDO** (IRE) 14
29 **ALCHIMIA** (FR) 1
34 **ALDBOROUGH** (IRE) 56
223 **ALDEDASH** (USA) 2
472 **ALDER MAIRI** (IRE) 1
434 **ALDERLEY ROVER** (IRE) 6
371 **ALDERLEY STAR** (IRE) 2
525 **ALDERLUCK** (IRE) 2
698 **ALDERMOOR** (USA) 1
489 **ALDERTUNE** (IRE) 4
304 **ALDERWAY** (IRE) 1
3 **ALDGATE** (USA) 46
397 **ALDO** (FR) 2
572 **ALDORA** (GB) C 24
299 **ALDWICK BAY** (IRE) 1
666 **ALECO** (GB) 17
111 **ALEGRA** (GB) 84
147 **ALEKSANDAR** (GB) 16
102 **ALENUSHKA** (GB) F 43
262 **ALESANDRO MANTEGNA** (IRE) 1
299 **ALESSIA** (GER) F 123
500 **ALEXANDER ALLIANCE** (IRE) C 11
147 **ALEXANDER CELEBRE** (IRE) F 72
27 **ALEXANDER COMPOSER** (IRE) C 42
573 **ALEXANDER GOLDMINE** (GB) C 78
261 **ALEXANDER OATS** (GB) 1
434 **ALEXANDER ROAD** (IRE) 7
408 **ALEXANDRA SIX** 42
318 **ALEXANDRE D'OR** (FR) 13
569 **ALEXANDROVA** (IRE) F 95
161 **ALEXIA REVEUSE** (IRE) C 41
606 **ALF THE AUDACIOUS** (IRE) 1
298 **ALFA BEAT** (IRE) 2
551 **ALFIE BROWN** (GB) 1
697 **ALFIE SPINNER** (IRE) 1
16 **ALFIE WILLS** (GB) 2
560 **ALFLORABUNDA** (GB) 1
527 **ALFLORAMOOR** (GB) 1
684 **ALFRAAMSEY** (GB) 1
506 **ALFRED HUTCHINSON** (GB) 1
473 **ALFRED JAMES** (GB) 1
261 **ALFRED OATS** (GB) 2
43 **ALFRESCO** (GB) 1
58 **ALGA REH** (USA) 56
306 **ALHABAN** (IRE) 1
144 **ALHUFOOF** (USA) F 5
380 **ALI BABA** (GB) 7
366 **ALIANTE** (GB) 44
467 **ALICE'S DANCER** (IRE) 13
468 **ALIMURE** (GB) 1

508 **ALINDJAR** (IRE) 14
212 **ALIS AQUILAE** (IRE) 1
355 **ALISDANZA** (GB) C 9
45 **ALIVE AND KICKING** (GB) 1
508 **ALIZARI** (IRE) 15
654 **ALJAMAAHEER** (IRE) 30
214 **ALJOSAN** (GB) 37
366 **ALKADI** (IRE) 45
219 **ALKANIA** (GB) 1
686 **ALKIFAF** (USA) C 19
49 **ALKIMOS** (IRE) 3
265 **ALL ABOUT TIMING** (IRE) 1
94 **ALL ABOUT YOU** (IRE) 1
660 **ALL ANNALENA** (IRE) 2
266 **ALL BLACK ROSE** (GB) 114
8 **ALL FOR A BUZZ** (GB) 1
16 **ALL FOR CASH** (GB) 3
246 **ALL FOR EVE** (GB) 1
374 **ALL FOR FREE** (IRE) 1
700 **ALL GOOD NEWS** (IRE) 27
534 **ALL MY HEART** (GB) 1
447 **ALL NIGHTER** (IRE) 11
660 **ALL OF A QUIVER** (GB) 27
370 **ALL ON JOHN** (GB) 1
543 **ALL OR NOTHIN** (IRE) 31
315 **ALL RIGHT NOW** (GB) 1
263 **ALL THAT REMAINS** (IRE) 1
111 **ALL THAT RULES** (GB) 24
321 **ALL THE ACES** (IRE) 2
371 **ALL THE FASHION** (IRE) 3
206 **ALL THE ROSES** (IRE) G 2
406 **ALL THE WINDS** (GER) 1
111 **ALL TIME** (GB) 3
111 **ALL TIME GREAT** (GB) F 85
12 **ALL WE KNOW** (GB) 2
55 **ALLA SPERANZA** (GB) 10
640 **ALLANARD** (IRE) 2
149 **ALLANIT** (GER) 1
681 **ALLARACKET** (IRE) G 2
472 **ALLDUNNANDUSTED** (IRE) 2
681 **ALLEANDOE** (GB) 3
473 **ALLEE GARDE** (FR) 3
529 **ALLEGRA BYRON** (GB) 24
619 **ALLEGRETTO** (GB) C 91
520 **ALLEGRO STAR** (IRE) 16
498 **ALLERTON** (IRE) 3
569 **ALLEZ HONGKONG** (GER) 21
111 **ALLFORMARY** (GB) 4
263 **ALLIED ANSWER** (GB) 1
223 **ALLIED CAUSE** (GB) F 45
35 **ALLIED POWERS** (IRE) 1
677 **ALLORA FLORA** (GB) 1
579 **ALLORO** (GB) 1
218 **ALLOW ME** (GB) 3
569 **ALLOWAY BLUE** (FR) 96
508 **ALLOWED** (GB) 16
460 **ALLTERRAIN** (IRE) 3
331 **ALLTHEKINGSHORSES** (IRE) 2
473 **ALLURE OF ILLUSION** (IRE) 4
200 **ALLURING STAR** (GB) 2
270 **ALLUSIVE POWER** (IRE) 1
564 **ALLY BLACK** (FR) 20
49 **ALMAAS** (USA) 72
614 **ALMAASEH** (IRE) C 33
474 **ALMADAN** (IRE) 1
266 **ALMAGEST** (GB) 2
507 **ALMAIL** (USA) 1
569 **ALMALYK** (FR) 97

49 **ALMANSOORA** (USA) C 116
19 **ALMARAI** (USA) F 107
111 **ALMASE** (USA) 25
447 **ALMATINKA** (IRE) F 55
686 **ALMATY EXPRESS** (GB) 1
362 **ALMIRAH** (GB) 19
654 **ALMOST GEMINI** (IRE) 31
546 **ALMOST HERE** (IRE) 1
654 **ALMOUTEZAH** (USA) F 88
368 **ALMOWJ** (GB) 1
191 **ALMUDER** (GB) 14
191 **ALMUFTARRIS** (GB) 15
456 **ALMUTAHAM** (USA) 1
107 **ALNAIR** (IRE) 20
408 **ALOARA** (FR) 43
654 **ALOHA** (GB) 89
145 **ALONG CAME ROSIE** (GB) 2
552 **ALORA MONEY** (GB) 1
384 **ALOYSIA** (GB) 9
339 **ALPANCHO** (GB) 1
542 **ALPATHAR** (IRE) C 2
364 **ALPENROT** (GB) F 17
247 **ALPHA DELTA WHISKY** (GB) 1
396 **ALPHA JULIET** (IRE) 1
268 **ALPHA ONE** (IRE) 1
283 **ALPHA TAURI** (USA) 1
639 **ALPHABETICAL ORDER** (GB) 2
104 **ALPINE BREEZE** (IRE) 1
304 **ALPINE EAGLE** (IRE) 2
193 **ALPINE MYSTERIES** (IRE) 44
55 **ALPINIST** (GB) 67
283 **ALQAAHIR** (USA) 1
193 **ALRAASED** (USA) 23
447 **ALSAABEQA** (USA) C 56
296 **ALSAHIL** (USA) 1
193 **ALSHADIYAH** (USA) F 45
682 **ALSHAKR** (GB) F 80
643 **ALSHAMATRY** (USA) F 50
451 **ALSHAZAH** (GB) 1
266 **ALSHMEMI** (USA) 32
8 **ALSO JO** (GB) 2
29 **ALSU** C 69
359 **ALTAN KHAN** (GB) 2
520 **ALTARIA** (GB) 17
567 **ALTERANTHELA** (IRE) 2
76 **ALTERNATOR** (IRE) 1
198 **ALTESSE DE SOU** (FR) G 1
359 **ALTOGETHER NOW** (IRE) G 3
219 **ALUMNA** (USA) 120
191 **ALUSHTA** (GB) 16
200 **ALUSTAR** (GB) F 67
287 **ALVAR** (USA) 1
695 **ALVARADO** (IRE) 6
119 **ALVERNIA** (USA) F 58
119 **ALVITUDE** (USA) 15
150 **ALWAARY** (USA) 1
643 **ALWAFFAA** (USA) 22
654 **ALWARGA** (USA) 32
415 **ALWAYS A WAY** (GB) 1
358 **ALWAYS ATTRACTIVE** (IRE) C 27
508 **ALWAYS AWESOME** (USA) F 59
178 **ALWAYS BEST** (GB) 1
374 **ALWAYS BOLD** (IRE) 2
126 **ALWAYS BE ONE** (GB) 1
145 **ALWAYS DIXIE** (IRE) 3
366 **ALWAYS EAGER** (GB) 46
366 **ALWAYS ENDS WELL** (IRE) 47
450 **ALWAYS GUNNER** (GB) 1

659 **ALWAYS RIGHT** (IRE) 1
328 **ALWAYS SATISFIED** (GB) 73
141 **ALWAYS THE LADY** (GB) 1
59 **ALWAYS WAINING** (IRE) 2
250 **ALWAYS WILLING** (IRE) 2
534 **ALWILDA** (GB) 41
654 **ALZAHRA** (GB) 33
191 **ALZAROOF** (USA) F 47
534 **ALZAVOLA** (GB) 42
219 **ALZUBRA** (GB) 121
633 **AM I BLUE** (GB) 1
157 **AMA JIMA** (GB) 1
681 **AMAAL** (USA) 4
180 **AMADEUS DENTON** (IRE) 25
507 **AMADEUS WOLFE TONE** (IRE) 13
200 **AMALFI STORM** (GB) C 68
74 **AMALIE** (IRE) F 57
474 **AMALRIC** (FR) 1
73 **AMANA** (USA) 1
259 **AMANDA WOLF** (IRE) 40
111 **AMARAJA** (GER) 26
73 **AMARELLA** (FR) G 2
507 **AMARICE** (GB) C 29
403 **AMARONI** (GB) 1
388 **AMARYSIA** (FR) 59
460 **AMAURY DE LUSIGNAN** (IRE) 4
27 **AMAZING AMORAY** (IRE) 1
320 **AMAZING DREAM** (IRE) C 13
460 **AMAZING DREAM** (IRE) G 100
383 **AMAZING KING** (IRE) 2
107 **AMAZING STAR** (IRE) 2
299 **AMAZING STORM** (IRE) 21
59 **AMAZING VALOUR** (IRE) 3
69 **AMAZINGREYCE** (GB) 1
161 **AMAZON BEAUTY** (IRE) C 42
363 **AMAZON TWILIGHT** (GB) 1
191 **AMAZONAS** (IRE) 48
666 **AMBALA** (GB) 1
503 **AMBER CLOUD** (GB) 4
524 **AMBER HEIGHTS** (GB) 1
651 **AMBER MILL** (GB) F 8
682 **AMBER ROMANCE** (IRE) 81
328 **AMBER SILK** (IRE) 15
67 **AMBER SPYGLASS** (GB) 9
141 **AMBER'S BLUFF** (GB) C 60
160 **AMBION WOOD** (IRE) 2
336 **AMBITIOUS BOY** (GB) 25
283 **AMBITIOUS ICARUS** (GB) 69
654 **AMBIVALENT** (IRE) 34
651 **AMBRIA** (ITY) F 9
585 **AMBROSE PRINCESS** (IRE) 2
654 **AMEERAT** (GB) F 90
111 **AMELIORATE** (IRE) 86
488 **AMENABLE** (IRE) 2
192 **AMERICA NOVA** (FR) C 19
569 **AMERICAN BEAUTY** (IRE) 22
460 **AMERICAN BLING** (USA) 101
438 **AMERICAN BLING** (USA) 4
695 **AMERICAN CRICKET** (IRE) 7
610 **AMERICAN LADIE** (GB) 1
658 **AMERICAN LIFE** (IRE) 2
662 **AMERICAN LOVER** (IRE) 1
154 **AMERICAN SPIN** (GB) 1
489 **AMERICAN TRILOGY** (IRE) 5
329 **AMETHYST** (IRE) F 24
550 **AMETHYST DAWN** (IRE) 1
55 **AMHRASACH** (IRE) 11
219 **AMIENS** (GB) 29

499 **AMIENS STREET** (IRE) 44
340 **AMIGAN LADY** (IRE) 3
296 **AMIR PASHA** (UAE) 3
108 **AMIRAH** (IRE) 58
567 **AMIRICO** (IRE) 3
109 **AMIS REUNIS** (GB) 9
364 **AMISTRESS** (GB) 1
27 **AMITOLA** (IRE) 2
685 **AMJAD** (GB) 1
586 **AMNO DANCER** (IRE) 1
657 **AMOK** (IRE) 3
288 **AMOR PATRICE** (GB) 1
191 **AMORALIST** (GB) 17
647 **AMORAS** (IRE) C 23
195 **AMORELIMONCELLO** (IRE) 1
360 **AMOSITE** (GB) 2
408 **AMOUR DU PUY NOIR** 44
102 **AMOUR PROPRE** (GB) 1
542 **AMOURE MEDICI** (GB) 14
19 **AMPHORA** (GB) 35
366 **AMPLEFORTH** (GB) 1
434 **AMRON LAD** (IRE) 8
101 **AMROTH BAY** (GB) 1
569 **AMSHAD** (FR) 23
74 **AMTHAL** (GB) 28
207 **AMTIRED** (GB) 2
4 **AMULREE** (GB) 1
700 **AMWELL STAR** (USA) C 33
711 **AMY THORPE** (GB) 1
434 **AN CAPALL MOR** (IRE) 9
55 **AN GHALANTA** (IRE) 12
55 **AN SAINCHEANN** (IRE) 13
274 **ANA BUACHAILL DANA** (GB) 1
511 **ANA NOVA** (FR) 43
654 **ANAAMIL** (FR) F 91
252 **ANABAA'S DANCE** (IRE) 2
74 **ANABEDWEYAH** (IRE) 29
359 **ANABRANCH** (IRE) F 36
161 **ANACONDA** (FR) 16
207 **ANAGANA KANDA** (USA) 3
12 **ANASTASIA VENTURE** (GB) F 24
336 **ANATHENA** (GB) 1
3 **ANATOLIAN** (GB) 3
312 **ANAY TURGE** (FR) 1
564 **ANBELLA** (FR) C 84
460 **ANCESTRAL DREAM** (GB) 5
200 **ANCIENT CROSS** (GB) 3
18 **ANCIENT GREECE** (GB) 1
657 **AND HE'S DREAMING** (IRE) 4
556 **AND THE MAN** (GB) 2
597 **ANDALIEB** (GB) 23
501 **ANDERIEGO** (IRE) 1
658 **ANDEX** (IRE) 3
263 **ANDHAAR** (GB) 3
604 **ANDIAMO VIA** (GB) 1
38 **ANDRASTA** (GB) 1
298 **ANDREA BELLEVICA** (IRE) 37
207 **ANDREO BAMBALEO** (GB) 4
326 **ANDREW NICK** (IRE) 2
569 **ANDUCAS** (FR) 24
82 **ANDY VIC** (IRE) 1
601 **ANGARIC** (FR) 1
446 **ANGE BLANC** (FR) 2
682 **ANGE BRIGHT** (IRE) 27
437 **ANGEL CAKE** (IRE) 10
696 **ANGEL GABRIAL** (IRE) 60
601 **ANGEL GRIGIO** (GB) 57
219 **ANGEL OAK** (GB) 122

225 **ANGEL OF MERCY** (GB) 1
476 **ANGEL SUN** (FR) 2
310 **ANGEL WARRIOR** (IRE) 11
447 **ANGELIC NOTE** (IRE) 12
19 **ANGELIC UPSTART** (IRE) 1
188 **ANGELO POLIZIANO** (GB) 1
328 **ANGELS WILL FALL** (IRE) 16
116 **ANGELS WILL FLY** (IRE) 14
573 **ANGILINA** (GB) 79
645 **ANGINOLA** (IRE) 10
214 **ANGINOLA** (IRE) 38
39 **ANGLES HILL** (IRE) 2
543 **ANGRY BARK** (USA) C 44
285 **ANISEED** (IRE) 17
519 **ANITOPIA** (GB) 2
49 **ANJAZ** (USA) 73
182 **ANJOMARBA** (IRE) 2
49 **ANNA PALARIVA** (IRE) C 117
654 **ANNA PALLIDA** (GB) C 92
564 **ANNA PAVLOVA** (GB) C 85
625 **ANNA'S ARCH** (IRE) 2
34 **ANNA'S PEARL** (GB) 57
249 **ANNA'S STORM** (GB) 25
56 **ANNABEL LEE** (FR) 32
357 **ANNAHALA** (IRE) G 1
408 **ANNAKOV** (GB) 45
658 **ANNAKRISTA** (GER) 4
214 **ANNALUNA** (IRE) 39
102 **ANNAWI** (GB) 44
53 **ANNELKO** (GB) 2
243 **ANNES ROCKET** (IRE) 1
460 **ANNESBROOK** (IRE) 6
617 **ANNIE ANSHAN** (IRE) 1
27 **ANNIE BEACH** (IRE) 31
484 **ANNIE CONFIDENTIAL** (IRE) 1
201 **ANNIE GOGH** (IRE) 103
601 **ANNIE HARVEY** (GB) C 58
488 **ANNIE WALKER** (IRE) 45
357 **ANNIE'S FORTUNE** (IRE) 22
461 **ANNIE'S PRIDE** (GB) 1
57 **ANNIESUELLA** (IRE) 18
472 **ANNIMATION** (IRE) 3
635 **ANNS BENEFIT** (IRE) 1
3 **ANOMALY** (GB) 47
461 **ANOTHER ALFIE** (GB) 2
201 **ANOTHER CITIZEN** (IRE) 1
466 **ANOTHER COCKTAIL** (GB) 62
178 **ANOTHER DIMENSION** (IRE) 4
458 **ANOTHER DUCHESS** (GB) 24
554 **ANOTHER KATE** (IRE) 1
344 **ANOTHER MANS CAUSE** (FR) G 1
434 **ANOTHER MIRACLE** (GB) 10
598 **ANOTHER MYSTERY** (GB) 1
446 **ANOTHER PALM** (IRE) 3
201 **ANOTHER SUNSET** (GB) 2
357 **ANOTHER TRY** (IRE) 2
450 **ANOTHER WISE KID** (IRE) 2
643 **ANQOODA** (USA) 23
321 **ANQUETTA** (IRE) 3
80 **ANRHEG** (GB) 1
407 **ANSWER DO** (GB) C 36
200 **ANSWERED PRAYER** (GB) F 69
384 **ANTHEA** (GB) C 39
276 **ANTIGONI** (IRE) C 14
220 **ANTIGUA SUNRISE** (IRE) 3
634 **ANTIHERO** (GB) 1
383 **ANTOELLA** (IRE) 3
161 **ANTON CHIGURH** (GB) 17

193 **ANTON DOLIN** (IRE) 2
658 **ANTONELLO** (IRE) 40
620 **ANTONIUS** (GB) 11
374 **ANY CURRENCY** (IRE) 3
434 **ANY GIVEN DAY** (IRE) 11
597 **ANY GIVEN DREAM** (IRE) 24
636 **ANY GIVEN MOMENT** (IRE) 1
387 **ANY OTHER DAY** (IRE) 13
663 **ANY THE WISER** (GB) 1
622 **ANYAULDIRON** (IRE) 1
625 **ANYCHANCEDAVE** (IRE) 3
220 **ANYTHING** (IRE) 41
659 **APACHE BLUE** (IRE) 2
334 **APACHE BRAVE** (IRE) 1
574 **APACHE DAWN** (GB) 1
615 **APACHE GLORY** (USA) 1
343 **APACHE JACK** (IRE) 2
446 **APACHE STRONGHOLD** (IRE) 4
501 **APACHE WARRIOR** (GB) 2
601 **APASSIONFORFASHION** (GB) 2
455 **APATURA DIK** (GB) 1
585 **APERITIF** (GB) 3
299 **APHORISM** (GB) C 124
29 **APHRODITE** (FR) 70
658 **API SA** (FR) F 56
658 **APISATA** (GER) 1
141 **APOLLO D'NEGRO** (IRE) 2
569 **APOLLO ELEVEN** (IRE) 25
35 **APOSTLE** (IRE) 17
266 **APOTHECARY** (GB) 33
534 **APPEAL** (IRE) 3
58 **APPEALING** (IRE) 20
352 **APPEASE** (GB) 18
336 **APPELONE** (GB) G 26
673 **APPLAUDE** (GB) 1
507 **APPLAUDERE** (GB) 14
110 **APPLAUSE FOR AMY** (IRE) 1
315 **APPLE BLOSSOM TIME** (IRE) 2
647 **APPLE SAUCE** (GB) F 24
681 **APPLEADAY** (IRE) 5
488 **APPLEBLOSSOM PEARL** (IRE) G 46
180 **APPLEBLOSSOM PEARL** (IRE) G 43
619 **APPROACH** (GB) C 92
237 **APPROVED QUALITY** (IRE) F 46
45 **APRESLEPETITBOIS** (GB) 2
102 **APRICOT SKY** 45
306 **APRIL FOOL** (GB) 2
73 **APRIL LEYF** (IRE) 25
473 **APT APPROACH** (IRE) 5
18 **AQUA ARDENS** (GER) 2
223 **AQUA JETER** (IRE) 20
366 **AQUA LAD** (GB) 2
682 **AQUA REGIA** (GB) 28
266 **AQUANAUT** (GB) 34
220 **AQUARIAN SPIRIT** (GB) 4
214 **AQUASULIS** (IRE) 40
259 **AQUILA CARINA** (GB) 41
91 **AQUILIFER** (IRE) 1
111 **AQUILLA** (IRE) 27
55 **AQUILONIUS** (IRE) 14
525 **ARAB LEAGUE** (IRE) 3
619 **ARAB SPRING** (GB) 93
266 **ARABESQUE** (GB) F 115
643 **ARABEYA** (USA) 24
71 **ARABIAN FLIGHT** (GB) 17
380 **ARABIAN HEIGHTS** (GB) 2
299 **ARABIAN PENINSULA** (USA) C 125
109 **ARABIAN RANCHES** (GB) 10

390 **ARABIAN SPELL** (IRE) F 21
220 **ARABIAN SPIRIT** (GB) 5
19 **ARABIAN STAR** (IRE) 1
534 **ARABIAN STORM** (IRE) 43
223 **ARABIC** (GB) 21
380 **ARALDUR** (FR) 3
296 **ARAMINTE** (GB) 4
285 **ARAQELLA** (GB) 72
434 **ARAUCARIA** (IRE) 12
123 **ARBALETTE** C 54
279 **ARBEO** (IRE) 1
219 **ARC LIGHTER** (USA) 30
513 **ARC WARRIOR** (FR) 1
366 **ARCH OF COLOURS** (IRE) 48
520 **ARCH VILLAIN** (IRE) 18
686 **ARCH WALKER** (IRE) 2
447 **ARCHBISHOP** (USA) 13
643 **ARCHELAO** (IRE) 1
372 **ARCHIE RICE** (USA) 1
296 **ARCHIE'S WISH** (GB) 5
19 **ARCHINA** (IRE) 36
321 **ARCTIC ACTRESS** (GB) 4
299 **ARCTIC ADMIRAL** (IRE) 126
157 **ARCTIC BEN** (IRE) 2
266 **ARCTIC COSMOS** (USA) 3
260 **ARCTIC COURT** (IRE) 1
373 **ARCTIC FLOW** (GB) 1
172 **ARCTIC GUNNER** (GB) 3
43 **ARCTIC LYNX** (IRE) 2
54 **ARCTIC MIRAGE** (GB) 1
531 **ARCTIC REACH** (GB) 2
43 **ARCTIC STRYKER** (GB) 15
103 **ARCTIC WATCH** (GB) 1
108 **ARCTIC WINGS** (GB) 1
422 **ARDBRAE LADY** (GB) C 28
531 **ARDENT GREEN GRAPE** (GB) 3
493 **ARDENT NUMBER** (GB) 1
405 **ARDERIN** (GB) 1
353 **ARDESIA** (IRE) 1
511 **ARDHA** (GB) 1
654 **ARDINGLY** (IRE) 93
380 **ARDLUI** (IRE) 4
573 **ARDMAY** (IRE) 36
105 **ARDNACLANCY** (IRE) 1
473 **ARE YA RIGHT CHIEF** (IRE) 6
318 **ARENGO** (IRE) 14
629 **ARES VALLIS** (IRE) F 19
404 **AREUWITMENOW** (IRE) 2
597 **AREYAAM** (USA) F 60
225 **ARGANTE CLAUDIUS** (IRE) 19
695 **ARGAUM** (IRE) 8
358 **ARGENT KNIGHT** (GB) 28
586 **ARGENTINE** (IRE) 2
270 **ARGENTINIAN TANGO** (IRE) 1
219 **ARIBAA** (GB) 31
366 **ARIOSO** (GB) 49
456 **ARISEA** (IRE) 2
542 **ARIYFA** (IRE) 3
145 **ARIZONA HIGH** (GB) 4
410 **ARIZONA JOHN** (IRE) 2
461 **ARIZONA RIVER** (GB) 3
599 **ARKAIM** (GB) 1
219 **ARKANSAS** (GB) 123
29 **ARLY** (FR) 71
93 **ARMAGNAC REBEL** (GB) 1
274 **ARMEDANDDANGEROUS** (IRE) 2
467 **ARMIGER** (GB) 14
58 **ARMOISE** (GB) 1

98 **ARNAUD** (IRE) 2
388 **ARNOLFINI** (IRE) 60
329 **AROSA** (IRE) C 25
379 **AROUND A POUND** (IRE) 1
166 **AROWANA** (IRE) 2
658 **ARQUES** (GER) 42
570 **ARRAN LAW** (IRE) 1
525 **ARRAYAN** (GB) 4
519 **ARRIVA LA DIVA** (GB) 3
283 **ARRIVADERCI** (GB) 3
619 **ARRIVE** (GB) C 94
659 **ARROW BARROW** (IRE) 3
542 **ARROW LAKE** (FR) 15
528 **ARROWMINT** (GB) 1
299 **ARROWSMITH** (GB) 127
488 **ARRY'S ORSE** (GB) 2
285 **ARSAADI** (IRE) 18
157 **ART BROKER** (IRE) 3
29 **ART COMTEMPORAIN** (USA) 72
201 **ART DZEKO** (GB) 66
366 **ART EYES** (USA) F 152
227 **ART HISTORY** (GB) 2
460 **ART NEWS** (IRE) 102
679 **ART OF GOLD** (IRE) 3
699 **ART PROFESSOR** (IRE) 3
183 **ART ROCK** (FR) 33
9 **ART SCHOLAR** (IRE) 3
434 **ART SCHOOL** (IRE) 13
9 **ART THIEF** (GB) 4
208 **ARTE DEL CALCIO** (GB) 11
116 **ARTEUS** (GB) 1
422 **ARTFUL LADY** (IRE) 19
254 **ARTHUR'S PASS** (GB) 1
331 **ARTHURIAN LEGEND** (GB) 3
51 **ARTIC JOURNEY** (IRE) 1
556 **ARTIC NIGHT** (FR) 3
157 **ARTICULATE** (IRE) 4
207 **ARTISAN** (GB) 5
318 **ARTISTE BERE** (FR) 43
442 **ARTISTIC JEWEL** (IRE) 12
569 **ARTISTIQUE** (IRE) C 98
99 **ARTLANA** (GB) 18
358 **ARTORIUS CASTUS** (GB) 29
332 **ARTY FARMER** (GB) 2
328 **ARUM LILY** (USA) F 74
585 **ARUMUN** (GB) 4
654 **ARYAAMM** (IRE) C 94
339 **AS DE FER** (FR) 2
104 **AS I AM** (IRE) 2
388 **ASAGAYA** (FR) 17
227 **ASAGAO** (GB) 2
49 **ASATIR** (USA) 74
203 **ASCALON** (GB) 1
436 **ASFURAH'S DREAM** (IRE) C 24
569 **ASHARNA** (IRE) C 99
86 **ASHBOURNE FOLLY** (IRE) 1
525 **ASHBRITTLE** (GB) 5
469 **ASHCOTT BOY** (GB) 1
358 **ASHDOWN LAD** (GB) 12
657 **ASHES HOUSE** (IRE) 5
695 **ASHFIELD'S DREAM** (GB) 9
341 **ASHKALARA** (GB) 1
525 **ASHKAZAR** (FR) 6
569 **ASHKIYR** (IRE) 26
442 **ASHOVER AMBER** (GB) F 19
612 **ASHPAN SAM** (GB) 12
663 **ASHTOWN BOY** (IRE) 2

180 **ASHVA** (USA) 2
360 **ASHWELL ROSE** (GB) C 48
147 **ASHYANE** (IRE) 17
285 **ASIAN TRADER** (GB) 19
49 **ASIFA** (IRE) 75
628 **ASK CAROL** (IRE) F 17
299 **ASK DAD** (GB) 128
62 **ASK THE THATCHER** (IRE) 1
439 **ASKALOTT** (IRE) 1
643 **ASKAR TAU** (FR) 2
176 **ASKAUD** (IRE) 2
643 **ASKER** (IRE) 3
424 **ASKMEROE** (IRE) 1
658 **ASPANTAU** (IRE) 5
713 **ASPARELLA** (GB) 12
219 **ASSAGIE** (IRE) 32
123 **ASSAULT ROYAL** 16
422 **ASSERTIVE DANCER** (USA) C 20
366 **ASSIZES** (GB) 50
614 **ASTER CASS** (IRE) 34
480 **ASTERALES** (GB) 2
40 **ASTERISK** (GB) 2
55 **ASTEROID BELT** (IRE) 15
474 **ASTON CANTLOW** (GB) 2
336 **ASTONISHED HARRY** (GER) 27
619 **ASTONISHING** (IRE) 95
619 **ASTORG** (USA) F 96
34 **ASTRA HALL** (IRE) 17
650 **ASTRACAD** (FR) 3
19 **ASTRAGAL** (GB) 3
642 **ASTRODREAMS** (GB) 40
642 **ASTROGOLD** (GB) 24
642 **ASTROLEO** (GB) 2
642 **ASTROLIBRA** (GB) 3
642 **ASTROMAGICK** (GB) 4
235 **ASTRONOMICAL** (IRE) 1
266 **ASTRONOMY DOMINE** (GB) 35
442 **ASTROPHYSICAL JET** (GB) 1
642 **ASTROSAPPHIRE** (GB) 41
642 **ASTROSCARLET** (GB) 25
451 **ASTRUM** (GB) 44
219 **ASULAYANA** (GB) 2
543 **ASUNCION** (USA) F 45
564 **ASYL** (IRE) 21
424 **ASYMMETRICAL** (IRE) 2
506 **AT AMAL** (IRE) G 22
328 **AT THE LIMIT** (GB) 17
694 **AT YOUR PERIL** (GB) 1
522 **ATA BOY** (IRE) 1
614 **ATACX** (IRE) 11
643 **ATALANTA BAY** (IRE) 51
658 **ATALEI** (GER) 43
654 **ATAMANA** (IRE) C 95
388 **ATARFE** (IRE) 18
306 **ATHAAKEEL** (IRE) 3
534 **ATHENIAN** (IRE) 12
283 **ATHENIAN GARDEN** (USA) 4
174 **ATHERSTONE HILL** (IRE) 1
550 **ATHLETIC** (GB) 1
407 **ATHLUMNEY LADY** (GB) F 37
49 **ATHREYAA** (GB) C 118
114 **ATHWAAB** (GB) 1
64 **ATLANTIC BEACH** (GB) 1
64 **ATLANTIC CYCLE** (IRE) 2
219 **ATLANTIC HIGH** (GB) C 124
654 **ATLANTIC LIGHT** (GB) F 96
489 **ATLANTIC ROLLER** (IRE) 6
200 **ATLANTIC STORY** (USA) 4

61 **ATLANTIS CROSSING** (IRE) 19
74 **ATMANNA** (GB) 30
29 **ATOMIC WAVES** (GB) 19
699 **ATOUCHBETWEENACARA** (IRE) 4
355 **ATTACK MINDED** (GB) 1
359 **ATTAGLANCE** (GB) 4
225 **ATTAIN** (GB) 20
201 **ATTANAGH** (IRE) C 104
496 **ATTENBOROUGH** (USA) 12
161 **ATTENSHUN** (IRE) 43
328 **ATTILIA** (GER) F 75
414 **ATTLONGGLAST** (GB) C 12
597 **ATTRACTION TICKET** (GB) 25
654 **ATTWAAL** (IRE) 35
24 **ATTYCRAN** (IRE) 3
579 **AUBERGE** (IRE) 2
564 **AUBREE** (FR) 86
655 **AUBRIETIA** (GB) 8
79 **AUBURN LADY** (GB) 1
191 **AUCTION** (IRE) 49
544 **AUDACIOUS** (GB) 1
658 **AUENDANCER** (GER) 6
120 **AUGHCARRA** (IRE) 1
657 **AUGUSTUS GIBBONS** (IRE) 6
619 **AUGUSTUS SNODGRASS** (IRE) 11
619 **AULD ALLIANCE** (IRE) 97
510 **AUNT GER** (IRE) 5
111 **AUNT JULIA** (GB) C 87
200 **AUNTIE JOY** (GB) 51
677 **AUNTIE KATHLEEN** (GB) G 4
698 **AUNTIE KATHRYN** (IRE) 12
19 **AUNTIE MABEL** (GB) 37
473 **AUPCHARLIE** (IRE) 7
239 **AUREATE** (GB) 1
651 **AURELIA** (GB) F 10
600 **AURELIO AURELI** (FR) 16
281 **AURENS** (IRE) 3
12 **AURENS** (IRE) 25
336 **AUREOLIN GULF** (GB) 28
55 **AURIFODINA** (IRE) 16
136 **AURORA SKY** (IRE) 1
606 **AURORAS ENCORE** (IRE) 3
318 **AURORE BERE** (FR) 44
511 **AUSONE** (FR) 44
527 **AUSSIE BLUE** (IRE) 2
221 **AUSSIE BOUND** (IRE) 9
387 **AUSSIE REIGNS** (GB) 33
328 **AUSTRALIA FAIR** (GB) 18
520 **AUTARCH** (USA) 19
640 **AUTHENTIC ACT** (IRE) 3
347 **AUTHENTIC CREATURE** (IRE) G 1
452 **AUTHENTIC SWING** (IRE) 10
366 **AUTHENTICATION** (GB) 51
458 **AUTHINGER** (IRE) 1
917 **AUTO MAC** (IRE) 1
225 **AUTOMOTIVE** (GB) 2
183 **AUTORITAIRE** (FR) 34
58 **AUTSPREAD** (GB) 57
174 **AUTUMN SPIRIT** (GB) 2
19 **AUTUMN FIRE** (GB) 38
159 **AUTUMN HAZE** (GB) 1
214 **AUTUMN STAR** (IRE) C 67
447 **AUTUMNAL** (IRE) G 14
3 **AUTUMNUS** (IRE) 48
61 **AVAILABLE** (IRE) 20
147 **AVALANCHE** (GB) 18
203 **AVALON BAY** (GB) 2

388 **AVANTE** (GB) 19
194 **AVEC MOI** (GB) 1
434 **AVENGING ACE** (IRE) 14
397 **AVERTIS** (GB) 3
601 **AVERTUOSO** (GB) 3
493 **AVESA** (GB) F 2
49 **AVIACION** (BRZ) C 119
660 **AVIADOR** (GER) 3
56 **AVIATOR** (FR) 18
619 **AVIETTA** (GB) 98
214 **AVISO** (GB) 1
220 **AVISON** (IRE) 6
206 **AVOCA PROMISE** (IRE) 3
564 **AVODALE** (IRE) 22
682 **AVOIDANCE** (USA) F 82
64 **AVON LIGHT** (GB) 3
352 **AVON RIVER** (GB) 1
376 **AVON SUPREME** (GB) 1
75 **AVONCHARM** (GB) 1
32 **AVONCREEK** (GB) 1
32 **AVONLINI** (GB) 2
299 **AVONMORE STAR** (GB) 2
588 **AVONROSE** (GB) 3
272 **AVONVALLEY** (GB) 1
104 **AVRUMI** (GB) 3
578 **AWAIT** (IRE) F 4
147 **AWAKE MY SOUL** (IRE) 19
531 **AWARD WINNER** (GB) 3
33 **AWAREINESS** (IRE) 1
237 **AWAYWITHEFAIRIES** (GB) 36
380 **AWESOME BELLA** (GB) 5
534 **AWESOME PEARL** (USA) 13
44 **AWESOME ROCK** (GB) 2
340 **AWKWARD MOMENT** (IRE) 4
131 **AWMAN** (GB) 1
665 **AXIOM** (GB) 1
388 **AXIONIKI** (IRE) 3
388 **AXIOPI** (FR) 20
276 **AY TAY TATE** (GB) 1
288 **AYAARAH** (IRE) 2
601 **AYASHA** (GB) 59
113 **AYE AYE DIGBY** (IRE) 1
131 **AYE WELL** (GB) 2
111 **AYSHEA** (GB) 2
193 **AYUN** (USA) F 46
318 **AZADE** (IRE) 1
588 **AZAMARA STAR** (GB) 29
508 **AZANARA** (IRE) 17
418 **AZARIA** (FR) 1
596 **AZEBRA** (GB) 1
299 **AZELLE** (GB) 129
657 **AZELMA** (GB) 7
58 **AZERODEGREE** (IRE) 21
564 **AZEVILLE** 23
583 **AZIONE** (GB) 1
508 **AZMIYNA** (IRE) 60
557 **AZULADA BAY** (IRE) 1
377 **AZYGOUS** (GB) 2
310 **AZZURRA DU CAPRIO** (IRE) 2
510 **B BARDOT** (FR) 13
329 **B FIFTY TWO** (IRE) 4
260 **BAAHER** (USA) 2
213 **BAAN** (USA) 2
49 **BAB AL SALAM** (USA) 4
353 **BABBLON BROOKE** (IRE) 2
168 **BABE HEFFRON** (IRE) 1
344 **BABICH BAY** (IRE) 2
700 **BABUSHKA'S GIRL** (GB) 28

521 **BABY DOTTIE** (GB) 1
485 **BABY DRIVER** (GB) 2
97 **BABY MAC** (GB) 2
254 **BABY MIX** (FR) 2
660 **BABY SHINE** (IRE) 4
588 **BABY STRANGE** (GB) 4
343 **BABY'S HOT** (IRE) 3
503 **BABYSITTER** (IRE) 5
220 **BACCARAT** (IRE) 42
296 **BACH PEDDLING** (IRE) 6
596 **BACH STREET GIRL** (IRE) 2
667 **BACH TO FRONT** (IRE) 1
244 **BACHELOR KNIGHT** (IRE) 1
597 **BACINELLA** (USA) C 61
254 **BACK BOB BACK** (IRE) 3
304 **BACK BURNER** (IRE) 3
39 **BACK IN A FLASH** (IRE) 3
473 **BACK IN FOCUS** (IRE) 8
458 **BACK OFF MATE** (IRE) 3
458 **BACK ON THE ROAD** (IRE) 3
472 **BACK TO MY PLACE** (IRE) 4
304 **BACKBENCH BLUES** (IRE) 79
35 **BACKCOURT** (USA) 18
394 **BACKFROMTHECONGO** (IRE) 1
394 **BACKSTREET BILLY** (IRE) 2
19 **BACKTRADE** (IRE) 39
14 **BADDI HEIGHTS** (FR) C 20
390 **BADEE'A** (IRE) F 22
508 **BADGED** (GB) 18
570 **BADGER FOOT** (IRE) 3
174 **BADGERS COVE** (IRE) 3
476 **BADGERS RETREAT** (IRE) 3
343 **BAFFIN ISLAND** (IRE) 4
496 **BAFFLED** (USA) F 49
304 **BAFFLES BRAINS** (IRE) 80
473 **BAGBER** (GB) 9
498 **BAGSY'S BRIDGE** (IRE) 4
336 **BAHAMIAN LAD** (GB) 2
283 **BAHARAT** (IRE) 5
654 **BAHEEJA** (GB) 36
74 **BAHIANO** (IRE) 3
266 **BAHJA** (USA) C 116
657 **BAHR NOTHING** (IRE) 8
495 **BAHRI BEAT** (IRE) 1
43 **BAHRI SHEEN** (IRE) 3
321 **BAI ZHU** (IRE) 5
212 **BAILADEIRA** (GB) 1
696 **BAILE ANRAI** (IRE) 2
107 **BAILE ATHA CLIATH** (IRE) 21
136 **BAILEYS AGINCOURT** (GB) 2
259 **BAILEYS BIGISHU** (GB) 15
699 **BAILEYS CONCERTO** (IRE) 5
366 **BAILEYS DUTCH** (GB) 52
259 **BAILEYS OVER ICE** (GB) 16
366 **BAILEYS STRIDER** (GB) 53
465 **BAILY BEAU** (GB) 1
465 **BAILY DUSK** (GB) 2
465 **BAILY GREEN** (IRE) 3
465 **BAILY ROCK** (IRE) 4
326 **BAILY STORM** (IRE) 3
573 **BAIN'S PASS** (IRE) 80
54 **BAJAN BEAR** (GB) 2
194 **BAJAN BELLE** (IRE) G 18
214 **BAJAN HERO** (IRE) 41
54 **BAJAN ROSE** (GB) C 12
380 **BAKBENSCHER** (GB) 6
564 **BAKI** (FR) 87
569 **BAL DE LA ROSE** (IRE) F 100

29 **BALADA SALE** (ARG) 2
193 **BALADY** (IRE) 24
31 **BALAJO** (FR) 1
407 **BALAMIYDA** (IRE) C 38
569 **BALANKIYA** F 101
447 **BALATON** (GB) 15
386 **BALBRIGGAN** (IRE) 2
213 **BALCARY BAY** (GB) 12
18 **BALDADASH** (IRE) 3
220 **BALDASSARRE** (IRE) 43
380 **BALDER SUCCES** (FR) 7
489 **BALDING BANKER** (IRE) 7
161 **BALDOVINA** (GB) F 44
380 **BALERINA** (FR) 8
398 **BALESTEEM** (GB) 1
525 **BALGARRY** (FR) 7
328 **BALI BREEZE** (IRE) F 76
503 **BALINROAB** (IRE) 6
118 **BALIVERNIER** (GB) 1
460 **BALIYA** (GB) G 7
408 **BALKAN HERO** 1
434 **BALLABRIGGS** (IRE) 15
469 **BALLAD OPERA** (GB) G 2
241 **BALLADE DE LA MER** (GB) 2
141 **BALLADONIA** (GB) C 61
7 **BALLARINA** (GB) 1
447 **BALLESTEROS** (IRE) 16
9 **BALLINACUBBY LASS** (IRE) 5
712 **BALLINARGH BOY** (GB) 1
712 **BALLINARGH GIRL** (GB) 2
667 **BALLINHASSIG** (IRE) 2
102 **BALLINLINA** (GB) 2
699 **BALLINTUBBER CROSS** (IRE) 6
161 **BALLISTA** (IRE) 2
654 **BALLOOR** (USA) 97
511 **BALLROOM BELLE** (IRE) 45
151 **BALLY GUNNER** (GB) 1
373 **BALLY LEGEND** (GB) 2
426 **BALLY SANDS** (IRE) 1
254 **BALLYALLIA MAN** (IRE) 4
696 **BALLYALTON** (IRE) 3
365 **BALLYBANKS** (IRE) 2
570 **BALLYBEN** (IRE) 3
610 **BALLYBOKER BOY** (IRE) 2
321 **BALLYBOUGH GORTA** (IRE) 6
543 **BALLYBRIGGAN** (IRE) 2
494 **BALLYCARBERY** (GB) 2
391 **BALLYCARNEY** (IRE) 2
473 **BALLYCASEY** (IRE) 10
503 **BALLYCLOUGH** (IRE) 7
150 **BALLYCLOUGH GALE** G 2
189 **BALLYCOLIN** (IRE) 1
518 **BALLYCRACKEN** (IRE) 1
568 **BALLYCROY BOY** (IRE) 1
676 **BALLYDAY** (IRE) 1
17 **BALLYDONAGH** (IRE) 1
86 **BALLYEGAN** (IRE) 2
650 **BALLYFITZ** (GB) 4
460 **BALLYFOY** (GB) 8
386 **BALLYGARVEY** (FR) 3
473 **BALLYHAUNIS** (GB) 11
447 **BALLYHEIGUE** (IRE) 17
174 **BALLYHOOLEY BOY** (IRE) 4
386 **BALLYLIFEN** (IRE) 4
118 **BALLYMACDUFF** (IRE) 2
252 **BALLYMAN** (IRE) 3
657 **BALLYMOAT** (GB) 9
420 **BALLYMURRY** (IRE) 3

609 **BALLYNAMONABONANZA** (GB) 1
699 **BALLYOLIVER** (GB) 7
386 **BALLYPATRICK** (IRE) 5
331 **BALLYQUIN QUEEN** (IRE) 4
657 **BALLYROCK** (IRE) 10
39 **BALLYROE RAMBLER** (IRE) 4
666 **BALLYSHONAGH** (GB) 35
610 **BALLYSPELLAN STORM** (IRE) 3
340 **BALLYSTEEN** (IRE) 1
42 **BALLYTURN BOY** (IRE) 2
59 **BALLYVESEY** (IRE) 4
381 **BALLYVONEEN** (IRE) 3
118 **BALLYVOQUE** (IRE) 3
16 **BALLYWATT** (IRE) 5
19 **BALNAHA** (GB) C 108
331 **BALSTHAR KING** (IRE) 5
200 **BALTI'S SISTER** (IRE) 52
519 **BALTIC BELLE** (IRE) C 23
543 **BALTIC BOMBER** (IRE) 32
91 **BALTIC FIZZ** (IRE) 22
204 **BALTIC FLYER** (IRE) 5
578 **BALTIC GIN** (IRE) 5
606 **BALTIC PATHFINDER** (IRE) 4
328 **BALTY BOYS** (IRE) 19
264 **BALUSTRADE** (IRE) 1
310 **BALWARAH** (IRE) C 18
310 **BALWYLLO** (IRE) 3
380 **BALZACCIO** (FR) 9
525 **BAMBOLEO** (FR) 8
24 **BAMPTON BECKS** (GB) 4
469 **BAN UISCE** (IRE) 3
19 **BANA WU** (GB) 40
499 **BANANA FLAMBE** (IRE) 2
454 **BAND OF THUNDER** (GB) 1
625 **BANDANAMAN** (IRE) 4
219 **BANDIDAZO** (USA) 33
601 **BANDSTAND** (GB) 4
19 **BANK BONUS** (GB) 41
49 **BANK MERGER** (USA) 1
436 **BANK ON BLACK** (IRE) 1
286 **BANKCITY** (FR) 1
388 **BANKRUPTCY** (USA) 21
219 **BANKS HILL** (GB) F 125
172 **BANKS ROAD** (IRE) 4
287 **BANNA BOIRCHE** (IRE) 2
366 **BANNOCK** (IRE) 54
201 **BANNOCKBURN BOY** (GB) 105
466 **BANOFFEE** (IRE) 63
178 **BANOGE** (IRE) 3
384 **BANOVALLUM** (GB) 40
614 **BANQUISE** (IRE) F 35
191 **BANTAM** (IRE) 50
395 **BANYAN TREE** (IRE) 1
573 **BAPAK CHINTA** (USA) 37
573 **BAPAK PINTAR** (GB) 38
263 **BAR DE LIGNE** (FR) 4
434 **BARAATHEN** (USA) 16
306 **BARACHIEL** (GB) 3
632 **BARATHEA DANCER** (IRE) 1
58 **BARBARELLA BLUE** (IRE) 22
79 **BARBARIAN** (GB) 2
696 **BARBATOS** (IRE) 1
321 **BARBERS SHOP** (GB) 7
496 **BARBERTON** (USA) 13
14 **BARBICAN** (GB) 1
616 **BARBIROLLI** (GB) 1
447 **BARBOUKH** (GB) C 57
642 **BARBSIZ** (IRE) 42

434 **BARDELI** (IRE) 17
552 **BARDOLET** (IRE) 2
43 **BAREBACK** (IRE) 16
570 **BARELLO ROAD** (GB) 4
321 **BARENGER** (IRE) 8
239 **BARISTA** (IRE) 2
147 **BARKIS** (GB) 20
7 **BARKSTON ASH** (GB) 2
570 **BARLIFFEY** (IRE) 5
599 **BARNACK** (GB) 2
203 **BARNACLE** (GB) 8
283 **BARNET FAIR** (GB) 6
525 **BARNEY COOL** (GB) 9
180 **BARNEY MCGREW** (IRE) 3
253 **BARNEY THE BEAR** (GB) 1
347 **BARNHILL BROWNIE** (IRE) 2
320 **BARNMORE** (GB) 1
538 **BARONS SPY** (IRE) 1
469 **BAROQUE MAN** (GB) 4
494 **BARR HEAD** (IRE) 3
161 **BARRACUDA BOY** (IRE) 45
695 **BARRAKILLA** (IRE) 10
200 **BARREN BROOK** (GB) 5
503 **BARRIE BURN** (IRE) 8
407 **BARRING ORDER** (IRE) F 39
404 **BARRISON** (GB) 3
364 **BARRISTERS BRIEF** (GB) 3
287 **BARROW ISLAND** (IRE) 3
23 **BARRY THE BARBER** (IRE) 1
29 **BARSAM** (FR) 73
625 **BARSEVENTYTWO** (IRE) 5
147 **BARTACK** (IRE) 73
495 **BARTERED BRIDE** (GB) 2
601 **BARTLEY** (GB) 25
58 **BARTOLOMEU** (GB) 23
490 **BARTON BOUNTY** (GB) 1
469 **BARTON DANTE** (GB) G 5
469 **BARTON FELIX** (GB) 6
612 **BARTON GIFT** (GB) 1
642 **BARWICK** (GB) 5
161 **BASANTEE** (GB) 18
404 **BASEBALL TED** (IRE) 4
101 **BASFORD BOB** (IRE) 2
191 **BASHAASH** (USA) 18
74 **BASHAMA** (GB) 4
19 **BASINGSTOKE** (IRE) 42
376 **BASLE** (GB) 2
16 **BASODA** (GB) 6
564 **BASSAMBA** (FR) 24
666 **BASSARA** (IRE) 18
511 **BASSEL** (FR) 2
328 **BASSETERRE** (IRE) 20
480 **BASSETT ROAD** (IRE) 3
446 **BAT MASTERSON** (IRE) 5
219 **BATAHOLA** (USA) 3
447 **BATASH** (IRE) 58
61 **BATCHELORS STAR** (IRE) 1
687 **BATCHWORTH BLAISE** (GB) 1
687 **BATCHWORTH BREEZE** (GB) F 2
687 **BATCHWORTH FIREFLY** (GB) 3
119 **BATED BREATH** (GB) 2
40 **BATGIRL** (GB) 3
68 **BATHCOUNTY** (IRE) 1
214 **BATHWICK BEAR** (IRE) 2
525 **BATHWICK BRAVE** (IRE) 10
233 **BATHWICK JUNIOR** (GB) 1
525 **BATHWICK QUEST** (IRE) 11
214 **BATHWICK STREET** (GB) 42

380 **BATONNIER** (FR) 10
642 **BATTERY POWER** (GB) 6
627 **BATTLE FOR GLORY** (IRE) 2
525 **BATTLE GROUP** (GB) 12
63 **BATTLE HONOUR** (GB) 1
695 **BATTLECAT** (GB) 11
650 **BATTLECRY** (GB) 5
413 **BATTLEDANCER** (GB) 1
15 **BATTLEFIELD BOB** (IRE) 1
12 **BATTLEOFTRAFALGAR** (GB) 3
147 **BATU** (IRE) 21
266 **BAUBLE** (USA) F 117
690 **BAVARIAN NORDIC** (USA) 1
91 **BAVARIAN PRINCESS** (USA) 2
220 **BAWAARDI** (IRE) 7
214 **BAWAARDI** (IRE) 3
695 **BAY CENTRAL** (IRE) 12
192 **BAY LAUREL** (IRE) 20
174 **BAY MAID** (GB) G 5
501 **BAY OF FIRES** (IRE) 3
9 **BAY OF NAPLES** (IRE) 6
469 **BAY OF PLENTY** (GB) C 7
388 **BAYAKA** (IRE) 7
447 **BAYAN** (IRE) 18
219 **BAYARGAL** (USA) 126
26 **BAYBSHAMBLES** (IRE) 2
43 **BAYLEYF** (IRE) 17
200 **BAYMIST** (GB) C 70
569 **BAYRIN** (FR) 27
400 **BAZART** (GB) 2
711 **BAZGUY** (GB) 2
684 **BE ALL MAN** (IRE) 2
52 **BE BOP ALOHA** (GB) G 3
200 **BE CALM** (GB) 53
254 **BE DEFINITE** (IRE) 5
625 **BE DEVIOUS** (GB) 6
347 **BE EXTRAORDINARY** (IRE) 3
3 **BE FABULOUS** (GER) 4
49 **BE HAPPY** (BRZ) C 120
111 **BE JOYFUL** (IRE) 29
321 **BE MY BELLE** (IRE) G 9
283 **BE MY DEPUTY** (IRE) 7
404 **BE MY LIGHT** (IRE) 5
219 **BE STILL** (USA) 34
321 **BE THERE IN FIVE** (IRE) 10
299 **BE VERY CAREFUL** (GB) 130
307 **BEA PERSUASIVE** (GB) 8
299 **BEACH CANDY** (IRE) 22
6 **BEACH RHYTHM** (USA) 1
304 **BEACHDALE LAD** (IRE) 4
266 **BEACHFIRE** (GB) 4
344 **BEACHWOOD BAY** (IRE) 4
498 **BEACON BRIGHT** (GB) 5
488 **BEACON LODGE** (IRE) 4
359 **BEAMAZED** (GB) 5
496 **BEAMING STAR** (USA) 50
659 **BEANEY TUNES** (GB) 4
161 **BEAR BEHIND** (IRE) 19
570 **BEAR DANCING** (GB) 6
429 **BEAR FOX BEN** (GB) 1
237 **BEAR WITH RUPERT** (GB) 1
321 **BEAR'S AFFAIR** (IRE) 11
89 **BEAT ALL OUT** (GB) 1
433 **BEAT OF THE BLUES** (GB) 2
12 **BEAT ROUTE** (GB) 1
570 **BEAT THE BAND** (GB) 7
27 **BEAT THE BELL** (GB) 3
436 **BEAT THE RAIN** (GB) F 25

695 **BEAT THE REF** (GB) 13
99 **BEAT THE RUSH** (GB) 1
490 **BEAT THE SHOWER** (GB) 2
327 **BEAT THE SYSTEM** (GB) 1
113 **BEAT UP** (GB) 2
285 **BEATEN UP** (GB) 1
9 **BEATING HARMONY** (GB) 7
511 **BEATRICE** (GB) 99
193 **BEATRICE AURORE** (IRE) 3
525 **BEATTIE GREEN** (GB) 13
391 **BEAU COLONEL** (FR) 3
659 **BEAU DANDY** (GB) 5
19 **BEAU DUKE** (IRE) 43
460 **BEAU FIGHTER** (GB) 9
607 **BEAU LAKE** (IRE) 2
273 **BEAU MISTRAL** (IRE) 9
414 **BEAUBRAV** (GB) 1
1 **BEAUCHAMP AQUA** (GB) 5
1 **BEAUCHAMP ASTRA** (GB) 22
1 **BEAUCHAMP BELLA** (GB) 23
1 **BEAUCHAMP BEST** (GB) 6
1 **BEAUCHAMP BOLD** (GB) 24
1 **BEAUCHAMP CASTLE** (GB) 7
1 **BEAUCHAMP ELLE** (GB) 25
1 **BEAUCHAMP ORANGE** (GB) 8
1 **BEAUCHAMP REBEL** (GB) 26
1 **BEAUCHAMP SUNSET** (GB) 27
102 **BEAUCHAMP ZORRO** (GB) 3
358 **BEAUFORT TWELVE** (GB) 13
474 **BEAUMONT COOPER** (GB) 21
268 **BEAUMONT'S PARTY** (IRE) 2
416 **BEAUTIFUL LANDO** (FR) 1
318 **BEAUTIFUL SY** (FR) 45
442 **BEAUTY PAGEANT** (IRE) 2
366 **BECAUSEWECAN** (USA) 3
614 **BECK CASS** (IRE) 36
465 **BECKETT ROCK** (GB) 3
698 **BECKFIELD POINT** (GB) 13
77 **BECKHANI** (GB) 1
384 **BECKY IN PINK** (USA) C 41
123 **BECQUANIS** (FR) 17
511 **BEDARA** (GB) F 100
10 **BEDARRA BOY** (GB) 1
223 **BEDAZZLED** (GB) 22
55 **BEDECKED** (GB) 68
455 **BEDIBYES** (GB) 2
201 **BEDLAM** (GB) 67
97 **BEDLOE'S ISLAND** (IRE) 3
433 **BEDOUIN BAY** (GB) 3
335 **BEE BUMBLE** (GB) 2
700 **BEE STING** (GB) 1
459 **BEE-BEE-GEE** (IRE) F 2
119 **BEECH GARDENS** (GB) G 16
57 **BEECH VIEW** (IRE) 1
299 **BEECHNUT** (IRE) C 131
471 **BEECHY BANK** (IRE) C 2
434 **BEER AND SKITTLES** (IRE) 18
593 **BEETUNA** (IRE) 3
436 **BEFOREIT'STOOLATE** (IRE) 16
283 **BEFORTYFOUR** (GB) 8
18 **BEGGAR'S BANQUET** (IRE) 36
42 **BEGGAR'S OPERA** (IRE) 3
498 **BEGGAR'S VELVET** (IRE) 6
687 **BEGGERS BELIEF** (GB) 9
687 **BEGGERS LUCK** (GB) 10
627 **BEGIN THE BEGUINE** (IRE) F 5
516 **BEGINNINGS** (USA) 2

508 **BEHANA** (IRE) 19
426 **BEHEST** (GB) 2
640 **BEHINDCLOSEDDOORS** (IRE) 4
695 **BEHTARINI** (GB) 14
570 **BEIDH TINE ANSEO** (IRE) 8
304 **BEIR BUA** (IRE) 5
234 **BEL TEMPO** (FR) F 4
314 **BELFIORE** (IRE) 1
18 **BELGIAN BILL** (GB) 4
225 **BELIEVE IN ME** (GB) 25
100 **BELINSKY** (IRE) 1
99 **BELINSKY** (IRE) 1
507 **BELLA BEGUINE** (GB) F 30
306 **BELLA BERTOLINI** (GB) C 36
111 **BELLA BERTOLINI** (GB) C 88
698 **BELLA CARMELA** (GB) 14
461 **BELLA CINDERELLA** (GB) 33
475 **BELLA MANA MOU** (IRE) 2
91 **BELLA NOIR** (GB) 3
466 **BELLA OPHELIA** (IRE) 33
178 **BELLA VENEZIA** (IRE) 7
559 **BELLABOOSH** (IRE) 1
123 **BELLACOOLA** (GER) C 55
80 **BELLAPAIS ABBEY** (IRE) 4
306 **BELLE BAYARDO** (IRE) 5
299 **BELLE DE CRECY** (IRE) 23
18 **BELLE DE FONTENAY** (FR) 5
270 **BELLE INDIGO** (IRE) 12
366 **BELLE JOSEPHINE** (GB) 4
253 **BELLE PARK** (GB) 2
329 **BELLE'S EDGE** (GB) C 26
591 **BELLEAU** (IRE) 2
486 **BELLFLOWER BOY** (IRE) 2
143 **BELLINGO** (GB) 1
433 **BELLS OF BERLIN** (GB) 30
321 **BELLVANO** (GER) 12
606 **BELMORE BARON** (GB) 5
219 **BELONGING** (GB) 127
129 **BELOVA** (IRE) 23
96 **BELOW THE DECK** (IRE) 1
199 **BEMUSED** (IRE) 1
447 **BEN CROY** (GB) 19
438 **BEN CROY** (GB) 5
344 **BEN EVA** (IRE) 4
652 **BEN TROVATO** (GB) 2
657 **BEN'S FOLLY** (IRE) 11
477 **BENANDONNER** (USA) 1
192 **BENARTIC** (GB) 2
374 **BENBANE HEAD** (USA) 4
650 **BENBENS** (IRE) 6
420 **BENCH WARRENT** (IRE) 4
292 **BENDANT** (GB) 1
260 **BENE LAD** (IRE) 3
469 **BENEATH** (GB) 8
424 **BENEFFICIENT** (IRE) 3
218 **BENEFICIAL REFORM** (IRE) 4
557 **BENEFIT CUT** (IRE) 2
313 **BENEFIT GAME** (IRE) 1
657 **BENEFIT OF YOUTH** (IRE) 12
446 **BENEMEADE** (IRE) 6
446 **BENEVOLENT** (IRE) 7
108 **BENGAL TIGER** (GB) 2
176 **BENGALINE** (GB) 19
18 **BENHEGO** (GB) 6
150 **BENHEIR** (IRE) 3
662 **BENIDORM** (GB) 2
391 **BENIGN DICTATOR** (IRE) 4
434 **BENJAMIN BITTERN** (IRE) 19

BENJARONG (GB) C 47
BENLUNA (IRE) 2
BENMADIGAN (IRE) 4
BENNELONG (GB) 4
BENNY BE GOOD (GB) 3
BENNY BOY (IRE) 1
BENNYNTHEJETS (IRE) 2
BENNYS MIST (IRE) 8
BENNYS WELL (IRE) 5
BENONI 46
BENOZZO GOZZOLI (GB) 5
BENSOON (GB) 28
BENTLEY (GB) 3
BENWAKI (FR) 18
BENZANNO (IRE) 44
BEOGRAD SNIPER (GB) 24
BERBERANA (IRE) 1
BERBICE (IRE) 4
BEREA BORU (IRE) 2
BEREA COURT (IRE) 3
BEREA VENTURE (IRE) 4
BERENGAR (IRE) 20
BERENICA (FR) F 20
BERGO (GER) 10
BERINGONPHEE (FR) 15
BERKELEY NOTE (IRE) G 13
BERLING (IRE) 4
BERLUSCA (IRE) 14
BERMONDSEY BOB (IRE) 2
BERMUXA (FR) C 24
BERNAEDELLI (IRE) 5
BERNIE THE BOLT (IRE) 4
BERNIE'S WEAPON (GB) 1
BERNIX (GB) 1
BERNIX (GB) 3
BERT THE ALERT (GB) 11
BERTBRAND (GB) 1
BERTIE BLU BOY (GB) 1
BERTIE BOO (GB) 8
BERTIE MILAN (IRE) 2
BERTIE ROYALE (GB) 6
BERTIE SOUTHSTREET (GB) 3
BERTIE'S DESIRE (GB) 4
BERTIELICIOUS (GB) 4
BERTIEWHITTLE (GB) 4
BERTOLIVER (GB) 2
BERWAAZ (GER) 5
BERWIN (GB) 10
BESCOT SPRINGS (IRE) 9
BESEECH (USA) 3
BESIDE THE FIRE (IRE) 3
BESITO (IRE) 15
BESPOKE JOE (GB) 77
BESSICHKA (GB) 16
BESSIE BLUES (GB) G 1
BEST BE CAREFUL (IRE) 1
BEST LOVED (IRE) 35
BEST LOVER (FR) 5
BEST ONE (GB) 6
BEST POLICY (USA) 20
BEST SERVED COLD (GB) 6
BEST TRIP (IRE) 9
BESTSELLER (GER) 1
BESTWOOD LODGE (GB) 1
BESTY (GB) 1
BETA BLOCKER (GB) 3
BETABOB (IRE) 2
BETAVIX (GB) 4

BETHEHOLYGOBBS (IRE) 3
BETILLA (IRE) F 62
BETTER BE MINE (IRE) 25
BETTERAS BERTIE (GB) 1
BETTY BOO (IRE) 13
BETTY BROOK (IRE) 8
BETTY BROWNEYES (GB) 3
BETTY JOHANNE (USA) F 51
BETTY'S PRIDE (GB) F 47
BETWEEN THE LINES (IRE) 12
BETWEEN US (GB) 14
BEVERLY HILL BILLY (GB) 1
BEVIS MARKS (USA) 55
BEVNOTT (IRE) 1
BEWARE CHALK PIT (IRE) 4
BEWITCH (GB) C 6
BEYEH (IRE) 9
BEYOND (IRE) 14
BEYOND CONCEIT (IRE) 9
BEYOND DESIRE (GB) 2
BEYOND THANKFUL (IRE) 6
BEYOND THE DREAM (USA) C 128
BEYOND THE TWEED (GB) 6
BEZANT (IRE) C 73
BHAKTI (IRE) 3
BHALTAIR (IRE) 21
BIBA DIVA (IRE) 14
BIBLE BELT (IRE) 6
BIBLE BLACK (IRE) 14
BID FOR GOLD (GB) 1
BIDABLE (GB) 2
BIG AUDIO (IRE) 6
BIG BAD BOO (GB) 1
BIG BAY (USA) 2
BIG BENJIE (GB) 2
BIG BERTIE (IRE) 1
BIG BETTY (GB) 1
BIG BUCK'S (FR) 8
BIG CREEK (IRE) 1
BIG DUFFY (GB) 2
BIG EARED FRAN (IRE) 3
BIG EASY (GER) 6
BIG FELLA THANKS (GB) 4
BIG GAME HUNTER (IRE) 6
BIG JAKE (GB) 2
BIG JOHNNY D (IRE) 26
BIG KAHUNA (GB) 4
BIG KNICKERS (GB) 9
BIG NEWS (GB) 3
BIG NOTE (GB) 45
BIG OCCASION (IRE) 15
BIG SAM (GB) 3
BIG SOCIETY (IRE) 7
BIG TALK (GB) 1
BIG THUNDER (GB) 44
BIG WATER (IRE) 7
BIG ZEB (IRE) 3
BIGALO'S LAURA B (IRE) 3
BIGGAR (IRE) 2
BIGGINS BOY (IRE) 46
BIJOU A MOI (GB) F 58
BIJOU DAN (GB) 4
BILASH (GB) 3
BILIDN (GB) 4
BILKO PAK (IRE) 5
BILL THE LAD (IRE) 1
BILLESLEY ROAD (GB) 7
BILLIE HALE (IRE) 22

BILLIE MAGERN (GB) 7
BILLIE'S MATE (IRE) G 3
BILLION DOLLAR KID (GB) 1
BILLSGREY (IRE) 3
BILLY BLADE (GB) 15
BILLY BONKERS (IRE) 12
BILLY BUTTONS (GB) 5
BILLY CADIZ (GB) 3
BILLY CADIZ (GB) 4
BILLY MERRIOTT (IRE) 9
BILLY MURPHY (GB) 2
BILLY NO NAME (IRE) 4
BILLY RED (GB) 3
BILLY TEAL (GB) 1
BILLY TWYFORD (IRE) 13
BILLYRAYVALENTINE (CAN) 37
BILLYTHEBLACKSMITH (IRE) 7
BILLYTHESHIP (IRE) 2
BIN END (GB) 2
BINABEE (GB) 36
BINCHE (USA) F 129
BINOCULAR (FR) 14
BINT ALAKAABER (IRE) 4
BINT ALMUKHTAR (IRE) 22
BINT BADDI (FR) F 12
BINT ELNADIM (IRE) 6
BIOGRAPHER (GB) 5
BIOGRAPHICAL (USA) 3
BIONDETTI (USA) 5
BIONIC (GB) C 89
BIRD DOG (GB) 1
BIRD'S EYE VIEW (GB) 12
BIRDIE (GB) F 27
BIRDLOVER (GB) 58
BIRDSONG (IRE) C 37
BIRDWATCHER (IRE) 3
BIRNIES BOY (GB) 2
BIRTHDAY BELLE (GB) C 4
BIRTHDAY STAR (IRE) 1
BIRTHDAY VENTURE (GB) F 47
BIRTHPLACE (USA) F 35
BIRZALI (FR) 4
BISCAYA BAY (GB) 36
BISHOP ROKO (GB) 17
BISHOP'S CASTLE (USA) 56
BISHOPHILL JACK (IRE) 7
BISHOPS HEIR (GB) 7
BISHOPSFURZE (IRE) 12
BIT A CRAIC (GB) 3
BIT BY BIT (GB) 17
BIT OF A CHANCE G 1
BIT OF A MADAM (GB) 16
BITAPHON (IRE) 3
BITE OF THE CHERRY (GB) 19
BITTA DASH (GB) 1
BITTER HARVEST (GB) 20
BITTER LEMON (GB) 19
BIVOUAC (UAE) 8
BIX (GB) 59
BIZNESS ACCOUNT (GB) 13
BLACK ANNIS BOWER (GB) 2
BLACK APALACHI (IRE) 5
BLACK BACCARA (GB) 2
BLACK CACHE (IRE) 3
BLACK COFFEE (GB) 3
BLACK DOUGLAS (IRE) 16
BLACK DRAGON (GB) 1
BLACK ICEMAN (GB) 3

394 **BLACK IS BEAUTIFUL** (FR) 4
383 **BLACK JACARI** (IRE) 4
299 **BLACK MASCARA** (IRE) 24
520 **BLACK MINSTREL** (IRE) 20
299 **BLACK MONK** (IRE) 132
35 **BLACK MOTIVE** (GB) 21
397 **BLACK OR RED** (IRE) 4
646 **BLACK PHANTOM** (IRE) 1
321 **BLACK POND** (USA) 15
147 **BLACK ROLLER** (GB) 74
33 **BLACK SAMBUCA** (GB) 3
141 **BLACK SPIRIT** (USA) 3
489 **BLACK THUNDER** (FR) 10
139 **BLACK TRIBAL** (IRE) F 27
237 **BLACKAMOOR ZARA** (GB) 37
299 **BLACKBERRY PIE** (USA) C 133
451 **BLACKDOWN FAIR** (GB) 27
225 **BLACKMORE** (GB) 3
473 **BLACKSTAIRMOUNTAIN** (IRE) 13
588 **BLACKSTONE VEGAS** (GB) 7
695 **BLACKTOFT** (USA) 17
160 **BLACKWATER BAY** (IRE) F 3
624 **BLACKWELL SYNERGY** (FR) 1
525 **BLADOUN** (IRE) 16
54 **BLAENAVON** (GB) F 21
208 **BLAINA** (GB) G 28
310 **BLAKE DEAN** (GB) 4
41 **BLAKENEYS PET** (IRE) 1
417 **BLANC DE CHINE** (IRE) 10
542 **BLANCHE DUBAWI** (IRE) 5
520 **BLANK CZECH** (IRE) 21
147 **BLASH** (GB) 23
150 **BLAST FREEZE** (IRE) G 4
570 **BLAZIN WHITE FACE** (IRE) 10
194 **BLAZING APOSTLE** (IRE) 2
380 **BLAZING BAILEY** (GB) 11
456 **BLAZING BAY** (IRE) 3
684 **BLAZING BOLTE** (GB) 3
108 **BLAZING BUCK** (GB) 3
659 **BLAZING BULL** (IRE) 6
636 **BLAZING DIVA** (IRE) 2
141 **BLAZING FIELD** (GB) 4
223 **BLAZING SPEED** (GB) 23
473 **BLAZING TEMPO** (IRE) 14
682 **BLEND** (GB) C 83
570 **BLENHEIM BROOK** (IRE) 11
380 **BLESS THE WINGS** (IRE) 12
102 **BLESS YOU** (GB) 4
35 **BLESSING** (GB) F 59
666 **BLESSING BOX** (GB) 36
129 **BLESSYOURPINKSOX** (IRE) F 25
642 **BLIMEY O'RILEY** (GB) 7
577 **BLINDING LIGHTS** (IRE) 1
433 **BLINDING MISSION** (IRE) F 48
286 **BLINKA ME** (GB) 2
496 **BLINKING** (GB) F 51
466 **BLISSAMORE** (GB) 34
446 **BLISSFUL MOMENT** (USA) 8
136 **BLITZED ECKIE** (IRE) 3
574 **BLIZZARD BLUES** (USA) 2
614 **BLOND MOMENT** (GB) F 38
299 **BLONDE** (IRE) 25
60 **BLONDE MAITE** (GB) 2
408 **BLONDE VIRGINIA** (FR) 2
298 **BLONDE VISION** (GB) 3
387 **BLOODSWEATANDTEARS** (GB) 1
573 **BLOSSOM** (GB) G 39
254 **BLOSSOM KING** (FR) 8

395 **BLOWING A HOOLIE** (IRE) 2
155 **BLOWN IT** (USA) 1
299 **BLUE AZURE** (USA) C 134
675 **BLUE BELL HOUSE** (IRE) 1
373 **BLUE BLOODED** (GB) 3
682 **BLUE BLUE SONG** (IRE) 84
3 **BLUE BUNTING** (USA) 6
446 **BLUE CANNON** (GB) 2
287 **BLUE CORNER** (IRE) 29
653 **BLUE COSSACK** (IRE) 2
2 **BLUE DEER** (IRE) 1
543 **BLUE DESTINATION** (GB) 3
366 **BLUE DUNE** (GB) 57
366 **BLUE DUSTER** (USA) C 153
35 **BLUE ECHO** (GB) C 60
265 **BLUE EYED MISS** (IRE) 2
573 **BLUE INDIGO** (GB) F 81
19 **BLUE IRIS** (GB) C 109
161 **BLUE JACK** (GB) 3
223 **BLUE LIGHTNING** (GB) C 46
373 **BLUE LOVELL** (IRE) 4
208 **BLUE LULLABY** (GB) C 29
387 **BLUE MISTRAL** (IRE) F 34
301 **BLUE MONOAKA** (GB) 1
307 **BLUE NILE** (IRE) F 14
662 **BLUE NOODLES** (GB) 3
654 **BLUE PARADE** (IRE) C 98
219 **BLUE PETREL** (USA) 37
219 **BLUE RAMBLER** (GB) 130
56 **BLUE RAPIDS** (IRE) 19
442 **BLUE REEMA** (IRE) C 21
496 **BLUE RHAPSODY** (GB) F 52
318 **BLUE SEA** (IRE) 16
476 **BLUE SHARK** (FR) 5
201 **BLUE SHOES** (IRE) 68
254 **BLUE SIGNAL** (IRE) 9
19 **BLUE SIREN** (GB) C 110
520 **BLUE SURF** (GB) 22
49 **BLUE TIGER** (GB) 76
493 **BLUE TOMATO** (GB) 1
664 **BLUE TOP** (GB) 19
74 **BLUE TREASURE** (GB) 31
566 **BLUE VELVET** (GB) F 1
682 **BLUEBELL PARK** (USA) C 85
572 **BLUEBERRY FIZZ** (IRE) 1
228 **BLUECROP BOY** (GB) 3
522 **BLUEGRASS BID** (USA) 2
42 **BLUELAND** (IRE) 4
391 **BLUES AND TWOS** (GB) 5
586 **BLUES JAZZ** (GB) 3
357 **BLUSHING AWAY** (USA) F 23
461 **BLUSHING HEART** (GB) G 34
588 **BLUSHING SUNRISE** (USA) F 38
336 **BOA** (GB) 4
266 **BOAST** (GB) F 118
29 **BOATHOUSE** (GB) 20
262 **BOB CASEY** (IRE) 5
304 **BOB LE BEAU** (IRE) 7
185 **BOB LEWIS** (GB) 1
10 **BOB RUN** (IRE) 3
8 **BOB'S DREAM** (IRE) 4
625 **BOB'S LADY TARA** (GB) 9
57 **BOB'S LEGEND** (IRE) 2
101 **BOB'S WORLD** (GB) 30
650 **BOBBIE MAGERN** (GB) 8
367 **BOBBITS WAY** (GB) 1
214 **BOBBLE BORU** (IRE) 4
535 **BOBBY DOVE** (GB) 1

525 **BOBBY EWING** (IRE) 17
124 **BOBBY'S DOLL** (GB) 1
168 **BOBBYBOARD** (IRE) 2
124 **BOBBYOW** (GB) 2
460 **BOBBYSCOT** (IRE) 13
696 **BOBCATBILLY** (IRE) 5
486 **BOBOWEN** (IRE) 3
45 **BOBS HER UNCLE** (GB) 13
262 **BOBS LAW** (IRE) 6
373 **BOBS PRESENT** (GB) 5
321 **BOBS WORTH** (IRE) 16
145 **BOCAMIX** (FR) 6
207 **BOCCIANI** (GER) 6
599 **BODIE** (GB) 3
424 **BOG WARRIOR** (IRE) 4
573 **BOGART** (GB) 40
217 **BOGEY HOLE** (IRE) 12
118 **BOGSIDE** (IRE) 4
501 **BOGSIDE THEATRE** (IRE) 4
620 **BOGSNOG** (IRE) 12
619 **BOHEMIAN DANCE** (IRE) 99
58 **BOHEMIAN MELODY** (GB) 2
329 **BOHEMIAN RHAPSODY** (IRE) 5
15 **BOHEMIAN ROCK** (GB) 3
117 **BOITE** (IRE) 33
228 **BOJANGLE** (IRE) 11
113 **BOLACHOIR** (IRE) 3
638 **BOLAND'S CORNER** (GER) 2
480 **BOLD ADVENTURE** (GB) 4
473 **BOLD BANKS** (IRE) 15
489 **BOLD CHIEF** (IRE) 11
46 **BOLD CROSS** (IRE) 1
534 **BOLD CUFFS** (GB) 15
243 **BOLD DAVID** (GB) 11
46 **BOLD DUKE** (GB) 2
331 **BOLD HENRY** (GB) 8
522 **BOLD IDENTITY** (IRE) 1
611 **BOLD INDIAN** (IRE) 1
699 **BOLD JACK** (IRE) 9
653 **BOLD LOVE** (GB) F 27
91 **BOLD MARC** (IRE) 4
537 **BOLD PERK** (IRE) 1
552 **BOLD RANSOM** (GB) 4
687 **BOLD RING** (GB) 5
570 **BOLD SIR BRIAN** (IRE) 12
374 **BOLD TARA** (GB) 5
29 **BOLDOGSAG** (FR) 21
219 **BOLINGBROKE** (IRE) 38
660 **BOLIVIA** (GER) 6
201 **BOLLIN FELIX** (GB) 3
392 **BOLLIN FERGUS** (GB) 1
461 **BOLLIN FIONA** (GB) 1
402 **BOLLIN FREDDIE** (GB) 1
201 **BOLLIN GRETA** (GB) 4
42 **BOLLIN JUDITH** (GB) 5
689 **BOLLIN JULIE** (GB) 1
333 **BOLLIN PIPER** (GB) 1
689 **BOLLIN RUTH** (GB) 3
381 **BOLLIN TAHINI** (GB) 4
201 **BOLLIN TOMMY** (GB) 69
471 **BOLLISTICK** (GB) 3
31 **BOLLYWOOD** (IRE) 2
358 **BOLSENA** (USA) F 30
617 **BOLT FROM THE BLUE** (GB) 3
654 **BOMBAZINE** (IRE) C 99
111 **BON ALLUMAGE** (GB) 30
437 **BON ROYALE** (GB) 3
264 **BON SPIEL** (GB) 2

266 **BONASH** (GB) C 119
29 **BONBONNIERE** (USA) 22
506 **BOND ARTIST** (IRE) 14
506 **BOND BABE** (GB) F 23
506 **BOND BLADE** (GB) 2
506 **BOND FASTRAC** (GB) 3
696 **BOND KATHLEEN** (GB) 6
506 **BOND PLATINUM CLUB** (GB) C 24
506 **BOND ROYALE** (GB) C 25
506 **BOND SHAKIRA** (GB) F 26
601 **BOND STYLE** (GB) 26
529 **BONDI MIST** (IRE) 25
71 **BONDIE** (GB) 2
19 **BONFIRE** (GB) 46
686 **BONKERS** (GB) F 20
161 **BONNE AMIE** (IRE) 46
16 **BONNE FEE** (GB) 8
29 **BONNE JOURNEE** (FR) 23
117 **BONNET DE DOUCHE** (IRE) 7
708 **BONNIE BELLE** (GB) C 22
651 **BONNIE BLADE** (GB) 5
208 **BONNIE BRAE** (GB) 1
566 **BONNIE BURNETT** (IRE) 2
488 **BONNIE CHARLIE** (GB) 5
440 **BONNIE PRINCE BLUE** (GB) 2
686 **BONNY ROSE** (GB) F 21
511 **BONTONI** (FR) 101
692 **BOO BOO BOOYAKASHA** (GB) 1
237 **BOO'S BOUNTY** (GB) 4
341 **BOOGIE DANCER** (GB) 2
257 **BOOGIE KNIGHT** (GB) 1
654 **BOOGIE SHOES** (GB) 3
219 **BOOK OF MANNERS** (GB) 131
59 **BOOK'EM DANNO** (IRE) 5
600 **BOOKEND** (GB) 1
360 **BOOKIESINDEX BOY** (GB) 5
360 **BOOKIESINDEXDOTNET** (GB) 41
643 **BOOM AND BUST** (IRE) 4
407 **BOOM TO BUST** (IRE) 1
329 **BOOMERANG BOB** (IRE) 6
198 **BOOMSHACKERLACKER** (IRE) 59
2 **BOOMTOWN** (GB) 2
332 **BOOSHA** (GB) 4
91 **BOOTS AND SPURS** (GB) 23
601 **BOP IT** (GB) 27
661 **BORDER BANDIT** (USA) 1
8 **BORDER FLORA** (GB) 5
30 **BORDER HILL JACK** (GB) 19
119 **BORDER LEGEND** (GB) 18
201 **BORDER REIVER** (GB) 5
123 **BORDER SONG** (FR) 19
31 **BORDER STATION** (IRE) 3
456 **BORDER TALE** (GB) 4
476 **BORDERHOPPER** (GB) 6
30 **BORDERLESCOTT** (GB) 1
366 **BORDONI** (USA) 58
219 **BORGHESA** (GER) C 132
564 **BORGO** 3
200 **BORIS GRIGORIEV** (IRE) 54
353 **BORIS THE BLADE** (GB) 3
43 **BORIS THE BOLD** (GB) 18
314 **BORN FOR DIAMONDS** (IRE) F 11
300 **BORN TO BE ACHAMP** (BRZ) 1
304 **BORN TO BENEFIT** (IRE) 8
510 **BORN TO RUN** (GB) 14
508 **BORN TO SEA** (IRE) 20
625 **BORN TO SHINE** (USA) 10
35 **BORN TO SURPRISE** (GB) 22

219 **BORN WILD** F 133
285 **BORNHOLM** (IRE) 20
226 **BORO SUPREME** (IRE) F 2
564 **BORODINO** 25
628 **BORUG** (USA) 1
434 **BORULER** (IRE) 23
446 **BOSE IKARD** (IRE) 10
433 **BOSONIC** (GB) 31
472 **BOSS IN BOOTS** (IRE) 6
108 **BOSTON BLUE** (GB) 4
473 **BOSTON BOB** (IRE) 16
618 **BOSTON COURT** (IRE) 1
626 **BOSTON GLOBE** (IRE) 1
304 **BOSTONS ANGEL** (IRE) 9
27 **BOSUN BREESE** (GB) 5
657 **BOTTMAN** (IRE) 14
107 **BOUCHER GARCON** (IRE) 3
323 **BOUGGATTI** (GB) 1
391 **BOUGGLER** (GB) 6
256 **BOUGUEREAU** (GB) 2
475 **BOUILLABAISSE** (IRE) 5
270 **BOULAY** (IRE) 2
511 **BOULBA D'ALBEN** (FR) 47
270 **BOUNCE** (FR) F 13
35 **BOUNCY BOUNCY** (GB) 4
658 **BOUND BY HONOUR** (SAF) 7
434 **BOUND FOR GLORY** (IRE) 24
201 **BOUNDARIES** (GB) 6
55 **BOUNDLESS HOPE** (IRE) 17
585 **BOUNDS AND LEAPS** (GB) 5
599 **BOUNTIFUL CATCH** (GB) 14
366 **BOUNTY SEEKER** (USA) 59
311 **BOURGELAT** (GB) 2
434 **BOURNE** (GB) 25
271 **BOVS CASTLE** (GB) 7
659 **BOW BADGER** (GB) 7
200 **BOW BRIDGE** (GB) F 71
337 **BOW FIDDLE** (IRE) 1
200 **BOW PEEP** (IRE) C 72
325 **BOW RIVER ARCH** (USA) 1
293 **BOW SCHOOL** (IRE) 2
357 **BOW TO NO ONE** (IRE) 3
54 **BOWDEN ROSE** (GB) G 13
366 **BOWDGER'S MAGIC** (GB) 5
473 **BOWFINGER** (IRE) 17
516 **BOWLED OUT** (GB) F 18
541 **BOWMANS WELL** (GB) 1
583 **BOWNTOBEBAD** (IRE) 2
643 **BOWSERS BRAVE** (GB) 5
473 **BOXER GEORG** (IRE) 18
471 **BOXER SHORTS** (GB) 4
279 **BOY OF BORU** (IRE) 2
517 **BOY THE BELL** (GB) 1
474 **BOYCHUK** (IRE) 4
686 **BRACKENDALE** (GB) 11
114 **BRACKLOON HIGH** (IRE) 2
390 **BRADAMANTE** (GB) C 23
45 **BRADBURY** (IRE) 3
623 **BRADDOCK ISLAND** (GB) 1
3 **BRAILSFORD** (IRE) 49
489 **BRAMPOUR** (IRE) 12
520 **BRAMSHAW** (USA) 1
520 **BRAMSHILL LASS** (GB) 23
476 **BRANDON THOMAS** (IRE) 7
73 **BRANDY SNAPPING** (GB) 26
228 **BRANDYWELL BOY** (IRE) 4
485 **BRANNOC** (IRE) 3
299 **BRANSON** (IRE) 135

204 **BRANSTON BERRY** (IRE) F 11
201 **BRANSTON GEM** (GB) F 106
461 **BRASINGAMAN ERIC** (GB) 5
461 **BRASINGAMAN ESPEE** (GB) 25
681 **BRASS MONKEY** (IRE) 7
110 **BRASS TAX** (IRE) 2
161 **BRAVE ACCLAIM** (IRE) 47
321 **BRAVE ALLIANCE** (IRE) 17
26 **BRAVE BATTLE** (GB) 3
139 **BRAVE DECISION** (GB) 1
573 **BRAVE DREAM** (GB) 2
151 **BRAVE ENOUGH** (USA) 2
136 **BRAVE HEART** (IRE) 4
208 **BRAVE KISS** (GB) 12
299 **BRAVE MADAM** (IRE) C 136
488 **BRAVE ONE** (IRE) 47
268 **BRAVE SPARTACUS** (IRE) 3
297 **BRAVERY SCOTCH** (IRE) 1
390 **BRAVESTAR** (IRE) 24
564 **BRAVIA** (GB) 26
12 **BRAVO ECHO** (GB) 5
283 **BRAVO KING** (IRE) 10
366 **BRAVO RAGAZZO** (IRE) 154
426 **BRAVO RIQUET** (FR) 3
306 **BRAZILIAN STYLE** (GB) C 37
191 **BRAZILIAN TERRACE** (GB) F 52
56 **BREAD LOFT** (FR) 1
390 **BREAD OF HEAVEN** (GB) F 25
43 **BREAK OF DAWN** (USA) F 32
318 **BREAK RANK** (USA) 17
15 **BREAK THE CHAIN** (GB) 3
342 **BREAKHEART** (IRE) 2
467 **BREAKING THE BANK** (GB) 15
248 **BREAKOUTTHEBOOZE** (IRE) 1
111 **BREATHE** (FR) F 90
228 **BREATHING SPACE** (GB) F 15
573 **BREATHLESS KISS** (USA) 3
654 **BREATHTAKING** (GB) F 100
508 **BRECCBENNACH** (GB) 61
118 **BREMER BAY** (IRE) 5
407 **BRENDAN BRACKAN** (IRE) 15
130 **BRENT PELHAM** (GB) 1
32 **BRET MAVERICK** (IRE) 4
597 **BRETON ROCK** (IRE) 62
320 **BRETT VALE** (IRE) 2
686 **BRIAN SPROUT** (GB) 3
237 **BRIAN'S BEST** (GB) 38
403 **BRIANNSTA** (IRE) 2
446 **BRIARY GAP** (IRE) 11
699 **BRICK RED** (GB) 10
569 **BRICMATE** (IRE) 28
511 **BRICTESSE** (FR) 48
410 **BRIDAL MEDIC** (GB) 2
415 **BRIDGE OF GOLD** (USA) 2
351 **BRIDGE THAT GAP** (GB) 1
673 **BRIDGE VALLEY** (GB) 2
3 **BRIDGEFIELD** (USA) 7
35 **BRIDGEHAMPTON** (GB) 23
9 **BRIDGETOWN** (GB) 10
311 **BRIDGEVILLE QUEEN** (GB) 2
441 **BRIDLINGTONBYGONES** (IRE) 2
520 **BRIEF CHAT** (USA) 24
205 **BRIEFCASE** (IRE) 1
8 **BRIERYHILL BOY** (GB) 6
299 **BRIGADE** (IRE) 137
321 **BRIGADIER MILLER** (GB) 18
358 **BRIGADOON** (GB) 1
219 **BRIGANTIN** (USA) 4

682 **BRIGHT AND CLEAR** (GB) F 86
661 **BRIGHT APPLAUSE** (GB) 2
164 **BRIGHT DECISION** (GB) 2
74 **BRIGHT GIRL** (IRE) 5
308 **BRIGHT HEART** (IRE) 4
117 **BRIGHT HOPE** (IRE) C 34
522 **BRIGHT LIGHT** (GB) 4
343 **BRIGHT LIGHT CITY** (IRE) 6
343 **BRIGHT NEW DAWN** (IRE) 7
164 **BRIGHT SPANGLE** (IRE) F 10
226 **BRIGHTON ROAD** (IRE) 3
556 **BRIJOMI QUEEN** (IRE) 6
684 **BRILLIANT BARCA** (GB) 4
374 **BRIMHAM BOY** (GB) 6
536 **BRIMLEY** (GB) 1
109 **BRIMSTONE HILL** (IRE) 11
570 **BRINDISI BREEZE** (IRE) 13
531 **BRING IT ON HOME** (GB) 6
650 **BRING ON THE JUDGE** (IRE) 9
207 **BRING SWEETS** (IRE) 7
482 **BRINGEWOOD BELLE** (GB) 1
482 **BRINGEWOOD BUNNY** (GB) 2
482 **BRINGEWOOD FOX** (GB) 3
526 **BRINK** (GB) 1
433 **BRIO** (GB) 4
123 **BRIONNE** (GER) 20
111 **BRISK BREEZE** (GER) C 91
534 **BRISTOL FASHION** (GB) 16
388 **BRIVIESCA** (GB) F 63
43 **BRIXA** (FR) C 33
68 **BRIXEN** (IRE) 3
321 **BROADBACKBOB** (IRE) 19
160 **BROADCAST** (GB) C 4
192 **BROADWAY BABE** (IRE) 6
299 **BROADWAY DUCHESS** (GB) 138
597 **BROADWAY HIT** (GB) C 63
75 **BROCKFIELD** (GB) 2
573 **BROCKLEBANK** (IRE) 41
161 **BROCKWELL** (GB) 20
268 **BROCKWELL ABBEY** (GB) 4
123 **BROCOTTES** (FR) 21
552 **BROCTUNE PAPA GIO** (GB) 5
18 **BROKEN ROMANCE** (IRE) F 38
299 **BROKEN SPECTRE** (GB) C 139
268 **BROKETHEGATE** (IRE) 5
183 **BRONCOLI** (FR) 2
299 **BRONTERRE** (GB) 26
643 **BRONZE ANGEL** (IRE) 25
620 **BRONZE BEAU** (GB) 1
460 **BRONZE CANNON** (USA) 14
180 **BROOK STAR** (IRE) 4
359 **BROOKLYN BROWNIE** (IRE) 6
564 **BROOKLYN THOMAS** (IRE) 27
404 **BROTHER BOB** (IRE) 6
436 **BROTHER RABBIT** (IRE) 17
606 **BROTHER SCOTT** (GB) 6
201 **BROTHER SUPERIOR** (GB) 70
422 **BROTHER TIGER** (GB) 21
326 **BROUGH ACADEMY** (IRE) 5
480 **BROUGHTON PLACE** (GB) 5
480 **BROUGHTON SANDS** (GB) 6
480 **BROUGHTONS BANDIT** (GB) 7
480 **BROUGHTONS CLASSIC** (GB) 8
480 **BROUGHTONS PARADIS** (IRE) 9
480 **BROUGHTONS STAR** (GB) 10
480 **BROUGHTONS SWINGER** (GB) 11
161 **BROUHAHA** (GB) 4
650 **BROUSSE EN FEUX** (FR) 10

161 **BROWN PANTHER** (GB) 5
283 **BROWN PETE** (IRE) 11
600 **BROWN TIGER** (IRE) 18
456 **BROWNEYES BLUE** (IRE) 5
699 **BROWNS BROOK** (IRE) 11
366 **BROXBOURNE** (IRE) 60
302 **BRUACH NA MARA** (IRE) 1
161 **BRUBECK** (IRE) 21
465 **BRUFF** (IRE) 7
102 **BRUNDON** (GB) 22
472 **BRUNETTE'SONLY** (IRE) 7
263 **BRUNSWICK GOLD** (GB) 5
450 **BRUNSWICK VALE** (IRE) 35
642 **BRUSHING** (GB) 8
695 **BRUSLINI** (FR) 18
388 **BRUYANTE** (GB) 22
35 **BRYANT PARK** (USA) 24
375 **BRYTER LAYTER** (GB) 10
573 **BU SAMRA** (IRE) 42
298 **BUACHAILL ALAINN** (IRE) 4
234 **BUAITEOIR** (IRE) 1
14 **BUBBLY BALLERINA** (GB) 14
14 **BUBBLY BOUNTY** (GB) 15
521 **BUBBLY BRAVEHEART** (IRE) 2
563 **BUBBLY BREEZE** (IRE) 1
498 **BUBBLY BRUCE** (IRE) 7
407 **BUCCANEER BOB** (IRE) 2
111 **BUCHANAN** (GB) 92
455 **BUCK BUNNIE** (GB) 4
566 **BUCK ON** (GB) G 3
658 **BUCKED OFF** (SAF) 8
321 **BUCKIE BOY** (IRE) 20
126 **BUCKLEY BOY** (GB) 8
347 **BUCKS R'US** (IRE) 5
201 **BUCKSHEE** (GB) 7
525 **BUDDY BOLERO** (IRE) 18
32 **BUDS BRUVVER** (GB) 25
487 **BUDSSON** (GB) 2
400 **BUDVA** (GB) 3
525 **BUENA VISTA** (IRE) 19
16 **BUFFALO BOB** (IRE) 9
647 **BUFFALOSPRINGFIELD** (GB) 2
49 **BUFFUM** (USA) 7
569 **BUGIE D'AMORE** (GB) 29
18 **BUGSY'S BABE** (GB) 60
18 **BUGSY'S BOY** (GB) 1
573 **BUKHOOR** (IRE) C 82
116 **BULL BAY** (GB) 15
399 **BULL FIVE** (GB) 1
367 **BULL MARKET** (IRE) 2
447 **BULLDOG BEASLEY** (USA) 21
111 **BULLET TRAIN** (GB) 4
304 **BULLOCK HARBOUR** (IRE) 10
55 **BUNAIRGEAD** (IRE) 70
434 **BUNCLODY** (GB) 26
384 **BUNDITTEN** (GB) C 42
473 **BUNDLE OF FUN** (IRE) 19
407 **BUNDLE OF JOY** (IRE) C 40
249 **BUNKERED AGAIN** (GB) 2
654 **BUNOOD** (IRE) F 101
564 **BUNOOK** (GB) 28
328 **BUNRAKU** (GB) 21
598 **BUNRATTY** (IRE) 2
55 **BUNREACHT** (USA) 71
74 **BUNTING** (GB) F 58
19 **BUONA FORTUNA** (GB) 111
447 **BURANO** (IRE) 22

70 **BURGUNDY BEAU** (GB) 1
49 **BURJ HATTA** (USA) 8
49 **BURJ NAHAR** (GB) 9
496 **BURKE'S ROCK** (GB) 15
304 **BURN AND TURN** (IRE) 11
407 **BURN THE BOATS** (IRE) 16
288 **BURNBRAKE** (GB) 3
265 **BURNELL** (IRE) 18
466 **BURNHAM** (GB) 35
176 **BURNHOPE** (GB) 20
407 **BURNIE BRAES** (IRE) 17
200 **BURNING PASSION** (GB) 55
29 **BURNING SUNSET** (GB) C 74
624 **BURNSWOOD** (IRE) 2
57 **BURNT CREAM** (GB) 3
451 **BURNT FINGERS** (IRE) 45
172 **BURNT ORCHID** (IRE) 5
198 **BURNTHILL** (IRE) 3
586 **BURNWYND BOY** (GB) 4
586 **BURNWYND SPIRIT** (IRE) 12
299 **BURSLEDON** (IRE) 140
191 **BURSTING BUBBLES** (IRE) 19
321 **BURTON PORT** (IRE) 21
191 **BURWAAZ** (GB) 20
48 **BURY PARADE** (IRE) 1
597 **BUSHMAN** (GB) 5
333 **BUSHWACKER** (IRE) 2
125 **BUSINESS BAY** (USA) 1
321 **BUSKER ROYAL** (GB) 22
214 **BUSSA** (GB) 5
236 **BUSSELL ALONG** (IRE) 1
704 **BUSTANINCH** (GB) 1
259 **BUSTER BROWN** (IRE) 17
589 **BUSY ISIT** (GB) 1
366 **BUTE HALL** (GB) 61
333 **BUTE STREET** (GB) 3
266 **BUTHELEZI** (USA) 5
637 **BUTTERFLIER** (GB) F 4
619 **BUTTERFLY COVE** (USA) F 100
285 **BUTTERFLY DREAM** (GB) 74
708 **BUTTON MOON** (IRE) 2
452 **BUXFIZZ** (USA) 1
593 **BUXOM** (IRE) 5
351 **BUXTON** (GB) 2
332 **BUYERS PREMIUM** (GB) 5
390 **BUZKASHI** (IRE) 6
91 **BUZZ LAW** (IRE) 5
169 **BY IMPLICATION** (GB) 4
34 **BY INVITATION** (USA) 18
700 **BY POPULAR DEMAND** (IRE) 2
38 **BYGONES FOR COINS** (IRE) 2
380 **BYGONES IN BRID** (IRE) 13
441 **BYGONES OF BRID** (IRE) 3
525 **BYGONES SOVEREIGN** (IRE) 20
19 **BYPASS** (GB) 47
362 **BYRESTEADS FARM** (GB) 2
507 **BYRON BLUE** (IRE) 15
237 **BYRON GET ONE FREE** (GB) 39
511 **BYRON SON** (IRE) 49
500 **BYRONIC HERO** (GB) 6
102 **BYTON** (GB) 23
219 **BYWORD** (GB) 7
273 **C P JOE** (IRE) 2
265 **C'EST MA SŒUR** (IRE) 24
330 **C'MON YOU IRONS** (IRE) 1
650 **C'MONTHEHAMMERS** (IRE) 11
145 **CABAL** (GB) 7
502 **CABARET GIRL** (GB) 1

183 **CABARETUNE** (FR) 3
456 **CABBYL DOO** (GB) 6
233 **CABO ROCHE** (GB) 2
161 **CABOODLE** (GB) 22
55 **CACHE CREEK** (IRE) C 72
373 **CADEAUX CERISE** (IRE) 6
176 **CADEAUX PEARL** (GB) 3
508 **CADENCE** (GB) C 62
19 **CADES REEF** (GB) 48
155 **CADGERS BRIG** (GB) 2
336 **CADMIUM LOCH** (GB) 5
570 **CADORE** (GB) 14
394 **CADOUDALAS** (FR) 5
473 **CADSPEED** (GB) 20
178 **CAERLAVEROCK** (GB) 5
58 **CAERLINA** (GB) C 58
643 **CAERWYN** (GB) 52
658 **CAFE AU LAIT** (GER) 57
519 **CAFE EXPRESS** (IRE) 19
49 **CAFE LATTE** (IRE) C 121
632 **CAHALA DANCER** (GB) 2
343 **CAHERONAUN** (IRE) 8
299 **CAI SHEN** (IRE) 3
640 **CAILIN NA RI** (IRE) 5
226 **CAIM HILL** (IRE) 4
462 **CAIPIRINIA** (IRE) F 26
372 **CAIRANNE** (GB) 2
19 **CAITLIN** (GB) 49
35 **CALA** (FR) C 61
237 **CALCULAITE** (GB) 5
215 **CALDERCRUIX** (USA) 1
655 **CALDY DANCER** (IRE) C 19
344 **CALEDONIA PRINCE** (GB) 5
466 **CALEDONIAN LAD** (GB) 36
386 **CALGARY BAY** (IRE) 7
433 **CALICO BAY** (IRE) 5
160 **CALICO ROSE** (GB) 5
299 **CALIFANTE** (GB) 141
58 **CALIFORNIA ENGLISH** (IRE) 25
316 **CALINE DE FROMENT** (FR) F 2
511 **CALIPATRIA** (GB) 3
304 **CALISSA** (IRE) 103
347 **CALL AT MIDNIGHT** (GB) 6
434 **CALL BACK** (GB) 27
383 **CALL IT ON** (IRE) 5
380 **CALL ME A STAR** (GB) 14
253 **CALL ME APRIL** (GB) 3
370 **CALL ME FRANKIE** (IRE) 2
659 **CALL ME MULLIGAN** (IRE) 8
473 **CALL THE POLICE** (IRE) 21
508 **CALL TO BATTLE** (IRE) 21
696 **CALL TO REASON** (IRE) 7
219 **CALLE FLORA** (USA) 39
312 **CALLERLILLY** (GB) 2
509 **CALLIE'S ANGEL** (GB) 5
315 **CALLIGRAPHY** (GB) F 13
540 **CALLISTO LIGHT** (GB) 1
509 **CALONNOG** (IRE) C 23
331 **CALUSA CALDERA** (GB) 9
3 **CALVADOS BLUES** (FR) 8
366 **CALYPSO CAY** (GB) 6
647 **CALYPSO CHARMS** (GB) F 25
362 **CALYPSO MAGIC** (IRE) 3
380 **CALYPSO PRINCESS** (GB) 15
312 **CALYPSO STAR** (GB) 3
327 **CALZAGHE** (IRE) 2
127 **CAMACHE QUEEN** (IRE) 1

111 **CAMARET** (IRE) F 93
391 **CAMAS BRIDGE** (GB) 7
119 **CAMBERLEY TWO** (GB) 3
266 **CAMBORNE** (GB) 6
698 **CAMBRIDGE DUCHESS** (GB) 15
593 **CAMDEN** (IRE) 6
130 **CAMELOPARDALIS** (GB) 8
463 **CAMERA SHY** (IRE) 1
654 **CAMERON HIGHLAND** (IRE) 37
610 **CAMINERO** (IRE) 4
251 **CAMISKY** (GB) 1
328 **CAMISOLE** (IRE) 78
446 **CAMLIN FLOW** (IRE) 12
201 **CAMP FIRE** (IRE) F 107
49 **CAMPANOLOGIST** (USA) 10
299 **CAMPANOLOGY** (GB) 27
336 **CAMPIGLIA** (GB) C 39
214 **CAMROCK STAR** (IRE) 43
181 **CAN DO LES** (IRE) 7
139 **CANADIAN DANEHILL** (IRE) 2
68 **CANADIAN DIAMOND** (IRE) 3
650 **CANADIAN DREAMER** (IRE) 12
161 **CANADIAN RED** (GB) 48
343 **CANALY** (IRE) 9
58 **CANARY WHARF** (IRE) 26
560 **CANAZTA** (GB) 2
344 **CANDELITA** (GB) 6
179 **CANDLEFORD** (GB) 1
119 **CANDOLUMINESCENCE** (GB) 59
236 **CANDY BUBBLE** (FR) 33
236 **CANDY COPPER** (GB) F 2
35 **CANDYCAKES** (IRE) 25
102 **CANE CAT** (IRE) 5
166 **CANKARA** (IRE) G 47
225 **CANNI THINKAAR** (IRE) 3
639 **CANNING VALE** (GB) 21
124 **CANNINGTON BROOK** (IRE) 5
30 **CANNIZARO HOUSE** (IRE) 18
695 **CANNON BOLT** (IRE) 2
627 **CANNON FIRE** (FR) 19
147 **CANNOT GIVE** (USA) 3
214 **CANON LAW** (IRE) 75
246 **CANOPY OF STARS** (GB) 6
333 **CANSHEBEMINE** (GB) 2
619 **CANTABILLY** (IRE) 4
600 **CANTAL** (GB) 13
447 **CANTICUM** (GB) 19
7 **CANTALOUPE** (GB) C 60
681 **CANTLOW** (GB) 8
67 **CANTARA** (GB) 18
609 **CANTOR** (GB) 1
660 **CANTRELL** (IRE) 2
326 **CANUSSPOTIT** (GB) 7
474 **CAP ELORN** (FR) 6
223 **CAP FALCO** (IRE) 5
573 **CAPACIOUS** (GB) 24
322 **CAPAILL LIATH** (IRE) 4
74 **CAPDALIGHT** (IRE) 2
299 **CAPE ALEX** (GB) 32
113 **CAPE APPEAL** (GB) 142
285 **CAPE BRETON** (IRE) 4
19 **CAPE CLASSIC** (IRE) 2
433 **CAPE CROSSING** (IRE) 50
227 **CAPE DANCER** (IRE) F 49
266 **CAPE DUTCH** (IRE) 4
321 **CAPE ELIZABETH** (IRE) 120
299 **CAPE EXPRESS** (IRE) 23
299 **CAPE JOY** (IRE) 28

485 **CAPE KIMBERLEY** (GB) 4
18 **CAPE MELODY** (GB) 8
614 **CAPE OF APPROVAL** (IRE) 13
78 **CAPE OF STORMS** (GB) 1
102 **CAPE PERON** (GB) 48
520 **CAPE PRIDE** (GB) 25
653 **CAPE RAINBOW** (GB) 20
625 **CAPE RISING** (GB) 11
387 **CAPE ROCK** (GB) 2
628 **CAPE SAFARI** (GB) 6
117 **CAPE SAMBA** (GB) 8
597 **CAPE SAVANNAH** (GB) 26
133 **CAPE SCHANCK** (GB) 1
359 **CAPE TRIBULATION** (GB) 7
304 **CAPE VIOLET** (GB) 81
35 **CAPELLA'S SONG** (IRE) 62
499 **CAPELLANUS** (IRE) 4
206 **CAPELLINI** (GB) 4
201 **CAPETOWN GIRL** (GB) F 108
193 **CAPHENE** (GB) 27
387 **CAPHIRA** (GB) 14
31 **CAPISCI** (IRE) 4
183 **CAPITAINE COURAGE** (IRE) 4
4 **CAPITAL VENTURE** (IRE) 3
408 **CAPITEUX** 46
447 **CAPITOL GAIN** (IRE) 23
682 **CAPONATA** (USA) 29
176 **CAPONE** (IRE) 4
3 **CAPORETTO** (USA) 50
695 **CAPPA BLEU** (IRE) 20
331 **CAPPAGH** (IRE) 10
358 **CAPPIELOW PARK** (GB) 17
3 **CAPPONI** (IRE) 9
714 **CAPRICIOUS LADY** (IRE) F 2
393 **CAPRICORN PRINCESS** (GB) G 1
476 **CAPRICORNUS** (USA) 8
203 **CAPRIOLE** (GB) F 14
466 **CAPRIOLLA** (GB) C 64
480 **CAPRISKA** (GB) 29
194 **CAPSTICK** (JPN) F 19
218 **CAPTAIN AMERICO** (IRE) 8
343 **CAPTAIN ARCEUS** (IRE) 10
246 **CAPTAIN BECKET** (GB) 3
466 **CAPTAIN BELLAMY** (USA) 1
328 **CAPTAIN BERTIE** (IRE) 1
695 **CAPTAIN BROWN** (GB) 21
119 **CAPTAIN CAT** (IRE) 19
331 **CAPTAIN CHRIS** (IRE) 11
685 **CAPTAIN CLAYTON** (IRE) 2
321 **CAPTAIN CONAN** (FR) 24
279 **CAPTAIN CRACKERS** (IRE) 3
321 **CAPTAIN CUTTER** (IRE) 25
98 **CAPTAIN DANCER** (IRE) 3
214 **CAPTAIN DIMITRIOS** (IRE) 7
201 **CAPTAIN DUNNE** (IRE) 8
590 **CAPTAIN HASTINGS** (IRE) 1
457 **CAPTAIN HERO** (IRE) 1
557 **CAPTAIN JOHN SMITH** (GB) 4
489 **CAPTAIN KELLY** (IRE) 13
214 **CAPTAIN KENDALL** (IRE) 44
231 **CAPTAIN LING** (GB) 2
89 **CAPTAIN LOUI** (IRE) 3
657 **CAPTAIN MOONMAN** (IRE) 15
268 **CAPTAIN NASH** (IRE) 6
236 **CAPTAIN OATS** (IRE) 3
337 **CAPTAIN PAULIE** (IRE) 2
573 **CAPTAIN RAMIUS** (IRE) 5
661 **CAPTAIN ROYALE** (IRE) 3

233 **CAPTAIN SCARLETT** (IRE) 3
283 **CAPTAIN SCOOBY** (GB) 12
400 **CAPTAIN SHARPE** (GB) 4
126 **CAPTAIN SMOOTHY** (GB) 2
146 **CAPTAIN STARLIGHT** (IRE) 23
703 **CAPTAIN SULLY** (IRE) 2
391 **CAPTAIN SUNSHINE** (GB) 8
522 **CAPTAIN TIDDS** (IRE) 5
557 **CAPTAIN WILSON** (GB) 5
513 **CAPTAIN WOODHOUSE** (GB) 3
500 **CAPTAIN'S DREAM** (IRE) 12
194 **CAPTAINRISK** (IRE) 3
619 **CAPTION** (GB) 14
223 **CAPTIVATOR** (GB) 3
495 **CAPTIVE HEART** F 3
366 **CAPTIVITY** (GB) 62
698 **CARA CARMELA** (GB) 3
285 **CARA GINA** (GB) 75
676 **CARA'S DELIGHT** (AUS) 2
249 **CARABINE** (USA) F 26
321 **CARABINIER** (FR) 26
360 **CARAMELITA** (GB) 6
75 **CARANBOLA** (GB) 3
117 **CARAVAN ROLLS ON** (GB) 1
657 **CARAVEL** (IRE) 16
494 **CARBERY SPIRIT** (IRE) F 4
166 **CARBIS BAY** (GB) 4
215 **CARBON PRINT** (USA) 2
447 **CARBON** (GB) 61
215 **CARD HIGH** (IRE) 6
215 **CARD LOVER** (GB) 3
708 **CARDI CRYSTAL** (IRE) 3
708 **CARDI KING** (GB) 4
285 **CARDIGAN** (IRE) 21
139 **CARDINAL** (GB) 3
274 **CARDINAL RICHELIEU** (IRE) 3
503 **CARDINAL ROSE** (GB) 9
597 **CARDINAL WALTER** (IRE) 27
319 **CARHENEY RIVER** (IRE) 1
276 **CARIBANA** (GB) F 15
213 **CARIBBEAN ACE** (IRE) 13
659 **CARIBBEAN RULES** (GB) 9
298 **CARIBBEAN SEA** (GB) 5
658 **CARIERO** (GER) 44
223 **CARINAE** (USA) F 47
679 **CARINYA** (IRE) 1
49 **CARISOLO** (GB) C 122
35 **CARLA** (FR) C 63
322 **CARLETON PLACE** (IRE) 3
489 **CARLICUE** (IRE) 14
129 **CARLTON BLUE** (IRE) 26
619 **CARLTON HOUSE** (USA) 1
277 **CARLTON MAC** (GB) 1
95 **CARLTON SCROOP** (FR) 1
611 **CARMELA MARIA** (GB) 2
309 **CARMELS GIFT** (IRE) F 1
19 **CARMEN'S CONCERTO** (GB) 51
127 **CARMENCITA** (GB) F 15
433 **CARNAC** (IRE) 6
494 **CARNELIAN** (IRE) 2
445 **CARNIVAL DREAM** (GB) 1
123 **CARNOUSTIE** (IRE) 22
43 **CARO MIO** (GB) C 34
10 **CAROLE'S DESTINY** (GB) 4
469 **CAROLE'S DESTRIER** (GB) 10
600 **CAROLINGIAN** (USA) 20
48 **CAROUSEL MUSIC** (GB) 2
580 **CARPENTRAS** (GB) 1
347 **CARPINCHO** (FR) 7

108 **CARR HALL** (IRE) 6
75 **CARRAGOLD** (GB) 4
645 **CARRAIGOONA** (IRE) F 15
206 **CARRIBS LEAP** (IRE) 5
141 **CARRICK A REDE** (IRE) 5
699 **CARRICKBOY** (IRE) 12
486 **CARRICKMINES** (IRE) 4
419 **CARRIES DARLING** (GB) 1
479 **CARRIETAU** (GB) 1
76 **CARRIG AN UISCE** (IRE) 2
420 **CARRIGLEA WOOD** (IRE) 5
331 **CARRIGMORNA KING** (IRE) 12
65 **CARRUTHERS** (GB) 2
465 **CARRY EACH OTHER** (IRE) 8
299 **CARRY ON CLAPPING** (IRE) 143
366 **CARRY ON KATIE** (USA) F 155
329 **CARSON DANCER** (USA) F 27
356 **CARTERS REST** (GB) 1
191 **CARTHAGINIAN** (IRE) 21
147 **CARTIMANDUA** (GB) F 76
471 **CARYS'S LAD** (GB) 5
432 **CASA BEX** (GB) 6
3 **CASAMENTO** (IRE) 10
658 **CASCADA** (GER) 45
396 **CASCO BAY** (GB) 2
183 **CASCO MOJADO** (GB) 35
219 **CASERTA** (GB) 40
499 **CASH AND GO** (IRE) 5
499 **CASH IS GOOD** (IRE) 6
592 **CASHEL KISS** (GB) G 16
617 **CASHEL ROSE** (IRE) 4
283 **CASHELGAR** (IRE) 13
564 **CASHMERE ROSE** (GB) 29
270 **CASIMIR ROAD** (IRE) 3
619 **CASKELENA** (IRE) 15
433 **CASPAR NETSCHER** (GB) 32
290 **CASPAR OF TARSUS** (IRE) 1
465 **CASPIAN PIPER** (IRE) 9
682 **CASSANDRA GO** (IRE) C 87
412 **CASSIUS** (IRE) 1
420 **CAST CADA** (IRE) 6
328 **CAST IN GOLD** (USA) F 79
354 **CAST IRON CASEY** (IRE) 1
34 **CASTA DIAMANTE** (GB) 59
204 **CASTALIAN SPRING** (IRE) 6
535 **CASTANET** (GB) F 2
49 **CASTAWAY QUEEN** (IRE) C 123
466 **CASTERNOVA** (GB) 2
597 **CASTILO DEL DIABLO** (IRE) 28
157 **CASTLE CONFLICT** (IRE) 5
42 **CASTLE MYTH** (USA) 6
419 **CASTLE WINGS** (IRE) 5
290 **CASTLEBOY WARRIOR** (IRE) 2
12 **CASTLEMORRIS KING** (GB) 6
503 **CASTLEROCK** (GB) 10
404 **CASTLES IN THE AIR** (GB) 8
404 **CASTLETOWN BRIDGE** (IRE) 7
489 **CASTLETOWNSEND** (IRE) 15
379 **CASTLEY LANE** (GB) 2
19 **CASUAL GLANCE** (GB) F 112
43 **CASUAL MOVER** (IRE) 4
651 **CASUAL REMARK** (IRE) F 6
642 **CAT ISLAND** (GB) 9
566 **CAT O' NINE TAILS** (GB) 4
376 **CAT QUEEN** (GB) 10
478 **CATALINAS DIAMOND** (IRE) 1
107 **CATALLOUT** (IRE) 4
283 **CATALYZE** (GB) 14

283 **CATAWOLLOW** (GB) 15
407 **CATCH A SMILE** (USA) C 41
525 **CATCH TAMMY** (IRE) 21
503 **CATCH THAT** (IRE) 11
640 **CATCH THE CASH** (IRE) 6
1 **CATCH THE CIDER** (GB) 28
59 **CATCH THE FIRE** (GB) 6
472 **CATCH THE RASCAL** (IRE) 8
597 **CATCH US** (FR) C 64
364 **CATCHANOVA** (IRE) 3
241 **CATCHER OF DREAMS** (IRE) 3
136 **CATCHING DREAMS** (IRE) C 62
447 **CATCHING STARS** (IRE) C 62
80 **CATCHY TUNE** (IRE) 7
552 **CATEGORICAL** (GB) 6
569 **CATERINA DE MEDICI** (FR) 30
447 **CATFISH** (IRE) 2
447 **CATHEDRAL** (GB) 24
219 **CATHERINE LINTON** (IRE) C 134
34 **CATHERINE PALACE** (GB) F 60
695 **CATHERINE'S RUN** (IRE) G 22
257 **CATHOLIC HILL** (USA) 2
403 **CATIVO CAVALLINO** (GB) 3
520 **CATO MINOR** (GB) 26
506 **CATRAMIS** (GB) 15
139 **CATS EYES** (GB) 16
206 **CATSPAN** (FR) 6
564 **CATTIVA GENEROSA** (GB) F 88
223 **CATWALK** (IRE) 25
266 **CAUCUS** (GB) 7
374 **CAUGHT BY WITNESS** (IRE) 7
63 **CAUGHT IN THE ACT** (IRE) 3
312 **CAUGHT INTHE LIGHT** (GB) 4
476 **CAUGHTONTHERIVER** (IRE) 9
646 **CAULFIELDS VENTURE** (IRE) 2
469 **CAUNAY** (IRE) 11
287 **CAUSEWAY SONG** (USA) C 58
650 **CAUSING CHAOS** (IRE) 13
643 **CAVALEIRO** (IRE) 26
657 **CAVALIER SPIRIT** (IRE) 17
412 **CAVALRY** (GB) G 2
435 **CAVALRY GUARD** (USA) 1
49 **CAVALRYMAN** (GB) 11
42 **CAVE OF THE GIANT** (IRE) 7
656 **CAVENDISH ROAD** (IRE) 1
77 **CAVITE ALPHA** (IRE) 2
640 **CAVITE ETA** (IRE) 7
77 **CAVITE GAMMA** (IRE) 3
519 **CAYMAN FOX** (GB) 5
227 **CAYMAN ISLANDS** (GB) 3
331 **CAYMAN KIRK** (GB) 13
49 **CAYMANS** (AUS) 12
619 **CAYUGA** (GB) 16
699 **CEANNLINE** (IRE) 13
395 **CEBONNE** (FR) 3
287 **CEBUANO** (GB) 4
619 **CECCHETTI METHOD** (IRE) 17
466 **CECILY PARSLEY** (GB) 3
489 **CEDRE BLEU** (FR) 16
299 **CEELO** (GB) 144
639 **CEEPEEGEE** (IRE) 5
111 **CEFIRA** (USA) F 94
682 **CELEBRITY SEVI** (IRE) 1
614 **CELERINA** (IRE) 1
489 **CELESTIAL HALO** (IRE) 17
534 **CELESTIAL RAY** (GB) 17
29 **CELESTIAL SEA** (GB) 75
640 **CELIAN** (FR) 8

285 CELLIST (GB) 22
156 CELTIC BALLAD (IRE) 1
304 CELTIC CAILIN (IRE) 12
183 CELTIC CELEB (IRE) 5
521 CELTIC CHARLIE (FR) 3
270 CELTIC CHARM (IRE) 4
499 CELTIC CUB (IRE) 7
682 CELTIC CUTIE (IRE) 30
292 CELTIC FELLA (IRE) 2
654 CELTIC FLING (GB) F 38
254 CELTIC INTRIGUE (IRE) 10
542 CELTIC SIXPENCE (IRE) 6
490 CELTIC STEP (GB) 3
450 CELTIC SULTAN (IRE) 5
335 CELTIC TORE (IRE) F 3
375 CELTS ESPERE (GB) 2
321 CELTUS (FR) 27
593 CENT PRIME (GB) F 7
285 CENTRAL FORCE (GB) C 76
619 CENTRED (GB) 101
475 CENTURIAN (IRE) 6
473 CEOL RUA (IRE) 22
366 CERCLE D'AMOUR (USA) C 156
7 CEREJEIRA (IRE) 3
58 CEREMONIAL JADE (UAE) 3
126 CERISE EN BLEU (FR) 3
388 CERITA F 64
381 CERIUM (IRE) 3
287 CERTERACH (IRE) 5
658 CESARE (GER) 9
254 CESIUM (FR) 11
265 CEST NOTRE GRIS (IRE) 25
329 CHA CHING (IRE) 7
696 CHABADA (JPN) 8
49 CHABAL (IRE) 13
33 CHAC DU CADRAN (FR) 4
511 CHACHA HEELS (FR) 50
111 CHACHAMAIDEE (IRE) 5
664 CHADFORD (GB) 1
698 CHALK AND CHEESE (USA) 16
237 CHAMBERS (IRE) 6
550 CHAMBLES (GB) 9
472 CHAMBRAY DANCER (IRE) 9
407 CHAMELEON (GB) C 42
434 CHAMIREY (FR) 28
473 CHAMPAGNE AGENT (IRE) 23
650 CHAMPAGNE FLORA (GB) 3
370 CHAMPAGNE JOHNNY (GB) 3
86 CHAMPAGNE ROSIE (GB) 3
677 CHAMPAGNE VALLEY (GB) 5
630 CHAMPERTY (IRE) 1
374 CHAMPION COURT (IRE) 8
130 CHAMPION TIPSTER (GB) F 13
326 CHAMPION VERSIONS (GB) 3
462 CHAMPOLUC (IRE) F 27
460 CHAMPS DE BLEU (IRE) 15
287 CHAN TONG (BRZ) F 59
331 CHANCE DU ROY (FR) 14
51 CHANCE ENCOUNTER (IRE) 2
55 CHANCE TO DANCE (IRE) 73
501 CHANCERY (USA) 5
496 CHANDELLE NO FIVE (USA) F 53
232 CHANDIGARH (IRE) 1
299 CHANDLERY (IRE) 29
646 CHANDOS (IRE) 3
403 CHANDRAYAAN (GB) 4
619 CHANGE COURSE (GB) C 102
547 CHANGING LANES (GB) 1

486 CHANGING THE GUARD (GB) 5
642 CHANKILLO (GB) 26
188 CHANT (IRE) 28
614 CHANTERELLE (IRE) C 14
139 CHANTILLY JEWEL (USA) 4
287 CHAPARRO (IRE) 6
270 CHAPATI (IRE) 5
303 CHAPEL HOUSE (GB) 1
390 CHAPELLE DU ROI (USA) 7
447 CHAPELLERIE (IRE) 25
304 CHAPERONED (IRE) 13
326 CHAPOLIMOSS (FR) 8
477 CHAPTER AND VERSE (IRE) 2
265 CHAPTER NINE (IRE) 3
533 CHARGEN (IRE) 1
476 CHARINGWORTH (IRE) 10
391 CHARIOT CHARGER (IRE) 9
467 CHARITABLE ACT (FR) 16
666 CHARITY BOX (IRE) 19
45 CHARLCOT (GB) 4
328 CHARLENE LACY (IRE) C 80
16 CHARLES (GB) 10
384 CHARLES CAMOIN (IRE) 1
461 CHARLES DE MILLE (GB) 6
321 CHARLES ONZE (FR) 28
277 CHARLES PARNELL (IRE) 2
18 CHARLES TYRWHITT 39
689 CHARLIE BUCKET (GB) 1
460 CHARLIE CHEESECAKE (IRE) 16
321 CHARLIE WINGNUT (IRE) 29
183 CHARLIZE (FR) 36
500 CHARLOTTE LAMB (GB) F 7
632 CHARLOTTE ROSINA (GB) 9
296 CHARLOTTE VALE (GB) C 51
713 CHARLOTTE'S BALL (IRE) 1
351 CHARLOTTEVALENTINA (IRE) C 7
452 CHARLTON (GB) 2
695 CHARM SCHOOL (GB) 23
506 CHARMEL'S DELIGHT (GB) 16
388 CHARMEUSE (IRE) 23
100 CHARMING GRACE (IRE) 4
670 CHARMING KNIGHT (IRE) 1
420 CHARMING LAD (IRE) 7
434 CHARMINSTER (IRE) 29
511 CHARMSTONE (USA) 4
588 CHAROLLES (GB) F 39
358 CHART (GB) 18
632 CHARTPLAN (IRE) 3
525 CHARTREUX (FR) 22
246 CHASE GATE (GB) 4
384 CHASIN' RAINBOWS (GB) 2
81 CHASING ACES (GB) 3
219 CHASING HALOS (USA) 6
343 CHASING SHADOWS (IRE) 11
588 CHATEAU LOLA (GB) 30
366 CHATTERATI (USA) 63
321 CHATTERBOX (IRE) 30
643 CHATTERER (IRE) 6
49 CHATURANGA (GB) C 124
109 CHAUD LAPIN (GB) 12
161 CHAUKAO (FR) C 49
600 CHEAM KSAH (IRE) 21
529 CHEAP STREET (GB) 2
180 CHEATING TIGER (IRE) 5
63 CHEATINGSIDEOFTOWN (IRE) 4
498 CHECKERBOARD (IRE) 8
111 CHECKPOINT (GB) 31
117 CHEDDAR GEORGE (GB) 2

58 CHEEKTOCHEEK (IRE) 59
129 CHEEKY GIRL (GB) C 27
593 CHEERS (GB) 8
276 CHEERS BUDDY (IRE) 2
201 CHEERS FOR THEA (GB) 9
237 CHEERY CAT (USA) 7
410 CHELSEA MICK (GB) 21
654 CHELWOOD GATE (IRE) 102
569 CHENDIYR (GB) 31
321 CHENEY MANOR (GB) 31
296 CHERNIK (IRE) 7
442 CHEROKEE STREAM (IRE) C 22
509 CHERREGO (USA) 4
626 CHERRY ALLEY (IRE) F 2
16 CHERRY LADY (GB) 11
266 CHERRY MALOTTE (GB) 121
19 CHERRY STREET (GB) 52
641 CHERRY TIGER (GB) 11
625 CHERRY TREE HILL (IRE) 12
16 CHERRY VINE (GB) 12
569 CHERRYXMA F 102
656 CHES JICARO (IRE) 2
27 CHESHIRE LADY (IRE) 6
134 CHESIL BEACH BOY (GB) 1
7 CHESTER ARISTOCRAT (GB) 14
700 CHESTER DEELYTE (IRE) 3
434 CHESTER LAD (GB) 30
630 CHESTER LEGEND (GB) 7
8 CHESTER RIDGE (GB) 7
641 CHESTER ROW (GB) 12
169 CHESTER'SLITTLEGEM (IRE) 27
256 CHESTHAM LAD (GB) 3
81 CHESTNUT BEN (IRE) 2
538 CHEVETON (GB) 2
358 CHEVIOT QUEST (IRE) 19
709 CHEVISE (IRE) 1
504 CHEVY TO THE LEVY (IRE) 1
208 CHEWOREE (GB) 13
29 CHEYENNE DREAM (GB) C 76
324 CHEYENNE RED (IRE) 1
698 CHEYLESMORE (IRE) 4
464 CHEZ VRONY (GB) 1
192 CHHOTA NAA (GB) 2
19 CHIBERTA KING (GB) 6
559 CHICAGO ALLEY (GB) 1
659 CHICAGO OUTFIT (IRE) 10
247 CHICARITO (GB) 7
469 CHICHARITO (IRE) 12
564 CHICHI KING (FR) 30
183 CHICHITEUSE (FR) 37
599 CHICKLEMIX (GB) 4
456 CHIEF DAN GEORGE (IRE) 7
404 CHIEF HECKLER (GB) 8
127 CHIEF OF MEN (GB) 2
219 CHIEF OF STAFF (GB) 7
111 CHIGNON (IRE) 32
111 CHIGUN (GB) 33
315 CHIK'S DREAM (GB) 6
466 CHIL THE KITE (GB) 37
50 CHILBURY HILL (IRE) 1
343 CHILL (IRE) 12
2 CHILLI GREEN (GB) 2
380 CHILLI ROSE (GB) 16
651 CHILLIANWALLAH (GB) 2
540 CHILLIE PEPPAR (GB) 2
226 CHILLY CHOCOLATE (IRE) 5
684 CHILWORTH LASS (IRE) 5
264 CHILWORTH SCREAMER (GB) 3

606 **CHINA EXCELS** (GB) 7
700 **CHINA HOUSE** (IRE) 4
447 **CHINA PINK** (GB) C 63
465 **CHINA ROCK** (IRE) 10
388 **CHINCHON** (IRE) 2
66 **CHINK OF LIGHT** (GB) 1
338 **CHIPPY** (IRE) 2
247 **CHISPA** (GB) C 13
503 **CHIT CHAT** (GB) 12
182 **CHJIMES** (IRE) 3
188 **CHLOE'S DREAM** (IRE) 29
450 **CHOC'A'MOCA** (IRE) 6
259 **CHOCCYWOCCYDOODAH** (GB) 18
49 **CHOCK A BLOCK** (IRE) 14
407 **CHOCOLATE HILLS** (FR) 18
161 **CHOCOLATE PURSUITS** (GB) 23
407 **CHOCOLATE PEARL** (USA) 19
391 **CHOICE WORDS** (USA) 10
80 **CHOIR GALLERY** (GB) C 13
201 **CHOISAN** (GB) 71
214 **CHOISIREZ** (IRE) 45
141 **CHOKUREI** (IRE) 6
508 **CHOLESKY** (IRE) 22
155 **CHOOKIE AVON** (GB) 3
155 **CHOOKIE HAMILTON** (GB) 4
155 **CHOOKIE ROYALE** (GB) 5
573 **CHOOSEDAY** (IRE) 43
299 **CHORAL** (GB) 2
102 **CHORAL BEE** (GB) 24
71 **CHORAL FESTIVAL** (GB) 3
199 **CHORD** (GB) 2
366 **CHORIST** (GB) C 157
237 **CHORISTER GIRL** (GB) 40
358 **CHORISTER SPORT** (IRE) 20
161 **CHOSEN CHARACTER** (GB) 4
506 **CHOSEN FOREVER** (GB) 4
635 **CHOSEN KEYS** (GB) 2
106 **CHOSEN ONE** (IRE) 1
460 **CHRIS PEA GREEN** (GB) 103
632 **CHRISSYCROSS** (IRE) 10
673 **CHRISTENING** (IRE) F 3
285 **CHRISTINGLE** (GB) 23
200 **CHRISTMAS CARNIVAL** (GB) 7
184 **CHRISTOPHER CHUA** (IRE) 17
256 **CHRISTOPHER WREN** (USA) 4
643 **CHRONIC FLAME** (TUR) 27
117 **CHUNKY DIAMOND** (IRE) 9
585 **CHURCH MUSIC** (IRE) 35
466 **CHURCH OF ENGLAND** (GB) 65
54 **CHURN DAT BUTTER** (USA) F 22
408 **CHUTIQUETTA** (FR) 47
379 **CIAN BOY** (IRE) 2
352 **CIARA BOO** (IRE) 19
699 **CICERON** (IRE) 14
647 **CIDER LOLLY** (GB) 3
439 **CIGALAS** (GB) 2
511 **CIGALON** (FR) 51
466 **CILL RIALAIG** (GB) 4
198 **CILRHIWRON** (GB) 4
228 **CINCIALLEGRA** (GB) F 16
698 **CINCINNATI KIT** (GB) 17
56 **CINDER'S POST** (FR) 34
16 **CINDERELLA ROSE** (GB) 13
434 **CINDERS AND ASHES** (GB) 31
564 **CINDY SHERMAN** (FR) 4
373 **CINEVATOR** (IRE) 7
219 **CINNAMON BAY** (GB) F 135
564 **CINTA** (GB) 5

658 **CIOCCOMIA** (GER) 46
183 **CIPRIANI** (FR) 6
129 **CIRCUMVENT** (GB) 1
260 **CIRCUS CLOWN** (IRE) 4
3 **CIRCUS MONDAO** (USA) 51
69 **CIRCUS POLKA** (USA) 2
599 **CIRCUS STAR** (IRE) 5
304 **CITIZENSHIP** (GB) 14
681 **CITRUS MARK** (GB) 9
666 **CITRUS STAR** (USA) 2
299 **CITY DAZZLER** (IRE) 30
433 **CITY GROUND** (USA) 8
433 **CITY LEGEND** (GB) 7
310 **CITY MAIDEN** (USA) C 19
147 **CITY OF CANTON** (IRE) 24
29 **CITY ON SEA** (IRE) 2
118 **CITY PLAYER** (IRE) 6
321 **CITY PRESS** (IRE) 32
55 **CITY SQUARE** (IRE) 74
3 **CITY STYLE** (USA) 11
504 **CITYAR** (FR) 2
119 **CITYSCAPE** (GB) 4
39 **CIVENA** (IRE) 5
373 **CIVIL DISOBEDIENCE** (GB) 8
650 **CIVIL SERVANT** (GB) 15
218 **CIVIL UNREST** (IRE) 9
9 **CLAIMANT** (IRE) 11
241 **CLANACHY** (GB) 4
655 **CLAPPED** (GB) 9
569 **CLAQUE** (FR) 32
347 **CLARA'S DREAM** (IRE) G 8
458 **CLARAGH NATIVE** (IRE) 4
135 **CLARESBURN** (GB) 3
391 **CLARET CLOAK** (IRE) 11
220 **CLARETINTHEBLOOD** (IRE) 44
299 **CLARICE ORSINI** (GB) F 145
695 **CLARION CALL** (GB) 24
565 **CLARIOR EX OBSCURO** (IRE) 1
569 **CLARIYN** (FR) 33
507 **CLARKSON** (IRE) 16
583 **CLASH DUFF** (IRE) 3
91 **CLASS MONITOR** (GB) 24
619 **CLASS WIN** (GB) 18
501 **CLASSIC COLORI** (IRE) 6
408 **CLASSIC CUT** (GB) 10
408 **CLASSIC DIVA** (GER) 48
292 **CLASSIC EURO** (IRE) 3
359 **CLASSIC FALCON** (IRE) 24
208 **CLASSIC PUNCH** (GB) 3
700 **CLASSIC QUARTET** (GB) F 29
700 **CLASSIC QUARTET** (GB) F 34
359 **CLASSIC RALLY** (GB) 8
520 **CLASSIC VINTAGE** (USA) 2
34 **CLASSIC VISION** (GB) F 61
283 **CLASSICAL CHLOE** (GB) 16
706 **CLASSICAL LAND** (GB) 2
501 **CLASSICAL MIST** (GB) 7
320 **CLASSICALLY** (IRE) 3
588 **CLASSY LASS** (GB) 31
688 **CLAUDE CARTER** (GB) 3
304 **CLAUSTRA** (FR) F 104
397 **CLAWS** (GB) C 48
191 **CLAXON** (FR) C 53
374 **CLE DE LUNE** (FR) G 9
433 **CLEAN BOWLED** (GB) 33
340 **CLEAN HILLS** (IRE) 8
376 **CLEAR ICE** (IRE) 3
655 **CLEAR IN THE WEST** (USA) F 20

184 **CLEAR PRAISE** (USA) 1
94 **CLEAR SAILING** (GB) 2
612 **CLEAR SPRING** (IRE) 3
67 **CLEAR WONDER** (GB) 6
572 **CLEARING HOUSE** (GB) 2
460 **CLEARWATER BAY** (IRE) 17
269 **CLEEVE CLOUD** (IRE) 1
364 **CLEMENT** (IRE) 31
55 **CLEOFILA** (IRE) 18
139 **CLERICAL** (USA) 5
593 **CLERK'S CHOICE** (IRE) 9
508 **CLESSIDRA** (IRE) 23
525 **CLEVER DICK** (GB) 23
54 **CLICHE** (IRE) F 23
499 **CLICKSNMORTAR** (IRE) 8
123 **CLICQUOT** (USA) 23
687 **CLIFFORDS REPRIEVE** (GB) 6
534 **CLINICAL** (GB) 4
658 **CLOCCA SAM** 10
55 **CLOCH CHORA** (IRE) 75
201 **CLOCKMAKER** (IRE) 10
507 **CLODHOPPER** (IRE) 17
55 **CLOGHER COVE** (IRE) 19
27 **CLON BRULEE** (IRE) 32
298 **CLONDAW WARRIOR** (IRE) 6
397 **CLONE DEVIL** (IRE) 41
362 **CLONUSKER** (IRE) 4
245 **CLOONAVERY** (IRE) 1
407 **CLOONKEARY** (GB) C 43
278 **CLORAN JACK** (IRE) 1
525 **CLOSE HOUSE** (GB) 24
223 **CLOSE REGARDS** (IRE) C 48
433 **CLOSE TO THE EDGE** (IRE) 8
452 **CLOSE TOGETHER** (IRE) 18
321 **CLOSE TOUCH** (GB) 33
628 **CLOUD CASTLE** (GB) F 18
201 **CLOUD HAWK** (IRE) 11
304 **CLOUDED THOUGHTS** (IRE) 15
446 **CLOUDGAZER** (IRE) 13
682 **CLOUDRACER** (IRE) 31
673 **CLOUDS OF GLORY** (GB) 6
266 **CLOUDSPIN** (USA) C 122
511 **CLOUDY BAY** (GER) F 102
478 **CLOUDY BOB** (IRE) 2
606 **CLOUDY DAWN** (GB) 8
336 **CLOUDY SPIRIT** (GB) 6
507 **CLOUDY START** (GB) 2
606 **CLOUDY TOO** (IRE) 9
487 **CLOUDY WAGER** (GB) 3
340 **CLOUGHMILE** (IRE) 9
479 **CLOUSEAU** (NZ) 1
248 **CLOVERS BOY** (GB) 2
119 **CLOWANCE ESTATE** (IRE) 20
699 **CLOWANCE HOUSE** (GB) 15
451 **CLOWANCE KEYS** (GB) 28
259 **CLUMBER PLACE** (GB) 1
197 **CLUNIE** (GB) G 13
529 **CLYFFE TOP** (GB) 3
543 **CMONBABYLITEMYFIRE** (IRE) 33
548 **CNOC MOY** (IRE) 1
614 **CNOCAN DIVA** (IRE) 2
454 **COACH LANE** (GB) 3
116 **COACH MONTANA** (IRE) 16
308 **COALBURN** (GB) 2
388 **COALIS** (GB) 65
283 **COASTAL PASSAGE** (GB) 17
105 **COASTLEY** (IRE) 2
123 **COASTLINE** (GB) C 56

337 **COAX** (GB) 3
157 **COBBLER'S QUEEN** (IRE) 6
444 **COCACOBANA** (IRE) 1
632 **COCHABAMBA** (IRE) 4
262 **COCK OF THE ROCK** (IRE) 7
34 **COCKATRICE** (GB) C 62
447 **COCKNEY CLASS** (USA) 3
328 **COCKNEY DANCER** (GB) 22
214 **COCKNEY FIRE** (GB) 46
116 **COCKNEY ROCKER** (GB) 17
117 **COCKNEY SPARROW** (GB) 10
331 **COCKNEY TRUCKER** (IRE) 15
201 **COCKTAIL CHARLIE** (GB) 12
682 **COCKTAIL HOUR** (IRE) 88
223 **COCO ROUGE** (IRE) 4
681 **COCOA MINNIE** (IRE) 10
521 **COCOHATCHEE** (GB) 4
74 **COCONUT QUEEN** (IRE) C 59
58 **COCOZZA** (USA) 4
531 **CODA AGENCY** (GB) 7
150 **CODDINGTON BOY** (GB) 5
434 **CODE BLUE** (GB) 32
601 **CODE SIX** (IRE) 28
416 **CODY WYOMING** (GB) 2
254 **COEUR DE FOU** (FR) 12
408 **COEUR DES AS** (FR) 3
80 **COFFEE CREAM** (GB) C 14
597 **COFFEE KING** (GB) 29
447 **COGITO** (USA) 26
614 **COIN OF COURAGE** (IRE) 15
460 **COIN OF THE REALM** (IRE) 18
681 **COIS FARRAIG** (GB) 11
445 **COLAMANDIS** (GB) 2
220 **COLBYOR** (GB) 45
695 **COLD HARBOUR** (GB) 25
380 **COLD KNIGHT** (GB) 17
237 **COLDITZ** (IRE) 8
561 **COLEBROOKE** (GB) 2
34 **COLIMA** (IRE) 19
454 **COLIN'S DESIRE** (GB) 4
111 **COLLADA** (IRE) C 95
201 **COLLATERAL DAMAGE** (IRE) 13
304 **COLLECTABLE** (GB) 82
659 **COLLEGE GREEN** (GB) 11
700 **COLLIERS CASTLE** (IRE) 5
299 **COLLINGBOURNEDUCIS** (IRE) 146
102 **COLLOQUIAL** (GB) 5
266 **COLOMBIAN** (IRE) 8
681 **COLONEL ALF** (GB) 12
196 **COLONEL FLAY** (GB) 1
27 **COLONEL MAK** (GB) 7
49 **COLONIAL** (IRE) 15
469 **COLONIAL HARRY** (GB) 13
265 **COLONUS** (IRE) 4
169 **COLORADO GOLD** (GB) 5
659 **COLORADO KID** (IRE) 12
58 **COLORFUL NOTION** (IRE) 27
588 **COLORI D'AMORE** (GB) 32
507 **COLOUR AND SPICE** (IRE) F 31
304 **COLOUR COORDINATED** (RE) F 83
366 **COLOUR GUARD** (GB) 7
442 **COLOUR MY WORLD** (GB) 23
436 **COLOUR OF LOVE** (IRE) 2
331 **COLOUR SQUADRON** (IRE) 16
18 **COLOUR THERAPY** (IRE) 61
49 **COLOUR VISION** (FR) 16
64 **COLOURBEARER** (IRE) 4
7 **COLOURS OF NATURE** (GB) 19

552 **COLUMBUS SECRET** (IRE) 7
675 **COLWYN BAY** (IRE) 2
29 **COLZA** (USA) C 77
146 **COMADOIR** (IRE) 1
472 **COMBUSTIBLE LADY** (IRE) 10
658 **COME AND FIGHT** (IRE) 11
107 **COME HERE YEW** (IRE) 5
153 **COME ON BLUE CHIP** (IRE) 9
488 **COME ON DAVE** (IRE) 48
645 **COME ON SAFARI** (IRE) 2
53 **COME OUT FIRING** (IRE) 3
501 **COMEDY ACT** (GB) 8
219 **COMEDY AWARD** (USA) 41
414 **COMEDY HOUSE** (GB) 2
547 **COMEHOMEQUIETLY** (IRE) 2
231 **COMERAGH KING** (GB) 3
182 **COMIC** (IRE) C 103
366 **COMICAL** (GB) 64
601 **COMMANCHE** (GB) 29
42 **COMMANCHE DAWN** (GB) 8
180 **COMMANCHE RAIDER** (IRE) 6
169 **COMMAND MARSHAL** (FR) 6
566 **COMMANDER VEEJAY** (GB) 5
71 **COMMANDINGPRESENCE** (USA) 4
619 **COMMEND** (GB) 19
89 **COMMERCE** (GB) 4
507 **COMMERCIAL** (IRE) 3
4 **COMMERCIAL EXPRESS** (IRE) 4
3 **COMMISSAR** (GB) 52
147 **COMMITMENT** (GB) 25
306 **COMMON CENTS** (GB) 26
564 **COMMON DENOMINATOR** (GB) 31
19 **COMMUNICATOR** (GB) 7
437 **COMMUNITY** (USA) 4
391 **COMPASSION** (GB) 12
655 **COMPLACENT** (IRE) 10
214 **COMPLEX** (GB) 47
520 **COMPLEX** (USA) F 52
61 **COMPLICATION** (GB) F 35
259 **COMPRADORE** (GB) C 42
34 **COMPTON** (GB) 20
1 **COMPTON AIR** (USA) 9
1 **COMPTON ASHDOWN** (GB) 10
1 **COMPTON BABY** (GB) 11
1 **COMPTON BELL** (GB) 12
1 **COMPTON BIRD** (GB) 13
1 **COMPTON CROFTER** (GB) 14
493 **COMPTON LAD** (GB) 4
1 **COMPTON MONARCH** (GB) 15
141 **COMPTON PRINCE** (GB) 26
1 **COMPTON RAINBOW** (GB) 16
1 **COMPTON SHUTTLE** (IRE) 17
1 **COMPTON SILVER** (GB) 29
1 **COMPTON TARGET** (IRE) 18
642 **COMRADE BOND** (GB) 10
19 **COMTESSE NOIRE** (CAN) C 113
49 **CON ARTIST** (IRE) 17
205 **CONAN'S ROCK** (GB) 19
588 **CONAS ATA TU** (GB) 33
219 **CONCENTRIC** (GB) F 136
283 **CONCORDIA NOTTE** (IRE) 70
61 **CONCUBINE** (IRE) C 36
706 **CONDARIAN** (IRE) 3
73 **CONDILESSA** (IRE) F 38
29 **CONDITION** (GB) C 78
376 **CONDUCTING** (GB) 4
601 **CONE DONKEY** (IRE) 30
65 **CONEYGREE** (GB) 3

330 **CONFIDE IN ME** (GB) 2
388 **CONFIDENTE** (IRE) 24
348 **CONFLICTOFINTEREST** (GB) 1
398 **CONFLUENCE** (GB) 4
621 **CONIGRE** (GB) 2
374 **CONINGTON** (GB) 10
70 **CONJOLA** (GB) 2
676 **CONJUROR'S BLUFF** (GB) 3
172 **CONN MAN** (IRE) 6
160 **CONNAK** (IRE) 6
358 **CONOWEN** (GB) 21
263 **CONQUISTO** (GB) 6
119 **CONSENTING** (GB) 21
219 **CONSERVATOIRE** (USA) 42
111 **CONSERVE** (GB) 96
109 **CONSIDER YOURSELF** (USA) 1
525 **CONSIGLIERE** (FR) 25
496 **CONSIGN** (GB) 54
32 **CONSISTANT** (GB) 5
434 **CONSTANT CONTACT** (GB) 33
444 **CONSTANT CUPID** (IRE) 2
123 **CONSTANT DESIRE** (IRE) 2
219 **CONSTELLATION** (GB) 1
285 **CONSTITUTE** (USA) C 77
205 **CONSULATE** (IRE) 2
374 **CONSULT** (GB) 11
433 **CONSULTANT STYLIST** (IRE) C 50
274 **CONTADOR** (IRE) 4
266 **CONTENTIOUS** (USA) F 123
111 **CONTINUUM** (GB) 34
619 **CONTRADICT** (GB) 103
18 **CONTRADIKTIVE** (IRE) 9
136 **CONVERTI** (GB) 6
345 **CONVINCE** (USA) 1
611 **CONVITEZZA** (GB) 3
399 **COOKIESHAKE** (GB) 2
153 **COOL AS CASH** (GB) 10
579 **COOL BARANCA** (GER) 3
699 **COOL CASCADE** (GB) 16
153 **COOL FANTASY** (IRE) 11
583 **COOL FRIEND** (IRE) 4
187 **COOL GEORGE** (GB) 1
161 **COOL HAND LUKE** (IRE) 24
450 **COOL IN THE SHADE** (GB) 7
328 **COOL MACAVITY** (IRE) 2
157 **COOL MERENDA** (IRE) G 7
682 **COOL METALLIC** (IRE) 89
434 **COOL MISSION** (IRE) 34
383 **COOL OPERATOR** (GB) 6
161 **COOL RUNNINGS** (IRE) 50
387 **COOL SKY** (GB) 15
559 **COOL SPRING** (IRE) G 7
105 **COOL STAR** (IRE) 3
380 **COOL STEEL** (IRE) 18
286 **COOL STRIKE** (UAE) 3
105 **COOL VIC** (IRE) 4
684 **COOLAGAD STAR** (IRE) 6
254 **COOLBEG** (IRE) 13
473 **COOLDINE** (IRE) 24
203 **COOLER CLIMES** (GB) 9
298 **COOLKING** (GB) 2
498 **COOPERS HILL** (GB) 9
298 **COOSAN BELLE** (IRE) 8
39 **COOTAMUNDRA** (IRE) 6
650 **COOTEHILL** (IRE) 16
214 **COOTEHILL LASS** (IRE) 8
299 **COPLOW** (GB) 31
352 **COPP THE LOT** (USA) 20

462 **COPPER CANYON** (GB) 1
531 **COPPER FALLS** (GB) 33
323 **COPPER ROSE** (USA) C 2
570 **COPPER'S GOLD** (IRE) 15
54 **COPPERWOOD** (GB) 3
446 **COPS AND ROBBERS** (GB) 14
459 **COPSEHILL GIRL** (IRE) 3
465 **COPSIANO** (IRE) 11
183 **COQUERELLE'S BEST** (GB) 53
466 **COQUET** (GB) 38
669 **COQUET HEAD** (GB) 1
533 **COQUETTE ROUGE** (IRE) F 7
410 **CORAL COVE** (GB) 3
361 **CORAL POINT** (IRE) 1
625 **CORAL SANDS** (GB) 13
318 **CORALINE** (GB) F 46
499 **CORBALLY CROSS** (IRE) 9
446 **CORBALLY GHOST** (IRE) 15
434 **CORDILLERA** (GB) 35
147 **CORININE** (IRE) C 77
58 **CORINTHIAN CASUAL** (IRE) 60
552 **CORKAGE** (IRE) 8
513 **CORKY DANCER** (GB) 4
95 **CORLOUGH MOUNTAIN** (GB) 2
532 **CORMORANT WHARF** (IRE) 2
437 **CORN MAIDEN** (GB) 11
299 **CORNICHE** (FR) 147
174 **CORNISH ICE** (GB) 6
266 **CORNROW** (GB) 124
433 **CORNUS** (GB) 9
507 **CORPORAL MADDOX** (GB) 4
299 **CORREGGIO** (GB) 148
509 **CORRIB** (IRE) 9
530 **CORRIB DRIFT** (USA) 1
141 **CORRYVRECKAN** (IRE) F 62
123 **CORSAGE** (USA) 24
111 **CORSETRY** (USA) 35
150 **CORSICAN BOY** (GB) 6
81 **CORSICAN BOY** (GB) 3
446 **CORSKEAGH ROYALE** (IRE) 16
634 **CORTINAS** (IRE) 3
9 **CORVETTE** (GB) 12
466 **COSIMO DE MEDICI** (GB) 5
111 **COSMIC CURIOUS** (GER) 97
220 **COSMIC HALO** (GB) 46
304 **COSMIC RHYTHM** (GB) 84
223 **COSSETED** (GB) 49
380 **COSWAY SPIRIT** (IRE) 19
214 **COTES DU RHONE** (IRE) 48
696 **COTILLION** (GB) 9
112 **COTSWOLD VILLAGE** (AUS) 1
254 **COTTAGE ACRE** (IRE) 14
75 **COTTAM DONNY** (GB) 5
75 **COTTAM STELLA** (GB) 6
3 **COTTESMORE** (USA) 53
237 **COTTON EASTER** (GB) G 41
642 **COTTON GRASS** (GB) 11
130 **COTTON KING** (GB) 2
227 **COTTON MILL** (GB) 6
266 **COTTON TRADER** (USA) 37
429 **COULD IT BE MAGIC** (GB) 2
446 **COULEUR FRANCE** (IRE) 17
600 **COULEUVRE** (USA) 22
572 **COULISSE** (IRE) F 14
619 **COUNSEL** (IRE) 20
501 **COUNT BERTONI** (IRE) 9
516 **COUNT CEPRANO** (IRE) 4
219 **COUNTERFEITER** (GB) 137

3 **COUNTERGLOW** (IRE) 54
380 **COUNTERPARTY** (GB) 20
3 **COUNTERSIGN** (GB) 55
33 **COUNTESS COMET** (IRE) 5
285 **COUNTESS FERRAMA** (GB) 25
505 **COUNTING HOUSE** (IRE) 2
9 **COUNTRY ROAD** (IRE) 13
289 **COUNTRYCRAFT** (GB) 1
466 **COUNTRYMAN** (GB) 66
543 **COUNTRYWIDE FLAME** (IRE) 4
656 **COUNTRYWIDE GIRL** (IRE) C 12
659 **COUNTY COLOURS** (GB) 3
520 **COUP DE GRACE** (IRE) 27
639 **COUP ROYALE** (FR) 7
299 **COUPE DE VILLE** (GB) 32
619 **COURAGE** (IRE) 21
573 **COURAGEOUS** (IRE) 6
132 **COURT AGAIN** (GB) 1
467 **COURT APPLAUSE** (IRE) 5
132 **COURT BEHIND** (GB) 2
391 **COURT BY SURPRISE** (IRE) 13
541 **COURT FINALE** (GB) 2
469 **COURT GAMBLE** (IRE) 14
541 **COURT HUMOUR** (GB) 3
391 **COURT IN MOTION** (IRE) 14
374 **COURT IN SESSION** (GB) 3
695 **COURT MINSTREL** (IRE) 26
111 **COURT PASTORAL** (GB) 98
347 **COURT RED HANDED** (IRE) 9
391 **COURT VICTORY** (IRE) 15
538 **COURT WING** (IRE) 3
366 **COURTESY CALL** (IRE) 65
331 **COURTING WHITNEY** (IRE) 17
529 **COURTLAND AVENUE** (IRE) 26
214 **COURTLAND KING** (IRE) 49
565 **COURTLY CONDUCT** (IRE) 2
466 **COUSIN KHEE** (GB) 6
473 **COUSIN VINNY** (IRE) 25
466 **COVENTINA** (IRE) F 67
556 **COVERHOLDER** (IRE) 7
141 **COVERT DECREE** (GB) 7
357 **COVETED** (GB) F 24
539 **COWBRIDGE** (IRE) 3
480 **COZY TIGER** (USA) 12
306 **COZZENE'S PRIDE** (USA) F 38
700 **CRABBIES GINGER** (GB) 6
700 **CRABBIES GOLD** (IRE) 7
251 **CRACK AT DAWN** (IRE) 2
489 **CRACK AWAY JACK** (GB) 18
694 **CRACK OF DAWN** (IRE) 1
201 **CRACKENTORP** (GB) 14
634 **CRACKERJAC BOY** (USA) 4
17 **CRACKERJACK** (GB) 1
570 **CRACKERJACK LAD** (IRE) 16
180 **CRACKING CHOICE** (IRE) 44
606 **CRAFTI BOOKIE** (IRE) 10
542 **CRAFTY ROBERTO** (GB) 7
464 **CRAGGANMORE CREEK** (GB) 2
578 **CRAIC SA CEILI** (IRE) F 6
435 **CRAICAJACK** (IRE) 2
412 **CRAICNEASY** (IRE) 3
696 **CRAIGLANDS** (IRE) 10
386 **CRAIGNURE** (IRE) 3
340 **CRAIGS DREAM** (IRE) 10
219 **CRANACH** (GB) 43
659 **CRANBERRY ICE** (GB) 14
298 **CRANKY CORNER** (GB) 9
262 **CRANNAGHMORE BOY** (IRE) 8

212 **CRANWORTH QUEST** (IRE) 3
340 **CRASH** (IRE) 11
366 **CRAVAT** (GB) 66
108 **CRAZY BOLD** (GER) 7
308 **CRAZY DAISY** 3
597 **CRAZY TOO** (IRE) 30
228 **CREAM TEASE** (GB) C 12
304 **CREATIVE PURSUIT** (IRE) 16
404 **CREDIT FOR LIFE** (IRE) 9
699 **CREDIT SWAP** (GB) 17
227 **CREEKSIDE** (GB) 7
35 **CREME ANGLAISE** (GB) 3
101 **CRESCENT BEACH** (IRE) 3
650 **CRESCENT ISLAND** (IRE) 17
339 **CRESSWELL CRUSADER** (GB) 3
299 **CRESTA STAR** (GB) 33
460 **CRETE** (IRE) 19
249 **CREW CUT** (IRE) 3
493 **CRICKET BOY** (GB) 5
93 **CRIDDA BOY** (GB) 2
201 **CRIED FOR YOU** (IRE) 72
681 **CRIME DONT PAY** (IRE) 13
488 **CRIMEA** (IRE) 6
447 **CRIMSON CHEER** (USA) 27
713 **CRIMSON MITRE** (GB) 2
78 **CRIMSON QUEEN** (GB) 3
310 **CRIMSON SEA** (IRE) 12
682 **CRIMSON SUNRISE** (IRE) 32
162 **CRIMSON TOPAZ** (GB) F 5
489 **CRIQTONIC** (FR) 19
489 **CRISTAL BONUS** (FR) 20
550 **CRISTAL GEM** (GB) 10
61 **CRISTALIYEV** (GB) 3
534 **CRITICAL POINT** (GB) 18
299 **CRIUS** (GB) 34
696 **CROAN ROCK** (IRE) 11
11 **CROCO BAY** (IRE) 1
250 **CROCO MISTER** (IRE) 3
283 **CROCODILE BAY** (IRE) 18
499 **CROCUS BAY** (IRE) 10
283 **CROESO BACH** (GB) G 82
612 **CROESO MAWR** (GB) 4
366 **CROFTAMIE** (GB) 67
175 **CROFTON ARCH** (GB) 1
175 **CROFTON LANE** (GB) 2
614 **CROI AN OR** (IRE) 16
331 **CROIX DE GUERRE** (IRE) 18
183 **CROIX MADAME** (FR) 7
254 **CROOKSHANKS** (IRE) 15
671 **CROP WALKER** (IRE) 1
508 **CROPLEY** (IRE) 24
169 **CROQUEMBOUCHE** (IRE) 28
446 **CROSS APPEAL** (IRE) 18
101 **CROSS KENNON** (IRE) 4
404 **CROSS OF HONOUR** (IRE) 10
310 **CROSS THE BOSS** (IRE) 5
503 **CROSS THE FLAGS** (IRE) 13
120 **CROSSGUARD** (USA) 2
506 **CROSSLEY** (GB) 17
388 **CROSSTOWN** (GB) 66
148 **CROWDED ROOM** (IRE) 1
450 **CROWN CHOICE** (GB) 8
366 **CROWN COUNSEL** (IRE) 8
299 **CROWN DEPENDENCY** (IRE) 35
436 **CROWN OF JEWELS** (USA) F 26
552 **CROWNING JEWEL** (GB) 9
462 **CROWNING STAR** (IRE) 8
343 **CROWNING VIRTUE** (IRE) 13

89 **CRUCHAIN** (IRE) 5
116 **CRUINN A BHORD** (GB) F 26
55 **CRUINNEAS** (IRE) 20
538 **CRUISE CONTROL** (GB) 4
50 **CRUISE IN STYLE** (IRE) 2
73 **CRUISE TOTHELIMIT** (IRE) 4
467 **CRUISER** (GB) 2
59 **CRUISING BYE** (GB) 7
383 **CRUMBLE** (GB) 7
526 **CRUNCHED** (GB) 2
321 **CRUZ ON TED** (GB) 34
119 **CRY FURY** (GB) 5
227 **CRY OF FREEDOM** (USA) 8
285 **CRY PEARL** (USA) 78
165 **CRYING GAME** (IRE) 1
3 **CRYING WOLF** (USA) 56
111 **CRYOSPHERE** (GB) 4
328 **CRYPTIC CHOICE** (IRE) 23
476 **CRYSTAL CHILD** (GB) 11
603 **CRYSTAL CLICHE** (GB) 1
35 **CRYSTAL CURLING** (IRE) F 64
660 **CRYSTAL GAL** (IRE) 8
508 **CRYSTAL HOUSE** (CHI) C 63
111 **CRYSTAL MONARCH** (IRE) 36
304 **CRYSTAL MORNING** (IRE) 17
259 **CRYSTAL PEAKS** (GB) 43
404 **CRYSTAL PRINCE** (GB) 11
390 **CRYSTAL REEF** (GB) F 26
321 **CRYSTAL ROCK** (GB) 35
35 **CRYSTAL SWAN** (IRE) F 65
522 **CRYSTAL SWING** (GB) 6
434 **CUBAN PIECE** (GB) 36
161 **CUBAN TASH** (GB) 51
34 **CUBANITA** (GB) 21
65 **CUCKOO PEN** (GB) 4
529 **CUCKOO ROCK** (IRE) 4
29 **CUCUMA** (FR) 79
321 **CUCUMBER RUN** (IRE) 36
113 **CUCURRI** (GB) 5
639 **CUE CARD** (GB) 8
552 **CUE TO CUE** (GB) 10
19 **CUISINE** (IRE) 114
86 **CULLAHILL** (IRE) 4
686 **CUMBRIAN CONCERTO** (GB) F 22
343 **CUMULUS NIMBUS** (GB) 14
529 **CUNNING ACT** (GB) 5
220 **CUNNING CLARETS** (IRE) 9
507 **CUORE** (IRE) 18
520 **CURACAO** (GB) 3
534 **CURIOUS MIND** (GB) 45
299 **CURL** (IRE) 149
446 **CURLEY BILL** (IRE) 19
666 **CURLY COME HOME** (GB) 20
95 **CURRAGH DANCER** (FR) 3
24 **CURRAHEE** (GB) 5
567 **CURRENT CLIMATE** (IRE) 5
489 **CURRENT EVENT** (FR) 21
652 **CURSUM PERFICIO** (GB) 2
489 **CURTAIN RAZER** (IRE) 22
3 **CURZON LINE** (GB) 57
380 **CUSTER OF THE WEST** (IRE) 21
311 **CUSTERS FLIGHT** (IRE) 3
403 **CUSTOM HOUSE** (IRE) 5
399 **CUT ACROSS** (IRE) 3
683 **CUT AND THRUST** (IRE) 1
129 **CUT NO ICE** (IRE) 8
191 **CUT SHORT** (USA) F 54
283 **CUT THE CACKLE** (IRE) 19

287 **CUTE CAIT** (GB) C 30
340 **CUTEASAFOX** (IRE) 12
358 **CUTHBERT** (GB) 1
496 **CUTTING IT FINE** (IRE) 16
509 **CWM CAT** (GB) 18
509 **CWMNI** (GB) 6
476 **CYBORA** (FR) 12
299 **CYCLONE** (GB) 150
285 **CYCLONE CONNIE** (GB) C 79
174 **CYDONIA** (IRE) 7
276 **CYFLYMDER** (IRE) 3
434 **CYGNET** (GB) 37
141 **CYNTHIA CALHOUN** (GB) C 27
571 **CYPRESS GROVE** (IRE) 1
419 **CYPRUSORMILAN** (GB) 3
191 **CYRUS SOD** (GB) 22
520 **CZECH IT OUT** (IRE) 53
593 **D'ARGENT CLOUD** (GB) 10
408 **D'ARTAGNAN** (GER) 4
552 **D'GIGI** (GB) 3
360 **D'URBERVILLE** (GB) 7
585 **DA PONTE** (GB) 6
601 **DA'QUONDE** (IRE) 5
170 **DAARTH** (GB) 1
207 **DAAWEITZA** (GB) 8
287 **DABADIYAN** (IRE) 60
299 **DABAWIYAH** (IRE) F 151
488 **DADDY WARBUCKS** (IRE) 49
198 **DADDY'SLITTLEGIRL** (GB) 5
124 **DADO MUSH** (GB) 3
93 **DADS BIRTHDAY** (GB) 1
328 **DAFFAASH** (USA) C 81
682 **DAFFERN SEAL** (IRE) 2
119 **DAFFYD** (GB) 22
466 **DAFFYDOWNDILLY** (GB) 7
74 **DAGHASH** (GB) 33
74 **DAGHASHAH** (GB) 34
116 **DAHAB GOLD** (IRE) 5
507 **DAHSHAH** (GB) C 32
65 **DAHTESTE** (GB) 5
329 **DAI E DAI** (USA) C 28
314 **DAINTIE DISH** (IRE) 12
59 **DAIS RETURN** (IRE) 8
214 **DAISY DAZE** (GB) 9
308 **DAISY DO** (IRE) F 12
29 **DAIVIKA** (USA) 80
286 **DAKOTA BOY** (IRE) 4
299 **DALANDRA** (GB) 152
380 **DALAVAR** (IRE) 22
460 **DALAYIR** (FR) 20
606 **DALDINI** (GB) 11
343 **DALE STREET** (IRE) 15
49 **DALGIG** 49
154 **DALHAAN** (USA) 2
161 **DALIANCE** (IRE) 25
287 **DALIYAN** (IRE) 31
35 **DALIYANA** (IRE) F 66
569 **DALKALA** (USA) 34
299 **DALKOVA** (GB) 36
460 **DALMO** (IRE) 104
569 **DALTARA** (IRE) C 103
569 **DALTAYA** (FR) C 104
569 **DALTIANA** (IRE) 35
508 **DALUKA** (IRE) 64
573 **DAM BEAUTIFUL** (GB) 44
351 **DAM CERTAIN** (GB) C 8
49 **DAMAR** (IRE) 77
45 **DAMASCUS SYMPHONY** (GB) 5

619 **DAMBUSTER** (IRE) 104
408 **DAME DE GUERRE** 5
601 **DAME LAURA** (IRE) C 60
111 **DAME'S VIOLET** (IRE) C 100
318 **DAMELINA** (FR) 2
357 **DAMSON** (FR) C 25
446 **DAN BOGAN** (IRE) 84
525 **DAN BREEN** (IRE) 26
249 **DAN DONNELLY** (IRE) 4
618 **DAN'S HEIR** (GB) 2
174 **DAN'S MARTHA** (GB) 8
18 **DANA'S PRESENT** (GB) 40
147 **DANADANA** (IRE) 2
592 **DANAFISIAK** (IRE) 17
422 **DANAHER** (GB) 1
331 **DANANDY** (IRE) 19
285 **DANAT AL ATHEER** (GB) 80
461 **DANBROOK** (IRE) 7
451 **DANCE** (GB) 29
655 **DANCE AND DANCE** (IRE) 1
201 **DANCE AWAY** (IRE) F 109
682 **DANCE CLEAR** (IRE) C 90
387 **DANCE COMPANY** (GB) 16
141 **DANCE EXPRESS** (IRE) 28
357 **DANCE FONTAINE** (IRE) C 26
310 **DANCE FOR GEORGIE** (GB) 13
501 **DANCE FOR JULIE** (IRE) 10
174 **DANCE FOR LIVVY** (IRE) 9
110 **DANCE ISLAND** (IRE) 3
219 **DANCE MOVES** (GB) 9
552 **DANCE OF TIME** (GB) 12
442 **DANCE ON** (GB) C 24
219 **DANCE ROUTINE** (GB) C 138
74 **DANCE SOLO** (GB) F 60
16 **DANCE TEMPO** (GB) 14
601 **DANCE THE RAIN** (GB) 31
362 **DANCE TIL MIDNIGHT** (GB) 5
126 **DANCE TO DESTINY** (GB) 4
171 **DANCE TO THE BLUES** (IRE) F 12
534 **DANCE TO THE STARS** (IRE) 5
564 **DANCE TOUPIE** (FR) 32
19 **DANCE WITH ME** (IRE) 53
296 **DANCEINTOTHELIGHT** (IRE) 5
400 **DANCEWITHTHEDEVIL** (IRE) 5
285 **DANCHAI** (GB) 26
91 **DANCHEUR** (IRE) 25
35 **DANCING ABBIE** (USA) F 67
552 **DANCING ART** (IRE) 13
388 **DANCING BELIEF** (IRE) 25
174 **DANCING DAFFODIL** (GB) 10
299 **DANCING DEBUT** (GB) C 153
268 **DANCING DIK** (GB) 2
321 **DANCING DUDE** (IRE) 37
588 **DANCING ELLIE MAE** (GB) 34
444 **DANCING EMILY** (IRE) 3
283 **DANCING FREDDY** (IRE) 20
688 **DANCING GIZMO** (GB) 4
104 **DANCING JACK** (FR) 4
60 **DANCING MAITE** (GB) 5
160 **DANCING MIST** (IRE) 7
55 **DANCING ON TURF** (IRE) 53
73 **DANCING PRIMO** (GB) 5
285 **DANCING RAIN** (IRE) 3
331 **DANCING ROYAL** (GB) 20
310 **DANCING STEPS** (GB) F 20
391 **DANCING TEASEL** (GB) 16
340 **DANCING TORNADO** (IRE) 13
115 **DANCING WAVE** (GB) 1

64 **DANCING WELCOME** (GB) 5
99 **DANDARRELL** (GB) 5
223 **DANDINO** (GB) 5
19 **DANDY** (GER) 54
180 **DANE BLUE** (IRE) F 45
207 **DANE COTTAGE** (GB) 9
304 **DANE STREET** (USA) 85
510 **DANE THYME** (GB) F 15
118 **DANEBROOK LAD** (IRE) 7
380 **DANEHILL DANTE** (IRE) 23
700 **DANEHILL PRINCESS** (IRE) C 35
314 **DANEHILL TAPDANCER** (IRE) 2
700 **DANEHILL'S DREAM** (GB) C 36
266 **DANEKING** (GB) 38
246 **DANEVA** (GB) 5
475 **DANGAN DAYLIGHT** (IRE) 7
447 **DANGEROUS MIDGE** (USA) 4
466 **DANGEROUS TO KNOW** (GB) 39
473 **DANI CATALONIA** (GB) 2
223 **DANI RIDGE** (IRE) F 50
287 **DANICK OF TIME** (IRE) 7
283 **DANIEL THOMAS** (IRE) 21
175 **DANIEL'S DREAM** (GB) 3
200 **DANIFAH** (IRE) F 73
714 **DANISH REBEL** (IRE) 3
619 **DANK** (GB) 22
434 **DANNCEYS HILL** (IRE) 38
665 **DANNIOS** (GB) 2
479 **DANNY JOHN BOY** (GB) 3
119 **DANSARA** (GB) C 60
299 **DANSILI DUAL** (IRE) 7
27 **DANSILI DUTCH** (IRE) 33
511 **DANSKER** (FR) 52
695 **DANTARI** (IRE) 27
8 **DANTE'S FROLIC** (GB) 8
57 **DANTES TERM** (IRE) F 4
366 **DANUBE RIVER** (GB) 68
568 **DANUM DIVA** (IRE) F 9
681 **DANVILLA** (GB) 14
625 **DANZELLINE** (GB) C 52
287 **DANZERINI** (USA) 32
471 **DANZIG FOX** (GB) 6
654 **DANZIG'S HUMOR** (USA) C 104
194 **DANZOE** (IRE) 4
481 **DAPHNE'S DOLL** (IRE) F 9
274 **DAPPLE PRINCE** (IRE) 5
456 **DAR ES SALAAM** (GB) 3
424 **DARA TANGO** (FR) 5
724 **DARAA** (IRE) 35
433 **DARAKTI** (IRE) 51
695 **DARCEYS DANCER** (IRE) 28
711 **DARCY MAY** (GB) 3
331 **DARE ME** (GB) 21
473 **DARE TO DOUBT** (GB) 37
299 **DARE TO DREAM** (GB) 37
298 **DARENJAN** (IRE) 10
111 **DARIA** (GER) 101
569 **DARIEN** (FR) 36
129 **DARING DAMSEL** (IRE) 7
696 **DARING INDIAN** (GB) 12
394 **DARING ORIGYN** (FR) 6
508 **DARING QUEEN** (IRE) 25
658 **DARING RUDOLPH** (GER) 12
18 **DARK AGES** (IRE) 41
686 **DARK ALBATROSS** (USA) F 23
531 **DARK AND DANGEROUS** (IRE) 8
384 **DARK CASTLE** (GB) 11
526 **DARK CELT** (IRE) 8

139 **DARK DIAMOND** (IRE) 28
328 **DARK DON** (IRE) 24
201 **DARK DUNE** (IRE) 5
585 **DARK ENERGY** (GB) 7
118 **DARK EXILE** (IRE) 8
628 **DARK FALCON** (IRE) 7
268 **DARK GLACIER** (IRE) 8
526 **DARK JUSTICE** (IRE) 14
500 **DARK OCEAN** (IRE) 13
117 **DARK ORCHID** (IRE) 11
219 **DARK ORCHID** (USA) 44
654 **DARK PROMISE** (GB) 4
446 **DARK PROSPECT** (GB) 20
526 **DARK RANGER** (GB) 3
625 **DARK RULER** (IRE) 47
71 **DARK RUMOUR** (IRE) 20
266 **DARK STRANGER** (GB) 39
118 **DARKAN ROAD** (GB) 9
507 **DARKEST NIGHT** (IRE) 33
321 **DARLAN** (GB) 38
49 **DARLEY SUN** (IRE) 18
285 **DARLING GRACE** (GB) 27
16 **DARNA** (GB) 15
153 **DARNATHEAN** (GB) 12
671 **DARNBOROUGH** (IRE) 2
564 **DARNETAL** (IRE) 33
473 **DARRFONAH** (IRE) C 19
473 **DARROUN** (IRE) 28
387 **DARROW** (IRE) 17
666 **DARSAN** (IRE) 3
410 **DART** (GB) 4
458 **DART QUEEN** (GER) 5
266 **DARTFORD** (USA) 40
593 **DARTFORD WARBLER** (IRE) 11
180 **DARTRIX** (GB) 26
433 **DARUBAND** (GB) 10
569 **DARVAZA** (USA) 37
352 **DARWIN STAR** (GB) 2
569 **DARYLA** (USA) 38
466 **DASH TO THE FRONT** (GB) F 68
208 **DASHIBA** (GB) C 30
654 **DASHING** (IRE) F 105
573 **DASHING EDDIE** (GB) 7
429 **DASHO** (GB) 3
109 **DASHWOOD** (GB) 2
299 **DAUNT** (GB) 38
183 **DAUPHINE RUSSE** (FR) 54
631 **DAVANA** (GB) 1
321 **DAVE'S DREAM** (GB) 39
72 **DAVERON** (IRE) 2
304 **DAVID'S DREAM** (GB) 18
550 **DAVIDS DILEMMA** (GB) 2
658 **DAWARIYA** (IRE) 13
55 **DAWN APPROACH** (IRE) 76
404 **DAWN COMMANDER** (GER) 12
466 **DAWN GALE** (IRE) 8
119 **DAWN GLORY** (GB) 23
433 **DAWN LIGHTNING** (GB) 34
38 **DAWN MYSTERY** (GB) 3
296 **DAWN RIDE** (IRE) 9
390 **DAWN SKY** (GB) 1
660 **DAWN TWISTER** (GER) 9
29 **DAWNING** (USA) 25
712 **DAWNING DAY** (IRE) G 7
591 **DAWNS GREY LIGHT** (GB) 3
310 **DAY BY DAY** (GB) C 21
617 **DAY OF DESTINY** (IRE) 5
200 **DAY OF THE EAGLE** (IRE) 9

169 **DAY ONE** (GB) 7
569 **DAYITA** (FR) 39
19 **DAYLIGHT** (GB) 115
391 **DAYMAR BAY** (IRE) 17
55 **DAYRINA** (IRE) 21
363 **DAYS OF GRACE** (IRE) F 11
264 **DAYS OF PLEASURE** (IRE) 4
344 **DAZAKHEE** (GB) 3
642 **DAZINSKI** (GB) 12
201 **DAZZLIN BLUEBELL** (IRE) 73
181 **DAZZLING BEGUM** (GB) 1
496 **DAZZLING DANCER** (GB) C 55
682 **DAZZLING PEARL** (GB) 33
700 **DAZZLING QUINTET** (GB) C 37
269 **DAZZLING RITA** (GB) 2
14 **DAZZLING VALENTINE** (GB) 2
338 **DAZZLING VIEW** (USA) F 18
476 **DE BOITRON** (FR) 13
695 **DE FAOITHESDREAM** (IRE) 29
374 **DE FORGOTTEN MAN** (IRE) 13
331 **DE LA BECH** (GB) 22
38 **DE LESSEPS** (USA) 4
185 **DE LUAIN GORM** (IRE) 2
658 **DE RIGUEUR** (GB) 14
265 **DE VESCI** (IRE) 5
490 **DE VINE MEMORY** (GB) 6
420 **DE WAITING GAME** (IRE) 8
298 **DE' ORO** (IRE) 11
223 **DEACON BLUES** (GB) 6
139 **DEAD COOL** (GB) 6
343 **DEAD DONE** (FR) 16
639 **DEAN'S GRANGE** (GB) 9
32 **DEAR BEN** (GB) 26
129 **DEAR CATCH** (GB) C 29
130 **DEAR MAURICE** (GB) 3
201 **DEAUVILLE FLYER** (GB) 16
619 **DEBATING SOCIETY** (IRE) 23
109 **DEBBIE DOO** (GB) 3
266 **DEBORAH** (GB) 125
340 **DEBT TO SOCIETY** (IRE) 14
3 **DEBUSSY** (IRE) 12
466 **DECANA** (GB) 7
19 **DECENT FELLA** (IRE) 8
101 **DECENT LORD** (IRE) 5
681 **DECEPTIVE** (GB) 15
365 **DECHIPER** (IRE) 3
306 **DECIDER** (USA) 7
171 **DECIDING MOMENT** (IRE) 2
550 **DECIMATE** (GB) 2
583 **DECIMUS** (IRE) 5
318 **DECISION** (FR) 47
161 **DECISION BY ONE** (GB) 26
525 **DECOY** (FR) 27
408 **DECURION** 49
119 **DEDICATION** (GB) 24
424 **DEDIGOUT** (IRE) 6
256 **DEE EE WILLIAMS** (IRE) 5
503 **DEED OF GIFT** (IRE) 14
180 **DEEP APPLAUSE** (GB) 3
680 **DEEP KING** (GB) 1
295 **DEEP PEARL** (GB) 1
373 **DEEP POCKETS** (IRE) 9
695 **DEEP PURPLE** (GB) 30
338 **DEEPRITIVE** (GB) F 2
201 **DEEPSAND** (IRE) 74
493 **DEER PARK LORD** (GB) 6
145 **DEERHURST** (GB) 8
75 **DEFENCE COUNCIL** (IRE) 7

479 **DEFERTO DELPHI** (GB) 4
493 **DEFI** (IRE) 7
119 **DEFINIGHTLY** (GB) 6
287 **DEFINING YEAR** (IRE) 8
135 **DEFINITE APPEAL** (IRE) 2
343 **DEFINITE CLASS** (IRE) 17
657 **DEFINITE DAWN** (IRE) 18
557 **DEFINITE LADY** (IRE) 6
699 **DEFINITE MEMORIES** (IRE) 18
499 **DEFINITE RIDGE** (IRE) 11
321 **DEFINITE RUBY** (IRE) 40
681 **DEFINITELY GLAD** (IRE) 5
111 **DEFY THE ODDS** (GB) 37
570 **DEGAS ART** (IRE) 17
266 **DEIA SUNRISE** (IRE) 41
274 **DEIANIRA** (IRE) 6
597 **DEIRA PHANTOM** (IRE) 65
489 **DEIREADH RE** (IRE) 23
384 **DELAGOA BAY** (IRE) 3
600 **DELANTERA** (FR) 36
404 **DELAYS EXPECTED** (IRE) 13
49 **DELEGATOR** (GB) 19
496 **DELFT** (GB) 17
381 **DELGANY GUNNER** (GB) 6
214 **DELIGHTFUL SLEEP** (GB) 10
570 **DELIGHTFULLY** (FR) 18
228 **DELISHUSS** (GB) 13
691 **DELLA SUN** (FR) 1
521 **DELLBUOY** (GB) 17
521 **DELLS BREEZER** (GB) 5
35 **DELMA** (IRE) 26
616 **DELORAIN** (IRE) 2
573 **DELORES ROCKET** (GB) 83
328 **DELPHIE QUEEN** (IRE) C 2
654 **DELPHINUS** (GB) C 106
552 **DELTA FORTY** (GB) 14
29 **DELTA SCUTI** (USA) 26
643 **DELWYN** (GB) 53
299 **DEMOCRETES** (GB) 39
555 **DEMOISELLE BOND** (GB) 2
705 **DEMOLITION** (GB) 1
529 **DEMOLITION JO** (GB) F 39
9 **DEMORA** (GB) 36
476 **DEN OF INIQUITY** (GB) 14
241 **DEN'S GIFT** (IRE) 8
380 **DENALI HIGHWAY** (GB) 24
188 **DENBIGH RAUR** (IRE) 30
29 **DENEBOLA** (USA) F 81
287 **DENOMINATOR** (IRE) 33
486 **DENTON** (NZ) 6
213 **DENTON DANCER** (GB) 14
334 **DENY** (GB) 2
146 **DEORAI** (IRE) 2
538 **DEPDEN** (IRE) 5
495 **DEPORTATION** (GB) 4
523 **DEPORTISTA** (GB) 1
550 **DEPRESSED** (GB) F 12
593 **DEPUTY DAN** (IRE) 12
503 **DEPUTY DOG** (IRE) 3
658 **DERAPOUR** (IRE) 15
370 **DERAWAR** (IRE) 4
9 **DEREK THE DIAMOND** (GB) 37
266 **DERIVATIVES** (IRE) 42
388 **DERKIOS** (IRE) 26
15 **DERMATOLOGISTE** (GB) 4
183 **DERNIERE CARTE** (FR) 55
377 **DERRY ANN** (GB) F 5
446 **DERRYVALE ROSE** (IRE) 21

59 **DERWEN PRYDE** (GB) 9
501 **DESCARO** (USA) 11
586 **DESERT AUCTION** (IRE) 5
510 **DESERT CLASSIC** (GB) F 16
61 **DESERT CRISTAL** (IRE) F 37
434 **DESERT CRY** (IRE) 39
19 **DESERT DONKEY** (IRE) 116
49 **DESERT GAZELLE** (USA) 78
188 **DESERT GOLD** (IRE) C 31
296 **DESERT HUNTER** (IRE) 9
433 **DESERT ICON** (IRE) 11
397 **DESERT ICON** (IRE) 5
380 **DESERT JOE** (IRE) 25
19 **DESERT LAW** (IRE) 9
430 **DESERT MOONLIGHT** (GB) 1
100 **DESERT NOVA** (IRE) 5
597 **DESERT PHANTOM** (USA) 6
573 **DESERT PHILOSOPHER** (GB) 45
35 **DESERT RED** (IRE) 27
191 **DESERT ROYALTY** (IRE) F 55
488 **DESERT SCEPTRE** (GB) G 50
214 **DESERT SCEPTRE** (GB) C 68
433 **DESERT STRIKE** (GB) 12
328 **DESERT STRIKE** (GB) 3
200 **DESERT VISION** (GB) 10
147 **DESERTED** (GB) 78
299 **DESERTION** (IRE) C 40
605 **DESERTMORE STAR** (IRE) 1
34 **DESLAYA** (IRE) 2
659 **DESPERADO** (IRE) 15
476 **DESPERATE DEX** (IRE) 15
400 **DESPERATE TIMES** (IRE) 6
189 **DESSIE GRAY** (IRE) 2
676 **DESTINATION AIM** (GB) 4
268 **DESTINY BLUE** (IRE) 9
336 **DESTINY OF A DIVA** (GB) 7
146 **DESTINY OF DREAMS** (GB) 3
135 **DESTINY RULES** (GB) 3
657 **DESTROYER DEPLOYED** (IRE) 19
101 **DETOUR AHEAD** (GB) 6
659 **DEUTERONOMY** (IRE) 16
473 **DEUTSCHLAND** (USA) 29
460 **DEUX ETOILES** (IRE) 21
141 **DEVDAS** (IRE) 2
366 **DEVERON** (USA) F 158
64 **DEVEZE** (IRE) 6
380 **DEVIL TO PAY** (GB) 26
200 **DEVIL YOU KNOW** (IRE) 11
446 **DEVILS PAINTBRUSH** (IRE) 22
76 **DEVILS RIVER** (IRE) 3
29 **DEVOIR DE MEMOIRE** (FR) 3
72 **DEVON DIVA** (GB) 3
681 **DEVON DRUM** (IRE) 17
287 **DEVONELLI** (IRE) 9
34 **DEVOTED** (GB) 2
570 **DEVOTION TO DUTY** (IRE) 19
647 **DEW REWARD** (IRE) 4
9 **DEWALA** (GB) 38
573 **DEWI CHINTA** (IRE) 84
380 **DHAAFER** (GB) 27
260 **DHAULAR DHAR** (IRE) 5
619 **DHELAAL** (GB) C 105
695 **DI KAPRIO** (FR) 31
183 **DIABLE DE JIM** (FR) 8
664 **DIABLO DANCER** (GB) 2
436 **DIABOLITO** (IRE) 18
569 **DIAKALI** (FR) 40

310 **DIAKTOROS** (IRE) 22
285 **DIALA** (IRE) 28
542 **DIAMOND BELLE** (GB) 16
690 **DIAMOND BLUE** (GB) 2
697 **DIAMOND BROOK** (GB) 2
184 **DIAMOND CHARLIE** (IRE) 2
47 **DIAMOND D'AMOUR** (IRE) 1
619 **DIAMOND DAME** (IRE) 24
653 **DIAMOND DEE** (GB) 3
697 **DIAMOND ECLIPSE** (IRE) 3
283 **DIAMOND FAY** (IRE) 22
659 **DIAMOND FRONTIER** (IRE) 17
697 **DIAMOND HARRY** (GB) 4
247 **DIAMOND MARKS** (IRE) 8
147 **DIAMOND MINE** (GB) 79
358 **DIAMOND NECKLACE** (USA) F 31
219 **DIAMOND REEF** (GB) C 139
705 **DIAMOND SUNRISE** (GB) 2
380 **DIAMOND SWEEPER** (IRE) 28
700 **DIAMOND TWISTER** (USA) 8
462 **DIAMOND VANESSA** (IRE) F 9
306 **DIAMOND VINE** (GB) 8
271 **DIAMOND VISION** (IRE) 1
525 **DIAMOND'S RETURN** (IRE) 28
447 **DIAMONDHEAD** (IRE) 28
655 **DIAMONDSINHEREYES** (IRE) 11
501 **DIANELLA** (IRE) C 46
614 **DIAVOLEZZA** (GB) 17
287 **DIBIYA** (IRE) C 61
275 **DICA** (FR) 1
268 **DICE** (IRE) 10
357 **DICEY VOWS** (GB) 4
414 **DICHOH** (GB) 3
117 **DICK BOS** (GB) 12
266 **DICK DOUGHTYWYLIE** (GB) 9
494 **DICKIE HENDERHOOP** (IRE) 6
283 **DICKIE LE DAVOIR** (GB) 23
200 **DICKY MINT** (GB) 56
459 **DIDDLEY DEE** (GB) 4
397 **DIDDUMS** (GB) 6
119 **DIDINA** (GB) F 61
123 **DIDN'T I TELL YOU** (IRE) F 57
123 **DIEPPE** (IRE) 25
99 **DIESCENTRIC** (USA) 6
219 **DIEVOTCHKA** (GB) F 140
101 **DIFFERENT DEE** (IRE) G 7
86 **DIFFERENT TRADES** (IRE) 5
382 **DIFLOCK** (GB) 1
473 **DIGEANTA** (GB) 30
659 **DIGG WHITAKER** (GB) 18
86 **DIGGER'S MATE** (GB) 6
700 **DIGGERS DAYDREAM** (IRE) 9
366 **DIGNIFY** (GB) C 159
139 **DIKANTA** (GB) 7
665 **DIKSIE DANCER** (GB) C 12
318 **DIKTABAMA** (FR) 3
654 **DILAG** (IRE) C 107
489 **DILDAR** (IRE) 24
385 **DILGURA** (GB) 18
434 **DILIGENT** (GB) 40
111 **DILIZA** (GB) C 102
207 **DILIZAN** (IRE) 50
315 **DIMAIRE** (GB) 4
520 **DIMAKYA** (USA) C 54
7 **DIMAN WATERS** (IRE) 4
450 **DIMASHQ** (GB) 9
223 **DIMENSION** (GB) 7
639 **DIMPSY TIME** (GB) 10

569 DINAFOR (FR) 41
55 DINARA (IRE) 22
286 DINARIUS (GB) 5
642 DINE OUT (GB) 27
380 DINAR (FR) 29
272 DINGAAN (IRE) 2
340 DINGALING (IRE) 15
657 DINGAT (IRE) 20
214 DINGLE TWO (IRE) 50
102 DINKUM DIAMOND (IRE) 6
372 DINNER DATE (GB) 3
18 DINNER GUEST (GB) 10
556 DINNY KENN (IRE) G 8
266 DINVAR DIVA (GB) 43
434 DIOCLES (IRE) 41
74 DIPLOMASI (GB) 6
682 DIPLOMAT (USA) 34
613 DIPLOMATIC (IRE) 1
310 DIPLOMATS DAUGHTER (GB) F 23
656 DIPPLE (GB) F 13
569 DIRAMA (FR) 1
686 DIRECT (GB) 12
596 DIRECT APPROACH (IRE) 3
62 DIRECT LINE (IRE) 2
558 DIRECTOR'S DREAM (IRE) 2
304 DIRECTOR'S FORUM (IRE) 19
113 DIRECTORSHIP (GB) 6
72 DIRTY BERTIE (FR) 4
201 DISCANTI (IRE) 17
113 DISCO DOLL (GB) 7
299 DISCO LIGHTS (GB) C 155
219 DISCOPHILIA (GB) 45
3 DISCOURSE (USA) 58
266 DISCOVERER (IRE) 44
218 DISCOVERIE (GB) 11
366 DISCREET BRIEF (IRE) C 160
573 DISCRESSION (GB) 46
54 DISHY GURU (GB) 14
511 DISMAY (GB) 5
12 DISPATCH BOX (GB) 7
450 DISPOL GRAND (IRE) 10
266 DISPOSITION (GB) 45
593 DISSOLVE (GB) F 13
19 DISTANT LOVE (IRE) 55
601 DISTANT MUSIC (GB) C 61
519 DISTANT SUN (USA) 6
543 DISTIME (IRE) 5
658 DISTINCTIVE IMAGE (USA) 16
285 DISTRICT ATTORNEY (IRE) 29
601 DIVA DONKEY (IRE) 32
328 DIVEA (GB) 25
35 DIVERGENCE (IRE) 68
476 DIVERS (FR) 16
60 DIVERTIMENTI (IRE) 4
358 DIVERTING (GB) 5
456 DIVINATORE (GB) 9
64 DIVINE CALL (GB) 7
564 DIVINE CREATION (FR) 6
326 DIVINE FOLLY (GB) 9
654 DIVINE GRACE (IRE) F 108
61 DIVINE PAMINA (IRE) 21
29 DIVINE PRESENCE (USA) 27
457 DIVINE RULE (IRE) 2
388 DIVISME (USA) 67
18 DIVY (FR) 11
678 DIX VILLEZ (FR) 2
206 DIXIE BULL (IRE) 7
406 DIXIE CASE (IRE) 2

299 DIXIE'S DREAM (IRE) 41
287 DIYALA (IRE) 34
207 DIZZY RIVER (IRE) 10
434 DJ MILAN (GB) 42
499 DO BRAZIL (GB) 12
49 DO IT ALL (USA) 20
570 DO IT FOR DALKEY (GB) 20
521 DO MORE BUSINESS (GB) 6
337 DOBERDAN (USA) 4
696 DOBLE VE (IRE) 13
155 DOC HAY (USA) 6
54 DOC HILL (GB) 15
283 DOCKSIDE STRIKE (GB) G 83
176 DOCOFTHEBAY (IRE) 5
488 DOCTOR CRANE (USA) 7
326 DOCTOR DAVID (GB) 10
330 DOCTOR HILARY (GB) 3
301 DOCTOR KINGSLEY (GB) 2
7 DOCTOR PARKES (GB) 5
440 DOCTOR ZHIVAGO (GB) 3
19 DOCTOR'S GIFT (GB) 117
497 DOCTORED (GB) 2
135 DODGE THE BULLET (GB) 4
189 DODGEY DREAM (GB) 3
489 DODGING BULLETS (GB) 25
208 DODO (IRE) 2
489 DOESLESSTHANME (IRE) 26
119 DOGSTAR (IRE) 25
19 DOLLAR BILL (GB) 56
456 DOLLAR MICK (IRE) 10
436 DOLLIES CHILD (IRE) 3
433 DOLLY BANTRY (GB) 52
225 DOLLY BAY (GB) 5
161 DOLLY COLMAN (IRE) 4
185 DOLLY PENROSE (GB) 3
481 DOLORES ORTIZ (IRE) 2
509 DOLPHIN STAMP (IRE) F 19
697 DOM D'ORGEVAL (FR) 5
318 DOM TOM (USA) 4
222 DOMBEYA (IRE) G 1
98 DOMINATION (GB) 4
249 DOMINIUM (USA) 5
476 DOMOLY (FR) 17
489 DOMTALINE (FR) 27
600 DON BOSCO (FR) 2
462 DON EDUARDO (GB) 28
7 DON JUAN (GB) 20
129 DON LIBRE (GB) 8
119 DON MARCO (GB) 62
10 DON POOLEONI (IRE) 5
488 DON'T CALL ME (IRE) 8
104 DON'T CALL ME TINY (IRE) 5
304 DON'T KNOW (IRE) 20
25 DON'T LOOK BACH (IRE) 1
333 DON'T PANIC (IRE) 5
384 DON'T TEMPT ME (IRE) 12
380 DONA (GB) 30
19 DONA ROYALE (IRE) C 118
147 DONATIA (GB) 26
227 DONATORIO (GB) 9
80 DONCASTER ROVER (USA) 3
644 DONNA ELVIRA (GB) 3
223 DONNAI (IRE) C 51
446 DONNAS PALM (IRE) 23
141 DONT TAKE ME ALIVE (GB) 30
419 DONT TELL PA (IRE) 4
101 DONT TELL SAILOR (IRE) 8
600 DONT TEUTCH (FR) 23

455 DONT WORRY (GB) 5
275 DONTCALLERTHAT (IRE) 2
207 DONTPAYTHEFERRYMAN (USA) 11
86 DONTSAYATHING (IRE) 7
659 DOOR BOY (IRE) 19
597 DORA CARRINGTON (IRE) F 66
466 DORA'S GIFT (GB) 40
543 DORA'S SISTER (IRE) 34
434 DORABELLE (IRE) 43
600 DORADE ROSE (FR) 3
705 DORBACK (GB) 3
360 DORCEUS (GB) 8
384 DORIS SOUTER (IRE) C 43
337 DORLESH WAY (IRE) 5
29 DORMELLO (IRE) 4
304 DORMERS GIRL (IRE) 86
474 DORMOUSE (FR) 3
501 DORN HILL (GB) C 47
619 DOROTHEA BROOKE (IRE) F 106
460 DOROTHY'S DANCING (IRE) 22
654 DORRATI (USA) C 109
27 DORRY K (IRE) 34
24 DORSET DORA (GB) 6
339 DORSET NAGA (GB) 4
347 DORSET SQUARE (IRE) 10
180 DOS AMIGOS (IRE) 27
501 DOT C C (USA) C 48
696 DOT OR FEATHER (IRE) 14
42 DOT'S DELIGHT (GB) 9
30 DOTTY DARROCH (GB) 3
279 DOUBLE BUD (GB) 4
711 DOUBLE CARPET (IRE) 4
640 DOUBLE DEFAULT (IRE) 9
422 DOUBLE DICE (GB) 2
161 DOUBLE DISCOUNT (IRE) 52
86 DOUBLE DIZZY (GB) 8
268 DOUBLE EXPRESSO (GB) 11
601 DOUBLE FANTASY (GB) F 33
637 DOUBLE FORTUNE (GB) 5
326 DOUBLE HANDFUL (GER) 11
488 DOUBLE PRECEDENT (GB) C 51
650 DOUBLE ROSS (IRE) 18
498 DOUBLE SILVER (GB) 10
397 DOUBLE STAKE (USA) F 42
529 DOUBLE STAR (GB) 40
646 DOUBLE THE TROUBLE (GB) 4
530 DOUBLE WHAMMY (GB) 2
366 DOUBLE YOUR MONEY (IRE) 161
511 DOUCEUR NOCTURNE (FR) 6
40 DOUCHKIRK (FR) 4
344 DOUGLAS (GB) 8
606 DOUGLAS JULIAN (GB) 12
119 DOURO (GB) 26
639 DOURYNA (GB) 11
569 DOUTZEN (IRE) 105
94 DOUZE POINTS (IRE) 3
385 DOVE COTTAGE (IRE) 1
672 DOVE HILL (IRE) 1
373 DOVECOTE WOOD (GB) 10
291 DOVER'S HILL (GB) 1
451 DOVILS DATE (GB) 30
556 DOWD'S DESTINY (IRE) 9
514 DOWN THE STRETCH (GB) 1
279 DOWNE PAYMENT (IRE) 5
73 DOWNHILL SKIER (IRE) 6
193 DOWNHILLER (IRE) 5
282 DOWNLAND (USA) F 6

299 **DOWNTON ABBEY** (IRE) 42
143 **DOWNTOWN BOY** (IRE) 2
593 **DOWNTOWN MANHATTAN** (IRE) 14
101 **DOWNWARD SPIRAL** (IRE) 9
434 **DOYLE CARTE** (GB) 44
91 **DOYNOSAUR** (GB) 6
601 **DOYOUKNOWWHOIAM** (GB) 34
708 **DOZY JOE** (GB) 5
592 **DR ALBERT** (GB) 18
396 **DR ANUBIS** (IRE) 3
40 **DR DARCEY** (GB) 5
516 **DR FINLEY** (IRE) 5
294 **DR FLYNN** (IRE) 1
520 **DR HOUSEMAN** (GB) 28
460 **DR THISTLE** (IRE) 23
111 **DR YES** (FR) 38
108 **DRACO BOY** (GB) 8
219 **DRAGON FALLS** (IRE) 46
274 **DRAGON MASTER** (IRE) 2
304 **DRAGON PULSE** (IRE) 87
185 **DRAGON'S DEN** (IRE) 4
460 **DRAGON'S ROOST** (IRE) 24
191 **DRAGONERA** (GB) 1
141 **DRAKES DRUM** (GB) 9
503 **DRAMATIC DUKE** (IRE) 16
570 **DRAMATIC JEWEL** (USA) 21
652 **DRAMATIC VICTORY** (IRE) 3
639 **DRAWN FREE** (IRE) 12
336 **DRAWN GOLD** (GB) 8
507 **DRAWNFROMTHEPAST** (IRE) 5
503 **DREAM AGAIN BOYS** (IRE) 17
233 **DREAM ALLIANCE** (GB) 4
597 **DREAM CAST** (GB) 67
524 **DREAM CATCHER** (FR) 2
503 **DREAM CATCHER** (SWE) 18
525 **DREAM ESTEEM** (GB) 29
647 **DREAM EXPRESS** (IRE) 3
331 **DREAM FUNCTION** (IRE) 23
705 **DREAM LASS** (IRE) G 4
176 **DREAM LODGE** (IRE) 6
214 **DREAM OF FORTUNE** (IRE) 11
428 **DREAM PERFORMANCE** (IRE) 1
628 **DREAM PROSPECTOR** (GB) 8
619 **DREAM TICKET** (USA) C 107
266 **DREAM TO BE MAID** (GB) 126
141 **DREAM TUNE** (GB) 31
228 **DREAM WHISPERER** (GB) 14
299 **DREAMALOT** (GB) C 156
583 **DREAMBROOK LADY** (IRE) 6
359 **DREAMERS OF DREAMS** (IRE) 9
310 **DREAMING OF RUBIES** (GB) 14
619 **DREAMS OF FIRE** (USA) 25
19 **DREAMSPEED** (IRE) 10
299 **DREAMWRITER** (USA) 43
214 **DREAMY CIARA** (GB) 69
308 **DREAMY NIGHTS** (GB) 4
49 **DRESS UNIFORM** (USA) C 125
146 **DRESSED IN LACE** (GB) 17
659 **DREVER ROUTE** (IRE) 20
666 **DRIFT AND DREAM** (GB) 4
58 **DRIFTING** (IRE) C 61
434 **DRILL SERGEANT** (GB) 45
275 **DRISHOGUE LAD** (IRE) 3
705 **DRIVE HOME** (USA) 5
226 **DRIVE ON LOCKY** (IRE) 6
473 **DRIVE ON REGARDLES** (IRE) 31
473 **DRIVE TIME** (USA) 32
174 **DROM** (GB) 11

211 **DROMBEG PRIDE** (IRE) 1
388 **DROMEOS** (GB) 68
637 **DROMORE HILL** (IRE) 6
428 **DROPPY'S** (IRE) 2
58 **DROPZONE** (USA) 28
593 **DRUM VALLEY** (GB) 15
136 **DRUMADOON** (IRE) 7
695 **DRUMBALOO** (IRE) 32
584 **DRUMBEATER** (IRE) 1
696 **DRUMLANG** (IRE) 15
458 **DRUMLISTER** (IRE) 6
637 **DRUMMERS DRUMMING** (USA) 7
141 **DRUMMOND** (GB) 32
685 **DRUMPELLIER** (IRE) 3
699 **DRUMSHAMBO** (USA) 19
522 **DRUSSELL** (IRE) 7
454 **DRYBROOK BEDOUIN** (GB) 5
57 **DUALAGI** (GB) 5
489 **DUALLA LORD** (IRE) 28
285 **DUBAI AIRSHOW** (GB) 81
450 **DUBAI BAY** (FR) 11
99 **DUBAI CELEBRATION** (GB) 7
321 **DUBAI CREST** (GB) 41
352 **DUBAI DELIGHT** (GB) 28
201 **DUBAI DESTINY** (GB) 75
601 **DUBAI HILLS** (GB) 6
202 **DUBAI KISS** (GB) 10
682 **DUBAI KITTEN** (USA) 35
3 **DUBAI PRINCE** (IRE) 14
9 **DUBAI RYTHM** (GB) 39
35 **DUBAI SPRING** (USA) 28
35 **DUBAI SUNSHINE** (IRE) 29
142 **DUBAIANSWER** (GB) 2
273 **DUBARA REEF** (IRE) 3
146 **DUBARSHI** (GB) 4
220 **DUBAWI CHEETAH** (IRE) 47
42 **DUBAWI DANCER** (GB) 5
299 **DUBAWI GOLD** (GB) 5
3 **DUBAWI ISLAND** (FR) 59
654 **DUBAWI SOUND** (GB) 5
508 **DUBAWI STAR** (GB) 2
619 **DUBBURG** (USA) 17
158 **DUBDAY** (GB) 108
147 **DUBIOUS** (GB) C 80
608 **DUBIOUS ESCAPADE** (IRE) 8
592 **DUBONNY** (GB) 2
626 **DUC DE REGNIERE** (FR) 3
654 **DUCAB** (GB) 110
477 **DUCAL** (GB) 3
543 **DUCHESS DORA** (IRE) 6
523 **DUCHESS OF MALFI** (IRE) 8
200 **DUCHESS THEATRE** (IRE) 12
201 **DUCHESSE SATIN** (IRE) 76
129 **DUCK OVER** (GB) C 30
198 **DUDLEYS DELIGHT** (GB) G 6
619 **DUKE COSIMO** (GB) 109
488 **DUKE LIAM** (IRE) 52
299 **DUKE OF CLARENCE** (GB) 44
665 **DUKE OF DESTINY** (IRE) 6
619 **DUKE OF FIRENZE** (GB) 26
331 **DUKE OF LUCCA** (GB) 24
267 **DUKE OF MALFI** (GB) 1
420 **DUKE OF MONMOUTH** (IRE) 9
556 **DUKE OF NAVAN** (IRE) 10
76 **DUKE OF ORMOND** (IRE) 4
147 **DUKE OF PERTH** (GB) 81
324 **DUKE OF RAINFORD** (GB) 2
525 **DUKES ART** (GB) 30

29 **DUKHAN** (FR) 28
237 **DULALLY** (GB) 9
147 **DULARAME** (GB) 27
233 **DULCEMARA** (IRE) 5
147 **DULKASHE** (IRE) 28
323 **DUMBFOUNDED** (FR) 3
613 **DUMNONI** (GB) F 6
343 **DUN MASC** (IRE) 18
420 **DUN SEE DEE** (IRE) 10
283 **DUNASKIN** (IRE) 24
310 **DUNBRODY** (FR) F 24
198 **DUNCANTHOMAS** (GB) 7
688 **DUNDOCK** (GB) 22
304 **DUNDRUM** (IRE) 21
71 **DUNE ISLAND** (IRE) 5
593 **DUNE SHINE** (GB) 16
226 **DUNEAVEY** (IRE) G 7
217 **DUNEEN DREAM** (USA) 1
19 **DUNGANNON** (GB) 11
699 **DUNGENESS** (GB) 20
226 **DUNGUIB** (IRE) 8
485 **DUNHOY** (IRE) 5
401 **DUNKELLY CASTLE** (IRE) 1
80 **DUNLOE** (GB) C 15
326 **DUNLOUGH BAY** (IRE) 12
446 **DUNMOE** (IRE) 24
220 **DUNMORE BOY** (IRE) 10
488 **DUNN'O** (IRE) 9
434 **DUNOWEN POINT** (IRE) 46
380 **DUNRAVEN PRINCE** (IRE) 4
331 **DUNRAVEN STORM** (IRE) 25
344 **DUNSEVERICK** (IRE) 9
80 **DUNYA** (GB) C 16
458 **DUOMO DI MILANO** (IRE) 7
111 **DURANTE ALIGHIERI** (GB) 6
362 **DURGAN** (GB) 6
197 **DURING THE WAR** (USA) 1
601 **DURRAH GREEN** (GB) F 62
33 **DUSHY LADY** (FR) 5
207 **DUSKY BOB** (IRE) 12
617 **DUSKY DAME** (GB) F 6
299 **DUST** (GB) C 157
628 **DUST DANCER** (GB) C 20
466 **DUSTER** (GB) 10
641 **DUSTY ANSWER** (GB) F 13
462 **DUSTY BLUEBELLS** (IRE) 2
647 **DUSTY DANE** (IRE) 4
387 **DUSTY RED** (GB) 18
442 **DUSTY STORM** (IRE) 25
266 **DUTCH DIAMOND** (GB) 46
446 **DUTCH HENRY** (IRE) 85
19 **DUTCH MASTER** (GB) 57
656 **DUTCH MISTRESS** (GB) 14
460 **DUTCH OLD MASTER** (GB) 105
390 **DUTCH SUPREME** (GB) 8
496 **DUTIFUL SON** (GB) 56
342 **DVINSKY** (USA) 3
511 **DYCTYNNA** (FR) 53
461 **DYLAN GEORGE** (GB) 26
183 **DYLAN PHILLY** (GB) 56
446 **DYLAN ROSS** (GB) 25
201 **DYLAN'S DREAM** (IRE) 77
336 **DYLANS VERSE** (IRE) 29
479 **DYNAMIC DRIVE** (IRE) 5
299 **DYNAMIC DUO** (GB) 43
460 **DYNAMIC IDOL** (USA) 25
55 **DYNAMITE DIXIE** (IRE) 23
525 **DYNASTE** (FR) 31

299 **DYNASTIC** (GB) 46
672 **DYSTONIA'S REVENGE** (IRE) 2
283 **DZESMIN** (POL) 25
561 **E MAJOR** (GB) 3
113 **EAGER TO BOW** (IRE) 8
363 **EAGLE NEBULA** (GB) 3
223 **EAGLE POWER** (IRE) 26
629 **EAGLE ROCK** (IRE) 1
654 **EAMAADD** (GB) 39
642 **EANANS BAY** (IRE) 9
539 **EARCOMESTHEDREAM** (IRE) 2
15 **EARL OF THOMOND** (IRE) 5
473 **EARLS QUARTER** (IRE) 33
658 **EARLSALSA** (GER) 18
698 **EARLSMEDIC** (GB) 5
328 **EARLY APPLAUSE** (GB) 4
510 **EARLY ONE MORNING** (GB) 17
569 **EARTH AMBER** (GB) 42
678 **EARTH CRYSTAL** (IRE) 3
489 **EARTH PLANET** (IRE) 29
461 **EASBY PARK** (GB) 8
47 **EASEMENT** (GB) 2
219 **EAST FIFTEEN** (GB) 47
299 **EAST TEXAS RED** (IRE) 158
507 **EASTBURY** (GB) 6
391 **EASTER DANCER** (GB) 18
489 **EASTER DAY** (IRE) 30
520 **EASTER DIVA** (IRE) 29
323 **EASTER FAYRE** (GB) 4
154 **EASTER LAD** (GB) 3
391 **EASTER METEOR** (IRE) 19
261 **EASTER QUEEN** (GB) 3
417 **EASTER SONG** (USA) C 18
261 **EASTER VIC** (GB) 4
58 **EASTERN AMOUR** (IRE) 29
178 **EASTERN BAZZAAR** (IRE) G 6
56 **EASTERN GLOW** (GB) 20
433 **EASTERN HILLS** (GB) 13
665 **EASTERN LILY** (USA) F 13
336 **EASTERN MAGIC** (IRE) 9
287 **EASTERN RULES** (IRE) 10
266 **EASTERN SUN** (IRE) 47
503 **EASTLAKE** (IRE) 19
296 **EASTLANDS LAD** (IRE) 44
673 **EASTWARD HO** (GB) 4
704 **EASY LED** (GB) 2
643 **EASY LIFE** (GB) 54
578 **EASY MOVER** (IRE) F 7
366 **EASY OPTION** (IRE) C 162
442 **EASY OVER** (IRE) 3
644 **EASY TERMS** (GB) 4
111 **EASY TO LOVE** (USA) C 103
108 **EASYDOESIT** (IRE) 9
508 **EBADIYLA** (IRE) F 65
508 **EBALVIYRA** (IRE) 26
434 **EBANOUR** (IRE) 47
390 **EBARAYA** (IRE) F 27
508 **EBAZAN** (USA) 27
460 **EBONY BOMB** (IRE) 26
420 **EBONY DIAMOND** (IRE) 11
101 **EBONY RIVER** (IRE) 10
520 **EBONY ROC** (GB) 55
146 **EBONY SONG** (USA) 5
306 **EBRAAM** (USA) 9
643 **EBTISAMA** (USA) 28
352 **ECECHEIRA** (GB) 21
247 **ECHO BRAVA** (GB) 14
668 **ECHO DANCER** (GB) 1

3 **ECHO OF DREAM** (GB) 60
74 **ECHO OF DUBAI** (IRE) 36
399 **ECHO OF THUNDER** (IRE) 9
508 **ECHOES IN THE WIND** (IRE) 28
306 **ECHOS OF MOTIVATOR** (GB) 10
29 **ECLAIR CLASSIC** (FR) 29
249 **ECLAT ROYALE** (GB) 27
577 **ECLIPSE AWARD** (IRE) 2
3 **ECLIPTIC** (USA) 15
366 **ECOSSAISE** (GB) 9
214 **ED** (GB) 70
357 **EDABIYA** (FR) F 27
152 **EDAS** (GB) 1
460 **EDDIE G** (IRE) 27
503 **EDDIE THE EAGLE** (IRE) 20
521 **EDE'SAJOLYGOODFELO** (GB) 7
564 **EDEN STAR** (FR) 34
424 **EDEYMI** (IRE) 7
489 **EDGARDO SOL** (FR) 31
681 **EDGBRIAR** (FR) 18
509 **EDGE OF LIGHT** (GB) F 24
55 **EDGE OF SANITY** (IRE) 24
681 **EDGEBURY** (GB) 19
110 **EDGEFOUR** (IRE) 4
681 **EDGEOVER** (GB) 20
2 **EDGEWATER** (IRE) 3
72 **EDGEWORTH** (IRE) 5
553 **EDGWARE ROAD** (GB) 2
62 **EDIESKAIA** (IRE) 3
494 **EDINBURGH GIN TIME** (GB) 7
153 **EDINBURGH KNIGHT** (IRE) 1
100 **EDITORS STORY** (GB) 6
99 **EDITORS STORY** (GB) 8
647 **EDLOMOND** (IRE) 7
501 **EDMAAJ** (IRE) 12
569 **EDMONTON** (GB) 106
294 **EDMUND** (IRE) 2
447 **EDRAAQ** (GB) 29
3 **EDUCATE** (GB) 61
650 **EDUCATED EVANS** (IRE) 19
171 **EDUCATED SON** (GB) 3
51 **EDWARD LEAR** (GB) 3
97 **EENY MAC** (IRE) 1
525 **EFFERVESCE** (IRE) 32
102 **EFFIGY** (GB) 7
403 **EFISIO PRINCESS** (GB) 6
182 **EFISTORM** (GB) 1
388 **EFTEOS** (FR) 69
600 **EGADE** (FR) 37
219 **EGOTIST** (IRE) 10
466 **EGRETTA** (IRE) 41
489 **EGYPT MILL SPIRIT** (IRE) 32
272 **EGYPTIAN LORD** (GB) 3
390 **EGYPTIAN QUEEN** (USA) C 28
49 **EHKAM** (USA) 79
49 **EHTEDAAM** (USA) 80
451 **EIGHT KEYS** (GB) 2
35 **EIGHT LETTERS** (USA) 30
434 **EIGHTEEN CARAT** (IRE) 48
29 **EIGHTFOLD PATH** (USA) 5
365 **EILA WHEELER** (GB) 4
241 **EILEAN EEVE** (GB) 5
300 **EILEEN'S GIRL** (IRE) F 2
55 **EINSTEINS FOLLY** (IRE) 77
192 **EISHIN ELEUTHERA** (IRE) C 21
97 **EIUM MAC** (GB) 10
166 **EJEED** (USA) 5
49 **EJLAAL** (IRE) C 126

654 **EKTIHAAM** (IRE) 40
43 **EL CALAFATE** (USA) 19
619 **EL CORDOBES** (IRE) 110
660 **EL DANCER** (GER) 10
283 **EL DECECY** (USA) 26
299 **EL DIAMANTE** (IRE) 47
610 **EL DIEGO** (IRE) 5
343 **EL FONTAN** (FR) 19
619 **EL GRECO** (IRE) 27
366 **EL LAIL** (USA) 69
687 **EL LIBERTADOR** (USA) 7
525 **EL LOBO** (FR) 33
56 **EL MARIACHI** (FR) 2
504 **EL MCGLYNN** (IRE) 14
321 **EL MONDO** (FR) 42
364 **EL MOROCCO** (USA) C 32
256 **EL PADRINO** (IRE) 6
458 **EL SORO** (FR) 8
501 **EL TORBELLINO** (IRE) 13
496 **ELA ATHENA** (GB) F 57
641 **ELA'S GIANT** (GB) F 14
700 **ELAMMATO** (IRE) 30
629 **ELAND ALLY** (GB) 2
496 **ELAS DIAMOND** (GB) 2
625 **ELAUYUN** (IRE) F 53
111 **ELBE** (GB) 39
388 **ELDANDY** (IRE) 27
321 **ELDRED** (IRE) 43
660 **ELEAZAR** (GER) 11
34 **ELECTRELANE** (GB) 23
454 **ELECTRIC MAYHEM** (GB) 6
161 **ELECTRIC QATAR** (GB) 27
266 **ELECTRICIAN** (GB) 48
141 **ELECTROLYSER** (IRE) 10
273 **ELEGANT DANCER** (IRE) 4
357 **ELEGANT FLIGHT** (GB) 11
201 **ELEGANT GIRL** (IRE) 78
9 **ELEGANT MUSE** (GB) 14
151 **ELEGANT OLIVE** (GB) 3
329 **ELEGANT PRIDE** (GB) F 29
436 **ELEGANT SISI** (IRE) 19
117 **ELEGANT TIMES** (IRE) F 35
391 **ELEGANT TOUCH** (IRE) 20
339 **ELEVEN FIFTY NINE** (GB) 5
147 **ELHAAME** (IRE) 82
182 **ELHAMRI** (GB) 5
476 **ELIADES RUN** (IRE) 18
446 **ELIJAH GARDNER** (IRE) 86
27 **ELIJAH PEPPER** (USA) 8
619 **ELIK** (IRE) 111
250 **ELITE BENEFICIAL** (IRE) 4
440 **ELITE HOPE** (USA) G 13
588 **ELITISTA** (FR) F 40
29 **ELITISTE** (IRE) 82
164 **ELIXIR DU LAC** (GB) 3
388 **ELIXOS** (FR) 28
287 **ELIZABETH COFFEE** (IRE) 11
74 **ELJOWZAH** (IRE) 7
366 **ELKHART** (IRE) 70
328 **ELLAAL** (GB) 26
715 **ELLANDSHE** (IRE) 1
510 **ELLANOVA** (GB) F 18
507 **ELLCON** (IRE) F 34
658 **ELLE BELLE** (IRE) 47
196 **ELLE DIVA** (IRE) 2
73 **ELLE REBELLE** (GB) 39
569 **ELLE SAME** (GB) 107
180 **ELLE WOODS** (IRE) 46

221 **ELLELL DUKE** (IRE) 10
352 **ELLEMUJIE** (GB) 3
643 **ELLEN** (IRE) F 55
364 **ELLEN DEAN** (GB) 4
592 **ELLEN MOONEY** (GB) F 19
509 **ELLEPHIL** (IRE) 7
69 **ELLERSLIE POSH** (GB) 3
357 **ELLIE IN THE PINK** (IRE) 5
73 **ELLIELUSIVE** (IRE) 7
375 **ELLIS** (GB) 3
507 **ELLWAY QUEEN** (USA) F 35
391 **ELMA JOYCE** (IRE) G 21
384 **ELMORA** (GB) 13
144 **ELNA BRIGHT** (GB) 1
408 **ELOGIEUX** 50
188 **ELOQUENT ISLE** (IRE) F 32
657 **ELSAFEER** (IRE) 21
74 **ELSHABAKIYA** (GB) 8
113 **ELSIE'S ORPHAN** (GB) 8
383 **ELSPETH'S BOY** (USA) 8
619 **ELTIFAAT** (IRE) 28
266 **ELTIQAA** (IRE) 49
482 **ELTON FOX** (GB) 4
3 **ELUDING** (GB) 62
208 **ELUSIVE FLAME** (GB) 14
265 **ELUSIVE GENT** (IRE) 6
149 **ELUSIVE HAWK** (IRE) 3
601 **ELUSIVE HEIR** (GB) 63
270 **ELUSIVE IN PARIS** (IRE) 14
188 **ELUSIVE ISLAND** (USA) 9
266 **ELUSIVE KATE** (USA) 1
55 **ELUSIVE MARETTE** (IRE) 78
27 **ELUSIVE PRINCE** (GB) 9
564 **ELUSIVE STORM** (FR) 35
433 **ELUSIVE WARRIOR** (USA) 14
447 **ELUSIVITY** (IRE) 5
643 **ELUTRAH** (GB) C 56
332 **ELY BROWN** (IRE) 6
654 **ELYASSAAT** (GB) 41
619 **ELYSIAN** (GB) 29
465 **ELYSIAN ROCK** (GB) 12
654 **ELZAAM** (AUS) 6
476 **ELZAHANN** (IRE) 19
508 **EMAZAR** (USA) 66
520 **EMBANKMENT** (GB) 30
682 **EMBASSY** (GB) C 91
511 **EMBOSS** (IRE) 7
212 **EMBRA** (IRE) 4
671 **EMBSAY CRAG** (GB) 3
480 **EMEEBEE** (GB) 13
49 **EMERALD COMMANDER** (IRE) 21
647 **EMERALD FIRE** (GB) C 26
283 **EMERALD GIRL** (IRE) 27
643 **EMERALD PEACE** (IRE) C 57
687 **EMERALD ROYAL** (GB) 8
666 **EMERALD SEA** (GB) 37
645 **EMERALD STORM** (USA) C 16
139 **EMERALD WILDERNESS** (IRE) 8
686 **EMERALDS SPIRIT** (IRE) 4
111 **EMILIO LARGO** (GB) 7
285 **EMILY BLAKE** (GB) F 82
366 **EMILY CARR** (IRE) 71
650 **EMILY'S FLYER** (IRE) 20
268 **EMIRATE ISLE** (GB) 12
49 **EMIRATES CHAMPION** (GB) 22
49 **EMIRATES DREAM** (USA) 23
597 **EMIRATES ECHO** (GB) 31
147 **EMIRATES QUEEN** (GB) 29

64 **EMIRATESDOTCOM** (GB) 8
597 **EMIRATI SPIRIT** (GB) 68
654 **EMKANAAT** (GB) 7
163 **EMMA SODA** (GB) 1
225 **EMMA'S GIFT** (IRE) 6
335 **EMMABEL** (GB) 4
247 **EMMAN BEE** (IRE) 9
607 **EMMASLEGEND** (GB) 3
299 **EMMUSKA** (GB) 48
49 **EMOTION PARADE** (ARG) C 127
479 **EMOTIVE** (GB) 6
452 **EMOUNA** (GB) C 19
476 **EMPEROR CHARLIE** (GB) 20
426 **EMPEROR COMMODOS** (GB) 4
660 **EMPEROR CONCERTO** (GB) 4
146 **EMPEROR JULIUS** (IRE) 24
231 **EMPEROR OF ROME** (IRE) 4
19 **EMPEROR VESPASIAN** (GB) 58
699 **EMPEROR'S CHOICE** (IRE) 21
526 **EMPEROR'S DAUGHTER** (GB) 15
489 **EMPIRE LEVANT** (USA) 33
475 **EMPIRE OF DIRT** (IRE) 36
520 **EMPIRICIST** (IRE) 56
299 **EMPOWERMENT** (GB) 159
285 **EMPRESS ADELAIDE** (GB) 83
304 **EMPRESS CATHERINE** (GB) 105
601 **EMPRESS JAIN** (GB) F 64
55 **EMPRESS OF ROME** (IRE) 2
434 **EMPRESS ORCHID** (GB) 49
434 **EMRANI** (USA) 50
682 **EMULOUS** (GB) 3
49 **ENAK** (ARG) 24
713 **ENCANTADORA** (IRE) 3
422 **ENCHANTED DREAM** (GB) 3
359 **ENCHANTED GARDEN** (GB) 4
573 **ENCHANTED PRINCESS** (GB) C 47
329 **ENCHANTING WAY** (GB) C 30
219 **ENCIPHER** (USA) 48
360 **ENCIRCLED** (GB) 9
3 **ENCKE** (USA) 63
352 **ENCLAVE** (GB) G 29
299 **ENCOURAGEMENT** (GB) C 160
208 **ENCOURAGING** (IRE) 15
682 **ENCRYPTED MESSAGE** (IRE) 36
511 **ENCYIA** (FR) 103
573 **END OF DREAMS** (USA) 48
384 **ENDEAR** (GB) F 14
579 **ENDEAVOR** (GB) 4
219 **ENDELLION** (USA) 49
601 **ENDERBY SPIRIT** (GB) 7
299 **ENDIS** (IRE) F 161
690 **ENDLESS APPLAUSE** (GB) 14
619 **ENDLESS LIGHT** (GB) 112
496 **ENDLESS LOVE** (IRE) F 58
681 **ENDOFDISCUSION** (IRE) 21
366 **ENDORSEMENT** (GB) C 163
299 **ENERGIZE** (FR) 49
366 **ENERY** (IRE) 72
525 **ENFANT DE LUNE** (FR) 34
447 **ENFIRAAJ** (USA) C 64
72 **ENGAI** (GER) 6
494 **ENGLISH CITY** (IRE) 8
508 **ENGLISH NIGHT** (IRE) 29
366 **ENGLISH SUMMER** (GB) 10
540 **ENGLISHGREEK** (IRE) 8
328 **ENGLISHMAN** (GB) 83
208 **ENGROSSING** (GB) 16
619 **ENOBLED** (GB) 113

542 **ENRICHING** (USA) 8
619 **ENROL** (GB) 30
467 **ENROLLER** (IRE) 3
328 **ENSEJAAM** (CAN) 27
94 **ENSNARE** (GB) 4
111 **ENTENTE CORDIALE** (IRE) F 104
174 **ENTERTAIN ME** (GB) 12
127 **ENTHRALL** (IRE) 9
58 **ENTHUSIASTIC** (GB) 5
285 **ENTICING** (IRE) C 84
285 **ENTIFAADHA** (GB) 30
625 **ENTIHAA** (GB) 14
223 **ENTITLEMENT** (GB) 27
225 **ENTRANCE** (GB) 7
496 **ENVIABLE** (IRE) 59
650 **EPEE CELESTE** (FR) 21
553 **EPIC STORM** (IRE) 3
43 **EPINEUSE** (GB) C 35
496 **EPIPHANY** (GB) C 60
111 **EPOQUE** (GB) 40
521 **EPSOM SALTS** (GB) 8
142 **EQTIRAAB** (IRE) 3
161 **EQUALIZER** (GB) 28
234 **EQUATION OF TIME** (GB) 5
601 **EQUINOX** (GB) 65
299 **EQUITISSA** (IRE) 162
366 **EQUITY CARD** (GB) 73
165 **EQUITY RELEASE** (GB) 2
614 **EQUITY SWAP** (IRE) 18
612 **EQUULEUS PICTOR** (GB) 5
473 **EQUUS MAXIMUS** (IRE) 34
366 **ERAADA** (GB) 74
321 **ERADICATE** (IRE) 44
388 **ERASMIOS** (FR) 70
697 **ERE ALFIE** (IRE) 6
55 **ERE YESTERDAY** (IRE) 79
43 **EREKA** (IRE) 5
456 **ERGO** (FR) 11
461 **ERICA STARPRINCESS** (GB) 35
321 **ERICHT** (IRE) 45
476 **ERIN DANCER** (IRE) 21
521 **ERMYNTRUDE** (GB) 9
573 **ERNE PROJECT** (IRE) F 85
299 **ERODIUM** (GB) 163
647 **ERREUR** (IRE) C 27
711 **ERRIGAL LAD** (GB) 5
705 **ERYCINA** (IRE) 6
192 **ES QUE** (GB) F 22
366 **ES QUE LOVE** (IRE) 75
71 **ESCAPE ARTIST** (GB) 6
415 **ESCAPE TO GLORY** (USA) 3
72 **ESCARDO** (GER) 7
489 **ESCORT'MEN** (IRE) 34
489 **ESCUDERO** (IRE) 35
172 **ESEEJ** (USA) 7
191 **ESHAAB** (USA) 23
266 **ESHTIBAAK** (IRE) 10
214 **ESHTYAAQ** (GB) 12
388 **ESLES** (FR) 3
702 **ESME RIDES A GAINE** (GB) 1
119 **ESPAGNOLETTE** (GB) 27
700 **ESPECIALLY RED** (IRE) 31
304 **ESPRESSO LADY** (IRE) 22
61 **ESPRIT DANSEUR** (GB) 22
622 **ESPRIT DE FER** (FR) 2
488 **ESPRIT DE MIDAS** (GB) 10
219 **ESSENTIELLE** (USA) 50
38 **ESSEXVALE** (IRE) 11

396 **ESTATE** (GB) 4
215 **ESTATES RECOVERY** (IRE) 4
193 **ESTEBSAAL** (IRE) 28
643 **ESTEDAAMA** (IRE) 29
403 **ESTEE WILL** (GB) 7
214 **ESTEEM** (GB) 13
643 **ESTEMAALA** (IRE) 30
682 **ESTERLINA** (IRE) F 92
619 **ESTIMATE** (IRE) 31
49 **ESTIQBAAL** (GB) 81
193 **ESTIRDAAD** (USA) 47
613 **ESTIONA** (GB) 2
49 **ESTOURAH** (IRE) 25
119 **ESTRELA** (GB) 28
570 **ET MAINTENANT** (FR) 22
366 **ETERNAL HEART** (IRE) 11
58 **ETERNITY RING** (GB) C 62
285 **ETHAARA** F 85
266 **ETHEL** (GB) 127
40 **ETHICS GIRL** (IRE) 6
86 **ETHIOPIA** (GB) 9
117 **ETICA** (IRE) F 36
19 **ETIZAAN** (IRE) F 119
193 **ETIZAAZ** (USA) C 48
3 **ETON DORNEY** (USA) 64
654 **ETON FOREVER** (IRE) 8
698 **ETON RIFLES** (IRE) 6
570 **ETXALAR** (FR) 23
314 **EUR ELUSIVE** (IRE) 3
505 **EURHYTHMIC** (IRE) 7
8 **EUROHUNTER** (IRE) 9
75 **EUROLINK CAFE** (GB) C 18
366 **EUROLINK RAINDANCE** (IRE) C 164
75 **EUROLINKA** (IRE) F 19
198 **EUROLIS** (FR) G 8
3 **EUROPE** (GB) 65
283 **EUROPEAN DREAM** (IRE) 28
585 **EUROQUIP BOY** (IRE) 8
585 **EUROQUIP ROSE** (GB) 36
585 **EUROQUIP SUSIE** (GB) 9
29 **EUROZONE** (GB) 30
299 **EURYSTHEUS** (IRE) 50
688 **EUSTON SQUARE** (GB) 6
219 **EVADING** (USA) 51
433 **EVANESCENT** (IRE) 35
619 **EVANGELIST** (GB) 114
628 **EVE** (GB) C 9
162 **EVELITH REGENT** (IRE) 1
381 **EVELLA** (IRE) 7
328 **EVELYN MAY** (IRE) 5
687 **EVEN BOLDER** (GB) 9
176 **EVEN STEVENS** (IRE) 7
281 **EVENSTORM** (USA) C 5
450 **EVER ROSES** (GB) 12
485 **EVER THE OPTIMIST** (IRE) 6
671 **EVERAARD** (USA) 4
110 **EVERDON BROOK** (IRE) 5
397 **EVERGREEN FOREST** (IRE) 7
597 **EVERLASTING DREAM** (GB) 69
299 **EVERLEIGH** (GB) 164
117 **EVERLONG** (GB) 13
462 **EVERREADYNEDDY** (GB) 29
462 **EVERVESCENT** (IRE) 10
146 **EVERYBODY KNOWS** (GB) 6
343 **EVERYTHING ZAIN** (IRE) 69
496 **EVIDENT** (IRE) 61
49 **EVIL EMPIRE** (GER) C 128
569 **EVITA** (GB) F 108

496 **EVOKE** (IRE) 62
476 **EWE ARE JOKING** (GB) 22
452 **EWELL PLACE** (IRE) 11
509 **EWENNY STAR** (GB) 20
266 **EX ORIENTE** (IRE) 51
388 **EXAMOS** (FR) 71
601 **EXCEEDANCE** (GB) 35
35 **EXCEEDEXPECTATIONS** (IRE) 31
613 **EXCEEDINGTHESTARS** (GB) 3
601 **EXCEL BOLT** (GB) 8
601 **EXCELETTE** (IRE) 36
422 **EXCELLENT AIM** (GB) 4
422 **EXCELLENT GUEST** (GB) 5
422 **EXCELLENT JEM** (GB) 22
366 **EXCELLENT MARINER** (IRE) 165
329 **EXCELLENT NEWS** (IRE) 8
64 **EXCELLENT VISION** (GB) 9
511 **EXCELLENTE ARTISTE** (IRE) 54
522 **EXCELSIOR ACADEMY** (GB) 8
461 **EXCLUSIVE DANCER** (GB) 27
387 **EXCLUSIVE WATERS** (IRE) 35
573 **EXCUSE ME** (GB) 8
340 **EXCUSE ME MARIA** (IRE) 16
310 **EXECUTIVE'S HALL** (IRE) 6
366 **EXEMPLARY** (GB) 12
592 **EXEPTIONAL GIRL** (GB) 3
510 **EXEXEL** (GB) F 19
287 **EXHILARATOR** (IRE) 12
682 **EXHORTATION** (GB) 37
551 **EXILES RETURN** (IRE) 2
640 **EXIT TO ANYWHERE** (GB) 10
662 **EXIT TO FREEDOM** (GB) 4
249 **EXKALIBER** (GB) 28
160 **EXMOOR RANGER** (IRE) 8
223 **EXNING HALT** (GB) 28
225 **EXOPUNTIA** (GB) 8
19 **EXORCET** (IRE) F 120
217 **EXOTIC FOREST** (GB) F 13
460 **EXPECTATION** (IRE) F 125
19 **EXPENSE CLAIM** (IRE) 59
621 **EXPENSIVE LEGACY** (GB) 3
49 **EXPERT FIGHTER** (USA) 82
657 **EXPLAINED** (IRE) 22
285 **EXPOSE** (GB) 4
489 **EXPRESS LEADER** (GB) 36
266 **EXPRESSIONISM** (GB) 52
520 **EXTRASOLAR** (GB) 57
40 **EXTREME CONVICTION** (IRE) 7
695 **EXTREME IMPACT** (GB) 33
35 **EXTREMELY ALERT** (GB) 32
432 **EXTREMELY SO** (GB) 1
288 **EYE FOR THE GIRLS** (GB) 4
366 **EYEDORO** (USA) 13
592 **EYES ON** (GB) 5
570 **EYRE APPARENT** (IRE) 24
552 **EYRE SQUARE** (IRE) 15
447 **EYRECOURT** (GB) C 65
463 **EZDIYAAD** (IRE) 2
27 **EZRA CHURCH** (IRE) 10
525 **FAASEL** (IRE) 35
45 **FAB LOLLY** (IRE) 21
434 **FABALU** (IRE) 51
141 **FABLED CITY** (USA) 33
417 **FABREZE** (GB) 1
321 **FABRIKA** (GB) 46
306 **FABULEUX CHERIE** (GB) C 39
328 **FABULOUS FAIRY** (USA) F 84
114 **FABULOUS FRED** (IRE) 3

496 **FABULOUSLY FAST** (USA) F 63
507 **FACE THE PROBLEM** (IRE) 7
406 **FADE TO GREY** (IRE) 3
328 **FADHAA** (IRE) 6
111 **FAFA O O** (IRE) 105
408 **FAGO** (FR) 6
646 **FAHA** (IRE) 5
695 **FAHRISEE** (IRE) 34
430 **FAILED THE TEST** (IRE) 2
331 **FAIR ALONG** (GER) 26
522 **FAIR BREEZE** (GB) 9
174 **FAIR CRUISE** (GB) F 13
174 **FAIR CRUISE** (GB) F 47
489 **FAIR DREAMER** (GB) 37
226 **FAIR OF CAPPAMORE** (IRE) 9
588 **FAIR PASSION** (GB) 8
420 **FAIR POINT** (IRE) 12
101 **FAIR REFLECTION** (GB) 11
296 **FAIR SPIN** (GB) 11
658 **FAIR STORM** (GER) 19
466 **FAIR TRADE** (GB) 11
184 **FAIR VALUE** (IRE) 3
496 **FAIREST** (IRE) 18
621 **FAIREY DELTA** (GB) 4
8 **FAIRLEE DUTCH** (GB) 10
569 **FAIRLY FAIR** (IRE) 43
18 **FAIRMILE** (GB) 12
338 **FAIRMONT** (IRE) F 19
331 **FAIROAK LAD** (IRE) 27
444 **FAIRVIEW SUE** (GB) 4
693 **FAIRWAY TO HEAVEN** (IRE) 6
668 **FAIRY ALISHA** (GB) 2
624 **FAIRY DAWN** (IRE) G 3
566 **FAIRY MIST** (GB) 6
285 **FAIRY OF THE NIGHT** (IRE) C 86
256 **FAIRY RATH** (GB) 7
304 **FAIRY WING** (GB) 23
219 **FAIRY WINGS** (USA) 52
153 **FAIRYINTHEWIND** (IRE) 13
671 **FAIRYNUFF** (GB) 5
408 **FAISSI FAISSI** 7
498 **FAITH KEEPER** (IRE) 11
658 **FAITH THE BID** (GER) 20
665 **FAITHFILLY** (IRE) 14
306 **FAITHFUL RULER** (USA) 11
74 **FAKHUUR** (GB) 9
573 **FALASTEEN** (IRE) 9
219 **FALCOMIX** (FR) 141
496 **FALCON IN FLIGHT** (GB) 19
639 **FALCON ISLAND** (GB) 13
496 **FALCON'S REIGN** (FR) 20
366 **FALCONINTHEDESERT** (GB) 76
296 **FALCUN** (GB) 12
266 **FALKLAND** (GB) 53
266 **FALLEN FOR YOU** (GB) 54
49 **FALLEN IDOL** (GB) 26
3 **FALLS OF LORA** (GB) 66
340 **FALSE ECONOMY** (IRE) 17
340 **FALSE MESSENGER** (IRE) 18
129 **FALUKA** (IRE) 31
97 **FAMA MAC** (GB) 5
682 **FAME AT LAST** (USA) F 93
119 **FAMILY** (USA) C 63
614 **FAMILY FOCUS** (IRE) C 39
150 **FAMILY THREE** (IRE) 7
39 **FAMOUS BALLERINA** (IRE) 7
682 **FAMOUS NAME** (GB) 4
49 **FAMOUS POET** (IRE) 83

58 **FAMUSA** (GB) 6
43 **FANCIFUL DANCER** (GB) C 36
467 **FANCOURT** (GB) 4
647 **FANCY FEATHERS** (IRE) C 28
34 **FANCY ROSE** (USA) F 24
107 **FANCY ROSE** (USA) C 26
123 **FANDEE** (USA) 5
49 **FANN** (USA) C 129
127 **FANNY MAY** (GB) 3
628 **FANNY'S FANCY** (GB) F 21
617 **FANNYTHEWUNDAHORSE** (IRE) 7
266 **FANOOS** (GB) 55
447 **FANTACISE** (GB) 66
569 **FANTANELLA** (IRE) 44
442 **FANTASTIC ACCOUNT** (GB) C 26
447 **FANTASTIC SANTANY** (GB) C 67
285 **FANTASTIC SPRING** (USA) C 87
30 **FANTASTIC STORM** (GB) 4
403 **FANTASY FIGHTER** (GB) 8
161 **FANTASY FRY** (GB) 7
139 **FANTASY GLADIATOR** (GB) 9
306 **FANTASY HERO** (GB) 27
619 **FANTASY IN BLUE** (GB) 115
478 **FANTINO** (GB) 4
58 **FANUNALTER** (GB) 7
141 **FAR EAST** (GB) 34
328 **FARADAY LIGHT** (IRE) F 85
107 **FARANG KONDIEW** (GB) 6
225 **FARAWAY LAND** (USA) 9
328 **FARBENSPIEL** (GB) C 86
530 **FARBREAGA** (IRE) 3
193 **FAREEDHA** (IRE) 29
286 **FAREWELLATMIDNIGHT** (GB) 6
129 **FARFALA** (FR) C 32
193 **FARHAAN** (USA) 30
49 **FARHH** (GB) 27
569 **FARIDPOUR** (IRE) 4
336 **FARINA** (IRE) G 40
34 **FARLOW** (IRE) 3
294 **FARM PIXIE** (IRE) 3
379 **FARMER FRANK** (GB) 4
706 **FARMER GUNNER** (GB) 4
538 **FARMERS DREAM** (IRE) 6
330 **FARMERS HILL** (GB) 4
654 **FARRAAJ** (IRE) 42
219 **FARRUCA** (FR) 53
366 **FASCINATING** (IRE) 14
390 **FASHION MODEL** (GB) F 29
268 **FASHION STAKES** (GB) 22
508 **FASHION STATEMENT** (GB) F 67
266 **FASHION TRADE** (GB) F 128
246 **FASINATOR** (GB) 6
183 **FAST FLIGHT** (FR) 38
221 **FAST ON** (GB) 11
285 **FAST OR FREE** (GB) 31
471 **FAST RUBY** (GB) 7
201 **FAST SHOT** (GB) 18
682 **FASTNESSE** (GB) 3
27 **FASTNET STORM** (IRE) 11
708 **FASTNETTE** (IRE) 6
408 **FATALITE** (GB) 51
569 **FATE** (FR) 46
58 **FATHER AND SON** (GB) 63
269 **FATHER PAT** (GB) 3
498 **FATHER PROBUS** (GB) 12
602 **FATHEY** (IRE) 1
460 **FATHOM FIVE** (IRE) 28
299 **FATHOMING** (USA) C 165

597 **FATHSTA** (IRE) 7
58 **FATTSOTA** (GB) 8
397 **FAULT** (GB) 8
331 **FAULTLESS FEELINGS** (IRE) 28
74 **FAURAN** (IRE) 37
318 **FAUVISM** (USA) 40
329 **FAUX PAS** (IRE) G 9
9 **FAVORITE GIRL** (GER) 15
503 **FAVOURED NATION** (IRE) 21
201 **FAVOURITE GIRL** (IRE) 19
201 **FAVOURS BRAVE** (GB) 20
266 **FAWAAYED** (IRE) 56
299 **FAWAAYID** (USA) F 166
135 **FAWDON** (GB) 5
201 **FAYR FALL** (IRE) 79
247 **FAYRE BELLA** (GB) 2
644 **FAZZA** (GB) 3
304 **FEABHRA** (IRE) 24
466 **FEALEVIEW LADY** (USA) C 69
266 **FEARLESS DREAM** (GB) 57
43 **FEARLESS LAD** (IRE) 37
601 **FEARLESS POET** (IRE) 9
192 **FEATHER** (USA) F 23
381 **FEATHERBED LANE** (IRE) 29
385 **FEATHERGRASS** (IRE) C 19
684 **FEB THIRTYFIRST** (IRE) 19
374 **FEDERSTAR** (GER) 14
429 **FEDORA** (IRE) 4
10 **FEEL THE FORCE** (IRE) 6
601 **FEEL THE HEAT** (GB) 13
338 **FEELING BLUE** (GB) F 20
207 **FEELING GOOD** (GB) 51
115 **FEELING PECKISH** (USA) 2
111 **FEELTHEDIFFERENCE** (GB) 41
447 **FEET OF FLAME** (USA) C 68
55 **FEILE BRIDE** (IRE) 80
55 **FEILE NA MBAN** (IRE) 81
329 **FEISTY CHAMPION** (IRE) 10
299 **FELD MARECHALE** (FR) C 167
364 **FELIN GRUVY** (GB) F 33
696 **FELIX DA HOUSECAT** (IRE) 16
466 **FELIX FABULLA** (GB) 10
473 **FELIX YONGER** (IRE) 35
714 **FELONA** (GB) F 9
653 **FELONA** (GB) F 28
625 **FELUCCA** (GB) C 54
511 **FEMME D'ESPERE** (GB) 4
511 **FEMME FATALE** (SWI) 8
17 **FEN FARM** (GB) 3
447 **FEN GUEST** (GB) C 69
266 **FENCING** (USA) 58
202 **FENELLA** (GB) G 1
588 **FENELLA FUDGE** (GB) 9
366 **FENNELL BAY** (IRE) 77
157 **FENNEY MILL** (GB) 8
657 **FENNIS BOY** (IRE) 23
573 **FENWICK GALE** (IRE) 86
273 **FERDY** (IRE) 10
55 **FERE GRANDIS** (USA) 25
388 **FEREVIA** (IRE) 72
608 **FERGAL MAEL DUIN** (GB) 1
472 **FERGALL** (IRE) 11
147 **FERLADIN** (GB) 30
654 **FERNANDA** (GB) C 94
188 **FERNDALE** (GB) 10
222 **FERNEY BOY** (GB) 2
55 **FERRYCARRIG** (IRE) 26
164 **FESTIVAL DREAMS** (GB) 4

658 **FEUERFUCHS** (GER) 58
347 **FEVER FEW** (GB) 23
458 **FEVER PITCH** (IRE) 9
200 **FEW AND FAR** (GB) 13
480 **FIBS AND FLANNEL** (GB) 14
91 **FICELLE** (IRE) 26
446 **FICKLE FORTUNE** (IRE) 26
503 **FIDDLEDEDEE** (IRE) 22
299 **FIDELIO'S MIRACLE** (USA) C 168
171 **FIDELIS** (IRE) 4
157 **FIDELOR** (FR) 9
80 **FIDGET** (GB) 17
715 **FIELD ELECT** (GB) 2
176 **FIELD FINNER** (GB) 8
507 **FIELD OF DREAM** (GB) 8
27 **FIELDGUNNER KIRKUP** (GER) 12
101 **FIENDISH FLAME** (IRE) 12
682 **FIERY AMBITION** (GB) 39
147 **FIERY LAD** (IRE) 3
658 **FIERY'S LEGACY** (GER) 59
362 **FIFI L'AMOUR** (IRE) 7
488 **FIFTEENTWO** (GB) 53
360 **FIFTH AUNTIE** (GB) 10
390 **FIG TREE DRIVE** (USA) F 30
285 **FIGARO** (GB) 5
342 **FIGARO FLYER** (IRE) 4
200 **FIGHTER BOY** (IRE) 14
394 **FIGHTING CHANCE** (IRE) 7
331 **FIGHTING FLYNN** (IRE) 30
331 **FILBERT** (IRE) 31
470 **FILE AND PAINT** (IRE) 1
503 **FILIPPO LIPPI** (IRE) 23
606 **FILL THE POWER** (IRE) 13
35 **FILS ANGES** (IRE) 69
448 **FILUN** (GB) 1
420 **FIN VIN DE LEU** (GER) 13
473 **FINAL APPROACH** (GB) 36
328 **FINAL CALL** (GB) 28
18 **FINAL DELIVERY** (GB) 42
489 **FINAL GIFT** (IRE) 38
357 **FINAL LEGACY** (USA) F 28
568 **FINAL TUNE** (IRE) 2
352 **FINALIST** (GB) 22
601 **FINALIZE** (GB) 66
593 **FINANCIAL CLIMATE** (IRE) 17
259 **FINBAR** (GB) 19
162 **FINBAR FLYNN** (GB) 2
334 **FINBIN** (IRE) 3
460 **FINCH FLYER** (IRE) 29
556 **FIND A KEY** (IRE) 11
180 **FINE ALTOMIS** (GB) 28
180 **FINE KINGDOM** (GB) 29
460 **FINE PAINTING** (IRE) 106
420 **FINE PARCHMENT** (IRE) 14
340 **FINE PRESENTATION** (IRE) 19
19 **FINE RESOLVE** (GB) 60
392 **FINE THE WORLD** (GB) 2
328 **FINE THREADS** (GB) 7
91 **FINEFRENZYROLLING** (IRE) 7
461 **FINELLAS FORTUNE** (GB) 9
34 **FINESSE** (GB) 25
331 **FINGAL BAY** (IRE) 32
111 **FINGER POPPIN** (GB) 106
321 **FINIAN'S RAINBOW** (IRE) 47
695 **FINISK ROSE** (IRE) 35
366 **FINITY RUN** (GER) 78
434 **FINLAY** (GB) 52
438 **FINLODEX** (GB) 1

495 **FINN MAC** (GB) 13
686 **FINN'S RAINBOW** (GB) 5
657 **FINNEGAN PADDY** (IRE) 24
115 **FINNEGANS RAINBOW** (GB) 3
110 **FINNS REFLECTION** 6
408 **FINORO** (GER) 52
622 **FINTAN** (GB) 3
55 **FIONNUAR** (IRE) 27
57 **FIORDALINDA** (GB) 6
619 **FIORENTE** (IRE) 2
650 **FIORENZA** (GB) 22
654 **FIRDAWS** (USA) 43
391 **FIRE AND RAIN** (FR) 22
432 **FIRE CHIEF** (GB) 2
380 **FIRE FIGHTER** (IRE) 32
693 **FIRE IN BABYLON** (IRE) 2
32 **FLAMING EXPRESS** (GB) 6
285 **FIREBEAM** (GB) 6
686 **FIREFLY** (GB) 13
10 **FIREITFROMYE** (IRE) 7
223 **FIRENZE** (GB) C 52
113 **FIRESCENT** (GB) 10
321 **FIREY KING** (IRE) 48
681 **FIRM ORDER** (GB) 22
219 **FIRST** (GB) C 142
626 **FIRST ACT** (GB) 4
358 **FIRST APPROVAL** (GB) C 32
457 **FIRST AVENUE** (GB) 3
553 **FIRST BATTALION** (IRE) 4
668 **FIRST BEE** (GB) F 3
259 **FIRST BID** (GB) 20
282 **FIRST CLASS** (GB) 1
201 **FIRST CLASS FAVOUR** (IRE) 21
443 **FIRST COMING** (GB) 1
29 **FIRST DATE** (GB) 31
657 **FIRST FANDANGO** (GB) 25
407 **FIRST FANTASY** (GB) C 44
9 **FIRST GLANCE** (GB) 40
299 **FIRST GLIMMER** (USA) C 169
75 **FIRST HARMONY** (GB) G 16
405 **FIRST IN COMMAND** (IRE) 2
321 **FIRST IN THE QUEUE** (IRE) 49
528 **FIRST LAD** (GB) 7
465 **FIRST LIEUTENANT** (IRE) 13
29 **FIRST MANDURO** (FR) 83
111 **FIRST MOHICAN** (GB) 8
666 **FIRST PENINSULAR** (GB) 38
75 **FIRST PHASE** (GB) 17
315 **FIRST POST** (IRE) 5
40 **FIRST PRESSING** (GB) 8
150 **FIRST QUARTER** (GB) 8
564 **FIRST RAINS** (GB) 7
625 **FIRST ROCK** (IRE) 15
119 **FIRST SECRETARY** (GB) 64
658 **FIRST STREAM** (GER) 21
183 **FIRST TO RISE** (FR) 57
259 **FIRST VOICE** (IRE) 21
302 **FISCAL NOMAD** (IRE) 2
446 **FISHER BRIDGE** (IRE) 27
547 **FISHING BRIDGE** (IRE) 3
150 **FISHOUTOFWATER** (IRE) 9
507 **FISTFUL OF DOLLARS** (IRE) 19
489 **FISTRAL BEACH** (IRE) 39
98 **FISTS OF FURY** (IRE) 5
374 **FITANDPROPERJOB** (GB) 15
67 **FITFUL SKIES** (IRE) 67
472 **FITOBUST** (IRE) 12
488 **FITZ FLYER** (IRE) 11

79 **FITZWARREN** (GB) 3
525 **FIULIN** (GB) 36
356 **FIVE BUCKS** (IRE) 2
647 **FIVE COOL KATS** (IRE) 8
489 **FIVE DREAM** (FR) 40
296 **FIVE FRANKS** (USA) 45
642 **FIVE HEARTS** (GB) 13
263 **FIVE OF WANDS** (GB) F 24
695 **FIVE OUT OF FIVE** (IRE) 36
226 **FIVE POINT PLAN** (GB) 10
620 **FIVE STAR JUNIOR** (USA) 3
583 **FIVE STAR WILSHAM** (IRE) 7
473 **FIVEFORTHREE** (IRE) 37
326 **FIVEWAYS** (IRE) 13
460 **FIX THE RIB** (IRE) 30
682 **FIXED GAZE** (USA) 40
666 **FLAG IS UP** (GB) 21
325 **FLAG OF GLORY** (GB) 2
49 **FLAG OFFICER** (GB) 8
655 **FLAMBOROUGH BREEZE** (GB) 12
101 **FLAME OF DIXIE** (IRE) 13
169 **FLAMEOFTHEFOREST** (IRE) 8
259 **FLAMES** (GB) C 44
573 **FLAMING ARROW** (IRE) 10
380 **FLAMING CHARLIE** (IRE) 33
639 **FLAMING CHARMER** (IRE) 14
423 **FLAMING CLINT** (GB) 1
499 **FLAMING DAWN** (IRE) 13
117 **FLAMING FERRARI** (IRE) 14
489 **FLAMING GORGE** (IRE) 41
302 **FLAMING POP** (IRE) 3
562 **FLAMING SPIRT** (GB) 3
629 **FLAMINGO CAY** (GB) 3
329 **FLAMINGO GUITAR** (USA) C 31
19 **FLAMJICA** (USA) C 121
59 **FLANAGAN** (IRE) 10
29 **FLANDRE** (USA) 32
111 **FLASH AND DAZZLE** (IRE) G 107
601 **FLASH CITY** (ITY) 11
139 **FLASH CRASH** (GB) 17
658 **FLASH FOX** (GER) 22
473 **FLASH OF GENIUS** (GB) 38
129 **FLASHBANG** (GB) 2
49 **FLASHING GREEN** (GB) C 130
366 **FLASHLIGHT** (GB) 166
220 **FLASHMAN** (GB) 48
508 **FLASHY APPROACH** (GB) 68
208 **FLASHYFRANK** (GB) 17
713 **FLAT CAP THURSDAY** (GB) 4
473 **FLAT OUT** (FR) 39
299 **FLAVIUS VICTOR** (IRE) 51
19 **FLAXEN FLARE** (IRE) 61
64 **FLAXEN LAKE** (GB) 10
268 **FLAYGRAY** (GB) 14
268 **FLAYMORE** (GB) 15
134 **FLEET DAWN** (GB) 7
9 **FLEETING FASHION** (GB) 41
362 **FLEETING MAN** (IRE) 20
172 **FLEETING MOON** (GB) C 12
417 **FLEETWOODMAXI** (USA) 2
64 **FLEETWOODSANDS** (IRE) 11
374 **FLEMENTIME** (IRE) 16
347 **FLEMI TWO TOES** (IRE) 1
650 **FLEMISH INVADER** (IRE) 23
707 **FLETCH AND LENNY** (IRE) 1
247 **FLETCHER CHRISTIAN** (GB) 15
619 **FLEUR DE CACTUS** (IRE) 32
34 **FLEUR DE LA VIE** (IRE) 26

626 **FLEUR DE VASSY** (GB) 5
658 **FLEURO** (GER) 23
466 **FLEXIBLE FLYER** (GB) 42
137 **FLICHITY** (IRE) 1
434 **FLICKA WILLIAMS** (IRE) 53
224 **FLIGHTY DANCER** (GB) F 3
380 **FLINTWOOD** (GB) G 34
556 **FLINTY BAY** (IRE) 12
7 **FLIPPING** (GB) 6
442 **FLIRTINASKIRT** (GB) 27
266 **FLIRTINI** (GB) 129
166 **FLIXTER** (GB) 6
549 **FLOAT MY BOAT** (GB) 1
358 **FLOATING MOUNTAIN** (GB) 4
408 **FLOGAROSE** 53
573 **FLORA BURN** (UAE) C 87
552 **FLORA'S PRIDE** (GB) 16
593 **FLORAFERN** (GB) 18
552 **FLORAROSSA** (GB) 17
588 **FLOREAT** (GB) 50
588 **FLORENTINE LADY** (GB) F 41
370 **FLORIDA FACT** (GB) G 5
19 **FLORIDA HEART** (GB) C 122
207 **FLORIO VINCITORE** (IRE) 13
78 **FLOTATION** (USA) 3
111 **FLOW** (USA) 108
272 **FLOW CHART** (IRE) 4
501 **FLOWER BOWL** (IRE) F 49
160 **FLOWER HAVEN** (GB) 9
25 **FLOWERBUD** (GB) 2
266 **FLUCTUATE** (USA) 59
696 **FLUCTUATION** (IRE) 17
573 **FLUFFY** (GB) G 49
407 **FLUIDITY** (GB) 2
615 **FLUMPS** (GB) 7
318 **FLUTE** (USA) F 48
290 **FLUTERS HOUSE** (GB) 3
304 **FLUTTERING LASHES** (USA) 88
18 **FLUTTERING ROSE** (GB) F 62
479 **FLY BY WHITE** (IRE) 7
387 **FLY HAAF** (IRE) 19
317 **FLY HOME** (GB) G 1
317 **FLY HOME** (GB) C 7
628 **FLY ME TO THE MOON** (GER) C 22
102 **FLY ON BY** (GB) 25
695 **FLY TOWN** (IRE) 37
108 **FLYFORD PRINCE** (GB) 10
108 **FLYFORD PRINCESS** (GB) 11
60 **FLYING APPLAUSE** (GB) 5
248 **FLYING AWARD** (IRE) 3
496 **FLYING FINISH** (FR) F 64
573 **FLYING HIGHEST** (GB) F 88
71 **FLYING KITTY** (GB) 1
459 **FLYING PHOEBE** (GB) 5
89 **FLYING PHOENIX** (GB) 6
433 **FLYING PICKETS** (IRE) 36
628 **FLYING POWER** (GB) 3
70 **FLYING RIDGE** (IRE) F 4
178 **FLYING SQUAD** (UAE) 7
116 **FLYING TRADER** (USA) 19
5 **FLYING TRUMP** (GB) 1
657 **FLYING VIC** (IRE) 26
454 **FLYING WHALE** (GB) 7
24 **FLYING WIND** (GB) G 27
155 **FLYLOWFLYLONG** (IRE) F 20
237 **FLYNN'S ISLAND** (IRE) 10
572 **FOCAIL EILE** (GB) 3

572 **FOCAIL MAITH** (GB) 4
570 **FOG PATCHES** (IRE) 25
489 **FOGGY'S WALL** (IRE) 42
467 **FOIE GRAS** (GB) 38
55 **FOINSE** (IRE) 28
569 **FOL AMI** (FR) 47
488 **FOL HOLLOW** (IRE) 12
284 **FOLIE A DEUX** (IRE) 1
543 **FOLK TUNE** (IRE) 7
24 **FOLLOW ON** (GB) 7
321 **FOLLOW THE FACTS** (GB) 51
433 **FOLLOW THE FLAG** (IRE) 15
239 **FOLLOW THE MASTER** (GB) 3
299 **FOLLOWEVERYRAINBOW** (GB) 170
93 **FOLLY FARM** (IRE) 4
466 **FOLLY LODGE** (GB) C 71
654 **FONDA** (USA) C 111
682 **FONT OF WISDOM** (IRE) 5
569 **FONTAINE GUERARD** (FR) C 109
391 **FONTANO** (FR) 23
364 **FONTLEY** (GB) 5
666 **FOOT TAPPER** (GB) 22
337 **FOOT THE BILL** (GB) 6
480 **FOOTSTEPSOFSPRING** (GB) 15
321 **FOR A LAUGH** (GB) 52
403 **FOR LIFE** (GB) 9
697 **FOR NON STOP** (GB) 7
405 **FOR SHIA AND LULA** (IRE) 8
390 **FOR WHAT** (USA) 2
440 **FORBIDDEN** (IRE) 4
4 **FORCEFIELD** (GB) 5
184 **FORCEFUL APPEAL** (USA) 4
257 **FORCRYINGOUTLOUD** (IRE) 9
297 **FOREIGN KING** (GB) 2
666 **FOREIGN LANGUAGE** (GB) F 23
329 **FOREIGN RELATION** (IRE) F 32
26 **FOREIGN RHYTHM** (IRE) 4
388 **FOREIGN TUNE** (GB) 29
214 **FOREST EDGE** (IRE) 51
373 **FOREST PENNANT** (IRE) 11
200 **FOREST PRIZE** (GB) F 74
472 **FOREST RHYTHM** (IRE) 13
141 **FOREST ROW** (GB) 35
266 **FOREVER AND EVER** (IRE) 60
601 **FOREVER BOND** (GB) F 67
304 **FOREVER GLORY** (IRE) 25
142 **FOREVER HOPE** (GB) 4
273 **FOREVER JANEY** (IRE) 11
321 **FOREVER PRESENT** (IRE) 53
446 **FOREVER SILVER** (IRE) G 28
117 **FOREVER TIMES** F 37
59 **FOREVER WAINING** (IRE) 11
506 **FOREVER'S GIRL** (GB) 5
123 **FOREWARNED** (IRE) C 59
672 **FORGE HOUSE** (IRE) 3
460 **FORGET IT** (GB) 31
573 **FORGET ME NOT LANE** (IRE) 50
299 **FORGIVE** (GB) 52
254 **FORGOTTEN GOLD** (IRE) 16
328 **FORGOTTEN HERO** (IRE) 29
25 **FORGOTTEN PROMISE** (GB) 1
682 **FORGOTTEN RULES** (IRE) 95
419 **FORJOETHEPLUMBER** (IRE) 5
116 **FORKS** (GB) 3
371 **FORMEDABLE** (IRE) 4
520 **FORMERLY HOT** (GB) 58
488 **FORMIDABLE GIRL** (USA) 13
530 **FORMIDABLE GUEST** (GB) 4

446 **FORMIDABLEOPPONENT** (IRE) 29
476 **FORMULATION** (IRE) 23
380 **FORRESTERS FOLLY** (GB) 35
299 **FORT BASTION** (IRE) 53
219 **FORT BELVEDERE** (GB) 11
299 **FORT KNOX** (GB) 171
123 **FORT TICONDEROGA** (IRE) 3
284 **FORT VIEW** (IRE) 2
35 **FORTIETH AND FIFTH** (IRE) 33
92 **FORTIFICATION** (USA) 1
462 **FORTRESS** (GB) F 30
19 **FORTROSE ACADEMY** (IRE) 62
603 **FORTUNA ROSE** (GB) 2
620 **FORTUNATE BID** (IRE) 4
564 **FORTUNE HUNTER** (FR) 36
592 **FORTUNELINI** (GB) 5
178 **FORTUNI** (IRE) 8
433 **FORTY PROOF** (IRE) 16
145 **FORTYSECOND STREET** (IRE) 9
509 **FORWARD FELINE** (IRE) 8
606 **FORWARD FLIGHT** (IRE) 14
445 **FORZARZI** (IRE) 3
321 **FORZY ORIGNY** (FR) 54
45 **FOSSGATE** (GB) 6
503 **FOUNDATION MAN** (IRE) 24
339 **FOUNTAIN CRUMBLE** (GB) C 6
446 **FOUNTAIN OF HONOUR** (IRE) 30
507 **FOUR BETTER** (GB) 20
465 **FOUR COMMANDERS** (IRE) 14
4 **FOUR FIDDLERS** (GB) 5
58 **FOUR LEAVES** (IRE) 30
384 **FOUR LEGS GOOD** (IRE) F 44
520 **FOUR NATIONS** (USA) 4
507 **FOUR RICHER** (GB) 21
653 **FOUR STEPS BACK** (GB) 4
274 **FOUR VALLIES** (IRE) F 8
139 **FOUR WINDS** (GB) 8
580 **FOUR-LEGGED FRIEND** C 3
9 **FOURACRES** (GB) 42
336 **FOURSQUARE FUNTIME** (GB) 30
321 **FOURTH ESTATE** (GB) 55
625 **FOURTH GENERATION** (IRE) 16
191 **FOURTH OF JUNE** (IRE) 24
391 **FOX APPEAL** (IRE) 24
113 **FOXHAVEN** (GB) 11
33 **FOXINTHECOTS** (GB) 7
30 **FOXLEY** (IRE) 5
320 **FOXSPUR** (IRE) 4
601 **FOXTROT ROMEO** (IRE) 37
299 **FOXY DANCER** (IRE) 172
7 **FOXY MUSIC** (GB) 1
535 **FRAAM LEA** (GB) 3
328 **FRABJOUS** (GB) F 87
219 **FRACTIONAL** (GB) 54
111 **FRAGONARD** (GB) 42
74 **FRAGRANCY** (FR) F 61
569 **FRALOGA** (IRE) C 110
200 **FRAMBROISE** (GB) C 75
387 **FRAMED** (GB) 20
469 **FRAN'S FOLLY** (GB) 15
318 **FRANCASTEL** (FR) 19
157 **FRANCESA** (GB) 10
147 **FRANCESCANA** (GB) 31
698 **FRANCIA** (GB) F 28
471 **FRANCIS ALBERT** (GB) 8
147 **FRANCISCAN** (GB) 4
320 **FRANCO IS MY NAME** (GB) 5
119 **FRANK MORGAN** (GB) 29

296 **FRANK THE SLINK** (GB) 13
111 **FRANKEL** (GB) 9
229 **FRANKIE FALCO** (GB) 1
489 **FRANKIE FIGG** (IRE) 43
296 **FRANKS A MILLION** (IRE) 14
650 **FRASCATI PARK** (IRE) 24
654 **FRASERS HILL** (GB) 44
433 **FRATELLINO** (GB) 17
647 **FRECKLE FACE** (GB) 9
434 **FRECKLETON** (GB) 54
294 **FRED BOJANGALS** (IRE) 4
316 **FRED GRASS** (GB) 3
600 **FRED LALLOUPET** (GB) 4
27 **FRED WILLETTS** (IRE) 13
69 **FREDA'S ROSE** (GB) 4
676 **FREDDIE BOLT** (GB) 5
118 **FREDDIE BROWN** (GB) 10
299 **FREDDY Q** (GB) 54
367 **FREDDY'S STAR** (IRE) 3
284 **FREDDY'S STAR** (IRE) 3
642 **FREDERICK ALFRED** (GB) 43
264 **FREDERICK WILLIAM** (GB) 5
466 **FREDERICKTHEGREAT** (GB) 43
696 **FREDO** (IRE) 18
262 **FREE ADVICE** (IRE) 9
566 **FREE ANGEL** (USA) F 14
684 **FREE FALLING** (GB) 7
42 **FREE SPEECH** (GB) 11
299 **FREE VERSE** (GB) 55
458 **FREE WORLD** (FR) 10
601 **FREE ZONE** (GB) 38
625 **FREEDOM** (GER) C 55
355 **FREEDOM FLYING** (GB) 2
35 **FREEZING LOVE** (USA) F 70
488 **FREMEN** (USA) 14
510 **FREMONT** (IRE) 1
611 **FRENCH APPLAUSE** (IRE) 4
123 **FRENCH FIFTEEN** (FR) 26
682 **FRENCH HEN** (USA) 41
231 **FRENCH HOLLOW** (GB) 5
3 **FRENCH NAVY** (GB) 10
321 **FRENCH OPERA** (GB) 56
130 **FRENCH QUARTET** (IRE) F 14
511 **FRENCH RULES** (FR) 15
664 **FRENCH SEVENTYFIVE** (GB) 3
101 **FRENCH TIES** (IRE) 14
119 **FRENI** (GER) F 65
155 **FREQUENCY** (GB) 7
534 **FRESA** (GB) 19
500 **FRESHER** (GB) C 14
160 **FRESHER FISHING** (IRE) 10
586 **FREYA TRICKS** (GB) G 16
200 **FRIDAYTHORPE** (IRE) 5
412 **FRIENDLY CRAIC** (IRE) F 8
340 **FRIENDLY SOCIETY** (IRE) 20
330 **FRIENDS OF AMA GI** (GB) 4
215 **FRIENDSHIP BAY** (GB) 5
208 **FRIENDSHIP IS LOVE** (IRE) 32
343 **FRISCO DEPOT** (GB) 20
494 **FRITH** (GB) 9
380 **FRIZZO** (FR) 36
384 **FROCK** (IRE) 15
34 **FROG HOLLOW** (GB) 27
283 **FROGNAL** (IRE) 29
360 **FROLIC ALONG** (IRE) 11
447 **FROND** (GB) F 70
310 **FRONT OF HOUSE** (IRE) 7
218 **FRONTIER BOY** (IRE) 12

326 **FRONTIER DANCER** (IRE) 14
650 **FRONTIER SPIRIT** (IRE) 25
91 **FRONTLINE PHANTOM** (IRE) 8
525 **FROSTED GRAPE** (GB) 37
58 **FROSTY BERRY** (GB) 31
360 **FROSTY FRIDAY** (GB) 12
476 **FROSTY LAD** (IRE) 24
685 **FROSTY LIGHT** (GB) G 4
9 **FROSTY RECEPTION** (GB) 16
116 **FROSTY SECRET** (GB) 20
385 **FROZEN OVER** (GB) 2
460 **FRUITY O'ROONEY** (GB) 32
232 **FU FIC FAS** (GB) 2
566 **FU WA** (USA) F 16
682 **FUDGE** (GB) C 96
496 **FUERTA VENTURA** (GB) F 65
117 **FUGITIVE MOTEL** (IRE) 15
172 **FUHGEDDABOUDIT** (GB) 3
366 **FULBRIGHT** (GB) 79
621 **FULGORA** (GB) 4
147 **FULGUR** (GB) 5
503 **FULL OF JOY** (IRE) 25
251 **FULL OV BEANS** (GB) 3
612 **FULL SHILLING** (IRE) 6
654 **FULL SWING** (GB) 45
260 **FULL TOSS** (GB) 6
446 **FULLY FUNDED** (USA) 31
213 **FULNEY** (GB) 15
461 **FUNCTION DREAMER** (GB) F 10
328 **FUNK SOUL BROTHER** (GB) 88
688 **FUNKY MUNKY** (GB) 7
496 **FURBELOW** (GB) 21
606 **FURIUS** (GB) 15
593 **FURROWS** (GB) 19
391 **FURTHER MORE** (IRE) 25
614 **FURTHER PROOF** (IRE) 19
285 **FURY** (GB) 7
147 **FURZANAH** (GB) 32
659 **FUSHE JO** (GB) 21
328 **FUSTAAN** (IRE) C 89
94 **FUTURE IMPACT** (IRE) 5
49 **FUTURE SECURITY** (IRE) 84
467 **FUZZY LOGIC** (IRE) 17

564 **GAANYA** (FR) 37
249 **GABBIANO** (GB) 29
265 **GABH MO LEITHSCEAL** (IRE) 7
35 **GABRIAL THE GREAT** (IRE) 34
597 **GABRIAL THE HERO** (USA) 32
573 **GABRIAL THE KING** (USA) 51
597 **GABRIAL'S GIFT** (GB) 33
366 **GABRIAL'S HOPE** (FR) 80
696 **GABRIAL'S KING** (GB) 61
366 **GABRIAL'S LAYLA** (GB) 81
220 **GABRIAL'S LEXI** (GB) 49
601 **GABRIAL'S PRINCESS** (IRE) 39
601 **GABRIAL'S STAR** (GB) 40
127 **GABRIEL'S LAD** (IRE) 10
448 **GADREEL** (IRE) 8
451 **GAELIC ICE** (GB) 31
460 **GAELIC SILVER** (FR) 33
228 **GAELIC WIZARD** (IRE) 5
388 **GAIETE** (GB) 73
120 **GAINSBOROUGH'S ART** (IRE) 9
446 **GAIUS MARIUS** (GB) 32
490 **GALA SPIRIT** (IRE) 5
476 **GALANT NUIT** (IRE) 25
483 **GALANTOS** (GER) 2
451 **GALATIAN** (GB) 3

223 **GALAXY HIGHFLYER** (GB) F 53
503 **GALAXY ROCK** (IRE) 26
366 **GALICIAN** (GB) 82
102 **GALILAHI** (GB) 50
682 **GALILEO'S CHOICE** (IRE) 6
460 **GALIOTTO** (GB) 34
123 **GALIPEA** (IRE) 4
600 **GALIPETTE** (GB) C 38
169 **GALLANT EAGLE** (IRE) 9
29 **GALLANT LEADER** (USA) 33
342 **GALLANTRY** (GB) 5
538 **GALLEGO** (GB) 7
619 **GALLEON** (GB) 33
219 **GALLERIA** (GB) 12
147 **GALLETTO** (IRE) 33
115 **GALLEY SLAVE** (IRE) 4
469 **GALLIMAUFRY** (GB) 16
266 **GALLIPOT** (GB) 61
521 **GALLOPING MINISTER** (IRE) 10
684 **GALLOPING QUEEN** (IRE) 8
657 **GALLOX BRIDGE** (GB) 27
318 **GALVESTON** (FR) 49
513 **GALWAY GEM** (FR) 5
304 **GALZIG** (IRE) 26
108 **GAMBATTE** (GB) 12
35 **GAMBLE** (GB) 71
695 **GAMBO** (IRE) 38
510 **GAME ALL** (IRE) 6
110 **GAME HALL** (IRE) 7
496 **GAME TAKEN** (GB) 22
3 **GAMILATI** (GB) 68
407 **GAMMA** (FR) C 45
511 **GAMMARTH** (FR) 9
614 **GAMRA** (FR) C 40
339 **GAN ON** (GB) 7
141 **GANAS** (IRE) 11
569 **GANDALAK** (FR) 48
10 **GANDALFE** (FR) 8
91 **GANGSTERBANKSTERS** (FR) 27
606 **GANSEY** (IRE) 16
308 **GAOTH NA MARA** (IRE) G 13
695 **GAP OF DUNLOE** (IRE) 5
496 **GARDE COTIERE** (USA) 3
499 **GARDE FREINET** (IRE) 45
285 **GARDEN ROW** (GB) 88
92 **GARDINER HARTE** (IRE) 2
24 **GARLETON** (GB) 3
573 **GARMELONA GIRL** (GB) 89
625 **GARRA MOLLY** (IRE) G 56
331 **GARROW'S LAW** (GB) 33
237 **GARSTANG** (GB) 11
534 **GARZONI** (GB) 20
430 **GASPAR** (IRE) 3
525 **GASPARA** (FR) 38
29 **GASPROM'S BRINED** (IRE) 34
534 **GASSIN GOLF** (GB) 21
219 **GATERIE** (GB) 55
475 **GATES OF ROME** (IRE) 9
600 **GATEWAY** (USA) F 39
266 **GATEWOOD** (GB) 11
266 **GATHERING** (USA) 62
161 **GAUL WOOD** (GB) 29
697 **GAUVAIN** (GER) 8
476 **GAVROCHE GAUGAIN** (FR) 26
544 **GAY GALLIVANTER** (GB) 2
18 **GAY ROMANCE** (GB) F 63
134 **GAY SLOANE** (GB) 3
524 **GAZBOOLOU** (GB) 3

526 **GEANIE MAC** (IRE) 9
460 **GEE DEE NEN** (GB) 35
206 **GEE HI** (IRE) 8
656 **GEE MAJOR** (GB) 3
109 **GEEAITCH** (GB) 13
129 **GEM OF WIZDOM** (IRE) 5
531 **GEMINI JIM** (IRE) 9
390 **GEMINIANI** (IRE) C 31
500 **GEMINUS** (IRE) 2
335 **GEMMASON** (GB) 5
111 **GEMS OF ARABY** (GB) F 109
373 **GENERAL GIRLING** (GB) 12
256 **GENERAL KUTUZOV** (IRE) 8
608 **GENERAL MELCHETT** (IRE) 2
321 **GENERAL MILLER** (GB) 57
707 **GENERAL ROSS** (IRE) 2
660 **GENERAL TING** (IRE) 13
602 **GENERAL TUFTO** (GB) 2
171 **GENERALYSE** (GB) 11
160 **GENEROUS BEAUTY** (GB) 11
472 **GENEROUS BOB** (GB) 14
225 **GENEROUS GENELLA** (GB) 10
108 **GENEROUS KENNY** (GB) 13
112 **GENES OF A DANCER** (AUS) 2
323 **GENEVA GEYSER** (GER) 5
3 **GENIUS BEAST** (USA) 17
119 **GENKI** (IRE) 7
380 **GENSTONE TRAIL** (GB) 37
254 **GENTLE BOB** (IRE) 17
250 **GENTLEMAN ANSHAN** (IRE) 5
458 **GENTLEMAN DUKE** (IRE) 3
169 **GENTLEMAN IS BACK** (USA) 10
268 **GENTLEMAN JEFF** (USA) 16
466 **GENTLEMAN JIMMY** (GB) 12
299 **GENTLY** (GB) C 173
326 **GENUINE PEARL** (IRE) 15
328 **GEOGRAPHIC** (USA) C 90
684 **GEORDIE BOY** (GB) 20
625 **GEORGE ADAMSON** (IRE) 17
18 **GEORGE BAKER** (IRE) 13
488 **GEORGE BENJAMIN** (GB) 15
35 **GEORGE CINQ** (GB) 72
283 **GEORGE FENTON** (GB) 71
573 **GEORGE FERNBECK** (GB) 11
12 **GEORGE GURU** (GB) 8
678 **GEORGE MY FRIEND** (GB) 4
697 **GEORGE NYMPTON** (GB) 9
451 **GEORGE THISBY** (GB) 4
657 **GEORGE WOOLF** (GB) 28
283 **GEORGEBERNARDSHAW** (IRE) 30
353 **GEORGEDOUBLEYOU** (IRE) 4
570 **GEORGES STREET** (IRE) 26
219 **GEORGETOWN** (GB) 144
625 **GEORGEY GIRL** (GB) 18
607 **GEORGIAN KING** (GB) 4
241 **GEORGIAN SILVER** (GB) 6
18 **GEORGIE THE FOURTH** (IRE) F 64
262 **GEORGIE WHALE** (GB) 10
18 **GEORGINA BAKER** 65
436 **GERALDINES LASS** (IRE) 4
219 **GERMANIC** (GB) 145
22 **GERRARD** (IRE) 1
299 **GERRARDS CROSS** (IRE) 174
59 **GET HOME NOW** (GB) 12
695 **GET IT ON** (IRE) 40
503 **GET ME OUT OF HERE** (IRE) 27
381 **GET READY TO GO** (IRE) 9
408 **GET YOUR WAY** 54

201 GETABUZZ (GB) 22
404 GETAWAY DRIVER (IRE) 14
43 GETCARTER (GB) 6
404 GETMEOUTHEDOLDRUMS (GB) 15
556 GETTING READY (IRE) 13
525 GEVREY CHAMBERTIN (FR) 39
434 GHAABESH (IRE) 55
658 GHAAYER (GB) 24
654 GHAIDAA (IRE) C 112
366 GHALAA (IRE) 83
74 GHAR SHOOP (IRE) 10
111 GHAZAL (USA) C 110
588 GHAZEER (IRE) 35
58 GHENWAH (FR) C 64
321 GHIMAAR (GB) 58
489 GHIZAO (GER) 44
219 GHOST ARMY (IRE) 56
696 GHOST OF A SMILE (IRE) 19
597 GHOST PROTOCOL (IRE) 34
111 GHOST RUNNER (IRE) 111
366 GHOST TRAIN (GB) 84
215 GHOSTWING (GB) 6
516 GHUFA (IRE) 6
266 GHUSOON (GB) 63
219 GIACINTA (GB) 57
113 GIANT ACT (GB) 12
326 GIANT O MURCHU (IRE) 16
124 GIANTSTEPSAHEAD (IRE) 19
18 GIB (IRE) F 66
321 GIBB RIVER (IRE) 59
496 GIDDY HEIGHTS (GB) 66
424 GIFT OF DGAB (IRE) 8
40 GIFT OF SILENCE (GB) 13
102 GIFTED DANCER (GB) 26
129 GIFTED GIRL (IRE) 10
515 GIFTED HEIR (IRE) 1
696 GIFTED LEADER (USA) 20
73 GIFTED SPIRIT (GB) 40
460 GIGONDAS (GB) 107
503 GILBARRY (IRE) 28
264 GILDED AGE (GB) 6
396 GILDED YOUTH (GB) 5
160 GILES CROSS (GB) 12
695 GILWEN GLORY (IRE) 41
117 GIMASHA (GB) F 38
304 GIMLI'S RETURN (IRE) 27
304 GIMLI'S ROCK (IRE) 28
635 GIN COBBLER (GB) 3
161 GIN TWIST (GB) 10
110 GINGER FIZZ (GB) 8
501 GINGER GREY (IRE) 14
462 GINGER MONKEY (IRE) 11
161 GINGER NOT BLONDE (USA) C 53
698 GINGER TED (IRE) 7
266 GINGERNUT (GB) 64
386 GINGERS REFLECTION (GB) 9
565 GINOLAD (AUS) 3
569 GIOFRA (GB) 2
331 GIORDANO BRUNO (IRE) 34
321 GIORGIO QUERCUS (FR) 60
227 GIREVOLE (GB) 10
460 GITANO HERNANDO (GB) 36
587 GIULIETTA DA VINCI (GB) 7
511 GIULIO CESARE (IRE) 10
210 GIVE A LOT (GB) 1
447 GIVE A WHISTLE (IRE) F 71
194 GIVE OR TAKE (GB) 5
39 GIVE US A HAND (IRE) 8

188 GIVEHERACHANCE (GB) 11
198 GIVEITACHANCE (IRE) 9
552 GIVEITAGO (GB) 44
304 GIVING ORDERS (IRE) 29
340 GIZZIT (IRE) 21
217 GLACIAL HARRY (GB) 2
6 GLADSTONE (IRE) 2
493 GLADYS AYLWARD (GB) G 8
654 GLADYS' GAL (GB) 9
641 GLAISDALE (GB) 4
475 GLAM GERRY (IRE) 10
299 GLAMADOUR (IRE) C 175
304 GLAMOROUS (GER) 30
223 GLANELY (IRE) 54
56 GLASCLUNE (IRE) 3
223 GLASS MOUNTAIN (IRE) 8
597 GLASS OFFICE (GB) 70
525 GLASSAWINE (GB) 40
511 GLASSIK (IRE) 56
476 GLASSON LAD (IRE) 27
172 GLASTONBERRY (GB) 9
466 GLAZE (GB) 44
391 GLEANN EAGAS (IRE) 26
688 GLEANN NA NDOCHAIS (IRE) 8
271 GLEANNACREIM (IRE) 2
366 GLEN ELLYN (GB) 85
328 GLEN GINNIE (IRE) 91
328 GLEN MOSS (GB) 30
220 GLEN'S DIAMOND (GB) 11
328 GLENARD (GB) 92
343 GLENBARROW (IRE) 21
466 GLENCAL (GB) F 72
659 GLENCREE (IRE) 22
57 GLENDUN ANNIE (IRE) 7
340 GLENELEG (IRE) 22
654 GLENMARA (USA) C 113
384 GLENNTEN (GB) 16
570 GLENORA GALE (IRE) 27
259 GLENRIDDING (GB) 2
386 GLENS BOY (IRE) 10
434 GLENWOOD KNIGHT (IRE) 56
86 GLENWOOD PRESENT (IRE) 10
156 GLIDEWELL (GB) 2
299 GLIDING LIGHT (USA) C 176
628 GLIMPSE (GB) F 23
556 GLINGERBANK (IRE) 14
556 GLINGERBURN (IRE) 15
643 GLINT (GB) C 58
619 GLITTERBALL (IRE) 34
619 GLITTERING GOLD (GB) 35
299 GLITTERING PRIZE (UAE) C 177
207 GLOBAL (GB) 14
49 GLOBAL CITY (IRE) 29
321 GLOBAL FELLA (IRE) 61
15 GLOBAL FLYER (GB) 6
299 GLOBAL ICON (IRE) 178
153 GLOBAL LEADER (IRE) 16
593 GLOBAL POWER (IRE) 20
55 GLOBAL REACH (IRE) 82
119 GLOBAL TREND (GB) C 66
207 GLOBAL VILLAGE (IRE) 15
391 GLOBAL WARMING (IRE) 27
343 GLOBALIZED (IRE) 22
55 GLOR NA MARA (IRE) 3
597 GLORIAM (USA) 35
665 GLORIOUS PROTECTOR (IRE) 15
665 GLORIOUS STAR (IRE) 16
321 GLORIOUS TWELFTH (IRE) 62

328 GLORY DAYS (GER) C 93
299 GLOSSY POSSE (GB) 179
585 GLOUCESTER (GB) 10
55 GLOVE SMITH (IRE) 83
658 GLOW STAR (SAF) 25
360 GO AMWELL (GB) 13
164 GO ANNIE (GB) 5
73 GO COURCHEVAL (GB) 27
308 GO DAN DO (GB) 5
654 GO DUTCH (IRE) 46
116 GO GO GADGET (GER) 4
260 GO GO GREEN (IRE) 7
331 GO LIMPOPO (GB) 35
169 GO NANI GO (GB) 11
446 GO NATIVE (IRE) 33
650 GO ON ARCH (IRE) 26
229 GO ON JACK (GB) 2
213 GO SET GO (GB) 3
283 GOAL (IRE) 31
650 GOAT CASTLE (IRE) 27
705 GOBAMA (GB) 7
150 GOD OF THE KOP (IRE) 10
424 GOD'S COUNTY (FR) 9
380 GODSMEJUDGE (IRE) 38
625 GOGEO (IRE) 19
220 GOING GREY (IRE) 50
709 GOING TWICE (GB) 2
476 GOING WRONG (GB) 28
31 GOLAN GUY (IRE) 5
684 GOLAN WAY (GB) 9
219 GOLBAHAR (IRE) 146
55 GOLD BAND (IRE) 84
49 GOLD CITY (IRE) 85
576 GOLD DEAL (GB) 4
496 GOLD EDITION (GB) 23
183 GOLD EXCHANGE (FR) 9
597 GOLD FALCON (IRE) 36
380 GOLD INGOT (GB) 39
191 GOLD LACE (IRE) 25
501 GOLD MAJESTY (GB) G 50
19 GOLD MINE (GB) 12
3 GOLD RALLY (USA) 69
200 GOLD RULES (GB) 16
183 GOLD SAVE THE KING (IRE) 10
299 GOLD SCEPTRE (GB) 56
573 GOLD STRIKE (GB) C 90
388 GOLDATOR (FR) 74
573 GOLDEN (FR) G 91
306 GOLDEN (FR) G 40
219 GOLDEN ANTIGUA (USA) C 147
219 GOLDEN AQUILA (IRE) 58
434 GOLDEN CALL (IRE) 57
252 GOLDEN CELEBRATION (GB) 5
272 GOLDEN CHARM (IRE) F 12
639 GOLDEN CHIEFTAIN (GB) 15
298 GOLDEN CLUBS (IRE) 38
67 GOLDEN COMPASS (GB) 2
466 GOLDEN DELICIOUS (GB) 13
184 GOLDEN DESERT (IRE) 5
328 GOLDEN DEW (IRE) C 94
237 GOLDEN DREAM (GB) 12
207 GOLDEN DREAM (IRE) 16
600 GOLDEN DREAMS (FR) 5
409 GOLDEN EMPEROR (IRE) 1
380 GOLDEN FIREBIRD (IRE) 40
501 GOLDEN FLYER (FR) G 51
490 GOLDEN FUTURE (GB) 6
583 GOLDEN GAEL (GB) 8

400 **GOLDEN GRAHAM** (GB) 7
337 **GOLDEN GROOM** (GB) 7
299 **GOLDEN JUBILEE** (USA) 57
700 **GOLDEN KING** (IRE) 10
219 **GOLDEN LILAC** (IRE) 13
58 **GOLDEN SHARE** (USA) 32
265 **GOLDEN SHOE** (IRE) 8
473 **GOLDEN SILVER** (FR) 40
208 **GOLDEN SONG** (GB) 18
189 **GOLDEN SPARKLE** (IRE) 4
364 **GOLDEN TEMPEST** (IRE) 6
364 **GOLDEN WATERS** (GB) 7
220 **GOLDENVEIL** (IRE) 12
183 **GOLDIE JOLIE** (FR) 39
55 **GOLDIROCKS** (IRE) 29
331 **GOLDMADCHEN** (GER) 36
19 **GOLDONI** (IRE) 63
147 **GOLDREAM** (GB) 34
32 **GOLDSTORM** (GB) 7
511 **GOLDY MOON** (GB) 104
318 **GOLF JUAN** (USA) 20
570 **GOLFER'S CROSSING** (IRE) 28
74 **GOLUBITSA** (IRE) F 62
600 **GONAWIN** (FR) 40
49 **GONBARDA** (GER) C 131
220 **GONE BY SUNRISE** (GB) 51
249 **GONE TO GROUND** (GB) 30
260 **GONINODAETHAT** (GB) 8
296 **GONOW** (GB) 15
389 **GOOCHYPOOCHYPRADER** (GB) 9
253 **GOOD AUTHORITY** (IRE) 4
573 **GOOD BOY JACKSON** (GB) 12
466 **GOOD GIRL** (GB) G 73
460 **GOOD LUCK CHARM** (GB) 108
366 **GOOD MORNING STAR** (IRE) 86
388 **GOOD NEWS** (FR) 4
18 **GOOD OLD PAUL** (IRE) 14
254 **GOOD ORDER** (GB) 18
80 **GOOD TIMIN'** (GB) 4
188 **GOODFELLOWS QUEST** (IRE) 12
384 **GOODIE GOODIE** (GB) 17
435 **GOODISON PARK** (GB) 3
24 **GOODLUKIN LUCY** (GB) 9
450 **GOODMANYOURSELF** (GB) 13
501 **GOODNESS** (GB) 15
193 **GOODWOOD ATLANTIS** (IRE) 31
201 **GOODWOOD MARCH** (GB) F 110
193 **GOODWOOD MIRAGE** (IRE) 49
42 **GOODWOOD STARLIGHT** (IRE) 12
655 **GOOGLETTE** (IRE) 2
417 **GOOSEBERRY BUSH** (GB) 3
534 **GOOSEBERRY FOOL** (GB) 23
283 **GORDY BEE** (USA) 32
114 **GORES ISLAND** (IRE) 4
495 **GOREY LANE** (IRE) 5
138 **GORGE** (AUS) 1
699 **GORGEHOUS LLIEGE** (FR) 22
276 **GORGEOUS GOBLIN** (IRE) 4
473 **GORGEOUS SIXTY** (FR) 41
487 **GORING ONE** (IRE) 4
487 **GORING TWO** (IRE) 5
53 **GORMANSTOWN CUCKOO** (GB) 5
92 **GORT NA MONA** (USA) 4
408 **GORVELLO** 55
102 **GOSBECK** (GB) 8
75 **GOSFORTH PARK** (GB) 8
619 **GOSPEL CHOIR** (GB) 36
380 **GOSPEL PREACHER** (GB) 41

332 **GOT ATTITUDE** (IRE) 7
657 **GOT THE URGE** (IRE) 29
646 **GOTOYOURPLAY** (IRE) 6
434 **GOTTANY O'S** (GB) 58
27 **GOTTCHER** (GB) 14
445 **GOUGANE** (GB) 4
525 **GOULANES** (IRE) 41
102 **GOURAY GIRL** (IRE) 9
71 **GOWER RULES** (IRE) 7
208 **GOWER SONG** (GB) F 33
478 **GOWITHDFLO** (IRE) 4
49 **GOZLAN** (USA) 86
191 **GRABLE** (GB) F 56
460 **GRABTHEGLORY** (IRE) 37
108 **GRACCHUS** (USA) 14
567 **GRACE AND FORTUNE** (GB) 6
576 **GRACE HULL** (GB) 7
686 **GRACEFUL AIR** (IRE) C 24
649 **GRACEFUL DESCENT** (FR) 1
204 **GRACEFUL LASS** (GB) F 12
214 **GRACEFUL SPIRIT** (GB) 14
321 **GRACEY BELLA** (IRE) 63
538 **GRACIE'S GAMES** (GB) 8
283 **GRACIE'S GIFT** (IRE) 33
388 **GRACILIA** (FR) 30
388 **GRACIOSILLA** (SPA) 31
243 **GRACIOUS GEORGE** (IRE) 12
610 **GRADUATION NIGHT** (GB) 6
388 **GRAFFITO** (FR) 32
531 **GRAFITE** (GB) 10
111 **GRAIL** (USA) F 112
573 **GRAMERCY** (IRE) 13
318 **GRAMMAR** (GB) 21
233 **GRAMS AND OUNCES** (GB) 6
586 **GRAN CANARIA QUEEN** (GB) 13
219 **GRAN MAESTRO** (USA) 59
446 **GRAN TORINO** (IRE) 34
705 **GRAND ART** (IRE) 8
140 **GRAND ARTICLE** (IRE) 3
145 **GRAND DAY OUT** (IRE) 10
141 **GRAND DENIAL** (IRE) 63
260 **GRAND DIAMOND** (IRE) 9
318 **GRAND DUC** (USA) 5
706 **GRAND FELLA** (IRE) 5
342 **GRAND HONOUR** (IRE) 6
657 **GRAND LAHOU** (IRE) 30
40 **GRAND LIAISON** (GB) 14
299 **GRAND SLAM MARIA** (FR) C 180
501 **GRAND SPLENDOUR** (GB) G 52
107 **GRAND STITCH** (USA) 6
61 **GRAND THEFT EQUINE** (GB) 7
569 **GRAND VADLA** (FR) C 111
49 **GRAND VENT** (IRE) 30
639 **GRAND VISION** (IRE) 16
116 **GRANDAD MAC** (GB) 5
404 **GRANDADS HORSE** (GB) 16
678 **GRANDE MONSIEUR** (FR) 5
496 **GRANDEAR** (IRE) 24
619 **GRANDILOQUENT** (GB) 37
489 **GRANDIOSO** (IRE) 45
321 **GRANDOUET** (FR) 64
525 **GRANDS CRUS** (FR) 42
446 **GRANGE HOUSE** (IRE) 35
153 **GRANNY ANNE** (IRE) 2
447 **GRANNY KELLY** (USA) C 72
14 **GRANNY MCPHEE** (GB) 3
45 **GRANSTON** (IRE) 7
117 **GRANULE** (GB) 39

101 **GRANVILLE ISLAND** (IRE) 15
664 **GRANWOOD** (GB) 4
558 **GRAPES HILL** (GB) 6
299 **GRAPHIC** (IRE) 58
536 **GRASSCUTTER** (IRE) 2
561 **GRASSFINCH** (GB) 4
266 **GRAVITATE** (GB) 65
298 **GRAY HESSION** (IRE) 12
328 **GRAY PEARL** (GB) 31
101 **GRAYCLIFFE** (IRE) 16
360 **GRAYFRIARS** (GB) 14
174 **GRAYLYN AMBER** (GB) 14
204 **GRAYLYN OLIVAA** (GB) 7
174 **GRAYLYN RUBY** (FR) 15
174 **GRAYLYN VALENTINO** (GB) 48
467 **GRAYSWOOD** (GB) 39
434 **GREAT BOSS** (GB) 59
525 **GREAT ENDEAVOUR** (IRE) 43
206 **GREAT ESTEEM** (IRE) 9
360 **GREAT EXPECTATIONS** (GB) 15
160 **GREAT GUSTO** (IRE) 13
266 **GREAT HEAVENS** (GB) 66
522 **GREAT HERO** (GB) 10
614 **GREAT HUZZAR** (IRE) 3
93 **GREAT KICKER** (IRE) 5
388 **GREAT MOON** (USA) 5
586 **GREAT NICANOR** (IRE) 14
573 **GREAT PHILOSOPHER** (IRE) 92
321 **GREAT REASON** (GB) 65
705 **GREAT ROAR** (USA) 9
384 **GREAT SHOT** (GB) 4
400 **GREAT SHOW** (GB) 8
597 **GREAT SOPRANO** (USA) 37
419 **GREAT SPAN** (IRE) 6
221 **GREAT SUMMER** (IRE) 12
49 **GREAT TIMES** (GER) 87
331 **GREAT TUSKER** (IRE) 37
343 **GREAT VALUE** (IRE) 23
570 **GREAT WISDOM** (IRE) 29
699 **GREAT'S AUTRECHENE** (FR) 23
619 **GREATEST** (FR) 38
507 **GREATEST DANCER** (IRE) 22
147 **GREATWOOD** (GB) 83
597 **GRECIAN AIR** (FR) F 71
572 **GRECIAN GODDESS** (IRE) 5
407 **GREEK CANYON** (IRE) 21
366 **GREEK COLONY** (GB) 87
169 **GREEK ISLANDS** (IRE) 12
540 **GREEK MUSIC** (GB) 9
3 **GREEK WAR** (IRE) 70
666 **GREELEY HOUSE** (GB) 5
183 **GREEN BANANAS** (FR) 11
304 **GREEN CHORUS** (IRE) 89
521 **GREEN EARTH** (IRE) 11
304 **GREEN ENERGY** (GB) 31
123 **GREEN FEES** (IRE) 27
30 **GREEN HOWARD** (GB) 6
111 **GREEN LASSY** (FR) C 113
520 **GREEN LEGACY** (USA) 31
310 **GREEN LIFE** (GB) F 25
592 **GREEN MITAS** (ITY) 20
107 **GREEN PARK** (IRE) 7
34 **GREEN PEARL** (IRE) 4
104 **GREEN TO GOLD** (GB) 6
460 **GREEN WADI** (GB) 38
283 **GREEN WARRIOR** (GB) 34
592 **GREEN WAVE** (ITY) 21
304 **GREENBELT STAR** (GB) 32

462 **GREENFLY** (GB) C 31
488 **GREENHEAD HIGH** (GB) 16
593 **GREENLAW** (GB) 21
592 **GREENMEETIC** (IRE) 6
54 **GREENSAND** (GB) F 24
477 **GREENSWARD** (GB) 4
329 **GREENVERA** (USA) F 33
266 **GREGORIAN** (GB) 67
418 **GRENANE** (IRE) 2
137 **GRENOLI** (FR) 2
399 **GRENOUILLERE** (USA) F 12
34 **GRETA D'ARGENT** (IRE) C 63
197 **GRETEL** (GB) F 14
38 **GRETHEL** (IRE) 5
191 **GRETNA** (GB) C 57
75 **GREY COMMAND** (USA) 9
657 **GREY CRUZEME** (USA) 31
597 **GREY FALCON** (FR) 38
394 **GREY GOLD** (GB) 8
359 **GREY LIFE** (GB) 11
596 **GREY LOCKER** (GB) 4
58 **GREY MIRAGE** (GB) 33
274 **GREY MISTRAL** (GB) F 9
223 **GREY SEAL** (GB) 29
635 **GREY WHISPER** (IRE) 4
391 **GREY WULFF** (GB) 28
102 **GREY'S ELEGY** (GB) 51
538 **GREYEMKAY** (GB) 9
420 **GREYFRIARS DRUMMER** (GB) 15
207 **GREYFRIARSCHORISTA** (GB) 17
452 **GREYLAMI** (IRE) 3
564 **GREYVENTURE** (FR) 38
446 **GRIESENAU** (IRE) 36
467 **GRIFFIN POINT** (IRE) 5
123 **GRIMOD** (FR) 28
378 **GRIMWITH** (GB) 1
695 **GRINDY** (IRE) 42
80 **GRIPPA** (GB) 8
183 **GRISE LEIGH** 12
201 **GRISSOM** (IRE) 23
220 **GRITSTONE** (GB) 13
652 **GRITTI PALACE** (IRE) 4
3 **GRIZZLE** (GB) 71
542 **GROOM LANDING** (PR) F 23
465 **GROOMED** (IRE) 15
178 **GROOVY DANCER** (GB) 9
397 **GROSS PROPHET** (GB) 9
299 **GROUNDWORK** (GB) 181
360 **GROUP LEADER** (GB) 16
434 **GROUSE LODGE** (IRE) 60
475 **GROVE FIELD** (IRE) 11
157 **GROVE PRIDE** (GB) 11
380 **GRUDGE** (GB) 6
380 **GRUMETI** (GB) 42
219 **GUADALAJARA** (GER) F 148
75 **GUADALOUP** (GB) F 20
19 **GUAJIRA** (FR) F 123
117 **GUANTANAMERA** (IRE) C 40
285 **GUARANTEE** (GB) 32
285 **GUARDA PAMPA** (GB) 33
3 **GUARDI** (IRE) 72
460 **GUARDS CHAPEL** (GB) 39
592 **GUAVA** (GB) 22
597 **GUCCI D'ORO** (USA) 39
498 **GUD DAY** (IRE) 13
390 **GUERMANTES** (GB) C 32
476 **GUESS AGAIN** (IRE) 29
585 **GUEST BOOK** (IRE) 11

681 **GUEST OF HONOUR** (FR) 23
58 **GUEST OF HONOUR** (IRE) 34
410 **GUGA** (IRE) 5
385 **GUILDED SPIRIT** (GB) 20
95 **GUILDED WARRIOR** (GB) 4
282 **GUILETTA** (IRE) 2
366 **GULF OF NAPLES** (IRE) 15
434 **GULF PUNCH** (GB) 61
601 **GULF STORM** (IRE) 41
501 **GULF STREAM LADY** (IRE) F 53
102 **GULL ROCK** (GB) 27
489 **GULLIBLE GORDON** (IRE) 46
391 **GULLINBURSTI** (IRE) 29
681 **GUMBALL** (GB) 24
606 **GUN AND MORE** (GB) 17
43 **GUNG HO JACK** (GB) 20
386 **GUNNA SOUND** (IRE) 11
536 **GUNNADOIT** (USA) 3
585 **GUNNER ROSE** (GB) 12
18 **GUNNER WILL** (IRE) 43
174 **GUNS OF LOVE** (IRE) 16
295 **GUNSHIP** (IRE) 2
585 **GUNSLINGER** (FR) 13
695 **GURTACRUE** (IRE) 43
91 **GURU GIRL** (GB) 28
219 **GURUTZIA** (GB) 60
304 **GUSH** (USA) 90
299 **GUSTO** (GB) 59
569 **GUYAPI** (GB) 49
699 **GUYDUS** (IRE) 24
142 **GWEN JOHN** (USA) F 16
647 **GWENS BOY** (GB) 10
191 **GWORN** (GB) 58
587 **GYMCRAK CYRANO** (IRE) C 6
491 **GYMDOLI** (GB) 1
600 **GYPSY HIGHWAY** (GB) 6
509 **GYPSY RIDER** (GB) 21
462 **GYPSY ROYAL** (IRE) F 32
27 **GYPSY WEDDING** (GB) 35
141 **HA'PENNY BEACON** (GB) C 64
220 **HAADEETH** (GB) 14
34 **HAAF A SIXPENCE** (GB) 28
200 **HAAF'N HAAF** (GB) 76
141 **HAAFACHANCE** (GB) 12
299 **HAAFHD HANDSOME** (GB) 60
450 **HAAJES** (GB) 14
285 **HAAMAAT** (IRE) 8
646 **HAAR** (GB) 7
380 **HABBIE SIMPSON** (GB) 43
654 **HABIBTI** (GB) C 114
119 **HABITA** (IRE) 30
664 **HABLA ME** (IRE) G 23
219 **HACHITA** (USA) C 149
406 **HACKETT** (IRE) 4
425 **HACKPENTHOMAS** (GB) 1
74 **HADAJ** (GB) 38
321 **HADRIAN'S APPROACH** (IRE) 66
201 **HADRIANS RULE** (IRE) 80
664 **HAIL TIBERIUS** (GB) 5
308 **HAIRY NIGHT** (IRE) F 14
299 **HAIRY ROCKET** (GB) 182
366 **HAJRAS** (IRE) 88
207 **HAKUNA MATATA** (IRE) 18
601 **HAKURAA** (IRE) 68
16 **HAL OF A LOVER** (GB) 16
406 **HALDIBARI** (IRE) 5
180 **HALF A BILLION** (IRE) 30
575 **HALF A CROWN** (IRE) 3

110 **HALF INCH** (GB) G 27
58 **HALFSIN** (IRE) 9
227 **HALIFAX** (IRE) 11
654 **HALL HEE** (IRE) F 115
55 **HALLA NA SAOIRE** (IRE) 85
220 **HALLA SAN** (GB) 15
328 **HALLAND PARK GIRL** (IRE) F 95
223 **HALLELUJAH** (GB) 9
254 **HALLEY** (FR) 19
466 **HALLING'S QUEST** (GB) 45
19 **HALLINGS COMET** (GB) 64
200 **HALLMARK HARRY** (GB) 17
410 **HALLSTATT** (IRE) 6
259 **HALOGEN** (GB) 22
681 **HALUCHA** (IRE) 25
3 **HAMAN** (CAN) 18
601 **HAMBLETON** (GB) 12
124 **HAMILTON HILL** (GB) 4
366 **HAMIS AL BIN** (IRE) 89
201 **HAMISH MCGONAGALL** (GB) 24
611 **HAMMER** (GB) 5
682 **HAMMERED SILVER** (IRE) 97
321 **HAMMERSLY LAKE** (IRE) 67
473 **HAMMERSMITH** (IRE) 42
166 **HAMMERWOOD** (GB) 7
488 **HAMOODY** (USA) 17
456 **HAMPSFELL** (GB) 12
573 **HAMZA** (IRE) 52
286 **HANAHOE** (GB) 7
511 **HANAMI** (GB) F 105
448 **HAND PAINTED** (GB) 2
569 **HANDANA** (IRE) 112
508 **HANDAZAN** (IRE) 30
338 **HANDFORD HENRY** (IRE) 3
169 **HANDHELD** (GB) 13
251 **HANDSOME BUDDY** (IRE) 4
16 **HANDSOME HARRY** (IRE) 16
360 **HANDSOME KING** (IRE) 17
49 **HANDSOME MAN** (IRE) 88
208 **HANDSOME MOLLY** (GB) 19
266 **HANDSOME RANSOM** (GB) 68
110 **HANDTHEPRIZEOVER** (GB) 9
639 **HANDY ANDY** (IRE) 17
311 **HANDY MANNY** (IRE) 4
430 **HANG UP MY BOOTS** (IRE) 4
208 **HANGIN WITH MY BUDS** (USA) C 34
556 **HANNAH JACQUES** (IRE) 16
55 **HANNAH'S SMILE** (IRE) 30
496 **HANNIBAL HAYES** (USA) 35
359 **HANNIBAL'S LODGER** (IRE) G 12
485 **HANOVERIAN BARON** (GB) 7
340 **HANS CRESCENT** (FR) 23
266 **HANSEATIC** (GB) 69
412 **HANSOMIS** (IRE) 4
191 **HANZADA** (USA) 59
529 **HAPPY CLAPPER** (GB) C 41
214 **HAPPY OMEN** (GB) C 71
511 **HAPPY WEDDING** (IRE) 11
298 **HARANGUE** (IRE) 13
74 **HARAQAAN** (GB) 39
508 **HARASIYA** (IRE) 69
285 **HARAYIR** (USA) F 89
259 **HARBOUR SANDS** (GB) 23
682 **HARBOUR SIDE** (GB) 42
299 **HARBOUR WATCH** (IRE) 61
446 **HARCHIE** (IRE) 37
564 **HARD DREAM** (IRE) 39
593 **HARD HOUSE** (GB) 22

666 **HARD ROAD** (GB) 24
270 **HARD ROCK CITY** (USA) 6
665 **HARD RUN** (GB) 4
411 **HARD TO NAME** (GB) 1
374 **HARD TO SWALLOW** (IRE) 17
586 **HARDROCK DIAMOND** (GB) 6
9 **HARDWICK BAY** (GB) 17
507 **HARDY BLUE** (IRE) 36
127 **HARDY PLUME** (GB) 11
507 **HARDY RED** (IRE) 87
201 **HAREBY** (IRE) 81
600 **HAREM LADY** (FR) 24
573 **HARLEM DANCER** (GB) C 93
124 **HARLEQUIN GIRL** (GB) 5
193 **HARLESTONE TIMES** (IRE) 6
193 **HARLESTONE WOOD** (GB) 32
542 **HARMONIE** (IRE) 17
626 **HAROUET** (FR) 6
681 **HARRIS GARDEN** (IRE) 26
659 **HARRIS HAWK** (GB) 23
285 **HARRIS TWEED** (GB) 9
689 **HARRY FLASHMAN** (GB) 5
178 **HARRY HANDSOME** (GB) 10
444 **HARRY HUNT** (GB) 5
706 **HARRY OSCAR** (IRE) 6
654 **HARRY PATCH** (GB) 10
664 **HARRY THE HAWK** (GB) 7
489 **HARRY THE VIKING** (GB) 47
16 **HARRY TOPPER** (GB) 17
460 **HARRY TRICKER** (GB) 40
278 **HARRY WESTON** (GB) 2
19 **HARRYANA** (GB) F 124
626 **HARRYS BOY** (GB) 7
274 **HARRYS GUNNER** (GB) 10
686 **HARRYS WHIM** (GB) 6
73 **HARRYS YER MAN** (GB) 8
508 **HARTANI** (GB) 31
45 **HARTFORTH** (GB) 7
643 **HARTING HILL** (GB) 7
496 **HARVARD N YALE** (USA) 26
54 **HARVEST MIST** (GB) 4
386 **HARVEST SONG** (IRE) 12
552 **HARVEY'S HOPE** (GB) 18
447 **HASAAD** (USA) 73
508 **HASANKA** (IRE) 62
447 **HASHEEMA** (IRE) C 74
29 **HASNA** (FR) 35
53 **HASSADIN** (GB) 6
141 **HASSLE** (IRE) 36
299 **HASTEN** (GB) C 183
237 **HASTY LADY** (GB) G 48
64 **HATHA ZAIN** (IRE) 26
598 **HATHAMORE** (GB) 3
73 **HATHAWAY** (IRE) 9
619 **HATHRAH** (IRE) C 116
328 **HATPIN** (GB) C 96
473 **HATS AND HEELS** (IRE) 43
43 **HATS OFF** (GB) 38
516 **HATTA STREAM** (IRE) 7
492 **HATTERS RIVER** (IRE) 1
1 **HAVANA BEAT** (IRE) 125
299 **HAVANA GOLD** (IRE) 184
390 **HAVE FAITH** (IRE) F 33
670 **HAVE YOU HAD YOURS** (IRE) 2
654 **HAVIN' A GOOD TIME** (IRE) 47
529 **HAVING A BALL** (GB) 6
374 **HAVINGOTASCOOBYDO** (IRE) 18
643 **HAWAAFEZ** (GB) 8

376 **HAWAANA** (IRE) 5
689 **HAWAII KLASS** (GB) 6
615 **HAWAIIAN FREEZE** (GB) 8
91 **HAWAIIAN STORM** (GB) 29
628 **HAWAWI** (GB) 3
84 **HAWK GOLD** (IRE) 1
612 **HAWK MOTH** (IRE) 7
543 **HAWK MOUNTAIN** (UAE) 8
503 **HAWK RUN** (GB) 29
489 **HAWKES POINT** (GB) 48
696 **HAWKESHEAD** (GB) 21
657 **HAWKHILL** (IRE) 32
588 **HAWKINO** (IRE) 36
220 **HAWKS REEF** (GB) 52
385 **HAWRIDGE KING** (GB) 3
451 **HAWRIDGE SONG** (GB) 5
385 **HAWRIDGE STAR** (IRE) 4
508 **HAY POINT** (GB) 32
318 **HAYA** (FR) 22
34 **HAYAKU** (IRE) 5
271 **HAYDEN GRACE** (GB) G 8
246 **HAYDENS MOUNT** (GB) 7
201 **HAYEK** (GB) 25
404 **HAYJACK** (GB) 17
597 **HAYLAMAN** (IRE) 8
287 **HAYLOFT** (IRE) 35
366 **HAYMARKET** (GB) 90
201 **HAZARDOUS** (GB) C 111
74 **HAZAZ** (IRE) 40
291 **HAZEL BROOK** (GB) 3
328 **HAZEL LAVERY** (IRE) 32
657 **HAZELDENE** (GB) 33
201 **HAZELRIGG** (IRE) 26
246 **HAZELWOOD** (GB) 8
560 **HAZY BAY** (GB) 3
585 **HAZY DAWN** (GB) 14
682 **HAZY GLOW** (IRE) 98
404 **HAZY TOM** (IRE) 18
34 **HE'S A HAWKER** (IRE) 9
452 **HE'S NO ANGEL** (IRE) 12
420 **HEAD HUNTED** (GB) 16
520 **HEAD OF STEAM** (USA) 5
405 **HEAD OF THE RIVER** (IRE) 3
472 **HEAD SPIN** (IRE) 15
79 **HEAD TO HEAD** (IRE) 4
299 **HEADING NORTH** (GB) 185
95 **HEADING TO FIRST** (GB) 9
199 **HEADLY'S BRIDGE** (IRE) 3
450 **HEADSTIGHT** (IRE) 36
639 **HEALTH IS WEALTH** (IRE) 18
503 **HEAR MY SONG** (IRE) 30
149 **HEARDUTHEFIRSTTIME** (IRE) 11
595 **HEART DANCER** (FR) 1
416 **HEART LAKE** (CAN) F 9
513 **HEART O ANNANDALE** (IRE) 6
296 **HEART OF DUBAI** (USA) 16
247 **HEARTSONG** (IRE) 10
639 **HEARTY ROYALE** (IRE) 19
111 **HEAT OF THE NIGHT** (GB) C 114
394 **HEATHCLIFF** (GB) 9
460 **HEATHCOTE** (GB) 41
606 **HEATHER GLEN** (IRE) 18
129 **HEATHER MIX** (GB) C 33
321 **HEATHER ROYAL** (GB) 68
511 **HEAVEN GREY** (USA) 57
35 **HEAVENLY BAY** (USA) F 73
552 **HEAVENLY CHORUS** (GB) 19
597 **HEAVENLY WHISPER** (IRE) F 72

233 **HEAVENSTOWN** (IRE) 7
366 **HEAVY METAL** (GB) 167
55 **HEAVY WEIGHT** (IRE) 31
446 **HECK THOMAS** (IRE) 38
43 **HECTON LAD** (USA) 7
394 **HECTOR'S CHOICE** (FR) 10
217 **HECTOR'S HOUSE** (GB) 3
643 **HEDDWYN** (IRE) 9
285 **HEERAAT** (IRE) 34
489 **HEEZ A CRACKER** (FR) 49
118 **HEEZ A STEEL** (IRE) 11
215 **HEEZAGREY** (IRE) 7
714 **HEEZMINE** (IRE) 4
299 **HEFNER** (GB) 62
188 **HEIDI'S DELIGHT** (IRE) 13
666 **HEIGHT OF SUMMER** (IRE) 6
201 **HEIGHTS RIDGE** (GB) 112
328 **HELEN SHARP** (GB) C 97
606 **HELENA OF TROY** (GB) 19
233 **HELENS VISION** (GB) 8
658 **HELGA** (GER) 48
534 **HELICONIA** (GB) 46
56 **HELIODORO** (FR) 4
699 **HELIOPSIS** (IRE) 25
395 **HELIUM** (FR) 4
639 **HELL'S BAY** (FR) 20
241 **HELLBENDER** (IRE) 7
3 **HELLENISTIC** (GB) 73
650 **HELLO BUD** (IRE) 28
597 **HELLO DUBAI** (GB) 40
597 **HELLO GLORY** (GB) 41
155 **HELLO GORGEOUS** (GB) 21
34 **HELLO SAILOR** (GB) 64
201 **HELLO STRANGER** (IRE) 82
564 **HELOISE** (FR) 89
599 **HELPSTON** (GB) 6
191 **HENDERSON BAND** (USA) C 60
328 **HENDRINA** (IRE) F 98
233 **HENDRY TRIGGER** (GB) 18
476 **HENNESSY** (IRE) 30
650 **HENOK** (FR) 29
555 **HENRIETTA HOLMES** (IRE) F 3
496 **HENRIETTA ROSE** (USA) 67
654 **HENRY ALLINGHAM** (GB) 48
307 **HENRY BEE** (GB) 53
366 **HENRY BOND** (GB) 1
366 **HENRY CLAY** (GB) 91
366 **HENRY GEORGE** (GB) 92
555 **HENRY HOLMES** (IRE) 2
160 **HENRY HOOK** (IRE) 14
243 **HENRY HURST** (IRE) 3
359 **HENRY JENKINS** (IRE) 13
160 **HENRY KING** (IRE) 15
56 **HENRY MORGANN** (FR) 5
380 **HENRY SAN** (IRE) 44
327 **HENRY THE FIRST** (IRE) 3
197 **HENRY'S HERO** (IRE) 7
180 **HENRYS GIFT** (GB) 8
654 **HENTIES BAY** (IRE) C 116
266 **HEPWORTH** (GB) 70
29 **HER STAR** (USA) 84
102 **HERBALIST** (GB) 52
651 **HERBERT** (GB) 2
331 **HERDSMAN** (IRE) 38
414 **HERE COMES JEANIE** (GB) 8
233 **HERE COMES MOSS** (GB) 5
19 **HERE COMES WHEN** (IRE) 126
586 **HERE NOW AND WHY** (IRE) 7

4 **HERE'S TO HARRY** (GB) 7
650 **HERECOMESTHEHOLLOW** (IRE) 30
264 **HERECOMESTHETRUTH** (IRE) 7
362 **HEREDITARY** (GB) 8
352 **HEREFORD BOY** (GB) 4
338 **HERES ACTION MAN** (GB) 4
115 **HERESELLIE** (IRE) 5
508 **HERMIA** (IRE) 71
219 **HERMINIA** (IRE) 150
200 **HERNANDO TORRES** (GB) 18
486 **HERNELLO** (IRE) 7
603 **HERO'S CALL** (GB) 3
520 **HERO'S STORY** (GB) 59
304 **HEROIC ENDEAVOUR** (IRE) 91
395 **HERON BAY** (GB) 7
660 **HERON REEF** (IRE) 14
218 **HERON'S MILL** (IRE) 13
321 **HERONRY** (GB) 69
150 **HERONS WELL** (GB) 11
501 **HEROSTATUS** (IRE) 17
460 **HERSCHEL** (IRE) 42
339 **HES OUR LAD** (IRE) 8
56 **HESIONE** (IRE) 21
192 **HESPERIDES** (GB) 7
213 **HESTON SOUND** (GB) 16
564 **HEURTEVENT** 40
518 **HEVER ROAD** (IRE) 2
639 **HEY BIG SPENDER** (IRE) 21
328 **HEY FIDDLE FIDDLE** (IRE) 33
328 **HEYAARAAT** (IRE) 34
204 **HEYWARD GIRL** (GB) 8
266 **HEZMAH** (GB) 12
310 **HI DANCER** (GB) 8
496 **HI FILWAH** (USA) 68
359 **HI GEORGE** (GB) 14
94 **HI LYLA** (IRE) C 12
684 **HI NOTE** (GB) 10
568 **HI SPEC** (IRE) 3
360 **HI TIDE** (IRE) 18
123 **HI YA PAL** (USA) 29
264 **HIBBA** (USA) 8
347 **HIBIKI** (IRE) 12
695 **HIDDEN** (GB) 44
597 **HIDDEN CHARM** (IRE) C 73
298 **HIDDEN CYCLONE** (IRE) 14
371 **HIDDEN FOX** (GB) 5
259 **HIDDEN GLORY** (GB) 3
328 **HIDDEN HEART** (USA) C 99
520 **HIDDEN JUSTICE** (IRE) 32
404 **HIDDEN KEEL** (GB) 19
534 **HIDDEN LINK** (GB) 47
196 **HIDDEN PLEASURE** (GB) 3
600 **HIDDEN RAINBOW** (IRE) 7
19 **HIDDEN VALLEY** (GB) 13
192 **HIDDENDALE** (IRE) F 24
260 **HIGGS BOSON** (GB) 10
327 **HIGGSY** (GB) 4
636 **HIGGY'S BOY** (IRE) 3
321 **HIGGY'S RAGAZZO** (FR) 70
656 **HIGH BALL ROLLER** (GB) 4
308 **HIGH CHART** (GB) F 15
458 **HIGH DESERT** (GER) 12
123 **HIGH ENDEAVOUR** (IRE) 30
218 **HIGH EXPECTATION** (GB) 14
352 **HIGH FINALE** (GB) F 30
653 **HIGH FIVE PRINCE** (IRE) 21
60 **HIGH FIVE SOCIETY** (GB) 6

254 **HIGH HO SHERIFF** (IRE) 20
606 **HIGH HOYLANDER** (GB) 20
630 **HIGH INTEREST** (GB) 3
223 **HIGH JINX** (IRE) 10
343 **HIGH KINGS** (GB) 24
386 **HIGH KITE** (IRE) 13
508 **HIGH MAINTENANCE** (GB) F 72
496 **HIGH MISWAKI** (FR) 27
220 **HIGH OFFICE** (GB) 16
434 **HIGH ON A HILL** (IRE) 62
342 **HIGH ON THE HOG** (IRE) 7
567 **HIGH OSCAR** (GB) 7
266 **HIGH PRAISE** (USA) F 130
296 **HIGH RANSOM** (GB) 17
519 **HIGH RESOLUTION** (GB) 7
472 **HIGH SAMANA** (GB) 16
511 **HIGH SPEED** (SWI) 12
249 **HIGH STANDING** (USA) 6
150 **HIGH STORM** (IRE) 12
147 **HIGH STRATOS** (GB) 35
3 **HIGH TWELVE** (IRE) 19
10 **HIGH VILLE** (IRE) 9
392 **HIGH VOLTAGE** (GB) 3
377 **HIGH WINDOW** (IRE) 6
81 **HIGHBURY HIGH** (IRE) 4
57 **HIGHCLIFFE** (GB) 8
614 **HIGHER LOVE** (IRE) F 41
332 **HIGHKINGOFMUNSTER** (IRE) 8
568 **HIGHLAND BRAVE** (IRE) 4
236 **HIGHLAND CADETT** (GB) 4
417 **HIGHLAND CASCADE** (GB) F 19
208 **HIGHLAND CASTLE** (GB) 4
669 **HIGHLAND CATHEDRAL** (GB) 7
624 **HIGHLAND CEILIDH** (IRE) G 4
141 **HIGHLAND DUKE** (IRE) 37
530 **HIGHLAND HARVEST** (GB) 5
19 **HIGHLAND KNIGHT** (IRE) 14
391 **HIGHLAND LODGE** (IRE) 30
500 **HIGHLAND LOVE** (GB) 3
682 **HIGHLAND MISS** (USA) 43
450 **HIGHLAND WARRIOR** (GB) 15
193 **HIGHLY LIKELY** (IRE) 33
111 **HIGHLY SKILLED** (GB) 43
292 **HIGHMEAD HARRY** (GB) 4
388 **HIGHPHAR** (FR) F 75
606 **HIGHRATE** (IRE) 21
104 **HIGHTOWN** (IRE) 7
55 **HIGHWATER EXPRESS** (IRE) 32
394 **HIGHWAY CODE** (USA) 11
313 **HIGHWAY JACK** (IRE) 3
533 **HIGHWAY WARRIOR** (GB) 6
156 **HIHARRY** (IRE) 3
338 **HIKKADUWA** (GB) 15
366 **HIKMA** (USA) 93
81 **HILALI** (IRE) 11
34 **HILARIOUS** (IRE) F 65
32 **HILBRE COURT** (USA) 8
404 **HILDISVINI** (IRE) 20
73 **HILL FARM DANCER** (GB) F 10
472 **HILL FORTS GLORIA** (IRE) 17
352 **HILL OF DREAMS** (IRE) 23
266 **HILL STREET** (IRE) 71
27 **HILLS OF DAKOTA** (IRE) 15
712 **HILLSIDE GIRL** (IRE) F 9
619 **HILLSTAR** (IRE) 117
260 **HILLVIEW BOY** (IRE) 11
431 **HILLWALK** (GB) 1
708 **HIMALAYAN MOON** (GB) 7

592 **HIMAYNA** (GB) 7
474 **HIMRAYN** (GB) 7
700 **HINDFORD OAK GOLD** (GB) 11
380 **HINDON ROAD** (GB) 45
19 **HINT OF MINT** (GB) 65
119 **HINT OF PROMISE** (GB) 31
489 **HINTERLAND** (FR) 50
155 **HINTON ADMIRAL** (GB) 8
321 **HINTON INDIANA** (GB) 71
387 **HINTON PEARL** (GB) F 36
34 **HIP** (GB) C 66
154 **HIP HIP HOORAY** (GB) 4
29 **HIPPOLYTO** (IRE) 85
147 **HIPPY HIPPY SHAKE** (GB) 36
434 **HIRAYNA** (IRE) G 63
682 **HISAABAAT** (IRE) 7
124 **HISCANO** (GB) 6
35 **HISPANIA** (IRE) 74
219 **HISTORIC FIND** (GB) 61
321 **HIT THE HEADLINES** (IRE) 72
682 **HIT THE JACKPOT** (IRE) 44
101 **HIT THE SWITCH** (IRE) 17
27 **HITCHENS** (IRE) 16
27 **HITHERTO** (GB) 48
516 **HITS ONLY CASH** (GB) 8
107 **HITS ONLY JUDE** (IRE) 8
254 **HOARE ABBEY** (IRE) 21
68 **HOBACK JUNCTION** (IRE) 5
469 **HOBB'S DREAM** (IRE) 17
397 **HOBSON** (GB) 10
672 **HOBSONS BAY** (IRE) 4
47 **HOCKENHEIM** (FR) 3
150 **HODGSON** (IRE) 13
503 **HOGAN'S BRIDGE** (IRE) 31
147 **HOH CHI MIN** (GB) C 84
45 **HOH HEDSOR** (GB) C 22
536 **HOH NELSON** (GB) 4
699 **HOHLETHELONELY** (GB) 26
56 **HOKEY POKEY** (FR) F 35
219 **HOKKAIDO** (GB) 151
49 **HOLBERG** (UAE) 31
94 **HOLCOMBE BOY** (GB) 6
695 **HOLD COURT** (GB) 45
489 **HOLD FAST** (IRE) 51
183 **HOLD MY HAND** (FR) 40
380 **HOLD ON JULIO** (GB) 46
637 **HOLD THE FORT** (IRE) 8
13 **HOLDEN CAULFIELD** (IRE) 1
485 **HOLDEN EAGLE** (GB) 3
570 **HOLE IN ONE** (GB) 30
340 **HOLEINTHEWALL BAR** (IRE) 24
534 **HOLISTIC** (GB) 24
417 **HOLLIE** (GB) 4
296 **HOLLINS** (GB) 18
476 **HOLLO LADIES** (IRE) 31
650 **HOLLOW BLUE SKY** (FR) 31
650 **HOLLOW HEARTBEAT** (GB) 32
380 **HOLLOW PENNY** (GB) 47
434 **HOLLOW TREE** (GB) 64
80 **HOLLOWINA** (GB) 18
614 **HOLLY BLUE** (GB) F 42
1 **HOLLY MARTINS** (GB) 19
511 **HOLLY POLLY** (GB) 58
705 **HOLLYGROVE SAMBA** (IRE) G 12
491 **HOLLYROCK** (GB) 2
467 **HOLLYWOOD ALL STAR** (IRE) 18
92 **HOLMWOOD LEGEND** (GB) 3
111 **HOLOGRAM** (GB) 44

201 **HOLY ANGEL** (IRE) 83
35 **HOLY EMPRESS** (IRE) 35
475 **HOLY SMOKES** (IRE) 12
12 **HOLYFIELD WARRIOR** (IRE) 9
503 **HOLYWELL** (IRE) 32
496 **HOMAGE** (IRE) 69
458 **HOME FARM** (IRE) 13
469 **HOME FROM THE HILL** (IRE) G 18
525 **HOME RUN** (GER) 44
643 **HOMEBOY** (IRE) 10
58 **HOMEGROWN** (IRE) C 65
20 **HOMEOFTHECLASSICS** (GB) C 7
472 **HOMER RUN** (IRE) 18
191 **HOMERIC** (IRE) 26
592 **HOMEWARD STRUT** (GB) 23
219 **HOMILY** (GB) 14
263 **HONEST JOHN** (GB) 7
405 **HONEST STRIKE** (USA) 4
653 **HONESTY PAYS** (GB) F 29
214 **HONEY OF A KITTEN** (USA) 15
561 **HONEYCREEPER** (GB) 5
664 **HONEYPOT LANE** (GB) 7
296 **HONG KONG ISLAND** (IRE) 19
166 **HONORINE DE DUCY** (FR) 8
619 **HONOUR** (IRE) 39
287 **HONOUR AND OBEY** (IRE) 36
323 **HONOUR HIGH** (GB) 6
49 **HONOUR SYSTEM** (IRE) 32
160 **HONOURABLE ARTHUR** (IRE) 16
446 **HONOURABLE EMPEROR** (IRE) 87
653 **HONOURABLE KNIGHT** (FR) 5
489 **HOO LA BALOO** (IRE) F 52
200 **HOOF IT** (GB) 19
267 **HOOKY'S DIAMOND** (GB) 2
102 **HOOLIGAN SEAN** (GB) 10
387 **HOONOSE** (GB) 21
61 **HOOVER** (GB) 4
458 **HOP IN** (IRE) 14
469 **HOPATINA** (IRE) 19
666 **HOPE ISLAND** (IRE) F 39
653 **HOPE POINT** (GB) 6
527 **HOPEAND** (GB) 3
503 **HOPEFUL START** (IRE) 33
107 **HOPES REBELLION** (GB) 23
450 **HOPPY'S FLYER** (FR) 16
404 **HORACE** (GB) 21
270 **HORATIAN** (USA) 4
501 **HORATIO CARTER** (GB) 18
697 **HORATIO HORNBLOWER** (IRE) 10
496 **HORNBOY** (GB) 70
498 **HORSHAM LAD** (IRE) 14
654 **HORSTED KEYNES** (IRE) 117
380 **HOT 'N SAUCY** (GB) C 48
634 **HOT 'N' HOLY** (GB) 5
317 **HOT CHERRY** (GB) 2
639 **HOT CHOICE** (GB) 22
117 **HOT DIGGITY** (FR) 41
35 **HOT MUSTARD** (GB) 75
39 **HOT OR WHAT** (IRE) 9
193 **HOT SPICE** (GB) 7
573 **HOT SUGAR** (USA) 53
194 **HOT TUB** (GB) 6
408 **HOTAL CALIFORNIA** (FR) 56
241 **HOTGROVE BOY** (GB) 8
705 **HOTHAM** (GB) 11
699 **HOUBLON DES OBEAUX** (FR) 27
318 **HOUGHTON HILL** (FR) 50
219 **HOULEUSE** (USA) 62

226 **HOUNDSCOURT** (IRE) 11
498 **HOUROFTIME** (IRE) 15
192 **HOUSE LIMIT** (GB) 8
366 **HOUSE OF ORANGE** (IRE) 168
227 **HOUSEPARTY** (GB) 12
556 **HOUSTON DYNIMO** (IRE) 17
619 **HOVERING** (IRE) C 118
553 **HOW NICE** (IRE) 5
45 **HOW SWEET IT IS** (IRE) 14
420 **HOW'S BUSINESS** (GB) 12
574 **HOW'S D STRAWBOSS** (IRE) 3
103 **HOW'S MY FRIEND** (GB) 2
434 **HOWABOUTNOW** (IRE) 65
699 **HOWARD'S LEGACY** (IRE) 28
155 **HOWARDS HEROINE** (IRE) C 22
493 **HOWARDS WAY** (GB) 9
208 **HOWEVER** (IRE) F 4
24 **HOWIZEE** (GB) 10
343 **HOWS THE CHAP** (IRE) 25
314 **HOYLAND COMMON** (IRE) F 4
74 **HUBOOD** (GB) 11
43 **HUCKING HARMONY** (IRE) F 39
108 **HUCKLEBERRY** (IRE) 15
520 **HUFF AND PUFF** (GB) 6
130 **HUGENOT** (IRE) 9
304 **HUGO DE VINDECY** (FR) 33
525 **HUGO DRAX** (GB) 45
287 **HUJAYLEA** (IRE) 13
500 **HULA BALLEW** (GB) C 15
661 **HULWA** (USA) 11
367 **HUMBEL BEN** (IRE) 4
563 **HUMBIE** (IRE) 2
447 **HUMBLE FIFTEEN** (USA) F 75
475 **HUME TOWER** (IRE) 13
183 **HUMHUM** (GB) 41
18 **HUMIDOR** (IRE) 15
285 **HUMMINGBIRD** (GB) 35
617 **HUMOUROUS** (IRE) 8
299 **HUMUNGOSAUR** (GB) 63
304 **HUNDRED SEN** (GB) 14
299 **HUNDRED YEAR FLOOD** (USA) F 186
161 **HUNG PARLIAMENT** (FR) 8
129 **HUNT A MISTRESS** (IRE) 11
92 **HUNT BALL** (IRE) 4
49 **HUNT'S LIGHT** (IRE) 33
705 **HUNTERS BELT** (IRE) 12
650 **HUNTERS LODGE** (IRE) 33
259 **HUNTING GONK** (GB) 24
383 **HUNTINGFORTREASURE** (GB) 9
35 **HUNTSMANS CLOSE** (IRE) 76
220 **HURLER AND FARMER** (IRE) 54
444 **HURRICANE ELECTRIC** (IRE) 6
366 **HURRICANE EMERALD** (IRE) 94
473 **HURRICANE FLY** (IRE) 44
391 **HURRICANE HENRY** (IRE) 31
697 **HURRICANE HERBIE** (IRE) 11
366 **HURRICANE HIGGINS** (IRE) 6
407 **HURRICANE HUGO** (IRE) 22
480 **HURRICANE HYMN** (IRE) 16
127 **HURRICANE IN DUBAI** (GB) 12
654 **HURRICANE IRENE** (IRE) C 118
570 **HURRICANE JACK** (GB) 31
222 **HURRICANE MAX** (IRE) 11
380 **HURRICANE MILLY** (IRE) 49
304 **HURRICANE RIDGE** (IRE) 92
124 **HURRICANE SPIRIT** (IRE) 7

366 **HURRIYA** (GB) 95
161 **HURRY HOME POPPA** (IRE) 54
34 **HURRY UP GEORGE** (GB) 29
267 **HURRY UP HARRY** (GB) 3
617 **HURRYONHARRY** (GB) 9
208 **HURSLEY HOPE** (IRE) 5
219 **HUSSAR BALLAD** (USA) 63
302 **HUSTLE 'N' FLOW** (IRE) 4
74 **HUWAYIT** (IRE) 12
127 **HUYGENS** (GB) 4
342 **HUZZAH** (IRE) 8
575 **HYDRANT** (GB) 2
329 **HYGROVE WELSHLADY** (IRE) 1
366 **HYPERLINK** (IRE) 96
705 **HYPNOSIS** (IRE) 13
534 **HYPNOTISM** (GB) 48
119 **HYPOTENEUSE** (IRE) C 67
471 **HYPOXIA** (GB) F 24
336 **HYSON** (GB) 31
443 **I AM THE MAN** (GB) 2
485 **I B A GEE GEE** (GB) 20
503 **I CAN RUN CAN YOU** (IRE) 34
300 **I CONFESS** (GB) 3
265 **I FOUGHT THE LAW** (GB) 12
552 **I GOT MUSIC** (GB) 20
260 **I GOT SUNSHINE** (GB) 12
114 **I KNOW THE CODE** (IRE) 5
19 **I LOVE ME** (GB) 15
347 **I NEED A HERO** (IRE) 13
567 **I NO UNDERSTAND** (IRE) 8
285 **I SAY** (GB) 90
422 **I SEE YOU** (GB) 23
147 **I STAND CORRECTED** (GB) 37
670 **I WITNESS** (IRE) 3
24 **I'LL BE FRANK** (GB) 11
365 **I'LL BE GOOD** (GB) 13
585 **I'LLDOIT** (GB) 15
114 **I'M A COLLEGE BOY** (IRE) 6
597 **I'M A DREAMER** (IRE) 9
434 **I'M A GANGSTER** (IRE) 67
18 **I'M FRAAM GOVAN** (GB) 16
165 **I'M IN THE PINK** (FR) 3
658 **I'M ON FIRE** (GER) 60
525 **I'M SO LUCKY** (GB) 46
114 **I'M SO SPECIAL** (IRE) 7
647 **I'M STILL THE MAN** (IRE) 21
625 **I'M SUPER TOO** (IRE) 20
525 **I'MSINGINGTHEBLUES** (IRE) 47
347 **I'VE BEEN FRAMED** (IRE) 14
111 **IBERIS** (GB) 115
531 **IBIZA SUNSET** (IRE) 11
476 **IBN HIYYAN** (USA) 32
49 **IBTAHAJ** (GB) 89
8 **ICANSEECLEARLYNOW** (GB) 8
320 **ICE 'N' EASY** (IRE) 6
188 **ICE** (IRE) 14
42 **ICE BELLINI** (GB) 13
314 **ICE BOUND** (IRE) 5
432 **ICE COLD BEX** (GB) 3
118 **ICE IMAGE** (IRE) 12
54 **ICE LOCH** (GB) 16
384 **ICE MISSILE** (GB) 18
466 **ICE NELLY** (IRE) 14
451 **ICE TRES** (GB) 32
620 **ICE TROOPER** (GB) 5
200 **ICEBLAST** (GB) 20
123 **ICEBRAKER** (IRE) 5
451 **ICEBUSTER** (GB) 6

54 **ICED OPAL** (GB) 17
366 **ICELANDER** (USA) 97
601 **ICHIMOKU** (GB) 69
201 **ICING** (GB) F 113
611 **ICING SUGAR** (GB) 6
286 **ICONOCLAST** (IRE) 8
690 **ICY BLUE** (GB) 3
681 **ICY COLT** (ARG) 27
130 **ICY QUIET** (GB) 4
534 **ICY REPLY** (GB) 49
529 **IDA INKLEY** (IRE) 27
445 **IDAROSE** (IRE) 8
296 **IDEALISM** (GB) 20
373 **IDENTIMIN** (GB) 13
452 **IDESIA** (IRE) C 20
366 **IDILIC CALM** (IRE) F 169
366 **IDLER** (IRE) 98
653 **IDOL DEPUTY** (IRE) 7
587 **IDRIS** (GER) 2
462 **IDYLLIC STAR** (IRE) 12
194 **IF AND WHEN** (GB) 7
715 **IF EVER** (IRE) 3
18 **IF I HAD HIM** (IRE) 17
228 **IF I WERE A BOY** (IRE) 6
287 **IF PER CHANCE** (IRE) 14
223 **IF SO** (GB) 30
609 **IF U BELIEVE** (IRE) 3
572 **IF WHAT AND MAYBE** (GB) 6
477 **IF YOU WHISPER** (IRE) 5
509 **IFAN** (IRE) 9
501 **IFANDBUTWHYNOT** (IRE) 19
180 **IFFRAAM** (IRE) 31
33 **IFONLYALFIE** (GB) 8
583 **IFYOULETMEFINISH** (IRE) 9
469 **IHEARDU** (GB) 2
49 **IHSAS** (USA) 90
49 **IHTIFAL** (GB) 91
49 **IHTIRAAM** (IRE) 92
388 **IKONE** (IRE) 76
591 **IKORODU ROAD** (GB) 4
383 **IKTIVIEW** (GB) 10
433 **IL BATTISTA** (GB) 49
446 **IL FENOMENO** (ITY) 39
477 **IL PAZZO** (GB) 11
460 **IL PORTICO** (GB) 43
696 **ILE DE RE** (FR) 22
161 **ILE DESERTE** (GB) F 55
81 **ILEWIN DUNDEE** (GB) 5
81 **ILEWIN JANINE** (IRE) G 6
81 **ILEWIN KIM** (GB) 7
600 **ILHABELA** (IRE) 8
298 **ILISSOS** (GB) 15
496 **ILLAUNGLASS** (IRE) 28
445 **ILLAWALLA** (GB) 5
159 **ILLEGALE** (IRE) 2
600 **ILLUSIO** (FR) 9
479 **ILLUSTRATION** (IRE) 8
410 **ILLUSTRIOUS FOREST** (GB) 7
61 **ILLUSTRIOUS LAD** (IRE) 23
107 **ILLUSTRIOUS PRINCE** (IRE) 9
400 **ILLYSANTACHRISTINA** (GB) 9
349 **ILONGUE** (FR) 1
306 **IMAGERY** (GB) 28
422 **IMAGINARY DIVA** (GB) 6
29 **IMBABALA** (GB) F 86
236 **IMDINA** (GB) G 19
462 **IMELDA MAYHEM** (GB) 13
496 **IMILOA** (USA) C 71

616 **IMJIN RIVER** (IRE) 3
139 **IMMEDIATELY** (GB) 29
241 **IMMORTELLE** (GB) F 17
306 **IMMORTOTALITY** (GB) 29
283 **IMOGEN LOUISE** (IRE) 35
299 **IMPEL** (GB) 64
337 **IMPERATOR AUGUSTUS** (IRE) 8
304 **IMPERIAL CASCADE** (IRE) 35
331 **IMPERIAL CIRCUS** (IRE) 39
197 **IMPERIAL FONG** (GB) 3
422 **IMPERIAL GUEST** (GB) 7
251 **IMPERIAL LAIDY** (IRE) 5
488 **IMPERIAL LEGEND** (IRE) 54
364 **IMPERIAL OAK** (GB) 34
125 **IMPERIAL ROYALE** (IRE) 2
390 **IMPERIAL WAVE** (IRE) 9
612 **IMPERIAL WEAPON** (IRE) 13
593 **IMPINELLA** (GB) 23
14 **IMPRIMIS TAGULA** (IRE) 4
388 **IMRIEL** (GB) 33
111 **IMROZ** (USA) F 116
628 **IMTITHAL** (IRE) 1
98 **IN A NUTSHELL** (IRE) 6
225 **IN LUCK** (GB) F 22
366 **IN MY LIFE** (IRE) F 170
256 **IN RAINBOWS** (GB) 28
657 **IN THE DOCK** (IRE) 34
450 **IN THE FASHION** (IRE) G 43
61 **IN THE LONG GRASS** (IRE) 5
150 **IN THE POST** (IRE) 14
385 **IN THE STOCKS** (GB) F 15
214 **INA POINT** (GB) 16
86 **INCA CAVE** (IRE) 11
188 **INCA CHIEF** (GB) 2
275 **INCA KOLA** (GB) 4
510 **INCENDIARY** (IRE) 7
223 **INCENDO** (GB) 11
394 **INCENTIVISE** (IRE) 12
366 **INCESSANT** (IRE) 99
119 **INCHINA** (GB) 32
198 **INCHLOCH** (GB) 10
704 **INCHMORE** (GB) F 3
201 **INCHY COO** (GB) 114
111 **INCOMING CALL** (USA) F 117
388 **INCROYABLE** (USA) 34
656 **INDE COUNTRY** (GB) 5
390 **INDE TIGRESS** (GB) 3
559 **INDEFINITE HOPE** (ITY) 4
488 **INDEGO BLUES** (GB) 55
573 **INDEPUB** (GB) 54
318 **INDEX LINKED** (GB) 6
543 **INDIAN ARROW** (GB) 9
299 **INDIAN ART** (GB) 6
192 **INDIAN BLOSSOM** (GB) 9
481 **INDIAN CHASE** (GB) 3
692 **INDIAN CITIZEN** (IRE) 2
489 **INDIAN DAUDAIE** (GB) F 53
259 **INDIAN DAYS** (GB) 4
72 **INDIAN DUMAANI** (GB) 8
490 **INDIAN EMPEROR** (IRE) 7
659 **INDIAN GROOM** (GB) 24
667 **INDIAN LEGEND** (IRE) F 3
447 **INDIAN LOVE BIRD** (GB) C 76
374 **INDIAN MISS** (GB) C 19
130 **INDIAN MOON** (GB) 10
79 **INDIAN OASIS** (GB) 5
566 **INDIAN OCEAN** (IRE) 7
3 **INDIAN PETAL** (GB) 74

574 **INDIAN PIPE DREAM** (IRE) 4
15 **INDIAN RIVER** (IRE) 7
529 **INDIAN SHUFFLE** (IRE) 7
221 **INDIAN ST JOVITE** (IRE) 1
139 **INDIAN TINKER** (GB) 18
488 **INDIAN TRAIL** (GB) 18
105 **INDIAN VOYAGE** (IRE) 5
384 **INDIANA BLUES** (GB) C 45
422 **INDIANA GUEST** (IRE) 24
188 **INDIESLAD** (GB) 3
299 **INDIGNANT** (GB) 187
127 **INDIGO MOON** (GB) 16
564 **INDRIYA** (GB) 41
181 **INDUS VALLEY** (IRE) 2
573 **INETROBIL** (IRE) 55
619 **INFATUATE** (GB) 119
147 **INFINITE HOPE** (USA) 38
329 **INFINITE JEST** (GB) 11
266 **INFIRMATION** (GB) 72
58 **INFORTUAL** (TUR) 35
157 **INGA BIRD** (GB) 12
702 **INGENTI** (GB) 2
27 **INGLEBY ARCH** (USA) 17
220 **INGLEBY SPIRIT** (GB) 17
440 **INGLEBY STAR** (IRE) 5
34 **INGOT OF GOLD** (GB) 67
534 **INHERITED** (GB) 50
343 **INISH ISLAND** (IRE) 26
496 **INITIATOR** (GB) 5
588 **INJAAZ** (GB) C 42
299 **INJUNCTION** (USA) 65
116 **INKA EXPRESS** (GB) 27
274 **INKBERROW ROSE** (IRE) 11
58 **INKLET** (GB) 10
110 **INKY MISS** (GB) 10
3 **INLER** (IRE) 20
366 **INNCLASSIC** (IRE) F 171
555 **INNER STEEL** (IRE) 5
467 **INNISCASTLE BOY** (GB) 19
266 **INNOCENT AIR** (GB) C 132
47 **INOOGOO** (IRE) 4
440 **INOURTHOUGHTS** (IRE) G 14
432 **INPURSUITOFFREEDOM** (GB) 4
49 **INQADH** (USA) 93
71 **INQUISITRESS** (GB) 8
285 **INSAAF** (GB) F 91
639 **INSIDE DEALER** (IRE) 23
711 **INSIDE KNOWLEDGE** (USA) 6
366 **INSIJAAM** (USA) C 172
237 **INSOLENCEOFOFFICE** (IRE) 13
219 **INSOUCIANTE** (IRE) 64
473 **INSPECTOR CLOUSEAU** (IRE) 45
327 **INSPECTOR QICS** (GB) 5
496 **INSTANCE** (GB) 4
682 **INSTANT UPDATE** (IRE) 99
139 **INSTRUCTRESS** (GB) 11
43 **INSTRUMENTALIST** (IRE) 21
373 **INSURED** (GB) 14
639 **INTAC** (GB) 24
219 **INTARSIA** (GER) 15
619 **INTEGRAL** (GB) 120
219 **INTELLO** (FR) 152
666 **INTENSE PINK** (GB) 25
35 **INTENT** (IRE) 36
645 **INTERAKT** (GB) 3
515 **INTERCHOICE STAR** (GB) 2
619 **INTERCONTINENTAL** (GB) C 121
111 **INTERLOCKING** (USA) 45

384 **INTERMISSION** (IRE) C 46
450 **INTERNATIONALDEBUT** (IRE) 17
111 **INTERVALE** (GB) 46
49 **INTHAR** (USA) 94
497 **INTHEJUNGLE** (IRE) 3
111 **INTIMACY** (IRE) 47
496 **INTIMIDATE** (GB) 72
447 **INTISHAAR** (IRE) C 77
451 **INTO THE WIND** (GB) 7
408 **INTO VINCERES** (GER) 8
263 **INTO WAIN** (USA) 8
61 **INTOMIST** (IRE) 24
19 **INTRANSIGENT** (GB) 66
191 **INTREPID QUEEN** (USA) C 61
619 **INTRINSIC** (GB) 122
3 **INTROVERT** (IRE) 21
299 **INTUITION** (GB) 66
328 **INUNDATE** (USA) 35
270 **INVELITE** (GB) 15
204 **INVENT** (GB) 1
338 **INVERARAY** (GB) F 21
189 **INVERLOCHY LAD** (IRE) 5
119 **INVESTIGATE** (GB) 33
266 **INVESTISSEMENT** (GB) 13
347 **INVESTMENT AFFAIR** (IRE) 15
496 **INVESTMENT EXPERT** (IRE) 73
607 **INVICTA LAKE** (GB) 5
380 **INVICTUS** (IRE) 50
588 **INVIGILATOR** (GB) 10
287 **INVINCIBLE ASH** (IRE) 15
193 **INVINCIBLE CARA** (IRE) 50
408 **INVINCIBLE DANCER** 9
273 **INVINCIBLE FORCE** (IRE) 5
107 **INVINCIBLE HERO** (IRE) 10
299 **INVINCIBLE RIDGE** (IRE) 7
55 **INVINCIBLE VINCE** (IRE) 33
49 **INVISIBLE HUNTER** (USA) 95
49 **INVISIBLE MAN** (GB) 34
488 **INXILE** (IRE) 19
603 **IONA DAYS** (IRE) 4
436 **IONISPHERE** (GB) 5
315 **IONWY** (GB) 7
147 **IPPIOS** (GB) 6
446 **IPSOS DU BERLAIS** (FR) 40
569 **IPSWICH** (GB) 113
3 **IPTISAM** (GB) 75
496 **IRIDESCENCE** (GB) 74
384 **IRIE UTE** (GB) 5
123 **IRIS GLORIA** (FR) 6
393 **IRIS'S FLYER** (GB) 2
408 **IRISH BOY** 57
450 **IRISH BOY** (IRE) 18
331 **IRISH BUCCANEER** (IRE) 40
55 **IRISH BULLETIN** (IRE) 86
552 **IRISH CHAPERONE** (GB) 2
502 **IRISH GUARD** (GB) 2
451 **IRISH JUGGER** (USA) 8
20 **IRISH LAW** (GB) 1
682 **IRISH STYLE** (IRE) C 100
69 **IRISH SYMPHONY** (IRE) 5
511 **IRISH TIGER** (FR) 59
360 **IRJA** (GB) G 42
213 **IRON BUTTERFLY** (GB) 17
380 **IRON CHANCELLOR** (IRE) 51
213 **IRON CONDOR** (GB) 4
527 **IRON CROSS** (IRE) 4
416 **IRON GREEN** (FR) 3
656 **IRON STEP** (GB) 6

406 **IRONICAL** (IRE) 6
390 **IRONICALLY** (IRE) 10
327 **IRONPIN** (GB) 6
18 **IRONS ON FIRE** (USA) 18
601 **IRRATIONAL** (GB) 42
573 **IRREPLACEABLE** (GB) 94
395 **IS IT ME** (USA) 6
556 **ISABELLE B** (IRE) 18
111 **ISATIS** (GB) 48
463 **ISDAAL** (GB) 3
658 **ISHAN** (GER) 26
272 **ISHETOO** (GB) 5
451 **ISHI** (GB) 33
437 **ISHIAMIRACLE** (GB) 12
380 **ISHIKAWA** (IRE) 52
336 **ISHISMART** (GB) 10
191 **ISHRAAK** (USA) F 62
335 **ISINGOLD** (GB) 6
61 **ISINGY RED** (FR) 6
451 **ISIS BLUE** (GB) 46
366 **ISLA AZUL** (IRE) C 173
4 **ISLA PATRIOT** (GB) 8
4 **ISLA PEARL FISHER** (GB) 9
19 **ISLAND DESTINY** (IRE) F 127
237 **ISLAND HOPPER** (GB) F 14
64 **ISLAND LEGEND** (IRE) 12
462 **ISLAND MELODY** (IRE) 14
666 **ISLAND QUEEN** (USA) F 40
237 **ISLAND SPRITE** (IRE) 15
695 **ISLANDMAGEE** (IRE) 46
26 **ISLE OF ELLIS** (IRE) 5
329 **ISLE OF SPICE** (USA) F 34
386 **ISLEOFHOPENDREAMS** (GB) 14
416 **ISLESMAN** (GB) 4
434 **ISOBAR** (GER) 68
119 **ISOBEL ROSE** (IRE) F 68
466 **ISOBELLA** (GB) 46
529 **ISOLA BELLA** (GB) 28
223 **ISOLA VERDE** (GB) 31
461 **ISOLDE'S RETURN** (GB) 28
219 **ISPANKA** (GB) 65
99 **ISTAN STAR** (USA) 19
520 **ISTHMUS** (GB) 33
182 **ISTIQDAAM** (GB) 7
219 **ISTRIANE** (IRE) 153
567 **IT WASN'T US** (IRE) 9
503 **IT'S A GIMME** (IRE) 35
18 **IT'S A GIRL THING** (IRE) 44
567 **IT'S A KILLER** (GB) 10
533 **IT'S A MANS WORLD** (GB) 2
34 **IT'S A PRIVILEGE** (GB) 30
397 **IT'S DUBAI DOLLY** (GB) 11
221 **IT'S FREEZING** (IRE) 2
200 **IT'S ME AND YOU** (GB) 21
597 **IT'S MY TIME** (GB) 42
647 **IT'S ONLY BUSINESS** (GB) 29
434 **IT'S OSCAR** (GB) 69
653 **IT'S TABOO** (GB) 30
18 **IT'S TWILIGHT TIME** (GB) C 67
219 **ITALIAN** (GB) 154
161 **ITALIAN AFFAIR** (GB) F 56
397 **ITALIAN GODDESS** (GB) F 49
601 **ITALIAN ICE** (GB) 43
357 **ITALIAN LADY** (USA) 12
482 **ITALIAN LEGACE** (IRE) 5
489 **ITALIAN MASTER** (GB) 54
534 **ITALIAN RIVIERA** (GB) 25
306 **ITALIAN TOM** (IRE) 12

569 **ITASCA** (FR) 50
366 **ITHOUGHTITWASOVER** (IRE) 17
200 **ITLAAQ** (GB) 22
193 **ITNAB** (GB) F 51
643 **ITOAAN** (USA) C 59
605 **ITS BOBKAT** (IRE) 2
379 **ITS MURPHY AGAIN** (IRE) 5
688 **ITS TOUGH** (IRE) 9
672 **ITSBEYONDAJOKE** (GB) 5
708 **ITSONLYMAKEBELIEVE** (IRE) 16
73 **ITSTHURSDAYALREADY** (GB) 11
456 **ITSTOOEARLY** (GB) 13
49 **ITTASAL** (GB) 96
654 **ITTIRAD** (USA) 11
194 **ITUM** (GB) 5
556 **ITZACLICHE** (IRE) 19
543 **IULUS** (GB) 10
283 **IVAN THE TERRIBLE** (IRE) 36
657 **IVAN VASILEVICH** (IRE) 35
299 **IVANIA** (GB) C 188
572 **IVER BRIDGE LAD** (GB) 7
55 **IVETA** (IRE) 34
639 **IVOR'S KING** (GB) 25
223 **IVORY GALA** (FR) F 55
283 **IVORY JAZZ** (GB) 37
569 **IVORY LAND** (FR) 3
564 **IVORY ROSE** (GB) 42
249 **IVORY SILK** (GB) 7
352 **IVORY'S JOY** (GB) F 31
665 **IVY LEAGUE STAR** (IRE) C 18
610 **IXORA** (IRE) 7
387 **IZ SHE** (GB) 3
123 **IZODAR** (FR) 31
338 **IZZA DIVA** (GB) 5
26 **IZZET** (GB) 6
266 **IZZI TOP** (GB) 14
696 **J J LEARY** (IRE) 62
601 **J R HARTLEY** (GB) 13
657 **J'ADHERE** (FR) 36
511 **J'N KA AVENUE** (FR) 60
654 **JAARYAH** (IRE) 12
628 **JABBARA** (IRE) C 24
56 **JABBERWOCKY** (GB) 22
12 **JACALOU** (GB) 18
451 **JACASA TOO** (GB) 34
569 **JACIRA** (FR) F 114
30 **JACK BARKER** (GB) 20
98 **JACK COOL** (IRE) 7
488 **JACK DAWKINS** (USA) 20
40 **JACK IRISH** (GB) 19
511 **JACK MALONE** (FR) 15
214 **JACK MY BOY** (IRE) 17
632 **JACK OF DIAMONDS** (IRE) 11
259 **JACK SMUDGE** (GB) 5
461 **JACK THE GENT** (IRE) 11
321 **JACK THE GIANT** (GB) 13
214 **JACK WHO'S HE** (IRE) 52
18 **JACK'S REVENGE** (IRE) 19
639 **JACKERS** (GB) 26
78 **JACKIE KIELY** (GB) 4
429 **JACKIE LOVE** (IRE) 5
339 **JACKIES SOLITAIRE** (GB) 9
374 **JACKO'S BOY** (GB) 20
439 **JACKOFHEARTS** (GB) 3
434 **JACKSON CAGE** (IRE) 70
299 **JACOB CATS** (GB) 67
27 **JACOB MCCANDLES** (GB) 18
452 **JACOBS SON** (GB) 4

259 **JADANNA** (IRE) 45
500 **JADE PET** (GB) F 16
35 **JADESNUMBERONE** (IRE) 77
657 **JAFFONNIEN** (FR) 37
285 **JAFOOL** (IRE) 36
511 **JAG WAR** (FR) 14
338 **JAGO'S GIRL** (GB) G 6
191 **JAISH** (USA) C 63
18 **JAKE'S DESTINY** (IRE) 45
58 **JAKKALBERRY** (IRE) 11
446 **JAKROS** (IRE) 41
631 **JALDARSHAAN** (IRE) 2
285 **JALEELA** (USA) F 92
614 **JALISCO** (FR) C 43
666 **JALISSA** (GB) F 41
654 **JALOUSIE** (IRE) C 119
124 **JAMAICA GRANDE** (GB) 8
658 **JAMAICA SUN** (GER) 49
263 **JAMARJO** (IRE) 9
387 **JAMBOBO** (GB) 22
496 **JAMBORETTA** (IRE) C 75
227 **JAMEEL** (USA) 13
139 **JAMEELA GIRL** (GB) 12
697 **JAMES DE VASSY** (FR) 12
400 **JAMES POLLARD** (IRE) 10
610 **JAMESSON** (IRE) 8
74 **JAMHARA** (GB) 41
407 **JAMMING** (IRE) 23
161 **JAMRAH** (IRE) C 57
618 **JAN SMUTS** (IRE) 3
509 **JANDEE** (GB) 22
619 **JANE AUSTEN** (IRE) F 123
698 **JANE LACHATTE** (IRE) 18
332 **JANET LINDUP** (GB) F 9
200 **JANET'S PEARL** (GB) 23
55 **JANEY MUDDLES** (IRE) 35
654 **JANISTRA** (USA) C 120
136 **JANUARY** (GB) 8
600 **JAPAN** (GER) C 41
689 **JAPP** (GB) 7
712 **JAQUES VERT** (FR) 3
488 **JARROW** (IRE) 21
452 **JASIE JAC** (IRE) 13
126 **JASMIN RAI** (GB) 5
501 **JASMINE BREEZE** (GB) G 54
433 **JATH** (GB) C 37
654 **JATHAABEH** (GB) F 121
650 **JAUNTY JOURNEY** (GB) 34
408 **JAVIRCO** (FR) 58
283 **JAWAAB** (GB) 38
691 **JAWAHAL DU MATHAN** (FR) 2
615 **JAWBREAKER** (IRE) 2
615 **JAWBREAKERONASTICK** (GB) 9
285 **JAWHAR** (IRE) 10
331 **JAWHARY** (GB) 41
214 **JAWKING** (GB) 53
476 **JAWS** (GB) 33
450 **JAY JAYS JOY** (GB) 19
712 **JAY KAY** (GB) 8
224 **JAY PEAS JACKO** (GB) 4
531 **JAYA BELLA** (IRE) 12
331 **JAYANDBEE** (IRE) 42
187 **JAYJAY VALENTINE** (GB) 2
473 **JAYO** (FR) 46
471 **JAZZ BABY** (IRE) F 26
446 **JAZZ CONCERTO** (IRE) 42
147 **JAZZ MASTER** (GB) 85
460 **JAZZ UP** (GB) F 126

444 **JE NE SAIS PLUS** (FR) 7
593 **JEANO DE TOULOUSE** (FR) 24
691 **JEANRY** (FR) 3
200 **JEER** (IRE) 24
299 **JEHANBUX** (USA) 8
569 **JEHANNEDARC** (IRE) 4
67 **JEMIMAVILLE** (IRE) 3
304 **JENARI** (IRE) 36
197 **JENNDALE** (GB) 8
642 **JENNIFER J** (GB) 29
713 **JENNY'S GOLD** (GB) 5
315 **JEREMY SUE** (IRE) 3
507 **JERICHO** (IRE) 23
360 **JERMATT** (GB) 43
366 **JERRE JO GLANVILLE** (USA) C 174
371 **JERRY LEE** (IRE) 6
407 **JERSEY LILLIE** (GB) C 46
685 **JERUFLO** (IRE) F 5
552 **JESSICA VALENTINE** (IRE) 22
308 **JESSIE** (GB) F 16
188 **JESSIE'S SPIRIT** (IRE) 15
111 **JET AWAY** (GB) 10
63 **JET MASTER** (IRE) 5
380 **JETNOVA** (IRE) 53
304 **JETSON** (IRE) 37
366 **JEU DE VIVRE** (IRE) 18
414 **JEWEL** (IRE) C 13
343 **JEWEL OF THE WEST** (IRE) 27
475 **JEWEL STAR** (IRE) 14
323 **JEWELLED** (GB) 7
304 **JEZKI** (IRE) 38
61 **JEZYAH** (USA) C 38
682 **JIBBOOM** (USA) C 101
74 **JIBOUTI** (IRE) 13
446 **JIM BOWIE** (IRE) 43
493 **JIM MARTIN** (GB) 5
617 **JIM TANGO** (FR) 10
393 **JIMBATAI** (IRE) 3
657 **JIMBILL** (IRE) 38
435 **JIMMY RYAN** (IRE) 4
141 **JIMMY STYLES** (GB) 13
469 **JIMMY THE LOLLIPOP** (IRE) 38
141 **JINKER NOBLE** (GB) 38
653 **JINKS AND CO** (GB) 31
519 **JINKY** (GB) 8
270 **JINSKYS GIFT** (IRE) F 16
407 **JINXY JILL** (GB) C 47
657 **JIVE MASTER** (IRE) 39
339 **JIVRY** (GB) 10
654 **JIWEN** (CAN) 13
35 **JO BOY** (GB) 4
700 **JOBEKANI** (GB) 12
102 **JOCASTA DAWN** (GB) 28
460 **JODAWES** (USA) 44
272 **JODEEKA** (GB) F 13
80 **JODRELL BANK** (IRE) F 19
529 **JODY BEAR** (GB) 8
407 **JOE EILE** (IRE) 3
366 **JOE LE TAXI** (IRE) 19
184 **JOE M** (GB) 18
529 **JOE PACKET** (GB) 9
496 **JOE PALOOKA** (IRE) 76
642 **JOE THE COAT** (GB) 30
253 **JOG ON KITTY** (GB) 5
446 **JOHANNISBERGER** (IRE) 44
19 **JOHN BISCUIT** (GB) 16
700 **JOHN CRABBIES** (FR) 13
207 **JOHN FORBES** (GB) 20

206 **JOHN GULLY** (IRE) 10
432 **JOHN LOUIS** (GB) 5
32 **JOHN POTTS** (GB) 9
209 **JOHN'S DELIGHT** (IRE) 1
166 **JOHN'S GEM** (GB) 9
535 **JOHN'S OSCAR** (IRE) 4
329 **JOHNNO** (GB) 12
520 **JOHNNY CASTLE** (GB) 7
283 **JOHNNY CAVAGIN** (GB) 72
322 **JOHNNY MULLEN** (IRE) 4
62 **JOHNNY OWEN** (IRE) 4
632 **JOHNNY SPLASH** (IRE) 12
304 **JOHNNYS LEGACY** (IRE) 39
503 **JOHNS SPIRIT** (IRE) 36
283 **JOHNSON'S CAT** (IRE) 73
472 **JOIN THE NAVY** (GB) 19
489 **JOIN TOGETHER** (IRE) 55
73 **JOIN UP** (GB) 12
380 **JOJABEAN** (GB) 54
332 **JOKER OF THE PACK** (IRE) 10
74 **JOLAH** (GB) 14
102 **JOLI SOLEIL** (GB) 29
541 **JOLI'S DAUGHTER** (GB) 4
404 **JOLIBOB** (IRE) 22
108 **JOLIE ETOILE** (GB) 16
183 **JOLIE NOCE** (FR) 13
141 **JOLIES DEE** (GB) F 65
250 **JOLLY BOYS OUTING** (IRE) 6
485 **JOLLY RANCH** (GB) 9
381 **JOLLY VALENTINE** (GB) 9
460 **JOLLY'S CRACKED IT** (FR) 109
240 **JOLLYGOODWELLDONE** (GB) 2
332 **JOMADE** (IRE) 11
437 **JONNIE SKULL** (IRE) 5
260 **JONNY DELTA** (GB) 13
201 **JONNY LESTERS HAIR** (IRE) 27
161 **JONNY MUDBALL** (GB) 9
237 **JONNY WOMBAT** (GB) 49
607 **JORDAN** (GB) 6
526 **JORDANS CHRISSY** (IRE) 4
573 **JORDANSTOWN** (GB) 95
376 **JORDAURA** (GB) 68
111 **JORUM** (GB) 49
299 **JOSAM** (GB) 68
331 **JOSEPH MERCER** (IRE) 43
583 **JOSH'S DREAMWAY** (IRE) 10
380 **JOSHING** (GB) 55
696 **JOSHUA** (GB) 23
155 **JOSHUA THE FIRST** (GB) 15
58 **JOSHUA TREE** (IRE) 12
399 **JOSHUA'S PRINCESS** (GB) C 13
604 **JOSIE LENNON** (GB) 10
643 **JOURNALISTIC** (USA) 31
705 **JOVIAL** (IRE) 14
304 **JOVIAL QUEEN** (IRE) 40
266 **JOVIALITY** (GB) 15
302 **JOXER** (IRE) 5
129 **JOY TO THE WORLD** (IRE) 12
629 **JOYFUL MOTIVE** (GB) 11
193 **JOYFUL SPIRIT** (IRE) 34
283 **JOYOUSLY** (GB) 39
111 **JOYRIDE** (GER) 50
434 **JUBAIL** (IRE) 71
466 **JUBILANTE** (GB) 74
299 **JUBILEE DIAMOND** (IRE) 189
376 **JUDAS JO** (FR) 11
364 **JUDD STREET** (GB) 8
306 **JUDGE 'N JURY** (GB) 13

373 **JUDGE DAVIS** (GB) 15
499 **JUDGE ROY BEAN** (IRE) 14
657 **JUDICIARY** (IRE) 40
436 **JUDIES CHILD** (IRE) 6
184 **JUHD** (IRE) 8
366 **JUKEBOX JURY** (IRE) 20
552 **JUKEBOX MELODY** (IRE) 23
359 **JULATTEN** (GB) G 37
193 **JULES** (IRE) F 52
8 **JULIA TOO** (GB) 11
343 **JULIE PRINCE** (IRE) 28
298 **JULIMARK** (IRE) 16
161 **JULIUS GEEZER** (IRE) 10
32 **JULY DAYS** (IRE) 10
283 **JULY SPECIALISTS** (GB) 74
534 **JULY WAITS** (USA) 51
508 **JUMAIRA TOWER** (IRE) 73
563 **JUMBY BAY** (IRE) 3
166 **JUMEIRAH LIBERTY** (GB) 17
299 **JUMEIRAH PALM STAR** (GB) 69
489 **JUMP CITY** (FR) 56
262 **JUMP UP** (GB) 11
62 **JUMPJACK FLINT** (GB) 5
639 **JUMPS ROAD** (GB) 27
696 **JUNE FRENCH** (IRE) 24
116 **JUNGLE BAY** (IRE) 8
266 **JUNGLE BEAT** (IRE) 73
525 **JUNIOR** (GB) 48
58 **JUNIOR COUNCIL** (IRE) C 66
447 **JUNIOR DIARY** (USA) 30
374 **JUNIOR JACK** (GB) 21
35 **JUNIPER GIRL** (IRE) C 78
580 **JUNKET** (GB) 2
19 **JUNO MINT** (GB) C 128
161 **JUNOOB** (GB) 11
183 **JUNZI** (FR) 58
460 **JUPITER STORM** (GB) 110
489 **JUST AMAZING** (FR) 57
482 **JUST ANOTHER JOKER** (GB) 6
636 **JUST AWAKE** (GB) 4
522 **JUST BENNY** (GB) 11
166 **JUST BEWARE** (GB) 11
557 **JUST BLUE** (GB) 7
506 **JUST BOND** (IRE) 6
712 **JUST CALL ME DAVE** (USA) 4
461 **JUST FABULOUS** (GB) 29
686 **JUST FIVE** (IRE) 7
299 **JUST IN LOVE** (GB) C 190
135 **JUST JORDAN** (GB) 6
684 **JUST JOSIE** (GB) 11
447 **JUST JULIE** (USA) C 78
174 **JUST KATES GIRL** (GB) 17
201 **JUST LIKE HEAVEN** (IRE) 84
188 **JUST LILLE** (IRE) 4
491 **JUST MADDIE** (GB) 3
27 **JUST PERFECT** (IRE) 36
557 **JUST PLAYFULL** (GB) 8
57 **JUST SAY PLEASE** (GB) 9
321 **JUST SIXTY** (IRE) 74
682 **JUST SPECIAL** (GB) C 102
50 **JUST SPOT** (GB) 3
491 **JUST STRIPE** (GB) 4
469 **JUST THE JOB** (IRE) 21
230 **JUST THE TONIC** (GB) 1
32 **JUST TIMMY MARCUS** (GB) 11
454 **JUST TOOTSIE** (GB) 8
640 **JUST TYN** (GB) 11
206 **JUST WALKING JACK** (GB) 11

134 **JUST WATCH OLLIE** (IRE) 4
19 **JUST WHEN** (GB) 67
431 **JUST WOOD** (FR) C 2
711 **JUST ZAK** (GB) 7
639 **JUSTABOUT** (GB) 28
561 **JUSTAZIPPY** (GB) 6
214 **JUSTBOOKIE DOT COM** (IRE) 18
44 **JUSTBOOKIES DOTNET** (GB) 2
228 **JUSTCALLMEHANDSOME** (GB) 7
99 **JUSTINE TIME** (IRE) 20
285 **JUSTINEO** (GB) 37
296 **JUSTJOE** (IRE) 37
220 **JUSTONEFORTHEROAD** (GB) 18
299 **JUVENAL** (IRE) 70
139 **JWALA** (GB) 19
538 **K ISLAND** (IRE) 10
328 **KAAFEL** (IRE) 36
682 **KAASEB** (USA) 45
284 **KABIRA** (GB) 4
569 **KADIANA** (IRE) F 115
227 **KADOODD** (IRE) 14
40 **KADOUCHSKI** (FR) 9
174 **KADUNA** (GB) 18
614 **KAFAYEF** (USA) C 44
16 **KAFFIE** (GB) 19
460 **KAHFRE** (GB) 45
507 **KAHINA** (GER) C 38
285 **KAHRUMAN** (USA) 38
35 **KAI** (GB) 37
570 **KAI BROON** (IRE) 32
351 **KAI MOOK** (GB) 3
3 **KAILANI** (GB) 76
129 **KAISER WILHELM** (IRE) 13
302 **KAKAGH** (IRE) 6
474 **KAKAPUKA** (GB) 8
19 **KAKATOSI** (GB) 17
321 **KAKI DE LA PREE** (FR) 75
639 **KALA PATTHAR** (GB) 29
508 **KALABAYA** (IRE) 3
564 **KALAHARI GOLD** (IRE) 8
476 **KALAHARI KING** (FR) 34
508 **KALAJAR** (USA) 33
29 **KALAMOS** (IRE) 36
366 **KALANA** (FR) C 175
339 **KALANI KING** (IRE) 11
569 **KALIK** (FR) 51
147 **KALILY** (GB) 39
111 **KALIMA** (GB) C 118
408 **KALIPSIS** (FR) 10
119 **KALITHEA** (GB) 69
200 **KALK BAY** (IRE) 25
365 **KALKAN BAY** (GB) 5
483 **KALMBEFORETHESTORM** (GB) 3
146 **KALOKAGATHIA** (IRE) 18
564 **KAMATE** (FR) 43
460 **KAMBIS** (GB) 46
283 **KAMES PARK** (IRE) 40
225 **KAMPAI** (GB) 11
123 **KANDYKAINE** (IRE) 32
123 **KANEL** (FR) 33
436 **KANES PASS** (IRE) 20
391 **KANGAROO COURT** (IRE) 32
506 **KANISFLUH** (GB) F 27
56 **KANOTIER** (FR) 6
262 **KANTURK** (IRE) 12
260 **KAOLAK** (USA) 14
714 **KAP WEST** (FR) 5
699 **KAPGA DE CERISY** (FR) 29

585 **KAPRICORNE** (FR) 16
183 **KAPSTADT** (FR) 59
408 **KAPTAINE** (FR) 59
139 **KARA'S VISION** (GB) 20
593 **KARACAS** (IRE) 25
511 **KARADARGENT** (FR) 106
488 **KARAKA JACK** (GB) 22
360 **KARAM ALBAARI** (IRE) 19
508 **KARATASH** (IRE) 34
1 **KARATE** (IRE) 2
26 **KARATE QUEEN** (GB) 7
508 **KARAWANA** (IRE) F 74
321 **KARAZHAN** (IRE) 76
1 **KARIM** (GB) 20
434 **KARINGA DREAM** (GB) 72
434 **KARINGA HEY** (GB) 73
494 **KARINGO** (GB) 10
552 **KARINGREASON** (GB) 24
214 **KARINSKI** (USA) C 72
372 **KARISTAR** (IRE) 7
287 **KARKASAR** (IRE) 37
569 **KARKIYN** (IRE) 116
508 **KARLIDI** (USA) 75
511 **KARLINHA** (IRE) 15
40 **KARMA CHAMELEON** (GB) 15
606 **KARMADICE** (GB) 22
566 **KARMAROUGE** (IRE) 8
434 **KARRICAL** (GB) 74
589 **KARSHAAN** (FR) 2
331 **KARTANIAN** (FR) 44
654 **KARTUZY** (JPN) C 122
299 **KARUGA** (GB) 71
593 **KASBADALI** (FR) 26
183 **KASBAH BISS** (FR) 42
183 **KASBAH BLISS** (FR) 14
35 **KASHGAR** (GB) 38
407 **KASHMIR PEAK** (IRE) 24
544 **KASHMIRI STAR** (GB) 7
569 **KASIGAR** (FR) 52
123 **KASLICKY** (FR) 34
600 **KASLIK** (GB) 10
619 **KASORA** (IRE) C 124
149 **KASSIODOR** (GER) 4
127 **KASTINI** (GB) 17
508 **KASTOVIA** (USA) 35
566 **KATA ROCK** (USA) 9
111 **KATARIYA** (IRE) C 119
643 **KATAYEB** (IRE) C 60
600 **KATCHAGUA** (FR) 25
54 **KATCHMORE** (IRE) 5
697 **KATEAL** (GB) 13
2 **KATHERINE DEUX** (FR) 23
543 **KATHERINE SEYMOUR** (GB) C 46
115 **KATHINDI** (IRE) 6
296 **KATHLATINO** (GB) 22
642 **KATHLEEN FRANCES** (GB) 14
174 **KATHLEENS PRIDE** (IRE) 19
451 **KATHRYN'S GLORY** (GB) 35
526 **KATIE GALE** 16
420 **KATIES TUITOR** (GB) 18
508 **KATIOLA** (IRE) 36
653 **KATMAI RIVER** (IRE) 8
56 **KATMANDOUNE** (FR) 7
682 **KATOOM** (IRE) C 103
500 **KATY O'HARA** (GB) F 17
358 **KATY'S SECRET** (GB) 5
332 **KAUTO RELKO** (FR) 12
489 **KAUTO STAR** (FR) 58

489 **KAUTO STONE** (FR) 59
380 **KAUTO THE ROC** (FR) 56
460 **KAVALOTI** (FR) 47
272 **KAVERI** (USA) C 14
174 **KAWA** (FR) 20
285 **KAWN** (GB) C 93
599 **KAYAAN** (GB) 7
408 **KAYAGUA** 60
695 **KAYALAR** (IRE) 47
650 **KAYBEEW** (GB) 35
151 **KAYCEE** (IRE) 4
585 **KAYEF** (GB) 17
650 **KAYF ARAMIS** (GB) 36
 75 **KAYF COMMANDER** (GB) 10
612 **KAYF PARADIS** (GB) 8
157 **KAYFLEUR** (GB) 43
362 **KAYFLIN** (FR) 9
454 **KAYFROU** (GB) 9
217 **KAYFTON PETE** (GB) 4
460 **KAYLEE** (GB) 111
496 **KAYLENA** (GB) 30
184 **KAYPEA** (GB) 19
381 **KAYSERSBERG** (FR) 10
 56 **KAZAYA** (FR) 8
119 **KAZEEM** (GB) G 34
525 **KAZLIAN** (FR) 49
308 **KEALBRA LADY** (GB) G 17
479 **KEALIGOLANE** (IRE) 9
461 **KEALSHORE** (GB) 12
567 **KECKERROCKERNIXES** (IRE) 11
614 **KEDLESTON** (IRE) 20
219 **KEEGSQUAW** (IRE) 66
377 **KEEN'S TOKEN** (GB) 7
619 **KEENE DANCER** (GB) 40
434 **KEENELAND** (FR) 75
395 **KEENES DAY** (FR) 7
211 **KEEP A WELCOME** (GB) 2
147 **KEEP IT DARK** (GB) 40
503 **KEEP KICKING** (GB) 37
381 **KEEP TALKING** (GB) 11
666 **KEEPAX** (GB) 26
111 **KEEPING TIME** (GB) 9
597 **KELADORA** (USA) F 74
321 **KELLS BELLE** (IRE) 77
476 **KELLYSTOWN LAD** (IRE) 35
447 **KELNER'S CROSS** (GB) 31
452 **KELTBRAY** (IRE) 5
252 **KELTIC CRISIS** (IRE) 6
491 **KELVINGROVE** (GB) 120
491 **KEMPSKI** (GB) 5
385 **KEN'S GIRL** (GB) 5
380 **KENAI PENINSULA** (GB) 57
657 **KENALECK** (GER) 41
605 **KENNELMAN** (IRE) 3
161 **KENNY POWERS** (GB) 31
467 **KENNY'S GIRL** (IRE) 40
 35 **KENSINGTON GARDENS** (GB) 79
203 **KENSWICK** (GB) 3
606 **KENT STREET** (IRE) 23
391 **KENTFORD GREY LADY** (GB) 33
564 **KENTUCKY BILL** (FR) 44
597 **KENTUCKY WARBLER** (IRE) C 75
442 **KENYAN CAT** (GB) 4
534 **KEPLER'S LAW** (GB) 6
511 **KEPRESH** (FR) 16
223 **KEPT** (GB) 32
508 **KERANIA** (IRE) F 76
473 **KERB APPEAL** (IRE) 47

137 **KERCABELLEC** (FR) 3
184 **KERFUFFLE** (IRE) 20
654 **KERIYKA** (IRE) C 123
110 **KERNEL VICTOR** (GB) 11
418 **KERSIVAY** (GB) 3
311 **KETTLE STREET** (IRE) 5
576 **KEY AMBITION** (GB) 5
629 **KEY APPOINTMENT** (GB) 12
681 **KEY CUTTER** (FR) 28
366 **KEY GOLD** (GB) 100
185 **KEY TO MILAN** (GB) 5
219 **KEY TO PEACE** (IRE) 155
321 **KEY TO THE WEST** (IRE) 78
654 **KEYAADI** (GB) 49
601 **KEYAKI** (FR) F 70
 24 **KEYAKI** (IRE) G 28
183 **KEYED UP** (FR) 15
664 **KEYHOLE KATE** (GB) 20
295 **KEYNEEMA** (GB) 3
321 **KEYS** (IRE) 79
488 **KEYS OF CYPRUS** (IRE) 23
 62 **KHACHATURIAN** (IRE) 6
225 **KHAJAALY** (IRE) 12
654 **KHAJOOL** (IRE) 50
628 **KHALEEJIYA** (IRE) 11
155 **KHANDAQ** (USA) 9
287 **KHAREZI** (IRE) 38
183 **KHASMA** (IRE) 43
 64 **KHATEER** (IRE) 13
233 **KHATELLA** (IRE) 19
 49 **KHAWLAH** (IRE) 35
285 **KHAZEENA** (GB) 39
203 **KHAZIUM** (IRE) 10
115 **KHESKIANTO** (IRE) 7
147 **KHIONE** (GB) 41
400 **KHORUN** (IRE) 11
191 **KHUBALA** (IRE) 27
 29 **KHUMBA MELA** (IRE) F 87
480 **KHUN JOHN** (IRE) 17
650 **KHYBER KIM** (GB) 37
543 **KIAMA BAY** (IRE) 11
 5 **KIAN'S DELIGHT** (IRE) 13
500 **KIAN'S JOY** (GB) 8
651 **KIBARAGUE** (GB) F 11
696 **KICKAHEAD** (USA) 25
499 **KICKHAMSTOWN** (IRE) 15
347 **KICKING TIME** (IRE) 16
282 **KICKINGTHELILLY** (GB) 3
321 **KID CASSIDY** (IRE) 80
488 **KID DYNAMITE** (GB) 56
111 **KID GLOVES** (GB) F 121
299 **KID SUITOR** (GB) 72
 14 **KIDLAT** (GB) 5
 49 **KIDNAPPED** (AUS) 36
434 **KIE** (IRE) 76
 32 **KIELTY'S FOLLY** (GB) 12
469 **KIERANN** (IRE) 22
500 **KIERON'S ROCK** (IRE) 9
275 **KIGALI** (IRE) F 11
397 **KIJIVU** (GB) 12
147 **KIKONGA** (GB) 86
561 **KIKOS** (FR) 7
397 **KILBURN** (GB) 13
250 **KILCASCAN** (GB) 7
649 **KILCASKIN STAR** (IRE) 2
151 **KILCOMMON PRIDE** (IRE) 5
419 **KILCREA** (IRE) 7
444 **KILCREA ASLA** (IRE) 8

591 **KILDARE KITTEN** (USA) 5
338 **KILDEE LASS** (GB) F 7
246 **KILDERRY DEAN** (IRE) 9
226 **KILFLORA** (GB) 12
606 **KILKENNY ALL STAR** (IRE) 24
624 **KILLCARA BOY** (GB) 5
635 **KILLEANEY PRINCESS** (IRE) 5
371 **KILLFINNAN CASTLE** (IRE) 7
321 **KILLIECRANKIE** (GB) 81
239 **KILLING ME SOFTLY** (GB) 4
113 **KILLORGLIN** (GB) 22
302 **KILLTILANE ROSE** (IRE) 7
498 **KILMACOWEN** (IRE) 16
469 **KILRUSH** (IRE) 23
525 **KILRYE** (IRE) 50
650 **KILVERGAN BOY** (IRE) 38
 35 **KIMBERELLA** (GB) 80
657 **KIMBERLITE KING** (IRE) 42
160 **KIMMERIDGE BAY** (GB) 17
557 **KINCORA COURT** (IRE) 9
111 **KIND** (IRE) C 122
391 **KIND OF EASY** (IRE) 34
268 **KINDER SCOUT** (GB) 17
391 **KINDLY NOTE** (GB) 35
147 **KINDU** (GB) 87
318 **KINETIC FORCE** (USA) F 51
534 **KINETICA** (GB) 26
555 **KING ALFRED** (IRE) 6
 38 **KING BERTOLINI** (IRE) 6
420 **KING BREX** (DEN) 19
371 **KING DIAMOND** (FR) 8
264 **KING EDMUND** (GB) 9
304 **KING FERDINAND** (GB) 41
543 **KING FINGAL** (IRE) 12
359 **KING FONTAINE** (IRE) 15
675 **KING GABRIEL** (IRE) 3
501 **KING IN WAITING** (IRE) 20
522 **KING JACK** (GB) 12
689 **KING KALIUM** (IRE) 8
538 **KING KIEREN** (IRE) 11
573 **KING KURT** (IRE) 14
310 **KING LAERTIS** (IRE) 15
230 **KING MAK** (GB) 2
659 **KING O'THE GYPSIES** (IRE) 25
270 **KING OF ARAN** (IRE) 7
219 **KING OF ARNOR** (GB) 16
415 **KING OF CADEAUX** (IRE) 4
 42 **KING OF CASTILE** (GB) 14
683 **KING OF CONNACHT** (GB) 2
111 **KING OF DUDES** (GB) 52
 7 **KING OF EDEN** (IRE) 8
569 **KING OF ENGLAND** (GB) 117
219 **KING OF ENGLAND** (GB) 156
699 **KING OF GLORY** (GB) 30
 35 **KING OF JAZZ** (IRE) 5
681 **KING OF KEYS** (GB) 9
299 **KING OF KUDOS** (IRE) 191
 7 **KING OF PARADISE** (IRE) 15
511 **KING OF SONG** (FR) 61
201 **KING OF THE CELTS** (IRE) 28
489 **KING OF THE NIGHT** (GB) 60
424 **KING OF THE REFS** (GB) 10
359 **KING OF THE WOLDS** (FR) 16
461 **KING OF THORNS** (IRE) 13
266 **KING OF WANDS** (GB) 16
 61 **KING OF WING** (GB) 25
108 **KING OLAV** (UAE) 17
299 **KING OLIVER** (GB) 192

391 **KING OZYMANDIAS** (GB) 36
664 **KING PENDA** (IRE) 8
661 **KING PIN** (GB) 4
479 **KING PUC** (GB) 10
531 **KING SPIRIT** (IRE) 13
299 **KING SUPREME** (IRE) 9
299 **KING TORUS** (IRE) 10
357 **KING VAHE** (IRE) 13
393 **KING ZEAL** (IRE) 4
37 **KING'S ALCHEMIST** (GB) 1
479 **KING'S CHORISTER** (GB) 11
18 **KING'S CIEL** (GB) 46
363 **KING'S COLOUR** (GB) 4
501 **KING'S COUNSEL** (IRE) 2
439 **KING'S ENVOY** (USA) 4
318 **KING'S FAREWELL** (GB) 23
2 **KING'S FUTURE** (GB) 6
434 **KING'S GRACE** (GB) 77
637 **KING'S REALM** (GB) 9
474 **KING'S ROAD** (GB) 9
657 **KING'S SUNSET** (IRE) 43
407 **KING'S WARRANT** (IRE) 25
214 **KING'S WHARF** (GB) 54
711 **KINGAROO** (IRE) 8
404 **KINGARRICK** (GB) 23
292 **KINGDOM OF HEAVEN** (IRE) 5
220 **KINGDOM OF MUNSTER** (IRE) 19
265 **KINGDOMFORTHEBRIDE** (IRE) 21
281 **KINGLAMI** (GB) 4
3 **KINGLET** (GB) 77
352 **KINGS 'N DREAMS** (GB) 5
626 **KINGS APOLLO** (GB) 24
380 **KINGS BAYONET** (GB) 58
183 **KINGS BLISS** (IRE) 16
556 **KINGS CANYON** (IRE) 20
321 **KINGS DESTINY** (GB) 82
629 **KINGS GAMBIT** (SAF) 4
552 **KINGS GREY** (IRE) 25
639 **KINGS LAD** (IRE) 30
321 **KINGS LODGE** (GB) 83
331 **KINGS MUSIC** (IRE) 45
254 **KINGS QUEEN** (IRE) 22
395 **KINGS STORY** (IRE) 8
203 **KINGSCOMBE** (USA) 11
366 **KINGSCROFT** (IRE) 21
58 **KINGSDESIRE** (IRE) 36
460 **KINGSFOLD BLAZE** (GB) F 112
460 **KINGSFOLD FLARE** (GB) 48
169 **KINGSGATE CHOICE** (IRE) 14
124 **KINGSHILL LAD** (IRE) 20
157 **KINGSMERE** (GB) 13
564 **KINGSTON** 45
332 **KINGSTON QUEEN** (IRE) 13
366 **KINGSVILLE** (IRE) 176
214 **KINGSWINFORD** (IRE) 19
207 **KINGSWINFORD** (IRE) 21
108 **KINKEEL** (IRE) 18
366 **KINLOCH CASTLE** (IRE) 101
200 **KINYRAS** (IRE) 26
182 **KIPCHAK** (IRE) 8
92 **KIRBYS GLEN** (IRE) 5
688 **KIRKAIG** (GB) 10
393 **KIRKHAMMERTON** (IRE) 5
183 **KIROCCO** (FR) 17
471 **KIRSTYS LAD** (GB) 10
147 **KIRTHILL** (IRE) 7
376 **KISHANDA** (GB) 7
352 **KISS A PRINCE** (GB) 6

111 **KISS MY HEART** (GB) 11
111 **KISSING** (GB) F 123
208 **KISSING TIME** (GB) C 35
409 **KIT CARSON** (IRE) 2
57 **KIT KAT KATE** (IRE) G 10
593 **KITCHEN LOAN** (GB) 27
467 **KITTENS** (GB) 20
564 **KITTLE** (IRE) 46
147 **KIWAYU** (GB) 42
180 **KIWI BAY** (GB) 9
3 **KIZ KULESI** (GB) 78
569 **KIZIL** (FR) 53
58 **KLANG VALLEY** (GB) 37
460 **KLARIBEL** (IRE) G 113
438 **KLARIBEL** (IRE) G 6
18 **KLEBB** (USA) 20
385 **KLEITOMACHOS** (IRE) 6
514 **KNAPP BRIDGE BOY** (GB) 2
119 **KNAPTON HILL** (GB) C 70
417 **KNAVE OF CLUBS** (IRE) 12
96 **KNICKERBOKERGLORY** (GB) 2
62 **KNIGHT BLAZE** (GB) 7
364 **KNIGHT CHARM** (GB) 35
487 **KNIGHT FLIGHT** (GB) 6
410 **KNIGHT IN PURPLE** (GB) 8
347 **KNIGHT LEGEND** (IRE) 17
223 **KNIGHT OWL** (IRE) 56
96 **KNIGHT VALLIANT** (GB) 3
488 **KNIGHT VISION** (GB) 57
520 **KNIGHT'S PARADE** (IRE) 60
193 **KNIGHTLY ESCAPADE** (GB) 8
610 **KNIGHTON COMBE** (GB) 9
394 **KNOCK A HAND** (IRE) 1
362 **KNOCK BOY** (IRE) 10
593 **KNOCKALONGI** (GB) 28
570 **KNOCKANDO** (GB) 33
118 **KNOCKARA BEAU** (IRE) 13
343 **KNOCKARA ONE** (IRE) 29
375 **KNOCKAVARDAGH BOY** (IRE) 5
659 **KNOCKAVILLA** (IRE) 26
214 **KNOCKER KNOWLES** (IRE) 55
98 **KNOCKFIERNA** (IRE) 8
446 **KNOCKGRAFFON KING** (IRE) 45
567 **KNOCKNAREEN BOY** (IRE) 12
419 **KNOCKRAHA LAD** (IRE) 8
455 **KNOCKVICAR** (IRE) 6
397 **KNOW NO FEAR** (IRE) 14
651 **KNOWE HEAD** (NZ) 3
501 **KNOWING LOOK** (GB) F 55
520 **KNOYDART** (USA) 34
223 **KOALA BEAR** (GB) 57
501 **KOALITION** (GB) 44
442 **KODIAC ISLAND** (GB) 13
664 **KODICIL** (IRE) 9
643 **KOGERSHIN** (USA) 32
418 **KOKA FAST** (FR) 4
58 **KOKO LOCA** (IRE) 38
515 **KOMREYEV STAR** (GB) 3
147 **KONA STORM** (GB) 43
460 **KONDAKOVA** (IRE) C 127
643 **KONSTANTIN** (IRE) 11
329 **KONZERT** (ITY) 35
207 **KOO AND THE GANG** (IRE) 22
629 **KOOL SHUFFLE** (GER) 5
681 **KOOLALA** (IRE) 30
705 **KOOLGREYCAT** (IRE) 26
367 **KORALSDARLING** (IRE) 5
474 **KORNATI KID** (GB) 10

193 **KORNGOLD** (GB) 9
283 **KOROLIEVA** (IRE) F 84
318 **KORTOBA** (USA) 24
268 **KOSTA BRAVA** (FR) 18
654 **KOTA SAS** (IRE) 14
141 **KOTDIJI** (GB) F 66
657 **KOULTAS KING** (IRE) 44
434 **KOUP DE KANON** (FR) 78
191 **KOZMINA** (IRE) F 64
529 **KOZMINA BAY** (GB) 29
147 **KRAKEN** (IRE) 88
388 **KREOUSA** (GB) 35
29 **KRISIA** (GB) F 88
593 **KRISTIANO** (IRE) 29
483 **KRISTOFFERSEN** (GB) 4
153 **KROSSKINA** (IRE) 17
93 **KRUSEMAN** (GB) 6
388 **KRYMKA** (IRE) 77
417 **KUANYAO** (IRE) 5
472 **KUCHAROVA** (IRE) 20
654 **KUDA HURAA** (IRE) 15
141 **KUDOZ** (GB) 39
629 **KUDU COUNTRY** (IRE) 6
256 **KUILSRIVER** (IRE) 9
56 **KUKURUN** (FR) 36
391 **KUMASI CLAN** (IRE) 37
380 **KUMBESHWAR** (GB) 59
223 **KUNEGUNDA** (GB) 33
259 **KUNG HEI FAT CHOY** (USA) 25
3 **KUNOOZ** (IRE) 79
391 **KUSADIKI** (GB) 38
111 **KUSHNARENKOVO** (GB) C 124
183 **KUSTER BEATON** (FR) 18
433 **KUWAIT MOON** (GB) 38
673 **KUWAIT STAR** (GB) 7
433 **KUWAIT STAR** (GB) 39
30 **KWIK TIME** (GB) 7
141 **KYANITE** (IRE) 40
32 **KYLE OF BUTE** (GB) 13
708 **KYLEAKIN LASS** (GB) 17
573 **KYLESKU** (IRE) 56
429 **KYLIN** (GB) 11
543 **KYLLACHY DANCER** (GB) 35
111 **KYLLACHY RISE** (GB) 125
387 **KYLLACHY SPIRIT** (GB) 4
30 **KYLLACHYKOV** (IRE) 8
263 **KYLLADDIE** (GB) 10
645 **KYNCRAIGHE** (IRE) 4
312 **KYOTO** (GER) 5
407 **KYTHIA** (IRE) C 48
26 **KYZER CHIEF** (GB) 8
400 **L FRANK BAUM** (IRE) 12
447 **L'AFFAIRE MONIQUE** (GB) C 79
102 **L'AMI LOUIS** (IRE) 11
384 **L'ARLESIENNE** (GB) 19
200 **L'ASTRE DE CHOISIR** (IRE) 27
33 **L'ELDORADO** (FR) 9
24 **L'EMINENCE GRISE** (IRE) 12
12 **L'HIRONDELLE** (IRE) 10
219 **L'ORFEO** (GB) 157
219 **LA ARENOSA** (IRE) 67
356 **LA BACOUETTEUSE** (FR) 3
508 **LA BARACCA** (IRE) 37
141 **LA BATAILLE** (USA) C 67
9 **LA BELLA VILLA** (GB) G 18
389 **LA BELLE AU BOIS** (IRE) 2
380 **LA BELLE DOYENNE** (GB) 60
699 **LA BELLE SAUVAGE** (GB) 31

332 **LA BRIGANTINE** (IRE) G 14
552 **LA CALINDA** (GB) 26
176 **LA CAPRIOSA** (GB) 9
682 **LA CORUNA** (GB) C 104
34 **LA DANGEVILLE** (GB) F 68
602 **LA DANSE CHAMPETRE** (GB) 3
104 **LA ESTRELLA** (USA) 8
332 **LA FILLE D'OSCAR** (IRE) 15
67 **LA GAZZETTA** (IRE) F 10
86 **LA MADONNINA** (IRE) 12
339 **LA MILANAISE** (GB) 12
658 **LA NEXT** (GER) 27
564 **LA NOE** (GB) 47
387 **LA PAMPITA** (IRE) 23
296 **LA PANTERA ROSA** (IRE) 23
452 **LA PASSIONATA** (GB) 14
511 **LA PELEGRINA** (USA) 17
496 **LA REINA** (USA) C 77
321 **LA REINE DE RIOGH** (IRE) 84
27 **LA SALIDA** (GB) 37
612 **LA SONADORA** (GB) 14
266 **LA SPEZIA** (IRE) C 133
219 **LA TOUR ROUGE** (GB) 69
511 **LA ULTIMA COPA** (FR) 62
418 **LA VERTE RUE** (USA) 5
597 **LA VIDA LOCA** (IRE) F 76
49 **LA VINCHINA** (GER) C 132
447 **LA VITA E BELLA** (IRE) F 80
123 **LA ZAM** (FR) 35
388 **LA ZUBIA** (GB) 36
654 **LAAHEB** (GB) 16
3 **LAAJOOJ** (IRE) 22
49 **LAATAFREET** (IRE) 37
619 **LABARINTO** (GB) 3
107 **LAC A DANCER** (IRE) 11
123 **LAC FONTANA** (FR) 36
304 **LACE** (IRE) F 106
3 **LACILY** (USA) 80
606 **LACKAMON** (GB) 25
616 **LACONICOS** (IRE) 4
421 **LADFROMHIGHWORTH** (GB) 1
506 **LADIES ARE FOREVER** (GB) 7
506 **LADIES IN CHICAGO** (GB) 8
412 **LADIES PRIDE** (GB) 5
529 **LADRAM BAY** (IRE) 30
247 **LADWEB** (GB) 16
201 **LADY ADVOCATE** (GB) 85
461 **LADY AMAKHALA** (GB) 14
123 **LADY ANA** (FR) 37
329 **LADY ANGOLA** (IRE) F 36
222 **LADY ANNE NEVILL** (GB) 3
397 **LADY ARABELLA** (IRE) 43
220 **LADY AUTHOR** (GB) 55
520 **LADY BARASTAR** (GB) 8
642 **LADY BELLATRIX** (GB) 31
695 **LADY BLADE** (IRE) G 48
252 **LADY BLING BLING** (GB) 7
688 **LADY BLUESKY** (GB) 11
375 **LADY BLYTHE** (GB) 6
302 **LADY BOULEA** (GB) 8
613 **LADY BRICKHOUSE** (GB) 4
257 **LADY BRIDGET** (GB) 4
272 **LADY BROOKIE** (GB) 6
634 **LADY BY RED** (IRE) 6
299 **LADY CALANTHA** (GB) 193
116 **LADY CAPRICE** (GB) 21
180 **LADY CHAPARRAL** (GB) 10

306 **LADY CRESTA** (IRE) 30
299 **LADY DARAYNA** (GB) C 194
509 **LADY DEANIE** (IRE) 10
681 **LADY DEDDINGTON** (GB) 31
230 **LADY DEL SOL** (GB) 3
191 **LADY ELGAR** (GB) C 28
58 **LADY ELGAR** (IRE) F 67
201 **LADY ELLEN** G 86
437 **LADY ELLICE** (GB) 6
219 **LADY ELLIOTT** (GB) 158
697 **LADY EVERYWHERE** (GB) 14
506 **LADY GAR GAR** (GB) 9
188 **LADY GEORGINA** (GB) F 33
304 **LADY GERONIMO** (IRE) 93
357 **LADY GIBRALTAR** (GB) 14
406 **LADY HANNAH** (GB) 7
207 **LADY HAWK** (GER) C 23
54 **LADY HEARTBEAT** (GB) 18
74 **LADY HEN** (GB) F 42
101 **LADY IDA** (GB) 18
297 **LADY JOJO** (IRE) 3
347 **LADY KARABAYA** (GB) 18
404 **LADY KARINGA** (GB) 24
625 **LADY KASHAAN** (IRE) 48
681 **LADY KATHLEEN** (GB) 32
500 **LADY KILDARE** (IRE) 4
601 **LADY LAYLA** (GB) 44
233 **LADY LECTRA** (GB) 3
276 **LADY LIBBY LAMB** (GB) 5
220 **LADY LOCH** (GB) 56
564 **LADY LYNCH** (FR) 48
336 **LADY LYRICIST** (GB) 32
366 **LADY MACDUFF** (GB) 102
285 **LADY MALET** (GB) 94
306 **LADY MANGO** (IRE) 14
117 **LADY MARSHALL** (FR) C 16
565 **LADY MAYDAY** (IRE) G 4
429 **LADY MORGANNA** (IRE) 6
283 **LADY NATILDA** (GB) F 85
433 **LADY NICKANDY** (IRE) 40
566 **LADY NORLELA** (GB) 10
193 **LADY OCARINA** (GB) 35
450 **LADY OF BILSTON** (IRE) G 44
653 **LADY OF BURGUNDY** (GB) 3
343 **LADY OF GLENCOE** (IRE) 30
451 **LADY OF LIMERICK** (IRE) C 47
155 **LADY OF WINDSOR** (IRE) F 23
230 **LADY OGLIER** (GB) 4
196 **LADY ON TOP** (IRE) 3
408 **LADY PASCALINE** (FR) 11
653 **LADY PERCY** (IRE) 22
506 **LADY PLATINUM CLUB** (GB) 10
461 **LADY POPPY** (GB) 36
647 **LADY PRODEE** (GB) 11
462 **LADY RAGAZZA** (IRE) F 33
531 **LADY ROMANZA** (IRE) 34
643 **LADY ROSAMUNDE** (GB) 12
429 **LADY ROYAL OAK** (IRE) 7
506 **LADY ROYALE** (GB) 11
504 **LADY RUMBA** (GB) 3
593 **LADY SINATRA** (GB) 30
625 **LADY SINGSPIEL** (IRE) C 57
450 **LADY SLEDMERE** (IRE) 20
223 **LADY STARDUST** (GB) C 58
645 **LADY SYLVIA** (GB) 11
146 **LADY TABITHA** (IRE) 25
382 **LADY THERMAL** (GB) 2
73 **LADY TYCOON** (GB) 28

174 **LADY VALTAS** (GB) 21
34 **LADY WHO** (GB) 69
257 **LADY WILLA** (IRE) 5
155 **LADY XARA** (IRE) F 24
74 **LADY ZONDA** (GB) C 63
78 **LADYDOLLY** (GB) 5
617 **LADYLLIAT** (FR) F 11
619 **LADYSHIP** (GB) 41
525 **LADYVIE** (FR) 51
573 **LAFFAN** (IRE) 57
496 **LAFIRMA** (USA) C 78
525 **LAFLAMMEDEGLORIE** (GB) 52
473 **LAGANBANK** (IRE) 48
569 **LAGO MINTO** (GB) 54
511 **LAGUNA QUEEN** (GB) 107
511 **LAGUNA SUN** (FR) 63
628 **LAHEEN** (GB) C 25
556 **LAHIB THE FIFTH** (IRE) 21
287 **LAHIBA** (IRE) F 39
196 **LAID BARE** (GB) 5
174 **LAIDBACK LEO** (GB) 22
460 **LAJDAAL** (USA) 49
299 **LAKE NAYASA** (GB) C 195
706 **LAKE STREET JANE VII** F 7
207 **LAKEMAN** (IRE) 24
195 **LAKOTA GHOST** (USA) 2
299 **LALECTRA** (GB) C 196
431 **LALINA** (GER) C 3
384 **LALINA** (GB) C 47
208 **LAMARITA** (GB) F 36
647 **LAMBLORD** (IRE) 12
59 **LAMBORO LAD** (IRE) 14
700 **LAMBRINI LACE** (IRE) 14
700 **LAMBRINI QUEEN** (GB) G 15
473 **LAMBRO** (IRE) 49
31 **LAMBRO RIVER** (IRE) 6
53 **LAMPS** (GB) 7
214 **LANA** (IRE) 56
520 **LANCASTER GATE** (GB) 35
695 **LANCETTO** (FR) 49
516 **LAND HAWK** (IRE) 9
366 **LANDAMAN** (IRE) 22
500 **LANDELA** (GB) C 18
564 **LANDELLES** (IRE) 49
472 **LANDERBEE** (IRE) 21
263 **LANDESHERR** (GER) 11
392 **LANDOLINO** (FR) 4
336 **LANDOWN LITTLEROCK** (GB) 33
489 **LANDSCAPE** (FR) 61
444 **LANEGUY** (FR) 9
418 **LANG SHINING** (IRE) 6
666 **LANGHAM LILY** (USA) 27
657 **LANGLEY** (GB) 45
632 **LANGLEY VALE** (GB) 13
617 **LANGTOON LASS** (GB) 12
639 **LANHYDROCK** (GB) 31
290 **LANSDOWNE PRINCESS** (GB) 4
654 **LANZANA** (IRE) C 124
476 **LAP OF HONOUR** (IRE) 36
682 **LAPIS BLUE** (IRE) 105
384 **LAPIS LAZULI** (GB) C 48
193 **LAQATAAT** (GB) C 53
123 **LARAMIE** (USA) F 60
320 **LARGO** (FR) F 15
442 **LARK IN THE PARK** (IRE) C 26
352 **LARKRISE STAR** (GB) 7
321 **LARKS LAD** (IRE) 85
565 **LARSEN BEE** (IRE) 5

102 **LARWOOD** (IRE) 30
266 **LASCAUX** (GB) 74
249 **LASER BLAZER** (GB) 8
619 **LASHYN** (USA) 42
123 **LAST ATTEMPT** (IRE) 7
201 **LAST BID** (GB) 87
219 **LAST BORN** (FR) 70
507 **LAST DREAM** (IRE) F 24
507 **LAST DREAM** (IRE) C 39
49 **LAST FIGHTER** (IRE) 97
226 **LAST INSTALMENT** (IRE) 13
99 **LAST OF THE DIXIES** (GB) 74
219 **LAST RHAPSODY** (IRE) F 159
467 **LAST SHADOW** (GB) 21
699 **LAST SHOT** (FR) 32
517 **LAST SOVEREIGN** (GB) 2
45 **LAST SUPPER** (GB) 15
219 **LAST TRAIN** (GB) 71
200 **LAST ZAK** (GB) 57
107 **LASTCHANCELUCAS** (GB) 27
635 **LASTING MEMORYS** (IRE) 6
182 **LASTKINGOFSCOTLAND** (IRE) 9
458 **LASTOFTHELEADERS** (IRE) 15
681 **LASTOFTHEMOHICANS** (FR) 33
699 **LATANIER** (FR) 33
463 **LATARADUD** (IRE) 4
534 **LATE NIGHT MOVIE** (IRE) 27
111 **LATE TELEGRAPH** (IRE) 11
194 **LATER IN LIFE** (GB) 20
263 **LATERLY** (IRE) 12
702 **LATEST FASHION** (IRE) 3
260 **LATIN REBEL** (IRE) 15
647 **LATIN SCHOLAR** (IRE) 13
620 **LATTE** (GB) 8
695 **LAUBERHORN** (GB) 50
358 **LAUDATION** (GB) 33
321 **LAUDATORY** (GB) 86
349 **LAUGHING GAME** (GB) 2
108 **LAUGHING JACK** (GB) 19
460 **LAUGHTON PARK** (GB) 50
264 **LAUNDE** (IRE) 10
73 **LAURA LAMP** (GB) 13
360 **LAURA'S BAIRN** (GB) 44
570 **LAUREATE DES LOGES** (FR) 34
270 **LAUREL CREEK** (IRE) 8
29 **LAURELINE** (FR) 89
49 **LAURENA** (GER) C 133
219 **LAUSANNE** (GB) 72
695 **LAVA LAMP** (GB) 51
526 **LAVENDER BAY** (GB) 17
93 **LAVENOAK LAD** (GB) 7
660 **LAVERRE** (IRE) 15
511 **LAW BLADE** (FR) 18
58 **LAW OF THE RANGE** (GB) 13
304 **LAW REBEL** (IRE) 42
625 **LAW TO HIMSELF** (IRE) 21
230 **LAWGIVER** (IRE) 5
501 **LAWLESS BRIDGET** (GB) F 56
328 **LAWN JAMIL** (USA) 37
19 **LAY TIME** (GB) 18
49 **LAYALI DUBAI** (USA) 98
260 **LAYBACH** (IRE) 16
410 **LAYLA'S BOY** (GB) 9
108 **LAYLA'S DANCER** (GB) 20
543 **LAYLA'S HERO** (IRE) 13
422 **LAYLA'S KING** (GB) 8
376 **LAYLINE** (IRE) 8
682 **LAYWAAN** (USA) F 106

74 **LAZEEZ** (USA) 43
394 **LE BEAU BAI** (FR) 14
391 **LE BEC** (FR) 39
29 **LE BILBOQUET** (GB) 37
608 **LE BURF** (FR) 3
525 **LE CHASSE SPLEEN** (FR) 53
180 **LE CHAT D'OR** (GB) 11
108 **LE CORVEE** (IRE) 21
43 **LE DELUGE** (FR) 40
408 **LE GRAND BABU** 12
395 **LE GRAND CHENE** (FR) 9
192 **LE GRANDE CHEVAL** (IRE) 25
183 **LE GRENELLE** (FR) 19
328 **LE MONTRACHET** (GB) F 100
312 **LE PERGOLESE** (FR) 6
660 **LE REVE** (IRE) 16
283 **LE REVEUR** (FR) 41
476 **LE ROI ROUGE** (FR) 37
408 **LE SHOCK** (GER) 13
476 **LE VERT GALANT** (FR) 38
225 **LEA VALLEY** (GB) 23
476 **LEADER OF THE GANG** (GB) 39
331 **LEADING CONTENDER** (IRE) 46
414 **LEADING STAR** (GB) 9
706 **LEAHNESS** (IRE) 8
496 **LEAHURST** (IRE) 5
393 **LEAN BURN** (GB) 6
390 **LEAN ON PETE** (IRE) 11
446 **LEAN TIMES** (IRE) 46
164 **LEANE** (IRE) G 6
302 **LEANNE** (IRE) 8
55 **LEARGAS** (IRE) 87
201 **LEASE LEND** (GB) 29
696 **LEATH ACRA MOR** (IRE) 26
276 **LEAVE IT TO LIB** G 11
644 **LEAVING ALONE** (USA) 6
446 **LECEILE** (USA) 47
112 **LECHLADE LASS** (GB) 3
10 **LEELU** (GB) 10
507 **LEENANE** (IRE) C 40
631 **LEES ANTHEM** (GB) 3
403 **LEFTY'S DOLLBABY** (USA) F 15
684 **LEG IRON** (FR) 12
601 **LEGAL BOND** (GB) 45
273 **LEGAL EAGLE** (FR) 6
55 **LEGAL FARCE** (IRE) 36
276 **LEGAL LEGACY** (GB) 6
132 **LEGAL LEGEND** (GB) 3
64 **LEGEND OF TARA** (USA) F 27
570 **LEGBEFOREWICKET** (GB) 35
655 **LEGENDARY** (GB) 13
33 **LEGENDARY HOP** (GB) 10
619 **LEGENDS** (IRE) 125
57 **LEGENDSOFTHEFALL** (IRE) F 11
185 **LEGION D'HONNEUR** (UAE) 6
29 **LEGISLATION** (GB) 23
55 **LEGS ON DISPLAY** (IRE) 88
362 **LEITH HILL DANCER** (GB) 11
689 **LEITH WALK** (IRE) 9
55 **LEITIR MOR** (IRE) 89
285 **LEITRIM KING** (IRE) 40
130 **LEKKA DING** (IRE) F 15
58 **LELAPS** (USA) 39
681 **LEMON DROP RED** (USA) 34
34 **LEMON PEARL** (GB) 70
681 **LEMON'S GENT** (GB) 35
699 **LENA'S BLUEBELL** (IRE) 34

343 **LENABANE** (IRE) 31
340 **LEND A HAND SON** (GB) 25
115 **LENDERKING** (FR) 8
653 **LENNOXWOOD** (IRE) 10
576 **LENNY BEE** (GB) 1
619 **LEO LUNA** (GB) 43
637 **LEOPARD HILLS** (IRE) 10
634 **LEOPOLD** (SLO) 7
366 **LEQQAA** (USA) 103
357 **LERICI** (USA) F 29
677 **LERIDA** (GB) 2
446 **LEROY PARKER** (IRE) 48
706 **LERUBIS** (FR) 9
418 **LES LANDES** (IRE) 7
49 **LES TROYENS** (GB) 38
666 **LES VERGUETTES** (IRE) 7
220 **LESANDA** (GB) 20
710 **LESCER'S LAD** (GB) 1
553 **LESLEY'S CHOICE** (GB) 6
542 **LESOTHO** (IRE) 18
29 **LET IT SLIP** (FR) 6
384 **LET YOUR LOVE FLOW** (IRE) 20
401 **LET'S BE FAMOUS** (IRE) 2
573 **LET'S FALL IN LOVE** (GB) 58
141 **LETHAL FORCE** (IRE) 41
276 **LETS GET IT ON** (IRE) F 12
321 **LETS GET SERIOUS** (IRE) 87
336 **LETS GO PRIMO** (GB) 34
380 **LETSBY AVENUE** (GB) 61
441 **LETTERWOMAN** (IRE) G 5
342 **LEVANTERA** (IRE) 9
223 **LEVI DRAPER** (GB) 34
433 **LEVITATE** (GB) 19
249 **LEWYN** (GB) 9
654 **LEXI STAR** (USA) F 125
434 **LEXI'S BOY** (IRE) 79
573 **LEXI'S HERO** (IRE) 15
696 **LEXI'S PRINCESS** (IRE) 27
254 **LEXICON LAD** (IRE) 23
49 **LEY HUNTER** (USA) 39
33 **LEYTE GULF** (USA) 11
564 **LHENY** (FR) 50
338 **LHOTSE SHERPA** (IRE) 16
534 **LIBER** (GB) 52
619 **LIBER NAUTICUS** (IRE) 126
487 **LIBERATION BELLE** (IRE) 7
586 **LIBERTY ISLAND** (IRE) 8
87 **LIBERTY SHIP** (GB) 9
265 **LIBERTY TO ROCK** (IRE) 9
511 **LIBR'ARTTIST** (GB) 108
299 **LIBRANNO** (GB) 11
183 **LIBRARY** (FR) 60
371 **LIBRE** (GB) 9
511 **LIBRE TEMPS** (FR) 19
357 **LIBRETTELA** (GB) 6
161 **LIBYS DREAM** (FR) 12
366 **LICENCE TO TILL** (USA) 23
690 **LICHEN ANGEL** (GB) 18
569 **LICORNE BLEUE** (USA) 55
473 **LIDAKAN** (FR) 50
380 **LIDAR** (FR) 62
8 **LIE FORRIT** (FR) 12
9 **LIEUTENANT DAN** (IRE) 19
608 **LIEUTENANT GEORGE** (IRE) 4
321 **LIEUTENANT MILLER** (GB) 88
520 **LIFE AND SOUL** (GB) 9
3 **LIFE AND TIMES** (USA) 24
496 **LIFE IS GOLDEN** (USA) 31

474 **LIFE LONG** (IRE) 11
480 **LIFE OF LAUGHTER** (USA) 18
321 **LIFESTYLE** (GB) 89
207 **LIFETIME** (IRE) 25
3 **LIGHT BURST** (GB) 81
543 **LIGHT FROM MARS** (GB) 14
55 **LIGHT HEAVY** (IRE) 37
266 **LIGHT JIG** (GB) C 134
366 **LIGHT ROSE** (IRE) 177
266 **LIGHT SHINE** (GB) 75
614 **LIGHT STORM CASS** (IRE) 45
106 **LIGHT THE CITY** (IRE) 2
460 **LIGHT WELL** (IRE) 51
507 **LIGHTED WAY** (GB) F 41
400 **LIGHTENING FIRE** (GB) 13
407 **LIGHTENING PEARL** (IRE) 26
200 **LIGHTENING ROD** (GB) 28
390 **LIGHTHOUSE** (GB) F 35
573 **LIGHTNING CLOUD** (IRE) 16
285 **LIGHTNING DEBUT** (GB) 95
460 **LIGHTNING SPIRIT** (GB) 52
699 **LIGHTNING STRIKE** (GER) 30
344 **LIGHTS OF BROADWAY** (IRE) 10
29 **LIGOVKA** (FR) 38
666 **LIGURIAN SEA** (GB) 28
647 **LIKE A BOY** (GB) 14
380 **LIKE A HURRICANE** (IRE) 63
642 **LIKE CLOCKWORK** (GB) 32
449 **LIKE ICE** (GB) 1
489 **LIKE MINDED** (GB) 62
58 **LIKE THE NIGHT** (GB) 40
489 **LIKEABLE ROGUE** (IRE) 63
624 **LIKEAROLLINGSTONE** (IRE) 6
642 **LIKELIKELIKELIKEIT** (GB) 15
337 **LIL ELLA** (IRE) 9
286 **LILAC BELLE** (GB) 9
201 **LILAC MIST** (GB) F 115
217 **LILEO** (IRE) 5
310 **LILIARGH** (IRE) 16
43 **LILIUM** (GB) C 41
260 **LILLIOFTHEBALLET** (IRE) 17
706 **LILLY DE ROME** (GB) 10
564 **LILY AMERICA** (FR) 51
511 **LILY BOLERO** (GB) F 109
529 **LILY IN PINK** (GB) 10
401 **LILY LILY** (GB) 3
422 **LIMEGREEN BOW** (GB) F 29
379 **LINCS LAD** (GB) 6
219 **LINDA RADLETT** (IRE) 73
414 **LINDA'S SCHOOLGIRL** (IRE) G 10
530 **LINDEN GRACE** (USA) C 6
336 **LINDEN ROSE** (GB) 35
686 **LINDEN'S LADY** (GB) F 25
198 **LINDENGROVE** (GB) 11
533 **LINDORO** (GB) 3
166 **LINDSAY'S DREAM** (GB) 12
365 **LINDSEYFIELD LODGE** (IRE) 6
49 **LINE AHEAD** (IRE) C 134
625 **LINE OF DUTY** (GB) 22
270 **LINENHALL LADY** (IRE) 17
351 **LINGTREN** (GB) 4
635 **LINK HOUSE APPEAL** (IRE) 7
328 **LINKABLE** (GB) 38
458 **LINNEL** (IRE) 16
625 **LINROYALE BOY** (USA) 23
615 **LION COURT** (IRE) 3
123 **LION KING** (FR) 8
16 **LION ON THE PROWL** (IRE) 20

147 **LIONHEART** (GB) 89
366 **LIONROCK** (FR) 104
473 **LIOS A CHOILL** (IRE) 51
626 **LIQUEUR ROSE** (GB) 8
384 **LIQUID SUNSHINE** (GB) 21
56 **LISA POST** (FR) 24
299 **LISA'S LEGACY** (GB) 197
320 **LISAHANE BOG** (GB) 7
275 **LISBON** (IRE) 5
640 **LISBON LION** (IRE) 12
405 **LISCAHILL KARELLA** (IRE) 5
320 **LISCUNE** (IRE) C 16
424 **LISDALEEN** (IRE) 11
596 **LISDONAGH HOUSE** (IRE) 5
91 **LISIERE** (GB) 30
199 **LISSELAN AMAZON** (IRE) 4
546 **LISSELAN GALAXY** (IRE) 2
400 **LISSELAN PLEASURE** (USA) 14
57 **LISSELTON CROSS** (IRE) 12
650 **LISTEN BOY** (IRE) 39
207 **LITEUP MY WORLD** (IRE) 26
366 **LITHOGRAPH** (USA) 105
219 **LITIGANT** (GB) 17
328 **LITMUS** (GB) 39
45 **LITTLE BOB** (GB) 9
347 **LITTLE CARMELA** (GB) 19
24 **LITTLE CASCADE** (GB) F 29
467 **LITTLE CHINA** (GB) 22
404 **LITTLE CHIP** (IRE) 25
141 **LITTLE CHOOSEY** (GB) 68
141 **LITTLE COTTONSOCKS** (GB) 14
18 **LITTLE COTTONSOCKS** (GB) 21
466 **LITTLE CURTSEY** (GB) 15
141 **LITTLE DUTCH GIRL** (GB) 42
319 **LITTLE EAGLET** (IRE) 2
453 **LITTLE FEE** (GB) 1
636 **LITTLE FIFI** (GB) 5
321 **LITTLE FRITZ** (GB) 90
58 **LITTLE GARCON** (USA) 14
434 **LITTLE GEORGE** (IRE) 80
659 **LITTLE HERCULES** (IRE) 27
153 **LITTLE JAZZ** (GB) 3
274 **LITTLE JIMMY** (GB) 12
201 **LITTLE JIMMY ODSOX** (IRE) 30
314 **LITTLE LIVE WIRE** (IRE) 6
503 **LITTLE MISS FLORA** (GB) 38
220 **LITTLE MR SUNSHINE** (GB) 57
342 **LITTLE PERISHER** (GB) 10
141 **LITTLE RAINBOW** (GB) 43
117 **LITTLE RED MINX** (IRE) 17
683 **LITTLE RICHARD** (IRE) 3
487 **LITTLE ROXY** (IRE) 8
546 **LITTLE WADHAM** (GB) 3
653 **LITTLECOTE LAD** (GB) 32
653 **LITTLECOTE LADY** (GB) 23
504 **LITTLEDEAN JIMMY** (IRE) 4
567 **LITTLEMISSPERFECT** (GB) 13
283 **LITTLEPORTNBRANDY** (IRE) 42
1 **LITTLESUZIE** (GB) 21
39 **LIVE ACT** (IRE) 10
434 **LIVELY BARON** (GB) 81
450 **LIVER BIRD** (GB) 21
55 **LIVIA GALILEI** (IRE) 38
641 **LIVING DESERT** (GB) 15
169 **LIVING IT LARGE** (FR) 15
511 **LIVING WELL** (GB) 64
570 **LIVVY INN** (USA) 36
318 **LIXIAN** (GB) F 52

201 **LIZZIE** (IRE) 31
19 **LIZZIE TUDOR** (GB) 129
30 **LIZZY'S DREAM** (GB) 9
328 **LLANARMON LAD** (IRE) 40
61 **LLEWELLYN** (GB) 7
219 **LLIA** (GB) C 160
263 **LOCAL HERO** (GER) 13
511 **LOCAL LOVER** (GB) 110
333 **LOCAL PRESENT** (IRE) 6
494 **LOCAL QUINE** (IRE) 11
342 **LOCAL SINGER** (IRE) 11
35 **LOCAL SPIRIT** (USA) F 81
473 **LOCH ARD** (IRE) 52
386 **LOCH BA** (IRE) 15
460 **LOCH FLEET** (IRE) 53
55 **LOCH GARMAN** (IRE) 90
213 **LOCH VERDI** (GB) F 20
424 **LOCHAN LACHA** (IRE) 12
180 **LOCHARIA** (GB) F 47
8 **LOCHORE** (IRE) 13
34 **LOCHRIDGE** (GB) F 71
24 **LOCKALANE** (GB) 13
9 **LOCKANTANKS** (GB) 20
563 **LOCKED INTHEPOCKET** (IRE) 4
294 **LOCKSTOWN** (GB) 5
219 **LOCKWOOD** (GB) 74
642 **LOCUM** (GB) 15
434 **LODEN** (GB) 82
650 **LODGICIAN** (IRE) 40
408 **LOFTE PLACE** 61
470 **LOGANS LEGEND** (IRE) 2
634 **LOGICAL APPROACH** (IRE) 8
358 **LOKI'S REVENGE** (GB) 6
668 **LOLA LOLA** (IRE) F 5
470 **LOLITA LEBRON** (IRE) 3
299 **LOLITA'S GOLD** (USA) F 198
573 **LOLLINA PAULINA** (GB) 59
519 **LOLLYPOP LADY** (GB) 20
21 **LOMBARDY BOY** (IRE) 1
460 **LOMBOK** (GB) 54
228 **LONDON AVENUE** (IRE) 8
446 **LONDON BRIDGE** (GB) 49
102 **LONDON SILVER** (GB) 31
213 **LONDON SKOLAR** (GB) 21
467 **LONDON WELSH** (GB) 2
384 **LONE FOOT LADDIE** (IRE) 22
569 **LONE RANGER** (FR) 5
592 **LONE STAR STATE** (IRE) 24
511 **LONELY TIGER** (GB) 65
691 **LONESOME BOATMAN** (IRE) 4
570 **LONG DISTANCE** (FR) 37
56 **LONG JOHN SILVER** (FR) 9
508 **LONG JOURNEY HOME** (IRE) 4
366 **LONG LOST LOVE** (GB) 106
579 **LONG RANGE** (GB) 5
321 **LONG RUN** (FR) 91
157 **LONGITUDE** (GB) 14
341 **LONGROW** (GB) 3
476 **LONGWAYTOTIPPERARY** (GB) 40
55 **LONRACH** (IRE) 39
129 **LOOK AT LULU** (GB) 34
61 **LOOK AT ME NOW** (GB) 26
336 **LOOK FOR LOVE** (GB) 11
597 **LOOK LEFT** (GB) 10
265 **LOOK NOBLE** (GB) 3
442 **LOOK ON BY** (GB) 29
663 **LOOK WHO'S TALKING** (GB) 3
219 **LOOKING** (GB) 75

219 **LOOKING AT GLORY** (IRE) 161
321 **LOOKING HOPEFUL** (IRE) 92
102 **LOOKING ON** (GB) 12
9 **LOOKING TANNED** (GB) 43
447 **LOOKS CAN KILL** (GB) 81
35 **LOOKS LIKE RAIN** (GB) 39
171 **LOOKS LIKE SLIM** (GB) 5
404 **LOOSE CHIPS** (GB) 26
321 **LOOSE PREFORMER** (IRE) 93
117 **LOQUACITY** (GB) F 42
507 **LORAINE** (GB) 42
709 **LORD ALDERVALE** (IRE) 3
348 **LORD ARATAN** (GER) 2
161 **LORD ASHLEY** (IRE) 58
694 **LORD BELLAMY** (IRE) 3
283 **LORD BUFFHEAD** (GB) 75
331 **LORD CREWE** (IRE) 47
7 **LORD FRANKLIN** (GB) 16
488 **LORD GAGA** (IRE) 58
473 **LORD GALE** (IRE) 53
157 **LORD GRANTHAM** (IRE) 5
287 **LORD KENMARE** (USA) 16
286 **LORD KENNEDY** (IRE) 10
111 **LORD NANDI** (GB) 53
420 **LORD OF HOUSE** (GER) 20
73 **LORD OF THE DANCE** (IRE) 14
639 **LORD OF THE DUNES** (GB) 32
647 **LORD OF THE STORM** (GB) 55
392 **LORD OF THE WING** (GB) 5
299 **LORD OFTHE SHADOWS** (IRE) 73
284 **LORD RAGNAR** (IRE) 5
254 **LORD RYEFORD** (IRE) 24
460 **LORD SINGER** (GB) 55
399 **LORD THEO** (GB) 4
16 **LORD TOMNODDY** (GB) 21
476 **LORD VILLEZ** (IRE) 41
700 **LORD WHEATHILL** (GB) 16
218 **LORD WISHES** (GB) 15
285 **LORDOFTHEHOUSE** (IRE) 11
617 **LORIENT EXPRESS** (IRE) 13
56 **LOS ABRIGOS** (FR) 25
260 **LOS NADIS** (GER) 18
426 **LOST ARCA** (FR) 5
220 **LOST CITY** (GB) 58
201 **LOST IN PARIS** (IRE) 32
49 **LOST IN THE MOMENT** (IRE) 40
639 **LOST TWO STARS** (IRE) 33
166 **LOSTAYER** (IRE) 13
43 **LOTARESPECT** (GB) 22
142 **LOTHIAN LASS** (IRE) F 17
358 **LOTHIAN SKY** (IRE) 22
408 **LOTTIE BELLE** 62
270 **LOTUS ROOTS** (GB) 18
219 **LOU SALOME** (GB) 162
226 **LOUDMOUTH** (IRE) 14
397 **LOUGH CORRIB** (USA) 15
610 **LOUGH DERG WAY** (IRE) 10
503 **LOUGH INCH** (IRE) 39
591 **LOUGHALDER** (IRE) 6
573 **LOUIS THE PIOUS** (GB) 17
219 **LOUISA M ALCOTT** (GB) 76
706 **LOUISE SAUVAGE** (GB) 11
201 **LOUKOUMI** (GB) 33
446 **LOUP DU SAUBOUAS** (FR) 50
360 **LOUPHOLE** (GB) 20
388 **LOUSSIA** (FR) 37
366 **LOUVE MYSTERIEUSE** (USA) F 178
498 **LOUXOR DES MOTTES** (FR) 17

119 **LOVAGE** (GB) 35
364 **LOVAT LANE** (GB) 9
32 **LOVCEN** (GER) 64
32 **LOVE CLUB** (GB) 14
111 **LOVE DIVINE** (GB) C 126
366 **LOVE EVERLASTING** (GB) F 179
35 **LOVE GROWS WILD** (USA) 40
78 **LOVE IN THE PARK** (GB) 6
690 **LOVE ISLAND** (GB) 15
619 **LOVE MAGIC** (GB) 127
366 **LOVE ME TENDER** (GB) C 180
74 **LOVE OF DUBAI** (USA) C 64
425 **LOVE OF TARA** (GB) 2
557 **LOVE TALE** (GB) 13
19 **LOVE TATOO** (GB) 68
150 **LOVE THE LORD** (IRE) G 15
30 **LOVE THING** (GB) C 21
139 **LOVE TO TARA** (GB) 21
107 **LOVE VALENTINE** (IRE) C 28
360 **LOVE YOU LOUIS** (GB) 21
477 **LOVE YOUR LOOKS** (GB) 6
117 **LOVEALOT** (GB) F 18
223 **LOVED ONE** (GB) 59
525 **LOVEINASANDDUNE** (GB) 10
525 **LOVES A BRAZILIAN** (IRE) 54
14 **LOVES THEME** (IRE) 6
685 **LOVEY DOVEY** (GB) 6
270 **LOVING KIND** (IRE) 19
641 **LOVING SPIRIT** (GB) 1
200 **LOW PASTURES** (GB) 58
617 **LOW REACTOR** (IRE) 14
226 **LOWANBEHOLD** (IRE) 15
699 **LOWER HOPE DANDY** (GB) 36
123 **LOWER LAKE** (FR) 61
266 **LOWNDES** (GB) 76
69 **LOWRY MAHER** (IRE) 6
488 **LOWTHER** (GB) 24
601 **LOWTHERWOOD** (GB) 46
64 **LOYAL ROYAL** (GB) 14
588 **LOYALTY** (GB) 11
185 **LOYAUTE** (FR) 7
359 **LUA DE ITAPOAN** (GB) 17
473 **LUC JORDAN** (GB) 53
695 **LUCAINDUBAI** (IRE) 52
619 **LUCANIN** (GB) 44
585 **LUCAS PITT** (GB) 18
564 **LUCAYAN** (FR) 52
543 **LUCCOMBE CHINE** (GB) 15
268 **LUCEMATIC** (GB) 19
570 **LUCIA BAY** (GB) 38
180 **LUCIES PRIDE** (IRE) F 48
384 **LUCIFERS SHADOW** (IRE) 23
318 **LUCILLE** C 7
415 **LUCKY** (IRE) C 12
182 **LUCKY ART** (USA) 10
328 **LUCKY BEGGAR** (IRE) 101
715 **LUCKY BELLE** (IRE) 4
169 **LUCKY BREEZE** (IRE) 16
273 **LUCKY DAN** (IRE) 7
232 **LUCKY DANCER** (FR) C 3
320 **LUCKY DATE** (FR) F 17
647 **LUCKY DIVA** (GB) 16
230 **LUCKY FOR SOME** (GB) 6
141 **LUCKY HENRY** (GB) 44
142 **LUCKY LANDING** (IRE) 5
101 **LUCKY LUKEY** (GB) 19
479 **LUCKY MELLOR** (GB) 12

331 **LUCKY MIX** (GB) 48
534 **LUCKY MONEY** (GB) 28
35 **LUCKY NORWEGIAN** (IRE) C 82
273 **LUCKY NUMBERS** (IRE) 8
329 **LUCKY OAKWOOD** (USA) C 37
202 **LUCKY PRINCE** (GB) 2
249 **LUCKY ROYALE** (GB) 10
35 **LUCKY SPIN** (GB) C 83
299 **LUCKY SUIT** (IRE) 199
202 **LUCKY SUN** (GB) 3
617 **LUCKY SUNNY** (IRE) 15
59 **LUCKY THUMB** (GB) 15
249 **LUCKY TRICKS** (GB) 11
68 **LUCKY VIC** (IRE) 6
625 **LUCKY WINDMILL** (GB) 24
564 **LUCRECE** (GB) 53
155 **LUCTOR EMERGO** (IRE) 16
219 **LUCUMON** (GER) 163
525 **LUCY'S PERFECT** (GB) 55
108 **LUGGERS HALL** (IRE) 22
139 **LUI REI** (ITY) 13
511 **LUISA MILLER** (GER) 66
352 **LUJEANIE** (GB) 8
101 **LUKEYS LUCK** (GB) 20
471 **LULU'S GIFT** (IRE) 11
328 **LULUA** (USA) C 102
600 **LUMIERE DU SOIR** (FR) 11
285 **LUMIERE NOIRE** (FR) F 96
43 **LUMIERE ROUGE** (FR) C 42
299 **LUMINDA** (IRE) C 200
476 **LUMPINI PARK** (GB) G 42
362 **LUNA LIGHTNING** (GB) 12
141 **LUNA ROSA** (IRE) 45
204 **LUNA VALE** (GB) 9
364 **LUNAR DEITY** (GB) 18
417 **LUNAR LIMELIGHT** (GB) 6
408 **LUNATORIO** (FR) 14
485 **LUNDY BAY** (GB) 10
485 **LUNDY SKY** (GB) 11
569 **LUNE D'OR** (FR) F 118
80 **LUNERAY** (FR) G 5
460 **LUPANAR** (GER) 56
27 **LUPIN POOTER** (GB) 38
581 **LUPITA** (IRE) 1
43 **LUPO D'ORO** (IRE) 23
223 **LURCHER** (GB) 35
176 **LUSCIVIOUS** (GB) 10
298 **LUSKA LAD** (IRE) 17
268 **LUTIN DU MOULIN** (FR) 20
477 **LUTINE BELL** (GB) 7
306 **LUTINE CHARLIE** (IRE) 15
32 **LUV U NOO** (GB) 15
19 **LYCA BALLERINA** (GB) C 130
130 **LYCIDAS** (GER) 11
388 **LYKASTOS** (IRE) 78
388 **LYKEA** (IRE) 79
373 **LYNFORD NAKITA** (GB) 16
352 **LYNFORYOU** (GB) 32
58 **LYNNWOOD CHASE** (USA) C 68
471 **LYON'S HILL** (GB) 12
343 **LYREEN LEGEND** (IRE) 32
534 **LYRIC PIECE** (GB) 53
109 **LYRIC POET** (USA) 5
191 **LYRIC STREET** (IRE) 2
583 **LYRICAL CHANT** (IRE) 11
462 **LYRICAL GANGSTER** (IRE) 15
24 **LYRICAL INTENT** (GB) 14

193 **LYSANDRA** (IRE) F 54
12 **LYSSIO** (GER) 11
321 **LYVIUS** (GB) 94
273 **M J WOODWARD** (GB) 12
33 **M'LADY ROUSSEAU** (IRE) 12
435 **MA FILLE SAUVAGE** (GB) 5
296 **MA KELLYS** (IRE) 46
102 **MA QUILLET** (GB) 13
654 **MAAKIRR** (IRE) 1
366 **MAASTRICHT** (IRE) 107
328 **MABAAHEJ** (USA) C 103
285 **MABAANY** (GB) 41
469 **MABEL TASMAN** (GB) 24
102 **MABEL'S SONG** (GB) 32
359 **MAC AEDA** (GB) 18
695 **MAC BEATTIE** (GB) 53
684 **MAC FEDERAL** (GB) 13
247 **MAC GILLE EOIN** (GB) 3
695 **MAC HALEN** (IRE) 54
55 **MAC LIR** (USA) 91
119 **MAC LOVE** (GB) 8
448 **MAC'S GREY** (GB) 3
223 **MAC'S POWER** (IRE) 12
223 **MAC'S SUPERSTAR** (FR) 60
547 **MACARTHUR** (GB) 4
451 **MACCABEES** (GB) 36
385 **MACDILLON** (GB) 7
276 **MACE THE ACE** (GB) 16
605 **MACK MILAN** (IRE) 4
352 **MACK'S SISTER** (GB) 9
566 **MACKEM BEAT** (GB) F 17
343 **MACKEYS FORGE** (IRE) 33
547 **MACRA NA FEIRME** (IRE) 5
476 **MACS ISLAND** (IRE) 43
452 **MACY ANNE** (IRE) 15
450 **MAD FOR FUN** (GB) 37
81 **MAD GEORGE** (IRE) 8
429 **MAD GINGER ALICE** (GB) 8
469 **MAD MAX** (IRE) 25
650 **MAD MOOSE** (IRE) 41
137 **MAD PROFESSOR** (IRE) 4
568 **MADAM ISSHE** (GB) 5
677 **MADAM LILIBET** (GB) 6
501 **MADAM MACIE** (IRE) 2
266 **MADAM NINETTE** (GB) C 135
382 **MADAM NOSO** (GB) 3
509 **MADAM TESSA** (IRE) 11
690 **MADAM VALENTINE** (GB) G 19
480 **MADAME ALLSORTS** (GB) 5
441 **MADAME BLAVATSKY** (FR) 6
336 **MADAME ELIZABETH** (GB) 41
102 **MADAME FEU** (GB) 33
607 **MADAME JASMINE** (GB) 7
451 **MADAME KINTYRE** (GB) 9
256 **MADAME PAPILLON** (GB) 10
146 **MADAME SCARLETT** (IRE) 26
447 **MADAME ST CLAIR** (IRE) 32
460 **MADAME STELLA** (FR) G 57
463 **MADAME TAVELURE** (GB) 5
619 **MADAME VESTRIS** (IRE) 128
543 **MADAMLILY** (IRE) 16
287 **MADAMOISELLE H** (IRE) 40
18 **MADAMOISELLE JONES** (GB) F 68
501 **MADDIE'S PEARL** (IRE) C 57
340 **MADE FOR SHARING** (IRE) 2
460 **MADE IN ITALY** (IRE) 58
424 **MADE IN TAIPAN** (IRE) 13
450 **MADE IN THE SHADE** (GB) 38

150 **MADE IN TIME** (IRE) 16
533 **MADEIRA MIST** (IRE) 4
151 **MADERSON BLUE** (IRE) 6
299 **MADGENTA** (IRE) 74
682 **MADHMOONAH** (IRE) 46
318 **MADRASA** (FR) 53
552 **MADRASA** (IRE) 27
366 **MADRILENE** (USA) 24
54 **MAE CIGAN** (FR) 6
466 **MAE ROSE COTTAGE** (IRE) 47
252 **MAELSTROM SEA** (GB) 8
193 **MAFETENG** (GB) 10
330 **MAFI** (IRE) 5
658 **MAGDA LENA** (GER) 28
450 **MAGDALENE** (FR) F 45
267 **MAGGIE BLUE** (IRE) 4
473 **MAGGIE CONNOLLY** (IRE) 55
450 **MAGGIE MEY** (IRE) 22
304 **MAGGIE NEARY** (IRE) 43
9 **MAGGIE PINK** (GB) 44
275 **MAGGIO** (FR) 6
223 **MAGHYA** (IRE) C 61
359 **MAGIC BLOOM** G 38
201 **MAGIC BOUNTY** (GB) 88
91 **MAGIC CAT** (GB) 9
299 **MAGIC CITY** (IRE) 75
178 **MAGIC ECHO** (GB) 11
289 **MAGIC HAZE** (GB) 2
331 **MAGIC MARMALADE** (IRE) 49
501 **MAGIC MILLIE** (GB) 23
219 **MAGIC MOTIF** (USA) 77
129 **MAGIC MUSIC** (IRE) C 35
237 **MAGIC PEAK** (IRE) F 50
359 **MAGIC PRESENT** (GB) 19
420 **MAGIC PROSPECT** (FR) 22
59 **MAGIC SHOW** (GB) 16
475 **MAGIC SPEAR** (IRE) 15
266 **MAGIC TREE** (UAE) F 136
317 **MAGICAL DANCER** (IRE) F 9
631 **MAGICAL DANCERS** (IRE) 8
27 **MAGICAL MACEY** (USA) 19
292 **MAGICAL MAN** (GB) 6
304 **MAGICAL MEMOIR** (IRE) 44
9 **MAGICAL MUSIC** (GB) C 201
299 **MAGICAL PEACE** (IRE) 3
422 **MAGICAL SPEEDFIT** (IRE) 9
693 **MAGICAL STAR** (GB) 3
480 **MAGICALMYSTERYTOUR** (IRE) 20
27 **MAGILINI** (IRE) 39
29 **MAGIQ RIO** (IRE) 39
496 **MAGIQUE** (IRE) 79
19 **MAGMA** (GB) 69
343 **MAGNANIMITY** (IRE) 34
404 **MAGNIFIQUE ETOILE** (GB) 27
32 **MAGNITUDE** (GB) 16
682 **MAGNOLIA RIDGE** (IRE) 107
119 **MAGOG** (GB) 71
160 **MAGOT DE GRUGY** (FR) 18
682 **MAHAAZEN** (IRE) 47
361 **MAHAB EL SHAMAAL** (GB) 2
169 **MAHADEE** (IRE) 17
420 **MAHAYOGIN** (USA) 23
695 **MAHER** (USA) 55
207 **MAHFAL** (FR) 27
49 **MAHKAMA** (USA) 99
219 **MAHNAZ** (IRE) 78
678 **MAID EQUAL** (GB) F 6
473 **MAID FROM MILAN** (IRE) 56

290 **MAID IN ENGLAND** (GB) 5
290 **MAID IN ENGLAND** (GB) F 9
290 **MAID IN ENGLAND** (GB) F 10
519 **MAID OF MEFT** (GB) 9
111 **MAID TO BELIEVE** (GB) F 127
304 **MAID TO MASTER** (IRE) 94
526 **MAIL EXPRESS** (IRE) G 18
130 **MAIN BEACH** (GB) 5
390 **MAIN LINE** (GB) 12
390 **MAIN SEQUENCE** (USA) 13
365 **MAINLAND** (USA) 7
29 **MAINSAIL** (GB) 40
186 **MAISON BRILLET** (IRE) 1
147 **MAISTRO** (IRE) 44
627 **MAITH GALORE** (IRE) 4
216 **MAIZY MISSILE** (IRE) 1
254 **MAJAALES** (USA) 25
254 **MAJALA** (FR) 26
597 **MAJEED** (GB) 77
222 **MAJESTIC BOUNTY** (GB) 12
682 **MAJESTIC CONCORDE** (IRE) 8
200 **MAJESTIC DREAM** (IRE) 29
578 **MAJESTIC EVICTION** (IRE) F 8
508 **MAJESTIC JASMINE** (IRE) 77
488 **MAJESTIC MANANNAN** (IRE) 59
461 **MAJESTIC MAYHEM** (IRE) 15
220 **MAJESTIC MYLES** (IRE) 21
285 **MAJESTIC SAKEENA** (GB) F 97
397 **MAJESTIC ZAFEEN** (GB) 44
330 **MAJESTUEUX** (GB) 6
111 **MAJESTY** (IRE) 128
256 **MAJOR BELLAMY** (GER) 11
547 **MAJOR DECISION** (IRE) 6
296 **MAJOR DOMO** (IRE) 24
506 **MAJOR MUSCARI** (IRE) 12
543 **MAJOR PARKES** (GB) 47
593 **MAJORICA KING** (IRE) 5
366 **MAJOUNE** (FR) C 181
283 **MAJURO** (IRE) 43
361 **MAJY D'AUTEUIL** (FR) 3
654 **MAKAASEB** (USA) C 126
147 **MAKAFEH** (GB) 90
569 **MAKANA** (FR) 56
705 **MAKARI** (GB) 15
604 **MAKBULLET** (GB) 2
384 **MAKE A FUSS** (GB) 24
407 **MAKE MY HEART SING** (USA) C 49
705 **MAKE UP** (GB) 27
473 **MAKE YOUR MARK** (IRE) 57
695 **MAKETHE MOSTOFNOW** (IRE) 56
657 **MAKHZOON** (USA) 46
327 **MAKIN A FUSS** (GB) 7
510 **MAKING EYES** (IRE) 2
654 **MALAAQ** (GB) C 127
108 **MALANOS** (IRE) 23
682 **MALAYAN MIST** (IRE) 9
201 **MALCHEEK** (IRE) 34
597 **MALEKAT JAMAL** (IRE) 43
111 **MALEKOV** (IRE) 54
467 **MALELANE** (IRE) C 41
8 **MALIBU DANCER** (IRE) 14
219 **MALICHO** (GB) 79
299 **MALIGNED** (USA) 76
573 **MALIHA** (IRE) 60
556 **MALIN BAY** (IRE) 22
86 **MALIN HEAD** (IRE) 13
259 **MALINDI** (GB) 26
510 **MALINGERING** (GB) 8

304 **MALLER TREE** (GB) 45
147 **MALLORY HEIGHTS** (IRE) 91
432 **MALLT** (IRE) 7
16 **MALLUSK** (IRE) 22
321 **MALT MASTER** (IRE) 95
550 **MALTEASE AH** (GB) 11
285 **MAMA QUILLA** (USA) 42
485 **MAMBO SPIRIT** (IRE) 12
422 **MAMOURA** (IRE) C 30
534 **MAN FROM SEVILLE** (GB) 54
49 **MAN OF ACTION** (USA) 41
116 **MAN OF ICE** (GB) 22
196 **MAN OF LEISURE** (GB) 6
176 **MAN OF MY WORD** (GB) 21
193 **MAN OF PLENTY** (GB) 36
131 **MAN OF PRINCIPLES** (IRE) 3
75 **MANA POOLS** (IRE) F 21
619 **MANAAL** (USA) F 129
266 **MANAAR** (USA) 77
696 **MANADAM** (FR) 28
380 **MANAGEMENT** (IRE) 65
495 **MANAGER MICK** (IRE) 6
606 **MANAHEJ** (USA) 26
55 **MANALISA** (IRE) 40
55 **MANALIVE** (IRE) 41
283 **MANANA MANANA** (GB) 44
193 **MANBAA** (USA) 37
43 **MANCUNIAN** (IRE) 8
511 **MAND CHICK** (GB) 67
8 **MANDAEAN** (GB) 82
230 **MANDALAY KING** (IRE) 7
635 **MANDARIN SUNSET** (IRE) 8
49 **MANDELLICHT** (IRE) C 135
299 **MANDEVILLE** (IRE) 202
325 **MANDHOOMA** (GB) 3
146 **MANDIANNA** (IRE) 19
569 **MANDISTANA** (FR) 57
219 **MANDORE** (IRE) 80
429 **MANDY'S HERO** (GB) 9
567 **MANELE BAY** (GB) 14
241 **MANGHAM** (IRE) 9
58 **MANGO LADY** (GB) C 69
42 **MANGONEL** (GB) 15
483 **MANICS MAN** (GB) 5
508 **MANIEREE** (IRE) 5
388 **MANIKARAA** (FR) 80
408 **MANJANO** 63
147 **MANKINI** (IRE) 45
312 **MANMOON** (FR) 7
659 **MANNERED** (GB) 28
699 **MANNLICHEN** (FR) 37
74 **MANOMINE** (GB) 44
201 **MANON'S SONG** (GB) C 116
374 **MANOR COURT** (IRE) 22
569 **MANSER FRIN** 59
660 **MANSHOOR** (IRE) 17
395 **MANSOLIAS** (FR) 10
476 **MANSONIEN L'AS** (FR) 44
219 **MANTILLA** (USA) 81
447 **MANTOBA** (GB) 6
663 **MANTON** (GB) 4
619 **MANUKA** (IRE) 45
600 **MANUKA** (USA) 26
193 **MANY A SLIP** (GB) 11
593 **MANY CLOUDS** (IRE) 32
40 **MANY LEVELS** (GB) 20
101 **MAOI CHINN TIRE** (IRE) 21

496 **MAORI DANCER** (USA) 32
249 **MAP OF LOVE** (IRE) 40
201 **MAPPIN TIME** (IRE) 35
699 **MARAAFEQ** (USA) 38
75 **MARABOUT** (IRE) 22
388 **MARACENA** (FR) 38
569 **MARADINI** (FR) 60
417 **MARAH MUSIC** (GB) 13
480 **MARAJAA** (IRE) 21
45 **MARAKABEI** (GB) C 23
249 **MARAMKOVA** (IRE) F 41
569 **MARASIMA** M 119
473 **MARASONNIEN** (FR) 58
217 **MARATIB** (USA) 6
201 **MARBLE SILVER** (IRE) 117
567 **MARBLE WALK** (IRE) 15
331 **MARCHAND D'ARGENT** (FR) 50
401 **MARCHING ORDERS** (IRE) 4
318 **MARCHING WEST** (USA) C 54
496 **MARCIANO** (IRE) 80
58 **MARCRET** (IRE) 15
61 **MARCUS ANTONIUS** (GB) 8
268 **MARDOOD** (GB) 21
699 **MARESCSOU** (FR) 39
161 **MARFORD MISSILE** (IRE) 32
668 **MARGARETS WISH** (GB) F 6
668 **MARGARETS WISH** (GB) G 4
328 **MARGATE** (GB) 41
296 **MARGO CHANNING** (GB) 47
35 **MARGOT DID** (IRE) 6
573 **MARHABA MALAYEEN** (IRE) 96
597 **MARHABA MALYOON** (IRE) 11
193 **MARHOONA** (USA) 38
266 **MARIA LETIZIA** (GB) 78
329 **MARIA MONTEZ** (GB) 13
466 **MARIA THERESA** (GB) F 75
58 **MARIA VEZZERA** (GB) 41
619 **MARIA'S CHOICE** (IRE) 46
201 **MARIACHI MAN** (GB) 36
434 **MARIAETTA** (IRE) C 83
193 **MARIANNES** (GB) 39
407 **MARIAS MAGIC** (GB) C 50
583 **MARIAS ROCK** (GB) 12
626 **MARICO** (FR) 7
542 **MARIE DE BLOIS** (IRE) F 24
264 **MARIE DEJA LA** (FR) 11
637 **MARIE DES ANGES** (FR) 11
166 **MARIE'S FANTASY** (GB) 23
117 **MARIELLA** (GB) 43
19 **MARIET** (GB) 70
19 **MARIKA** (GB) F 131
60 **MARINA BALLERINA** (GB) 7
69 **MARINA BAY** (GB) 7
123 **MARINA PICCOLA** (IRE) 38
60 **MARINA'S OCEAN** (GB) 8
111 **MARINE GIRL** (GB) 55
3 **MARINER'S CROSS** (IRE) 83
16 **MARINESIDE** (FR) 23
420 **MARINGO BAY** (IRE) 24
242 **MARINO PRINCE** (FR) 1
384 **MARINUS** (IRE) 25
473 **MARITO** (GER) 59
29 **MARIUS** (FR) 41
184 **MARJONG** (GB) 23
449 **MARJU KING** (IRE) 2
307 **MARK ANTHONY** (IRE) 2
237 **MARK OF MEYDAN** (GB) 16
110 **MARK THE BOOK** (IRE) 12

16 **MARK TWAIN** (IRE) 24
102 **MARKAB** (GB) 14
579 **MARKADAM** (GB) 6
394 **MARKED MAN** (IRE) 15
73 **MARKET PUZZLE** (IRE) 15
73 **MARKSBURY** (GB) 16
147 **MARKTTAG** (GB) 92
374 **MARLENO** (GER) 23
681 **MARLEY ROCA** (IRE) 36
139 **MARMALADE MOON** (GB) 22
643 **MARMAS** (GB) 34
610 **MARODIMA** (FR) 11
564 **MARONI** (GB) 9
510 **MAROON MACHINE** (IRE) 3
299 **MAROUSSIE** (FR) C 203
569 **MARQUE ROYALE** (GB) C 120
466 **MARRIED FOR MONEY** (USA) C 76
642 **MARSH DRAGON** (GB) 45
207 **MARSH WARBLER** (GB) 28
373 **MARSHAL ZHUKOV** (IRE) 17
543 **MARSHALL ART** (GB) 36
178 **MARSHMALLOW** (GB) 12
543 **MARSTER PARKES** (GB) 17
298 **MART LANE** (IRE) 18
161 **MARTHA** (IRE) F 59
200 **MARTHA'S WAY** (IRE) 59
19 **MARTIAL ART** (IRE) 132
525 **MARTIAL LAW** (IRE) 56
285 **MARTIAN** (IRE) 98
148 **MARTIN CASH** (IRE) 2
619 **MARTIN CHUZZLEWIT** (IRE) 47
243 **MARTIN'S SHADOW** (GB) 4
318 **MARTINI** (GER) 55
18 **MARTYR** (GB) 22
489 **MARTYS MISSION** (IRE) 64
331 **MARUFO** (IRE) 51
496 **MARULA** (IRE) F 81
180 **MARVELLOUS VALUE** (IRE) 12
642 **MARVO** (GB) 16
462 **MARY FILDES** (IRE) 16
149 **MARY KATE O'BRIEN** (GB) 5
653 **MARY SEA** (FR) F 33
2 **MARY'S PET** (GB) 4
666 **MARYQUEENOFSCOTS** (IRE) C 42
119 **MARZANTE** (GB) 9
654 **MASAAFAT** (GB) C 128
30 **MASAI KING** (IRE) 22
451 **MASAI MOON** (GB) 10
573 **MASAMAH** (IRE) 18
628 **MASANDRA** (IRE) C 26
74 **MASAYA** (GB) 15
325 **MASHDOOD** (USA) 4
420 **MASKED MAN** (IRE) 25
266 **MASKED MARVEL** (GB) 17
628 **MASKUNAH** (IRE) F 27
325 **MASLAK** (IRE) 5
441 **MASON DAVID BROWN** (IRE) 7
441 **MASON HINDMARSH** (GB) 8
634 **MASRA** (GB) 9
33 **MASS HYSTERIA** (IRE) 13
180 **MASS RALLY** (IRE) 13
350 **MASSAMS LANE** (GB) 1
529 **MASSANNIE** (IRE) 11
401 **MASSAPOAG** (IRE) 5
699 **MASSENA** (IRE) 40
543 **MASSINI LOTTO** (IRE) 18
455 **MASSINI SUNSET** (IRE) 7
525 **MASSINI'S MAGUIRE** (IRE) 57

287 **MASSIYN** (IRE) 41
688 **MASTER ACT** (IRE) 12
128 **MASTER ALF** (IRE) 1
492 **MASTER ALFREDO** (GB) 2
118 **MASTER BEAU** (GB) 14
601 **MASTER BOND** (GB) 47
17 **MASTER CARDOR VISA** (IRE) 4
180 **MASTER CHIPPER** (GB) 32
185 **MASTER COBBLER** (IRE) 8
334 **MASTER CONOR** (IRE) 4
706 **MASTER COSPECTOR** (GB) 12
254 **MASTER CYNK** (GB) 27
395 **MASTER D'OR** (FR) 11
457 **MASTER DARCY** (GB) 4
321 **MASTER FIDDLE** (GB) 96
583 **MASTER FLIGHT** (GB) 13
601 **MASTER LEON** (GB) 14
503 **MASTER MILAN** (IRE) 40
620 **MASTER MOON** (GB) 13
670 **MASTER MURPHY** (GB) 4
312 **MASTER NEO** (GB) 7
366 **MASTER OF AGES** (IRE) 108
525 **MASTER OF ARTS** (USA) 58
155 **MASTER OF DANCE** (IRE) 10
32 **MASTER OF DISGUISE** (GB) 9
60 **MASTER OF SONG** (GB) 9
321 **MASTER OF THE GAME** (IRE) 97
321 **MASTER OF THE HALL** (IRE) 98
650 **MASTER OF THE SEA** (IRE) 42
299 **MASTER OF WAR** (GB) 204
525 **MASTER OVERSEER** (IRE) 59
601 **MASTER ROONEY** (GB) 15
157 **MASTER SOMERVILLE** (GB) 16
88 **MASTER T** (USA) 1
62 **MASTER'N COMMANDER** (GB) 9
476 **MASTERFUL ACT** (USA) 45
624 **MASTEROFTHEBREE** (IRE) 7
49 **MASTEROFTHEROLLS** (GB) 42
572 **MASTERS BLAZING** (GB) 15
525 **MASTERS CLUB** (GB) 16
219 **MASTERSTROKE** (USA) 82
338 **MATA HARI BLUE** (GB) 8
588 **MATAAJIR** (GB) 12
516 **MATAALEB** (GB) 10
373 **MATAKO** (FR) 18
357 **MATAVIA BAY** (IRE) 7
697 **MATERIAL BOY** (GB) 15
87 **MATERIANA** (IRE) 2
388 **MATHEMATICIENNE** (IRE) 39
299 **MATIKANEHAMATADORI** (JPN) F 205
222 **MATILDA PEACE** (GB) F 13
145 **MATMATA DE TENDRON** (FR) 11
388 **MATREAS** (FR) 6
469 **MATROW'S LADY** (IRE) 26
264 **MATTORAL** (GB) 12
525 **MATUHI** (GB) 60
34 **MATURED** (GB) 31
628 **MAURI MOON** (GB) C 28
374 **MAURICETHEATHLETE** (IRE) 24
503 **MAURITION** (GER) 41
650 **MAVALENTA** (IRE) 43
201 **MAVEN** (GB) 37
34 **MAVERIK** (GB) 6
49 **MAWAARIK** (USA) C 136
360 **MAWAAKEF** (IRE) 22
191 **MAWAAL** (GB) 29
447 **MAWAARED** (GB) C 82

619 **MAWAQEET** (USA) 48
619 **MAWASEM** (GB) 49
207 **MAWJOODAH** (GB) 29
18 **MAWSEM** (IRE) 23
16 **MAX BYGRAVES** (GB) 25
21 **MAX LAURIE** (FR) 2
180 **MAXAMILLION BOUNTY** (GB) 14
279 **MAXIMIX** (GB) 6
124 **MAXIYOW** (IRE) 9
385 **MAY BE SOME TIME** (GB) 8
541 **MAY COURT** (GB) 5
511 **MAY DANCE** (FR) 111
310 **MAY DAY QUEEN** (IRE) F 26
529 **MAY FOX** (GB) F 42
653 **MAY'S BOY** (GB) 11
299 **MAYAAR** (USA) C 206
108 **MAYAN FLIGHT** (IRE) 24
201 **MAYBEAGREY** (GB) 89
483 **MAYBEESWAY** (GB) 6
97 **MAYBEME** (GB) 6
243 **MAYDREAM** (GB) 5
344 **MAYFORDE JACK** (GB) 21
15 **MAYOLYNN** (USA) 8
501 **MAYOMAN** (IRE) 24
158 **MAYOR OF KILCOCK** (GB) 1
481 **MAYSARAH** (IRE) F 20
220 **MAYSON** (GB) 22
217 **MAYTHETENTH** (IRE) 7
3 **MAYWOOD** (GB) 25
14 **MAZ** (GB) 7
628 **MAZAAYA** (USA) F 29
98 **MAZAGEE** (FR) 9
287 **MAZARAK** (IRE) 42
564 **MAZAYYEN** (GB) 54
654 **MAZEYDD** (GB) 52
325 **MAZIJ** (GB) 6
115 **MAZOVIAN** (USA) 9
153 **MCBIRNEY** (GB) 4
283 **MCCONNELL** (USA) 45
651 **MCCOOL BANNANAS** (GB) 4
237 **MCCROHAN** (IRE) 17
436 **MCMONAGLE** (USA) 7
359 **MCMURROUGH** (IRE) 20
149 **ME FEIN** (GB) 6
692 **ME JULIE** (GB) 3
287 **MEA PARVITAS** (IRE) 43
490 **MEADOW MIX** (GB) 8
629 **MEAN IT** (IRE) 13
219 **MEANDRE** (FR) 18
147 **MEASURE** (GB) F 93
180 **MECCA'S TEAM** (GB) 15
9 **MECOX BAY** (IRE) 21
35 **MECOX MEADOW** (USA) 41
366 **MEDAL OF VALOUR** (JPN) 25
307 **MEDAM** (GB) 9
619 **MEDDLING** (GB) 130
619 **MEDEA** (IRE) 50
380 **MEDERMIT** (FR) 66
285 **MEDHYAAR** (GB) 43
91 **MEDIA HYPE** (GB) 10
662 **MEDIA JURY** (GB) 5
365 **MEDIA STARS** (GB) 8
248 **MEDIC MAN** (IRE) 4
446 **MEDICAL CARD** (IRE) 51
249 **MEDICEAN MAN** (GB) 12
147 **MEDICI MUSIC** (GB) 46
201 **MEDICI TIME** (GB) 38
271 **MEDICINAL** (IRE) 3

534 **MEDICOE** (GB) 55
664 **MEDIEVAL BISHOP** (IRE) 21
380 **MEDINAS** (FR) 67
708 **MEDITATION** (GB) F 18
360 **MEDITERRANEAN SEA** (IRE) 23
259 **MEDLAUR** (GB) 27
214 **MEET JOE BLACK** (IRE) 57
469 **MEET ME AT DAWN** (GB) 27
666 **MEET ME HALFWAY** (GB) 43
531 **MEET THE CRITICS** (IRE) 14
447 **MEETING IN PARIS** (IRE) 83
296 **MEETINGS MAN** (IRE) 25
3 **MEEZNAH** (USA) 26
695 **MEGABILL** (IRE) 57
483 **MEGAGRACE** (GB) 7
71 **MEGALALA** (IRE) 9
408 **MEGALYPOS** (FR) 64
620 **MEGAMUNCH** (IRE) 14
19 **MEGAN'S MOTIVATOR** (GB) 19
460 **MEGASTAR** (GB) 59
65 **MEGASTYLE** (GB) 6
397 **MEGLIO ANCORA** (GB) 16
404 **MEGZZAMS BOY** (IRE) 28
447 **MEHDI** (IRE) 33
388 **MEHITABEL** (FR) 40
219 **MEI** (FR) 83
666 **MEIA NOITE** (GB) 8
401 **MEIRIG'S DREAM** (IRE) 6
150 **MEISTER ECKHART** (IRE) 17
713 **MEKONG MISS** (GB) 6
75 **MELANDRE** (GB) C 23
118 **MELANGE** (USA) 15
364 **MELATONINA** (IRE) C 36
388 **MELEAGROS** (IRE) 41
385 **MELLIFLUOUS** (IRE) F 21
304 **MELLIFONT ABBEY** (IRE) 4G
666 **MELLOR** (GB) 29
388 **MELODIQUE** (FR) 81
390 **MELODRAMA** (IRE) 14
390 **MELODRAMATIC** (IRE) C 36
272 **MELODY ISLAND** (IRE) F 15
366 **MELPOMENE** (GB) C 182
509 **MELROSE GOLD** (GB) 12
606 **MELUA MARIE** (GB) 27
19 **MELVIN THE GRATE** (IRE) 133
227 **MEMORABILIA** (GB) 15
158 **MEMORIES OF GOLD** (IRE) 2
665 **MEMORIZE** (IRE) 19
207 **MEMORY CLOTH** (GB) 30
214 **MEMPHIS MAN** (GB) 20
169 **MEN DON'T CRY** (IRE) 29
325 **MENADATI** (USA) 7
29 **MENARDAIS** (FR) 42
49 **MENDIP** (USA) 43
388 **MENEAS** (FR) 82
647 **MENEUR** (FR) 17
247 **MENHA** (GB) 4
388 **MENISKA** (FR) 43
597 **MENNETOU** (IRE) F 78
331 **MENORAH** (IRE) 52
699 **MENTALIST** (FR) 41
388 **MENYLLOS** (GB) 43
299 **MEON MIX** (GB) C 207
219 **MER DE CORAIL** (IRE) C 165
643 **MERAYAAT** (FR) F 61
705 **MERCERS ROW** (GB) 16
260 **MERCHANT OF DUBAI** (GB) 19
296 **MERCHANT OF MEDICI** (GB) 26

682 **MERCHANT ROYAL** (IRE) 10
262 **MERCURY BAY** (IRE) 13
111 **MEREVALE** (GB) 56
390 **MERIBEL** (USA) F 37
659 **MERIDIAN CITY** (IRE) 29
549 **MERIDIEM** (GB) 2
513 **MERIGO** (FR) 7
489 **MERRION SQUARE** (IRE) 65
241 **MERRION TIGER** (IRE) 10
662 **MERRJANAH** (GB) 6
266 **MERRY JAUNT** (USA) 79
503 **MERRY KING** (IRE) 42
669 **MERRY MINSTER** (GB) 3
556 **MERRYDOWN** (IRE) 23
343 **MERRYDOWN VINTAGE** (IRE) 35
299 **MESHARDAL** (GER) 208
58 **MESMERIZED** (GB) 70
664 **MESSINA** (IRE) G 24
59 **MESSIRE CHIPIE** (FR) 26
471 **METHAALY** (IRE) 13
74 **METHAYEL** (IRE) 5
90 **METROPOLITAN CHIEF** (GB) 1
219 **MEXICALI** (IRE) 19
215 **MEXICAN BOB** (GB) 8
628 **MEXICAN HAWK** (USA) C 30
35 **MEXICAN WAVE** (GB) 42
690 **MEY BLOSSOM** (GB) 4
237 **MEYDAN STYLE** (USA) 18
251 **MEZARAT** (ITY) 6
328 **MEZMAAR** (GB) 42
59 **MEZZANISI** (IRE) 17
512 **MEZZOTINT** (IRE) 42
511 **MEZZOTINTO** (FR) 20
220 **MFIFTYTHREE FORD** (IRE) 59
511 **MI AMOR** (SWI) 21
368 **MI MAN SAM** (IRE) 2
437 **MI REGALO** (GB) 7
447 **MIA MADONNA** (GB) 7
689 **MIA MATRIARCH** (GB) 10
197 **MIA'S BOY** (GB) 8
544 **MIAKORA** (GB) 3
91 **MIAMI GATOR** (IRE) 11
639 **MIBLEU** (IRE) 34
74 **MIBLISH** (GB) 45
160 **MIC'S DELIGHT** (IRE) 19
220 **MICA MIKA** (IRE) 23
27 **MICHAEL'S NOOK** (GB) 20
646 **MICHEAL FLIPS** (IRE) 8
489 **MICHEL LE BON** (FR) 66
266 **MICHELANGELO** (GB) 80
292 **MICHIGAN ASSASSIN** (FR) 2
571 **MICHIGAN D'ISOP** (FR) 2
408 **MICHTO** 15
107 **MICK SLATES** (IRE) 24
39 **MICK THE TOOTH** (IRE) 11
522 **MICK'S DANCER** (GB) 13
446 **MICKELSON** (IRE) 52
695 **MICKMACMAGOOLE** (IRE) 58
631 **MICKY MAC** (IRE) 5
698 **MICKY P** (GB) 8
283 **MICKY'S KNOCK OFF** (IRE) 46
19 **MICQUUS** (IRE) 71
268 **MICRO MISSION** (IRE) 22
403 **MICROLIGHT** (GB) 10
326 **MID DIV AND CREEP** (GB) 17
467 **MIDAS MOMENT** (GB) 6
113 **MIDAS WAY** (GB) 13
466 **MIDAZ** (GB) 77

490 **MIDDLEBROOK** (IRE) 9
450 **MIDDLETON FLYER** (IRE) 39
55 **MIDFIELD GENERAL** (IRE) 92
380 **MIDNIGHT APPEAL** (GB) 68
352 **MIDNIGHT BAHIA** (GB) 24
17 **MIDNIGHT CHARMER** (GB) 5
469 **MIDNIGHT CHASE** (GB) 28
215 **MIDNIGHT CHOICE** (GB) 9
535 **MIDNIGHT DOVE** (GB) 9
620 **MIDNIGHT DREAM** (FR) 15
364 **MIDNIGHT FEAST** (GB) 10
9 **MIDNIGHT FUN** (GB) 22
347 **MIDNIGHT GAMBLE** (GB) 20
473 **MIDNIGHT GAME** (GB) 60
16 **MIDNIGHT HAZE** (GB) 26
373 **MIDNIGHT LIRA** (GB) 19
681 **MIDNIGHT LOVER** (GB) G 37
660 **MIDNIGHT MACARENA** (GB) 18
76 **MIDNIGHT MAISIE** (GB) 5
201 **MIDNIGHT MARTINI** (GB) 39
339 **MIDNIGHT MINX** (GB) 13
183 **MIDNIGHT MIRACLE** (IRE) 61
682 **MIDNIGHT MUSIC** (IRE) 11
473 **MIDNIGHT OIL** (GB) 61
469 **MIDNIGHT OPERA** (GB) 29
16 **MIDNIGHT OSCAR** (IRE) 27
299 **MIDNIGHT PARTNER** (IRE) F 209
380 **MIDNIGHT PRAYER** (GB) 69
237 **MIDNIGHT RETURN** (IRE) 19
666 **MIDNIGHT RIDER** (IRE) 9
380 **MIDNIGHT SAIL** (GB) 70
53 **MIDNIGHT SEQUEL** (GB) 17
507 **MIDNIGHT SKY** (GB) C 43
57 **MIDNIGHT SPIRIT** (GB) 13
682 **MIDNIGHT THOUGHTS** (USA) 108
188 **MIDNIGHT TRYST** (GB) 16
525 **MIDNIGHT TUESDAY** (FR) 61
588 **MIDNITE MOTIVATION** (GB) 37
111 **MIDSUMMER** (GB) F 129
111 **MIDSUMMER SUN** (GB) 12
307 **MIEREVELD** (GB) 3
183 **MIEUXDARQUEJAMAIS** (FR) 44
472 **MIGHT AS WELL** (GB) 22
3 **MIGHTY AMBITION** (USA) 84
220 **MIGHTY CLARETS** (IRE) 24
640 **MIGHTY MAGNUS** (IRE) 13
326 **MIGHTY MAMBO** (GB) 18
160 **MIGHTY MONTY** (GB) 20
410 **MIGHTY MOTIVE** (GB) 2
394 **MIGHTY RIVER** (IRE) 16
657 **MIGHTY SNAZY** (GB) 47
111 **MIGHTY YAR** (IRE) 130
654 **MIJHAAR** (GB) 17
473 **MIKAEL D'HAGUENET** (FR) 62
191 **MIKDAAR** (IRE) 30
49 **MIKE'S WILDCAT** (USA) C 137
460 **MIKHAIL GLINKA** (IRE) 60
699 **MIKO DE BEAUCHENE** (FR) 42
262 **MILANEEN** (GB) 14
321 **MILANELLA** (IRE) 99
268 **MILANS MAN** (IRE) 23
531 **MILANS WELL** (IRE) 15
639 **MILARROW** (IRE) 35
600 **MILEDOUSHE** (FR) 42
593 **MILGEN BAY** (GB) 33
424 **MILITARY BOWL** (USA) 14
104 **MILITARY MAN** (GB) 9
200 **MILL END DANCER** (GB) 77

410 **MILL MICK** (GB) 10
386 **MILLERS GLEN** (IRE) 16
466 **MILLERS PUDSEY** (GB) 16
610 **MILLERS REEF** (IRE) 12
399 **MILLIBAR** (IRE) 10
331 **MILLIE O'BRIEN** (GB) 53
383 **MILLIEJANE** (GB) 11
564 **MILLION** (FR) 55
654 **MILLISTAR** (GB) F 129
593 **MILLY MALONE** (IRE) 34
141 **MILLY'S GIFT** (GB) 69
249 **MILLYANT** (GB) C 42
24 **MILLYMIX** (FR) G 30
200 **MILLYMONKIN** (GB) 60
394 **MILO MILAN** (IRE) 17
446 **MILT YARBERRY** (GB) 88
283 **MILTON OF CAMPSIE** (GB) 47
110 **MIMIS BONNET** (FR) G 13
654 **MIN BANAT ALREEH** (IRE) 53
29 **MINAKSHI** (FR) 7
569 **MINATLYA** F 121
119 **MINCE** (GB) 36
712 **MIND SHOWER** (IRE) 5
413 **MINDEN MARCH** (GB) 2
529 **MINDER** (GB) 12
217 **MINELLA BLISS** (IRE) 8
404 **MINELLA BOYS** (IRE) 29
321 **MINELLA CLASS** (IRE) 100
503 **MINELLA FOR STEAK** (IRE) 43
321 **MINELLA FORFITNESS** (IRE) 101
567 **MINELLA MISTAKE** (IRE) 16
322 **MINELLA SPECIAL** (IRE) 5
489 **MINELLA STARS** (IRE) 67
326 **MINELLA THEATRE** (IRE) 19
112 **MINETY LASS** (GB) 4
169 **MINGUN BELL** (USA) 18
636 **MINI BECK** (GB) 6
689 **MINI THE MINX** (IRE) 11
338 **MINI'S DESTINATION** (GB) 9
3 **MINIDRESS** (GB) 85
19 **MINIMISE RISK** (GB) 72
237 **MINISTEROFINTERIOR** (GB) 20
460 **MINISTRY** (GB) 61
100 **MINKIE MOON** (IRE) 7
80 **MINNE WA WA** (GB) 9
31 **MINNEAPOLIS** (GB) 7
681 **MINNIE O'GRADY** (IRE) G 38
619 **MINOAN DANCER** (IRE) 51
428 **MINOR CHORD** (GB) 3
619 **MINORITY INTEREST** (GB) 52
553 **MINORTRANSGRESSION** (USA) 7
343 **MINSK** (FR) 36
9 **MINSKY MINE** (IRE) 23
268 **MINSTER SHADOW** (GB) 24
360 **MINSTRELS GALLERY** (IRE) 45
569 **MINTLY FRESH** (USA) C 137
266 **MINWAH** (IRE) 81
299 **MIRAAJ** (IRE) 210
266 **MIRABILIS** (USA) F 137
55 **MIRACLE CURE** (IRE) 48
657 **MIRACLE HOUSE** (IRE) 49
141 **MIRACLE MAID** (GB) 46
193 **MIRACOLIA** (IRE) F 55
318 **MIRACOLO** (FR) 25
465 **MIRADANE** (GB) 16
178 **MIRAGE DORE** (FR) 13
424 **MIRIAM'S DREAM** (IRE) 15
385 **MIRIAM'S SONG** (GB) 16

626 **MIRIFIC** (FR) 10
29 **MIRINA** (FR) F 91
201 **MIRRORED** (GB) 40
614 **MISCHIEF N MAYHEM** (GB) 46
593 **MISCHIEVOUS MILLY** (GB) 35
299 **MISDEMEANOUR** (IRE) 77
57 **MISEFI** (GB) 14
573 **MISERE** (GB) 19
283 **MISERERE MEI** (IRE) 76
564 **MISFAAT** (USA) 56
74 **MISHHAR** (IRE) 46
360 **MISHRIF** (GB) 24
193 **MISK KHITAAM** (USA) 12
619 **MISLEADING LADY** (GB) C 131
29 **MISRAI** (IRE) 92
306 **MISRED MELISSA** (IRE) 31
579 **MISS ABBEY** (GB) 7
343 **MISS ACCURATE** (IRE) 37
35 **MISS AIX** (GB) 17
299 **MISS ASTRAGAL** (IRE) 78
597 **MISS AZEZA** (GB) 44
321 **MISS BALLANTYNE** (GB) 102
107 **MISS BEAT** (IRE) 12
111 **MISS BEATRIX** (GB) C 131
511 **MISS BESTSY** (IRE) 68
643 **MISS BLAKENEY** (GB) 35
30 **MISS BLINK** (GB) 10
711 **MISS BLOOM** (GB) 17
90 **MISS BOOTYLISHES** (GB) 2
444 **MISS BROWNES FANCY** (IRE) 10
19 **MISS CAP ESTEL** (GB) 73
282 **MISS CATO** (GB) 4
511 **MISS CATSY** (IRE) 22
447 **MISS COMPLEX** (GB) 34
499 **MISS CONCEPTION** (IRE) 16
612 **MISS CONDUCT** (GB) 15
299 **MISS CORINNE** (GB) C 211
643 **MISS DARLEY** (GB) 13
223 **MISS DASHWOOD** (GB) 36
494 **MISS DEEFIANT** (GB) 3
573 **MISS DELILA** (USA) F 97
55 **MISS DYLAN** (IRE) 43
55 **MISS EKATERINA** (IRE) 44
447 **MISS ELEGANCE** (GB) 8
690 **MISS ELLA JADE** (GB) 16
511 **MISS EMMA MAY** (IRE) F 112
380 **MISS EXHIBITIONIST** (GB) 71
454 **MISS FLEUR** (GB) 10
143 **MISS FLEURIE** (GB) F 5
566 **MISS FORTYWINKS** (GB) 7
482 **MISS HARRIET LEWIS** (GB) 7
15 **MISS HILTON** (GB) 9
681 **MISS HOLBECK GHYLL** (GB) 39
299 **MISS INDIGO** (GB) C 212
59 **MISS KALIFA** (IRE) 18
384 **MISS KINABALU** (GB) F 49
643 **MISS KINGWOOD** (GB) 14
625 **MISS LACEY** (IRE) 53
174 **MISS LADYBIRD** (USA) 23
700 **MISS LAMBRINI** (GB) F 38
700 **MISS LAMBRINI** (GB) G 32
146 **MISS LEGAL EAGLE** (IRE) 27
696 **MISS LUCKY PENNY** (GB) 29
657 **MISS MAYFAIR** (IRE) 49
266 **MISS MELTEMI** (IRE) C 138
442 **MISS METICULOUS** (GB) 30
610 **MISS MILBORNE** (GB) 13
651 **MISS MIRASOL** (GB) F 12

573 **MISS MISSION** (IRE) F 98
708 **MISS MOCCA** (GB) 23
174 **MISS MORN** (IRE) 24
499 **MISS NOMER** (IRE) 17
344 **MISS P** (GB) 11
266 **MISS PENTON** (GB) F 139
30 **MISS POLLY ANYA** (GB) 11
197 **MISS POLLY PLUM** (GB) 5
564 **MISS POST OFFICE** (FR) 57
274 **MISS POWDERKEG** (GB) 13
214 **MISS PURITY PINKER** (IRE) 58
266 **MISS QUEEN** (USA) C 140
294 **MISS ROYELLO** (GB) G 6
294 **MISS ROYELLO** (GB) F 9
299 **MISS SACHA** (IRE) C 213
248 **MISS SAFFRON** (GB) 5
299 **MISS SERENDIPITY** (IRE) F 214
249 **MISS SOCIALITE** (GB) 31
107 **MISS ST TROPEZ** (GB) C 29
353 **MISS SUNFLOWER** (GB) 5
333 **MISS TENACIOUS** (GB) 7
660 **MISS THEA** (GB) 19
699 **MISS TIQUE** (IRE) 43
193 **MISS TOPSY TURVY** (IRE) 13
353 **MISS TOSCA** (IRE) 6
496 **MISS UNIVERSITY** (USA) F 82
534 **MISS VISTAERO** (GB) 56
161 **MISS WELLS** (IRE) C 60
342 **MISS WHIPPY** (GB) 12
32 **MISSHOLLYGOLIGHTLY** (GB) 18
586 **MISSILE ATTACK** (IRE) 9
635 **MISSING YOU** (IRE) 9
503 **MISSION COMPLETE** (IRE) 44
661 **MISSION IMPOSSIBLE** (GB) 5
108 **MISSIONAIRE** (USA) 25
653 **MISSISH** G 12
366 **MISSISIPI STAR** (IRE) F 183
447 **MISSISSIPPI** (GB) 35
266 **MISSOURI BELLE** (GB) 82
454 **MISSTREE DANCER** (GB) 11
18 **MISSUS MILLS** (IRE) 47
657 **MIST THE BOAT** (GB) 50
610 **MISTA ROSSA** (GB) 14
55 **MISTEIREACH** (USA) 45
511 **MISTER BAWI** (FR) 113
334 **MISTER BLOOM** (IRE) 5
45 **MISTER BOB** (GER) 16
614 **MISTER CARTER** (IRE) 4
380 **MISTER CHANCER** (IRE) 72
321 **MISTER DILLON** (GB) 103
535 **MISTER FIZZ** (GB) 6
540 **MISTER FROSTY** (IRE) 3
234 **MISTER GREEN** (FR) 2
503 **MISTER HYDE** (IRE) 45
43 **MISTER MACKENZIE** (GB) 24
488 **MISTER MANANNAN** (IRE) 25
75 **MISTER MARCASITE** (GB) 24
556 **MISTER MARKER** (IRE) 24
451 **MISTER MUSICMASTER** (GB) 37
522 **MISTER NEWBY** (GB) 14
511 **MISTER RYAN** (FR) 69
185 **MISTER SNOWBALL** (FR) 9
380 **MISTER STICKLER** (GB) 73
600 **MISTER TEE** (FR) 43
536 **MISTER TWIRLEY** (IRE) 5
476 **MISTER WALL STREET** (FR) 46
312 **MISTER WISEMAN** (GB) 9
647 **MISTERAY** (GB) 30

625 **MISTIC SUN** (GB) G 59
434 **MISTOFFELEES** (GB) 84
480 **MISTRESS COOPER** (GB) F 32
180 **MISTRESS OF ROME** (GB) 33
299 **MISTRESS THAMES** (GB) C 215
605 **MISTY CLOUD** (GB) 5
116 **MISTY SECRET** (IRE) 28
192 **MITCH RAPP** (USA) 10
27 **MITCHELL** (GB) 49
625 **MITCHELL'S WAY** (GB) 25
27 **MITCHUM** (GB) 40
477 **MITIE MOUSE** (GB) 12
367 **MIX N MATCH** (GB) 6
284 **MIX N MATCH** (GB) 6
111 **MIXORA** (USA) 57
123 **MIXTURE** (GB) C 62
311 **MIYAJIMA** (GB) 6
287 **MIZANI** (IRE) 44
49 **MIZBAH** (GB) 100
49 **MIZWAAJ** (GB) 101
287 **MIZZAVA** (IRE) 62
86 **MIZZURKA** (GB) 14
34 **MME SANS GENE** (GB) 72
215 **MNARANI** (IRE) 10
12 **MO STOPHER** (GB) F 12
366 **MOATAZ** (USA) 109
451 **MOBAASHER** (USA) 11
117 **MOCENIGO** (IRE) 44
328 **MODEL PUPIL** (GB) 43
460 **MODERATOR** (GB) 114
569 **MODERN EAGLE** (GER) 123
3 **MODERN HISTORY** (IRE) 27
682 **MODERN ROMANCE** (IRE) 48
619 **MODERN TUTOR** (GB) 53
111 **MODESTA** (IRE) F 132
388 **MODESTIE** (FR) 83
29 **MODESTY'S WAY** (USA) 93
49 **MODEYRA** (GB) 44
254 **MODULE** (FR) 28
40 **MODUN** (GB) 45
456 **MOGHAAYER** (GB) 14
223 **MOHAIR** (GB) 37
684 **MOHANAD** (IRE) 14
180 **MOHAWK RIDGE** (GB) 16
503 **MOHAYER** (IRE) 46
147 **MOHEDIAN LADY** (IRE) 8
106 **MOHEEBB** (GB) 3
393 **MOHI RAHRERE** (IRE) 7
119 **MOIDORE** (GB) 37
3 **MOJAVE** (GB) 86
201 **MOJOLIKA** (GB) 41
193 **MOKARABA** (GB) F 56
654 **MOKBIL** (IRE) 54
614 **MOLDOWNEY** (GB) 21
160 **MOLESKIN** (IRE) 21
471 **MOLKO JACK** (FR) 14
366 **MOLL'S GAP** (GB) 110
597 **MOLLY BROWN** (GB) C 79
315 **MOLLY JONES** (GB) 10
119 **MOLLY MELLO** (GB) F 72
259 **MOLLY PITCHER** (IRE) C 46
516 **MOLLY PITCHER** (IRE) C 13
103 **MOLLY ROUND** (GB) 22
562 **MOLLYCARRS TOPCLIF** (GB) 2
562 **MOLLYCARRSBREKFAST** (GB) 3
124 **MOLLYOW** (IRE) 10
321 **MOLOTOF** (FR) 104
285 **MOMALORKA** (GB) 99

388 **MOMBAKA** (GB) 44
193 **MOMBASA** (GB) 57
467 **MOMENT IN THE SUN** (GB) 24
191 **MOMENT JUSTE** (GB) 3
19 **MOMENT OF TIME** (GB) 20
35 **MOMENTARY** (GB) 43
570 **MOMKINZAIN** (USA) 39
659 **MOMOTARO** (IRE) 30
299 **MON AMI JOLIE** (USA) 12
271 **MON CHEVALIER** (IRE) 4
657 **MON DESIR** (FR) 51
557 **MON HOMME** (GB) 3
699 **MON MOME** (FR) 44
489 **MON PARRAIN** (FR) 68
301 **MON ROMIER** (GB) 3
666 **MON VISAGE** (GB) 7
405 **MONADREEN DANCER** (GB) 6
227 **MONARCH'S WAY** (GB) 16
84 **MONASH LAD** (IRE) 2
118 **MONASHEE** (IRE) 16
113 **MONASHEE ROCK** (IRE) 14
446 **MONASTRELL** (GB) 53
390 **MONAWARA** (IRE) C 38
147 **MONAWER** (GB) 94
585 **MONBEG DUDE** (IRE) 19
569 **MONBLUE** (GB) 6
511 **MONDAY NIGHT** (SWI) 70
18 **MONDEGO** (GER) 24
193 **MONDSCHEIN** (GB) C 58
362 **MONESSA** (IRE) 21
129 **MONETS SECRET** (GB) 36
588 **MONEY BRIDGE** (GB) 13
423 **MONEY DIEU** (IRE) 2
451 **MONEY MONEY MONEY** (GB) 12
681 **MONEYMIX** (GB) 40
237 **MONICA GELLER** (GB) F 51
366 **MONICKER** (GB) 111
681 **MONKEY MILAN** (IRE) 41
446 **MONKSLAND** (IRE) 54
705 **MONKTON VALE** (IRE) 17
111 **MONNAVANNA** (GB) C 133
206 **MONNOW MADE** (IRE) 12
176 **MONNOYER** (GB) 22
321 **MONO MAN** (IRE) 105
268 **MONOCO MAN** (IRE) 25
635 **MONOGRAM** (GB) 10
34 **MONOPOLI** (GB) 32
408 **MONPILOU** (FR) 16
654 **MONROE** (GB) 55
52 **MONROE PARK** (IRE) 1
129 **MONS CALPE** (IRE) 3
619 **MONSHAK** (IRE) 54
480 **MONSIEUR BROUGHTON** (GB) 22
254 **MONSIEUR CADOU** (FR) 29
371 **MONSIEUR GEORGES** (FR) 10
360 **MONSIEUR JAMIE** (GB) 25
139 **MONSIEUR JOE** (IRE) 14
201 **MONSIEUR JOURDAIN** (FR) 42
30 **MONSIEUR PONTAVEN** (FR) 12
529 **MONSIEUR RIEUSSEC** (GB) 43
219 **MONST** (IRE) 34
387 **MONSTER MUNCHIE** (JPN) 5
219 **MONTAGNE MAGIQUE** (FR) C 166
136 **MONTAGNETTE** (GB) G 9
424 **MONTAN** (FR) 16
597 **MONTASER** (IRE) 45
380 **MONTBAZON** (FR) 74
219 **MONTCLAIR** (IRE) 167

601 **MONTE CASSINO** (IRE) 16
150 **MONTE CAVALLO** (SAF) 18
631 **MONTE PATTINO** (USA) 6
452 **MONTEREY** (IRE) 6
3 **MONTEROSSO** (GB) 28
122 **MONTEVETRO** (GB) 1
55 **MONTFERRAT** (IRE) 93
618 **MONTHLY MEDAL** (GB) 4
299 **MONTIRIDGE** (IRE) 216
268 **MONTOYA'S SON** (IRE) 26
366 **MONTPARNASSE** (IRE) 26
380 **MONTURGEON** (FR) 75
315 **MONTY FAY** (IRE) 11
374 **MONTY'S REVENGE** (IRE) 25
651 **MONUMENTAL MAN** (GB) 7
208 **MONYMUSK** (GB) 20
115 **MONZINO** (USA) 10
328 **MOODHILL** (GB) 44
467 **MOODY DANCER** (GB) 25
299 **MOODY MARGARET** (GB) F 217
357 **MOON CRYSTAL** (GB) F 30
262 **MOON DEVIL** (IRE) 15
659 **MOON INDIGO** (GB) 31
611 **MOON MELODY** (GER) 7
473 **MOON OVER MANDALAY** (GER) 63
420 **MOON OVER MIAMI** (GER) 26
34 **MOON PEARL** (USA) 33
569 **MOON QUADRILLE** (FR) 61
619 **MOON SEARCH** (GB) C 132
62 **MOON STREAM** (GB) 9
366 **MOON TRIP** (GB) 112
600 **MOON'S WHISPER** (USA) F 90
600 **MOONDAY SUN** (USA) 27
34 **MOON'S MY NAME** (GB) 7
266 **MOONGLOW** (GB) 83
338 **MOONLARK** (GB) 10
390 **MOONLIGHT DANCE** (USA) C 39
543 **MOONLIGHT DRIVE** (IRE) 19
254 **MOONLIGHT MAGGIE** (GB) 3
223 **MOONMAIDEN** (GB) C 62
123 **MOONSAIL** (USA) 39
682 **MOONSHED** (USA) 49
325 **MOONSHINE RUBY** (GB) 8
619 **MOONSHIP** (GB) 55
34 **MOONSTONE MAGIC** (GB) 34
527 **MOONSTREAKER** (GB) 5
299 **MOONVALE** (GB) 218
293 **MOONWIND** (IRE) 3
171 **MOOR HAMPSHIRE** (IRE) G 6
635 **MOOR RED** (GB) 11
711 **MOORGATE LASS** (GB) 9
373 **MOORLAND SUNSET** (GB) 20
159 **MOORLANDS JACK** (GB) 3
159 **MOORLANDS MIST** (GB) 4
220 **MOORSIDE MAGIC** (GB) 60
525 **MOOSE MORAN** (USA) 62
222 **MOOTABAR** (IRE) 4
417 **MORACHE MUSIC** (GB) 7
440 **MORAL ISSUE** (GB) 8
111 **MORALITY** (GB) C 37
111 **MORANT BAY** (IRE) 58
457 **MORAR** (GB) 5
654 **MORATAB** (IRE) 56
377 **MORCAT** (GB) F 8
699 **MORE BALLET MONEY** (GB) 45
629 **MORE BOTTLE** (IRE) 14
579 **MORE EQUITY** (GB) 8

69 **MORE FOR LESS** (GB) 8
439 **MORE SHENNANIGANS** (GB) 5
299 **MORE THAN WORDS** (IRE) 79
254 **MORENITO** (FR) 31
440 **MORERMALOKE** (GB) 7
531 **MORESTEAD** (IRE) 16
460 **MORESWEETS 'N LACE** (GB) 62
34 **MORETTA BLANCHE** (GB) 42
671 **MORGAN BE** (GB) 6
141 **MORILLES** (GB) 47
643 **MORINDA** (GB) 36
197 **MORMORAN** (GB) 9
673 **MORNA'S GLORY** (GB) 8
308 **MORNIN RESERVES** (GB) 6
364 **MORNING CALL** (GB) 19
266 **MORNING CHARM** (USA) 18
122 **MORNING FAREWELL** (GB) 2
15 **MORNING MOMENT** (GB) 10
237 **MORNING SUNSHINE** (IRE) 21
55 **MORNING WITH IVAN** (GB) 94
527 **MOROCCHIUS** (USA) 6
266 **MOROCCO** (GB) 84
526 **MOROCCO MOON** (GB) 10
3 **MORROW** (GB) 87
29 **MORTGA** (FR) 43
482 **MORTIMERS CROSS** (GB) 8
447 **MORTITIA** (GB) 9
509 **MOSA MINE** (GB) 13
254 **MOSCOW CHANCER** (IRE) 32
366 **MOSCOW CIRCUS** (IRE) 184
478 **MOSCOW IN APRIL** (IRE) 5
570 **MOSCOW MISCHIEF** (GB) 40
349 **MOSCOW MULE** (GB) 3
181 **MOSCOW OZNICK** (GB) 3
434 **MOSCOW PRESENTS** (IRE) 85
386 **MOSCOW RED** (IRE) 17
594 **MOSCOW SUMFINN** (IRE) 1
266 **MOSHAAGIB** (USA) 85
550 **MOSQUETA** (GB) 4
654 **MOSSBRAE** (GB) 57
460 **MOSSINI** (IRE) 63
321 **MOSSLEY** (IRE) 106
448 **MOSSMANN GORGE** (GB) 4
452 **MOSSTANG** 21
304 **MOSSTOWN** (IRE) 47
447 **MOST IMPROVED** (IRE) 36
331 **MOSTLY BOB** (IRE) 54
296 **MOTAFARRED** (IRE) 27
75 **MOTHER CORRIGAN** (IRE) C 25
576 **MOTHER JONES** (GB) 2
516 **MOTIRANI** (GB) 11
534 **MOTIVADO** (GB) 7
522 **MOTOU** (FR) 15
283 **MOTTLEY CREWE** (GB) 48
556 **MOUFATANGO** (FR) 25
699 **MOUJIK BORGET** (FR) 46
444 **MOULIN TOUR** (FR) 11
696 **MOUNT ABORA** (IRE) 30
219 **MOUNT ELBRUS** (GB) F 168
336 **MOUNT HOLLOW** (GB) 12
287 **MOUNT KLINOVEC** (IRE) F 63
147 **MOUNT MACEDON** (GB) 95
698 **MOUNT MAYDAY** (IRE) 19
433 **MOUNT MCLEOD** (IRE) 41
407 **MOUNT MERU** (GB) 27
639 **MOUNT OSCAR** (IRE) 36
18 **MOUNT ST MISTRESS** (GB) 48
300 **MOUNTAIN CAT** (IRE) 4

141 **MOUNTAIN CHAIN** (USA) F 70	102 **MRS HUFFEY** (GB) 35
434 **MOUNTAIN HIKER** (IRE) 86	572 **MRS KANNING** (GB) F 17
299 **MOUNTAIN HOLLY** (GB) F 219	666 **MRS KANNING** (GB) C 44
193 **MOUNTAIN RANGE** (IRE) 14	285 **MRS MARSH** (GB) C 100
610 **MOUNTAIN RETREAT** (IRE) 15	434 **MRS MCCLINTOCK** (IRE) G 88
460 **MOUNTAINEER** (FR) 64	711 **MRS MEDLEY** (GB) 10
650 **MOUNTAINOUS** (IRE) 44	626 **MRS PADDY JACK** (IRE) G 11
226 **MOUNTHENRY LADY** (IRE) G 16	657 **MRS PEACHEY** (IRE) 28
460 **MOUNTRATH** (GB) 65	657 **MRS PEACOCK** (IRE) 52
178 **MOUNTSKIP** (GB) 14	440 **MRS SNAFFLES** (IRE) F 15
473 **MOURAD** (IRE) 64	328 **MRS WARREN** (GB) 104
508 **MOURAMARA** (IRE) C 78	525 **MS CORDELIA** (USA) 64
433 **MOUSIE** (GB) 42	191 **MUARRAB** (GB) 31
339 **MOVE ALONG** (GB) 14	193 **MUBARAZA** (IRE) 40
55 **MOVE TO STRIKE** (IRE) 95	285 **MUBKERA** (IRE) C 101
295 **MOVING WINGS** (IRE) 4	499 **MUBROOK** (USA) 18
256 **MOY RIVER** (IRE) 12	597 **MUBTADI** (GB) 12
682 **MOY WATER** (IRE) F 109	654 **MUCH FASTER** (IRE) F 130
129 **MOYNAHAN** (USA) 4	466 **MUCH WANTS MORE** (IRE) 17
75 **MOZAYADA** (USA) 11	18 **MUCHMORDASH** (GB) 25
473 **MOZOLTOV** (GB) 65	198 **MUD MONKEY** (GB) 12
160 **MR BACHSTER** (IRE) 22	74 **MUDISH** (IRE) 17
639 **MR BINGLEY** (GB) 37	76 **MUDITA MOMENT** (IRE) 6
434 **MR CHIPPY** (IRE) 87	119 **MUFFLED** (USA) C 73
568 **MR CHOCOLATE DROP** (IRE) 6	450 **MUFTARRES** (IRE) 23
525 **MR CHOW** (GB) 63	191 **MUGAZALA** (IRE) 32
3 **MR CHURCHILL** (IRE) 88	49 **MUHAMEE** (IRE) 104
296 **MR CRYSTAL** (FR) 28	399 **MUHANDIS** (IRE) 5
507 **MR DAVID** (USA) 9	643 **MUHARRER** (GB) 37
600 **MR DOYEN** (GB) 12	447 **MUHDIQ** (IRE) 6
460 **MR FICKLE** (IRE) 115	446 **MUIRHEAD** (IRE) 55
597 **MR FONG** (GB) 46	573 **MUJA FAREWELL** (GB) C 99
363 **MR HENDRIX** (GB) 6	488 **MUJAADEL** (USA) 26
160 **MR HOOPER** (GB) 23	285 **MUJADORA** (IRE) 102
489 **MR HUDSON** (IRE) 69	631 **MUJAHOPE** (GB) 7
660 **MR JAY DEE** (GB) 20	643 **MUJANNAD** (IRE) 38
61 **MR KNIGHTLEY** (IRE) 27	285 **MUJANNADA** (USA) 44
615 **MR MALLO** (GB) 10	285 **MUKHADRAM** (GB) 45
494 **MR MANSSON** (IRE) 13	596 **MUKTARA** (IRE) 6
619 **MR MAYNARD** (GB) 56	283 **MUKTASB** (USA) 49
343 **MR MEANER** (GB) 38	245 **MULAAZEM** (GB) 2
489 **MR MOLE** (IRE) 7	643 **MULAQEN** (GB) 15
606 **MR MOONSHINE** (IRE) 28	253 **MULBERRY BRITE** (GB) 6
684 **MR MUDDLE** (GB) 15	16 **MULDOON'S PICNIC** (IRE) 29
498 **MR ONE TOO** (IRE) 18	116 **MULL OF KILLOUGH** (IRE) 7
102 **MR OPULENCE** (GB) 34	424 **MULLEADY** (IRE) 17
296 **MR PERCEPTIVE** (IRE) 29	344 **MULLINS WAY** (USA) 12
550 **MR PLOD** (GB) 5	357 **MULTI BLESSING** (GB) 15
552 **MR PUCK** (IRE) 28	266 **MULTICOLOUR WAVE** (IRE) F 141
529 **MR PYRAMUS** (GB) 13	520 **MULTILATERAL** (USA) 36
248 **MR REDWOOD** (GB) 6	417 **MULTIPLY** (GB) 14
380 **MR ROBERTO** (GB) 76	73 **MULTIPOWER** (GB) 30
157 **MR ROBINSON** (FR) 17	287 **MULTITASKING** (GB) 45
265 **MR ROCKNROLL** (GB) 11	619 **MUMAYEZA** (GB) F 133
635 **MR SHAHADY** (IRE) 12	59 **MUMBLES HEAD** (IRE) 19
625 **MR SINGLETON** (IRE) 26	570 **MUMGOS DEBUT** (IRE) 41
124 **MR SKIPITON** (IRE) 11	124 **MUMMYOW** (IRE) 13
664 **MR SNOOZY** (GB) 22	161 **MUNAAWASHAT** (IRE) F 61
231 **MR SYNTAX** (IRE) 6	276 **MUNAAWIB** (GB) 7
296 **MR TALLYMAN** (GB) 30	102 **MUNCHKIN** (GB) 6
522 **MR TINGLE** (GB) 16	401 **MUNICH** (IRE) 7
400 **MR UDAGAWA** (GB) 15	180 **MUNICIPAL** (IRE) 49
124 **MR WILLIS** (GB) 12	58 **MUNIFICENCE** (GB) 43
267 **MR WOODS** (GB) 5	569 **MUNK** (IRE) 7
73 **MRS AWKWARD** (GB) 29	591 **MUNLOCHY BAY** (GB) 7
407 **MRS BROWN** (GB) C 51	155 **MUNSARIM** (IRE) 11
384 **MRS CASH** (IRE) 26	682 **MUNTASAF** (IRE) 50
364 **MRS GREELEY** (GB) 11	

49 **MUNTASIR** (IRE) 103
619 **MUQANTARA** (USA) 57
685 **MURAAFIQ** (USA) 11
42 **MURCHAN HIGH** (IRE) 16
298 **MURCHU** (IRE) 8
655 **MUREEFA** (USA) F 21
367 **MURFREESBORO** (GB) 7
118 **MURKLE BOY** (GB) 17
681 **MURPHY'S CHOICE** (GB) 42
334 **MURRELL** (GB) 6
457 **MUSASHI** (IRE) 6
29 **MUSCAT** (GB) 44
321 **MUSH MIR** (IRE) 107
241 **MUSIC IN EXILE** (USA) F 18
174 **MUSIC IN THE AIR** (GB) 25
146 **MUSIC MAN** (IRE) 28
700 **MUSICAL BRIDGE** (GB) 17
328 **MUSICAL HORIZON** (USA) C 105
307 **MUSICAL LEAP** (GB) 6
307 **MUSICAL STRIKE** (GB) 10
198 **MUSICAL WEDGE** (GB) 13
75 **MUSICOLOGY** (USA) F 26
19 **MUSIKHANI** (GB) 134
102 **MUSKAT LINK** (GB) 53
666 **MUSKOKA DAWN** (USA) C 45
207 **MUSNAD** (GB) 31
285 **MUSSOORIE** (FR) C 103
364 **MUST BE ME** (GB) 37
155 **MUSTAFEED** (USA) 12
564 **MUSTAHEEL** (IRE) 58
451 **MUSTAJED** (GB) 13
654 **MUTAALEQ** (IRE) 58
266 **MUTAFAAKIR** (IRE) 86
169 **MUTANAKER** (GB) 19
643 **MUTANAWWER** (GB) 39
49 **MUTARJIM** (USA) 104
654 **MUTASADDER** (USA) 59
193 **MUTHABARA** (IRE) F 59
318 **MUTIN** (FR) 56
314 **MUTISKA** (IRE) 7
534 **MUTUAL REGARD** (IRE) 29
285 **MUWAKLEH** (GB) F 104
268 **MUWALLA** (GB) 27
662 **MUZDAAN** (IRE) 60
471 **MUZEY'S PRINCESS** (GB) 15
294 **MUZHIL** (IRE) 47
434 **MWALESHI** (GB) 89
407 **MY** (GB) F 52
108 **MY BEST MAN** (GB) 26
117 **MY BODY IS A CAGE** (IRE) 19
451 **MY BOY GINGER** (GB) 38
525 **MY BROTHER SYLVEST** (GB) 65
609 **MY BROTHERS WILL** (IRE) 4
226 **MY DELIGHT** (IRE) G 17
3 **MY DESTINATION** (IRE) 89
654 **MY DUBAI** (IRE) C 131
141 **MY ESPOIR** (GB) 48
408 **MY FAIR LADY** 65
662 **MY FAIR LILY** (GB) 7
448 **MY FAITHFUL ANNIE** (IRE) 5
463 **MY FARMER GIRL** (GB) 6
55 **MY FERE LADY** (USA) 46
360 **MY FLAME** (GB) 26
49 **MY FREEDOM** (IRE) 46
386 **MY FRIEND RIQUET** (FR) 18
505 **MY FRIEND SANDY** (GB) 4
488 **MY GACHO** (IRE) 27
714 **MY GRUNTER** (IRE) 6

642 **MY GUARDIAN ANGEL** (GB) 33
597 **MY HEART'S DEELITE** (USA) F 80
328 **MY HEARTS RACING** (IRE) 106
24 **MY IDEA** (GB) 15
254 **MY INHERITANCE** (IRE) 33
243 **MY JEANIE** (IRE) 6
696 **MY KINGDOM** (IRE) 31
49 **MY LEADER** (USA) 105
341 **MY LEGAL LADY** (GB) 4
306 **MY LORD** (GB) 16
111 **MY MARIAM** (GB) F 134
259 **MY MATE JAKE** (IRE) 6
108 **MY MATE LES** (GB) 27
616 **MY MATE MAL** (GB) 5
336 **MY MATE MAX** (GB) 13
503 **MY MATE VINNIE** (IRE) 47
326 **MY MATILDA** (GB) 20
485 **MY METEOR** (GB) 13
404 **MY MISS LUCY** (GB) 30
685 **MY MUM MO** (GB) 7
306 **MY NAME IS SAM** (GB) 7
273 **MY NEW ANGEL** (IRE) 13
110 **MY NOSY ROSY** (GB) 14
597 **MY OWN EYES** (IRE) 47
573 **MY PEARL** (IRE) 61
161 **MY PRETTY** (GB) 33
117 **MY PROPELLER** (IRE) 20
299 **MY QUEENIE** (GB) 80
110 **MY RENAISSANCE** (GB) 28
363 **MY SCAT DADDY** (USA) 7
384 **MY SHARONA** (GB) 27
186 **MY SILVER LILLY** (GB) 2
99 **MY SINGLE MALT** (IRE) 9
653 **MY SISTER** (GB) 13
589 **MY SPACE** (GB) 3
57 **MY SUMMER DAY** (GB) 15
321 **MY TENT OR YOURS** (IRE) 108
471 **MY TIME** (GB) 25
189 **MY UNCLE JACK** (GB) 6
504 **MY VIKING BAY** (IRE) 5
570 **MY ZEAL** (GB) 42
188 **MYANNE** (GB) 3
360 **MYBOYALFIE** (GB) 27
29 **MYCENAEAN** (USA) 45
38 **MYFOURTHBOY** (GB) 7
705 **MYJESTIC MELODY** (IRE) 18
517 **MYKIA** (GB) 3
654 **MYLINGTON MAID** (GB) 61
492 **MYLORD COLLONGES** (FR) 3
219 **MYPRECIOUSBLUE** (GB) 85
106 **MYRAID** (GB) 4
219 **MYRTLEWOOD** (IRE) 86
160 **MYSOCKS** (GB) 24
16 **MYSORTOFMAN** (GB) 30
299 **MYSTERIAL** (GB) 220
49 **MYSTERIAL** (USA) C 138
19 **MYSTERIOUS MAN** (IRE) 74
334 **MYSTERIOUS WORLD** (IRE) 7
219 **MYSTERIX** (IRE) F 169
642 **MYSTERY STAR** (IRE) 17
583 **MYSTIC APPEAL** (IRE) 14
304 **MYSTIC DESIR** (FR) 48
178 **MYSTIC ECHO** (GB) 15
35 **MYSTIC EDGE** (GB) 8
592 **MYSTIC HALO** (GB) 8
129 **MYSTIC MELODY** (IRE) 14
519 **MYSTICAL AYR** (IRE) C 24
299 **MYSTICAL MOMENT** (GB) 221

146 **MYSTICAL SAPPHIRE** (GB) 29
194 **MYSTICAL WITCH** (GB) 21
198 **MYSULA** (GB) 14
186 **MYTARA** (GB) 3
447 **MYTH AND MAGIC** (IRE) F 84
407 **MYTHICAL ECHO** (USA) C 53
326 **MZURI BAY** (GB) 21
169 **NAABEGHA** (GB) 20
241 **NAAFETHA** (IRE) 11
191 **NABAT SEIF** (USA) 65
254 **NACARAT** (FR) 34
200 **NACHO LIBRE** (GB) 30
604 **NADEEN** (IRE) 3
109 **NADEMA ROSE** (IRE) 14
321 **NADIYA DE LA VEGA** (FR) 109
654 **NADMAH** (GB) 132
471 **NAFA** (IRE) 16
573 **NAGHAM** (IRE) 62
699 **NAGPUR** (FR) 47
540 **NAHEELL** (GB) 4
659 **NAHNEH** (IRE) 32
654 **NAHRAIN** (GB) 18
476 **NAIAD DU MISSELOT** (FR) 47
29 **NAISSANCE ROYALE** (IRE) C 94
617 **NAJLAA** (GB) 16
74 **NAJRAAN** (GB) 18
634 **NAKURU BREEZE** (IRE) 17
538 **NALEDI** (GB) 7
3 **NAMECHECK** (GER) 29
8 **NAMED AFTER NINA** (GB) 15
200 **NAMEITWHATYOULIKE** (GB) 61
215 **NAMIR** (IRE) 11
639 **NAMPOUR** (FR) 38
260 **NAMWAHJOBO** (IRE) 20
226 **NANCYMAR** (GB) G 18
148 **NANCYS BRIDGE** (IRE) G 3
192 **NANDO'S DREAM** (GB) F 26
237 **NANI JANI** (GB) 42
662 **NANT SAESON** (IRE) 11
511 **NANTY** F 114
390 **NANTYGLO** (GB) F 40
55 **NAOISE** (IRE) 5
161 **NAOMI WILDMAN** (GB) C 62
34 **NAPOLEON'S MUSE** (IRE) 35
365 **NAPOLETANO** (ITY) 9
191 **NARCISSIST** (GB) 33
147 **NARGYS** (IRE) 96
111 **NARLA** (GB) 59
569 **NARMINA** (IRE) F 124
219 **NARUKO** (USA) 87
573 **NASHARRA** (IRE) 20
564 **NASHEED** (USA) C 91
628 **NASIJ** (USA) F 31
488 **NASRI** (GB) 28
387 **NASSAU STORM** (GB) 24
614 **NASSMA** (IRE) F 47
164 **NATAANI** (IRE) 7
299 **NATAGORA** (FR) F 222
19 **NATASHA ROSTOVA** (GB) 75
266 **NATHANIEL** (IRE) 19
55 **NATIONAL FIBRE** (IRE) 47
366 **NATIONAL HERO** (IRE) 113
18 **NATIONAL HOPE** (IRE) 26
321 **NATIVE BEAUTY** (GB) 110
331 **NATIVE BREEZE** (IRE) 55
185 **NATIVE BRIAN** (IRE) 10
654 **NATIVE COLONY** (GB) 19
171 **NATIVE GALLERY** (IRE) 7

508 **NATIVE KHAN** (FR) 6
672 **NATIVE OPTIMIST** (IRE) 6
304 **NATIVE PALM** (IRE) 49
59 **NATURAL ACTION** (GB) 20
111 **NATURAL BLOOM** (GB) 60
553 **NATURAL HIGH** (GB) 8
607 **NATURAL SPRING** (GB) 8
329 **NAUGHTICAL** (GB) 14
57 **NAUGHTY NELL** (GB) F 19
285 **NAUSICAA** (USA) F 105
124 **NAVAHO SPIRIT** (GB) 21
357 **NAVAJO CHARM** (GB) 16
357 **NAVAJO CHIEF** (GB) 8
601 **NAVAJO NIGHTS** (GB) 71
706 **NAVAL DISPATCH** (GB) G 13
219 **NAVARRE** (GB) 88
597 **NAVE** (USA) 13
597 **NAVIGATION TRACK** (GB) 14
570 **NAVY LIST** (FR) 43
193 **NAWWAAR** (USA) 41
511 **NAXXOS** (FR) 71
466 **NAZREEF** (GB) 18
619 **NAZYM** (IRE) 134
151 **NEAR GERMANY** (IRE) 7
567 **NEAR THE WATER** (IRE) 17
150 **NEARBY** (GB) 19
424 **NEAREST THE PIN** (IRE) 18
201 **NEARLY A GIFT** (IRE) 90
344 **NEARLY A MILDRED** (GB) F 13
162 **NEARLY DECENT** (GB) F 3
433 **NEAT SWEEP** (IRE) 20
682 **NEBRAAS** (GB) F 110
191 **NEBRASKA LADY** (IRE) C 34
682 **NEBRASKA TORNADO** (USA) F 111
184 **NECESSITY** (GB) 7
619 **NECKLACE** (GB) C 135
446 **NED BUNTLINE** (GB) 56
705 **NEDRICO** (GB) 19
191 **NEEDLES AND PINS** (IRE) F 66
143 **NEEDWOOD PARK** (GB) 3
592 **NEEDWOOD RIDGE** (GB) 9
648 **NEEDY MCCREDIE** (GB) 1
664 **NEFELI** (IRE) F 25
191 **NEGIN** (GB) 35
476 **NEGUS DE BEAUMONT** (FR) 48
266 **NEHAAM** (GB) 20
534 **NEIGE D'ANTAN** (GB) 30
215 **NEIGHBOURHOOD** (USA) 12
139 **NELINA** (GB) 30
259 **NELLA SOFIA** (GB) 7
366 **NELLIE BLY** (GB) 185
19 **NELLIE FORBUSH** (GB) 135
511 **NELLIE GWYN** (GB) F 115
570 **NELLIEDONETHAT** (IRE) 44
356 **NELSON DU RONCERAY** (FR) 4
447 **NELSON'S BAY** (GB) 38
153 **NELSON'S BOUNTY** (GB) 5
321 **NELSON'S BRIDGE** (IRE) 111
198 **NELTARA** (GB) 15
160 **NEMETAN** (FR) 25
118 **NEMI** (CZE) 18
497 **NEMO SPIRIT** (IRE) 4
653 **NEMOROSA** (GB) F 34
18 **NENGE MBOKO** (GB) 69
95 **NEOPHILIA** (IRE) 96
304 **NEPALI PRINCESS** (IRE) 95
489 **NEPTUNE COLLONGES** (FR) 71
207 **NEPTUNE EQUESTER** (GB) 32

366 **NEPTUNE'S BRIDE** (USA) C 186
614 **NERO EMPEROR** (IRE) 22
29 **NERVI** (FR) 95
462 **NESAAH'S PRINCESS** (GB) C 34
49 **NESHLA** (GB) C 139
397 **NESNAAS** (USA) 17
496 **NET WHIZZ** (USA) 33
460 **NETHERBY** (GB) 66
299 **NETLEY MARSH** (GB) 81
636 **NETMINDER** (IRE) 7
655 **NETTIE** (GB) 14
418 **NEUILLY** (GB) 8
410 **NEUTRAFA** (IRE) 11
203 **NEVAEH** (GB) 12
19 **NEVER A DOUBT** (GB) F 136
219 **NEVER ANOTHER** (USA) 89
328 **NEVER AWAY** (GB) F 107
507 **NEVER CAN TELL** (IRE) 10
619 **NEVER FOREVER** (GB) 58
38 **NEVER IN** (IRE) 12
366 **NEVER IS A PROMISE** (USA) C 187
629 **NEVER PERFECT** (IRE) 15
609 **NEVER ROAM** (IRE) 5
328 **NEVER SATISFIED** (GB) 45
8 **NEVILLE WOODS** (GB) 16
185 **NEW CHRISTMAS** (USA) 11
460 **NEW CODE** (GB) 67
366 **NEW DECADE** (GB) 114
19 **NEW FFOREST** (GB) 137
447 **NEW HAVENS** (GB) F 85
665 **NEW LEYF** (IRE) 3
520 **NEW ORDER** (GB) F 61
80 **NEW PEARL** (IRE) 20
682 **NEW PHASE** (IRE) 12
543 **NEW PLANET** (IRE) 20
55 **NEW REGALIA** (GB) 97
180 **NEW RICH** (GB) 50
99 **NEW ROMANTIC** (GB) 22
227 **NEW YEAR'S EVE** (GB) 17
14 **NEWBY LODGE** (IRE) 8
516 **NEWINGTON** (GB) 14
469 **NEWMANS BOY** (GB) 30
562 **NEWNHAM FLYER** (IRE) 4
119 **NEWNTON LODGE** (GB) 38
543 **NEWPORT ARCH** (GB) 21
55 **NEWS AT SIX** (IRE) 98
446 **NEWS CARVER** (IRE) 57
266 **NEWS DESK** (GB) 87
674 **NEWSDAY** (IRE) 1
659 **NEWSPAGE** (IRE) 33
404 **NEWTON TONIC** (GB) 31
678 **NEWYEARSRESOLUTION** (IRE) 7
299 **NEXT CRY** (USA) 82
66 **NEXT EDITION** (IRE) 2
420 **NEXT HIGHT** (GB) 27
380 **NEXT MAN IN** (IRE) 77
556 **NEXT TO NOWHERE** (IRE) 26
450 **NEZAMI** (IRE) 24
366 **NEZHENKA** (GB) 27
124 **NGINA** (GB) 14
9 **NHA TRANG** (IRE) 24
588 **NIALLY NOO** (GB) 14
142 **NIALLY NOO** (GB) 6
397 **NIBANI** (IRE) 18
192 **NIC NOK** (GB) 11
318 **NICE ASSOCIATION** (FR) 8
511 **NICE MATIN** (USA) C 116
366 **NICE ROSE** (GB) 115

249 **NICE STYLE** (IRE) 13
588 **NICE TUNE** (GB) F 43
256 **NICEBOY** (IRE) 13
34 **NICEOFYOUTOTELLME** (GB) 36
699 **NICEONEFRANKIE** (GB) 48
702 **NICEONEMYSON** (GB) 6
489 **NICHE MARKET** (IRE) 72
665 **NICHOLASCOPERNICUS** (IRE) 7
287 **NICK'S NIKITA** (IRE) F 64
601 **NICKEL SILVER** (GB) 4
266 **NICKELS AND DIMES** (IRE) 142
174 **NICKS POWER** (IRE) 26
504 **NICKY NUTJOB** (GER) 6
660 **NICOLA BELLA** (IRE) F 30
511 **NICOLE** (FR) 23
160 **NICTO DE BEAUCHENE** (FR) 26
191 **NIDHAAL** (IRE) F 67
496 **NIGER** (IRE) 34
486 **NIGHT ALLIANCE** (IRE) 8
141 **NIGHT AND DANCE** (IRE) 15
19 **NIGHT CARNATION** (GB) 21
259 **NIGHT FLASH** (GB) 28
219 **NIGHT GARDEN** (USA) 90
84 **NIGHT GROOVE** (IRE) 3
552 **NIGHT IN MILAN** (IRE) 29
55 **NIGHT INVADER** (IRE) 48
153 **NIGHT LILY** (IRE) 6
299 **NIGHT OF JOY** (IRE) C 223
200 **NIGHT OWL** (GB) C 78
115 **NIGHT REVELLER** (IRE) 11
380 **NIGHT ROSE** (GB) 78
511 **NIGHT SERENADE** (IRE) 24
306 **NIGHT TRADE** (IRE) 17
511 **NIGHT WAVE** (FR) 72
358 **NIGHT'S WATCH** (GB) 34
511 **NIGHTDANCE SUN** (GER) F 117
422 **NIHAL** (IRE) F 31
142 **NIKNAD** (GB) 18
650 **NIKOLA** (FR) 45
682 **NILE VENTURE** (GB) 51
600 **NILSON** (GER) 28
119 **NIMBLE THIMBLE** (USA) 39
29 **NIMBUS STAR** (GB) 46
366 **NIMIETY** (GB) 116
141 **NINA ROSE** (GB) 55
283 **NINE BEFORE TEN** (IRE) 50
476 **NINE DE SIVOLA** (FR) 49
285 **NINE REALMS** (GB) 46
268 **NINE STORIES** (IRE) 28
124 **NINE TO FIVE** (GB) F 15
58 **NINER'S HOME** (USA) C 71
72 **NINFEA** (IRE) 9
511 **NINNARELLA** (FR) 73
358 **NIP AND TUCK** (GB) 23
495 **NIPPY NIKKI** (GB) 7
240 **NISAAL** (IRE) 3
318 **NITZA** (FR) 9
76 **NO BUTS** (GB) 8
237 **NO COMEBACKS** (GB) G 43
237 **NO COMEBACKS** (GB) F 52
466 **NO COMPROMISE** (GB) 48
9 **NO DIAMOND** (GB) 25
259 **NO DOMINION** (IRE) 29
157 **NO DUFFER** (GB) 18
19 **NO FRILLS** (IRE) C 138
597 **NO HERETIC** (GB) 15
390 **NO JET LAG** (USA) 41
666 **NO JUSTICE** (GB) 11

353 **NO LADY** (GB) 7
102 **NO LARKING** (IRE) 15
489 **NO LOOSE CHANGE** (IRE) 73
450 **NO MEAN TRICK** (USA) 25
110 **NO MORE TROUBLE** (GB) G 15
404 **NO NO BINGO** (IRE) 32
542 **NO PLAN B** (IRE) 19
606 **NO PLANNING** (GB) 29
201 **NO POPPY** (IRE) 43
603 **NO PRINCIPLES** (GB) 5
304 **NO PROBLEM** (GB) 107
119 **NO QUEST** (IRE) C 74
642 **NO RULES** (GB) 18
525 **NO SECRETS** (IRE) 66
380 **NO SUBSTITUTE** (IRE) 79
585 **NO THROUGH ROAD** (GB) 20
188 **NO TIME TO CRY** (GB) 17
507 **NO TIME TO LOSE** (GB) 25
614 **NO WAY** (IRE) F 48
617 **NO WAY HOZAY** (GB) 17
608 **NOAKARAD DE VERZEE** (FR) 5
219 **NOBILIS** (GB) 91
556 **NOBLE ALAN** (GER) 27
99 **NOBLE ATTITUDE** (GB) 10
328 **NOBLE BULL** (IRE) 108
340 **NOBLE CHIC** (GB) 7
597 **NOBLE CITIZEN** (USA) 16
394 **NOBLE CRUSADER** (USA) 18
285 **NOBLE DEED** (GB) 106
436 **NOBLE FOUR** (IRE) 8
193 **NOBLE GIFT** (GB) 60
15 **NOBLE LEGEND** (GB) 11
111 **NOBLE MISSION** (GB) 61
329 **NOBLE PEARL** (GER) F 38
707 **NOBLE PERK** (GB) 3
625 **NOBLE SCHOLAR** (GB) 27
660 **NOBLE SILK** (GB) 8
442 **NOBLE STORM** (USA) 5
63 **NOBLE TIGER** (IRE) G 6
527 **NOBLE WITNESS** (IRE) 7
516 **NOBODY LOVES ME** (GB) 15
699 **NOBUNAGA** (GB) 49
450 **NOCTILUCENT** (JPN) F 46
496 **NOCTURN** (GB) 35
363 **NOCTURNAL LADY** (GB) F 8
689 **NODDA HIGH KID** (GB) 12
254 **NODEBATEABOUTIT** (GB) 35
434 **NODFORM RICHARD** (GB) 90
441 **NODFORMS VIOLET** (IRE) 9
496 **NOGUCHI** (IRE) 6
659 **NOIR ANGELIS** (GB) 34
489 **NOLAND** (GB) 74
511 **NOLAS LOLLY** (IRE) F 118
283 **NOLECCE** (GB) 51
29 **NOLENE** (FR) 96
171 **NOM DE GUERRE** (IRE) 8
271 **NOMAD** (FR) 5
345 **NOMADIC FAITH** (GB) 2
338 **NOMADIC WARRIOR** (GB) 11
256 **NOMECHEKI** (FR) 14
257 **NOMOREBLONDES** (GB) 26
466 **NON DOM** (IRE) 19
629 **NONSENSE** (IRE) F 20
508 **NOOR AL WATAN** (GB) 79
108 **NOOR EL HOUDAH** (IRE) F 55
204 **NOOR EL HOUDAH** (IRE) C 13
511 **NOOR FOREVER** (FR) F 119
34 **NOOSA BOY** (GB) 37

419 **NORAS FANCY** (IRE) 9
194 **NORCROFT** (GB) 9
418 **NORDIC LIGHT** (USA) 9
666 **NORFOLK SKY** (GB) 30
367 **NORISAN** (GB) 8
34 **NORLANDER** (GB) 38
59 **NORMALLY** (GB) 9
564 **NORMAN STORM** (FR) 92
491 **NORMINSTER** (GB) 6
127 **NORPHIN** (GB) 18
384 **NORSE BLUES** (GB) 6
56 **NORSE KING** (FR) 27
208 **NORSE SONG** (GB) 21
56 **NORSE WARRIOR** (FR) 7
688 **NORTH BROOK** (IRE) 13
397 **NORTH CAPE** (USA) 19
246 **NORTH LONDON** (GB) 10
534 **NORTH POLE** (GB) 57
16 **NORTH STACK** (GB) 31
299 **NORTH STAR BOY** (IRE) 83
63 **NORTHERN ACRES** (GB) 7
4 **NORTHERN FLAME** (IRE) 10
9 **NORTHERN GENES** (AUS) 26
525 **NORTHERN JEM** (GB) 67
619 **NORTHERN MEETING** (IRE) 136
49 **NORTHERN MELODY** (GB) C 140
407 **NORTHERN MISCHIEF** (USA) C 54
19 **NORTHERN OUTLOOK** (GB) 76
184 **NORTHERN SPY** (USA) 8
161 **NORTHERN STAR** (IRE) 63
61 **NORTHERN TERRITORY** (IRE) 28
625 **NORTHSIDE PRINCE** (IRE) 28
69 **NORTHUMBERLAND** (GB) 9
375 **NORTHWOLD** (GB) 7
661 **NORTON GIRL** (GB) 6
214 **NORVILLE** (IRE) 21
511 **NORWEGIAN LADY** (FR) 74
320 **NORWOOD LANE** (GB) 10
420 **NOSECOND CHANCE** (IRE) 28
488 **NOSEDIVE** (GB) 29
299 **NOT BAD FOR A BOY** (IRE) 84
276 **NOT MY CHOICE** (IRE) 5
19 **NOT RIGG** (USA) 139
700 **NOT SO GENEROUS** (IRE) C 39
331 **NOT SO PRUDENT** (IRE) 56
18 **NOT SO SURE DICK** (IRE) 27
360 **NOT TIL MONDAY** (IRE) 28
184 **NOTABADGIRL** (GB) 21
184 **NOTABADLAD** (GB) 9
682 **NOTABLE GRADUATE** (IRE) 13
89 **NOTABOTHERONME** (IRE) 7
583 **NOTARFBAD** (GB) 15
408 **NOTARIO HAS** (FR) 66
284 **NOTCANTDOIT** (IRE) 7
253 **NOTHING PERSONAL** (GB) 7
510 **NOTHING'S SIMPLE** (GB) 9
526 **NOTHINGBUTTHETRUTH** (IRE) 5
75 **NOTJUSTAPRETTYFACE** (USA) F 27
57 **NOTNOWIVORHEADACHE** (GB) 20
462 **NOTNOWSTANLEY** (GB) 17
511 **NOTTINGHAM ROAD** (FR) 75
525 **NOTUS DE LA TOUR** (FR) 68
336 **NOUAILHAS** (GB) 14
242 **NOUNOU** (GB) 2
133 **NOUS VOILA** (IRE) 7
366 **NOVA CYNGI** (USA) C 188
564 **NOVA KEDIET** (USA) 10
73 **NOVA NIMPH** (GB) 31

331 **NOVA SAM** (FR) 57
564 **NOVA VALOREM** (IRE) 11
469 **NOVABRIDGE** (GB) 31
30 **NOVALIST** (GB) 13
555 **NOVEL DANCER** (GB) 7
111 **NOVELLARA** (GB) C 135
480 **NOVELLEN LAD** (IRE) 23
219 **NOVELTY SEEKER** (USA) 92
306 **NOVERRE TO GO** (IRE) 18
214 **NOVIKOV** (GB) 22
223 **NOVIRAK** (IRE) 13
451 **NOW** (GB) 14
366 **NOW IT BEGINS** (GB) C 189
677 **NOW THEN SAM** (GB) 3
123 **NOW WE CAN** (GB) 40
529 **NOW WHAT** (GB) 14
434 **NOWURHURLIN** (IRE) 91
299 **NOYELLES** (IRE) F 224
166 **NOZIC** (FR) 14
654 **NSX** (GB) C 62
573 **NSX** (GB) C 100
154 **NUBA** (IRE) 5
214 **NUBAR BOY** (GB) 23
614 **NUBAR LADY** (IRE) C 49
650 **NUDGE AND NURDLE** (IRE) 46
658 **NUGGET** (FR) 29
626 **NUISANCE** (GB) 12
511 **NUIT D'ETE** (GER) 25
383 **NUMBER ONE GUY** (GB) 12
338 **NUMBER THEORY** (GB) 12
531 **NUMBERCRUNCHER** (IRE) 17
299 **NUMERAL** (IRE) 13
56 **NUMEROLOGIE** (FR) 10
463 **NUMEROLOGY** (FR) 7
45 **NUMERUS CLAUSUS** (FR) C 24
451 **NUMIDE** (FR) 15
283 **NURSE DOMINATRIX** (IRE) 77
436 **NUTAKOVA** (GB) 9
388 **NUTELLO** (USA) 45
331 **NUTIN FANCY** (IRE) 58
570 **NUTS N BOLTS** (GB) 45
388 **NYMFIA** (FR) 7
111 **NYRAMBA** (GB) C 136
6 **O CROTAIGH** (IRE) 6
384 **O MA LAD** (IRE) 7
607 **O MALLEY'S OSCAR** (IRE) 9
217 **OAK LEAVES** (GB) 9
188 **OAKBROOK** (GB) 18
552 **OAKLANDS ELISE** (GB) 30
289 **OAKWELL** (IRE) 3
534 **OASIS CANNES** (GB) 58
34 **OASIS DANCER** (GB) 9
321 **OASIS KNIGHT** (IRE) 112
366 **OASIS LOVE** (IRE) 117
19 **OASIS SPIRIT** (GB) 140
80 **OATCAKE** (GB) C 21
130 **OBLIGADA** (IRE) 6
19 **OBLIGE** (GB) F 141
387 **OBLITEREIGHT** (IRE) 25
529 **OBSCURITY** (IRE) 15
298 **OBSESSION** (GB) 20
4 **OCARINA** (FR) 11
52 **OCCASIONALLY YOURS** (IRE) 2
572 **OCEAN BAY** (GB) 8
611 **OCEAN BLUFF** (GB) 8
108 **OCEAN COUNTESS** (IRE) 28
108 **OCEAN LEGEND** (IRE) 29

529 **OCEAN MYTH** (GB) 31
572 **OCEAN TEMPEST** (GB) 18
147 **OCEAN VIEW** (USA) C 97
3 **OCEAN WAR** (GB) 30
572 **OCEAN'S MINSTREL** (GB) 9
19 **OCEANA DREAMER** (IRE) 77
391 **OCEANA GOLD** (GB) 40
219 **OCEANLINER** (USA) 170
572 **OCEANS DESTINATION** (GB) 10
366 **OCEANWAY** (USA) 28
476 **OCKEY DE NEULLIAC** (FR) 50
171 **OCULIST** (GB) 9
628 **ODABELLA'S CHARM** (GB) F 32
208 **ODABELLA'S CHARM** (GB) G 22
700 **ODD BALL** (IRE) 18
24 **ODDSMAKER** (IRE) 16
180 **ODDYSEY** (IRE) 34
208 **ODIN** (IRE) 6
658 **ODIT** (GER) 50
637 **OENOLOGUE** (FR) 12
357 **OETZI** (GB) 9
201 **OFF CAMERA** (GB) C 118
201 **OFF CHANCE** (GB) 44
357 **OFF MESSAGE** (IRE) C 31
391 **OFF THE GROUND** (IRE) 41
531 **OFFBEAT SAFARIS** (IRE) 18
553 **OFFICER IN COMMAND** (USA) 9
250 **OFFICIALLY MODERN** (IRE) 8
68 **OFFICIER DE RESERVE** (FR) 7
58 **OGARITMO** (GB) 44
561 **OGEE** (GB) 8
456 **OH BOY OH BOY** (GB) 23
380 **OH CRICK** (FR) 80
333 **OH DEAR OH DEAR** (GB) 8
480 **OH FOR SURE** (IRE) 30
569 **OH LADY BE GOOD** (FR) 62
141 **OH MY DAYS** (IRE) 17
696 **OH NO NOT HARRY** (FR) 32
56 **OH OH** (FR) 11
579 **OH RIGHT** (IRE) 9
570 **OH SO BEAUTIFUL** (IRE) 46
407 **OH SO LUCY** (IRE) 28
458 **OH SO QUAINT** (IRE) 25
647 **OH SO ROSIE** (IRE) F 31
666 **OH SO SASSY** (GB) 46
666 **OH SO SPICY** (GB) 12
639 **OHIO GOLD** (IRE) 39
167 **OHMS LAW** (GB) 1
5 **OICHE GHEALAI** (IRE) 49
200 **OIL STRIKE** (GB) 31
5 **OILINDA** (GB) 84
639 **OISEAU DE NUIT** (FR) 40
505 **OKAFRANCA** (IRE) 5
3 **OKIMONO** (GB) 90
642 **OLD BOY TED** (GB) 19
256 **OLD DREAMS** (IRE) 7
223 **OLD HUNDRED** (IRE) 14
395 **OLD MAGIC** (GB) 12
209 **OLD SI** (IRE) 2
101 **OLD STYLE** (IRE) 22
201 **OLD TESTAMENT** (GB) 45
643 **OLD TIMES SAKE** (TUR) 40
639 **OLD TRICKS** (IRE) 41
699 **OLD WAY** (IRE) 50
150 **OLD WIGMORE** (GB) 20
331 **OLDRIK** (GB) 59
516 **OLIMAMU** (IRE) 12
305 **OLIVER'S GOLD** (GB) 1

646 **OLIVIA'S LAD** (GB) 16
161 **OLLIANNA** (IRE) 13
91 **OLLON** (USA) 12
254 **OLOFI** (FR) 36
682 **OLYMPIAD** (IRE) 14
449 **OLYMPIAN** (FR) 3
395 **OLYMPIAN BOY** (IRE) 13
471 **OLYNARD** (IRE) 17
388 **OLYNTHOS** (IRE) 8
511 **OMANA** (FR) 76
441 **OMANI REBEL** (GB) 10
19 **OMAR KHAYYAM** (GB) 78
561 **OMARURU** (GB) 9
29 **OMBRIE** (GB) F 97
442 **OMEGA CENTAURI** (GB) 6
656 **OMID** (GB) 7
564 **OMINOUS** (GB) 59
184 **OMMADAWN** (IRE) F 24
313 **OMMEGA** (FR) 4
434 **OMOKOROA** (IRE) 92
10 **ON BORROWED WINGS** (IRE) 11
476 **ON GOSSAMER WINGS** (IRE) 51
473 **ON HIS OWN** (IRE) 66
525 **ON KHEE** (GB) 69
699 **ON MY LIVING LIFE** (IRE) 51
226 **ON MY OWN** (IRE) 19
643 **ON MY OWN** (TUR) 41
315 **ON POINT** (GB) F 14
51 **ON THE BRIDGE** (IRE) 4
200 **ON THE BRINK** (GB) F 79
254 **ON THE CASE** (GB) 37
283 **ON THE CUSP** (IRE) 52
451 **ON THE FEATHER** (IRE) 16
200 **ON THE HOOF** (GB) 62
254 **ON THE MONEY** (GB) 38
614 **ON THE NILE** (IRE) F 50
551 **ON THE RAZ** (GB) 3
476 **ON THE RIGHT PATH** (GB) 52
642 **ON THE ROCKS** (GB) 34
256 **ON TREND** (IRE) 16
446 **ON YOUR EOIN** (IRE) 58
333 **ON YOUR MAX** (GB) 9
613 **ONCEAPONATIME** (IRE) 5
322 **ONCLE KID** (FR) 6
287 **ONDEAFEARS** (IRE) 17
219 **ONDOYANTE** (IRE) 93
312 **ONE AND ALL** (IRE) 10
71 **ONE COOL CHICK** (GB) 10
247 **ONE COOL DANCER** (IRE) 11
658 **ONE DAY SHADOW** (GER) 51
304 **ONE FINE DAY** (IRE) 96
556 **ONE FOR HARRY** (IRE) 28
556 **ONE FOR HOCKY** (IRE) 29
233 **ONE FOR JOULES** (IRE) 10
434 **ONE FOR LOU** (GB) 93
201 **ONE FOR LUCK** (GB) 46
35 **ONE KOOL DUDE** (GB) 44
333 **ONE LAST DREAM** (GB) 13
321 **ONE LUCKY LADY** (GB) 113
38 **ONE MORE CENT** (GB) 8
374 **ONE MORE COOKIE** (IRE) 26
280 **ONE MORE DINAR** (FR) 1
462 **ONE MORE ROMAN** (IRE) 18
376 **ONE MORE ROMAN** (IRE) 12
200 **ONE OF TWINS** (GB) 32
488 **ONE PURSUIT** (IRE) 30
634 **ONE ROSE** (GB) C 18
336 **ONE SCOOP OR TWO** (GB) 15

49 **ONE SO MARVELLOUS** (GB) C 141
390 **ONE SO WONDERFUL** (GB) C 42
150 **ONE TERM** (IRE) 21
214 **ONE WAY OR ANOTHER** (AUS) 24
328 **ONE WORD MORE** (IRE) 109
363 **ONEIRIC** (GB) 5
80 **ONELADYOWNER** (GB) 6
625 **ONEOFAPEAR** (IRE) 29
645 **ONERTOTHER** (IRE) 7
153 **ONGOODFORM** (IRE) 7
662 **ONIZ TIPTOES** (IRE) 8
219 **ONLY A PLEASURE** (IRE) 94
296 **ONLY A ROUND** (IRE) 48
270 **ONLY EXCEPTION** (IRE) 20
79 **ONLY FOR YOU** (GB) 10
42 **ONLY HOPE** (IRE) 17
296 **ONLY ORSENFOOLSIES** (GB) 49
360 **ONLY TEN PER CENT** (IRE) 29
476 **ONLY THE BEST** (GB) 53
322 **ONLY VINTAGE** (USA) 7
197 **ONLY WITNESS** (IRE) 19
194 **ONWARD** (GB) 6
194 **ONWARDS'N'UPWARDS** (GB) 10
654 **OOJOOBA** (GB) 64
344 **OOLALA LADY** (IRE) 14
259 **OOMPH** (GB) C 47
433 **OPEN COUNTRY** (IRE) 21
218 **OPEN DE L'ISLE** (IRE) 16
321 **OPEN HEARTED** (GB) 114
19 **OPEN WATER** (IRE) 79
489 **OPENING BATSMAN** (IRE) 75
203 **OPENING CEREMONY** (USA) C 15
223 **OPENLY** (GB) 38
614 **OPENNESS** (GB) C 51
643 **OPERA BOX** (IRE) 16
384 **OPERA BUFF** (GB) 28
299 **OPERA FLUTE** (IRE) 85
19 **OPERA GAL** (IRE) 22
629 **OPERA NORTH** (GB) 7
699 **OPERA OG** (IRE) 52
199 **OPERA PRINCE** (GB) 5
188 **OPERA RIDGE** (IRE) F 35
310 **OPERATEUR** (IRE) 9
31 **OPERATING** (IRE) 50
35 **OPERATION TRACER** (GB) 45
531 **OPHELIA'S KISS** (GB) 20
619 **OPINION** (IRE) 59
3 **OPINION POLL** (IRE) 31
219 **OPPOSITE** (IRE) 95
92 **OPTIMISTIC DUKE** (IRE) 6
575 **OPTION MONEY** (GB) 5
520 **OPUS** (IRE) 37
58 **OPUS CACTUS** (USA) 72
182 **OPUS MAXIMUS** (IRE) 11
476 **OR D'OUDAIRIES** (FR) 54
63 **OR DE GRUGY** (FR) 8
472 **OR SING ABOUT** (FR) 23
226 **ORAN FLYER** (IRE) 20
349 **ORANG OUTAN** (FR) 4
699 **ORANGE GIZMO** (IRE) 53
110 **ORANGEADAY** (IRE) 16
384 **ORATORIAN** (FR) 29
300 **ORATORY** (IRE) 5
180 **ORBIT THE MOON** (IRE) 17
646 **ORCHARD ROAD** (USA) 9
33 **ORDELIA** (GB) 14
658 **ORDENSRITTER** (GER) 30

364 **ORDERS FROM ROME** (IRE) 20
157 **ORDRE DE BATAILLE** (FR) 19
29 **ORELLANA** (USA) C 98
388 **ORFNEA** (FR) 46
458 **ORGANISEDCONFUSION** (IRE) 17
601 **ORIANE** (GB) C 72
699 **ORIENTAL CAT** (GB) 54
87 **ORIENTAL CAVALIER** (GB) 3
49 **ORIENTAL DANCE** (GB) C 142
358 **ORIENTAL SCOT** (GB) 7
446 **ORIGINAL OPTION** (IRE) 59
650 **ORIGINAL PRANKSTER** (IRE) 47
572 **ORINOCCO** (GB) 19
248 **ORION EXPRESS** (GB) 7
511 **ORION LOVE** (GB) 120
511 **ORION MOON** (FR) 77
228 **ORLA** (FR) 9
358 **ORLENA** (USA) G 8
434 **ORLITTLEBYLITTLE** (GB) 94
564 **ORMEL** (GB) 60
471 **ORPEN BID** (IRE) 18
115 **ORPEN WIDE** (IRE) 12
243 **ORPEN'ARRY** (IRE) 2
221 **ORPENS PEACH** (IRE) 3
106 **ORPSIE BOY** (IRE) 5
369 **ORREZZO** (GER) 1
604 **ORSIPPUS** (USA) 4
457 **ORSM** (GB) 7
299 **ORTACK ROCK** (IRE) 86
214 **ORTEA** (GB) 19
137 **ORTEGA** (FR) 5
169 **ORTHODOX LAD** (GB) 21
483 **ORVITA** (FR) 8
693 **ORWELLIAN** (GB) 7
447 **ORWELLIAN** (GB) 39
460 **ORZARE** (IRE) 68
499 **OSANA** (FR) 19
3 **OSCAN** (USA) 91
279 **OSCAR BABY** (IRE) 7
40 **OSCAR BERNADOTTE** (GB) 10
322 **OSCAR CHARLIE** (IRE) 8
18 **OSCAR CLOSE** (IRE) 28
424 **OSCAR DAN DAN** (IRE) 19
331 **OSCAR DAVY** (IRE) 60
344 **OSCAR FLYER** (IRE) 15
298 **OSCAR GALE** (IRE) 21
695 **OSCAR GOGO** (IRE) 59
321 **OSCAR NOMINEE** (IRE) 115
256 **OSCAR PAPA** (GB) 17
396 **OSCAR RAINBOW** (GB) 6
201 **OSCAR ROMEO** (IRE) 47
657 **OSCAR SIERRA** (IRE) 53
178 **OSCAR STANLEY** (IRE) 16
695 **OSCAR SUNSET** (IRE) 60
344 **OSCAR TANNER** (IRE) 16
174 **OSCAR TOM** (IRE) 27
321 **OSCAR WHISKY** (IRE) 116
16 **OSCAR'S SECRET** (IRE) 32
321 **OSCARA DARA** (IRE) 117
489 **OSCARGO** (IRE) 76
360 **OSCARS JOURNEY** (GB) 49
304 **OSCARS WELL** (IRE) 51
489 **OSCARSLAD** (IRE) 77
569 **OSCEOLA** (IRE) 63
113 **OSIRIS WAY** (GB) 15
424 **OSIRIXAMIX** (IRE) 20
264 **OSMOSIA** (FR) 13
658 **OSORIOS TRIAL** (GER) 31

321 **OSRIC** (IRE) 118
80 **OSSIANA** (IRE) C 22
9 **OSSIE ARDILES** (IRE) 27
139 **OSSIE'S DANCER** (GB) 23
632 **OSTENTATION** (GB) 5
180 **OSTEOPATHIC REMEDY** (IRE) 18
314 **OSTJESSY** (IRE) F 12
404 **OSTLAND** (GER) 33
654 **OSUS** (USA) 65
663 **OTAGE DE BRION** (FR) 5
116 **OTTAVINO** (IRE) 23
583 **OTTER MIST** (GB) 16
659 **OTTO QUERCUS** (FR) 35
321 **OTTO THE GREAT** (FR) 119
117 **OTTO THE GREAT** (FR) 21
408 **OTTOSTAR** 67
476 **OUEST ECLAIR** (FR) 55
191 **OUIJA BOARD** (GB) F 68
192 **OULIANOVSK** (IRE) C 27
395 **OUMEYADE** (FR) 14
460 **OUR COOL CAT** (IRE) 116
73 **OUR EM** (GB) 17
525 **OUR FATHER** (IRE) 70
384 **OUR FAYE** (GB) C 50
385 **OUR FOLLY** (GB) 9
542 **OUR GAL** (GB) 9
653 **OUR GOLDEN BOY** (IRE) 14
79 **OUR GOLDEN BOY** (IRE) 7
657 **OUR ISLAND** (GB) 54
9 **OUR IVOR** (GB) 46
220 **OUR JOE MAC** (IRE) 25
573 **OUR JONATHAN** (GB) 21
517 **OUR MATE JOE** (IRE) 4
434 **OUR MICK** (GB) 95
473 **OUR MONTY** (IRE) 67
192 **OUR PHYLLI VERA** (IRE) 12
555 **OUR PLAY** (IRE) 3
588 **OUR PRINCESS ELLIE** (USA) 15
447 **OUR SHEILA** (GB) C 86
98 **OUR VINNIE** (IRE) 10
557 **OURS** (FR) 11
695 **OURSININLAW** (IRE) 61
147 **OUT DO** (GB) 47
499 **OUT NOW** (IRE) 20
682 **OUT OF REACH** (GB) C 112
184 **OUT OF THE STORM** (GB) 10
508 **OUT OF TIME** (FR) F 80
188 **OUTBACK** (IRE) 19
570 **OUTLAW TOM** (IRE) 47
283 **OUTLAW TORN** (IRE) 78
14 **OUTPOST** (IRE) 9
331 **OUTRAGEOUS REQUEST** (GB) 61
308 **OUTSIDE ART** (GB) 18
199 **OUTSIDE THE BOX** (GB) 6
391 **OUZBECK** (FR) 42
520 **OVATORY** (GB) 62
334 **OVER AND ABOVE** (IRE) 8
715 **OVER THE CLYDE** (GB) 5
352 **OVER THE LIMIT** (IRE) F 25
454 **OVER THE RUBICON** (IRE) 12
434 **OVERAFRICA** (IRE) 96
359 **OVERBRANCH** (GB) 21
131 **OVERLADY** (GB) 4
502 **OVERLAY** (GB) 3
254 **OVERNIGHT FAME** (IRE) 39
436 **OVERNOVA** (IRE) 10
24 **OVERPRICED** (GB) 17
207 **OVERRULE** (USA) 34

539 **OVERTON LAD** (GB) 3
434 **OVERTURN** (IRE) 97
550 **OVERWHELM** (GB) 6
139 **OVERWING** (IRE) C 31
268 **OVERYOU** (GB) 29
321 **OWEN GLENDOWER** (IRE) 120
264 **OWNER OCCUPIER** (GB) 14
3 **OXBOW** (FR) 92
415 **OXFORD CHARLEY** (USA) 7
321 **OZETA** (FR) 121
34 **PABUSAR** (GB) 10
593 **PACCO** (FR) 36
682 **PACELLI ROAD** (IRE) 52
53 **PACHA D'OUDAIRIES** (FR) 8
489 **PACHA DU POLDER** (FR) 78
74 **PACHANGA** (GB) F 65
526 **PACIFIC HEIGHTS** (IRE) 11
3 **PACIFIC ISLANDS** (IRE) 93
569 **PACIFIQUE** (IRE) 8
124 **PACK OF CARDS** (IRE) 22
55 **PACK THE PUNCH** (IRE) 99
543 **PACQUIAO** (IRE) 48
223 **PAD THE WALLET** (USA) C 63
17 **PADDLEYOUROWNCANOE** (IRE) 6
657 **PADDY PARTRIDGE** (GB) 55
287 **PADDY THE CELEB** (IRE) 18
455 **PADDY THE YANK** (IRE) 8
329 **PADDYFROMMENLO** (IRE) 15
131 **PADDYS UNYOKE** (IRE) 5
318 **PADINA** C 10
481 **PADOVA** (GB) 4
416 **PADRE ETERNO** (GB) 5
299 **PAELLA** (IRE) 225
55 **PAENE MAGNUS** (IRE) 50
686 **PAGE** (GB) C 26
511 **PAGERA** (IRE) 26
108 **PAHENTE** (GB) 30
597 **PAINT THE TOWN** (IRE) C 81
404 **PAINTBALL** (IRE) 34
434 **PAINTED SKY** (GB) 98
625 **PAINTED TAIL** (IRE) 30
525 **PAINTER MAN** (IRE) 71
191 **PAIRUMANN PRINCESS** (IRE) C 69
522 **PAK JACK** (IRE) 17
503 **PALACE JESTER** (GB) 48
387 **PALACE MOON** (GB) 6
508 **PALACE OF WINDS** (IRE) 81
619 **PALACE WEEKEND** (USA) C 137
3 **PALADIN** (FR) 94
299 **PALAIS GLIDE** (GB) 14
418 **PALANOUR** (FR) 10
19 **PALATINE DANCER** (IRE) C 142
543 **PALAWI** (IRE) 22
266 **PALAZZO BIANCO** (GB) 21
682 **PALE MIMOSA** (IRE) 53
214 **PALE ORCHID** (GB) 60
256 **PALE RIDER** (IRE) 18
355 **PALISANDRA** (USA) F 10
534 **PALLASATOR** (GB) 31
390 **PALMERAIE** (USA) C 43
266 **PALMETTE** (GB) 88
61 **PALOMA'S PRINCE** (IRE) 29
526 **PALOS CONTI** (FR) 6
117 **PALUS SAN MARCO** (IRE) 22
228 **PALWINA** (FR) 5
334 **PAMAK D'AIRY** (FR) 9
434 **PAMPANITO** (GB) 99
404 **PAMPELONNE** (IRE) 35

332 **PAMPERED MOLLY** (IRE) G 16
208 **PAN GALACTIC** (USA) C 38
699 **PANAMA PETRUS** (FR) 55
29 **PANAMAX** (IRE) 47
100 **PANASHKA** (IRE) 8
388 **PANCORBO** (USA) 47
446 **PANDORAMA** (IRE) 60
400 **PANDORICA** (GB) 16
658 **PANESIDORA** (GER) 61
654 **PANETTONE** (IRE) 66
123 **PANFILO** (GB) 9
460 **PANJO BERE** (FR) 69
511 **PANTHEOR** (FR) 78
316 **PANTHERS RUN** (GB) 4
550 **PANTS** (GB) F 13
380 **PANTXOA** (FR) 81
266 **PANZANELLA** (GB) 89
606 **PAPA CARUSO** (GB) 30
360 **PAPAGENO** (GB) 30
4 **PAPAMOA** (GB) 12
440 **PAPARAAZI** (IRE) 8
508 **PAPAYA** (GB) 82
452 **PAPERETTO** (GB) 7
698 **PAPHOS** (GB) 9
268 **PAPILLON PARC** (GB) 30
650 **PAPRADON** (GB) 48
43 **PAQUITA** (IRE) C 43
700 **PARA SIEMPRE** (GB) C 40
304 **PARADIS DE THAIX** (FR) 52
657 **PARADISE EXPECTED** (GB) 56
34 **PARADISE ISLE** (USA) F 73
415 **PARADISE SEA** (GB) 8
91 **PARADISE SPECTRE** (GB) 13
285 **PARAKOPI** (IRE) C 107
111 **PARALLAX** (IRE) 137
29 **PARAMITA** (FR) 48
147 **PARAMYTHI** (IRE) 85
109 **PARANDIH** (USA) 15
629 **PARC DE LAUNAY** (GB) 16
556 **PARC DES PRINCES** (USA) 30
402 **PARCHMENT** (IRE) 2
517 **PARDOVEN** (IRE) 12
569 **PAREO** (FR) 9
315 **PARHELION** (GB) 6
256 **PARIGINO** (FR) 19
462 **PARIS GLORY** (USA) C 35
285 **PARIS ROSE** (GB) 108
55 **PARISH HALL** (IRE) 51
466 **PARISIAN PRINCESS** (IRE) 49
573 **PARISIAN PYRAMID** (IRE) 22
488 **PARK'S GIRL** (GB) C 66
569 **PARKER RIDGE** (FR) 125
614 **PARKERS MILL** (IRE) 5
336 **PARKSIDE PROSPECT** (GB) F 42
617 **PARKY** (IRE) 18
29 **PARLE MOI** (IRE) 99
366 **PARLEY** (USA) 118
3 **PARLOUR GAMES** (GB) 32
39 **PARNELL STREET** (IRE) 65
19 **PARQUE ATLANTICO** (GB) 80
304 **PARRAMATTA** (IRE) 53
254 **PARSNIP PETE** (GB) 40
494 **PARSON'S PUNCH** (GB) 14
446 **PARSONS PISTOL** (IRE) 61
499 **PARTHIAN EMPIRE** (GB) 21
714 **PARTICIPATION** (GB) 7
573 **PARTNER** (IRE) 23
469 **PARTY CHARMER** (GB) G 32

366 **PARTY LINE** (GB) 119
341 **PARTY PALACE** (GB) 5
117 **PARVENUE** (FR) F 45
24 **PAS TROP TARD** (FR) 18
529 **PASAKA BOY** (GB) 44
256 **PASCHA BERE** (FR) 24
489 **PASCO** (SWI) 79
607 **PASS ME BY** (GB) 10
517 **PASS MUSTER** (GB) 5
458 **PASS THE HAT** (GB) 18
511 **PASSAGE DU CAIRE** (FR) 121
111 **PASSAGE OF TIME** (GB) C 138
473 **PASSAGE VENDOME** (FR) 68
511 **PASSARINHO** (IRE) 79
164 **PASSATO** (GER) 8
56 **PASSING CLOUD** (FR) 12
80 **PASSING HOUR** (USA) C 23
32 **PASSING MOMENT** (GB) 19
111 **PASSING PARADE** (GB) 139
226 **PASSING THROUGH** (GB) 21
387 **PASSION PLAY** (GB) 7
511 **PASSIOR** (FR) 80
567 **PASTORAL JET** (GB) 18
466 **PASTORAL PLAYER** (GB) 20
241 **PASTORAL PREY** (GB) 19
74 **PASTORAL PRIDE** (GB) 19
446 **PAT GARRETT** (IRE) 62
161 **PATACAKE PATACAKE** (USA) F 64
600 **PATAGONIA** (FR) 13
644 **PATAVIUM** (IRE) 7
146 **PATAVIUM PRINCE** (IRE) 7
588 **PATCH PATCH** (GB) 16
331 **PATEESE** (FR) 62
266 **PATEGONIA** (GB) 90
336 **PATH FINDER** (FR) 36
564 **PATH OF HOPE** (USA) 61
564 **PATH OF JUSTICE** (USA) 62
564 **PATH OF LIFE** (USA) 63
194 **PATIENCE** (GB) 11
224 **PATRICIAS PRIDE** (IRE) 1
194 **PATRICK DEE** (GB) 12
55 **PATRIMONIUM** (IRE) 52
197 **PATRIOTIC** (IRE) 7
380 **PATSY FINNEGAN** (GB) 82
223 **PATTIMECH** (USA) C 64
394 **PAUL REVERE** (IRE) 19
391 **PAUSE AND CLAUSE** (IRE) 43
283 **PAVEMENT GAMES** (GB) 53
705 **PAVERS STAR** (GB) 28
219 **PAVIE** (USA) 20
331 **PAVILLON BLEU** (FR) 63
658 **PAWELLA** (GER) F 62
285 **PAWPRINTS** (IRE) 47
147 **PAY THE BANK** C 98
94 **PAYBACK** (GB) 13
619 **PAYPHONE** (GB) F 138
569 **PAZARI** (FR) 64
407 **PC HENRY** (GB) 29
573 **PEA SHOOTER** (GB) 63
251 **PEACE CORPS** (GB) 7
56 **PEACE KEEPER** (FR) 13
109 **PEACE SEEKER** (GB) 7
266 **PEACE TIME** (GER) F 143
364 **PEACE TREATY** (GB) 38
511 **PEACEFUL LOVE** (GB) 12
646 **PEACEFUL RIVER** (IRE) G 10
556 **PEACHEY MOMENT** (USA) 31
397 **PEACHEZ** (GB) 20

542 **PEADAR MIGUEL** (GB) 10
407 **PEAK MARIA'S WAY** (USA) C 55
115 **PEAK SEASONS** (IRE) 13
657 **PEAKS OF FIRE** (IRE) 57
299 **PEARL ACCLAIM** (IRE) 226
534 **PEARL ANGEL** (IRE) 59
648 **PEARL BELL** (IRE) 87
666 **PEARL BLUE** (IRE) 13
19 **PEARL BOUNTY** (IRE) 143
34 **PEARL BRIDGE** (GB) 74
19 **PEARL CASTLE** (IRE) 144
201 **PEARL CATCHER** (GB) 91
117 **PEARL DIVA** (IRE) 23
34 **PEARL FROST** (GB) 39
34 **PEARL MIX** (IRE) 40
27 **PEARL NOTE** (GB) 50
127 **PEARL OPERA** (GB) 5
573 **PEARL RANSOM** (IRE) 101
698 **PEARL REBEL** (GB) 20
29 **PEARL REWARD** (USA) 29
80 **PEARL SEA** (IRE) 24
27 **PEARL SECRET** (GB) 41
534 **PEARL SPICE** (IRE) 60
102 **PEARL STREET** (USA) 54
489 **PEARL SWAN** (IRE) 80
417 **PEARL TRADER** (FR) C 21
285 **PEARL WAR** (USA) 48
129 **PEARLFIELDS** (IRE) 8
129 **PEARLS FROM SYDNEY** (GB) 15
564 **PEARLS OR PASSION** 64
564 **PEARLY AVENUE** (GB) 93
157 **PEARLYSTEPS** (GB) 20
201 **PEAU DOUCE** (FR) 65
201 **PEBBLEGLEN** (IRE) 48
614 **PECTIN** (FR) 9
434 **PEDDLERS CROSS** (IRE) 100
223 **PEDIMENT** (GB) C 65
501 **PEEDEEQUE** (GB) 25
650 **PEG LEG** (GB) 49
552 **PEGASUS PRINCE** (USA) 31
304 **PEGGARTY** (USA) 54
229 **PEHERA BOY** (GB) 3
401 **PEINTRE DU ROI** (USA) 8
569 **PEINTURE ABSTRAITE** (GB) 10
654 **PEKAN STAR** (GB) 23
473 **PEKING TO PARIS** (IRE) 69
509 **PELHAM CRESCENT** (IRE) 14
597 **PELICAN BAY** (GB) 82
161 **PELICAN ROCK** (GB) 34
318 **PEMBINA** (IRE) 26
3 **PEMBREY** (GB) 95
671 **PEN GWEN** (FR) 7
55 **PEN TO PAPER** (IRE) 100
570 **PENA DORADA** (IRE) 48
214 **PENANG CINTA** (GB) 25
328 **PENANG PEARL** (FR) F 110
286 **PENANGDOUBLE O ONE** (GB) 11
399 **PENBRYN** (USA) 6
602 **PENDERYN** (GB) 4
73 **PENDLE LADY** (IRE) 32
284 **PENDOUN** (GB) 8
207 **PENDRAGON** (USA) 35
695 **PENELOPE PIPS** (GB) 62
219 **PENGLAN PAVILION** (USA) 171
34 **PENINSULA** (GB) 41
501 **PENITENT** (GB) 26
400 **PENN DA BENN** (FR) 17
380 **PENNANT PRINCESS** (GB) G 83

256 **PENNEYROSE BAY** (GB) G 21
614 **PENNISTON LINE** (IRE) 23
328 **PENNY CROSS** (GB) F 111
148 **PENNY FARTHING** (GB) F 4
542 **PENNY HA'PENNY** (GB) C 25
391 **PENNY MAX** (GB) 44
552 **PENNYS PRIDE** (IRE) F 32
213 **PENNYWEIGHT** (GB) 22
59 **PENSION PLAN** (GB) 22
344 **PENSNETT BAY** (GB) 17
520 **PENTAMETER** (GB) 38
699 **PENTIFFIC** (NZ) 56
479 **PENTON HOOK** (GB) 13
416 **PEPELINA** (IRE) 6
699 **PEPITE ROSE** (FR) 57
457 **PEPITO COLLONGES** (FR) 8
460 **PEPLUM** (FR) 70
417 **PEPONI** (GB) 8
466 **PEPPERMINT GREEN** (GB) F 78
198 **PEQENO DIABLO** (IRE) 16
134 **PEQUENITA** (GB) G 5
127 **PERCY'S GIFT** (IRE) 19
18 **PERCYTHEPINTO** (IRE) 49
447 **PERDICULA** (IRE) C 88
643 **PERDU** (GB) 62
227 **PERE BLANC** (IRE) 18
328 **PERENNIAL** (GB) 46
29 **PERENNITE** (FR) 8
708 **PERFECT CH'I** (IRE) 8
141 **PERFECT CRACKER** (GB) 18
141 **PERFECT DELIGHT** (GB) 49
117 **PERFECT EXAMPLE** (IRE) 24
141 **PERFECT FANTASY** (IRE) 8
473 **PERFECT GENTLEMAN** (IRE) 70
29 **PERFECT HAND** (GB) C 100
19 **PERFECT MISSION** (GB) 23
249 **PERFECT OUTLOOK** (GB) 14
61 **PERFECT PASTIME** (GB) 9
200 **PERFECT PASTURE** (GB) 80
34 **PERFECT POLICY** (GB) 42
299 **PERFECT POSE** (IRE) 227
19 **PERFECT RESPONSE** (GB) 81
42 **PERFECT SHOT** (GB) 18
141 **PERFECT SILENCE** (GB) 19
446 **PERFECT SMILE** (IRE) 63
654 **PERFECT STEP** (IRE) 67
19 **PERFECT TREASURE** (IRE) C 145
141 **PERFECT TRIBUTE** (GB) 20
306 **PERFECTO TIEMPO** (IRE) 33
600 **PERFIDIE** (IRE) F 44
660 **PERFORCE** (GB) 29
55 **PERFUME DAYS** (IRE) 101
198 **PERGAMON** (IRE) 17
583 **PERICOLOSO** (IRE) 18
447 **PERILS OF JOY** (IRE) C 89
3 **PERIPHERY** (USA) 96
435 **PERIWINKLE WAY** (GB) 9
557 **PERKIN WARBECK** (GB) 12
306 **PERLACHY** (GB) 19
43 **PEROVSKIA** (USA) C 44
227 **PERPETUALLY** (IRE) 19
698 **PERSARIO** (GB) F 30
619 **PERSEPOLIS** (FR) 139
681 **PERSIAN AVENUE** (IRE) G 43
530 **PERSIAN BUDDY** (GB) 7
33 **PERSIAN GATES** (IRE) 15
467 **PERSIAN HERALD** (GB) 7
358 **PERSIAN LASS** (IRE) F 35

628 **PERSIAN SEA** (UAE) C 33
331 **PERSIAN SNOW** (IRE) 64
123 **PERSISTE ET SIGNE** (FR) 10
200 **PERTEMPS NETWORKS** (GB) 33
296 **PERTUIS** (IRE) 31
488 **PERYLLYS** (GB) F 67
272 **PERYLLYS** (GB) F 16
452 **PESHAWAR** (GB) F 22
499 **PESOTO** (FR) 22
452 **PETARA BAY** (GB) 14
479 **PETE** (GB) 14
487 **PETE THE FEAT** (IRE) 9
466 **PETE THE PASTOR** (GB) 21
461 **PETELLA** (GB) 16
366 **PETER ANDERS** (GB) 120
496 **PETER MARTINS** (USA) 7
139 **PETER'S PLEASURE** (GB) 24
299 **PETHER'S MOON** (IRE) 228
460 **PETIT ECUYER** (FR) 71
603 **PETIT FLEUR** (GB) 6
321 **PETIT ROBIN** (FR) 122
219 **PETITE NOBLESSE** (FR) 96
520 **PETITE NYMPHE** (GB) C 63
299 **PETITE SPECTRE** (GB) F 229
257 **PETITO** (IRE) 6
283 **PETOMIC** (IRE) 54
64 **PETRARCHAN** (GB) 15
17 **PETRARCHICK** (USA) 7
618 **PETROCELLI** (GB) 5
94 **PETROGLYPH** (GB) 7
147 **PETROL** (GB) 49
517 **PETSAS PLEASURE** (GB) 6
650 **PETTIFOUR** (IRE) 50
698 **PETTOCHSIDE** (GB) 21
243 **PEVERIL PANDORA** (GB) 8
222 **PEYTO PRINCESS** (GB) F 14
111 **PHAENOMENA** (IRE) 140
466 **PHANTOM RANCH** (GB) 50
198 **PHAR AGAIN** (IRE) 18
713 **PHARBAR** (IRE) G 7
522 **PHARDESSA** (GB) 18
110 **PHARE ISLE** (IRE) 17
599 **PHEIDIAS** (GB) 8
249 **PHENOMENA** (GB) 32
201 **PHI PHI** (FR) C 119
695 **PHIDIPPIDES** (IRE) 63
183 **PHIL MAN** (IRE) 45
160 **PHILADELPHUS** (GB) 27
434 **PHILANDER** (GB) 101
220 **PHILHARMONIC HALL** (IRE) 26
487 **PHILIPEDEFROXFIELD** (GB) 10
299 **PHILIPSTOWN** (GB) 87
592 **PHLORIAN** (GB) 10
364 **PHLUKE** (GB) 12
655 **PHOEBE WOODSTOCK** (IRE) C 22
212 **PHOENICIAN BLAZE** (GB) 8
450 **PHOENIX CLUBS** (IRE) 40
137 **PHOENIX DES MOTTES** (FR) 6
433 **PHOENIX FLAME** (GB) 24
215 **PHOENIX FLIGHT** (IRE) 13
268 **PHOENIX LADY** (GB) 31
625 **PHOENIX RETURNS** (IRE) 31
193 **PHONIC** (IRE) 15
111 **PHOSPHORESCENCE** (IRE) 141
397 **PHOTO OPPORTUNITY** (GB) 21
622 **PHOTOGENIQUE** (FR) 5
646 **PIANO CONCERTO** (USA) 11
511 **PIANO SHOW** (USA) 27

214 **PICALILLY** (GB) 61
144 **PICANSORT** (GB) 2
658 **PICCOLA** (GER) 52
32 **PICCOLO EXPRESS** (GB) 20
176 **PICENO** (IRE) 11
466 **PICK A LITTLE** (GB) 22
119 **PICK THREE** (GB) 40
157 **PICKAMUS** (FR) 21
473 **PICKAPOCKETORTWO** (IRE) 71
400 **PICOT DE SAY** (GB) 18
121 **PICOT DE SAY** (GB) 1
460 **PICTURE DEALER** (GB) 117
492 **PICTURE IN THE SKY** (IRE) 4
321 **PICTURE POST** (USA) 123
489 **PICTURE THIS** (IRE) 81
34 **PICURA** (GB) 43
442 **PIDDIE'S POWER** (GB) 7
78 **PIE POUDRE** (GB) 7
328 **PIECE OF CAKE** (GB) 47
219 **PIEPOWDER COURT** (IRE) 172
265 **PIERRE D'OR** (IRE) 23
18 **PIERS GAVESTON** (FR) 50
650 **PIGEON ISLAND** (GB) 51
534 **PIGEON POWER** (GB) 61
142 **PILGRIM DANCER** (IRE) 7
29 **PILGRIM SOUL** (FR) 101
374 **PILGRIMS LANE** (IRE) 27
299 **PILGRIMS REST** (GB) 88
172 **PILKAYSKI** (GB) 10
476 **PILLAR OF HERCULES** (IRE) 56
589 **PIMBURY** (IRE) 4
3 **PIMPERNEL** (IRE) 97
591 **PIN D'ESTRUVAL** (FR) 8
542 **PINACOTHEQUE** (IRE) C 26
700 **PINBALL** (IRE) 19
141 **PINDROP** (GB) 51
219 **PINE CREEK** (GB) 21
226 **PINEAU DE RE** (FR) 22
606 **PINEROLO** (GB) 31
608 **PINGOU DE LA VIRE** (FR) 6
194 **PININI** (GB) F 13
433 **PINK BELINI** (GB) 43
654 **PINK DAMSEL** (IRE) 68
462 **PINK DELIGHT** (IRE) 19
376 **PINK EVIE** (GB) 13
177 **PINK LADY** (FR) F 1
447 **PINK SOVIETSTAIA** (FR) C 90
34 **PINK TEQUILA** (GB) 44
226 **PINKEEN LADY** (IRE) G 23
389 **PINNACLE OFPASSION** (IRE) 3
220 **PINOT** (GB) 61
490 **PINOTAGE** (GB) 10
45 **PINTRADA** (GB) 10
597 **PINTURA** (GB) 17
625 **PIONEER BOY** (USA) 49
569 **PIONEER GIRL** (GB) 126
200 **PIOUS** (GB) C 81
531 **PIPE BANNER** (GB) 21
475 **PIPE LADY** (IRE) 16
200 **PIPER CHEROKEE** (GB) 63
614 **PIPER HILL** (IRE) 6
201 **PIPER'S ASH** (USA) C 120
366 **PIPER'S LASS** (IRE) 190
287 **PIPERS CHOICE** (IRE) 19
397 **PIPERS PIPING** (IRE) 22
473 **PIQUE SOUS** (FR) 72
569 **PIRACICABA** (GER) 65
400 **PIRAN** (IRE) 19

312 **PIRANS CAR** (GB) 11
696 **PIRATE'S GOLD** (IRE) 33
525 **PIRAYA** (FR) 72
424 **PIRES** (GB) 21
407 **PIRI WANGO** (GB) 30
219 **PIRIKA** (GB) 22
331 **PIROULET** (FR) 65
372 **PISCEAN** (USA) 4
49 **PISCO SOUR** (USA) 47
619 **PISTOL** (IRE) 60
476 **PISTOL BASC** (FR) 57
395 **PISTOLET DOVE** (IRE) 15
408 **PISTOLET JAUNE** 68
55 **PITCH 'N TOSS** (IRE) 102
200 **PITKIN** (GB) 34
481 **PITTON RIVERS** (GB) 5
98 **PITTONI** (IRE) 11
247 **PIUS PARKER** (IRE) 12
661 **PIVOTAL PROSPECT** (GB) 7
614 **PIVOTAL ROCK** (IRE) 7
188 **PIVOTAL ROLE** (GB) C 20
520 **PIVOTAL SILENCE** (GB) 64
520 **PIVOTMAN** (GB) 10
74 **PIVOTTING** (GB) F 66
259 **PIZZICATO** (GB) F 48
275 **PLACE D'ARMES** (IRE) G 12
18 **PLACE IN MY HEART** (GB) 51
466 **PLACE THAT FACE** (IRE) 6
29 **PLANET ELDER** (GB) 9
331 **PLANET OF SOUND** (GB) 66
543 **PLANETEX** (IRE) 37
390 **PLANETOID** (IRE) 3
619 **PLASTIKI** (GB) 61
380 **PLATINUM LEADER** (IRE) F 84
698 **PLATINUM PRINCESS** (GB) F 31
366 **PLATTSBURGH** (USA) 29
21 **PLAY IT SAM** (GB) 3
529 **PLAY STREET** (GB) 32
304 **PLAY THE MARKET** (IRE) 55
597 **PLAY TIGER** (FR) 48
619 **PLAYBILL** (GB) 140
156 **PLAYFUL GIRL** (IRE) 4
501 **PLAYING THE FIELD** (IRE) 27
174 **PLAYING WITH FIRE** (IRE) 28
123 **PLAYLAND** (GB) 11
162 **PLEASANT DREAMS** (GB) F 6
446 **PLEASE TALK** (IRE) 64
147 **PLEASURE BENT** (GB) 99
254 **PLEASURE ISLAND** (IRE) 41
699 **PLEIN POUVOIR** (FR) 58
606 **PLENMELLER** (IRE) 32
328 **PLENTY OF SUGAR** (CAN) C 112
489 **PLENTY POCKET** (FR) 82
208 **PLUM BAY** (GB) 23
600 **PLUM FAIRY** (GB) C 45
608 **PLUM PUDDING** (FR) 7
219 **PLUMBA** (GB) 173
695 **PLUNKETT** (IRE) 64
520 **PLUS FOURS** (USA) 39
218 **PLUS JAMAIS** (FR) 17
198 **PLUS TU METS** (FR) G 19
511 **PLUTARQUE** (FR) 28
283 **POBS TROPHY** (GB) 55
567 **POCKET ACES** (IRE) 19
147 **POCKET WATCH** (GB) 50
397 **POCKETWOOD** (GB) 23
220 **PODGIES BOY** (GB) 27
389 **PODIUM DANCER** (GB) 4

141 **POET** (GB) 21
27 **POET'S PLACE** (USA) 22
141 **POETIC DANCER** (GB) 52
299 **POETIC LORD** (GB) 89
208 **POETIC POWER** (IRE) 24
451 **POETIC VERSE** (GB) 48
54 **POETRY WRITER** (GB) 19
511 **POINCON DE FRANCE** (IRE) 9
488 **POINT AT ISSUE** (IRE) 60
708 **POINT DU JOUR** (FR) 9
20 **POINT NORTH** (IRE) 2
35 **POINT OF CONTROL** (GB) 85
469 **POINT OF REFERENCE** (IRE) 3
363 **POINT PERFECT** (GB) F 12
454 **POINT VIEW** (IRE) 13
161 **POINTED ARCH** (IRE) F 65
556 **POINTLESS** (GB) 32
5 **POKER DE SIVOLA** (FR) 58
18 **POKER HOSPITAL** (GB) 52
593 **POKERHUNTRESS** (GB) 37
260 **POKFULHAM** (IRE) 21
108 **POLAR AURORAS** (GB) 31
620 **POLAR CHIEF** (GB) 16
359 **POLAR GUNNER** (GB) 22
285 **POLAR VENTURE** (GB) 49
16 **POLARBROOK** (IRE) 33
511 **POLARIX** (GB) 30
208 **POLDHU** (GB) F 39
592 **POLEMICA** (IRE) 11
3 **POLICE FORCE** (USA) 98
214 **POLISH BELLE** (GB) C 73
304 **POLISHED ROCK** (IRE) 108
489 **POLISKY** (FR) 83
200 **POLITBUREAU** (GB) 35
365 **POLITELYSED** (GB) 10
697 **POLITEO** (FR) 16
285 **POLITESSE** (USA) F 109
491 **POLITICAL PADDY** (GB) 7
33 **POLLEN JOCK** (GB) 16
397 **POLLY ADLER** 24
153 **POLLY HOLDER** (IRE) 8
656 **POLLY MCGINTY** (GB) 5
321 **POLLY PEACHUM** (IRE) 124
573 **POLO** (GB) F 64
600 **POLTAVA** (FR) C 46
206 **POLURRIAN** (IRE) 13
139 **POLY BLUE** (FR) 32
299 **POLY POMONA** (GB) 90
689 **POLYANTHUS JONES** (GB) G 13
192 **POLYDAMOS** (GB) 13
266 **POLYGON** (USA) 22
219 **POLYTECHNICIEN** (USA) 23
520 **POMARINE** (USA) 40
266 **POMEROL** 144
473 **POMME TIEPY** (FR) 73
266 **POMODORO** (GB) 145
34 **POMPEIA** (GB) 75
534 **PONCHO** (GB) 32
9 **PONTE DI ROSA** (GB) 28
304 **PONTIAC** (FR) 56
201 **PONTY ACCLAIM** (IRE) 92
59 **PONTYATES** (GB) 23
299 **POOLE HARBOUR** (IRE) 91
525 **POOLE MASTER** (GB) 73
220 **POONTOON** (IRE) 22
507 **POOR DUKE** (IRE) 44
473 **POPCORN** (FR) 74
117 **POPOLO** (IRE) C 46

282 **POPPY CAREW** (IRE) C 7
460 **POPPY COME RUNNING** (IRE) 72
107 **POPPY GOLIGHTLY** (GB) 13
481 **POPPY GREGG** (GB) 6
111 **POPULAR** (GB) 62
399 **POPULAR CHOICE** (GB) 11
227 **POPULATION** (GB) 20
489 **POQUELIN** (FR) 84
526 **PORGY** (GB) 7
570 **PORRIDGE** (GB) 49
466 **PORT CHARLOTTE** (GB) 52
73 **PORT HILL** (GB) 18
192 **PORT PROVIDENCE** (GB) F 28
402 **PORT VIEW** (IRE) 3
328 **PORTELLE** (GB) F 113
329 **PORTENTOUS** (GB) F 39
448 **PORTHGWIDDEN BEACH** (USA) 6
582 **PORTMEADE** (GB) 1
467 **PORTMEIRION** (GB) F 42
270 **PORTO VENERE** (IRE) G 22
328 **PORTODORA** (USA) F 114
534 **PORTRAIT** (GB) 62
460 **PORTRAIT EMOTION** (IRE) 73
487 **PORTRAIT ROYALE** (IRE) 11
111 **PORTRAITOFMYLOVE** (IRE) 63
515 **PORTRUSH STORM** (GB) 4
351 **POSE** (GB) 5
141 **POSEIDON GREY** (IRE) 53
490 **POSH BIRD** (GB) 11
333 **POSH EMILY** (GB) 10
304 **POSH FROCK** (GB) 97
534 **POSITION** (GB) 33
458 **POSITIVE VIBES** (GB) 26
619 **POSITIVELY** (GB) 62
366 **POSSESSION** (GB) C 191
194 **POSSESSIVE LADY** F 14
117 **POSSIBLY** (GB) 25
157 **POSSOL** (FR) 22
318 **POSTALE** (GB) 27
597 **POSTE RESTANTE** (GB) 83
682 **POSTERITY** (IRE) F 113
657 **POSTMASTER** (GB) 58
696 **POSTSCRIPT** (IRE) 34
329 **POTENTIALE** (GB) 2
705 **POULE DE LUXE** (IRE) G 20
489 **POUNGACH** (FR) 85
29 **POUPEE FLASH** (USA) 49
345 **POUR CHANGER** (FR) 3
380 **POUVOIR** (FR) 85
521 **POW R JACK** (GB) 12
177 **POWER MAN** (IRE) 2
111 **POWER OF FUTURE** (GER) F 142
650 **POWER PACK JACK** (IRE) 52
700 **POWERBALL** (IRE) 20
207 **POWERFUL AMBITION** (IRE) 36
440 **POWERFUL PIERRE** (GB) 9
501 **POWERFUL PRESENCE** (IRE) 28
577 **POWERFULLBEAT** (GB) 3
34 **POYLE TODREAM** (GB) 11
511 **PRAIRIE BELLA** (FR) 81
188 **PRAIRIE SUN** (GER) F 36
511 **PRAIRIE SUNSET** (GB) 123
59 **PRANKSTER** (GB) 24
525 **PRASINA RUSSATA** (IRE) 74
207 **PRAVDA STREET** (GB) 37
705 **PRAXIOS** (GB) 21
191 **PRAYER** (IRE) C 70
61 **PRAYERS FOR RAIN** (IRE) C 39

279 **PRE RAPHAELITE** (FR) 8
213 **PRECINCT** (GB) 23
300 **PRECIOUS LASS** (IRE) 6
249 **PRECISION FIVE** (GB) 33
511 **PRECOCIOUS STAR** (IRE) C 124
318 **PREFERENTIAL** (GB) 28
474 **PREFERRED LIES** (IRE) 12
352 **PREMATURE** (GB) 26
201 **PREMIER CHOICE** (GB) 93
556 **PREMIER DANE** (IRE) 33
218 **PREMIER GRAND CRU** (FR) 18
290 **PREMIER PRINCESS** G 6
208 **PREMIER PRIZE** (GB) F 40
556 **PREMIER SAGAS** (FR) 34
161 **PREMIER STEPS** (IRE) 66
666 **PREMIO LOCO** (USA) 14
645 **PREMIUM COFFEE** (GB) 5
645 **PRESBURG** (IRE) 13
407 **PRESCIENT** (IRE) 4
196 **PRESENT ACCEPTED** (GB) 7
141 **PRESENT DAY** (GB) 54
697 **PRESENT M'LORD** (IRE) 17
465 **PRESENT POTENTIAL** (IRE) 17
308 **PRESENT STORY** (GB) 7
169 **PRESENT TO YOU** (IRE) 22
444 **PRESENTED** (IRE) 12
525 **PRESENTING ACE** (GB) 75
489 **PRESENTING ARMS** (IRE) 86
23 **PRESENTING DR T** (IRE) 2
461 **PRESQUE PERDRE** (GB) 17
329 **PRESS BARON** (GB) 16
5 **PRESSTHEREDBUTTON** (IRE) 2
619 **PRESUME** (GB) 63
184 **PRESUMIDO** (IRE) 25
147 **PRESVIS** (GB) 9
280 **PRET A THOU** (FR) 2
318 **PRETTY CLEAR** (USA) C 57
39 **PRETTY HAPPY** (IRE) 13
597 **PRETTY MAJESTIC** (IRE) C 84
564 **PRETTY PANTHER** (FR) 94
425 **PRETTY PENNY** (GB) 3
299 **PRETTY PRIMO** (GB) 92
10 **PREUTY BOY** (FR) 12
19 **PRICE LIST** (USA) 82
625 **PRICELESS ART** (IRE) 32
119 **PRICELESS JEWEL** (GB) 41
200 **PRICES LANE** (GB) 36
588 **PRICKLES** (GB) 17
360 **PRIDE OF MINE** (GB) 31
473 **PRIDE OFTHE PARISH** (IRE) 75
617 **PRIDEUS** (IRE) 17
559 **PRIDEWAY** (IRE) F 5
388 **PRIEGO** (USA) 9
484 **PRIEST FIELD** (IRE) 7
254 **PRIEST ISLAND** (IRE) 42
91 **PRIESTLEY'S REWARD** (IRE) 31
390 **PRIMA LUCE** (IRE) C 44
695 **PRIMA PORTA** (GB) 65
446 **PRIMA VISTA** (GB) 12
466 **PRIMACY** (IRE) 53
223 **PRIMAEVAL** (IRE) 15
227 **PRIMARIES** (IRE) 21
156 **PRIME DESIGN** (IRE) 5
292 **PRIME EDITION** (GB) 8
597 **PRIME RUN** (GB) 49
564 **PRIME WINNER** (GB) 95
119 **PRIMEVERE** (IRE) 10
493 **PRIMO WAY** (GB) 11

494 PRIMROSE TIME (GB) 15
473 PRIMROSEANDBLUE (IRE) 76
43 PRINCE AYOOB (GB) 9
49 PRINCE BISHOP (IRE) 48
8 PRINCE BLACKTHORN (IRE) 17
403 PRINCE BLUE (GB) 11
626 PRINCE BUSTER (GB) 12
481 PRINCE CHARLEMAGNE (IRE) 7
473 PRINCE DE BEAUCHENE (FR) 77
408 PRINCE DES GABIERS (FR) 17
15 PRINCE DES MARAIS (FR) 12
380 PRINCE DU SEUIL (GB) 86
682 PRINCE ERIK (GB) 15
383 PRINCE FREDDIE (GB) 7
573 PRINCE GABRIAL (IRE) 65
538 PRINCE GOLAN (IRE) 13
200 PRINCE JAMES (GB) 37
62 PRINCE N POACHERS (GB) 10
170 PRINCE NAMID (GB) 2
249 PRINCE OF BURMA (IRE) 15
474 PRINCE OF DENIAL (IRE) 13
169 PRINCE OF DREAMS (GB) 23
343 PRINCE OF IVAGH (GB) 6
629 PRINCE OF JOHANNE (IRE) 8
483 PRINCE OF KING (GB) 9
3 PRINCE OF ORANGE (IRE) 99
588 PRINCE OF PASSION (CAN) 18
321 PRINCE OF PIRATES (IRE) 125
698 PRINCE OF PROPHETS (IRE) 32
511 PRINCE OF SOFIA (FR) 82
2 PRINCE OF SORRENTO (GB) 5
12 PRINCE OF THEBES (IRE) 13
604 PRINCE OF VASA (IRE) 5
468 PRINCE SAMOS (IRE) 2
49 PRINCE SIEGFRIED (FR) 49
474 PRINCE TAIME (FR) 14
267 PRINCE TAM (GB) 6
489 PRINCE TOM (GB) 87
299 PRINCE'S TRUST (GB) 230
523 PRINCEABLE LADY (IRE) F 3
331 PRINCELY PLAYER (IRE) 67
698 PRINCELY SUM (IRE) 22
237 PRINCEOFPERFECTION (GB) 44
711 PRINCEOFTHEDESERT (GB) 11
124 PRINCESS ALESSIA (GB) 23
451 PRINCESS ANNABELLE (GB) 39
597 PRINCESS DANAH (IRE) F 85
706 PRINCESS DIVA (GB) F 14
7 PRINCESS ELLIS (GB) G 21
73 PRINCESS GAIL (IRE) 19
682 PRINCESS HIGHWAY (USA) 54
146 PRINCESS ICICLE (GB) 8
506 PRINCESS KHELEYF (GB) 18
317 PRINCESS KIERA (GB) 3
619 PRINCESS KRIS (GB) F 141
58 PRINCESS LEONA (IRE) C 73
387 PRINCESS LEXI (IRE) 8
700 PRINCESS MADAEN (IRE) F 41
146 PRINCESS MAYA (GB) 20
510 PRINCESS PALMER (GB) 10
67 PRINCESS PALMER (GB) 7
308 PRINCESS QUEST (GB) 19
58 PRINCESS RAYA (GB) C 74
384 PRINCESS SABAAH (IRE) F 51
304 PRINCESS SINEAD (IRE) 98
422 PRINCESS SPEEDFIT (FR) C 32
416 PRINCESS STEPH (IRE) 7
219 PRINCESS TAISE (USA) F 174

73 PRINCESS TAMINA (IRE) 33
403 PRINCESSE WILLOW (GB) 12
585 PRINCESSE FLEUR (GB) 21
37 PRINCESSE KATIE (IRE) 2
321 PRISTINE (IRE) 126
191 PRITHEE (GB) C 71
534 PRIVACY ORDER (GB) 63
366 PRIVATE CAPTAIN (IRE) 192
358 PRIVATE EQUITY (GB) 9
511 PRIVATE JET (FR) 31
390 PRIVATE LIFE (FR) C 45
682 PRIVATE LINE (USA) F 114
328 PRIVATE MEANS (GB) 48
657 PRIVATE STORY (USA) 59
629 PRIVILEGED SPEECH (USA) F 21
596 PRIZE FIGHTER (IRE) 7
274 PRIZE POINT (GB) 14
114 PRIZE POPPY (GB) 9
3 PRIZEFIGHTING (USA) 33
356 PROBABLY GEORGE (GB) 5
321 PROBLEMA TIC (IRE) 127
306 PRODIGALITY (GB) 20
299 PRODUCER (GB) 93
485 PROFAB BOY (GB) 14
708 PROFESSOR JOHN (IRE) 10
27 PROFILE STAR (IRE) 42
27 PROFILE STORM (IRE) 43
19 PROFIT AGAIN (IRE) 83
139 PROHIBIT (GB) 15
397 PROHIBITION (IRE) 25
420 PROLINX (IRE) 29
629 PROMISE OF LOVE (GB) F 22
264 PROMISED WINGS (GER) 15
489 PROMISING ANSHAN (GB) 88
619 PROMISING LEAD (GB) C 142
9 PRONOUNCE (GB) 29
227 PROOF (IRE) 22
266 PROOFREADER (GB) 91
387 PROPER CHARLIE (GB) 9
65 PROPER VILLAN (IRE) 7
107 PROPHESY (IRE) 25
215 PROPHETE DE GUYE (FR) 14
119 PROPONENT (IRE) 11
570 PROSECCO (IRE) 50
489 PROSPECT WELLS (GB) 89
34 PROSPERA (IRE) 76
390 PROTANTO (IRE) 15
446 PROTARAS (USA) 66
55 PROTOTYPE (GB) F 103
398 PROUD CHIEFTAIN (GB) 2
485 PROUD SCHOLAR (GB) 5
625 PROUD TIMES (USA) 33
29 PROVENCE VERTE (IRE) 102
460 PROWSE (GB) F 118
619 PROXIMITY (GB) 64
366 PRUSSIAN (GB) 121
321 PRYDE ROCK (GB) 128
460 PSI (USA) 74
447 PSYCHIC (IRE) C 91
424 PSYCHO (IRE) 22
601 PTOLEMAIC (GB) 48
549 PTOLOMEOS (GB) 3
507 PUCK'S CASTLE (GB) C 45
632 PUCON (GB) 14
396 PUDSEY HOUSE (GB) 36
584 PUERTO AZUL (IRE) 2
302 PUFF OF MAGIC (IRE) F 10
593 PUFFIN BILLY (IRE) 38

366 PUGNACIOUS (IRE) 122
516 PULL THE PIN (IRE) 16
550 PULLMEN (GB) 7
601 PULSATILLA (GB) 18
619 PULVERIZE (USA) 65
321 PUNCHESTOWNS (FR) 129
182 PUNCHING (GB) 12
3 PUNITA (USA) 100
99 PUNTA BALUARTE (GB) 11
273 PUNTA LARA LADY (IRE) 14
389 PUR DE SIVOLA (FR) 5
499 PUR STYLE (FR) 23
178 PURCELL'S BRIDGE (FR) 17
366 PURE EXCELLENCE (GB) 193
59 PURE FAITH (IRE) 25
129 PURE GOLD (GB) C 37
19 PURE SONG (GB) F 146
266 PURIFICATION (IRE) 23
260 PURKAB (GB) 22
59 PURLANDO (GER) 26
384 PURLEY QUEEN (IRE) 30
18 PURPLE 'N GOLD (IRE) 53
462 PURPLE AFFAIR (IRE) 20
3 PURPLE BAY (USA) 101
423 PURPLE MONEY (IRE) 3
9 PURPLE RAIN (IRE) C 51
628 PURPLE TIGER (IRE) F 34
628 PURPLE TIGER (IRE) F 12
467 PURRING (USA) F 43
285 PURSUE (GB) 50
220 PURSUIT OF PASSION (GB) 28
619 PURSUITOEXCELLENCE (IRE) 4
530 PUSH ME (GB) 8
373 PUSH TO EXIT (GB) 21
129 PUTERI WENTWORTH (GB) C 38
386 PUTIACCA BELLA (FR) 19
437 PUTIN (IRE) 8
461 PUY D'ARNAC (FR) 18
700 PUYOL (IRE) 21
9 PUZZLING (GB) F 47
178 PYJAMA GAME (IRE) 13
583 PYLEIGH LASS (GB) 18
101 PYRACANTHA (GB) 23
12 PYTHEAS (USA) 14
266 QAADIRA (USA) 92
147 QAHRIMAN (GB) 10
525 QALINAS (FR) 76
564 QAMARYA (USA) 66
147 QANAN (GB) 51
328 QANNAAS (USA) 49
546 QARAARAT (IRE) 4
654 QASIRAH (IRE) F 133
331 QASPAL (FR) 68
73 QEETHAARA (USA) 20
508 QEWY (IRE) 83
404 QHILIMAR (FR) 36
391 QIANSHAN LEADER (IRE) 45
657 QOUBILAI (FR) 61
68 QRACKERS (FR) 8
331 QROKTOU (FR) 69
570 QUACITY (FR) 51
509 QUADRA HOP (IRE) 15
657 QUADRATO (GER) 62
458 QUADRI (GB) F 28
473 QUADRILLON (FR) 78
393 QUAHADI (IRE) 8
684 QUAILS HOLLOW (IRE) 16

198 **QUALITEE** (GB) 20
283 **QUALITY ART** (USA) 56
147 **QUALITY PEARL** (USA) 52
646 **QUALYPSO D'ALLIER** (FR) 12
151 **QUAM CELERRIME** (GB) 8
111 **QUAN YIN** (IRE) F 143
381 **QUANAH PARKER** (IRE) 12
301 **QUAND JE REVE DE TOI** (FR) 4
183 **QUAND REVERRAIJE** (FR) 46
359 **QUANNAPOWITT** (IRE) 23
321 **QUANTITATIVEEASING** (IRE) 130
569 **QUANZHOU** (FR) 66
22 **QUAPRILAND** (FR) 2
473 **QUAQUO DE FLOTTE** (FR) 79
450 **QUAROMA** (GB) 27
419 **QUARRYVALE** (IRE) 10
699 **QUARTZ DE THAIX** (FR) 59
487 **QUARTZ DU MONTCEAU** (FR) 12
708 **QUASI CONGAREE** (GER) 11
183 **QUATRE ARPENTS** (FR) 62
495 **QUAY MEADOW** (IRE) 8
275 **QUAY MOMENT** (IRE) F 13
198 **QUAYSIDE COURT** (IRE) 21
503 **QUAZY DE JOIE** (FR) 49
620 **QUBUH** (IRE) 6
692 **QUE VIVO** (FR) 4
366 **QUEEN OF DENMARK** (USA) 30
18 **QUEEN OF EPIRUS** (GB) 29
417 **QUEEN OF HEAVEN** (GB) 1
498 **QUEEN OF MANTUA** (GB) C 35
628 **QUEEN'S BEST** (GB) C 35
474 **QUEEN'S CHOICE** (IRE) 15
366 **QUEEN'S ESTATE** (GER) C 39
391 **QUEEN'S FOREST** (IRE) 46
15 **QUEEN'S LEADER** (GB) F 13
713 **QUEEN'S PAWN** (IRE) 8
662 **QUEEN'S PRINCESS** (GB) 4
299 **QUEEN'S PUDDING** (IRE) C 231
19 **QUEEN'S STAR** (GB) 84
12 **QUEENIE'S STAR** (IRE) 15
639 **QUEENS BAY** (GB) 42
652 **QUEENS FANTASY** (GB) G 5
50 **QUEENS GROVE** (GB) 4
201 **QUEENS REVENGE** (GB) 94
614 **QUEENS VISIT** (GB) 24
16 **QUEENSWOOD BAY** (GB) 34
364 **QUEENY'S PRINCESS** (IRE) C 39
659 **QUEL BALLISTIC** (GB) 37
444 **QUEL BRUERE** (FR) 13
456 **QUEL ELITE** (FR) 15
473 **QUEL ESPRIT** (FR) 80
408 **QUEL PLAISIR** (GB) 69
650 **QUELQU'UN COMME TOI** (FR) 53
266 **QUENCHED** (GB) C 146
157 **QUENTIN COLLONGES** (FR) 23
95 **QUERIDO** (GER) 6
3 **QUERNSTONE** (USA) 102
542 **QUERY** (USA) C 27
564 **QUESERAISJESANSTOI** (IRE) C 96
147 **QUEST FOR PEACE** (IRE) 11
407 **QUESTAMA** (GB) C 56
266 **QUESTIONING** (IRE) 24
656 **QUESTIONNAIRE** (IRE) 9
640 **QUETZAL** (IRE) 14
473 **QUEVEGA** (FR) 81
393 **QUIAMO MALTA** (FR) 9
510 **QUICK BITE** (IRE) 11
86 **QUICK EXIT** (GB) G 15

55 **QUICK FIZZ** (IRE) 104
682 **QUICK GLIMPSE** (GB) 55
49 **QUICK WIT** (GB) 50
319 **QUICKLY ORIGNY** (FR) 3
218 **QUICUYO** (GER) 19
447 **QUIERO GANAR** (USA) F 40
160 **QUIET CONFIDENCE** (IRE) G 28
516 **QUIET COUNSEL** (IRE) F 19
219 **QUIET DIPLOMACY** (IRE) 175
16 **QUIET WHISPER** (IRE) 35
55 **QUILL AND VELLUM** (IRE) 6
367 **QUINCY DES PICTONS** (FR) 9
570 **QUINDER SPRING** (FR) 52
287 **QUINMASTER** (USA) 20
462 **QUINSMAN** (GB) 3
525 **QUINTE DU CHATELET** (FR) 77
607 **QUIPE ME POSTED** (FR) 11
473 **QUISCOVER FONTAINE** (FR) 82
529 **QUITE A CATCH** (IRE) 16
611 **QUITE SPARKY** (GB) 9
359 **QUITE THE MAN** (IRE) 24
475 **QUITO DE LA ROQUE** (FR) 17
570 **QUITO DU TRESOR** (FR) 53
86 **QUIX** (GB) 16
74 **QUIXOTE** (IRE) 48
466 **QUIZ MISTRESS** (GB) 23
414 **QUIZ TIME** (GB) C 14
444 **QUIZWORK** (FR) 14
655 **QUIZZED** (GB) 15
617 **QUO VISTA** (IRE) 20
525 **QUOCOTIEP** (FR) 78
380 **QUOTICA DE POYANS** (FR) 87
332 **QUOUSKO DE L'ISOP** (FR) 17
358 **QUSHCHI** (GB) 10
374 **R CRAIG** (IRE) 28
450 **RA JUNIOR** (USA) 28
463 **RAAMZ** (IRE) 8
328 **RAASEKHA** (GB) 8
338 **RABSHIH** (IRE) F 22
19 **RACE AND STATUS** (IRE) 147
185 **RACEY LACEY** (GB) 12
236 **RACING WITH ANGELS** (GB) 5
321 **RACKHAM LEROUGE** (FR) 131
573 **RACY** (GB) 24
564 **RADAMES** (FR) 12
65 **RADETSKY MARCH** (IRE) 8
526 **RADIANCY** (IRE) F 19
318 **RADIATION** (FR) 58
699 **RADICAL IMPACT** (IRE) 60
682 **RADIO CALL** (GB) 56
442 **RADIO GAGA** (GB) 14
34 **RADIOACTIVE** (GB) 45
504 **RADMORES OSCAR** (GB) 7
504 **RADMORES REVENGE** (GB) 8
204 **RAFAAF** (IRE) 2
299 **RAFALE** (GB) 232
336 **RAFEEJ** (GB) 125
339 **RAFFA** (GB) 15
384 **RAFFINN** (GB) 31
58 **RAGDA** (GB) 16
183 **RAGEUR** (FR) 20
73 **RAGGED STAFF** (IRE) 21
479 **RAGGIOS BOY** (GB) 15
325 **RAGHDAAN** (GB) 9
161 **RAGTIME BLUES** (GB) C 67
29 **RAHEB** (GB) 50
366 **RAHEEBA** (GB) 126

19 **RAHY'S PROMISE** (USA) 85
381 **RAIFTEIRI** (IRE) 13
434 **RAILWAY DILLON** (IRE) 102
553 **RAILWAY RICO** (IRE) 10
588 **RAIMOND RIDGE** (IRE) 19
488 **RAIN DELAYED** (IRE) 31
407 **RAIN FLOWER** (FR) C 57
434 **RAIN MAC** (GB) 103
556 **RAIN STOPS PLAY** (IRE) 35
110 **RAINBOW DANCER** (IRE) 18
208 **RAINBOW END** (GB) C 41
366 **RAINBOW GOLD** (IRE) 127
159 **RAINBOW HAZE** (GB) 5
111 **RAINBOW LAKE** (GB) F 144
569 **RAINBOW QUARTZ** (IRE) 67
151 **RAINBOW RICHES** (GB) 10
712 **RAINBOW SPECTRUM** (FR) F 10
450 **RAINBOW TREASURE** (IRE) F 47
307 **RAINBOWS GUEST** (IRE) C 15
407 **RAINDROP** (GB) C 58
366 **RAINESTORM** (FR) 194
218 **RAINING HORSE** (FR) 20
320 **RAINSBOROUGH** (GB) 8
161 **RAINY DAY SONG** (GB) C 68
336 **RAINY NIGHT** (GB) 16
473 **RAISE HELL** (GB) 83
94 **RAISE THE RAFTERS** (IRE) 8
29 **RAISONNABLE** (GB) F 103
614 **RAJA** (IRE) C 53
460 **RAJAMAND** (FR) 75
111 **RAJARATNA** (GB) 145
321 **RAJDHANI EXPRESS** (GB) 132
628 **RAJEEM** (GB) F 36
699 **RAJEEVA** (IRE) 61
681 **RAJNAGAN** (FR) 44
507 **RAKAAN** (IRE) 11
588 **RAKATA** (USA) C 44
630 **RAKERIN LAD** (IRE) 4
462 **RAKTICATE** (IRE) 36
33 **RAKTIMAN** (FR) 17
296 **RALEIGH QUAY** (IRE) 32
595 **RAMATUEL** (FR) 2
543 **RAMBLER** (GB) G 49
360 **RAMBO WILL** (GB) 32
252 **RAMBRIDGE COPSE** (GB) 9
49 **RAMONA** (GB) C 143
489 **RAMSES DE MARCIGNY** (FR) 90
665 **RANCHO CUCAMONGA** (IRE) C 20
160 **RANDJO** (FR) 29
145 **RANGEFINDER** (GB) 12
489 **RANGITOTO** (IRE) 91
188 **RANGOONED** (GB) 37
191 **RANIN** (GB) C 72
489 **RANJAAN** (FR) 92
699 **RANJOBAIE** (FR) 62
16 **RANNOCH MOOR** (GB) 36
328 **RANSOM NOTE** (GB) 9
682 **RANSOMED ROSE** (GB) 57
174 **RAPHIELL** (IRE) 29
507 **RAPHIMIX** (GB) F 46
55 **RAPID APPROACH** (IRE) 105
336 **RAPID HEAT LAD** (IRE) 37
503 **RAPID INCREASE** (IRE) 50
682 **RAPID RANSOM** (USA) F 115
460 **RAPID WATER** (GB) 76
155 **RAPSGATE** (IRE) C 25
473 **RAPTOR** (FR) 84
495 **RAPTUROUS** (GB) F 11

296 **RAPTUROUS APPLAUSE** (GB) 33
123 **RAQUETTE** (GB) 41
343 **RARE BOB** (IRE) 40
64 **RARE FLING** (USA) C 28
101 **RARE RUBY** (IRE) 24
381 **RASAM ALDAAR** (GB) 14
385 **RASH JUDGEMENT** (GB) 10
307 **RASMANI** (GB) F 16
364 **RASPBERRY FIZZ** (GB) 21
49 **RASSAM** (IRE) 12
488 **RASSELAS** (IRE) 32
372 **RASTEAU** (IRE) 5
503 **RATE OF KNOTS** (IRE) 51
639 **RATEABLE VALUE** (GB) 43
71 **RATHER COOL** (GB) 11
39 **RATHER CURIOUS** (IRE) 14
343 **RATHFEIGH** (IRE) 41
465 **RATHLIN** (GB) 18
657 **RATHNAROUGHY** (IRE) 63
473 **RATTAN** (USA) 85
606 **RATTLIN** (GB) 33
540 **RAUCOUS BEHAVIOUR** (USA) 5
619 **RAUSHAN** (IRE) 143
592 **RAVANCHI** (GB) 12
404 **RAVASTREE** (IRE) 37
391 **RAVENCLAW** (IRE) 47
659 **RAVENS SECRET** (GB) 38
8 **RAVENSBILL** (IRE) 18
666 **RAVENSBURG** (GB) 47
688 **RAVI RIVER** (IRE) 14
207 **RAVI RIVER** (IRE) 38
58 **RAVING MONSUN** (GB) 45
447 **RAWAAFED** (IRE) 41
434 **RAWAAJ** (GB) 104
19 **RAWAKI** (IRE) 24
414 **RAY DIAMOND** (GB) 4
360 **RAY OF JOY** (GB) 33
380 **RAYA STAR** (GB) 88
221 **RAYBERTS PET** (IRE) 4
542 **RAYNELL** (GB) 11
508 **RAYOUNABAD** (IRE) 84
570 **RAYSROCK** (IRE) 54
642 **RAYVIN BLACK** (GB) 35
569 **RAYYANA** (IRE) C 127
343 **RAZ DE MAREE** (FR) 42
508 **RAZIA** (IRE) 85
328 **RAZORBILL** (USA) 50
619 **RAZZLE** (USA) C 144
307 **RAZZLE DAZZLE 'EM** (GB) 11
418 **REACH OUT** (GB) 11
116 **REACHFORTHEBUCKS** (GB) 8
511 **READ OVER** (FR) 83
576 **READY** (IRE) 8
86 **READY OR NOT** (IRE) 17
698 **REAL CAT** (USA) F 33
434 **REAL MILAN** (IRE) 105
434 **REALIGNMENT** (IRE) 106
695 **REALISATION** (USA) 66
9 **REALITY SHOW** (IRE) 30
466 **REALIZE** (GB) 79
434 **REALMONT** (FR) 107
446 **REALT DUBH** (IRE) 67
556 **REALT MOR** (IRE) 36
588 **REAPING** (GB) 20
279 **REAR GUNNER** (IRE) 9
304 **REAR VIEW** (GB) 57
29 **REARRANGE** (GB) 51
310 **REASON TO BELIEVE** (IRE) 10

552 **REASONABLE FORCE** (GB) 33
123 **REASONS** (USA) 12
127 **REBECCA ROMERO** (GB) 6
89 **REBECCAS CHOICE** (IRE) 8
670 **REBECCAS ROSE** (IRE) 5
696 **REBEL DANCER** (FR) 35
489 **REBEL DU MAQUIS** (FR) 93
245 **REBEL HIGH** (IRE) 3
299 **REBEL MAGIC** (GB) 233
420 **REBEL MELODY** (IRE) 30
69 **REBEL NELL** (GB) 10
489 **REBEL REBELLION** (IRE) 94
3 **REBEL SONG** (IRE) 103
606 **REBEL SWING** (GB) 34
422 **REBELLIOUS GUEST** (GB) 25
460 **REBLIS** (FR) 77
447 **REBUKE** (USA) F 92
663 **RECIF DE THAIX** (FR) 6
407 **RECITE** (JPN) F 59
141 **RECKLESS ABANDON** (GB) 71
496 **RECKONING** (IRE) 36
434 **RECORD BREAKER** (IRE) 108
573 **RECTIFY** (IRE) F 102
364 **RECTORY LANE** (GB) 40
299 **RED ADAIR** (GB) 234
420 **RED ADMIRAL** (USA) 31
74 **RED AGGRESSOR** (IRE) 49
259 **RED ALEX** (GB) 30
362 **RED ANCHOR** (IRE) 13
407 **RED ARMY BLUES** (IRE) 5
328 **RED ART** (IRE) 51
485 **RED AVALANCHE** (IRE) 15
447 **RED BANDANNA** (IRE) C 93
7 **RED BARON** (IRE) 17
496 **RED BATON** (GB) 83
116 **RED BAY** (GB) 24
209 **RED BURN** (GB) 3
191 **RED CADEAUX** (GB) 4
285 **RED CAMELLIA** (GB) C 110
106 **RED CAPE** (FR) 6
422 **RED CATKIN** (GB) 33
188 **RED CHARMER** (IRE) 38
585 **RED CURRENT** (GB) 22
214 **RED DAGGER** (IRE) 26
227 **RED DEVIL BOYS** (IRE) 23
543 **RED DUKE** (GB) 38
299 **RED EMPRESS** (GB) C 235
72 **RED FLASH** (IRE) 10
619 **RED HALO** (IRE) 66
266 **RED HAND** (USA) 93
329 **RED HEAVEN** (GB) C 40
642 **RED HERMES** (IRE) 36
188 **RED HIGHLITES** (IRE) 39
29 **RED HURRICANE** (IRE) 52
207 **RED INCA** (GB) 39
91 **RED JADE** (GB) 14
328 **RED JAZZ** (USA) 15
579 **RED KINGDOM** (IRE) 10
461 **RED KOKO** (IRE) 37
170 **RED LANCER** (GB) 3
632 **RED LARKSPUR** (IRE) 15
287 **RED LASER** (IRE) 46
257 **RED LAW** (IRE) 7
618 **RED LITE** (GB) 6
191 **RED LOVER** (GB) 5
434 **RED MERLIN** (IRE) 109

391 **RED MILE** (FR) 48
192 **RED MISCHIEF** (IRE) 14
635 **RED MYST** (IRE) 13
199 **RED NOT BLUE** (IRE) 7
27 **RED OCTOBER** (IRE) 51
366 **RED ORATOR** (GB) 128
234 **RED PROTECTOR** (IRE) 6
204 **RED QUARTET** (IRE) 10
43 **RED RAMESSES** (IRE) 25
336 **RED RANI** (GB) 17
510 **RED RED WINE** (GB) 20
296 **RED RHYTHM** (GB) 34
329 **RED RITA** (IRE) C 41
327 **RED RIVER RUN** (GB) 8
650 **RED RIVERMAN** (GB) 54
434 **RED ROCCO** (IRE) 110
650 **RED ROUBLE** (GB) 55
629 **RED SEAL** (GB) 17
328 **RED SENOR** (IRE) 53
299 **RED SEVENTY** (GB) 94
511 **RED SHOT** (FR) 125
705 **RED SKIPPER** (GB) 22
477 **RED SOMERSET** (USA) 8
117 **RED SPADES** (IRE) 3
412 **RED TANBER** (IRE) 6
328 **RED TRUMP** (GB) 54
496 **RED TURBAN** (GB) 84
543 **RED TYKE** (IRE) F 33
654 **RED VALE** (IRE) F 134
622 **RED WHISPER** (GB) 6
645 **RED YARN** (GB) 6
141 **RED YELLOW BLUE** (USA) F 72
299 **REDACT** (GB) 95
214 **REDAIR** (IRE) 62
331 **REDBRIDGE REBEL** (GB) 70
58 **REDCLUE** (IRE) 46
424 **REDERA** (IRE) 23
50 **REDGRAVE DANCER** (GB) 5
459 **REDHOTDOC** (GB) 6
600 **REDIAL** (GB) 29
480 **REDINESSENCE** (IRE) 24
489 **REDLYNCH ROCK** (GB) 95
201 **REDMOLLY** (GB) 49
331 **REDUNDERTHEBED** (IRE) 71
655 **REDVERS** (IRE) 3
328 **REDWOOD** (GB) 11
61 **REE'S RASCAL** (IRE) 10
462 **REELI SILLI** (GB) C 37
33 **REELWILL** (FR) 18
61 **REEM ONE** (IRE) 11
19 **REEMAS** (GB) 53
299 **REFECTORY** (IRE) 148
299 **REFLECT** (IRE) 15
496 **REFLECTED GLORY** (AUS) 37
223 **REFRACTOR** (IRE) 16
18 **REFRESHESHEPARTS** (USA) 54
15 **REFUSAL** (GB) 14
72 **REG'S RUBY** (GB) 11
201 **REGAL ACCLAIM** (GB) 95
61 **REGAL APPROVAL** (GB) 11
146 **REGAL ART** (GB) 21
266 **REGAL AURA** (GB) 94
344 **REGAL BROOK** (GB) 18
57 **REGAL CURTSY** (GB) F 22
339 **REGAL ENCORE** (IRE) 16
373 **REGAL FLOW** (GB) 22
80 **REGAL LADY** (GB) 10
488 **REGAL PARADE** (GB) 33

460 **REGAL PARK** (IRE) 78
160 **REGAL PRESENCE** (IRE) 30
320 **REGAL RAVE** (USA) 9
496 **REGAL REALM** (GB) 38
74 **REGAL RIBAND** (GB) F 67
496 **REGAL SILK** (GB) 85
147 **REGAL STEP** (GB) C 100
625 **REGAL SWAIN** (IRE) 34
458 **REGAL TIE** (IRE) 27
111 **REGENCY** (GER) 64
64 **REGENCY ART** (IRE) 16
397 **REGGAE RHYTHM** (IRE) 26
366 **REGGAE STAR** (GB) 195
699 **REGINALDINHO** (UAE) 63
467 **REGISTER** (IRE) 26
287 **REGULATION** (IRE) 47
676 **REGY FROM SEDGY** (GB) 6
676 **REGYTHELION** (GB) 7
447 **REIGN OF FIRE** (IRE) C 94
91 **REIGNIER** (GB) 15
299 **REIGNS OF GLORY** (IRE) 96
434 **REINDEER DIPPIN** (GB) 111
49 **REINE ZAO** (FR) C 144
46 **REINETTE O'BRY** (GB) 3
328 **REINSTATED** (IRE) C 115
318 **REITERATE** (GB) 29
147 **REJUVENATION** (IRE) C 101
699 **RELAX** (FR) 64
299 **RELAY** (GB) 236
488 **RELEASE THE FUNDS** (IRE) 61
18 **RELENTLESS HARRY** (IRE) 55
569 **RELIABLE MAN** (GB) 11
201 **RELIGHT MY FIRE** (GB) 121
569 **RELINQUISH** (GB) 67
569 **RELIZANE** (GB) 68
299 **REMBRANDT** (IRE) 237
501 **REMEDY** (GB) C 58
304 **REMEMBER ALEXANDER** (GB) 99
321 **REMEMBER NOW** (IRE) 133
263 **REMEMBER ROCKY** (GB) 25
111 **REMINISCE** (GB) 146
329 **REMIX** (IRE) 17
588 **REMMYNISS** (GB) 21
29 **REMOTE ROMANCE** (USA) F 104
699 **RENARD** (FR) 65
490 **RENDL BEACH** (IRE) 12
549 **RENEGE THE JOKER** (GB) 4
19 **RENEGOTIATE** (GB) 86
184 **RENOIR'S LADY** (GB) 11
192 **RENOWNED** (IRE) C 15
681 **REPEAT BUSINESS** (IRE) 45
534 **REPEATER** (GB) 34
258 **REPLICATOR** (GB) 1
542 **REPOSER** (FR) 12
3 **REPRESENTATION** (USA) 104
19 **REPUTABLE** (GB) C 149
407 **REQUESTED PLEASURE**
        (IRE) C 60
160 **REQUIN** (FR) 31
147 **REQUIRE** (GB) 53
708 **REQUISITE** (GB) 12
201 **RESIDENCE AND SPA** (IRE) 50
285 **RESILIENT** (IRE) 4
645 **RESISTANCE HEROINE** (GB) C 17
226 **RESOLUTE BAY** (IRE) 24
682 **RESOLUTE RESPONSE** (IRE) 116
397 **RESPLENDENT ALPHA** (GB) 27
400 **RESPLENDENT LIGHT** (GB) 20

466 **RESPONSIVE** (GB) 54
19 **RESTAURATEUR** (IRE) 87
331 **RESTE GOSSE** (FR) 72
256 **RESTE JEUNE** (FR) 22
137 **RESTER VRAI** (FR) 7
404 **RESTEZEN D'ARMOR** (FR) 38
336 **RESTLESS BAY** (IRE) 18
174 **RESTLESS HARRY** (GB) 30
556 **RESTORATION** (FR) 37
385 **RESURGE** (IRE) 11
318 **RESURGENT** (GB) 30
620 **RESUSCITATOR** (USA) 7
43 **RETAINAGE** (USA) C 45
519 **RETREAT CONTENT** (IRE) 10
49 **RETRIEVE** (AUS) 51
43 **RETROMANIA** (IRE) 26
657 **REV IT UP** (IRE) 64
257 **REVAADER** (GB) 8
433 **REVE DE NUIT** (USA) 23
697 **REVE DE SIVOLA** (FR) 18
433 **REVE DU JOUR** (IRE) 44
711 **REVEAL THE LIGHT** (GB) 12
328 **REVEAL THE STAR** (USA) 55
328 **REVELETTE** (USA) 56
619 **REVERED CITIZEN** (USA) 68
119 **REVERT** (USA) 42
276 **REVEUR** (FR) F 17
355 **REVOLVING WORLD** (IRE) 3
215 **REVUPCLOVER** (IRE) 15
641 **REWARDED** (GB) 5
119 **REX IMPERATOR** (GB) 43
337 **REX ROMANORUM** (IRE) 10
701 **REXMEHEAD** (IRE) 1
404 **REY NACARADO** (IRE) 39
380 **REYAMOUR** (GB) 89
92 **REYMYSTERIO** (IRE) 7
561 **REYNO** (GB) 10
460 **REZWAAN** (GB) 79
438 **REZWAAN** (GB) 2
496 **RHADEGUNDA** (GB) C 86
34 **RHAGORI** (GB) 46
299 **RHAMNUS** (GB) 238
325 **RHINESTONE REBEL** (IRE) 10
650 **RHUM** (FR) 56
282 **RHUMBA RAGE** (USA) F 8
259 **RHYME ROYAL** (GB) 31
570 **RHYMERS HA'** (GB) 55
130 **RHYMING SKY** (GB) 7
161 **RHYTHM OF LIGHT** (GB) 14
474 **RHYTHM SEEKER** (GB) 16
617 **RHYTON** (IRE) 21
462 **RIBALD** (GB) C 21
658 **RIBBERY** (GER) 63
223 **RIBBONS** (GB) 66
269 **RICARDO'S CHANCE** (GB) 4
45 **RICH AGAIN** (IRE) 17
522 **RICH BUDDY** (GB) 19
29 **RICH COAST** (GB) 10
682 **RICH DARK INK** (USA) 117
45 **RICH FOREVER** (IRE) 25
515 **RICH HARVEST** (USA) 5
179 **RICH HILL** (GB) 2
553 **RICH KAYF** (GB) 11
132 **RICH LIVE** (FR) 4
476 **RICH LORD** (GB) 59
190 **RICH MAID** (IRE) 1
299 **RICHARD SENIOR** (GB) 239
305 **RICHARD THE THIRD** (GB) 2

160 **RICHARD'S SUNDANCE** (IRE) 32
625 **RICHEN** (USA) G 60
271 **RICHENDA** (GB) F 9
142 **RICHIE ROB** (GB) 8
696 **RICHMOND** (FR) 36
343 **RICK** (FR) 43
161 **RICZAR** (GB) 15
287 **RIDAYEF** (IRE) 21
111 **RIDDLE MASTER** (GB) 65
653 **RIDGEWAY HAWK** (GB) 15
391 **RIDGEWAY POPPY** (GB) 49
653 **RIDGEWAY SAPPHIRE** (GB) 16
111 **RIDGEWAY STORM** (IRE) 147
286 **RIF** (FR) 12
394 **RIFLEMAN** (IRE) 20
306 **RIFLESSIONE** (GB) 21
682 **RIFQAH** (USA) C 118
699 **RIGADIN DE BEAUCHENE** (FR) 66
665 **RIGGINS** (IRE) 4
237 **RIGHT CREDENTIALS** (GB) 23
447 **RIGHT DIVINE** (IRE) 42
664 **RIGHT ENOUGH** (GB) 10
117 **RIGHT EXPECTATION** (IRE) 26
239 **RIGHT MOVE** (IRE) 5
233 **RIGHT OPTION** (IRE) 11
45 **RIGHT RESULT** (IRE) 18
357 **RIGHT STEP** (GB) 10
460 **RIGHT STUFF** (FR) 80
447 **RIGHT TO DREAM** (IRE) 43
285 **RIGHT TO RULE** (IRE) 51
272 **RIGHTCAR** (GB) 7
272 **RIGHTCAR DOMINIC** (GB) 8
108 **RIGID** (GB) 32
265 **RIGID ROCK** (FR) 12
657 **RIGIDITY** (GB) 65
55 **RIGOLETTA** (IRE) 53
476 **RIGUEZ DANCER** (GB) 60
699 **RILEYEV** (FR) 67
3 **RILEYSKEEPINGFAITH** (GB) 34
547 **RIME AVEC GENTIL** (FR) 7
547 **RIMINI** (FR) 8
28 **RINCE DONN** (IRE) 1
254 **RING BO REE** (IRE) 43
55 **RING CRAFT** (IRE) 106
197 **RING FOR BAILEYS** (GB) 10
129 **RING THE RELATIVES** (GB) C 39
8 **RINGAROUND** (GB) 19
529 **RINGMOOR DOWN** (GB) F 45
574 **RINGSEND ROSE** (IRE) 5
494 **RINNAGREE ROSIE** (GB) 16
408 **RIO ATHENAS** (FR) 18
136 **RIO CARLOS** (IRE) 10
488 **RIO COBOLO** (IRE) 34
49 **RIO DE LA PLATA** (USA) 52
188 **RIO GRANDE** (GB) 21
108 **RIO MILAN** (GB) 33
520 **RIO ROYALE** (IRE) 11
690 **RIO SANDS** (GB) 5
142 **RIO'S GIRL** (GB) 9
34 **RIO'S PEARL** (GB) 77
690 **RIO'S ROSANNA** (IRE) 6
654 **RIOJA RESERVA** (GB) 69
34 **RIOT OF COLOUR** (GB) 47
447 **RIOTOUS APPLAUSE** (GB) C 95
174 **RIPOFF** (GB) 31
266 **RIPPLED** (GB) 95
191 **RIPPLES MAID** (GB) F 36
337 **RIPRISTINI** (IRE) 11

585 **RIPTIDE** (GB) 23
35 **RISHIKESH** (GB) 9
305 **RISING KHELEYF** (IRE) 3
299 **RISING LEGEND** (GB) 240
495 **RISK IT** (GB) 9
456 **RISK RUNNER** (IRE) 16
380 **RISKAREAS** (FR) 90
462 **RISKIE THINGS** (GB) F 38
659 **RISKIER** (GB) 39
35 **RISKIT FORA BISKIT** (IRE) 86
682 **RITE OF PASSAGE** (GB) 16
547 **RITH BOB** (FR) 3
343 **RIVAGE D'OR** (FR) 44
563 **RIVAL D'ESTRUVAL** (FR) 5
708 **RIVAS RHAPSODY** (IRE) 13
661 **RIVER ARDECHE** (GB) 8
395 **RIVER D'OR** (FR) 16
142 **RIVER DRAGON** (IRE) 10
418 **RIVER DU NORD** (FR) 19
22 **RIVER EXIT** (FR) 3
299 **RIVER FANTASY** (USA) C 241
329 **RIVER FLOW** (USA) F 42
283 **RIVER GRAND** (IRE) F 86
321 **RIVER MAIGUE** (IRE) 134
338 **RIVER NESS** (GB) F 13
38 **RIVER NOVA** (GB) 13
364 **RIVER PAGEANT** (GB) 22
410 **RIVER PURPLE** (GB) 16
695 **RIVER RHAPSODY** (IRE) 67
297 **RIVER SALTS** (IRE) G 4
351 **RIVER TAFF** (GB) 6
318 **RIVERAIN** (FR) 31
587 **RIVERAIN** (GB) C 7
466 **RIVERINE** (GB) C 80
380 **RIVERMOUTH** (GB) 91
383 **RIVERSIDE POPPET** (GB) 14
321 **RIVERSIDE THEATRE** (GB) 135
288 **RIVIERA RED** (IRE) 5
695 **RIVIERA STARS** (GB) 68
483 **RIVIERE RUBY** (GB) 10
166 **RIVIERE RUBY** (GB) 15
220 **RIVINGTON** (GB) 63
511 **RIWAN** (FR) 32
508 **RIYABA** (IRE) 86
564 **RJWA** (IRE) 67
262 **ROAD SHOW** (GB) 16
331 **ROALCO DE FARGES** (FR) 73
264 **ROANSTAR** (GB) 16
29 **ROATAN** (GB) 11
49 **ROAYH** (USA) 53
331 **ROB CONTI** (FR) 74
552 **ROBBIE** (GB) 34
457 **ROBBY BOBBY** (GB) 9
27 **ROBEMA** (GB) F 52
266 **ROBEMAKER** (GB) 25
343 **ROBERTO GOLDBACK** (IRE) 45
473 **ROBIN ANGEVIN** (GB) 86
331 **ROBIN DE CREUSE** (FR) 75
655 **ROBIN HOODS BAY** (GB) 4
312 **ROBIN OF SPRING** (FR) 12
178 **ROBIN'S COMMAND** (IRE) 19
489 **ROBINSON COLLONGES** (FR) 96
696 **ROBOBAR** (FR) 37
198 **ROBOUGG** (FR) 22
436 **ROBYN RUA** (IRE) 11
215 **ROC DE GUYE** (FR) 16
318 **ROCAILLE** (FR) 59
511 **ROCCARINA** (FR) 126

499 **ROCCO'S HALL** (IRE) 24
318 **ROCHELLE** (FR) 32
358 **ROCK A DOODLE DOO** (IRE) 11
477 **ROCK ANTHEM** (IRE) 9
299 **ROCK BAND** (GB) 97
519 **ROCK CANYON** (IRE) 21
285 **ROCK CRITIC** (GB) 112
682 **ROCK CRITIC** (IRE) 17
80 **ROCK LILY** (GB) C 25
593 **ROCK ME GENTLY** (GB) 39
219 **ROCK MY SOUL** (IRE) 24
496 **ROCK OF AGES** (GB) 39
386 **ROCK OF ALLEN** (IRE) 20
99 **ROCK OF DEAUVILLE** (IRE) 12
265 **ROCK OF FIRE** (IRE) 13
35 **ROCK OF MONET** (GB) 46
384 **ROCK ON CANDY** (GB) 32
489 **ROCK ON RUBY** (GB) 97
400 **ROCK PEAK** (IRE) 21
268 **ROCK RELIEF** (IRE) 32
654 **ROCK SALT** (GB) C 135
520 **ROCK SONG** (GB) 41
299 **ROCK SUPREME** (GB) 98
29 **ROCK'N'ROLL DREAM** (IRE) 9
650 **ROCKABILLY** (FR) 57
147 **ROCKALONG** (IRE) C 25
23 **ROCKANDAHARDPLACE** (IRE) 3
408 **ROCKBURN** 70
299 **ROCKBURST** (GB) C 242
285 **ROCKCIDE** (USA) C 113
480 **ROCKET ROB** (IRE) 25
700 **ROCKETBALL** (IRE) 22
127 **ROCKFELLA** (IRE) 9
465 **ROCKFIELD ABBEY** (GB) 19
58 **ROCKGOAT** (IRE) 47
265 **ROCKIN N REELIN** (USA) 14
299 **ROCKINANTE** (FR) 99
476 **ROCKING AND REELIN** (GB) 61
157 **ROCKITEER** (IRE) 24
249 **ROCKME COCKNEY** (GB) 34
119 **ROCKPOOL** (GB) 75
180 **ROCKTHERUNWAY** (IRE) 35
263 **ROCKWEILLER** (GB) 14
489 **ROCKY CREEK** (IRE) 98
10 **ROCKY ELSOM** (USA) 13
503 **ROCKY RACCOON** (IRE) 52
33 **ROCKY REBEL** (GB) 19
19 **ROCKY REEF** (GB) 88
42 **ROCKY RYAN** (IRE) 19
473 **ROCKYABOYA** (IRE) 87
417 **RODE TWO DESTINY** (IRE) 15
61 **RODRIGO DE FREITAS** (IRE) 12
91 **RODRIGO DE TORRES** (GB) 16
254 **RODY** (FR) 44
362 **ROE VALLEY** (IRE) 14
507 **ROEDEAN** (IRE) 26
564 **ROERO** (FR) 68
489 **ROGER BEANTOWN** (IRE) 99
321 **ROGER SEZ** (IRE) 96
21 **ROGUE DANCER** (FR) 4
698 **ROGUE REPORTER** (IRE) 23
525 **ROI DE ROSE** (FR) 79
408 **ROI DE TREVE** 19
321 **ROI TOSCAN** (FR) 136
321 **ROJO VIVO** (FR) 137
246 **ROLANTA** (FR) 11
178 **ROLE ON** (IRE) 20
294 **ROLECARR** (IRE) 7

328 **ROLEXA** (GB) C 116
543 **ROLL OF THUNDER** (GB) 40
8 **ROLL OVER ROSE** (IRE) 20
331 **ROLL THE DICE** (IRE) 76
489 **ROLLING ACES** (IRE) 100
476 **ROLLWITHTHEPUNCHES** (GB) 62
473 **ROLLY BABY** (FR) 88
387 **ROMAN AROUND** (GB) 26
544 **ROMAN FLAME** (GB) 4
539 **ROMAN LANDING** (GB) 4
384 **ROMAN MYST** (IRE) 33
222 **ROMAN RULER** (FR) 5
161 **ROMAN SEAL** (IRE) 35
57 **ROMAN SENATE** (IRE) 21
30 **ROMAN SIOUX** (IRE) 14
54 **ROMAN STRAIT** (GB) 7
407 **ROMANCING** (GB) C 61
637 **ROMANESCO** (FR) 13
147 **ROMANOFF** (IRE) 102
111 **ROMANTIC** (IRE) 66
285 **ROMANTIC RETREAT** (GB) F 114
614 **ROMANTIC STROLL** (IRE) 25
219 **ROMANTICA** (GB) 97
673 **ROMANTICIZE** (GB) 5
51 **ROMANY QUEST** (GB) 5
659 **ROMANY RYME** (GB) 40
673 **ROMANY SPIRIT** (IRE) 9
111 **ROME** (GB) 148
191 **ROMEO MONTAGUE** (IRE) 6
151 **ROMNEY MARSH** (GB) 9
5 **ROMPER STOMPER** (GB) 3
380 **ROMULUS D'ARTAIX** (FR) 92
642 **RON** (GB) 20
260 **RONALD GEE** (IRE) 23
113 **RONDEAU** (GB) 16
601 **RONINSKI** (IRE) 19
296 **RONNIE RHINO** (GB) 35
366 **ROO** (GB) C 196
700 **ROODEE GIANT** (IRE) 23
64 **ROODEE QUEEN** (GB) 17
364 **ROODLE** (GB) 13
51 **ROOFTOP RAINBOW** (IRE) 6
279 **ROPARTA AVENUE** (GB) 10
503 **ROPER** (IRE) 53
444 **RORY BOY** (GB) 15
178 **ROS CASTLE** (IRE) 21
304 **ROS THE BOSS** (IRE) F 109
193 **ROSA BURN** (GB) 61
496 **ROSA CLARA** (FR) 40
601 **ROSA LUXEMBURG** (GB) 20
10 **ROSAFI** (IRE) G 14
296 **ROSAIRLIE** (IRE) 36
141 **ROSAMIXA** (FR) C 73
569 **ROSAWA** (FR) C 128
366 **ROSBY WAVES** (USA) 129
632 **ROSCO FLYER** (IRE) 6
654 **ROSCOE** (GB) 70
643 **ROSE AURORA** (IRE) 17
237 **ROSE BOUNTY** (GB) G 53
269 **ROSE DE RITA** (GB) 5
29 **ROSE ET NOIRE** (IRE) 54
101 **ROSE KARANJA** (GB) G 25
35 **ROSE MADDER** (GB) 47
75 **ROSE OF MOONCOIN** (IRE) F 28
10 **ROSE OF SALOME** (IRE) G 15
525 **ROSE OF THE MOON** (IRE) 80
390 **ROSE PARADE** (GB) F 46
654 **ROSE SEASON** (GB) 71

252 **ROSE THYNE** (IRE) G 10
564 **ROSEBERY AVENUE** (FR) 69
645 **ROSEIN** (GB) F 18
299 **ROSELYN** (GB) C 243
612 **ROSENBLATT** (GER) 9
286 **ROSENEATH** (IRE) 13
569 **ROSENSAUM** (GB) 129
19 **ROSERROW** (GB) 89
83 **ROSES LEGEND** (GB) 7
203 **ROSEWATER** (GER) F 16
462 **ROSEWOOD LAD** (GB) 4
601 **ROSIE HALL** (IRE) 73
119 **ROSIE PROBERT** (GB) 44
602 **ROSIE RAYMOND** (GB) 5
466 **ROSINKA** (IRE) F 81
457 **ROSOFF** (IRE) 10
343 **ROSS NA RIGH** (IRE) 46
76 **ROSSBRIN** (IRE) 8
91 **ROSSELLI** (IRE) 32
223 **ROSSETTI** (GB) 17
63 **ROSSINI'S DANCER** (GB) 9
119 **ROSSLYN CASTLE** (GB) 45
404 **ROSSMORE LAD** (IRE) 40
3 **ROSTRUM** (FR) 35
213 **ROSY OUTLOOK** (USA) C 24
440 **ROSY SCINTILLA** (IRE) F 16
174 **ROTHRES** (FR) 32
299 **ROTUNDA** (GB) C 244
681 **ROUBILIAC** (USA) 46
223 **ROUBLE** (GB) 67
160 **ROUDOUDOU VILLE** (FR) 33
299 **ROUGEMONT** (IRE) 100
328 **ROUGETTE** (GB) 12
657 **ROUGH TIMES** (GB) 66
331 **ROUGHAM** (GB) 77
573 **ROUGHLYN** (GB) 66
663 **ROULEZ COOL** (GB) 7
505 **ROUND THE HORN** (IRE) 6
489 **ROUND TOM** (FR) 101
109 **ROUNDELAY** (GB) 16
339 **ROUQUINE SAUVAGE** (GB) 17
318 **ROUTINE** (USA) C 60
61 **ROWAN LIGHTENING** 41
517 **ROWAN LODGE** (IRE) 7
61 **ROWAN RHAPSODY** 30
61 **ROWAN RIDGE** (GB) 13
73 **ROWAN SPIRIT** (GB) 22
486 **ROWAN TIGER** (GB) 9
489 **ROWDY RAMPAGE** (IRE) 102
570 **ROWDY ROCHER** (IRE) 56
362 **ROWE PARK** (GB) 15
233 **ROWLESTONE LAD** (GB) 12
174 **ROXANE BRUERE** (FR) 33
569 **ROXELANA** (IRE) 69
496 **ROXELANA** (IRE) 41
520 **ROXY FLYER** (IRE) 12
40 **ROY ROCKET** (FR) 21
307 **ROY'S LEGACY** (GB) 12
585 **ROYAL ACCLAMATION** (IRE) 24
397 **ROYAL ALCOR** (IRE) 28
634 **ROYAL AND ANCIENT** (IRE) 10
339 **ROYAL ANNOUNCEMENT** (GB) 18
708 **ROYAL AWARD** (GB) 9
259 **ROYAL BAJAN** (USA) 8
147 **ROYAL BALLET** (GB) 103
38 **ROYAL BLADE** (IRE) 9
366 **ROYAL BLUE** (GB) F 197
304 **ROYAL BLUE STAR** (IRE) 58

543 **ROYAL BONSAI** (GB) 23
89 **ROYAL BOX** (GB) 9
299 **ROYAL CHALLIS** (GB) 245
489 **ROYAL CHARM** (FR) 103
53 **ROYAL CHATELIER** (FR) 9
5 **ROYAL CITY** (GB) 4
391 **ROYAL COMMISSION** (IRE) 50
201 **ROYAL COMPOSER** (IRE) 51
131 **ROYAL CURTSY** (GB) 6
503 **ROYAL DIAMOND** (GB) 54
200 **ROYAL DISTANT** (USA) C 82
127 **ROYAL DUTCH** (GB) 13
233 **ROYAL ENCHANTRESS** (GB) 13
383 **ROYAL ENTOURAGE** (GB) 15
342 **ROYAL ENVOY** (IRE) 13
326 **ROYAL ETIQUETTE** (IRE) 22
212 **ROYAL GIG** (GB) 9
639 **ROYAL GUARDSMAN** (GB) 44
283 **ROYAL INTRUDER** (GB) 57
500 **ROYAL JENRAY** (GB) 19
607 **ROYAL KICKS** (FR) 12
237 **ROYAL LADYBIRD** (GB) 24
411 **ROYAL MACKINTOSH** (GB) 2
476 **ROYAL MILE** (GB) 63
647 **ROYAL MISTRESS** (GB) F 32
259 **ROYAL NASHKOVA** (GB) C 49
339 **ROYAL NATIVE** (GB) 19
207 **ROYAL OPERA** (GB) 40
111 **ROYAL PECULIAR** (GB) 13
372 **ROYAL PREMIER** (IRE) 6
237 **ROYAL PREMIUM** (GB) 2
27 **ROYAL PROFILE** (GB) 23
191 **ROYAL RAZZINI** (GB) 7
150 **ROYAL REVERIE** (GB) 22
385 **ROYAL REYAH** (GB) 17
650 **ROYAL RIVIERA** (GB) 58
666 **ROYAL ROCK** (GB) 15
508 **ROYAL SEA** (IRE) 38
285 **ROYAL SECRETS** (IRE) F 115
253 **ROYAL SELECTION** (IRE) 8
519 **ROYAL STRAIGHT** (GB) 11
64 **ROYAL SUPREMACY** (IRE) C 29
625 **ROYAL SWAIN** (GB) 35
643 **ROYAL TRIX** (GB) 42
259 **ROYAL TROOPER** (IRE) 9
98 **ROYAL VIC** (IRE) 12
65 **ROYAL VILLAN** (IRE) 9
508 **ROYAL VISIT** (IRE) 39
285 **ROYALE FIGURINE** (IRE) C 116
657 **ROYALE PERFORMANCE** (GB) 67
141 **ROYALE RANSOM** (GB) 55
697 **ROYALE'S CHARTER** (GB) 19
286 **ROYAUME BLEU** (FR) 14
233 **ROYBUOY** (GB) 14
192 **ROZ** (GB) 29
699 **ROZOLENN** (FR) 68
35 **RUACANA** (GB) 48
2 **RUBAN** (IRE) 105
489 **RUBEN COTTER** (GB) 104
533 **RUBI DIA** (GB) 4
508 **RUBICON BAY** (GB) 8
508 **RUBINA** (IRE) 40
359 **RUBIPRESENT** (IRE) 25
147 **RUBRICS** (IRE) 55
49 **RUBY AFFAIR** (IRE) C 145
657 **RUBY BAY** (IRE) 68
34 **RUBY BROOK** (GB) 12
16 **RUBY CROWN** (GB) 37

397 **RUBY DOO** (GB) 29
447 **RUBY GLASS** (IRE) 44
472 **RUBY GLOW** (GB) 24
40 **RUBY IN THE DUST** (GB) 11
267 **RUBY JOY** (GB) F 7
35 **RUBY NIGHT** (IRE) 49
703 **RUBY VALENTINE** (FR) 3
59 **RUDANPHAST** (IRE) 27
513 **RUDEMEISTER** (IRE) 8
68 **RUDINERO** (IRE) 9
634 **RUFF DIAMOND** (USA) 11
116 **RUFUS STONE** (USA) 9
102 **RUGGED CROSS** (GB) 36
160 **RUGGED JACK** (FR) 34
255 **RUGGED JEM** (IRE) 1
328 **RUGOSA** (GB) 57
299 **RULE BOOK** (IRE) 101
657 **RULER OF ALL** (IRE) 69
212 **RULER'S HONOUR** (IRE) 5
380 **RULING PARTY** (GB) 93
364 **RUM PUNCH** (GB) 23
663 **RUMBAVU** (IRE) 8
671 **RUMBLE OF THUNDER** (IRE) 8
49 **RUMH** (GER) 54
287 **RUMMAGING** (IRE) 22
469 **RUN ALONG BOY** (GB) 34
573 **RUN FAT LASS RUN** (GB) 103
447 **RUN IT TWICE** (IRE) 96
364 **RUN OF THE DAY** (GB) 24
59 **RUN TO FLY** (IRE) 28
340 **RUN WITH THE WIND** (IRE) 28
55 **RUNAIOCHT** (IRE) 107
392 **RUNAROUND RITA** (FR) 6
699 **RUNAWAY GREEN** (FR) 69
111 **RUNNING DEER** (IRE) 9
318 **RUNNING DEER** (USA) 33
146 **RUNNING MATE** (IRE) 9
445 **RUNNING WATER** (GB) 6
666 **RUNNINGLIKETHEWIND** (IRE) 48
72 **RUNSHAN** (IRE) 12
659 **RUNSWICK RELAX** (GB) 41
119 **RUNWAY GIRL** (IRE) 46
102 **RUPEETOUPS** (GB) 16
669 **RUPERT BEAR** (GB) 4
90 **RUPERT BRUSH** (GB) 3
317 **RUPERT'S PRINCESS** (IRE) C 8
665 **RUSCELLO** (IRE) 8
110 **RUSH CAD** (FR) 19
3 **RUSLAND** (IRE) 106
394 **RUSSE BLANC** (FR) 21
619 **RUSSELLIANA** (GB) 69
236 **RUSSELLSTOWN BOY** (GB) 5
507 **RUSSIAN BULLET** (GB) 27
472 **RUSSIAN CONQUEST** (GB) 25
381 **RUSSIAN FLAG** (FR) 15
263 **RUSSIAN GEORGE** (IRE) 15
352 **RUSSIAN ICE** (GB) 10
529 **RUSSIAN RAVE** (GB) 17
619 **RUSSIAN REALM** (GB) 145
174 **RUSSIAN ROMANCE** (IRE) 34
529 **RUSSIAN RUMBA** (IRE) 33
116 **RUSSIAN SILK** (GB) C 29
219 **RUSSIAN SNOWS** (IRE) C 176
219 **RUSSIAN SOCIETY** (GB) C 177
212 **RUSSIAN WINTER** (GB) 6
185 **RUSSIE WITH LOVE** (GB) 13
188 **RUST** (IRE) 40
380 **RUSTARIX** (FR) 94

480 **RUSTIC DEACON** (GB) 26
237 **RUSTIC GOLD** (GB) 26
705 **RUSTIC PRINCESS** (IRE) C 29
273 **RUSTY ROCKET** (IRE) 15
18 **RUTHERGLEN** (GB) 90
700 **RYAN STYLE** (IRE) 24
699 **RYDALIS** (FR) 70
318 **RYDE** F 61
327 **RYDON PYNES** (GB) 9
329 **RYE** (IRE) F 43
36 **RYE CROSS** (IRE) 1
619 **RYE HOUSE** (IRE) 70
394 **RYE ROCKET** (GB) 22
283 **RYEDALE DANCER** (IRE) 58
645 **RYEDALE LASS** (GB) 7
201 **RYEDANE** (IRE) 52
283 **RYLEE MOOCH** (GB) 59
681 **RYSBRACK** (USA) 47
366 **RYTHMIC** (GB) 130
570 **RYTON RUNNER** (IRE) 57
218 **SA SUFFIT** (FR) 21
628 **SAABIQ** (USA) C 37
628 **SAABOOG** (GB) 13
49 **SAAMIDD** (GB) 55
55 **SAANA** (IRE) C 108
654 **SABAWEEYA** (GB) 13
180 **SABLONNE** (USA) C 51
220 **SABORE** (GB) 64
520 **SABORIDO** (USA) 13
511 **SABRATAH** (GB) 33
519 **SABRATHA** (IRE) 12
35 **SABRE** (GB) 87
619 **SABRE TOOTH** (IRE) 71
357 **SABREON** (GB) C 32
629 **SABRINA BROWN** (GB) F 23
693 **SABYS GEM** (IRE) 4
471 **SACCO D'ORO** (GB) 19
285 **SACRE COEUR** (GB) F 117
66 **SACRE TOI** (FR) 3
191 **SACRED LOVE** (IRE) C 37
669 **SACRED MOUNTAIN** (GB) 5
243 **SACRED PEARL** (IRE) C 13
111 **SACRED SONG** (FR) F 149
497 **SACRILEGE** (GB) 5
176 **SACROSANCTUS** (GB) 12
669 **SADDLE PACK** (IRE) 5
508 **SADDLER'S ROCK** (IRE) 7
424 **SADDLERS STORM** (IRE) 24
100 **SADDLERS' SECRET** (GB) 9
237 **SADDLERS' SUPREME** (FR) 27
3 **SADEEK'S SONG** (USA) 36
331 **SADLER'S RISK** (IRE) 78
53 **SADLER'S STAR** (GER) 10
49 **SADMA** (GB) 107
570 **SAFARI ADVENTURES** (IRE) 58
331 **SAFARI JOURNEY** (USA) 79
387 **SAFARI SUNSEEKER** (IRE) 27
328 **SAFARJAL** (IRE) 58
366 **SAFE HOUSE** (IRE) 131
326 **SAFE INVESTMENT** (USA) 23
201 **SAFFA GARDEN** (IRE) C 122
201 **SAFFA HILL** (GB) 97
374 **SAFFRON LORD** (GB) 29
43 **SAFFRON PARK** (GB) 27
93 **SAFFRON SAM** (GB) 8
318 **SAFI WAFI** (IRE) 34
157 **SAFRAN DE COTTE** (FR) 25

480 **SAFWAAN** (GB) 27
123 **SAGA BOREALE** (USA) 42
434 **SAGA DE TERCEY** (FR) 112
161 **SAGA LOUT** (GB) 69
24 **SAGA SURPRISE** (FR) 19
569 **SAGARIYA** (FR) 70
569 **SAGAWARA** (GB) 71
534 **SAGESSE** (GB) 64
659 **SAGLIERE** (GB) 42
466 **SAGRAMOR** (GB) 24
643 **SAHARA BELLE** (USA) C 63
654 **SAHARA LADY** (IRE) F 136
457 **SAHARA SUNSHINE** (GB) 11
18 **SAHARAN AIR** (IRE) 56
12 **SAHARIA** (GB) 16
357 **SAHARIRI** (IRE) F 33
53 **SAHRATI** (GB) 11
408 **SAHYAP** 71
641 **SAIGON** (GB) 6
508 **SAIK** (USA) F 87
225 **SAIL HOME** (GB) 13
40 **SAIL PAST** (GB) 16
603 **SAILOR'S SOVEREIGN** (FR) 25
499 **SAILORS WARN** (IRE) 25
553 **SAINGLEND** (GB) 12
657 **SAINT ARE** (FR) 70
219 **SAINT BAUDOLINO** (IRE) 98
417 **SAINT BONIFACE** (GB) 16
287 **SAINT BY DAY** (IRE) 23
408 **SAINT DE GARDE** (FR) 72
286 **SAINT DENIS** (FR) 15
192 **SAINT HELENA** (IRE) 3
467 **SAINT HILARY** (GB) 27
54 **SAINT IRENE** (GB) 20
643 **SAINT JEROME** (IRE) 64
59 **SAINT LUKE** (IRE) 29
86 **SAINT PERAY** (FR) 18
489 **SAINT ROQUE** (FR) 105
29 **SAINT THOMAS** (FR) 105
410 **SAINT THOMAS** (IRE) 13
73 **SAINTE ECALINE** 73
467 **SAINTE ROQUE** 74
59 **SAINTLY LADY** (IRE) 30
614 **SAINTLY SPEECH** (USA) C 54
602 **SAIRAAM** (IRE) 6
285 **SAITARA** (GB) 52
49 **SAJJHAA** (GB) 56
146 **SAKHEE'S PEARL** (GB) 10
34 **SAKHEERA** (GB) 48
117 **SAKHYA** (FR) C 47
588 **SAKTOON** (USA) 22
397 **SALAAHEB** (IRE) 45
3 **SALACIA** (GB) 35
249 **SALALAH** (GB) F 43
564 **SALAMANSA** (FR) 70
25 **SALEAL** (GB) 8
188 **SALEROSA** (IRE) 5
208 **SALFORD ART** (IRE) 25
208 **SALFORD DREAM** (GB) 26
58 **SALFORD EXCEL** (GB) 75
208 **SALFORD PRINCE** (IRE) 7
108 **SALFORD ROSE** (GB) 34
12 **SALIENT** (GB) 17
488 **SALIK TAG** (USA) 35
564 **SALISBURY BLUE** (FR) 71
644 **SALLY FRIDAY** (IRE) 8
259 **SALLY PEPPER** (USA) 32

7 **SALLY'S SWANSONG** (GB) 9
241 **SALLY'S TWINS** (GB) G 12
380 **SALMANAZAR** (GER) 95
400 **SALONTYRE** (GER) 22
597 **SALOOMY** (GB) 50
503 **SALPIERRE** (IRE) 55
466 **SALSA STEPS** (USA) F 82
125 **SALSKA** (GB) G 4
125 **SALSKA** (GB) F 3
358 **SALTIRE BLUE** (GB) 24
522 **SALTO D'ALBAIN** (FR) 20
489 **SALUBRIOUS** (IRE) 106
304 **SALUDOS** (IRE) 59
525 **SALUT FLO** (FR) 81
286 **SALUT HONORE** (FR) 16
183 **SALUT L'AMI** (FR) 21
248 **SALUT L'AS** (FR) 8
116 **SALUTARY** (GB) 25
180 **SALVA** (GB) G 52
625 **SALVINIA** (USA) F 36
552 **SAM D'OC** (FR) 35
531 **SAM HALL** (FR) 22
456 **SAM LORD** (GB) 17
690 **SAM NOMBULIST** (GB) 7
689 **SAM PATCH** (GB) 14
539 **SAM'S PRIDE** (GB) 5
619 **SAMAAH** (IRE) 72
214 **SAMADILLA** (IRE) C 74
473 **SAMAIN** (GER) 89
219 **SAMANA CAY** (USA) 99
461 **SAMARINNDA** (IRE) G 30
534 **SAMARKAND** (IRE) 8
708 **SAMASANA** (IRE) 20
564 **SAMBA CHRYSS** (IRE) 72
3 **SAMBA KING** (GB) 108
213 **SAMBA NIGHT** (IRE) 18
56 **SAMBALA** (IRE) C 37
282 **SAMBALA** (IRE) C 5
161 **SAMBARINA** (IRE) C 70
552 **SAMBELUCKY** (IRE) 36
650 **SAME DIFFERENCE** (IRE) 59
366 **SAMEDI** (GB) 132
408 **SAMETEGAL** 75
652 **SAMIZDAT** (FR) 6
117 **SAMMINDER** (IRE) 27
597 **SAMMY ALEXANDER** (GB) 18
688 **SAMMY SPIDERMAN** (GB) 15
54 **SAMMYMAN** (GB) 8
447 **SAMOAN** (IRE) 45
476 **SAMSON COLLONGES** (FR) 64
380 **SAMSONS SON** (GB) 96
53 **SAMUEL GEORGE** (GB) 12
442 **SAMURAI SWORD** (GB) 37
699 **SAMURAI WAY** (GB) 71
388 **SAMYNTHA** (FR) 48
599 **SAN ANTONIO** (GB) 9
434 **SAN BELLINO** (GB) 113
476 **SAN CASSIANO** (IRE) 65
128 **SAN JOSE** (IRE) 2
134 **SAN MARINO** (FR) 6
564 **SAN PEDRO** 73
561 **SAN TELM** (IRE) 11
109 **SANAD** (IRE) 17
569 **SANARIYA** (IRE) F 130
225 **SANCHO PANZA** (GB) 14
43 **SANCIA** (IRE) C 46
489 **SANCTUAIRE** (FR) 107
385 **SAND ORCHID** (GB) 22

496 **SAND PIRATE** (CAN) C 87
1 **SAND SKIER** (GB) 3
34 **SANDBANKS SIZZLER** (IRE) 13
447 **SANDBETWEENOURTOES** (IRE) 46
363 **SANDFRANKSKIPSGO** (GB) 9
144 **SANDFRANKSKIPSGO** (GB) 4
111 **SANDGLASS** (GB) F 150
286 **SANDOFTHECOLOSSEUM** (IRE) 17
619 **SANDS OF FORTUNE** (IRE) 73
207 **SANDS OF VATERSAY** (GB) 41
696 **SANDTIME** (IRE) C 63
130 **SANDTIME** (IRE) F 16
3 **SANDUSKY** (GB) 38
241 **SANDWITH** (GB) 3
564 **SANDY'S CHARM** (FR) 13
610 **SANDY'S DOUBLE** (GB) 16
157 **SANDYNOW** (IRE) 26
467 **SANGRAIL** (GB) 28
600 **SANIMA** (IRE) 47
311 **SANITY** (IRE) 7
219 **SANJIDA** (IRE) F 178
447 **SANKATY LIGHT** (USA) F 150
108 **SANNIBEL** (GB) 35
496 **SANS FRONTIÈRES** (IRE) 8
418 **SANS SA DAME** (FR) 13
59 **SANSILI** (GB) 31
511 **SANSIWA** (IRE) 84
201 **SANTA FE STINGER** (GB) 123
447 **SANTA SOPHIA** (IRE) C 97
570 **SANTA'S SON** (IRE) 59
460 **SANTADELACRUZE** (GB) 119
408 **SANTALINE** 76
59 **SANTAMINA** (IRE) 32
299 **SANTARINI** (IRE) 102
434 **SANTAVINO** (IRE) G 114
108 **SANTERA** (IRE) 36
519 **SANTIAGO BOY** (GB) 13
43 **SANTIBURI GIRL** (GB) F 47
700 **SANTINHO** (IRE) 25
699 **SANTO THOMAS** (FR) 72
107 **SANTRY** (GB) 30
288 **SAOI** (IRE) 35
645 **SAPHILA** (IRE) F 19
585 **SAPHIR RIVER** (FR) 25
254 **SAPHIRE NIGHT** (GB) 45
682 **SAPPHIRE** (IRE) 4
472 **SAPPHIRE ROUGE** (IRE) 26
473 **SARABAD** (FR) 90
178 **SARABELLE** (FR) 22
308 **SARAH'S ART** (IRE) 8
681 **SARANDO** (GB) 48
578 **SARANGOO** (GB) 1
573 **SARDANAPALUS** (GB) 67
74 **SAREEAH** (IRE) 50
246 **SARENICE** (FR) 12
697 **SARIKA** (FR) 20
569 **SARKIYLA** (FR) 72
699 **SAROQUE** (IRE) 73
394 **SARRACO** (FR) 23
49 **SARRSAR** (GB) 57
343 **SARTEANO** (FR) 47
625 **SARTINGO** (IRE) 37
249 **SASHEEN** (GB) 16
116 **SASKIA'S DREAM** (GB) 10
346 **SASLONG** (GB) 133
217 **SASSANIAN** (IRE) 10
372 **SASSI SIOUX** (GB) 8
500 **SATANIC BEAT** (IRE) 10

522 **SATICON** (GB) 21
161 **SATIN CAPE** (IRE) C 71
350 **SATINDRA** (IRE) 2
29 **SATOPANTH** (GB) 55
331 **SATOU** (IRE) 80
558 **SATWA BALLERINA** (GB) 3
488 **SAUCY BROWN** (IRE) 36
530 **SAUCY BUCK** (IRE) 9
43 **SAUCY CAT** (IRE) 28
520 **SAUCY MINX** (GB) 65
380 **SAUDI PEARL** (IRE) 97
597 **SAUNTA** (GB) 17
657 **SAUTE** (GB) 71
534 **SAVANNA LA MAR** (USA) 4
16 **SAVANT BLEU** (FR) 38
181 **SAVARONOLA** (USA) 4
149 **SAVARONOLA** (USA) 7
123 **SAVE HER NAME** (FR) 43
107 **SAVE THE BEES** (GB) 14
625 **SAVEIRO** (FR) 38
424 **SAVELLO** (IRE) 25
39 **SAVELLO** (IRE) 15
503 **SAVES TIME** (IRE) 56
619 **SAVIDA** (IRE) 74
304 **SAVILLE ROW** (IRE) 60
318 **SAVOIR** (FR) 62
214 **SAVVY SHOPPER** (USA) F 75
460 **SAWAGO** (FR) 81
74 **SAWAHILL** (GB) 20
699 **SAWPIT SAMBA** (FR) 74
699 **SAWPIT SUPREME** (GB) 75
402 **SAXBY** (IRE) 4
653 **SAXON HOUSE** (IRE) 17
191 **SAXON SOLDIER** (GB) 73
519 **SAXONETTE** (GB) 14
643 **SAYEDAH** (IRE) C 65
188 **SAYING GRACE** (FR) F 41
49 **SAYTARA** (IRE) 108
359 **SCALES** (IRE) 26
170 **SCALLEYS RUN** (GB) 4
226 **SCAMALLACH** (IRE) 25
32 **SCAMPERDALE** (GB) 21
681 **SCAMPI BOY** (IRE) 49
117 **SCARABOCIO** (GB) 28
655 **SCARBOROUGH LILY** (GB) 5
643 **SCARLET BELLE** (GB) 43
556 **SCARLET FIRE** (IRE) 38
214 **SCARLET ROCKS** (IRE) 27
70 **SCARLET RUBY** (GB) 3
8 **SCARLET RUBY** (GB) 21
336 **SCARLET STRAND** (GB) 43
599 **SCARLET WHISPERS** (GB) 15
241 **SCARLET WOMAN** (GB) C 20
643 **SCARLETT FEVER** (GB) 44
174 **SCARLETT O'TARA** (GB) 35
447 **SCARLETT ROSE** (GB) F 98
219 **SCATINA** (IRE) F 179
366 **SCATTER DICE** (IRE) 134
302 **SCEAL SIOG** (IRE) G 11
55 **SCEILG** (IRE) 109
188 **SCENTPASTPARADISE** (GB) 42
486 **SCHINDLER'S GOLD** (IRE) 10
343 **SCHINKEL** (IRE) 48
359 **SCHINKEN OTTO** (IRE) 27
503 **SCHISM** (GB) 57
519 **SCHMOOZE** (IRE) 22
511 **SCHNAPS** (FR) 85
473 **SCHOLARS MATE** (IRE) 91

304 **SCHOLARS PRINCESS** (IRE) 61
626 **SCHOLASTICA** (GB) 14
102 **SCHOOL FEES** (GB) 37
42 **SCHOOL FOR SCANDAL** (IRE) 20
420 **SCHUMPTERS LAD** (IRE) 32
58 **SCIAMPIN** (GB) 17
55 **SCINTILLULA** (IRE) 110
559 **SCOGLIO** (GB) 6
657 **SCORCHED SON** (IRE) 72
150 **SCOTER FONTAINE** (FR) 23
214 **SCOTSBROOK CLOUD** (GB) 28
626 **SCOTSBROOK LEGEND** (GB) 15
473 **SCOTSIRISH** (IRE) 92
267 **SCOTSWELL** (GB) 8
98 **SCOTTISH BOOGIE** (IRE) 13
101 **SCOTTISH CLOVER** (GB) G 26
113 **SCOTTISH GLEN** (GB) 17
213 **SCOTTISH STAR** (GB) 5
619 **SCOTTISH VESPERS** (IRE) 75
410 **SCOURIE BAY** (GB) 14
61 **SCOUTING FOR GIRLS** (IRE) 31
688 **SCRAPPER SMITH** (IRE) 16
214 **SCRIBE** (IRE) 29
38 **SCRIPT** (GB) 14
19 **SCRIPTURE** (IRE) F 151
358 **SCRIPTURIST** (GB) 25
598 **SCRIPTWRITER** (IRE) 4
147 **SCRUPUL** (IRE) 56
392 **SCULASTIC** (GB) 7
29 **SE LA VIE** (FR) C 106
19 **SEA ANEMONE** (GB) 90
447 **SEA CHORUS** (GB) F 99
275 **SEA CLIFF** (IRE) 7
147 **SEA FEVER** (FR) 57
123 **SEA FIGHT** (USA) 13
201 **SEA FLOWER** (IRE) 53
466 **SEA FRET** (GB) 55
607 **SEA FURY** (IRE) 13
351 **SEA JADE** (IRE) C 9
3 **SEA LORD** (IRE) 39
619 **SEA MOON** (GB) 5
119 **SEA OF HEARTBREAK** (IRE) 12
29 **SEA OF LAUGHTER** (USA) 107
98 **SEA OF THUNDER** (IRE) 14
248 **SEA SAFFRON** (GB) 9
26 **SEA SALT** (GB) 9
299 **SEA SHANTY** (USA) 246
147 **SEA SMOKE** (IRE) 58
19 **SEA SOLDIER** (IRE) 25
643 **SEA THE FLAMES** (IRE) 18
318 **SEA TRIAL** (FR) 35
647 **SEAGREEN** (IRE) C 33
388 **SEAHORSE** (FR) 84
223 **SEAL OF APPROVAL** (IRE) 39
102 **SEAL ROCK** (GB) 17
237 **SEAMSTER** (GB) 28
102 **SEAMUS SHINDIG** (GB) 18
657 **SEAN OG KATY** (IRE) 73
329 **SEARCH AND RESCUE** (USA) 18
111 **SEARING HEAT** (USA) 14
34 **SEASIDE SIZZLER** (GB) 14
259 **SEASON SPIRIT** (GB) 33
499 **SEATTLE DRIVE** (IRE) 26
208 **SEATTLE RIBBON** (USA) C 42
188 **SEATTLE SOUNDER** (IRE) 22
60 **SEAWOOD** (GB) 10
564 **SEBIA** 74
289 **SECOND AFFAIR** (IRE) F 4

165 **SECOND BROOK** (IRE) 4
520 **SECOND OF MAY** (GB) C 66
152 **SECOND REEF** (GB) 2
54 **SECOND TO NUN** (IRE) 9
49 **SECRECY** (GB) 58
34 **SECRET ART** (IRE) 78
392 **SECRET ASSASSIN** (IRE) 8
116 **SECRET ASSET** (IRE) 11
18 **SECRET BEAU** (GB) 71
67 **SECRET BLEND** (GB) C 11
49 **SECRET CHARM** (IRE) C 146
30 **SECRET CITY** (IRE) 15
647 **SECRET COMBE** (IRE) C 34
367 **SECRET DANCER** (IRE) 10
476 **SECRET DESERT** (GB) 66
380 **SECRET EDGE** (GB) 98
147 **SECRET ENVOY** (GB) 59
467 **SECRET ERA** (GB) 8
711 **SECRET LODGE** (GB) 13
442 **SECRET LOOK** (GB) 31
511 **SECRET MARKS** (GB) 86
569 **SECRET NIGHT** (USA) 73
441 **SECRET PAST** (IRE) 11
327 **SECRET QUEEN** (GB) 66
223 **SECRET QUEST** (GB) 40
508 **SECRET SEA** (IRE) 41
534 **SECRET SONG** (GB) 66
466 **SECRET TALENT** (GB) 83
500 **SECRET VENUE** (GB) 5
20 **SECRET VIRTUE** (GB) 3
622 **SECRET WHISPER** (GB) C 7
622 **SECRET WHISPER** (GB) F 8
306 **SECRET WITNESS** (GB) 7
321 **SECRET WORLD** (IRE) 138
219 **SECRETE** (FR) 100
102 **SECRETLY** (GB) 55
58 **SECRETS AWAY** (IRE) 48
136 **SECURON LADY** (GB) F 11
307 **SEDGWICK** (GB) 5
201 **SEE CLEARLY** (GB) 98
266 **SEE EMILY PLAY** (IRE) 96
713 **SEE MORE TRICKS** (GB) F 9
240 **SEE THE LEGEND** (GB) 4
700 **SEE THE STORM** (GB) 26
30 **SEE VERMONT** (GB) 16
640 **SEE WHAT HAPPENS** (IRE) 15
34 **SEE YOU LATER** (GB) F 79
160 **SEEBRIGHT** (GB) 35
285 **SEE MAL AHA** (USA) C 118
434 **SEEDLESS** (GB) 115
206 **SEEDSMAN** (GB) 14
343 **SEEFOOD** (IRE) 49
61 **SEEK THE FAIR LAND** (GB) 14
141 **SEEKING MAGIC** (GB) 22
4 **SEEKING POWER** (IRE) 13
507 **SEEKING THE FUN** (USA) F 47
35 **SEEMENOMORE** (GB) 88
130 **SEFEMM** (GB) C 17
600 **SEGUIDA** (USA) 31
160 **SEIGNEUR DE GUERRE** (FR) 36
476 **SEIGNEUR DES BOIS** (FR) 67
456 **SEIZE** (GB) 18
564 **SEL DE PROVENCE** (FR) 97
75 **SELDOM** (GB) 12
543 **SELECT COMMITTEE** (GB) 24
686 **SELECTIVE SPIRIT** (GB) 14
328 **SELF CENTRED** (GB) 59
711 **SELF EMPLOYED** (GB) 14

119 **SELFARA** (GB) 47
520 **SELFSAME** (USA) 42
299 **SELINKA** (GB) C 247
442 **SELIQUE** (GB) C 32
102 **SELKIE'S FRIEND** (GB) 5
45 **SELKIRK SKY** (GB) C 26
74 **SEMAYYEL** (IRE) 51
147 **SEMEEN** (GB) 60
321 **SEMI COLON** (FR) 139
208 **SENATOR BONG** (GB) 43
268 **SENDALI** (GB) 33
699 **SENDINPOST** (GB) 76
476 **SENDIYM** (GB) 68
112 **SENESCHAL** (GB) 5
81 **SENIORS PET** (IRE) 9
233 **SENNA DA SILVA** (GB) F 21
366 **SENNOCKIAN STORM** (USA) 31
635 **SENOR ALCO** (GB) F 14
221 **SENOR TOMMIE** (IRE) 5
424 **SENSATIONAL SEMA** (IRE) 26
111 **SENSE OF JOY** (GB) C 151
682 **SENSE OF PURPOSE** (IRE) 19
219 **SENSE OF STYLE** (USA) F 180
632 **SENSIBILITY** (GB) C 20
299 **SENSUAL** (GB) 248
285 **SENTARIL** (GB) 53
503 **SENTIMENTALJOURNEY** (IRE) 58
54 **SENTOSA** (GB) 10
321 **SENTRY DUTY** (GB) 140
681 **SEPTEMBER BLAZE** (GB) 50
111 **SEPTENARIUS** (USA) 68
538 **SEPTOS** (GB) 14
619 **SEQUENCE** (FR) 76
226 **SEQUIN SLIPPERS** (IRE) G 26
328 **SEQUOIA** (GB) 60
59 **SERANWEN** (IRE) 33
304 **SEREIN** (IRE) 62
552 **SEREN GRIS** (GB) 37
552 **SEREN ROUGE** (GB) 38
129 **SERENATA** (IRE) 40
686 **SERENDIPITY BLUE** (GB) 15
511 **SERENITY STAR** (GB) 34
123 **SEREZ** (GB) 63
259 **SERGEANT ABLETT** (GB) 10
579 **SERGEANT PINK** (IRE) 11
18 **SERGEANT TROY** (IRE) 30
430 **SERIOUS BREACH** (GB) 5
511 **SERPINA** (GB) C 127
58 **SERRENIA** (IRE) F 76
111 **SET DREAMS** (GB) 69
16 **SET IN HER WAYS** (IRE) 39
621 **SET TO GO** (GB) 3
35 **SET TO MUSIC** (IRE) 10
333 **SETTER'S PRINCESS** (GB) 11
513 **SETTLEDOUTOFCOURT** (IRE) 9
331 **SEVEN DAYS** (IRE) 81
260 **SEVEN IS LUCKY** (IRE) 24
111 **SEVEN MAGICIANS** (USA) C 152
611 **SEVEN STARS** (GB) 10
569 **SEVEN SUMMITS** (GER) 74
534 **SEVEN VEILS** (IRE) 35
321 **SEVEN WOODS** (IRE) 141
45 **SEVEN YEAR ITCH** (IRE) 19
386 **SEVENTH HUSSAR** (GB) 21
285 **SEVENTH SIGN** (GB) 54
420 **SEVENTH SKY** (GER) 33
654 **SEVERIANO** (USA) 137
639 **SEW ON TARGET** (IRE) 45

388 **SEXY** (FR) 85
585 **SEYMOUR ALFIE** (GB) 26
585 **SEYMOUR ERIC** (GB) 27
703 **SEYMOUR LEGEND** (GB) 4
164 **SGT ROBERTS** (GB) 78
614 **SHAANARA** (IRE) F 26
285 **SHABIBA** (USA) C 119
654 **SHABORA** (IRE) 73
619 **SHADA** (IRE) 77
569 **SHADARPOUR** (IRE) 75
373 **SHADDAII** (FR) 23
51 **SHADES OF AUTUMN** (IRE) 7
141 **SHADES OF GREY** (GB) 23
539 **SHADESOFNAVY** (GB) 6
689 **SHADOW BOXER** (GB) 15
35 **SHADOW ROLL** (IRE) F 89
200 **SHADOWS LENGTHEN** (GB) 38
606 **SHADRACK** (GB) 35
380 **SHADY LANE** (GB) 99
366 **SHAGWA** (IRE) 198
451 **SHAHDAROBA** (IRE) 49
452 **SHAHMINA** (IRE) C 23
258 **SHAHRAZAD** (IRE) 3
654 **SHAHZAN** (IRE) 21
102 **SHAIYADIMA** (IRE) C 56
508 **SHAIYZAR** (IRE) 42
321 **SHAKALAKABOOMBOOM** (IRE) 142
254 **SHAKE THE BARLEY** (IRE) 46
640 **SHAKER STYLE** (USA) 16
473 **SHAKERVILZ** (FR) 93
525 **SHAKING HANDS** (IRE) 82
462 **SHAKTI** (GB) F 39
508 **SHALAMAN** (IRE) 43
108 **SHALAMBAR** (IRE) 37
381 **SHALATINA** (GB) 16
654 **SHALEEK** (GB) 74
697 **SHALIMAR FROMENTRO** (FR) 21
573 **SHALL WE DANCE** (GB) C 68
462 **SHALL WE TELL** (GB) C 40
34 **SHALLIKA** (IRE) G 49
227 **SHALLOON** (IRE) 24
525 **SHALLOW BAY** (GB) 83
34 **SHALLOW GROUND** (IRE) C 80
690 **SHALOO DIAMOND** (GB) 8
442 **SHALUCA** (GB) 8
299 **SHAMAAL NIBRAS** (USA) 103
460 **SHAMAHAN** (GB) 120
682 **SHAMANA** (USA) C 119
473 **SHAMAR** (FR) 94
628 **SHAMARDELIAH** (IRE) 14
569 **SHAMDARA** (IRE) C 131
180 **SHAMDARLEY** (IRE) 19
328 **SHAME ON YOU** (IRE) 61
146 **SHAMIR** (GB) 11
569 **SHAMIYRA** (IRE) 76
160 **SHAMMICK BOY** (IRE) 37
508 **SHAMOODA** (GB) 44
556 **SHAMOUR** (IRE) 39
569 **SHAMSIKHAN** (IRE) 77
263 **SHAN BLUE** (IRE) 16
200 **SHAN VALLEY** (IRE) 39
205 **SHANANN STAR** (IRE) 3
631 **SHANAVAZ** (GB) 9
465 **SHANE ROCK** (IRE) 20
699 **SHANGANI** (USA) 77
54 **SHANGAZI** (USA) F 25
226 **SHANIV** (IRE) 27
118 **SHANNAGARRY** (IRE) 19

626 **SHANNON NATIVE** (IRE) G 16
650 **SHANNONS BOY** (IRE) 60
134 **SHANNONS BOY** (IRE) 7
287 **SHANROD** (IRE) 24
266 **SHANTARAM** (GB) 97
414 **SHANTOU BREEZE** (IRE) 5
592 **SHARADIYA** (IRE) F 13
468 **SHARADIYN** (GB) 3
42 **SHARAKTI** (IRE) 21
147 **SHARAREH** (GB) 104
108 **SHARE OPTION** (GB) 38
247 **SHARED MOMENT** (IRE) 5
123 **SHAREEL** (FR) 64
508 **SHARESHA** (IRE) C 88
508 **SHARESTAN** (IRE) 8
569 **SHARETA** (IRE) 12
640 **SHARGA** (IRE) 2
635 **SHARIVARRY** (FR) 15
475 **SHARIYAN** (IRE) 21
508 **SHARLEEZ** (IRE) F 89
346 **SHARLENE'S QUEST** (IRE) 1
131 **SHARNEY SIKE** (IRE) 7
237 **SHARP AND CHIC** (GB) 29
287 **SHARP AND SMART** (IRE) 48
682 **SHARP CRISP AIR** (IRE) 120
682 **SHARP POINT** (IRE) C 121
188 **SHARP SHOES** (IRE) 6
440 **SHARP SOVEREIGN** (USA) 10
503 **SHARPSHOOTER** (GB) 59
147 **SHARQAWIYAH** (GB) 105
142 **SHARWAKOM** (IRE) 11
34 **SHASTYE** (IRE) F 81
447 **SHATARAH** (GB) C 100
705 **SHATIN SPIRIT** (IRE) 30
285 **SHATTER** (FR) 55
352 **SHAUNAS SPIRIT** (IRE) 11
451 **SHAVANSKY** (GB) 17
328 **SHAWKA** (GB) 62
588 **SHAWKANTANGO** (GB) 23
588 **SHAWS DIAMOND** (USA) 24
29 **SHAYALINA** (FR) 13
58 **SHBAKNI** (USA) F 77
355 **SHE WHO DARES WINS** (GB) 5
355 **SHE WHO DARES WINS** (IRE) G 4
302 **SHE'S A DREAMER** (IRE) G 12
362 **SHE'S HUMBLE** (IRE) 16
362 **SHE'S JOLLY** (IRE) 17
266 **SHE'S LATE** 147
496 **SHE'S LOADED** (USA) C 88
103 **SHE'S ON THE CASE** (IRE) 4
308 **SHE'S UNTOUCHABLE** (GB) 9
694 **SHE'SOLOVELY** (IRE) 4
508 **SHEBELLA** (IRE) 45
508 **SHEER BLISS** (IRE) F 90
569 **SHEHILA** (IRE) 132
43 **SHEIKH THE REINS** (IRE) 29
597 **SHEIKHZAYEDROAD** (GB) 52
462 **SHEILA'S BUDDY** (GB) 22
549 **SHEILA'S CASTLE** (IRE) 7
452 **SHEILA'S SECRET** (IRE) C 24
146 **SHELAGH** (IRE) 12
508 **SHELFORD** (IRE) 46
496 **SHELL GARLAND** (USA) C 89
648 **SHELOMOH** (IRE) 2
508 **SHEMAKA** (IRE) F 91
569 **SHEMBARA** (IRE) 78
410 **SHEMP** (GB) 15
569 **SHENDAMA** (FR) 79

19 **SHENKARA** (IRE) C 152
458 **SHENZHOU** (GB) 19
340 **SHERCO SPORTS** (IRE) 29
118 **SHERIFF HALL** (IRE) 20
166 **SHERJAWY** (IRE) 16
451 **SHERMAN MCCOY** (GB) 18
321 **SHERNANDO** (GB) 143
220 **SHERRY CHERIE** (IRE) 65
650 **SHERWANI WOLF** (IRE) 61
507 **SHESASMARTLADY** (IRE) F 48
529 **SHESHA BEAR** (GB) 18
167 **SHESLIKETHEWIND** (GB) 2
390 **SHESTHEMAN** (GB) 16
220 **SHEVINGTON** (GB) 66
299 **SHEWALKSINBEAUTY** (IRE) 16
451 **SHIELALIGH** (GB) C 50
366 **SHIELDMAIDEN** (USA) 32
473 **SHIFA** (GB) 95
573 **SHIFTING GOLD** (IRE) 25
71 **SHIFTING STAR** (IRE) 12
49 **SHIHAB** (IRE) 109
569 **SHIKARPOUR** (IRE) 133
199 **SHILPA** (IRE) 8
619 **SHIMMERING SAL** (GB) 146
654 **SHIMMERING SURF** (IRE) 22
628 **SHIMNA** (GB) F 38
457 **SHINE IN TIME** (IRE) 12
299 **SHINE LIKE A STAR** (GB) F 249
391 **SHINING EMBERS** (IRE) 51
671 **SHINING LIGHTS** (IRE) G 9
219 **SHINKO HERMES** (IRE) F 181
610 **SHINKO MOON** (GB) 17
418 **SHIP'S HILL** (IRE) 14
336 **SHIPBOARD ROMANCE** (IRE) 19
325 **SHIRATAKI** (IRE) 11
222 **SHIRLS SON SAM** (GB) 6
466 **SHIROCCO STAR** (GB) 56
407 **SHISHA THREESIXTY** (IRE) 6
579 **SHOAL BAY DREAMER** (GB) 12
420 **SHOCKINGTIMES** (IRE) 34
525 **SHOEGAZER** (GB) 84
643 **SHOHRAH** (IRE) F 147
285 **SHOLAAN** (IRE) 56
642 **SHOMBERG** (GB) 37
318 **SHOMOUKH** (USA) 36
318 **SHOMUS** (USA) 37
520 **SHOOGLE** (USA) C 67
475 **SHOOTIN THE BREEZE** (IRE) 19
513 **SHOOTING TIMES** (GB) 10
285 **SHORE PERFORMER** (IRE) 57
531 **SHOREACRES** (IRE) 23
619 **SHORT DANCE** (USA) F 147
664 **SHORT SUPPLY** (USA) 11
434 **SHORT TAKES** (USA) 116
573 **SHOSHONI WIND** (GB) 26
499 **SHOT FROM THE HIP** (GER) 27
19 **SHOT IN THE DARK** (IRE) 91
202 **SHOTAVODKA** (IRE) 85
97 **SHOTLEY MAC** (GB) 7
97 **SHOTLEY MUSIC** (GB) 11
149 **SHOUDA** (IRE) 8
682 **SHOW COURT** (IRE) 58
35 **SHOW ME THE LINE** (GB) 50
595 **SHOW PUBLIC** (FR) 3
520 **SHOWBIZ** (IRE) C 68
433 **SHOWBOATING** (GB) 24
446 **SHOWERING** (GB) F 89
619 **SHOWLADY** (USA) C 148

193 **SHOWMEPOWER** (IRE) 42
507 **SHOWMESOMETHING** (IRE) F 49
220 **SHOWSINGER** (GB) 67
655 **SHRAAYEF** (GB) C 23
98 **SHRAPNEL** (IRE) 15
655 **SHREDDING** (IRE) 16
328 **SHROPSHIRE** (IRE) 13
655 **SHUAILY** (PER) C 24
654 **SHUBAAT** (GB) 23
13 **SHUFFLEWING** (IRE) 2
10 **SHUIL ROYALE** (IRE) 16
49 **SHUJA** (USA) 110
407 **SHUKHOV** (IRE) 31
573 **SHULAMMITE WOMAN** (FR) C 104
519 **SHUNKAWAKHAN** (IRE) 15
569 **SHUTTERFLY** (IRE) 80
503 **SHUTTHEFRONTDOOR** (IRE) 60
147 **SHUTTLE** (GB) 106
451 **SHY** (GB) 19
643 **SHY ROSA** (USA) 45
13 **SI BIEN** (FR) 3
214 **SI SEALY** (IRE) 63
55 **SIANSA** (IRE) 54
123 **SIBERIAN FREEZE** (IRE) 44
263 **SIBLING RIVALRY** (GB) 17
473 **SICILIAN SECRET** (IRE) 96
166 **SID** (GB) 17
19 **SIDE GLANCE** (GB) 26
657 **SIEGLINDE** (FR) 74
102 **SIENA STREET** (GB) 39
682 **SIERRA RED** (IRE) 122
35 **SIGN MANUAL** (GB) 51
299 **SIGN OF THE ZODIAC** (IRE) 250
441 **SIGN PRO** (IRE) 32
218 **SIGNALMAN** (GB) 22
19 **SIGNATURE DISH** (IRE) 153
292 **SIGNE D'ESTRUVAL** (FR) 9
520 **SIGNED UP** (GB) 43
458 **SIGNELLA** (GB) F 29
385 **SIGNIFICANT MOVE** (GB) 12
654 **SIGNOR SASSI** (GB) 75
485 **SIGNORA FRASI** (IRE) 16
285 **SIGURWANA** (USA) 58
614 **SIKARA** (IRE) 8
488 **SILAAH** (GB) 37
388 **SILASOL** (IRE) 86
381 **SILBY** (GB) 17
184 **SILCA KEY** (FR) 26
467 **SILENCE IS EASY** (GB) 29
91 **SILENCEOFTHEWIND** (USA) 17
73 **SILENT AMBITION** (GB) 34
615 **SILENT DECISION** (USA) 4
306 **SILENT ENERGY** (IRE) 34
219 **SILENT FIRE** (IRE) 182
529 **SILENT LAUGHTER** (GB) 34
588 **SILENT MIRACLE** (IRE) F 45
360 **SILENT MISTRESS** (GB) 46
49 **SILENT MOMENT** (USA) 111
460 **SILENT SAM** (GB) 82
357 **SILENT WATERS** (GB) F 34
299 **SILENZIO** (GB) 17
657 **SILICIUM** (FR) 75
142 **SILK** (IRE) G 15
579 **SILK DRUM** (IRE) 13
682 **SILK KIMONO** (GB) 59
357 **SILK LAW** (IRE) G 17
155 **SILK MEADOW** (IRE) C 26
694 **SILK OATS** (GB) F 5

519 **SILK POINT** (IRE) F 25
694 **SILK ROSE** (GB) 6
102 **SILK ROUTE** (GB) 57
147 **SILK SARI** (GB) 107
358 **SILKE TOP** (GB) 26
299 **SILKEE SUPREME** (GB) 104
19 **SILKEN DALLIANCE** (GB) F 154
139 **SILKEN EXPRESS** (IRE) 25
157 **SILKEN PEARLS** (GB) G 27
188 **SILKEN SATINWOOD** (IRE) 23
40 **SILKEN THOUGHTS** (GB) 12
124 **SILKY BLEU** (GB) 24
657 **SILKY BOB** (IRE) 76
252 **SILKY LADY** (IRE) 11
384 **SILLY BILLY** (IRE) 8
26 **SILLY GILLY** (IRE) 10
620 **SILLY MID-ON** (GB) G 9
395 **SILMI** (GB) 17
564 **SILOE** (FR) 75
469 **SILSULA** (GB) 35
233 **SILVA FLINT** (GB) 15
450 **SILVANUS** (IRE) 29
73 **SILVAS ROMANA** (IRE) 35
71 **SILVEE** (GB) 13
593 **SILVER ACCORD** (IRE) 40
486 **SILVER ADONIS** (IRE) 11
225 **SILVER ALLIANCE** (GB) 15
18 **SILVER BANDANA** (USA) C 72
625 **SILVER BLAZE** (GB) 50
366 **SILVER BULLITT** (GB) 33
268 **SILVER BY CHOICE** (GB) 34
664 **SILVER CAROUSEL** (GB) 12
39 **SILVER CAVALIER** (GB) 9
298 **SILVER CIRCLE** (IRE) 22
682 **SILVER CONCORDE** (GB) 20
69 **SILVER DIVO** (GB) 11
10 **SILVER DOLLARS** (FR) 17
391 **SILVER FOOTNOTE** (GB) 52
564 **SILVER GREEN** (FR) 14
434 **SILVER GYPSY** (IRE) 117
554 **SILVER KATE** (IRE) 2
666 **SILVER LACE** (IRE) 31
347 **SILVER LILY** (IRE) 21
119 **SILVER LIME** (USA) 48
94 **SILVER LINNET** (IRE) 9
460 **SILVER MARIZAH** (IRE) 121
43 **SILVER MISS** (FR) F 48
477 **SILVER NATIVE** (IRE) 13
219 **SILVER PEARL** (GB) 183
619 **SILVER PIVOTAL** (IRE) C 149
249 **SILVER QUEST** (GB) C 44
34 **SILVER RIDGE** (IRE) 82
519 **SILVER RIME** (FR) 16
386 **SILVER ROQUE** (FR) 22
19 **SILVER SAMBA** (GB) 92
684 **SILVER SIX** (GB) 21
634 **SILVER SPEECH** (GB) 12
237 **SILVER STEEL** (IRE) 3
503 **SILVER STIRRUP** (IRE) 61
304 **SILVER SYCAMORE** (USA) 100
446 **SILVER TASSIE** (GB) 68
461 **SILVER TIGRESS** (GB) 19
249 **SILVER TURN** (GB) 3
433 **SILVER WIND** (GB) 25
561 **SILVER WREN** (GB) 12
695 **SILVERBURN** (IRE) 69
446 **SILVERHAND** (IRE) 69
129 **SILVERHEELS** (IRE) 16

578 **SILVERRICA** (IRE) 9
611 **SILVERS SPIRIT** (GB) 11
201 **SILVERY MOON** (IRE) 54
489 **SILVINIACO CONTI** (FR) 108
698 **SIM SALA BIM** (GB) 10
74 **SIMAYILL** (GB) 21
473 **SIMENON** (IRE) 3
468 **SIMHAL** (GB) 4
366 **SIMLA BIBI** (GB) C 199
343 **SIMON GRAY** (GB) 50
207 **SIMONSIDE** (GB) 42
321 **SIMONSIG** (GB) 144
501 **SIMPLE JIM** (FR) 29
572 **SIMPLE RHYTHM** (GB) 11
115 **SIMPLIFIED** (GB) 14
600 **SIMPLON** (GB) 32
364 **SIMPLY** (GB) 25
454 **SIMPLY BEN** (IRE) 14
556 **SIMPLY NED** (IRE) 40
420 **SIMPLY STRONG** (IRE) 35
394 **SIMPLY WINGS** (IRE) 24
705 **SIMPSON MILLAR** (GB) 31
489 **SIN BIN** (IRE) 109
473 **SIN PALO** (GB) 98
74 **SINAADI** (IRE) 68
661 **SINATRAMANIA** (GB) 9
18 **SINBAD THE SAILOR** (GB) 31
569 **SINDAJAN** (IRE) 13
29 **SINDIRANA** (IRE) F 92
508 **SINDJARA** (USA) 47
446 **SINE METU** (IRE) 70
287 **SINETTA** (IRE) 49
299 **SINFONICO** (IRE) 18
686 **SING AND DANCE** (GB) F 8
686 **SING AND DANCE** (GB) G 16
68 **SING SING SING** (FR) 10
259 **SINGALAT** (GB) 34
511 **SINGAPORE JOY** (IRE) 35
511 **SINGAPORE ZEN** (IRE) 128
55 **SINGE THE TURF** (IRE) 7
564 **SINGERSIDE** (IRE) 76
191 **SINGERSONGWRITER** (GB) 74
30 **SINGEUR** (IRE) 17
388 **SINGING** (FR) 87
58 **SINGING DIVA** (IRE) C 78
388 **SINGLE** (FR) 88
529 **SINGLE GIRL** (GB) 35
328 **SINGLE MARKET** (USA) F 117
74 **SINGSPIEL SPIRIT** (GB) 52
200 **SINGZAK** (GB) 9
654 **SINISTER** (GB) 138
287 **SINIYYA** (GB) C 65
564 **SINNKOSAKO** 77
61 **SIOUX CITY SUE** (GB) 15
9 **SIOUXIES DREAM** (GB) 48
31 **SIOUXME** (GB) 8
467 **SIOUXPERHERO** (IRE) 30
295 **SIR BATHWICK** (IRE) 5
447 **SIR BEDIVERE** (IRE) 47
262 **SIR BENFRO** (GB) 17
150 **SIR BERE** (FR) 24
625 **SIR BOREAS HAWK** (GB) 39
471 **SIR BOSS** (IRE) 20
509 **SIR BRUNO** (FR) 16
473 **SIR DES CHAMPS** (FR) 99
489 **SIR DU BEARN** (FR) 110
306 **SIR DYLAN** (GB) 35

328 **SIR FREDLOT** (IRE) 63
176 **SIR GEOFFREY** (IRE) 13
517 **SIR GEORGE** (IRE) 8
520 **SIR GLANTON** (IRE) 44
366 **SIR GRAHAM WADE** (FR) 135
380 **SIR HARRY ORMESHER** (GB) 100
9 **SIR IKE** (IRE) 31
619 **SIR JOHN HAWKWOOD** (IRE) 78
59 **SIR JOHNSON** (GB) 34
583 **SIR KEZBAAH** (IRE) 19
90 **SIR LOIN** (GB) 4
220 **SIR LOUIS** (GB) 29
520 **SIR MIKE** (GB) 45
149 **SIR MOZART** (IRE) 9
99 **SIR NOD** (GB) 13
285 **SIR PALOMIDES** (USA) 59
328 **SIR PEDRO** (GB) 64
299 **SIR PRANCEALOT** (IRE) 251
19 **SIR QUINTIN** (IRE) 93
220 **SIR REGINALD** (GB) 30
503 **SIR ROGER** (IRE) 62
606 **SIR TAMBURLANE** (IRE) 36
625 **SIR TANTALLUS HAWK** (GB) 40
161 **SIR TREVOR** (IRE) 36
339 **SIR TYTO** (IRE) 20
543 **SIR WINDSORLOT** (IRE) 41
160 **SIR WINSTON** (IRE) 38
460 **SIRCOZY** (IRE) 83
489 **SIRE COLLONGES** (FR) 111
460 **SIRE DE GRUGY** (FR) 84
223 **SIREN SOUND** (GB) C 68
643 **SIRENA** (GER) F 67
408 **SIRENE JO** 77
200 **SIRIOUS OSS** (GB) 64
16 **SIRIUS CHESNUT** (GB) 40
352 **SIRIUS PROSPECT** (USA) 12
19 **SIRIUS SUPERSTAR** (GB) 27
659 **SIRMUHTA** (FR) 43
27 **SIRVINO** (GB) 24
102 **SIRYENA** (GB) C 58
418 **SISSI GUIHEN** (FR) 15
320 **SISTER GURU** (GB) 11
654 **SISTER MOONSHINE** (FR) C 139
304 **SISTER ROCKS** (USA) 101
30 **SISTER SIOUX** (IRE) 18
287 **SISTER SOX** (IRE) F 50
318 **SISTER SWANK** (USA) C 63
321 **SISTINE** (GB) 145
659 **SITTING TENNANT** (GB) 44
254 **SIVOLA DE SIVOLA** (FR) 47
283 **SIX DIAMONDS** (GB) 60
647 **SIX OF CLUBS** (GB) 18
446 **SIX STONE NED** (IRE) 71
176 **SIX WIVES** (GB) 14
715 **SIXTIES ROCK** (GB) 6
681 **SIXTY SOMETHING** (FR) 51
447 **SIYADAH** (USA) C 101
569 **SIYENICA** (FR) 134
183 **SIYOUMA**(IRE) 22
299 **SIZE** (IRE) 105
553 **SIZING AMERICA** (IRE) 13
473 **SIZING SAHARA** (GB) 100
34 **SIZZLER** (GB) 83
116 **SKATING OVER** (USA) 30
501 **SKENAKILLA CROSS** (IRE) 30
43 **SKETCHY EVIDENCE** (USA) 10
56 **SKHOLANTA** (FR) 29
657 **SKI SUNDAY** (GB) 77

119 **SKIABLE** (IRE) C 76
98 **SKIBABE** (IRE) 16
686 **SKIDDAW SECRET** (GB) 9
79 **SKIDDAW VIEW** (GB) 8
266 **SKILFUL** (GB) 26
321 **SKINT** (GB) 146
383 **SKIP THE PRESENT** (IRE) 16
556 **SKIPPERS BRIG** (IRE) 41
659 **SKIRLAW** (IRE) 45
366 **SKIRMISH** (GB) 136
473 **SKORCHER** (IRE) 101
619 **SKY BOAT** (IRE) 79
374 **SKY CALLING** (GB) 30
259 **SKY CROSSING** (GB) 35
410 **SKY DIAMOND** (IRE) 16
625 **SKY HIGH DIVER** (IRE) 41
219 **SKY HUNTER** (GB) 184
191 **SKY KHAN** (GB) 38
299 **SKY LANTERN** (IRE) 252
489 **SKY WATCH** (IRE) 112
130 **SKYBLUE** (GB) 12
73 **SKYERON** (GB) 36
379 **SKYFIRE** (GB) 7
152 **SKYLARKER** (USA) 3
588 **SKYLLA** (GB) 25
586 **SKYSTREAM** (IRE) 10
366 **SKYTRAIN** (GB) 200
254 **SLAM** (GB) 48
475 **SLATE LADY** (IRE) 20
283 **SLATEY HEN** (IRE) 61
510 **SLEAVE SILK** (IRE) F 21
111 **SLEEK** (GB) 153
66 **SLEEP IN FIRST** (FR) 4
682 **SLEEPING BEAUTY** (IRE) 123
160 **SLEEPING CITY** (FR) 39
198 **SLEEPING DU GRANIT** (FR) 23
569 **SLEEPING GIANT** (GER) 135
66 **SLEEPING POLICEMAN** (FR) 5
388 **SLEEPING STORM** (IRE) F 89
20 **SLEEPY BLUE OCEAN** (GB) 4
466 **SLEEPY HOLLOW** (GB) 25
283 **SLEEPY LUCY** (GB) 79
642 **SLEIGH BELLS** (GB) 38
440 **SLEIGHTS BOY** (IRE) 11
386 **SLICK OPERATOR** (IRE) 23
499 **SLIEVEARDAGH** (IRE) 28
489 **SLIGHTLY TANNED** (IRE) 113
266 **SLIP FREE** (GB) 148
534 **SLIP OF THE TONGUE** (GB) 67
617 **SMACK DOWN** (GB) 22
380 **SMAD PLACE** (FR) 101
434 **SMADYNIUM** (FR) 118
381 **SMALL AND MIGHTY** (GB) 18
86 **SMALL FLY** (GB) 19
654 **SMALL FORTUNE** (GB) C 140
442 **SMALL STEPS** (IRE) 15
601 **SMALLJOHN** (GB) 21
434 **SMART ACT** (IRE) 14
451 **SMART AFFAIR** (GB) 40
58 **SMART ASS** (IRE) F 79
108 **SMART CATCH** (IRE) 39
561 **SMART EXIT** (IRE) 13
476 **SMART MISTRESS** (GB) 69
366 **SMART STEP** (GB) 34
501 **SMARTY SOCKS** (IRE) 31
30 **SMIDDY HILL** (GB) 23
186 **SMILE FOR US** (GB) 4
471 **SMIRFY'S SILVER** (GB) 21

446 **SMITHFIELD** (IRE) 72
434 **SMITHY THE HORSE** (IRE) 120
287 **SMOKEN ROSA** (USA) C 66
641 **SMOKETHATTHUNDERS** (IRE) 16
16 **SMOKEY GEORGE** (GB) 41
642 **SMOKEY OAKEY** (IRE) 21
29 **SMOKING SUN** (USA) 56
679 **SMOKY CLOUD** (IRE) 2
442 **SMOOCH** (GB) F 33
122 **SMOOTH SOVEREIGN** (IRE) 3
447 **SMOOTHTALKINRASCAL** (IRE) 102
606 **SMUDGER** (GB) 27
388 **SMYRNES** (FR) 49
447 **SNAKE'S HEAD** (GB) C 103
123 **SNAKESTONE** (GB) 45
331 **SNAP TIE** (IRE) 82
511 **SNAPE MALTINGS** (IRE) 36
689 **SNAPPING TURTLE** (IRE) 16
178 **SNOOKER** (GER) 23
220 **SNOOKY** (GB) 68
439 **SNOOZE N YOU LOSE** (GB) 6
495 **SNOW ALERT** (GB) 10
488 **SNOW BAY** (GB) 38
150 **SNOW BLIZZARD** (IRE) 25
192 **SNOW CRYSTAL** (IRE) F 30
445 **SNOW DANCER** (IRE) 4
191 **SNOW FAIRY** (IRE) 8
666 **SNOW HILL** (GB) 16
190 **SNOW PATROL** (GB) 2
34 **SNOW RIDGE** (GB) 15
569 **SNOW SIGN** (FR) 81
352 **SNOW TROOPER** (GB) 13
224 **SNOWBERRY HILL** (USA) 2
266 **SNOWBRIGHT** (GB) 149
388 **SNOWDAY** (FR) 90
713 **SNOWDON LILY** (GB) F 10
101 **SNOWED IN** (IRE) 31
336 **SNOWY DAWN** (GB) 44
329 **SNOWY DAY IN LA** (IRE) F 44
447 **SNOWY INDIAN** (GB) C 104
199 **SNOWY VALLEY** (GB) 9
218 **SNUKER** (GB) 23
701 **SO BAZAAR** (IRE) 2
299 **SO CHEEKY** (GB) 106
331 **SO FINE** (GB) 83
14 **SO IS SHE** (IRE) 10
155 **SO WISE** (USA) 13
473 **SO YOUNG** (FR) 102
510 **SOAP WARS** (GB) 4
366 **SOAPY DELIGHT** (GB) 137
654 **SOARING SPIRITS** (IRE) 141
424 **SOBER SAILOR** (IRE) 27
219 **SOBLUE** (IRE) 185
588 **SOCIABLE** (GB) F 46
503 **SOCIAL REALISM** (IRE) 63
328 **SOCIETY PEARL** (IRE) 118
223 **SOCIETY ROCK** (IRE) 18
444 **SOCIETY SHARES** (IRE) 16
585 **SOCIETY VENUE** (GB) 28
509 **SOFIA ROYALE** (GB) F 7
60 **SOFIAS NUMBER ONE** (USA) 11
388 **SOFT LIPS** (GB) 50
24 **SOFT SPOKEN GUY** (IRE) 20
239 **SOFTLY KILLING ME** (GB) 6
299 **SOGNO VERDE** (IRE) C 253
427 **SOHAPPYHARRY** (GB) 1
641 **SOHAR** (GB) 2
27 **SOHCAHTOA** (IRE) 25

641 **SOHO DANCER** (GB) 17
641 **SOHO ROCKS** (GB) 7
511 **SOHO ROSE** (IRE) 87
641 **SOHO SPIRIT** (GB) 8
641 **SOHO SUSIE** (GB) 9
466 **SOHRAAB** (GB) 26
380 **SOIR D'ESTRUVAL** (FR) 102
587 **SOITSAKAI** (GB) 3
386 **SOIXANTE** (FR) 24
388 **SOJO** (USA) 91
529 **SOKOA** (USA) F 36
266 **SOLACE** (USA) 150
313 **SOLAISE EXPRESS** (GB) 5
201 **SOLANGE** (IRE) 99
58 **SOLAR DEITY** (IRE) 49
308 **SOLAR FLARE** (IRE) G 20
55 **SOLAR OUTBURST** (IRE) 111
111 **SOLAR SKY** (GB) 15
534 **SOLAR VIEW** (IRE) 36
657 **SOLARAS EXHIBITION** (IRE) 78
60 **SOLARMAITE** (GB) 14
55 **SOLAS NA GREINE** (IRE) F 52
321 **SOLDATINO** (FR) 147
279 **SOLE AGENT** (IRE) 11
64 **SOLE DANSER** (IRE) 18
681 **SOLE SURVIVOR** (FR) 52
380 **SOLEIL D'AVRIL** (FR) 103
408 **SOLEIL VERT** (FR) 20
64 **SOLEMN** (GB) 19
655 **SOLEMN OATH** (USA) 17
219 **SOLENSI** (GER) 101
407 **SOLENT RIDGE** (IRE) 17
338 **SOLERA TIME** (GB) 17
466 **SOLFILIA** (GB) 57
218 **SOLIS** (GER) 24
239 **SOLITARY PALM** (IRE) 7
321 **SOLIWERY** (FR) 148
321 **SOLIX** (FR) 149
473 **SOLL** (GB) 103
416 **SOLVA** (GB) F 10
309 **SOLWAY BAY** (GB) 2
309 **SOLWAY BROOK** (IRE) 3
309 **SOLWAY DORNAL** (GB) 4
309 **SOLWAY ROSE** (GB) G 5
309 **SOLWAY SAM** (GB) 6
309 **SOLWAY STAR** (GB) 7
98 **SOLWHIT** (FR) 17
219 **SOMALIAN** (IRE) 102
35 **SOME DIVA** (GB) C 90
293 **SOME LAD** (IRE) 4
460 **SOME SLAM** (IRE) 85
473 **SOME TARGET** (IRE) 104
572 **SOMEMOTHERSDOHAVEM** (GB) 20
238 **SOMERBY** (GB) 4
386 **SOMERSBY** (IRE) 25
604 **SOMERSET ISLAND** (IRE) 6
55 **SOMETHING GRACEFUL** (GB) 55
260 **SOMETHING SILVER** (GB) 25
573 **SOMETHINGBOUTMARY** (GB) 105
304 **SOMETHINGDIFFERENT** (IRE) 63
681 **SOMEWHATINEVITABLE** (IRE) 53
508 **SOMEWHERE** (IRE) 48
149 **SOMMERSTURM** (GER) 10
434 **SON OF FLICKA** (GB) 121
344 **SON OF MAY** (GB) 22
62 **SON OF SWALLOW** (IRE) 11
281 **SON OF THE CAT** (USA) 2
366 **SON VIDA** (IRE) 35

525 **SONA SASTA** (IRE) 86
507 **SONDEDURO** (GB) 28
146 **SONDRAY** (GB) 13
285 **SONG AND DANCE MAN** (GB) 120
371 **SONG FOR JESS** (IRE) F 11
153 **SONG OF JOY** (IRE) 14
7 **SONG OF PARKES** (GB) 12
501 **SONG OF THE SIREN** (GB) 32
639 **SONG SUNG BLUE** (IRE) 46
111 **SONGBIRD** (IRE) 70
653 **SONGBIRD BLUES** (GB) 24
74 **SONGBOOK** (GB) C 69
49 **SONGCRAFT** (IRE) 59
221 **SONGJIANG** (GB) 6
660 **SONGSMITH** (GB) 21
510 **SONIC NIGHT** (IRE) F 22
526 **SONKO** (GB) 12
318 **SONNY** (FR) 11
43 **SONNY G** (IRE) 9
696 **SONOFAGUN** (FR) 38
489 **SONOFVIC** (IRE) 114
531 **SONORAN SANDS** (IRE) 24
155 **SONSIE LASS** (GB) 17
115 **SOPHIE'S BEAU** (USA) 15
436 **SOPHIES ECHO** (IRE) 21
55 **SOPHISTICATED HEIR** (IRE) 113
476 **SOPHONIE** (FR) 70
208 **SOPRAN MARIDA** (IRE) C 44
592 **SOPRAN NAD** (ITY) 14
260 **SOPRANO** (GER) 26
208 **SORCELLERIE** (GB) 45
458 **SORCEROR** (FR) 20
223 **SORN** (IRE) 69
275 **SORROW** (FR) 14
511 **SORRY WOMAN** (FR) 129
713 **SORSE** (GB) 11
654 **SORTITA** (GER) C 142
147 **SORYAH** (IRE) 108
124 **SOS BRILLANTE** (CHI) 16
642 **SOSUMI** (GB) F 46
688 **SOTOVIK** (IRE) 17
184 **SOTTOVOCE** (GB) 12
263 **SOUDAIN** (FR) 18
240 **SOUL ANGEL** (GB) 5
268 **SOUL BID** (IRE) 35
270 **SOUL CUSTODY** (CAN) 9
267 **SOUL MAGIC** (IRE) 9
286 **SOUND ACCORD** (IRE) 18
155 **SOUND ADVICE** (GB) 18
517 **SOUND AMIGO** (IRE) 9
654 **SOUND HEARTS** (USA) 76
373 **SOUND STAGE** (GB) 24
247 **SOUNDBYTE** (GB) 6
405 **SOURCE OF LIGHT** (IRE) 9
184 **SOURIRE** (GB) C 27
473 **SOUS LES CIEUX** (FR) 15
108 **SOUTER POINT** (USA) 40
460 **SOUTH CAPE** (GB) 86
416 **SOUTH KENTER** (USA) 8
47 **SOUTH LEINSTER** (IRE) 5
147 **SOUTHERLY** (GB) 61
61 **SOUTHERN MIGRATION** (USA) F 42
366 **SOUTHERN STATE** (USA) 36
451 **SOUTHERNESS** (GB) 20
373 **SOUTHFIELD THEATRE** (IRE) 25
194 **SOUTHWARK NEWSMAN** (GB) 15
194 **SOUTHWARKNEWSFLASH** (GB) F 22
248 **SOUTHWAY STAR** (GB) 10

35 **SOUVENIR** (GB) 91
35 **SOVEREIGN DEBT** (IRE) 52
130 **SOVEREIGN SEAL** (GB) C 18
53 **SOVEREIGN SPIRIT** (IRE) 13
188 **SOVEREIGN STREET** (GB) 7
364 **SOVEREIGN WATERS** (GB) 26
496 **SOVEREIGN'S HONOUR** (USA) C 90
512 **SOVEREIGNS LEGACY** (GB) 1
223 **SOVIET DREAM** (GB) 41
275 **SOVIET PRINCESS** (GB) G 15
19 **SOVIET ROCK** (IRE) 155
43 **SOWETO STAR** (IRE) 12
36 **SOY ALEGRE** (IRE) G 2
338 **SOYALANG** (FR) C 23
169 **SPA'S DANCER** (IRE) 24
420 **SPACE MISSION** (GB) 36
304 **SPACE RACE** (GB) 64
328 **SPACE RAIDER** (AUS) 65
184 **SPACE STATION** (GB) 13
200 **SPACE WAR** (GB) 41
375 **SPACECRAFT** (IRE) 8
57 **SPACEMAN** (GB) 16
696 **SPAGETTI WESTERN** (IRE) 39
501 **SPAHI** (FR) 33
338 **SPANGLE** (GB) F 24
299 **SPANISH ART** (GB) 254
304 **SPANISH AURIGA** (GB) 65
418 **SPANISH BOUNTY** (GB) 16
404 **SPANISH CRUISE** (GB) 41
193 **SPANISH DUKE** (IRE) 16
99 **SPANISH LEGACY** (GB) 23
214 **SPANISH NEEDLE** (GB) C 76
657 **SPANISH OPTIMIST** (IRE) 79
336 **SPANISH PLUME** (GB) 20
438 **SPANISH SPRINGS** (IRE) C 8
58 **SPANISH WEDDING** (GB) 50
658 **SPARK** (GER) 53
641 **SPARK OF GENIUS** (GB) 10
544 **SPARK SEPT** (FR) C 114
219 **SPARKLE PLENTY** (IRE) 186
612 **SPARKLING AIR** (GB) 10
11 **SPARKLING HAND** (GB) 2
220 **SPARKLING PORTRAIT** (GB) 1
614 **SPARKLING ROCK** (IRE) 27
606 **SPARKLING TARA** (GB) 38
665 **SPARKS MIGHT FLY** (GB) 9
92 **SPARKY MAY** (GB) 8
696 **SPARTAN KING** (IRE) 40
466 **SPARTAN SPIRIT** (IRE) 27
259 **SPARTILLA** (GB) 36
7 **SPAVENTO** (IRE) 11
54 **SPEAK SOFTLY TO ME** (USA) F 26
61 **SPEAK THE TRUTH** (IRE) 16
682 **SPEAKING OF WHICH** (FR) 60
420 **SPEAR THISTLE** (GB) 37
29 **SPEARTOOTH** (GB) 14
585 **SPECIAL CASE** (IRE) C 29
552 **SPECIAL CATCH** (IRE) 39
511 **SPECIAL FAVOUR** (GB) 88
698 **SPECIAL GREEN** (FR) C 34
657 **SPECIAL MATE** (GB) 80
200 **SPECIAL MIX** (GB) 42
193 **SPECIAL MOMENT** (IRE) F 62
643 **SPECIAL PARK** (USA) C 68
699 **SPECIAL ROBON** (FR) 78
19 **SPECIAL TOUCH** (GB) C 156
256 **SPECIALAGENT ALFIE** (GB) 23
3 **SPECIFIC** (IRE) 109

111 **SPECIFIC GRAVITY** (FR) 16
191 **SPECKLED HILL** (GB) 75
496 **SPEECH** (GB) C 91
19 **SPEED COP** (IRE) C 157
321 **SPEED MASTER** (IRE) 150
511 **SPEED OF ANABAA** (IRE) 130
328 **SPEED SONG** (GB) F 119
657 **SPEED STEED** (IRE) 81
422 **SPEEDFIT GIRL** (IRE) 10
432 **SPEEDI MOUSE** (GB) 8
614 **SPEEDWAY CASS** (IRE) 55
531 **SPEEDY DIRECTA** (GER) 25
511 **SPEEDY MARTIN** (GB) 89
102 **SPEEDY WRITER** (GB) 59
405 **SPEEDY YAKI** (IRE) 10
194 **SPEEDYFIX** (GB) 16
485 **SPELLMAKER** (GB) 21
219 **SPELLWORK** (USA) 103
535 **SPENCER LEA** (GB) 7
223 **SPENSLEY** (IRE) 19
27 **SPES NOSTRA** (IRE) 16
204 **SPESSARTINE** (IRE) 14
45 **SPEY SONG** (IRE) 11
644 **SPHINX** (FR) 9
653 **SPICE FAIR** (GB) 18
397 **SPICE RUN** (GB) 30
592 **SPICEY** (GB) F 25
309 **SPICEY CUT** G 8
434 **SPIDER PALM** (IRE) 122
614 **SPIDER ZAGATO** (IRE) 28
501 **SPIEKEROOG** (GB) 34
495 **SPIELBOUND** (GB) F 12
147 **SPIETA** (GB) 109
147 **SPIFER** (IRE) 12
388 **SPILIADA** (FR) 92
690 **SPIN A WISH** (GB) 9
683 **SPIN AGAIN** (IRE) 4
645 **SPIN CAST** (GB) 8
436 **SPINAIMANWIN** (IRE) F 27
180 **SPINATRIX** (GB) 20
276 **SPINNING GOLD** (GB) F 18
306 **SPINNING RIDGE** (IRE) 23
643 **SPINNING SILK** (IRE) 46
89 **SPINNING WATERS** (GB) 10
119 **SPIRAEA** (GB) 77
219 **SPIRAL SEA** (IRE) 104
235 **SPIRIT CALLING** (IRE) 2
699 **SPIRIT D'ARMOR** (FR) 79
153 **SPIRIT MAN** (GB) 13
456 **SPIRIT OF A NATION** (IRE) 19
657 **SPIRIT OF ADJISA** (IRE) 82
525 **SPIRIT OF BARBADOS** (IRE) 87
682 **SPIRIT OF CONCORDE** (GB) 61
450 **SPIRIT OF CONISTON** (GB) 30
64 **SPIRIT OF GONDREE** (IRE) 20
433 **SPIRIT OF GRACE** (IRE) 26
253 **SPIRIT OF LAKE** (IRE) 9
161 **SPIRIT OF PARKES** (GB) 72
404 **SPIRIT OF SHANKLY** (GB) 42
225 **SPIRIT OF SHARJAH** (IRE) 16
191 **SPIRIT OF THE LAW** (IRE) 39
362 **SPIRIT OF XAAR** (IRE) 18
321 **SPIRIT RIVER** (IRE) 151
321 **SPIRIT SON** (IRE) 152
29 **SPIRITJIM** (FR) 109
111 **SPIRITOFTOMINTOUL** (GB) 71
325 **SPIRITONTHEMOUNT** (USA) 12
154 **SPIRITUAL ART** (GB) 6

19 **SPIRITUAL STAR** (IRE) 94
564 **SPIRITUS HIT** (GB) 78
564 **SPIRITUS QUEEN** (GB) 79
511 **SPIRO** (GB) 90
360 **SPITFIRE** (GB) 34
3 **SPLASH POINT** (USA) 40
266 **SPLENDID LIGHT** (GB) 27
712 **SPLENDID SENORITA** (IRE) 6
489 **SPOCK** (FR) 115
503 **SPOIL ME** (IRE) 64
364 **SPOKE TO CARLO** (GB) 27
676 **SPOKESPERSON** (USA) 8
494 **SPORTED AND PLAYED** (IRE) 17
53 **SPORTING BOY** (IRE) 14
664 **SPORTING GOLD** (GB) 77
343 **SPORTINGTHEME** (GB) 51
434 **SPORTS LINE** (IRE) 123
499 **SPORTSMASTER** (IRE) 29
631 **SPOSALIZIO** (IRE) 10
465 **SPOT FINE** (GB) 21
34 **SPOT PRIZE** (USA) C 84
503 **SPOT THE BALL** (IRE) 65
285 **SPOTLIGHT** (GB) C 121
38 **SPREAD BOY** (IRE) 10
708 **SPREE** (IRE) F 24
571 **SPRING BAY** (GB) 3
61 **SPRING CLEAN** (FR) F 43
299 **SPRING GLORY** (GB) C 255
374 **SPRING MOON** (IRE) 31
49 **SPRING OF FAME** (USA) 60
509 **SPRING SECRET** (GB) 17
263 **SPRINGFIELD RAKI** (GB) 19
188 **SPRINGKELL JAKE** (GB) 22
180 **SPRINGINMYSTEP** (IRE) 36
7 **SPRINGTIME PARKES** (GB) G 22
321 **SPRINTER SACRE** (FR) 153
219 **SPRITZA** (IRE) C 187
200 **SPRITZERIA** (GB) F 83
222 **SPRUZZO** (GB) 7
299 **SPUTNIK SWEETHEART** (GB) 107
116 **SPYDER** (GB) 12
91 **SPYKES BAY** (USA) 33
299 **SQUAD** (GB) 14
299 **SQUARE PANTS** (USA) F 256
564 **SQUAW DANCE** (GB) C 98
241 **SQUIRE TRELAWNEY** (GB) 14
291 **SQUIRREL WOOD** (IRE) 2
654 **SRI PUTRA** (GB) 24
566 **SRIMENANTI** (GB) 11
111 **SRINAGAR GIRL** (GB) 72
329 **SSAFA** (GB) 3
467 **ST ATHAN** (GB) 31
9 **ST IGNATIUS** (GB) 32
23 **ST MARYS HALL** (GB) 4
499 **ST MAXIME** (IRE) 30
488 **ST MORITZ** (IRE) 39
501 **ST OSWALD** (GB) 35
157 **STACCATO VALTAT** (IRE) 28
467 **STACEYMAC** (IRE) F 44
504 **STAFFORD CHARLIE** (GB) 9
384 **STAG HILL** (IRE) 34
19 **STAGE ATTRACTION** (IRE) 28
31 **STAGECOACH DANMAN** (IRE) 9
606 **STAGECOACH JASPER** (GB) 39
606 **STAGECOACH PEARL** (GB) 40
391 **STAIGUE FORT** (GB) 53
244 **STAMP DUTY** (IRE) 2
252 **STAN'S THE MAN** (GB) 12

476 **STAND CLEAR** (GB) 71
94 **STAND GUARD** (GB) 10
415 **STAND TO REASON** (IRE) 6
318 **STANDARD BEARER** (GB) 12
129 **STANDING BEAR** (IRE) 41
452 **STANDING STRONG** (IRE) 9
336 **STANDPOINT** (GB) 21
479 **STANLEY BRIDGE** (GB) 16
220 **STANLEY RIGBY** (GB) 31
143 **STANROAD** (GB) 4
625 **STANSONNIT** (GB) 42
317 **STANWELL** (GB) 4
671 **STAR BEAT** (GB) 10
78 **STAR BELUCKY** (GB) 8
597 **STAR BONITA** (IRE) 53
180 **STAR CITY** (IRE) 37
642 **STAR COMMANDER** (GB) 22
681 **STAR COUNCEL** (IRE) G 54
415 **STAR FOR LIFE** (IRE) 3
214 **STAR GALAXY** (IRE) 30
380 **STAR HILL** (GB) 104
434 **STAR IN FLIGHT** (GB) 124
452 **STAR KINGDOM** (IRE) 16
366 **STAR LAHIB** (GB) 138
298 **STAR NEUVILLE** (IRE) 23
525 **STAR OF ANGELS** (GB) 88
396 **STAR OF GERMANY** (IRE) 7
499 **STAR OF MASSINI** (IRE) 31
642 **STAR OF MISSOURI** (GB) 47
35 **STAR OF ROHM** (GB) 92
328 **STAR OF SILIGO** (USA) C 120
564 **STAR OF SUNDAY** (FR) 99
573 **STAR PROFILE** (FR) F 106
619 **STAR RATING** (IRE) 80
422 **STAR REBEL** (GB) 11
214 **STAR ROVER** (IRE) 31
575 **STAR SIGN** (GB) G 7
613 **STARBECK** (IRE) C 8
611 **STARBIRD** (GB) 12
266 **STARBOARD** (GB) 98
45 **STARBOTTON** (GB) 27
129 **STARFISH** (IRE) C 42
387 **STARFLEET** (GB) F 37
397 **STARGAZY** (GB) 31
511 **STARKS** (FR) C 131
55 **STARLAND** (IRE) 115
569 **STARLET'S SISTER** (IRE) 82
199 **STARLIGHT SECRET** (GB) 10
531 **STARLIGHT SYMPHONY** (IRE) 35
304 **STARLING LADY** (GB) 66
167 **STARLIT EVE** (GB) 3
10 **STARLUCK** (IRE) 18
328 **STARRING** (FR) F 121
699 **STARS DU GRANITS** (FR) 80
461 **STARS LEGACY** (GB) 31
266 **STARSCOPE** (GB) 19
160 **STARSKY DES MOTTES** (FR) 40
682 **STARSTRUCK** (IRE) 62
49 **START RIGHT** (GB) 61
451 **STARVING MARVIN** (GB) 21
71 **STARWATCH** (GB) 14
321 **STATE BENEFIT** (GB) 154
328 **STATE CRYSTAL** (IRE) F 122
614 **STATE CRYSTAL** (IRE) F 29
331 **STATE DEPARTMENT** (GB) 84
695 **STATE OF PLAY** (GB) 70
321 **STATE SENATOR** (USA) 155
55 **STATESMANSHIP** (GB) 8

123 **STATU QUO** (FR) 46
161 **STATUA** (IRE) F 73
19 **STATURE** (IRE) 95
109 **STATUS SYMBOL** (IRE) 8
600 **STAY COOL** (FR) 15
499 **STAYING ARTICLE** (IRE) 32
567 **STEADY GAZE** (GB) 20
339 **STEADY GIRLFRIEND** (GB) 21
55 **STEADY HAND** (IRE) 56
409 **STEADYS BREEZE** (GB) 3
201 **STEAL THE CURTAIN** (GB) 55
404 **STEALING THE LINE** (IRE) 43
516 **STEAM CUISINE** (GB) C 20
183 **STEED** (FR) 23
711 **STEEL CITY BOY** (IRE) 15
412 **STEEL MAN** (IRE) 7
217 **STEEL RAIN** (GB) 11
75 **STEEL STOCKHOLDER** (GB) 13
214 **STEELCUT** (GB) 32
632 **STEELE TANGO** (USA) 7
287 **STEELY GRACE** (IRE) 51
361 **STEEPLEOFCOPPER** (IRE) 4
366 **STEER BY THE STARS** (IRE) 201
29 **STELLA BERINE** F 110
117 **STELLA DEL MATTINO** (USA) C 48
29 **STELLA DIVINE** (FR) 57
702 **STELLA MARRIS** (GB) 4
13 **STELLAR CAUSE** (USA) 4
9 **STELLAR EXPRESS** (IRE) 49
29 **STELWAY** (FR) 58
285 **STENCIVE** (GB) 60
460 **STENTORIAN** (IRE) 87
601 **STEPHARLIE** (GB) 49
695 **STEPHEN'S GREEN** (USA) 71
467 **STEPPER POINT** (GB) 32
12 **STEPPIN OUT** (GB) F 26
12 **STEPPIN OUT** (GB) F 18
654 **STEPS** (IRE) 25
304 **STEPS TO FREEDOM** (IRE) 67
18 **STEPTURN** (GB) 57
34 **STEREOTYPICAL** (GB) 50
696 **STEVIE GEE** (IRE) 41
657 **STEWARTS HOUSE** (IRE) 83
359 **STICK TOGETHER** (GB) 28
361 **STICKERS** (GB) 5
192 **STICKLEBACK** (GB) 16
259 **STILETTOESINTHEMUD** (IRE) 11
24 **STILL CALM** (GB) 21
597 **STILL I'M A STAR** (IRE) 54
111 **STIPULATE** (GB) 73
119 **STIR TRADER** (IRE) 49
19 **STIRRING BALLAD** (GB) 96
147 **STOICAL** (IRE) 13
456 **STOLEN MOMENTS** (FR) 20
391 **STOLEN THUNDER** (GB) 54
619 **STOMACHION** (IRE) 150
43 **STONE OF FOLCA** (GB) 13
272 **STONEACRE JOE JOE** (GB) 8
272 **STONEACRE LAD** (IRE) 10
272 **STONEACRE THIRSK** (IRE) 17
155 **STONEFIELD FLYER** (IRE) 19
343 **STONEMASTER** (IRE) 52
657 **STONETHROWER** (IRE) 84
343 **STONEY** 53
380 **STONEY'S TREASURE** (GB) 105
573 **STOP FLIRTING** (GB) 69
311 **STOP N STARE** (IRE) 8
268 **STOP ON** (GB) 36

304 **STOP ROAD LAD** (IRE) 68
522 **STOP THE SHOW** (IRE) 22
671 **STOPPED OUT** (GB) 11
248 **STORM ALERT** (GB) 11
203 **STORM HAWK** (IRE) 4
100 **STORM IN FRONT** (IRE) F 10
422 **STORM KING** (GB) 26
501 **STORM LADY** (FR) F 59
682 **STORM LIGHTNING** (GB) 63
366 **STORM LILY** (GB) C 202
408 **STORM OF SAINTLY** 78
422 **STORM RUNNER** (GB) 12
331 **STORM SHADOW** (IRE) 85
640 **STORM SURGE** (IRE) 17
503 **STORM SURVIVOR** (IRE) 66
129 **STORMBOUND** (IRE) 17
650 **STORMHOEK** (IRE) 62
542 **STORMIN GORDON** (IRE) 20
19 **STORMING** (IRE) 158
14 **STORMING BERNARD** (USA) 16
434 **STORMING GALE** (IRE) 125
213 **STORMING REDD** (GB) 6
570 **STORMION** (IRE) 60
24 **STORMONT BRIDGE** (GB) 22
616 **STORMS RANSOM** (IRE) 8
317 **STORMWORTHY MISS** (IRE) G 5
317 **STORMWORTHY MISS** (IRE) C 10
91 **STORMY GLAZ** (FR) 34
383 **STORMY MORNING** (GB) 17
207 **STORMY WEATHER** (FR) 43
460 **STORMY WEATHER** (GB) C 128
259 **STORMY WHATEVER** (FR) 37
695 **STORMYISLAND AHEAD** (GB) 72
462 **STORY** (GB) F 41
387 **STORY WRITER** (GB) 28
240 **STORYMAKER** (GB) 6
699 **STOW** (GB) 81
343 **STOWREE BUD** (IRE) 54
407 **STRADA COLORATO** (IRE) 32
147 **STRADA FACENDO** (USA) 6
447 **STRAIGHT SHOT** (IRE) 48
473 **STRAIN OF FAME** (GB) 106
168 **STRAND LINE** (IRE) 3
226 **STRANGE ENCOUNTER** (IRE) 28
55 **STRAPLESS** (IRE) 116
362 **STRATEGIC ACTION** (IRE) 22
597 **STRATEGIC BID** (GB) 19
129 **STRATEGIC MOUNT** (GB) 5
50 **STRATEGIC PLAN** (FR) 6
564 **STRATEGIE** 80
145 **STRATHAIRD** (IRE) 13
626 **STRATHCAL** (GB) 17
191 **STRATHNAVER** (GB) 40
101 **STRATOSPHERE** (GB) G 27
141 **STRATOSPHERIC** (GB) F 74
336 **STRAVERSJOY** (GB) 22
628 **STRAWBERRY FLAVOUR** (GER) 15
180 **STRAWBERRY LOLLY** (GB) C 53
31 **STRAWBERRY VILLA** (GB) 10
58 **STRAWBERRYMYSTIQUE** (GB) 6
266 **STREAMER** (GB) 151
14 **STREET ANGEL** (IRE) 17
262 **STREET DANCE** (IRE) 18
525 **STREET ENTERTAINER** (IRE) 89
654 **STREET FIRE** (IRE) C 143
123 **STREET LIGHTNING** (FR) F 65
249 **STREET POWER** (USA) 18
285 **STREET STAR** (USA) C 122

447 **STREET STYLE** (IRE) C 105
298 **STREETS OF NEWYORK** (GB) 24
364 **STRENGTH AND STAY** (IRE) 14
43 **STREWTH** (IRE) 14
529 **STRICTLY MINE** (GB) 37
14 **STRICTLY PINK** (IRE) 11
14 **STRICTLY SILVER** (IRE) 18
619 **STRIDENT FORCE** (GB) 81
1 **STRIDING EDGE** (IRE) 4
61 **STRIKE A POSE** (IRE) 32
398 **STRIKE FORCE** (GB) 3
80 **STRIKE HARD** (IRE) F 26
29 **STRIKE LIGHTLY** (GB) F 111
355 **STRIKEMASTER** (IRE) 6
506 **STRIKER TORRES** (IRE) 13
231 **STRIKING PRIORITE** (GB) 7
451 **STRIKING WILLOW** (GB) 3
628 **STRING QUARTET** (IRE) C 39
299 **STRING THEORY** (IRE) 151
299 **STRINGER BELL** (GB) 108
299 **STRINGS** (GB) C 257
252 **STRIPE ME BLUE** (GB) 13
161 **STRIPPED BEAR** (GB) F 74
29 **STRIX** (GB) 112
494 **STROBE** (GB) 18
689 **STRONG EDITION** (IRE) G 17
436 **STRONG HEATHER** (IRE) G 12
664 **STRONG KNIGHT** (GB) 13
299 **STRONG SUIT** (USA) 19
35 **STRONG VIGILANCE** (IRE) 11
404 **STRONGBOWS LEGEND** (GB) 44
123 **STRONGER** (GB) F 47
503 **STRONGLY SUGGESTED** (GB) 67
275 **STRONGPOINT** (IRE) 8
127 **STROPPY** (GB) F 124
681 **STRUANMORE** (GB) 55
59 **STRUMBLE HEAD** (IRE) 35
451 **STUDIOUS MICHAEL** (GB) 41
476 **STUFF OF DREAMS** (GB) 72
682 **STUNNED SILENCE** (USA) 64
601 **STUNNING ICON** (GB) 50
141 **STUNNING ROSE** (IRE) C 75
266 **STUNNING VIEW** (USA) 100
127 **STUPENDA** (GB) 20
214 **STYLE AND PANACHE** (IRE) 33
169 **STYLE MARGI** (IRE) 25
123 **STYLE VENDOME** (FR) 66
447 **STYLIST** (IRE) C 106
569 **SUAMA** (FR) 83
328 **SUBITO** (GB) F 123
695 **SUBLIME TALENT** (IRE) 73
17 **SUBTLE APPROACH** (IRE) 8
19 **SUBTLE DIFFERENCE** (IRE) 159
192 **SUBTLE EMBRACE** (IRE) 17
67 **SUBTLE KNIFE** (GB) 8
180 **SUBTLE MOVE** (GB) G 54
489 **SUBTLE SOVEREIGN** (IRE) 116
147 **SUBTRACTION** (IRE) 63
380 **SUBURBAN BAY** (GB) 106
117 **SUBURBAN WAR** (GB) 29
461 **SUCCINCT** (GB) F 31
56 **SUCH A MAJ** (IRE) 14
434 **SUD PACIFIQUE** (IRE) 126
30 **SUDDEN INTEREST** (FR) C 24
42 **SUDDEN LIGHT** (IRE) 22
14 **SUDDEN WISH** (IRE) 19
176 **SUDDENLY SUSAN** (IRE) 15
467 **SUEDEHEAD** (GB) 33

58 **SUEGIOO** (FR) 51
489 **SUERTE AL SALTO** (IRE) 117
408 **SUERTE PARA TODOS** 79
220 **SUFFICE** (GB) 70
616 **SUFFOLINI** (GB) 6
114 **SUGAR AND SPICE** (GB) 10
306 **SUGAR BEET** (GB) 24
343 **SUGAR BULLET** (IRE) 55
467 **SUGAR LOAF** (GB) 34
526 **SUGAR PRINCE** (GB) 13
441 **SUGAR SANDS** (GB) 13
533 **SUGARLOAF SARAH** (GB) 5
424 **SUGHERA** (IRE) 28
12 **SUHAILAH** (GB) 19
390 **SUHAILI** (GB) 4
90 **SUHAYL STAR** (IRE) 5
408 **SUITE A COEUR** 80
27 **SUITS ME** (GB) 27
447 **SUJET BELLAGIO** (GB) 49
249 **SULIS MINERVA** (IRE) 19
86 **SULPIUS** (GER) 20
420 **SUM LAFF** (IRE) 38
476 **SUMAK** (FR) 73
184 **SUMANI** (FR) 15
200 **SUMITRA** (GB) C 84
29 **SUMMER BREEZE** (GB) F 113
686 **SUMMER CRUSH** (USA) F 27
200 **SUMMER DAZE** (USA) C 85
280 **SUMMER DE BAUNE** (FR) 3
58 **SUMMER DREAM** (IRE) 80
56 **SUMMER WAVE** (IRE) F 38
169 **SUMMERINTHECITY** (IRE) 26
191 **SUMMERS LEASE** (GB) F 76
654 **SUMMERSTRAND** (IRE) C 144
466 **SUMMERTIME PARKES** (GB) F 84
699 **SUMMERY JUSTICE** (IRE) 82
147 **SUMMIT SURGE** (IRE) 14
285 **SUN CENTRAL** (GB) 61
359 **SUN CLOUD** (IRE) 29
108 **SUN DREAM** (GB) 41
499 **SUN FISHER** (GB) 33
670 **SUN LADY** (FR) 6
55 **SUN ON THE RUN** (IRE) 117
177 **SUN QUEST** (GB) 3
466 **SUN SEAL** (GB) 58
686 **SUN SEASONS** (IRE) F 28
670 **SUNARRI** (IRE) 7
328 **SUNBULA** (USA) 124
59 **SUNDAY CITY** (JPN) 36
117 **SUNDAY TIMES** (GB) 30
556 **SUNDOWN TRAIL** (IRE) 42
682 **SUNDRENCHED COAST** (USA) 65
328 **SUNDUS** (USA) C 125
321 **SUNGLASSES** (IRE) 156
460 **SUNLEY PEACE** (GB) 88
19 **SUNNY BANK** (GB) 97
641 **SUNNY HOLLOW** (GB) 18
220 **SUNNY SIDE UP** (IRE) 71
460 **SUNNY SPELLS** (GB) 89
503 **SUNNYHILLBOY** (GB) 68
266 **SUNPASS** (GB) 101
450 **SUNRAIDER** (IRE) 31
541 **SUNRISE COURT** (GB) 6
357 **SUNRISE DANCE** (GB) 18
287 **SUNRISE SONG** (IRE) 52
183 **SUNRISE SPIRIT** (FR) 24
600 **SUNSEEK** (GB) 33
95 **SUNSET BOULEVARD** (IRE) 7

477 **SUNSET KITTY** (USA) 10
652 **SUNSET PARK** (IRE) G 7
252 **SUNSET PLACE** (GB) 14
255 **SUNSET SONG** (GB) 2
298 **SUNSET STANZA** (GB) 25
157 **SUNSETTEN** (IRE) 29
451 **SUNSHINE BUDDY** (GB) 23
108 **SUPA SEEKER** (USA) 42
466 **SUPAHEART** (GB) 59
32 **SUPASTARQUEEN** (USA) 22
513 **SUPER ALLY** (IRE) 11
218 **SUPER BABY** (FR) 25
298 **SUPER COLLIDER** (GB) 26
660 **SUPER DIRECTA** (GER) 22
521 **SUPER DUPLEX** (GB) 13
434 **SUPER DUTY** (IRE) 127
373 **SUPER FORMEN** (FR) 26
166 **SUPER FRANK** (IRE) 18
473 **SUPER SONIC BOOM** (IRE) 107
326 **SUPER VILLAN** (GB) 24
656 **SUPERCAST** (IRE) 10
407 **SUPERCHARGED** (GB) 8
34 **SUPERCILIARY** (GB) 51
418 **SUPERDUPER** (GB) 17
447 **SUPERNOVA HEIGHTS** (IRE) 107
682 **SUPERNOVAE** (GB) 66
543 **SUPERPLEX** (GB) 42
285 **SUPERSTAR LEO** (IRE) F 123
223 **SUPERSTICION** (GB) 42
426 **SUPRALUNARY** (GB) 6
226 **SUPREME BOB** (IRE) 29
298 **SUPREME BUILDER** (GB) 27
473 **SUPREME CAROLINA** (IRE) 108
498 **SUPREME DE PAILLE** (IRE) 20
226 **SUPREME FAVOUR** (IRE) G 30
573 **SUPREME LUXURY** (IRE) 70
119 **SUPREME QUEST** (GB) 50
61 **SUPREME ROCK** (GB) 33
337 **SUPREME RULER** (IRE) 12
422 **SUPREME SPIRIT** (IRE) 13
165 **SUPREME TEAM** (IRE) 5
569 **SUPREME WISDOM** (GB) 14
131 **SUPRISE VENDOR** (IRE) 8
600 **SUR MA VIE** (USA) F 48
35 **SURAJ** (GB) 53
525 **SURE JOSIE SURE** (FR) 90
157 **SURE THING** (FR) 30
436 **SURE THYNE** (IRE) 13
503 **SURF AND TURF** (IRE) 69
219 **SURF CLUB** (USA) F 188
447 **SURF THE WEB** (IRE) C 108
321 **SURFING** (FR) 157
180 **SURREALIST** (ITY) G 38
632 **SURREY DREAM** (IRE) 16
123 **SURVEYANCE** (USA) 48
436 **SUSIESCOT** (IRE) 22
166 **SUSSEX LASS** (GB) 19
681 **SUSSEX SUNSET** (GB) 56
699 **SUSTAINABILITY** (IRE) 83
18 **SUTTON SID** (GB) 73
647 **SUTTON STORM** (GB) 19
249 **SUTTON VENY** (GB) 20
610 **SUTTON WHO** (IRE) 18
213 **SUZI'S A CLASS ACT** (GB) 7
161 **SUZIE FONG** (GB) C 75
332 **SUZIE GREY** (IRE) 18
161 **SUZUKI** (IRE) C 76
569 **SVIATOPOLK** (USA) 84

50 **SWAINS MEADOW** (GB) 7
483 **SWAINSON** (USA) 11
296 **SWALEDALE LAD** (IRE) 37
160 **SWALING** (IRE) 41
218 **SWALLOW** (FR) 26
58 **SWALLOW** (TUR) 52
19 **SWAN SONG** (GB) 98
521 **SWANINSTOCKWELL** (IRE) 14
531 **SWANSBROOK** (IRE) 26
3 **SWEDISH SAILOR** (GB) 110
643 **SWEEPING STORY** (USA) C 69
451 **SWEET ALABAMA** (GB) 51
438 **SWEET CHARITY** (USA) C 7
80 **SWEET GRACE** (GB) 11
388 **SWEET IRON** (USA) 51
380 **SWEET IRONY** (FR) 107
19 **SWEET LIBERTA** (GB) 99
180 **SWEET LIGHTNING** (GB) 21
19 **SWEET MANDOLIN** (GB) F 160
39 **SWEET MARIA** (IRE) 17
146 **SWEET MARWELL** (IRE) 8
568 **SWEET MIRASOL** (IRE) 7
473 **SWEET MY LORD** (FR) 109
682 **SWEET MYSTERY** (IRE) 67
516 **SWEET NAMIBIA** (IRE) C 21
18 **SWEET OPHELIA** (GB) 58
653 **SWEET OVATION** (GB) 25
95 **SWEET PICCOLO** (GB) 9
61 **SWEET PICKLE** (GB) F 44
203 **SWEET POSSESSION** (USA) 5
503 **SWEET PRINCE** (GB) 70
249 **SWEET SECRET** (GB) 50
55 **SWEET SHOP** (GB) C 118
360 **SWEET SUGAR** (FR) 35
34 **SWEET SURPRISE** (GB) C 85
542 **SWEET TIMES** (GB) F 21
307 **SWEET VERA** (GB) 6
400 **SWEET WORLD** (GB) 23
462 **SWEETEST FRIEND** (IRE) 23
653 **SWEETEST REVENGE** (IRE) C 35
673 **SWEETNESSANDLIGHT** (GB) 10
654 **SWEETSFORMYSWEET** (USA) F 145
504 **SWENDAB** (IRE) 10
682 **SWERVE** (GB) 68
296 **SWERVINIRVIN** (GB) 38
366 **SWIFT ALHAARTH** (IRE) 37
434 **SWIFT ARROW** (IRE) 128
323 **SWIFT BLADE** (IRE) 8
357 **SWIFT CEDAR** (IRE) 35
331 **SWIFT CHAP** (GB) 86
188 **SWIFT ENCOUNTER** (IRE) 25
657 **SWIFT ESCAPE** (GB) 85
191 **SWIFT GIFT** (GB) 9
460 **SWIFT LORD** (IRE) 90
466 **SWIFT WINGED** (GB) 60
107 **SWIFTLY DONE** (IRE) 15
488 **SWILLY FERRY** (USA) 40
697 **SWINCOMBE FLAME** (GB) 22
650 **SWINCOMBE ROCK** (GB) 63
339 **SWINCOMBE STONE** (GB) 22
488 **SWINDLING** (GB) G 62
376 **SWING ALONE** (IRE) 14
525 **SWING BILL** (FR) 91
525 **SWING BOWLER** (GB) 92
311 **SWING THE LEAD** (IRE) F 9
176 **SWINGER** (GB) 16
696 **SWINGING HAWK** (GER) 42
552 **SWINGING SULTAN** (GB) 40

193 **SWINGKEEL** (IRE) 17
129 **SWINGLAND** (GB) 18
296 **SWISH DISH** (CAN) 39
25 **SWISS ART** (IRE) 4
208 **SWISS DREAM** (GB) 8
208 **SWISS FRANC** (GB) 9
657 **SWISS GUARD** (GB) 86
603 **SWISS ROSE** (GB) F 8
208 **SWISS SPIRIT** (GB) 27
666 **SWITCH ON** (GB) 49
200 **SWITCHBACK** (GB) 43
696 **SWITCHED OFF** (GB) 43
161 **SWITCHER** (IRE) 37
366 **SWITZERLAND** (IRE) 139
285 **SWNYMOR** (IRE) 62
147 **SWOP** (IRE) 15
446 **SWORD OF DESTINY** (IRE) 73
515 **SWORDS** (GB) 6
299 **SWYNFORD LADY** (IRE) C 258
677 **SWYNFORD PLEASURE** (GB) F 7
650 **SYBARITE** (FR) 64
611 **SYCHO FRED** (IRE) 13
4 **SYDNEY COVE** (IRE) 14
434 **SYDNEY PAGET** (IRE) 129
219 **SYLVAN SONG** (USA) 105
501 **SYMBOLISM** (IRE) 36
32 **SYMPHONIC DANCER** (USA) 23
89 **SYMPHONY OF DREAMS** (GB) 11
89 **SYMPHONY OF LIGHT** (GB) 12
433 **SYMPHONY OF SPACE** (GB) 45
153 **SYMPHONY STAR** (IRE) 15
447 **SYMPHONY TIME** (IRE) 50
111 **SYMPOSIA** (GB) 74
29 **SYNCHRONIC** (GB) 114
299 **SYNCHRONICITY** (IRE) 109
503 **SYNCHRONISED** (IRE) 71
147 **SYNCOPATE** (GB) 64
699 **SYNDICATION** (IRE) 84
237 **SYNERGIE** (IRE) G 45
237 **SYNERGIE** (IRE) G 54
457 **SYNTHE DAVIS** (FR) 13
534 **SZABO'S ART** (GB) 68
285 **TA AJABB** (GB) 63
144 **TAAJUB** (IRE) 3
463 **TAARESH** (IRE) 9
241 **TAB'S GIFT** (GB) F 21
690 **TABARET** (GB) 10
519 **TABIET** (GB) 17
232 **TABRINA** (IRE) C 4
471 **TACKSWOP** (IRE) 22
3 **TACTFULLY** (IRE) 111
35 **TACTICIAN** (GB) 12
696 **TADABEER** (GB) 44
519 **TADALAVIL** (GB) 18
49 **TADMIR** (USA) 112
219 **TADORNE** (FR) C 189
643 **TADRIS** (USA) F 70
408 **TADZIO** (FR) 21
328 **TAFAANI** (FR) F 126
619 **TAFAASEEL** (USA) 152
654 **TAFAWUK** (USA) 78
259 **TAFFE** (GB) 38
681 **TAFIKA** (GB) 57
129 **TAFIYA** (GB) C 43
597 **TAGHREED** (IRE) C 86
19 **TAGLIETELLE** (GB) 100
440 **TAGULA BREEZE** (IRE) 12
352 **TAGULA NIGHT** (IRE) 14

49 **TAHAAMAH** (GB) 62
141 **TAHARA** (IRE) F 76
655 **TAHIR** (GB) F 25
93 **TAHITI DANCER** (GB) 9
606 **TAHITI PEARL** (IRE) 44
35 **TAHLIA REE** (IRE) 54
573 **TAHNEE MARA** (IRE) 71
328 **TAHRIR** (IRE) F 127
315 **TAHTHEEB** (IRE) F 15
608 **TAIGAN** (IRE) 8
466 **TAIKOO** (GB) 28
3 **TAILORING** (IRE) 112
296 **TAIPANS GIRL** (IRE) G 40
328 **TAJAWWUB** (USA) 66
49 **TAJRIBA** (IRE) 113
73 **TAKAJAN** (IRE) 23
508 **TAKAR** (IRE) 49
597 **TAKAWIRI** (IRE) F 87
113 **TAKE A NOTE** (GB) 23
240 **TAKE A SPIN** (GB) 7
422 **TAKE COVER** (GB) 14
397 **TAKE IT THERE** (GB) 32
150 **TAKE OF SHOC'S** (IRE) 26
525 **TAKE OVER SIVOLA** (FR) 93
336 **TAKE ROOT** (GB) 23
3 **TAKE TEN** (GB) 41
489 **TAKE THE BREEZE** (FR) 118
285 **TAKE THE PLUNGE** (GB) C 124
504 **TAKE TWO** (GB) 15
488 **TAKEALOOKATMENOW** (IRE) 68
53 **TAKEITFROMALADY** (IRE) 52
489 **TAKEROC** (FR) 119
304 **TAKEYOURCAPOFF** (IRE) 69
705 **TAKEYOURTIME** (GB) G 23
436 **TAKING CHANCES** (IRE) 23
619 **TAKRICE** (GB) F 153
343 **TALAB** (GB) 56
467 **TALBOT GREEN** (GB) 9
458 **TALBOT ROAD** (IRE) 21
643 **TALEEF** (GB) F 71
34 **TALENT** (GB) 86
664 **TALENT SCOUT** (IRE) 14
619 **TALES OF GRIMM** (USA) 82
343 **TALES OF MILAN** (IRE) 57
688 **TALESOFRIVERBANK** (GB) 18
485 **TALINAS ROSE** (IRE) C 22
332 **TALK D'ARON** (FR) 19
510 **TALK OF THE NORTH** (GB) 12
131 **TALKIN SENCE** (IRE) 9
556 **TALKIN THOMAS** (IRE) 43
331 **TALKONTHESTREET** (IRE) 87
296 **TALLULA** (IRE) 50
496 **TALWAR** (IRE) 42
682 **TALWEEN** (GB) 69
249 **TALYA'S STORM** (GB) 35
161 **TAMALETTA** (IRE) 77
664 **TAMANACO** (IRE) 15
220 **TAMAREEN** (IRE) 32
395 **TAMARILLO GROVE** (IRE) 18
525 **TAMARINBLEU** (FR) 94
49 **TAMARRUD** (GB) 114
442 **TAMASOU** (IRE) 9
595 **TAMBOUR MAJOR** (FR) 4
700 **TAMBRINI LAD** (GB) 42
628 **TAMDIID** (USA) C 40
397 **TAMINO** (GB) 33
193 **TANAGHUM** (GB) C 63
35 **TANAMI DESERT** (GB) C 93

109 **TANASIE** (GB) F 18
450 **TANCRED SPIRIT** (GB) 32
369 **TANCREDI** (SWE) 2
657 **TANERKO EMERY** (FR) 87
157 **TANEYS LEADER** (IRE) G 31
32 **TANFORAN** (GB) 24
511 **TANGATCHEK** (IRE) 91
601 **TANGERINE TREES** (GB) 22
699 **TANGO DE JUILLEY** (FR) 85
33 **TANGO IN THE NIGHT** (GB) 20
34 **TANGO SKY** (IRE) 53
208 **TANGO TONIC** (IRE) C 46
362 **TANGTASTIC** (IRE) 23
183 **TANIN** 25
499 **TANJUNG AGAS** (IRE) 34
321 **TANKS FOR THAT** (IRE) 158
331 **TANNERMAN** (IRE) 88
119 **TANTAMOUNT** (GB) 51
380 **TANTE SISSI** (FR) 108
652 **TANTI'S STORM** (IRE) G 8
119 **TANTINA** (USA) F 78
29 **TANTRIS** (FR) 115
573 **TANWIR** (GB) F 107
570 **TANZANITE BAY** (GB) 61
489 **TAOUFICK DU SEUIL** (FR) 120
570 **TAP NIGHT** (USA) 62
200 **TAPIS LIBRE** (GB) 44
19 **TAPPANAPPA** (IRE) 29
435 **TAQAAT** (USA) 6
503 **TAQUIN DU SEUIL** (FR) 72
650 **TARA ROSE** (GB) 65
434 **TARA ROYAL** (GB) 130
657 **TARA WARRIOR** (GB) 88
290 **TARABELA** (GB) 7
339 **TARADREWE** (GB) 23
318 **TARAF** (GB) 38
508 **TARAKALA** (IRE) F 93
461 **TARANTELLA LADY** (GB) 20
659 **TARAS JOY** (IRE) 46
31 **TARAS D'ALBEN** (FR) 11
525 **TARATATA SIVOLA** (FR) 95
478 **TARATEENO** (GB) 6
572 **TARBELA** (IRE) F 12
654 **TARFSHI** (GB) F 146
154 **TARGET SCORE** (GB) 7
695 **TARKARI** (IRE) 74
350 **TARKESAR** (IRE) 3
658 **TARKHEENA PRINCE** (USA) 32
473 **TARLA** (FR) 110
434 **TARLAN** (GB) 131
233 **TARMAC GIRL** (GB) 16
101 **TARN HOWS** (IRE) 28
387 **TARNEEM** (USA) F 38
188 **TARO TYWOD** (IRE) 26
220 **TAROOQ** (USA) 33
620 **TARQUIN** (IRE) 10
420 **TARQUINIUS** (FR) 39
408 **TARQUINO** (FR) 81
407 **TARRSILLE** (IRE) 9
102 **TART AND A HALF** (GB) G 40
254 **TARTAK** (FR) 49
259 **TARTAN GUNNA** (GB) 12
366 **TARTAN JURA** (GB) 38
131 **TARTAN SNOW** (GB) 10
543 **TARTAN TIGER** (IRE) 25
19 **TARTAN TRIP** (GB) 30
119 **TARTARY** (IRE) 79
193 **TARTEEL** (USA) C 64

29 **TARTESSIAN** (IRE) 59
442 **TARTIFLETTE** (GB) 16
685 **TARUMA** (FR) 8
503 **TARVINI** (IRE) 73
193 **TASHAWAK** (IRE) C 65
373 **TASHEBA** (GB) 27
219 **TASHELKA** (FR) F 190
400 **TASTE THE WINE** (GB) 24
183 **TASTEVIN** (FR) 26
567 **TATENEN** (FR) 21
404 **TATISPOUT** (FR) 45
197 **TATTING** (GB) 11
708 **TATTY** (GB) 21
538 **TAURUS TWINS** (GB) 15
714 **TAVALU** (USA) 8
366 **TAWAAFUR** (GB) C 140
473 **TAWAAGG** (GB) 111
686 **TAWAAJUD** (USA) F 29
285 **TAWAASUL** (GB) 64
287 **TAWARIYKA** (GB) 53
78 **TAWSEEF** (IRE) 9
66 **TAX BENEFIT** (IRE) 6
488 **TAX FREE** (IRE) 41
671 **TAXI DES OBEAUX** (FR) 12
115 **TAYARAT** (IRE) 16
643 **TAYIBAH** (IRE) F 72
501 **TAZAAMUN** (IRE) 37
619 **TAZAHUM** (GB) 6
654 **TAZWEED** (GB) 79
434 **TC SPITFIRE** (IRE) 132
166 **TCHANG GOON** (FR) 20
556 **TCHATCHACOYA** (IRE) G 44
56 **TCHERNICHEVA** (FR) 30
570 **TCHICO POLOS** (FR) 63
329 **TEA BREAK** (GB) F 45
610 **TEA CADDY** (GB) 19
285 **TEACHER** (IRE) 65
150 **TEAFORTHREE** (IRE) 27
660 **TEALISSIO** (GB) 23
545 **TEALS STAR** (GB) 1
268 **TEARS FROM HEAVEN** (USA) 37
521 **TECKTAL** (FR) 15
318 **TECLA** (IRE) 64
197 **TECTONIC** (FR) 12
489 **TED SPREAD** (GB) 121
424 **TED VEALE** (IRE) 29
283 **TED'S BROTHER** (IRE) 62
696 **TEDDY'S REFLECTION** (IRE) 45
682 **TEEBA** (USA) C 124
90 **TEEN AGER** (FR) 6
588 **TEENAGE DREAM** (IRE) 26
598 **TEENAGE IDOL** (FR) 5
284 **TEENAGE KICKS** (IRE) 9
606 **TEENANDO** (FR) 42
47 **TEERIE EXPRESS** (GB) 6
136 **TEGAN LEE** (GB) 12
366 **TEIDE PEAK** (IRE) 141
388 **TEKTEA** (FR) 52
119 **TELAMON** (IRE) 80
388 **TELETI** (FR) 53
503 **TELL ME Y** (IRE) 74
446 **TELLEGIO** (GB) 74
467 **TELLMETHINGS** (GB) 10
117 **TELWAAR** (GB) 31
573 **TEMBLADORA** (IRE) C 108
318 **TEMESTIOS** (FR) 65
478 **TEMLETT** (IRE) 7
266 **TEMPEST FUGIT** (IRE) 102

110 **TEMPEST RIVER** (IRE) 20
570 **TEMPLE LEADER** (GB) G 64
503 **TEMPLE LORD** (FR) 75
442 **TEMPLE MEADS** (GB) 10
64 **TEMPLE ROAD** (IRE) 21
501 **TEMPLEFIRE** (GER) 38
331 **TEMPLER** (IRE) 89
473 **TEMPO DU CAMP** (FR) 112
56 **TEN POLE FELICE** (GB) 31
695 **TEMPTING PARADISE** (IRE) 75
475 **TEN BOB** (IRE) 21
585 **TEN POLE TUDOR** (GB) 30
192 **TENABLE** (GB) F 31
307 **TENANCY** (IRE) 7
387 **TENAVON** (GB) 10
315 **TENBRIDGE** (GB) 12
262 **TENBY JEWEL** (GB) 19
38/ **TENDERLY PLACE** (GB) 29
315 **TENEBRAE** (IRE) F 16
7 **TENHOO** (GB) 12
92 **TENITEMSPLUSTOAST** (GB) 9
473 **TENNIS CAP** (IRE) 113
654 **TENOR** (IRE) 147
699 **TENOR NIVERNAIS** (FR) 86
520 **TENTATIVE** (USA) F 69
619 **TENURE** (GB) 83
322 **TENZING** (IRE) 9
296 **TERENZIUM** (IRE) 41
525 **TERFEL'S TOSCAR** (IRE) 96
473 **TERMINAL** (FR) 114
531 **TERRA BLEU** (IRE) 27
374 **TESHALI** (IRE) 32
191 **TESTOSTERONE** (IRE) 10
29 **TETBURY** (USA) 60
112 **TETBURY LASS** (GB) 6
226 **TETE A QUEUE** (FR) 31
511 **TETH** (GB) 92
321 **TETLAMI** (IRE) 159
696 **TEUTONIC KNIGHT** (IRE) 46
181 **TEVEZ** (GB) 5
8 **TEVIOT LASS** (GB) 22
14 **TEWIN WOOD** (GB) 12
604 **TEXAS HOLDEM** (IRE) 7
446 **TEXAS JACK** (IRE) 75
222 **THACKERAY** (GB) 8
43 **THAI DYE** (UAE) C 49
288 **THALIA GRACE** (GB) 7
619 **THAMARA** (USA) C 154
219 **THANDISWA** (IRE) 106
629 **THANE OF CAWDOR** (IRE) 18
360 **THANK YOU JOY** (GB) 36
564 **THANKS AGAIN** (IRE) F 100
321 **THANKS FOR COMING** (GB) 160
447 **THANKSGIVING DAY** (USA) 109
124 **THARAWAL** (IRE) 25
543 **THARAWAL LADY** (IRE) 50

34 **THARWA** (IRE) C 87
489 **THAT'LL DO** (GB) 122
556 **THAT'LL DO NICELY** (IRE) 45
489 **THAT'LLDOBOY** (FR) 123
696 **THAT'S SOME MILAN** (IRE) 47
137 **THAT'S THE DEAL** (IRE) 8
29 **THAT'S THE SPIRIT** (FR) 61
142 **THATCHERITE** (IRE) 12
695 **THATS BEN** (IRE) 76
643 **THAWABEL** (IRE) 47
174 **THE ABSENT MARE** (GB) 36
410 **THE BANANA MAN** (GB) 17
534 **THE BARONET** (GB) 37
94 **THE BAY BANDIT** (GB) 11
150 **THE BEAR TRAP** (IRE) 28
366 **THE BELLS O PEOVER** (GB) 39
496 **THE BEST DOCTOR** (IRE) 92
318 **THE BEST LAWYER** (USA) 39
304 **THE BIG EASY** (IRE) 70
657 **THE BIG FREEZE** (IRE) 89
567 **THE BISHOPS BABY** (IRE) 22
660 **THE BLACK BARON** (IRE) 24
541 **THE BLONDE EMPEROR** (GB) 7
644 **THE BLUE BANANA** (IRE) 10
672 **THE BOOZY BISHOP** (IRE) 7
583 **THE BOSS** (IRE) 20
473 **THE BOSSES COUSIN** (IRE) 115
96 **THE BRAVETRAVELLER** (IRE) 4
304 **THE BULL HAYES** (IRE) 71
501 **THE BUSKA** (IRE) 39
102 **THE CALLING CURLEW** (GB) 19
142 **THE CARDEN ARMS** (GB) 13
213 **THE CAT CREATION** (HOL) 8
394 **THE CHAZER** (IRE) 25
364 **THE CHEKA** (IRE) 15
27 **THE CLAN MACDONALD** (GB) 44
483 **THE CLYDA ROVER** (IRE) 12
650 **THE COCKNEY MACKEM** (IRE) 66
54 **THE COMPOSER** (GB) 11
102 **THE CONFESSOR** (GB) 20
271 **THE CONJURER** (FR) 6
181 **THE COULBECK KID** (GB) 8
340 **THE CRAFTY BUTCHER** (IRE) 30
647 **THE DANCING LORD** (GB) 22
254 **THE DARLING BOY** (GB) 50
174 **THE DE THAIX** (FR) 37
108 **THE DERRY** (GB) 43
634 **THE DIAL HOUSE** (GB) 13
331 **THE DISENGAGER** (IRE) 90
646 **THE DRUIDS NEPHEW** (IRE) 14
225 **THE DUCKING STOOL** (IRE) 17
409 **THE DUNION** (GB) 4
157 **THE FALKLANDER** (GB) 32
132 **THE FAST FROG** (IRE) 5
625 **THE FERICK** (IRE) 43
586 **THE FIERY CROSS** (GB) 11
626 **THE FLAMING MATRON** (IRE) 18
340 **THE FLYING DUSTMAN** (FR) 31
266 **THE FUGUE** (GB) 103
201 **THE FUN CRUSHER** (GB) 56
688 **THE GALLOPING SHOE** (GB) 19
299 **THE GATLING BOY** (IRE) 259
72 **THE GIANT BOLSTER** (GB) 13
384 **THE GIVING TREE** (IRE) 35
696 **THE GOLDMEISTER** (IRE) 48
489 **THE GOSSMOOR YANK** (IRE) 124
650 **THE GREAT ALFIE** (GB) 67
64 **THE GREY ONE** (IRE) 22

571 **THE GRIFTER** (GB) 4
467 **THE GURU OF GLOOM** (IRE) 11
86 **THE HAPPY WARRIOR** (GB) 21
475 **THE HARD HAT** (IRE) 22
487 **THE HARDY BOY** (GB) 13
665 **THE HIGH MAN** (GB) 5
476 **THE HOLLINWELL** (GB) 74
146 **THE HOLYMAN** (IRE) 14
505 **THE HUDNALLS** (IRE) 7
694 **THE HUMBEL BUTLER** (IRE) 7
370 **THE HUMBEL MONK** (IRE) 6
465 **THE HURL** (IRE) 22
303 **THE IRON GIANT** (IRE) 2
697 **THE ITALIAN YOB** (IRE) 23
504 **THE JAILER** (GB) 11
150 **THE JIGSAW MAN** (IRE) 29
340 **THE JOB IS RIGHT** (GB) 32
150 **THE JUGOPOLIST** (IRE) 30
407 **THE KERNIGAL** (IRE) 33
489 **THE KNOXS** (GB) 125
15 **THE LAODICEAN** (GB) 15
287 **THE LAST DON** (IRE) 25
391 **THE LAST NIGHT** (FR) 55
603 **THE LAST SELECTION** (GB) 9
499 **THE LEGAL ARTICLE** (IRE) 35
531 **THE LEMONPIE** (GER) 28
525 **THE LITTLE MINX** (GB) 97
9 **THE LOCK MASTER** (IRE) 33
640 **THE LODGE ROAD** (IRE) 18
359 **THE MAGIC BISHOP** (GB) 30
20 **THE MAGIC OF RIO** (GB) 5
35 **THE MANX MISSILE** (GB) 94
665 **THE MANX TOUCH** (IRE) C 21
299 **THE MASCOT** (GB) 260
473 **THE MIDNIGHT CLUB** (IRE) 116
124 **THE MIGHTIE QUIN** (GB) 17
115 **THE MIGHTY MOD** (USA) 17
489 **THE MINACK** (GB) 126
640 **THE MONGOLIAN** (IRE) 19
214 **THE MONGOOSE** (GB) 34
380 **THE MUMPER** (IRE) 109
287 **THE MUNSTER MAORI** (IRE) 26
650 **THE MUSICAL GUY** (GB) 68
257 **THE NAME IS DON** (IRE) 11
257 **THE NAME IS FRANK** (GB) 9
317 **THE NAMES HARRY** (GB) 6
113 **THE NAMES JAMES** (GB) 18
650 **THE NEW ONE** (GB) 69
489 **THE NIGHTINGALE** (FR) 127
266 **THE NILE** (GB) 104
384 **THE NOBLE ORD** (GB) 36
180 **THE OIL MAGNATE** (GB) 22
373 **THE OMEN** (GB) 28
162 **THE OSTEOPATH** (IRE) 4
525 **THE PACKAGE** (GB) 98
4 **THE PADDY PREMIUM** (FR) 15
359 **THE PANAMA KID** (IRE) 31
473 **THE PAPARAZZI KID** (IRE) 117
45 **THE PEN** (GB) F 20
525 **THE PIER** (IRE) 99
150 **THE PLAYFUL PRIEST** (IRE) 31
71 **THE PLOUGHMAN** (GB) 19
259 **THE POWER OF ONE** (FR) 50
489 **THE PRETENDER** (GB) 128
525 **THE PRIME VIPER** (GB) 100
174 **THE QUANTUM KID** (GB) 38
333 **THE QUARTERJACK** (GB) 14
304 **THE QUIET HAWK** (IRE) 72

16 **THE RAINBOW HUNTER** (GB) 42
499 **THE REAL ARTICLE** (IRE) 36
343 **THE REAL TARGET** (IRE) 58
499 **THE REAL TYSON** (IRE) 37
407 **THE REAPER** (IRE) 10
61 **THE RECTIFIER** (USA) 17
381 **THE RED LAIRD** (GB) 19
489 **THE REFORMER** (IRE) 129
407 **THE RESISTANCE** (IRE) 11
108 **THE RIGHT TIME** (GB) 44
695 **THE ROCKIES** (IRE) 77
150 **THE ROMFORD PELE** (IRE) 32
329 **THE ROYAL** (GB) 19
347 **THE ROYAL BROMPTON** (GB) 22
497 **THE SAUCY SNIPE** (GB) 6
86 **THE SAWYER** (BEL) 22
564 **THE SHACK** (IRE) 15
461 **THE SHY MAN** (IRE) 21
338 **THE SNORER** (GB) 14
322 **THE SOCIETY MAN** (IRE) 10
314 **THE SPAILPIN FANAC** (IRE) 9
570 **THE STARBOARD BOW** (GB) 65
10 **THE STRAWBERRY ONE** (GB) 19
698 **THE STRIG** (GB) 11
614 **THE TALLY HO KID** (IRE) 30
525 **THE TATKIN** (IRE) 101
340 **THE TELAVARA** (IRE) 33
634 **THE THIRSTY BRICKY** (IRE) 8
632 **THE TICHBORNE** (IRE) 8
685 **THE TIDDLY TADPOLE** (GB) 9
191 **THE TIGER** (GB) 11
658 **THE TIPSY TANGERINE** 54
525 **THE TRACEY SHUFFLE** (GB) 102
55 **THE VISITOR** (IRE) 125
499 **THE WAY WE WERE** (IRE) 38
200 **THE WAYWARD LORD** (IRE) 34
434 **THE WEATHERMAN** (IRE) 133
243 **THE WEE CHIEF** (IRE) 9
692 **THE WEE MIDGET** (GB) 5
283 **THE WHICH DOCTOR** (GB) 63
321 **THE WHITE ADMIRAL** (IRE) 161
374 **THE WICKED KIPPER** (GB) 33
406 **THE WINGED ASSASIN** (USA) 8
19 **THE WIZARD OF AUS** (IRE) 161
108 **THE YANK** (GB) 56
469 **THE YOUNG MASTER** (GB) 39
187 **THEATRE DIVA** (IRE) 3
639 **THEATRE GUIDE** (IRE) 47
68 **THEATRELANDS** (GB) 11
639 **THEATRICAL STAR** (GB) 48
617 **THEBOYFROMBRAZIL** (IRE) 23
254 **THECIRCLEOFTRUST** (FR) 51
572 **THECORNISHCOCKNEY** (GB) 21
572 **THECORNISHCOWBOY** (GB) 22
185 **THEDEBOFTHEYEAR** (GB) 14
505 **THEDREAMSTILLALIVE** (IRE) 8
109 **THEEBAH** (GB) F 19
298 **THEGONDOLIER** (IRE) 28
446 **THEGREATJOHNBROWNE** (IRE) 76
503 **THEHILLOFUISNEACH** (IRE) 76
19 **THELADYINQUESTION** (GB) 31
473 **THELEZE** (FR) 118
624 **THELIFEOF** (IRE) 8
657 **THELOBSTERCATCHER** (GB) 90
489 **THEMILANHORSE** (IRE) 130
665 **THEN 'N NOW** (GB) C 22
619 **THEODORE GERICAULT** (IRE) 155
681 **THEODORE LAMB** (GB) 58

486 **THEOLOGIST** (IRE) 12
263 **THEOLOGY** (GB) 20
620 **THEORIE** (FR) G 17
472 **THERE AND THEN** (GB) 27
283 **THERE'S NO RULES** (GB) 80
5 **THEREDBALLOON** (GB) 5
516 **THERESNONEEDFORDAT** (IRE) 17
237 **THETASTEOFPARADISE** (GB) 31
266 **THETURNOFTHESUN** (IRE) 105
380 **THETWINCAMDRIFT** (IRE) 110
507 **THICKET** (GB) F 50
266 **THIMAAR** (USA) 28
468 **THINK** (GB) 5
74 **THINK FAST** (IRE) 22
218 **THINK GREEN** (GB) 27
414 **THINK IT OVER** (IRE) F 11
201 **THINKING** (GB) 57
639 **THIRD INTENTION** (IRE) 49
191 **THIRD PARTY** (GB) F 77
200 **THIRTEEN SHIVERS** (IRE) 46
689 **THIRTY DAYS OUT** (IRE) 18
104 **THIS IS ME** (GB) 10
161 **THIS IS NICE** (IRE) 78
20 **THIS ONES FOR EDDY** (GB) 6
571 **THIS WAY** (IRE) 5
119 **THISTLE BIRD** (GB) 13
637 **THISTLE STIKK** (GB) 14
681 **THOM THUMB** (IRE) 59
504 **THOMAS BELL** (GB) 12
111 **THOMAS CHIPPENDALE** (IRE) 75
174 **THOMAS CRAPPER** (GB) 39
55 **THOMAS DYLAN** (IRE) 60
424 **THOMAS EDISON** (IRE) 30
127 **THOMASINA** (GB) 21
110 **THORESBY** (IRE) 21
218 **THORLAK** (FR) 28
588 **THORNCLIFFER** (GB) 27
522 **THORNTON ALICE** (GB) 23
654 **THORNTOUN PICCOLO** (GB) C 148
34 **THORPE** (IRE) 88
558 **THORPE BAY** (GB) 5
183 **THORZIEN** (FR) 47
266 **THOUGHT WORTHY** (USA) 106
473 **THOUSAND STARS** (FR) 119
446 **THOUVA** (FR) 77
146 **THRASOS** (IRE) 22
299 **THREE AM TOUR** (IRE) 110
366 **THREE BARDS** (IRE) 142
299 **THREE CHOIRS** (IRE) 261
708 **THREE CROWNS** (GB) 25
488 **THREE DARLINGS** (IRE) 64
682 **THREE KINGDOMS** (IRE) 70
298 **THREE MOUNTAINVIEW** (IRE) 29
496 **THREE SUGARS** (AUS) 43
265 **THREE WAY STRETCH** (IRE) 15
207 **THREE WHITE SOCKS** (IRE) 44
447 **THREE WRENS** (IRE) C 110
690 **THREEPENCE** (GB) 20
93 **THUNDER CHILD** (GB) 10
407 **THUNDER MOON** (IRE) 34
373 **THUNDER ON** (GB) 29
498 **THUNDER SHEIK** (IRE) 21
176 **THUNDERBALL** (GB) 17
434 **THUNDERCRACK** (IRE) 134
118 **THUNDERING HOME** (GB) 32
176 **THUNDERSTRUCK** (GB) 18
552 **THURNHAM** (GB) 41
55 **THUS FAR** (USA) 126

34 **THWART** (GB) 89
391 **THYMELESS** (GB) 56
388 **TIA KIA** (IRE) 10
681 **TIAGRA** (GB) 60
318 **TIBALDI** (FR) 40
408 **TIBERIUS** (GER) 82
422 **TIBERIUS CLAUDIUS** (IRE) 15
146 **TICK TOCK LOVER** (GB) 15
444 **TICKATACK** (IRE) 17
613 **TICKI TORI** (IRE) C 7
380 **TICKITY BLEUE** (GB) 111
386 **TICKLE ME** (IRE) 26
111 **TICKLED PINK** (IRE) 76
489 **TIDAL BLUE** (IRE) 131
391 **TIDAL DANCE** (IRE) 57
221 **TIDAL STAR** (GB) 7
573 **TIDDLIWINKS** (GB) 27
511 **TIDESPRING** (IRE) 37
148 **TIERNAN'S TERROR** (IRE) 5
328 **TIFARITI** (USA) C 128
55 **TIFFILIA** (IRE) 61
511 **TIFONGO** (GB) 93
55 **TIGER AT HEART** (IRE) 62
114 **TIGER BAY** (IRE) 11
111 **TIGER CLIFF** (IRE) 77
415 **TIGER CUB** (GB) 10
542 **TIGER GIRL** (GB) 13
434 **TIGER MAGUIRE** (IRE) 135
285 **TIGER MIST** (IRE) F 125
695 **TIGER O'TOOLE** (IRE) 78
188 **TIGER PRINCE** (IRE) 43
695 **TIGER RAG** (FR) 79
180 **TIGER REIGNS** (GB) 13
35 **TIGER SPICE** (IRE) C 95
462 **TIGER SUNSET** (IRE) 42
200 **TIGER WEBB** (GB) 47
234 **TIGER WHO** (GB) 3
225 **TIGER'S HOME** (GB) 26
346 **TIGER'S JACEY** (IRE) 2
656 **TIGERBILL** (GB) 11
222 **TIGERINO** (IRE) 9
632 **TIGERS TALE** (IRE) 17
698 **TIGERTOO** (IRE) 24
102 **TIGHT FIT** (GB) 60
213 **TIGHT LIPPED** (IRE) 19
266 **TIGHTLACED** (USA) 107
17 **TIGNELLO** (IRE) 9
489 **TIGRE D'ARON** (IRE) 132
366 **TIGRESA** (IRE) 143
503 **TIGRESSE BLEUE** (GB) 77
608 **TIHUI SEPT** (GB) 9
400 **TIJORI** (IRE) 25
169 **TIJUCA** (IRE) 30
475 **TILE LADY** (IRE) 23
465 **TILLAHOW** (IRE) 23
201 **TILLIEMINT** (IRE) 58
613 **TILLY'S DREAM** (GB) F 9
207 **TILOS GEM** (IRE) 45
299 **TILSTARR** (IRE) 262
360 **TILSWORTH GLENBOY** (GB) 37
174 **TILT DU CHATELIER** (FR) 40
391 **TIM THE CHAIR** (IRE) 58
508 **TIMAROUN** (USA) 50
19 **TIME AWAY** (IRE) F 162
639 **TIME BOOK** (IRE) 50
373 **TIME DO** (FR) 30
102 **TIME FOR A TIGER** (GB) 41
437 **TIME FOR HARRY** (GB) 9

681 **TIME FOR RUPERT** (IRE) 61
404 **TIME FOR SPRING** (IRE) 46
108 **TIME MEDICEAN** (GB) 45
614 **TIME OF MY LIFE** (IRE) 31
218 **TIME OUT** (IRE) 29
3 **TIME PRISONER** (USA) 42
108 **TIME SQUARE** (FR) 46
645 **TIME TO DANCE** (GB) 14
180 **TIME TO EXCEL** (GB) 39
81 **TIME TO PLAY** (GB) 10
472 **TIME TO THINK** (GB) 28
202 **TIMEFORAGIN** (GB) 4
27 **TIMELESS ELEGANCE** (IRE) 28
3 **TIMELINE** (GB) 43
111 **TIMEPIECE** (GB) 17
193 **TIMES UP** (GB) 18
695 **TIMESAWASTIN** (GB) 80
400 **TIMETORING** (GB) 26
508 **TIMIKAR** (USA) 94
92 **TIMMIES GONE** (IRE) 10
397 **TIMOCRACY** (GB) 34
157 **TIMPO** (FR) 33
67 **TIN PAN ALLEY** (GB) 4
695 **TIN POT MAN** (IRE) 81
202 **TINA THYNE** (IRE) F 5
141 **TINA'S SPIRIT** (IRE) 56
465 **TINAKELLYLAD** (IRE) 24
686 **TINAREENA** (IRE) C 30
221 **TINAS EXHIBITION** (IRE) 8
681 **TINDARO** (FR) 62
406 **TINELYRA** (IRE) 9
600 **TINGE** (USA) C 49
460 **TINGLING** (USA) F 129
10 **TINGO IN THE TALE** (IRE) 23
403 **TINKERBELL WILL** (GB) 13
619 **TINLEY LODGE** (GB) 84
566 **TINSELTOWN** (GB) 12
315 **TINSHU** (IRE) 7
467 **TINTERN** (GB) F 45
220 **TINY TEMPER** (IRE) 44
119 **TIOMAN LEGEND** (GB) 52
654 **TIOMAN PEARL** (GB) 80
183 **TIP TOE** (FR) 27
606 **TIPPERING** (IRE) 43
510 **TIPPING OVER** (IRE) 23
127 **TIPSY GIRL** (GB) 8
606 **TIPSY INDIAN** (GB) 44
201 **TIPTOEAWAY** (IRE) 59
12 **TIRADITO** (USA) 20
254 **TIRE LARIGOT** (FR) 52
390 **TIS ROCK 'N' ROLL** (USA) 17
539 **TISFREETDREAM** (IRE) 7
18 **TISH BAY** (GB) 33
433 **TISLAAM** (IRE) 27
321 **TISTORY** (FR) 162
321 **TITAN DE SARTI** (FR) 163
653 **TITAN DIAMOND** (IRE) 19
387 **TITAN TRIUMPH** (GB) 11
634 **TITANIA** (GB) G 15
512 **TITCH STRIDER** (IRE) 2
123 **TITIAN TIME** (USA) F 67
570 **TITO BUSTILLO** (FR) 66
61 **TITUS BOLT** (IRE) 34
249 **TITUS GENT** (GB) 22
447 **TITUS MILLS** (IRE) 10
462 **TITUS STAR** (IRE) 24
366 **TMAAM** (USA) 40
366 **TO THE SEA** (USA) 144

201 **TOBACCO** (GB) 125
299 **TOBACCO ROAD** (IRE) 263
323 **TOBAGO** (GB) 9
460 **TOBAGO BAY** (GB) 91
55 **TOBANN** (IRE) 127
499 **TOBAR NA GAOISE** (IRE) 39
511 **TOBERMORY** (IRE) C 132
359 **TOBETALL** (GB) 14
75 **TOBRATA** (GB) 14
157 **TOBY BELCH** (IRE) 34
355 **TOBY MAC** (GB) 7
450 **TOBY TYLER** (GB) 33
391 **TOCCA FERRO** (FR) 59
208 **TOCHAR BAN** (USA) F 47
505 **TODAREISTODO** (GB) 9
57 **TODAY'S THE DAY** (GB) C 23
26 **TOFFEE NOSE** (GB) 11
329 **TOFFEE VODKA** (IRE) F 46
125 **TOFFEEPOT** (GB) 5
343 **TOFINO BAY** (FR) 59
249 **TOGA TIGER** (GB) 23
542 **TOLDYA** (GB) F 28
24 **TOLEDO GOLD** (IRE) 23
160 **TOLKEINS TANGO** (IRE) 42
446 **TOM HORN** (IRE) 78
174 **TOM O'TARA** (GB) 41
352 **TOM RED** (GB) 27
610 **TOM SANG** (FR) 20
99 **TOM SAWYER** (GB) 14
305 **TOM WADE** (IRE) 4
147 **TOMAHAWK CHIEF** (IRE) 110
686 **TOMASINI** (GB) 17
705 **TOMBELLINI** (IRE) 24
517 **TOMBI** (USA) 10
336 **TOMINATOR** (GB) 24
111 **TOMINTOUL MAGIC** (IRE) 154
226 **TOMMIE MILAN** (IRE) 32
425 **TOMMY TIGER** (GB) 4
116 **TOMMY'S SECRET** (GB) 31
635 **TOMMYSTEEL** (IRE) 16
564 **TOMOOHAT** (USA) F 101
647 **TOMORROW'S WORLD** (IRE) F 35
166 **TOMS RIVER TESS** (IRE) 21
161 **TOMWAY** (GB) 38
594 **TOMZATACKMAN** (IRE) 2
691 **TON-CHEE** (GB) 5
456 **TONGALOOMA** (GB) 21
489 **TONIC MELLYSSE** (FR) 133
141 **TONLE SAP** (IRE) 57
434 **TONVADOSA** (GB) 136
321 **TONY DINOZZO** (FR) 164
451 **TONY HOLLIS** (GB) 91
331 **TONY STAR** (FR) 91
336 **TOO AMBITIOUS** (GB) 38
448 **TOOKA** (GB) 7
108 **TOOLEY WOODS** (IRE) 57
337 **TOOMAN LANE** (IRE) 13
180 **TOORAH LAURA LA** (USA) C 55
473 **TOOSTRONG** (FR) 120
157 **TOOT SWEET** (IRE) 35
711 **TOOTHACHE** (GB) 6
16 **TOP BENEFIT** (IRE) 43
201 **TOP BID** (GB) 60
23 **TOP BOB** (IRE) 5
388 **TOP CHILL** (FR) 93
19 **TOP COP** (GB) 101
110 **TOP DANCER** (FR) 22
253 **TOP DESIGN** (GB) 10

619 **TOP DIKTAT** (GB) 7
141 **TOP FROCK** (IRE) 58
446 **TOP MAN MICHAEL** (IRE) 90
321 **TOP OF THE RANGE** (IRE) 165
119 **TOP OFFER** (GB) 53
174 **TOP ROSE** (GB) 42
511 **TOP SAUCE** (GB) C 133
472 **TOP SMART** (GB) 29
475 **TOP SPIN** (IRE) 24
183 **TOP TRIP** (GB) 48
525 **TOP WOOD** (FR) 103
642 **TOPAMICHI** (GB) 48
19 **TOPANGA CANYON** (GB) 102
293 **TOPAZ BAY** (GB) 5
388 **TOPAZE BLANCHE** (IRE) 94
404 **TOPAZE COLLONGES** (FR) 47
110 **TOPENHALL** (IRE) 23
249 **TOPFLIGHT PRINCESS** (GB) 36
387 **TOPIARY** (FR) C 39
10 **TOPOLSKI** (IRE) 20
447 **TOPPLED** (IRE) 51
642 **TOPTEMPO** (GB) 39
183 **TOPZA** (FR) 63
55 **TOQUETTE** (IRE) 128
650 **TOREADOR** (FR) 70
123 **TOREODORA** (FR) 49
573 **TORERO** (GB) 72
699 **TORGAMAH LAD** (IRE) 87
321 **TORNADE D'ESTRUVAL** (FR) 166
695 **TORNADE DE GUYE** (FR) 82
366 **TORNADO BATTLE** (GB) 203
434 **TORNADO BOB** (IRE) 137
496 **TORNADO FORCE** (FR) 9
695 **TORNADO IN MILAN** (IRE) 83
299 **TORONADO** (IRE) 264
380 **TORPHICHEN** (GB) 112
213 **TORRAN SOUND** (GB) 9
388 **TORREMOLINOS** (FR) 54
53 **TORRENTIAL RAINE** (GB) 15
243 **TORRES DEL PAINE** (GB) 10
564 **TORRESTRELLA** (IRE) C 102
181 **TORTILLA** (IRE) 6
573 **TORTONI** (IRE) 73
275 **TORTUEUSE** (IRE) 9
446 **TORUS OR YOU** (IRE) G 79
254 **TORY MASSINI** (IRE) 53
260 **TOSHI** (USA) 27
632 **TOSS A COIN** (IRE) 18
569 **TOSS THE DICE** (IRE) 15
474 **TOTAL EFFECTS** (IRE) 17
330 **TOTAL OBSESSION** (GB) 7
434 **TOTAL REBELLION** (IRE) 138
374 **TOTAL SUBMISSION** (GB) 34
396 **TOTAL VICTORY** (GB) 8
147 **TOTALIZE** (GB) 65
299 **TOTALLY DOMINANT** (USA) 111
366 **TOTALLY YOURS** (IRE) C 204
657 **TOTO CORDE MEO** (IRE) 91
489 **TOUBAB** (FR) 134
544 **TOUCAN TANGO** (IRE) 5
111 **TOUCH GOLD** (IRE) 78
696 **TOUCH OF IRISH** (GB) 49
25 **TOUCH OF STYLE** (IRE) 5
218 **TOUCH OF TWEED** (IRE) 30
634 **TOUCH TONE** (GB) 16
251 **TOUGH COOKIE** (IRE) 8
658 **TOUGHNESS DANON** (GB) 33
511 **TOUJOURS** (GER) 94

365 **TOULOUSE EXPRESS** (IRE) 11
321 **TOUR D'ARGENT** (FR) 167
650 **TOUR DES CHAMPS** (FR) 71
29 **TOUR EIFFEL** (FR) 62
696 **TOURIST** (GB) 50
461 **TOURTIERE** (GB) 22
481 **TOUS LES DEUX** (GB) 8
657 **TOUT REGULIER** (GB) 92
408 **TOUT ROUGE** 22
318 **TOUTE ALLURE** (USA) 41
379 **TOUZ MASTER** (FR) 8
200 **TOWBEE** (GB) 65
466 **TOWN MOUSE** (GB) 85
658 **TOWN REBEL** (IRE) 34
708 **TOWY BOY** (GB) 14
479 **TOY GUN** (IRE) 17
259 **TOYMAKER** (GB) 13
298 **TRABAJO** (IRE) 30
360 **TRACHONITIS** (IRE) 38
595 **TRACKANAIS** (FR) 5
215 **TRACKMATE** (GB) 17
64 **TRADE CENTRE** (GB) 23
266 **TRADE COMMISSIONER** (IRE) 29
380 **TRADE ON** (GB) 113
75 **TRADE SECRET** (GB) 15
597 **TRADE STORM** (GB) 20
119 **TRADER JACK** (GB) 54
447 **TRADER SECRET** (IRE) C 111
321 **TRADEWINDS** (FR) 168
55 **TRADING LEATHER** (IRE) 129
444 **TRADITIONAL BOB** (IRE) 18
650 **TRAFALGAR** (FR) 72
404 **TRAFALGAR ROAD** (IRE) 48
12 **TRAFALGAR SQUARE** (GB) 21
420 **TRAFFIC CHAOS** (IRE) 40
462 **TRAFFIC SISTER** (USA) 5
573 **TRAIL BLAZE** (IRE) 74
266 **TRAIL OF TEARS** (IRE) 108
682 **TRAIN OF THOUGHT** (IRE) 21
695 **TRAITOR** (GB) 84
499 **TRANQUIL SEA** (IRE) 40
111 **TRANQUIL TIGER** (GB) 18
658 **TRANQUIL WATERS** (IRE) 35
501 **TRANS SONIC** (GB) 40
640 **TRANSACT** (IRE) 20
308 **TRANSEGGSELENCE** (GB) 10
538 **TRANSFER** (GB) 16
21 **TRANSFORMER** (IRE) 5
628 **TRANSITION TIME** (USA) F 41
201 **TRANSMIT** (IRE) 61
13 **TRANSVESTITE** (IRE) 5
408 **TRAPRAIN** 83
304 **TRASNAGH** (IRE) 73
299 **TRAVELLER'S TALES** (IRE) 112
58 **TRAVELLING** (GB) 53
499 **TRAVIS MCGEE** (FR) 41
424 **TRAZAR** (FR) 31
507 **TREADWELL** (IRE) 12
113 **TREASURE ACT** (GB) 19
511 **TREASURE ROCK** (IRE) 134
682 **TREASURE THE RIDGE** (IRE) 71
520 **TREASURED DREAM** (GB) 46
458 **TREAT YOURSELF** (IRE) 22
161 **TREBLE HEIGHTS** (IRE) C 79
108 **TRECASE** (GB) 47
219 **TREE TOPS** (GB) F 191
294 **TREEHOUSE** (GB) 8
611 **TREGARO** (FR) 14

93 **TREGONY BRIDGE** (GB) 11
119 **TREKKING** (USA) F 81
86 **TRENCHANT** (GB) 23
520 **TREND IS MY FRIEND** (USA) 47
117 **TREND LINE** (IRE) 4
249 **TRENDING** (IRE) 37
627 **TRENDY CELT** (IRE) G 6
511 **TRES BLUE** (IRE) 135
27 **TRES CORONAS** (IRE) 29
511 **TRES DANCE** (IRE) 95
9 **TRESABELLA** (GB) 50
394 **TRESOR DE BONTEE** (FR) 26
66 **TRESOR DE L'ISLE** (FR) 7
227 **TRESPASSER** (IRE) 25
547 **TREV TARA** (GB) 10
318 **TREVE** (FR) 66
388 **TREVIERES** (FR) 11
391 **TREVIS** (GB) 60
658 **TREVOSE** (FR) 55
529 **TRI PAC** (IRE) C 46
254 **TRIANGULAR** (USA) 54
110 **TRIBAL DANCE** (IRE) 24
352 **TRIBOULEY** (GB) 15
588 **TRICK OF ACE** (USA) F 47
520 **TRICKED** (GB) C 70
625 **TRICKSOFTHETRADE** (IRE) 44
599 **TRICKY TREE** (IRE) 10
253 **TRICOR** (GB) 11
98 **TRIFOLIUM** (FR) 18
380 **TRIGGER THE LIGHT** (GB) 114
331 **TRIGGERMAN** (GB) 92
270 **TRIKIRK** (IRE) 10
439 **TRILBY** (GB) G 7
666 **TRINKILA** (USA) F 50
578 **TRIO OF TRIX** (GB) 3
321 **TRIOLO D'ALENE** (FR) 169
72 **TRIOMPHAL** (FR) 14
259 **TRIOOMPH** (GB) 39
540 **TRIP SWITCH** (GB) 6
449 **TRIP THE LIGHT** (GB) 4
249 **TRIPLE ASPECT** (IRE) 24
187 **TRIPLE BLUFF** (IRE) 4
496 **TRIPLE CHARM** (GB) 10
64 **TRIPLE DREAM** (GB) 24
501 **TRIPLE EDITION** (USA) C 60
383 **TRIPLE EIGHT** (IRE) 18
397 **TRIPLE SALCHOW** (IRE) 46
58 **TRIPLE SHARP** (GB) F 82
219 **TRIPLE THREAT** (FR) 192
506 **TRIPLE TRICKS** (GB) C 28
506 **TRIPLE TRICKS** (IRE) G 19
29 **TRIPLE WITCHING** (USA) 63
276 **TRIPTI** (IRE) C 19
695 **TRIPTICO** (FR) 85
184 **TRISHA'S BOY** (IRE) 22
618 **TRISKAIDEKAPHOBIA** (FR) 7
564 **TROIS LUNES** (FR) 81
3 **TROIS VALLEES** (USA) 113
99 **TROJAN GIFT** (USA) 15
540 **TROJAN ROCKET** (IRE) 7
626 **TROJAN SUN** (IRE) 19
569 **TROON** (FR) 85
682 **TROON** (USA) 22
695 **TROOPER CLARENCE** (GB) 86
555 **TROOPER KIT** (GB) 9
30 **TROOPER ROYAL** (GB) 25
263 **TROOPINGTHECOLOUR** (GB) 21
525 **TROP FORT** (FR) 104

388 **TROPAIOS** (GB) 55
456 **TROPENFEUER** (FR) 22
388 **TROPHY BABY** (GB) 56
237 **TROPICAL BACHELOR** (IRE) 32
266 **TROPICAL BEAT** (GB) 30
188 **TROPICAL BREEZE** (IRE) C 44
237 **TROPICAL CORAL** (GB) G 33
26 **TROPICAL DUKE** (GB) 12
115 **TROPICAL SKY** (IRE) 18
266 **TROPICAL SONG** (GB) 152
287 **TROTTING WEASEL** (IRE) 27
343 **TROUBLED** (IRE) 60
108 **TROUBLETIMESTWO** (FR) 48
109 **TROUNCE** (GB) F 20
520 **TROVARE** (USA) 14
318 **TROYA** (FR) 67
174 **TROYAN** (IRE) 43
321 **TROZULON** (FR) 170
657 **TRUCKERS BENEFIT** (IRE) 93
298 **TRUCKERS DELIGHT** (IRE) 31
332 **TRUCKERS PRINCESS** (IRE) 20
657 **TRUE BLUE** (IRE) 94
506 **TRUE BOND** (GB) 20
304 **TRUE CHARACTER** (IRE) 74
495 **TRUE MELODY** (IRE) F 14
520 **TRUE PRINCE** (USA) 48
116 **TRUE SATIRE** (GB) 13
153 **TRUE SPIRIT** (GB) 19
442 **TRULLITTI** (IRE) C 34
299 **TRUMPET MAJOR** (IRE) 113
475 **TRUPENNY BIT** (IRE) 25
92 **TRUQ CHOUET** (FR) 11
183 **TRUQUE** (FR) 28
201 **TRUST FUND BABE** (IRE) 100
403 **TRUST ME BOY** (GB) 14
201 **TRUSTAN TIMES** (IRE) 62
364 **TRUSTING** (IRE) 28
31 **TRY CATCH ME** (IRE) 12
388 **TRYLKO** (USA) C 95
321 **TSAR ALEXANDRE** (FR) 171
619 **TSAR'S PRIDE** (GB) F 156
380 **TSARINOVA** (GB) 115
446 **TUCKER CASEY** (IRE) 91
26 **TUDOR BEAT** (GB) 13
499 **TUGBOAT** (IRE) 42
310 **TUIBAMA** (IRE) 17
564 **TUIGA** (FR) C 103
468 **TUKITINYASOK** (IRE) 6
331 **TULIA DE GRAVELLE** (GB) 93
219 **TULIPS** (IRE) 107
256 **TULLAMORE DEW** (IRE) 24
19 **TULLIUS** (IRE) 32
284 **TULLOW BOY** (GB) 10
628 **TULLYNALLY** (GB) C 42
558 **TUMBLED AGAIN** (GB) 4
572 **TUMBLEOWTASHOES** (GB) 23
690 **TUMBLEWIND** (GB) 21
49 **TUMOOH** (IRE) 115
384 **TUNDRIDGE** (GB) 37
183 **TUNE IN** (FR) 49
466 **TUNNAGER GROVE** (GB) 61
237 **TUNZA THE LION** (GB) 34
645 **TUPPENNY** (GB) F 20
191 **TURAMA** (GB) 41
331 **TURANJO BELLO** (FR) 94
473 **TURBAN** (FR) 121
282 **TURBAN HEIGHTS** (IRE) F 9
8 **TURBO ISLAND** (GB) 23

671 **TURBOLINAS** (FR) 13
400 **TURBULANCE** (IRE) 27
166 **TURBULENT PRIEST** (GB) 22
461 **TURF TRIVIA** (GB) 23
511 **TURFBLUTE** (GER) 136
14 **TURJUMAN** (USA) 13
500 **TURN BACK** (GB) G 20
407 **TURN ME LOOSE** (USA) F 62
380 **TURN OVER SIVOLA** (FR) 116
357 **TURNED TO GOLD** (IRE) 19
654 **TURNING LEAF** (IRE) F 149
160 **TUROYAL** (FR) 43
564 **TURTLE BOW** (FR) C 104
564 **TURTLE GREEN** (FR) 82
326 **TURTLETHOMAS** (IRE) 25
343 **TUSA EIRE** (IRE) 61
654 **TUSCAN FUN** (GB) 150
380 **TUSCAN GOLD** (GB) 117
42 **TUSCANY STAR** (IRE) 23
367 **TUSKAR** (USA) 11
699 **TUSKAR ROCK** (FR) 88
366 **TUSSIE MUSSIE** (GB) 205
556 **TUTCHEC** (FR) 46
325 **TUXEDO** (GB) 13
285 **TWEED** (GB) 126
542 **TWEEDLE DEE** (GB) 22
626 **TWEEDLEDRUM** (GB) 20
178 **TWEEDO PARADISO** (NZ) 24
451 **TWEED LADY** (GB) 42
16 **TWELVE ROSES** (GB) 44
147 **TWELVE STRINGS** (GB) 66
169 **TWENTY ONE CHOICE** (IRE) 31
696 **TWENTYFOURCARAT** (IRE) 51
126 **TWENTYNINEBLACK** (FR) 6
275 **TWENTYPOUNDLUCK** (IRE) 10
641 **TWICE BITTEN** (GB) 3
606 **TWICE LUCKY** (GB) 45
111 **TWICE OVER** (GB) 19
588 **TWICE RED** (GB) 28
359 **TWIGLET THE PIGLET** (GB) 33
473 **TWIGLINE** (FR) 122
203 **TWILIGHT ANGEL** (GB) 6
155 **TWILIGHT BELLE** (IRE) C 27
102 **TWILIGHT MISTRESS** (GB) C 61
397 **TWIN BARRELS** (GB) 35
487 **TWIN BUD** (GB) 14
241 **TWIN EDGE** (GB) 15
55 **TWIN FOCUS** (IRE) 63
230 **TWIN IVAN** (IRE) 9
223 **TWIN SHADOW** (IRE) 43
19 **TWIN SOUL** (IRE) 33
35 **TWINKLED** (GB) 13
473 **TWINLIGHT** (FR) 123
503 **TWIRLING MAGNET** (IRE) 78
653 **TWITCH HILL** (GB) F 36
188 **TWO CITIES** (GB) 37
123 **TWO FOR TWO** (IRE) 14
510 **TWO IN THE PINK** (GB) 24
321 **TWO OSCARS** (IRE) 172
547 **TWO SHOOK MEN** (IRE) 11
471 **TWO TURTLE DOVES** (IRE) 23
698 **TYCHAIOS** (GB) 35
386 **TYCOONS REFLECTION** (IRE) 27
390 **TYPHON** (USA) 47
374 **TYPHON DE GUYE** (FR) 35
467 **TYPOGRAPHY** (GB) 35
696 **TYRANA** (GER) 52
506 **TYRE GIANT DOT COM** (GB) 21

659 **TYRONE HOUSE** (IRE) 47
9 **TYSOE LAD** (GB) 34
536 **TYUP POMPEY** (IRE) 6
278 **U B CAREFULL** (GB) 3
664 **UBI ACE** (GB) 16
65 **UBIQUE** (IRE) 10
219 **UCCELLINA** (FR) 108
408 **UCELLO CONTI** (FR) 23
218 **UEUETEOTL** (FR) 31
171 **UFFA FOX** (IRE) 10
219 **UFOLOGUE** (FR) 25
695 **UGO** (USA) 87
183 **UHLAN BUTE** (FR) 29
219 **UIGHUR** (FR) 26
183 **UKISSDAWINNA** (FR) 30
572 **UKRAINE** (IRE) C 25
366 **UKRAINIAN** (FR) 145
111 **UKRAINIAN PRINCESS** (GB) 79
374 **UKRAINIAN STAR** (FR) 36
489 **ULCK DU LIN** (FR) 135
266 **ULFAH** (USA) F 153
697 **ULIS DE VASSY** (FR) 24
227 **ULLSWATER** (IRE) 26
441 **ULTIEP** (FR) 14
207 **ULTIMATE** (GB) 46
343 **ULTIMATE RISK** (IRE) 62
564 **ULTIME BERE** (FR) 16
619 **ULTRASONIC** (USA) 85
583 **ULTRAVOX** (GB) 21
180 **ULUWATU** (IRE) F 40
380 **ULYS DU CHARMIL** (FR) 118
266 **UMAYYAD** (IRE) 109
183 **UMBRAGE** (FR) 31
408 **UMIRO** (FR) 24
83 **UMORISTIC** (FR) 2
214 **UMPH** (FR) 64
358 **UMTHOULAH** (IRE) C 36
242 **UMVERTI** (GB) 3
473 **UN ATOUT** (FR) 124
697 **UN AMI** (FR) 25
697 **UN BON P'TIT GARS** (FR) 26
258 **UNA VITA PIUS** (IRE) 2
682 **UNACCOMPANIED** (IRE) 23
573 **UNASSAILABLE** (GB) 109
408 **UNATOU D'ESTRUVAL** 25
283 **UNBREAK MY HEART** (IRE) 64
543 **UNCLE BRYN** (GB) 26
531 **UNCLE DERMOT** (IRE) 29
113 **UNCLE FRED** (GB) 20
331 **UNCLE JIMMY** (IRE) 95
339 **UNCLE JOHNNY** (GB) 24
473 **UNCLE JUNIOR** (IRE) 125
126 **UNCLE PELDER** (IRE) 7
529 **UNCLE PETTIT** (IRE) 19
364 **UNCLE ROGER** (IRE) 29
543 **UNCLE TIMMY** (GB) 43
490 **UNCUT STONE** (IRE) 13
333 **UNDERLAY UNDERLAY** (GB) 12
435 **UNDERSTUDY** (USA) 7
19 **UNDERWRITTEN** (GB) 103
321 **UNE ARTISTE** (FR) 173
374 **UNE DAME D'OR** (FR) 37
408 **UNE DE CIERGUES** (FR) 26
585 **UNE DES BIEFFES** (FR) 31
270 **UNESCORTED** (IRE) 21
35 **UNEX BOSCH** (GB) 55
129 **UNEX CANALETTO** (GB) 19
525 **UNEX DEGAS** (IRE) 105

604 **UNEX GOYA** (IRE) 8
328 **UNEX MONA LISA** (GB) 67
696 **UNEX PICASSO** (GB) 53
12 **UNEX RENOIR** (GB) 22
218 **UNEX VALADON** (GB) 32
174 **UNFORGETTABLE** (FR) 44
418 **UNIFORM RUBY** (GB) 18
407 **UNION CITY BLUES** (IRE) 12
207 **UNION ISLAND** (IRE) 47
408 **UNIONISTE** (FR) 27
408 **UNITED PARK** 28
34 **UNITED PASSION** (GB) C 90
3 **UNIVERSAL** (IRE) 114
681 **UNIVOQUE** (FR) 63
573 **UNKNOWN REBEL** (IRE) 28
108 **UNLIMITED** (GB) 49
585 **UNNECESSARY XPENSE** (GB) 32
29 **UNNEFER** (FR) 15
408 **UNO D'ESTRUVAL** 29
664 **UNO VALOROSO** (FR) 17
301 **UNOITMAKESSENSE** (IRE) 5
489 **UNPARTOU** (FR) 136
147 **UNQUENCHABLE** (USA) C 111
682 **UNREACHABLE** (USA) 72
299 **UNREACHABLE STAR** (GB) F 265
447 **UNRESTRAINED** (USA) F 112
408 **UNTIL PASS** (FR) 84
573 **UNTOLD MELODY** (GB) 75
332 **UNWANTED GIFT** (IRE) 21
466 **UP AT DAWN** (GB) F 86
473 **UP OU THAT** (FR) 126
200 **UP TEN DOWN TWO** (IRE) 66
473 **UP THE BEAT** (GB) 127
568 **UP THE CREEK** (FR) F 8
404 **UP TO SOMETHING** (FR) 49
157 **UP TO THE MARK** (FR) 36
474 **UP WITH THE LARK** (GB) 18
472 **UP YOUR GAME** (IRE) 30
157 **UPBEAT COBBLER** (FR) 37
85 **UPHAM ATOM** (GB) 1
376 **UPHOLD** (GB) 9
522 **UPPER DECK** (IRE) 24
366 **UPPER ECHELON** (GB) 206
219 **UPPER HOUSE** (IRE) 109
385 **UPPERCUT** (GB) 13
682 **UPPERVILLE** (IRE) F 125
619 **UPRISE** (GB) 86
408 **UPSILON BLEU** (FR) 30
447 **UPSKITTLED** (GB) C 113
696 **UPTHEMSTEPS** (FR) 54
31 **UPTON MEAD** (IRE) 13
185 **UPTON OAKS** (GB) 15
408 **URAK** 31
219 **URANY** (GB) 110
697 **URBAIN DE SIVOLA** (FR) 27
508 **URBAN BALL** (IRE) 51
570 **URBAN KODE** (FR) 67
408 **URBI D'ESTRUVAL** 32
665 **URBICUS** (GB) 23
625 **URBONITE** (IRE) 51
408 **URFE D'ESTRUVAL** (FR) 33
408 **URGENCE D'ESTRUVAL** 34
619 **URIAH HEEP** (FR) 87
91 **URSULA** (IRE) 19
408 **URSULO DU RIB** 35
408 **URVE BRUERE** (FR) 36
219 **URYALE** (FR) C 193
29 **US LAW** (IRE) 116

299 **USAIN COLT** (GB) 114
408 **USER ET ABUSER** (FR) 37
415 **USER NAME** (USA) 11
219 **USHANA** (GB) 194
19 **USHINDI** (IRE) C 163
84 **USQUEABACH** (GB) 4
110 **USSEE** (FR) 25
473 **UT DE SIVOLA** (FR) 128
408 **UTO** 38
256 **UTOPIAN** (FR) 25
147 **UTOPIAN** (GB) 67
388 **UTOPIQUE** (USA) 96
388 **UTRERA** (FR) 57
226 **UTRILLO'S ART** (IRE) 33
266 **UTTERANCE** (GB) 110
645 **UVA FRAGOLA** (GB) F 21
408 **UZES D'ESTRUVAL** (FR) 39
565 **VAALWATER** (IRE) 6
25 **VACARIO** (GER) 6
569 **VADAMAR** (FR) 16
569 **VADAZA** (FR) C 136
569 **VADERANA** (FR) 86
447 **VADORGA** (GB) C 114
200 **VAGABOND CHANTEUSE** (GB) F 86
49 **VAGUE** (USA) C 147
408 **VAILLANCE** 85
600 **VAL DE SAANE** (IRE) 50
699 **VAL MONDO** (GER) 89
569 **VALAMAR** (FR) 137
597 **VALANDRAUD** (FR) F 88
661 **VALANTINO OYSTER** (IRE) 10
496 **VALBCHEK** (IRE) 44
436 **VALBUCCA** (FR) 14
214 **VALDAN** (FR) 35
79 **VALDEMAR** (GB) 9
380 **VALDEZ** (GB) 119
573 **VALE OF BELVOIR** (IRE) F 110
43 **VALE OF LINGFIELD** (IRE) 30
452 **VALE VIEW** (FR) C 25
466 **VALENCHA** (GB) 29
700 **VALENCIA** (FR) F 43
119 **VALENCIA** (GB) 55
520 **VALENTINE BAND** (USA) C 71
395 **VALENTINE BHOY** (GB) 9
97 **VALENTINE'S GIFT** (GB) 8
363 **VALENTINO ROCKS** (GB) 10
9 **VALENTINO SWING** (GB) 35
16 **VALENTO** (GB) 45
201 **VALETTO** (IRE) 126
285 **VALIANT** (GB) 66
119 **VALIANT GIRL** (GB) 55
299 **VALIANTLY** (GB) C 266
573 **VALID MOVE** (USA) C 111
505 **VALID POINT** (IRE) 10
352 **VALID REASON** (GB) 16
61 **VALIDATE** (GB) F 45
511 **VALIDOR** (FR) 38
147 **VALIDUS** (GB) 68
569 **VALIMA** (FR) C 138
569 **VALIYR** (IRE) 17
266 **VALJARV** (IRE) F 154
570 **VALLANI** (GB) 68
266 **VALLEE DES REVES** (USA) C 155
657 **VALLEY LAD** (IRE) 95
299 **VALLEY OF DESTINY** (GB) 115
440 **VALLEY OF THE MOON** (IRE) F 17
653 **VALLEY QUEEN** (GB) 26
220 **VALLEY TIGER** (GB) 35

503 **VALLEY VIEW** (IRE) 79
626 **VALMARI** (IRE) 21
108 **VALMINA** (GB) 50
174 **VALRENE** (GB) 45
511 **VALSE BLEUE** (GB) 96
74 **VALSE MYSTIQUE** (IRE) F 70
702 **VALSESIA** (IRE) 5
285 **VALTINA** (GB) 127
570 **VAMIZI** (IRE) 69
418 **VAMOS** (IRE) 19
299 **VAN DE CAPPELLE** (IRE) C 116
61 **VAN DE CAPPELLE** (IRE) C 18
357 **VAN DER ART** (GB) 20
529 **VAN DOESBURG** (IRE) 20
366 **VAN ELLIS** (GB) 146
176 **VAN GO GO** (GB) 23
19 **VAN PERCY** (IRE) 164
397 **VANADIUM** (GB) 36
408 **VANIKA PLACE** 86
408 **VANILLA CRUSH** (FR) 87
410 **VANILLA RUM** (GB) 18
123 **VANILOQUIO** (IRE) 50
80 **VANITYCASE** (IRE) C 27
635 **VANNIN** (IRE) 17
91 **VANTAA** (IRE) 20
388 **VARDARIS** (IRE) 97
111 **VARIETY SHOW** (IRE) 80
511 **VARING** (FR) 137
219 **VARSOVIAN** (IRE) 195
55 **VASANTA NAVARATRI** (IRE) 64
388 **VASIAS** (FR) 12
204 **VASILY** (GB) 3
473 **VAST CONSUMPTION** (IRE) 129
111 **VASTLY** (USA) 81
408 **VATULEHE** 88
408 **VAUDAIRE** 89
408 **VAUTOUR** 90
697 **VEAUCE DE SIVOLA** (FR) 29
508 **VEDANI** (IRE) 52
285 **VEERAYA** (GB) 128
646 **VEHEMENT** (GB) 15
321 **VEILED** (GB) 174
543 **VEILED APPLAUSE** (GB) 27
161 **VEILED BEAUTY** (IRE) F 80
408 **VEILLE AU GRAIN** 91
339 **VELATOR** (GB) 25
408 **VELEHA** (FR) 92
446 **VELESGO** (IRE) 80
417 **VELLENA** (GB) F 22
696 **VELOCE** (GB) 55
705 **VELOSO** (FR) 25
619 **VELOUETTE** (GB) C 157
147 **VELOX** (GB) 112
129 **VELVET STAR** (IRE) 20
283 **VELVET VIC** (IRE) 65
193 **VELVETINA** (IRE) 66
366 **VENA AMORIS** (USA) 147
286 **VENCEREMOS** (IRE) 19
380 **VENDOR** (FR) 120
117 **VENEGAZZU** (IRE) 32
555 **VENETIAN LAD** (GB) 10
460 **VENETIAN VIEW** (IRE) 122
698 **VENETIAS DREAM** (IRE) 25
47 **VENITZIA** (IRE) 7
672 **VENOGE** (GB) F 112
499 **VENTO DI PONENTE** (IRE) 43
318 **VENTOUX** (GB) 42
220 **VENTURA COVE** (IRE) 36

226 **VENTURE CAPITAL** (IRE) 34
35 **VENTURI** (GB) C 96
442 **VENUTIUS** (GB) 11
180 **VERA RICHARDSON** (IRE) 41
55 **VERBAL HONESTY** (IRE) 130
102 **VERBAL INTRIGUE** (USA) C 62
433 **VERBEECK** (GB) 46
569 **VEREMA** (FR) 87
655 **VERGE** (IRE) 18
601 **VERINCO** (GB) 23
599 **VERMUYDEN** (GB) 16
564 **VERNITA GREEN** (FR) 105
564 **VERONA** 83
225 **VERONA BAY** (FR) 24
320 **VERONICA FRANCO** (GB) F 18
259 **VEROON** (FR) 14
214 **VERSE OF LOVE** (GB) 65
643 **VERTIBES** (GB) 19
408 **VERTIGE DE COTTE** (FR) 93
108 **VERTUEUX** (FR) 51
206 **VERY EDGY** (IRE) 15
73 **VERY FIRST BLADE** (GB) 37
503 **VERY STYLISH** (IRE) 80
325 **VERY WELL RED** (GB) 14
442 **VESPASIA** (GB) 17
473 **VESPER BELL** (IRE) 130
364 **VESTIBULE** (GB) 41
3 **VEZZALI** (USA) 115
434 **VFORVICTORY** (GER) 139
272 **VHUJON** (FR) 11
570 **VIA ARCHIMEDE** (USA) 70
287 **VIA BALLYCROY** (IRE) 54
460 **VIA GALILEI** (IRE) 92
599 **VIABLE** (GB) 11
391 **VIC AR AGHAIDH** (IRE) 61
343 **VIC VENTURI** (IRE) 63
157 **VICE ET VERTU** (FR) 44
408 **VICE ROI GEORGES** 94
460 **VICGERNIC** (GB) 123
34 **VICKERS VIMY** (GB) 54
19 **VICKSBURG** (IRE) 165
339 **VICS STAR** (IRE) 26
488 **VICTOIRE DE LYPHAR** (IRE) 42
552 **VICTOR HEWGO** (GB) 42
420 **VICTOR LEUDORUM** (IRE) 41
600 **VICTORIA COLLEGE** (FR) F 51
93 **VICTORIA ROSE** (IRE) 12
219 **VICTORIAN BEAUTY** (USA) 111
485 **VICTORIAN BOUNTY** (GB) 17
172 **VICTORIAN NUMBER** (FR) 11
384 **VICTORICA** (USA) F 52
388 **VICTORINNA** (FR) 13
339 **VICTORS SERENADE** (IRE) 27
394 **VICTORY GUNNER** (IRE) 27
659 **VICTORY ROCK** (IRE) 48
635 **VICTORY SURGE** (IRE) 18
424 **VICTRIX GALE** (IRE) 32
102 **VIENNESE VERSE** (GB) 63
299 **VIEWPOINT** (IRE) 117
650 **VIKING BLOND** (FR) 73
659 **VIKING CHIEF** (IRE) 49
106 **VIKING DANCER** (GB) 7
16 **VIKING RIDGE** (IRE) 46
213 **VIKING ROSE** (IRE) 10
298 **VIKING SPLASH** (GB) 32
192 **VIKING STORM** (GB) 4
180 **VIKING WARRIOR** (IRE) 24
460 **VILLA NOVA** (IRE) F 130

686 **VILLA REIGNS** (GB) 18
192 **VILLA ROYALE** (GB) 18
328 **VILLAGE GREEN** (GB) 68
25 **VILLAGE SECRET** (GB) 7
331 **VILLAGE VIC** (IRE) 96
39 **VILLAGE WHISPERS** (IRE) 18
219 **VILLARRICA** (USA) C 196
467 **VILLENEUVE** (GB) 36
511 **VILLERAMBERT** (FR) 97
503 **VIMIERO** (USA) 81
332 **VIN DE ROY** (FR) 22
435 **VINCES** (GB) 8
404 **VINCITORE** (FR) 50
72 **VINEMAN** (GB) 15
552 **VINETTA** (GB) 43
408 **VINGT DIEUX** (FR) 95
462 **VINGT ET UNE** (FR) F 43
57 **VINNIE'S GIRL** (IRE) 17
178 **VINNY GAMBINI** (IRE) 25
460 **VINO GRIEGO** (FR) 93
442 **VINO VERITAS** (USA) C 35
406 **VINOMORE** (GB) 10
520 **VINTAAJ WAY** (IRE) 49
312 **VINTAGE FABRIC** (USA) 13
7 **VINTAGE GRAPE** (IRE) 13
33 **VINTAGE RED** (GB) 21
606 **VINTAGE STAR** (IRE) 46
201 **VINTAGE TIMES** (IRE) 63
161 **VINTAGE TIPPLE** (IRE) C 81
161 **VIOLA D'AMOUR** (IRE) 58
387 **VIOLA DA GAMBA** (IRE) 30
328 **VIOLA ROYALE** (IRE) F 129
511 **VIOLANTE** (USA) 39
543 **VIOLENT VELOCITY** (IRE) 28
682 **VIOLET HOUR** (USA) 126
304 **VIOLET LASHES** (USA) 102
658 **VIOLET'S GIFT** (IRE) 36
489 **VIOLIN DAVIS** (FR) 137
639 **VIRGINIA ASH** (IRE) 51
390 **VIRGINIA GALILEI** (IRE) 18
329 **VIRGINIA GALLICA** (IRE) 20
299 **VIRTUOUS** (GB) C 267
569 **VISALIA** (IRE) 88
19 **VISCOUNT VERT** (IRE) 104
263 **VISCOUNT VICTOR** (IRE) 22
569 **VISINOVA** (FR) 89
408 **VISION DES CHAMPS** 96
569 **VISIONNAIRE** (FR) C 139
283 **VISIONS OF JOHANNA** (USA) 66
308 **VISITATION** (GB) G 11
682 **VISTA BELLA** (GB) C 127
111 **VITA NOVA** (IRE) 20
27 **VITAL CALLING** (GB) 45
656 **VITAL MERLIN** (GB) 15
654 **VITAL STATISTICS** (GB) C 151
147 **VITALIZE** (GB) 69
601 **VITE** (IRE) 51
604 **VITO VOLTERRA** (IRE) 9
688 **VITTACHI** (GB) 20
397 **VITZNAU** (IRE) 37
501 **VIVA COLONIA** (IRE) 41
220 **VIVA RONALDO** (IRE) 37
208 **VIVA VETTORI** (GB) 10
19 **VIVACIOUS WAY** (IRE) 105
569 **VIVACITE** (FR) 90
408 **VIVALKO** 97
504 **VIVARINI** (GB) 13
520 **VIVIANI** (IRE) 15

285 **VIVID BLUE** (GB) 67
8 **VIVONA HILL** (GB) 24
647 **VIVRE LA SECRET** (GB) 20
254 **VIVRE LIBRE** (GB) 55
410 **VIZEAN** (IRE) 19
366 **VOCATIONAL** (USA) 148
365 **VODKA RED** (IRE) 12
321 **VODKAONTHEROCKS** (IRE) 175
619 **VODNIK** (IRE) 158
115 **VOGARTH** (GB) 19
331 **VOLADOR** (IRE) 97
408 **VOLCAN D'AINAY** 98
380 **VOLCAN SURPRISE** (FR) 121
64 **VOLCANIC DUST** (GB) 25
496 **VOLDEMORT** (BRZ) 45
475 **VOLER LA VEDETTE** (IRE) 26
682 **VOLEUSE DE COEURS** (IRE) 73
366 **VOLIERE** (GB) C 207
474 **VOLITO** (GB) 19
420 **VOLTIGGER HILL** (GER) 42
511 **VOLVORETAS CAPE** (GB) 98
585 **VON GALEN** (GB) 33
191 **VOODOO PRINCE** (GB) 12
218 **VOSGES** (FR) 33
408 **VOSTOK** (FR) 99
408 **VOTEZ POUR MOI** 100
183 **VOUS MEME** (FR) 50
285 **VOW** (GB) 68
111 **VOX POP** (GB) 155
183 **VOYAGE A VENISE** (FR) 32
318 **VOYAGEUSE** (FR) 68
489 **VRAI VERT** (IRE) 138
12 **VRENNAN** (GB) F 27
408 **VUELTA DE CAMPANA** 101
566 **VULCAN BELLE** F 13
404 **VULCANITE** (GB) 51
408 **VULPIO** 102
476 **VUVUZELA** (GB) 75
573 **VYATKA** (GB) F 113
283 **WAABEL** (GB) 67
117 **WAAFIAH** (GB) F 49
643 **WAAFID** (USA) 48
682 **WAAHEB** (USA) 24
325 **WAAHEJ** (GB) 15
508 **WAAHY** (IRE) 95
357 **WACHIWI** (IRE) C 36
546 **WADHAM HILL** (GB) 5
476 **WADNAAN** (GB) 76
53 **WADSWICK BEN** (GB) 16
30 **WAFFLE** (GB) 30
74 **WAHYLAH** (IRE) 53
619 **WAILA** (GB) 159
469 **WAIT NO MORE** (IRE) 36
192 **WAITINGONACLOUD** (GB) F 32
511 **WAITRESS** (USA) 40
451 **WAKE UP GIRL** (GB) 25
276 **WAKE UP SIOUX** (IRE) 13
58 **WAKEUP LITTLE SUZY** (IRE) 83
298 **WAKHAN** (IRE) 33
573 **WAKING WARRIOR** (GB) 29
658 **WAKY LI** (GER) 37
108 **WALDEN PRINCE** (GB) 52
219 **WALDLERCHE** (GB) 112
266 **WALDMARK** (GER) C 156
553 **WALDSEE** (GER) 14
556 **WALDVOGEL** (IRE) 47
180 **WALK IN MY SHADOW** (IRE) C 56
434 **WALK LIKE A MAN** (IRE) 140

263 **WALKABOUT CREEK** (IRE) 23
380 **WALKON** (FR) 122
682 **WALNUT HILL** (GB) 74
659 **WALSER** (GB) 50
19 **WALTER WHITE** (IRE) 166
378 **WALTHAM ABBEY** (GB) 2
600 **WANDESTA** (GB) C 52
266 **WANNABE LOVED** (GB) 111
266 **WANNABE YOUR MAN** (GB) 157
78 **WAR OF THE ROSES** (IRE) 10
486 **WAR PARTY** (GB) 13
501 **WAR POET** (GB) 42
525 **WAR SINGER** (GB) 106
414 **WARBOND** (GB) 6
220 **WARCROWN** (IRE) 72
616 **WARDEN BOND** (GB) 7
193 **WARLU WAY** (GB) 19
531 **WARNE'S WAY** (IRE) 30
18 **WARNERFORD** (GB) 3
10 **WARNING CRY** (IRE) G 21
430 **WARRANTS A NAME** (IRE) 6
474 **WARREN CHASE** (IRE) 20
201 **WARRICK BROWN** (GB) 101
496 **WARRIGAL** (GB) 93
112 **WARRIOR NATION** (FR) 7
298 **WARRIOR ONE** (GB) 34
177 **WARSAW PACT** (IRE) 4
547 **WARWICKSHIRE** (IRE) 12
40 **WASABI** (IRE) 17
508 **WASABI'S HOUSE** (IRE) 53
503 **WASHINGTON ROAD** (IRE) 82
191 **WASPY** (GB) 42
74 **WATANEE** (GB) 54
298 **WATCH AMIGO** (IRE) 35
433 **WATCH CHAIN** (IRE) 28
251 **WATCH HOUSE** (IRE) 9
619 **WATCHABLE** (GB) 160
219 **WATCHFUL EYES** (IRE) 113
24 **WATCHMEGO** (GB) 24
111 **WATER FOUNTAIN** (GB) C 156
525 **WATER GARDEN** (FR) 107
199 **WATER RAIL** (GB) 11
110 **WATER ROSE** (GB) 26
114 **WATER STRATFORD** (GB) G 12
412 **WATER STRATFORD** (IRE) F 9
391 **WATER WAGTAIL** (GB) 62
119 **WATERCLOCK** (GB) 56
260 **WATERCOLOURS** (IRE) 28
643 **WATERED SILK** (GB) 20
567 **WATERGATE** (IRE) 23
265 **WATERHOUSE** (IRE) 16
336 **WATERLINE TWENTY** (IRE) C 45
446 **WATERLOO CHATEAU** (IRE) 81
544 **WATERLOO DOCK** (GB) 6
439 **WATERSKI** (GB) 8
525 **WATERUNDER** (IRE) 108
266 **WATERWAYS** (GB) C 158
334 **WATERPOD** (GB) 10
654 **WATHEEQ** (USA) 81
254 **WATLEDGE** (FR) 56
185 **WATS ON LUCKY** (GB) 16
696 **WATT BRODERICK** (GB) 64
107 **WATTS UP SON** (GB) 16
354 **WAVE POWER** (IRE) 2
597 **WAVEGUIDE** (IRE) 55
399 **WAVERTREE WARRIOR** (IRE) 7
508 **WAVING** (GB) 54
380 **WAY BACK WHEN** (GB) 123

29 WAY OF LOVE (FR) 64
226 WAY TO SUCCESS (IRE) 35
34 WAYNE MANOR (IRE) 55
42 WAYWARD GLANCE (GB) 24
696 WAYWARD PRINCE (GB) 56
442 WAYWARD WIND (GB) 18
280 WAYWOOD PRINCESS (GB) 4
35 WE ARE CITY (GB) 97
467 WE HAVE A DREAM (GB) 12
301 WE NEVER GIVE UP (IRE) 6
200 WE'LL DEAL AGAIN (GB) 48
55 WE'LL GO WALKING (IRE) 131
597 WE'RE IN THE RED (IRE) 89
643 WEAAM (IRE) 49
49 WEALTHY (GB) 64
385 WEAPON OF CHOICE (IRE) 14
406 WEAPON OF WAR (IRE) 11
98 WEAPON'S AMNESTY (IRE) 19
529 WEATHER BABE (GB) 27
447 WEB OF INTRIGUE (GB) C 115
583 WEBBERYS DREAM (GB) 22
100 WEBBOW (IRE) 17
99 WEBBOW (IRE) 16
16 WEDGER PARDY (IRE) 47
162 WEDGEWOOD STAR (GB) G 7
96 WEE BUNS (GB) 7
689 WEE WILLOW (GB) F 19
706 WEET IN NERJA (GB) 15
24 WEETFROMTHECHAFF (GB) 25
434 WEIRD AL (IRE) 141
686 WELCOME APPROACH (GB) 10
587 WELCOME LU (GB) C 8
165 WELCOME STRANGER (GB) 6
86 WELD'S PRIDE (GB) 24
698 WELEASE BWIAN (IRE) 26
472 WELL GREEN (IRE) 31
503 WELL HELLO THERE (IRE) 83
660 WELL METT (IRE) 25
240 WELL OILED (IRE) 8
285 WELL PAINTED (GB) 69
460 WELL REFRESHED (GB) 94
391 WELL REGARDED (IRE) 63
601 WELL WISHES (GB) 52
601 WELLS LYRICAL (IRE) 24
534 WELSH BARD (GB) 21
161 WELSH CAKE (GB) F 82
306 WELSH DANCER (GB) 25
71 WELSH INLET (IRE) 15
520 WELSH NAYBER (GB) 50
467 WELSH ROYALE (GB) 37
467 WELSH VALLEY (USA) F 46
300 WENDY'SGREYHORSE (GB) 7
569 WENGE (USA) C 140
74 WEOOD (IRE) 55
446 WESLEY HARDIN (IRE) 82
157 WESSEX KING (IRE) 38
483 WEST BAY HOOLIE (GB) 13
404 WEST BRIT (IRE) 52
78 WEST COAST DREAM (GB) 11
600 WEST COUNTRY (USA) 34
60 WEST END LAD (GB) 12
380 WEST END ROCKER (IRE) 124
90 WEST LEAKE (IRE) 8
328 WEST LEAKE DIMAN (GB) 69
328 WEST LEAKE HARE (IRE) 70
619 WEST OF THE MOON (IRE) 161
24 WESTENDJACK (GB) 26
695 WESTER ROSS (IRE) 88

174 WESTERLY BREEZE (IRE) 46
328 WESTERN APPEAL (USA) F 130
321 WESTERN APPROACHES (GB) 176
496 WESTERN ARISTOCRAT (USA) 11
343 WESTERN CHARMER (GB) 64
42 WESTERN HIGH (GB) 25
233 WESTERN KATE (IRE) 17
420 WESTERN KING (IRE) 43
298 WESTERN LEADER (IRE) 36
321 WESTERN MOVIE (GB) 177
387 WESTERN PEARL (GB) 12
538 WESTERN PRIDE (GB) 17
34 WESTERN PRIZE (GB) 16
394 WESTERN WHISKY (FR) 28
446 WESTHAVEN (GB) 83
700 WESTLIFE (IRE) C 44
414 WESTLIN' WINDS (IRE) 19
207 WESTLIN' WINDS (IRE) 48
254 WESTON LODGE (IRE) 57
329 WESTWARD HOPE (USA) 21
596 WESTWIRE TOBY (GB) 8
285 WESTWITHTHENIGHT (IRE) 70
55 WEXFORD OPERA (IRE) 132
58 WHAILEYY (IRE) 19
458 WHAT A CHARM (IRE) 23
8 WHAT A DREAM (GB) 5
489 WHAT A FRIEND (GB) 139
650 WHAT A GOOD NIGHT (IRE) 74
688 WHAT A STEEL (IRE) 21
266 WHAT A TREASURE (IRE) C 159
650 WHAT A WARRIOR (IRE) 75
220 WHAT ABOUT YOU (IRE) 38
304 WHAT AN ARTICLE (IRE) 75
650 WHAT AN OSCAR (IRE) 76
583 WHAT ER SAY (GB) 23
256 WHAT WILL YOU SAY (GB) 26
95 WHAT'S FOR TEA (GB) 8
517 WHAT'S THE POINT (GB) 11
573 WHAT'S UP (GB) 76
567 WHATAGOA (IRE) 24
587 WHATLINGTON (IRE) 4
107 WHATS FOR PUDDING (IRE) 17
340 WHATS HAPPENING (IRE) 34
39 WHATS ON THE MENU (IRE) 19
659 WHATS UP WOODY (IRE) 51
438 WHATS YOUR STORY (GB) 3
657 WHATSHALLWEDO (GB) 96
654 WHATSOFUNNY (IRE) 82
191 WHAZZIS (GB) F 78
198 WHEELAVIT (IRE) 24
139 WHEN WE COLLIDE (GB) 26
522 WHENEVER (GB) 25
154 WHERE'S JOSIE (GB) 8
397 WHERE'S REILEY (USA) 38
414 WHERE'S SUSIE (GB) 7
530 WHERES JOHNNY (GB) 10
503 WHERES THE HARE (IRE) 84
695 WHERES WAL (IRE) 89
117 WHEY SAUCE (JPN) 5
354 WHEYAYE (GB) 8
522 WHICHEVER (GB) 26
299 WHIMSICAL (IRE) 118
460 WHINGING WILLIE (IRE) 124
15 WHINSTONE BOY (IRE) 16
450 WHIP IT IN (IRE) 41
55 WHIP STORM (IRE) 133
320 WHIPCRACKAWAY (IRE) 12

19 WHIPLASH WILLIE (GB) 34
55 WHIPLESS (IRE) 9
447 WHIPPER'S BOY (IRE) 116
684 WHIPPERWAY (IRE) 17
73 WHIPPHOUND (GB) 24
606 WHISKEY RIDGE (IRE) 47
80 WHISKY BRAVO (GB) 12
230 WHISKY MAGIC (IRE) 8
489 WHISKY YANKEE (GB) 140
321 WHISPER (FR) 178
436 WHISPER COOL (IRE) 15
696 WHISPERING BOB (IRE) 57
343 WHISPERING HILLS (IRE) 65
420 WHISPERING JACK (GB) 44
496 WHISPERING WARRIOR (IRE) 46
62 WHISPERING WIND (IRE) 12
417 WHISTLING BUDDY (GB) 22
503 WHISTLING SENATOR (IRE) 85
460 WHITBY JACK (GB) 95
655 WHITBY JET (IRE) 6
530 WHITCOMBE SPIRIT (GB) 11
300 WHITE DEER (USA) 8
359 WHITE DIAMOND (GB) 34
529 WHITE FLIGHT (GB) 38
328 WHITE FROST (IRE) 14
145 WHITE FUSION (GB) 14
597 WHITE NILE (GB) 56
342 WHITE SHIFT (IRE) 14
343 WHITE STAR LINE (IRE) 66
612 WHITECREST (GB) 11
645 WHITSTABLE NATIVE (GB) 9
375 WHITTLE ROCK (GB) F 9
420 WHO OWNS ME (IRE) 45
222 WHO'S SHIRL (GB) 10
553 WHODATHOUGHT (IRE) 15
325 WHODUNIT (UAE) 16
256 WHOLELOTTALOVE (GB) 27
107 WHOZTHECAT (IRE) 18
178 WHY ARE YOU ASKING (IRE) 26
496 WHY AREEB (GB) 94
304 WHY BUT WHY (USA) 76
575 WHY SO SERIOUS (GB) 6
344 WICKED WENCH (GB) 23
404 WIDE RECEIVER (IRE) 53
35 WIDOW FLOWER (GB) 56
266 WIDYAAN (IRE) 112
447 WIENER WALD (USA) F 117
660 WIESENTRAUM (GER) 26
489 WIFFY CHATSBY (IRE) 141
102 WIGGY SMITH (GB) 21
35 WIGMORE HALL (IRE) 14
200 WIGRAM'S TURN (USA) 49
223 WIJAYA (GB) 44
157 WILD CARD (GB) 39
688 WILD CHILD LUCY (GB) 22
111 WILD COCO (GER) 21
404 WILD DESERT (FR) 54
534 WILD DIAMOND (GB) 69
466 WILD GARDENIA (GB) F 87
50 WILD GROUND (GB) 8
392 WILD IN WOOLLY (FR) 9
496 WILD OCEAN (GB) 95
601 WILD SAUCE (GB) 53
488 WILDCAT WIZARD (USA) 43
529 WILDE AT HEART (IRE) 22
218 WILDE PASTURES (IRE) 34
472 WILDE RUBY (IRE) 32
496 WILDOMAR (GB) 47

299 **WILDSPLASH** (USA) C 268
146 **WILFRED PICKLES** (IRE) 16
45 **WILL NOT** (GB) 12
692 **WILL SCARLET** (IRE) 6
97 **WILLBEME** (GB) 9
625 **WILLIAM HAIGH** (GB) 45
262 **WILLIAM HOGARTH** (GB) 20
297 **WILLIAM MORGAN** (GB) 2
708 **WILLIAM'S WAY** (GB) 15
695 **WILLIAM'S WISHES** (IRE) 90
8 **WILLIE HALL** (GB) 26
665 **WILLIE WAG TAIL** (USA) 10
328 **WILLIES WONDER** (IRE) 71
49 **WILLING FOE** (USA) 65
380 **WILLOUGHBY HEDGE** (GB) 125
360 **WILLOW BEAUTY** (GB) 47
266 **WILLOW BECK** (GB) 113
219 **WILLOW BREEZE** (GB) 114
682 **WILLOW ISLAND** (IRE) 75
360 **WILLOW THE ROSE** (GB) 39
404 **WILLOW'S SAVIOUR** (GB) 55
366 **WILLPOWER** (IRE) 149
606 **WILLY C** (GB) 48
461 **WILLY MCBAY** (GB) 32
108 **WILMING** (GB) F 53
249 **WILTSHIRE LIFE** (IRE) 38
213 **WILY FOX** (GB) 11
628 **WIMPLE** (USA) F 43
571 **WIN A HAND** (GB) G 6
311 **WIN FOR US** (IRE) 10
619 **WINCE** (GB) F 162
105 **WINCES WELL** (IRE) 6
220 **WIND SHUFFLE** (GER) 39
407 **WINDBENEATHMYWINGS** (IRE) C 63
260 **WINDFIELD TRICK** (IRE) 29
366 **WINDHOEK** (GB) 208
157 **WINDS AND WAVES** (IRE) 40
285 **WINDS OF TIME** (IRE) F 129
657 **WINDS OF WAR** (IRE) 97
614 **WINDSOCKS** (GB) 9
397 **WINDSOR KNIGHTS** (GB) 39
73 **WINDSOR ROSE** (IRE) 41
285 **WINDY LANE** (GB) 71
400 **WINE 'N DINE** (GB) 28
699 **WING MIRA** (IRE) 90
662 **WING N PRAYER** (IRE) 10
161 **WING STEALTH** (IRE) F 83
242 **WINGED FARASI** (GB) 4
56 **WINGLAND** (FR) 39
587 **WINGMAN** (IRE) 5
91 **WINGS OF APOLLO** (IRE) 21
525 **WINGS OF ICARUS** (IRE) 109
657 **WINGS OF SMOKE** (IRE) 98
424 **WINGTIPS** (FR) 33
496 **WINNER'S CALL** (GB) C 96
496 **WINNER'S WISH** (GB) 48
619 **WINNERS CHANT** (IRE) F 163
658 **WINNIESTAR** (GER) 38
321 **WINNING HABIT** (GB) 179
460 **WINNING SPARK** (USA) 96
706 **WINROB** (GB) 16
193 **WINSA** (USA) F 67
118 **WINSTONE** (IRE) 21
556 **WINTER ALCHEMY** (IRE) 48
13 **WINTER BREAK** (IRE) G 6
632 **WINTER DRESS** (GB) 19
161 **WINTER HILL** (GB) 40
234 **WINTER ICE** (GB) F 7

508 **WINTER LION** (IRE) 96
29 **WINTER SOLSTICE** (GB) C 117
3 **WINTER SUN** (GB) 116
266 **WINTER SUNRISE** (GB) F 160
299 **WINTER WHITE** (IRE) 269
141 **WINTER'S NIGHT** (IRE) 24
219 **WINTERGREEN** (IRE) 115
293 **WINTERWOOD** (IRE) 6
321 **WISE MOVE** (IRE) 180
357 **WISE VENTURE** (IRE) 21
462 **WISECRAIC** (GB) 6
450 **WISEMAN'S DIAMOND** (USA) 34
488 **WISH AGAIN** (GB) 65
344 **WISHBONE** (IRE) 19
173 **WISHES AND STARS** (IRE) 1
652 **WISHES OR WATCHES** (IRE) 9
462 **WISHFORMORE** (IHt) 7
331 **WISHFUL THINKING** (GB) 98
385 **WISHING GATE** (IRE) 23
599 **WISTOW** (GB) 12
55 **WITCH OF FIFE** (USA) F 66
505 **WITCH'S HAT** (IRE) 11
485 **WITCHRY** (GB) 18
129 **WITCHY MOMENTS** (IRE) 21
585 **WITH HINDSIGHT** (IRE) 34
680 **WITH SPEED** (GER) 2
640 **WITHOUT EQUAL** (GB) 21
200 **WITHOUT PREJUDICE** (USA) 50
50 **WITHY MILLS** (GB) 9
3 **WITNESSED** (GB) 117
462 **WIZBY** (GB) F 25
626 **WOGAN** (GB) 22
329 **WOHAIDA** (IRE) F 47
98 **WOLF HALL** (IRE) 20
374 **WOLF MOON** (IRE) 38
461 **WOLF SHIELD** (IRE) 24
106 **WOLF SPIRIT** (IRE) 8
599 **WOM** (GB) 13
615 **WONDERWINDER** (IRE) 5
696 **WONMORENOMORE** (IRE) C 209
283 **WOOD CHORUS** (GB) F 87
220 **WOOD FAIRY** (GB) 40
232 **WOOD WHITE** (UAE) C 5
650 **WOOD YER** (IRE) 77
690 **WOODACRE** (GB) 11
321 **WOODBANK** (GB) 181
283 **WOODBECK** (GB) G 88
226 **WOODBINE WILLIE** (IRE) 36
201 **WOODCOCK MOON** (GB) C 127
113 **WOODCOTE PLACE** (GB) 21
578 **WOODEN KING** (IRE) 2
366 **WOODLAND ORCHID** (IRE) C 209
447 **WOODLAND SCENE** (IRE) 52
525 **WOODLARK ISLAND** (IRE) 110
43 **WOODMAVEN** (USA) C 50
685 **WOODMORE** (IRE) 51
434 **WOODPOLE ACADEMY** (IRE) 142
444 **WOODSIDE** (GB) G 20
299 **WOODWIN** (IRE) C 270
259 **WOODY BAY** (GB) 51
659 **WOODY WALLER** (GB) 52
617 **WOODYS BROTHER** (IRE) 24
489 **WOOLCOMBE FOLLY** (IRE) 142
422 **WOOLFALL SOVEREIGN** (IRE) 16
460 **WOOLFALL TREASURE** (GB) 97
493 **WOOLFE** (GB) C 12
524 **WOOLSTON FERRY** (IRE) 4
696 **WOOP WOOP** (IRE) 59

409 **WOR LASS** (GB) 5
68 **WORDINESS** (GB) 12
417 **WORDISMYBOND** (GB) 17
432 **WORDS COME EASY** (GB) 9
527 **WORDY'S BOY** (GB) 8
489 **WORKBENCH** (FR) 143
666 **WORLD CLASS** (GB) 32
111 **WORLD DOMINATION** (USA) 22
204 **WORLD HERITAGE** (GB) 4
447 **WORTH** (GB) 32
579 **WORTH A KING'S** (GB) 14
534 **WORTHADD** (IRE) 9
639 **WOSAYU** (GB) 52
690 **WOTALAD** (GB) 22
690 **WOTATOMBOY** (GB) 12
219 **WOVEN LACE** (GB) 116
319 **WRAY CASTLE** (IRE) 4
299 **WREATHS OF EMPIRE** (IRE) 119
265 **WREKIN ROCK** (IRE) 17
203 **WRENINGHAM** (GB) 7
226 **WRIGHT FLYER** (IRE) 37
285 **WRONG KEY** (IRE) C 130
111 **WROTHAM HEATH** (GB) 82
219 **WYBORNE** (GB) 117
444 **WYCHWOODS DANCER** (GB) 21
444 **WYCHWOODS MIST** (GB) 22
72 **WYCK HILL** (IRE) 16
520 **WYE VALLEY** (GB) 51
434 **WYMOTT** (IRE) 143
451 **WYNDHAM WAVE** (GB) 43
292 **WYNN DARWI** (IRE) 10
260 **WYSE HILL TEABAGS** (GB) 30
639 **XAARCET** (IRE) 53
304 **XAVIERA** (IRE) C 110
296 **XCLAIM** (GB) 42
531 **XENOPHON** (GB) 31
488 **XILERATOR** (IRE) 44
3 **XIN XU LIN** (BRZ) 44
329 **XINBAMA** (IRE) 22
508 **XINJI** (IRE) C 97
183 **XPO UNIVERSEL** 51
60 **XPRES MAITE** (GB) 13
684 **YA HAFED** (IRE) 18
3 **YAA SALAM** (GB) 118
49 **YAA WAYL** (GB) 66
380 **YABADABADOO** (GB) 126
531 **YACHT LONDON LADY** (GB) 32
107 **YAHRAB** (IRE) 19
193 **YAIR HILL** (IRE) 20
124 **YAJBER** (USA) 26
194 **YAKAMA** (IRE) 17
384 **YAKY ROMANI** (IRE) F 53
43 **YALDING DANCER** (GB) 31
43 **YALDING DUTCH** (GB) 51
619 **YANABEEAA** (USA) 88
693 **YANKEE STORM** (GB) 5
480 **YAQOOTAH** (USA) F 33
682 **YARASTAR** (GB) F 128
407 **YARIA** (IRE) F 64
480 **YARRA VALLEY** (GB) 31
501 **YAS MARINA** (USA) 43
49 **YASIR** (USA) 67
507 **YASMIN SATINE** (IRE) C 51
447 **YAZDI** (IRE) 54
706 **YEAH** (GB) 17
91 **YEEOOW** (IRE) 35
123 **YELLOW AND GREEN** (GB) 51
93 **YELLOW JERSEY** (GB) 13

257 **YELLOW PRINTER** (GB) 10
682 **YELLOW ROSEBUD** (IRE) 76
706 **YELLOWSHRUBMARINE** (GB) 18
18 **YENSI** (GB) 35
220 **YEOMANOFTHEGUARD** (GB) 73
451 **YES CHEF** (GB) 26
665 **YES IT'S THE BOY** (USA) 11
123 **YES MY LOVE** (IRE) C 68
451 **YES TWO** (GB) 52
10 **YESYOUCAN** (IRE) 22
689 **YINFORTHEROAD** (IRE) 20
101 **YIPPEE KIYAY** (IRE) 21
300 **YKIKAMOOCOW** (GB) 9
12 **YMIR** (GB) 23
376 **YOGIC FLYER** (GB) 15
573 **YORK GLORY** (USA) 30
296 **YORKIST** (IRE) 43
188 **YORKSHIRE ICON** (GB) 45
511 **YORKSHIRE LASS** (IRE) 41
142 **YORKSTERS PRINCE** (GB) 14
283 **YOSSI** (IRE) 68
469 **YOU CAN OF COURSE** (IRE) 37
654 **YOU DON'T LOVE ME** (IRE) 83
249 **YOU GOT THE LOVE** (IRE) 39
606 **YOU KNOW YOURSELF** (IRE) 49
503 **YOU'RE SO SPECIAL** (FR) 86
665 **YOU'RE THE BOSS** (GB) 24
321 **YOU'RE THE TOP** (FR) 182
237 **YOU'RELIKEMEFRANK** (GB) 35
538 **YOU'VE BEEN MOWED** (GB) 18
29 **YOUDA** (IRE) 65
157 **YOUM JAMIL** (USA) 41
141 **YOUNG AND DARING** (USA) F 77
343 **YOUNG DALE** (IRE) 67
521 **YOUNG DOTTIE** (GB) 16
601 **YOUNG FREDDIE** (IRE) 54
321 **YOUNG HURRICANE** (IRE) 183
422 **YOUNG JACKIE** (GB) 17
444 **YOUNG JIM** (IRE) 23
422 **YOUNG LISA** (GB) 27
174 **YOUNG LOU** (GB) 49
498 **YOUNG MAGS** (IRE) 22
452 **YOUNG PRINCE** (IRE) 17
422 **YOUNG SIMON** (GB) 18
617 **YOUNG SPARKY** (IRE) 25
394 **YOUNG VICTORIA** (GB) 29
614 **YOUR PAL TAL** (GB) 56
136 **YOUR TURN NOW** (IRE) 13
287 **YOUR VILLAGE** (IRE) C 67
141 **YOUR WORD** (GB) 59
405 **YOURINTHEWILL** (USA) 7
573 **YOURS** (GB) 31
534 **YOURS EVER** (GB) 39
673 **YPRES** (GB) 11
569 **YSOLDINA** (FR) F 141
276 **YUNGABURRA** (IRE) 9
364 **YURITUNI** (GB) 16
366 **ZA'LAN** (USA) 150
56 **ZAAFRAN** (FR) 40
193 **ZAAHYA** (IRE) 43
475 **ZAARITO** (IRE) 27
508 **ZABARAJAD** (IRE) 9
476 **ZACANA** (FR) 77
433 **ZACYNTHUS** (IRE) 29
473 **ZADARSKA** (IRE) 131
3 **ZAEEM** (GB) 119
654 **ZAFARANA** (GB) 26
501 **ZAFARAYA** (IRE) F 61

508 **ZAFARQAND** (IRE) 10
352 **ZAFEEN'S PEARL** (GB) 17
569 **ZAFERI** (IRE) 142
201 **ZAFFY** (IRE) 102
344 **ZAFISIO** (IRE) 20
696 **ZAFONIC STAR** (GB) 65
108 **ZAFRANAGAR** (IRE) 54
218 **ZAFRITA** (GB) 35
283 **ZAGALETA** (GB) G 89
360 **ZAGALINIS SPEECH** (GB) 40
328 **ZAGHRUTA** (USA) C 131
331 **ZAGOVA** (IRE) 91
397 **ZAHAADID** (FR) G 50
464 **ZAHEEB** (GB) 3
157 **ZAHIRAH MOON** (GB) 42
643 **ZAHRAAN** (IRE) 21
654 **ZAHRAT DUBAI** (GB) C 152
473 **ZAIDPOUR** (FR) 132
508 **ZAINDA** (IRE) 98
99 **ZAKATAL** (GB) 17
287 **ZAKREET** (GB) 77
508 **ZALANTOUN** (IRE) 55
321 **ZAMA ZAMA** (GB) 184
119 **ZAMARELLE** (GB) 57
308 **ZAMBEZI** (USA) F 21
699 **ZAMDY MAN** (GB) 91
657 **ZAMINA** (IRE) 99
682 **ZAMINAST** (GB) 25
693 **ZAMMY** (GB) 8
387 **ZAMURAI** (GB) 31
508 **ZAND** (IRE) 99
19 **ZANETTO** (IRE) 167
444 **ZANIR** (FR) 24
654 **ZANOTTI** (GB) 84
35 **ZANOUBIA** (USA) F 57
543 **ZAPLAMATION** (IRE) 29
682 **ZAQRAH** (USA) F 129
111 **ZARANNDA** (IRE) C 157
366 **ZARARA** (USA) C 210
657 **ZARAZAR** (GB) 100
569 **ZARDAKA** (IRE) 143
287 **ZARIYNA** (IRE) 56
569 **ZARKALAN** (IRE) 91
287 **ZARKALIA** (GB) C 68
489 **ZARKANDAR** (IRE) 144
161 **ZARLA** (GB) 84
183 **ZARNIT** (FR) 52
40 **ZAROSA** (IRE) 18
391 **ZARRAFAKT** (IRE) 64
218 **ZARU** (FR) 36
610 **ZAVA RIVER** (IRE) 21
366 **ZAVIER** (FR) 151
407 **ZAWARIQ** (GB) C 65
569 **ZAYANIDA** (IRE) C 144
290 **ZAYDAR** (FR) 8
43 **ZAYNAH** (IRE) F 52
697 **ZAYNAR** (FR) 28
145 **ZAZAMIX** (FR) 15
71 **ZAZOUS** (GB) 16
666 **ZE KING** (GB) 33
391 **ZEBRANO** (GB) 65
615 **ZED CANDY** (FR) 6
147 **ZEE ZEE GEE** (GB) F 113
664 **ZEFOOHA** (IRE) 18
56 **ZEGODLESSMAN** (FR) 15
569 **ZELAMAR** (FR) 92
55 **ZELIE MARTIN** (IRE) 134

460 **ZELOS DIKTATOR** (GB) 98
56 **ZEMIRO** (FR) 16
529 **ZEN FACTOR** (GB) 23
195 **ZENAAD** (USA) 3
619 **ZENAAT** (GB) 89
642 **ZENARINDA** (GB) 23
266 **ZENDA** (GB) C 161
219 **ZENJI** (USA) 197
626 **ZENNOR** (GB) 23
343 **ZERASHAN** (IRE) 68
407 **ZERMATT** (IRE) 35
29 **ZERO GRAVITY** (GB) 66
119 **ZERO MONEY** (IRE) 14
569 **ZEWARA** (GB) C 145
111 **ZEYRAN** (IRE) 83
102 **ZHIGGY'S STARDUST** (GB) 42
74 **ZIBET** (GB) F 71
619 **ZIBILENE** (GB) C 164
129 **ZIEFHD** (GB) 22
466 **ZIEKHANI** (GB) 88
214 **ZIGAZAG** (GB) 66
67 **ZIGGY LEE** (GB) 5
660 **ZIGGY ZAGGY** (GB) F 31
555 **ZIGZAGA** (IRE) 11
283 **ZILKHA** (GB) F 81
312 **ZIMBABWE** (FR) 14
219 **ZIMBALI** (FR) 198
191 **ZIMIRA** (IRE) 43
56 **ZIMRI** (FR) 17
129 **ZING WING** (GB) 6
364 **ZINGANA** (GB) 30
429 **ZIP LOCK** (IRE) 10
74 **ZIRAUN** (GB) 23
201 **ZITENKA** (IRE) 64
359 **ZOENICIBEL** (GB) 35
388 **ZOGRAFIA** (FR) 58
543 **ZOMERLUST** (GB) 30
355 **ZOOM IN** (GB) 8
219 **ZOUBROVKA** (USA) 118
460 **ZOUTI** (FR) 99
654 **ZOWAINA** (GB) 85
266 **ZUIDER ZEE** (GER) 31
619 **ZUMBI** (IRE) 90
433 **ZUNIGA'S DATE** (USA) C 53
366 **ZUT ALORS** (IRE) C 211
387 **ZUZU ANGEL** (IRE) 32
614 **ZVONAREAVE** (IRE) 10

LATE ENTRIES

MR AUGUSTINE LEAHY, Kilmallock

Postal: **Clogher, Kilmallock, Co. Limerick, Ireland**
Contacts: PHONE (00353) 639 0676   FAX (00353) 63 90676   MOBILE (00353) 872 580 296
E-MAIL susanleahy@eircom.net

1 **BALLYHEIGH (IRE)**, 5, b g Oscar (IRE)—Miss Snapdragon (IRE)
2 **BIG BAD LILY (IRE)**, 4, b f Big Bad Bob (IRE)—Ginger Lily (IRE)
3 **DESERT CROP**, 4, b f Shirocco (GER)—Yield
4 **FANTASTIC BOB (IRE)**, 5, b br g Big Bad Bob (IRE)—Fantastic Fantasy (IRE)
5 **GRA GEAL MO CHROI (IRE)**, 7, br m Imperial Ballet (IRE)—Shyshiyra (IRE)
6 **HONEY POUND (IRE)**, 4, b g Big Bad Bob (IRE)—Moon Review (USA)
7 **MOENCHENGLADBACH (IRE)**, 4, b g Stardan (IRE)—Dusseldorf (IRE)
8 **PERILOUSLY (USA)**, 4, ch f Mr Greeley (USA)—Shin Feign (USA)
9 **RHEINLAND (IRE)**, 6, b m Humbel (USA)—Dusseldorf (IRE)

THREE-YEAR-OLDS

10 **CEOL NA MARA**, b f Strategic Prince—Isobel Rose (IRE)
11 **DANEQUEST (IRE)**, b g Stardan (IRE)—Tinquest
12 **DROMBEG'S CHOICE (IRE)**, ch f Choisir (AUS)—St Catherine (IRE)

TWO-YEAR-OLDS

13 B f 14/2 Amadeus Wolf—Arzachena (FR) (Grand Lodge (USA))
14 Ch f 24/3 Papal Bull—Daneway (Danehill Dancer (IRE))
15 B br f 30/4 Big Bad Bob (IRE)—Lake Millstatt (IRE) (Magical Strike (USA))
16 B f 20/1 Moss Vale (IRE)—Marefonic (Zafonic (USA)) (656)
17 Ch c 16/5 Papal Bull—Marinka (Pivotal) (1477)
18 B f 23/2 Papal Bull—Rainbow Lass (Rainbow Quest (USA))
19 B f 16/4 Papal Bull—Serramanna (Grand Lodge (USA)) (410)

Assistant Trainer: Susan Leahy

MR RICHARD BRABAZON, Co. Kildare

Postal: **Rangers Lodge, The Curragh, Co. Kildare, Ireland**
Contacts: PHONE 00353 (0) 45 441259   FAX 00353 (0) 45 441906   MOBILE 00353 (0) 87 2515626
E-MAIL richardbrabazon@eircom.net WEBSITE www.richardbrabazon.ie

1 **LIGHTENING STRICKS (IRE)**, 5, b h King's Best (USA)—Opera Comique (FR) **Mrs Alice Perry**
2 **PLACERE (IRE)**, 4, ch f Noverre (USA)—Puppet Play (IRE) **Mrs F. D. McAuley**
3 **TORETTO (IRE)**, 4, ch g Peintre Celebre (USA)—Petite-D-Argent **R. Brabazon**

THREE-YEAR-OLDS

4 **KORBOUS (IRE)**, ch g Choisir (AUS)—Puppet Play (IRE) **Mrs F. D. McAuley**

Assistant Trainer: Michelle Cox

STOP PRESS Additional horses

The following additional horses were received too late to be included in the trainer's main list

MR JEREMY GASK, Warminster

1 **MAGIC SECRET**, 4, b g Trade Fair—Just Devine (IRE) **Carmel Stud**
2 **PRANA (USA)**, 4, b f Proud Citizen (USA)—Javana (USA) **The Prana Syndicate**

THREE-YEAR-OLDS

3 **FINE FINALE**, b c Lucky Story (USA)—Lamees (USA) **C. R. Withers**
4 **LANA MAE**, ch f Proclamation (IRE)—Saharan Song (IRE) **BKL Partners**
5 **MIRRACLE BALLAD**, b c Singspiel (IRE)—Emulate **Follow The Flag Partnership**
6 **RED HOT SECRET**, ch f Three Valleys (USA)—Princess Miletrian (IRE) **Carmel Stud**

TWO-YEAR-OLDS

7 **LUCKY STARS**, ch f 21/4 Lucky Story (USA)—Cosmic Countess (IRE) (Lahib (USA)) **Gracelands Stud**

MR MIKE MURPHY, Westoning

1 **HURRICANE LADY (IRE)**, 4, b f Hurricane Run (IRE)—Yaria (IRE) **Mr Borgatti & Mr Moir**
2 4, Ch g Dr Fong (USA)—Kembla **M. Murphy**
3 **LA FORTUNATA**, 5, b m Lucky Story (USA)—Phantasmagoria **Mr J. Patton**
4 **SERVOCA (CAN)**, 6, gr g El Prado (IRE)—Cinderellaslipper (USA) **M. Murphy**
5 **STARCLASS**, 5, b m Starcraft (NZ)—Classic Millennium **Mr Borgatti & Mr Moir**

THREE-YEAR-OLDS

6 B f Royal Applause—Limonia (GER) **M. Murphy**
7 **REGALO ROSADO**, ch f Cadeaux Genereux—Pinkai (IRE) **Goff, Hoskins, Hyde, Lobo & Smithx2**

TWO-YEAR-OLDS

8 B g 6/4 Sakhee's Secret—Limonia (GER) (Perugino (USA)) **M. Murphy**

Mr KEVIN RYAN, Hambleton

1 **ADVANCED**, 9, b g Night Shift (USA)—Wonderful World (GER)
2 **ARGANIL (USA)**, 7, ch g Langfuhr (CAN)—Sherona (USA) **Mr M & Mrs C McGeever**
3 **BAJAN TRYST (USA)**, 6, b br g Speightstown (USA)—Garden Secrets (USA) **Mrs M Forsyth & Mrs R G Hillen**
4 **BEAUTIFUL DAY**, 4, b g Piccolo—Evening **Mr Guy Reed**
5 **DICKIE'S LAD (IRE)**, 4, b g Diamond Green (FR)—Shadow Mountain **Duddy, McNulty & Duncan**
6 **LE TOREADOR**, 7, ch g Piccolo—Peggy Spencer **Mr Guy Reed**
7 **LOVE DELTA (USA)**, 5, b br g Seeking The Gold (USA)—Delta Princess (USA) **Mrs R G Hillen**
8 **MURURA (IRE)**, 5, b g Green Desert (USA)—Victoria Regia (IRE) **Mrs R. G. Hillen**
9 **REEM STAR**, 4, b f Green Tune (USA)—Arlecchina (GER) **Mr Ahmed Ali**
10 **TRIBAL MYTH (IRE)**, 5, b g Johannesburg (USA)—Shadow Play (USA) **Mr & Mrs K. S. Hughes & Dr J. Gozzard**

THREE-YEAR-OLDS

11 **DOZY (IRE)**, ch f Exceed And Excel (AUS)—Star Profile (IRE) **D Redvers & J H & S M Wall**
12 **KATHLEENSLUCKYLAD (IRE)**, b c Antonius Pius (USA)—Jacobina **Miss R. Galligan**
13 **MINNIE DIVA (IRE)**, b f Multiplex—Looker **Mr N & Mrs G Cable**
14 **NATURALMENTE (IRE)**, b f Captain Rio—Blusienka (IRE) **Mr Roger Peel**
15 **O'GORMAN**, b g Sleeping Indian—Harryana **We Haven't Told The Wives Syndicate**

TWO-YEAR-OLDS

16 Ch f 12/3 Beat Hollow—Cavernista (Lion Cavern (USA)) **SCB Ltd**

Mr JOHN WAINWRIGHT, Malton

1 **KEEP FIGHTING,** 4, ch f Monsieur Bond (IRE)—Baron Rhodes **Mr Ian Barran & Mr Paul Rhodes**
2 4, Ch f Monsieur Bond (IRE)—Landofheartsdesire (IRE)

THREE-YEAR-OLDS

3 B g Elusive City (USA)—Landofheartsdesire (IRE)
4 **MEDECIS MOUNTAIN,** b g Medecis—Moon Cat (IRE) **Sam Enwright**
5 B f Kyllachy—Palm Cove (UAE)

TWO-YEAR-OLDS

6 **FOREST PHILLY (IRE),** b f 5/4 Moss Vale (IRE)—Red Beach (IRE) (Turtle Island (IRE)) **Phil Cooper**
7 **KNOCKAMANY BENDS (IRE),** b c 13/3 Majestic Missile (IRE)—
Sweet Compliance (Safawan) (9851) **Mr & Mrs D Brown**

RECRUIT WINNING STAFF

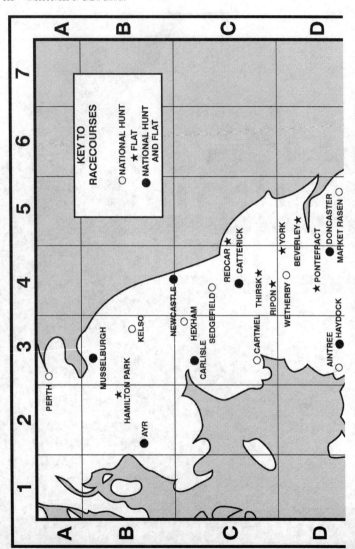

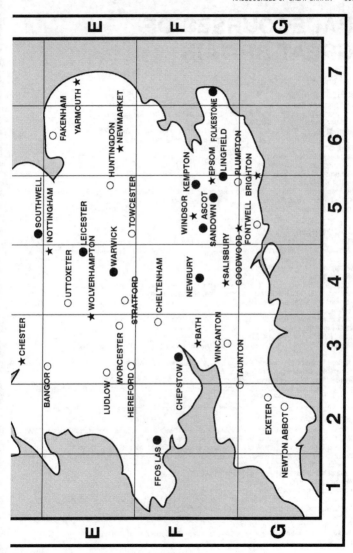

RACECOURSES OF GREAT BRITAIN

AINTREE (L.H)
Grand National Course: Triangular, 2m 2f (16) 494y run-in with elbow. Perfectly flat. A severe test for both horse and rider, putting a premium on jumping ability, fitness and courage.
Mildmay Course: Rectangular, 1m 4f (8) 260y run-in. A very fast course with sharp bends.
Address: Aintree Racecourse, Ormskirk Road, Aintree, Liverpool, l 9 5AS Tel: (0151) 523 2600
Fax: (0151) 522 2920 E-mail: aintree@rht.net Website: www.aintree.co.uk
Clerk of the Course: Andrew Tulloch (07831) 315104
Managing Director: Julian Thick
Going Reports: (0151) 523 2600.
Stabling: 162 boxes allocated in strict rotation. Facilities are available on the course for up to 100 stable staff. (0151) 522 2937.
By Road: North of the City, near the junction of the M57 and M58 with the A59 (Preston).
By Rail: Aintree Station is adjacent to the Stands, from Liverpool Central.
By Air: Liverpool (Speke) Airport is 10 miles. Helicopter landing facility by prior arrangement.

ASCOT (R.H)
Flat: Right-handed triangular track just under 1m 6f in length. The Round course descends from the 1m 4f start into Swinley Bottom, the lowest part of the track. It then turns right-handed and joins the Old Mile Course, which starts on a separate chute. The course then rises to the right-handed home turn over a new underpass to join the straight mile course. The run-in is about 3f, rising slightly to the winning post. The whole course is of a galloping nature with easy turns.
N.H. Triangular, 1m 6f (10) 240y run-in mostly uphill. A galloping course with an uphill finish, Ascot provides a real test of stamina. The fences are stiff and sound jumping is essential, especially for novices.
Address: Ascot Racecourse, Ascot, Berkshire SL5 7JX Tel: (08707) 271 234 Fax: (08704) 601250 Website: www.ascot.co.uk
Clerk of the Course: Chris Stickels (01344) 878502/(07970) 621440
Chief Executive: Charles Barnett
Going Reports: Day: (01344) 878502
Stabling: 175 boxes. Free, with shavings, straw or paper provided. Tel: (01344) 878454
Fax: (0870) 4214755
By Road: West of the town on the A329. Easy access from the M3 (Junction 3) and the M4 (Junction 6). Car parking adjoining the course and Ascot Heath.
By Rail: Regular service from Waterloo to Ascot (500y from the racecourse).
By Air: Helicopter landing facility at the course. London (Heathrow) Airport 15 miles, White Waltham Airfield 12 miles (01427 718800).

AYR (L.H)
Flat: A left-handed, galloping, flat oval track of 1m 4f with a 4f run-in. The straight 6f is essentially flat.
N.H. Oval, 1m 4f (9) 210y run-in. Relatively flat and one of the fastest tracks in Great Britain. It is a well-drained course and the ground rarely becomes testing. Suits the long-striding galloper.
Address: Ayr Racecourse, Whitletts Road, Ayr KA8 0JE Tel: (01292) 264179 Fax: (01292) 610140 Website: www.ayr-racecourse.co.uk
Clerk of the Course: Emma Marley (07881) 908702
Managing Director: Geoff Green
Going Reports: Contact Clerk of the Course as above.
Stabling: 175 boxes. Free stabling and accommodation for lads and lasses. Tel: (01292) 264179 ext 141.
By Road: East of the town on the A758. Free parking for buses and cars.
By Rail: Ayr Station (trains on the half hour from Glasgow Central). Journey time 55 minutes.
Buses and taxis also to the course.
By Air: Prestwick International Airport (10 minutes), Glasgow Airport (1 hour).

BANGOR-ON-DEE (L.H)

N.H. Circular, 1m 4f (9) 325y run-in. Apart from some 'ridge and furrow', this is a flat course notable for three sharp bends, especially the paddock turn. Suits handy, speedy sorts and is ideal for front-runners.
Address: Bangor-On-Dee Racecourse, Overton Road, Bangor-On-Dee, Wrexham. LL13 0DA
Tel: (01978) 782081, Fax: (01978) 780985 Website: www.bangorondeeraces.co.uk
Racecourse Manager/Clerk of the Course: Andrew Morris
Chief Executive: Richard Thomas
General Manager: Jeannie Chantler
Going Reports: Contact Clerk of the Course as above.
Stabling: 85 stables, allotted on arrival. Shavings (straw on request). Applications to the Manager.
Tel: (01978) 782081.
By Road: 5 miles South-East of Wrexham, off the B5069.
By Rail: Wrexham Station (bus or taxi to the course).
By Air: Helicopters may land by prior arrangement with Clerk of the Course at entirely their own risk.

BATH (L.H)

Flat: Galloping, left-handed, level oval of 1m 4f 25y, with long, stiff run-in of about 4f which bends to the left. An extended chute provides for races over 5f 11y and 5f 161y.
Address: The Racecourse, Lansdown, Bath BA1 9BU. Tel: (01225) 424609 Fax: (01225) 444415.
Website: www.bath-racecourse.co.uk
Clerk of the Course: Katie Stephens (07866) 698163
Going Reports: Contact Clerk of the Course as above.
Stabling: 120 boxes. Free stabling and accommodation for lads and lasses. Tel: (01225) 424609
By Road: 2 miles North-West of the City (M4 Junction 18) at Lansdown. Unlimited free car and coach parking space immediately behind the stands. Special bus services operate from Bath to the racecourse.
By Rail: Bath Station (from Paddington).
By Air: Bristol or Colerne Airports. Helicopter landing facilities available by prior arrangement.

BEVERLEY (R.H)

Flat: A right-handed oval of 1m 3f, generally galloping, with an uphill run-in of two and a half furlongs. The 5f course is very stiff.
Address: Beverley Race Co. Ltd., York Road, Beverley, Yorkshire HU17 9QZ
Tel: (01482) 867488/882645.Website: www.beverley-racecourse.co.uk
Racecourse Manager & Clerk of the Course: Sally Iggulden (07850) 458605
Going Reports: Tel: (01482) 867488/882645 or Head Groundsman (Mr. J Morley) (07885) 678186
Stabling: 111 boxes. Free stabling. Accommodation available for lads and lasses
Tel: (01482) 867488/882645.
By Road: 7 miles from the M62 (Junction 38) off the A1035. Free car parking opposite the course.
Owners and Trainers use a separate enclosure.
By Rail: Beverley Station (Hull-Scarborough line). Occasional bus service to the course (1 mile).

BRIGHTON (L.H)

Flat: Left-handed, 1m 4f horseshoe with easy turns and a run-in of three and a half furlongs. Undulating and sharp, the track suits handy types.
Address: Brighton Racecourse, Brighton, East Sussex BN2 2XZ Tel: (01273) 603580 Fax: (01273) 673267
Website: www.brighton-racecourse.co.uk
Clerk of the Course: Edward Arkell (07977) 587713
General Manager: Callum MacKay
Going Reports: Available on www.brighton-racecourse.co.uk or contact main office/Clerk of the Course as above
Stabling: 102 boxes. Stabling & accommodation: Tel: (01273) 603580, available on request.
By Road: East of the city on the A27 (Lewes Road). There is a car park adjoining the course.
By Rail: Brighton Station (from Victoria on the hour, London Bridge or Portsmouth). Special bus service to the course from the station (approx 2 miles).
By Air: Helicopters may land by prior arrangement.

CARLISLE (R.H)

Flat: Right-handed, 1m 4f pear-shaped track. Galloping and undulating with easy turns and a stiff uphill run-in of three and a half furlongs. 6f course begins on an extended chute.
N.H. Pear-shaped, 1m 5f (9) 300y run-in uphill. Undulating and a stiff test of stamina, ideally suited to the long-striding thorough stayer. Three mile chases start on a chute, and the first fence is only jumped once. Ground tends to be either very fast or very soft.

Address: Carlisle Racecourse, Durdar Road, Carlisle CA2 4TS Tel: (01228) 554700 Fax: (01228) 554747
Website: www.carlisle-races.co.uk
Raceday Clerks of the Course: Andrew Tulloch (07831) 315104 & Kirkland Tellwright (07748) 181595
General Manager: Richard Clements
Going Reports: (01228) 554700 (recorded) or contact Clerk of the Course above
Stabling: 98 boxes. Stabling and accommodation available on request. Please phone Head Groundsman
on (07889) 987542, or Fax Stable Office on (01228) 554747 by 1pm day before racing.
By Road: 2 miles south of the city (Durdar Road). Easy access from the M6 (Junction 42).
The car park is free (adjacent to the course).
By Rail: Carlisle Station (2 miles from the course).
By Air: Helicopter landing facility by prior arrangement.

CARTMEL (L.H)
N.H.: Oval, 1m 1f (6) 800y run-in. Almost perfectly flat but very sharp, with the longest run-in in the country,
approximately half a mile. The fences are stiff but fair.
Address: Cartmel Racecourse, Cartmel, nr Grange-Over-Sands, Cumbria LA11 6QF Tel: (01539) 536340.
Out of season: (01539) 533335 Fax: (01539) 536004 Website: www.cartmel-racecourse.co.uk
Managing Director: Jonathan Garrett
Clerk of the Course: Anthea Morshead (07837) 559861
Racecourse Manager: Shaun Hodgson (07779) 315104
Club Secretary: Mrs Bray (01539) 533434
Going Reports: (01539) 536340 or contact Clerk of the Course as above.
Stabling: 75 boxes. Boxes and accommodation for lads and lasses is limited. Prior booking is required by
12noon the day before racing (01539) 534609.
By Road: 1 mile West of the town, 2 miles off the B5277 (Grange-Haverthwaite road). M6 (Junction 36).
By Rail: Cark-in-Cartmel Station (2½ miles) (Carnforth-Barrow line). Raceday bus service.
By Air: Light aircraft facilities available at Cark Airport (4 miles from the course). Helicopter landing facility
at the course, by prior arrangement only.

CATTERICK (L.H)
Flat: A sharp, left-handed, undulating oval of 1m 180y with a downhill run-in of 3f.
N.H. Oval, 1m 1f (9) 240y run-in. Undulating, sharp track that favours the handy, front-running sort, rather
than the long-striding galloper.
Address: The Racecourse, Catterick Bridge, Richmond, North Yorkshire DL10 7PE Tel: (01748) 811478
Fax: (01748) 811082 Website: www.catterickbridge.co.uk
General Manager & Clerk of the Course: Fiona Needham (07831) 688625
Going Reports: Contact Clerk of the Course as above
Stabling: 116 Boxes. Allotted on arrival.
By Road: The course is adjacent to the A1, 1 mile North-West of the town on the A6136.
There is a free car park.
By Rail: Darlington Station (special buses to course - 14 mile journey).
By Air: Helicopters can land by prior arrangement. Fixed wing planes contact RAF Leeming
Tel: 01677 423041

CHELTENHAM (L.H)
Old Course: Oval, 1m 4f (9) 350y run-in. A testing, undulating track with stiff fences.
The ability to stay is essential.
New Course: Oval, 1m 5f (10) 220y run-in. Undulating, stiff fences, testing course, uphill for the final
half-mile.
Address: Cheltenham Racecourse, Prestbury Park, Cheltenham, Gloucestershire GL50 4SH
Tel: (01242) 513014 Fax: (01242) 224227 Website: www.cheltenham.co.uk
Managing Director: Edward Gillespie
Director of Racing & Clerk of the Course: Simon Claisse (07785) 293966
Going Reports: Available from 6 days before racing (01242) 513014 (option 2, then 6)
Stabling: 299 boxes. Ample stabling and accommodation for lads.
Apply to the Stable Manager (01242) 537602 or 521950.
By Road: 1.5 miles North of the town on the A435. M5 (Junction 10 or 11).
By Rail: Cheltenham Station. Buses and taxis to course.
By Air: Helicopter landing site to the North-East of the stands.

CHEPSTOW (L.H)

Flat: A left-handed, undulating oval of about 2m, with easy turns, and a straight run-in of 5f. There is a straight track of 1m 14y.

N.H. Oval, 2m (11) 240y run-in. Many changing gradients, five fences in the home straight.

Favours the long-striding front-runner, but stamina is important.

Address: Chepstow Racecourse, Chepstow, Monmouthshire NP16 6BE Tel: (01291) 622260

Fax: (01291) 627061 Website: www.chepstow-racecourse.co.uk

Clerk of the Course: Keith Ottesen (07813) 043453

Acting General Manager: Rebecca Joy

Going Reports: Contact Clerk of the Course as above.

Stabling: 106 boxes, allotted on arrival. Limited accommodation for lads and lasses.

Apply: (01291) 622260.

By Road: 1 mile North-West of the town on the A466. (1 mile from Junction 22 of the M4 (Severn Bridge) or M48 Junction 2. There is a free public car park opposite the Stands entrance.

By Rail: Chepstow Station (from Paddington, change at Gloucester or Newport).

The course is 1 mile from station.

By Air: Helicopter landing facility in the centre of the course.

CHESTER (L.H)

Flat: A level, sharp, left-handed, circular course of 1m 73y, with a short run-in of 230y.

Chester is a specialists' track which generally suits the sharp-actioned horse.

Address: The Racecourse, Chester CH1 2LY Tel: (01244) 304600 Fax: (01244) 304648 Website:

www.chester-races.co.uk

Racecourse Manager/Clerk of the Course: Andrew Morris

Chief Executive: Richard Thomas

Going Reports: Contact Main Office (01244) 304600

Stabling: 138 boxes and accommodation. Tel: (01244) 324880 or (01244) 304610

By Road: The course is near the centre of the city on the A548 (Queensferry Road). The Owners and Trainers car park is adjacent to the Leverhulme Stand. There is a public car park in the centre of the course.

By Rail: Chester Station (¾ mile from the course). Services from Euston, Paddington and Northgate.

By Air: Hawarden Airport (2 miles). Helicopters are allowed to land on the racecourse by prior arrangement only.

DONCASTER (L.H)

Flat: A left-handed, flat, galloping course of 1m 7f 110y, with a long run-in which extends to a straight mile.

N.H. Conical, 2m (11) 247y run-in. A very fair, flat track ideally suited to the long-striding galloper.

Address: Doncaster Racecourse, Leger Way, Doncaster DN2 6BB Tel: (01302) 304200,

Fax: (01302) 323271 Email: info@doncaster-racecourse.co.uk

Website: www.doncaster-racecourse.co.uk

Clerk of the Course: Jon Pullin (01302) 304200 or (07775) 943341

Managing Director: Mark Spincer

Going Reports: Contact Clerk of the Course as above or Estate Manager (07831) 260373.

Stabling: 147 boxes. Free stabling and accommodation. Tel: (01302) 304200

By Road: East of the town, off the A638 (M18 Junctions 3 & 4). Club members car park reserved.

Large public car park free and adjacent to the course.

By Rail: Doncaster Central Station (from King's Cross). Special bus service from the station (1 mile).

By Air: Helicopter landing facility by prior arrangement only. Doncaster Robin Hood Airport is 15 minutes from the racecourse.

EPSOM (L.H)

Flat: Left-handed and undulating with easy turns, and a run-in of just under 4f. The straight 5f course is also undulating and downhill all the way, making it the fastest 5f in the world.

Address: The Racecourse, Epsom Downs, Surrey, KT18 5LQ. Tel: (01372) 726311, Fax (01372) 748253

Website: www.epsomderby.co.uk

Clerk of the Course: Andrew Cooper. Tel: (01372) 726311, Mobile: (07774) 230850.

Managing Director: Rupert Trevelyan

Going Reports: Contact Clerk of the Course as above.

Stabling: 108 boxes. Free stabling and accommodation. Tel: (01372) 460454

By Road: 2 miles South of the town on the B290 (M25 Junctions 8 & 9). For full car park particulars apply to: The Club Secretary, Epsom Grandstand, Epsom Downs, Surrey KT18 5LQ. Tel: (01372) 726311.

By Rail: Epsom, Epsom Downs or Tattenham Corner Stations (trains from London Bridge, Waterloo, Victoria). Regular bus services run to the course from Epsom and Morden Underground Station.
By Air: London (Heathrow) and London (Gatwick) are both within 30 miles of the course.
Heliport (Derby Meeting only) apply to Hascombe Aviation. Tel: (01279) 680291.

EXETER (R.H)

N.H.: Oval, 2m (11) 300y run-in uphill. Undulating with a home straight of half a mile. A good test of stamina, suiting the handy, well-balanced sort.
Address: Exeter Racecourse, Kennford, Exeter, Devon EX6 7XS Tel: (01392) 832599 Fax: (01392) 833454
Email: Exeter@thejockeyclub.co.uk Website: www.exeter-racecourse.co.uk
Clerk of the Course: Barry Johnson (07976) 791578
General Manager: Alice Everitt
Going Reports: Contact Clerk of the Course as above.
Stabling: 90 loose boxes at the course. Sleeping accommodation and canteen for both lads and lasses by prior arrangement. Apply to Racecourse Office. Tel: (01392) 832599 by 12 noon on day before racing.
By Road: The course is at Haldon, 5 miles South-West of Exeter on the A38 (Plymouth) road, 2 miles East of Chudleigh.
By Rail: Exeter (St Davids) Station. Free bus service to course.
By Air: Helicopters can land by prior arrangement.

FAKENHAM (L.H)

N.H. Square, 1m (6) 200y run-in. On the turn almost throughout and undulating, suiting the handy front-runner. The going rarely becomes heavy.
Address: The Racecourse, Fakenham, Norfolk NR21 7NY Tel: (01328) 862388 Fax: (01328) 855908
email: info@fakenhamracecourse.co.uk Website: www.fakenhamracecourse.co.uk
Clerk of the Course & Chief Executive: David Hunter Tel: (01328) 862388 Mobile: (07767) 802206.
Going Reports: Contact Clerk of the Course as above.
Stabling: 70 boxes available. Tel: (01328) 862388 Fax: (01328) 855908.
By Road: 1 mile South of the town on the B1146 (East Dereham) road.
By Rail: Norwich Station (26 miles) (Liverpool Street line),
King's Lynn (22 miles) (Liverpool Street/Kings Cross).
By Air: Helicopter landing facility in the centre of the course by prior arrangement only.

FFOS LAS (L.H)

Flat & N.H. : The track is a 60m wide, basically flat, 1m4f oval with sweeping bends.
Address: Ffos Las Racecourse, Trimsaran, Carmarthenshire, SA17 4DE Tel: (01554) 811092
Fax: (01554) 811037 Website: www.ffoslasracecourse.com
Clerk of the Course & General Manager: Tim Long (07966) 893531
Going Reports: Contact Clerk of the Course as above.
Stabling: 120 box stable yard.
By Road: From the east take J48 from the M4 and join the A4138 to Llanelli, then follow the brown tourist signs to the racecourse. From the west take the A48 to Carmarthen then the A484 to Kidwelly before following the brown signs.
By Air: The course has the facilities to land helicopters on race days.

FOLKESTONE (R.H)

Flat: Right-handed, undulating, circuit of 1m 3f, with a two and a half furlong run-in.
There is a straight 6f course.
N.H. Oval, 1m 3f (8) chases 220y run-in, hurdles 250y run-in. An undulating course with easy fences, not particularly suitable for the long-striding galloper.
Address: Folkestone Racecourse, Westenhanger, Hythe, Kent CT21 4HX Tel: (01303) 266407
Fax: (01303) 260185 Website: www.folkestone-racecourse.co.uk
Racecourse Manager: Emma Santer
Clerk of the Course: Andy Waitt (07973) 939840
Going Reports: Contact Clerk of the Course as above
Stabling: 93 boxes allotted in rotation. Advance notice required for overnight accommodation, by noon on the day prior to racing. (01303) 266407.
By Road: 6 miles West of town at Westenhanger. Easy access from Junction 11 of the M20.
Car park adjoins stands.
By Rail: Westenhanger Station adjoins course. Trains from Charing Cross.
By Air: Helicopter landing facility by prior arrangement.

FONTWELL PARK (Fig. 8)

N.H. 2m (7) 230y run-in with left-hand bend close home. The figure-of-eight chase course suits handy types and is something of a specialist's track. The left-handed hurdle course is oval, one mile round with nine hurdles per two and a quarter miles.

Address: Fontwell Park Racecourse, nr Arundel, West Sussex BN18 0SX Tel: (01243) 543335
Fax: (01243) 543904 Website: www.fontwellpark.co.uk
Clerk of the Course: Edward Arkell (07977) 587713
Executive Director: Phil Bell
Going Reports: (01243) 543335 during office hours.
Stabling: 90 boxes. Limited accommodation.
If arriving the day before the meeting, contact: Tel: (01243) 543335.
By Road: South of village at the junction of the A29 (Bognor) and A27 (Brighton-Chichester) roads.
By Rail: Barnham Station (2 miles). Brighton-Portsmouth line (access via London Victoria).
By Air: Helicopter landing facility by prior arrangement with the Clerk of the Course.

GOODWOOD (R.H)

Flat: A sharp, undulating, essentially right-handed track with a long run-in. There is also a straight six furlong course.
Address: Goodwood Racecourse Ltd., Goodwood, Chichester, West Sussex PO18 0PX
Tel: (01243) 755022, Fax: (01243) 755025 Website:www.goodwood.co.uk
Managing Director: Adam Waterworth
Clerk of the Course: Seamus Buckley (07774) 100223
Going Reports: (01243) 755022 (recorded message) or Clerk of the Course.
Stabling: Free stabling and accommodation for runners (130 well equipped boxes at Goodwood House). Please book in advance. Subsidised canteen and recreational facilities. Tel: (01243) 755022/755036.
By Road: 6 miles North of Chichester between the A286 & A285. There is a car park adjacent to the course. Ample free car and coach parking.
By Rail: Chichester Station (from Victoria or London Bridge). Regular bus service to the course (6 miles).
By Air: Helicopter landing facility by prior arrangement (01243 755030). Goodwood Airport 2 miles (taxi to the course).

HAMILTON PARK (R.H)

Flat: Sharp, undulating, right-handed course of 1m 5f with a five and a half furlong, uphill run-in. There is a straight track of 6f.
Address: Hamilton Park Racecourse, Bothwell Road, Hamilton, Lanarkshire ML3 0DW Tel: (01698) 283806
Fax: (01698) 286621 Website:www.hamilton-park.co.uk
Racing Manager & Clerk of the Course: Hazel Peplinski (01698) 283806 (raceday). Mobile: (07774) 116733.
Fax: (01698) 286621
Chief Executive: Vivien Kyles (01698) 283806
Going Reports: Track Manager: (07736) 101130 or Clerk of the Course.
Stabling: Free stabling (102 boxes) and accommodation on request. Tel: (01698) 284892 or Office.
By Road: Off the A72 on the B7071 (Hamilton-Bothwell road). (M74 Junction 5). Free parking for cars and buses.
By Rail: Hamilton West Station (1 mile).
By Air: Glasgow Airport (20 miles).

HAYDOCK PARK (L.H)

Flat: A galloping, almost flat, oval track, 1m 5f round, with a run-in of four and a half furlongs and a straight six furlong course.
N.H. Oval, 1m 5f (10) 440y run-in. Flat, galloping chase course. The hurdle track, which is sharp, is inside the chase course and has some tight bends.
Address: Haydock Park Racecourse, Newton-le-Willows, Merseyside WA12 0HQ Tel: (01942) 402609
Fax: (01942) 270879 Website: www.haydock-park.co.uk
Clerk of the Course: Kirkland Tellwright (01942) 725963 or (07748) 181595
Managing Director: Dickon White
Going Reports: Contact Clerk of the Course as above or Head Groundsman (07831) 849298

Stabling: 124 boxes. Applications to be made to the Racecourse for stabling and accommodation.
Tel: (01942) 725963 or (01942) 402615 (racedays).
By Road: The course is on the A49 near Junction 23 of the M6.
By Rail: Newton-le-Willows Station (Manchester-Liverpool line) is 2.5 miles from the course. Earlstown 3
miles from the course. Warrington Bank Quay and Wigan are on the London to Carlisle/Glasgow line.
By Air: Landing facilities in the centre of the course for helicopters and planes not exceeding 10,000lbs
laden weight. Apply to the Sales Office.

HEREFORD (R.H)

N.H.: Square, 1m 4f (9) 300y run-in. The turns, apart from the final one that is on falling ground, are easily
negotiated, placing the emphasis on speed rather than stamina. A handy position round the home turn is
vital, as winners rarely come from behind. The hurdle track is on the outside of the chase course.
Address: Hereford Racecourse, Roman Road, Holmer, Hereford HR4 9 QU Tel: (01432) 273560,
Fax: (01432) 352807 Website: www.hereford-racecourse.co.uk
Clerk of the Course: Keith Ottesen (07813) 043453
General Manager: Darren Cook
Going Reports: (01432) 273560 (weekdays) or Clerk of the Course
Stabling: 105 boxes allocated on arrival. Apply to the Stabling Manager, The Racecourse House, Roman
Road, Holmer, Hereford. Tel: (01432) 273560.
By Road: 1 mile North West of the City centre off the A49 (Leominster) road.
By Rail: Hereford Station (1 mile from the course).
By Air: Helicopter landing facility in the centre of the course by arrangement with the Clerk of the Course,
and entirely at own risk.

HEXHAM (L.H)

N.H.: Oval, 1m 4f (10) 220y run-in. An undulating course that becomes very testing when the ground is
soft, it has easy fences and a stiff uphill climb to the finishing straight, which is on a separate spur.
Address: Hexham Racecourse, The Riding, Hexham, Northumberland NE46 2JP Tel: (01434) 606881
Fax: (01434) 605814, Racedays: (01434) 603738. Email: admin@hexham-racecourse.co.uk Website:
www.hexham-racecourse.co.uk
Chief Executive: Charles Enderby
Clerk of the Course: James Armstrong (01434) 606881 or (07801) 166820
Going Reports: Contact Clerk of the Course as above
Stabling: 93 Boxes allocated in rotation.
Please book stabling and accommodation the day before by fax: (01434) 605814.
By Road: 1.5 miles South-West of the town off the B6305.
By Rail: Hexham Station (Newcastle-Carlisle line). Free bus to the course.
By Air: Helicopter landing facility in centre of course (by special arrangement only).

HUNTINGDON (R.H)

N.H.: Oval, 1m 4f (9) 200y run-in. Perfectly flat, galloping track with a tricky open ditch in front of the
stands. The two fences in the home straight can cause problems for novice chasers. Suits front runners.
Address: The Racecourse, Brampton, Huntingdon, Cambridgeshire PE28 4NL Tel: (01480) 453373
Fax: (01480) 455275 Website:www.huntingdon-racecourse.co.uk
Clerk of the Course: Sulekha Varma
Managing Director: Sophie Hodgkinson
Going Reports: Tel: (01480) 453373 or (07990) 774295
Stabling: 100 boxes available. Allotted on arrival. Telephone Racecourse Office.
By Road: The course is situated at Brampton, 2 miles West of Huntingdon on the A14.
Easy access from the A1 (½ mile from the course).
By Rail: Huntingdon Station. Buses and taxis to course.
By Air: Helicopter landing facility by prior arrangement.

KELSO (L.H)

N.H.: Oval, 1m 3f (9) 440y run-in uphill. Rather undulating with two downhill fences opposite the stands,
Kelso suits the nippy, front-running sort, though the uphill run to the finish helps the true stayer.
The hurdle course is smaller and very sharp with a tight turn away from the stands.
Address: Kelso Racecourse, Kelso, Roxburghshire TD5 7SX Tel: (01668) 280800
Website:www.kelso-races.co.uk
Clerk of the Course: Hazel Peplinski (07774) 116733

Managing Director & Secretary: Richard M. Landale, c/o Sale & Partners, 18-20 Glendale Road, Wooler, Northumberland NE71 6DW. Tel: (01668) 280800.
Going Reports: Racecourse: (01573) 224822 Groundsman Tel: (07774) 172527
Stabling: 94 boxes allotted in rotation. Reservations for stabling and accommodation for lads and lasses at the racecourse, please phone Head Groundsman Tel: (01573) 224767 or
Racecourse stables: (01573) 224822 from 3pm the day before racing.
By Road: 1 mile North of the town, off the B6461.
By Rail: Berwick-upon-Tweed Station. 23 mile bus journey to Kelso.
By Air: Helicopters can land at course by arrangement, fixed wing aircraft Winfield, regular aircraft Edinburgh.

KEMPTON PARK (R.H)

Flat: A floodlit Polytrack circuit opened in March 2006. A 10f outer track accommodates races over 6f, 7f, 1m, 1m 3f, 1m 4f and 2m. The 8f inner track caters for races over 5f and 1m 2f.
N.H. Triangular, 1m 5f (10) 175y run-in. Practically flat; sharp course where the long run between the last obstacle on the far side and the first in the home straight switches the emphasis from jumping to speed. The hurdles track is on the outside of the chase track. The fences have been rebuilt and the water jump removed. The course crosses the Polytrack at two points on each circuit.
Address: Kempton Park Racecourse, Sunbury-on-Thames, Middlesex TW16 5AQ Tel: (01932) 782292 Fax: (01932) 782044 Raceday Fax: (01932) 779525 Website: www.kempton.co.uk Email: kempton@rht.net
Clerk of the Course & Director of Racing: Brian Clifford (07880) 784484
Managing Director: Amy Starkey
Raceday Office Manager: Beverley Frith
Going Reports: (01932) 782292 if unavailable contact Clerk of the Course as above
Stabling: 117 boxes. Allocated on arrival. Prior booking required for overnight stay. Tel: (01932) 782292
By Road: On the A308 near Junction 1 of the M3.
By Rail: Kempton Park Station (from Waterloo).
By Air: London (Heathrow) Airport 6 miles.

LEICESTER (R.H)

Flat: Stiff, galloping, right-handed oval of 1m 5f, with a 5f run-in. There is a straight course of seven furlongs.
N.H. Rectangular, 1m 6f (10) 250y run-in uphill. An undulating course with an elbow 150y from the finish, Leicester can demand a high degree of stamina, for the going can become extremely heavy and the last three furlongs are uphill.
Address: Leicester Racecourse, Oadby, Leicester LE2 4AL. Tel: (0116) 2716515 Fax: (0116) 2711746
Website:www.leicester-racecourse.co.uk
Clerk of the Course: Jimmy Stevenson (0116) 2712115 or (07774) 497281
General Manager: David Maykels (0116) 2716515
Going Reports: Recorded message (0116) 2710875 or contact Clerk of the Course as above.
Stabling: 108 boxes. Allocated on arrival. Canteen opens at 7.30a.m. Tel: (0116) 271 2115.
By Road: The course is 2.5 miles South-East of the City on the A6 (M1, Junction 21). The car park is free.
By Rail: Leicester Station (from St Pancras) is 2.5 miles.
By Air: Helicopter landing facility in the centre of the course.

LINGFIELD PARK (L.H)

Flat, Turf: A sharp, undulating left-handed circuit, with a 7f 140y straight course.
Flat, Polytrack: The left-handed all-weather polytrack is 1m 2f round, with an extended chute to provide a 1m 5f start. It is a sharp, level track with a short run-in.
N.H. Conical, 1m 5f (10) 200y run-in. Severely undulating with a tight downhill turn into the straight, the chase course suits front runners and those of doubtful resolution.
Address: Lingfield Park Racecourse, Lingfield, Surrey RH7 6PQ Tel: (01342) 834800 Fax: (01342) 832833
Website: www.lingfield-racecourse.co.uk
Clerk of the Course: Neil Mackenzie Ross (01342) 831720 Mobile: (07917) 326977
Managing Director: Paul Shrimpton
Going Reports: Contact Clerk of the Course as above.
Stabling: 106 boxes. For details of accommodation tel: (01342) 831718. Advance notice for overnight accommodation required before 12 noon on the day before racing.
By Road: South-East of the town off the A22 (M25 Junction 6). Ample free parking.
By Rail: Lingfield Station (regular services from London Bridge and Victoria). ½m walk to the course.
By Air: London (Gatwick) Airport 10 miles. Helicopter landing facility south of wind-sock.

LUDLOW (R.H)

N.H. Oval, 1m 4f (9) 185y run-in. The chase course is flat and has quite sharp bends into and out of the home straight, although long-striding horses never seem to have any difficulties. The hurdle course is on the outside of the chase track and is not so sharp.

Address: Ludlow Race Club Ltd, The Racecourse, Bromfield, Ludlow, Shropshire SY8 2BT
Tel: (01584) 856221 (Racedays) or see below. Website:www.ludlowracecourse.co.uk
Club Secretary & Clerk of the Course: Bob Davies. Tel: (01584) 856221, Mobile (07970) 861533,
Fax: (01584) 856217 Email: bobdavies@ludlowracecourse.co.uk
Going Reports: Contact Clerk of the Course as above or Groundsman Tel: (01584) 856289 or (07970) 668353
Stabling: Free and allocated on arrival. 100 stables, mainly cardboard with a limited number of shavings and straw. Tel: (01584) 856221.
By Road: The course is situated at Bromfield, 2 miles North of Ludlow on the A49.
By Rail: Ludlow Station (Hereford-Shrewsbury line) 2 miles.
By Air: Helicopter landing facility in the centre of the course by arrangement with the Clerk of the Course and entirely at own risk.

MARKET RASEN (R.H)

N.H. Oval, 1m 2f (8) 250y run-in. A sharp, undulating course with a long run to the straight,
Market Rasen favours the handy, front-running type.

Address: Market Rasen Racecourse, Legsby Road, Market Rasen, Lincolnshire LN8 3EA Tel: (01673)
843434 Fax: (01673) 844532 Website: www.marketrasenraces.co.uk
Clerk of the Course: To be Announced
Managing Director: Pip Kirkby
Going Reports: Contact Clerk of the Course as above.
Stabling: 86 boxes at the course, allocated on arrival.
Accommodation for lads and lasses is by reservation only. Tel: (01673) 842307 (racedays only)
By Road: The town is just off the A46, and the racecourse is one mile East of the town on the A631.
Free car parks and racecards.
By Rail: Market Rasen Station 1 mile (King's Cross - Cleethorpes line).
By Air: Helicopter landing facility by prior arrangement only.

MUSSELBURGH (R.H)

Flat: A sharp, level, right-handed oval of 1m 2f, with a run-in of 4f. There is an additional 5f straight course.
N.H. Rectangular, 1m 3f (8) 150y run-in (variable). A virtually flat track with sharp turns, suiting the handy, front-running sort. Drains well.

Address: Musselburgh Racecourse, Linkfield Road, Musselburgh, East Lothian EH21 7RG
Tel: (0131) 665 2859 (Racecourse) Fax: (0131) 653 2083 Website:www.musselburgh-racecourse.co.uk
Clerk of the Course: Harriet Graham (07843) 380401
General Manager: Bill Farnsworth (07710) 536134
Going Reports: Contact main office as above or Clerk of the Course.
Stabling: 101 boxes.
Free stabling. Accommodation provided. Tel: (07773) 048638, Stables (racedays): (0131) 665 2796.
By Road: The course is situated at Musselburgh, 5 miles East of Edinburgh on the A1.
Car park, adjoining course, free for buses and cars.
By Rail: Waverley Station (Edinburgh). Local Rail service to Musselburgh.
By Air: Edinburgh (Turnhouse) Airport 30 minutes

NEWBURY (L.H)

Flat: Left-handed, oval track of about 1m 7f, with a slightly undulating straight mile. The round course is level and galloping with a four and a half furlong run-in. Races over the round mile and 7f 60y start on the adjoining chute.
N.H. Oval, 1m 6f (11) 255y run-in. Slightly undulating, wide and galloping in nature. The fences are stiff and sound jumping is essential. One of the fairest tracks in the country.

Address: The Racecourse, Newbury, Berkshire RG14 7NZ Tel: (01635) 40015 Fax: (01635) 528354
Website: www.newbury-racecourse.co.uk
Managing Directors: Stephen Higgins & Sarah Hordern.
Raceday Clerk: Richard Osgood (07977) 426947
Going Reports: Clerk of the Course as above.
Stabling: 164 boxes. Free stabling and accommodation for lads and lasses. Tel: (01635) 40015.
By Road: East of the town off the A34 (M4, Junction 12 or 13). Car park, adjoining enclosures, free.

By Rail: Newbury Racecourse Station, adjoins course.
By Air: Light Aircraft landing strip East/West. 830 metres by 30 metres wide. Helicopter landing facilities.

NEWCASTLE (L.H)

Flat: Galloping, easy, left-handed oval of 1m 6f, with an uphill 4f run-in. There is a straight course of 1m 8y.
N.H. Oval, 1m 6f (11) 220y run-in. A gradually rising home straight of four furlongs makes this galloping track a true test of stamina, especially as the ground can become very heavy. The fences are rather stiff.
Address: High Gosforth Park, Newcastle-Upon-Tyne NE3 5HP Tel: (0191) 236 2020 Fax: (0191) 236 7761
Website: www.newcastle-racecourse.co.uk
Clerk of the Course: James Armstrong (07801) 166820
Managing Director: Simon Lane
Stabling: 135 boxes. Stabling Free. It is essential to book accommodation in advance.
Apply via the Racecourse Office.
Going Reports: Contact Clerk of the Course as above or Head Groundsman (07860) 274289.
By Road: 4 miles North of city on the A6125 (near the A1). Car and coach park free.
By Rail: Newcastle Central Station (from King's Cross), a free bus service operates from South Gosforth and Regent Centre Metro Station.
By Air: Helicopter landing facility by prior arrangement. The Airport is 4 miles from the course.

NEWMARKET (R.H)

Rowley Mile Course: There is a straight ten furlong course, which is wide and galloping. Races over 12f or more are right-handed. The Rowley course has a long run-in and a stiff finish.
July Course: Races up to a mile are run on the Bunbury course, which is straight. Races over 10f or more are right-handed, with a 7f run-in. Like the Rowley course, the July track is stiff.
Address: Newmarket Racecourse, Newmarket, Suffolk CB8 0TG Tel: (01638) 663482 (Main Office), (01638) 663762 (Rowley), (01638) 675416 (July) Fax: Rowley (01638) 675340. Fax: July (01638) 675410
Website: www.newmarketracecourses.co.uk
Clerk of the Course: Michael Prosser, Westfield House, The Links, Newmarket.
Tel: (01638) 675504 or (07802) 844578
Managing Director: Stephen Wallis
Going Reports: Contact main office or Clerk of the Course as above
Stabling: 100 boxes. Free accommodation available at the Links Stables. Tel: (01638) 662200 or (07747) 766614
By Road: South-West of the town on the A1304 London Road (M11 Junction 9). Free car parking at the rear of the enclosure. Annual Badge Holders' car park free all days; Free courtesy bus service from Newmarket Station, Bus Station and High Street, commencing 90 minutes prior to the first race, and return trips up to 60 minutes after the last race.
By Rail: Infrequent rail service to Newmarket Station from Cambridge (Liverpool Street) or direct bus service from Cambridge (13 mile journey).
By Air: Landing facilities for light aircraft and helicopters on racedays at both racecourses.
See Flight Guide. Cambridge Airport 11 miles.

NEWTON ABBOT (L.H)

N.H. Oval, 1m 2f (7) 300y run-in. Flat with two tight bends and a water jump situated three fences from home. The nippy, agile sort is favoured. The run-in can be very short on the hurdle course.
Address: Newton Abbot Races Ltd., Kingsteignton Road, Newton Abbot, Devon TQ12 3AF
Tel: (01626) 353235 Fax: (01626) 336972 Website:www.newtonabbotracing.com
Clerk of the Course/Estate Manager: Jason Loosemore (07766) 228109
Managing Director: Pat Masterson. Tel: (01626) 353235 Fax: (01626) 336972 Mobile: (07917) 830144.
Going reports: Clerk of the Course as above.
Stabling: 80 boxes, allocated on arrival. Tel: (07766) 202938
By Road: North of the town on the A380. Torquay 6 miles, Exeter 17 miles.
By Rail: Newton Abbot Station (from Paddington) ¾ mile. Buses and taxis operate to and from the course.
By Air: Helicopter landing pad in the centre of the course.

NOTTINGHAM (L.H)

Flat: Left-handed, galloping, oval of about 1m 4f, and a run-in of four and a half furlongs.
Flat with easy turns.
Address: Nottingham Racecourse, Colwick Park, Nottingham NG2 4BE Tel: 0870 8507634
Fax: (0115) 958 4515 Website: www.nottinghamracecourse.co.uk

Clerk of the Course: To be Announced
Managing Director: Pip Kirkby
Going Reports: Contact main office as above or Clerk of the Course.
Stabling: 122 boxes allotted on arrival. Hostel for lads and lasses. Tel: (0870) 850 7634
By Road: 2 miles East of the City on the B686.
By Rail: Nottingham (Midland) Station. Regular bus service to course (2 miles).
By Air: Helicopter landing facility in the centre of the course.

PERTH (R.H)

N.H. Rectangular, 1m 2f (8) 283y run-in. A flat, easy track with sweeping turns. Not a course for the long-striding galloper. An efficient watering system ensures that the ground rarely gets hard.
Address: Perth Racecourse, Scone Palace Park, Perth PH2 6BB Tel: (01738) 551597 Fax: (01738) 553021
Website: www.perth-races.co.uk
Clerk of the Course: Harriet Graham (07843) 380401
General Manager: Sam Morshead Tel: (01738) 551597 Mobile: (07768) 868848
Secretary: Mrs M Reid
Going Reports: Groundsman: (07899 034012) or contact Clerk of the Course as above.
Stabling: 96 boxes and accommodation for lads and lasses Tel: (01738) 551597. Stables
Tel: (01738) 621604 (racedays only).
By Road: 4 miles North of the town off the A93.
By Rail: Perth Station (from Dundee) 4 miles. There are buses to the course.
By Air: Scone Airport (3.75 miles). Edinburgh Airport 45 minutes.

PLUMPTON (L.H)

N.H.: Oval, 1m 1f (7) 200y run-in uphill. A tight, undulating circuit with an uphill finish, Plumpton favours the handy, fast jumper. The ground often gets heavy, as the course is based on clay soil.
Address: Plumpton Racecourse, Plumpton, East Sussex, BN7 3AL Tel: (01273) 890383
Fax: (01273) 891557 Website: www.plumptonracecourse.co.uk
Clerk of the Course: Mark Cornford (07759) 151617
Chief Executive: Claire Sheppard
Going Reports: Tel: (01273) 890383, or (07759) 151617.
Stabling: 76 boxes. Advance notice required for overnight arrival. Tel: (07759) 151617
By Road: 2 miles North of the village off the B2116.
By Rail: Plumpton Station (from Victoria) adjoins course.
By Air: Helicopter landing facility by prior arrangement with the Clerk of the Course.

PONTEFRACT (L.H)

Flat: Left-handed oval, undulating course of 2m 133y, with a short run-in of 2f. It is a particularly stiff track with the last 3f uphill.
Address: Pontefract Park Race Co. Ltd., The Park, Pontefract, West Yorkshire Tel: (01977) 781307
(Racedays) Fax: (01977) 781850 Website: www.pontefract-races.co.uk
Clerk of the Course: Richard Hamill (07808) 965402
Managing Director: Norman Gundill (01977) 781307 (Office), (01977) 620649 (Home)
Going Reports: Contact Office as above, or Clerk of the Course
Stabling: 113 boxes. Stabling and accommodation must be reserved. They will be allocated on a first come-first served basis. Tel: (01977) 702323
By Road: 1 mile North of the town on the A639. Junction 32 of M62. Free car park adjacent to the course.
By Rail: Pontefract Station (Tanshelf, every hour to Wakefield), 1½ miles from the course. Regular bus service from Leeds.
By Air: Helicopters by arrangement only. (Nearest Airfields: Robin Hood (Doncaster), Sherburn-in-Elmet, Yeadon (Leeds/Bradford).

REDCAR (L.H)

Flat: Left-handed, level, galloping, oval course of 14f with a straight run-in of 5f. There is also a straight 8f.
Address: Redcar Racecourse, Redcar, Cleveland TS10 2BY Tel: (01642) 484068 Fax: (01642) 488272
Website: www.redcarracing.com
Clerk of the Course: Jonjo Sanderson Tel: (01642) 484068 Mobile: (07766) 022893
General Manager: Amy Fair
Going Reports: Contact main office as above or Clerk of the Course.
Stabling: 144 Boxes available. Tel: Stables (01642) 484068 or racedays only (01642) 484254).

By Road: In town off the A1085. Free parking adjoining the course for buses and cars.
By Rail: Redcar Station (¼ mile from the course).
By Air: Landing facilities at Turners Arms Farm (600yds runway) Yearby, Cleveland. 2 miles South of the racecourse - transport available. Teeside airport (18 miles west of Redcar).

RIPON (R.H)
Flat: A sharp, undulating, right-handed oval of 1m 5f, with a 5f run-in. There is also a 6f straight course.
Address: Ripon Racecourse, Boroughbridge Road, Ripon, North Yorkshire HG4 1UG Tel: (01765) 530530
Fax: (01765) 698900 E-mail: info@ripon-races.co.uk Website: www.ripon-races.co.uk
Clerk of the Course & Managing Director: James Hutchinson, Tel: (01765) 530530, Mobile (07860) 679904.
Raceday Fax: (01765) 603341
Going Reports: Tel: (01765) 603696 or Head Groundsman (07976) 960177
Stabling: Trainers requiring stabling (103 boxes available) are requested to contact Stable Manager prior to 12 noon the day before racing. Tel: (01765) 604135
By Road: The course is situated 2 miles South-East of the city, on the B6265. There is ample free parking for cars and coaches. For reservations apply to the Secretary.
By Rail: Harrogate Station (11 miles), or Thirsk (15 miles). Bus services to Ripon.
By Air: Helicopters only on the course. Otherwise Leeds/Bradford airport.

SALISBURY (R.H)
Flat: Right-handed and level, with a run-in of 4f. There is a straight 8f track. The last half mile is uphill, providing a stiff test of stamina.
Address: Salisbury Racecourse, Netherhampton, Salisbury, Wiltshire SP2 8PN Tel: (01722) 326461
Fax: (01722) 412710 Website: www.salisburyracecourse.co.uk
Clerk of the Course & General Manager: Jeremy Martin (07880) 744999
Going Reports: Contact Clerk of the Course as above
Stabling: Free stabling (114 boxes) and accommodation for lads and lasses, apply to the Stabling Manager (01722) 327327.
By Road: 3 miles South-West of the city on the A3094 at Netherhampton. Free car park adjoins the course.
By Rail: Salisbury Station is 3.5 miles (from London Waterloo). Bus service to the course.
By Air: Helicopter landing facility near the ten furlong start.

SANDOWN PARK(R.H)
Flat: An easy right-handed oval course of 1m 5f with a stiff straight uphill run-in of 4f. Separate straight 5f track is also uphill. Galloping.
N.H. Oval, 1m 5f (11) 220y run-in uphill. Features seven fences on the back straight, the last three (Railway Fences) are very close together and can often decide the outcome of races. The stiff uphill climb to the finish puts the emphasis very much on stamina, but accurate-jumping, free-running sorts are also favoured. Hurdle races are run on the Flat course.
Address: Sandown Park Racecourse, Esher, Surrey KT10 9AJ Tel: (01372) 464348 Fax: (01372) 470427
www.sandown.co.uk
Clerk of the Course: Andrew Cooper, Sandown Park, Esher, Surrey. Tel: (01372) 461213
Mobile: (07774) 230850.
Managing Director: David Mackinnon
Going Reports: (01372) 461212.
Stabling: 110 boxes. Free stabling and accommodation for lads and lasses. Tel: (01372) 463511.
By Road: 4 miles South-West of Kingston-on-Thames, on the A307 (M25 Junction 10).
By Rail: Esher Station (from Waterloo) adjoins the course.
By Air: London (Heathrow) Airport 12 miles.

SEDGEFIELD (L.H)
N.H. Oval, 1m 2f (8) 200y run-in: Hurdles 200y run-in. Undulating with fairly tight turns and does not suit the big, long-striding horse.
Address: Sedgefield Racecourse, Sedgefield, Stockton-on-Tees, Cleveland TS21 2HW
Tel: (01740) 621925 (Office) Fax: (01740) 620663 Website: www.sedgefield-racecourse.co.uk
Clerk of the Course: Charlie Moore Tel: (01287) 711233, Mobile (07764) 255500.
General Manager: Jill Williamson
Going Reports: Tel: (01740) 621925 or contact Clerk of the Course as above
Stabling: 116 boxes filled in rotation. No forage. Accommodation for horse attendants:
Tel: (01740) 621925

By Road: ³/₄ mile South-West of the town, near the junction of the A689 (Bishop Auckland) and the A177 (Durham) roads. The car park is free.
By Rail: Darlington Station (9 miles). Durham Station (12 miles).
By Air: Helicopter landing facility in car park area by prior arrangement only.

SOUTHWELL (L.H)

Flat, Turf: Tight left-handed track.
Flat, Fibresand: Left-handed oval, Fibresand course of 1m 2f with a 3f run-in. There is a straight 5f. Sharp and level, Southwell suits front-runners.
N.H. Oval, 1m 1f (7) 220y run-in. A tight, flat track with a short run-in, suits front-runners.
Address: Southwell Racecourse, Rolleston, Newark, Nottinghamshire NG25 0TS Tel: (01636) 814481
Fax: (01636) 812271 Website: www.southwell-racecourse.co.uk
Clerk of the Course: Roderick Duncan (07772) 958685
Managing Director: Dave Roberts
Going Reports: Contact Clerk of the Course as above.
Stabling: 113 boxes at the course. Applications for staff and horse accommodation to be booked by noon the day before racing on (01636) 814481.
By Road: The course is situated at Rolleston, 3 miles South of Southwell, 5 miles from Newark.
By Rail: Rolleston Station (Nottingham-Newark line) adjoins the course.
By Air: Helicopters can land by prior arrangement.

STRATFORD-ON-AVON (L.H)

N.H. Triangular, 1m 2f (8) 200y run-in. Virtually flat with two tight bends, and quite a short home straight. A sharp and turning course, Stratford-on-Avon suits the well-balanced, handy sort.
Address: Stratford Racecourse, Luddington Road, Stratford-upon-Avon, Warwickshire CV37 9SE
Tel: (01789) 267949 Fax: (01789) 415850 Website: www.stratfordracecourse.net
Clerk of the Course & Managing Director: Stephen Lambert. Mobile (07836) 384932. Home (01608) 674354
Assistant to Managing Director: Ilona Barnett
Going reports: Contact main office as above or Head Groundsman Tel: (07770) 623366.
Stabling: 89 boxes allotted on arrival. Advance notice must be given for overnight stays.
Tel: (01789) 267949.
By Road: 1 mile from the town centre, off the A429 (Evesham road).
By Rail: Stratford-on-Avon Station (from Birmingham New Street or Leamington Spa) 1 mile.
By Air: Helicopter landing facility by prior arrangement.

TAUNTON (R.H)

N.H. Elongated oval, 1m 2f (8) 150y run-in uphill. Sharp turns, especially after the winning post, with a steady climb from the home bend. Suits the handy sort.
Address: Taunton Racecourse, Orchard Portman, Taunton, Somerset TA3 7BL
Tel: (01823) 337172 (Office) Fax: (01823) 325881 Website: www.tauntonracecourse.co.uk
Clerk of the Course: Michael Trickey, The Racecourse, Taunton, Somerset TA3 7BL. Tel: (01823) 337172
General Manager: Bob Young
Going reports: Contact Clerk of the Course as above, or Head Groundsman (after 4.30pm) (07971) 695132.
Stabling: 90 boxes allotted on arrival. Advance bookings for long journeys.
Apply to the Stable Manager, c/o The Racecourse (01823) 337172
By Road: 2 miles South of the town on the B3170 (Honiton) road (M5 Junction 25).
By Rail: Taunton Station 2½ miles. There are buses and taxis to course.
By Air: Helicopter landing facility by prior arrangement.

THIRSK (L.H)

Flat: Left-handed, oval of 1m 2f with sharp turns and an undulating run-in of 4f. There is a straight 6f track.
Address: The Racecourse, Station Road, Thirsk, North Yorkshire YO7 1QL Tel: (01845) 522276
Fax: (01845) 525353. Website: www.thirskracecourse.net
Clerk of the Course: Christopher Tetley (07860) 919661
Going reports: Contact main office or Clerk of the Course as above
Club Secretary: Mr J McNaught
Stabling: 110 boxes. For stabling and accommodation apply to the Racecourse Tel: (01845) 522096
By Road: West of the town on the A61. Free car park adjacent to the course for buses and cars.
By Rail: Thirsk Station (from King's Cross). 1/2 mile from the course.

By Air: Helicopters can land by prior arrangement. Tel: Racecourse (01845) 522276.
Fixed wing aircraft can land at RAF Leeming. Tel: (01677) 423041.
Light aircraft at Bagby. Tel: (01845) 597385 or (01845) 537555.

TOWCESTER (R.H)

N.H. Square, 1m 6f (10) 200y run-in uphill. The final six furlongs are uphill. One of the most testing tracks in the country with the emphasis purely on stamina.
Address: The Racecourse, Easton Neston, Towcester, Northants NN12 7HS Tel: (01327) 353414
Fax: (01327) 358534 Website: www.towcester-racecourse.co.uk
Clerk of the Course: Robert Bellamy (07836) 241458
General Manager: Kevin Ackerman.
Going Reports: Tel: (01327) 353414 or contact Clerk of the Course as above.
Stabling: 101 stables in a new block. Allocated on arrival. Please contact racecourse in advance for overnight stabling / accommodation (01327) 350200.
By Road: 1 mile South-East of the town on the A5 (Milton Keynes road). M1 (Junction 15a).
By Rail: Northampton Station (Euston) 9 miles, buses to Towcester; or Milton Keynes (Euston) 12 miles, taxis available.
By Air: Helicopters can land by prior arrangement with the Racecourse Manager.

UTTOXETER (L.H)

N.H. Oval, 1m 2f (8) 170y run-in. A few undulations, easy bends and fences and a flat home straight of over half a mile. Suits front-runners, especially on the two mile hurdle course.
Address: The Racecourse, Wood Lane, Uttoxeter, Staffordshire ST14 8BD Tel: (01889) 562561
Fax: (01889) 562786 Website: www.uttoxeter-racecourse.co.uk
Clerk of the Course: Charlie Moore (07764) 255500
General Manager: David MacDonald
Going Reports: Contact main office or Clerk of the Course as above.
Stabling: 102 boxes, allotted on arrival. Tel: (01889) 562561. Overnight and Accommodation requirements must be notified in advance as no hostel at course.
By Road: South-East of the town off the B5017 (Marchington Road).
By Rail: Uttoxeter Station (Crewe-Derby line) adjoins the course.
By Air: Helicopters can land by prior arrangement with the raceday office.

WARWICK (L.H)

Flat: Left-handed, sharp, level track of 1m 6f 32y in circumference, with a run-in of two and a half furlongs.
N.H. Circular, 1m 6f (10) 240y run-in. Undulating with tight bends, five quick fences in the back straight and a short home straight, Warwick favours handiness and speed rather than stamina.
Address: Warwick Racecourse, Hampton Street, Warwick CV34 6HN Tel: (01926) 491553
Fax: (01926) 403223 Website: www.warwickracecourse.co.uk
Clerk of the Course: Sulekha Varma
Managing Director: Huw Williams
Going Reports: Contact main office or Clerk of the Course as above.
Stabling: 117 boxes allocated on arrival or by reservation (01926) 491553.
By Road: West of the town on the B4095 adjacent to Junction 15 of the M40.
By Rail: Warwick or Warwick Parkway Stations.
By Air: Helicopters can land by prior arrangement with the Clerk of the Course.

WETHERBY (L.H)

N.H. Oval, 1m 4f (9) 200y run-in slightly uphill. A flat, very fair course which suits the long-striding galloper.
Address: The Racecourse, York Road, Wetherby, LS22 5EJ Tel: (01937) 582035 Fax: (01937) 588021
Website: www.wetherbyracing.co.uk
Clerk of the Course & Chief Executive: Jonjo Sanderson (07831) 437453
Going reports: Tel: (01937) 582035, or Head Groundsman: (07880) 722586
Stabling: 91 boxes allocated on arrival. Accommodation available. Tel: (01937) 582035 or from 2pm day before racing (01937) 582074.
By Road: East of the town off the B1224 (York Road). Adjacent to the A1. Excellent bus and coach facilities. Car park free.
By Rail: Leeds Station 12 miles. Buses to Wetherby.
By Air: Helicopters can land by prior arrangement

WINCANTON (R.H)

N.H. Rectangular, 1m 3f (9) 200y run-in. Good galloping course where the going rarely becomes heavy. The home straight is mainly downhill.

Address: Wincanton Racecourse, Wincanton, Somerset BA9 8BJ Tel: (01963) 32344 Fax: (01963) 34668
Website: www.wincantonracecourse.co.uk

Clerk of the Course: Barry Johnson (07976) 791578

General Manager: Steve Parlett

Going Reports: Contact Racecourse Office as above.

Stabling: 94 boxes allocated on arrival, overnight accommodation must be booked in advance.
Apply to the Stable Manager, Wincanton Racecourse. Tel: (01963) 32344.

By Road: 1 mile North of the town on the B3081.

By Rail: Gillingham Station (from Waterloo) or Castle Cary Station (from Paddington). Buses and taxis to the course.

By Air: Helicopter landing area is situated in the centre of the course.

WINDSOR (Fig. 8)

Flat: Figure eight track of 1m 4f 110y. The course is level and sharp with a long run-in. The 6f course is essentially straight.

Address: Royal Windsor Racecourse, Maidenhead Road, Windsor, Berkshire SL4 5JJ Tel: (01753) 498400
Fax: (01753) 830156. Website: www.windsor-racecourse.co.uk

Clerk of the Course: To be Announced

Managing Director: Daniel Clark

Going Reports: Contact Clerk of the Course as above.

Stabling: 114 boxes available. Reservation required for overnight stay and accommodation only.
Tel: (07825) 603236 or (01753) 498405 (racedays).

By Road: North of the town on the A308 (M4 Junction 6).

By Rail: Windsor Central Station (from Paddington) or Windsor & Eton Riverside Station (from Waterloo).

By Air: London (Heathrow) Airport 15 minutes. Also White Waltham Airport (West London Aero Club) 15 minutes.

River Bus: 7 mins from Barry Avenue promenade at Windsor.

WOLVERHAMPTON (L.H)

Flat: Left-handed oval of 1m, with a run-in of 380y. A level track with sharp bends, the Polytrack surface, in use since October 2004, generally rides slower than that at Lingfield.

Address: Wolverhampton Racecourse, Dunstall Park, Gorsebrook Road, Wolverhampton WV6 0PE
Tel: (01902) 390000 Fax: (01902) 421621 Website: www.wolverhampton-racecourse.co.uk

Clerk of the Course: Fergus Cameron (07971) 531162

General Manager: Dave Roberts

Going Reports: Contact Main Office as above

Stabling: 103 boxes allotted on arrival. Applications for lads and lasses, and overnight stables must be made to Racecourse by noon on the day before racing. Tel: (07971) 531162. Fax: (01902) 421621.

By Road: 1 mile North of city on the A449 (M54 Junction 2 or M6 Junction 12). Car parking free of charge.

By Rail: Wolverhampton Station (from Euston) 1 mile.

By Air: Halfpenny Green Airport 8 miles.

WORCESTER (L.H)

N.H. Elongated oval, 1m 5f (9) 220y run-in. Flat with easy turns, Worcester is a very fair, galloping track.

Address: Worcester Racecourse, Pitchcroft, Worcester WR1 3EJ Tel: (01905) 25364 Fax: (01905) 617563
Website: www.worcester-racecourse.co.uk

Clerk of the Course: Fergus Cameron (07971) 531162.

Managing Director: Dave Roberts (01905) 25364.

Going Reports: Contact Clerk of the Course as above, or (01905) 25364 (racedays).

Stabling: 97 boxes allotted on arrival. Overnight accommodation for lads and lasses in Worcester.
Tel: (01905) 25364 Fax: (01905) 617563.

By Road: West of the city off the A449 (Kidderminster road) (M5 Junc 8).

By Rail: Foregate Street Station, Worcester (from Paddington) ¾ mile.

By Air: Helicopter landing facility in the centre of the course, by prior arrangement only.

YARMOUTH (L.H)
Flat: Left-handed, level circuit of 1m 4f, with a run-in of 5f. The straight course is 8f long.
Address: The Racecourse, Jellicoe Road, Great Yarmouth, Norfolk NR30 4AU Tel: (01493) 842527
Fax: (01493) 843254 Website: www.greatyarmouth-racecourse.co.uk
Clerk of the Course: Richard Aldous (07738) 507643
General Manager: Glenn Tubby
Going Reports: Contact Main Office or Clerk of the Course as above
Stabling: 127 boxes available. Allocated on arrival. Tel: (01493) 855651 (racedays only) or racecourse office.
By Road: 1 mile East of town centre (well sign-posted from A47 & A12).
By Rail: Great Yarmouth Station (1 mile). Bus service to the course.
By Air: Helicopter landing available by prior arrangement with Racecourse Office

YORK (L.H)
Flat: Left-handed, level, galloping track, with a straight 6f. There is also an adjoining course of 6f 214y.
Address: The Racecourse, York YO23 1EX Tel: (01904) 683932 Fax: (01904) 611071
Website: www.yorkracecourse.co.uk
Clerk of the Course and Chief Executive: William Derby (07812) 961176
Assistant Clerk of the Course: Anthea Morshead
Going Reports: Contact (01904) 683932 or Clerk of the Course as above.
Stabling: 177 boxes available Tel: (01904) 706317 (Racedays) or (07712) 676434.
By Road: 1 mile South-East of the city on the A1036.
By Rail: 1½ miles York Station (from King's Cross). Special bus service from station to the course.
By Air: Light aircraft and helicopter landing facilities available at Rufforth aerodrome (5,000ft tarmac runway). £20 landing fee-transport arranged to course. Leeds/Bradford airport (25 miles).

THE INVESTEC DERBY (CLASS 1)
EPSOM, SATURDAY JUNE 2ND

HORSE	TRAINER	HORSE	TRAINER
A'JUBA	Saeed bin Suroor	CHENDIYR (FR)	A. de Royer Dupre, France
AAZIF (IRE)	John Dunlop	CHERRY STREET	Andrew Balding
ACCREDIT (IRE)	Mahmood Al Zarooni	CHEVIOT QUEST (IRE)	William Jarvis
ACT OF WAR (IRE)	Aidan O'Brien, Ireland	CHICAGO (IRE)	Aidan O'Brien, Ireland
ACTOR (IRE)	Jeremy Noseda	CHOLESKY (IRE)	John M. Oxx, Ireland
AEGAEUS	Ed Dunlop	CITY OF CANTON (IRE)	Luca Cumani
AFTER THE STORM	Aidan O'Brien, Ireland	COLONSAY (USA)	
AIRD SNOUT (USA)	David Simcock	COMMEND	Sir Michael Stoute
ALBAYAN (IRE)	Saeed bin Suroor	COMMON CENTS	Ronald Harris
ALBION	A. Fabre, France	CONTINUUM	Sir Henry Cecil
ALEKSANDAR	Luca Cumani	COSMO BELLE AME	M. Saito, Japan
ALFAATEH (USA)	Brian Meehan	COTTESMORE (USA)	Mahmood Al Zarooni
ALINDJAR (IRE)	John M. Oxx, Ireland	COUNSEL (IRE)	Sir Michael Stoute
ALIZARI (IRE)	John M. Oxx, Ireland	COUNTERSIGN	Mahmood Al Zarooni
ALJAMAAHEER (IRE)	Roger Varian	CRANACH	A. Fabre, France
ALL THAT RULES	Sir Henry Cecil	CROPLEY (IRE)	John M. Oxx, Ireland
ALMAAS (USA)	Saeed bin Suroor	CRYING WOLF (USA)	Mahmood Al Zarooni
AL MAMZAR (IRE)	David Simcock	CRYSTAL MONARCH (IRE)	Sir Henry Cecil
ALMOST GEMINI (IRE)	Roger Varian	DALIANCE (IRE)	Tom Dascombe
ALMUFTARRIS (USA)	Ed Dunlop	DANDY (GER)	Andrew Balding
AL NAWRAS	F. Head, France	DANEKING	John Gosden
AL SAHAM	Saeed bin Suroor	DARIEN (FR)	A. de Royer Dupre, France
ALSHMEMI (USA)	John Gosden	DAVID LIVINGSTON (IRE)	Aidan O'Brien, Ireland
AMIENS	Aidan O'Brien, Ireland	DAWERANN (IRE)	John M. Oxx, Ireland
AMIRA'S PRINCE (IRE)	David Wachman, Ireland	DELTA SCUTI (USA)	P. Bary, France
ANGEL GABRIAL (IRE)	Ian Williams	DESERT PHILOSOPHER	Kevin Ryan
APOLLO (IRE)	Aidan O'Brien, Ireland	DREAM TUNE	Clive Cox
APOLLO ELEVEN (IRE)	A. de Royer Dupre, France	DR YES (FR)	Sir Henry Cecil
ARCTIC GALAXY (CAN)	John Gosden	DUBAWI ISLAND (FR)	Mahmood Al Zarooni
ASTROLOGY (IRE)	Aidan O'Brien, Ireland	DYNASTIC	Richard Hannon
ATHENS (IRE)	Aidan O'Brien, Ireland	EAST MEETS WEST (IRE)	Aidan O'Brien, Ireland
AUTHENTICATION	Mark Johnston	EBAZAN (USA)	John M. Oxx, Ireland
AUTUMNUS (IRE)	Mahmood Al Zarooni	EDUCATE	Mahmood Al Zarooni
BALTY BOYS (IRE)	Charles Hills	EHKAM (USA)	Saeed bin Suroor
BASSETERRE (IRE)	Charles Hills	EHTEDAAM (USA)	Saeed bin Suroor
BATTLE OF SARATOGA (IRE)	Aidan O'Brien, Ireland	EL GRECO (IRE)	Sir Michael Stoute
BENBECULA	William Haggas	ELLAAL	Charles Hills
BIOGRAPHER	David Lanigan	EL NAMOOSE	Saeed bin Suroor
BISHOP'S CASTLE (USA)	Mark Johnston	ELTIFAAT (IRE)	Sir Michael Stoute
BOHEMIAN RHAPSODY (IRE)	J. W. Hills	ELYASSAAT	Roger Varian
BONANZA	Aidan O'Brien, Ireland	EMIRATES ECHO	David Simcock
BONFIRE	Andrew Balding	ENCKE (USA)	Mahmood Al Zarooni
BORDONI (USA)	Mark Johnston	ENCRYPTED MESSAGE (IRE)	D. K. Weld, Ireland
BORN TO SEA (IRE)	John M. Oxx, Ireland	ENERGIA EROI (FR)	P. Bary, France
BRIDGEHAMPTON	Michael Bell	ENERGIZE (FR)	Richard Hannon
BROCKWELL	Tom Dascombe	ENGLISH NIGHT (IRE)	John M. Oxx, Ireland
BUCKINGHAM GATE (IRE)	Aidan O'Brien, Ireland	ENGROSSING	David Elsworth
BURNHAM	Hughie Morrison	ENTIFAADHA	William Haggas
BUSTER BROWN (IRE)	James Given	EQUALIZER	Tom Dascombe
CALGACUS (IRE)	D. K. Weld, Ireland	ERNEST HEMINGWAY (IRE)	Aidan O'Brien, Ireland
CALL TO BATTLE (IRE)	John M. Oxx, Ireland	ESHAAB (USA)	Ed Dunlop
CAMELOT	Aidan O'Brien, Ireland	ESTEBSAAL (IRE)	John Dunlop
CAMERON HIGHLAND (IRE)	Roger Varian	EUROPE (IRE)	Mahmood Al Zarooni
CANARY WHARF (IRE)	Marco Botti	EXACT	Aidan O'Brien, Ireland
CAPTIVITY	Mark Johnston	EXTERMINATE (IRE)	E. Lynam, Ireland
CARDINAL WALTER (IRE)	David Simcock	EXTREMELY ALERT	Michael Bell
CASTILO DEL DIABLO (IRE)	David Simcock	FA'IZ (IRE)	
CAVALEIRO (IRE)	Marcus Tregoning	FALKLAND (IRE)	John Gosden
CAYUGA	Sir Michael Stoute	FARHAAN (USA)	John Dunlop
CHAMONIX (IRE)	Aidan O'Brien, Ireland	FAST OR FREE	William Haggas
CHAPELLE DU ROI (USA)	David Lanigan	FATHER OF SCIENCE (IRE)	Aidan O'Brien, Ireland

HORSE	TRAINER	HORSE	TRAINER
FENCING (USA)	John Gosden	LOOPDELOO (IRE)	E. Lynam, Ireland
FENNELL BAY (IRE)	Mark Johnston	LOTHIAN SKY (IRE)	William Jarvis
FILATORE (IRE)		LUCANIN	Sir Michael Stoute
FORGOTTEN HERO (IRE)	Charles Hills	LUNAYIR (FR)	A. de Royer Dupre, France
FORT SAM HOUSTON	Aidan O'Brien, Ireland	MAAKIRR (IRE)	Roger Varian
FRASERS HILL	Roger Varian	MAIMON (IRE)	
FRONTIER (GER)	Aidan O'Brien, Ireland	MANALIVE (IRE)	J. S. Bolger, Ireland
FULL SWING	Roger Varian	MANDOUR (USA)	A. de Royer Dupre, France
FURNER'S GREEN (IRE)	Aidan O'Brien, Ireland	MANKINI (IRE)	Luca Cumani
FUTURE SECURITY (IRE)	Saeed bin Suroor	MANNHEIM (IRE)	Aidan O'Brien, Ireland
GABRIAL'S KING (IRE)	Ian Williams	MANUKA (IRE)	Sir Michael Stoute
GABRIAL THE GREAT (IRE)	Michael Bell	MARCHESE MARCONI (IRE)	Aidan O'Brien, Ireland
GHOSTLY BRIGHT (USA)		MARINER'S CROSS (IRE)	Mahmood Al Zarooni
GINGERNUT	John Gosden	MARSHGATE LANE (USA)	Mahmood Al Zarooni
GLADIATOR KING (IRE)	Aidan O'Brien, Ireland	MARTIN CHUZZLEWIT (IRE)	Sir Michael Stoute
GOLDIROCKS (IRE)	J. S. Bolger, Ireland	MATAIEA	A. de Royer Dupre, France
GOLD RALLY (USA)	Mahmood Al Zarooni	MAWASEM	Sir Michael Stoute
GOOD OF LUCK	Mick Channon	METALMARK (IRE)	
GRANDILOQUENT	Sir Michael Stoute	MEZMAAR	Charles Hills
GREATEST (IRE)	Sir Michael Stoute	MICHELANGELO	John Gosden
GREAT RULER (USA)	Aidan O'Brien, Ireland	MICKDAAM (IRE)	
GREAT SOPRANO (USA)	David Simcock	MIGHTY AMBITION (USA)	Mahmood Al Zarooni
GREAT TIMES (GER)	Saeed bin Suroor	MINIMISE RISK	Andrew Balding
GREEN LEGACY (USA)	Amanda Perrett	MINORITY INTEREST	Sir Michael Stoute
GUEST OF HONOUR (IRE)	Marco Botti	MISTER BOB (GER)	James Bethell
HABESH (IRE)	M. Halford, Ireland	MOONSHED (USA)	D. K. Weld, Ireland
HAIL (IRE)	Aidan O'Brien, Ireland	MOONSHIP	Sir Michael Stoute
HAJRAS (IRE)	Mark Johnston	MOSHAAGIB (USA)	John Gosden
HALLING'S QUEST	Hughie Morrison	MR MOONLIGHT (IRE)	J. E. Pease, France
HANDAZAN (IRE)	John M. Oxx, Ireland	MUBARAZA (IRE)	John Dunlop
HANDSOME MAN (IRE)	Saeed bin Suroor	MUHAMEE (IRE)	Saeed bin Suroor
HANDSOME RANSOM	John Gosden	MUHARRER	Marcus Tregoning
HANSEATIC	John Gosden	MUKHADRAM	William Haggas
HAYMARKET	Mark Johnston	MULHEB (USA)	D. K. Weld, Ireland
HIGHFLYING (IRE)	Aidan O'Brien, Ireland	MUSTAKSHIF	J. E. Hammond, France
HIGH STRATOS	Luca Cumani	MUTAALEQ (IRE)	Roger Varian
HIT THE JACKPOT (IRE)	D. K. Weld, Ireland	MUTAAWED (USA)	F. Chappet, France
HOMERIC (IRE)	Ed Dunlop	MUTARJIM (USA)	Saeed bin Suroor
IBTAHAJ	Saeed bin Suroor	MUTASADDER (USA)	Roger Varian
IFFRAAM (IRE)	Michael Dods	MY DESTINATION (IRE)	Mahmood Al Zarooni
I HAVE A DREAM	Aidan O'Brien, Ireland	MYSTERIOUS MAN (IRE)	Andrew Balding
IMPERIAL MONARCH (IRE)	Aidan O'Brien, Ireland	MYSTICAL WIND (IRE)	Aidan O'Brien, Ireland
INNER PATH (USA)	J. E. Pease, France	NARCISSIST (IRE)	Ed Dunlop
INTHAR (USA)	Saeed bin Suroor	NASHVILLE (IRE)	David Wachman, Ireland
INVISIBLE HUNTER (USA)	Saeed bin Suroor	NAVARRE	A. Fabre, France
IPTISAM	Mahmood Al Zarooni	NEPHRITE	Aidan O'Brien, Ireland
JARRAH		NEVER ANOTHER (USA)	A. Fabre, France
JUNGLE BEAT (IRE)	John Gosden	NEW YOUMZAIN (FR)	Mick Channon
JUPITER STORM	Gary Moore	NIGHT FLASH (GER)	James Given
KALAJAR (USA)	John M. Oxx, Ireland	NOAH WEBSTER (IRE)	Aidan O'Brien, Ireland
KALIK (FR)	A. de Royer Dupre, France	NOBLE MISSION	Sir Henry Cecil
KASHGAR	Michael Bell	NO DOMINION (IRE)	James Given
KIZIL (FR)	A. de Royer Dupre, France	OBBOORR	Roger Varian
KINGLET (USA)	Mahmood Al Zarooni	OFFER (IRE)	Aidan O'Brien, Ireland
KING OF DUDES	Sir Henry Cecil	OMAR KHAYYAM	Andrew Balding
KING OF THE PICTS (IRE)	E. Lynam, Ireland	OPINION (IRE)	Sir Michael Stoute
KIWAYU	Luca Cumani	OPTIMIST (IRE)	David Wachman, Ireland
LAGO MINTO	A. de Royer Dupre, France	OPUS (IRE)	Amanda Perrett
LAHAAG	John Gosden	ORDER (IRE)	Aidan O'Brien, Ireland
LAST TRAIN	A. Fabre, France	OSCAN (USA)	Mahmood Al Zarooni
LAWN JAMIL (USA)	Charles Hills	PACIFIC HEIGHTS (IRE)	Tim Pitt
LEARN (IRE)	Aidan O'Brien, Ireland	PADDYFROMMENLO (IRE)	J. W. Hills
LEBRON (IRE)	Aidan O'Brien, Ireland	PARAMYTHI (IRE)	Luca Cumani
LEO LUNA	Sir Michael Stoute	PARISH HALL (IRE)	J. S. Bolger, Ireland
LEQQAA (USA)	Mark Johnston	PEMBREY	Mahmood Al Zarooni
LEYLAND (IRE)	H. Hotger, Germany	PERENNIAL	Charles Hills
LIONROCK (FR)	Mark Johnston	PERFECT HEART	

HORSE	TRAINER
PETITE NOBLESSE (FR)	Aidan O'Brien, Ireland
PISTOL (IRE)	Sir Michael Stoute
PLACE VENDOME (IRE)	Aidan O'Brien, Ireland
PRINCE OF ORANGE (IRE)	Mahmood Al Zarooni
PRIVATE TREASURE (IRE)	Aidan O'Brien, Ireland
PULVERIZE (USA)	Sir Michael Stoute
PURPLE BAY (IRE)	Mahmood Al Zarooni
RAWAAFED (IRE)	Brian Meehan
REGENCY (GER)	Sir Henry Cecil
REIGNS OF GLORY (IRE)	Richard Hannon
REPRESENTATION (USA)	Mahmood Al Zarooni
ROCKALONG (IRE)	Luca Cumani
ROCK OF AGES	Jeremy Noseda
ROCK SONG	Amanda Perrett
ROCK SUPREME (IRE)	Richard Hannon
ROSERROW	Andrew Balding
ROYAL EMPIRE (IRE)	Saeed bin Suroor
RUBRICS (IRE)	Luca Cumani
RUGGED CROSS	Henry Candy
RULE BOOK (IRE)	Richard Hannon
RYE HOUSE (IRE)	Sir Michael Stoute
SADMA	Saeed bin Suroor
SCARABOCIO	Peter Chapple-Hyam
SCOTTISH VESPERS (IRE)	Sir Michael Stoute
SCRUPUL (IRE)	Luca Cumani
SEA FEVER (IRE)	Luca Cumani
SEASON SPIRIT	James Given
SECRETARY OF STATE (IRE)	Aidan O'Brien, Ireland
SECRET ENVOY	Luca Cumani
SEPTENARIUS (USA)	Sir Henry Cecil
SEVENTH SIGN	William Haggas
SHADARPOUR (IRE)	A. de Royer Dupre, France
SHAIYZAR (IRE)	John M. Oxx, Ireland
SHALAMAN (IRE)	John M. Oxx, Ireland
SHAMSIKHAN (IRE)	A. de Royer Dupre, France
SHANTARAM	John Gosden
SHARENI (IRE)	John M. Oxx, Ireland
SHIELD (IRE)	Aidan O'Brien, Ireland
SHIHAB (IRE)	Saeed bin Suroor
SHUJA (USA)	Saeed bin Suroor
SIDEREUS NUNCIUS (IRE)	Aidan O'Brien, Ireland
SIR GRAHAM WADE (IRE)	Mark Johnston
SKY KHAN	Ed Dunlop
SKYPHOS (IRE)	Aidan O'Brien, Ireland
SMOKING SUN (USA)	P. Bary, France
SONDEDURO	Jamie Osborne
SOUTHERLY	Luca Cumani
SOVIET DREAM	James Fanshawe
SPACIOUS SKY (USA)	J. E. Pease, France
SPEAKING OF WHICH (IRE)	D. K. Weld, Ireland
SPORTING GOLD (IRE)	Roger Varian
STAR FOR LIFE (USA)	Mikael Magnusson
STENCIVE	William Haggas
STORMBOUND (IRE)	Paul Cole
SUBORDINATE (GER)	Mark Johnston
SUN CENTRAL (USA)	William Haggas
SUNEAGLE (IRE)	P. J. Prendergast, Ireland
SUPREME ROCK	Jim Boyle
SURAJ	Michael Bell
SWITZERLAND (IRE)	Mark Johnston
SWNYMOR (IRE)	William Haggas
SYNCHRONICITY (IRE)	Richard Hannon
TADMIR (USA)	Saeed bin Suroor
TAIGAN (USA)	Aidan O'Brien, Ireland
TAJAMAL (IRE)	Saeed bin Suroor
TAJAWWUB (USA)	Charles Hills
TAKAR (IRE)	John M. Oxx, Ireland

HORSE	TRAINER
TAMARRUD	Saeed bin Suroor
TASRIH (USA)	Saeed bin Suroor
TENTH STAR (IRE)	Aidan O'Brien, Ireland
THAT'S PLENTY (IRE)	Tracey Collins, Ireland
THE LOST LEGION (IRE)	D. K. Weld, Ireland
THETURNOFTHESUN (IRE)	John Gosden
THOMAS CHIPPENDALE (IRE)	Sir Henry Cecil
THOMAS DYLAN (IRE)	J. S. Bolger, Ireland
THOMASGAINSBOROUGH (IRE)	Aidan O'Brien, Ireland
THOUGHT WORTHY (USA)	John Gosden
TIBET (IRE)	Aidan O'Brien, Ireland
TIMAROUN (USA)	John M. Oxx, Ireland
TOKYO BROWN (USA)	Heather Main
TOP BILLING	John Gosden
TOP OFFER	Roger Charlton
TOTALLY DOMINANT (USA)	Richard Hannon
TOTOM CHIEF	Gay Kelleway
TOWER ROCK (IRE)	Aidan O'Brien, Ireland
TREASURE THE RIDGE (IRE)	D. K. Weld, Ireland
TREND IS MY FRIEND (USA)	Amanda Perrett
TRIUMPHANT (IRE)	Aidan O'Brien, Ireland
TROON (FR)	A. de Royer Dupre, France
UMAYYAD (IRE)	John Gosden
UNANIMOUS (IRE)	Aidan O'Brien, Ireland
UNEX MICHELANGELO (IRE)	John Gosden
UNIVERSAL (IRE)	Mahmood Al Zarooni
URIAH HEEP (FR)	Sir Michael Stoute
URSA MAJOR (IRE)	
USTURA (USA)	Saeed bin Suroor
UTOPIAN	Luca Cumani
UTTERANCE	John Gosden
VALIANT	William Haggas
VALIDUS	Luca Cumani
VAN ELLIS	Mark Johnston
VEDANI (IRE)	John M. Oxx, Ireland
VENEGAZZU (IRE)	Peter Chapple-Hyam
VIGIL (IRE)	Aidan O'Brien, Ireland
VITALIZE	Luca Cumani
WAFOUD	Saeed bin Suroor
WARCROWN (IRE)	Richard Fahey
WARWICK AVENUE (IRE)	Aidan O'Brien, Ireland
WAVING	John M. Oxx, Ireland
WEAAM (IRE)	Marcus Tregoning
WHITE NILE (IRE)	D. K. Weld, Ireland
WIMPOLE STREET (IRE)	Aidan O'Brien, Ireland
WINDSOR PARK (IRE)	Aidan O'Brien, Ireland
WROTE (IRE)	Aidan O'Brien, Ireland
WROTHAM HEATH	Sir Henry Cecil
WYBORNE	A. Fabre, France
ZALANTOUN (IRE)	John M. Oxx, Ireland
ZARKALAN (IRE)	A. de Royer Dupre, France
ZAROUD (IRE)	John M. Oxx, Ireland
ZELAMAR (FR)	A. de Royer Dupre, France
EX ADORATION (USA)	Sir Michael Stoute
EX EXHIBIT ONE (USA)	
EX IRJA	J. R. Jenkins
EX ISUZU DREAM (JPN)	
EX KESTREL QUEST (USA)	
EX LADY ELGAR (IRE)	Ed Dunlop
EX POLICALLE (FR)	
EX VADAPOLINA (FR)	A. de Royer Dupre, France

THE BET AT BLUESQ.COM
EUROPEAN FREE HANDICAP
NEWMARKET CRAVEN MEETING 2012
(ON THE ROWLEY MILE COURSE)
WEDNESDAY APRIL 18TH

The Bet at Bluesq.com European Free Handicap (Class 1) (Listed race) with total prize fund of £30,000 for two-year-olds only of 2011 which are included in the European 2-y-o Thoroughbred Rankings or which, in 2011, either ran in Great Britain or ran for a trainer who at the time was licensed by the British Horseracing Authority, and are Rated 100 or above; lowest weight 7st 12lbs; highest weight 9st 7lbs. Penalty for a winner after December 31st 2011, 5 lbs. Seven furlongs.

Rating		st	lb	Rating		st	lb
119	CAMELOT (GB)	9	7	110	FARRAAJ (IRE)	8	12
119	DABIRSIM (FR)	9	7	110	NEPHRITE (GB)	8	12
117	DADDY LONG LEGS (USA)	9	5	110	REPLY (IRE)	8	12
117	HARBOUR WATCH (IRE)	9	5	110	REQUINTO (IRE)	8	12
117	PARISH HALL (IRE)	9	5	110	ROGER SEZ (IRE)	8	12
117	POWER (GB)	9	5	110	SAIGON (GB)	8	12
116	DRAGON PULSE (IRE)	9	4	110	TENTH STAR (IRE)	8	12
116	ELUSIVE KATE (USA)	9	4	110	WADING (IRE)	8	12
116	MANDAEAN (GB)	9	4	109	BAPAK CHINTA (USA)	8	11
116	MAYBE (IRE)	9	4	109	BURWAAZ (GB)	8	11
115	BEST TERMS (GB)	9	3	109	DISCOURSE (USA)	8	11
115	MOST IMPROVED (IRE)	9	3	109	FACTORY TIME (IRE)	8	11
115	WROTE (IRE)	9	3	109	REDACT (IRE)	8	11
114	BRONTERRE (GB)	9	2	109	ROCKINANTE (FR)	8	11
114	CASPAR NETSCHER (GB)	9	2	109	ROMAN SOLDIER (IRE)	8	11
114	DAVID LIVINGSTON (IRE)	9	2	109	SHUMOOS (USA)	8	11
114	LA COLLINA (IRE)	9	2	109	SPIRITUAL STAR (IRE)	8	11
114	TRUMPET MAJOR (IRE)	9	2	109	SUNDAY TIMES (GB)	8	11
113	AKEED MOFEED (GB)	9	1	108	ASTROLOGY (IRE)	8	10
113	CRIUS (IRE)	9	1	108	BONFIRE (GB)	8	10
113	CRUSADE (USA)	9	1	108	GAMILATI (GB)	8	10
113	FRENCH FIFTEEN (FR)	9	1	108	LEARN (IRE)	8	10
113	FURNER'S GREEN (IRE)	9	1	108	STEPPER POINT (GB)	8	10
112	ABTAAL (USA)	9	0	107	ENTIFAADHA (GB)	8	9
112	LYRIC OF LIGHT (GB)	9	0	107	TALWAR (IRE)	8	9
112	RED DUKE (USA)	9	0	107	WEST LEAKE DIMAN (IRE)	8	9
112	RESTIADARGENT (FR)	9	0	106	ANGELS WILL FALL (IRE)	8	8
112	SOFAST (FR)	9	0	106	BOGART (GB)	8	8
112	TAI CHI (GER)	9	0	106	FORT BASTION (IRE)	8	8
112	TOUGH AS NAILS (IRE)	9	0	106	NAYARRA (IRE)	8	8
112	ZIP TOP (IRE)	9	0	106	PIMPERNEL (IRE)	8	8
111	CHANDLERY (IRE)	8	13	106	ST BARTHS (GB)	8	8
111	FALLEN FOR YOU (GB)	8	13	106	TELL DAD (GB)	8	8
111	FAMILY ONE (FR)	8	13	105	B FIFTY TWO (IRE)	8	7
111	FENCING (USA)	8	13	105	BOOMERANG BOB (IRE)	8	7
111	FIRE LILY (IRE)	8	13	105	CHARLES THE GREAT (IRE)	8	7
111	FREDERICK ENGELS (GB)	8	13	105	COUPE DE VILLE (IRE)	8	7
111	LIGHTENING PEARL (IRE)	8	13	105	GRAY PEARL (GB)	8	7
111	LILBOURNE LAD (IRE)	8	13	105	GUSTO (GB)	8	7
111	SALURE (GB)	8	13	105	LETHAL FORCE (IRE)	8	7
111	SAMITAR (GB)	8	13	105	LETSGOROUNDAGAIN (IRE)	8	7
111	VENETO (FR)	8	13	105	PERENNIAL (GB)	8	7
110	BALTY BOYS (IRE)	8	12	105	PONTY ACCLAIM (IRE)	8	7
110	BANNOCK (IRE)	8	12	104	CALEDONIA LADY (GB)	8	6

Rating		st	lb	Rating		st	lb
104	CHUNKY DIAMOND (IRE)	8	6	101	ARTISTIC JEWEL (IRE)	8	3
104	FALLS OF LORA (IRE)	8	6	101	BAYLEYF (IRE)	8	3
104	RUSSELLIANA (GB)	8	6	101	FIRDAWS (USA)	8	3
104	VOCATIONAL (USA)	8	6	101	MEHDI (IRE)	8	3
103	CALEDONIAN SPRING (IRE)	8	5	101	QUESTING (GB)	8	3
103	EUREKA (IRE)	8	5	101	ZUMBI (IRE)	8	3
103	FOXTROT ROMEO (IRE)	8	5	100	CROWN DEPENDENCY (IRE)	8	2
103	MISS WORK OF ART (GB)	8	5	100	DIJARVO (GB)	8	2
103	SILVERHEELS (IRE)	8	5	100	EKTIHAAM (IRE)	8	2
103	STONEFIELD FLYER (GB)	8	5	100	FARHAAN (USA)	8	2
102	ALSINDI (IRE)	8	4	100	GABRIAL THE KING (USA)	8	2
102	BANA WU (GB)	8	4	100	HAZAZ (IRE)	8	2
102	GATEPOST (IRE)	8	4	100	JANEY MUDDLES (IRE)	8	2
102	INETROBIL (IRE)	8	4	100	KINGLET (USA)	8	2
102	JUSTINEO (GB)	8	4	100	MISS LAHAR (GB)	8	2
102	REGAL REALM (GB)	8	4	100	PRODUCER (GB)	8	2
102	WHIP RULE (IRE)	8	4	100	TELWAAR (GB)	8	2

WORLD THOROUGHBRED RANKINGS

for three-year-olds rated 115 or greater by the International Federation of Horseracing Authorities. Horses rated 110 to 114 are not part of the World Rankings but have been rated by the European Pattern Committee

Rating	Trained
136 FRANKEL (GB)	GB
128 DANEDREAM (GER)	GER
126 DREAM AHEAD (USA)	GB
126 EXCELEBRATION (IRE)	GB
126 NATHANIEL (IRE)	GB
123 ORFEVRE (JPN)	JPN
123 SEPOY (AUS)	AUS
123 STRONG SUIT (USA)	GB
122 CALEB'S POSSE (USA)	USA
122 MEANDRE (FR)	FR
122 POUR MOI (IRE)	FR
122 RELIABLE MAN (GB)	FR
121 ANIMAL KINGDOM (USA)	USA
121 ATLANTIC JEWEL (AUS)	AUS
121 IMMORTAL VERSE (IRE)	FR
121 MASKED MARVEL (GB)	GB
121 SEA MOON (GB)	GB
121 SHACKLEFORD (USA)	USA
121 UNCLE MO (USA)	USA
120 GALIKOVA (FR)	FR
120 MISTY FOR ME (IRE)	IRE
120 RULER ON ICE (USA)	USA
120 SHARETA (IRE)	FR
120 TREASURE BEACH (GB)	IRE
119 BEATEN UP (GB)	GB
119 BRILLIANT SPEED (USA)	USA
119 CARLTON HOUSE (USA)	GB
119 HELMET (AUS)	AUS
119 ROYAL DELTA (USA)	USA
119 SEVILLE (GER)	IRE
118 BUBBLE CHIC (FR)	FR
118 COIL (USA)	USA
118 GOLDEN LILAC (IRE)	FR
118 MANAWANUI (AUS)	AUS
118 MOONLIGHT CLOUD (GB)	FR
118 STAY THIRSTY (USA)	USA
118 TO HONOR AND SERVE (USA)	USA
118 TOGETHER (IRE)	IRE
118 TURBULENT DESCENT (USA)	USA
118 VARIETY CLUB (SAF)	SAF
118 ZOFFANY (IRE)	IRE
117 ASTROLOGY (USA)	USA
117 BLUE BUNTING (USA)	GB
117 CENSUS (IRE)	GB
117 CRACKERJACK KING (IRE)	ITY
117 DANCING RAIN (IRE)	GB
117 DIALED IN (USA)	USA
117 DUBAWI GOLD (GB)	GB
117 IT'S TRICKY (USA)	USA
117 MEMPHIS TENNESSEE (IRE)	IRE
117 MR COMMONS (USA)	USA
117 MUTUAL TRUST (GB)	FR
117 NAHRAIN (GB)	GB
117 PLUM PRETTY (USA)	USA
117 R HEAT LIGHTNING (USA)	USA
117 RODERIC O'CONNOR (IRE)	IRE

Rating	Trained
117 SUPER EASY (NZ)	SIN
117 THE FACTOR (USA)	USA
117 VADAMAR (FR)	FR
117 WILBURN (USA)	USA
117 WIN VARIATION (JPN)	JPN
117 ZAZU (USA)	USA
116 BROWN PANTHER (GB)	GB
116 EARL OF TINSDAL (GER)	GER
116 FLASHPOINT (USA)	USA/USA
116 MOSHEEN (AUS)	AUS
116 MUCHO MACHO MAN (USA)	USA
116 NATIVE KHAN (FR)	GB
116 NEHRO (USA)	USA
116 PREMIER PEGASUS (USA)	USA
116 REAL IMPACT (JPN)	JPN
116 SANGSTER (NZ)	NZ
116 SLOW PACE (USA)	FR
116 SMART MISSILE (AUS)	AUS
116 STREAMA (AUS)	AUS
116 WALDPARK (GER)	GER
116 WINTER MEMORIES (USA)	USA
115 ARCHARCHARCH (USA)	USA
115 AVENTURA (JPN)	JPN
115 AWESOME FEATHER (USA)	USA
115 BARAAN (FR)	FR
115 COLOMBIAN (IRE)	GB
115 FOXWEDGE (AUS)	AUS
115 INDUNA (AUS)	AUS
115 MANIEREE (IRE)	IRE
115 MARKETING MIX (CAN)	USA
115 MASTER OF HOUNDS (USA)	IRE
115 MIDNIGHT INTERLUDE (USA)	USA
115 NEEBRAS (IRE)	GB
115 PISCO SOUR (USA)	GB
115 RATTLESNAKE BRIDGE (USA)	USA
115 SADDLER'S ROCK (IRE)	IRE
115 SOLDAT (USA)	USA
115 ST JOHN'S RIVER (USA)	USA
115 SURFRIDER (IRE)	FR
115 TESTOSTERONE (IRE)	FR
115 TIN HORSE (IRE)	FR
114 ARRIGO (GER)	GER
114 BANIMPIRE (IRE)	IRE
114 BIBLE BELT (IRE)	IRE
114 CAZALS (IRE)	ITY
114 GLORIOUS SIGHT (IRE)	FR
114 MARGOT DID (GB)	GB
114 ORACLE (IRE)	IRE
114 QUEST FOR PEACE (IRE)	GB
114 SANDY'S CHARM (FR)	FR
114 TAZAHUM (USA)	USA
113 DREAM PEACE (IRE)	FR
113 DUBAI PRINCE (IRE)	GB
113 GLASWEGIAN (GB)	FR
113 LAUGHING LASHES (USA)	IRE
113 RECITAL (FR)	IRE

Rating	Age	Trained
113 SNEAK A PEEK (ITY)		ITY
113 WESTERN ARISTOCRAT (USA)		GB
113 WILD COCO (GER)		GB
113 WONDER OF WONDERS (USA)		IRE
112 AL KAZEEM (GB)		GB
112 CASAMENTO (IRE)		GB
112 DJUMAMA (IRE)		GER
112 ELZAAM (AUS)		GB
112 FIELD OF MIRACLES (IRE)		GB
112 IBICENCO (GER)		GER
112 LIBRANNO (GB)		GB
112 NAMIBIAN (IRE)		GB
112 PRAIRIE STAR (FR)		FR
112 SOLEMIA (IRE)		FR
111 BEATRICE AURORE (IRE)		GB
111 CHILWORTH LAD (GB)		GB
111 DUNBOYNE EXPRESS (IRE)		IRE
111 DUX SCHOLAR (GB)		GB
111 EPIC LOVE (IRE)		FR
111 GRAND VENT (IRE)		FR
111 MAWINGO (GER)		GER
111 THEO DANON (GER)		GER
111 WAVERING (IRE)		FR
111 ZIYARID (IRE)		FR
110 ALANZA (IRE)		IRE
110 AMETRIN (IRE)		GER
110 ANAM ALLTA (IRE)		IRE

Rating	Trained
110 BARBICAN (GB)	GB
110 CODEMASTER (GB)	GB
110 COLOUR VISION (FR)	GB
110 COOL DUDE (FR)	FR
110 DALARUA (IRE)	FR
110 DOMINANT (IRE)	GB
110 FRENCH NAVY (GB)	GB
110 GAILY GAME (GB)	FR
110 HAVANE SMOKER (GB)	FR
110 HAYA LANDA (FR)	FR
110 HUNTER'S LIGHT (IRE)	GB
110 IZZI TOP (GB)	GB
110 KING OF ARNOR (GB)	FR
110 KREEM (GB)	GB
110 MAJESTIC MYLES (IRE)	GB
110 MAQAASID (GB)	GB
110 MISS LAGO (IRE)	FR
110 PAUSANIAS (GB)	GB
110 SAPPHIRE (IRE)	IRE
110 SET TO MUSIC (IRE)	GB
110 SHANKARDEH (IRE)	FR
110 SIRIUS PROSPECT (USA)	GB
110 SLUMBER (GB)	GB
110 SPIRIT QUARTZ (IRE)	ITY
110 VENOMOUS (GB)	FR
110 WIZZ KID (IRE)	FR

OLDER HORSES 2011

For four-year-olds and up rated 115 or greater by the International Federation of Horseracing Authorities. Horses rated 110 to 114 are not part of the World Rankings but have been rated by the European Pattern Committee

Rating	Age	Trained
132 BLACK CAVIAR (AUS)	5	AUS
128 CIRRUS DES AIGLES (FR)	5	FR
127 CANFORD CLIFFS (IRE)	4	GB
127 REWILDING (GB)	4	GB
126 SO YOU THINK (NZ)	5	IRE
125 ROCKET MAN (AUS)	6	SIN
125 TWICE OVER (GB)	6	GB
125 WORKFORCE (GB)	4	GB
124 DROSSELMEYER (USA)	4	USA
124 GOLDIKOVA (IRE)	6	FR
124 ST NICHOLAS ABBEY (IRE)	4	IRE
123 ACCLAMATION (USA)	5	USA
123 AMERICAIN (USA)	6	FR
123 TIZWAY (USA)	6	USA
122 AMBITIOUS DRAGON (NZ)	5	HK
122 BEHKABAD (FR)	4	FR
122 CAPE BLANCO (IRE)	4	IRE
122 DICK TURPIN (IRE)	4	GB
122 GAME ON DUDE (USA)	4	USA
122 HAY LIST (AUS)	6	AUS
122 J J THE JET PLANE (SAF)	7	SAF
122 PLANTEUR (IRE)	4	FR
122 SNOW FAIRY (IRE)	4	GB
122 TOSEN JORDAN (JPN)	5	JPN
122 VICTOIRE PISA (JPN)	4	JPN
121 AWAIT THE DAWN (USA)	4	IRE
121 BYWORD (GB)	5	FR
121 CITYSCAPE (GB)	5	GB
121 COURT VISION (USA)	6	USA
121 DARK SHADOW (JPN)	4	JPN

Rating	Age	Trained
121 EARNESTLY (JPN)	6	JPN
121 FAME AND GLORY (GB)	5	IRE
121 MONTEROSSO (GB)	4	UAE
121 SACRED KINGDOM (AUS)	8	HK
121 SARAFINA (FR)	4	FR
121 TEAKS NORTH (USA)	4	USA
121 TRANSCEND (JPN)	5	JPN
121 TWIRLING CANDY (USA)	4	USA
121 WISE DAN (USA)	4	USA
120 BUENA VISTA (JPN)	5	JPN
120 DEACON BLUES (GB)	4	GB
120 EISHIN FLASH (JPN)	4	JPN
120 GIO PONTI (USA)	6	USA
120 HAVRE DE GRACE (USA)	4	USA
120 HIRUNO D'AMOUR (JPN)	4	JPN
120 JIMMY CHOUX (NZ)	4	NZ
120 MIDDAY (GB)	5	GB
120 MORE JOYOUS (NZ)	5	AUS
120 PELUSA (JPN)	4	JPN
120 PORTUS BLENDIUM (USA)	5	USA
120 PRESVIS (GB)	7	GB
120 TO THE GLORY (JPN)	4	JPN
120 TURALLURE (USA)	4	USA
120 WHOBEGOTYOU (AUS)	6	AUS
120 WORTHADD (IRE)	4	ITY
119 ABLE ONE (NZ)	9	HK
119 AMAZOMBIE (USA)	5	USA
119 BIG DRAMA (USA)	5	USA
119 BLIND LUCK (USA)	4	USA
119 BOLD SILVANO (SAF)	5	UAE

Rating	Age	Trained	Rating	Age	Trained
119 **FLAT OUT** (USA)	5	USA	116 **ABTERRA BLUE** (AUS)	5	HK
119 **GREEN DESTINY** (IRE)	4	GB	116 **ALGOL** (GB)	7	HK
119 **JAGUAR MAIL** (JPN)	7	JPN	116 **ANNOUNCE** (GB)	4	FR
119 **MUFHASA** (NZ)	7	NZ	116 **ARUNA** (USA)	4	USA
119 **RAJSAMAN** (FR)	4	FR	116 **AWESOME MARIA** (USA)	4	USA
119 **SHOCKING** (AUS)	6	AUS	116 **BEAUTY FLASH** (NZ)	6	HK
119 **SMILING TIGER** (USA)	4	USA	116 **BEROUNI** (FR)	5	HK
119 **STACELITA** (FR)	5	USA	116 **CAMPANOLOGIST** (USA)	6	GB
118 **BATED BREATH** (GB)	4	GB	116 **CAPTAIN OBVIOUS** (AUS)	6	SIN
118 **DEAN'S KITTEN** (USA)	4	USA	116 **CARACORTADO** (AUS)	4	USA
118 **DUNADEN** (FR)	5	FR	116 **CHAMP PEGASUS** (USA)	5	USA
118 **DURBAN THUNDER** (GER)	5	GER	116 **DANCEWITHTHEDEVIL** (SAF)	5	SAF
118 **EISHIN APOLLON** (USA)	4	JPN	116 **DANLEIGH** (AUS)	8	AUS
118 **EUROEARS** (USA)	7	USA	116 **DISTORTED LEGACY** (USA)	4	USA
118 **FORCE FREEZE** (USA)	6	USA	116 **DRUNKEN SAILOR** (IRE)	6	GB
118 **GET STORMY** (USA)	5	USA	116 **DUNCAN** (GB)	5	GB
118 **GITANO HERNANDO** (GB)	5	UAE	116 **EMULOUS** (GB)	4	IRE
118 **HEART OF DREAMS** (AUS)	6	AUS	116 **FAMOUS NAME** (GB)	6	IRE
118 **HOOF IT** (GB)	4	GB	116 **GINGERBREAD MAN** (AUS)	4	SIN
118 **IGUGU** (AUS)	4	SAF	116 **GLASS HARMONIUM** (IRE)	5	AUS
118 **IRIAN** (GER)	5	HK	116 **HAVELOCK** (USA)	4	USA
118 **LION TAMER** (NZ)	4	NZ	116 **JUKEBOX JURY** (IRE)	5	GB
118 **LUCK OR DESIGN** (IRE)	4	HK	116 **KINGDOM OF FIFE** (GB)	5	AUS
118 **PERFECT SHIRL** (USA)	4	CAN	116 **LITTLE BRIDGE** (NZ)	5	HK
118 **RIO DE LA PLATA** (USA)	6	GB	116 **LITTORIO** (AUS)	7	AUS
118 **RULERSHIP** (JPN)	4	JPN	116 **LOVE CONQUERS ALL** (AUS)	5	AUS
118 **SAHPRESA** (USA)	6	FR	116 **LUCAS CRANACH** (GER)	4	GER
118 **SHIMRAAN** (FR)	4	FR	116 **MENDIP** (USA)	4	UAE
118 **SKYSURFERS** (GB)	5	UAE	116 **MUSICAL ROMANCE** (USA)	4	USA
118 **SMART FALCON** (JPN)	6	JPN	116 **NIGHT MAGIC** (GER)	5	GER
118 **TRAILBLAZER** (JPN)	4	JPN	116 **PIERRE JOURDAN** (SAF)	5	SAF
118 **UNRIVALED BELLE** (USA)	5	USA	116 **PINKER PINKER** (AUS)	4	AUS
118 **XTENSION** (IRE)	4	HK	116 **PRINCE WILL I AM** (USA)	4	USA
118 **ZAZOU** (GER)	4	GER	116 **PROHIBIT** (GB)	6	GB
117 **ALIANTHUS** (GER)	6	GER	116 **RANSOM NOTE** (GB)	4	GB
117 **BETTER THAN EVER** (AUS)	5	SIN	116 **ROYAL BENCH** (IRE)	4	FR
117 **COURAGEOUS CAT** (USA)	5	USA	116 **SANAGAS** (GER)	5	USA
117 **CRYSTAL CAPELLA** (GB)	6	GB	116 **SCENIC SHOT** (AUS)	9	AUS
117 **DESCARADO** (NZ)	4	AUS	116 **SINCERO** (AUS)	4	AUS
117 **DUBAWI HEIGHTS** (GB)	4	USA	116 **THUMBS UP** (NZ)	7	HK
117 **ENTRAPMENT** (AUS)	5	HK	116 **TRUSTING** (AUS)	5	AUS
117 **FANUNALTER** (GB)	5	GB	116 **ULTRA BLEND** (USA)	5	USA
117 **FIFTH PETAL** (JPN)	5	JPN	116 **WALL STREET** (NZ)	7	NZ
117 **GOLDEN SWORD** (GB)	5	UAE	115 **ALAINMAAR** (FR)	5	GB
117 **HILDA'S PASSION** (USA)	4	USA	115 **ALBERT THE FAT** (AUS)	7	AUS
117 **JACKSON BEND** (USA)	4	USA	115 **ALWAYS A PRINCESS** (USA)	4	USA
117 **JAKKALBERRY** (IRE)	5	ITY	115 **ALWAYS CERTAIN** (AUS)	5	SIN
117 **JERANIMO** (USA)	5	USA	115 **ASK THE MOON** (USA)	5	USA
117 **JOY AND FUN** (NZ)	8	HK	115 **BETTER BE THE ONE** (USA)	5	SIN
117 **MUFARRH** (IRE)	4	UAE	115 **BIG CITY LIFE** (SAF)	6	SAF
117 **MUSIR** (USA)	5	UAE	115 **BIRDRUN** (USA)	5	USA
117 **NEVER RETREAT** (USA)	6	USA	115 **BLACK PIRANHA** (AUS)	8	AUS
117 **OPINION POLL** (IRE)	5	GB	115 **BOURBON BAY** (USA)	5	USA
117 **RANGIRANGDOO** (NZ)	7	AUS	115 **BRAVURA** (SAF)	5	SAF
117 **REGALLY READY** (USA)	4	USA	115 **CALVADOS BLUES** (FR)	5	UAE
117 **REKINDLED INTEREST** (AUS)	4	AUS	115 **CEDARBERG** (AUS)	5	AUS
117 **ROSE KINGDOM** (JPN)	4	JPN	115 **CENTENNIAL PARK** (NZ)	6	AUS
117 **SARAH LYNX** (IRE)	4	FR	115 **CHINCHON** (IRE)	6	FR
117 **SASSY IMAGE** (USA)	4	USA	115 **COMIC STRIP** (GB)	9	HK
117 **SCALO** (GER)	4	GER	115 **CROWN OF THORNS** (USA)	6	USA
117 **SIDNEY'S CANDY** (USA)	4	USA	115 **DANON CHANTILLY** (JPN)	4	JPN
117 **SILVER POND** (FR)	4	FR	115 **DANON COME ON** (JPN)	5	JPN
117 **SOCIETY ROCK** (IRE)	4	GB	115 **DAO DAO** (AUS)	8	AUS
117 **VOILA ICI** (IRE)	4	ITY	115 **DECISION TIME** (AUS)	4	AUS
117 **WHAT A WINTER** (SAF)	4	SAF	115 **DERBAAS** (USA)	5	UAE
117 **WIGMORE HALL** (IRE)	4	GB	115 **ESCAMONDA** (ARG)	6	SIN
117 **WINCHESTER** (USA)	6	USA	115 **ESPOIR CITY** (JPN)	6	JPN

Rating		Age	Trained
115	**ESTEJO** (GER)	7	GER
115	**FLUKE** (BRZ)	6	USA
115	**FURIOSO** (JPN)	7	JPN
115	**GIANT OAK** (USA)	5	USA
115	**GIANT RYAN** (USA)	5	USA
115	**HARRIS TWEED** (GB)	4	GB
115	**HOLD IT HARVEY** (AUS)	7	NZ
115	**ILOVETHISCITY** (AUS)	4	AUS
115	**KASBAH BLISS** (FR)	9	FR
115	**KINSHASA NO KISEKI** (AUS)	8	JPN
115	**LEY HUNTER** (USA)	4	FR
115	**LIBERIAN FREIGHTER** (USA)	6	USA
115	**LINTON** (AUS)	5	AUS
115	**LITTLE MIKE** (USA)	4	USA
115	**MELITO** (AUS)	5	AUS
115	**MIDAS TOUCH** (GB)	4	AUS
115	**MONSIEUR CHEVALIER** (IRE)	4	GB
115	**MONTECCHIO** (IRE)	4	HK
115	**MORNING LINE** (USA)	4	USA
115	**MR MEDICI** (IRE)	6	HK
115	**MUSKETIER** (GER)	9	CAN
115	**NOBLE CONQUEROR** (AUS)	9	HK
115	**OKEN BRUCE LEE** (JPN)	6	JPN
115	**PAST MASTER** (SAF)	5	SAF
115	**PLAYING GOD** (AUS)	4	AUS
115	**POET'S VOICE** (GB)	4	GB
115	**RED CADEAUX** (GB)	5	GB
115	**REDWOOD** (GB)	5	GB
115	**RETRIEVE** (AUS)	4	AUS
115	**RULE** (USA)	4	USA
115	**SACRED CHOICE** (AUS)	6	AUS
115	**SARATOGA BLACK** (IRE)	4	ITY
115	**SECRET ADMIRER** (AUS)	4	AUS
115	**SEHREZAD** (IRE)	6	GER
115	**SHAMALGAN** (FR)	4	CHR
115	**SHAMROCKER** (NZ)	4	AUS
115	**SHEA SHEA** (SAF)	4	SAF
115	**SIDE GLANCE** (GB)	4	GB
115	**SIGHT WINNER** (NZ)	8	HK
115	**SNAAFY** (USA)	7	UAE
115	**SOLE POWER** (GB)	5	IRE
115	**SRI PUTRA** (GB)	5	GB
115	**STATELY VICTOR** (USA)	4	USA
115	**STRONG RETURN** (JPN)	5	JPN
115	**SUNNY KING** (IRE)	8	HK
115	**SWIFT ALLIANCE** (AUS)	6	AUS
115	**SWITCH** (USA)	5	USA
115	**TACKLEBERRY** (USA)	4	USA
115	**TANGERINE TREES** (GB)	6	GB
115	**TEMPLE OF BOOM** (AUS)	5	AUS
115	**THE APACHE** (SAF)	4	SAF
115	**TRAPPE SHOT** (USA)	4	USA
115	**TRIPLE ELEGANCE** (AUS)	5	AUS
115	**TYPHOON TRACY** (AUS)	6	AUS
115	**VITA NOVA** (IRE)	4	GB
115	**WAIKATO** (NZ)	8	SIN
115	**WAR ARTIST** (AUS)	8	FR
115	**WONDER ACUTE** (JPN)	5	JPN
115	**ZACK HALL** (FR)	4	FR
115	**ZAVITE** (NZ)	9	AUS
114	**BEST DATING** (IRE)	4	FR
114	**CLASS IS CLASS** (IRE)	5	GB
114	**ELLE SHADOW** (IRE)	4	GER
114	**GENKI** (IRE)	7	GB
114	**HAMISH MCGONAGALL** (GB)	6	GB
114	**INDIAN DAYS** (GB)	6	GB
114	**IVORY LAND** (FR)	4	FR

Rating		Age	Trained
114	**JET AWAY** (GB)	4	GB
114	**JOSHUA TREE** (IRE)	4	GB
114	**MEEZNAH** (USA)	4	GB
114	**NAKAYAMA FESTA** (JPN)	5	JPN
114	**PREMIO LOCO** (USA)	7	GB
114	**SECRET ASSET** (IRE)	6	GB
114	**SOMMERABEND** (GB)	4	GER
114	**STAR WITNESS** (AUS)	4	AUS
114	**TIMEPIECE** (GB)	4	GB
114	**VANJURA** (GER)	4	GER
113	**BE FABULOUS** (GER)	4	FR
113	**BLUE BAJAN** (IRE)	9	GB
113	**BRIGANTIN** (USA)	4	FR
113	**CHACHAMAIDEE** (IRE)	4	GB
113	**CLOWANCE** (GB)	6	GB
113	**DAGDA MOR** (ITY)	4	ITY
113	**DANDINO** (GB)	4	GB
113	**GENTOO** (FR)	7	FR
113	**HITCHENS** (IRE)	6	GB
113	**ILLO** (GER)	5	AUS
113	**KINGSGATE NATIVE** (IRE)	6	GB
113	**LORD CHAPARRAL** (IRE)	4	ITY
113	**MASAMAH** (IRE)	5	GB
113	**POET** (GB)	6	GB
113	**SET THE TREND** (GB)	5	GB
113	**SILVERSIDE** (USA)	5	FR
113	**TAC DE BOISTRON** (FR)	4	FR
113	**TRES ROCK DANON** (FR)	5	GER
112	**AIZAVOSKI** (IRE)	5	FR
112	**AMOUR PROPRE** (GB)	5	GB
112	**BEACON LODGE** (IRE)	6	GB
112	**CIMA DE PLUIE** (GB)	4	ITY
112	**CITY LEADER** (IRE)	6	GB
112	**DREAM EATER** (IRE)	6	GB
112	**EMERALD COMMANDER** (IRE)	4	GB
112	**INXILE** (IRE)	6	GB
112	**IRISH FLAME** (SAF)	5	SAF
112	**LAAHEB** (GB)	5	GB
112	**LOLLY FOR DOLLY** (IRE)	4	IRE
112	**MANIGHAR** (FR)	5	GB
112	**MARINOUS** (FR)	5	FR
112	**NATIVE RULER** (GB)	5	GB
112	**OUR JONATHAN** (GB)	4	GB
112	**POLYTECHNICIEN** (USA)	5	FR
112	**PRINCE SIEGFRIED** (FR)	5	GB
112	**PRINCIPAL ROLE** (USA)	4	GB
112	**QUIZA QUIZA QUIZA** (GB)	5	ITY
112	**RED JAZZ** (USA)	4	GB
112	**ROYAL ROCK** (GB)	7	GB
112	**RUSSIAN TANGO** (GER)	4	GER
112	**SAJJHAA** (GB)	4	GB
112	**STEELE TANGO** (USA)	6	GB
112	**STRAWBERRYDAIQUIRI** (GB)	5	GB
112	**VERDE-MAR** (BRZ)	4	FR
112	**VISCOUNT NELSON** (USA)	4	IRE
112	**WATAR** (IRE)	6	FR
112	**ZINABAA** (FR)	6	FR
111	**AFRICAN STORY** (GB)	4	GB
111	**AGENT SECRET** (IRE)	5	FR
111	**DELEGATOR** (GB)	5	GB
111	**ETON RIFLES** (IRE)	6	GB
111	**GERTRUDE BELL** (GB)	4	GB
111	**I'M A DREAMER** (IRE)	4	GB
111	**INVINCIBLE ASH** (IRE)	6	IRE
111	**IVER BRIDGE LAD** (GB)	4	GB
111	**LOST IN THE MOMENT** (IRE)	4	GB
111	**MAR ADENTRO** (FR)	5	FR

Rating		Age	Trained
111	**MARCHAND D'OR** (FR)	8	FR
111	**MARCRET** (ITY)	4	ITY
111	**OVERDOSE** (GB)	6	HUN
111	**SAGA DREAM** (FR)	5	FR
111	**TASTAHIL** (IRE)	7	GB
111	**TERTULLUS** (FR)	8	NOR
111	**TIMES UP** (GB)	5	GB
110	**AFSARE** (GB)	4	GB
110	**ALCOHUAZ** (CHI)	6	SWE
110	**ALLIED POWERS** (IRE)	6	GB
110	**ALTANO** (GER)	5	GER
110	**AMICO FRITZ** (GER)	5	FR
110	**ANTARA** (GER)	5	GB
110	**ARCTIC COSMOS** (USA)	4	GB
110	**ASKAR TAU** (FR)	6	GB
110	**CAVALRYMAN** (GB)	5	GB
110	**CELTIC CELEB** (IRE)	4	FR
110	**DANCE AND DANCE** (IRE)	5	GB
110	**FERDOOS** (GB)	4	GB/GB
110	**FIRST CITY** (GB)	5	GB

Rating		Age	Trained
110	**FOX HUNT** (IRE)	4	GB
110	**GALILEO'S CHOICE** (IRE)	5	IRE
110	**MAHBOOBA** (AUS)	4	SAF
110	**MASHOOR** (FR)	4	FR
110	**MODUN** (IRE)	4	GB
110	**NEHAAM** (GB)	5	GB
110	**ONE CLEVER CAT** (IRE)	5	FR
110	**PACHATTACK** (USA)	5	GB
110	**PASSION FOR GOLD** (USA)	4	GB
110	**PRINCE BISHOP** (IRE)	4	GB
110	**RITE OF PASSAGE** (GB)	7	IRE
110	**ROCKHORSE** (IRE)	6	ITY
110	**SECRECY** (GB)	5	GB
110	**SILVER VALNY** (FR)	5	FR
110	**SIR LANDO** (GB)	4	NOR
110	**SKINS GAME** (GB)	5	FR
110	**SMOOTH OPERATOR** (GER)	5	GER
110	**SWEET LIGHTNING** (GB)	6	GB
110	**TIMOS** (GER)	6	FR
110	**VAGABOND SHOES** (IRE)	4	FR

RACEFORM CHAMPIONS 2012
THREE-YEAR-OLDS AND UP

5f-6f

BLACK CAVIAR	133
HAY LIST	127
ROCKET MAN	127
SEPOY	127
BIG DRAMA	125
DEACON BLUES	125
J J THE JETPLANE	125
DREAM AHEAD	124
HOOF IT	124
SACRED KINGDOM	124

7f-9f

FRANKEL	139
CANFORD CLIFFS	130
DREAM AHEAD	129
EXCELEBRATION	129
WISE DAN	128
CALEB'S POSSE	127
GOLDIKOVA	126
SMILING TIGER	126
STRONG SUIT	126
THE FACTOR	126
UNCLE MO	126
AMBITIOUS DRAGON	125
FLAT OUT	125
HAVRE DE GRACE	125
GOLDIKOVA	125
TIZWAY	125
WHOBEGOTYOU	125

10f-12f

CIRRUS DES AIGLES	130
REWILDING	130
SO YOU THINK	129
DANEDREAM	128
ORFEVRE	128
WORKFORCE	128
ANIMAL KINGDOM	126
DROSSELMEYER	126
NATHANIEL	126
TOSEN JORDAN	126
SEA MOON	126
TWICE OVER	126
ACCLAMATION	125
AWAIT THE DAWN	125
BEHKABAD	125
FLAT OUT	125
SARAFINA	125
SHOCKING	125
SNOW FAIRY	125

13+f

AMERICAIN	127
ORFEVRE	125
MASKED MARVEL	124
ST NICHOLAS ABBEY	124
HIRUNO D'AMOUR	122
SADDLERS ROCK	122
DUNADEN	121
FAME AND GLORY	121
SEA MOON	121
OPINION POLL	120

RACEFORM CHAMPIONS 2011
TWO-YEAR-OLDS

5f-6f

DABIRSIM	120	CRUSADE	114
HARBOUR WATCH	117	LA COLLINA	114
BEST TERMS	114	LILBOURNE LAD	112
CASPAR NETSCHER	114		

7f+

CAMELOT	119	BRONTERRE	115
PARISH HALL	118	DAVID LIVINGSTON	115
POWER	118	ELUSIVE KATE	115
DRAGON PULSE	117	WROTE	115
MOST IMPROVED	116		

MEDIAN TIMES 2011

The following Raceform median times are used in the calculation of the Split Second speed figures. They represent a true average time for the distance, which has been arrived at after looking at the winning times for all races over each distance within the past five years, except for those restricted to two or three-year-olds.

Some current race distances have been omitted as they have not yet had a sufficient number of races run over them to produce a reliable average time.

ASCOT

5f 1m 1.20	1m Round 1m 40.70	2m 3m 29.00
6f 1m 14.40	1m Straight 1m 40.60	2m 4f 4m 24.80
6f 110y 1m 20.80	1m 2f 2m 7.00	2m 5f 159y 4m 49.40
7f 1m 27.20	1m 4f 2m 32.50	

AYR

5f 59.40	1m 1m 43.80	1m 5f 13y 2m 54.00
6f 1m 12.40	1m 1f 20y 1m 57.50	1m 7f 3m 20.40
7f 50y 1m 33.40	1m 2f 2m 12.00	2m 1f 105y 4m 0.50

BATH

5f 11y 1m 2.50	1m 2f 46y 2m 11.00	1m 5f 22y 2m 52.00
5f 161y 1m 11.20	1m 3f 144y 2m 30.60	2m 1f 34y 3m 51.90
1m 5y 1m 40.80		

BEVERLEY

5f 1m 3.50	1m 100y 1m 47.60	1m 4f 16y 2m 39.80
7f 100y 1m 33.80	1m 1f 207y 2m 7.00	2m 35y 3m 39.80

BRIGHTON

5f 59y 1m 2.30	6f 209y 1m 23.10	1m 1f 209y 2m 3.60
5f 213y 1m 10.20	7f 214y 1m 36.00	1m 3f 196y 2m 32.70

CARLISLE

5f 1m 0.80	7f 200y 1m 40.00	1m 6f 32y 3m 7.50
5f 193y 1m 13.70	1m 1f 61y 1m 57.60	2m 1f 52y 3m 53.00
6f 192y 1m 27.10	1m 3f 107y 2m 23.10	

CATTERICK

5f 59.80	7f 1m 27.00	1m 5f 175y 3m 3.60
5f 212y 1m 13.60	1m 3f 214y 2m 38.90	1m 7f 177y 3m 32.00

CHEPSTOW

5f 16y 59.30	1m 14y 1m 36.20	2m 49y 3m 38.90
6f 16y 1m 12.00	1m 2f 36y 2m 10.60	2m 2f 4m 3.60
7f 16y 1m 23.20	1m 4f 23y 2m 39.00	

CHESTER

5f 16y 1m 1.00	7f 122y 1m 33.80	1m 5f 89y 2m 52.80
5f 110y 1m 6.20	1m 2f 75y 2m 11.20	1m 7f 195y 3m 28.00
6f 18y 1m 13.80	1m 3f 79y 2m 24.80	2m 2f 147y 4m 4.80
7f 2y 1m 26.50	1m 4f 66y 2m 38.50	

DONCASTER

5f 1m 0.50	7f 1m 26.30	1m 4f 2m 34.90
5f 140y 1m 8.80	1m Straight 1m 39.30	1m 6f 132y 3m 7.40
6f 1m 13.60	1m Round 1m 39.70	2m 110y 3m 40.40
6f 110y 1m 19.90	1m 2f 60y 2m 9.40	2m 2f 3m 55.00

EPSOM

5f	55.70	7f	1m 23.30	1m 2f 18y	2m 9.70
6f	1m 9.40	1m 114y	1m 46.10	1m 4f 10y	2m 38.90

FFOS LAS

5f	58.30	1m 2f	2m 9.40	1m 6f	3m 3.80
6f	1m 10.00	1m 4f	2m 37.40	2m	3m 30.00
1m	1m 41.00				

FOLKESTONE

5f	3m 30.00	1m 1f 149y	2m 4.90	1m 7f 92y	3m 29.70
6f	1m 12.70	1m 4f	2m 40.90	2m 93y	3m 37.20
7f Straight	1m 27.30				

GOODWOOD

5f	58.40	1m 1f	1m 56.30	1m 6f	3m 3.60
6f	1m 12.20	1m 1f 192y	2m 8.00	2m	3m 29.00
7f	1m 26.90	1m 3f	2m 26.50	2m 5f	4m 31.00
1m	1m 39.90	1m 4f	2m 38.40		

HAMILTON

5f 4y	4m 31.00	1m 1f 36y	1m 59.70	1m 4f 17y	2m 38.60
6f 5y	1m 12.20	1m 3f 16y	2m 25.60	1m 5f 9y	2m 53.90
1m 65y	1m 48.40				

HAYDOCK

5f	1m 0.80	7f	1m 30.90	1m 3f 200y	2m 34.00
5fl	1m 0.80	1m	1m 42.90	1m 6f	3m 1.20
6f	1m 13.80	1m 30y	1m 44.70	2m 45y	3m 36.00
6fl	1m 13.80	1m 2f 95y	2m 16.00		

KEMPTON (A.W)

5f	1m 0.50	1m	1m 39.80	1m 4f	2m 34.50
6f	1m 13.10	1m 2f	2m 8.00	2m	3m 30.10
7f	1m 26.00	1m 3f	2m 21.90		

LEICESTER

5f 2y	3m 30.10	7f 9y	1m 26.20	1m 1f 218y	2m 7.90
5f 218y	1m 13.00	1m 60y	1m 45.10	1m 3f 183y	2m 33.90

LINGFIELD

5f	58.20	7f 140y	1m 32.30	1m 3f 106y	2m 31.50
6f	1m 11.20	1m 1f	1m 56.60	1m 6f	3m 10.00
7f	1m 23.30	1m 2f	2m 10.50	2m	3m 34.80

LINGFIELD (A.W)

5f	58.80	1m	1m 38.20	1m 5f	2m 46.00
6f	1m 11.90	1m 2f	2m 6.60	2m	3m 25.70
7f	1m 24.80	1m 4f	2m 33.00		

MUSSELBURGH

5f	1m 0.40	1m 1f	1m 53.90	1m 6f	3m 5.30
7f 30y	1m 29.00	1m 4f 100y	2m 42.00	2m	3m 33.50
1m	1m 41.20	1m 5f	2m 52.00		

NEWBURY

5f 34y	1m 1.40	1m Straight	1m 39.70	1m 3f 5y	2m 21.20
6f 8y	1m 13.00	1m 7y Round	1m 38.70	1m 4f 5y	2m 35.50
6f 110y	1m 19.30	1m 1f	1m 55.50	1m 5f 61y	2m 52.00
7f Straight	1m 25.70	1m 2f 6y	2m 8.80	2m	3m 32.00

NEWCASTLE

5f	1m 1.10	1m Round	1m 45.30	1m 4f 93y	2m 45.60
6f	1m 14.60	1m 3y Straight	1m 43.40	1m 6f 97y	3m 11.30
7f	1m 27.80	1m 2f 32y	2m 11.90	2m 19y	3m 39.40

NEWMARKET (ROWLEY)

5f Rowley	59.10	1m 1f Rowley	1m 51.70	1m 6f Rowley	2m 57.00
6f Rowley	1m 12.20	1m 2f Rowley	2m 5.80	2m Rowley	3m 30.50
7f Rowley	1m 25.40	1m 4f Rowley	2m 32.00	2m 2f Rowley	3m 56.80
1m Rowley	1m 38.60				

NEWMARKET (JULY)

5f July	59.10	1m July	1m 40.00	1m 5f July	2m 44.00
6f July	1m 12.50	1m 2f July	2m 5.50	1m 6f 175y July	3m 8.40
7f July	1m 25.70	1m 4f July	2m 32.90	2m 24y July	3m 27.00

NOTTINGHAM

5f 13y	1m 1.00	1m 75y	1m 45.60	1m 6f 15y	3m 7.30
6f 15y	1m 14.90	1m 2f 50y	2m 11.70	2m 9y	3m 30.30

PONTEFRACT

5f	1m 3.30	1m 2f 6y	2m 13.70	2m 1f 216y	3m 56.20
6f	1m 16.90	1m 4f 8y	2m 40.80	2m 5f 122y	4m 51.00
1m 4y	1m 45.90	2m 1f 22y	3m 44.60		

REDCAR

5f	58.60	1m	1m 38.00	1m 6f 19y	3m 4.70
6f	1m 11.80	1m 1f	1m 53.00	2m 4y	3m 31.40
7f	1m 24.50	1m 2f	2m 7.10		

RIPON

5f	1m 0.70	1m 1f	1m 54.70	1m 4f 10y	2m 36.70
6f	1m 13.00	1m 1f 170y	2m 5.40	2m	3m 31.80
1m	1m 41.40				

SALISBURY

5f	1m 1.00	1m	1m 43.50	1m 4f	2m 38.00
6f	1m 14.80	1m 1f 198y	2m 9.90	1m 6f 21y	3m 7.40
6f 212y	1m 28.60				

SANDOWN

5f 6y	1m 1.60	1m 1f	1m 55.70	1m 6f	3m 4.50
7f 16y	1m 29.50	1m 2f 7y	2m 10.50	2m 78y	3m 38.70
1m 14y	1m 43.30				

SOUTHWELL (A.W)

5f	59.70	1m	1m 43.70	1m 6f	3m 8.30
6f	1m 16.50	1m 3f	2m 28.00	2m	3m 45.50
7f	1m 30.30	1m 4f	2m 41.00		

THIRSK

5f	59.60	7f	1m 27.20	1m 4f	2m 36.20
6f	1m 12.70	1m	1m 40.10	2m	3m 28.30

WARWICK

5f	59.60	7f 26y	1m 24.60	1m 4f 134y	2m 44.60
5f 110y	1m 5.90	1m 22y	1m 41.00	1m 6f 213y	3m 19.00
6f	1m 11.80	1m 2f 188y	2m 21.10		

WINDSOR

5f 10y.................... 1m 0.30	1m 67y.......................... 1m 44.70	1m 3f 135y 2m 29.50
6f........................... 1m 13.00	1m 2f 7y.........................2m 8.70	

WOLVERHAMPTON (A.W)

5f 20y.................... 1m 2.30	1m 141y....................... 1m 50.50	1m 5f 194y..................... 3m 6.00
5f 216y.................. 1m 15.00	1m 1f 103y.....................2m 1.70	2m 119y....................... 3m 41.80
7f 32y................... 1m 29.60	1m 4f 50y.......................2m 41.10	

YARMOUTH

5f 43y.................... 1m 2.70	1m 3y.......................... 1m 40.60	1m 3f 101y 2m 28.70
6f 3y..................... 1m 14.40	1m 1f............................ 1m 55.80	1m 6f 17y....................... 3m 7.60
7f 3y..................... 1m 26.60	1m 2f 21y.......................2m 10.50	2m................................ 3m 32.40

YORK

5f.............................. 59.30	1m.............................. 1m 38.80	1m 6f.............................. 3m 0.20
5f 89y.................... 1m 4.10	1m 208y...................... 1m 52.00	2m 88y......................... 3m 34.50
6f........................... 1m 11.90	1m 2f 88y.......................2m 12.50	2m 2f............................. 3m 58.20
7f........................... 1m 25.30	1m 4f.............................2m 33.20	

RACEFORM RECORD TIMES (FLAT)

ASCOT

DISTANCE	TIME	AGE	WEIGHT	GOING	HORSE	DATE		
5f	59.17 secs	2	8-12	Good To Firm	**MAQAASID**	Jun	16	2010
5f	57.44 secs	3	9-1	Good To Firm	**MISS ANDRETTI**	Jun	19	2007
6f	1m 12.46	2	9-1	Good To Firm	**HENRYTHENAVIGATOR**	Jun	19	2007
6f	1m 12.19	3	8-6	Good To Firm	**PERFECT TRIBUTE**	April	19	2011
7f	1m 27.9	2	7-12	Good To Firm	**RELATIVE ORDER**	Aug	11	2007
7f	1m 24.94	3	8-12	Good To Firm	**RAINFALL**	July	16	2010
7f	1m 25.89	6	8-12	Good	**ADVANCED**	Sep	26	2009
1m (Rnd)	1m 39.55	2	8-12	Good	**JOSHUA TREE**	Sep	26	2009
1m (Rnd)	1m 38.32	3	9-0	Good To Firm	**GHANAATI**	Jun	19	2009
1m (Str)	1m 37.16	5	9-0	Good To Firm	**INVISIBLE MAN**	Jun	16	2010
1m 2f	2m 02.52	5	9-3	Good	**CIRRUS DES AIGLES**	Oct	15	2011
1m 4f	2m 26.78	4	9-7	Good	**HARBINGER**	July	24	2010
2m	3m 24.13	3	9-1	Good To Firm	**HOLBERG**	May	2	2007
2m 4f	4m 16.92	6	9-2	Good To Firm	**RITE OF PASSAGE**	Jun	17	2010
2m 5f 159y	4m 47.79	7	9-2	Good To Firm	**BERGO**	Jun	19	2010

AYR

DISTANCE	TIME	AGE	WEIGHT	GOING	HORSE	DATE		
5f	56.9 secs	2	8-11	Good	**BOOGIE STREET**	Sep	18	2003
5f	55.68 secs	3	8-11	Good To Firm	**LOOK BUSY**	Jun	21	2008
6f	1m 09.7	2	7-10	Good	**SIR BERT**	Sep	17	1969
6f	1m 08.37	5	8-6	Good To Firm	**MAISON DIEU**	Jun	21	2008
7f 50y	1m 28.9	2	9-0	Good	**TAFAAHUM**	Sep	19	2003
7f 50y	1m 28.2	4	9-2	Good To Firm	**FLUR NA H ALBA**	Jun	21	2003
1m	1m 39.2	2	9-0	Good	**KRIBENSIS**	Sep	17	1986
1m	1m 36.0	4	7-13	Firm	**SUFI**	Sep	16	1959
1m 1f 20y	1m 50.3	4	9-3	Good	**RETIREMENT**	Sep	19	2003
1m 2f	2m 04.0	4	9-9	Good To Firm	**ENDLESS HALL**	July	17	2000
1m 2f 192y	2m 13.3	4	9-0	Good To Firm	**AZZAAM**	Sep	18	1991
1m 5f 13y	2m 45.8	4	9-7	Good To Firm	**EDEN'S CLOSE**	Sep	18	1993
1m 7f	3m 13.1	3	9-4	Good	**ROMANY RYE**	Sep	19	1991
2m 1f 105y	3m 45.0	4	6-13	Good	**CURRY**	Sep	16	1955

BATH

DISTANCE	TIME	AGE	WEIGHT	GOING	HORSE	DATE		
5f 11y	59.50 secs	2	9-2	Firm	**AMOUR PROPRE**	July	24	2008
5f 11y	58.75 secs	3	8-12	Firm	**ENTICING**	May	1	2007
5f 161y	1m 08.7	2	8-12	Firm	**QALAHARI**	July	24	2008
5f 161y	1m 08.1	6	9-0	Firm	**MADRACO**	May	22	1989
1m 5y	1m 40.3	2	8-12	Good To Firm	**KHASSAH**	Sep	9	1999
1m 5y	1m 37.2	5	8-12	Good To Firm	**ADOBE**	Jun	17	2000
1m 2f 46y	2m 05.6	3	9-0	Good To Firm	**CONNOISSEUR BAY**	May	29	1998
1m 3f 144y	2m 25.74	3	9-0	Hard	**TOP OF THE CHARTS**	Sep	8	2005
1m 5f 22y	2m 47.2	4	10-0	Firm	**FLOWN**	Aug	13	1991
2m 1f 34y	3m 43.4	6	7-9	Firm	**YAHESKA**	Jun	14	2003

BEVERLEY

DISTANCE	TIME	AGE	WEIGHT	GOING	HORSE	DATE		
5f	1m 01.0	2	8-2	Good To Firm	ADDO	July	17	2001
5f	1m 00.1	4	9-5	Firm	PIC UP STICKS	Apr	16	2003
7f 100y	1m 31.1	2	9-0	Firm	MAJAL	July	30	1991
7f 100y	1m 29.5	3	7-8	Firm	WHO'S TEF	July	30	1991
1m 100y	1m 43.3	2	9-0	Firm	ARDEN	Sep	24	1986
1m 100y	1m 42.2	3	8-4	Firm	LEGAL CASE	Jun	14	1989
1m 1f 207y	2m 01.00	3	9-7	Good To Firm	EASTERN ARIA	Aug	29	2009
1m 4f 16y	2m 34.88	6	10-0	Firm	WEE CHARLIE CASTLE	Aug	30	2009
2m 35y	3m 29.5	4	9-2	Good To Firm	RUSHEN RAIDER	Aug	14	1996

BRIGHTON

DISTANCE	TIME	AGE	WEIGHT	GOING	HORSE	DATE		
5f 59y	1m.00.1	2	9-0	Firm	BID FOR BLUE	May	6	1993
5f 59y	59.3 secs	4	8-9	Firm	PLAY HEVER GOLF	May	26	1993
5f 213y	1m 08.1	2	8-9	Firm	SONG MIST	July	16	1996
5f 213y	1m 07.3	3	8-9	Firm	THIRD PARTY	Jun	3	1997
5f 213y	1m 07.3	5	9-1	Good To Firm	BLUNDELL LANE	May	4	2000
6f 209y	1m 19.9	2	8-11	Hard	RAIN BURST	Sep	15	1988
6f 209y	1m 19.4	4	9-3	Good To Firm	SAWAKI	Sep	3	1991
7f 214y	1m 32.8	2	9-7	Firm	ASIAN PETE	Oct	3	1989
7f 214y	1m 30.5	5	8-11	Firm	MYSTIC RIDGE	May	27	1999
1m 1f 209y	2m 04.7	2	9-0	Good To Soft	ESTEEMED MASTER	Nov	2	2001
1m 1f 209y	1m 57.2	3	9-0	Firm	GET THE MESSAGE	Apr	30	1984
1m 3f 196y	2m 25.8	4	8-2	Firm	NEW ZEALAND	July	4	1985

CARLISLE

DISTANCE	TIME	AGE	WEIGHT	GOING	HORSE	DATE		
5f	1m 00.1	2	8-5	Firm	LA TORTUGA	Aug	2	1999
5f	59.3 secs	5	8-12	Firm	FRIAR TUCK	July	21	2000
5f 193y	1m 12.45	2	9-6	Good To Firm	MUSICAL GUEST	Sep	11	2005
5f 193y	1m 10.83	4	9-0	Good To Firm	BO MCGINTY	Sep	11	2005
6f 206y	1m 26.5	2	9-4	Hard	SENSE OF PRIORITY	Sep	10	1991
6f 206y	1m 25.3	4	9-1	Firm	MOVE WITH EDES	July	6	1996
7f 200y	1m 37.34	5	9-7	Good To Firm	HULA BALLEW	Aug	17	2005
7f 214y	1m 44.6	2	8-8	Firm	BLUE GARTER	Sep	9	1980
1m 1f 61y	1m 53.8	3	9-0	Firm	LITTLE JIMBOB	Jun	14	2004
1m 3f 107y	2m 22.25	5	9-6	Good To Firm	OVERRULE	Jun	24	2009
1m 3f 206y	2m 29.13	5	9-8	Good To Firm	TEMPSFORD	Sep	19	2005
1m 6f 32y	3m 02.2	6	8-10	Firm	EXPLOSIVE SPEED	May	26	1994

CATTERICK

DISTANCE	TIME	AGE	WEIGHT	GOING	HORSE	DATE		
5f	57.7 secs	2	9-0	Good To Firm	VERDE ALITALIA	Sep	21	1991
5f	57.1 secs	4	8-7	Firm	KABCAST	July	7	1989
5f 212y	1m 11.4	2	9-4	Firm	CAPTAIN NICK	July	11	1978
5f 212y	1m 09.8	9	8-13	Good To Firm	SHARP HAT	May	30	2003
7f	1m 24.1	2	8-11	Firm	LINDA'S FANTASY	Sep	18	1982
7f	1m 22.5	6	8-7	Firm	DIFFERENTIAL	May	31	2003
1m 3f 214y	2m 30.5	3	8-8	Good To Firm	RAHAF	May	30	2003
1m 5f 175y	2m 54.8	3	8-5	Firm	GERYON	May	31	1984
1m 7f 177y	3m 20.8	4	7-11	Firm	BEAN BOY	July	8	1982

CHEPSTOW

DISTANCE	TIME	AGE	WEIGHT	GOING	HORSE	DATE	
5f 16y	57.6 secs	2	8-1	Firm	MICRO LOVE	July	8 1986
5f 16y	56.8 secs	3	8-4	Firm	TORBAY EXPRESS	Sep	15 1979
6f 16y	1m 09.4	2	9-0	Firm	ROYAL FIFI	Sep	9 1989
6f 16y	1m 08.8	4	8-6	Firm	AFRICAN REX	May	12 1987
7f 16y	1m 20.8	2	9-0	Good To Firm	ROYAL AMARETTO	Sep	12 1996
7f 16y	1m 19.3	3	9-0	Firm	TARANAKI	Sep	18 2001
1m 14y	1m 33.1	2	8-11	Good To Firm	SKI ACADEMY	Aug	28 1995
1m 14y	1m 31.6	3	8-13	Firm	STOLI	Sep	18 2001
1m 2f 36y	2m 04.1	5	8-9	Hard	LEONIDAS	July	5 1983
1m 2f 36y	2m 04.1	5	7-8	Good To Firm	IT'S VARADAN	Sep	9 1989
1m 2f 36y	2m 04.1	3	8-5	Good To Firm	ELA ATHENA	July	23 1999
1m 4f 23y	2m 31.0	3	8-9	Good To Firm	SPRITSAIL	July	13 1989
1m 4f 23y	2m 31.0	7	9-6	Hard	MAINTOP	Aug	27 1984
2m 49y	3m 27.7	4	9-0	Good To Firm	WIZZARD ARTIST	July	1 1989
2m 2f	3m 56.4	5	8-7	Good To Firm	LAFFAH	July	8 2000

CHESTER

DISTANCE	TIME	AGE	WEIGHT	GOING	HORSE	DATE	
5f 16y	59.94 secs	2	9-2	Good To Firm	LEIBA LEIBA	June	26 2010
5f 16y	59.2 secs	3	10-0	Firm	ALTHREY DON	July	10 1964
6f 18y	1m 13.2	2	8-11	Good To Firm	ACE OF PARKES	July	11 1998
6f 18y	1m 12.7	3	8-3	Good To Firm	PLAY HEVER GOLF	May	4 1993
6f 18y	1m 12.7	6	9-2	Good	STACK ROCK	Jun	23 1993
7f 2y	1m 26.2	2	8-4	Good To Firm	BY HAND	Aug	31 1991
7f 2y	1m 23.75	5	8-13	Good To Firm	THREE GRACES	July	9 2005
7f 122y	1m 35.0	2	9-0	Firm	DOUBLE VALUE	Sep	1 1972
7f 122y	1m 30.91	3	8-12	Good To Firm	CUPID'S GLORY	Aug	18 2005
1m 2f 75y	2m 7.15	3	8-8	Good To Firm	STOTSFOLD	Sep	23 2006
1m 3f 79y	2m 22.17	3	8-12	Good To Firm	PERFECT TRUTH	May	6 2009
1m 4f 66y	2m 34.2	3	8-11	Good To Firm	OLD VIC	May	9 1989
1m 5f 89y	2m 45.4	5	8-11	Firm	RAKAPOSHI KING	May	7 1987
1m 7f 195y	3m 24.5	7	7-11	Good To Firm	MOONLIGHT QUEST	July	30 1995
2m 2f 147y	3m 58.59	7	9-2	Good To Firm	GREENWICH MEANTIME	May	9 2007

DONCASTER

DISTANCE	TIME	AGE	WEIGHT	GOING	HORSE	DATE	
5f	58.1 secs	2	9-5	Good To Firm	SAND VIXEN	Sep	11 2009
5f	57.2 secs	6	9-12	Good To Firm	CELTIC MILL	Sep	9 2004
5f 140y	1m 07.2	2	9-0	Good To Firm	CARTOGRAPHY	Jun	29 2003
5f 140y	1m 05.6	9	9-10	Good	HALMAHERA	Sep	8 2004
6f	1m 09.6	2	8-11	Good	CAESAR BEWARE	Sep	8 2004
6f	1m 09.56	3	8-10	Good To Firm	PROCLAIM	May	30 2009
6f 110y	1m 17.22	2	8-3	Good To Firm	SWILLY FERRY	Sep	10 2009
7f	1m 22.6	2	9-1	Good To Firm	LIBRETTIST	Sep	8 2004
7f	1m 21.6	3	9-4	Good To Firm	PASTORAL PURSUITS	Sep	9 2004
1m Str	1m 36.5	2	8-6	Good To Firm	SINGHALESE	Sep	9 2004
1m Rnd	1m 35.4	2	9-0	Good To Firm	PLAYFUL ACT	Sep	9 2004
1m Str	1m 35.52	4	8-9	Good To Firm	DREAM LODGE	July	24 2008
1m Rnd	1m 34.46	4	8-12	Good To Firm	STAYING ON	April	18 2009
1m 2f 60y	2m 13.4	2	8-8	Good	YARD BIRD	Nov	6 1981
1m 2f 60y	2m 04.81	4	8-13	Good To Firm	RED GALA	Sep	12 2007
1m 4f	2m 27.48	3	8-4	Good To Firm	SWIFT ALHAARTH	Sep	10 2011
1m 6f 132y	3m 00.44	3	9-0	Good To Firm	MASKED MARVEL	Sep	10 2011
2m 110y	3m 34.4	4	9-12	Good To Firm	FARSI	Jun	12 1992
2m 2f	3m 48.41	4	9-4	Good To Firm	SEPTIMUS	Sep	14 2007

EPSOM

DISTANCE	TIME	AGE	WEIGHT	GOING	HORSE	DATE		
5f	55.0 secs	2	8-9	Good To Firm	**PRINCE ASLIA**	Jun	9	1995
5f	53.6 secs	4	9-5	Firm	**INDIGENOUS**	Jun	2	1960
6f	1m 07.8	2	8-11	Good To Firm	**SHOWBROOK**	Jun	5	1991
6f	1m 07.21	5	9-13	Good To Firm	**MAC GILLE EOIN**	July	2	2009
7f	1m 21.3	2	8-9	Good To Firm	**RED PEONY**	July	29	2004
7f	1m 20.1	4	8-7	Firm	**CAPISTRANO**	Jun	7	1972
1m 114y	1m 42.8	2	8-5	Good To Firm	**NIGHTSTALKER**	Aug	30	1988
1m 114y	1m 40.7	3	8-6	Good To Firm	**SYLVA HONDA**	Jun	5	1991
1m 2f 18y	2m 03.5	5	7-13	Good	**CROSSBOW**	Jun	7	1967
1m 4f 10y	2m 32.3	3	9-0	Good To Firm	**WORKFORCE**	Jun	5	2010

FFOS LAS

DISTANCE	TIME	AGE	WEIGHT	GOING	HORSE	DATE		
5f	57.06 secs	2	9-3	Good To Firm	**MR MAJEIKA**	May	5	2011
5f	56.35 secs	5	8-8	Good	**HAAJES**	Sep	12	2009
6f	1m 9.93	2	9-0	Good To Firm	**LUNAR DEITY**	May	26	2010
6f	1m 7.80	8	8-4	Good To Firm	**THE JAILER**	May	5	2011
1m	1m 40.61	2	9-0	Good To Firm	**SHARAAYEEN**	Sep	13	2009
1m	1m 37.12	5	9-0	Good To Firm	**ZEBRANO**	May	5	2011
1m 2f	2m 04.85	8	8-12	Good To Firm	**PELHAM CRESCENT**	May	5	2011
1m 4f	2m 32.61	5	9-8	Good To Firm	**LADY OF BURGUNDY**	July	11	2011
1m 6f	2m 58.61	4	9-7	Good To Firm	**LADY ECLAIR**	July	12	2010
2m	3m 29.86	4	9-7	Good	**BLACK OR RED**	July	21	2009

FOLKESTONE

DISTANCE	TIME	AGE	WEIGHT	GOING	HORSE	DATE		
5f	58.4 secs	2	9-2	Good To Firm	**PIVOTAL**	Nov	6	1995
5f	58.18 secs	4	8-8	Good To Firm	**BLACK BACCARA**	April	12	2011
6f	1m 10.8	2	8-9	Good	**BOOMERANG BLADE**	July	16	1998
6f	1m 09.38	4	9-6	Good To Firm	**MUNADDAM**	Sep	18	2006
6f 189y	1m 23.7	2	8-11	Good	**HEN HARRIER**	July	3	1996
6f 189y	1m 22.0	4	10-0	Firm	**NEUWEST**	Jun	28	1996
7f (str)	1m 25.01	2	9-0	Good To Firm	**DONA ALBA**	Sep	2	2007
7f (str)	1m 23.76	3	8-11	Good To Firm	**WELSH CAKE**	Sep	18	2006
1m 1f 149y	1m 59.7	3	8-6	Good To Firm	**DIZZY**	July	23	1991
1m 4f	2m 33.2	4	8-8	Hard	**SNOW BLIZZARD**	Jun	30	1992
1m 7f 92y	3m 23.1	3	9-11	Firm	**MATA ASKARI**	Sep	12	1991
2m 93y	3m 34.9	3	8-12	Good To Firm	**CANDLE SMOKE**	Aug	20	1996

GOODWOOD

DISTANCE	TIME	AGE	WEIGHT	GOING	HORSE	DATE		
5f	57.51 secs	2	9-0	Good	**REQUINTO**	July	26	2011
5f	56.0 secs	5	9-0	Good To Firm	**RUDI'S PET**	July	27	1999
6f	1m 09.8	2	8-11	Good To Firm	**BACHIR**	July	28	1999
6f	1m 09.1	6	9-0	Good To Firm	**TAMAGIN**	Sep	12	2009
7f	1m 24.9	2	8-11	Good To Firm	**EKRAAR**	July	29	1999
7f	1m 23.8	3	8-7	Firm	**BRIEF GLIMPSE**	July	25	1995
1m	1m 37.21	2	9-0	Good	**CALDRA**	Sep	9	2006
1m	1m 35.61	4	8-9	Good To Firm	**SPECTAIT**	Aug	4	2006
1m 1f	1m 52.8	3	9-6	Good	**VENA**	July	27	1995
1m 1f 192y	2m 02.81	3	9-3	Good To Firm	**ROAD TO LOVE**	Aug	3	2006
1m 3f	2m 23.0	3	8-8	Good To Firm	**ASIAN HEIGHTS**	May	22	2001
1m 4f	2m 31.5	3	8-10	Firm	**PRESENTING**	July	25	1995
1m 6f	2m 58.05	4	9-6	Good To Firm	**EASTERN ARIA**	July	29	2010
2m	3m 21.55	5	9-10	Good To Firm	**YEATS**	Aug	3	2006
2m 4f	4m 11.7	3	7-10	Firm	**LUCKY MOON**	Sep	2	1990

HAMILTON

DISTANCE	TIME	AGE	WEIGHT	GOING	HORSE	DATE		
5f 4y	57.95 secs	2	8-8	Good To Firm	ROSE BLOSSOM	May	29	2009
6f 5y	1m 10.0	2	8-12	Good To Firm	BREAK THE CODE	Aug	24	1999
6f 5y	1m 09.3	4	8-7	Firm	MARCUS GAME	July	11	1974
1m 65y	1m 45.8	2	8-11	Firm	HOPEFUL SUBJECT	Sep	24	1973
1m 65y	1m 42.7	6	7-7	Firm	CRANLEY	Sep	25	1972
1m 1f 36y	1m 53.6	5	9-6	Good To Firm	REGENT'S SECRET	Aug	10	2005
1m 3f 16y	2m 19.32	3	8-1	Good To Firm	CAPTAIN WEBB	May	16	2008
1m 3f 16y	2m 20.7	5	9-8	Good To Firm	WADI	July	20	2000
1m 4f 17y	2m 30.52	5	9-10	Good To Firm	RECORD BREAKER	Jun	10	2009
1m 5f 9y	2m 45.1	6	9-6	Firm	MENTALASANYTHIN	Jun	14	1995

HAYDOCK

DISTANCE	TIME	AGE	WEIGHT	GOING	HORSE	DATE		
5f (Inner)	57.67 secs	4	9-4	Good To Firm	SOLE POWER	May	21	2011
5f	59.2 secs	2	9-4	Firm	MONEY FOR NOTHING	Aug	21	1964
5f	57.15 secs	3	8-11	Good To Firm	FLEETING SPIRIT	Sep	3	2005
6f	1m 09.9	4	9-0	Good To Firm	IKTAMAL	Sep	7	1996
7f 30y	1m 29.4	2	9-0	Good To Firm	APPREHENSION	Sep	7	1996
7f 30y	1m 27.2	4	9-4	Firm	INDIAN KING	Jun	5	1982
1m 30y	1m 40.6	2	8-12	Good To Firm	BESIEGE	Sep	7	1996
1m	1m 40.07	3	8-2	Good	SAGRAMOR	May	21	2011
1m 2f 95y	2m 09.95	3	8-8	Good	JUKEBOX JURY	Aug	8	2009
1m 3f 200y	2m 26.4	5	8-2	Firm	NEW MEMBER	July	4	1970
1m 6f	2m 58.46	3	8-10	Good To Firm	MESHTRI	Sep	27	2008
2m 45y	3m 27.0	4	8-13	Firm	PRINCE OF PEACE	May	26	1984
2m 1f 130y	3m 55.0	3	8-12	Good	CRYSTAL SPIRIT	Sep	8	1990

KEMPTON (A.W)

DISTANCE	TIME	AGE	WEIGHT	GOING	HORSE	DATE		
5f	58.96	2	8-6	Standard	GLAMOROUS SPIRIT	Nov	28	2008
5f	58.50	5	9-4	Standard	PISCEAN	Oct	21	2010
6f	1m 11.44	2	9-5	Standard	SIGNS IN THE SAND	Oct	6	2010
6f	1m 11.02	4	8-13	Standard	MAC'S POWER	Sept	27	2010
7f	1m 24.73	2	9-3	Standard	STORM FORCE	Nov	3	2007
7f	1m 23.29	5	8-11	Standard	PRIMAEVAL	Nov	16	2011
1m	1m 38.13	2	8-12	Standard	PRIMEVERE	Oct	13	2010
1m	1m 35.73	3	8-9	Standard	WESTERN ARISTOCRAT	Sep	5	2011
1m	1m 36.58	6	9-2	Standard	RIGGINS	Nov	27	2010
1m 2f	2m 3.77	6	8-13	Standard	KANDIDATE	Mar	29	2008
1m 3f	2m 16.98	5	9-6	Standard	IRISH FLAME	Nov	10	2011
1m 4f	2m 29.33	4	9-3	Standard	PRINCE BISHOP	Nov	2	2011
2m	3m 24.70	4	10-1	Standard	SPICE FAIR	Oct	27	2011

LEICESTER

DISTANCE	TIME	AGE	WEIGHT	GOING	HORSE	DATE		
5f 2y	58.4 secs	2	9-0	Firm	CUTTING BLADE	Jun	9	1986
5f 2y	57.85 secs	5	9-5	Good To Firm	THE JOBBER	Sep	18	2006
5f 218y	1m 10.1	2	9-0	Firm	THORDIS	Oct	24	1995
5f 218y	1m 09.12	6	8-12	Good To Firm	PETER ISLAND	Apr	25	2009
7f 9y	1m 22.6	2	9-0	Good To Firm	MARIE DE MEDICI	Oct	6	2009
7f 9y	1m 20.8	3	8-7	Firm	FLOWER BOWL	Jun	9	1986
1m 60y	1m 44.05	2	8-11	Good To Firm	CONGRESSIONAL	Sep	6	2005
1m 60y	1m 41.89	5	9-7	Good To Firm	VAINGLORY	Jun	18	2009
1m 1f 218y	2m 05.3	2	9-1	Good To Firm	WINDSOR CASTLE	Oct	14	1996
1m 1f 218y	2m 02.4	3	8-11	Firm	EFFIGY	Nov	4	1985
1m 1f 218y	2m 02.4	4	9-6	Good To Firm	LADY ANGHARAD	Jun	18	2000
1m 3f 183y	2m 27.1	5	8-12	Good To Firm	MURGHEM	Jun	18	2000

LINGFIELD (TURF)

DISTANCE	TIME	AGE	WEIGHT	GOING	HORSE	DATE		
5f	57.07 secs	2	9-0	Good To Firm	QUITE A THING	June	11	2011
5f	56.09 secs	3	9-4	Good To Firm	PERFECT TRIBUTE	May	7	2011
6f	1m 08.36	2	8-12	Good To Firm	FOLLY BRIDGE	Sep	8	2009
6f	1m 08.2	6	9-10	Firm	AL AMEAD	July	2	1986
7f	1m 21.3	2	7-6	Firm	MANDAV	Oct	3	1980
7f	1m 20.1	3	8-7	Good To Firm	ZELAH	May	13	1998
7f 140y	1m 29.9	2	8-12	Firm	RATHER WARM	Nov	7	1978
7f 140y	1m 26.7	3	8-6	Good To Firm	HIAAM	Jul	11	1987
1m 1f	1m 52.4	4	9-2	Good To Firm	QUANDARY	July	15	1995
1m 2f	2m 04.6	3	9-3	Firm	USRAN	July	15	1989
1m 3f 106y	2m 23.3	3	8-5	Firm	NIGHT-SHIRT	July	14	1990
1m 6f	2m 59.1	5	9-5	Firm	IBN BEY	July	1	1989
2m	3m 23.7	3	9-5	Good To Firm	LAURIES CRUSADOR	Aug	13	1988

LINGFIELD (A.W)

DISTANCE	TIME	AGE	WEIGHT	GOING	HORSE	DATE		
5f	58.29 secs	2	8-8	Standard	SMOKEY RYDER	Dec	14	2008
5f	57.26 secs	3	8-12	Standard	MAGIC GLADE	Feb	27	2007
6f	1m 09.99	2	8-12	Standard	SWISS DIVA	Nov	19	2008
6f	1m 09.61	6	9-0	Standard	EXCUSEZ MOI	Feb	23	2008
6f	1m 09.61	4	9-5	Standard	JACONET	Sep	4	2009
7f	1m 23.68	2	8-4	Standard	YOUNG DOTTIE	Oct	21	2008
7f	1m 22.7	6	9-12	Standard	VORTEX	Apr	9	2005
1m	1m 36.38	2	9-0	Standard	GOODISON GLORY	Nov	19	2008
1m	1m 34.77	4	9-3	Standard	BAHARAH	Oct	30	2008
1m 2f	2m 01.79	5	9-0	Standard	CUSOON	Feb	24	2007
1m 4f	2m 28.10	3	8-10	Standard	FALCATIV	Feb	2	2007
1m 5f	2m 41.08	3	8-8	Standard	MISCHIEF MAKER	Oct	30	2008
2m	3m 20.07	4	9-0	Standard	NIGHT CRUISE	Aug	8	1992

MUSSELBURGH

DISTANCE	TIME	AGE	WEIGHT	GOING	HORSE	DATE		
5f	57.7 secs	2	8-2	Firm	ARASONG	May	16	1994
5f	57.3 secs	3	8-12	Firm	CORUNNA	Jun	3	2000
7f 30y	1m 27.46	2	8-8	Good	DURHAM REFLECTION	Sep	14	2009
7f 30y	1m 27.1	5	8-12	Good	DIAMOND DECORUM	Jun	18	2001
1m	1m 40.3	2	8-12	Good To Firm	SUCCESSION	Sep	26	2004
1m	1m 36.83	3	9-5	Good To Firm	GINGER JACK	July	13	2010
1m 1f	1m 50.42	8	8-11	Good To Firm	DHAULAR DHAR	Sep	3	2010
1m 4f	2m 33.7	3	9-11	Firm	ALEXANDRINE	Jun	26	2000
1m 4f 100y	2m 36.80	3	8-3	Good To Firm	HARRIS TWEED	Jun	5	2010
1m 5f	2m 47.51	6	9-11	Good To Firm	DIMASHQ	July	31	2008
1m 6f	2m 59.2	3	9-7	Firm	FORUM CHRIS	July	3	2000
2m	3m 28.1	3	8-1	Good To Firm	WARRING KINGDOM	Sep	13	1999

NEWBURY

DISTANCE	TIME	AGE	WEIGHT	GOING	HORSE	DATE		
5f 34y	59.1 secs	2	8-6	Good To Firm	SUPERSTAR LEO	July	22	2000
5f 34y	59.2 secs	3	9-5	Good To Firm	THE TRADER	Aug	18	2001
6f 8y	1m 11.07	2	8-4	Good To Firm	BAHATI	May	30	2009
6f 8y	1m 09.42	3	8-11	Good To Firm	NOTA BENE	May	13	2005
7f	1m 24.1	2	8-11	Good To Firm	HAAFHD	Aug	15	2003
7f	1m 21.5	3	8-4	Good To Firm	THREE POINTS	July	21	2000
1m	1m 37.5	2	9-1	Good To Firm	WINGED CUPID	Sep	16	2005
1m	1m 33.59	6	9-0	Firm	RAKTI	May	14	2005
1m 1f	1m 49.6	3	8-0	Good To Firm	HOLTYE	May	21	1995
1m 2f 6y	2m 1.2	3	8-7	Good To Firm	WALL STREET	July	20	1996
1m 3f 5y	2m 16.5	3	8-9	Good To Firm	GRANDERA	Sep	22	2001
1m 4f 5y	2m 28.26	4	9-7	Good To Firm	AZAMOUR	Jul	23	2005
1m 5f 61y	2m 44.9	5	10-0	Good To Firm	MYSTIC HILL	July	20	1996
2m	3m 25.4	8	9-12	Good To Firm	MOONLIGHT QUEST	July	19	1996

NEWCASTLE

DISTANCE	TIME	AGE	WEIGHT	GOING	HORSE	DATE		
5f	58.8 secs	2	9-0	Firm	ATLANTIC VIKING	Jun	4	1997
5f	58.0 secs	4	9-2	Firm	PRINCESS OBERON	July	23	1994
6f	1m 11.98	2	9-3	Good	PEARL ARCH	Sep	6	2010
6f	1m 10.58	4	9-9	Good To Firm	JONNY MUDBALL	June	26	2010
7f	1m 24.2	2	9-0	Good To Firm	ISCAN	Aug	31	1998
7f	1m 23.3	4	9-2	Good To Firm	QUIET VENTURE	Aug	31	1998
1m 3y	1m 37.1	2	8-3	Good To Firm	HOH STEAMER	Aug	31	1998
1m 3y	1m 37.3	3	8-8	Good To Firm	ITS MAGIC	May	27	1999
1m 1f 9y	2m 03.2	2	8-13	Soft	RESPONSE	Oct	30	1993
1m 1f 9y	1m 58.4	3	8-8	Good To Firm	INTRODUCING	Aug	6	2003
1m 2f 32y	2m 06.5	3	8-11	Firm	MISSIONARY RIDGE	July	29	1990
1m 4f 93y	2m 37.3	5	8-12	Firm	RETENDER	Jun	25	1994
1m 6f 97y	3m 06.4	3	9-6	Good To Firm	ONE OFF	Aug	6	2003
2m 19y	3m 24.3	4	8-10	Good	FAR CRY	Jun	26	1999

NEWMARKET (ROWLEY)

DISTANCE	TIME	AGE	WEIGHT	GOING	HORSE	DATE		
5f	58.76 secs	2	8-5	Good To Firm	VALIANT ROMEO	Oct	3	2002
5f	56.8 secs	6	9-2	Good To Firm	LOCHSONG	Apr	30	1994
6f	1m 09.56	2	8-12	Good To Firm	BUSHRANGER	Oct	3	2008
7f	1m 22.39	2	8-12	Good To Firm	ASHRAM	Oct	2	2008
7f	1m 22.2	4	9-5	Good To Firm	PERFOLIA	Oct	17	1991
1m	1m 35.7	2	9-0	Good To Firm	FORWARD MOVE	Sep	21	2004
1m	1m 34.07	4	9-0	Good To Firm	EAGLE MOUNTAIN	Oct	3	2008
1m 1f	1m 47.26	5	8-12	Good To Firm	MANDURO	Apr	19	2007
1m 2f	2m 04.6	2	9-4	Good	HIGHLAND CHIEFTAIN	Nov	2	1985
1m 2f	2m 00.13	3	8-12	Good	NEW APPROACH	Oct	18	2008
1m 4f	2m 26.07	3	8-9	Good To Firm	MOHEDIAN LADY	Sept	22	2011
1m 6f	2m 51.59	3	8-7	Good	ART EYES	Sep	29	2005
2m	3m 18.64	5	9-6	Good To Firm	TIMES UP	Sept	22	2011
2m 2f	3m 47.5	3	7-12	Hard	WHITEWAY	Oct	15	1947

NEWMARKET (JULY)

DISTANCE	TIME	AGE	WEIGHT	GOING	HORSE	DATE		
5f	58.5 secs	2	8-10	Good	SEDUCTRESS	July	10	1990
5f	56.09 secs	6	9-11	Good	BORDERLESCOTT	Aug	22	2008
6f	1m 10.35	3	8-11	Good	ELNAWIN	Aug	22	2008
6f	1m 09.5	3	8-13	Good To Firm	STRAVINSKY	July	9	1999
7f	1m 23.96	2	8-12	Good	DISCOURSE	Aug	6	2011
7f	1m 22.5	3	9-7	Firm	HO LENG	July	9	1998
1m	1m 37.47	2	8-13	Good	WHIPPERS LOVE	Aug	28	2009
1m	1m 35.5	3	8-6	Good To Firm	LOVERS KNOT	July	8	1998
1m 110y	1m 44.1	3	8-11	Good	GOLDEN SNAKE	Apr	15	1999
1m 2f	2m 00.9	4	9-3	Good To Firm	ELHAYQ	May	1	1999
1m 4f	2m 25.11	3	8-11	Good	LUSH LASHES	Aug	22	2008
1m 6f 175y	3m 04.2	3	8-5	Good	ARRIVE	July	11	2001
2m 24y	3m 20.2	7	9-10	Good	YORKSHIRE	July	11	2001

NOTTINGHAM

DISTANCE	TIME	AGE	WEIGHT	GOING	HORSE	DATE		
5f 13y	57.9 secs	2	8-9	Firm	HOH MAGIC	May	13	1994
5f 13y	57.6 secs	6	9-2	Good To Firm	CATCH THE CAT	May	14	2005
6f 15y	1m 11.4	2	8-11	Firm	JAMEELAPI	Aug	8	1983
6f 15y	1m 10.0	4	9-2	Firm	AJANAC	Aug	8	1988
1m 75y	1m 45.23	2	9-0	Good To Firm	TACTFULLY	Sept	28	2011
1m 75y	1m 42.25	5	9-1	Good To Firm	RIO DE LA PLATA	June	2	2010
1m 2f 213y	2m 02.3	2	9-0	Firm	AYAABI	July	21	1984
1m 2f 50y	2m 9.54	4	9-12	Good To Firm	GENEVA GEYSER	July	3	2010
1m 2f 50y (I)	2m 10.61	6	8-13	Firm	SHAVANSKY	April	27	2010
1m 6f 15y	2m 57.8	3	8-10	Firm	BUSTER JO	Oct	1	1985
2m 9y	3m 25.25	3	9-5	Good	BULWARK	Sep	27	2005
2m 2f 18y	3m 55.1	9	9-10	Good To Firm	PEARL RUN	May	1	1990

PONTEFRACT

DISTANCE	TIME	AGE	WEIGHT	GOING	HORSE	DATE		
5f	1m 01.1	2	9-0	Firm	GOLDEN BOUNTY	Sep	20	2001
5f	1m 00.8	4	8-9	Firm	BLUE MAEVE	Sep	29	2004
6f	1m 14.0	2	9-3	Firm	FAWZI	Sep	6	1983
6f	1m 12.6	3	7-13	Firm	MERRY ONE	Aug	29	1970
1m 4y	1m 42.8	2	9-13	Firm	STAR SPRAY	Sep	6	1970
1m 4y	1m 41.3	4	8-9	Firm	NIGRASINE	Sep	20	2001
1m 2f 6y	2m 12.8	2	9-0	Good To Firm	WARBROOK	Oct	2	1995
1m 2f 6y	2m 08.2	4	7-8	Hard	HAPPY HECTOR	July	9	1979
1m 4f 8y	2m 33.72	3	8-7	Firm	AJAAN	Aug	8	2007
2m 1f 22y	3m 40.67	4	8-7	Good To Firm	PARADISE FLIGHT	Jun	6	2005
2m 1f 216y	3m 51.1	3	8-8	Firm	KUDZ	Sep	9	1986
2m 5f 122y	4m 47.8	4	8-4	Firm	PHYSICAL	May	14	1984

REDCAR

DISTANCE	TIME	AGE	WEIGHT	GOING	HORSE	DATE		
5f	56.9 secs	2	9-0	Firm	MISTER JOEL	Oct	24	1995
5f	56.01 secs	10	9-3	Firm	HENRY HALL	Sep	20	2006
6f	1m 08.8	2	8-3	Good To Firm	OBE GOLD	Oct	2	2004
6f	1m 08.6	3	9-2	Good To Firm	SIZZLING SAGA	Jun	21	1991
7f	1m 21.28	2	9-3	Firm	KAROO BLUE	Sep	20	2006
7f	1m 21.0	3	9-1	Firm	EMPTY QUARTER	Oct	3	1995
1m	1m 34.37	2	9-0	Firm	MASTERSHIP	Sep	20	2006
1m	1m 32.42	4	10-0	Firm	NANTON	Sep	20	2006
1m 1f	1m 52.4	2	9-0	Firm	SPEAR	Sep	13	2004
1m 1f	1m 48.5	5	8-12	Firm	MELLOTTIE	July	25	1990
1m 2f	2m 10.1	2	8-11	Good	ADDING	Nov	10	1989
1m 2f	2m 01.4	5	9-2	Firm	ERADICATE	May	28	1990
1m 3f	2m 17.2	3	8-9	Firm	PHOTO CALL	Aug	7	1990
1m 5f 135y	2m 54.7	6	9-10	Firm	BRODESSA	Jun	20	1992
1m 6f 19y	2m 59.81	4	9-1	Good To Firm	ESPRIT DE CORPS	Sep	11	2006
2m 4y	3m 24.9	3	9-3	Good To Firm	SUBSONIC	Oct	8	1991

RIPON

DISTANCE	TIME	AGE	WEIGHT	GOING	HORSE	DATE		
5f	57.8 secs	2	8-8	Firm	SUPER ROCKY	July	5	1991
5f	57.6 secs	5	8-5	Good	BROADSTAIRS BEAUTY	May	21	1995
6f	1m 10.9	2	8-11	Good	KAHIR ALMAYDAN	Aug	28	1995
6f	1m 09.8	4	9-8	Good To Firm	TADEO	Aug	16	1997
6f	1m 09.8	5	7-10	Firm	QUOIT	July	23	1966
1m	1m 39.79	2	8-6	Good	TOP JARO	Sep	24	2005
1m	1m 36.62	4	8-11	Good To Firm	GRANSTON	Aug	29	2005
1m 1f	1m 50.4	3	9-2	Good To Firm	BOLD WORDS	Apr	9	1997
1m 2f	2m 02.6	3	9-4	Firm	SWIFT SWORD	July	20	1990
1m 4f 10y	2m 31.40	4	8-8	Good To Firm	DANDINO	Apr	16	2011
2m	3m 27.07	5	9-12	Good To Firm	GREENWICH MEANTIME	Aug	30	2005

SALISBURY

DISTANCE	TIME	AGE	WEIGHT	GOING	HORSE	DATE		
5f	59.3 secs	2	9-0	Good To Firm	AJIGOLO	May	12	2005
5f	59.4 secs	3	8-11	Firm	BELLSABANGING	May	5	1993
6f	1m 12.1	2	8-0	Good To Firm	PARISIAN LADY	Jun	10	1997
6f	1m 11.09	3	9-0	Firm	L'AMI LOUIS	May	1	2011
6f 212y	1m 25.9	2	9-0	Firm	MORE ROYAL	Jun	29	1995
6f 212y	1m 24.91	3	9-4	Firm	CHILWORTH LAD	May	1	2011
1m	1m 40.48	2	8-13	Firm	CHOIR MASTER	Sep	17	2002
1m	1m 38.29	3	8-7	Good To Firm	LAYMAN	Aug	11	2005
1m 1f 198y	2m 04.81	3	8-5	Good To Firm	PRIMEVERE	Aug	10	2011
1m 4f	2m 31.6	3	9-5	Good To Firm	ARRIVE	Jun	27	2001
1m 6f 15y	2m 59.4	3	8-6	Good To Firm	TABAREEH	Sep	2	1999

SANDOWN

DISTANCE	TIME	AGE	WEIGHT	GOING	HORSE	DATE		
5f 6y	59.4 secs	2	9-3	Firm	TIMES TIME	July	22	1982
5f 6y	58.8 secs	6	8-9	Good To Firm	PALACEGATE TOUCH	Sep	17	1996
7f 16y	1m 26.56	2	9-0	Good To Firm	RAVEN'S PASS	Sep	1	2007
7f 16y	1m 26.3	3	9-0	Firm	MAWSUFF	Jun	14	1983
1m 14y	1m 41.1	2	8-11	Firm	REFERENCE POINT	Sep	23	1986
1m 14y	1m 39.0	3	8-8	Firm	LINDA'S FANTASY	Aug	19	1983
1m 1f	1m 54.6	2	8-8	Good To Firm	FRENCH PRETENDER	Sep	20	1988
1m 1f	1m 52.4	7	9-3	Good To Firm	BOURGAINVILLE	Aug	11	2005
1m 2f 7y	2m 02.1	4	8-11	Firm	KALAGLOW	May	31	1982
1m 3f 91y	2m 21.6	4	8-3	Firm	AYLESFIELD	July	7	1984
1m 6f	2m 56.9	4	8-7	Good To Firm	LADY ROSANNA	July	19	1989
2m 78y	3m 29.86	4	9-0	Good To Firm	KING OF WANDS	July	3	2010

SOUTHWELL (TURF)

DISTANCE	TIME	AGE	WEIGHT	GOING	HORSE	DATE		
6f	1m 15.03	2	9-3	Good	TREPA	Sep	6	2006
6f	1m 13.48	4	8-10	Good	PARIS BELL	Sep	6	2006
7f	1m 27.56	2	9-7	Good	HART OF GOLD	Sep	6	2006
7f	1m 25.95	3	9-0	Good	AEROPLANE	Sep	6	2006
1m 2f	2m 7.47	3	8-11	Good To Firm	DESERT AUTHORITY	Sep	7	2006
1m 3f	2m 20.13	4	9-12	Good	SANCHI	Sep	6	2006
1m 4f	2m 34.4	5	9-3	Good To Firm	CORN LILY	Aug	10	1991
2m	3m 34.1	5	9-1	Good To Firm	TRIPLICATE	Sep	20	1991

SOUTHWELL (A.W)

DISTANCE	TIME	AGE	WEIGHT	GOING	HORSE	DATE		
5f	57.85 secs	2	9-3	Standard	ARCTIC FEELING	Mar	31	2010
5f	56.80 secs	5	9-7	Standard	GHOSTWING	Jan	3	2012
6f	1m 14.0	2	8-5	Standard	PANALO	Nov	8	1989
6f	1m 13.3	3	9-2	Standard	RAMBO EXPRESS	Dec	18	1990
7f	1m 27.1	2	8-2	Standard	MYSTIC CRYSTAL	Nov	20	1990
7f	1m 26.8	5	8-4	Standard	AMENABLE	Dec	13	1990
1m	1m 38.0	2	8-9	Standard	ALPHA RASCAL	Nov	13	1990
1m	1m 38.0	2	8-10	Standard	ANDREW'S FIRST	Dec	30	1989
1m	1m 37.2	3	8-6	Standard	VALIRA	Nov	3	1990
1m 3f	2m 21.5	4	9-7	Standard	TEMPERING	Dec	5	1990
1m 4f	2m 33.9	4	9-12	Standard	FAST CHICK	Nov	8	1989
1m 6f	3m 01.6	3	7-7	Standard	QUALITAIR AVIATOR	Dec	1	1989
1m 6f	3m 01.6	3	7-8	Standard	EREVNON	Dec	29	1990
2m	3m 37.6	9	8-12	Standard	OLD HUBERT	Dec	5	1990

THIRSK

DISTANCE	TIME	AGE	WEIGHT	GOING	HORSE	DATE		
5f	57.2 secs	2	9-7	Good To Firm	PROUD BOAST	Aug	5	2000
5f	56.1 secs	7	8-0	Firm	SIR SANDROVITCH	Jun	26	2003
6f	1m 09.2	2	9-6	Good To Firm	WESTCOURT MAGIC	Aug	25	1995
6f	1m 08.8	6	9-4	Firm	JOHAYRO	July	23	1999
7f	1m 23.7	2	8-9	Firm	COURTING	July	23	1999
7f	1m 22.8	4	8-5	Firm	SILVER HAZE	May	21	1988
1m	1m 37.9	2	9-0	Good To Firm	SUNDAY SYMPHONY	Sep	4	2004
1m	1m 34.8	4	8-13	Firm	YEARSLEY	May	5	1990
1m 4f	2m 29.9	5	9-12	Firm	GALLERY GOD	Jun	4	2001
2m	3m 22.3	3	8-10	Firm	TOMASCHEK	Aug	1	1964

WARWICK

DISTANCE	TIME	AGE	WEIGHT	GOING	HORSE	DATE		
5f	57.95 secs	2	8-9	Good To Firm	AMOUR PROPRE	Jun	26	2008
5f	57.8 secs	5	9-4	Good To Firm	ANOTHER EPISODE	Aug	29	1994
5f 110y	1m 03.6	5	8-6	Good To Firm	DIZZY IN THE HEAD	Jun	27	2004
6f	1m 11.22	2	9-3	Good To Firm	HURRICANE HYMNBOOK	Sep	15	2007
6f	1m 09.44	5	8-12	Good To Firm	PETER ISLAND	Jun	26	2008
7f 26y	1m 22.9	2	9-3	Good To Firm	COUNTRY RAMBLER	Jun	20	2004
7f 26y	1m 21.2	3	8-11	Good To Firm	LUCKY SPIN	Jun	19	2004
1m 22y	1m 37.1	3	8-11	Firm	ORINOCOVSKY	Jun	26	2002
1m 2f 188y	2m 14.98	4	8-12	Good To Firm	RONALDSAY	Jun	16	2008
1m 4f 134y	2m 39.5	3	8-13	Good To Firm	MAIMANA	Jun	22	2002
1m 6f 135y	3m 07.5	3	9-7	Good To Firm	BURMA BAY	July	2	1999
2m 39y	3m 30.6	5	8-1	Good To Firm	RENAISSANCE LADY	Jun	27	2001

WINDSOR

DISTANCE	TIME	AGE	WEIGHT	GOING	HORSE	DATE		
5f 10y	58.69 secs	2	9-0	Good To Firm	CHARLES THE GREAT	May	23	2011
5f 10y	58.08 secs	5	8-13	Good To Firm	TAURUS TWINS	April	4	2011
6f	1m 10.5	2	9-5	Good To Firm	CUBISM	Aug	17	1998
6f	1m 09.89	4	9-0	Good To Firm	BATED BREATH	May	23	2011
1m 67y	1m 42.46	2	8-9	Good To Firm	TIGER CUB	Oct	10	2011
1m 67y	1m 40.19	4	9-4	Good	NATIONALISM	June	25	2011
1m 2f 7y	2m 03.0	3	9-1	Firm	MOOMBA MASQUERADE	May	19	1990
1m 3f 135y	2m 21.5	3	9-2	Firm	DOUBLE FLORIN	May	19	1980

WOLVERHAMPTON (A.W)

DISTANCE	TIME	AGE	WEIGHT	GOING	HORSE	DATE		
5f 20y	1m 01.13	2	8-8	Standard To Fast	YUNGABURRA	Nov	8	2006
5f 20y	1m 00.22	5	9-3	Standard	DEERSLAYER	Aug	30	2011
5f 216y	1m 12.61	2	9-0	Standard To Fast	PRIME DEFENDER	Nov	8	2006
7f 32y	1m 27.7	2	9-5	Standard	BILLY DANE	Aug	14	2006
7f 32y	1m 26.86	6	9-3	Standard	BORDER MUSIC	Mar	10	2007
1m 141y	1m 48.08	2	8-9	Standard To Fast	WORLDLY	Aug	30	2006
1m 141y	1m 46.48	3	8-9	Standard	GITANO HERNANDO	Sep	17	2009
1m 1f 103y	1m 57.34	4	8-13	Standard	BAHAR SHUMAAL	Oct	28	2006
1m 4f 50y	2m 34.75	5	8-13	Standard To Fast	FANTOCHE	May	3	2007
1m 5f 194y	2m 59.85	6	9-12	Standard To Fast	VALANCE	Aug	30	2006
2m 119y	3m 35.85	5	8-11	Standard To Fast	MARKET WATCHER	Nov	21	2006

YARMOUTH

DISTANCE	TIME	AGE	WEIGHT	GOING	HORSE	DATE		
5f 43y	1m 00.4	2	8-6	Good To Firm	EBBA	July	26	1999
5f 43y	1m 00.2	3	8-11	Firm	CHARM BIRD	Sep	15	1988
6f 3y	1m 10.4	2	9-0	Firm	LANCHESTER	Aug	15	1988
6f 3y	1m 10.0	3	8-10	Good To Firm	TIPSY CREEK	Aug	10	1997
7f 3y	1m 22.2	2	9-0	Good To Firm	WARRSHAN	Sep	14	1988
7f 3y	1m 22.12	4	9-4	Good To Firm	GLENBUCK	Apr	26	2007
1m 3y	1m 36.3	2	8-2	Good To Firm	OUTRUN	Sep	15	1988
1m 3y	1m 33.9	3	8-8	Firm	BONNE ETOILE	Jun	27	1995
1m 1f	1m 53.01	3	8-13	Good To Firm	DUBAWI DANCER	July	12	2011
1m 2f 21y	2m 02.83	2	8-9	Firm	REUNITE	July	18	2006
1m 3f 101y	2m 23.1	3	8-9	Firm	RAHIL	July	1	1993
1m 6f 17y	2m 57.8	3	8-2	Good To Firm	BARAKAT	July	24	1990
2m	3m 26.7	4	8-2	Good To Firm	ALHESN	July	26	1999
2m 2f 51y	3m 56.8	4	9-10	Firm	PROVENCE	Sep	19	1991

YORK

DISTANCE	TIME	AGE	WEIGHT	GOING	HORSE	DATE		
5f 3y	57.33 secs	2	9-0	Good To Firm	STAR ROVER	Aug	19	2009
5f 3y	56.2 secs	3	9-9	Good To Firm	OASIS DREAM	Aug	21	2003
5f 89y	1m 2.31	2	9-3	Good To Firm	EL VIENTO	Sept	5	2010
5f 89y	1m 2.31	6	9-5	Good To Firm	BARNEY MCGREW	Aug	18	2009
6f	1m 9.28	2	8-12	Good To Firm	SHOWCASING	Aug	19	2009
6f	1m 08.58	7	9-4	Firm	CAPE OF GOOD HOPE	Jun	16	2005
7f	1m 22.45	2	9-0	Good To Firm	ELUSIVE PIMPERNEL	Aug	18	2009
7f	1m 21.85	4	8-11	Good	CHACHAMAIDEE	May	21	2011
1m	1m 36.24	3	9-2	Good To Firm	CAPPONI	Jul	10	2010
1m 205y	1m 52.4	2	8-1	Good To Firm	ORAL EVIDENCE	Oct	6	1988
1m 208y	1m 46.76	5	9-8	Good To Firm	ECHO OF LIGHT	Sep	5	2007
1m 2f 88y	2m 05.29	3	8-11	Good To Firm	SEA THE STARS	Aug	18	2009
1m 3f 198y	2m 27.4	4	9-4	Good To Firm	ISLINGTON	Aug	20	2003
1m 6f	2m 54.96	4	9-0	Good To Firm	TACTIC	May	22	2010
1m 7f 195y	3m 18.4	3	8-0	Good To Firm	DAM BUSTERS	Aug	16	1988
2m 88y	3m 30.63	4	9-1	Good To Firm	ASKAR TAU	Aug	19	2009

TOP FLAT JOCKEYS IN BRITAIN 2011

W-R	%	JOCKEY	2ND	3RD	TOTAL PRIZE	WIN PRIZE
177-1209	15%	PAUL HANAGAN	171	147	1,553,345	897,284
167-1053	16%	SILVESTRE DE SOUSA	140	112	1,236,638	764,122
154-933	17%	KIEREN FALLON	123	113	1,879,837	1,026,091
130-722	18%	RICHARD HUGHES	98	86	2,653,776	1,771,219
128-1330	10%	LUKE MORRIS	152	160	671,592	380,446
124-721	17%	JAMIE SPENCER	88	97	1,828,874	1,114,384
115-794	14%	ADAM KIRBY	91	93	719,925	426,595
106-620	17%	WILLIAM BUICK	77	77	2,527,960	1,854,849
103-638	16%	JOE FANNING	89	72	587,987	401,345
101-531	19%	RYAN MOORE	84	56	2,640,027	1,066,792
100-735	14%	TOM QUEALLY	72	59	2,562,513	1,871,453
97-738	13%	NEIL CALLAN	98	86	1,033,430	586,994
96-826	12%	DANE O'NEILL	108	106	684,900	352,894
94-701	13%	PHILLIP MAKIN	66	73	837,640	629,282
94-798	12%	JIM CROWLEY	84	82	824,543	513,514
93-1028	9%	TOM EAVES	103	110	542,333	322,693
88-574	15%	HAYLEY TURNER	73	62	925,920	766,423
87-731	12%	GRAHAM GIBBONS	90	86	527,298	325,808
78-627	12%	ROBERT WINSTON	59	87	555,624	377,673
78-635	12%	SEB SANDERS	73	82	514,760	314,075
77-750	10%	SHANE KELLY	93	82	602,578	348,018
76-584	13%	GEORGE BAKER	70	65	613,723	355,486
76-639	12%	JAMES DOYLE	71	67	290,937	193,416
72-367	20%	FRANKIE DETTORI	57	43	2,231,104	1,684,110
71-781	9%	CATHY GANNON	93	98	378,621	197,074
68-589	12%	EDDIE AHERN	74	68	823,900	575,394
67-530	13%	MARTIN HARLEY	62	53	277,118	170,097
67-588	11%	JIMMY FORTUNE	72	55	978,740	605,618
67-592	11%	FREDERIK TYLICKI	57	62	438,187	305,541
64-531	12%	RICHARD KINGSCOTE	64	55	390,179	262,907
63-483	13%	KIERAN O'NEILL	50	62	297,710	182,100
63-533	12%	WILLIAM CARSON	45	43	219,016	161,546
63-575	11%	DAVID PROBERT	51	57	536,827	348,366
63-627	10%	STEVE DROWNE	61	58	677,256	314,133
61-762	8%	LIAM KENIRY	77	79	308,656	168,736
58-465	12%	TED DURCAN	45	56	590,240	373,514
57-576	10%	P J McDONALD	59	58	291,140	185,378
56-368	15%	RICHARD HILLS	58	48	838,976	315,570
56-653	9%	FERGUS SWEENEY	66	71	278,449	188,817
55-482	11%	ANDREA ATZENI	45	49	238,589	155,071
54-532	10%	IAN MONGAN	58	69	798,131	562,279
54-785	7%	CHRIS CATLIN	77	77	380,494	151,519
53-497	11%	MARTIN DWYER	50	46	546,063	343,954
52-503	10%	DAVID ALLAN	53	61	525,721	286,936
51-626	8%	MARTIN LANE	57	72	302,999	163,295
50-421	12%	BARRY McHUGH	38	39	224,420	161,130
50-721	7%	JAMES SULLIVAN	80	58	315,631	205,730
49-487	10%	FRANNY NORTON	61	59	404,966	253,095
47-380	12%	HARRY BENTLEY	44	35	286,801	199,937
46-302	15%	PAT DOBBS	37	29	340,996	236,180

TOP FLAT TRAINERS IN BRITAIN 2011

TRAINER	LEADING HORSE	W-R	2ND	3RD	4TH	TOTAL PRIZE	WIN PRIZE
RICHARD HANNON	Canford Cliffs	218-1408	205	158	149	3,726,396	2,283,589
A P O'BRIEN	So You Think	16-81	10	10	10	2,894,456	1,408,506
SIR HENRY CECIL	Frankel	55-285	44	32	33	2,750,157	2,094,982
JOHN GOSDEN	Nathaniel	99-553	75	84	57	2,529,369	1,828,265
MAHMOOD AL ZAROONI	Blue Bunting	81-409	57	50	42	1,874,348	1,469,722
RICHARD FAHEY	Miss Work Of Art	151-1224	137	122	118	1,650,127	980,328
SIR MICHAEL STOUTE	Workforce	53-366	63	50	40	1,554,607	596,991
MARK JOHNSTON	Namibian	179-1311	157	143	100	1,550,631	927,711
KEVIN RYAN	Bogart	133-797	100	78	53	1,326,031	984,501
WILLIAM HAGGAS	Dancing Rain	76-423	72	62	38	1,228,089	848,955
MICK CHANNON	Samitar	92-801	91	112	75	1,080,893	605,061
ANDREW BALDING	Charles The Great	70-543	74	60	54	971,676	620,393
SAEED BIN SUROOR	Delegator	58-375	61	46	40	921,445	494,862
TIM EASTERBY	Hamish McGonagall	90-902	88	101	87	882,568	481,298
DAVID SIMCOCK	Dream Ahead	46-371	51	50	39	803,988	565,049
A FABRE	Pour Moi	1-3	1	1	0	749,733	709,625
BRIAN MEEHAN	Mehdi	59-542	52	50	52	748,605	375,824
MME C BARANDE-BARBE	Cirrus Des Aigles	1-1	0	0	0	737,230	737,230
DAVID NICHOLLS	St Moritz	93-944	92	90	60	714,534	403,824
ROGER CHARLTON	Bated Breath	43-233	32	20	25	713,403	284,117
ROGER VARIAN	Dominant	53-272	35	25	36	702,386	387,237
JAMES FANSHAWE	Deacon Blues	32-201	36	14	18	698,357	609,452
LUCA CUMANI	Drunken Sailor	45-319	54	34	23	677,506	356,471
ED DUNLOP	Snow Fairy	54-388	43	41	41	650,899	209,840
MARCO BOTTI	Excelebration	46-274	43	32	27	636,721	271,055
HUGHIE MORRISON	Pastoral Player	50-352	37	30	28	580,023	454,663
CLIVE COX	Beacon Lodge	52-375	37	62	35	575,570	302,357
MICHAEL BELL	Margot Did	44-322	41	31	23	574,823	375,995
B W HILLS	Ransom Note	50-326	47	38	23	561,673	247,508
DAVID BARRON	Hitchens	57-398	52	47	38	486,023	255,917
DAVID O'MEARA	Smarty Socks	48-423	52	51	40	479,370	297,865
TOM DASCOMBE	Brown Panther	51-456	53	49	37	466,291	220,653
JOHN DUNLOP	Times Up	48-321	32	31	37	447,186	322,747
BRYAN SMART	Excelette	69-489	57	55	44	440,297	265,886
JEREMY NOSEDA	Talwar	62-257	27	38	23	424,165	281,304
ALAN MCCABE	Caspar Netscher	61-640	78	75	45	394,517	260,825
CHARLES HILLS	Hazel Lavery	20-152	20	18	14	388,922	165,402
DAVID ELSWORTH	Eton Rifles	30-224	25	26	18	376,910	254,698
DAVID EVANS	Norville	77-841	102	104	67	372,951	207,644
BRIAN ELLISON	Moyenne Corniche	53-371	48	29	28	368,076	271,316
SIR MARK PRESCOTT BT	Coeus	54-251	30	36	17	366,449	274,351
ALAN BAILEY	Barbican	40-267	27	34	26	359,565	284,615
RALPH BECKETT	Moon Pearl	56-369	48	46	33	358,540	199,901
MICHAEL EASTERBY	Hoof It	39-470	44	40	33	342,930	244,463
ROBERT COLLET	Immortal Verse	1-4	1	1	0	310,677	141,925
MICHAEL DODS	Sweet Lightning	39-404	47	50	34	301,165	187,809
J S BOLGER	Parish Hall	2-11	1	1	1	301,050	236,540
HENRY CANDY	Dinkum Diamond	23-217	32	26	21	297,753	132,127
JIM GOLDIE	Hawkeyethenoo	35-358	35	35	43	290,481	174,353
CHRIS WALL	Premio Loco	26-228	18	26	14	275,227	180,233

TOP FLAT OWNERS IN BRITAIN IN 2011

OWNER	LEADING HORSE	W-R	2ND	3RD	4TH	TOTAL PRIZE	WIN PRIZE
K ABDULLA	FRANKEL	63-325	43	38	33	3,470,858	2,312,596
GODOLPHIN	BLUE BUNTING	139-784	118	96	82	2,795,794	1,964,584
HAMDAN AL MAKTOUM	MAQAASID	100-649	92	78	66	1,151,387	538,584
DR MARWAN KOUKASH	NEVER CAN TELL	74-500	58	51	36	978,826	661,977
SMITH, MRS MAGNIER, TABOR	ST NICHOLAS ABBEY	5-20	2	4	1	874,960	341,166
SHEIKH HAMDAN BIN MOHAMMED AL M'	NAMIBIAN	84-532	74	49	46	860,938	523,876
MRS J MAGNIER, M TABOR & D SMITH	POUR MOI	2-13	0	1	2	828,438	743,651
LADY ROTHSCHILD	NATHANIEL	12-49	5	5	8	805,376	741,357
JEAN-CLAUDE-ALAIN DUPOUY	CIRRUS DES AIGLES	1-1	0	0	0	737,230	737,230
M TABOR, D SMITH & MRS JOHN MAGNIER	POWER	7-34	6	3	6	733,952	305,482
ANDREW TINKLER	TELL DAD	34-246	32	31	16	716,456	369,680
SMITH/MAGNIER/TABOR/DATO TAN/YAHAYA	SO YOU THINK	1-3	2	0	0	592,420	226,840
B E NIELSEN	MASKED MARVEL	10-45	5	4	5	429,042	374,782
KHALIFA DASMAL	DREAM AHEAD	4-34	2	3	1	417,482	397,515
THE QUEEN	CARLTON HOUSE	16-98	13	11	8	399,945	169,276
MRS J WOOD	STRONG SUIT	15-132	18	18	15	365,408	212,222
CHEVELEY PARK STUD	REGAL REALM	32-210	28	34	26	355,111	171,929
H R H PRINCESS HAYA OF JORDAN	ZUIDER ZEE	25-153	20	24	17	348,519	191,185
M J & L A TAYLOR	DANCING RAIN	3-7	1	0	1	340,442	330,810
MRS ANGIE BAILEY	BOGART	12-71	5	4	4	314,691	287,223
HEFFER SYND, TABOR & SMITH	CANFORD CLIFFS	2-3	1	0	0	305,772	241,272
PEARL BLOODSTOCK LTD	LIGHTENING PEARL	15-77	5	4	11	301,908	213,961
JABER ABDULLAH	FACTORY TIME	24-203	30	29	24	297,569	115,527
COUPE DE VILLE PARTNERSHIP	COUPE DE VILLE	4-6	1	0	0	297,532	290,649
N & O DHANDSA & J & Z WEBSTER	SAMITAR	4-23	5	3	1	278,366	204,616
J & P HOPPER & M MORRIS	DEACON BLUES	4-5	1	0	0	263,300	260,795
ANAMOINE LIMITED	SNOW FAIRY	0-12	2	3	2	257,176	0
SAEED MANANA	WAHYLAH	16-236	21	22	15	254,488	147,040
SALEH AL HOMAIZI & IMAD AL SAGAR	GREEN DESTINY	7-44	6	4	5	252,030	209,576
R C STRAUSS	IMMORTAL VERSE	1-2	0	1	0	249,525	141,925
MRS J S BOLGER	PARISH HALL	2-6	0	0	0	244,879	236,540
SHEIKH SULTAN BIN KHALIFA AL NAHYAN	VITA NOVA	18-86	9	18	7	242,086	97,429
SIMON GIBSON	SOCIETY ROCK	3-15	1	0	0	237,229	230,314
J C SMITH	HIGHLAND KNIGHT	18-163	16	18	18	235,706	141,463
MANFREDINI/TABOR/SMITH/MAGNIER	EXCELEBRATION	0-1	1	0	0	215,000	0
MRS JOHN MAGNIER	REPLY	1-3	0	0	1	212,663	207,293
JOHN STOCKER	BARBICAN	14-65	8	9	3	208,982	177,211
JOHN MANLEY	DICK TURPIN	5-12	1	1	2	208,963	156,954
DASMAL, RIX, BARR, MORLEY, PENNEY	PROHIBIT	1-4	0	2	0	208,537	170,310
T REDMAN AND P PHILIPPS	MARGOT DID	3-6	0	1	2	202,677	195,804
NORMANDIE STUD LTD	DUNCAN	7-33	7	2	4	199,195	124,992
OWEN PROMOTIONS LIMITED	BROWN PANTHER	7-28	5	3	3	187,448	57,095
IRAJ PARVIZI	MEHDI	5-34	4	6	1	185,717	65,960
CHARLES WENTWORTH	CASPAR NETSCHER	13-85	12	11	5	182,395	146,363
GEORGE STRAWBRIDGE	NIGHT CARNATION	13-56	4	6	9	182,081	114,632
A D SPENCE	JUKEBOX JURY	13-134	14	23	14	175,798	75,126
SIR ROBERT OGDEN	CLUB OCEANIC	21-97	13	13	5	171,030	120,001
LORDSHIP STUD	SWISS DREAM	8-44	8	6	3	170,837	94,859
P A BYRNE	AULD BURNS	5-23	5	2	2	169,112	151,240
H R H SULTAN AHMAD SHAH	SRI PUTRA	12-43	4	6	3	165,722	64,154

TOP FLAT HORSES IN BRITAIN 2011

HORSE (AGE)	WIN & PLACE £	W-R	TRAINER	OWNER	BREEDER
FRANKEL (3)	1,106,235	5-5	Sir Henry Cecil	K Abdulla	Juddmonte Farms Ltd
NATHANIEL (3)	746,518	3-5	John Gosden	Lady Rothschild	Kincorth Investments Inc
CIRRUS DES AIGLES (5)	737,230	1-1	Mme C Barande-Barbe	J-C-A Dupouy & Xavier Niel	Y Lelimouzin & B Deschamps
POUR MOI (3)	709,625	1-1	A Fabre	Mrs John Magnier, M Tabor & D Smith	Lynch Bages Ltd
SO YOU THINK (5)	592,420	1-3	A P O'Brien	Smith/Magnier/Tabor/ Dato Tan/Tunku Yahaya	M J Moran & Piper Farm Ltd
TWICE OVER (6)	466,802	2-5	Sir Henry Cecil	K Abdulla	Juddmonte Farms Ltd
MIDDAY (5)	435,663	2-5	Sir Henry Cecil	K Abdulla	Juddmonte Farms Ltd
BLUE BUNTING (3)	414,283	2-4	Mahmood Al Zarooni	Godolphin	B M Kelley
DREAM AHEAD (3)	367,287	2-3	David Simcock	Khalifa Dasmal	Darley
MASKED MARVEL (3)	352,993	3-5	John Gosden	B E Nielsen	Newsells Park Stud
WORKFORCE (4)	350,522	1-3	Sir Michael Stoute	K Abdulla	Juddmonte Farms Ltd
DANCING RAIN (3)	337,266	3-4	William Haggas	M J & L A Taylor	Swettenham Stud
CANFORD CLIFFS (4)	305,772	2-3	Richard Hannon	The Heffer Syndicate, M Tabor & D Smith	S And S Hubbard Rodwell
ST NICHOLAS ABBEY (4)	300,581	2-3	A P O'Brien	D Smith, Mrs J Magnier, M Tabor	Barton Bldstock & Villiers Synd
EXCELEBRATION (3)	298,053	1-4	Marco Botti	Manfredini, Tabor, Smith & Magnier	Owenstown Stud
COUPE DE VILLE (2)	297,532	4-6	Richard Hannon	Coupe de Ville Partnership	Flor Ryan
TREASURE BEACH (3)	297,385	1-2	A P O'Brien	Smith, Magnier, Tabor	Ashley House Stud
BOGART (2)	269,491	3-5	Kevin Ryan	Mrs Angie Bailey	Toby Barker
FAME AND GLORY (5)	268,118	2-2	A P O'Brien	Mrs F Hay, D Smith, Mrs J Magnier,M Tabor	Ptarmigan Bloodstock & Miss K Rausing
SAMITAR (2)	264,340	2-6	Mick Channon	Nick & Olga Dhandsa & John & Zoe Webster	Norman Court Stud
DEACON BLUES (4)	263,300	4-5	James Fanshawe	Jan & Peter Hopper & Michelle Morris	Mr & Mrs K W Grundy, Mr & Mrs P Hopper
OPINION POLL (5)	259,246	2-5	Mahmood Al Zarooni	Godolphin	Darley
IMMORTAL VERSE (3)	249,525	1-2	Robert Collet	R C Strauss	Kilfrush Stud
TELL DAD (2)	247,615	3-10	Richard Hannon	Andrew Tinkler	Wallace Holmes & Partners
SOCIETY ROCK (4)	233,995	1-5	James Fanshawe	Simon Gibson	San Gabriel Investments
DUBAWI GOLD (3)	227,355	3-7	Richard Hannon	Andrew Tinkler	A H Bennett
REWILDING (4)	227,080	1-2	Mahmood Al Zarooni	Godolphin	Watership Down Stud
REPLY (2)	224,886	1-3	A P O'Brien	Mrs Magnier/Tabor/ Smith/Mordukhovitch	Mrs C Regalado-Gonzalez
CARLTON HOUSE (3)	219,780	1-2	Sir Michael Stoute	Her Majesty The Queen	Darley
GREEN DESTINY (4)	212,888	4-7	William Haggas	Saleh Al Homaizi & Imad Al Sagar	Mubkera Syndicate
PROHIBIT (6)	208,537	1-4	Robert Cowell	Dasmal, Rix, Barr, Morley, Mrs Penney	Juddmonte Farms Ltd
MARGOT DID (3)	202,677	3-6	Michael Bell	T Redman And P Philipps	N Hartery
SNOW FAIRY (4)	201,095	0-3	Ed Dunlop	Anamoine Limited	Windflower Overseas Holdings Inc
PARISH HALL (2)	179,770	1-1	J S Bolger	Mrs J S Bolger	J S Bolger
BROWN PANTHER (3)	177,358	3-6	Tom Dascombe	Owen Promotions Limited	Owen Promotions Ltd
BATED BREATH (4)	176,950	2-7	Roger Charlton	K Abdulla	Juddmonte Farms Ltd
AWAIT THE DAWN (4)	165,669	2-3	A P O'Brien	M Tabor, Mrs J Magnier & D Smith	Juddmonte Farms Inc
STRONG SUIT (3)	165,176	3-4	Richard Hannon	Qatar Bloodstock Ltd	Mcdowell Farm, Gainsborough Farm Et Al
BARBICAN (3)	161,495	6-10	Alan Bailey	John Stocker	Hascombe & Valiant Studs
SEA MOON (3)	160,932	2-3	Sir Michael Stoute	K Abdulla	Juddmonte Farms Ltd
AULD BURNS (3)	159,639	2-7	Richard Hannon	P A Byrne	Simon Tindall
MOYENNE CORNICHE (6)	147,820	1-6	Brian Ellison	D Gilbert, M Lawrence, A Bruce	J L C Pearce
CASPAR NETSCHER (2)	143,398	3-9	Alan McCabe	Charles Wentworth	Meon Valley Stud

TOP NH JOCKEYS IN BRITAIN 2010/11

W-R	%	JOCKEY	2ND	3RD	TOTAL PRIZE
218-885	25%	A P MCCOY	137	91	1,871,512
151-784	19%	RICHARD JOHNSON	116	110	1,442,328
95-490	19%	JASON MAGUIRE	79	62	1,233,427
79-531	15%	PAUL MOLONEY	76	75	606,000
78-535	15%	PADDY BRENNAN	61	58	780,924
77-606	13%	GRAHAM LEE	80	68	600,075
74-466	16%	TOM O'BRIEN	41	59	483,389
65-541	12%	BRIAN HUGHES	68	60	456,369
63-556	11%	TOM SCUDAMORE	84	55	717,038
61-235	26%	BARRY GERAGHTY	40	18	1,225,057
61-491	12%	AIDAN COLEMAN	50	54	431,821
59-487	12%	SAM TWISTON-DAVIES	50	53	505,920
57-366	16%	DOUGIE COSTELLO	55	36	444,400
56-427	13%	DARYL JACOB	47	47	687,036
52-375	14%	ROBERT THORNTON	69	53	586,471
47-417	11%	JAMIE MOORE	53	42	311,307
42-323	13%	NICK SCHOLFIELD	36	34	270,747
41-284	14%	WAYNE HUTCHINSON	35	32	322,457
39-245	16%	FELIX DE GILES	20	31	204,265
39-448	9%	LEIGHTON ASPELL	46	56	230,719
36-319	11%	JIMMY DERHAM	47	35	203,009
36-340	11%	SAM THOMAS	38	30	406,644
35-304	12%	JAMES REVELEY	46	36	240,288
35-328	11%	ANDREW TINKLER	40	42	217,757
35-354	10%	RICHIE MCLERNON	21	40	210,855
35-378	9%	DENIS O'REGAN	42	34	229,459
34-295	12%	BARRY KENIRY	34	44	154,116
33-234	14%	DAVID BASS	23	34	243,664
32-283	11%	TIMMY MURPHY	29	20	424,209
31-150	21%	NOEL FEHILY	23	17	375,317
30-285	11%	PETER TOOLE	35	35	184,656
29-206	14%	HARRY SKELTON	29	28	291,390
29-314	9%	CAMPBELL GILLIES	33	41	197,996
28-258	11%	JOE TIZZARD	37	28	281,435
28-304	9%	PETER BUCHANAN	35	29	228,144
27-206	13%	JACK DOYLE	14	21	213,821
26-106	25%	R WALSH	15	16	1,121,128
26-193	13%	PAUL GALLAGHER	15	19	168,295
26-281	9%	RICHIE MCGRATH	23	31	134,192
25-256	10%	SEAN QUINLAN	16	30	135,355
25-309	8%	RHYS FLINT	34	32	182,916
24-209	11%	DONAL DEVEREUX	28	22	131,966
24-237	10%	CHARLIE POSTE	25	24	113,851
24-241	10%	RYAN MANIA	29	18	120,929
23-224	10%	WARREN MARSTON	21	25	125,436
22-235	9%	WILSON RENWICK	22	21	126,508
22-275	8%	WILL KENNEDY	22	31	193,058
22-394	6%	ANDREW THORNTON	32	48	182,030
21-226	9%	IAN POPHAM	29	25	264,545
21-261	8%	JOHNNY FARRELLY	23	19	129,993

TOP NH TRAINERS IN BRITAIN 2010/11

TRAINER	LEADING HORSE	W-R	2ND	3RD	4TH	TOTAL PRIZE	WIN PRIZE
PAUL NICHOLLS	BIG BUCK'S	134-583	89	81	55	2,424,059	1,607,886
NICKY HENDERSON	LONG RUN	153-612	76	68	54	2,210,465	1,591,676
DONALD McCAIN	BALLABRIGGS	100-588	97	64	54	1,286,133	954,456
PHILIP HOBBS	MENORAH	86-556	76	78	52	1,163,552	817,243
DAVID PIPE	GRANDS CRUS	65-504	63	47	46	999,942	545,872
NIGEL TWISTON-DAVIES	IMPERIAL COMMANDER	97-711	74	81	77	988,425	668,971
ALAN KING	MEDERMIT	84-600	102	83	56	900,660	528,023
JONJO O'NEILL	ALBERTAS RUN	94-750	70	75	64	861,735	526,606
EVAN WILLIAMS	STATE OF PLAY	90-595	86	85	59	647,447	355,650
TIM VAUGHAN	BESHABAR	91-563	82	59	66	573,106	427,605
HOWARD JOHNSON	TIDAL BAY	60-368	50	39	35	524,195	330,615
W P MULLINS	HURRICANE FLY	4-35	3	5	2	483,874	318,454
COLIN TIZZARD	CUE CARD	41-328	50	36	35	436,281	248,666
PETER BOWEN	ALWAYS WAINING	60-384	60	39	43	396,962	271,237
FERDY MURPHY	POKER DE SIVOLA	29-321	38	32	34	392,034	219,089
GORDON ELLIOTT	CARLITO BRIGANTE	35-123	29	7	7	365,016	280,026
NICK WILLIAMS	DIAMOND HARRY	17-116	15	13	19	352,498	247,711
TOM GEORGE	NACARAT	18-224	29	26	25	341,862	228,764
LUCINDA RUSSELL	SILVER BY NATURE	41-343	43	40	38	323,903	227,531
GARY MOORE	VIA GALILEI	45-390	54	40	33	304,187	171,450
VENETIA WILLIAMS	CICERON	38-372	29	42	37	264,405	164,601
SUE SMITH	STAGECOACH PEARL	40-361	29	31	22	258,496	197,878
CHARLIE LONGSDON	MINELLA BOYS	44-233	38	27	23	258,091	177,548
PAUL WEBBER	EDGBRIAR	28-203	23	19	25	256,818	161,252
EMMA LAVELLE	COURT IN MOTION	30-206	21	21	24	257,910	188,293
HENRY DE BROMHEAD	SIZING EUROPE	2-11	1	3	0	228,601	207,480
BRIAN ELLISON	BOTHY	21-108	12	17	16	223,407	129,160
MILTON HARRIS	CHANINBAR	32-311	38	36	36	222,214	114,520
NEIL MULHOLLAND	MIDNIGHT CHASE	21-206	33	10	24	202,968	119,174
M M LYNCH	OSCAR TIME	0-1	1	0	0	201,590	0
MALCOLM JEFFERSON	KING FONTAINE	26-208	30	22	16	183,900	105,581
KIM BAILEY	SARDE	38-200	16	29	21	183,438	141,015
IAN WILLIAMS	WAYWARD PRINCE	25-199	33	19	19	175,966	106,146
VICTOR DARTNALL	GILES CROSS	26-145	18	14	11	162,431	92,197
RICHARD LEE	LE BEAU BAI	26-166	19	21	18	151,872	95,928
PATRICK RODFORD	HOLMWOOD LEGEND	12-60	7	6	6	148,147	101,658
CHARLIE MANN	FINE PARCHMENT	20-202	27	25	23	147,165	91,852
REBECCA CURTIS	THE JIGSAW MAN	28-150	19	14	21	146,207	89,872
NICKY RICHARDS	MONET'S GARDEN	18-189	17	20	19	143,866	108,204
JENNIE CANDLISH	CROSS KENNON	15-111	14	12	13	138,637	79,291
HENRIETTA KNIGHT	SOMERSBY	6-150	11	13	12	133,813	25,899
DR RICHARD NEWLAND	ACT OF KALANISI	22-108	9	13	10	133,691	102,200
JOHN WADE	ALWAYS RIGHT	13-116	13	12	12	128,270	90,634
BRENDAN POWELL	PULLYOURFINGEROUT	22-222	25	24	28	128,175	78,166
LAWNEY HILL	TO ARMS	26-143	21	11	21	121,933	86,850
MARTIN KEIGHLEY	CHAMPION COURT	19-176	22	19	13	116,840	68,346
OLIVER SHERWOOD	ERIC'S CHARM	24-213	26	22	25	117,058	75,862
KEITH REVELEY	CATEGORICAL	22-164	25	23	15	112,832	68,257
C A MURPHY	BIG ZEB	1-3	1	0	0	111,407	42,959
NICK GIFFORD	TULLAMORE DEW	17-128	17	14	15	110,363	64,552

TOP NH OWNERS IN BRITAIN IN 2010/11

OWNER	LEADING HORSE	W-R	2ND	3RD	4TH	TOTAL PRIZE	WIN PRIZE
TREVOR HEMMINGS	Ballabriggs	32-204	27	23	8	951,634	822,164
JOHN P MCMANUS	Don't Push It	84-650	56	63	44	818,997	430,610
THE STEWART FAMILY	Big Buck's	14-74	12	10	5	549,563	455,226
ANDREA & GRAHAM WYLIE	Tidal Bay	46-242	35	28	16	439,552	268,438
MRS DIANA L WHATELEY	Menorah	16-67	16	6	6	425,531	349,338
ROBERT WALEY-COHEN	Long Run	3-14	0	2	1	422,669	405,674
CLIVE D SMITH	Master Minded	4-14	1	4	0	300,025	220,901
T G LESLIE	Peddlers Cross	15-76	21	12	6	293,848	114,965
WALTERS PLANT HIRE LTD	Oscar Whisky	21-78	6	9	10	275,260	222,938
GIGGINSTOWN HOUSE STUD	Carlito Brigante	6-29	0	2	5	262,511	218,150
MICHAEL BUCKLEY	Finian's Rainbow	15-46	7	1	2	245,152	163,859
D A JOHNSON	Poker De Sivola	8-85	9	6	8	222,270	123,079
ANN & ALAN POTTS PARTNERSHIP	Sizing Europe	2-6	0	2	0	213,005	207,480
GEORGE CREIGHTON & MRS ROSE BOYD	Hurricane Fly	1-1	0	0	0	210,937	210,937
R WALEY-COHEN/SIR MARTIN & S BROUGHTON	Oscar Time	0-1	1	0	0	201,590	0
SIMON W CLARKE	Nacarat	2-14	1	1	4	173,871	141,790
JOHN WADE	Always Right	22-156	20	15	10	164,447	118,626
ROGER STANLEY & YVONNE REYNOLDS III.	Grands Crus	3-5	2	0	0	155,089	78,085
J HALES	Al Ferof	6-31	1	2	5	144,725	136,653
PAUL DUFFY DIAMOND PARTNERSHIP	Diamond Harry	4-14	0	3	2	140,694	122,068
JIMMY NESBITT PARTNERSHIP	Riverside Theatre	2-3	1	0	0	138,817	100,315
PAUL MURPHY	Carole's Legacy	7-18	6	2	0	136,844	68,252
PAUL K BARBER	Denman	0-3	1	1	0	129,697	0
MRS JEAN R BISHOP	Cue Card	5-14	4	1	2	125,731	51,529
POTENSIS LIMITED & CHRIS GILES	Zarkandar	3-3	0	0	0	125,727	125,727
OUR FRIENDS IN THE NORTH	Imperial Commander	1-4	0	0	0	112,660	112,660
SIMON MUNIR	Grandouet	9-66	13	11	5	110,057	38,807
MRS M FINDLAY & MIDDLEHAM PARK RACING X.	Beshabar	1-1	0	0	0	102,618	102,618
ALAN PETERSON	Massini's Maguire	6-34	0	5	2	101,795	89,429
TONY BLOOM	Little Josh	3-12	0	0	1	101,248	95,946
POTENSIS LIMITED	Silviniaco Conti	6-20	2	3	5	100,814	76,658
MRS T P RADFORD	Somersby	1-42	5	5	6	96,932	2,276
HAMMER & TROWEL SYNDICATE	Thousand Stars	1-4	1	0	1	96,925	39,431
MR & MRS RAYMOND ANDERSON GREEN	Merigo	9-104	19	11	7	94,487	31,985
R E R WILLIAMS	Courella	24-98	14	10	9	94,236	73,988
ANDREW L COHEN	Quinz	4-34	2	6	5	90,490	79,876
LADY CLARKE	Midnight Chase	5-13	0	0	1	88,873	72,803
TERRY WARNER	Oiseau De Nuit	1-37	7	10	2	84,779	42,757
E A P SCOULLER	Bostons Angel	2-10	0	1	3	84,149	78,016
MR & MRS WILLIAM RUCKER	State Of Play	7-39	7	5	4	83,710	24,360
DAVID SEWELL	Montbazon	10-35	5	3	0	82,197	63,488
C G ROACH	The Tother One	5-36	5	5	4	82,055	29,957
THE NOT AFRAID PARTNERSHIP	Bobs Worth	4-4	0	0	0	80,126	80,126
POWER PANELS ELECTRICAL SYSTEMS LTD	Tartak	4-24	5	3	3	79,899	50,065
N A TWISTON-DAVIES	Baby Run	9-62	10	10	8	79,684	49,475
DAN GILBERT	Bothy	3-19	3	1	3	78,529	20,165
SIR ROBERT OGDEN	Giorgio Quercus	11-45	2	4	2	77,724	49,311
BRIAN DERRICK	Holmwood Legend	6-21	3	1	3	77,201	63,332
MRS S SMITH	Douglas Julian	17-135	10	13	4	76,931	61,085
JARED SULLIVAN & SIMON BROWN	Gauvain	2-10	3	0	2	76,815	34,887

TOP NH HORSES
IN BRITAIN 2010/11

HORSE (AGE)	WIN & PLACE £	W-R	TRAINER	OWNER	BREEDER
BALLABRIGGS (10)	542,788	3-4	Donald McCain	Trevor Hemmings	Mrs S L Jackson
LONG RUN (6)	403,733	2-3	Nicky Henderson	Robert Waley-Cohen	Mrs Marie-Christine Gabeur
BIG BUCK'S (8)	256,379	4-4	Paul Nicholls	The Stewart Family	Henri Poulat
MASTER MINDED (8)	220,901	4-5	Paul Nicholls	Clive D Smith	Marie-Christine Gabeur
HURRICANE FLY (7)	210,937	1-1	W P Mullins	G Creighton & Mrs R Boyd	Agricola Del Parco
OSCAR TIME (10)	201,590	0-1	M M Lynch	R Waley-Cohen/	Edmond Coleman
				Sir Martin & S Broughton	
ALBERTAS RUN (10)	195,553	1-5	Jonjo O'Neill	Trevor Hemmings	Oliver And Salome Brennan
SIZING EUROPE (9)	182,432	1-1	Henry De Bromhead	Ann & Alan Potts Prtship	Mrs Angela Bracken
NACARAT (10)	172,732	2-5	Tom George	Simon W Clarke	Francis Maze
OSCAR WHISKY (6)	170,762	3-4	Nicky Henderson	Walters Plant Hire Ltd	Stephanie Hanly
GRANDS CRUS (6)	155,089	3-5	David Pipe	R Stanley & Y Reynolds III	Jean-Marie Prost Alamartine
MENORAH (6)	152,441	2-3	Philip Hobbs	Mrs Diana L Whateley	Mrs E Grant &Miss A Brislane
PEDDLERS CROSS (6)	141,281	2-4	Donald McCain	T G Leslie	Mrs A Delaney
POQUELIN (8)	139,842	2-5	Paul Nicholls	The Stewart Family	Georges Sandor & Eric Becq
RIVERSIDE THEATRE (7)	138,817	2-3	Nicky Henderson	Jimmy Nesbitt Partnership	Goldford Stud
DENMAN (11)	129,697	0-3	Paul Nicholls	Paul K Barber	Colman O'Flynn
ZARKANDAR (4)	125,727	3-3	Paul Nicholls	Potensis Ltd & Chris Giles	H H The Aga Khan's Studs S C
BESHABAR (9)	120,106	2-4	Tim Vaughan	Mrs M Findlay &	John Cotter
				Middleham Park Racing X	
IMPERIAL COMMANDER (10)	112,660	1-2	Nigel Twiston-Davies	Our Friends In The North	Laurence J Flynn
FINIAN'S RAINBOW (8)	112,527	4-5	Nicky Henderson	Michael Buckley	J O'Keeffe
CAPTAIN CHRIS (7)	108,851	2-6	Philip Hobbs	Mrs Diana L Whateley	Mrs Noreen Walsh
WISHFULL THINKING (8)	106,651	3-6	Philip Hobbs	Mrs Diana L Whateley	Cobhall Court Stud
DON'T PUSH IT (11)	100,890	0-5	Jonjo O'Neill	John P McManus	Dominick Vallely
DIAMOND HARRY (8)	99,767	1-1	Nick Williams	Paul Duffy Diamond Prtship	Mrs A L Wood
LITTLE JOSH (9)	99,022	2-4	Nigel Twiston-Davies	Tony Bloom	Michael Kearns
SILVINIACO CONTI (5)	89,631	3-5	Paul Nicholls	Potensis Limited	Patrick Joubert
MIDNIGHT CHASE (9)	86,133	4-6	Neil Mulholland	Lady Clarke	Conkwell Grange Stud Ltd
CAROLE'S LEGACY (7)	82,222	1-5	Nicky Henderson	Paul Murphy	Paul Murphy
POKER DE SIVOLA (8)	80,278	1-3	Ferdy Murphy	D A Johnson	Gilles Trapenard
BOBS WORTH (6)	80,126	4-4	Nicky Henderson	The Not Afraid Partnership	Mrs L Eadie
BOSTONS ANGEL (7)	74,113	1-1	Mrs John Harrington	E A P Scoullar	P A D Scoullar
KAUTO STAR (11)	72,828	0-2	Paul Nicholls	Clive D Smith	Mme Henri Aubert
TIDAL BAY (10)	71,871	0-5	Howard Johnson	Andrea & Graham Wylie	John Dorgan
QUINZ (7)	71,870	3-5	Philip Hobbs	Andrew L Cohen	Michael Blond
CARLITO BRIGANTE (5)	70,295	2-4	Gordon Elliott	Gigginstown House Stud	Ballylinch Stud
BINOCULAR (7)	70,030	2-4	Nicky Henderson	John P McManus	Elie Lellouche
AL FEROF (6)	69,388	3-5	J Hales		J Rauch & G Chenu
BIG ZEB (10)	68,448	0-1	C A Murphy	Patrick Joseph Redmond	Lyle Buttimer
CUE CARD (5)	67,995	2-5	Colin Tizzard	Mrs Jean R Bishop	R T Crellin
GAUVAIN (9)	67,706	1-5	Nick Williams	J Sullivan & S Brown	Stall Epona
HOLMWOOD LEGEND (10)	65,644	3-9	Patrick Rodford	Brian Derrick	Mrs P M Underhill
KALAHARI KING (10)	64,981	0-5	Ferdy Murphy	Mrs J Morgan	Henri Malard
OISEAU DE NUIT (9)	64,191	1-8	Colin Tizzard	Terry Warner	Guy Cherel
SOMERSBY (7)	63,417	0-5	Henrietta Knight	Mrs T P Radford	Miss Nicola Ann Adams
SPIRIT SON (5)	63,185	3-4	Nicky Henderson	Michael Buckley	Anne & Jean-Marc Baudrelle
MEDERMIT (7)	62,871	3-7	Alan King	The Dunkley & Reilly Prtship	Philippe Gasdoue
NEARBY (7)	61,832	3-9	Philip Hobbs	Andy Ash	Juddmonte Farms Ltd
TARTAK (8)	60,260	2-6	Tom George	Power Panels Elec Syst. Ltd	Francis & Colette Cottebrune
SPARKY MAY (6)	59,951	4-6	Patrick Rodford	Bill Muddyman	Ruxley Holdings Ltd
SAINT ARE (5)	58,239	1-5	Tim Vaughan	D W Fox	Jacques Cypres

LEADING SIRES OF 2011 IN GREAT BRITAIN AND IRELAND

STALLION	BREEDING	RNRS	WNRS	WINS	WIN MONEY	PLACES	PLACE MONEY	TOTAL
GALILEO (IRE)	by Sadler's Wells (USA)	222	87	121	3888164	271	1394903	5283067
MONTJEU (IRE)	by Sadler's Wells (USA)	130	51	76	2425151	194	494276	2919427
OASIS DREAM (GB)	by Green Desert (USA)	179	75	107	1315073	308	986370	2301443
DANSILI (GB)	by Danehill (USA)	161	65	95	1048073	219	660555	1708629
HIGH CHAPARRAL (IRE)	by Sadler's Wells (USA)	101	37	57	1107745	159	543402	1651147
DANEHILL DANCER (IRE)	by Danehill (USA)	182	67	99	971646	315	586052	1557697
EXCEED AND EXCEL (AUS)	by Danehill (USA)	170	64	102	843977	284	604823	1448800
PIVOTAL (GB)	by Polar Falcon (USA)	157	80	119	870598	272	520727	1391325
HOLY ROMAN EMPEROR (IRE)	by Danehill (USA)	115	48	84	834077	204	521040	1355117
DUBAWI (IRE)	by Dubai Millennium (GB)	115	50	74	609333	191	588496	1197828
INVINCIBLE SPIRIT (IRE)	by Green Desert (USA)	189	78	107	710804	332	455023	1165828
CAPE CROSS (IRE)	by Green Desert (USA)	174	67	92	613558	264	433858	1047446
ACCLAMATION (GB)	by Royal Applause (GB)	166	68	100	569729	289	473630	1043359
ROCK OF GIBRALTAR (IRE)	by Danehill (USA)	100	43	63	791026	161	249291	1040317
SHAMARDAL (USA)	by Giant's Causeway (USA)	105	50	71	622647	171	260645	883293
DYNAFORMER (USA)	by Roberto (USA)	38	15	20	736335	56	139947	876282
KING'S BEST (USA)	by Kingmambo (USA)	111	31	41	330680	141	524394	855074
MEDICEAN (GB)	by Machiavellian (USA)	144	45	71	507760	209	315379	823138
HURRICANE RUN (IRE)	by Montjeu (IRE)	74	28	43	441809	119	364584	806393
INTIKHAB (USA)	by Red Ransom (USA)	74	29	48	298591	108	497032	795622
KYLLACHY (GB)	by Pivotal (GB)	153	73	118	505588	297	276769	782357
BAHAMIAN BOUNTY (GB)	by Cadeaux Genereux	123	51	84	563894	212	207386	771380
EVEN TOP (IRE)	by Topanoora	1	1	1	737230	0	0	737230
STREET CRY (IRE)	by Machiavellian (USA)	72	29	39	407857	112	328563	736420
SELKIRK (USA)	by Sharpen Up	98	43	62	495498	143	224787	720285

LEADING SIRES OF 2011
(GREAT BRITAIN, IRELAND AND OVERSEAS)

STALLION	BREEDING	DOMESTIC WNRS	WINS	WIN MONEY	OVERSEAS WNRS	WINS	WIN MONEY	TOTAL
GALILEO (IRE)	by Sadler's Wells (USA)	87	121	3888164	53	77	3025233	6913397
MONTJEU (IRE)	by Sadler's Wells (USA)	51	76	2425151	52	92	3092896	5518047
DUBAWI (IRE)	by Dubai Millennium (GB)	50	74	609333	44	75	2365549	2974882
SAKHEE (USA)	by Bahri (USA)	24	38	236514	28	52	2622663	2859177
TIGER HILL (IRE)	by Danehill (USA)	24	36	332032	33	47	2465553	2797586
HIGH CHAPARRAL (IRE)	by Sadler's Wells (USA)	37	57	1107745	42	71	1501605	2609350
DANEHILL DANCER (IRE)	by Danehill (USA)	67	99	971646	48	78	1395719	2367365
OASIS DREAM (GB)	by Green Desert (USA)	75	107	1315073	57	115	927648	2242721
DANSILI (GB)	by Danehill (USA)	65	95	1048073	62	101	1138409	2186483
CAPE CROSS (IRE)	by Green Desert (USA)	67	92	613588	40	56	1529681	2143269
SHAMARDAL (USA)	by Giant's Causeway (USA)	50	71	622647	46	85	1474382	2097030
PIVOTAL (GB)	by Polar Falcon (USA)	80	119	870598	59	101	1203267	2073865
KING'S BEST (USA)	by Kingmambo (USA)	31	41	330680	60	94	1499686	1830365
ROCK OF GIBRALTAR (IRE)	by Danehill (USA)	43	63	791026	62	102	946985	1738011
EXCEED AND EXCEL (AUS)	by Danehill (USA)	64	102	843977	37	80	834460	1678436
INVINCIBLE SPIRIT (IRE)	by Green Desert (USA)	78	107	710804	61	100	939179	1649984
DALAKHANI (IRE)	by Darshaan	22	35	358937	27	37	1177565	1536503
HAWK WING (USA)	by Woodman (USA)	22	33	161976	70	115	1372184	1534160
VERGLAS (IRE)	by Highest Honor (IRE)	25	41	159137	68	118	1341156	1500292
KYLLACHY (GB)	by Pivotal (GB)	73	118	505588	41	72	970586	1476174
REFUSE TO BEND (IRE)	by Sadler's Wells (USA)	39	58	188237	71	139	1285307	1473544
MEDICEAN (GB)	by Machiavellian (GB)	45	71	507760	55	99	910221	1417980
SINGSPIEL (IRE)	by In The Wings	29	44	234037	59	107	1108572	1342609
FOOTSTEPSINTHESAND (GB)	by Giant's Causeway (USA)	30	55	334467	45	78	922711	1257178
INTIKHAB (USA)	by Red Ransom (USA)	29	48	298591	34	54	948957	1247547

LEADING TWO-YEAR-OLD SIRES OF 2011 IN GREAT BRITAIN AND IRELAND

STALLION	BREEDING	RNRS	WNRS	WINS	WIN MONEY	PLACES	PLACE MONEY	TOTAL
HOLY ROMAN EMPEROR (IRE)	by Danehill (USA)	78	30	41	383369	130	367019	750888
OASIS DREAM (GB)	by Green Desert (USA)	52	16	23	488588	58	182964	671552
ACCLAMATION (GB)	by Royal Applause (GB)	66	29	41	345878	100	204756	550634
GALILEO (IRE)	by Sadler's Wells (USA)	74	22	27	435543	55	87990	523332
EXCEED AND EXCEL (AUS)	by Danehill (USA)	67	24	36	267320	100	197732	465052
CLODOVIL (IRE)	by Danehill (USA)	39	17	23	365544	56	70528	436072
ROCK OF GIBRALTAR (IRE)	by Danehill (USA)	40	12	15	320092	43	112700	432793
DANSILI (GB)	by Danehill (USA)	45	18	23	261832	38	161159	422992
BAHAMIAN BOUNTY (GB)	by Cadeaux Genereux	24	6	9	278235	27	80376	358611
STREET CRY (IRE)	by Machiavellian (USA)	36	15	21	246368	31	46410	292778
INTIKHAB (USA)	by Red Ransom (USA)	15	7	11	160158	20	125596	285754
INVINCIBLE SPIRIT (IRE)	by Green Desert (USA)	53	18	22	169068	86	116370	285438
MONTJEU (IRE)	by Sadler's Wells (USA)	28	6	10	216803	20	19212	236020
KYLLACHY (GB)	by Pivotal (GB)	38	21	29	141333	71	82646	223979
KODIAC (GB)	by Danehill (USA)	34	17	20	151779	64	63880	215659
DANEHILL DANCER (IRE)	by Danehill (USA)	43	14	16	104468	44	67502	171970
ROYAL APPLAUSE (GB)	by Waajib	54	20	27	90871	88	78092	168963
KHELEYF (USA)	by Green Desert (USA)	47	11	18	71537	80	88581	160119
CHOISIR (AUS)	by Danehill Dancer (IRE)	37	13	15	94869	43	53907	148776
MARJU (IRE)	by Last Tycoon	16	2	4	130946	10	17276	148222
MR GREELEY (USA)	by Gone West (USA)	13	2	3	109302	9	24527	133829
BERTOLINI (USA)	by Danzig (USA)	31	10	15	65137	43	63509	128645
DUBAWI (IRE)	by Dubai Millennium (GB)	35	12	13	67580	35	57602	125182
PIVOTAL (GB)	by Polar Falcon (USA)	31	12	14	82045	36	36715	118760
CAPE CROSS (IRE)	by Green Desert (USA)	51	10	10	51904	45	66638	118542

LEADING FIRST CROP SIRES OF 2011 IN GREAT BRITAIN AND IRELAND

STALLION	BREEDING	RNRS	WNRS	WINS	WIN MONEY	PLACES	PLACE MONEY	TOTAL
DUTCH ART (GB)	by Medicean (GB)	50	27	39	256784	93	167896	424770
DARK ANGEL (IRE)	by Acclamation (GB)	62	27	44	193645	134	197780	391425
TEOFILO (IRE)	by Galileo (IRE)	51	15	18	320480	42	58212	378692
EXCELLENT ART (GB)	by Pivotal (GB)	49	17	24	144253	68	163604	307857
RED CLUBS (IRE)	by Red Ransom (USA)	66	29	44	177256	110	91204	268460
STRATEGIC PRINCE (GB)	by Dansili (GB)	41	13	18	145558	43	83487	229045
AMADEUS WOLF (GB)	by Mozart (IRE)	55	17	24	118423	78	62401	180824
LAWMAN (FR)	by Invincible Spirit (IRE)	30	11	13	64928	30	92389	157317
DYLAN THOMAS (IRE)	by Danehill (USA)	38	10	11	73421	43	74866	148287
BALTIC KING (GB)	by Danetime (IRE)	15	6	7	18289	25	100443	118733
HARD SPUN (USA)	by Danzig (USA)	13	5	7	54611	21	46226	100837
SIR PERCY (GB)	by Mark Of Esteem (IRE)	26	10	16	65096	35	34925	100021
SCAT DADDY (USA)	by Johannesburg (USA)	2	2	3	67337	1	4020	71357
JEREMY (USA)	by Danehill Dancer (IRE)	23	4	4	25949	21	44942	70891
COCKNEY REBEL (IRE)	by Val Royal (IRE)	23	10	13	44793	41	22927	67719
MOSS VALE (IRE)	by Shinko Forest (IRE)	38	9	13	46922	26	18058	64980
MULTIPLEX (GB)	by Danehill (USA)	20	9	11	25885	35	26069	51954
HELIOSTATIC (IRE)	by Galileo (IRE)	6	4	6	40623	7	10835	51457
VITAL EQUINE (IRE)	by Danetime (IRE)	11	4	6	25946	19	16943	42888
THREE VALLEYS (USA)	by Diesis	39	7	8	21076	38	18359	39435
AUTHORIZED (IRE)	by Montjeu (IRE)	35	7	7	24947	20	14099	39046
NOTNOWCATO (GB)	by Inchinor (GB)	21	6	6	18889	15	11293	30183
ECHO OF LIGHT (GB)	by Dubai Millennium	26	4	4	11411	22	15856	27268
MANDURO (GER)	by Monsun (GER)	25	3	3	10877	24	12695	23572
MISU BOND (IRE)	by Danehill Dancer (IRE)	9	3	6	14889	13	6484	21373

LEADING MATERNAL GRANDSIRES OF 2011 IN GREAT BRITAIN AND IRELAND

STALLION	BREEDING	RNRS	WNRS	WINS	WIN MONEY	PLACES	PLACE MONEY	TOTAL
SADLER'S WELLS (USA)	by Northern Dancer	385	142	201	1583241	585	1543285	3126526
DANEHILL (USA)	by Danzig (USA)	247	92	140	2386059	395	618319	3004378
DARSHAAN	by Shirley Heights	222	81	109	1660749	322	627721	2288470
MARK OF ESTEEM (IRE)	by Darshaan	79	32	53	1302324	150	649574	1952398
INDIAN RIDGE	by Ahonoora	170	73	116	1280409	297	649929	1930338
GREEN DESERT (USA)	by Danzig (USA)	217	79	132	914710	322	629240	1543950
SILVER HAWK (USA)	by Roberto (USA)	39	17	29	994728	61	393083	1387811
KINGMAMBO (USA)	by Mr Prospector (USA)	74	29	35	541334	143	579212	1120595
TIGHTS (USA)	by Nijinsky (CAN)	1	1	4	754275	2	365580	1119855
RAINBOW QUEST (USA)	by Blushing Groom (FR)	176	59	81	676165	288	386621	1062785
LINAMIX (FR)	by Mendez (FR)	70	32	57	825137	121	139555	964692
CAERLEON (USA)	by Nijinsky (CAN)	101	26	40	772564	132	178197	950761
SHIRLEY HEIGHTS	by Mill Reef (USA)	72	24	41	640883	96	275462	916345
CADEAUX GENEREUX	by Young Generation	132	49	71	625351	167	151946	777297
ROYAL ACADEMY (USA)	by Nijinsky (CAN)	128	42	61	398644	220	360994	759638
SEPTIEME CIEL (USA)	by Seattle Slew (USA)	13	5	7	748764	12	6568	755332
WOODMAN (USA)	by Mr Prospector (USA)	121	44	68	497178	154	249873	747052
SELKIRK (USA)	by Sharpen Up	151	64	97	448460	214	295350	743810
NASHWAN (USA)	by Blushing Groom (FR)	114	45	70	512822	188	226916	739738
UNFUWAIN (USA)	by Northern Dancer	103	39	59	422531	141	278002	700532
BARATHEA (IRE)	by Sadler's Wells (USA)	139	39	71	448249	209	251462	699710
NIGHT SHIFT (USA)	by Northern Dancer	164	72	106	418419	294	269098	687517
MARJU (IRE)	by Last Tycoon	76	30	47	504720	111	176412	681132
DISTANT VIEW (USA)	by Mr Prospector (USA)	45	18	27	372342	68	258430	630772
SINGSPIEL (IRE)	by In The Wings	60	29	36	388971	100	226506	615477

FLAT STALLIONS' EARNINGS FOR 2011

(includes every stallion who sired a winner on the Flat in Great Britain and Ireland in 2011)

STALLIONS	RNRS	STARTS	WNRS	WINS	PLACES	TOTAL (£)
ABOU ZOUZ (USA)	1	4	1	1	0	2264.15
ACCLAMATION (GB)	166	938	68	100	289	1043358.59
ACCORDION	4	12	1	1	6	14676.72
ACTEUR FRANCAIS (USA)	1	8	1	1	3	3664.64
ACT ONE (GB)	30	134	7	11	37	55265.97
AD VALOREM (USA)	34	220	13	23	60	100799.32
AGNES WORLD (USA)	4	27	2	2	4	5687.80
AKBAR (IRE)	1	7	1	1	1	2072.38
ALAMSHAR (IRE)	2	14	1	1	3	7495.69
ALDEBARAN (USA)	5	28	3	5	8	16209.60
ALHAARTH (IRE)	69	323	27	38	103	395887.80
ALJABR (USA)	4	19	2	5	3	14313.66
ALKAADHEM (GB)	1	9	1	3	1	16400.86
ALMATY (IRE)	1	16	1	3	2	5222.11
ALMUTAWAKEL (GB)	5	42	2	3	16	36235.44
ALZAO (USA)	3	10	1	3	4	8321.03
AMADEUS WOLF (GB)	55	254	17	24	78	180824.16
AMERICAN POST (GB)	6	32	1	1	11	6355.35
ANABAA (USA)	20	108	7	10	27	120919.69
AND BEYOND (IRE)	4	24	1	2	8	6303.34
ANTONIUS PIUS (USA)	68	335	12	21	65	125167.40
ANY GIVEN SATURDAY (USA)	4	8	1	1	5	9796.42
A P INDY (USA)	1	6	1	1	2	2824.27
APRIL NIGHT (FR)	1	8	1	1	2	2205.45
APTITUDE (USA)	10	29	2	2	8	15505.18
ARAAFA (IRE)	36	196	8	10	43	41611.63
ARAGON	1	10	1	1	4	4381.35
ARAGORN (IRE)	4	24	1	1	11	8073.31
ARAKAN (USA)	25	135	9	16	26	252356.27
ARCH (USA)	30	146	11	16	53	112879.88
ASHKALANI (IRE)	3	15	1	1	1	3743.24
ATRAF (GB)	13	75	4	4	16	17248.88
AUCTION HOUSE (USA)	40	230	11	14	64	75594.55
AUSSIE RULES (USA)	54	287	20	29	75	209014.18
AUTHORIZED (IRE)	35	72	7	7	20	39045.60
AVERTI (IRE)	11	81	4	8	15	23764.93
AVONBRIDGE (GB)	90	540	26	42	149	213340.06
AWESOME AGAIN (CAN)	3	11	1	4	4	3778.77
AZAMOUR (IRE)	55	220	19	25	83	431611.08
BACHELOR DUKE (USA)	38	189	11	17	43	97018.60
BAHAMIAN BOUNTY (GB)	123	767	51	84	212	771280.10
BAHHARE (USA)	7	49	3	3	16	12743.33
BAHRI (USA)	24	106	8	12	32	87669.79
BALLET MASTER (USA)	5	36	2	4	10	10516.58
BALMONT (USA)	15	53	3	6	14	34760.50
BALTIC KING (GB)	15	97	6	7	25	118732.68
BANDINI (USA)	1	2	1	1	0	1535.39
BANYUMANIK (IRE)	2	3	1	1	1	2251.00
BARATHEA (IRE)	74	378	19	25	110	194909.64
BEAT ALL (USA)	9	68	2	3	20	45633.73
BEAT HOLLOW (GB)	68	390	37	63	119	521008.15
BELLAMY ROAD (USA)	1	6	1	2	2	4082.35
BENEFICIAL (GB)	3	11	1	1	8	12135.78
BERING	3	18	1	1	5	7686.92
BERNARDINI (USA)	23	71	7	9	22	108149.47
BERNSTEIN (USA)	11	46	3	7	16	36906.07
BERTOLINI (USA)	160	962	54	87	249	470734.77
BEST OF THE BESTS (IRE)	12	88	4	11	22	42391.90

STALLIONS	RNRS	STARTS	WNRS	WINS	PLACES	TOTAL (£)
BIG BAD BOB (IRE)	32	154	15	21	45	436553.23
BIG SHUFFLE (USA)	7	31	1	2	6	10838.29
BIRDSTONE (USA)	1	10	1	2	3	5485.65
BLUE DAKOTA (IRE)	6	37	1	1	5	3361.39
BOB'S RETURN (IRE)	3	25	2	4	12	31413.81
BOLD EDGE (GB)	15	123	5	10	38	45496.14
BOLD FACT (USA)	14	121	5	11	34	49087.22
BOLLIN ERIC (GB)	6	40	3	7	9	32895.04
BROKEN VOW (USA)	4	17	1	1	2	7200.10
BYRON (GB)	61	296	19	29	93	182847.63
CACIQUE (IRE)	8	40	5	7	15	231376.27
CADEAUX GENEREUX	68	380	25	45	118	333615.37
CAMACHO (GB)	35	240	15	22	82	178329.41
CAPE CROSS (IRE)	174	823	67	92	264	1047445.65
CAPE TOWN (IRE)	3	6	1	1	2	2908.56
CAPTAIN RIO (GB)	105	616	34	46	130	311252.45
CARNEGIE (IRE)	1	13	1	2	5	6302.80
CATCHER IN THE RYE (IRE)	31	147	7	12	40	48905.18
CAYMAN KAI (IRE)	4	34	2	4	10	14231.41
CELTIC SWING (GB)	33	201	17	27	55	200974.50
CENTRAL PARK (IRE)	4	32	1	2	4	5603.90
CENTURY CITY (IRE)	1	5	1	2	1	3272.38
CHEROKEE RUN (USA)	5	22	1	4	6	15431.14
CHEVALIER (IRE)	30	151	10	13	45	190553.39
CHICHICASTENANGO (FR)	2	11	2	2	4	34404.77
CHINEUR (FR)	52	369	24	30	115	186244.44
CHOISIR (AUS)	108	603	45	61	168	455394.69
CITY ON A HILL (USA)	6	40	1	2	6	6697.50
CLASSIC CLICHE (IRE)	1	4	1	1	1	7711.90
CLODOVIL (IRE)	62	298	22	29	105	581629.03
COCKNEY REBEL (IRE)	23	107	10	13	41	67719.40
COMMANDER COLLINS (IRE)	1	8	1	1	2	15456.89
COMMANDS (AUS)	2	7	1	1	3	2537.82
COMPTON ADMIRAL (GB)	12	66	2	3	14	11819.64
COMPTON PLACE (GB)	111	690	44	65	213	715343.15
CONGAREE (USA)	1	12	1	1	3	7526.33
CONSOLIDATOR (USA)	4	21	2	4	5	24982.24
COUNTRY REEL (USA)	3	15	2	2	7	7367.39
COURTEOUS (GB)	1	8	1	1	2	2600.85
COZZENE (USA)	11	66	2	3	26	44461.09
CRAFTY PROSPECTOR (USA)	1	16	1	1	10	8340.38
CRAIGSTEEL (GB)	3	12	1	1	5	5953.27
CROCO ROUGE (IRE)	3	15	1	1	4	5520.07
CRYPTOCLEARANCE (USA)	2	14	1	4	5	10872.18
CUVEE (USA)	2	11	1	1	4	52222.24
CYRANO DE BERGERAC	4	18	2	2	3	9214.49
DAAWE (USA)	3	16	1	1	3	3171.13
DAGGERS DRAWN (USA)	18	90	3	7	21	36810.76
DALAKHANI (IRE)	81	299	22	35	90	506363.00
DALIAPOUR (IRE)	1	3	1	1	1	2886.40
DANBIRD (AUS)	23	105	5	8	28	44289.96
DANEHILL (USA)	6	35	2	5	10	17407.77
DANEHILL DANCER (IRE)	182	925	67	99	315	1557697.14
DANETIME (IRE)	34	336	18	27	105	211476.53
DANROAD (AUS)	11	66	3	4	6	16394.66
DANSILI (GB)	161	682	65	95	219	1708628.81
DANZERO (AUS)	3	24	2	5	3	14967.52
DANZIG (USA)	3	16	1	2	4	9912.21
DARK ANGEL (IRE)	62	334	27	44	134	391425.29
DARNAY (GB)	2	33	1	2	11	8497.38
DASHING BLADE	6	20	3	3	6	15126.18
DAYLAMI (IRE)	22	104	9	10	31	109324.39
DEEP IMPACT (JPN)	2	16	1	2	9	8860.34

STALLIONS	RNRS	STARTS	WNRS	WINS	PLACES	TOTAL (£)
DEFINITE ARTICLE (GB)	8	22	2	2	6	10435.39
DELLA FRANCESCA (USA)	4	22	1	1	6	7488.61
DENOUNCE (GB)	5	26	1	3	6	9768.26
DEPLOY	4	16	1	1	1	3053.68
DEPORTIVO (GB)	10	57	4	7	14	25331.60
DESERT KING (IRE)	5	15	1	1	4	3183.66
DESERT MILLENNIUM (IRE)	1	9	1	3	3	9791.85
DESERT PRINCE (IRE)	25	175	10	13	44	89386.29
DESERT STORY (IRE)	2	13	1	2	7	11578.80
DESERT STYLE (IRE)	40	221	15	20	66	99145.96
DESERT SUN (GB)	21	134	5	6	35	63170.78
DIAMOND GREEN (FR)	59	305	17	25	72	166322.08
DIESIS	14	64	8	10	11	185028.03
DIKTAT (GB)	77	461	22	41	123	660985.68
DILSHAAN (GB)	8	58	4	8	17	68641.88
DISCREET CAT (USA)	2	5	1	1	0	3234.50
DISTANT MUSIC (USA)	12	67	4	5	19	39445.81
DISTANT VIEW (USA)	3	20	1	1	3	4065.32
DISTORTED HUMOR (USA)	22	84	10	11	24	128918.06
DIXIELAND BAND (USA)	3	16	2	2	7	7616.94
DIXIE UNION (USA)	10	24	2	2	12	14331.72
DOCKSIDER (USA)	3	28	2	2	11	44540.76
DOMEDRIVER (IRE)	13	61	4	6	13	47354.52
DONERAILE COURT (USA)	5	25	1	3	10	10978.12
DOYEN (IRE)	46	245	16	26	67	132317.80
DR DEVIOUS (IRE)	1	6	1	1	3	37157.75
DR FONG (USA)	69	385	26	37	128	194674.11
DR MASSINI (IRE)	3	10	1	1	5	41756.95
DUBAI DESTINATION (USA)	125	682	47	76	231	593961.80
DUBAWI (IRE)	115	549	50	74	191	1197828.34
DUTCH ART (GB)	50	231	27	39	93	424770.29
DYLAN THOMAS (IRE)	38	113	10	11	43	148287.43
DYNAFORMER (USA)	38	127	15	20	56	876281.78
DYNASTY (SAF)	1	2	1	1	0	4075.47
ECHO OF LIGHT (GB)	26	83	4	4	22	27267.72
E DUBAI (USA)	3	31	2	3	11	14284.15
EFISIO	9	82	4	9	25	96937.25
EL CORREDOR (USA)	6	20	1	1	0	4758.62
ELMHURST BOY (GB)	1	12	1	1	4	3038.88
ELNADIM (USA)	34	188	10	13	49	231190.06
EL PRADO (IRE)	10	41	4	5	11	35374.64
ELUSIVE CITY (USA)	89	501	26	45	155	375214.93
ELUSIVE QUALITY (USA)	53	280	21	34	108	294991.63
EMPEROR FOUNTAIN	1	11	1	1	5	6771.84
EMPIRE MAKER (USA)	14	44	4	6	12	123133.77
ENCOSTA DE LAGO (AUS)	20	119	11	15	36	126675.86
ERHAAB (USA)	6	41	4	5	16	33486.58
ESSENCE OF DUBAI (USA)	2	20	1	1	5	3077.78
EUROSILVER (USA)	1	9	1	2	2	6277.68
EVEN TOP (IRE)	1	1	1	1	0	737230.00
EXCEED AND EXCEL (AUS)	170	945	64	102	284	1448799.65
EXCELLENT ART (GB)	49	184	17	24	68	307857.01
EXCHANGE RATE (USA)	3	9	1	1	4	12454.65
FAIR MIX (IRE)	2	18	1	2	5	5282.68
FALBRAV (IRE)	14	77	5	8	19	112215.12
FANTASTIC LIGHT (USA)	47	284	17	33	80	252096.52
FASLIYEV (USA)	68	460	20	42	109	212697.01
FATH (USA)	34	283	17	27	68	181802.12
FAYRUZ	9	48	3	6	15	106743.70
FIREBREAK (GB)	29	148	8	13	43	84823.40
FIRST SAMURAI (USA)	3	15	1	1	8	11095.50
FIRST TRUMP (GB)	7	41	3	5	12	18168.03
FIVE STAR DAY (USA)	2	29	2	5	15	43625.65

STALLIONS	RNRS	STARTS	WNRS	WINS	PLACES	TOTAL (£)
FLEETWOOD (IRE)	3	13	1	1	4	4694.87
FOOTSTEPSINTHESAND (GB)	76	448	30	55	148	638527.10
FOREST CAMP (USA)	5	30	2	2	4	15368.51
FORESTRY (USA)	8	52	4	7	15	25544.12
FORZANDO	5	31	1	1	4	5276.37
FOXHOUND (USA)	9	60	2	2	17	18726.89
FRAAM (GB)	30	190	10	17	49	133557.49
FUSAICHI PEGASUS (USA)	12	48	1	1	18	11779.51
GALILEO (IRE)	222	775	87	121	271	5283066.91
GENEROUS (IRE)	19	88	6	11	29	177131.16
GENTLEMAN'S DEAL (IRE)	11	61	3	6	17	20469.16
GHOSTZAPPER (USA)	2	7	1	2	2	13436.93
GIANT'S CAUSEWAY (USA)	59	244	19	28	76	457646.73
GOLAN (IRE)	11	59	5	7	8	28059.51
GOLDEN SNAKE (USA)	6	26	2	3	6	11704.63
GONE WEST (USA)	8	39	4	10	17	129694.59
GOODRICKE (GB)	4	13	1	1	2	6576.00
GRAND LODGE (USA)	15	51	4	5	9	13049.57
GRAND SLAM (USA)	9	47	2	3	8	13695.81
GREAT EXHIBITION (USA)	5	23	2	4	3	19827.58
GREAT PALM (USA)	4	10	1	1	1	7379.31
GREEN DESERT (USA)	77	498	36	60	132	424206.67
GREEN TUNE (USA)	9	46	3	3	14	27307.69
GROOM DANCER (USA)	6	37	3	3	7	13186.32
GULCH (USA)	4	16	2	2	2	4970.35
HAAFHD (GB)	99	526	42	69	162	351449.81
HALLING (USA)	80	381	33	47	126	615247.47
HAMAIRI (IRE)	1	10	1	1	2	1988.01
HANDSOME RIDGE (GB)	1	20	1	3	4	6047.59
HARD SPUN (USA)	13	39	5	7	21	100837.35
HARLAN'S HOLIDAY (USA)	4	16	2	2	6	8238.55
HARMONIC WAY (GB)	1	9	1	2	7	10856.52
HAWKEYE (IRE)	4	14	1	2	2	8300.75
HAWK WING (USA)	91	450	22	33	133	378897.32
HELIOSTATIC (IRE)	6	26	4	6	7	51457.43
HELISSIO (FR)	2	5	1	2	0	21931.00
HENNESSY (USA)	6	44	4	6	16	54822.55
HENNY HUGHES (USA)	3	6	1	1	2	5474.36
HERNANDO (FR)	34	153	8	14	41	152109.44
HIGH CHAPARRAL (IRE)	101	453	37	57	159	1651147.47
HIGH ESTATE	2	13	1	2	4	7564.09
HIGH YIELD (USA)	3	31	2	3	14	31008.26
HOLY ROMAN EMPEROR (IRE)	115	582	48	84	204	1355117.35
HORSE CHESTNUT (SAF)	4	33	2	4	6	10799.89
HUNTING LION (IRE)	6	25	1	1	3	3648.00
HURRICANE RUN (IRE)	74	322	28	43	119	806393.06
HURRICANE SKY (AUS)	1	8	1	2	0	2900.19
HUSSONET (USA)	2	10	1	1	3	2496.10
ICEMAN (GB)	81	491	36	56	142	307075.08
IFFRAAJ (GB)	97	510	32	47	162	348212.31
IMPERIAL BALLET (IRE)	14	70	3	7	10	30760.27
IMPERIAL DANCER (GB)	22	122	8	14	33	51784.67
INCHINOR (GB)	9	63	3	3	16	42364.12
INCLUDE (USA)	1	3	1	1	1	8318.97
INDESATCHEL (IRE)	36	175	7	9	49	65131.76
INDIAN DANEHILL (IRE)	16	96	6	6	17	25515.84
INDIAN HAVEN (GB)	24	116	9	13	41	101589.52
INDIAN LODGE (IRE)	2	10	2	2	3	4087.58
INDIAN RIDGE	31	231	12	18	68	120822.10
INDIAN ROCKET (GB)	2	13	1	1	3	3517.25
IN THE WINGS	13	62	4	8	13	29183.19
INTIKHAB (USA)	74	368	29	48	108	795622.14
INVINCIBLE SPIRIT (IRE)	189	998	78	107	332	1165827.81

STALLIONS	RNRS	STARTS	WNRS	WINS	PLACES	TOTAL (£)
IRON MASK (USA)	8	55	3	9	13	50367.70
ISHIGURU (USA)	66	438	27	44	144	323764.50
IVAN DENISOVICH (IRE)	28	126	4	12	37	58504.68
JADE ROBBERY (USA)	5	16	1	1	6	4070.83
JAMMAAL (GB)	1	11	1	1	2	5810.35
JAZIL (USA)	4	14	2	3	2	14689.41
JEREMY (USA)	23	83	4	4	21	70890.53
JOE BEAR (IRE)	3	15	1	1	3	17678.82
JOHANNESBURG (USA)	47	282	22	41	65	368020.78
JOHAR (USA)	2	7	2	4	2	37220.67
JOSR ALGARHOUD (IRE)	21	118	9	19	38	61645.62
KAHYASI	9	30	2	2	12	16079.80
KALANISI (IRE)	16	67	6	9	17	43994.19
KAYF TARA (GB)	7	35	2	2	7	6380.84
KEY OF LUCK (USA)	29	146	10	15	38	93154.55
KHELEYF (USA)	124	775	38	56	245	428217.99
KING CHARLEMAGNE (USA)	18	135	5	7	35	27268.02
KINGMAMBO (USA)	33	107	11	14	53	344641.32
KINGSALSA (USA)	4	30	1	5	8	15109.58
KING'S BEST (USA)	111	509	31	41	141	855073.63
KING'S THEATRE (IRE)	12	27	2	2	6	9399.74
KIRKWALL (GB)	2	3	1	1	1	2681.52
KITTEN'S JOY (USA)	8	26	3	3	7	19396.46
KODIAC (GB)	67	407	30	44	139	337213.60
KOMAITE (USA)	3	27	2	2	8	12106.81
KORNADO (GB)	1	6	1	1	1	2526.35
KRIS KIN (USA)	9	39	1	2	10	16290.96
KUROFUNE (USA)	1	4	1	1	2	9433.00
KUTUB (IRE)	3	8	1	1	2	2771.53
KYLLACHY (GB)	153	1050	73	118	297	782356.73
LAHIB (USA)	8	52	3	6	23	21767.20
LAKE CONISTON (IRE)	4	29	1	2	7	7682.20
LANDO (GER)	6	21	1	2	8	7907.08
LANGFUHR (CAN)	7	48	4	4	20	43922.14
LAWMAN (FR)	30	94	11	13	30	157316.91
LEMON DROP KID (USA)	16	74	6	8	27	102899.42
LEND A HAND (GB)	9	57	2	4	17	21121.12
LEROIDESANIMAUX (BRZ)	3	28	2	5	9	22461.49
LE VIE DEI COLORI (GB)	21	157	7	16	41	82294.31
LIBRETTIST (USA)	57	261	16	21	78	200674.87
LIL'S BOY (USA)	4	11	2	2	4	7650.68
LINAMIX (FR)	15	44	3	4	11	120275.49
LION HEART (USA)	9	29	1	1	6	10072.79
LOMITAS (GB)	13	55	3	4	12	12522.50
LOST SOLDIER (USA)	1	5	1	1	1	19889.01
LUCKY OWNERS (NZ)	7	33	1	1	9	6648.15
LUCKY STORY (USA)	43	268	16	29	69	126650.48
LUJAIN (USA)	23	175	9	10	47	53260.81
MACHIAVELLIAN (USA)	19	151	7	8	48	90635.81
MACHO UNO (USA)	2	11	1	1	5	10944.57
MAJESTIC MISSILE (IRE)	41	180	10	13	44	177111.20
MAKBUL	15	85	5	7	24	54604.42
MANDURO (GER)	25	74	3	3	24	23571.57
MARIA'S MON (USA)	11	56	4	5	21	76457.60
MARJU (IRE)	64	298	16	25	93	496450.90
MARK OF ESTEEM (IRE)	40	198	7	8	65	83260.71
MASAD (IRE)	1	11	1	2	1	3441.75
MEDAALY (GB)	1	11	1	3	5	6381.87
MEDAGLIA D'ORO (USA)	19	53	5	5	18	43373.16
MEDALLIST (USA)	1	6	1	1	1	3197.09
MEDECIS (GB)	21	121	7	10	35	73564.02
MEDICEAN (GB)	144	669	45	71	209	823138.43
MERDON MELODY	1	12	1	2	4	6560.48

STALLIONS	RNRS	STARTS	WNRS	WINS	PLACES	TOTAL (£)
MIESQUE'S SON (USA)	1	4	1	2	2	4190.05
MILAN (GB)	2	4	1	1	1	17586.21
MILK IT MICK (GB)	7	34	1	1	9	7407.64
MILWAUKEE BREW (USA)	1	11	1	1	3	5000.00
MIND GAMES (GB)	22	172	10	18	48	120143.85
MINESHAFT (USA)	3	23	1	1	10	9262.60
MINGUN (USA)	2	13	1	1	5	6636.59
MISU BOND (IRE)	9	49	3	6	13	21373.23
MIZZEN MAST (USA)	18	89	9	10	27	43633.68
MODIGLIANI (USA)	19	99	4	7	33	47389.86
MONASHEE MOUNTAIN (USA)	11	50	3	3	7	10163.89
MONSIEUR BOND (IRE)	63	422	30	50	138	401283.64
MONSUN (GER)	29	86	9	13	26	177435.82
MONTJEU (IRE)	130	539	51	76	194	2919426.90
MORE THAN READY (USA)	19	103	6	8	31	49311.05
MOSS VALE (IRE)	38	121	9	13	26	64980.36
MOST WELCOME	6	42	3	7	7	34874.54
MOTIVATOR (GB)	81	345	29	36	103	409410.26
MOZART (IRE)	9	61	3	4	13	39283.35
MR GREELEY (USA)	50	216	15	22	65	289231.74
MTOTO	8	60	5	7	22	31340.82
MUHTARRAM (USA)	6	35	2	2	15	13155.96
MUHTATHIR (GB)	11	49	5	6	11	24336.23
MUJADIL (USA)	38	243	12	23	68	208535.73
MUJAHID (USA)	36	264	15	27	73	135063.77
MULL OF KINTYRE (USA)	32	176	9	12	59	76350.29
MULTIPLEX (GB)	20	96	9	11	35	51953.51
MY BEST VALENTINE (GB)	3	20	1	1	4	3790.55
NAMID (GB)	69	407	23	33	111	287571.81
NASHWAN (USA)	3	16	1	1	2	2073.60
NAYEF (USA)	79	277	21	29	83	223267.21
NEEDWOOD BLADE (GB)	75	404	25	37	99	156479.65
NIGHT SHIFT (USA)	31	211	15	24	64	233796.98
NORSE DANCER (IRE)	14	63	6	8	17	77082.83
NORTH LIGHT (IRE)	5	16	3	3	5	31485.47
NOTNOWCATO (GB)	21	67	6	6	15	30182.89
NOVERRE (USA)	83	533	34	58	133	404899.00
OASIS DREAM (GB)	179	874	75	107	308	2301443.14
OBSERVATORY (USA)	32	152	10	18	56	536840.10
OCTAGONAL (NZ)	1	5	1	1	2	15706.90
OFFICER (USA)	7	34	2	2	9	20095.57
OLDEN TIMES (GB)	5	38	3	5	19	122548.33
ONE COOL CAT (USA)	81	470	27	39	126	260629.81
ON THE RIDGE (IRE)	3	11	1	1	1	5836.21
ORATORIO (IRE)	113	595	42	60	206	597401.51
ORIENTATE (USA)	7	42	3	3	15	17317.87
ORPEN (USA)	36	173	11	17	46	138676.72
OSORIO (GER)	4	26	1	3	6	9552.05
OUTOFTHEBOX (USA)	1	9	1	1	3	2829.25
PAIRUMANI STAR (IRE)	2	16	1	3	2	21913.80
PARIS HOUSE (GB)	4	10	3	3	3	61633.13
PASSING GLANCE (GB)	5	28	2	4	10	88020.17
PASTORAL PURSUITS (GB)	60	311	23	35	96	572211.27
PEARL OF LOVE (IRE)	9	53	1	2	9	7122.17
PEINTRE CELEBRE (USA)	40	155	14	19	50	250067.50
PERRYSTON VIEW (GB)	2	19	1	1	4	2987.00
PERUGINO (USA)	4	27	1	2	7	5864.86
PETARDIA (GB)	1	16	1	5	3	14270.70
PETIONVILLE (USA)	2	16	1	2	1	3702.54
PHOENIX REACH (IRE)	21	108	5	11	27	70687.61
PICCOLO (GB)	95	637	34	63	175	269701.82
PIVOTAL (GB)	157	783	80	119	272	1391325.36
PLATINI (GER)	1	2	1	1	0	28385.00

STALLIONS	RNRS	STARTS	WNRS	WINS	PLACES	TOTAL (£)
PLEASANTLY PERFECT (USA)	1	5	1	1	1	1836.85
POINT GIVEN (USA)	4	26	1	1	4	2497.36
POLAR FALCON (USA)	1	9	1	1	1	2718.85
POLIGLOTE (GB)	1	6	1	2	2	33166.40
POLISH PRECEDENT (USA)	6	31	1	1	5	16998.55
POLISH SUMMER (GB)	1	3	1	1	2	16206.90
POSSE (USA)	1	10	1	2	3	4499.41
PRIMO VALENTINO (IRE)	19	94	6	11	28	38903.12
PRINCE SABO	1	20	1	1	4	3781.60
PRIOLO (USA)	3	16	1	2	5	4954.64
PRIZED (USA)	1	7	1	1	4	100422.50
PROCLAMATION (IRE)	44	195	7	12	53	53107.24
PROUD ACCOLADE (USA)	1	2	1	1	1	5073.40
PROUD CITIZEN (USA)	19	93	4	4	25	59822.04
PULPIT (USA)	8	37	2	2	10	20499.53
PURGE (USA)	2	7	1	1	1	2102.18
PURSUIT OF LOVE (GB)	14	72	1	1	15	9771.46
PYRUS (USA)	20	127	6	16	37	90773.88
QUIET AMERICAN (USA)	2	8	1	1	2	6402.67
RAHY (USA)	30	164	13	27	61	420204.33
RAIL LINK (GB)	17	51	4	4	9	20704.09
RAINBOW QUEST (USA)	18	91	6	9	33	108020.72
RAISE A GRAND (IRE)	7	35	1	2	7	7356.96
RAKTI (GB)	16	90	7	11	23	36658.11
RAMBLING BEAR (GB)	7	32	1	2	2	4536.59
RAPHANE (USA)	1	6	1	1	1	13163.79
REDBACK (GB)	58	334	12	16	89	146721.90
RED BULLET (USA)	1	3	1	1	0	1535.39
RED CLUBS (IRE)	66	363	29	44	110	268459.71
REDOUTE'S CHOICE (AUS)	9	33	6	9	16	150229.54
RED RANSOM (USA)	73	395	25	30	130	334317.38
REEL BUDDY (USA)	16	81	4	6	19	31245.12
REFUSE TO BEND (IRE)	108	596	39	58	173	307987.66
RESET (AUS)	29	177	13	21	46	102202.88
RESPLENDENT GLORY (IRE)	7	35	2	6	8	15430.41
REVOQUE (IRE)	5	18	1	1	6	9702.12
ROCK HARD TEN (USA)	4	19	1	1	11	5789.20
ROCK OF GIBRALTAR (IRE)	100	537	43	63	161	1040316.97
ROMANOV (IRE)	1	6	1	1	2	15130.98
ROMAN RULER (USA)	5	57	2	3	16	23488.57
ROSSINI (USA)	13	70	4	6	9	21502.68
ROUVRES (FR)	1	6	1	1	1	2800.32
ROYAL APPLAUSE (GB)	169	1062	61	89	319	523897.09
ROYAL DRAGON (USA)	1	9	1	2	1	6901.41
SADDLERS' HALL (IRE)	2	11	1	2	6	7635.15
SADLER'S WELLS (USA)	68	274	26	34	73	304257.28
SAFFRON WALDEN (FR)	7	20	1	1	0	1704.25
SAHM (USA)	6	30	1	1	3	136802.24
SAINT BALLADO (CAN)	1	2	1	1	0	1706.00
SAKHEE (USA)	62	285	24	38	91	327718.61
SAMPOWER STAR (GB)	3	28	2	3	9	17470.75
SAMUM (GER)	3	12	1	1	3	5193.32
SCAT DADDY (USA)	2	7	2	3	1	71356.66
SEA FREEDOM (GB)	1	9	1	3	3	6383.96
SECOND EMPIRE (IRE)	5	38	3	7	17	31691.04
SEEKING THE GOLD (USA)	14	84	5	6	16	21145.48
SELKIRK (USA)	98	451	43	62	143	720284.71
SENDAWAR (IRE)	5	17	1	2	8	8765.97
SESARO (USA)	2	22	1	1	8	6729.16
SHAHRASTANI (USA)	1	9	1	1	1	3409.98
SHAMARDAL (USA)	105	475	50	71	171	883292.69
SHINKO FOREST (IRE)	16	99	7	10	19	105090.36
SHIROCCO (GER)	39	147	9	14	43	289113.86

STALLIONS	RNRS	STARTS	WNRS	WINS	PLACES	TOTAL (£)
SHOLOKHOV (IRE)	1	8	1	1	2	7586.85
SILVANO (GER)	3	24	1	1	7	54069.68
SILVER DEPUTY (CAN)	5	33	2	3	14	12186.99
SILVER PATRIARCH (IRE)	7	28	2	2	4	9130.64
SINGSPIEL (IRE)	101	442	29	44	144	448187.57
SINNDAR (IRE)	22	75	9	15	18	145919.80
SIR PERCY (GB)	26	102	10	16	35	100021.20
SKI CHIEF (USA)	1	7	1	2	3	4525.78
SLEEPING INDIAN (GB)	59	328	25	39	94	236421.04
SMART STRIKE (CAN)	18	82	6	8	28	115565.50
SMARTY JONES (USA)	8	33	3	3	8	18121.18
SNURGE	1	3	1	1	1	5744.85
SONGANDAPRAYER (USA)	5	28	1	1	8	13373.42
SONGLINE (SWE)	1	6	1	1	2	2397.90
SOVEREIGN WATER (FR)	1	5	1	1	1	3121.51
SOVIET STAR (USA)	30	187	12	22	45	118426.62
SPARTACUS (IRE)	22	84	4	6	19	32389.93
SPECTRUM (IRE)	9	82	3	7	19	20453.35
SPEIGHTSTOWN (USA)	22	78	10	16	22	125032.69
SPINNING WORLD (USA)	12	108	7	12	34	110221.39
SRI PEKAN (USA)	1	8	1	2	1	18191.25
STARBOROUGH (GB)	3	11	1	2	4	30652.56
STARCRAFT (NZ)	19	115	5	14	37	166863.15
STARDAN (IRE)	5	19	1	1	4	14405.18
STATUE OF LIBERTY (USA)	55	340	18	26	94	154602.80
ST JOVITE (USA)	1	8	1	1	3	4027.25
STORM CAT (USA)	10	67	6	7	25	52982.15
STORM CREEK (USA)	1	5	1	1	0	1364.80
STORMING HOME (GB)	23	139	11	20	40	127266.74
STORMY ATLANTIC (USA)	14	79	6	9	27	82925.41
STORMY RIVER (FR)	3	16	1	1	5	4753.29
STRATEGIC PRINCE (GB)	41	182	13	18	43	229044.68
STRAVINSKY (USA)	7	64	3	3	27	47252.37
STREET CRY (IRE)	72	319	29	39	112	736420.14
STREET SENSE (USA)	5	15	1	2	8	11354.35
STRIKING AMBITION (GB)	20	86	5	8	17	36958.25
SUCCESSFUL APPEAL (USA)	4	20	1	2	8	13653.99
SULAMANI (IRE)	24	137	9	14	35	106214.33
SUNDAY BREAK (JPN)	3	9	2	2	2	8751.24
SUPERIOR PREMIUM (GB)	10	78	2	4	23	24674.17
SWAIN (IRE)	9	59	3	4	18	47709.99
TAGULA (IRE)	59	379	22	39	94	521391.41
TALAASH (IRE)	1	5	1	1	1	2120.50
TALE OF THE CAT (USA)	13	91	7	9	22	89054.94
TAMARISK (IRE)	4	27	2	3	8	15944.40
TAMURE (IRE)	3	14	1	2	3	9039.83
TAPIT (USA)	4	27	1	1	10	7731.55
TENDULKAR (USA)	2	7	1	2	2	60369.45
TEOFILIO (IRE)	4	21	1	3	8	9840.55
TEOFILO (IRE)	51	123	15	18	42	378692.07
TERTULLIAN (USA)	4	34	1	2	7	12068.19
THEATRICAL	6	31	4	11	6	31728.44
THREE VALLEYS (USA)	39	149	7	8	38	39434.88
THUNDER GULCH (USA)	3	41	1	3	15	10813.10
TIGER HILL (IRE)	86	385	24	36	106	411997.52
TILLERMAN (GB)	6	39	2	3	12	9829.04
TIMELESS TIMES (USA)	3	32	1	1	9	5397.03
TIPSY CREEK (USA)	6	47	2	4	10	10041.84
TITUS LIVIUS (FR)	40	326	21	40	95	229680.67
TIZNOW (USA)	5	38	2	3	9	12676.49
TOBOUGG (IRE)	94	448	33	52	116	228538.82
TOCCET (USA)	3	11	2	2	2	4565.64
TOMBA (GB)	12	83	5	9	23	45285.39

STALLIONS	RNRS	STARTS	WNRS	WINS	PLACES	TOTAL (£)
TRADE FAIR (GB)	49	285	19	28	87	155966.03
TRADITIONALLY (USA)	9	73	4	10	15	38532.67
TRANS ISLAND (GB)	41	235	16	31	70	141108.73
TUMBLEWEED RIDGE (GB)	6	23	2	4	5	12562.22
TURTLE ISLAND (IRE)	2	13	1	3	4	6583.40
TWO PUNCH (USA)	1	6	1	1	2	3615.20
UNBRIDLED'S SONG (USA)	1	4	1	1	3	4204.52
VAL ROYAL (FR)	46	300	13	22	82	198736.99
VAN NISTELROOY (USA)	15	48	2	2	15	24832.52
VERGLAS (IRE)	96	508	25	41	135	301589.75
VETTORI (IRE)	14	82	5	10	17	48427.49
VICAR (USA)	1	14	1	1	6	5995.70
VICTORY MOON (SAF)	1	4	1	2	2	64352.15
VIKING RULER (AUS)	11	31	2	3	5	11343.82
VISION OF NIGHT (GB)	1	18	1	2	9	9918.52
VITAL EQUINE (IRE)	11	54	4	6	19	42888.21
VOLOCHINE (IRE)	1	11	1	2	2	4048.49
WAR CHANT (USA)	14	74	6	9	27	110402.32
WEET-A-MINUTE (IRE)	2	19	1	3	4	6378.83
WHERE OR WHEN (IRE)	30	157	8	13	44	80665.39
WHIPPER (USA)	48	241	19	34	79	298831.48
WHITMORE'S CONN (USA)	1	6	1	1	2	6472.30
WHYWHYWHY (USA)	3	20	2	2	4	9292.15
WINDSOR KNOT (IRE)	9	30	1	1	13	10411.52
WISEMAN'S FERRY (USA)	3	24	2	4	3	12193.00
WITH APPROVAL (CAN)	13	79	4	9	30	35058.89
XAAR (GB)	33	166	9	11	39	139845.88
YANKEE GENTLEMAN (USA)	4	21	3	6	8	46321.43
YES IT'S TRUE (USA)	9	39	1	3	8	7082.30
ZAFEEN (FR)	37	222	17	24	69	107796.88
ZAFONIC (USA)	7	32	3	3	10	8458.16
ZAHA (CAN)	9	43	2	3	10	11136.70
ZAMINDAR (USA)	43	159	16	20	53	240163.17
ZIETEN (USA)	2	11	1	1	2	1701.23

BY KIND PERMISSION OF WEATHERBYS

NH STALLIONS' EARNINGS FOR 2010/11

(includes every stallion who sired a winner over jumps in Great Britain and Ireland in 2010/11)

STALLIONS	RNRS	STARTS	WNRS	WINS	PLACES	TOTAL (£)
AAHSAYLAD	6	18	2	3	4	17899.06
ACATENANGO (GER)	13	70	5	5	22	35781.83
ACCESS SKI	5	25	2	4	5	12786.59
ACCLAMATION (GB)	15	42	4	6	10	25432.63
ACCORDION	131	513	39	54	162	925996.38
ACT ONE (GB)	13	45	3	5	13	18373.22
ADNAAN (IRE)	3	10	1	1	3	3267.25
AGENT BLEU (FR)	4	18	2	3	10	28586.90
AGNES WORLD (USA)	5	23	2	2	6	9930.88
AKHDARI (USA)	1	6	1	2	3	60260.30
ALA HOUNAK	1	9	1	3	3	29423.61
ALAMO BAY (USA)	3	21	2	2	10	21909.52
ALBANO (IRE)	1	2	1	2	0	4143.47
ALBERTO GIACOMETTI (IRE)	1	3	1	1	2	41501.73
ALDERBROOK (GB)	120	435	32	52	128	414769.19
ALEXIUS (IRE)	2	12	1	1	3	6650.45
ALFLORA (IRE)	191	657	39	58	173	522004.02
ALHAARTH (IRE)	53	207	11	17	65	173534.43
ALI-ROYAL (IRE)	3	9	1	1	2	2057.17
ALJABR (USA)	9	36	4	4	13	64628.13
ALKALDE (GER)	2	6	2	2	2	27064.85
ALMAARAD	4	11	2	2	5	5645.03
AL NAMIX (FR)	3	13	1	3	8	72380.95
ALWUHUSH (USA)	2	16	2	3	5	31132.31
ALZAO (USA)	8	34	3	3	8	23620.05
AMILYNX (FR)	10	25	1	1	2	2876.02
AMONG MEN (USA)	1	11	1	2	4	5728.66
ANABAA (USA)	20	116	10	13	42	74446.08
ANABAA BLUE (GB)	6	22	4	6	5	30428.74
ANSHAN	190	757	57	98	200	924733.81
ANTARCTIQUE (IRE)	5	24	1	1	4	15600.84
ANTONIUS PIUS (USA)	15	53	4	4	12	19691.25
APPLE TREE (FR)	7	44	3	7	21	71160.72
APRIL NIGHT (FR)	11	45	3	5	11	43295.89
APTITUDE (USA)	2	8	1	2	5	37521.24
ARCH (USA)	9	25	1	1	8	8213.54
ARCTIC LORD	23	91	7	10	22	63763.35
AREION (GER)	1	6	1	2	0	3436.57
ARKADIAN HERO (USA)	8	44	1	1	11	9191.82
ARTAN (IRE)	1	8	1	1	2	3705.76
ARZANNI	9	21	2	3	3	23081.70
ASHKALANI (IRE)	17	41	2	2	8	9174.93
ASHLEY PARK (IRE)	1	4	1	3	1	8998.65
ASSESSOR (IRE)	7	28	3	4	15	43029.82
ASTAIR (FR)	1	4	1	2	1	7364.50
ASTARABAD (USA)	16	51	6	11	17	85073.92
ATRAF (GB)	14	74	4	5	29	40162.78
AUCTION HOUSE (USA)	10	23	1	4	3	13078.21
AVERTI (IRE)	7	26	1	1	13	9200.34
AVONBRIDGE (GB)	9	21	1	1	2	2141.99
AZAMOUR (IRE)	15	41	4	7	2	146702.37
BABY TURK	5	22	2	4	8	49497.70
BACH (IRE)	82	261	15	19	36	93713.31
BACHELOR DUKE (USA)	9	25	1	3	8	59019.81
BACHIR (IRE)	3	10	1	1	4	14247.79
BADOLATO (USA)	1	9	1	2	5	8076.95
BAHHARE (USA)	13	73	6	10	20	128602.87
BAHRI (USA)	16	73	8	11	20	61233.35
BAL HARBOUR (GB)	7	23	1	2	8	10642.90
BALLA COVE	4	9	1	1	1	3604.19

STALLIONS	RNRS	STARTS	WNRS	WINS	PLACES	TOTAL (£)
BALLEROY (USA)	3	10	1	1	4	8489.70
BALLET ROYAL (USA)	1	4	1	1	2	3692.20
BALLINGARRY (IRE)	6	19	1	1	7	8962.19
BANDMASTER (USA)	9	34	2	2	11	15792.92
BANYUMANIK (IRE)	1	15	1	3	6	15479.56
BARATHEA (IRE)	50	203	14	18	57	294803.26
BASANTA (IRE)	14	46	2	2	14	35691.08
BEAT ALL (USA)	73	288	13	21	60	122533.21
BEAT HOLLOW (GB)	24	86	7	12	30	95269.62
BEAUCHAMP KING (GB)	10	25	1	2	7	11146.86
BEDAWIN (FR)	1	12	1	3	5	12980.52
BELMEZ (USA)	1	4	1	1	1	11094.50
BE MY NATIVE (USA)	2	6	1	1	1	10811.46
BENEFICIAL (GB)	322	1307	85	132	357	1273989.38
BENNY THE DIP (USA)	6	22	1	3	6	20351.04
BERING	9	30	5	6	4	78201.34
BERTOLINI (USA)	31	87	5	6	16	25891.87
BEST OF THE BESTS (IRE)	10	38	1	1	8	7739.84
BIG SHUFFLE (USA)	7	26	1	3	8	14478.54
BISHOP OF CASHEL (GB)	25	86	5	6	25	33082.95
BLACK MINNALOUSHE (USA)	3	16	1	2	6	16254.32
BLACK SAM BELLAMY (IRE)	10	28	4	8	6	59670.76
BLUE OCEAN (USA)	5	16	1	1	4	9644.63
BLUEPRINT (IRE)	37	140	8	9	46	51412.56
BLUSHING FLAME (USA)	4	20	1	1	7	7234.23
BOB BACK (USA)	175	651	49	80	191	901384.29
BOB'S RETURN (IRE)	100	363	25	32	101	279261.99
BODY GLOVE (ARG)	2	7	1	1	0	2055.30
BOLLIN ERIC (GB)	19	49	1	2	11	7744.91
BONBON ROSE (FR)	2	8	1	2	3	6025.10
BRAVEFOOT (GB)	12	45	4	4	8	22109.56
BRIAN BORU (GB)	26	94	6	10	20	51662.00
BRIER CREEK (USA)	8	31	5	8	5	64866.88
BROADWAY FLYER (USA)	28	91	9	14	36	86634.56
BROKEN HEARTED	23	86	4	4	30	45649.49
BULINGTON (FR)	9	34	3	6	13	31777.00
BUSY FLIGHT (GB)	14	31	1	1	8	11682.18
BYZANTIUM (FR)	1	2	1	1	1	3262.25
CABALLO RAPTOR (CAN)	3	6	1	1	1	6301.62
CACHET NOIR (USA)	2	7	1	1	3	16069.98
CADEAUX GENEREUX	9	43	5	9	7	25084.82
CADOUBEL (FR)	1	8	1	1	0	1951.50
CADOUDAL (FR)	23	86	12	25	23	841746.30
CALIFET (FR)	4	22	3	5	9	23528.04
CAPE CROSS (IRE)	34	112	8	8	39	72501.34
CAPTAIN RIO (GB)	24	77	5	8	27	67310.94
CARNIVAL DANCER (GB)	6	23	2	3	7	9604.00
CARROLL HOUSE	39	126	4	7	30	79731.23
CARROWKEEL (IRE)	7	21	1	2	3	6277.87
CATCHER IN THE RYE (IRE)	47	135	12	18	33	133234.16
CAT'S CAREER (USA)	2	4	1	1	1	2237.70
CAYMAN KAI (IRE)	4	18	2	3	5	9970.37
CELTIC SWING (GB)	24	95	5	11	24	63857.11
CENTRAL PARK (IRE)	10	28	1	1	8	6235.98
CENTURY CITY (IRE)	1	12	1	3	7	19482.30
CHAMBERLIN (FR)	1	2	1	1	1	5426.85
CHARENTE RIVER (IRE)	8	38	3	3	8	21390.33
CHARMER	7	25	1	1	10	20344.22
CHARNWOOD FOREST (IRE)	6	18	2	2	1	8543.99
CHEF DE CLAN (FR)	4	14	1	2	4	11843.08
CHESTER HOUSE (USA)	2	7	1	2	1	31812.50
CHEVALIER (IRE)	14	55	6	7	14	27700.39
CHOISIR (AUS)	14	43	2	4	11	19111.65
CHRISTOPHENE (USA)	3	11	1	4	2	57088.50

STALLIONS	RNRS	STARTS	WNRS	WINS	PLACES	TOTAL (£)
CHURLISH CHARM (GB)	3	10	1	1	2	1990.63
CITY HONOURS (USA)	44	160	13	15	33	100134.32
CITY ON A HILL (USA)	4	18	1	1	5	11917.90
CLASSIC CLICHE (IRE)	82	304	20	30	95	194461.19
CLERKENWELL (USA)	7	23	1	2	9	12523.47
CLODOVIL (IRE)	5	19	2	2	9	42381.27
CLOSE CONFLICT (USA)	21	59	5	7	8	32098.44
CLOUDINGS (IRE)	47	203	14	20	54	101299.42
COIS NA TINE (IRE)	5	17	1	1	4	3997.60
COLONEL COLLINS (USA)	5	13	1	1	2	6179.90
COLONIAL AFFAIR (USA)	1	6	1	1	3	3986.20
COMMANCHE RUN	20	66	2	3	13	11935.79
COMMANDER COLLINS (IRE)	15	60	3	4	11	21717.31
COMMANDS (AUS)	1	4	1	1	2	3183.85
COMPTON ADMIRAL (GB)	4	19	1	2	5	9081.80
COMTE DU BOURG (FR)	3	10	1	1	1	4465.14
CORONADO'S QUEST (USA)	2	7	1	1	1	2964.90
CORROUGE (USA)	13	35	1	3	11	21781.73
COTATION (GB)	2	7	1	1	3	2500.81
COURT CAVE (IRE)	21	77	5	6	20	62942.56
COZZENE (USA)	5	31	2	2	7	10056.61
CRAIGSTEEL (GB)	34	140	11	15	43	132772.88
CROCO ROUGE (IRE)	5	30	1	1	13	32080.15
CRYPTOCLEARANCE (USA)	1	5	1	2	1	9909.75
CURTAIN TIME (IRE)	5	15	3	3	2	55499.90
CYBORG (FR)	13	67	7	8	28	55943.17
DAGGERS DRAWN (USA)	18	44	3	3	9	17552.45
DALAKHANI (IRE)	20	63	6	7	11	41002.66
DALIAPOUR (IRE)	5	21	4	5	11	31460.80
DANCING HIGH	6	23	2	2	10	12165.76
DANEHILL (USA)	7	22	3	4	9	22023.93
DANEHILL DANCER (IRE)	45	141	10	17	40	146547.70
DANETIME (IRE)	4	15	1	1	5	24884.27
DANSILI (GB)	37	160	10	14	49	133908.34
DARAZARI (IRE)	10	29	2	2	10	59738.21
DARK MOONDANCER (GB)	19	56	5	5	15	32647.04
DARNAY (GB)	22	69	3	4	15	17796.30
DARSHAAN	9	30	1	1	10	13703.92
DASHING BLADE	9	46	2	4	11	21352.58
DAYLAMI (IRE)	60	258	13	23	72	182415.45
DEFINITE ARTICLE (GB)	141	506	37	55	145	467764.34
DELLA FRANCESCA (USA)	4	17	1	2	4	11345.50
DENEL (FR)	5	22	2	2	5	20249.72
DENHAM RED (FR)	2	7	1	1	1	30586.25
DEPLOY	43	126	11	17	26	154500.81
DESERT KING (IRE)	12	48	1	1	12	8775.42
DESERT PRINCE (IRE)	30	143	12	15	36	122560.06
DESERT STYLE (IRE)	16	47	1	2	9	8886.46
DESERT SUN (GB)	14	44	1	3	8	33850.89
DIESIS	18	75	4	6	24	57825.23
DIKTAT (GB)	38	154	7	8	42	68682.42
DILSHAAN (GB)	13	55	4	8	17	78011.25
DISCOVER D'AUTEUIL (FR)	9	44	4	7	20	111623.74
DISTANT MUSIC (USA)	7	31	2	3	12	20626.62
DISTORTED HUMOR (USA)	2	11	1	2	3	4707.96
DOCKSIDER (USA)	5	29	2	5	8	33849.55
DOLPHIN STREET (FR)	3	7	1	1	4	16818.88
DOLPOUR	8	38	1	1	13	14872.16
DOM ALCO (FR)	15	60	10	17	18	403724.62
DOMEDRIVER (IRE)	12	42	2	2	7	18135.21
DOUBLE ECLIPSE (IRE)	12	36	3	4	9	25828.59
DOUBLETOUR (USA)	3	8	1	1	2	3109.90
DOUBLE TRIGGER (IRE)	52	208	17	24	61	141805.54
DOUNBA (FR)	2	8	1	1	1	15014.57

STALLIONS	RNRS	STARTS	WNRS	WINS	PLACES	TOTAL (£)
DOYEN (IRE)	10	30	4	6	11	71358.38
DR DEVIOUS (IRE)	5	20	1	2	6	13111.63
DREAM WELL (FR)	3	12	1	2	1	5124.45
DR FONG (USA)	35	150	10	16	55	124012.79
DR MASSINI (IRE)	95	396	32	55	118	467962.19
DUBAI DESTINATION (USA)	31	123	12	18	28	80496.26
DUBAWI (IRE)	4	24	2	6	9	27416.64
DUSHYANTOR (USA)	63	206	12	17	69	250305.58
DYNAFORMER (USA)	16	65	5	5	15	27946.43
EAST OF HEAVEN (IRE)	1	4	1	1	1	6393.81
EL CONQUISTADOR	5	13	1	1	3	6715.50
ELMAAMUL (USA)	10	43	3	4	14	20695.49
ELNADIM (USA)	7	23	2	3	6	15279.32
ELUSIVE QUALITY (USA)	5	17	3	5	6	48151.73
EMPEROR FOUNTAIN	17	46	1	1	14	10239.68
EMPEROR JONES (USA)	3	12	1	1	3	4311.40
EMPIRE MAKER (USA)	5	15	1	1	4	10022.77
ENCOSTA DE LAGO (AUS)	1	6	1	1	2	3853.57
ENRIQUE (GB)	2	8	1	2	4	82854.54
ENVIRONMENT FRIEND (GB)	33	123	4	10	27	168280.90
EPERVIER BLEU	3	6	1	1	2	8309.80
EPISTOLAIRE (IRE)	4	14	1	1	4	8988.84
ERHAAB (USA)	21	67	4	10	19	35172.47
ERINS ISLE	3	8	1	1	1	23584.07
ERMINIUS (GER)	1	8	1	1	2	4513.10
EUROBUS	7	28	2	3	6	17290.39
EVENING WORLD (FR)	2	10	1	1	5	64191.50
EVEN TOP (IRE)	6	21	2	2	4	11740.54
EVE'S ERROR	3	21	1	1	8	6991.68
EXCEED AND EXCEL (AUS)	4	7	1	1	1	3592.45
EXECUTIVE PERK	14	46	2	3	15	15330.86
EXIT TO NOWHERE (USA)	102	317	14	19	70	144036.32
FADO (FR)	2	10	2	3	4	12766.92
FAHRIS (IRE)	2	7	1	2	2	9213.70
FAIR MIX (IRE)	17	45	5	5	12	39513.33
FALBRAV (IRE)	5	21	1	1	6	4117.70
FANTASTIC LIGHT (USA)	47	136	6	9	31	76749.86
FASLIYEV (USA)	15	52	2	6	14	48022.52
FATH (USA)	12	36	3	3	9	21087.53
FIREBREAK (GB)	2	6	1	1	2	2780.85
FIRST TRUMP (GB)	7	27	2	4	4	12811.45
FITZCARRALDO (ARG)	1	7	1	2	2	12460.17
FLEETWOOD (IRE)	20	77	4	5	29	34090.96
FLEMENSFIRTH (USA)	271	989	70	95	293	1181738.62
FLYING LEGEND (USA)	17	100	4	4	26	45696.88
FLYING SPUR (AUS)	3	12	1	3	2	12130.15
FOOTSTEPSINTHESAND (GB)	4	25	2	4	9	17962.86
FOREST WILDCAT (USA)	4	23	1	2	4	15998.81
FOURSTARS ALLSTAR (USA)	39	155	5	6	48	58863.21
FOURTH OF JUNE (USA)	1	8	1	2	1	7905.09
FOXHOUND (USA)	10	44	3	4	14	25568.63
FRAAM (GB)	25	97	5	7	23	57382.66
FRAGRANT MIX (IRE)	11	33	1	2	16	54697.41
FREEDOM CRY (GB)	4	9	1	2	2	24682.85
FRENCH GLORY	1	5	1	1	3	37864.00
FRUITS OF LOVE (USA)	19	64	4	5	26	63893.50
FUNNY BABY (FR)	5	16	1	3	6	14073.82
FUSAICHI PEGASUS (USA)	8	37	3	4	7	15115.11
GALILEO (IRE)	56	228	18	29	83	254158.11
GARDE ROYALE	7	37	4	5	15	69832.43
GARUDA (IRE)	5	17	2	2	7	7652.54
GENEROUS (IRE)	56	185	17	21	57	111960.19
GERMANY (USA)	11	48	3	3	15	78333.35
GIANT'S CAUSEWAY (USA)	30	106	5	6	29	59463.78

STALLIONS	RNRS	STARTS	WNRS	WINS	PLACES	TOTAL (£)
GLACIAL STORM (USA)	38	139	10	12	41	79960.41
GOLAN (IRE)	24	72	6	8	15	58012.28
GOLD AWAY (IRE)	7	27	3	4	11	32403.70
GOLDEN SNAKE (USA)	8	31	2	2	9	9070.98
GOLDEN TORNADO (IRE)	18	85	5	9	21	133697.54
GOLDMARK (USA)	23	80	3	7	18	36890.38
GOLDNEYEV (USA)	3	21	2	7	6	24120.44
GOOD THYNE (USA)	17	70	2	3	29	114833.66
GOOFALIK (USA)	3	8	1	2	2	17287.77
GOTHLAND (FR)	11	31	2	2	5	7907.57
GOVERNOR BROWN (USA)	2	7	2	2	3	25302.44
GRAND LODGE (USA)	22	107	9	16	38	83520.28
GRAND PLAISIR (IRE)	10	45	4	5	15	85202.64
GRAND TRESOR (FR)	8	24	1	1	7	9510.06
GRAPE TREE ROAD (GB)	23	48	1	1	6	6738.84
GREAT PALM (USA)	88	277	10	14	49	162382.07
GREEN DESERT (USA)	5	17	1	1	0	4579.65
GREENSMITH	1	5	1	1	2	3456.50
GREEN TUNE (USA)	7	24	2	2	7	16026.42
GREY RISK (FR)	3	21	2	3	12	134137.99
GROOM DANCER (USA)	24	83	5	6	21	59457.84
GUNNER B	10	30	3	3	9	19586.90
HAAFHD (GB)	8	24	3	4	8	95246.09
HALLING (USA)	33	113	9	11	36	121572.43
HAMAIRI (IRE)	1	5	1	2	2	8506.98
HAMAS (IRE)	7	14	1	1	2	3787.35
HATIM (USA)	1	5	1	1	2	2831.65
HAWKEYE (IRE)	8	28	2	2	4	7964.78
HAWK WING (USA)	39	131	5	6	40	42718.39
HELISSIO (FR)	5	13	1	1	6	5563.28
HERNANDO (FR)	48	197	15	22	74	208869.24
HERON ISLAND (IRE)	65	188	18	24	41	107393.45
HIGH CHAPARRAL (USA)	43	141	10	10	47	81439.76
HIGHEST HONOR (FR)	13	63	4	8	22	95644.72
HIGH-RISE (IRE)	13	38	1	1	7	7179.69
HIGH ROLLER (IRE)	13	63	4	5	13	26188.03
HOUMAYOUN (FR)	12	53	2	3	11	49100.14
HOUSAMIX (FR)	1	5	1	1	3	10204.60
HUBBLY BUBBLY (USA)	20	83	4	4	21	29613.49
HUMBEL (USA)	22	101	6	9	32	45725.03
IDRIS (IRE)	4	22	1	2	7	13881.03
IMPERIAL BALLET (IRE)	21	106	5	6	29	56833.55
IMPERIAL DANCER (GB)	3	12	1	2	3	5830.79
I'M SUPPOSIN (IRE)	3	7	1	2	3	6915.65
INCHINOR (GB)	14	68	5	7	23	47949.77
IN COMMAND (IRE)	1	5	1	2	3	21746.50
INDIAN DANEHILL (IRE)	40	180	11	16	40	131311.58
INDIAN HAVEN (GB)	9	34	1	3	11	20541.86
INDIAN RIDGE	24	87	4	5	27	45933.31
INDIAN RIVER (FR)	6	19	1	1	5	8142.26
INDIAN ROCKET (GB)	2	15	1	1	5	5373.43
INFANTRY	1	7	1	2	3	6803.43
INSAN (USA)	14	48	6	9	14	44502.83
INSATIABLE (IRE)	11	44	2	2	11	12477.22
IN THE WINGS	29	110	7	10	26	119390.60
INTIKHAB (USA)	20	75	6	7	19	152643.93
INVINCIBLE SPIRIT (IRE)	21	69	5	11	16	90164.89
ISHIGURU (USA)	4	18	1	1	4	4115.70
JADE ROBBERY (USA)	7	25	3	4	8	21162.48
JAMESMEAD	3	14	1	1	6	7121.82
JAMMAAL (GB)	4	8	1	1	3	3741.37
JEUNE HOMME (USA)	1	11	1	2	7	24091.97
JIMBLE (FR)	8	23	1	2	4	7186.40
JOHAN CRUYFF (GB)	2	6	1	1	3	13398.23

STALLIONS	RNRS	STARTS	WNRS	WINS	PLACES	TOTAL (£)
JOHANNESBURG (USA)	14	66	5	6	16	40210.16
JOHANN QUATZ (FR)	4	20	2	2	9	25830.10
JOHN FRENCH	2	9	1	1	2	2633.20
JOLLY JAKE (NZ)	6	13	1	1	3	5662.51
JOSR ALGARHOUD (IRE)	23	51	3	3	15	16875.86
JUMBO HIRT (USA)	3	18	1	1	7	9716.87
JUPITER ISLAND	1	13	1	1	7	4957.23
JURADO (USA)	6	28	3	4	11	72913.54
KABOOL (GB)	1	2	1	1	1	1394.55
KADALKO (FR)	10	38	5	5	14	49211.68
KADASTROF (FR)	14	56	5	8	20	28147.07
KADEED (IRE)	7	18	1	1	2	5716.36
KAHTAN (GB)	7	17	1	1	1	2068.37
KAHYASI	44	222	15	19	72	269168.83
KAIETEUR (USA)	1	9	1	1	2	6530.98
KALANISI (IRE)	35	125	9	15	39	135294.84
KALDOUNEVEES (FR)	7	33	5	7	11	44818.23
KALMOSS (FR)	2	8	1	1	1	4681.75
KAPGARDE (FR)	25	96	4	8	25	37784.42
KARINGA BAY	144	537	30	36	153	248040.60
KASMAYO (GB)	4	15	1	1	6	8486.89
KAYF TARA (GB)	157	560	37	47	202	435928.46
KENDOR (FR)	5	25	2	2	9	36527.57
KEY OF LUCK (USA)	34	141	13	20	38	201119.91
KHALKEVI (IRE)	3	7	1	1	4	8322.83
KHELEYF (USA)	9	35	2	6	9	35894.31
KIER PARK (IRE)	2	12	1	1	3	2449.46
KING CHARLEMAGNE (USA)	12	45	2	2	6	13962.21
KING CUGAT (USA)	1	4	1	2	0	6283.55
KINGMAMBO (USA)	10	48	4	5	19	27932.85
KINGSALSA (USA)	5	25	3	6	10	51510.80
KING'S BEST (USA)	60	230	13	17	73	163936.81
KING'S THEATRE (IRE)	202	868	82	132	269	1574475.63
KIRKWALL (GB)	15	37	2	5	4	25300.80
KIZITCA (FR)	1	6	1	1	3	3377.82
KOMAITE (USA)	3	16	2	3	1	10726.50
KOMTUR (USA)	1	3	1	1	0	6411.50
KOTASHAAN (FR)	13	46	1	1	7	7983.96
KOUROUN (FR)	2	8	1	1	4	4623.90
KRIS	4	18	1	1	5	6861.41
KRIS KIN (USA)	12	25	1	1	3	3598.52
KYLLACHY (GB)	15	45	4	6	8	25905.22
LAHIB (USA)	53	214	15	27	42	186422.07
LAHINT (USA)	2	8	1	2	3	139842.58
LANCASTRIAN	1	1	1	1	0	6505.00
LANDO (GER)	8	43	4	8	13	83464.77
LARGESSE (GB)	6	21	1	1	5	4428.47
LAVERON (GB)	20	71	3	5	23	154802.74
LAVIRCO (GER)	17	69	5	8	15	118620.87
LEADING COUNSEL (USA)	12	42	2	2	17	45943.16
LEAR SPEAR (USA)	5	20	2	2	8	24442.55
LECROIX (GER)	2	9	1	1	3	8568.80
LE FOU (IRE)	2	5	2	2	3	11522.20
LEMON DROP KID (USA)	6	31	3	6	15	49248.97
LEND A HAND (GB)	17	68	4	7	18	105040.26
LESOTHO (USA)	5	15	1	1	7	8678.80
LE VIE DEI COLORI (GB)	3	12	2	4	4	28027.13
LIGHTS OUT (FR)	1	4	1	1	2	4064.47
LIL'S BOY (USA)	9	32	1	1	6	8706.20
LIMNOS (JPN)	6	17	1	1	3	4562.66
LINAMIX (FR)	21	99	6	8	25	64460.83
LION HEART (USA)	3	10	1	1	3	4756.47
LITTLE BIGHORN	5	18	1	1	5	3966.15
LOMITAS (GB)	32	171	14	23	56	211649.25

STALLIONS	RNRS	STARTS	WNRS	WINS	PLACES	TOTAL (£)
LONE BID (FR)	1	2	1	1	1	2754.25
LORD AMERICO	82	292	18	22	69	178227.12
LORD AVIE (USA)	1	10	1	1	6	8800.43
LORD OF APPEAL (GB)	34	125	7	12	28	106221.74
LORD OF MEN (GB)	6	27	3	3	10	19245.51
LOST WORLD (IRE)	19	80	8	12	24	134844.40
LOUP SAUVAGE (USA)	22	62	3	3	9	9760.78
LOUP SOLITAIRE (USA)	7	28	2	2	6	17283.03
LUCKY DREAM (FR)	3	18	1	2	7	11034.17
LUCKY STORY (USA)	10	27	1	1	5	4742.06
LUSO (GB)	149	560	27	41	133	330665.62
LUTE ANTIQUE (FR)	10	26	1	2	7	21362.94
MACHIAVELLIAN (USA)	19	100	7	10	32	106825.49
MACHIAVELLIAN TSAR (FR)	1	1	1	1	0	1507.22
MAILLE PISTOL (FR)	2	11	1	1	3	4251.80
MAKBUL	11	42	2	2	14	11302.47
MALINAS (GER)	4	9	2	2	3	4724.78
MANSONNIEN (FR)	21	100	7	13	33	232715.53
MARATHON (USA)	8	25	1	1	7	7082.32
MARESCA SORRENTO (FR)	13	65	5	7	20	50940.86
MARIA'S MON (USA)	3	7	1	1	2	5310.20
MARIGNAN (FR)	18	75	7	8	22	60477.40
MARJU (IRE)	26	99	6	8	36	61166.92
MARK OF ESTEEM (IRE)	36	136	6	10	38	68765.75
MARLY RIVER (FR)	2	5	1	1	0	3252.50
MARMATO	1	6	1	2	0	4228.25
MARTALINE (GB)	11	32	6	6	18	67947.70
MASTER WILLIE	2	5	1	2	1	4795.61
MEDAALY (GB)	4	13	1	3	4	63111.05
MEDICEAN (GB)	42	177	12	18	53	147277.18
MIDNIGHT LEGEND (GB)	75	325	27	49	100	484203.46
MIESQUE'S SON (USA)	3	16	1	2	10	50703.91
MILAN (GB)	171	559	40	51	157	338877.93
MINSTER SON	25	106	8	10	33	70982.00
MISSED FLIGHT (GB)	7	27	3	4	6	14344.97
MISTER BAILEYS (GB)	8	34	3	5	11	52904.00
MISTER LORD (USA)	14	63	1	1	21	17580.13
MISTER MAT (FR)	13	54	4	6	10	55793.42
MOHAAJIR (USA)	13	47	3	3	17	20088.84
MONASHEE MOUNTAIN (USA)	13	50	3	5	9	20229.68
MONSUN (GER)	17	67	7	10	17	96793.32
MONT BASILE (FR)	2	16	2	2	5	11920.51
MONTJEU (IRE)	95	406	29	45	135	944111.77
MONTJOY (USA)	2	12	2	3	1	10833.60
MOONAX (IRE)	20	66	4	5	17	24906.71
MORESPEED	3	10	2	2	5	43725.00
MOSCOW SOCIETY (USA)	100	361	22	32	106	269314.24
MOTIVATOR (GB)	9	36	2	3	12	16313.74
MR COMBUSTIBLE (IRE)	26	98	5	6	28	48101.63
MR GREELEY (USA)	6	20	2	4	3	17402.45
MT LIVERMORE (USA)	1	16	1	2	6	6495.87
MTOTO	16	72	5	9	17	37873.97
MUHTARRAM (USA)	21	84	7	10	28	66342.30
MUHTATHIR (GB)	7	16	2	2	7	28579.54
MUJADIL (USA)	8	24	1	1	3	4860.65
MUJAHID (USA)	24	88	6	9	32	59450.60
MUKADDAMAH (USA)	1	5	1	1	1	2600.64
MULL OF KINTYRE (USA)	33	131	11	18	34	126739.29
MUROTO	7	19	2	2	7	14579.14
MY RISK (FR)	1	7	1	3	4	23135.45
NAHEEZ (USA)	15	61	1	1	20	30805.02
NAMAQUALAND (USA)	3	20	1	3	8	24442.70
NAMID (GB)	13	31	2	2	6	14902.22
NASHAMAA	1	5	1	1	1	10252.50

STALLIONS	RNRS	STARTS	WNRS	WINS	PLACES	TOTAL (£)
NASHWAN (USA)	3	18	1	2	4	5229.29
NAYEF (USA)	27	83	7	7	22	40402.73
NEEDLE GUN (IRE)	55	171	9	12	32	74413.90
NEEDWOOD BLADE (GB)	11	48	1	3	12	17984.37
NETWORK (GER)	9	44	6	10	20	192506.30
NEW FRONTIER (IRE)	29	143	11	13	46	117577.50
NIGHT SHIFT (USA)	13	38	1	1	10	8837.73
NIKOS	21	94	10	16	29	295314.58
NO EXCUSE NEEDED (GB)	4	16	1	1	7	14361.65
NOMADIC WAY (USA)	20	85	6	8	25	39104.43
NONONITO (FR)	3	11	1	1	6	6879.69
NORWICH	64	208	9	13	46	151803.73
NOVERRE (USA)	22	91	7	8	24	37741.12
NUMEROUS (USA)	4	17	1	2	5	11268.14
OASIS DREAM (GB)	8	44	3	4	12	22444.28
OBSERVATORY (USA)	20	72	3	3	28	37706.27
OCEAN OF WISDOM (USA)	1	7	1	1	1	3500.54
OCTAGONAL (NZ)	4	23	1	1	2	4883.39
OFFICIEL (FR)	3	7	1	1	4	4632.95
OKAWANGO (USA)	5	23	3	4	8	42835.75
OLD VIC	235	810	68	104	239	1013802.79
ONE COOL CAT (USA)	13	44	4	10	7	92495.87
OPENING VERSE (USA)	1	8	1	1	4	8730.08
ORATORIO (IRE)	9	18	1	1	5	4818.52
ORIENTATE (USA)	1	3	1	1	1	2861.10
ORPEN (USA)	36	140	8	12	34	77105.30
OSCAR (IRE)	342	1251	88	118	334	1718692.91
OSCAR SCHINDLER (IRE)	27	64	2	3	14	30510.05
OUR ACCOUNT (USA)	1	4	1	2	0	2637.20
OVERBURY (IRE)	125	456	30	40	114	287383.99
PAIRUMANI STAR (IRE)	6	21	1	1	7	7933.87
PANORAMIC	9	23	3	4	6	39948.74
PAOLINI (GER)	1	7	1	1	3	5357.25
PARTHIAN SPRINGS (GB)	15	55	4	5	24	53822.90
PASSING GLANCE (GB)	5	24	3	5	4	16448.74
PASSING SALE (FR)	10	26	2	2	6	9203.48
PASTERNAK (GB)	19	75	3	4	21	119081.83
PAST GLORIES	3	11	2	2	3	8401.90
PASTORAL PURSUITS (GB)	2	8	1	1	1	3351.37
PEINTRE CELEBRE (USA)	18	70	8	13	17	95464.81
PELDER (IRE)	2	14	1	1	1	5712.39
PENTIRE (GB)	2	11	1	1	5	17222.55
PERPENDICULAR (GB)	5	17	1	1	3	7056.06
PERUGINO (USA)	7	26	1	1	7	11011.58
PETOSKI	7	32	2	3	9	13945.12
PHANTOM BREEZE	3	12	1	1	6	6413.34
PHARDANTE (FR)	6	27	3	3	11	15589.37
PICCOLO (GB)	15	64	2	3	19	16701.42
PIERRE (GB)	22	67	4	6	11	27460.20
PILSUDSKI (IRE)	22	52	2	2	12	12229.95
PISTOLET BLEU (IRE)	47	210	13	20	68	501483.59
PITCHOUNET (FR)	1	4	1	1	1	4780.50
PIVOTAL (GB)	34	115	11	19	37	242085.91
PLATINI (GER)	7	17	1	3	6	21208.65
POINT GIVEN (USA)	4	31	1	1	14	10845.72
POLIGLOTE (GB)	11	43	3	5	13	83722.85
POLISH PRECEDENT (USA)	12	34	4	4	9	22074.96
POLISH SUMMER (GB)	7	24	1	2	3	28193.72
PORTRAIT GALLERY (IRE)	32	135	8	11	42	128050.40
POSIDONAS (GB)	8	37	2	4	10	28260.68
PRESENTING (GB)	344	1211	85	136	353	2033378.87
PRIMATICO (USA)	1	5	1	1	0	3123.00
PRIMITIVE RISING (USA)	11	25	1	1	9	29291.53
PRIMO VALENTINO (IRE)	10	22	2	2	6	9006.57

STALLIONS	RNRS	STARTS	WNRS	WINS	PLACES	TOTAL (£)
PRIOLO (USA)	8	29	1	1	10	16452.49
PRIZED (USA)	1	7	1	2	3	37862.47
PROTEKTOR (GER)	1	5	1	2	2	4724.73
PUBLISHER (USA)	8	21	2	4	5	14015.14
PURSUIT OF LOVE (GB)	11	55	1	1	22	20362.51
PYRUS (USA)	10	29	3	3	9	24060.52
QUWS (GB)	27	102	4	6	30	62961.42
RAGMAR (FR)	19	54	2	4	11	35643.38
RAHY (USA)	7	30	1	1	5	11577.90
RAINBOW HIGH (GB)	13	50	4	4	12	18237.56
RAINBOW QUEST (USA)	22	61	1	2	15	17023.47
RAINTRAP (GB)	4	21	3	4	7	17213.14
RAISE A GRAND (IRE)	13	74	2	2	26	20709.55
RAJPOUTE (FR)	2	9	1	1	4	17149.07
RAKAPOSHI KING	21	94	7	8	31	46475.46
RAMBLING BEAR (GB)	3	13	1	2	4	10818.45
RASHAR (GB)	42	166	9	9	41	73544.18
REDBACK (GB)	14	42	5	5	13	76377.70
RED RANSOM (USA)	27	111	10	12	40	150577.18
RED SUNSET	2	11	1	2	1	6016.68
REEL BUDDY (USA)	5	11	1	1	4	3395.20
RELIGIOUSLY (USA)	8	38	2	4	10	17748.89
REPRIMAND	5	35	2	2	11	15732.47
RESET (AUS)	16	40	1	1	11	25096.75
REVOQUE (IRE)	49	153	4	4	42	43073.13
RIBERETTO	3	10	1	1	2	4410.18
RIDGEWOOD BEN (GB)	4	9	1	1	1	2614.46
RIGHT WIN (IRE)	8	21	2	3	3	61309.09
RISK ME (FR)	1	6	1	2	1	4581.94
RIVERHEAD (USA)	2	7	1	1	1	1850.23
RIVIERA (FR)	1	4	1	1	3	5805.03
ROAKARAD	4	15	1	2	5	13185.55
ROBELLINO (USA)	10	45	5	8	11	22054.96
ROBERTICO (GB)	4	19	3	4	7	16439.48
ROBIN DES CHAMPS (FR)	28	112	11	16	33	320801.81
ROBIN DES PRES (FR)	13	59	3	6	20	46492.57
ROCHESSON (FR)	5	12	1	1	1	6137.93
ROCK CITY	10	38	2	2	9	8949.67
ROCK HOPPER	21	86	2	4	5	28	30558.28
ROCK OF GIBRALTAR (IRE)	41	170	14	23	69	206698.45
ROI DE ROME (USA)	14	42	2	2	10	23846.95
ROMANY RYE (GB)	4	16	1	1	8	6164.49
ROSELIER (FR)	13	31	3	3	11	46791.97
ROSSINI (USA)	13	42	3	4	9	20511.04
ROYAL ANTHEM (USA)	7	35	4	7	13	35334.22
ROYAL APPLAUSE (GB)	31	138	6	8	39	37097.81
RUDIMENTARY (USA)	66	263	16	25	67	185290.31
RUNYON (IRE)	5	19	1	1	3	8617.39
SABIANGO (GER)	1	5	1	1	1	7435.01
SABREHILL (USA)	3	7	2	2	3	23576.00
SADDLERS' HALL (IRE)	173	686	37	51	206	437238.47
SADLER'S WELLS (USA)	87	395	34	47	123	412336.42
SAFETY CATCH (USA)	11	29	3	3	11	15313.24
SAGACITY (FR)	14	77	5	7	18	39205.02
SAGAMIX (FR)	6	14	1	2	4	28927.63
SAINT DES SAINTS (FR)	10	43	5	12	11	215921.15
SAINT PREUIL (FR)	13	34	1	1	11	8741.14
SAKHEE (USA)	27	93	9	9	38	62886.69
SASSANIAN (USA)	21	72	3	5	27	102002.01
SAYAARR (USA)	1	2	1	1	1	2268.45
SAYARSHAN (FR)	18	54	2	2	10	12323.05
SCRIBANO (GB)	12	40	1	1	8	11407.30
SEA RAVEN (IRE)	17	58	7	8	19	121316.90
SECOND EMPIRE (IRE)	16	45	3	4	18	119332.04

STALLIONS	RNRS	STARTS	WNRS	WINS	PLACES	TOTAL (£)
SECOND SET (IRE)	3	13	1	1	4	5432.45
SECRET SINGER (FR)	1	8	1	1	4	8325.60
SELKIRK (USA)	36	138	9	12	40	83411.87
SENDAWAR (IRE)	6	30	3	6	9	35127.01
SESARO (USA)	4	18	1	2	5	11992.56
SHAANMER (IRE)	7	27	1	2	13	29047.21
SHAHRASTANI (USA)	20	61	2	2	15	26916.88
SHAMARDAL (USA)	4	11	1	1	6	4980.84
SHAMBO	11	37	6	7	8	25409.08
SHANTOU (USA)	19	46	9	10	7	47017.17
SHERNAZAR	47	181	13	16	63	150857.71
SHEYRANN	5	18	1	2	4	7437.04
SHINKO FOREST (IRE)	8	27	2	4	6	12281.60
SHOLOKHOV (IRE)	3	8	1	2	1	35415.93
SILVANO (GER)	5	11	1	1	2	11740.53
SILVER PATRIARCH (IRE)	99	341	26	36	89	243500.55
SIMON DU DESERT (FR)	4	36	3	5	18	52325.73
SIMPLY GREAT (FR)	18	67	4	6	13	49349.81
SINGSPIEL (IRE)	22	79	7	9	24	172451.49
SINNDAR (IRE)	23	73	6	10	14	141122.38
SIR HARRY LEWIS (USA)	76	256	16	22	80	335880.72
SKI CHIEF (USA)	4	19	2	3	9	57163.59
SKY SWALLOW (FR)	1	8	1	4	1	11287.76
SLEEPING CAR (FR)	31	101	5	6	36	54275.77
SLIP ANCHOR	12	33	3	5	13	44584.56
SMADOUN (FR)	10	32	5	7	13	211488.72
SNURGE	54	204	18	30	50	212420.09
SOLAR ONE (FR)	2	4	1	1	2	6028.55
SOLON (GER)	4	19	3	3	11	109414.64
SONGLINE (SWE)	1	8	1	1	4	4913.05
SON OF SHARP SHOT (IRE)	6	25	1	1	5	7148.76
SONUS (IRE)	27	97	7	9	15	45363.87
SOVEREIGN WATER (FR)	13	40	4	6	13	50811.48
SOVIET STAR (USA)	29	122	3	6	26	33548.23
SPADOUN (FR)	6	24	2	3	12	14766.11
SPARTACUS (IRE)	21	80	4	7	26	45027.58
SPECTRUM (IRE)	26	121	7	9	35	149245.71
SPINNING WORLD (USA)	5	16	2	3	3	19933.83
SRI PEKAN (USA)	3	4	1	1	1	4830.30
STARBOROUGH (GB)	3	21	3	8	9	41065.49
STARCRAFT (NZ)	9	18	3	3	3	12640.24
START FAST (FR)	1	5	1	2	0	13217.70
STATUE OF LIBERTY (USA)	20	66	4	5	10	42143.87
STERNKOENIG (IRE)	1	5	1	1	3	67706.00
STORMIN FEVER (USA)	2	5	1	1	0	5331.20
STORMING HOME (GB)	11	38	2	3	16	21374.19
STOWAWAY (GB)	26	80	9	15	18	140230.34
STRATEGIC CHOICE (USA)	16	64	7	9	11	43825.14
STREET CRY (IRE)	10	39	3	4	8	19594.54
SUBOTICA (FR)	9	40	4	8	10	28072.57
SUBTLE POWER (IRE)	23	75	4	7	15	42419.54
SULAMANI (IRE)	14	47	3	5	20	28113.21
SUMMER SUSPICION (JPN)	1	10	1	1	7	4761.07
SUNDAY SILENCE (USA)	4	35	2	3	12	27984.42
SUNSHINE STREET (USA)	16	53	2	4	16	40954.70
SUPREME LEADER	112	421	30	39	109	404902.13
SUPREME SOUND (GB)	7	34	2	4	7	15965.21
SURE BLADE (USA)	4	17	2	2	4	6153.45
SWAIN (IRE)	6	31	4	7	11	39871.16
SYSTEMATIC (GB)	3	20	1	2	9	11035.77
TAGULA (IRE)	19	56	2	3	22	22676.45
TAIPAN (IRE)	50	205	15	21	74	190331.96
TAJRAASI (USA)	2	9	1	2	4	19681.42
TAKE RISKS (FR)	13	54	3	4	24	70941.69

STALLIONS	RNRS	STARTS	WNRS	WINS	PLACES	TOTAL (£)
TALKIN MAN (CAN)	11	32	2	3	3	16249.40
TAMAYAZ (CAN)	25	83	3	3	17	19159.23
TAMURE (IRE)	15	51	2	2	17	10877.76
TAWRRIFIC (NZ)	1	13	1	1	5	8809.75
TEENOSO (USA)	3	13	1	1	2	2218.47
TEL QUEL (FR)	20	68	4	6	13	33584.13
TERIMON	39	131	4	6	28	39627.09
TERTULLIAN (USA)	5	32	1	1	6	3756.80
THEATRICAL	8	36	3	6	8	36956.51
THEATRICAL CHARMER	3	12	1	2	3	14613.75
THEN AGAIN	3	15	1	1	3	4532.25
TIDARO (USA)	4	19	1	1	2	7737.76
TIGER HILL (IRE)	30	90	3	5	24	72253.52
TIKKANEN (USA)	18	60	5	9	22	44717.48
TILLERMAN (GB)	8	28	3	3	8	26980.26
TIPSY CREEK (USA)	3	20	1	1	5	4692.02
TIRAAZ (USA)	11	32	3	7	9	138859.08
TITUS LIVIUS (FR)	13	31	2	2	3	8807.18
TOBOUGG (IRE)	61	230	12	18	62	129967.34
TOPANOORA	28	112	8	11	34	119852.97
TOP OF THE WORLD	1	13	1	2	6	11396.50
TOUCH OF GREY	1	8	1	1	1	2754.25
TRADITIONALLY (USA)	20	77	3	3	24	28064.43
TRAGIC ROLE (USA)	11	51	2	5	11	19488.36
TRANS ISLAND (GB)	38	130	8	12	37	76088.84
TREASURE HUNTER	1	4	1	2	0	2810.70
TREMPOLINO (USA)	24	101	7	10	37	126476.48
TRUE BRAVE (USA)	3	14	1	1	3	3431.85
TURGEON (USA)	24	101	9	13	38	78712.99
TURTLE ISLAND (IRE)	94	359	30	39	81	307196.39
ULTIMATELY LUCKY (IRE)	4	19	1	1	2	2428.85
UMISTIM (GB)	2	7	1	2	0	3492.97
UN DESPERADO (FR)	10	33	1	2	9	13396.19
UNFUWAIN (USA)	9	27	2	2	8	108909.61
UNGARO (GER)	13	59	3	4	23	41698.48
UNTIL SUNDOWN (USA)	1	1	1	1	0	4274.34
URBAN OCEAN (FR)	3	11	1	1	1	2648.43
USEFUL (FR)	9	43	2	3	13	13338.81
USTINOV (AUS)	1	3	1	1	1	2513.52
VAGUELY PLEASANT (FR)	3	8	1	1	4	7109.66
VALANJOU (FR)	1	13	1	1	3	7287.61
VALANOUR (IRE)	2	20	1	2	3	8756.25
VAL ROYAL (FR)	22	60	6	7	8	36287.41
VALSEUR (USA)	1	7	1	2	1	9411.50
VAN NISTELROOY (USA)	2	10	1	1	5	7081.30
VARESE (FR)	3	22	1	1	7	10958.90
VERGLAS (IRE)	26	80	6	8	19	41064.30
VERTICAL SPEED (FR)	5	11	1	1	7	16911.45
VETTORI (IRE)	26	103	8	10	27	48446.70
VICTORY NOTE (USA)	4	12	1	4	2	29803.60
VIDEO ROCK (FR)	22	96	7	9	35	71956.78
VIKING RULER (AUS)	11	43	3	4	10	33285.79
VILLAGE STAR (FR)	1	4	1	1	2	147164.28
VILLEZ (USA)	8	40	2	2	16	24301.78
VISIONARY (FR)	2	10	1	1	7	21567.73
WAR CHANT (USA)	9	51	3	3	21	22396.66
WARCRAFT (USA)	5	13	1	1	6	5744.78
WEET-A-MINUTE (IRE)	3	10	2	2	5	7364.87
WELD	9	28	1	1	5	4425.45
WELDNAAS (USA)	5	17	1	1	4	2816.98
WELL CHOSEN (GB)	5	18	1	1	4	4266.52
WELSH LION (IRE)	6	16	1	1	1	6992.67
WESTERNER (GB)	15	26	2	3	11	11835.60
WHERE OR WHEN (IRE)	26	88	4	4	26	25399.66

STALLIONS	RNRS	STARTS	WNRS	WINS	PLACES	TOTAL (£)
WHIPPER (USA)	4	14	1	1	2	4523.75
WHITMORE'S CONN (USA)	6	13	1	1	4	6376.69
WINDSOR CASTLE (GB)	13	35	2	3	12	16444.54
WINGED LOVE (IRE)	70	289	20	32	93	405697.12
WINNING SMILE (FR)	2	7	1	2	2	9924.17
WISEMAN'S FERRY (USA)	1	9	1	1	6	11208.83
WITH THE FLOW (USA)	2	15	1	2	6	12357.74
WITNESS BOX (USA)	82	333	19	31	115	254207.51
WIZARD KING (GB)	21	73	1	2	12	19946.89
WOODBOROUGH (USA)	4	11	1	1	4	3589.77
WOODMAN (USA)	3	17	1	1	3	3251.95
WOODS OF WINDSOR (USA)	10	31	2	5	5	25098.76
XAAR (GB)	25	91	4	5	24	30911.05
ZAFEEN (FR)	7	17	1	1	4	7049.87
ZAFFARAN (USA)	36	146	9	12	52	202124.52
ZAFONIC (USA)	5	17	1	3	3	23651.22
ZAGREB (USA)	32	111	4	4	39	31106.02
ZAHA (CAN)	10	23	3	3	5	8227.54
ZILZAL (USA)	10	47	4	9	10	62180.58
ZINAAD (GB)	3	12	1	2	3	11016.10

BY KIND PERMISSION OF WEATHERBYS

YOUR
£10,000
OPPORTUNITY!

HIGH-PRICED YEARLINGS OF 2011 AT TATTERSALLS SALES

The following yearlings realised 62,000 guineas and over at Tattersalls Sales in 2011:-

Name and Breeding	Purchaser	Guineas
NAZYM (IRE) CH F GALILEO (IRE) - BRIGID (USA)	C GORDON-WATSON BS	1700000
FAFA O O (IRE) B F GALILEO (IRE) - WITCH OF FIFE (USA)	SIR R OGDEN	850000
B F GALILEO (IRE) - GWYNN (IRE)	BADGERS BS	800000
PHAENOMENA (IRE) CH F GALILEO (IRE) - CAUMSHINAUN (IRE)	COURSE INVESTMENT	700000
B C OASIS DREAM (GB) - KASSIOPEIA (IRE)	D O'BYRNE	700000
B F GALILEO (IRE) - PEACE TIME (GER)	BADGERS BS	600000
B C MONTJEU (IRE) - DANCE PARADE (USA)	D O'BYRNE	520000
B C NEW APPROACH (IRE) - LADY MILETRIAN (IRE)	JOHN FERGUSON BS	500000
PASSING PARADE (GB) B F CAPE CROSS (IRE) - MODEL QUEEN (USA)	C GORDON-WATSON BS	500000
B C DANSILI (GB) - FLAWLY (GB)	D O'BYRNE	480000
B C NEW APPROACH (IRE) - LADEENA (IRE)	JOHN FERGUSON BS	450000
B F GALILEO (IRE) - EVITA (GB)	AL SHAHANIA STUD	430000
B F GALILEO (IRE) - BLUE SYMPHONY (GB)	CHEVELEY PARK STUD	410000
B F OASIS DREAM (GB) - POLITESSE (USA)	MRS A SKIFFINGTON	400000
B C DANEHILL DANCER (IRE) - ANNA PALLIDA (GB)	C GORDON-WATSON BS	400000
B F GALILEO (IRE) - IONIAN SEA (GB)	D O'BYRNE	400000
RAUSHAN (IRE) GR F DALAKHANI (IRE) - CHIANG MAI (IRE)	C GORDON-WATSON BS	400000
B C ACCLAMATION (GB) - BOLD DESIRE (GB)	D O'BYRNE	370000
B C OASIS DREAM (GB) - BIRIYANI (IRE)	A COLE	360000
B C PIVOTAL (GB) - KITTY MATCHAM (IRE)	BADGERS BS	360000
B C CAPE CROSS (IRE) - MUSICAL TREAT (GB)	JOHN FERGUSON BS	360000
B C MONTJEU (IRE) - BUCK ASPEN (USA)	D O'BYRNE	360000
CH F GALILEO (IRE) - MRS LINDSAY (USA)	CHEVELEY PARK STUD	350000
RESILIENT (IRE) B C SHAMARDAL (USA) - ZITHER (GB)	BLANDFORD BS	350000
B C CAPE CROSS (IRE) - AQUARELLE BLEUE (GB)	SHADWELL ESTATE CO	340000
B C DUKE OF MARMALADE (IRE) - NIGHT FROLIC (GB)	D O'BYRNE	340000
B F GALILEO (IRE) - SECRET GARDEN (IRE)	BLANDFORD BS	340000
B C DANEHILL DANCER (IRE) - TANAMI DESERT (GB)	BLANDFORD BS	340000
AVIETTA (IRE) GR F DALAKHANI (IRE) - ALABASTRINE (GB)	CHEVELEY PARK STUD	340000
B C SHAMARDAL (USA) - PRIMA LUCE (IRE)	BLANDFORD BS	330000
B C GALILEO (IRE) - APPROACH (GB)	AL SHAHANIA STUD	320000
B F OASIS DREAM (GB) - INTERCHANGE (IRE)	D O'BYRNE	320000
B C ACCLAMATION (GB) - BENDIS (GER)	S HILLEN	310000
B F GALILEO (IRE) - RIVER BELLE (GB)	RICHARD FRISBY BS	310000
CH F PIVOTAL (GB) - AIMING (GB)	A O NERSES	310000
B C GALILEO (IRE) - L'ANCRESSE (IRE)	UMM QARN MANAGEMENT	300000
B F DANEHILL DANCER (IRE) - ASNIERES (USA)	HUGO MERRY BS	300000
B C INVINCIBLE SPIRIT (IRE) - FONDA (USA)	SHADWELL ESTATE CO	280000
B C INVINCIBLE SPIRIT (IRE) - LULUA (USA)	SHADWELL ESTATE	280000
CH C PIVOTAL (GB) - SELINKA (GB)	F CONLON	280000
B C MONTJEU (IRE) - TIME OVER (GB)	D O'BYRNE	270000
B F GALILEO (IRE) - CANDY MOUNTAIN (GB)	UMM QARN MANAGEMENT	260000
B F ROYAL APPLAUSE (GB) - NEVER A DOUBT (GB)	JOHN WARREN BS	260000
B C DANSILI (GB) - SILVER PIVOTAL (IRE)	C GORDON-WATSON BS	260000
B C EXCEED AND EXCEL (AUS) - TEMPLE OF THEBES (IRE)	HONG KONG JOCKEY CLUB	260000
B F NEW APPROACH (IRE) - PARK ROMANCE (GB)	JOHN FERGUSON BS	260000
CH C RAVEN'S PASS (USA) - RISE AND FALL (USA)	JOHN FERGUSON BS	260000
CH C SIR PERCY (GB) - BOMBAZINE (IRE)	A O NERSES	260000
B F PIVOTAL (GB) - FINLAGGAN (GB)	BLANDFORD BS	250000
GR F NEW APPROACH (IRE) - HOTELGENIE DOT COM (GB)	GILL RICHARDSON BS	250000
B C TEOFILO (IRE) - RAMONA (GB)	JOHN FERGUSON BS	250000
CH C DUBAWI (IRE) - LAURENA (GB)	JOHN FERGUSON BS	250000
B C RAVEN'S PASS (USA) - LOVE EXCELLING (FR)	JOHN WARREN BS	240000
CH F PIVOTAL (GB) - MISS PENTON (GB)	HUGO LASCELLES BS	240000
B C INVINCIBLE SPIRIT (IRE) - GHAZAL (USA)	VENDOR	240000
ELIK (IRE) B F DALAKHANI (IRE) - ELOPA (GER)	C GORDON-WATSON BS	240000
B C TEOFILO (IRE) - FANN (USA)	PETER & ROSS DOYLE BS	240000
B G DUKE OF MARMALADE (IRE) - SHERIFA (GER)	ANTHONY STROUD BS	230000
ABSOLUTELY SO (IRE) B C ACCLAMATION (GB) - WEEK END (GB)	JOHN WARREN BS	230000
B F GALILEO (IRE) - SHASTYE (IRE)	VENDOR	230000
HANZADA (USA) B/BR F ARCH (USA) - CHOCOLATE MAUK (USA)	C GORDON-WATSON BS	225000
B C ACCLAMATION (GB) - WRONG KEY (IRE)	A O NERSES	220000
OVATORY (GB) B C ACCLAMATION (GB) - MILLSINI (GB)	PETER & ROSS DOYLE BS	220000
BL C NEW APPROACH (IRE) - COMIC (IRE)	SHADWELL ESTATE CO	220000
B C CAPE CROSS (IRE) - MISS INTIMATE (USA)	JOHN FERGUSON BS	220000
BR F DUKE OF MARMALADE (IRE) - INCHMAHOME (GB)	D O'BYRNE	220000
B C INVINCIBLE SPIRIT (IRE) - GOLDTHROAT (IRE)	JOHN FERGUSON BS	220000

Name and Breeding	Purchaser	Guineas
B C KHELEYF (USA) - BLUE ECHO (GB)	A O NERSES	220000
CH F DANEHILL DANCER (IRE) - NORTHERN GULCH (USA)	C GORDON-WATSON BS	220000
MESHARDAL (GER) B C SHAMARDAL (USA) - MELODY FAIR (IRE)	PETER & ROSS DOYLE BS	220000
B C KYLLACHY (GB) - EGO (GB)	PETER & ROSS DOYLE BS	220000
CH C PIVOTAL (GB) - JAMBORETTA (IRE)	M YOUNGS	215000
B C NAYEF (USA) - ALLEGRETTO (IRE)	SHADWELL ESTATE CO	210000
CH F KYLLACHY (GB) - TRIPLE SHARP (GB)	A O NERSES	210000
CH C DANEHILL DANCER (IRE) - ONE SO WONDERFUL (GB)	C GORDON-WATSON BS	210000
B C EXCELLENT ART (GB) - MRS MARSH (GB)	JOHN WARREN BS	210000
CH C DALAKHANI (IRE) - RHADEGUNDA (GB)	RABBAH BS	210000
B C INVINCIBLE SPIRIT (IRE) - ZIBILENE (GB)	C GORDON-WATSON BS	200000
PARALLAX (IRE) B C GALILEO (IRE) - MOONLIGHT'S BOX (USA)	VENDOR	200000
B C TEOFILO (IRE) - DANCE TROUPE (GB)	JOHN FERGUSON BS	200000
B C STREET CRY (IRE) - DANELETA (IRE)	SHADWELL ESTATE CO	200000
DALANDRA (GB) B F MONTJEU (IRE) - DALASYLA (IRE)	PETER & ROSS DOYLE BS	200000
RED BATON (GB) B F EXCEED AND EXCEL (AUS) - RUBY ROCKET (USA)	CHEVELEY PARK STUD	200000
B C CAPE CROSS (IRE) - ATHENIAN WAY (GB)	JOHN FERGUSON BS	200000
B C MONTJEU (IRE) - BEYOND THE DREAM (USA)	D O'BYRNE	200000
B C DANEHILL DANCER (IRE) - HAWALA (IRE)	STEPHEN HILLEN BS	200000
B C ACCLAMATION (GB) - MISS CORINNE (GB)	PETER & ROSS DOYLE BS	200000
B C DUBAWI (IRE) - PURE (GB)	JOHN FERGUSON BS	200000
B C GALILEO (IRE) - DISTINCTIVE LOOK (IRE)	VENDOR	195000
FORT KNOX (GB) B C DUBAWI (IRE) - SAVANNAH BELLE (GB)	VENDOR	190000
MAKAFEH (GB) B C ELUSIVE QUALITY (USA) - DEMISEMIQUAVER (GB)	JOHN WARREN BS	190000
B C DUBAWI (IRE) - STRINGS (GB)	PETER & ROSS DOYLE BS	190000
B C NEW APPROACH (IRE) - DRESS UNIFORM (USA)	JOHN FERGUSON BS	190000
B C MONTJEU (IRE) - WHOS MINDIN WHO (IRE)	A COLE	190000
B F DANEHILL DANCER (IRE) - MASSAROSSA (GB)	D O'BYRNE	190000
BRECCBENNACH (GB) B C OASIS DREAM (GB) - NEXT (IRE)	CHEVELEY PARK STUD	180000
B F INVINCIBLE SPIRIT (IRE) - MAINE LOBSTER (USA)	JOHN FERGUSON BS	180000
B C AUTHORIZED (IRE) - ZELDA (IRE)	JOHN FERGUSON BS	180000
SOVIET ROCK (IRE) B C ROCK OF GIBRALTAR (IRE) - ANNA KARENINA (USA)	JOHN WARREN BS	180000
B/BR C ELUSIVE QUALITY (USA) - ALTA MODA (GB)	SHADWELL ESTATE CO	180000
KELVINGROVE (IRE) B C HURRICANE RUN (IRE) - SILVERSWORD (FR)	C DE MOUBRAY	180000
B F ZAMINDAR (USA) - MENNETOU (IRE)	BLANDFORD BS	180000
B F SELKIRK (USA) - HAVE FAITH (IRE)	C GORDON-WATSON BS	180000
B C ACCLAMATION (GB) - INTREPID QUEEN (USA)	SHADWELL ESTATE	180000
B F MARJU (IRE) - MUCH FASTER (IRE)	A O NERSES	180000
B F DANEHILL DANCER (IRE) - JANE AUSTEN (IRE)	VENDOR	175000
B C EXCEED AND EXCEL (AUS) - LADY LINKS (GB)	JOHN FERGUSON BS	170000
GR C DARK ANGEL (IRE) - MISS INDIGO (GB)	PETER & ROSS DOYLE BS	170000
B C OASIS DREAM (GB) - CAPE MERINO (GB)	JOHN FERGUSON BS	170000
B C DANEHILL DANCER (IRE) - ROSE OF PETRA (IRE)	D O'BYRNE	170000
CH F RAVEN'S PASS (USA) - MULTICOLOUR WAVE (IRE)	JOHN FERGUSON BS	170000
CH F EXCEED AND EXCEL (AUS) - LIGHTHOUSE (GB)	J BRUMMITT	170000
B C ACCLAMATION (GB) - WITH COLOUR (GB)	DAVID REDVERS BS	165000
B C ACCLAMATION (GB) - GRAND SLAM MARIA (FR)	PETER & ROSS DOYLE BS	165000
CH C IFFRAAJ (GB) - KHIBRAAT (GB)	SHADWELL ESTATE	160000
B F DUKE OF MARMALADE (IRE) - BOAST (GB)	BLANDFORD BS	160000
CH F ELUSIVE QUALITY (USA) - LOUVE MYSTERIEUSE (USA)	JOHN FERGUSON BS	160000
B C ACCLAMATION (GB) - GOLD HUSH (USA)	C GORDON-WATSON BS	160000
RICHARD SENIOR (GB) B C CAPE CROSS (IRE) - SABRIA (USA)	PETER & ROSS DOYLE BS	160000
B C EXCEED AND EXCEL (AUS) - MISS MELTEMI (IRE)	JOHN FERGUSON BS	160000
CH C DUBAWI (IRE) - SALEE (IRE)	HONG KONG JOCKEY CLUB	160000
B F TEOFILO (IRE) - VASSIANA (FR)	NORRIS/HUNTINGDON	160000
CH F RAVEN'S PASS (USA) - BADEE'A (IRE)	J BRUMMITT	160000
B C SHAMARDAL (USA) - NESHLA (GB)	R O'GORMAN BS	160000
B C GALILEO (IRE) - GLINTING DESERT (IRE)	BADGERS BS	155000
KNIGHT OWL (GB) B C ROCK OF GIBRALTAR (IRE) - MISS IVANHOE (IRE)	C GORDON-WATSON BS	155000
B F LEMON DROP KID (USA) - CUT SHORT (USA)	D SIMCOCK	155000
B C HENRYTHENAVIGATOR (USA) - GLATISANT (GB)	J MAGNIER	150000
B C INVINCIBLE SPIRIT (IRE) - DIAMOND DILEMMA (IRE)	JOHN WARREN BS	150000
PLEASURE BENT (GB) B C DANSILI (GB) - NITYA (FR)	C GORDON-WATSON BS	150000
B C INVINCIBLE SPIRIT (IRE) - LA CONQUISTADORA (GB)	JOHN FERGUSON BS	150000
B C OASIS DREAM (GB) - MAID TO BELIEVE (GB)	COURSE INVESTMENT	150000
CH C TAMAYUZ (GB) - FOR EVVA SILCA (GB)	BIG RED FARM	150000
CH F GALILEO (IRE) - MYSTICAL LADY (IRE)	BBA (IRELAND)	150000
B C MONTJEU (IRE) - LLIA (GB)	D O'BYRNE	150000
B F MOUNT NELSON (GB) - SPECIFICALLY (USA)	BADGERS BS	150000
B C SINGSPIEL (IRE) - MAJOUNE (FR)	M JOHNSTON	150000
B F MONTJEU (IRE) - TREE TOPS (GB)	D O'BYRNE	150000

Name and Breeding	Purchaser	Guineas
B F DANEHILL DANCER (IRE) - MYTH AND MAGIC (IRE)	HUGO MERRY BS	150000
B C RAVEN'S PASS (USA) - DELPHINUS (GB)	R VARIAN	150000
B C PIVOTAL (GB) - VIRTUOUS (GB)	RICHARD FRISBY BS	150000
B C STRATEGIC PRINCE (GB) - STARFISH (IRE)	C GORDON-WATSON BS	150000
B C GREEN DESERT (USA) - THORNTOWN PICCOLO (GB)	BLANDFORD BS	150000
CH C DUKE OF MARMALADE (IRE) - APACHE DREAM (IRE)	BLANDFORD BS	150000
B C ROYAL APPLAUSE (GB) - UMLILO (GB)	J O'BYRNE	150000
B F GALILEO (IRE) - DAPPRIMA (GER)	VENDOR	150000
B C TEOFILO (IRE) - PASSAGEWAY (USA)	JOHN FERGUSON BS	150000
B F LEMON DROP KID (USA) - CHALAMONT (IRE)	BLANDFORD BS	150000
B C RED CLUBS (IRE) - LADY ALEXANDER (IRE)	HONG KONG JOCKEY CLUB	150000
B C MONTJEU (IRE) - GHURRA (USA)	DAVID REDVERS BS	150000
B F MULTIPLEX (GB) - SHEMRIYNA (IRE)	GILL RICHARDSON BS	145000
CH C GIANT'S CAUSEWAY (USA) - VIKING'S COVE (USA)	HUGO MERRY BS	145000
CH C KYLLACHY (GB) - CLINET (USA)	BLANDFORD BS	145000
B F IFFRAAJ (GB) - RED VALE (IRE)	STEPHEN HILLEN BS	145000
B C EXCEED AND EXCEL (AUS) - BROADWAY HIT (GB)	HUGO MERRY BS	145000
GR C DALAKHANI (IRE) - VFNTURI (GB)	BLANDFORD BS	140000
B F DANEHILL DANCER (IRE) - FOOLISH ACT (IRE)	BBA (IRELAND)	140000
B C HIGH CHAPARRAL (IRE) - MOORE'S MELODY (IRE)	R BOFFEY	135000
CH C PEINTRE CELEBRE (USA) - SQUARE THE CIRCLE (GB)	W HAGGAS	135000
CH C NEW APPROACH (IRE) - SPOTLIGHT (GB)	JOHN WARREN BS	135000
B C PIVOTAL (GB) - QUEBRADA (IRE)	VENDOR	130000
B F TAMAYUZ (GB) - MIRACOLIA (IRE)	SHADWELL ESTATE	130000
B C INVINCIBLE SPIRIT (IRE) - FAIRY OF THE NIGHT (IRE)	SHADWELL ESTATE CO	130000
B F EXCEED AND EXCEL (AUS) - SOMETHING BLUE (GB)	SHADWELL ESTATE CO	130000
B F HENRYTHENAVIGATOR (USA) - DIAMOND NECKLACE (USA)	R WYLIE	130000
CONTRADICT (GB) B F RAVEN'S PASS (USA) - ACTS OF GRACE (USA)	A O NERSES	130000
B C DANEHILL DANCER (IRE) - NORDHOCK (USA)	VENDOR	130000
DUKE COSIMO (GB) CH C PIVOTAL (GB) - NANNINA (GB)	VENDOR	130000
BR F DANSILI (GB) - JOUET (GB)	FORM BS	130000
GR F EXCELLENT ART (GB) - DIVINE GRACE (IRE)	R VARIAN	125000
CH C NEW APPROACH (IRE) - ALL'S FORGOTTEN (USA)	J O'BYRNE	125000
B C TAMAYUZ (GB) - KINDLING (GB)	SACKVILLEDONALD	125000
CH C NEW APPROACH (IRE) - MISS QUEEN (USA)	BLANDFORD BS	125000
B C ELUSIVE CITY (USA) - PARAKOPI (IRE)	W HAGGAS	125000
B F DUKE OF MARMALADE (IRE) - HIGHER LOVE (IRE)	J O'BYRNE	125000
B F DUBAWI (IRE) - VALJARV (IRE)	JOHN FERGUSON BS	125000
B F DANEHILL DANCER (IRE) - MINE EXCAVATION (FR)	J O'BYRNE	125000
AJMAN BRIDGE (GB) CH C DUBAWI (IRE) - RICE MOTHER (IRE)	C GORDON-WATSON BS	125000
B F INVINCIBLE SPIRIT (IRE) - NEEDLES AND PINS (IRE)	A O NERSES	120000
CH C NEW APPROACH (IRE) - ONE SO MARVELLOUS (GB)	JOHN FERGUSON BS	120000
MAN FROM SEVILLE (GB) CH C DUKE OF MARMALADE (IRE) - BASANTI (USA)	SIR M PRESCOTT	120000
B C MEDICEAN (GB) - LILLI MARLANE (GB)	HONG KONG JOCKEY CLUB	120000
B F MOUNT NELSON (GB) - ENTENTE CORDIALE (IRE)	C DE MOUBRAY	120000
CH C NAYEF (USA) - MOOD INDIGO (IRE)	SHADWELL ESTATE	120000
B F MONSUN (GER) - CELEBRE VADALA (FR)	J HAMMOND	120000
B/BR C AUTHORIZED (IRE) - HENTIES BAY (GB)	C GORDON-WATSON BS	120000
CH C BAHAMIAN BOUNTY (GB) - ROSLEA LADY (IRE)	DAVID REDVERS BS	120000
CH C EXCEED AND EXCEL (AUS) - SISTER MOONSHINE (FR)	R VARIAN	120000
B F MONTJEU (IRE) - MADEIRA MIST (IRE)	VENDOR	120000
CH F NEW APPROACH (IRE) - ANNEE LUMIERE (IRE)	PETER & ROSS DOYLE BS	120000
CH C PIVOTAL (GB) - COURTING (GB)	J GOSDEN	120000
CH C DUKE OF MARMALADE (IRE) - MUBKERA (IRE)	A O NERSES	120000
B C CAPE CROSS (GB) - LIKEABLE (GB)	JOHN FERGUSON BS	115000
B C TEOFILO (IRE) - ISRAAR (GB)	JOHN WARREN BS	115000
B F DANEHILL DANCER (IRE) - MOUNT KLINOVEC (IRE)	M O'TOOLE	115000
ASK DAD (GB) B C INTIKHAB (USA) - DON'T TELL MUM (IRE)	D WOODS	115000
B C MEDICEAN (GB) - SOAR (GB)	SACKVILLEDONALD	115000
CH C SINGSPIEL (IRE) - MOONMAIDEN (GB)	RABBAH BS	115000
B C OASIS DREAM (GB) - MANHATTAN DREAM (USA)	JOHN FERGUSON BS	115000
B C CAPE CROSS (GB) - ISLA AZUL (IRE)	M JOHNSTON	115000
B C NEW APPROACH (IRE) - ENDORSEMENT (GB)	M JOHNSTON	110000
CH C NAYEF (USA) - RED CAMELLIA (GB)	SHADWELL ESTATE	110000
B C STORMY ATLANTIC (USA) - ROSE OF ZOLLERN (IRE)	THE HONG KONG JOCKEY CLUB	110000
B F PIVOTAL (GB) - SPEED SONG (GB)	BBA (IRELAND)	110000
B C DANSILI (GB) - VITAL STATISTICS (GB)	R VARIAN	110000
CH C IFFRAAJ (GB) - HURRICANE IRENE (IRE)	R VARIAN	110000
B F EXCELLENT ART (GB) - DOCTRINE (GB)	M O'TOOLE	110000
CH C PIVOTAL (GB) - STRAWBERRY FLEDGE (USA)	SACKVILLEDONALD	110000
SORYAH (IRE) B F SHAMARDAL (USA) - DIRTYBIRDIE (GB)	C GORDON-WATSON BS	110000

Name and Breeding	Purchaser	Guineas
GR C SHAMARDAL (USA) - PRINCESS SERENA (USA)	JOHN WARREN BS	110000
B C DUBAWI (IRE) - DREAM QUEST (GB)	JOHN FERGUSON BS	110000
B C CAPE CROSS (IRE) - KAHLUA KISS (GB)	M JOHNSTON	110000
B C SHAMARDAL (USA) - CASTAWAY QUEEN (IRE)	JOHN FERGUSON BS	110000
B C DYLAN THOMAS (IRE) - GOLDEN DEW (IRE)	BBA (IRELAND)	110000
SNOWBRIGHT (GB) B F PIVOTAL (GB) - SNOW GRETEL (IRE)	CHEVELEY PARK STUD	110000
B C SIR PERCY (GB) - TIGER SPICE (GB)	A O NERSES	110000
B F ACCLAMATION (GB) - ABINGTON ANGEL (GB)	M V MAGNIER	110000
B C ELUSIVE CITY (USA) - ROCK SALT (GB)	SHADWELL ESTATE	105000
B C COMPTON PLACE (GB) - GUERMANTES (GB)	J BRUMMITT	105000
B F OASIS DREAM (GB) - JUNO MARLOWE (IRE)	M V MAGNIER	105000
B/BR C HIGH CHAPARRAL (IRE) - PAY THE BANK	C GORDON-WATSON BS	105000
B C ACCLAMATION (GB) - WILDSPLASH (USA)	RICHARD FRISBY BS	105000
B C CAPE CROSS (IRE) - ANBELLA (FR)	SHADWELL ESTATE CO	105000
B/BR F NEW APPROACH (IRE) - IDILIC CALM (IRE)	M JOHNSTON	100000
B F NEW APPROACH (IRE) - DEVERON (USA)	M JOHNSTON	100000
B F DUKE OF MARMALADE (IRE) - SQUARE PANTS (USA)	PETER & ROSS DOYLE BS	100000
B F TAMAYUZ (GB) - FEMME FATALE (GB)	A PERRETT	100000
B F OASIS DREAM (GB) - VANISHING POINT (USA)	CROMWELL BS	100000
GR C DALAKHANI (IRE) - CLARA BOW (IRE)	B O'RYAN	100000
B C SHAMARDAL (USA) - LANZANA (GB)	VENDOR	100000
B C HARD SPUN (USA) - STORMY BLESSING (USA)	C GORDON-WATSON BS	100000
KYLLACHY RISE (GB) B C KYLLACHY (GB) - UP AND ABOUT (GB)	C DE MOUBRAY	100000
GLANELY (IRE) B C EXCEED AND EXCEL (AUS) - BON TON ROULET (GB)	ANTHONY STROUD BS	100000
CH C DUKE OF MARMALADE (IRE) - A P EASY (USA)	D O'BYRNE	100000
B C MR GREELEY (USA) - KUSHNARENKOVO (GB)	BBA (IRELAND)	100000
B C EXCEED AND EXCEL (AUS) - BLUE PARADE (IRE)	BLANDFORD BS	100000
B C AUTHORIZED (IRE) - ZIVANIA (IRE)	JOHN FERGUSON BS	100000
B C HENRYTHENAVIGATOR (USA) - SAINTLY SPEECH (USA)	CORMAC MCCORMACK BS	100000
B C OASIS DREAM (GB) - SEDNA (IRE)	BRIAN GRASSICK BS	100000
B C ACCLAMATION (GB) - KONDAKOVA (IRE)	G L MOORE	100000
CH F NEW APPROACH (IRE) - TIME AWAY (IRE)	VENDOR	100000
B C ACCLAMATION (GB) - APPLAUD (USA)	VENDOR	100000
STRICTLY SILCA (GB) CH F DANEHILL DANCER (IRE) - SILCA CHIAVE (GB)	VENDOR	100000
B C DANEHILL DANCER (IRE) - LUCKY SPIN (GB)	KERN/LILLINGSTON ASS	100000
B C NAYEF (USA) - EMERALD PEACE (IRE)	OLIVER ST LAWRENCE BS	100000
LIVING DESERT (GB) GR C OASIS DREAM (GB) - SELL OUT (GB)	RICHARD FRISBY BS	100000
B C HOLY ROMAN EMPEROR (IRE) - DELISHA (GB)	R BOFFEY	98000
B C BAHAMIAN BOUNTY (GB) - RISE (GB)	C GORDON-WATSON BS	95000
CH C DUTCH ART (GB) - EVASIVE QUALITY (FR)	SACKVILLEDONALD	95000
B C HENRYTHENAVIGATOR (USA) - ST HELENS SHADOW (USA)	STEPHEN HILLEN BS	95000
B F DUKE OF MARMALADE (IRE) - COMERAINCOMESHINE (IRE)	BLANDFORD BS	95000
CH C SAKHEE'S SECRET (GB) - DISCO LIGHTS (GB)	PETER & ROSS DOYLE BS	95000
B C INVINCIBLE SPIRIT (IRE) - SINDUDA (GB)	PETER & ROSS DOYLE BS	95000
B F CAPE CROSS (IRE) - NANTYGLO (GB)	M O'TOOLE	95000
B F ACCLAMATION (GB) - ALMOND FLOWER (IRE)	TALLY-HO STUD	95000
B C RED CLUBS (IRE) - TIFARITI (USA)	BBA (IRELAND)	92000
B F CAPE CROSS (GB) - FASLEN (USA)	KERN/LILLINGSTON ASS	90000
B F ACCLAMATION (GB) - DANI RIDGE (IRE)	RABBAH BS	90000
B F ROYAL APPLAUSE (GB) - THIRD PARTY (GB)	SHADWELL ESTATE	90000
B C MONTJEU (IRE) - GAMRA (IRE)	B O'RYAN	90000
CH C PIVOTAL (GB) - STARLIGHT DREAMS (USA)	VENDOR	90000
B C NOTNOWCATO (GB) - LUMINDA (IRE)	E DUNLOP	90000
B C ROCK OF GIBRALTAR (IRE) - SIREN SOUND (GB)	ANTHONY STROUD BS	90000
GR C INTIKHAB (USA) - THE MANX TOUCH (IRE)	SACKVILLEDONALD	90000
B F EXCELLENT ART (GB) - PARTY FEET (IRE)	D WACHMAN	90000
B C SHAMARDAL (USA) - TREBLE SEVEN (USA)	M JOHNSTON	90000
B F INVINCIBLE SPIRIT (IRE) - DOLYDILLE (IRE)	CROMWELL BS	90000
GLEE CLUB (GB) B F KYLLACHY (GB) - PENMAYNE (GB)	BBA (GERMANY)	90000
B C ROYAL APPLAUSE (GB) - ROLEXA (GB)	SHADWELL ESTATE	90000
B F OASIS DREAM (GB) - BIANCA NERA (GB)	RABBAH BS	90000
B C AUTHORIZED (IRE) - MATHOOL (IRE)	RABBAH BS	90000
B C AZAMOUR (IRE) - ZARA'S BIRTHDAY (IRE)	D WOODS	88000
B C ROYAL APPLAUSE (GB) - CRYSTAL POWER (USA)	BRIAN GRASSICK BS	88000
B C DYLAN THOMAS (IRE) - DUBIOUS (GB)	C GORDON-WATSON BS	87000
B C MEDAGLIA D'ORO (USA) - BECKY IN PINK (USA)	PETER & ROSS DOYLE BS	85000
B C MANDURO (GER) - GAZE (GB)	JOHN WARREN BS	85000
CH C KYLLACHY (GB) - CONSTITUTE (USA)	JOHN WARREN BS	85000
B C DALAKHANI (IRE) - YUMMY MUMMY (GB)	ANTHONY STROUD BS	85000
BR F EXCEED AND EXCEL (AUS) - TURNING LEAF (IRE)	WILL EDMEADES BS	85000
B C ROCK OF GIBRALTAR (IRE) - WALDMARK (GER)	BLANDFORD BS	85000

Name and Breeding	Purchaser	Guineas
B C DANEHILL DANCER (IRE) - SHOWBIZ (IRE)	J DELAHOOKE	85000
B C MEDAGLIA D'ORO (USA) - FIRST GLIMMER (USA)	PETER & ROSS DOYLE BS	85000
CH C PIVOTAL (GB) - DANCE A DREAM (GB)	JOHN WARREN BS	85000
B C TEOFILO (IRE) - RUBY AFFAIR (IRE)	JOHN FERGUSON BS	85000
B C GALILEO (IRE) - BYWAYOFTHESTARS (GB)	BIG RED FARM	85000
SECRET SONG (GB) B C SINGSPIEL (IRE) - CONFIDANTE (USA)	SIR M PRESCOTT	85000
B C MANDURO (GER) - MAKHSUSAH (IRE)	R BOFFEY	82000
CH F EXCEED AND EXCEL (AUS) - PARADISE ISLE (GB)	DAVID REDVERS BS	80000
CH C EXCEED AND EXCEL (AUS) - PSYCHIC (GB)	MCKEEVER BS	80000
B C INVINCIBLE SPIRIT (IRE) - THREE WRENS (IRE)	MCKEEVER BS	80000
B C DUKE OF MARMALADE (IRE) - BLUE AZURE (USA)	PETER & ROSS DOYLE BS	80000
B C BAHAMIAN BOUNTY (GB) - AGE OF CHIVALRY (IRE)	R O'RYAN	80000
B F PIVOTAL (GB) - DANCE OF LIGHT (USA)	CHEVELEY PARK STUD	80000
B F SHAMARDAL (USA) - BAIZE (GB)	VENDOR	80000
B C EXCEED AND EXCEL (AUS) - ZULEIKA DOBSON (GB)	ANGIE LODER BS	80000
B F HOLY ROMAN EMPEROR (IRE) - ELLEN (IRE)	OLIVER ST LAWRENCE BS	80000
CH F DUTCH ART (GB) - MAKARA (GB)	GILL RICHARDSON BS	80000
BRAVESTAR (IRE) B C LAWMAN (FR) - HIGH FIDELITY (GER)	C GORDON-WATSON BS	80000
CH C GIANT'S CAUSEWAY (USA) - NORTHERN MISCHIEF (USA)	DAVID REDVERS BS	80000
CH F SHAMARDAL (USA) - LA VITA E BELLA (IRE)	MCKEEVER BS	80000
BIG THUNDER (GB) GR C DALAKHANI (IRE) - CHARLOTTE O FRAISE (IRE)	HIGHFLYER BS	80000
B/BR C ANY GIVEN SATURDAY (USA) - PIRATE'S BOOTY (CAN)	VENDOR	80000
CH C TEOFILO (IRE) - IN A SILENT WAY (IRE)	JOHN FERGUSON BS	80000
B C DYLAN THOMAS (IRE) - KARAMIYNA (IRE)	BLANDFORD BS	80000
CH C PIVOTAL (GB) - MI ANNA (GER)	DAVID REDVERS BS	80000
B C CAPE CROSS (IRE) - ETERNITY RING (GB)	M BOTTI	80000
B F DUKE OF MARMALADE (IRE) - MINOR POINT (GB)	JOHN WARREN BS	80000
B C NEW APPROACH (IRE) - CLAXON (GB)	GEOFFREY HOWSON BS	80000
HAVANA GOLD (IRE) B C TEOFILO (IRE) - JESSICA'S DREAM (IRE)	MRS A SKIFFINGTON	80000
CH C COMPTON PLACE (GB) - HASTEN (USA)	PETER & ROSS DOYLE BS	80000
CH F MEDICEAN (GB) - FLEUR DE LIS (GB)	HRAB	80000
B F SHAMARDAL (USA) - FASHION TRADE (GB)	R O'GORMAN BS	80000
CH F NEW APPROACH (IRE) - SAMDANIYA (GB)	J O'BYRNE	80000
CH C DUKE OF MARMALADE (IRE) - GREEN CASTLE (IRE)	MOCKLERSHILL	80000
BR C MONSUN (GER) - GEMINIANI (IRE)	C GORDON-WATSON BS	80000
CH C RAVEN'S PASS (USA) - DISCREET BRIEF (IRE)	M JOHNSTON	80000
B C DUKE OF MARMALADE (IRE) - LISCUNE (IRE)	PCF RACING	80000
B F SHIROCCO (GER) - LOVE AND LAUGHTER (IRE)	BBA (GERMANY)	80000
B C INVINCIBLE SPIRIT (IRE) - DUNDEL (IRE)	SHADWELL ESTATE CO	80000
B F OASIS DREAM (GB) - MAGDALENE (GB)	M CROSSMAN	80000
CAMISOLE (IRE) BR F TEOFILO (IRE) - SLEEVELESS (USA)	BBA (IRELAND)	78000
B C ACCLAMATION (GB) - BENTLEY'S BUSH (GB)	C GORDON-WATSON BS	78000
B C SHAMARDAL (USA) - LOVE ME TENDER (GB)	M JOHNSTON	78000
B F DALAKHANI (IRE) - SHESASMARTLADY (IRE)	VENDOR	75000
B C SAKHEE (USA) - FOREST FIRE (SWE)	SHADWELL ESTATE CO	75000
B F AUTHORIZED (IRE) - INCOMING CALL (USA)	C DE MOUBRAY	75000
SORN (IRE) CH C GALILEO (IRE) - DAME AGAIN (AUS)	VENDOR	75000
NEW RICH (GB) B C BAHAMIAN BOUNTY (GB) - BLING BLING (GB)	D WOODS	75000
B C ELUSIVE CITY (USA) - DIAMOND LIGHT (USA)	ANTHONY STROUD BS	75000
B C MUJADIL (USA) - VANITY (IRE)	J ODCHAZEL	75000
CH C RAVEN'S PASS (USA) - SANTOLINA (USA)	HUGO MERRY BS	75000
B C AUTHORIZED (IRE) - MISS HEPBURN (USA)	JOHN FOOTE BS	75000
B F EXCELLENT ART (GB) - PIETRA DURA (GB)	J O'BYRNE	75000
B F INVINCIBLE SPIRIT (IRE) - MATIKANEHAMATIDORI (JPN)	PETER & ROSS DOYLE BS	75000
B C KYLLACHY (GB) - ETERNAL BEAUTY (USA)	BRIAN GRASSICK BS	75000
B F GREEN DESERT (USA) - DOROTHEA BROOKE (IRE)	C GORDON-WATSON BS	75000
GR F DALAKHANI (IRE) - IN THE LIMELIGHT (IRE)	GILL RICHARDSON BS	75000
CH C BERTOLINI (USA) - ARIAN DA (GB)	PETER & ROSS DOYLE BS	75000
B C OASIS DREAM (GB) - WORLD'S HEROINE (USA)	RICHARD FRISBY BS	75000
GR C DALAKHANI (IRE) - ARGENT DU BOIS (USA)	W R MUIR	75000
B C CAPE CROSS (IRE) - STREET STAR (USA)	SHADWELL ESTATE	75000
RUN IT TWICE (IRE) B C DARK ANGEL (IRE) - ALINDA (IRE)	ANGIE LODER BS	75000
B C DUTCH ART (GB) - ROTUNDA (GB)	PETER & ROSS DOYLE BS	75000
B C CAPE CROSS (IRE) - BRIGHT HOPE (IRE)	ELEDY SRL	75000
CH C ELUSIVE QUALITY (USA) - FLIP FLOP (FR)	VENDOR	74000
B C CAPE CROSS (IRE) - ELIZABETHAN AGE (IRE)	E DUNLOP	72000
KROSSKINA (IRE) B F CAPE CROSS (IRE) - DIEVOTCHKINA (IRE)	P D'ARCY	72000
B F CAPE CROSS (IRE) - NOYELLES (IRE)	E DUNLOP	72000
B F INVINCIBLE SPIRIT (IRE) - PARISIAN ELEGANCE (GB)	MOCKLERSHILL STABLES	72000
B F AUTHORIZED (IRE) - NAJMATI (GB)	JOHN FERGUSON BS	72000
CH C RAVEN'S PASS (USA) - WATERWAYS (IRE)	JOHN FERGUSON BS	72000

Name and Breeding	Purchaser	Guineas
B C TEOFILO (IRE) - FANTASTIC SPRING (USA)	JILL LAMB BS	72000
CH F GALILEO (IRE) - KITE MARK (GB)	C MARNANE	72000
MUSIKHANI (GB) B F DALAKHANI (IRE) - MUSICANNA (GB)	PITCHALL FARM STUD	72000
DALGIG (GB) B C NEW APPROACH (IRE) - BRIGHT HALO (IRE)	H CANDY	70000
B C ECHO OF LIGHT (GB) - MANTLE (GB)	R O'GORMAN BS	70000
B C AZAMOUR (IRE) - GLENMARA (USA)	A D SPENCE	70000
B C EXCEED AND EXCEL (AUS) - SAABIQ (USA)	CORMAC MCCORMACK BS	70000
TILSTARR (IRE) B F SHAMARDAL (USA) - VAMPIRE QUEEN (GB)	PETER & ROSS DOYLE BS	70000
B C TEOFILO (IRE) - WATER FOUNTAIN (GB)	BBA (IRELAND)	70000
B C NAYEF (USA) - DANEHILL DREAMER (USA)	SHADWELL ESTATE	70000
CH C EXCEED AND EXCEL (AUS) - SNOWY INDIAN (GB)	MCKEEVER BS	70000
B C SHAMARDAL (USA) - STEAM CUISINE (GB)	KILLARNEY GLEN	70000
B C EXCEED AND EXCEL (AUS) - MONNAVANNA (IRE)	C DE MOUBRAY	70000
B F SINGSPIEL (IRE) - MAGIC TREE (UAE)	BADGERS BS	70000
B C ROYAL APPLAUSE (GB) - OCEAN VIEW (USA)	C GORDON-WATSON BS	70000
B F RED CLUBS (IRE) - FUERTA VENTURA (IRE)	BADGERS BS	70000
BR F KHELEYF (USA) - PIZZICATO (GB)	B RAYMOND	70000
CH C FIREBREAK (GB) - DAYVILLE (USA)	GEOFFREY HOWSON BS	70000
CH F PIVOTAL (GB) - MY FIRST ROMANCE (GB)	VENDOR	70000
B C GREEN DESERT (USA) - ROSIE'S POSY (IRE)	J O'BYRNE	70000
B C DALAKHANI (IRE) - COYOTE (GB)	M JOHNSTON	70000
B C DUTCH ART (GB) - MAID TO DANCE (GB)	BRIAN GRASSICK BS	68000
B C DANEHILL DANCER (IRE) - GILDED VANITY (GB)	BLANDFORD BS	68000
B C BERNSTEIN (USA) - HANGIN WITHMY BUDS (USA)	PETER & ROSS DOYLE BS	68000
B C DUKE OF MARMALADE (IRE) - ARDBRAE LADY (GB)	G MARGARSON	68000
B C EXCEED AND EXCEL (AUS) - MAGIC MUSIC (IRE)	C GORDON-WATSON BS	67000
EMPIRICIST (IRE) B C HOLY ROMAN EMPEROR (IRE) - CHARAIG (GB)	PETER & ROSS DOYLE BS	67000
CH C BAHAMIAN BOUNTY (GB) - MAMOURA (IRE)	G MARGARSON	67000
B C CHEROKEE RUN (USA) - MENIATARRA (USA)	M CROSSMAN	65000
B F INVINCIBLE SPIRIT (IRE) - ISABELLA GLYN (IRE)	RABBAH BS	65000
CH F DALAKHANI (IRE) - WHAZZIS (GB)	VENDOR	65000
B C MEDICEAN (GB) - PAPPAS RUBY (USA)	HUGO MERRY BS	65000
SWITCH ON (GB) B C OASIS DREAM (GB) - NOODLE SOUP (USA)	VENDOR	65000
B C KHELEYF (USA) - LAUNCH TIME (USA)	GILL RICHARDSON BS	65000
BR F ROCK OF GIBRALTAR (IRE) - GEMS OF ARABY (GB)	H CECIL	65000
B F GIANT'S CAUSEWAY (USA) - LADY LINDA (USA)	VENDOR	65000
CH C STARCRAFT (NZ) - SHUAILY (PER)	FARRINGTON BS	65000
B C LAWMAN (FR) - PINK SOVIETSTAIA (FR)	ANGIE LODER BS	65000
SINAADI (IRE) B F KYLLACHY (GB) - QUANTUM (IRE)	RABBAH BS	65000
B/BR F FOOTSTEPSINTHESAND (GB) - ZEE ZEE GEE (GB)	GEOFFREY HOWSON BS	65000
ELLE WOODS (IRE) B F LAWMAN (FR) - LADY LIVIUS (IRE)	A TINKLER	65000
B C BAHAMIAN BOUNTY (GB) - LATENT LOVER (GB)	LAKIN BS	65000
B F RAVEN'S PASS (USA) - MACADAMIA (IRE)	VENDOR	65000
B C HALLING (USA) - L'AFFAIRE MONIQUE (GB)	ANGIE LODER BS	65000
HAVANA BEAT (IRE) B C TEOFILO (IRE) - SWEET HOME ALABAMA (IRE)	A BALDING	65000
B C SHAMARDAL (USA) - PETONELLAJILL (GB)	VENDOR	65000
B C HIGH CHAPARRAL (IRE) - PALATINE DANCER (IRE)	D ELSWORTH	65000
B C DUTCH ART (GB) - PIOUS (GB)	M W EASTERBY	65000
B C DUKE OF MARMALADE (IRE) - KATRINA (IRE)	W HAGGAS	65000
B F ELUSIVE QUALITY (USA) - HUCKING HOT (GB)	VENDOR	65000
GLENARD (GB) B C ARCH (USA) - OLAYA (USA)	BBA (IRELAND)	65000
B C MOUNT NELSON (GB) - PAN GALACTIC (USA)	D ELSWORTH	65000
B F SPEIGHTSTOWN (USA) - UNRESTRAINED (USA)	MCKEEVER BS	65000
B/BR C GHOSTZAPPER (USA) - TUSTARTA (USA)	CROMWELL BS	65000
BOOMSHACKERLACKER (IRE) GR C DARK ANGEL (IRE) - ALLEGRINA (IRE)	ANGIE LODER BS	65000
B C MONTJEU (IRE) - PUCE (GB)	W BROWNE	65000
B C HERNANDO (FR) - TRULLITTI (IRE)	OLIVER ST LAWRENCE BS	62000
CLOSE AT HAND (GB) B F EXCEED AND EXCEL (AUS) - CLASSIC REMARK (IRE)	C GORDON-WATSON BS	62000
B F DUBAWI (IRE) - CAPISTRANO DAY (USA)	VENDOR	62000
B C INTIKHAB (USA) - MASSADA (GB)	DAVID REDVERS BS	62000
RED RED WINE (GB) B C DUTCH ART (GB) - ATNAB (USA)	A DUARTE	62000
MARHABA MALAYEEN (IRE) B C DUTCH ART (GB) - POYLE CAITLIN (IRE)	STEPHEN HILLEN BS	62000
GR C DUKE OF MARMALADE (IRE) - SANTA SOPHIA (GB)	MCKEEVER BS	62000
B C MOUNT NELSON (GB) - RED ROSES STORY (FR)	A PERRETT	62000
B C ELUSIVE CITY (USA) - GLAMADOUR (IRE)	PETER & ROSS DOYLE BS	62000
CYCLONE (GB) B C TEOFILO (IRE) - ASCOT CYCLONE (USA)	A TINKLER	62000
B C FASTNET ROCK (AUS) - BELDARIAN (IRE)	VENDOR	62000

HIGH-PRICED YEARLINGS OF 2011 AT GOFFS
The following yearlings realised 36,000 euros and over at Goffs Sales in 2011:-

Name and Breeding	Purchaser	Euros
CH F NEW APPROACH (IRE) - POSTERITY (IRE)	SHADWELL ESTATE	350000
B F ARCH (USA) - PRINCESS KRIS (GB)	SHADWELL ESTATE	340000
GR F GALILEO (IRE) - ALTITUDE (GB)	SIR R OGDEN	300000
B C MONTJEU (IRE) - MAYANO SOPHIA (IRE)	SIR R OGDEN	300000
BR F MARJU (IRE) - MAYENNE (USA)	SHADWELL ESTATE	260000
GR F VERGLAS (IRE) - LIMPOPO (GB)	O COLE	210000
B C GALILEO (IRE) - KENTUCKY WARBLER (IRE)	S HILLEN	205000
B C DUKE OF MARMALADE (IRE) - BOWSTRING (IRE)	BBA (IRELAND)	200000
B C OASIS DREAM (GB) - HOVERING (IRE)	C GORDON-WATSON BS	200000
B C MONTJEU (IRE) - SPRITZA (IRE)	D L O'BYRNE	200000
B F DUKE OF MARMALADE (IRE) - SUPERFONIC (FR)	D L O'BYRNE	190000
B C DUKE OF MARMALADE (IRE) - DUST FLICKER (GB)	A COLE	190000
GR C TEOFILO (IRE) - CASSANDRA GO (IRE)	SHADWELL ESTATE	180000
B C CAPE CROSS (IRE) - BRAZILIAN SAMBA (IRF)	HONG KONG JOCKEY CLUB	180000
CH F TEOFILO (IRE) - SCARLETT ROSE (GB)	HUGO MERRY BS	180000
B/DR F HARD SPUN (USA) - TELL SEATTLE (USA)	SHADWELL ESTATE	170000
B/BR F TAMAYUZ (GB) - NEVERLETME GO (IRE)	SHADWELL ESTATE	170000
B C DANEHILL DANCER (IRE) - QUAD'S MELODY (IRE)	HUGO MERRY BS	170000
B F GALILEO (IRE) - SOMETHING MON (USA)	VENDOR	170000
B C GALILEO (IRE) - STARCHY (GB)	D L O'BYRNE	170000
B F SHAMARDAL (USA) - CARIBBEAN ESCAPE (GB)	JOHN FERGUSON BS	170000
B F ACCLAMATION (GB) - YARASTAR (GB)	B O'RYAN	165000
B/BR F DALAKHANI (IRE) - BRIOLETTE (IRE)	HUGO MERRY BS	160000
B F MARJU (IRE) - ATALINA (FR)	B O'RYAN	150000
B C INVINCIBLE SPIRIT (IRE) - GRECIAN DANCER (GB)	SACKVILLEDONALD	150000
CH C GALILEO (IRE) - GRECIAN BRIDE (IRE)	BBA (IRELAND)	150000
B F NEW APPROACH (IRE) - TADKIYRA (IRE)	PETER ROSS DOYLE BS	100000
B C HURRICANE RUN (IRE) - CLOSE REGARDS (IRE)	ANTHONY STROUD BS	100000
B C KYLLACHY (GB) - GRAND LUCRE (USA)	HONG KONG JOCKEY CLUB	100000
B F OASIS DREAM (GB) - HAZARAYNA (GB)	JOHN FERGUSON BS	100000
CH C HAATEF (USA) - BEZANT (IRE)	SHADWELL ESTATE	100000
B F ELUSIVE CITY (USA) - JIOCONDA (IRE)	BARRONSTOWN STUD	100000
CH C GALILEO (IRE) - MOHICAN PRINCESS (GB)	D L O'BYRNE	95000
B C TAPIT (USA) - AMERICAN JEWEL (USA)	BBA (IRELAND) (P.S.)	95000
B F ROYAL APPLAUSE (GB) - CZARNA ROZA (GB)	JOHN FERGUSON BS	95000
B C EXCELLENT ART (GB) - VESTAVIA (IRE)	SACKVILLEDONALD	95000
CH C SAKHEE'S SECRET (GB) - FUDGE (GB)	B O'RYAN	92000
B F INVINCIBLE SPIRIT (IRE) - BERNIQUE (USA)	BBA (IRELAND)	90000
CH F BARATHEA (IRE) - PETITE SPECTRE (IRE)	PETER & ROSS DOYLE BS	90000
DUSKY QUEEN (IRE) B F SHAMARDAL (USA) - SANNA BAY (IRE)	R O'RYAN	90000
CH C NEW APPROACH (IRE) - PALACE WEEKEND (USA)	C GORDON-WATSON BS	90000
B F INVINCIBLE SPIRIT (IRE) - MOY WATER (IRE)	B O'RYAN	87000
B F ACCLAMATION (GB) - CLAUSTRA (GB)	COURSE INVESTMENT	85000
B F JEREMY (USA) - NEBRAAS (GB)	SKYMARC FARM	85000
B F DARK ANGEL (IRE) - SERIOUS DELIGHT (GB)	DAVID REDVERS BS	85000
B C TAMAYUZ (GB) - TRULY YOURS (IRE)	SHADWELL ESTATE	85000
B C DUTCH ART (GB) - RING OF LOVE (GB)	HONG KONG JOCKEY CLUB	85000
CH F SAKHEE'S SECRET (GB) - MARTHA (IRE)	SACKVILLEDONALD (P.S.)	80750
B F HOLY ROMAN EMPEROR (IRE) - FARTHINGALE (IRE)	CORMAC MCCORMACK BS	80000
B C ELUSIVE CITY (USA) - L-WAY FIRST (IRE)	E LYNAM	80000
GR F DALAKHANI (IRE) - KARMIFIRA (FR)	GROVE STUD	80000
B C MONTJEU (IRE) - WOODLAND ORCHID (IRE)	M JOHNSTON	80000
B C GALILEO (IRE) - LONGING TO DANCE (GB)	BBA (IRELAND)	80000
B C ACCLAMATION (GB) - NIGHT SPHERE (IRE)	J WARREN	80000
B C IFFRAAJ (GB) - REIGN OF FIRE (IRE)	MCKEEVER BS	80000
B C ACCLAMATION (GB) - MEDINA (IRE)	HIGHFIELD FARM	80000
CH F DANEHILL DANCER (IRE) - UGO FIRE (IRE)	F BARRY	80000
B F DYLAN THOMAS (IRE) - NO WAY (IRE)	CORMAC MCCORMACK BS	80000
B C LAWMAN (FR) - FERNANDA (GB)	B O'RYAN	80000
B C DUKE OF MARMALADE (IRE) - MALA MALA (IRE)	D WACHMAN	80000
B F INVINCIBLE SPIRIT (IRE) - SHARAPOVA (IRE)	M O'TOOLE	80000
B C ORATORIO (IRE) - RING THE RELATIVES (GB)	P COLE	80000
B C INVINCIBLE SPIRIT (IRE) - FLOWER OF KENT (USA)	NNT LTD	76000
CH F MR GREELEY (USA) - MARZELLINE (USA)	BALLYHANE STUD	75000
GR F RED CLUBS (IRE) - SHAWANNI (GB)	SACKVILLEDONALD	75000
SHORE STEP (IRE) BR C FOOTSTEPSINTHESAND (GB) - CHATHAM ISLANDS (USA)	GILL RICHARDSON BS	75000
B F GALILEO (IRE) - IN MY LIFE (IRE)	M JOHNSTON	75000
B C DANEHILL DANCER (IRE) - AKUNA BAY (USA)	BADGERS BS	75000

Name and Breeding	Purchaser	Euros
GR C VERGLAS (IRE) - HEART'S DESIRE (IRE)	R O'RYAN	75000
B F SHAMARDAL (USA) - PACIFIC GROVE (GB)	STAMINA TURF	75000
B C AUTHORIZED (IRE) - CHATURANGA (GB)	JOHN FERGUSON BS	75000
CH C DANEHILL DANCER (IRE) - AUNT JULIA (GB)	M SAID AL-NUAMI	75000
CH C KYLLACHY (GB) - REPUTABLE (GB)	MCKEEVER BS	72000
B F INVINCIBLE SPIRIT (IRE) - SCRIPTURE (IRE)	MCKEEVER BS	70000
B C ACCLAMATION (GB) - INDIENNE (IRE)	SACKVILLEDONALD	70000
DOUBLE DISCOUNT (IRE) B C INVINCIBLE SPIRIT (IRE) - BRYANSTOWN GIRL (IRE)	SACKVILLEDONALD	70000
CH F TEOFILO (IRE) - OUT OF TIME (IRE)	KEVIN ROSS BS	68000
B C INVINCIBLE SPIRIT (IRE) - VADORGA (GB)	MCKEEVER BS	65000
CAPE APPEAL (GB) B F CAPE CROSS (IRE) - SHEBOYGAN (IRE)	PETER & ROSS DOYLE BS	65000
CARRY ON CLAPPING (IRE) B F ACCLAMATION (GB) - EMBASSY BELLE (IRE)	PETER & ROSS DOYLE BS	65000
GLEN GINNIE (IRE) BR F RED CLUBS (IRE) - BELSAY (IRE)	BBA (IRELAND)	65000
AJMANI (IRE) B C KHELEYF (USA) - PASSARELLE (USA)	J WARREN	65000
B F INTIKHAB (USA) - VIOLA ROYALE (IRE)	BBA (IRELAND)	65000
B F LAWMAN (FR) - BRAYDEEN (IRE)	SOUTHERN BS	65000
B F EXCELLENT ART (GB) - SUBITO (GB)	BBA (IRELAND)	65000
B C EXCEED AND EXCEL (AUS) - CRINKLE (IRE)	SACKVILLEDONALD	65000
B C ELUSIVE CITY (USA) - LUCKY NORWEGIAN (IRE)	J WARREN	64000
GR C VERGLAS (IRE) - ALIKHLAS (IRE)	A O'RYAN	62000
B F DUKE OF MARMALADE (IRE) - THRIFT (IRE)	CORMAC MCCORMACK BS (P.S.)	62000
B F MOUNT NELSON (GB) - STATUA (IRE)	SACKVILLEDONALD	60000
C KYLLACHY (GB) - SOME DIVA (GB)	J ALLISON	60000
TAKE IT EASY (GER) B C SHAMARDAL (USA) - TAKE MY HAND (GER)	BLANDFORD BS	60000
B/BR C KHELEYF (USA) - SNAP CRACKLE POP (IRE)	RABBAH BS	60000
B C ORATORIO (IRE) - JUS'CHILLIN' (IRE)	PETER & ROSS DOYLE BS	60000
CH C RAVEN'S PASS (USA) - SADINGA (IRE)	GILL RICHARDSON BS	60000
B C CAPE CROSS (IRE) - INTERIM PAYMENT (USA)	MAB AGENCY	60000
CH C SAKHEE'S SECRET (GB) - QUEEN'S PUDDING (IRE)	PETER & ROSS DOYLE BS	60000
BR/GR C VERGLAS (IRE) - OVAL OFFICE (GB)	S HILLEN	60000
B F VAN NISTELROOY (USA) - MISS ZAFONIC (FR)	J FERGUSON	58000
B F SHAMARDAL (USA) - FOREPLAY (USA)	PETER & ROSS DOYLE BS	57000
CH C TAMAYUZ (GB) - JUST SPECIAL (GB)	B O'RYAN	55000
B C ROYAL APPLAUSE (GB) - JUST JULIE (USA)	BBA	55000
B C DUKE OF MARMALADE (IRE) - EL SOPRANO (IRE)	VENDOR	55000
CH C EXCELLENT ART (GB) - GRANNY KELLY (USA)	MCKEEVER BS	55000
B C SHIROCCO (GER) - SHUHRAH (USA)	J I O'BYRNE	55000
B F ACCLAMATION (GB) - TALAH (IRE)	P TWOMEY	53000
B C DYLAN THOMAS (IRE) - TANGO TONIC (IRE)	GLENVALE STUD	53000
B C WHIPPER (USA) - GLYMPSE (IRE)	MCKEEVER BS	52000
ORGILGO BAY (IRE) B C LAWMAN (FR) - THIRD DIMENSION (IRE)	J MCCONNELL	52000
CH C TAMAYUZ (GB) - CRADLE BRIEF (IRE)	F BARRY	50000
BR F LAWMAN (FR) - FARADAY LIGHT (IRE)	BBA (IRELAND)	50000
CH F SHAMARDAL (USA) - ELSHAMMS (GB)	PETER & ROSS DOYLE BS	50000
BR C JEREMY (USA) - KHAYRAT (IRE)	MOCKLERSHILL	50000
TANGHAN (IRE) B C INVINCIBLE SPIRIT (IRE) - ROSE DE FRANCE (IRE)	R O'RYAN	50000
B C ACCLAMATION (GB) - PERILS OF JOY (IRE)	A LODER	50000
B C FRACAS (IRE) - MADAEN (USA)	B O'RYAN	50000
BR C SHAMARDAL (USA) - RED BANDANNA (IRE)	OLIVER ST LAWRENCE BS	50000
STEER BY THE STARS (IRE) B F PIVOTAL (GB) - MUNDUS NOVUS (USA)	A ROSS	50000
B F ELUSIVE CITY (USA) - MY FUNNY VALENTINE (GB)	R O'RYAN	50000
B F BERNARDINI (USA) - DYNA'S DESTINY (USA)	MOCKLERSHILL	50000
B/BR F ARCH (USA) - DEFENSIVE BOAST (USA)	FORM BS (P.S.)	50000
B C LEROIDESANIMAUX (BRZ) - GUIDING LIGHT (USA)	PETER & ROSS DOYLE BS	50000
EXCLUSIVE WATERS (IRE) B C ELUSIVE CITY (USA) - PELICAN WATERS (IRE)	PORTANOVA BS	50000
B C CAPE CROSS (IRE) - ARRAY OF STARS (IRE)	VENDOR	50000
B F MONTJEU (IRE) - SLOW SAND (USA)	SACKVILLEDONALD	50000
B C MOSS VALE (IRE) - EMMA'S STAR (ITY)	F BARRY	50000
B F NAYEF (USA) - BENEVENTA (GB)	P DEEGAN	50000
CH F GALILEO (IRE) - PESCIA (IRE)	J I O'BYRNE	50000
CH/GR C VERGLAS (IRE) - DAZZLING DANCER (GB)	J ALLISON	50000
B F MOUNT NELSON (GB) - LA GANDILIE (FR)	VENDOR	48000
B F DALAKHANI (IRE) - WATERSHIP CRYSTAL (IRE)	FORM BS	48000
B F SHAMARDAL (USA) - NASSMA (IRE)	VENDOR	48000
CH C HURRICANE RUN (IRE) - VALE VIEW (FR)	T G & B B MILLS	47000
B C ACCLAMATION (GB) - ASHEYANA (IRE)	K PRENDERGAST	47000
B/BR C FOOTSTEPSINTHESAND (GB) - ZAWARIQ (IRE)	G LYONS	46000
CH F GALILEO (IRE) - ROCK QUEEN (IRE)	VENDOR	46000
BR F DANSILI (GB) - WESTERLY GALE (USA)	T EASTERBY	46000
B F CAPE CROSS (IRE) - LAURELDEAN LADY (IRE)	M JOHNSTON	45000
SANJURO (IRE) BR C MANDURO (GER) - KIND REGARDS (IRE)	GILL RICHARDSON BS	45000

Name and Breeding	Purchaser	Euros
B F DANEHILL DANCER (IRE) - GLAMOUR (IRE)	VENDOR	45000
B C CAPE CROSS (IRE) - KHATELA (IRE)	MAB AGENCY	45000
CH C SHAMARDAL (USA) - PIVOTAL'S PRINCESS (IRE)	MOCKLERSHILL	45000
B F HENRYTHENAVIGATOR (USA) - AUDIT (USA)	J I O'BYRNE	45000
B F INVINCIBLE SPIRIT (IRE) - GREEK SYMPHONY (IRE)	J FERGUSON	45000
B C DYLAN THOMAS (IRE) - TANGO TONIC (IRE)	D ELSWORTH	45000
B F DUKE OF MARMALADE (IRE) - MOONBI RIDGE (IRE)	SEELAND INT	45000
EMPERORS HERO (IRE) B C HOLY ROMAN EMPEROR (IRE) - SERENGETI DAY (USA)	F BARRY	44000
B F DUKE OF MARMALADE (IRE) - MOORETOWN LADY (IRE)	GILL RICHARDSON BS	44000
B F HURRICANE RUN (IRE) - FOREIGN RELATION (IRE)	B O'BYRNE	44000
B C MARJU (IRE) - QUEEN'S QUEST (GB)	J MCCARTAN	43000
B C AZAMOUR (IRE) - ZARA'S BIRTHDAY (GB)	R ALLCOCK	43000
B C NEW APPROACH (IRE) - COY (IRE)	JOHN FERGUSON BS	42000
BR F ROCK OF GIBRALTAR (IRE) - SILVER MITZVA (IRE)	VENDOR	42000
B C CAPE CROSS (IRE) - SPARKLE OF STONES (FR)	VENDOR	42000
CH C MOUNT NELSON (GB) - WALDBLUME (GER)	SACKVILLEDONALD	42000
B C HOLY ROMAN EMPEROR (IRE) - TWO MARKS (GB)	J WHOLEY	42000
CH C BIG BROWN (USA) - SUGAR PLUM S J Π (USA)	F ZWICKY	42000
JADESNUMBERONE (IRE) B F AUTHORIZED (IRE) - GABRIELLA (GB)	J WARREN	42000
B C KHELEYF (USA) - JOURNEY'S END (IRE)	OAK TREE FARM	42000
CAPELLA'S SONG (IRE) B F ORATORIO (IRE) - BRIGHT BANK (IRE)	RICHARD FRISBY BS	42000
B C ORATORIO (IRE) - BALAMIYDA (IRE)	DAVID REDVERS BS	42000
B C DUBAWI (IRE) - ANOSTI (GB)	VENDOR	42000
B F MOUNT NELSON (GB) - GIVE A WHISTLE (IRE)	NEWSELLS PARK STUD	42000
B F PIVOTAL (GB) - BON NUIT (IRE)	BLANDFORD BS	42000
SLIP OF THE TONGUE (GB) CH C ZAMINDAR (USA) - KISWAHILI (GB)	SIR M PRESCOTT	42000
B F JEREMY (USA) - KOURNIKOVA (SAF)	DAVID REDVERS BS	42000
B C ACCLAMATION (GB) - KONDAKOVA (IRE)	G & D BS	42000
B C PIVOTAL (GB) - KITZA (IRE)	M JOHNSTON	41000
HIDDEN LINK (GB) B C RAIL LINK (GB) - GLOVED HAND (GB)	SIR M PRESCOTT	40000
CH C TAMAYUZ (GB) - FOLLOW MY LEAD (GB)	C GORDON-WATSON BS	40000
B F DUKE OF MARMALADE (IRE) - STARRY MESSENGER (GB)	SKYMARC FARM (P.S.)	40000
B C ACCLAMATION (GB) - SAHARA SKY (IRE)	TRANFORD	40000
B F MONTJEU (IRE) - VENERATION (GB)	GRAIGUESHEEN STUD (P.S.)	40000
B F HALLING (USA) - JAZZ BABY (IRE)	H BUTLER	40000
B F DUKE OF MARMALADE (IRE) - CRYSTAL CURLING (IRE)	F BARRY (P.S.)	40000
B C DARK ANGEL (IRE) - VADAROUSSE (GER)	J OSBORNE	40000
B F HOLY ROMAN EMPEROR (IRE) - CROSSANZA (IRE)	BALLYHANE STUD	40000
B F TAPIT (USA) - CATLIKE DANCER (USA)	BBA (IRELAND)	40000
CH C MANDURO (GER) - MEON MIX (GB)	B O'RYAN	40000
B F LAWMAN (FR) - KAZINOKI (UAE)	K PRENDERGAST	40000
CH F EXCELLENT ART (GB) - LISFANNON (GB)	D WACHMAN	40000
B F SHAMARDAL (USA) - OREGON TRAIL (USA)	MOCKLERSHILL	40000
B F SAKHEE'S SECRET (GB) - LAKE LADOGA (GB)	P DEEGAN	40000
B F NEW APPROACH (IRE) - CENTIFOLIA (FR)	S VIDAL	40000
CURL (IRE) B F DUKE OF MARMALADE (IRE) - FRINGE (GB)	PETER & ROSS DOYLE BS	40000
B F VERGLAS (IRE) - REGALLINE (IRE)	E LYNAM	40000
B/BR F MR GREELEY (USA) - VICTORICA (USA)	RATHMORE STUD	40000
B F OASIS DREAM (GB) - ROYAL BLUE (GB)	MOCKLERSHILL	40000
BR/GR F ACCLAMATION (GB) - MASAADER (USA)	BBA (IRELAND)	40000
CH F ELUSIVE CITY (USA) - CATCH THE SEA (IRE)	DAVID REDVERS BS	40000
B C SAKHEE'S SECRET (GB) - FIRST FANTASY (GB)	G LYONS	40000
B F ELUSIVE CITY (USA) - MIDNIGHT PARTNER (IRE)	PETER & ROSS DOYLE BS	38000
B C ACCLAMATION (GB) - MOVIE QUEEN (GB)	C MARNANE	38000
B C INVINCIBLE SPIRIT (IRE) - SAOIRE (GB)	J COLLINS	38000
B C JEREMY (USA) - OSTRUSA (AUT)	C MARNANE	38000
B C EXCELLENT ART (GB) - PUCK'S CASTLE (GB)	A DUARTE	38000
B F JEREMY (USA) - MISSKINTA (IRE)	BRIAN GRASSICK BS	38000
B C LAWMAN (FR) - REQUESTED PLEASURE (IRE)	G LYONS	38000
B C ROYAL APPLAUSE (GB) - HIDDEN HEART (USA)	BBA (IRELAND)	38000
B C INVINCIBLE SPIRIT (IRE) - BRAZILIAN BRIDE (IRE)	K KEIGHTLEY	38000
CH C DANEHILL DANCER (IRE) - RAIN FLOWER (IRE)	G LYONS	37000
B F KHELEYF (USA) - MAMONTA (IRE)	DAVID REDVERS BS	37000
AUSSIE REIGNS (IRE) B C AUSSIE RULES (USA) - ROHAIN (IRE)	PORTANOVA BS	36000
B F ROYAL APPLAUSE (GB) - ASK CAROL (IRE)	ANTHONY STROUD BS	36000
GR C VERGLAS (IRE) - SEVI'S CHOICE (USA)	GILL RICHARDSON BS	36000
B F SOVIET STAR (USA) - GRAVIERES (FR)	BLANDFORD BS	36000
CH C IFFRAAJ (GB) - LIVIUS LADY (IRE)	F ZWICKY	36000
B C HAATEF (USA) - IKAN (IRE)	C MARNANE	36000

HIGH-PRICED YEARLINGS OF 2011 AT DONCASTER SALES

The following yearlings realised 29,523 guineas and over at Doncaster Sales in 2011:-

Name and Breeding	Purchaser	Guineas
B C OASIS DREAM (GB) - RONALDSAY (GB)	E FITZPATRICK	266666
B F MONSIEUR BOND (IRE) - FOREVER BOND (GB)	D WOODS	140000
B C ACCLAMATION (GB) - LYCA BALLERINA (GB)	J WARREN	109523
B C ACCLAMATION (GB) - KERIYKA (GB)	MCKEEVER BS	100000
SANDREAMER (IRE) B F OASIS DREAM (GB) - ALSHARQ (IRE)	GILL RICHARDSON BS	80952
B C KYLLACHY (GB) - GLEAM OF LIGHT (IRE)	RICHARD FRISBY BS	80952
B C ELNADIM (USA) - SELKIRK ROSE (IRE)	D REDVERS	78095
B C KYLLACHY (GB) - MOLLY BROWN (GB)	BLANDFORD BS	76190
B C KYLLACHY (GB) - IVANIA (GB)	PETER & ROSS DOYLE BS	76190
B F ORATORIO (IRE) - GILDED EDGE (GB)	A O'RYAN	76190
B C KHELEYF (USA) - BALLADONIA (GB)	BLANDFORD BS	76190
B C KYLLACHY (GB) - FEN GUEST (GB)	MCKEEVER BS	74285
GR C ACCLAMATION (GB) - NEW DEAL (GB)	D REDVERS	71428
B C KHELEYF (USA) - MADAM NINETTE (GB)	JOHN FERGUSON BS	71428
B C IFFRAAJ (GB) - BRAVE MADAM (IRE)	PETER & ROSS DOYLE BS	68571
GR F ACCLAMATION (GB) - BANDANNA (GB)	JANE ALLISON BS	66666
B C ACCLAMATION (GB) - FATHOMING (USA)	PETER & ROSS DOYLE BS	66666
BR C KHELEYF (USA) - SPIRITUAL AIR (GB)	J WARREN	66666
DANSILI DUAL (IRE) B C DANSILI (GB) - JEWEL IN THE SAND (IRE)	D WOODS	66666
MISCHIEF N MAYHEM (GB) B F NAYEF (USA) - MAIL THE DESERT (IRE)	C MCCORMACK	66666
B C FOOTSTEPSINTHESAND (GB) - FARBENSPIEL (IRE)	BBA (IRELAND)	66666
B C KHELEYF (USA) - KISSING TIME (GB)	D ELSWORTH	66666
B F EXCEED AND EXCEL (AUS) - POPPO'S SONG (CAN)	GILL RICHARDSON BS	66666
BARRACUDA BOY (IRE) B C BAHAMIAN BOUNTY - MADAME BOULANGERE (GB)	D SACKVILLE	64761
CH F PIVOTAL (GB) - NOELANI (IRE)	ANTHONY STROUD BS	64761
B C EXCEED AND EXCEL (AUS) - PRAYER (IRE)	JANE ALLISON BS	63809
COLLINGBOURNEDUCIS (IRE) B C BAHAMIAN BOUNTY - QUICKSTYX (GB)	PETER & ROSS DOYLE BS	62857
BLACK MONK (IRE) B C DARK ANGEL (IRE) - DOUBLE EIGHT (IRE)	PETER & ROSS DOYLE BS	62857
B F KYLLACHY (GB) - NAUSICAA (USA)	VENDOR	61904
B F PASTORAL PURSUITS (GB) - CLARICE ORSINI (GB)	AMANDA SKIFFINGTON BS	61904
B C CHOISIR (AUS) - ACIDANTHERA (GB)	PETER & ROSS DOYLE BS	61904
B C OASIS DREAM (GB) - ALEXANDER ALLIANCE (IRE)	J O'KEEFFE	61904
FUNK SOUL BROTHER (GB) B C COCKNEY REBEL (IRE) - SWEET AFTON (IRE)	BBA (IRELAND)	61904
B/GR F DUBAWI (IRE) - GREY AGAIN (GB)	D REDVERS	60000
B C SHAMARDAL (USA) - NOVA CYNGI (USA)	JOHN FERGUSON BS	59047
RISKIT FORA BISKIT (IRE) B F KODIAC (GB) - MISS BRIEF (IRE)	RICHARD FRISBY BS	57142
B C ELUSIVE CITY (USA) - TRANQUIL SKY (GB)	PETER & ROSS DOYLE BS	57142
B F MORE THAN READY (USA) - BETTY JOHANNE (USA)	JANE ALLISON BS	57142
B C ACCLAMATION (GB) - DEA CAELESTIS (FR)	R J O'RYAN	57142
B C KYLLACHY (GB) - RELINQUISHED (GB)	PETER & ROSS DOYLE BS	55238
CH C ENGLISH CHANNEL (USA) - ARABIAN PENINSULA (USA)	PETER & ROSS DOYLE BS	53333
MONTIRIDGE (IRE) B C RAMONTI (FR) - ELEGANT RIDGE (IRE)	PETER & ROSS DOYLE BS	52380
CH C DUTCH ART (GB) - ARCULINGE (GB)	D ARMSTRONG	52380
CH C MOUNT NELSON (GB) - ALEXIA REVEUSE (IRE)	D SACKVILLE	52380
B C RED CLUBS (IRE) - DREAMALOT (GB)	PETER & ROSS DOYLE BS	52380
SAINT JEROME (IRE) B C JEREMY (USA) - EMINENCE GIFT (GB)	PETER & ROSS DOYLE BS	52380
B C KHELEYF (USA) - CATCHING STARS (IRE)	MCKEEVER BS	52380
KING OF KUDOS (IRE) B C ACCLAMATION (GB) - PERUGINA (GB)	D WOODS	51428
B C KYLLACHY (GB) - REGENT'S PARK (GB)	BLANDFORD BS	51428
B C JEREMY (USA) - COMPRADORE (GB)	ANTHONY STROUD BS	49523
B C ACCLAMATION (GB) - SUBTLE AFFAIR (IRE)	HIGHFIELD FARM	49523
B C ORATORIO (IRE) - RED RITA (IRE)	A SKIFFINGTON	49523
CH C SLEEPING INDIAN (GB) - CARLA (FR)	WILL EDMEADES BS	49523
CH C DUKE OF MARMALADE (IRE) - LICORNE (GB)	VENDOR	47619
B C ORATORIO (IRE) - MISS SACHA (GB)	BBA (IRELAND)	47619
B F CAPTAIN RIO (GB) - AGONY AUNT (GB)	D REDVERS	47619
CH F MOUNT NELSON (GB) - LACEWORK (GB)	R J O'RYAN	45714
B C INVINCIBLE SPIRIT (IRE) - MOSAIQUE BEAUTY (IRE)	BLANDFORD BS	45714
B/GR C AUSSIE RULES (USA) - JUSOOR (USA)	HUGO MERRY BS	45714
CH C COMPTON PLACE (GB) - FORTHEFIRSTTIME (GB)	R J O'RYAN	45714
B F PIVOTAL (GB) - SATIN FINISH (IRE)	GLOBAL EQUINE	43809
MRS WARREN (GB) B F KYLLACHY (GB) - BOLD BUNNY (GB)	C POWELL	42857
B C ORATORIO (IRE) - ALWAYS ATTRACTIVE (GB)	BLANDFORD BS	42857
CH C DANROAD (AUS) - OUR EMMY LOU (GB)	R O SHEEN BS	42857
EMPOWERMENT (IRE) B C ELUSIVE CITY (USA) - MAIMANA (IRE)	PETER & ROSS DOYLE BS	42857
B C SAKHEE'S SECRET (GB) - MALELANE (IRE)	W R MUIR	42857
CH C DUTCH ART (GB) - NAOMI WILDMAN (USA)	D SACKVILLE	42857

Name and Breeding	Purchaser	Guineas
NELSON'S ROCK (GB) B C MOUNT NELSON (GB) - REALLY RANSOM (GB)	GILL RICHARDSON BS	41904
B C EXCEED AND EXCEL (AUS) - PAPABILE (USA)	C MARNANE	40952
B G KHELEYF (USA) - MISS LACEY (IRE)	D WOODS	40952
B C EXCEED AND EXCEL (AUS) - WUNDERS DREAM (IRE)	B O'RYAN	40952
B C ACCLAMATION (GB) - DIVERT (IRE)	POWERSTOWN STUD	40000
B F SHAMARDAL (USA) - NILASSIBA (GB)	BLANDFORD BS	40000
B F KYLLACHY (GB) - XTRASENSORY (GB)	J WARREN	40000
B F KYLLACHY (GB) - NEVER AWAY (GB)	BBA (IRELAND)	40000
B C ROYAL APPLAUSE (GB) - HELEN SHARP (GB)	BBA (IRELAND)	40000
B C DANEHILL DANCER (IRE) - CHAMPAKA (IRE)	S AL NAEMI MUBARAK	40000
B F CAPE CROSS (IRE) - YARIA (IRE)	VENDOR	40000
CUISINE (IRE) B C HOLY ROMAN EMPEROR (IRE) - SAMORRA (IRE)	BADGER BS	40000
B C BAHAMIAN BOUNTY (GB) - DUST (GB)	D BARKER	40000
B C DARK ANGEL (IRE) - RIHANA (IRE)	S AL NAEMI MUBARAK	38095
B F ROYAL APPLAUSE (GB) - SILVER KESTREL (USA)	BLANDFORD BS	38095
B C REFUSE TO BEND (IRE) - ANNOUNCING PEACE (GB)	GILL RICHARDSON BS	38095
B C COMPTON PLACE (GB) - LAKE NAYASA (GB)	PETER & ROSS DOYLE BS	38095
B F DUTCH ART (GD) - ILE DESERTE (GB)	SACKVILLEDONALD	38095
CH F MONSIEUR BOND (IRE) - TIBESTI (GB)	A TURTON	38095
B C PASTORAL PURSUITS (GB) - MISS WELLS (IRE)	D SACKVILLE	38095
B C HAATEF (USA) - OPENNESS (GB)	C MCCORMACK	38095
B C CAPE CROSS (IRE) - THIELLA (USA)	BLANDFORD BS	38095
B F MONSIEUR BOND (IRE) - KANISFLUH (GB)	SOUTH YORKSHIRE RACING	37142
DARK DIAMOND (IRE) B C DARK ANGEL (IRE) - MOON DIAMOND (GB)	M CROSSMAN	36190
CH C BAHAMIAN BOUNTY (GB) - SNAKE'S HEAD (GB)	AGENT ALLISON	36190
B C ROYAL APPLAUSE (GB) - OUR FAYE (GB)	PETER & ROSS DOYLE BS	36190
B C ELUSIVE CITY (USA) - VANITYCASE (IRE)	J FRETWELL	36190
B/GR C DARK ANGEL (IRE) - DEAR CATCH (IRE)	O COLE	36190
GR F DARK ANGEL (IRE) - OWDBETTS (IRE)	B SMART	36190
ENGLISHMAN (GB) B C ROYAL APPLAUSE (GB) - TESARY (GB)	HILLWOOD BS	34285
ONE WORD MORE (IRE) B C THOUSAND WORDS (GB) - SOMOUSHE (IRE)	G HOWSON	34285
B C KODIAC (GB) - ALEXANDER ELIOTT (GB)	J FOLEY	34285
B C ANTONIUS PIUS (USA) - EMBERS OF FAME (IRE)	GILL RICHARDSON BS	34285
MIRAAJ (IRE) B C IFFRAAJ (GB) - MY-LORRAINE (IRE)	PETER & ROSS DOYLE BS	34285
CH C HAAFHD (GB) - ANNA OLEANDA (IRE)	COMPTON BEAUCHAMP	34285
B C PRESENTING (GB) - LA MARIANNE (IRE)	HIGHFLYER BS	34285
FILS ANGES (IRE) GR C DARK ANGEL (IRE) - LA PIAF (FR)	R L W FRISBY (P.S.)	33333
B C ROYAL APPLAUSE (GB) - ROCK LILY (GB)	J FRETWELL	33333
BR C COCKNEY REBEL (IRE) - VINO VERITAS (USA)	J FRETWELL	33333
B F SLEEPING INDIAN (GB) - VALE OF BELVOIR (IRE)	STEPHEN HILLEN BS	33333
B C CAPTAIN MARVELOUS (IRE) - BRATISLAVA (GB)	C MARNANE	32380
B C MOUNT NELSON (GB) - LADY GIN (USA)	BLANDFORD BS	32380
CH F BAHAMIAN BOUNTY (GB) - HALLAND PARK GIRL (GB)	BBA (IRELAND)	32380
HATS OFF (GB) B C ROYAL APPLAUSE (GB) - MIRIAM (GB)	J BEST	31428
CH F EXCEED AND EXCEL (AUS) - HMS PINAFORE (IRE)	P TWOMEY	31428
GR C DARK ANGEL (IRE) - XEMA (GB)	S HILLEN	31428
B C INVINCIBLE SPIRIT (IRE) - ALARME BELLE (GB)	C MARNANE	31428
GREAT PHILOSOPHER (IRE) CH C CHOISIR (AUS) - SANDBOX TWO (IRE)	S HILLEN	31428
FLETCHER CHRISTIAN (GB) B C BAHAMIAN BOUNTY (GB) - LADY DOMINATRIX (IRE)	C R MARKS	30476
THIS IS NICE (IRE) CH F EXCEED AND EXCEL (AUS) - SPANISH QUEST (GB)	D SACKVILLE	30476
B/BR F STREET BOSS (USA) - STRIKE HARD (IRE)	J FRETWELL	30476
B F REDBACK (GB) - NICE ONE CLARE (IRE)	PETER & ROSS DOYLE BS	30476
B C SHAMARDAL (USA) - LUNAR LUSTRE (IRE)	MEADOWVIEW STABLES	30476
TWO IN THE PINK (IRE) B F CLODOVIL (IRE) - SECRET CIRCLE (IRE)	A DUARTE	30476
B C DARK ANGEL (IRE) - FUN TIME (GB)	E BALDING	30476
CH C REDBACK (GB) - FEET OF FLAME (USA)	MCKEEVER BS	30476
B C GREEN DESERT (USA) - ROYAL GRACE (GB)	ROBIN O'RYAN BS	30476
CH C PASTORAL PURSUITS (GB) - PREFERENCE (GB)	PETER & ROSS DOYLE BS	29523
B C SAINT DES SAINTS (FR) - AULNE RIVER (IRE)	N GILCHRIST	29523
B C KODIAC (GB) - ATISHOO (IRE)	C MARNANE	29523
B C DUKE OF MARMALADE (IRE) - MYTHOLOGIE (FR)	ANTHONY STROUD BS	29523
B C PROCLAMATION (IRE) - ROCKBURST (GB)	PETER & ROSS DOYLE BS	29523
MANCHESTAR (GB) B C ELUSIVE CITY (USA) - GRANDE TERRE (IRE)	ROBIN O'RYAN BS	29523

HIGH-PRICED YEARLINGS OF 2011 AT TATTERSALLS IRELAND SALES

The following yearlings realised 16,000 euros and over at Tattersalls Ireland Sales in 2011:-

Name and Breeding	Purchaser	Euros
CH C DUKE OF MARMALADE (IRE) - LITERACY (USA)	MOCKLERSHILL	70000
BR C ROCK OF GIBRALTAR (IRE) - ALMAASEH (IRE)	J O'BYRNE	65000
B C HOLY ROMAN EMPEROR (IRE) - BALTING LASS (IRE)	PALATINATE TB	62000
B F KING'S THEATRE (IRE) - J'Y RESTE (FR)	GOLDFORD STUD	62000
B G KING'S THEATRE (IRE) - CINCUENTA (IRE)	HIGHFLYER BS	60000
B C ACCLAMATION (GB) - VINTAGE TIPPLE (IRE)	SACKVILLEDONALD	58000
B C DYLAN THOMAS (IRE) - SOFTLY TREAD (IRE)	PETER & ROSS DOYLE BS	52000
BR F HOLY ROMAN EMPEROR (IRE) - WEEKEND FLING (USA)	BBA (IRELAND)	50000
B C ELNADIM (USA) - DANCE CLEAR (IRE)	B O'RYAN	50000
B C PEINTRE CELEBRE (USA) - HOMEGROWN (IRE)	A DUARTE	50000
B C INVINCIBLE SPIRIT (IRE) - COACHELLA (GB)	VENDOR	48000
B F KAYF TARA (GB) - FAIRY BLAZE (IRE)	VENDOR	48000
B G PRESENTING (GB) - NAMLOC (IRE)	GATTERSTOWN STUD	47000
B C AUTHORIZED (IRE) - YAZMIN (IRE)	LYNN LODGE STUD	45000
BL G PRESENTING (GB) - CAILIN ALAINN (IRE)	VENDOR	45000
B C ACCLAMATION (GB) - HONKY TONK SALLY (GB)	A BALDING	42000
B G HIGH CHAPARRAL (IRE) - DAWN BID (IRE)	J GREEN	42000
B C DUTCH ART (GB) - ICE PALACE (GB)	C MARNANE	41000
B G KING'S THEATRE (IRE) - THE SHAN GANG (IRE)	J O'BYRNE	40000
B G SCORPION (IRE) - ERINS LOVE (IRE)	GATTERSTOWN STUD	38000
B G KAYF TARA (GB) - MAIDEN VOYAGE (GB)	J O'BYRNE	38000
CH C JOHANNESBURG (USA) - ROSE BOURBON (USA)	S HILLEN	37000
B G ROBIN DES CHAMPS (FR) - WHAT A MEWSMENT (IRE)	HIGHFLYER BS	37000
B C RAMONTI (FR) - ROYAL ESTEEM (GB)	C MARNANE	36000
LORD ASHLEY (IRE) CH C IFFRAAJ (GB) - MRS DALLOWAY (IRE)	SACKVILLEDONALD	36000
B C HAATEF (USA) - FOTINI (IRE)	C MARNANE	36000
B G MOTIVATOR (GB) - DARARIYNA (IRE)	HIGHFLYER BS	36000
B C SHIROCCO (GER) - KATARIYA (IRE)	M AL NAEMI	35000
B C THOUSAND WORDS (GB) - LUCY LIU (IRE)	C MARNANE	35000
B F RED CLUBS (IRE) - ALEXANDER WONDER (IRE)	D REDVERS	35000
B F INVINCIBLE SPIRIT (IRE) - LADY CIRCE (USA)	TALLY HO STUD	34000
B C AMADEUS WOLF (GB) - YASMIN SATINE (IRE)	BALLYHANE STUD	34000
B C KYLLACHY (GB) - FLY IN STYLE (GB)	PALATINATE TB	32000
B C CHOISIR (AUS) - LA TINTORETTA (IRE)	D WACHMAN	30000
GR F DARK ANGEL (IRE) - HAPPY TALK (IRE)	BRIAN GRASSICK BS	30000
BR C SAKHEE'S SECRET (GB) - DANCING NELLY (GB)	C MARNANE	30000
B F ANTONIUS PIUS (USA) - AWAIT (IRE)	M S SAUNDERS	30000
B G MILAN (GB) - GRANDY INVADER (IRE)	HIGHFLYER BS	30000
B G ROBIN DES CHAMPS (FR) - ANNS PRESENT (IRE)	HIGHFLYER BS	30000
B C KING'S THEATRE (IRE) - STARRY LADY (IRE)	J O'BYRNE	30000
B F DUKE OF MARMALADE (IRE) - OTELCALIFORNI (USA)	E FITZPATRICK	29000
BR C ROCK OF GIBRALTAR (IRE) - JALISCO (FR)	F STACK	29000
B C WITH APPROVAL (CAN) - QUIP (GB)	B O'RYAN	28000
B F STRATEGIC PRINCE (GB) - ELLANOVA (GB)	A SKIFFINGTON	28000
B F OASIS DREAM (GB) - KIRK (GB)	J CULLINAN	28000
B G PRESENTING (GB) - BALLYGILL HEIGHTS (IRE)	HIGHFLYER BS	27000
CH C KHELEYF (USA) - MAID OF AILSA (USA)	MEADOWVIEW STABLES	26000
B F CHEVALIER (IRE) - WESTCOTE (USA)	P & R DOYLE	26000
BR C FOOTSTEPSINTHESAND (GB) - EASY GOING (GB)	PALATINATE TB	26000
B F KODIAC (GB) - ANNUS IUCUNDUS (IRE)	P TWOMEY	26000
CH C ROCK OF GIBRALTAR (IRE) - TOORAH LAURA LA (USA)	M DODS	26000
B C BAHAMIAN BOUNTY (GB) - DOLLAR BIRD (IRE)	M FITZGIBBON	26000
SANTO DE LUNE (FR) GR C SAINT DES SAINTS (FR) - TIKIDOUN (FR)	WOODHILL STUD	26000
B C DARK ANGEL (IRE) - BAKEWELL TART (IRE)	VENDOR	25000
B F HIGH CHAPARRAL (IRE) - SILLY GAME (IRE)	P HICKEY	25000
CH F KHELEYF (USA) - KALIMANTA (IRE)	E LYNAM	25000
B C ORATORIO (IRE) - JAZZIE (FR)	EADLING FARM	25000
B C REDBACK (GB) - AMBER'S BLUFF (GB)	C COX	25000
CH F DUKE OF MARMALADE (IRE) - PERIHELION (IRE)	BBA (IRELAND)	25000
ANTARCTIC PRINCE (IRE) GR C VERGLAS (IRE) - QUEENIE (GB)	F BARRY	25000
B F KAYF TARA (GB) - NOVACELLA (FR)	J O'BYRNE	25000
B G FLEMENSFIRTH (USA) - KESTRAL HEIGHTS (IRE)	VENDOR	24000
B C ROCK OF GIBRALTAR (IRE) - SWEEPING STORY (USA)	M TREGONING	23000
B C REFUSE TO BEND (IRE) - DONA ROYALE (IRE)	A BALDING	23000
CH C PIVOTAL (GB) - DAZZLE (GB)	BBA (IRELAND)	22500
LADY MEDICI (GB) CH F MEDICEAN (GB) - JESTING (GB)	F BARRY	22000
B C HURRICANE RUN (IRE) - CLINGING VINE (USA)	B O'RYAN	22000

Name and Breeding	Purchaser	Euros
B G OSCAR (IRE) - LISSELTON LADY (IRE)	HIGHFLYER BS	22000
B F ACCLAMATION (GB) - MAHARANI (USA)	C MARNANE	22000
CH C HERNANDO (FR) - HEAT OF THE NIGHT (GB)	M AL NAEMI	22000
B C LAWMAN (FR) - CAERLINA (IRE)	M AL NAEMI	22000
B G KALANISI (IRE) - MARVELLOUS DREAM (FR)	VENDOR	22000
GR C MOTIVATOR (GB) - BARATHIKI (GB)	JANDA BS	21000
B F ELNADIM (USA) - DAUNTING LADY (IRE)	CHIMAX SRL	21000
RED CHARMER (IRE) B C RED CLUBS (IRE) - GOLDEN CHARM (IRE)	A DUFFIELD	21000
B C STRATEGIC PRINCE (GB) - JOLIE CLARA (FR)	BELIAR BS	21000
B C HAATEF (USA) - HAZARDOUS (GB)	T EASTERBY	21000
CH C CAPTAIN RIO (GB) - LUCKY COIN (GB)	TALLY HO STUD	21000
B F TAGULA (IRE) - GLAMOROUS LADY (IRE)	R O'RYAN	20000
B F HIGH CHAPARRAL (IRE) - DANSE CLASSIQUE (IRE)	F BARRY	20000
B C CAPTAIN MARVELOUS (IRE) - KELSO MAGIC (USA)	K MCGIVERN	20000
BR C MAJESTIC MISSILE (IRE) - BALANCE THE BOOKS (GB)	N TINKLER	20000
GR/RO C AUSSIE RULES (USA) - DHAKHIRAH (IRE)	B O'HAIRE	20000
CH C SAKHEE'S SECRET (GB) - MI AMOR (IRE)	C MARNANE	20000
B C MAJESTIC MISSILE (IRE) - GINGER NOT BLONDE (USA)	SACKVILLEDONALD	20000
B G KALANISI (IRE) - GLEN'S ENCORE (IRE)	GLEADHILL HOUSE	20000
B C RAIL LINK (GB) - WYOMING (GB)	J HARRINGTON	20000
B G KING'S THEATRE (IRE) - IRISH MYSTICS (IRE)	T COLEMAN	20000
B C KHELEYF (USA) - ENGRAVING (GB)	A BOTTI	20000
B C KHELEYF (USA) - SEA SEARCHER (USA)	B O'RYAN	20000
CH C PRESENTING (GB) - HUSHABY (IRE)	VENDOR	20000
BR G PRESENTING (GB) - MY NAME'S NOT BIN (IRE)	VENDOR	19000
B C KHELEYF (USA) - WINDBENEATHMYWINGS (IRE)	G LYONS	19000
B G KALANISI (IRE) - FULL IMPERATRICE (FR)	VENDOR	19000
B/BR C HOLY ROMAN EMPEROR (IRE) - BRAARI (USA)	A AGOSTINO	18500
BR G PRESENTING (GB) - PAUMAFI (IRE)	G HAINE	18500
B C WHIPPER (USA) - DANEMARQUE (AUS)	BBA (IRELAND)	18000
B C KODIAC (GB) - CATCH A SMILE (USA)	G LYONS	18000
B G KALANISI (IRE) - MUSICAL SHAN (IRE)	RATHBARRY STUD	18000
B C CAMACHO (GB) - LUCKY DANCER (FR)	SACKVILLEDONALD	17500
B F HOLY ROMAN EMPEROR (IRE) - LUNADINE (FR)	J C BS	17500
B C CAPTAIN MARVELOUS (IRE) - QUEENFISHER (GB)	C MARNANE	17500
BR C FOOTSTEPSINTHESAND (GB) - HURRICANE LILY (IRE)	SPRINGFORT STUD	17500
B C MOSS VALE (IRE) - INDIANA ANNIE (IRE)	CHIMAX SRL	17000
BR G PRESENTING (GB) - SPRING FLOWER (IRE)	R ROHAN	17000
B C KYLLACHY (GB) - AFRICAN QUEEN (IRE)	PALATINATE TB	17000
GR C VERGLAS (IRE) - MISS ST TROPEZ (GB)	D CARROLL	17000
B G FLEMENSFIRTH (USA) - KESTRAL HEIGHTS (IRE)	RATHMORE STUD	17000
CH C SLEEPING INDIAN (GB) - REMEDY (IRE)	E O'GORMAN	16500
GR C CAMACHO (GB) - DOCKLANDS GRACE (USA)	FINAL FURLONG BS	16500
B C ELUSIVE CITY (USA) - JAMRAH (USA)	SACKVILLEDONALD	16500
CH G ROBIN DES CHAMPS (FR) - GLEBE DREAM (IRE)	MOUNT EATON STUD	16500
CH C BACHELOR DUKE (USA) - KAYAK (GB)	BELIAR BS	16000
B F DARK ANGEL (IRE) - POLLY JONES (USA)	MAB AGENCY	16000
B F MARJU (IRE) - MAC MELODY (IRE)	N HAYES	16000
B C EXCELLENT ART (GB) - CHAMELEON (GB)	G LYONS	16000
B F AMADEUS WOLF (GB) - ROSY DUDLEY (IRE)	FINAL FURLONG BS	16000
B C ANTONIUS PIUS (USA) - LADY LUCIA (IRE)	N TINKLER	16000
B C HOLY ROMAN EMPEROR (IRE) - KESTREL QUEST (USA)	W HACKER	16000
STARLIGHT SYMPHONY (IRE) B F ORATORIO (IRE) - PHILLIPPA (IRE)	B O'RYAN	16000
B C COMPTON PLACE (GB) - FANCY ROSE (USA)	D CARROLL (P.S.)	16000
BR F ROCK OF GIBRALTAR (IRE) - DAPPLE DAWN (IRE)	G DEVLIN	16000
B F BAHAMIAN BOUNTY (GB) - COMPLICATION (GB)	PETER & ROSS DOYLE BS	16000
B C KHELEYF (USA) - NORTH EAST BAY (USA)	CHIMAX SRL	16000
B C ORATORIO (IRE) - PRAYERS FOR RAIN (USA)	TAHI STUD	16000
B C MUJADIL (USA) - UNDERTONE (IRE)	HARROWGATE BS	16000
B F ACCLAMATION (GB) - PITRIZZIA (IRE)	C MARNANE	16000
CH C FLEMENSFIRTH (USA) - CHANTOUE ROYALE (FR)	B O'BYRNE	16000

2000 GUINEAS STAKES (3y) Newmarket-1 mile

Year	Owner	Winner and Price	Jockey	Trainer	Second	Third	Ran	Time
1970	C Engelhard's	NIJINSKY (4/7)	L Piggott	V O'Brien	Yellow God.	Roi Soleil	14	1 41.54
1971	Mrs J Hislop's	BRIGADIER GERARD (11/2)	J Mercer	R Hern.	Mill Reef.	My Swallow	6	1 39.20
1972	Sir J Thorn's	HIGH TOP (85/40)	W Carson	B Van Cutsem	Roberto.	Sun Prince	12	1 40.82
1973	Mrs B Davis's	MON FILS (50/1)	F Durr.	R Hannon	Noble Decree.	Sharp Edge	18	1 42.97
1974	Mme M Berger's	NONOALCO (19/2)	Y Saint Martin	F Boutin	Giacometti.	Apalachee	12	1 39.53
1975	C d'Alessio's	BOLKONSKI (33/1)	G Dettori	H Cecil	Grundy.	Dominion	24	1 39.53
1976	C d'Alessio's	WOLLOW (evens)	G Dettori	H Cecil	Vitiges.	Thieving Demon.	17	1 38.09
1977	N Schibbye's	NEBBIOLO (20/1)	G Curran	K Prendergast.	Tachypous.	The Minstrel	18	1 38.54
1978	J Hayter's	ROLAND GARDENS (28/1)	F Durr.	D Sasse	Remainder Man.	Wath Nan.	19	1 47.33
1979	A Shead's	TAP ON WOOD (20/1)	S Cauthen	B Hills	Kris.	Young Generation	20	1 43.60
1980	K Abdulla's	KNOWN FACT (14/1)	W Carson	J Tree	Posse.	Night Alert	14	1 40.46
	(Nureyev finished first but was disqualified)							
1981	Mrs A Muinos's	TO-AGORI-MOU (5/2)	G Starkey	G Harwood	Mattaboy.	Bel Bolide	19	1 41.43
1982	G Oldham's	ZINO (8/1)	F Head	F Boutin	Wind and Wuthering.	Tender King	26	1 37.13
1983	R Sangster's	LOMOND (9/1)	Pat Eddery	V O'Brien	Tolomeo.	Muscatite	16	1 43.87
1984	R Sangster's	EL GRAN SENOR (15/8)	Pat Eddery	V O'Brien	Chief Singer.	Lear Fan.	9	1 37.41
1985	K Abdulla's	SHADEED (4/5)	L Piggott	M Stoute.	Bairn.	Supreme Leader.	14	1 37.41
1986	K Abdulla's	DANCING BRAVE (15/8)	G Starkey	G Harwood	Green Desert.	Huntingdale.	15	1 40.00
1987	J Horgan's	DON'T FORGET ME (9/1)	W Carson	R Hannon	Bellotto.	Midyan.	24	1 36.74
1988	H H Aga Khan's	DOYOUN (4/5)	W R Swinburn	M Stoute.	Charmer.	Bellefella.	9	1 41.73
1989	Hamdan Al-Maktoum's	NASHWAN (3/1)	W Carson	R Hern.	Exbourne.	Danehill.	14	1 36.44
1990	John Horgan's	TIROL (9/1)	M Kinane	C Brittain	Machiavellian.	Anshan.	14	1 35.84
1991	Lady Beaverbrook's	MYSTIKO (13/2)	M Roberts	C Chapple-Hyam.	Lycius.	Ganges.	14	1 37.83
1992	R Sangster's	RODRIGO DE TRIANO (6/1)	L Piggott	C Chapple-Hyam.	Lucky Lindy.	Pursuit of Love.	16	1 38.37
1993	K Abdulla's	ZAFONIC (5/6)	Pat Eddery	A Fabre.	Barathea.	Bin Ajwaad.	14	1 35.32
1994	G R Bailey Ltd's	MISTER BAILEYS (16/1)	J Weaver	M Johnston	Grand Lodge.	Colonel Collins	23	1 35.08
1995	Sheikh Mohammed's	PENNEKAMP (9/2)	T Jarnet	A Fabre.	Celtic Swing.	Bahri.	11	1 35.16
1996	Godolphin's	MARK OF ESTEEM (8/1)	L Dettori	Sir M Suroor	Even Top.	Bijou D'Inde	13	1 37.59
1997	M Tabor & Mrs J Magnier's	ENTREPRENEUR (11/2)	M Kinane	M Stoute.	Revoque.	Poleen	16	1 35.64
1998	M Tabor & Mrs J Magnier's	KING OF KINGS (7/2)	M Kinane	A O'Brien	Lend A Hand.	Border Arrow	18	1 39.25
1999	Godolphin's	ISLAND SANDS (10/1)	L Dettori	S Bin Suroor	Enrique.		16	1 37.14
	(Run on July Course)							
2000	Saeed Suhail's	KING'S BEST (13/2)	K Fallon	Sir M Stoute.	Giant's Causeway.	Barathea Guest.	27	1 37.77
2001	Lord Weinstock's	GOLAN (11/1)	K Fallon	Sir M Stoute.	Tamburaine.	Frenchmans Bay.	18	1 37.48
2002	Sir A Ferguson & Mrs J Magnier's	ROCK OF GIBRALTAR (9/1)	J Murtagh	A O'Brien	Hawk Wing.	Redback.	22	1 36.50
2003	Moyglare Stud Farm's	REFUSE TO BEND (9/2)	P J Smullen	D Weld	Zafeen.	Norse Dancer.	20	1 37.98
2004	Hamdan Al Maktoum's	HAAFHD (11/2)	R Hills	B Hills	Snow Ridge.	Azamour.	14	1 36.60
2005	Mr M Tabor & Mrs John Magnier's	FOOTSTEPSINTHESAND (13/2)	K Fallon	A O'Brien	Rebel Rebel.	Kandidate	19	1 36.10
2006	Mrs M Tabor, Mr M Tabor & Mr D Smith's	GEORGE WASHINGTON (6/4)	K Fallon	A O'Brien	Sir Percy.	Olympian Odyssey.	14	1 36.80
2007	P Cunningham's	COCKNEY REBEL (25/1)	O Peslier.	G Huffer	Vital Equine.	Dutch Art.	24	1 35.28
2008	Mrs J Magnier's	HENRYTHENAVIGATOR (11/1)	J Murtagh	A P O'Brien.	New Approach.	Stubbs Art.	15	1 39.14
2009	C Tsui's	SEA THE STARS (8/1)	M Kinane	J Oxx.	Delegator.	Gan Amhas.	15	1 35.88
2010	M Offenstadt's	MAKFI (33/1)	C Lemaire	M Delzangles	Dick Turpin.	Canford Cliffs.	19	1 36.35
2011	K Abdulla's	FRANKEL (1/2)	T Queally	H Cecil	Dubawi Gold.	Native Khan.	13	1 37.30

1000 GUINEAS STAKES (3y fillies) Newmarket-1 mile

Year	Owner	Winner and Price	Jockey	Trainer	Second	Third	Ran	Time
1970	Jean, Lady Ashcombe's	HUMBLE DUTY (3/1)	L Piggott	P Walwyn	Gleam	Black Satin	12	1 42.13
1971	F Hue-Williams's	ALTESSE ROYALE (25/1)	Y Saint Martin	J W Watts	Super Honey	Catherine Wheel	10	1 40.90
1972	Mrs R Stanley's	WATERLOO (8/1)	E Hide	N Murless	Marisela	Rose Dubarry	18	1 39.49
1973	G Pope's	MYSTERIOUS (11/1)	G Lewis	N Murless	Jacinth	Shellshock	14	1 40.32
1974	The Queen's	HIGHCLERE (12/1)	J Mercer	R Hern	Polygamy	Mrs Twiggywinkle	15	1 42.40
1975	Mrs D O' Kelly's	NOCTURNAL SPREE (14/1)	J Roe	S Murless	Girl Friend	Joking Apart	14	1 41.65
1976	D Wildenstein's	FLYING WATER (2/1)	Y Saint Martin	A Penna	Konafa	Kesar Queen	25	1 37.83
1977	Mrs E Kettlewell's	MRS MCARDY (16/1)	E Hide	M W Easterby	Freeze the Secret	Sanedtki	18	1 40.87
1978	R Bonnycastle's	ENSTONE SPARK (35/1)	E Johnson	B Hills	Fair Salinia	Seraphima	16	1 41.56
1979	Helena Springfield Ltd's	ONE IN A MILLION (evens)	J Mercer	H Cecil	Abbeydale	Yanuka	18	1 43.06
1980	O Phipps's	QUICK AS LIGHTNING (12/1)	B Rouse	J Dunlop	Our Home	Mrs Penny	23	1 41.89
1981	H Joel's	FAIRY FOOTSTEPS (6/4)	L Piggott	H Cecil	Tolmi	Go Leasing	14	1 40.43
1982	Sir P Oppenheimer's	ON THE HOUSE (33/1)	J Reid	H Wragg	Time Charter	Dione	15	1 40.45
1983	Maktoum Al-Maktoum's	MA BICHE (5/2)	F Head	C Brittain	Favoridge	Habibti	18	1 41.71
1984	M Lemos's	PEBBLES (8/1)	P Robinson	C Brittain	Meis El-Reem	Desirable	15	1 38.18
1985	Sheikh Mohammed's	OH SO SHARP (2/1)	S Cauthen	H Cecil	Al Bahathri	Bella Colora	17	1 36.85
1986	H Ranier's	MIDWAY LADY (10/1)	R Cochrane	B Hanbury	Maysoon	Sonic Lady	17	1 41.54
1987	S Aland's	MIESQUE (15/8)	F Head	F Boutin	Milligram	Interval	12	1 38.48
1988	Sheikh Mohammed's	RAVINELLA (4/5)	G W Moore	Mme C Head	Dabaweyaa	Diminuendo	10	1 40.88
1989	Hamdan Al-Maktoum's	MUSICAL BLISS (7/2)	W R Swinburn	M Stoute	Kerrera	Aldbourne	14	1 42.69
1990	Hamdan Al-Maktoum's	SALSABIL (6/4)	W Carson	J Dunlop	Heart of Joy	Negligent	14	1 42.06
1991	Hamdan Al-Maktoum's	SHADAYID (4/6)	W Carson	J Dunlop	Kooyonga	Crystal Gazing	15	1 38.06
1992	Mohamed Obaid's	HATOOF (10/1)	W R Swinburn	Mme C Head	Marling	Kenbu	15	1 38.18
1993	R Sangster's	SAYYEDATI (4/1)	W R Swinburn	C Brittain	Niche	Aljan	12	1 39.45
1994	Hamdan Al-Maktoum's	LAS MENINAS (12/1)	J Reid	Mme C Head	Balanchine	Coup de Genie	13	1 37.34
1995	Hamdan Al-Maktoum's	HARAYIR (5/1)	R Hills	M Stoute	Aqaarid	Moonshell	16	1 36.71
1996	Wafic Said's	BOSRA SHAM (10/11)	Pat Eddery	H Cecil	Matiya	Bint Shadayid	16	1 36.72
1997	Greenbay Stables Ltd's	SLEEPYTIME (5/1)	K Fallon	H Cecil	Oh Nellie	Dazzle	13	1 37.75
1998	Godolphin's	CAPE VERDI (5/1)	L Dettori	S Bin Suroor	Shahtoush	Exclusive	16	1 37.66
1999	K Abdulla's	WINCE (100/30)	K Fallon	H Cecil	Wannabe Grand	Valentine Waltz	22	1 37.91
	(Run on July Course)							
2000	Hamdan Al-Maktoum's	LAHAN (14/1)	R Hills	J Gosden	Princess Ellen	Petrushka	18	1 36.38
2001	Sheikh Ahmed Al Maktoum's	AMEERAT (11/1)	P Robinson	J Jarvis	Muwakleh	Toroca	18	1 36.36
2002	Godolphin's	KAZZIA (14/1)	L Dettori	S Bin Suroor	Snowfire	Alasha	19	1 37.85
2003	Cheveley Park Stud's	RUSSIAN RHYTHM (12/1)	K Fallon	Sir M Stoute	Six Perfections	Intercontinental	16	1 38.43
2004	Duke of Roxburghe's	ATTRACTION (11/2)	K Darley	M Johnston	Sundrop	Hathrah	20	1 36.70
2005	Mrs John Magnier & M M Tabor's	VIRGINIA WATERS (12/1)	K Fallon	A O'Brien	Maids Causeway	Vista Bella	13	1 36.50
2006	Mr Sly, Dr Davies & Mrs P Sly's	SPECIOSA (10/1)	M Fenton	Mrs P Sly	Confidential Lady	Nasheej	21	1 40.50
2007	M Ryan's	FINSCEAL BEO (5/4)	K Manning	J Bolger	Arch Swing	Simply Perfect	15	1 34.94
2008	S Friborg's	NATAGORA (11/4)	C Lemaire	P Bary	Spacious	Saoirse Abu	14	1 38.99
2009	Hamdan Al-Maktoum's	GHANAATI (20/1)	R Hills	B Hills	Cuis Ghaire	Super Sleuth	17	1 34.22
2010	K Abdulla's	SPECIAL DUTY (9/2)	S Pasquier	Mme C Head-Maarek	Jacqueline Quest	Gile Na Greine	17	1 39.66
	(The first two placings were reversed by the Stewards)							
2011	Godolphin's	BLUE BUNTING (16/1)	L Dettori	M Al Zarooni	Together	Maqaasid	18	1 39.27

OAKS STAKES (3y fillies) Epsom-1 mile 4 furlongs 10 yards

Year	Owner	Winner and Price	Jockey	Trainer	Second	Third	Ran	Time
1975	J Morrison's	JULIETTE MARNY (12/1)	J Piggott	A Penna	Val's Dream	Moonlight Night	14	2 39.10
1976	D Wildenstein's	PAWNEESE (6/5)	Y Saint Martin	A Penna	Roses for the Star	African Dancer	12	2 35.25
1977	The Queen's	DUNFERMLINE (6/1)	W Carson	D Weld	Freeze the Secret	Vaguely Deb	13	2 36.53
1978	S Hanson's	FAIR SALINIA (8/1)	G Starkey	M Stoute	Dancing Maid	Suni	15	2 36.82
1979	J Morrison's	SCINTILLATE (20/1)	Pat Eddery	J Tree	Bonnie Isle	Britannia's Rule	14	2 34.33
1980	R Hollingsworth's	BIREME (9/2)	W Carson	R Hern	Vielle	The Dancer	11	2 34.33
1981	Mrs B Firestone's	BLUE WIND (3/1)	L Piggott	D Weld	Madam Gay	Leap Lively	14	2 40.93
1982	R Barnett's	TIME CHARTER (12/1)	W Newnes	H Candy	Slightly Dangerous	Last Feather	13	2 34.21
1983	Sir M Sobell's	SUN PRINCESS (6/1)	W Carson	R Hern	Acclimatise	New Coins	13	2 40.98
1984	Sir R McAlpine's	CIRCUS PLUME (4/1)	L Piggott	J Dunlop	Poquito Queen		15	2 38.97
1985	Sheikh Mohammed's	OH SO SHARP (6/4)	S Cauthen	H Cecil	Triptych	Dubian	15	2 41.37
1986	H Ranier's	MIDWAY LADY (15/8)	R Cochrane	B Hanbury	Untold	Maysoon	15	2 35.60
1987	Sheikh Mohammed's	UNITE (11/1)	W R Swinburn	M Stoute	Bourbon Girl	Three Tails	11	2 38.17
1988	Sheikh Mohammed's	DIMINUENDO (7/4)	S Cauthen	H Cecil	Sudden Love	Animatrice	11	2 35.02
1989	Saeed Maktoum Al Maktoum's	SNOW BRIDE (13/2)	S Cauthen	H Cecil	Roseate Tern	Mamaluna	9	2 34.22

(Alysa finished first but was disqualified)

Year	Owner	Winner and Price	Jockey	Trainer	Second	Third	Ran	Time
1990	Hamdan Al-Maktoum's	SALSABIL (2/1)	W Carson	J Dunlop	Game Plan	Knight's Baroness	8	2 38.70
1991	Maktoum Al-Maktoum's	JET SKI LADY (50/1)	C Roche	J Bolger	Shamshir	Shadayid	11	2 37.30
1992	W J Gredley's	USER FRIENDLY (5/1)	G Duffield	C Brittain	All At Sea	Pearl Angel	14	2 39.77
1993	Sheikh Mohammed's	INTREPIDITY (5/1)	M Roberts	A Fabre	Royal Ballerina	Oakmead	14	2 34.19
1994	Godolphin's	BALANCHINE (6/1)	L Dettori	H Ibrahim	Wind In Her Hair	Hawajiss	10	2 40.37
1995	Maktoum Al Maktoum/ Godolphin's	MOONSHELL (3/1)	L Dettori	S Bin Suroor	Dance A Dream	Pure Grain	10	2 35.44

Year	Owner	Winner and Price	Jockey	Trainer	Second	Third	Ran	Time
1996	Wafic Said's	LADY CARLA (100/30)	Pat Eddery	H Cecil	Pricket	Mezzogiorno	11	2 35.55
1997	K Abdulla's	REAMS OF VERSE (5/6)	K Fallon	H Cecil	Gazelle Royale	Crown of Light	12	2 35.59
1998	Mrs D Nagle & Mrs J Magnier's	SHAHTOUSH (12/1)	M Kinane	A O'Brien	Bahr	Midnight Line	8	2 38.23
1999	F Salman's	RAMRUMA (3/1)	K Fallon	H Cecil	Noushkey	Zahrat Dubai	10	2 38.72
2000	Lordship Stud's	LOVE DIVINE (9/4)	T Quinn	H Cecil	Kalypso Katie	Melikah	10	2 43.11
2001	Mrs D Nagle & Mrs J Magnier's	IMAGINE (9/4)	M Kinane	A O'Brien	Flight of Fancy	Relish The Thought	14	2 36.70
2002	Godolphin's	KAZZIA (100/30)	L Dettori	S Bin Suroor	Quarter Moon	Shadow Dancing	14	2 44.52
2003	W S Farish III's	CASUAL LOOK (10/1)	M Dwyer	A Balding	Yesterday	Summitville	15	2 38.07
2004	Lord Derby's	OUIJA BOARD (7/2)	K Fallon	E Dunlop	All Too Beautiful	Punctilious	12	2 35.40
2005	Hamdan Al Maktoum's	ESWARAH (11/4)	K Fallon	M Jarvis	Something Exciting	Pictava	12	2 39.00
2006	Mrs J Magnier, Mr M Tabor & Mr D Smith's	ALEXANDROVA (9/4)	K Fallon	A O'Brien	Rising Cross	Short Skirt	10	2 37.42

Year	Owner	Winner and Price	Jockey	Trainer	Second	Third	Ran	Time
2007	Niarchos Family's	LIGHT SHIFT (13/2)	T Durcan	H Cecil	Peeping Fawn	All My Loving	14	2 40.38
2008	J H Richmond-Watson's	LOOK HERE (33/1)	J Sanders	M Bell	Moonstone	Katiya	16	2 36.99
2009	Lady Bamford's	SARISKA (9/4)	J Spencer	M Bell	Midday	High Heeled	10	2 35.28
2010	Aramone Ltd's	SNOW FAIRY (9/1)	R Moore	E Dunlop	Remember When	Rumoush	15	2 35.77

(Meezrah finished second but was disqualified)

Year	Owner	Winner and Price	Jockey	Trainer	Second	Third	Ran	Time
2011	M J & L A Taylor's	DANCING RAIN (20/1)	J Murtagh	W Haggas	Wonder of Wonders	Izzi Top	13	2 41.73

DERBY STAKES (3y) Epsom–1 mile 4 furlongs 10 yards

Year	Owner	Winner and Price	Jockey	Trainer	Second	Third	Ran	Time
1969	A Budgett's	BLAKENEY (15/2)	E Johnson	A Budgett	Shoemaker	Prince Regent	26	2 40.30
1970	C Engelhard's	NIJINSKY (11/8)	L Piggott	V O'Brien	Gyr	Stintino	11	2 34.68
1971	P Mellon's	MILL REEF (100/30)	G Lewis	I Balding	Linden Tree	Irish Ball	21	2 37.14
1972	J Galbreath's	ROBERTO (3/1)	L Piggott	V O'Brien	Rheingold	Pentland Firth	22	2 36.09
1973	A Budgett's	MORSTON (25/1)	E Hide	A Budgett	Cavo Doro	Freefoot	25	2 35.92
1974	Mrs N Phillips's	SNOW KNIGHT (50/1)	B Taylor	P Nelson	Imperial Prince	Giacometti	18	2 35.04
1975	Dr C Vittadini's	GRUNDY (5/1)	Pat Eddery	P Walwyn	Nobiliary	Hunza Dancer	18	2 35.35
1976	N B Hunt's	EMPERY (10/1)	L Piggott	M Zilber	Relkino	Oats	23	2 35.69
1977	R Sangster's	THE MINSTREL (5/1)	L Piggott	V O'Brien	Hot Grove	Blushing Groom	22	2 36.44
1978	Lord Halifax's	SHIRLEY HEIGHTS (8/1)	G Starkey	J Dunlop	Hawaiian Sound	Remainder Man.	25	2 35.30
1979	Sir M Sobell's	TROY (6/1)	W Carson	W Hern	Dickens Hill	Northern Man.	23	2 36.59
1980	Mrs A Plesch's	HENBIT (7/1)	W Carson	W Hern	Master Willie	Rankin	24	2 34.77
1981	H H Aga Khan's	SHERGAR (10/11)	W Swinburn	M Stoute	Glint of Gold	Scintillating Air	18	2 34.40
1982	R Sangster's	GOLDEN FLEECE (3/1)	Pat Eddery	V O'Brien	Touching Wood	Silver Hawk	18	2 34.27
1983	E Moller's	TEENOSO (9/2)	L Piggott	G Wragg	Carlingford Castle	Shearwalk.	21	2 49.07
1984	L Miglitti's	SECRETO (14/1)	C Roche	D O'Brien	El Gran Senor	Mighty Flutter	17	2 39.12
1985	Lord H. de Walden's	SLIP ANCHOR (9/4)	S Cauthen	H Cecil	Law Society	Damister.	14	2 36.23
1986	H H Aga Khan's	SHAHRASTANI (11/2)	W Swinburn	M Stoute	Dancing Brave	Mashkour	17	2 37.13
1987	L Freedman's	REFERENCE POINT (6/4)	S Cauthen	H Cecil	Most Welcome	Bellotto	19	2 33.90
1988	H H Aga Khan's	KAHYASI (11/1)	R Cochrane	L Cumani	Glacial Storm	Doyoun.	14	2 33.84
1989	Hamdan Al-Maktoum's	NASHWAN (5/4)	W Carson	W Hern	Terimon.	Cacoethes	12	2 34.90
1990	K Abdulla's	QUEST FOR FAME (7/1)	Pat Eddery	R Charlton	Blue Stag	Elmaamul.	18	2 37.26
1991	F Salman's	GENEROUS (9/1)	A Munro	P Cole	Marju	Star of Gdansk.	13	2 34.00
1992	Sidney H Craig's	DR DEVIOUS (8/1)	J Reid	P Chapple-Hyam	St Jovite	Silver Wisp.	18	2 36.19
1993	K Abdulla's	COMMANDER IN CHIEF (15/2)	M Kinane	H Cecil	Blue Judge	Blues Traveller.	16	2 34.51
1994	Hamdan Al-Maktoum's	ERHAAB (7/2)	W Carson	J Dunlop	King's Theatre	Colonel Collins.	25	2 34.16
1995	Saeed Maktoum Al Maktoum's	LAMMTARRA (14/1)	W Swinburn	S Bin Suroor	Tamure.	Presenting.	15	2 32.31
1996	K Dasmal's	SHAAMIT (12/1)	M Hills	W Haggas	Dushyantor	Shantou.	20	2 35.05
1997	L Knight's	BENNY THE DIP (11/1)	W Ryan	J Gosden	Silver Patriarch.	Romanov.	13	2 35.77
1998	Sheikh Mohammed Obaid Al Maktoum's	HIGH-RISE (20/1)	O Pesilier	L Cumani	City Honours	Border Arrow	15	2 33.88
1999	Thoroughbred Corporation's	OATH (13/2)	K Fallon	H Cecil	Dalapour	Eeet All.	16	2 37.43
2000	H H Aga Khan's	SINNDAR (7/1)	J Murtagh	J Oxx	Sakhee.	Beat Hollow.	15	2 36.75
2001	M Tabor & Mrs J Magnier's	GALILEO (11/4)	M Kinane	A O'Brien	Golan.	Tobougg.	12	2 33.27
2002	M Tabor & Mrs J Magnier's	HIGH CHAPARRAL (7/2)	J Murtagh	A O'Brien	Hawk Wing	Moon Ballad.	12	2 39.45
2003	Saeed Suhail's	KRIS KIN (6/1)	K Fallon	Sir M Stoute	The Great Gatsby.	Alamshar.	20	2 33.35
2004	Ballymacoll Stud's	NORTH LIGHT (7/2)	K Fallon	Sir M Stoute	Rule Of Law	Let The Lion Roar.	14	2 33.70
2005	The Royal Ascot Racing Club's	MOTIVATOR (3/1)	J Murtagh	M Bell	Walk In The Park.	Dubawi.	13	2 35.60
2006	A E Pakenham's	SIR PERCY (6/1)	M Dwyer	M Tregoning	Dragon Dancer	Dylan Thomas.	18	2 35.20
2007	Salah Al Homaizi & Imad Al Sagar's	AUTHORIZED (5/4)	L Dettori	P Chapple-Hyam	Eagle Mountain.	Aqaleem.	17	2 34.77
2008	HRH Princess Haya of Jordan's	NEW APPROACH (5/1)	K Manning	J Bolger	Tartan Bearer	Casual Conquest.	16	2 36.50
2009	C Tsui's	SEA THE STARS (11/4)	M Kinane	J Oxx	Fame And Glory	Masterofthehorse.	12	2 36.74
2010	K Abdulla's	WORKFORCE (6/1)	R Moore	Sir M Stoute	At First Sight.	Rewilding.	12	2 31.33
2011	Mrs John Magnier, M Tabor &	POUR MOI (4/1)	M Barzalona	A Fabre	Treasure Beach.	Carlton House.	13	2 34.54

ST LEGER STAKES (3y) Doncaster-1 mile 6 furlongs 132 yards

Year	Owner	Winner and Price	Jockey	Trainer	Second	Third	Ran	Time
1969	G Oldham's	INTERMEZZO (7/1)	R Hutchinson	H Wragg	Ribofilio	Prince Consort	11	3 11.80
1970	C Engelhard's	NIJINSKY (2/7)	L Piggott	V O'Brien	Meadowville	Politico	9	6.40
1971	Mrs J Rogerson's	ATHENS WOOD (5/2)	L Piggott	H T Jones	Homeric	Falkland	8	3 14.90
1972	O Phipps's	BOUCHER (3/1)	L Piggott	V O'Brien	Our Mirage	Ginevra	8	28.71
1973	W Behrens's	PELEID (28/1)	F Durr	W Elsey	Buoy	Duke of Ragusa	13	3 8.21
1974	Lady Beaverbrook's	BUSTINO (11/10)	J Mercer	R Hern	Giacometti	Riboson	10	9.02
1975	C St George's	BRUNI (11/10)	A Murray	R Price	King Pellinore	Libra's Rib	12	3 9.02
1976	D Wildenstein's	CROW (6/1)	Y Saint-Martin	R Penna	Secret Man	Scallywag	15	13.17
1977	The Queen's	DUNFERMLINE (10/1)	W Carson	R Hern	Alleged	Classic Example	13	5.17
1978	M Lemos's	JULIO MARINER (28/1)	E Hide	C Brittain	Le Moss	M-Lolshan	14	4.94
1979	A Rolland's	SON OF LOVE (20/1)	A Lequeux	R Collet	Soleil Noir	Niniski	17	9.02
1980	H Joel's	LIGHT CAVALRY (3/1)	J Mercer	H Cecil	Water Mill	World Leader	7	11.48
1981	Sir J Astor's	CUT ABOVE (28/1)	J Mercer	R Hern	Glint of Gold	Bustomi	7	3 11.60
1982	Maktoum Al Maktoum's	TOUCHING WOOD (7/1)	P Cook	H T Jones	Zilos	Diamond Shoal	15	3.53
1983	Sir M Sobell's	SUN PRINCESS (11/8)	W Carson	H Cecil	Esprit du Nord	Carlingford Castle	10	16.65
1984	I Allan's	COMMANCHE RUN (7/4)	L Cumani	L Cumani	Baynoun	Alphabatim	11	9.93
1985	Sheikh Mohammed's	OH SO SHARP (8/1)	S Cauthen	H Cecil	Phardante	Lanfranco	8	3 7.13
1986	Duchess of Norfolk's	MOON MADNESS (9/2)	Pat Eddery	J Dunlop	Celestial Storm	Untold	8	5.03
1987	L Freedman's	REFERENCE POINT (4/11)	S Cauthen	H Cecil	Mountain Kingdom	Dry Dock	7	5.91
1988	Lady Beaverbrook's	MINSTER SON (15/2)	W Carson	N A Graham	Diminuendo	Sheriff's Star	6	6.80
1989	C St George's	MICHELOZZO (6/4)	S Cauthen	H Cecil	Sapience	Roseate Tern	6	3 20.72
	(Run at Ayr)							
1990	M Arbib's	SNURGE (7/2)	T Quinn	P Cole	Hellenic	River God	8	3 8.78
1991	K Abdulla's	TOULON (5/2)	Pat Eddery	A Fabre	Saddlers' Hall	Micheletti	10	3.12
1992	W J Gredley's	USER FRIENDLY (7/4)	G Duffield	C Brittain	Sonus	Bonny Scot	9	5.48
1993	Mrs G A E Smith's	BOB'S RETURN (3/1)	P Robinson	M Tompkins	Armiger	Edbaysaan	8	7.85
1994	Sheikh Mohammed's	MOONAX (40/1)	Pat Eddery	B Hills	Broadway Flyer	Double Trigger	9	4.19
1995	Godolphin's	CLASSIC CLICHE (100/30)	L Dettori	S bin Suroor	Minds Music	Istidaad	11	9.74
1996	Sheikh Mohammed's	SHANTOU (8/1)	L Dettori	J Gosden	Dushyantor	Samraan	10	5.10
1997	P Winfield's	SILVER PATRIARCH (5/4)	Pat Eddery	J Dunlop	Vertical Speed	The Fly	10	6.92
1998	Godolphin's	NEDAWI (5/2)	J Reid	S bin Suroor	High and Low	Sunshine Street	9	5.61
1999	Godolphin's	MUTAFAWEQ (11/2)	R Hills	S bin Suroor	Ramruma	Adair	9	2.75
2000	N Jones'	MILLENARY (11/4)	T Quinn	J Dunlop	Air Marshall	Chimes At Midnight	11	2.58
2001	M Tabor & Mrs J Magnier's	MILAN (13/8)	M Kinane	A O'Brien	Demophilos	Mr Combustible	10	5.16
2002	Sir Neil Westbrook's	BOLLIN ERIC (7/1)	K Darley	T Easterby	Highest	Bandari	8	2.92
2003	Mrs J Magnier's	BRIAN BORU (5/4)	J P Spencer	A O'Brien	High Accolade	Phoenix Reach	12	4.64
2004	Godolphin's	RULE OF LAW (3/1)	K McEvoy	S bin Suroor	Quiff	Tycoon	8	6.20
2005	Mrs J Magnier & M Tabor's	SCORPION (10/11)	L Dettori	A O'Brien	The Geezer	Tawqeet	6	19.00
2006	Mrs S Roy's	SIXTIES ICON (11/8)	L Dettori	J Noseda	The Last Drop	Red Rocks	11	57.20
	(Run at York)							
2007	G Strawbridge's	LUCARNO (7/2)	J Fortune	J Gosden	Mahler	Honolulu	11	3 1.90
2008	Ballymacoll Stud's	CONDUIT (8/1)	L Dettori	Sir M Stoute	Unsung Heroine	Look Here	14	7.92
2009	Godolphin's	MASTERY (14/1)	T Durcan	S bin Suroor	Kite Wood	Monitor Closely	8	4.81
2010	Ms R Hood & R Geffen's	ARCTIC COSMOS (12/1)	W Buick	J Gosden	Midas Touch	Corsica	10	3.12
2011	B Nielsen's	MASKED MARVEL (15/2)	W Buick	J Gosden	Brown Panther	Sea Moon	9	0.44

KING GEORGE VI AND QUEEN ELIZABETH STAKES Ascot-1 mile 4 furlongs

Year	Owner	Winner and Price	Jockey	Trainer	Second	Third	Ran	Time
1971	P Mellon's	MILL REEF 3-8-7 (8/13)	G Lewis	I Balding	Ortis	Acclimatization	10	2 32.56
1972	Mrs J Hislop's	BRIGADIER GERARD 4-9-7 (8/13)	J Mercer	R Hern	Parnell	Riverman	9	2 32.91
1973	N B Hunt's	DAHLIA 3-8-4 (10/1)	W Pyers	M Zilber	Rheingold	Our Mirage	12	2 30.43
1974	N B Hunt's	DAHLIA 4-9-4 (15/8)	L Piggott	M Zilber	Highclere	Dankaro	10	3 03.03
1975	Dr C Vittadini's	GRUNDY 3-8-7 (4/5)	P Eddery	P Walwyn	Bustino	Dahlia	11	2 26.98
1976	D Wildenstein's	PAWNEESE 3-8-5 (9/4)	Y Saint Martin	A Penna	Bruni	Orange Bay	10	2 36.36
1977	R Sangster's	THE MINSTREL 3-8-8 (7/4)	L Piggott	V O'Brien	Orange Bay	Exceller	11	2 30.48
1978	D McCall's	ILE DE BOURBON 3-8-8 (12/1)	J Reid	R F Houghton	Hawaiian Sound	Montcontour	14	2 30.53
1979	Sir M Sobell's	TROY 3-8-8 (2/5)	W Carson	R Hern	Gay Mecene	Ela-Mana-Mou	7	2 33.75
1980	S Weinstock's	ELA-MANA-MOU 4-9-7 (11/4)	W Carson	R Hern	Mrs Penny	Gregorian	7	2 35.39
1981	H H Aga Khan's	SHERGAR 3-8-8 (2/5)	W Swinburn	M Stoute	Madam Gay	Fingals Cave	7	2 35.40
1982	A Ward's	KALAGLOW 4-9-7 (13-2)	G Starkey	G Harwood	Assert	Glint of Gold	9	2 31.58
1983	E Barnett's	TIME CHARTER 4-9-4 (5/1)	J Mercer	H Candy	Diamond Shoal	Sun Princess	9	2 30.78
1984	E Moller's	TEENOSO 4-9-7 (13/2)	L Piggott	G Wragg	Sadler's Wells	Tolomeo	13	2 27.95
1985	Lady Beaverbrook's	PETOSKI 3-8-8 (12/1)	W Carson	W Hern	Oh So Sharp	Rainbow Quest	12	2 27.61
1986	K Abdulla's	DANCING BRAVE 3-8-8 (6/4)	Pat Eddery	G Harwood	Shardari	Triptych	9	2 29.49
1987	L Freedman's	REFERENCE POINT 3-8-8 (11/10)	S Cauthen	H Cecil	Celestial Storm	Triptych	9	2 34.63
1988	Hamdan Al-Maktoum's	MTOTO 5-9-7 (4/1)	M Roberts	A C Stewart	Unitwain	Tony Bin	10	2 37.33
1989	Sheikh Ahmed Al Maktoum	NASHWAN 3-8-8 (2/9)	W Carson	R Hern	Cacoethes	Top Class	7	2 32.27
1990	Sheikh Mohammed's	BELMEZ 3-8-9 (15/2)	M Kinane	H Cecil	Old Vic	Assatis	11	2 30.76
1991	Mrs V K Payson's	GENEROUS 3-8-9 (4/5)	A Munro	P Cole	Sanglamore	Rock Hopper	9	2 28.99
1992	F Salman's	ST JOVITE 3-8-9 (4/5)	S Craine	J Bolger	Saddlers' Hall	Opera House	9	2 30.85
1993	Sheikh Mohammed's	OPERA HOUSE 5-9-7 (8/1)	M Roberts	M Stoute	White Muzzle	Commander in Chief	8	2 33.94
1994	Sheikh Mohammed's	KING'S THEATRE 3-8-9 (12/1)	M Kinane	H Cecil	White Muzzle	Wagon Master	10	2 28.92
1995	Saeed Maktoum	LAMMTARRA 3-8-9 (9/4)	L Dettori	S Bin Suroor	Pentire	Strategic Choice	7	2 31.01
1996	Mollers Racing's	PENTIRE 4-9-7 (100/30)	M Hills	G Wragg	Classic Cliche	Shaamit	8	2 28.11
1997	Godolphin's	SWAIN 5-9-7 (16/1)	J Reid	S Bin Suroor	Pilsudski	Helissio	8	2 36.45
1998	Godolphin's	SWAIN 6-9-7 (11/2)	L Dettori	S Bin Suroor	High-Rise	Royal Anthem	8	2 29.06
1999	Godolphin's	DAYLAMI 5-9-7 (3/1)	L Dettori	S Bin Suroor	Nedawi	Fruits of Love	7	2 29.35
2000	M Tabor's	MONTJEU 4-9-7 (1/3)	M Kinane	J Hammond	Fantastic Light	Daliapour	12	2 29.98
2001	Mrs J Magnier & M Tabor's	GALILEO 3-8-9 (1/2)	M Kinane	A O'Brien	Fantastic Light	Hightori	12	2 27.71
2002	Execs of the late Lord Weinstock's	GOLAN 4-9-7 (11/2)	K Fallon	Sir M Stoute	Nayef	Zindabad	7	2 29.70
2003	H H Aga Khan	ALAMSHAR 3-8-9 (13/2)	J Murtagh	J Oxx	Sulamani	Kris Kin	11	2 33.26
2004	Godolphin's	DOYEN 4-9-7 (11/10)	L Dettori	S Bin Suroor	Hard Buck	Sulamani	12	2 33.10
2005	H H Aga Khan's (Run at Newbury)	AZAMOUR 4-9-7 (5/2)	M Kinane	J Oxx	Norse Dancer	Bago	12	2 28.20
2006	M Tabor's	HURRICANE RUN 4-9-7 (5/6)	C Soumillon	A Fabre	Electrocutionist	Hear's Cry	6	2 30.20
2007	Mrs J Magnier & M Tabor's	DYLAN THOMAS 4-9-7 (5/4)	J Murtagh	A O'Brien	Youmzain	Maraahel	8	2 31.10
2008	Mrs J Magnier & M Tabor's	DUKE OF MARMALADE 4-9-7 (4/6)	J Murtagh	A O'Brien	Papal Bull	Youmzain	9	2 27.91
2009	Ballymacoll Stud's	CONDUIT 4-9-7 (13/8)	R Moore	Sir M Stoute	Tartan Bearer	Ask	6	2 28.73
2010	Highclere Thoroughbred Racing (Adm. Rous)'s	HARBINGER 4-9-7 (4/1)	O Peslier	Sir M Stoute	Cape Blanco	Youmzain	6	2 26.78
2011	Lady Rothschild's	NATHANIEL 3-8-9 (11/2)	W Buick	J Gosden	Workforce	St Nicholas Abbey	5	2 35.07

PRIX DE L'ARC DE TRIOMPHE Longchamp-1 mile 4 furlongs

Year	Owner	Winner and Price	Jockey	Trainer	Second	Third	Ran	Time
1970	A Plesch's	SASSAFRAS 3-8-10 (19/1)	Y Saint Martin	F Mathet	Nijinsky	Miss Dan	15	2 29.70
1971	P Mellon's	MILL REEF 3-8-10 (7/10)	G Lewis	I Balding	Pistol Packer	Cambrizzia	18	2 28.90
1972	Countess M Batthyany's	SAN SAN 3-8-7 (37/2)	F Head	A Penna	Rescousse	Homeric	19	2 38.60
1973	H Zeisel's	RHEINGOLD 4-9-6 (77/10)	L Piggott	B Hills	Allez France	Hard to Beat	27	2 35.80
1974	D Wildenstein's	ALLEZ FRANCE 4-9-3 (1/2)	Y Saint Martin	A Penna	Comtesse de Loir	Margouillat	20	2 36.90
1975	W Zeitelhack's	STAR APPEAL 5-9-6 (119/1)	G Starkey	T Grieper	On My Way	Comtesse de Loir	24	2 33.40
1976	J Wertheimer's	IVANJICA 4-9-3 (75/10)	F Head	A Head	Crow	Youth	20	2 33.60
1977	R Sangster's	ALLEGED 3-8-11 (38/10)	L Piggott	V O'Brien	Balmerino	Crystal Palace	26	2 30.60
1978	R Sangster's	ALLEGED 4-9-4 (7/5)	L Piggott	V O'Brien	Trillon	Dancing Maid	18	2 36.10
1979	Mme G Head's	THREE TROIKAS 3-8-8 (88/10)	F Head	Mme C Head	Le Marmot	Troy	22	2 28.90
1980	R Sangster's	DETROIT 3-8-8 (67/10)	P Eddery	O Douieb	Argument	Ela-Mana-Mou	20	2 28.00
1981	J Wertheimer's	GOLD RIVER 4-9-1 (53/1)	G W Moore	A Head	Bikala	April Run	24	2 35.20
1982	H Aga Khan's	AKIYDA 3-8-8 (43/4)	Y Saint Martin	A Mathet	Ardross	Awaasif	17	2 37.00
1983	D Wildenstein's	ALL ALONG 4-9-1 (173/10)	W Swinburn	P Biancone	Sun Princess	Luth Enchantee	26	2 28.10
1984	D Wildenstein's	SAGACE 4-9-4 (29/10)	Y Saint Martin	P Biancone	Northern Trick	All Along	22	2 39.10
1985	K Abdulla's	RAINBOW QUEST 4-9-4 (71/10)	Pat Eddery	J Tree	Sagace	Kozana	15	2 29.50
	(The first two placings were reversed after the Stewards)							
1986	K Abdulla's	DANCING BRAVE 3-8-11 (11/10)	Pat Eddery	G Harwood	Bering	Triptych	15	2 27.70
1987	P de Moussac's	TREMPOLINO 3-8-11 (20/1)	Pat Eddery	A Fabre	Tony Bin	Triptych	11	2 26.30
1988	Mrs V Gaucci del Bono's	TONY BIN 5-9-4 (14/1)	J Reid	L Camici	Mtoto	Boyatino	24	2 27.30
1989	A Balzarini's	CARROLL HOUSE 4-9-4 (19/1)	M Kinane	M Jarvis	Behera	Saint Andrews	19	2 30.80
1990	B McNall's	SAUMAREZ 3-8-11 (15/1)	G Mosse	N Clement	Epervier Bleu	Snurge	21	2 31.40
1991	B Chalhoub's	SUAVE DANCER 3-8-11 (37/10)	C Asmussen	J Hammond	Magic Night	Pistol Bleu	14	2 31.40
1992	O Lecerf's	SUBOTICA 4-9-4 (88/10)	T Jarnet	A Fabre	User Friendly	Vert Amande	18	2 37.90
1993	D Tsui's	URBAN SEA 4-9-1 (37/1)	E Saint Martin	J Lesbordes	White Muzzle	Opera House	23	2 37.90
1994	Sheikh Mohammed's	CARNEGIE 3-8-11 (3/1)	T Jarnet	A Fabre	Hernando	Apple Tree	20	2 31.10
1995	Saeed Maktoum Al Maktoum's	LAMMTARRA 3-8-11 (2/1)	L Dettori	S Bin Suroor	Freedom Cry	Swain	16	2 31.80
1996	E Sarasola's	HELISSIO 3-8-11 (18/10)	O Peslier	E Lellouche	Pilsudski	Oscar Schindler	16	2 29.90
1997	D Wildenstein's	PEINTRE CELEBRE 3-8-11 (22/10)	O Peslier	A Fabre	Pilsudski	Borgia	18	2 24.60
1998	J-L Lagardere's	SAGAMIX 3-8-11 (5/2)	O Peslier	A Fabre	Leggera	Tiger Hill	14	2 34.50
1999	H H Aga Khan's	MONTJEU 3-8-11 (6/4)	M Kinane	J Oxx	El Condor Pasa	Croco Rouge	14	2 38.50
2000	H H Aga Khan's	SINNDAR 3-8-11 (6/4)	J Murtagh	J Oxx	Egyptband	Volvoreta	10	2 36.10
2001	Godolphin's	SAKHEE 4-9-5 (22/10)	L Dettori	S Bin Suroor	Aquarelliste	Sagacity	17	2 36.70
2002	Godolphin's	MARIENBARD 5-9-5 (158/10)	L Dettori	S Bin Suroor	Sulamani	High Chaparral	13	2 26.70
2003	H H Aga Khan's	DALAKHANI 3-8-11 (9/4)	C Soumillon	A De Royer-Dupre	Mubtaker	High Chaparral	13	2 32.30
2004	Niarchos Family's	BAGO 3-8-11 (10/1)	T Gillet	J E Pease	Cherry Mix	Ouija Board	13	2 32.00
2005	M Tabor's	HURRICANE RUN 3-8-11 (11/4)	K Fallon	A Fabre	Westerner	Bago	15	2 25.00
2006	K Abdulla's	RAIL LINK 3-8-11 (11/4)	S Pasquier	A Fabre	Pride	Hurricane Run	8	2 27.40
	(Deep Impact disqualified from third placing)							
2007	Mrs J Magnier & M Tabor's	DYLAN THOMAS 4-9-5 (11/2)	K Fallon	A O'Brien	Youmzain	Sagara	12	2 28.50
2008	H H Aga Khan's	ZARKAVA 3-8-8 (13/8)	C Soumillon	A De Royer-Dupre	Youmzain	Soldier of Fortune/It's Gino	16	2 28.80
2009	C Tsui's	SEA THE STARS 3-8-11 (4/6)	M Kinane	J Oxx	Youmzain	Cavalryman	19	2 26.30
2010	K Abdulla's	WORKFORCE 3-8-11 (6/1)	R Moore	Sir M Stoute	Nakayama Festa	Sarafina	8	2 35.30
2011	Gestut Burg Eberstein & T Yoshida's	DANEDREAM 3-8-8 (20/1)	A Starke	P Schiergen	Shareta	Snow Fairy	16	2 24.49

GRAND NATIONAL STEEPLECHASE Aintree-4m 4f

Year	Winner and Price	Age & Weight	Jockey	Second	Third	Ran	Time
1967	FOINAVON (100/1)	9 10 0	J Buckingham	Honey End	Red Alligator	44	9 49.60
1968	RED ALLIGATOR (100/7)	9 10 0	B Fletcher	Moidore's Token	Different Class	45	9 28.60
1969	HIGHLAND WEDDING (100/9)	12 10 4	E Harty	Steel Bridge	Rondetto	30	9 30.80
1970	GAY TRIP (15/1)	8 11 5	P Taaffe	Vulture	Miss Hunter	28	9 38.00
1971	SPECIFY (28/1)	9 10 13	J Cook	Black Secret	Astbury	38	9 34.20
1972	WELL TO DO (14/1)	9 10 1	G Thorner	Gay Trip	Black Secret/General Symons	42	10 08.40
1973	RED RUM (9/1)	8 10 5	B Fletcher	Crisp	L'Escargot	38	9 01.90
1974	RED RUM (11/1)	9 12 0	B Fletcher	L'Escargot	Charles Dickens	42	9 20.30
1975	L'ESCARGOT (13/2)	12 11 3	T Carberry	Red Rum	Spanish Steps	31	9 31.10
1976	RAG TRADE (14/1)	10 10 12	J Burke	Red Rum	Eyecatcher	32	9 20.90
1977	RED RUM (9/1)	12 11 8	T Stack	Churchtown V.	Eyecatcher	42	9 30.30
1978	LUCIUS (14/1)	9 10 9	B R Davies	Sebastian V.	Drumroan	37	9 33.90
1979	RUBSTIC (25/1)	10 10 0	M Barnes	Zongalero	Rough and Tumble	34	9 52.90
1980	BEN NEVIS (40/1)	12 10 12	Mr C Fenwick	Rough and Tumble	The Pilgarlic	30	10 17.40
1981	ALDANITI (10/1)	11 10 13	R Champion	Spartan Missile	Royal Mail.	39	9 47.20
1982	GRITTAR (7/1)	9 11 5	Mr C Saunders	Hard Outlook	Loving Words.	39	9 12.60
1983	CORBIERE (13/1)	8 11 4	B de Haan	Greasepaint	Yer Man	41	9 47.04
1984	HALLO DANDY (13/1)	10 10 2	N Doughty	Greasepaint	Corbiere	40	9 21.04
1985	LAST SUSPECT (50/1)	11 10 5	H Davies	Mr Snugfit	Corbiere	40	9 42.70
1986	WEST TIP (15/2)	9 10 11	R Dunwoody	Young Driver	Classified	40	9 33.00
1987	MAORI VENTURE (28/1)	11 10 13	S C Knight	The Tsarevich	Lean Ar Agha dh	40	9 19.30
1988	RHYME 'N'REASON (10/1)	9 11 0	B Powell	West Tip	Monanore	40	9 53.50
1989	LITTLE POLVEIR (28/1)	12 10 3	J Frost	Durham Edition.	The Thinker	40	10 06.80
1990	MR FRISK (16/1)	11 10 6	Mr M Armytage	Durham Edition.	Rinus.	38	8 47.80
1991	SEAGRAM (12/1)	11 10 6	N Hawke	Garrison Savannah.	Auntie Dot.	40	9 29.90
1992	PARTY POLITICS (14/1)	8 10 7	C Llewellyn	Romany King	Laura's Beau.	40	9 06.30
1993	Race Void - false start						
1994	MINNEHOMA (16/1)	11 10 8	R Dunwoody	Just So	Moorcroft Boy	36	10 18.80
1995	ROYAL ATHLETE (40/1)	12 10 6	J Titley	Party Politics	Over The Deel	35	9 04.00
1996	ROUGH QUEST (7/1)	10 10 7	M Fitzgerald	Encore Un Peu.	Superior Finish.	27	9 00.80
1997	LORD GYLLENE (14/1)	9 10 0	A Dobbin	Suny Bay	Camelot Knight	36	9 05.80
1998	EARTH SUMMIT (7/1)	10 10 5	C Llewellyn	Suny Bay	Samlee.	37	10 51.40
1999	BOBBYJO (10/1)	9 10 0	P Carberry	Blue Charm	Call It A Day	32	9 14.00
2000	PAPILLON (10/1)	9 10 12	R Walsh	Mely Moss	Niki Dee.	40	9 09.70
2001	RED MARAUDER (33/1)	11 10 11	R Guest	Smarty.	Blowing Wind	40	11 00.10
2002	BINDAREE (20/1)	8 10 4	J Culloty	What's Up Boys	Blowing Wind	40	9 09.00
2003	MONTY'S PASS (16/1)	10 10 7	B J Geraghty	Supreme Glory.	Amberleigh House.	40	9 21.70
2004	AMBERLEIGH HOUSE (16/1)	12 10 10	G Lee	Clan Royal	Lord Atterbury	39	9 20.30
2005	HEDGEHUNTER (7/1)	9 11 1	R Walsh	Royal Auclair	Simply Gifted	40	9 20.80
2006	NUMBERSIXVALVERDE (11/1)	10 10 8	N Madden	Hedgehunter.	Clan Royal	40	9 41.00
2007	SILVER BIRCH (33/1)	10 10 6	R M Power	McKelvey.	Slim Pickings	40	9 13.60
2008	COMPLY OR DIE (7/1)	9 10 9	T Murphy	King John's Castle	Snowy Morning.	40	9 16.60
2009	MON MOME (100/1)	9 11 0	A P McCoy	Comply Or Die	My Will	40	9 32.90
2010	DON'T PUSH IT (10/1)	10 11 5	A P McCoy	Black Apalachi	State Of Play	40	9 04.60
2011	BALLABRIGGS (14/1)	10 11 10	J Maguire	Oscar Time	Don't Push It.	40	9 01.20

WINNERS OF GREAT RACES

LINCOLN HANDICAP
Doncaster-1m

2002	**ZUCCHERO** 6-8-13	23
2003	**PABLO** 4-8-11	24
2004	**BABODANA** 4-9-10	24
2005	**STREAM OF GOLD** 4-9-10	22
*2006	**BLYTHE KNIGHT** 6-8-10	30
**2007	**VERY WISE** 5-8-11	20
2008	**SMOKEY OAKEY** 4-8-9	21
2009	**EXPRESSO STAR** 4-8-12	20
2010	**PENITENT** 4-9-2	21
2011	**SWEET LIGHTNING** 6-9-4	21

*Run at Redcar
**Run at Newcastle

GREENHAM STAKES (3y)
Newbury-7f

2002	**REDBACK** 9-0	10
2003	**MUQBIL** 9-0	8
2004	**SALFORD CITY** 9-0	10
2005	**INDESATCHEL** 9-0	9
2006	**RED CLUBS** 9-0	5
2007	**MAJOR CADEAUX** 9-0	6
2008	**PACO BOY** 9-0	8
2009	**VOCALISED** 9-0	8
2010	**DICK TURPIN** 9-0	5
2011	**FRANKEL** 9-0	6

EUROPEAN FREE HANDICAP (3y)
Newmarket-7f

2002	**TWILIGHT BLUES** 9-5	8
2003	**INDIAN HAVEN** 9-1	6
2004	**BRUNEL** 8-13	11
2005	**KAMAKIRI** 8-10	8
2006	**MISU BOND** 8-13	8
2007	**PRIME DEFENDER** 9-5	7
2008	**STIMULATION** 9-3	11
2009	**OUQBA** 8-9	10
2010	**RED JAZZ** 9-6	7
2011	**PAUSANIAS** 8-12	6

CRAVEN STAKES (3y)
Newmarket-1m

2002	**KING OF HAPPINESS** 8-9	6
2003	**HURRICANE ALAN** 8-9	7
2004	**HAAFHD** 8-9	5
2005	**DEMOCRATIC DEFICIT** 8-12	8
2006	**KILLYBEGS** 8-12	9
2007	**ADAGIO** 8-12	8
2008	**TWICE OVER** 8-12	10
2009	**DELEGATOR** 8-12	7
2010	**ELUSIVE PIMPERNEL** 8-12	9
2011	**NATIVE KHAN** 8-12	6

JOCKEY CLUB STAKES
Newmarket-1m 4f

2002	**MARIENBARD** 5-8-12	9
2003	**WARRSAN** 5-8-9	6
2004	**GAMUT** 5-8-9	7
2005	**ALKAASED** 5-8-9	5
2006	**SHIROCCO** 5-8-9	7
2007	**SIXTIES ICON** 4-9-3	5
2008	**GETAWAY** 5-9-1	10

2009	**BRONZE CANNON** 4-8-12	3
2010	**JUKEBOX JURY** 4-9-3	5
2011	**DANDINO** 4-8-11	6

CHESTER VASE (3y)
Chester-1m 4f 66yds

2002	**FIGHT YOUR CORNER** 8-10	8
2003	**DUTCH GOLD** 8-10	4
2004	**RED LANCER** 8-10	6
2005	**HATTAN** 8-10	5
2006	**PAPAL BULL** 8-12	5
2007	**SOLDIER OF FORTUNE** 9-2	4
2008	**DOCTOR FREMANTLE** 8-12	8
2009	**GOLDEN SWORD** 8-12	8
2010	**TED SPREAD** 8-12	7
2011	**TREASURE BEACH** 8-12	5

CHESTER CUP
Chester-2m 2f 147yds

2002	**FANTASY HILL** 6-8-9	18
2003	**HUGS DANCER** 6-8-11	16
2004	**ANAK PEKAN** 4-8-2	17
2005	**ANAK PEKAN** 5-9-6	17
2006	**ADMIRAL** 5-8-1	17
2007	**GREENWICH MEANTIME** 7-9-2	17
2008	**BULWARK** 6-9-4	17
2009	**DARAAHEM** 4-9-0	17
2010	**MAMLOOK** 6-8-12	17
2011	**OVERTURN** 7-8-13	17

OAKS TRIAL (3y fillies)
Lingfield-1m 3f 106yds

2002	**BIRDIE** 8-8	7
2003	**SANTA SOPHIA** 8-8	8
2004	**BARAKA** 8-8	5
2005	**CASSYDORA** 8-10	6
2006	**SINDIRANA** 8-10	10
2007	**KAYAH** 8-12	7
2008	**MIRACLE SEEKER** 8-12	6
2009	**MIDDAY** 8-12	9
2010	**DYNA WALTZ** 8-12	5
2011	**ZAIN AL BOLDAN** 8-12	9

DERBY TRIAL (3y)
Lingfield-1m 3f 106yds

2002	**BANDARI** 8-7	6
2003	**FRANKLINS GARDENS** 8-7	6
2004	**PERCUSSIONIST** 8-7	4
2005	**KONG** 8-10	5
2006	**LINDA'S LAD** 9-3	5
2007	**AQALEEM** 8-12	7
2008	**ALESSANDRO VOLTA** 8-12	5
2009	**AGE OF AQUARIUS** 8-12	5
2010	**BULLET TRAIN** 8-12	7
2011	**DORDOGNE** 8-12	6

MUSIDORA STAKES (3y fillies)
York-1m 2f 88yds

2002	**ISLINGTON** 8-8	5
2003	**CASSIS** 8-8	8
2004	**PUNCTILIOUS** 8-8	6
2005	**SECRET HISTORY** 8-10	6
2006	**SHORT SKIRT** 8-12	6
2007	**PASSAGE OF TIME** 9-1	5

2008 **LUSH LASHES** 8-12 8
2009 **SARISKA** 8-12 6
2010 **AVIATE** 8-12 8
2011 **JOVIALITY** 8-12 5

DANTE STAKES (3y)
York-1m 2f 88yds
2002 **MOON BALLAD** 8-11 9
2003 **MAGISTRETTI** 8-11 10
2004 **NORTH LIGHT** 8-11 10
2005 **MOTIVATOR** 8-11 6
2006 **SEPTIMUS** 9-0 6
2007 **AUTHORIZED** 9-0 6
2008 **TARTAN BEARER** 9-0 6
2009 **BLACK BEAR ISLAND** 9-0 10
2010 **CAPE BLANCO** 9-0 5
2011 **CARLTON HOUSE** 9-0 10

YORKSHIRE CUP
York-1m 5f 194yds before 2007
2002 **ZINDABAD** 6-8-9 7
2003 **MAMOOL** 4-8-9 8
2004 **MILLENARY** 7-8-13 10
2005 **FRANKLINS GARDENS** 5-8-10 9
2006 **PERCUSSIONIST** 5-8-12 7
2007 **SERGEANT CECIL** 8-9-3 10
2008 **GEORDIELAND** 7-8-12 5
2009 **ASK** 6-8-13 8
2010 **MANIFEST** 4-8-12 8
2011 **DUNCAN** 6-9-2 8

DUKE OF YORK STAKES
York-6f
2002 **INVINCIBLE SPIRIT** 5-9-5 12
2003 **TWILIGHT BLUES** 4-9-2 15
2004 **MONSIEUR BOND** 4-9-2 15
2005 **THE KIDDYKID** 5-9-2 11
2006 **STEENBERG** 7-9-2 16
2007 **AMADEUS WOLF** 4-9-2 17
2008 **ASSERTIVE** 5-9-7 17
2009 **UTMOST RESPECT** 5-9-7 16
2010 **PRIME DEFENDER** 6-9-7 12
2011 **DELEGATOR** 5-9-7 14

LOCKINGE STAKES
Newbury-1m
2002 **KELTOS** 4-9-0 10
2003 **HAWK WING** 4-9-0 6
2004 **RUSSIAN RHYTHM** 4-8-11 15
2005 **RAKTI** 6-9-0 8
2006 **PEERESS** 5-8-11 8
2007 **RED EVIE** 4-8-11 8
2008 **CREACHADOIR** 4-9-0 11
2009 **VIRTUAL** 4-9-0 11
2010 **PACO BOY** 5-9-0 9
2011 **CANFORD CLIFFS** 4-9-0 7

HENRY II STAKES
Sandown-2m 78yds
2002 **AKBAR** 6-9-0 11
2003 **MR DINOS** 4-9-3 10
2004 **PAPINEAU** 4-8-12 9
2005 **FIGHT YOUR CORNER** 6-9-0 16
2006 **TUNGSTEN STRIKE** 5-9-2 7
2007 **ALLEGRETTO** 4-9-0 7
2008 **FINALMENTE** 6-9-2 8
2009 **GEORDIELAND** 8-9-2 7
2010 **AKMAL** 4-9-0 9
2011 **BLUE BAJAN** 9-9-2 8

TEMPLE STAKES
Haydock-5f
(Run at Sandown before 2008)
2002 **KYLLACHY** 4-9-3 11
2003 **AIRWAVE** 3-9-0 7
*2004 **NIGHT PROSPECTOR** 4-9-4 12
2005 **CELTIC MILL** 7-9-4 13
2006 **REVERENCE** 5-9-4 12
2007 **SIERRA VISTA** 7-9-1 8
2008 **FLEETING SPIRIT** 3-8-11 12
2009 **LOOK BUSY** 4-9-1 9
2010 **KINGSGATE NATIVE** 5-9-4 9
2011 **SOLE POWER** 4-9-4 12
*Run at Epsom

BRIGADIER GERARD STAKES
Sandown-1m 2f 7yds
2002 **POTEMKIN** 4-8-10 4
2003 **SIGHTS ON GOLD** 4-8-10 8
2004 **BANDARI** 5-8-10 9
2005 **NEW MORNING** 4-8-7 5
2006 **NOTNOWCATO** 4-9-3 6
2007 **TAKE A BOW** 6-9-0 7
2008 **SMOKEY OAKEY** 4-9-0 14
2009 **CIMA DE TRIOMPHE** 4-9-0 12
2010 **STOTSFOLD** 7-9-0 8
2011 **WORKFORCE** 4-9-7 8

CORONATION CUP
Epsom-1m 4f 10yds
2002 **BOREAL** 4-9-0 6
2003 **WARRSAN** 5-9-0 9
2004 **WARRSAN** 6-9-0 11
2005 **YEATS** 4-9-0 7
2006 **SHIROCCO** 5-9-0 6
2007 **SCORPION** 5-9-0 7
2008 **SOLDIER OF FORTUNE** 4-9-0 11
2009 **ASK** 6-9-0 9
2010 **FAME AND GLORY** 4-9-0 8
2011 **ST NICHOLAS ABBEY** 4-9-0 5

BOND TYRES TROPHY
(2009-10 Reg Griffin Memorial Trophy)
(2008 Betfair Sprint)
(William Hill Trophy before 2008)
York-6f
2002 **ARTIE** 7-10 20
2003 **DAZZLING BAY** 8-2 19
2004 **TWO STEP KID** 8-9 20
2005 **TAX FREE** 8-9 20
2006 **PRINCE TAMINO** 8-13 18
2007 ABANDONED
2008 **BRAVE PROSPECTOR** 9-0 19
2009 **SWISS DIVA** 9-1 20
2010 **VICTOIRE DE LYPHAR** 8-7 20
2011 **LEXI'S HERO** 8-11 20

QUEEN ANNE STAKES
Ascot-1m
2002 **NO EXCUSE NEEDED** 4-9-2 12
2003 **DUBAI DESTINATION** 4-9-0 10
2004 **REFUSE TO BEND** 4-9-0 16
*2005 **VALIXIR** 4-9-0 7
2006 **AD VALOREM** 4-9-0 7
2007 **RAMONTI** 5-9-0 8
2008 **HARADASUN** 5-9-0 11
2009 **PACO BOY** 4-9-0 9

2010	**GOLDIKOVA** 5-8-11	10
2011	**CANFORD CLIFFS** 4-9-0	7

*Run at York

PRINCE OF WALES'S STAKES

Ascot-1m 2f

2002	**GRANDERA** 4-9-0	12
2003	**NAYEF** 5-9-0	10
2004	**RAKTI** 5-9-0	10
*2005	**AZAMOUR** 4-9-0	8
2006	**OUIJA BOARD** 5-8-11	7
2007	**MANDURO** 5-9-0	6
2008	**DUKE OF MARMALADE** 4-9-0	12
2009	**VISION D'ETAT** 4-9-0	8
2010	**BYWORD** 4-9-0	12
2011	**REWILDING** 4-9-0	7

*Run at York

ST JAMES'S PALACE STAKES (3y)

Ascot-1m

2002	**ROCK OF GIBRALTAR** 9-0	9
2003	**ZAFEEN** 9-0	11
2004	**AZAMOUR** 9-0	11
*2005	**SHAMARDAL** 9-0	8
2006	**ARAAFA** 9-0	11
2007	**EXCELLENT ART** 9-0	8
2008	**HENRYTHENAVIGATOR** 9-0	8
2009	**MASTERCRAFTSMAN** 9-0	10
2010	**CANFORD CLIFFS** 9-0	9
2011	**FRANKEL** 9-0	9

*Run at York

COVENTRY STAKES (2y)

Ascot-6f

2002	**STATUE OF LIBERTY** 8-12	16
2003	**THREE VALLEYS** 8-12	13
2004	**ICEMAN** 8-12	13
*2005	**RED CLUBS** 8-12	14
2006	**HELLVELYN** 8-12	21
2007	**HENRYTHENAVIGATOR** 9-1	20
2008	**ART CONNOISSEUR** 9-1	18
2009	**CANFORD CLIFFS** 9-1	13
2010	**STRONG SUIT** 9-1	13
2011	**POWER** 9-1	23

*Run at York

KING EDWARD VII STAKES (3y)

Ascot-1m 4f

2002	**BALAKHERI** 8-10	7
2003	**HIGH ACCOLADE** 8-11	8
2004	**FIVE DYNASTIES** 8-11	5
*2005	**PLEA BARGAIN** 8-11	5
2006	**PAPAL BULL** 8-12	9
2007	**BOSCOBEL** 8-12	9
2008	**CAMPANOLOGIST** 8-12	9
2009	**FATHER TIME** 8-12	12
2010	**MONTEROSSO** 8-12	8
2011	**NATHANIEL** 8-12	10

*Run at York

JERSEY STAKES (3y)

Ascot-7f

2002	**JUST JAMES** 8-11	15
2003	**MEMBERSHIP** 8-10	14
2004	**KHELEYF** 8-10	15
*2005	**PROCLAMATION** 8-13	21
2006	**JEREMY** 9-1	14
2007	**TARIQ** 9-1	15

2008	**AQLAAM** 9-1	16
2009	**OUQBA** 9-1	16
2010	**RAINFALL** 8-12	13
2011	**STRONG SUIT** 9-6	9

*Run at York

WINDSOR FOREST STAKES
(fillies & mares)

Ascot-1m

2004	**FAVOURABLE TERMS** 4-8-12	10
*2005	**PEERESS** 4-8-9	8
2006	**SOVIET SONG** 6-8-12	10
2007	**NANNINA** 4-8-12	9
2008	**SABANA PERDIDA** 5-8-12	13
2009	**SPACIOUS** 4-8-12	9
2010	**STRAWBERRYDAIQUIRI** 4-8-12	10
2011	**LOLLY FOR DOLLY** 4-8-12	13

*Run at York

QUEEN MARY STAKES (2y fillies)

Ascot-5f

2002	**ROMANTIC LIASON** 8-8	19
2003	**ATTRACTION** 8-10	14
2004	**DAMSON** 8-10	17
*2005	**FLASHY WINGS** 8-10	17
2006	**GILDED** 8-12	15
2007	**ELLETELLE** 8-12	21
2008	**LANGS LASH** 8-12	17
2009	**JEALOUS AGAIN** 8-12	13
2010	**MAQAASID** 8-12	18
2011	**BEST TERMS** 8-12	14

*Run at York

CORONATION STAKES (3y fillies)

Ascot-1m

2002	**SOPHISTICAT** 9-0	11
2003	**RUSSIAN RHYTHM** 9-0	9
2004	**ATTRACTION** 9-0	11
*2005	**MAIDS CAUSEWAY** 9-0	10
2006	**NANNINA** 9-0	15
2007	**INDIAN INK** 9-0	13
2008	**LUSH LASHES** 9-0	11
2009	**GHANAATI** 9-0	10
2010	**LILLIE LANGTRY** 9-0	13
2011	**IMMORTAL VERSE** 9-0	12

*Run at York

ROYAL HUNT CUP

Ascot-1m

2002	**NORTON** 5-8-9	30
2003	**MACADAMIA** 4-8-13	32
2004	**MINE** 6-9-5	31
*2005	**NEW SEEKER** 5-9-0	22
2006	**CESARE** 5-8-8	30
2007	**ROYAL OATH** 4-9-0	26
2008	**MR AVIATOR** 4-9-5	29
2009	**FORGOTTEN VOICE** 4-9-1	25
2010	**INVISIBLE MAN** 4-8-9	29
2011	**JULIENAS** 4-8-8	28

*Run at York

QUEEN'S VASE (3y)

Ascot-2m

2002	**MAMOOL** 8-11	14
2003	**SHANTY STAR** 8-11	12
2004	**DUKE OF VENICE** 8-11	10
*2005	**MELROSE AVENUE** 8-11	10

2006 **SOAPY DANGER** 9-1 11
2007 **MAHLER** 9-1 15
2008 **PATKAI** 9-1 12
2009 **HOLBERG** 9-1 14
2010 **MIKHAIL GLINKA** 9-1 12
2011 **NAMIBIAN** 9-1 11
*Run at York

GOLDEN JUBILEE STAKES
Ascot-6f
2002 **MALHUB** 4-9-4 12
2003 **CHOISIR** 4-9-4 17
2004 **FAYR JAG** 5-9-4 14
*2005 **CAPE OF GOOD HOPE** 7-9-4 15
2006 **LES ARCS** 6-9-4 18
2007 **SOLDIER'S TALE** 6-9-4 21
2008 **KINGSGATE NATIVE** 3-8-11 17
2009 **ART CONNOISSEUR** 3-8-11 14
2010 **STARSPANGLEDBANNER** 4-9-4 24
2011 **SOCIETY ROCK** 4-9-4 16
*Run at York

NORFOLK STAKES (2y)
Ascot-5f
2002 **BARON'S PIT** 8-12 12
2003 **RUSSIAN VALOUR** 8-12 8
2004 **BLUE DAKOTA** 8-12 9
*2005 **MASTA PLASTA** 8-12 12
2006 **DUTCH ART** 9-1 11
2007 **WINKER WATSON** 9-1 11
2008 **SOUTH CENTRAL** 9-1 11
2009 **RADIOHEAD** 9-1 11
2010 **APPROVE** 9-1 12
2011 **BAPAK CHINTA** 9-1 15
*Run at York

GOLD CUP
Ascot-2m 4f
2002 **ROYAL REBEL** 6-9-2 15
2003 **MR DINOS** 4-9-0 12
2004 **PAPINEAU** 4-9-0 13
*2005 **WESTERNER** 6-9-2 17
2006 **YEATS** 5-9-2 12
2007 **YEATS** 6-9-2 14
2008 **YEATS** 7-9-2 10
2009 **YEATS** 8-9-2 9
2010 **RITE OF PASSAGE** 6-9-2 12
2011 **FAME AND GLORY** 5-9-2 15
*Run at York

RIBBLESDALE STAKES (3y fillies)
Ascot-1m 4f
2002 **IRRESISTIBLE JEWEL** 8-8 15
2003 **SPANISH SUN** 8-11 9
2004 **PUNCTILIOUS** 8-11 9
*2005 **THAKAFAAT** 8-11 9
2006 **MONT ETOILE** 8-12 11
2007 **SILKWOOD** 8-12 12
2008 **MICHITA** 8-12 9
2009 **FLYING CLOUD** 8-12 10
2010 **HIBAAYEB** 8-12 11
2011 **BANIMPIRE** 8-12 12
*Run at York

HARDWICKE STAKES
Ascot-1m 4f
2002 **ZINDABAD** 6-8-12 7
2003 **INDIAN CREEK** 5-8-9 9
2004 **DOYEN** 4-8-9 6
*2005 **BANDARI** 6-8-9 6
2006 **MARAAHEL** 5-9-0 8
2007 **MARAAHEL** 6-9-0 7
2008 **MACARTHUR** 4-9-0 9
2009 **BRONZE CANNON** 4-9-3 9
2010 **HARBINGER** 4-9-0 11
2011 **AWAIT THE DAWN** 4-9-0 9
*Run at York

WOKINGHAM STAKES
Ascot-6f
2002 **CAPRICHO** 5-8-11 28
2003 **RATIO** 5-9-3 dead heated with
     FAYR JAG 4-9-6 29
2004 **LAFI** 5-8-13 29
*2005 **IFFRAAJ** 4-9-6 17
2006 **BALTIC KING** 6-9-10 26
2007 **DARK MISSILE** 4-8-6 26
2008 **BIG TIMER** 4-9-2 22
2009 **HIGH STANDING** 4-8-12 26
2010 **LADDIES POKER TWO** 5-8-11 27
2011 **DEACON BLUES** 4-9-4 25
*Run at York

KING'S STAND STAKES
Ascot-5f
2002 **DOMINICA** 3-8-7 15
2003 **CHOISIR** 4-9-7 20
2004 **THE TATLING** 7-9-2 19
*2005 **CHINEUR** 4-9-2 16
2006 **TAKEOVER TARGET** 7-9-7 28
2007 **MISS ANDRETTI** 6-9-1 20
2008 **EQUIANO** 3-8-12 13
2009 **SCENIC BLAST** 5-9-4 15
2010 **EQUIANO** 5-9-4 20
2011 **PROHIBIT** 6-9-4 19
*Run at York

NORTHUMBERLAND PLATE
Newcastle-2m 19yds
2002 **BANGALORE** 6-9-5 16
2003 **UNLEASH** 4-8-11 20
2004 **MIRJAN** 8-8-3 19
2005 **SERGEANT CECIL** 6-8-8 20
2006 **TOLDO** 4-8-2 20
2007 **JUNIPER GIRL** 4-8-11 20
2008 **ARC BLEU** 7-8-2 18
2009 **SOM TALA** 6-8-8 17
2010 **OVERTURN** 6-8-7 19
2011 **TOMINATOR** 4-8-5 19

ECLIPSE STAKES
Sandown-1m 2f 7yds
2002 **HAWK WING** 3-8-10 5
2003 **FALBRAV** 5-9-7 15
2004 **REFUSE TO BEND** 4-9-7 12
2005 **ORATORIO** 3-8-10 7
2006 **DAVID JUNIOR** 4-9-7 9
2007 **NOTNOWCATO** 5-9-7 8
2008 **MOUNT NELSON** 4-9-7 8
2009 **SEA THE STARS** 3-8-10 10

| 2010 | TWICE OVER 5-9-7 | 5 |
| 2011 | SO YOU THINK 5-9-7 | 5 |

LANCASHIRE OAKS (fillies and mares)
Haydock-1m 3f 200yds

2002	MELLOW PARK 3-8-5	6
2003	PLACE ROUGE 4-9-3	12
2004	PONGEE 4-9-3	8
2005	PLAYFUL ACT 3-8-5	8
2006	ALLEGRETTO 3-8-6	8
*2007	TURBO LINN 4-9-5	12
2008	ANNA PAVLOVA 5-9-8	9
2009	BARSHIBA 5-9-5	8
2010	BARSHIBA 6-9-5	10
2011	GERTRUDE BELL 4-9-5	7

*Run at Newmarket

CHERRY HINTON STAKES (2y fillies)
Newmarket-6f

2002	SPINOLA 8-9	9
2003	ATTRACTION 8-12	8
2004	JEWEL IN THE SAND 8-9	10
2005	DONNA BLINI 8-9	8
2006	SANDER CAMILLO 8-12	10
2007	YOU'RESOTHRILLING 8-12	14
2008	PLEASE SING 8-12	8
2009	MISHEER 8-12	10
2010	MEMORY 8-12	7
2011	GAMILATI 8-12	11

BUNBURY CUP
(Run as 32Red Trophy in 2010)
Newmarket-7f

*2002	MINE 4-8-12	16
2003	PATAVELLIAN 5-9-1	20
2004	MATERIAL WITNESS 7-9-3	19
2005	MINE 7-9-9	18
2006	MINE 8-9-10	19
2007	GIGANTICUS 4-8-8	18
2008	LITTLE WHITE LIE 4-9-0	18
2009	PLUM PUDDING 6-9-10	19
2010	ST MORITZ 4-9-1	19
2011	BRAE HILL 5-9-1	20

*Capricho disqualified from first place dead-heat

PRINCESS OF WALES'S STAKES
Newmarket-1m 4f

2002	MILLENARY 5-9-2	7
2003	MILLENARY 6-9-2	6
2004	BANDARI 5-9-2	8
2005	GAMUT 6-9-2	5
2006	SOAPY DANGER 3-8-3	4
2007	PAPAL BULL 4-9-2	12
2008	LUCARNO 4-9-7	6
2009	DOCTOR FREMANTLE 4-9-2	9
2010	SANS FRONTIERES 4-9-2	8
2011	CRYSTAL CAPELLA 6-8-13	8

JULY STAKES (2y)
Newmarket-6f

2002	MISTER LINKS 8-10	10
2003	NEVISIAN LAD 8-10	8
2004	CAPTAIN HURRICANE 8-10	7
2005	IVAN DENISOVICH 8-10	11
2006	STRATEGIC PRINCE 8-12	9
2007	WINKER WATSON 9-1	13
2008	CLASSIC BLADE 8-12	7

2009	ARCANO 8-12	11
2010	LIBRANNO 8-12	5
2011	FREDERICK ENGELS 8-12	7

FALMOUTH STAKES (fillies & mares)
Newmarket-1m

2002	TASHAWAK 3-8-6	9
2003	MACADAMIA 4-9-1	8
2004	SOVIET SONG 4-9-1	7
2005	SOVIET SONG 5-9-1	7
2006	RAJEEM 3-8-10	7
2007	SIMPLY PERFECT 3-8-10	7
2008	NAHOODH 3-8-10	11
2009	GOLDIKOVA 4-9-5	8
2010	MUSIC SHOW 3-8-10	8
2011	TIMEPIECE 4-9-5	11

JULY CUP
Newmarket-6f

2002	CONTINENT 5-9-5	14
2003	OASIS DREAM 3-8-13	16
2004	FRIZZANTE 5-9-2	20
2005	PASTORAL PURSUITS 4-9-5	19
2006	LES ARCS 6-9-5	15
2007	SAKHEE'S SECRET 3-8-13	18
2008	MARCHAND D'OR 5-9-5	13
2009	FLEETING SPIRIT 4-9-2	13
2010	STARSPANGLEDBANNER 4-9-5	14
2011	DREAM AHEAD 3-8-13	16

PRINCESS MARGARET STAKES (2y fillies)
Ascot-6f

2002	RUSSIAN RHYTHM 8-9	6
2003	RIVER BELLE 8-9	9
2004	SOAR 8-9	6
*2005	MIXED BLESSING 8-9	12
2006	SCARLET RUNNER 8-12	10
2007	VISIT 8-12	13
2008	AFRICAN SKIES 8-12	16
2009	LADY OF THE DESERT 8-12	9
2010	SORAAYA 8-12	11
2011	ANGELS WILL FALL 8-12	7

*Run at Newbury

STEWARDS' CUP
Goodwood-6f

2002	BOND BOY 5-8-2	28
2003	PATAVELLIAN 5-8-11	29
2004	PIVOTAL POINT 4-8-11	28
2005	GIFT HORSE 5-9-7	27
2006	BORDERLESCOTT 4-9-5	27
2007	ZIDANE 5-9-1	27
2008	CONQUEST 4-8-9	27
2009	GENKI 5-9-1	26
2010	EVENS AND ODDS 6-8-10	28
2011	HOOF IT 4-10-0	27

GORDON STAKES (3y)
Goodwood-1m 4f

2002	BANDARI 8-13	4
2003	PHOENIX REACH 8-10	10
2004	MARAAHEL 8-10	8
2005	THE GEEZER 8-10	5
2006	SIXTIES ICON 9-0	7
2007	YELLOWSTONE 9-0	10
2008	CONDUIT 9-0	6

2009 **HARBINGER** 9-0 9
2010 **REBEL SOLDIER** 9-0 10
2011 **NAMIBIAN** 9-3 10

SUSSEX STAKES
Goodwood-1m
2002 **ROCK OF GIBRALTAR** 3-8-13 5
2003 **REEL BUDDY** 5-9-7 9
2004 **SOVIET SONG** 4-9-4 11
2005 **PROCLAMATION** 3-8-13 12
2006 **COURT MASTERPIECE** 6-9-7 7
2007 **RAMONTI** 5-9-7 8
2008 **HENRYTHENAVIGATOR** 3-8-13 6
2009 **RIP VAN WINKLE** 3-8-13 8
2010 **CANFORD CLIFFS** 3-8-13 7
2011 **FRANKEL** 3-8-13 4

RICHMOND STAKES (2y)
Goodwood-6f
*2002 **REVENUE** 8-11 9
2003 **CARRIZO CREEK** 8-11 7
2004 **MONTGOMERY'S ARCH** 8-11 8
2005 **ALWAYS HOPEFUL** 8-11 6
2006 **HAMOODY** 9-0 7
2007 **STRIKE THE DEAL** 9-0 9
2008 **PROLIFIC** 9-0 12
2009 **DICK TURPIN** 9-0 6
2010 **LIBRANNO** 9-3 9
2011 **HARBOUR WATCH** 9-0 10
*Elusive City disqualified from first place

KING GEORGE STAKES
Goodwood-5f
2002 **AGNETHA** 3-8-7 14
2003 **THE TATLING** 6-9-0 9
2004 **RINGMOOR DOWN** 5-8-11 12
2005 **FIRE UP THE BAND** 6-9-0 12
2006 **LA CUCARACHA** 5-8-11 18
2007 **MOORHOUSE LAD** 4-9-0 17
2008 **ENTICING** 4-8-11 12
2009 **KINGSGATE NATIVE** 4-9-0 17
2010 **BORDERLESCOTT** 8-9-0 15
2011 **MASAMAH** 5-9-0 11

GOODWOOD CUP
Goodwood-2m
2002 **JARDINES LOOKOUT** 5-9-2 9
2003 **PERSIAN PUNCH** 10-9-4 9
2004 **DARASIM** 6-9-4 9
2005 **DISTINCTION** 6-9-5 10
2006 **YEATS** 5-9-10 15
2007 **ALLEGRETTO** 4-9-5 15
2008 **YEATS** 7-9-12 8
2009 **SCHIAPARELLI** 6-9-7 10
2010 **ILLUSTRIOUS BLUE** 7-9-7 10
2011 **OPINION POLL** 5-9-5 15

MOLECOMB STAKES (2y)
Goodwood-5f
2002 **WUNDERS DREAM** 8-7 13
2003 **MAJESTIC MISSILE** 8-12 9
2004 **TOURNEDOS** 8-12 13
2005 **STRIKE UP THE BAND** 9-1 15
2006 **ENTICING** 8-11 10
2007 **FLEETING SPIRIT** 8-11 16
2008 **FINJAAN** 9-0 11
2009 **MONSIEUR CHEVALIER** 9-0 11

2010 **ZEBEDEE** 9-0 12
2011 **REQUINTO** 9-0 13

NASSAU STAKES (fillies and mares)
Goodwood-1m 1f 192yds
2002 **ISLINGTON** 3-8-6 10
2003 **RUSSIAN RHYTHM** 3-8-6 8
2004 **FAVOURABLE TERMS** 4-9-2 6
2005 **ALEXANDER GOLDRUN** 4-9-3 11
2006 **OUIJA BOARD** 5-9-5 7
2007 **PEEPING FAWN** 3-8-10 8
2008 **HALFWAY TO HEAVEN** 3-8-10 9
2009 **MIDDAY** 3-8-10 10
2010 **MIDDAY** 4-9-6 6
2011 **MIDDAY** 5-9-6 6

HUNGERFORD STAKES
Newbury-7f
2002 **REEL BUDDY** 4-8-13 10
2003 **WITH REASON** 5-8-13 11
2004 **CHIC** 4-8-11 13
2005 **SLEEPING INDIAN** 4-9-0 9
2006 **WELSH EMPEROR** 7-9-3 9
2007 **RED EVIE** 4-9-4 10
2008 **PACO BOY** 3-9-0 9
2009 **BALTHAZAAR'S GIFT** 6-9-3 9
2010 **SHAKESPEAREAN** 3-8-13 7
2011 **EXCELEBRATION** 3-8-13 9

GEOFFREY FREER STAKES
Newbury-1m 5f 61yds
2002 **MUBTAKER** 5-9-3 7
2003 **MUBTAKER** 6-9-3 5
2004 **MUBTAKER** 7-9-3 4
2005 **LOCHBUIE** 4-9-3 5
2006 **ADMIRAL'S CRUISE** 4-9-3 5
2007 **PAPAL BULL** 4-9-7 8
2008 **SIXTIES ICON** 5-9-5 10
2009 **KITE WOOD** 3-8-8 8
2010 **SANS FRONTIERES** 4-9-8 8
2011 **CENSUS** 3-8-6 10

INTERNATIONAL STAKES
York-1m 2f 88yds
2002 **NAYEF** 4-9-5 7
2003 **FALBRAV** 5-9-5 8
2004 **SULAMANI** 5-9-5 9
2005 **ELECTROCUTIONIST** 4-9-5 7
2006 **NOTNOWCATO** 4-9-5 7
2007 **AUTHORIZED** 3-8-11 7
*2008 **DUKE OF MARMALADE** 4-9-5 9
2009 **SEA THE STARS** 3-8-11 4
2010 **RIP VAN WINKLE** 4-9-5 9
2011 **TWICE OVER** 6-9-5 5
*Run at Newmarket over 1m 2f

GREAT VOLTIGEUR STAKES (3y)
York-1m 4f
2002 **BANDARI** 3-8-9 6
2003 **POWERSCOURT** 8-9 9
2004 **RULE OF LAW** 8-9 7
2005 **HARD TOP** 8-9 10
2006 **YOUMZAIN** 8-12 9
2007 **LUCARNO** 8-12 9
*2008 **CENTENNIAL** 8-12 5
2009 **MONITOR CLOSELY** 8-12 7

```
2010  REWILDING 8-12..................................10
2011  SEA MOON 8-12....................................8
```
*Run at Goodwood

YORKSHIRE OAKS (fillies and mares)
York-1m 4f
```
2002  ISLINGTON 3-8-8...............................11
2003  ISLINGTON 4-9-4.................................8
2004  QUIFF 3-8-8.........................................8
2005  PUNCTILIOUS 4-9-4............................11
2006  ALEXANDROVA 3-8-11..........................6
2007  PEEPING FAWN 3-8-11..........................7
*2008 LUSH LASHES 3-8-11............................6
2009  DAR RE MI 4-9-7..................................6
2010  MIDDAY 4-9-7.......................................8
2011  BLUE BUNTING 3-8-11...........................8
```
*Run at Newmarket

EBOR HANDICAP
York-1m 6f (1m 5f 194yds before 2007)
```
2002  HUGS DANCER 5-8-5.............................22
2003  SAINT ALEBE 4-8-8..............................22
2004  MEPHISTO 5-9-4...................................19
2005  SERGEANT CECIL 6-8-12........................20
2006  MUDAWIN 5-8-4....................................19
2007  PURPLE MOON 4-9-4.............................19
*2008 ALL THE GOOD 5-9-0.............................20
2009  SESENTA 5-8-8.....................................19
2010  DIRAR 5-9-1.........................................20
2011  MOYENNE CORNICHE 6-8-10...................20
```
*Run as Newburgh Handicap at Newbury over 1m 5f 61 yds

GIMCRACK STAKES (2y)
York-6f
```
2002  COUNTRY REEL 8-11.............................11
2003  BALMONT 8-11.......................................9
2004  TONY JAMES 8-11.................................11
2005  AMADEUS WOLF 8-11.............................13
2006  CONQUEST 8-12......................................6
2007  SIR GERRY 8-12.....................................8
*2008 SHAWEEL 8-12......................................12
2009  SHOWCASING 8-12..................................6
2010  APPROVE 9-1........................................11
2011  CASPAR NETSCHER 8-12..........................9
```
*Run at Newbury

NUNTHORPE STAKES
York-5f
```
2002  KYLLACHY 4-9-11..................................17
2003  OASIS DREAM 9-9-9.................................8
2004  BAHAMIAN PIRATE 9-9-11.......................12
2005  LA CUCARACHA 4-9-8.............................16
2006  REVERENCE 5-9-11................................14
2007  KINGSGATE NATIVE 2-8-1.......................16
*2008 BORDERLESCOTT 6-9-11.........................14
2009  BORDERLESCOTT 7-9-11.........................16
2010  SOLE POWER 3-9-9................................12
2011  MARGOT DID 3-9-6.................................15
```
*Run at Newmarket

PRESTIGE STAKES (2y fillies)
Goodwood-7f
```
2002  GEMINIANI 8-9.......................................8
2003  GRACEFULLY 8-9.....................................6
2004  DUBAI SURPRISE 8-9..............................12
2005  NANNINA 8-9..........................................9
2006  SESMEN 9-0..........................................10
```

```
2007  SENSE OF JOY 9-0..................................7
2008  FANTASIA 9-0.......................................10
2009  SENT FROM HEAVEN 9-0...........................8
2010  THEYSKENS' THEORY 9-0..........................7
2011  REGAL REALM 9-0....................................6
```

CELEBRATION MILE
Goodwood-1m
```
2002  TILLERMAN 6-9-1....................................7
2003  PRIORS LODGE 5-9-1...............................6
2004  CHIC 4-8-12...........................................7
2005  CHIC 5-8-12...........................................8
2006  CARADAK 5-9-1.......................................6
2007  ECHELON 5-8-12......................................8
2008  RAVEN'S PASS 3-8-9................................5
2009  DELEGATOR 3-8-9....................................7
2010  POET'S VOICE 3-8-9.................................4
2011  DUBAWI GOLD 3-8-9.................................7
```

SOLARIO STAKES (2y)
Sandown-7f 16yds
```
2002  FOSS WAY 8-11......................................11
2003  BARBAJUAN 8-11......................................8
2004  WINDSOR KNOT 8-11................................8
2005  OPERA CAPE 8-11....................................7
2006  DRUMFIRE 9-0.........................................8
2007  RAVEN'S PASS 9-0...................................9
2008  SRI PUTRA 9-0.......................................11
2009  SHAKESPEAREAN 9-0.................................8
2010  NATIVE KHAN 9-0.....................................6
2011  TALWAR 9-0............................................4
```

SPRINT CUP
Haydock-6f
```
2002  INVINCIBLE SPIRIT 5-9-0........................14
2003  SOMNUS 3-8-12......................................10
2004  TANTE ROSE 4-8-11................................19
2005  GOODRICKE 3-8-12..................................17
2006  REVERENCE 5-9-3....................................11
2007  RED CLUBS 4-9-3....................................14
*2008 AFRICAN ROSE 3-8-12.............................15
2009  REGAL PARADE 5-9-3...............................14
2010  MARKAB 7-9-3........................................13
2011  DREAM AHEAD 3-9-1................................16
```
*Run at Doncaster

SEPTEMBER STAKES
Kempton-1m 4f Polytrack
(run on turf before 2006)
```
2002  ASIAN HEIGHTS 4-9-3...............................6
2003  MUBTAKER 6-9-8.....................................5
2004  MAMOOL 5-9-3.........................................4
*2005 IMPERIAL STRIDE 4-9-8.............................6
2006  KANDIDATE 4-9-4.....................................6
2007  STEPPE DANCER 4-9-4..............................7
2008  HATTAN 6-9-7.........................................12
2009  KIRKLEES 5-9-9......................................10
2010  LAAHEB 4-9-4..........................................9
2011  MODUN 4-9-4...........................................7
```
*Run at Newmarket

MAY HILL STAKES (2y fillies)
Doncaster-1m
```
2002  SUMMITVILLE 8-9.....................................9
2003  KINNAIRD 8-10.......................................10
2004  PLAYFUL ACT 8-10....................................8
2005  NASHEEJ 8-13.........................................8
```

*2006 **SIMPLY PERFECT** 8-12 9
2007 **SPACIOUS** 8-12 12
2008 **RAINBOW VIEW** 9-1 7
2009 **POLLENATOR** 8-12 7
2010 **WHITE MOONSTONE** 8-12 7
2011 **LYRIC OF LIGHT** 8-12 8
*Run at York

PORTLAND HANDICAP
Doncaster-5f 140yds
2002 **HALMAHERA** 7-8-13 22
2003 **HALMAHERA** 8-9-4 22
2004 **HALMAHERA** 9-9-10 22
2005 **OUT AFTER DARK** 4-8-12 21
*2006 **FANTASY BELIEVER** 8-8-13 19
2007 **FULLANDBY** 5-8-13 21
2008 **HOGMANEIGH** 5-9-6 21
2009 **SANTO PADRE** 5-9-4 22
2010 **POET'S PLACE** 5-9-4 22
2011 **NOCTURNAL AFFAIR** 5-9-5 21
*Run at York over 5f 89yds

PARK HILL STAKES (fillies and mares)
Doncaster-1m 6f 132yds
2002 **ALEXANDER THREE D** 3-8-5 5
2003 **DISCREET BRIEF** 3-8-5 8
2004 **ECHOES IN ETERNITY** 4-9-3 10
2005 **SWEET STREAM** 5-9-3 11
*2006 **RISING CROSS** 3-8-7 7
2007 **HI CALYPSO** 3-8-7 14
2008 **ALLEGRETTO** 5-9-4 8
2009 **THE MINIVER ROSE** 3-8-6 9
2010 **EASTERN ARIA** 4-9-4 12
2011 **MEEZNAH** 4-9-4 7
*Run at York

DONCASTER CUP
Doncaster-2m 2f
2002 **BOREAS** 7-9-1 8
2003 **PERSIAN PUNCH** 10-9-4 6
2004 **MILLENARY** 7-9-4 dead heated with
         KASTHARI 5-9-1 8
2005 **MILLENARY** 8-9-4 7
*2006 **SERGEANT CECIL** 7-9-4 8
2007 **SEPTIMUS** 4-9-4 8
2008 **HONOLULU** 4-9-1 8
2009 **ASKAR TAU** 4-9-4 5
2010 **SAMUEL** 6-9-1 10
2011 **SADDLER'S ROCK** 3-8-1 7
*Run at York

CHAMPAGNE STAKES (2y)
Doncaster-7f
2002 **ALMUSHAHAR** 8-10 11
2003 **LUCKY STORY** 9-0 8
2004 **ETLAALA** 8-10 10
2005 **CLOSE TO YOU** 8-10 dead heated with
         SILENT TIMES 8-10 7
*2006 **VITAL EQUINE** 8-12 8
2007 **MCCARTNEY** 8-12 10
2008 **WESTPHALIA** 8-12 7
2009 **POET'S VOICE** 8-12 7
2010 **SAAMIDD** 8-12 8
2011 **TRUMPET MAJOR** 8-12 5
*Run at York

FLYING CHILDERS STAKES (2y)
Doncaster-5f
2002 **WUNDERS DREAM** 8-12 14
2003 **HOWICK FALLS** 8-12 13
2004 **CHATEAU ISTANA** 8-12 11
2005 **GODFREY STREET** 8-12 9
*2006 **WI DUD** 9-0 9
2007 **FLEETING SPIRIT** 8-11 8
2008 **MADAME TROP VITE** 8-11 12
2009 **SAND VIXEN** 8-11 10
2010 **ZEBEDEE** 9-0 10
2011 **REQUINTO** 9-0 10
*Run at York

AYR GOLD CUP
Ayr-6f
2002 **FUNFAIR WANE** 3-9-3 28
2003 **QUITO** 6-8-6 26
2004 **FUNFAIR WANE** 5-8-6 24
2005 **PRESTO SHINKO** 4-9-2 28
2006 **FONTHILL ROAD** 6-9-2 23
2007 **ADVANCED** 4-9-9 27
2008 **REGAL PARADE** 4-8-10 28
2009 **JIMMY STYLES** 5-9-2 26
2010 **REDFORD** 5-9-2 26
2011 **OUR JONATHAN** 4-9-6 26

MILL REEF STAKES (2y)
Newbury-6f 8yds
2002 **ZAFEEN** 8-12 8
2003 **BYRON** 8-12 10
2004 **GALEOTA** 8-12 9
2005 **COOL CREEK** 8-12 13
2006 **EXCELLENT ART** 9-1 6
2007 **DARK ANGEL** 9-1 6
2008 **LORD SHANAKILL** 9-1 9
2009 **AWZAAN** 9-1 6
2010 **TEMPLE MEADS** 9-1 7
2011 **CASPAR NETSCHER** 9-4 9

CUMBERLAND LODGE STAKES
Ascot-1m 4f
2002 **SYSTEMATIC** 3-8-6 5
2003 **HIGH ACCOLADE** 3-8-11 5
2004 **HIGH ACCOLADE** 4-9-0 9
*2005 **MUBTAKER** 8-9-0 8
2006 **YOUNG MICK** 4-9-0 8
2007 **ASK** 4-9-3 8
2008 **SIXTIES ICON** 5-9-3 5
2009 **MAWATHEEQ** 4-9-0 12
2010 **LAAHEB** 4-9-3 6
2011 **QUEST FOR PEACE** 3-8-7 7
*Run at Newmarket

FILLIES' MILE (2y fillies)
Ascot-1m
2002 **SOVIET SONG** 8-10 10
2003 **RED BLOOM** 8-10 7
2004 **PLAYFUL ACT** 8-10 9
*2005 **NANNINA** 8-12 6
2006 **SIMPLY PERFECT** 8-12 8
2007 **LISTEN** 8-12 7
2008 **RAINBOW VIEW** 8-12 8
2009 **HIBAAYEB** 8-12 9
2010 **WHITE MOONSTONE** 8-12 5
*2011 **LYRIC OF LIGHT** 8-12 8
*Run at Newmarket

ROYAL LODGE STAKES (2y)
Ascot-1m
2002	AL JADEED 8-11	9
2003	SNOW RIDGE 8-11	10
2004	PERFECTPERFORMANCE 8-11	8
*2005	LEO 8-11	8
2006	ADMIRALOFTHEFLEET 8-12	7
2007	CITY LEADER 8-12	11
2008	JUKEBOX JURY 8-12	8
2009	JOSHUA TREE 8-12	10
2010	FRANKEL 8-12	5
*2011	DADDY LONG LEGS 8-12	6

*Run at Newmarket

CHEVELEY PARK STAKES (2y fillies)
Newmarket-6f
2002	AIRWAVE 8-11	6
2003	CARRY ON KATIE 8-11	10
2004	MAGICAL ROMANCE 8-11	10
2005	DONNA BLINI 8-11	10
2006	INDIAN INK 8-12	11
2007	NATAGORA 8-12	14
2008	SERIOUS ATTITUDE 8-12	16
2009	SPECIAL DUTY 8-12	8
2010	HOORAY 8-12	11
2011	LIGHTENING PEARL 8-12	9

MIDDLE PARK STAKES (2y)
Newmarket-6f
2002	OASIS DREAM 8-11	10
*2003	BALMONT 8-11	13
2004	AD VALOREM 8-11	9
2005	AMADEUS WOLF 8-11	6
2006	DUTCH ART 8-12	9
2007	DARK ANGEL 8-12	9
2008	BUSHRANGER 8-12	9
2009	AWZAAN 8-12	5
2010	DREAM AHEAD 8-12	8
2011	CRUSADE 8-12	16

*Three Valleys disqualified from first place

SUN CHARIOT STAKES
(fillies and mares)
Newmarket-1m
2002	DRESS TO THRILL 3-8-10	10
2003	ECHOES IN ETERNITY 3-8-10	10
2004	ATTRACTION 3-8-11	5
2005	PEERESS 4-9-0	10
2006	SPINNING QUEEN 3-8-12	5
2007	MAJESTIC ROI 3-8-11	9
2008	HALFWAY TO HEAVEN 3-8-13	10
2009	SAHPRESA 4-9-2	8
2010	SAHPRESA 5-9-2	11
2011	SAHPRESA 6-9-3	8

CAMBRIDGESHIRE
Newmarket-1m 1f
2002	BEAUCHAMP PILOT 4-9-5	30
2003	CHIVALRY 4-8-1	34
2004	SPANISH DON 6-8-7	32
2005	BLUE MONDAY 4-9-3	30
2006	FORMAL DECREE 3-8-9	33
2007	PIPEDREAMER 3-8-12	34
2008	TAZEEZ 4-9-2	28
2009	SUPASEUS 6-9-1	32
2010	CREDIT SWAP 5-8-7	35
2011	PRINCE OF JOHANNE	32

QIPCO BRITISH CHAMPIONS SPRINT STAKES
Ascot-6f
(formerly Diadem Stakes)
| 2011 | DEACON BLUES 4-9-0 | 16 |

QUEEN ELIZABETH II STAKES (BRITISH CHAMPIONS MILE)
Ascot-1m
2002	WHERE OR WHEN 3-8-11	5
2003	FALBRAV 5-9-1	8
2004	RAKTI 5-9-1	11
*2005	STARCRAFT 5-9-1	6
2006	GEORGE WASHINGTON 3-8-13	8
2007	RAMONTI 5-9-3	7
2008	RAVEN'S PASS 3-8-13	7
2009	RIP VAN WINKLE 3-8-13	4
2010	POET'S VOICE 3-8-13	8
2011	FRANKEL 3-9-0	8

*Run at Newmarket

QIPCO BRITISH CHAMPIONS LONG DISTANCE CUP
(formerly Jockey Club Cup, run at Newmarket)
Ascot-2m
| 2011 | FAME AND GLORY 5-9-0 | 10 |

QIPCO BRITISH CHAMPIONS FILLIES' AND MARES' STAKES
(formerly Pride Stakes, run at Newmarket)
Ascot-1m 4f
| 2011 | DANCING RAIN 3-8-10 | 10 |

QIPCO CHAMPION STAKES (BRITISH CHAMPIONS MIDDLE DISTANCE)
Ascot-1m 2f
(Prior to 2011 run at Newmarket)
2002	STORMING HOME 4-9-2	11
2003	RAKTI 4-9-2	12
2004	HAAFHD 3-8-11	11
2005	DAVID JUNIOR 3-8-11	15
2006	PRIDE 6-9-0	8
2007	LITERATO 3-8-12	12
2008	NEW APPROACH 3-8-12	11
2009	TWICE OVER 4-9-3	14
2010	TWICE OVER 5-9-3	10
2011	CIRRUS DES AIGLES 5-9-3	12

CORNWALLIS STAKES (2y)
Ascot-5f
2002	PEACE OFFERING 8-12	11
2003	MAJESTIC MISSILE 9-1	11
*2004	CASTELLETTO 8-9	11
**2005	HUNTER STREET 8-12	12
2006	ALZERRA 8-1	10
2007	CAPTAIN GERRARD 9-0	12
2008	AMOUR PROPRE 9-0	19
2009	OUR JONATHAN 9-0	17
2010	ELECTRIC WAVES 8-11	14
2011	PONTY ACCLAIM 8-11	16

*Run at Newmarket
**Run at Salisbury

DEWHURST STAKES (2y)
Newmarket-7f
2002	TOUT SEUL 9-0	16
2003	MILK IT MICK 9-0	12
2004	SHAMARDAL 9-0	9
2005	SIR PERCY 9-0	8
2006	TEOFILO 9-1	15
2007	NEW APPROACH 9-1	10
2008	INTENSE FOCUS 9-1	13
2009	BEETHOVEN 9-1	15
2010	FRANKEL 9-1	6
2011	PARISH HALL 9-1	9

ROCKFEL STAKES (2y fillies)
Newmarket-7f
2002	LUVAH GIRL 8-9	11
2003	CAIRNS 8-9	10
2004	MAIDS CAUSEWAY 8-12	8
2005	SPECIOSA 8-9	14
2006	FINSCEAL BEO 9-2	14
2007	KITTY MATCHAM 8-12	10
2008	LAHALEEB 8-12	15
2009	MUSIC SHOW 8-12	11
2010	CAPE DOLLAR 8-12	10
2011	WADING 8-12	9

CHALLENGE STAKES
Newmarket-7f
2002	NAYYIR 4-9-0	17
2003	JUST JAMES 4-9-0	11
2004	FIREBREAK 5-9-4	12
2005	LE VIE DEI COLORI 5-9-0	15
2006	SLEEPING INDIAN 5-9-3	16
2007	MISS LUCIFER 3-8-12	15
2008	STIMULATION 3-9-1	15
2009	ARABIAN GLEAM 5-9-3	9
2010	RED JAZZ 3-9-1	14
2011	STRONG SUIT 3-9-5	8

TWO-YEAR-OLD TROPHY (2y)
Redcar-6f
2002	SOMNUS 8-12	18
2003	PEAK TO CREEK 9-0	23
2004	OBE GOLD 8-3	24
2005	MISU BOND 9-0	24
2006	DANUM DANCER 8-3	24
2007	DUBAI DYNAMO 9-2	23
2008	TOTAL GALLERY 8-9	22
2009	LUCKY LIKE 8-6	22
2010	LADIES ARE FOREVER 7-12	22
2011	BOGART 8-12	22

CESAREWITCH
Newmarket-2m 2f
2002	MISS FARA 7-8-0	36
2003	LANDING LIGHT 8-9-4	36

2004	CONTACT DANCER 5-8-2	34
2005	SERGEANT CECIL 6-9-8	34
2006	DETROIT CITY 4-9-1	31
2007	LEG SPINNER 6-8-11	33
2008	CARACCIOLA 11-9-6	32
2009	DARLEY SUN 3-8-6	32
2010	AIM TO PROSPER 6-7-13	32
2011	NEVER CAN TELL 4-8-11	33

HORRIS HILL STAKES (2y)
Newbury-7f
2002	MAKHLAB 8-9	10
2003	PEAK TO CREEK 8-9	9
2004	CUPID'S GLORY 8-9	13
2005	HURRICANE CAT 8-9	13
2006	DIJEERR 8-12	10
2007	BEACON LODGE 8-12	11
2008	EVASIVE 8-12	13
2009	CARNABY STREET 8-12	14
2010	KLAMMER 8-12	10
2011	TELL DAD 8-12	14

RACING POST TROPHY (2y)
Doncaster-1m
2002	BRIAN BORU 9-0	9
2003	AMERICAN POST 9-0	4
2004	MOTIVATOR 9-0	8
2005	PALACE EPISODE 9-0	7
*2006	AUTHORIZED 9-0	14
2007	IBN KHALDUN 9-0	12
2008	CROWDED HOUSE 9-0	15
2009	ST NICHOLAS ABBEY 9-0	11
2010	CASAMENTO 9-0	10
2011	CAMELOT 9-0	5

*Run at Newbury

NOVEMBER HANDICAP
Doncaster-1m 4f
2002	RED WINE 3-8-1	23
2003	TURBO 4-9-2	24
2004	CARTE DIAMOND 3-9-6	24
2005	COME ON JONNY 3-8-0	21
*2006	GROUP CAPTAIN 4-9-5	20
2007	MALT OR MASH 3-8-10	21
2008	TROPICAL STRAIT 5-8-13	21
2009	CHARM SCHOOL 4-8-12	23
2010	TIMES UP 4-8-13	22
2011	ZUIDER ZEE 4-8-13	23

*Run at Windsor

WINNERS OF PRINCIPAL RACES IN IRELAND

IRISH 2000 GUINEAS (3y)
The Curragh-1m
2002	ROCK OF GIBRALTAR 9-0	7
2003	INDIAN HAVEN 9-0	16

2004	BACHELOR DUKE 9-0	8
2005	DUBAWI 9-0	8
2006	ARAAFA 9-0	11
2007	COCKNEY REBEL 9-0	12

2008 **HENRYTHENAVIGATOR** 9-0.................5
2009 **MASTERCRAFTSMAN** 9-0...................9
2010 **CANFORD CLIFFS** 9-0....................13
2011 **RODERIC O'CONNOR** 9-0...................8

TATTERSALLS GOLD CUP
The Curragh-1m 2f 110yds
2002 **REBELLINE** 4-8-11...........................8
2003 **BLACK SAM BELLAMY** 4-9-0................8
2004 **POWERSCOURT** 4-9-0........................6
2005 **GREY SWALLOW** 4-9-0........................6
2006 **HURRICANE RUN** 4-9-0......................3
2007 **NOTNOWCATO** 5-9-0..........................9
2008 **DUKE OF MARMALADE** 4-9-0................6
2009 **CASUAL CONQUEST** 4-9-0...................5
2010 **FAME AND GLORY** 4-9-0.....................6
2011 **SO YOU THINK** 5-9-1........................5

IRISH 1000 GUINEAS (3y fillies)
The Curragh-1m
2002 **GOSSAMER** 9-0..............................15
2003 **YESTERDAY** 9-0..............................8
2004 **ATTRACTION** 9-0............................15
2005 **SAOIRE** 9-0.................................18
2006 **NIGHTIME** 9-0..............................15
2007 **FINSCEAL BEO** 9-0.........................11
2008 **HALFWAY TO HEAVEN** 9-0..................13
2009 **AGAIN** 9-0..................................16
2010 **BETHRAH** 9-0...............................19
2011 **MISTY FOR ME** 9-0.........................15

IRISH DERBY (3y)
The Curragh-1m 4f
2002 **HIGH CHAPARRAL** 9-0.......................9
2003 **ALAMSHAR** 9-0...............................9
2004 **GREY SWALLOW** 9-0.........................10
2005 **HURRICANE RUN** 9-0.........................9
2006 **DYLAN THOMAS** 9-0..........................8
2007 **SOLDIER OF FORTUNE** 9-0..................11
2008 **FROZEN FIRE** 9-0...........................11
2009 **FAME AND GLORY** 9-0.......................11
2010 **CAPE BLANCO** 9-0...........................10
2011 **TREASURE BEACH** 9-0........................8

IRISH OAKS (3y fillies)
The Curragh-1m 4f
2002 **MARGARULA** 9-0.............................12
2003 **VINTAGE TIPPLE** 9-0.......................11
2004 **OUIJA BOARD** 9-0............................7
2005 **SHAWANDA** 9-0..............................13
2006 **ALEXANDROVA** 9-0............................6
2007 **PEEPING FAWN** 9-0..........................12
2008 **MOONSTONE** 9-0.............................14
2009 **SARISKA** 9-0...............................10
2010 **SNOW FAIRY** 9-0............................15
2011 **BLUE BUNTING** 9-0...........................9

PHOENIX STAKES (2y)
The Curragh-6f
2002 **SPARTACUS** 9-0..............................9
2003 **ONE COOL CAT** 9-0...........................7
2004 **DAMSON** 8-11................................6
2005 **GEORGE WASHINGTON** 9-0...................7
2006 **HOLY ROMAN EMPEROR** 9-1.................7
2007 **SAOIRSE ABU** 8-12..........................6
2008 **MASTERCRAFTSMAN** 9-1.....................5
2009 **ALFRED NOBEL** 9-1..........................8

2010 **ZOFFANY** 9-1................................7
2011 **LA COLLINA** 8-12............................9

IRISH CHAMPION STAKES
Leopardstown-1m 2f
2002 **GRANDERA** 4-9-4.............................7
2003 **HIGH CHAPARRAL** 4-9-4.....................7
2004 **AZAMOUR** 3-8-11.............................8
2005 **ORATORIO** 3-8-11...........................10
2006 **DYLAN THOMAS** 3-9-0........................5
2007 **DYLAN THOMAS** 4-9-7........................6
2008 **NEW APPROACH** 3-9-0........................8
2009 **SEA THE STARS** 3-9-0........................9
2010 **CAPE BLANCO** 3-9-0..........................6
2011 **SO YOU THINK** 5-9-7.........................6

IRISH CAMBRIDGESHIRE
The Curragh-1m
2002 **MASANI** 3-9-7..............................21
2003 **DEFINITE BEST** 5-8-5.......................15
2004 **DUE RESPECT** 4-8-10........................18
2005 **KESTREL CROSS** 3-9-1.......................20
2006 **QUINMASTER** 4-10-1.........................22
2007 **JALMIRA** 6-8-13.............................24
2008 **TIS MIGHTY** 5-8-1..........................21
2009 **POET** 4-9-9................................27
2010 **HUJAYLEA** 7-8-3............................25
2011 **CASTLE BAR SLING** 6-8-11..................21

MOYGLARE STUD STAKES (2y fillies)
The Curragh-7f
2002 **MAIL THE DESERT** 8-11.......................9
2003 **NECKLACE** 8-11.............................11
2004 **CHELSEA ROSE** 8-11.........................12
2005 **RUMPLESTILTSKIN** 8-11.......................9
2006 **MISS BEATRIX** 8-12..........................12
2007 **SAOIRSE ABU** 8-12...........................9
2008 **AGAIN** 8-12.................................12
2009 **TERMAGANT** 8-12.............................7
2010 **MISTY FOR ME** 8-12.........................12
2011 **MAYBE** 9-1...................................8

NATIONAL STAKES (2y)
The Curragh-7f
2002 **REFUSE TO BEND** 9-0.........................7
2003 **ONE COOL CAT** 9-0...........................8
2004 **DUBAWI** 9-0.................................7
2005 **GEORGE WASHINGTON** 9-0...................7
2006 **TEOFILO** 9-1................................6
2007 **NEW APPROACH** 9-1...........................9
2008 **MASTERCRAFTSMAN** 9-1.....................7
2009 **KINGSFORT** 9-1..............................6
2010 **PATHFORK** 9-1...............................9
2011 **POWER** 9-1..................................9

IRISH ST LEGER
The Curragh-1m 6f
2002 **VINNIE ROE** 4-9-9...........................8
2003 **VINNIE ROE** 5-9-9...........................6
2004 **VINNIE ROE** 6-9-8..........................13
2005 **COLLIER HILL** 7-9-8.........................9
2006 **KASTORIA** 5-9-7.............................8
2007 **YEATS** 6-9-11...............................9
2008 **SEPTIMUS** 5-9-11............................9
2009 **ALANDI** 4-9-11..............................8
2010 **SANS FRONTIERES** 4-9-11...................8
2011 **DUNCAN** 6-9-11 dead heated with..........6
     JUKEBOX JURY 5-9-11........................6

IRISH CESAREWITCH
The Curragh-2m
2002	**AMERICAN GOTHIC** 4-9-0	18
2003	**ZIMBABWE** 3-8-0	17
2004	**ESSEX** 4-7-9	20
2005	**CLARA ALLEN** 7-8-0	17
2006	**IKTITAF** 5-8-8	16
2007	**SANDYMOUNT EARL** 4-9-3	21
2008	**SUAILCE** 3-8-1	28
2009	**DANI CALIFORNIA** 5-8-0	29
2010	**BRIGHT HORIZON** 3-8-7	23
2011	**MINSK** 3-8-9	19

BOYLESPORTS.COM HURDLE
Leopardstown-2m
(Pierse Hurdle before 2010)
(MCR Hurdle in 2011)
2002	**ADAMANT APPROACH** 8-11-1	26
2003	**XENOPHON** 7-10-11	28
2004	**DROMLEASE EXPRESS** 6-10-4	19
2005	**ESSEX** 5-10-8	21
2006	**STUDMASTER** 6-10-3	27
2007	**SPRING THE QUE** 8-10-3	30
2008	**BARKER** 7-10-6	28
2009	**PENNY'S BILL** 7-9-9	29
2010	**PUYOL** 8-10-10	30
2011	**FINAL APPROACH** 5-10-9	26
2012	**CITIZENSHIP** 6-10-3	30

IRISH CHAMPION HURDLE
Leopardstown-2m
2003	**LIKE-A-BUTTERFLY** 9-11-5	5
2004	**FOREMAN** 6-11-10	8
2005	**MACS JOY** 6-11-10	6
2006	**BRAVE INCA** 8-11-10	7

2007	**HARDY EUSTACE** 10-11-10	8
2008	**SIZING EUROPE** 6-11-10	6
2009	**BRAVE INCA** 11-11-10	9
2010	**SOLWHIT** 6-11-10	7
2011	**HURRICANE FLY** 7-11-10	5
2012	**HURRICANE FLY** 8-11-10	5

HENNESSY COGNAC GOLD CUP
Leopardstown-3m
2002	**ALEXANDER BANQUET** 9-12-0	5
2003	**BEEF OR SALMON** 7-12-0	5
2004	**FLORIDA PEARL** 12-11-12	7
2005	**RULE SUPREME** 9-11-12	7
2006	**BEEF OR SALMON** 10-11-12	7
2007	**BEEF OR SALMON** 11-11-12	5
2008	**THE LISTENER** 9-11-10	8
2009	**NEPTUNE COLLONGES** 8-11-10	6
2010	**JONCOL** 7-11-10	7
2011	**KEMPES** 8-11-10	9

IRISH GRAND NATIONAL
Fairyhouse-3m 5f
2002	**THE BUNNY BOILER** 8-9-9	17
2003	**TIMBERA** 9-10-12	21
2004	**GRANIT D'ESTRUVAL** 10-10-0	28
2005	**NUMBERSIXVALVERDE** 9-10-1	26
2006	**POINT BARROW** 8-10-8	26
2007	**BUTLER'S CABIN** 7-10-4	29
2008	**HEAR THE ECHO** 7-10-0	23
2009	**NICHE MARKET** 8-10-5	30
2010	**BLUESEA CRACKER** 8-10-4	26
2011	**ORGANISEDCONFUSION** 6-9-13	25

WINNERS OF PRINCIPAL RACES IN FRANCE

PRIX GANAY
Longchamp-1m 2f 110yds
2002	**AQUARELLISTE** 4-8-13	7
2003	**FAIR MIX** 5-9-2	9
2004	**EXECUTE** 7-9-2	8
2005	**BAGO** 4-9-2	9
2006	**CORRE CAMINOS** 4-9-2	7
2007	**DYLAN THOMAS** 4-9-2	8
2008	**DUKE OF MARMALADE** 4-9-2	6
2009	**VISION D'ETAT** 4-9-2	8
2010	**CUTLASS BAY** 4-9-2	9
2011	**PLANTEUR** 4-9-2	7

POULE D'ESSAI DES POULAINS (3y)
Longchamp-1m
2002	**LANDSEER** 9-2	13
2003	**CLODOVIL** 9-2	10
2004	**AMERICAN POST** 9-2	7
2005	**SHAMARDAL** 9-2	15
2006	**AUSSIE RULES** 9-2	11
2007	**ASTRONOMER ROYAL** 9-2	14
2008	**FALCO** 9-2	19
2009	**SILVER FROST** 9-2	6
2010	**LOPE DE VEGA** 9-2	15
2011	**TIN HORSE** 9-2	14

POULE D'ESSAI DES POULICHES (3y fillies)
Longchamp-1m
2002	**ZENDA** 9-0	17
2003	**MUSICAL CHIMES** 9-0	12
2004	**TORRESTRELLA** 9-0	13
2005	**DIVINE PROPORTIONS** 9-0	8
*2006	**TIE BLACK** 9-0	13
2007	**DARJINA** 9-0	13
2008	**ZARKAVA** 9-0	14
2009	**ELUSIVE WAVE** 9-0	11
**2010	**SPECIAL DUTY** 9-0	10
2011	**GOLDEN LILAC** 9-0	16

*Price Tag disqualified from first place
**Liliside disqualified from first place

PRIX SAINT-ALARY (3y fillies)
Longchamp-1m 2f
2002	**MAROTTA** 9-0	12
2003	**FIDELITE** 9-0	9
2004	**ASK FOR THE MOON** 9-0	7
2005	**VADAWINA** 9-0	8
2006	**GERMANCE** 9-0	8
2007	**COQUERELLE** 9-0	6
2008	**BELLE ET CELEBRE** 9-0	7

2009	**STACELITA** 9-0	.7
2010	**SARAFINA** 9-0	.9
2011	**WAVERING** 9-0	.12

PRIX JEAN PRAT (3y)

Chantilly-1m (1m 1f before 2005)

2002	**ROUVRES** 9-2	.8
2003	**VESPONE** 9-2	.8
2004	**BAGO** 9-2	.8
2005	**TURTLE BOWL** 9-2	.8
2006	**STORMY RIVER** 9-2	.11
2007	**LAWMAN** 9-2	.7
2008	**TAMAYUZ** 9-2	.16
2009	**LORD SHANAKILL** 9-2	.9
2010	**DICK TURPIN** 9-2	.8
2011	**MUTUAL TRUST** 9-2	.7

PRIX D'ISPAHAN

Longchamp-1m 1f 55yds

2002	**BEST OF THE BESTS** 5-9-2	.4
2003	**FALBRAV** 5-9-2	.8
2004	**PRINCE KIRK** 4-9-2	.5
2005	**VALIXIR** 4-9-2	.8
2006	**LAVEROCK** 4-9-2	.11
2007	**MANDURO** 5-9-2	.5
2008	**SAGEBURG** 4-9-2	.6
2009	**NEVER ON SUNDAY** 4-9-2	.9
2010	**GOLDIKOVA** 5-8-13	.8
2011	**GOLDIKOVA** 6-8-13	.9

PRIX DU JOCKEY CLUB (3y)

Chantilly-1m 2f 110yds (1m 4f before 2005)

2001	**ANABAA BLUE** 9-2	.14
2002	**SULAMANI** 9-2	.15
2003	**DALAKHANI** 9-2	.7
2004	**BLUE CANARI** 9-2	.15
2005	**SHAMARDAL** 9-2	.17
2006	**DARSI** 9-2	.15
2007	**LAWMAN** 9-2	.20
2008	**VISION D'ETAT** 9-2	.20
2009	**LE HAVRE** 9-2	.17
2010	**LOPE DE VEGA** 9-2	.22
2011	**RELIABLE MAN** 9-2	.16

PRIX DE DIANE (3y fillies)

Chantilly-1m 2f 110yds

2002	**BRIGHT SKY** 9-0	.15
2003	**NEBRASKA TORNADO** 9-0	.10
2004	**LATICE** 9-0	.17
2005	**DIVINE PROPORTIONS** 9-0	.10
2006	**CONFIDENTIAL LADY** 9-0	.16
2007	**WEST WIND** 9-0	.14
2008	**ZARKAVA** 9-0	.13
2009	**STACELITA** 9-0	.12
2010	**SARAFINA** 9-0	.9
2011	**GOLDEN LILAC** 9-0	.9

GRAND PRIX DE PARIS (3y)

Longchamp-1m 4f (1m 2f before 2005)

2002	**KHALKEVI** 9-2	.6
2003	**VESPONE** 9-2	.11
2004	**BAGO** 9-2	.4
2005	**SCORPION** 9-2	.9
2006	**RAIL LINK** 9-2	.9
2007	**ZAMBEZI SUN** 9-2	.7
2008	**MONTMARTRE** 9-2	.13
2009	**CAVALRYMAN** 9-2	.8

2010	**BEHKABAD** 9-2	.9
2011	**MEANDRE** 9-2	.7

GRAND PRIX DE SAINT-CLOUD

Saint-Cloud-1m 4f

2002	**ANGE GABRIEL** 4-9-8	.6
2003	**ANGE GABRIEL** 5-9-9	.10
2004	**GAMUT** 5-9-9	.10
2005	**ALKAASED** 5-9-2	.11
2006	**PRIDE** 6-8-13	.6
2007	**MOUNTAIN HIGH** 5-9-2	.6
2008	**YOUMZAIN** 5-9-2	.9
2009	**SPANISH MOON** 5-9-2	.10
2010	**PLUMANIA** 4-8-13	.7
2011	**SARAFINA** 4-8-13	.5

PRIX MAURICE DE GHEEST

Deauville-6f 110yds

2002	**MAY BALL** 5-8-13	.9
2003	**PORLEZZA** 4-8-12	.12
2004	**SOMNUS** 4-9-2	.18
2005	**WHIPPER** 4-9-2	.13
2006	**MARCHAND D'OR** 3-8-11	.17
2007	**MARCHAND D'OR** 4-9-2	.13
2008	**MARCHAND D'OR** 5-9-2	.16
2009	**KING'S APOSTLE** 5-9-2	.12
2010	**REGAL PARADE** 6-9-2	.15
2011	**MOONLIGHT CLOUD** 3-8-8	.13

PRIX JACQUES LE MAROIS

Deauville-1m

2002	**BANKS HILL** 4-9-1	.8
2003	**SIX PERFECTIONS** 3-8-9	.12
2004	**WHIPPER** 3-8-11	.10
2005	**DUBAWI** 3-8-11	.6
2006	**LIBRETTIST** 4-9-4	.10
2007	**MANDURO** 5-9-4	.6
2008	**TAMAYUZ** 3-8-11	.8
2009	**GOLDIKOVA** 4-9-0	.9
2010	**MAKFI** 3-8-11	.8
2011	**IMMORTAL VERSE** 3-8-8	.12

PRIX MORNY (2y)

Deauville-6f

2002	**ELUSIVE CITY** 9-0	.6
2003	**VESPONE** 9-0	.8
2004	**DIVINE PROPORTIONS** 8-11	.9
2005	**SILCA'S SISTER** 8-11	.7
2006	**DUTCH ART** 9-0	.7
2007	**MYBOYCHARLIE** 8-13	.6
2008	**BUSHRANGER** 9-0	.14
2009	**ARCANO** 9-0	.5
2010	**DREAM AHEAD** 9-0	.11
2011	**DABIRSIM** 9-0	.7

PRIX DU MOULIN DE LONGCHAMP

Longchamp-1m

2002	**ROCK OF GIBRALTAR** 3-8-11	.7
2003	**NEBRASKA TORNADO** 3-8-8	.14
2004	**GREY LILAS** 3-8-8	.11
2005	**STARCRAFT** 5-9-2	.9
2006	**LIBRETTIST** 4-9-2	.8
2007	**DARJINA** 3-8-8	.9
2008	**GOLDIKOVA** 3-8-8	.11
2009	**AQLAAM** 4-9-2	.9
2010	**FUISSE** 4-9-2	.6
2011	**EXCELEBRATION** 3-8-11	.8

CRITERIUM INTERNATIONAL (2y)
Saint-Cloud-1m
2002 **DALAKHANI** 9-0...5
2003 **BAGO** 9-0..7
2004 **HELIOS QUERCUS** 9-0...................................8
2005 **CARLOTAMIX** 9-0...6
2006 **MOUNT NELSON** 9-0...................................10
2007 **THEWAYYOUARE** 9-0...................................6
2008 **ZAFISIO** 9-0...11
2009 **JAN VERMEER** 9-0.......................................7
2010 **RODERIC O'CONNOR** 9-0............................10
2011 **FRENCH FIFTEEN** 9-0..................................11

PRIX VERMEILLE (fillies and mares)
Longchamp-1m 4f
(for 3yo fillies only prior to 2004)
2002 **PEARLY SHELLS** 9-0.....................................11
2003 **MEZZO SOPRANO** 9-0..................................11
2004 **SWEET STREAM** 4-9-2.................................13
2005 **SHAWANDA** 3-8-7...6
2006 **MANDESHA** 3-8-7...11
2007 **MRS LINDSAY** 3-8-9.....................................10
2008 **ZARKAVA** 3-8-8..12
*2009 **STACELITA** 3-8-8..12
2010 **MIDDAY** 4-9-3..12
2011 **GALIKOVA** 3-8-8..6
*Dar Re Mi disqualified from first place

PRIX DU CADRAN
Longchamp-2m 4f
2002 **GIVE NOTICE** 5-9-2......................................16
2003 **WESTERNER** 4-9-2.......................................10
2004 **WESTERNER** 5-9-6...8
2005 **REEFSCAPE** 4-9-2.......................................10
2006 **SERGEANT CECIL** 7-9-2................................7
2007 **LE MIRACLE** 6-9-2...6
2008 **BANNABY** 5-9-2...11
2009 **ALANDI** 4-9-2...12
2010 **GENTOO** 6-9-2...8
2011 **KASBAH BLISS** 9-9-2...................................10

PRIX DE L'ABBAYE DE LONGCHAMP
Longchamp-5f
2002 **CONTINENT** 5-9-11.......................................20
2003 **PATAVELLIAN** 5-9-11...................................19
2004 **VAR** 5-9-11..15
2005 **AVONBRIDGE** 5-9-11...................................17
2006 **DESERT LORD** 6-9-11...................................14
2007 **BENBAUN** 6-9-11...17
*2008 **MARCHAND D'OR** 5-9-11.............................17
2009 **TOTAL GALLERY** 3-9-11...............................16
2010 **GILT EDGE GIRL** 4-9-7.................................21
2011 **TANGERINE TREES** 6-9-11...........................15
* re-run after false start

PRIX MARCEL BOUSSAC (2y fillies)
Longchamp-1m
2002 **SIX PERFECTIONS** 8-11...............................10
2003 **DENEBOLA** 8-11..16
2004 **DIVINE PROPORTIONS** 8-11.........................10

2005 **RUMPLESTILTSKIN** 8-11..............................15
2006 **FINSCEAL BEO** 8-11....................................13
2007 **ZARKAVA** 8-11..10
2008 **PROPORTIONAL** 8-11...................................16
2009 **ROSANARA** 8-11...11
2010 **MISTY FOR ME** 8-11......................................8
2011 **ELUSIVE KATE** 8-11.......................................5

PRIX JEAN-LUC LAGARDERE (2y)
(Grand Criterium before 2003)
Longchamp-7f
2002 **HOLD THAT TIGER** 9-0.................................14
2003 **AMERICAN POST** 9-0....................................6
2004 **ORATORIO** 9-0..6
2005 **HORATIO NELSON** 9-0..................................6
2006 **HOLY ROMAN EMPEROR** 9-0.........................9
2007 **RIO DE LA PLATA** 9-0....................................8
2008 **NAAQOOS** 9-0...7
2009 **SIYOUNI** 9-0..7
2010 **WOOTTON BASSETT** 9-0................................9
2011 **DABIRSIM** 9-0...7

PRIX DE LA FORET
Longchamp-7f
2002 **DEDICATION** 3-8-11.....................................10
2003 **ETOILE MONTANTE** 3-8-11............................10
2004 **SOMNUS** 4-9-2...7
2005 **COURT MASTERPIECE** 5-9-2..........................8
2006 **CARADAK** 5-9-3...14
2007 **TOYLSOME** 8-9-2...13
2008 **PACO BOY** 3-9-0..8
2009 **VARENAR** 3-9-0...14
2010 **GOLDIKOVA** 5-8-13......................................10
2011 **DREAM AHEAD** 3-9-0......................................8

PRIX ROYAL-OAK
Longchamp-1m 7f 110yds
2002 **MR DINOS** 3-8-9...7
2003 **WESTERNER** 4-9-4......................................14
2004 **WESTERNER** 5-9-4...8
2005 **ALCAZAR** 10-9-4..11
2006 **MONTARE** 4-9-1...11
2007 **ALLEGRETTO** 4-9-1......................................11
2008 **YEATS** 7-9-4...11
2009 **ASK** 6-9-4...9
2010 **GENTOO** 6-9-4...10
2011 **BE FABULOUS** 4-9-1.....................................14

CRITERIUM DE SAINT-CLOUD (2y)
Saint-Cloud-1m 2f
2002 **ALBERTO GIACOMETTI** 9-0..........................10
2003 **VOIX DU NORD** 9-0......................................10
2004 **PAITA** 8-11..7
2005 **LINDA'S LAD** 9-0..5
2006 **PASSAGE OF TIME** 8-11...............................13
2007 **FULL OF GOLD** 9-0..10
2008 **FAME AND GLORY** 9-0..................................11
2009 **PASSION FOR GOLD** 9-0...............................10
2010 **RECITAL** 9-0..10
2011 **MANDAEAN** 9-0...8

WINNERS OF OTHER OVERSEAS RACES

DUBAI WORLD CUP
Meydan-1m 2f Tapeta
(Run at Nad Al Sheba over 1m 2f on dirt before 2010)
2002	STREET CRY 4-9-0	11
2003	MOON BALLAD 4-9-0	11
2004	PLEASANTLY PERFECT 6-9-0	12
2005	ROSES IN MAY 5-9-0	12
2006	ELECTROCUTIONIST 5-9-0	11
2007	INVASOR 5-9-0	7
2008	CURLIN 4-9-0	12
2009	WELL ARMED 6-9-0	14
2010	GLORIA DE CAMPEAO 7-9-0	14
2011	VICTOIRE PISA 4-9-0	14

KENTUCKY DERBY
Churchill Downs-1m 2f dirt
2002	WAR EMBLEM 9-0	18
2003	FUNNY CIDE 9-0	16
2004	SMARTY JONES 9-0	18
2005	GIACOMO 9-0	20
2006	BARBARO 9-0	20
2007	STREET SENSE 9-0	20
2008	BIG BROWN 9-0	20
2009	MINE THAT BIRD 9-0	19
2010	SUPER SAVER 9-0	20
2011	ANIMAL KINGDOM 9-0	19

BREEDERS' CUP TURF
Various courses-1m 4f
2002	HIGH CHAPARRAL 3-8-9	8
2003	JOHAR 4-9-0 dead heated with	
	HIGH CHAPARRAL 4-9-0	9
2004	BETTER TALK NOW 5-9-0	8
2005	SHIROCCO 4-9-0	13
2006	RED ROCKS 3-8-10	11
2007	ENGLISH CHANNEL 5-9-0	8
2008	CONDUIT 3-8-9	7
2009	CONDUIT 4-9-0	7
2010	DANGEROUS MIDGE 4-9-0	7
2011	ST NICHOLAS ABBEY 4-9-0	9

BREEDERS' CUP CLASSIC
Various courses-1m 2f dirt/pro-ride
2002	VOLPONI 4-9-0	12
2003	PLEASANTLY PERFECT 5-9-0	10
2004	GHOSTZAPPER 4-9-0	13
2005	SAINT LIAM 5-9-0	13
2006	INVASOR 4-9-0	13
2007	CURLIN 3-8-9	9
2008	RAVEN'S PASS 3-8-9	12
2009	ZENYATTA 5-8-11	12
2010	BLAME 4-9-0	12
2011	DROSSELMEYER 4-9-0	12

MELBOURNE CUP
Flemington-2m
2002	MEDIA PUZZLE 5-8-4	23
2003	MAKYBE DIVA 4-8-0	23
2004	MAKYBE DIVA 5-8-11	24
2005	MAKYBE DIVA 6-9-2	24
2006	DELTA BLUES 5-8-11	23
2007	EFFICIENT 4-8-8	21
2008	VIEWED 5-8-5	24
2009	SHOCKING 4-8-0	23
2010	AMERICAIN 5-8-8	23
2011	DUNADEN 5-8-8	23

JAPAN CUP
Tokyo-1m 4f
2002	FALBRAV 4-9-0	16
2003	TAP DANCE CITY 6-9-0	18
2004	ZENNO ROB ROY 4-9-0	16
2005	ALKAASED 5-9-0	18
2006	DEEP IMPACT 4-9-0	11
2007	ADMIRE MOON 4-9-0	18
2008	SCREEN HERO 4-9-0	17
2009	VODKA 5-8-10	18
*2010	ROSE KINGDOM 3-8-9	18
2011	BUENA VISTA 5-8-9	16

*Buena Vista disqualified from first place

WINNERS OF PRINCIPAL NATIONAL HUNT RACES

HENNESSY COGNAC GOLD CUP H'CAP CHASE
Newbury-3m 2f 110yds
*2002	GINGEMBRE 8-10-13	25
2003	STRONG FLOW 6-11-0	21
2004	CELESTIAL GOLD 6-10-5	14
2005	TRABOLGAN 6-11-9	19
2006	STATE OF PLAY 6-11-4	16
2007	DENMAN 7-11-12	18
2008	MADISON DU BERLAIS 7-11-4	15
2009	DENMAN 9-11-12	19
2010	DIAMOND HARRY 7-10-0	20

2011	CARRUTHERS 8-10-4	18

*Be My Royal disqualified from first place

KING GEORGE VI CHASE
Kempton-3m
2002	BEST MATE 7-11-10	10
2003	EDREDON BLEU 11-11-10	12
2004	KICKING KING 6-11-10	13
*2005	KICKING KING 7-11-10	9
2006	KAUTO STAR 6-11-10	9
2007	KAUTO STAR 7-11-10	7
2008	KAUTO STAR 8-11-10	10

2009	**KAUTO STAR** 9-11-10	13
**2010	**LONG RUN** 6-11-10	9
2011	**KAUTO STAR** 11-11-10	7

*Run at Sandown
**Run in January 2011

WELSH NATIONAL H'CAP CHASE
Chepstow-3m 5f 110yds

2002	**MINI SENSATION** 9-10-4	16
2003	**BINDAREE** 9-10-9	14
2004	**SILVER BIRCH** 7-10-5	17
2005	**L'AVENTURE** 6-10-4	18
2006	**HALCON GENELARDAIS** 6-11-3	18
2007	**MIKO DE BEAUCHENE** 7-10-5	18
2008	**NOTRE PERE** 7-11-0	20
2009	**DREAM ALLIANCE** 8-10-8	18
*2010	**SYNCHRONISED** 8-11-6	18
2011	**LE BEAU BAI** 8-10-1	20

*Run in January 2011

VICTOR CHANDLER CHASE
(Handicap before 2008)
Ascot-2m 1f (2m before 2008)

2003	ABANDONED	
2004	**ISIO** 8-10-5	13
*2005	**WELL CHIEF** 6-11-10	10
**2006	**TYSOU** 9-11-2	10
2007	ABANDONED	
2008	**TAMARINBLEU** 8-11-7	7
2009	**MASTER MINDED** 6-11-7	5
2010	**TWIST MAGIC** 8-11-7	7
2011	**MASTER MINDED** 8-11-7	9
2012	**SOMERSBY** 8-11-7	8

*Run at Cheltenham
**Run at Sandown

TOTESPORT TROPHY H'CAP HURDLE
Newbury-2m 110yds

2002	**COPELAND** 7-11-7	16
2003	**SPIRIT LEADER** 7-10-0	27
2004	**GEOS** 9-10-9	25
2005	**ESSEX** 5-11-6	25
2006	ABANDONED	
2007	**HEATHCOTE** 5-10-6	20
2008	**WINGMAN** 6-10-0	24
2009	ABANDONED	
2010	**GET ME OUT OF HERE** 6-10-6	23
2011	**RECESSION PROOF** 5-10-8	15

RACING POST H'CAP CHASE
Kempton-3m

2002	**GUNTHER MCBRIDE** 7-10-3	14
2003	**LA LANDIERE** 8-11-7	12
2004	**MARLBOROUGH** 12-11-12	11
2005	**FARMER JACK** 9-11-12	16
*2006	**INNOX** 10-11-0	15
2007	**SIMON** 8-11-5	10
2008	**GUNGADU** 8-11-12	15
2009	**NACARAT** 8-10-13	20
2010	**RAZOR ROYALE** 8-10-5	13
2011	**QUINZ** 7-11-0	16

*Run at Sandown

SUPREME NOVICES' HURDLE
Cheltenham-2m 110yds

2002	**LIKE-A-BUTTERFLY** 8-11-3	28
2003	**BACK IN FRONT** 6-11-8	19
2004	**BRAVE INCA** 6-11-7	19
2005	**ARCALIS** 5-11-7	20

2006	**NOLAND** 5-11-7	20
2007	**EBAZIYAN** 6-11-7	22
2008	**CAPTAIN CEE BEE** 7-11-7	22
2009	**GO NATIVE** 6-11-7	20
2010	**MENORAH** 5-11-7	18
2011	**AL FEROF** 6-11-7	15

ARKLE CHALLENGE TROPHY (NOVICES' CHASE)
Cheltenham-2m

2002	**MOSCOW FLYER** 8-11-8	12
2003	**AZERTYUIOP** 6-11-8	9
2004	**WELL CHIEF** 5-11-3	16
2005	**CONTRABAND** 7-11-7	19
2006	**VOY POR USTEDES** 5-11-2	14
2007	**MY WAY DE SOLZEN** 7-11-7	13
2008	**TIDAL BAY** 7-11-7	14
2009	**FORPADYDEPLASTERER** 7-11-7	17
2010	**SIZING EUROPE** 8-11-7	12
2011	**CAPTAIN CHRIS** 7-11-7	10

CHAMPION HURDLE
Cheltenham-2m 110yds

2002	**HORS LA LOI II** 7-12-0	15
2003	**ROOSTER BOOSTER** 9-12-0	17
2004	**HARDY EUSTACE** 7-11-10	14
2005	**HARDY EUSTACE** 8-11-10	14
2006	**BRAVE INCA** 8-11-10	18
2007	**SUBLIMITY** 7-11-10	10
2008	**KATCHIT** 5-11-10	10
2009	**PUNJABI** 6-11-10	23
2010	**BINOCULAR** 6-11-10	12
2011	**HURRICANE FLY** 7-11-10	11

QUEEN MOTHER CHAMPION CHASE
Cheltenham-2m

2002	**FLAGSHIP UBERALLES** 8-12-0	12
2003	**MOSCOW FLYER** 9-12-0	11
2004	**AZERTYUIOP** 7-11-10	8
2005	**MOSCOW FLYER** 11-11-10	8
2006	**NEWMILL** 8-11-10	12
2007	**VOY POR USTEDES** 6-11-10	10
2008	**MASTER MINDED** 5-11-10	8
2009	**MASTER MINDED** 6-11-10	12
2010	**BIG ZEB** 9-11-10	9
2011	**SIZING EUROPE** 9-11-10	11

NEPTUNE INVESTMENT MANAGEMENT NOVICES' HURDLE
(Royal & SunAlliance Hurdle until 2007,
Ballymore Hurdle 2008-9)
Cheltenham-2m 5f

2002	**GALILEO** 6-11-7	27
2003	**HARDY EUSTACE** 6-11-7	19
2004	**FUNDAMENTALIST** 6-11-7	15
2005	**NO REFUGE** 5-11-7	20
2006	**NICANOR** 5-11-7	14
2007	**MASSINI'S MAGUIRE** 6-11-7	15
2008	**FIVEFORTHREE** 6-11-7	16
2009	**MIKAEL D'HAGUENET** 5-11-7	14
2010	**PEDDLERS CROSS** 5-11-7	17
2011	**FIRST LIEUTENANT** 6-11-7	12

RSA CHASE
(Royal & SunAlliance Chase before 2009)
(Cheltenham-3m

2002	**HUSSARD COLLONGES** 7-11-4	19
2003	**ONE KNIGHT** 7-11-4	9

2004	**RULE SUPREME** 8-11-4	10
2005	**TRABOLGAN** 7-11-4	9
2006	**STAR DE MOHAISON** 5-10-8	15
2007	**DENMAN** 7-11-4	17
2008	**ALBERTAS RUN** 7-11-4	11
2009	**COOLDINE** 7-11-4	15
2010	**WEAPON'S AMNESTY** 7-11-4	9
2011	**BOSTONS ANGEL** 7-11-4	12

WORLD HURDLE
(Stayers' Hurdle before 2005)
Cheltenham-3m

2002	**BARACOUDA** 7-11-10	16
2003	**BARACOUDA** 8-11-10	11
2004	**IRIS'S GIFT** 7-11-10	10
2005	**INGLIS DREVER** 6-11-10	12
2006	**MY WAY DE SOLZEN** 6-11-10	20
2007	**INGLIS DREVER** 8-11-10	17
2008	**INGLIS DREVER** 9-11-10	17
2009	**BIG BUCK'S** 6-11-10	14
2010	**BIG BUCK'S** 7-11-10	14
2011	**BIG BUCK'S** 8-11-10	13

TRIUMPH HURDLE (4y)
Cheltenham-2m 1f

2002	**SCOLARDY** 11-0	28
2003	**SPECTROSCOPE** 11-0	27
2004	**MADE IN JAPAN** 11-0	23
2005	**PENZANCE** 11-0	23
2006	**DETROIT CITY** 11-0	17
2007	**KATCHIT** 11-0	23
2008	**CELESTIAL HALO** 11-0	14
2009	**ZAYNAR** 11-0	18
2010	**SOLDATINO** 11-0	17
2011	**ZARKANDAR** 11-0	23

CHELTENHAM GOLD CUP
Cheltenham-3m 2f 110yds

2002	**BEST MATE** 7-12-0	18
2003	**BEST MATE** 8-12-0	15
2004	**BEST MATE** 9-11-10	10
2005	**KICKING KING** 7-11-10	15
2006	**WAR OF ATTRITION** 7-11-10	22
2007	**KAUTO STAR** 7-11-10	18
2008	**DENMAN** 8-11-10	12
2009	**KAUTO STAR** 9-11-10	16
2010	**IMPERIAL COMMANDER** 9-11-10	11
2011	**LONG RUN** 6-11-0	13

FESTIVAL TROPHY CHASE
Cheltenham-2m 5f

2005	**THISTHATANDTOTHER** 9-11-3	12
2006	**FONDMORT** 10-11-0	11
2007	**TARANIS** 6-11-0	9
2008	**OUR VIC** 10-11-10	9
2009	**IMPERIAL COMMANDER** 8-11-10	10
2010	**ALBERTAS RUN** 9-11-10	13
2011	**ALBERTAS RUN** 10-11-10	11

TOTESPORT BOWL CHASE
(Martell Cup Chase before 2005)
(Betfair Bowl Chase 2005-8)
Aintree-3m 1f

2002	**FLORIDA PEARL** 10-11-12	6
2003	**FIRST GOLD** 10-11-12	7
2004	**TIUTCHEV** 11-11-12	8
2005	**GREY ABBEY** 11-11-12	8
2006	**CELESTIAL GOLD** 8-11-8	9
2007	**EXOTIC DANCER** 7-11-12	5
2008	**OUR VIC** 10-11-10	5
2009	**MADISON DU BERLAIS** 8-11-10	10
2010	**WHAT A FRIEND** 7-11-7	5
2011	**NACARAT** 10-11-7	6

AINTREE HURDLE
Aintree-2m 4f

2002	**ILNAMAR** 6-11-7	14
2003	**SACUNDAI** 6-11-7	11
2004	**RHINESTONE COWBOY** 8-11-7	11
2005	**AL EILE** 5-11-7	9
2006	**ASIAN MAZE** 7-11-0	9
2007	**AL EILE** 7-11-7	11
2008	**AL EILE** 8-11-7	9
2009	**SOLWHIT** 5-11-7	16
2010	**KHYBER KIM** 8-11-7	7
2011	**OSCAR WHISKY** 6-11-7	8

SCOTTISH GRAND NATIONAL (H'CAP CHASE)
Ayr-4m 110 yds (4m 1f before 2007)

2002	**TAKE CONTROL** 8-10-6	18
2003	**RYALUX** 10-10-5	19
2004	**GREY ABBEY** 10-11-12	28
2005	**JOES EDGE** 8-9-11	20
2006	**RUN FOR PADDY** 10-10-2	30
2007	**HOT WELD** 8-9-9	23
2008	**IRIS DE BALME** 8-9-7	24
2009	**HELLO BUD** 11-10-9	17
2010	**MERIGO** 9-10-0	30
2011	**BESHABAR** 9-10-4	28

BET365 GOLD CUP (H'CAP CHASE)
(Attheraces Gold Cup 2002-3,
Betfred Gold Cup 2004-7)
Sandown-3m 5f 110yds

2002	**BOUNCE BACK** 6-10-9	20
2003	**AD HOC** 9-10-10	16
2004	**PUNTAL** 8-11-4	18
2005	**JACK HIGH** 10-10-0	19
2006	**LACDOUDAL** 7-11-5	18
2007	**HOT WELD** 8-10-0	10
2008	**MONKERHOSTIN** 11-10-13	19
2009	**HENNESSY** 8-10-7	14
2010	**CHURCH ISLAND** 11-10-5	19
2011	**POKER DE SIVOLA** 8-10-12	18

DISTANCE CONVERSION

5f	1,000m	10f	2,000m	15f	3,000m	20f	4,000m
6f	1,200m	11f	2,200m	16f	3,200m	21f	4,200m
7f	1,400m	12f	2,400m	17f	3,400m	22f	4,400m
8f	1,600m	13f	2,600m	18f	3,600m		
9f	1,800m	14f	2,800m	19f	3,800m		

LEADING TRAINERS ON THE FLAT: 1898-2011

1898 R Marsh	1936 J Lawson	1974 P Walwyn
1899 J Porter	1937 C Boyd-Rochfort	1975 P Walwyn
1900 R Marsh	1938 C Boyd-Rochfort	1976 H Cecil
1901 J Huggins	1939 J L Jarvis	1977 M V O'Brien
1902 R S Sievier	1940 F Darling	1978 H Cecil
1903 G Blackwell	1941 F Darling	1979 H Cecil
1904 P P Gilpin	1942 F Darling	1980 W Hern
1905 W T Robinson	1943 W Nightingall	1981 M Stoute
1906 Hon G Lambton	1944 Frank Butters	1982 H Cecil
1907 A Taylor	1945 W Earl	1983 W Hern
1908 C Morton	1946 Frank Butters	1984 H Cecil
1909 A Taylor	1947 F Darling	1985 H Cecil
1910 A Taylor	1948 C F N Murless	1986 M Stoute
1911 Hon G Lambton	1949 Frank Butters	1987 H Cecil
1912 Hon G Lambton	1950 C H Semblat	1988 H Cecil
1913 R Wootton	1951 J L Jarvis	1989 M Stoute
1914 A Taylor	1952 M Marsh	1990 H Cecil
1915 P P Gilpin	1953 J L Jarvis	1991 P Cole
1916 R C Dawson	1954 C Boyd-Rochfort	1992 R Hannon
1917 A Taylor	1955 C Boyd-Rochfort	1993 H Cecil
1918 A Taylor	1956 C F Elsey	1994 M Stoute
1919 A Taylor	1957 C F N Murless	1995 J Dunlop
1920 A Taylor	1958 C Boyd-Rochfort	1996 Saeed bin Suroor
1921 A Taylor	1959 C F N Murless	1997 M Stoute
1922 A Taylor	1960 C F N Murless	1998 Saeed bin Suroor
1923 A Taylor	1961 C F N Murless	1999 Saeed bin Suroor
1924 R C Dawson	1962 W Hern	2000 Sir M Stoute
1925 A Taylor	1963 P Prendergast	2001 A O'Brien
1926 F Darling	1964 P Prendergast	2002 A O'Brien
1927 Frank Butters	1965 P Prendergast	2003 Sir M Stoute
1928 Frank Butters	1966 M V O'Brien	2004 Saeed bin Suroor
1929 R C Dawson	1967 C F N Murless	2005 Sir M Stoute
1930 H S Persse	1968 C F N Murless	2006 Sir M Stoute
1931 J Lawson	1969 A M Budgett	2007 A O'Brien
1932 Frank Butters	1970 C F N Murless	2008 A O'Brien
1933 F Darling	1971 I Balding	2009 Sir M. Stoute
1934 Frank Butters	1972 W Hern	2010 R Hannon
1935 Frank Butters	1973 C F N Murless	2011 R Hannon

CHAMPION JOCKEYS ON THE FLAT: 1896-2011

1896 M Cannon	164	1919 S Donoghue	129	1941 H Wragg	71
1897 M Cannon	145	1920 S Donoghue	143	1942 G Richards	67
1898 O Madden	161	1921 S Donoghue	141	1943 G Richards	65
1899 S Loates	160	1922 S Donoghue	102	1944 G Richards	88
1900 L Reiff	143	1923 S Donoghue	89	1945 G Richards	104
1901 O Madden	130	C Elliott	89	1946 G Richards	212
1902 W Lane	170	1924 C Elliott	106	1947 G Richards	269
1903 O Madden	154	1925 G Richards	118	1948 G Richards	224
1904 O Madden	161	1926 T Weston	95	1949 G Richards	261
1905 E Wheatley	124	1927 G Richards	164	1950 G Richards	201
1906 W Higgs	149	1928 G Richards	148	1951 G Richards	227
1907 W Higgs	146	1929 G Richards	135	1952 G Richards	231
1908 D Maher	139	1930 F Fox	129	1953 G Richards	191
1909 F Wootton	165	1931 G Richards	145	1954 D Smith	129
1910 F Wootton	137	1932 G Richards	190	1955 D Smith	168
1911 F Wootton	187	1933 G Richards	259	1956 D Smith	155
1912 F Wootton	118	1934 G Richards	212	1957 A Breasley	173
1913 D Maher	115	1935 G Richards	217	1958 D Smith	165
1914 S Donoghue	129	1936 G Richards	174	1959 D Smith	157
1915 S Donoghue	62	1937 G Richards	216	1960 L Piggott	170
1916 S Donoghue	43	1938 G Richards	206	1961 A Breasley	171
1917 S Donoghue	42	1939 G Richards	155	1962 A Breasley	179
1918 S Donoghue	66	1940 G Richards	68	1963 A Breasley	176

1964 L Piggott.....................140	1981 L Piggott 179	1998 K Fallon 185
1965 L Piggott.....................160	1982 L Piggott 188	1999 K Fallon 200
1966 L Piggott.....................191	1983 W Carson 159	2000 K Darley 152
1967 L Piggott.....................117	1984 S Cauthen 130	2001 K Fallon 166
1968 L Piggott.....................139	1985 S Cauthen 195	2002 K Fallon 144
1969 L Piggott.....................163	1986 Pat Eddery 176	2003 K Fallon 208
1970 L Piggott.....................162	1987 S Cauthen 197	2004 L Dettori 192
1971 L Piggott.....................162	1988 Pat Eddery 183	2005 J Spencer 163
1972 W Carson 132	1989 Pat Eddery 171	2006 R Moore 180
1973 W Carson 164	1990 Pat Eddery 209	2007 S Sanders 190
1974 Pat Eddery 148	1991 Pat Eddery 165	J Spencer 190
1975 Pat Eddery 164	1992 M Roberts 206	2008 R Moore 186
1976 Pat Eddery 162	1993 Pat Eddery 169	2009 R Moore 174
1977 Pat Eddery 176	1994 L Dettori 233	2010 P Hanagan 191
1978 W Carson 182	1995 L Dettori 211	2011 P Hanagan 165
1979 J Mercer 164	1996 Pat Eddery 186	
1980 W Carson 166	1997 K Fallon 196	

LEADING OWNERS ON THE FLAT: 1895-2011

1895 Ld de Rothschild	1934 H.H. Aga Khan	1973 Mr N B Hunt
1896 Ld de Rothschild	1935 H.H. Aga Khan	1974 Mr N B Hunt
1897 Mr J Gubbins	1936 Ld Astor	1975 Dr C Vittadini
1898 Ld de Rothschild	1937 H.H. Aga Khan	1976 Mr D Wildenstein
1899 Duke of Westminster	1938 Ld Derby	1977 Mr R Sangster
1900 H.R.H. The Prince of Wales	1939 Ld Rosebery	1978 Mr R Sangster
1901 Sir G Blundell Maple	1940 Lord Rothermere	1979 Sir M Sobell
1902 Mr R S Sievier	1941 Ld Glanely	1980 S Weinstock
1903 Sir James Miller	1942 His Majesty	1981 H.H. Aga Khan
1904 Sir James Miller	1943 Miss D Paget	1982 Mr R Sangster
1905 Col W Hall Walker	1944 H.H. Aga Khan	1983 Mr R Sangster
1906 Ld Derby (late)	1945 Ld Derby	1984 Mr R Sangster
1907 Col W Hall Walker	1946 H.H. Aga Khan	1985 Sheikh Mohammed
1908 Mr J B Joel	1947 H.H. Aga Khan	1986 Sheikh Mohammed
1909 Mr "Fairie"	1948 H.H. Aga Khan	1987 Sheikh Mohammed
1910 Mr "Fairie"	1949 H.H. Aga Khan	1988 Sheikh Mohammed
1911 Ld Derby	1950 M M Boussac	1989 Sheikh Mohammed
1912 Mr T Pilkington	1951 M M Boussac	1990 Mr Hamdan Al-Maktoum
1913 Mr J B Joel	1952 H. H. Aga Khan	1991 Sheikh Mohammed
1914 Mr J B Joel	1953 Sir Victor Sassoon	1992 Sheikh Mohammed
1915 Mr L Neumann	1954 Her Majesty	1993 Sheikh Mohammed
1916 Mr E Hulton	1955 Lady Zia Wernner	1994 Mr Hamdan Al-Maktoum
1917 Mr "Fairie"	1956 Maj L B Holliday	1995 Mr Hamdan Al-Maktoum
1918 Lady James Douglas	1957 Her Majesty	1996 Godolphin
1919 Ld Glanely	1958 Mr J McShain	1997 Sheikh Mohammed
1920 Sir Robert Jardine	1959 Prince Aly Khan	1998 Godolphin
1921 Mr S B Joel	1960 Sir Victor Sassoon	1999 Godolphin
1922 Ld Woolavington	1961 Maj L B Holliday	2000 H.H. Aga Khan
1923 Ld Derby	1962 Maj L B Holliday	2001 Godolphin
1924 H.H. Aga Khan	1963 Mr J R Mullion	2002 Mr Hamdan Al-Maktoum
1925 Ld Astor	1964 Mrs H E Jackson	2003 K Abdullah
1926 Ld Woolavington	1965 M J Ternynck	2004 Godolphin
1927 Ld Derby	1966 Lady Zia Wernham	2005 Mr Hamdan Al-Maktoum
1928 Ld Derby	1967 Mr H J Joel	2006 Godolphin
1929 H.H. Aga Khan	1968 Mr Raymond R Guest	2007 Godolphin
1930 H.H. Aga Khan	1969 Mr D Robinson	2008 HRH Princess Haya of Jordan
1931 Mr J A Dewar	1970 Mr C Engelhard	2009 Mr Hamdan Al-Maktoum
1932 H.H. Aga Khan	1971 Mr P Mellon	2010 K Abdullah
1933 Ld Derby	1972 Mrs J Hislop	2011 K Abdullah

LEADING SIRES ON THE FLAT: 1895-2011

1895 St Simon	1900 St Simon	1905 Gallinule
1896 St Simon	1901 St Simon	1906 Persimmon
1897 Kendal	1902 Persimmon	1907 St Frusquin
1898 Galopin	1903 St Frusquin	1908 Persimmon
1899 Orme	1904 Gallinule	1909 Cyllene

1910 Cyllene	1944 Fairway	1978 Mill Reef (USA)
1911 Sundridge	1945 Hyperion	1979 Petingo
1912 Persimmon	1946 Hyperion	1980 Pitcairn
1913 Desmond	1947 Nearco	1981 Great Nephew
1914 Polymelus	1948 Big Game	1982 Be My Guest (USA)
1915 Polymelus	1949 Nearco	1983 Northern Dancer
1916 Polymelus	1950 Fair Trial	1984 Northern Dancer
1917 Bayardo	1951 Nasrullah	1985 Kris
1918 Bayardo	1952 Tehran	1986 Nijinsky (CAN)
1919 The Tetrarch	1953 Chanteur II	1987 Mill Reef (USA)
1920 Polymelus	1954 Hyperion	1988 Caerleon (USA)
1921 Polymelus	1955 Alycidon	1989 Blushing Groom (FR)
1922 Lemberg	1956 Court Martial	1990 Sadler's Wells (USA)
1923 Swynford	1957 Court Martial	1991 Caerleon (USA)
1924 Son-in-Law	1958 Mossborough	1992 Sadler's Wells (USA)
1925 Phalaris	1959 Petition	1993 Sadler's Wells (USA)
1926 Hurry On	1960 Aureole	1994 Sadler's Wells (USA)
1927 Buchan	1961 Aureole	1995 Sadler's Wells (USA)
1928 Phalaris	1962 Never Say Die	1996 Sadler's Wells (USA)
1929 Tetratema	1963 Ribot	1997 Sadler's Wells (USA)
1930 Son-in-Law	1964 Chamossaire	1998 Sadler's Wells (USA)
1931 Pharos	1965 Court Harwell	1999 Sadler's Wells (USA)
1932 Gainsborough	1966 Charlottesville	2000 Sadler's Wells (USA)
1933 Gainsborough	1967 Ribot	2001 Sadler's Wells (USA)
1934 Blandford	1968 Ribot	2002 Sadler's Wells (USA)
1935 Blandford	1969 Crepello	2003 Sadler's Wells (USA)
1936 Fairway	1970 Northern Dancer	2004 Sadler's Wells (USA)
1937 Solario	1971 Never Bend	2005 Danehill (USA)
1938 Blandford	1972 Queen's Hussar	2006 Danehill (USA)
1939 Fairway	1973 Vaguely Noble	2007 Danehill (USA)
1940 Hyperion	1974 Vaguely Noble	2008 Galileo (IRE)
1941 Hyperion	1975 Great Nephew	2009 Danehill Dancer (IRE)
1942 Hyperion	1976 Wolver Hollow	2010 Galileo (IRE)
1943 Fairway	1977 Northern Dancer	2011 Galileo (IRE)

LEADING BREEDERS ON THE FLAT: 1911-2011

1911 Ld Derby (late)	1941 Ld Glanely	1970 Mr E P Taylor
1912 Col. W Hall Walker	1942 National Stud	1971 Mr P Mellon
1913 Mr J B Joel	1943 Miss D Paget	1972 Mr J Hislop
1914 Mr J B Joel	1944 Ld Rosebery	1973 Claiborne Farm
1915 Mr L Neumann	1945 Ld Derby	1974 Mr N B Hunt
1916 Mr E Hulton	1946 Lt- Col H Boyd-Rochfort	1975 Overbury Stud
1917 Mr "Fairie"	1947 H.H. Aga Khan	1976 Dayton Ltd
1918 Lady James Douglas	1948 H.H. Aga Khan	1977 Mr E P Taylor
1919 Ld Derby	1949 H.H. Aga Khan	1978 Cragwood Estates Inc
1920 Ld Derby	1950 M M Boussac	1979 Ballymacoll Stud
1921 Mr S B Joel	1951 M M Boussac	1980 P Clarke
1922 Ld Derby	1952 H. H. Aga Khan	1981 H.H. Aga Khan
1923 Ld Derby	1953 Mr F Darling	1982 Someries Stud
1924 Lady Sykes	1954 Maj L B Holliday	1983 White Lodge Stud
1925 Ld Astor	1955 Someries Stud	1984 Mr E P Taylor
1926 Ld Woolavington	1956 Maj L B Holliday	1985 Dalham Stud Farms
1927 Ld Derby	1957 Eve Stud	1986 H.H. Aga Khan
1928 Ld Derby	1958 Mr R Ball	1987 Cliveden Stud
1929 Ld Derby	1959 Prince Aly Khan and the late	1988 H. H. Aga Khan
1930 Ld Derby	H.H. Aga Khan	1989 Mr Hamdan Al- Maktoum
1931 Ld Dewar	1960 Eve Stud Ltd	1990 Capt. Macdonald- Buchanan
1932 H.H. Aga Khan	1961 Eve Stud Ltd	1991 Barronstown Stud
1933 Sir Alec Black	1962 Maj L B Holliday	1992 Swettenham Stud
1934 H.H. Aga Khan	1963 Mr H F Guggenheim	1993 Juddmonte Farms
1935 H.H. Aga Khan	1964 Bull Run Stud	1994 Shadwell Farm & Estate Ltd
1936 Ld Astor	1965 Mr J Ternynck	1995 Shadwell Farm & Estate Ltd
1937 H.H. Aga Khan	1966 Someries Stud	1996 Sheikh Mohammed
1938 Ld Derby	1967 Mr H J Joel	1997 Sheikh Mohammed
1939 Ld Rosebery	1968 Mill Ridge Farm	1998 Sheikh Mohammed
1940 Mr H E Morriss	1969 Lord Rosebery	1999 H. H. The Aga Khan's Studs

2000 H. H. The Aga Khan's Studs	2004 Juddmonte	2008 Darley
2001 Shadwell Farm & Estate Ltd	2005 Shadwell Farm & Estate Ltd	2009 Darley
2002 Gainsborough Stud	2006 Darley	2010 Juddmonte
2003 Juddmonte	2007 Darley	2011 Juddmonte

LEADING TRAINERS OVER JUMPS: 1946-2011

1946-47 F T T Walwyn	1968-69 T F Rimell	1990-91 M C Pipe
1947-48 F T T Walwyn	1969-70 T F Rimell	1991-92 M C Pipe
1948-49 F T T Walwyn	1970-71 F T Winter	1992-93 M C Pipe
1949-50 P V F Cazalet	1971-72 F T Winter	1993-94 D Nicholson
1950-51 T F Rimell	1972-73 F T Winter	1994-95 D Nicholson
1951-52 N Crump	1973-74 F T Winter	1995-96 M C Pipe
1952-53 M V O'Brien	1974-75 F T Winter	1996-97 M C Pipe
1953-54 M V O'Brien	1975-76 T F Rimell	1997-98 M C Pipe
1954-55 H R Price	1976-77 F T Winter	1998-99 M C Pipe
1955-56 W Hall	1977-78 F T Winter	1999-00 M C Pipe
1956-57 N Crump	1978-79 M H Easterby	2000-01 M C Pipe
1957-58 F T T Walwyn	1979-80 M H Easterby	2001-02 M C Pipe
1958-59 H R Price	1980-81 M H Easterby	2002-03 M C Pipe
1959-60 P V F Cazalet	1981-82 M W Dickinson	2003-04 M C Pipe
1960-61 T F Rimell	1982-83 M W Dickinson	2004-05 M C Pipe
1961-62 H R Price	1983-84 M W Dickinson	2005-06 P F Nicholls
1962-63 K Piggott	1984-85 F T Winter	2006-07 P F Nicholls
1963-64 F T T Walwyn	1985-86 N J Henderson	2007-08 P F Nicholls
1964-65 P V F Cazalet	1986-87 N J Henderson	2008-09 P F Nicholls
1965-66 H R Price	1987-88 D R C Elsworth	2009-10 P F Nicholls
1966-67 H R Price	1988-89 M C Pipe	2010-11 P F Nicholls
1967-68 Denys Smith	1989-90 M C Pipe	

CHAMPION JOCKEYS OVER JUMPS: 1901-2011

Prior to the 1925-26 season the figure relates to racing between January and December

1901	F Mason	58	1934-35 G Wilson	73	1967-68 J Gifford	82
1902	F Mason	67	1935-36 G Wilson	57	1968-69 B R Davies	77
1903	P Woodland	54	1936-37 G Wilson	45	T Biddlecombe	77
1904	F Mason	59	1937-38 G Wilson	59	1969-70 B R Davies	91
1905	F Mason	73	1938-39 T F Rimell	61	1970-71 G Thorner	74
1906	F Mason	58	1939-40 T F Rimell	24	1971-72 B R Davies	89
1907	F Mason	59	1940-41 G Wilson	22	1972-73 R Barry	125
1908	P Cowley	65	1941-42 R Smyth	12	1973-74 R Barry	94
1909	R Gordon	45	1942-43 No racing		1974-75 T Stack	82
1910	E Piggott	67	1943-44 No racing		1975-76 J Francome	96
1911	W Payne	76	1944-45 H Nicholson	15	1976-77 T Stack	97
1912	I Anthony	78	T F Rimell	15	1977-78 J J O'Neill	149
1913	E Piggott	60	1945-46 T F Rimell	54	1978-79 J Francome	95
1914	Mr J R Anthony	60	1946-47 J Dowdeswell	58	1979-80 J J O'Neill	117
1915	E Piggott	44	1947-48 B Marshall	66	1980-81 J Francome	105
1916	C Hawkins	17	1948-49 T Moloney	60	1981-82 J Francome	120
1917	W Smith	15	1949-50 T Moloney	95	P Scudamore	120
1918	G Duller	17	1950-51 T Moloney	83	1982-83 J Francome	106
1919	Mr H Brown	48	1951-52 T Moloney	99	1983-84 J Francome	131
1920	F B Rees	64	1952-53 F Winter	121	1984-85 J Francome	101
1921	F B Rees	65	1953-54 R Francis	76	1985-86 P Scudamore	91
1922	J Anthony	78	1954-55 T Moloney	67	1986-87 P Scudamore	123
1923	F B Rees	64	1955-56 F Winter	74	1987-88 P Scudamore	132
1924	F B Rees	108	1956-57 F Winter	80	1988-89 P Scudamore	221
1925	E Foster	76	1957-58 F Winter	82	1989-90 P Scudamore	170
1925-26 T Leader	61	1958-59 T Brookshaw	83	1990-91 P Scudamore	141
1926-27 F B Rees	59	1959-60 S Mellor	68	1991-92 P Scudamore	175
1927-28 W Stott	88	1960-61 S Mellor	118	1992-93 R Dunwoody	173
1928-29 W Stott	65	1961-62 S Mellor	80	1993-94 R Dunwoody	197
1929-30 W Stott	77	1962-63 J Gifford	70	1994-95 R Dunwoody	160
1930-31 W Stott	81	1963-64 J Gifford	94	1995-96 A P McCoy	175
1931-32 W Stott	77	1964-65 T Biddlecombe	114	1996-97 A P McCoy	190
1932-33 G Wilson	61	1965-66 T Biddlecombe	102	1997-98 A P McCoy	253
1933-34 G Wilson	56	1966-67 J Gifford	122	1998-99 A P McCoy	186

1999-00 A P McCoy 245	2003-04 A P McCoy 209	2007-08 A P McCoy 140
2000-01 A P McCoy 191	2004-05 A P McCoy 200	2008-09 A P McCoy 186
2001-02 A P McCoy 289	2005-06 A P McCoy 178	2009-10 A P McCoy 195
2002-03 A P McCoy 256	2006-07 A P McCoy 184	2010-11 A P McCoy 218

LEADING OWNERS OVER JUMPS: 1946-2011

(Please note that prior to the 1994-95 season the leading owner was determined by win prizemoney only)

1946-47 Mr J J McDowell	1968-69 Mr B P Jenks	1990-91 Mr P Piller
1947-48 Mr J Proctor	1969-70 Mr E R Courage	1991-92 Whitcombe Manor
1948-49 Mr W F Williamson	1970-71 Mr F Pontin	Racing Stables Ltd
1949-50 Mrs L Brotherton	1971-72 Capt T A Forster	1992-93 Mrs J Mould
1950-51 Mr J Royle	1972-73 Mr N H Le Mare	1993-94 Pell-Mell Partners
1951-52 Miss D Paget	1973-74 Mr N H Le Mare	1994-95 Roach Foods Limited
1952-53 Mr J H Griffin	1974-75 Mr R Guest	1995-96 Mr A T A Wates
1953-54 Mr J H Griffin	1975-76 Mr P B Raymond	1996-97 Mr R Ogden
1954-55 Mrs W H E Welman	1976-77 Mr N H Le Mare	1997-98 Mr D A Johnson
1955-56 Mr L Carver	1977-78 Mrs O Jackson	1998-99 Mr J P McManus
1956-57 Mrs Geoffrey Kohn	1978-79 Snailwell Stud Co Ltd	1999-00 Mr R Ogden
1957-58 Mr D J Coughlan	1979-80 Mr H J Joel	2000-01 Sir R Ogden
1958-59 Mr J E Bigg	1980-81 Mr R J Wilson	2001-02 Mr D A Johnson
1959-60 Miss W H Wallace	1981-82 Sheikh Ali Abu Khamsin	2002-03 Mr D A Johnson
1960-61 Mr C Vaughan	1982-83 Sheikh Ali Abu Khamsin	2003-04 Mr D A Johnson
1961-62 Mr N Cohen	1983-84 Sheikh Ali Abu Khamsin	2004-05 Mr D A Johnson
1962-63 Mr P B Raymond	1984-85 T Kilroe and Son Ltd	2005-06 Mr J P McManus
1963-64 Mr J K Goodman	1985-86 Sheikh Ali Abu Khamsin	2006-07 Mr J P McManus
1964-65 Mrs M Stephenson	1986-87 Mr H J Joel	2007-08 Mr D A Johnson
1965-66 Duchess of Westminster	1987-88 Miss Juliet E Reed	2008-09 Mr J P McManus
1966-67 Mr C P T Watkins	1988-89 Mr R Burridge	2009-10 Mr J P McManus
1967-68 Mr H S Alper	1989-90 Mrs Harry J Duffey	2010-11 Mr T Hemmings

LEADING AMATEUR RIDERS OVER JUMPS: 1947-2011

1947-48 Ld Mildmay 22	1968-69 Mr R Tate 17	1989-90 Mr P McMahon 15
1948-49 Ld Mildmay 30	1969-70 Mr M Dickinson 23	1990-91 Mr K Johnson 24
1949-50 Ld Mildmay 38	1970-71 Mr J Lawrence 17	1991-92 Mr M P Hourigan 24
1950-51 Mr P Chisman 13	1971-72 Mr W Foulkes 26	1992-93 Mr A Thornton 26
1951-52 Mr C Straker 19	1972-73 Mr R Smith 56	1993-94 Mr J Greenall 21
1952-53 Mr A H Moralee 22	1973-74 Mr A Webber 21	1994-95 Mr D Parker 16
1953-54 Mr A H Moralee 22	1974-75 Mr R Lamb 22	1995-96 Mr J Culloty 40
1954-55 Mr A H Moralee 13	1975-76 Mr P Greenall 25	1996-97 Mr R Thornton 30
1955-56 Mr R McCreery 13	Mr G Jones 25	1997-98 Mr S Durack 41
Mr A H Moralee 13	1976-77 Mr P Greenall 27	1998-99 Mr A Dempsey 47
1956-57 Mr R McCreery 23	1977-78 Mr G Sloan 23	1999-00 Mr P Flynn 41
1957-58 Mr J Lawrence 18	1978-79 Mr T G Dun 26	2000-01 Mr T Scudamore 24
1958-59 Mr J Sutcliffe 18	1979-80 Mr O Sherwood 29	2001-02 Mr D Crosse 19
1959-60 Mr G Kindersley 22	1980-81 Mr P Webber 32	2002-03 Mr C Williams 23
1960-61 Sir W Pigott-Brown 28	1981-82 Mr D Browne 28	2003-04 Mr O Nelmes 14
1961-62 Mr A Biddlecombe 30	1982-83 Mr D Browne 33	2004-05 Mr T Greenall 31
1962-63 Sir W Pigott-Brown 28	1983-84 Mr S Sherwood 28	2005-06 Mr T O'Brien 32
1963-64 Mr S Davenport 32	1984-85 Mr S Sherwood 30	2006-07 Mr T Greenall 31
1964-65 Mr M Gifford 15	1985-86 Mr T Thomson Jones ... 25	2007-08 Mr T Greenall 23
1965-66 Mr C Collins 24	1986-87 Mr T Thomson Jones ... 19	2008-09 Mr O Greenall 23
1966-67 Mr C Collins 33	1987-88 Mr T Thomson Jones ... 15	2009-10 Mr O Greenall 41
1967-68 Mr R Tate 30	1988-89 Mr P Fenton 18	2010-11 Mr R Mahon 19

LEADING SIRES OVER JUMPS: 1986-2011

1986 Deep Run	1994-95 Strong Gale	2003-04 Be My Native (USA)
1987 Deep Run	1995-96 Strong Gale	2004-05 Supreme Leader
1988 Deep Run	1996-97 Strong Gale	2005-06 Supreme Leader
1989 Deep Run	1997-98 Strong Gale	2006-07 Presenting
1989-90 Deep Run	1998-99 Strong Gale	2007-08 Old Vic
1990-91 Deep Run	1999-00 Strong Gale	2008-09 Presenting
1991-92 Deep Run	2000-01 Be My Native (USA)	2009-10 Presenting
1992-93 Deep Run	2001-02 Be My Native (USA)	2010-11 Presenting
1993-94 Strong Gale	2002-03 Be My Native (USA)	

JOCKEYS' AGENTS

Jockeys' Agents and their Contact Details

Agent	Telephone	Mobile/Email	Fax
NICKY ADAMS	01488 72004/72964	07796 547659 nadams52@yahoo.com	
NEIL ALLAN	01243 543870	07825 549081 aneil@aol.com	
NIGEL BAXTER	01942 269972	07973 561521 nigelbaxter@blueyonder.co.uk	01942 269989
PAUL BRIERLEY	01434 608212	07824 828750 paulbrierley@hotmail.co.uk	
CHRIS BROAD	01452 760482/447	07836 622858 c.j.broad@talk21.com	01452 760394
MR A. BURKE	01638 602208	07825 330392 anyprice2001@hotmail.com	
LIZ BUTTERWORTH	01768 361363	07917 717346 lizb345@hotmail.com	
PAUL CLARKE	01638 660804	07885 914306 paul.clarke79@btinternet.com	
RAY COCHRANE	01223 812008	07798 651247	
DANIEL CREIGHTON		07597 945219 danielcreighton@hotmail.com	
SIMON DODDS	01509 852344/852254	07974 924735 simon.dodds@btinternet.com	
JACQUI DOYLE	01672 871894	07831 880678 doyleracing@yahoo.co.uk	

Agent	Telephone	Mobile/Email	Fax
SHIPPY ELLIS	01638 668484	07860 864864 shippysjockeys@btconnect.com	01638 660946
TONY ELVES	01233 363445	07969 051306 tony.elves@yahoo.co.uk	
JOHN W FORD	01954 261122	07830 294210 john.ford47@btinternet.com	
MARK FURNASS		07988 203831 jockeysagent@gmail.com	
MARK GILCHRIST	01903 883356	07810 821787 shaz.gilly@hotmail.co.uk	01903 883797
PAUL GRUNDY	01845 597850	07760 993936 wpgi@btinternet.com	
MICHAEL HAGGAS	01638 660811	07740 624550 mhaggas@ntlworld.com	
RICHARD HALE	01768 88699	07909 520542 richardhale77@hotmail.co.uk	
DAVID HARRISON	0161 4087888	07592 767206 davidpharrison@hotmail.com	
ALAN HARRISON	01969 625006	07846 187991 ahjockagent60@yahoo.co.uk	0560 2729293
RICHARD HARRISON	01325 732186/182	richard694@btinternet.co.uk	
TONY HIND	01638 724997	07807 908599 tonyhind@jockeysagents.com	
GAVIN HORNE	01392 423352/01638 552206	07914 897170/07787 748712 gavin.horne@hotmail.co.uk	
RUSS JAMES	01653 699466	07947 414001 russjames2006@btinternet.com	01653 691455

Agent	Telephone	Mobile/Email	Fax
BRUCE JEFFREY	01750 21521	07747 854684 brucejeffrey@live.co.uk	
GUY JEWELL	01672 861231	07765 248859 guyjewell@btconnect.com	01672 861231
ANDREW LEWIS	01908 365945	07838 506594 andrew.lewis11@sky.com	
ANDY MACHIN	01924 210015	07941 422016 andy@andymachin.com	
SARA-LOUISE METCALFE	01635 298067	07900 207018 troopersjockeys@hotmail.co.uk	
LOUISE MILLMAN	01884 266620	07740 932791 rod.millman@ic24.net	
PHILIP MITCHELL	01372 273729	07836 231462 philip@downshouse.com	01372 278701
LEE NEWTON	01302 724679	07710 422437 newton808@btinternet.com	
TERRY NORMAN	01279 419395	07900 525033 tjnorman@hotmail.co.uk	01279 432619
GARETH OWEN	01638 428007	07958 335206 willowracing@gmail.com	
SHASHI RIGHTON	01353 688081	07825 318350 slasher74@aol.com	
DAVE ROBERTS	01737 761369	07860 234342 daveroberts.racing@ntlworld.com	
JOHN ROBERTSON	01284 850805/850807	07860 235151 jockeys@btinternet.com	01284 850807
WILLIE RYAN	01638 666644	07775 858285 willieryan1@hotmail.com	

Agent	Telephone	Mobile/Email	Fax
ROBERT STRONGE	01635 248710	07887 521333 robert@stronge4380.freeserve.co.uk	
SAM STRONGE	01488 72818	07775 727778 sam.stronge@virgin.net	01488 73790
GARY THOMSON	01642 873152	07722 059231/07986 607014 garythomson73@yahoo.com	01284 850807
JENNIFER WALSH	00353 45883704	00353 87258025 jennifer@ruby-walsh.com	00353 45871929
IAN WARDLE	01793 688858/688859	07831 865974 ian.wardlex@googlemail.com	

FLAT JOCKEYS

Riding weights and contact details

An index of agents appears on page 687

Jockey	Weight	Agent
EDDIE AHERN	8 - 5	Mr W. Ryan
AHMED AJTEBI	8 - 3	Mr S. T. Dodds
DAVID ALLAN	8 - 7	Mr S. M. Righton
PADDY ASPELL	9 - 0	Mr R. A. Hale
ANDREA ATZENI	7 - 12	Mr Paul Clarke
GEORGE BAKER	9 - 0	Mr G. D. Jewell
GARY BARTLEY	8 - 8	Mr R. A. Hale
MATTIE BATCHELOR	9 - 4	Mr Dave Roberts\
		Mr Mark Gilchrist
PADRAIG BEGGY	8 - 5	Mr R. A. Hale
TRAVIS BLOCK	8 - 9	Mr G. J. Horne
WILLIAM BUICK	8 - 6	Mr M. R. Haggas
ROBERT L. BUTLER	8 - 10	Mr R. A. Hale
NEIL CALLAN	8 - 7	Mr S. T. Dodds
WILLIAM CARSON	8 - 2	Mr Neil Allan
CHRIS CATLIN	8 - 3	Mr N. M. Adams
JOHN CAVANAGH	8 - 4	Mr John W. Ford
NEIL CHALMERS	8 - 4	Miss S. L. Metcalfe
CHRIS D. COGAN	8 - 0	Mr A. D. Lewis
PAT COSGRAVE	8 - 7	Mr S. M. Righton
MARK COUMBE	8 - 7	Mr Mark Gilchrist
STEPHEN CRAINE	8 - 9	Mr Mark Gilchrist
EDDIE CREIGHTON	8 - 5	Mr Daniel Creighton
JIM CROWLEY	8 - 7	Mr G. D. Jewell
TONY CULHANE	8 - 7	Mr Mark Gilchrist
SILVESTRE DE SOUSA	7 - 12	Mr G. R. Owen
FRANKIE DETTORI	8 - 7	Mr R. Cochrane
PAT DOBBS	8 - 6	Mr Tony Hind
STEVIE DONOHOE	8 - 5	Mr S. T. Dodds
JAMES DOYLE	8 - 7	Ms J. M. Doyle
STEVE DROWNE	8 - 6	Mr I. P. Wardle
TED DURCAN	8 - 5	Mr D. P. Harrison
MARTIN DWYER	8 - 4	Mr G. R. Owen
TOM EAVES	8 - 7	Mr R. A. Hale
ANDREW ELLIOTT	8 - 2	Mr N. A. Baxter
KIEREN FALLON	8 - 5	Mr T. J. Norman
JOE FANNING	8 - 2	Mr W. P. Grundy
DURAN FENTIMAN	7 - 12	Mr Alan Harrison
MICKY FENTON	8 - 7	Mr L. Newton
ROYSTON FFRENCH	8 - 3	Mr S. T. Dodds
ROBBIE FITZPATRICK	8 - 6	Mr S. M. Righton
JIMMY FORTUNE	8 - 9	Mr Tony Hind
DOMINIC FOX	7 - 12	M. Furnass
CATHY GANNON	7 - 12	Mr Neil Allan
NATALIA GEMELOVA	7 - 9	M. Furnass
GRAHAM GIBBONS	8 - 4	Mr L. Newton
SALEEM GOLAM	8 - 4	Mr Alan Harrison
JAMIE GOLDSTEIN	8 - 7	Mr Mark Gilchrist
J-P GUILLAMBERT	8 - 9	Mr G. D. Jewell
MARC HALFORD	8 - 6	Mr Daniel Creighton
TONY HAMILTON	8 - 3	Mr R. A. Hale
PAUL HANAGAN	8 - 0	Mr R. A. Hale
KELLY HARRISON	8 - 0	Mr Alan Harrison
ROBERT HAVLIN	8 - 6	Mr I. P Wardle
MICHAEL HILLS	8 - 0	Mr B. J. Robertson
RICHARD HILLS	8 - 4	Mr B. J. Robertson
SAM HITCHCOTT	8 - 5	Mr N. M. Adams
DARRYLL HOLLAND	8 - 7	Mr G. R. Owen
RICHARD HUGHES	8 - 7	Mr Tony Hind
LIAM JONES	8 - 4	Mr Paul Clarke
SHANE KELLY	8 - 7	Mr G. J. Horne
LIAM KENIRY	8 - 7	Mr N. M. Adams
RUSS KENNEMORE	8 - 8	Mr L. R. James
RICHARD KINGSCOTE	8 - 4	Mr G. D. Jewell
ADAM KIRBY	8 - 11	Mr N. M. Adams
MARTIN LANE	8 - 0	07549 982481
MARK LAWSON	8 - 7	S. Stronge
JAMIE MACKAY	7 - 12	Mr L. Newton
NICKY MACKAY	7 - 12	Mr Paul Clarke
PHILLIP MAKIN	8 - 9	Mr R. A. Hale
KYLIE MANSER	8 - 7	07920 772182
JEMMA MARSHALL	7 - 13	Mr A. D. Lewis
PATRICK MATHERS	8 - 0	Mr R. A. Hale
ADRIAN McCARTHY	7 - 13	Mr N. A. Baxter
DANIELLE McCREERY	7 - 7	Mr L. R. James
FRANKIE McDONALD	7 - 12	Mr N. M. Adams
P. J. McDONALD	8 - 4	Mr R. A. Hale
BARRY McHUGH	8 - 4	Mr R. A. Hale
TOM McLAUGHLIN	8 - 8	Mr G. J. Horne
IVA MILICKOVA	8 - 0	07814 475787
JAMES MILLMAN	8 - 11	Mrs L. S. Millman
JACK MITCHELL	8 - 8	Mr Philip Mitchell
IAN MONGAN	8 - 9	Mr N. M. Adams
RYAN MOORE	8 - 7	07764 926452
LUKE MORRIS	8 - 0	Mr Neil Allan
ANDREW MULLEN	8 - 0	Mr S. M. Righton
RICHARD MULLEN	8 - 5	Mr Tony Hind
PAUL MULRENNAN	8 - 6	Mr R. A. Hale
LEE NEWMAN	8 - 6	Mr Alan Harrison
LEE NEWNES	8 - 7	Mr John W. Ford
ADRIAN NICHOLLS	8 - 2	Mr S. M. Righton
DAVID NOLAN	8 - 12	Mr R. A. Hale
P. NOLAN	8 - 4	07985 445118
FRANNY NORTON	8 - 0	Mr I. P. Wardle
DARAGH O'DONOHOE	8 - 4	07956 612898
SLADE O'HARA	8 - 10	07789 195750
DANE O'NEILL	8 - 6	Mr N. M. Adams
TADHG O'SHEA	8 - 2	Mr G. D. Jewell
GILMAR PEREIRA	8 - 7	07765596278
LAURA PIKE	7 - 13	S. Stronge
HARRY POULTON	8 - 9	Mr R. T. Harrison
RUSSELL PRICE	8 - 7	078173 17359
DAVID PROBERT	7 - 12	Miss S. L. Metcalfe
TOM QUEALLY	8 - 6	Mr T. Elves
AMIR QUINN	8 - 9	07957948040
JIMMY QUINN	7 - 12	Mr G. J. Horne
PAUL QUINN	7 - 12	Mr S. M. Righton
SEB SANDERS	8 - 7	Mr G. R. Owen
VICTOR SANTOS	7 - 12	0762 608 9222
RICHARD SMITH	8 - 4	077209 15405
JAMIE SPENCER	8 - 6	Mr D. P Harrison
MICHAEL STAINTON	8 - 6	Mr John W. Ford
ANN STOKELL	8 - 2	07814 579982
KRISTIN STUBBS	8 - 7	07932 977279
JAMES SULLIVAN	7 - 12	Mr R. A. Hale
FERGUS SWEENEY	8 - 8	Mr N. M. Adams

DALE SWIFT	8 - 7	Mr R. A. Hale
L. SWIFT	9 - 0	01653 658537
RICHARD THOMAS	8 - 2	Mr I. P. Wardle
DANIEL TUDHOPE	8 - 7	Mr Alan Harrison
HAYLEY TURNER	8 - 2	Mr G. D. Jewell
FREDERIK TYLICKI	8 - 6	Mr R. A. Hale
LEE VICKERS	8 - 10	07515 876829
A. WHELAN	8 - 4	Mr A. D. Lewis
ROBERT WINSTON	8 - 6	Mr S. T. Dodds

APPRENTICES

Riding weights and contact details

An index of agents appears on page 687

LUCY ALEXANDER (N. W. Alexander)	9 - 0	Mr R. A. Hale
NATHAN ALISON (Jim Boyle)	7 - 12	Mr S. M. Righton
ROSS ATKINSON (Tom Dascombe)	8 - 4	Mr R. A. Hale
TOBY ATKINSON (Marco Botti)	8 - 4	Mr Paul Clarke
LEAH-ANNE AVERY (J. W. Hills)	8 - 2	c/o 01488 731 44
LAURA BARRY (Richard Fahey)	7 - 12	Mr R. A. Hale
LUCY K. BARRY (Clive Cox)	8 - 4	Mr L. R. James
JOSH BAUDAINS (Jo Hughes)	8 - 0	c/o 07900 680 189
HARRY BENTLEY (Gary Moore)	7 - 9	Mr G. D. Jewell
ADAM BESCHIZZA (William Haggas)	8 - 0	Mr John W. Ford
CHARLES BISHOP (Mick Channon)	8 - 0	Miss S. L. Metcalfe
PAUL BOOTH (Dean Ivory)	7 - 10	Mr A. D. Lewis
BRADLEY BOSLEY (John Ryan)	7 - 0	c/o 01638 664 172
DANNY BROCK (Chris Wall)	8 - 0	Mr W. Ryan
HENRY BROOKE (Donald McCain)	8 - 13	Mr R. A. Hale
THOMAS BROWN (Andrew Balding)	8 - 3	Mr Mark Gilchrist
JULIE BURKE (Kevin Ryan)	7 - 13	Mr R. A. Hale
HAYLEY BURTON (Luca Cumani)	8 - 3	c/o 01638 665 432
DARYL BYRNE (Mark Johnston)	8 - 5	Mr G. R. Owen\Mr Alan Harrison
ADAM CARTER (Tim Easterby)	8 - 0	Mr N. A. Baxter
GEORGE CHALONER (Richard Fahey)	8 - 5	Mr R. A. Hale
AARON CHAVE (Michael Attwater)	8 - 6	Mr N. A. Baxter
RYAN CLARK (Stuart Williams)	8 - 2	c/o 01638 560143
TIM CLARK (Sir Mark Prescott Bt)	8 - 3	Miss S. L. Metcalfe
MATTHEW COSHAM (David Evans)	8 - 0	Mr Neil Allan
JOSH CRANE (Chris Dwyer)	8 - 5	Mr A. D. Lewis
ALAN CREIGHTON (Edward Creighton)	8 - 12	Mr Daniel Creighton
DANIEL CREMIN (Jim Boyle)	8 - 0	c/o 01372 748 800
NED CURTIS (Roger Curtis)	8 - 0	c/o 07836 320 690
RAUL DA SILVA (Jeremy Gask)	7 - 12	Mr Neil Allan
MATTHEW DAVIES (George Baker)	8 - 5	c/o 01725 518889
PATRICK DONAGHY (Michael Dods)	8 - 0	Mr R. A. Hale
GEORGE DOWNING (Tony Carroll)	8 - 4	Mr L. R. James
KATIE DOWSON (Micky Hammond)	8 - 0	c/o 07808 572 777
SOPHIE DOYLE (Jamie Osborne)	7 - 11	Ms J. M. Doyle
JACK DUERN (Reg Hollinshead)	7 - 4	Mr L. R. James
RYAN DUTHIE (Gary Moore)	9 - 0	c/o 01403 891 912
THOMAS DYER (Clive Cox)	7 - 12	c/o 01488 730 72
NATASHA EATON (Alan Bailey)	7 - 12	M. Furnass
CHARLES EDDERY (Richard Guest)	8 - 0	c/o 07760 755741
SHANNON EDMONDSON (Willie Musson)	8 - 3	c/o 01638 663371
D. E. EGAN (Ronald Harris)	7 - 8	Mr Neil Allan
RICHARD EVANS (David Evans)	9 - 0	c/o 01873 890 837
JOHN FAHY (Clive Cox)	8 - 2	Mr N. M. Adams
NEIL FARLEY (Declan Carroll)	7 - 7	c/o 07801 553 779
JENNIFER FERGUSON (Olivia Maylam)	8 - 0	Mr Daniel Creighton
ROB J FITZPATRICK (Alan McCabe)	7 - 12	c/o 07766 302 092
GERARD GALLIGAN (Nigel Twiston-Davies)	8 - 12	c/o 07836 664 440
NOEL GARBUTT (Rae Guest)	7 - 2	Mr L. R. James
THOMAS GARNER (Warren Greatrex)	9 - 5	Mr Dave Roberts
PAUL HAINEY (Gay Kelleway)	7 - 9	c/o 07974 948768
MARTIN HARLEY (Joseph Tuite)	8 - 5	Mr T. Elves
DANIEL HARRIS (Christine Dunnett)	7 - 10	c/o 07775 793 523
JASON HART (Declan Carroll)	8 - 0	Mr Alan Harrison
ALICE HAYNES (David Simcock)	7 - 12	Mr A. D. Lewis
JOSEPH HAYNES (Andrew Balding)	7 - 7	c/o 01635 298210
THOMAS HEMSLEY (Michael Bell)	8 - 1	c/o 07802 264 514
DEAN HESLOP (David Barron)	8 - 2	Mr Alan Harrison

PATRICK HILLS (J. W. Hills)	8 - 5	Mr W. Ryan
MALIN HOLMBERG (Roger Varian)	8 - 0	c/o 01638 661702
MATTHEW HOPKINS (Alan Berry)	7 - 9	c/o 07880 553 515
TALIB HUSSAIN (Luca Cumani)	8 - 1	c/o 01638 665 432
CHARLOTTE JENNER (Laura Mongan)	8 - 4	c/o 07788 122942
ROSIE JESSOP (Sir Mark Prescott Bt)	7 - 13	Mr G. R. Owen
SHANE B. KELLY (Richard Fahey)	8 - 2	Mr R. A. Hale
DAVID KENNY (George Baker)	8 - 4	Mr L. R. James
MICHAEL KENNY (Declan Carroll)	7 - 12	c/o 07801 553 779
RACHEAL KNELLER (Mark Usher)	8 - 2	Mr R. T. Harrison
MATTHEW LAWSON (Charles Hills)	8 - 0	Mr Mark Gilchrist
MARTIN LEONARD (Sheena West)	8 - 5	c/o 01273 621 303
SEAN LEVEY (Richard Hannon)	8 - 6	Mr Tony Hind
NORA LOOBY (Alan McCabe)	7 - 4	Mr John W. Ford
KEVIN LUNDIE (David Evans)	7 - 0	c/o 01873 890 837
LEONNA MAYOR (Alastair Lidderdale)	8 - 0	Mr I. P. Wardle
MATTHEW MCGHEE (Bill Moore)	8 - 4	c/o 07834 884 060
PAUL MCGIFF (Kevin Ryan)	7 - 7	c/o 01845 597 622
ADAM MCLEAN (Andrew Balding)	8 - 3	c/o 01635 298210
LUKE MCNIFF (David Barron)	8 - 7	Mr Alan Harrison
CHRISTY MEWS (Pam Sly)	7 - 4	c/o 01733 270 298
DANIELLE MOONEY (Nigel Tinkler)	7 - 12	Mr John W. Ford
EVA MOSCROP (Nigel Tinkler)	7 - 10	c/o 07836 384 225
JADE MUGGERIDGE (Brian Meehan)	8 - 12	c/o 01672 517 191
ANTIOCO MURGIA (Mahmood Al Zarooni)	8 - 3	
MICHAEL J. MURPHY (Ed Walker)	8 - 6	Mr A. D. Lewis
CLAIRE MURRAY (David Brown)	8 - 5	c/o 07889 132931
JORDAN NASON (Geoffrey Harker)	8 - 3	c/o 07803 116412
GEMMA NELLIST (Marco Botti)	7 - 12	c/o 07775 803 007
JUSTIN NEWMAN (Bryan Smart)	8 - 8	M. Furnass
NICOLE NORDBLAD (Hans Adielsson)	7 - 3	Mr Neil Allan
HANNAH NUNN (John Berry)	7 - 7	Mr L. Newton
MICHAEL O'CONNELL (David Nicholls)	8 - 7	Mr S. T. Dodds
KIERAN O'NEILL (Richard Hannon)	7 - 6	Mr Tony Hind
RICHARD OLD (Mrs K. Burke)	7 - 13	Mr A. D. Lewis
JAKE PAYNE (Bill Turner)	8 - 0	S. Stronge
SIMON PEARCE (Andrew Balding)	7 - 12	Mr N. M. Adams
PAUL PICKARD (Brian Ellison)	8 - 0	Mr N. A. Baxter
EDWARD PIERCE (Bryan Smart)	8 - 7	c/o 07748 634 797
BRENDAN POWELL (Colin Tizzard)	8 - 1	Mr G. D. Jewell\Mr Dave Roberts
RYAN POWELL (J. S. Moore)	7 - 12	Mr N. M. Adams
JAMES ROGERS (William Muir)	8 - 1	Mr L. R. James
ACCURSIO ROMEO (Brett Johnson)	8 - 2	c/o 07768 697 141
LUKE ROWE (Mrs K. Burke)	8 - 3	Mr Mark Gilchrist
AMY RYAN (Kevin Ryan)	8 - 3	Mr R. A. Hale
AMY SCOTT (Henry Candy)	7 - 9	M. Furnass
DAVID SIMMONSON (Michael Easterby)	8 - 2	Mr R. A. Hale
KIRSTEN SMITH (Martin Bosley)	7 - 12	c/o 07778 938 040
ROSS SMITH (Linda Perratt)	8 - 5	c/o 07931 306 147
ROBERT SPENCER (Mark Usher)	8 - 1	c/o 07831 873 531
JESSICA STEVEN (Terry Clement)	6 - 0	c/o 07885 674474
LUKE STRONG (Tim Walford)	8 - 4	M. Furnass
RYAN TATE (Clive Cox)	7 - 13	c/o 01488 730 72
JORDAN TAYLOR (Luca Cumani)	7 - 12	c/o 01638 665 432
SHIRLEY TEASDALE (David Nicholls)	7 - 13	Mr S. M. Righton
STEPHANIE THEWLIS (Sir Mark Prescott Bt)	8 - 2	c/o 01638 662 117
BRIAN TOOMEY (Kevin Ryan)	9 - 3	Mr Dave Roberts
LEE TOPLISS (Richard Fahey)	8 - 5	Mr R. A. Hale
JORDAN UYS (Alan Jarvis)	8 - 4	c/o 01296 730707
JEAN VAN OVERMEIRE (Roger Varian)	8 - 4	c/o 01638 661702
DAVID WARREN (Pat Eddery)	8 - 0	c/o 01844 296 153
RYAN WHILE (Bill Turner)	8 - 0	c/o 07932 100173
GARRY WHILLANS (Alan Swinbank)	8 - 6	Mr R. A. Hale
JONATHAN WILLETTS (Andrew Balding)	7 - 12	c/o 01635 298210
BEN WILLIAMS (Tom Dascombe)	8 - 3	c/o 01948 820485
FRANCESCA WOLITER (Peter Niven)	7 - 4	c/o 07860 260 999

JUMP JOCKEYS

Riding weights and contact details

An index of agents appears on page 687

LEIGHTON ASPELL	10 - 0	07971 675127
JAMES BANKS	9 - 7	Mr L. R. James
MATTIE BATCHELOR	9 - 7	Mr Dave Roberts\
		Mr Mark Gilchrist
COLIN BOLGER	10 - 0	Mr C. D. Broad
MARK BRADBURNE	10 - 4	07773 327377
PADDY BRENNAN	10 - 0	Mr Dave Roberts
PETER BUCHANAN	10 - 0	Mr R. A. Hale
ALAIN CAWLEY	9 - 10	Mr Dave Roberts
STEVEN CLEMENTS	10 - 5	Mr C. D. Broad
AIDAN COLEMAN	10 - 0	S. Stronge
DANNY COOK	10 - 0	Mr R. A. Hale
DOUGIE COSTELLO	9 - 10	Mr Dave Roberts
DAVE CROSSE	10 - 0	Mr L. R. James
JAMES DAVIES	10 - 0	Mr L. R. James
FEARGHAL DAVIS	10 - 0	Mr G. J. Thomson
FELIX DE GILES	10 - 0	Mr Dave Roberts
JIMMY DERHAM	9 - 11	Mr C. D. Broad
JACK DOYLE	10 - 2	07799 623272
ROBERT DUNNE	9 - 9	Mr Daniel Creighton
DOMINIC ELSWORTH	10 - 2	Mr Dave Roberts
DAVID ENGLAND	10 - 0	Mr C. D. Broad
DONAL FAHY	10 - 0	S. Stronge
JAN FALTEJSEK	10 - 0	Mr Paul Brierley
JOHNNY FARRELLY	10 - 0	07811 113363
NOEL FEHILY	10 - 0	Mr C. D. Broad
ALISTAIR FINDLAY	10 - 0	Mr Paul Brierley
RHYS FLINT	10 - 5	Mr Dave Roberts
HADDEN FROST	10 - 0	Mr Dave Roberts
STEVEN GAGAN	10 - 0	01768 351354
BARRY GERAGHTY	10 - 3	Mr Dave Roberts
CAMPBELL GILLIES	10 - 0	Mr Paul Brierley
ANDREW GLASSONBURY	10 - 2	01884 840 715
MARC GOLDSTEIN	9 - 9	07974 414363
MARK GRANT	10 - 1	Mr C. D. Broad
RACHAEL GREEN	9 - 7	01308 868272
BRIAN HARDING	10 - 0	Mr R. A. Hale
LIAM HEARD	10 - 3	Mr C. D. Broad
CHRIS HONOUR	10 - 0	Mr Dave Roberts
BRIAN HUGHES	9 - 10	Mr R. A. Hale
WAYNE HUTCHINSON	10 - 0	Mr C. D. Broad
DARYL JACOB	10 - 2	Mr C. D. Broad
KENNY JOHNSON	10 - 0	07774 131121
RICHARD JOHNSON	10 - 0	Mr Dave Roberts
SAM JONES	10 - 0	Mr Dave Roberts
WAYNE KAVANAGH	9 - 7	07894330363
BARRY KENIRY	10 - 0	Mr Dave Roberts
WILL KENNEDY	10 - 0	Mr Dave Roberts
PHIL KINSELLA	10 - 0	Mr R. A. Hale
ADRIAN LANE	10 - 0	Mr C. D. Broad
GRAHAM LEE	10 - 0	Mr R. A. Hale
JASON MAGUIRE	10 - 5	Mr C. D. Broad
RYAN MANIA	10 - 0	Mr J. B. Jeffrey
MICHAEL MCALISTER	10 - 0	Mr Paul Brierley
JIMMY MCCARTHY	10 - 0	Mr L. R. James
A. P. MCCOY	10 - 4	Mr Dave Roberts
RICHIE MCGRATH	10 - 0	Mr R. A. Hale
RICHIE MCLERNON	9 - 9	S. Stronge
KEITH MERCER	10 - 0	Mr R. A. Hale
ALEX MERRIAM	10 - 0	Mr L. R. James
TOM MESSENGER	10 - 0	Mr L. R. James
JODIE MOGFORD	10 - 0	Mr Dave Roberts
PAUL MOLONEY	10 - 0	Mr Dave Roberts
JAMIE MOORE	10 - 0	Mr Robert Stronge
TIMMY MURPHY	10 - 0	Mr C. D. Broad
TOM O'BRIEN	10 - 0	Mr Dave Roberts
TOM O'CONNOR	10 - 2	S. Stronge
STEPHEN O'DONOVAN	10 - 4	Mr C. D. Broad
ALAN O'KEEFFE	10 - 5	Mr Dave Roberts
DENIS O'REGAN	10 - 2	S. Stronge
HENRY OLIVER	10 - 0	0770 106 8759
TOMMY PHELAN	9 - 10	Mr Dave Roberts
ADAM POGSON	10 - 8	07977016155
CHARLIE POSTE	10 - 0	Mr Dave Roberts
MARK QUINLAN	9 - 9	Mr Dave Roberts
SEAN QUINLAN	10 - 0	Mr C. D. Broad
WILSON RENWICK	10 - 0	Mr R. A. Hale
JAMES REVELEY	10 - 0	Mr R. A. Hale
NICK SCHOLFIELD	10 - 0	Mr Dave Roberts
TOM SCUDAMORE	10 - 0	Mr Dave Roberts
TOM SIDDALL	10 - 0	Mr Dave Roberts
HARRY SKELTON	10 - 0	Mr Dave Roberts
LEE STEPHENS	10 - 0	07966 386166
CHARLIE STUDD	9 - 9	Mr L. R. James
GERRY SUPPLE	10 - 7	07767790947
GARETH THOMAS	9 - 12	07775 933621
SAM THOMAS	10 - 9	S. Stronge
ANDREW THORNTON	10 - 2	Mr Dave Roberts
ROBERT THORNTON	10 - 0	Mr C. D. Broad
ANDREW TINKLER	10 - 0	Mr Dave Roberts
JOE TIZZARD	10 - 5	S. Stronge
LIAM TREADWELL	10 - 0	Mr Dave Roberts
GERARD TUMELTY	10 - 0	Mr C. D. Broad
SAM TWISTON-DAVIES	9 - 9	Mr C. D. Broad
ROBERT WALFORD	10 - 0	07815 116209
R. WALSH	10 - 1	Miss J. Walsh
EWAN WHILLANS	9 - 11	Mr Paul Brierley
CHRISTIAN WILLIAMS	10 - 0	Mr Dave Roberts

CONDITIONALS

Their employer and contact details

An index of agents appears on page 687

Name	Weight	Contact
NATHAN ADAMS (Laura Mongan)	9 - 10	c/o 07788 122942
JOSEPH AKEHURST (Gary Moore)	9 - 12	Mr Robert Stronge
LUCY ALEXANDER (N. W. Alexander)	9 - 0	Mr R. A. Hale
GEORGE BARTLETT (Venetia Williams)	9 - 10	Mr L. R. James
DAVID BASS (Nicky Henderson)	10 - 0	Mr Dave Roberts
JOEL BELBIN (James Moffatt)	10 - 1	Mr G. J. Thomson
THOMAS BELLAMY (David Pipe)	9 - 7	Mr C. D. Broad
JAMES BEST (Philip Hobbs)	9 - 7	Mr Dave Roberts
JONATHON BEWLEY (George Bewley)	10 - 0	Mr J. B. Jeffrey
PAUL BOHAN (Ian Williams)	9 - 12	c/o 01564 822 392
HENRY BROOKE (Donald McCain)	9 - 7	Mr R. A. Hale
MICHAEL BYRNE (Tim Vaughan)	10 - 0	Mr Dave Roberts
SHANE BYRNE (Sue Smith)	10 - 5	Mr L. R. James\Miss E. J. Butterworth
TOM CANNON (Chris Gordon)	10 - 0	Mr Dave Roberts
PETER CARBERRY (Richard Phillips)	9 - 6	Mr Dave Roberts
HARRY CHALLONER (Venetia Williams)	9 - 4	S. Stronge\Mr R. A. Hale
BEN CLARKE (Simon Burrough)	10 - 0	Mr L. R. James
EMMA CLUTTERBUCK (Alan King)	9 - 5	c/o 01793 815 009
GRANT COCKBURN (Lucinda Russell)	9 - 7	Mr R. A. Hale
JOE COLLIVER (Micky Hammond)	9 - 7	Mr R. A. Hale
AODHAGAN CONLON (Rebecca Curtis)	10 - 0	Mr Dave Roberts
NATHAN COOK (Tom Symonds)	9 - 4	c/o 07823324649
ED COOKSON (Kim Bailey)	9 - 10	c/o 01242 890 241
JOE CORNWALL (John Cornwall)	9 - 7	c/o 07939 557091
RYAN CRAWFORD (Anthony Honeyball)	10 - 0	c/o 01308 867452
MATT CRAWLEY (Lucy Wadham)	10 - 0	c/o 07980 545 776
CHRIS DAVIES (Philip Hobbs)	10 - 0	Mr Dave Roberts
HARRY DERHAM (Paul Nicholls)	9 - 7	c/o 01749 860 656
GARY DERWIN (Nicky Henderson)	9 - 7	Mr L. R. James
DONAL DEVEREUX (Peter Bowen)	9 - 11	Mr Dave Roberts
LEE EDWARDS (Tony Carroll)	9 - 11	Mr C. D. Broad
DONOVAN ELDIN (Richard Rowe)	9 - 8	c/o 07831 345636
JONATHAN ENGLAND (Sue Smith)	9 - 7	Mr C. D. Broad
LEE EVANS (Rebecca Curtis)	10 - 4	c/o 07970 710 690
CONOR FLANNELLY (Donald McCain)	9 - 0	c/o 01829 720 352
THOMAS FLINT (John Flint)	10 - 0	Mr Dave Roberts
ANTHONY FREEMAN (Fergal O'Brien)	9 - 7	Mr C. D. Broad
CRAIG GALLAGHER (Ben Haslam)	9 - 6	Mr R. A. Hale
THOMAS GARNER (Warren Greatrex)	9 - 5	Mr Dave Roberts
ZACHERY-JAMES GAUGHAN (Sue Smith)	9 - 5	c/o 07903 311959
C. P. GEOGHEGAN (Philip Hobbs)	9 - 10	Mr G. J. Thomson
ED GLASSONBURY (Victor Dartnall)	10 - 0	Mr Dave Roberts
GEMMA GRACEY-DAVISON (Zoe Davison)	9 - 3	Mr Robert Stronge
JAKE GREENALL (Henry Daly)	9 - 12	Mr Dave Roberts
CHARLES GREENE (Kim Bailey)	10 - 0	Mr C. D. Broad
MATT GRIFFITHS (Philip Hobbs)	10 - 0	Mr Dave Roberts
ANDRIAS GUERIN (Neil Mulholland)	9 - 7	Mr Robert Stronge
PETER HATTON (Alan King)	9 - 7	Mr Dave Roberts
GILES HAWKINS (Philip Hobbs)	9 - 11	Mr Dave Roberts
FRANCIS HAYES (David Pipe)	9 - 2	c/o 01884 840715
HARRY HAYNES (Lisa Harrison)	9 - 11	Mr Robert Stronge\Mr R. A. Hale
DANIEL HISKETT (Martin Keighley)	9 - 7	Mr Dave Roberts
JAMES HUXHAM (Henrietta Knight)	9 - 7	c/o 07860 110153
CHARLIE HUXLEY (Alan King)	10 - 0	c/o 01793 815 009
KYLE JAMES (Brian Ellison)	9 - 11	Mr L. R. James
COREY JONES (Martin Bosley)	9 - 7	c/o 07778 938 040
TONY KELLY (Ferdy Murphy)	10 - 0	c/o 01969 622 289
ARRON KENNEDY (Robin Dickin)	10 - 0	c/o 07979 518 593

Name (Trainer)	Weight	Contact
JASON KIELY (Tim Vaughan)	9 - 7	c/o 01446 771 626
RICHARD KILLORAN (Nicky Henderson)	9 - 11	Mr Dave Roberts
JOHN KINGTON (Donald McCain)	9 - 11	Mr Dave Roberts
ROBERT KIRK (Tim Vaughan)	9 - 3	Mr Dave Roberts
GARRY LAVERY (Malcolm Jefferson)	9 - 4	c/o 07710 502 044
EDMOND LINEHAN (Nicky Henderson)	9 - 4	Mr Dave Roberts
MAURICE LINEHAN (Jonjo O'Neill)	9 - 10	c/o 01386 584 209
RYAN MAHON (Paul Nicholls)	9 - 11	Mr Dave Roberts
MARK MARRIS (Sarah Humphrey)	9 - 12	Mr L. R. James
ROBERT MCCARTH (Ferdy Murphy)	9 - 12	Mr R. A. Hale
JEREMIAH MCGRATH (Nicky Henderson)	10 - 0	Mr Dave Roberts
CIARAN MCKEE (Alan King)	9 - 6	Mr C. D. Broad
ROSIE MCKEE (Lucy Wadham)	8 - 13	c/o 07980 545 776
DARYL MILLAR (John Wade)	9 - 9	Mr Paul Brierley
TOM MOLLOY (Graeme McPherson)	10 - 0	Mr Robert Stronge
JOSHUA MOORE (Gary Moore)	10 - 0	Mr Robert Stronge
KILLIAN MOORE (Graeme McPherson)	9 - 4	Mr Dave Roberts
NATHAN MOSCROP (James Ewart)	10 - 4	Mr R. A. Hale
STEPHEN MULQUEEN (Maurice Barnes)	9 - 4	Mr Paul Brierley
ADAM NICOL (Andrew Crook)	9 - 9	Mr Paul Brierley
CONOR O'FARRELL (David Pipe)	9 - 11	S. Stronge
DARREN O'KEEFFE (Seamus Mullins)	10 - 0	Mr L. R. James
LEE OSWIN (Gary Moore)	10 - 2	c/o 01403 891 912
JOSEPH PALMOWSKI (George Moore)	9 - 6	c/o 07711 321117
IAN POPHAM (Martin Keighley)	9 - 11	Mr Dave Roberts
BRENDAN POWELL (Colin Tizzard)	8 - 2	Mr G. D. Jewell\Mr Dave Roberts
DEAN PRATT (John Quinn)	9 - 7	Mr R. A. Hale
DAVID PRICHARD (Paul Nicholls)	9 - 7	Mr Dave Roberts
JACK QUINLAN (John Ferguson)	9 - 0	Mr Dave Roberts
GERALD QUINN (Tom George)	9 - 7	S. Stronge
CONOR QUISH (Emma Lavelle)	9 - 7	c/o 01264 735412
CONOR RING (Evan Williams)	9 - 4	c/o 07950 381227
JAMES ROBINSON (Kate Walton)	9 - 10	Mr L. R. James
GARY RUTHERFORD (Harriet Graham)	9 - 7	Mr J. B. Jeffrey
GAVIN SHEEHAN (Charlie Mann)	9 - 5	Mr C. D. Broad
SHANE SHORTALL (Ian Williams)	9 - 13	c/o 01564 822 392
NATHAN SWEENEY (Bob Buckler)	9 - 0	Mr Dave Roberts
C. D. TIMMONS (Oliver Sherwood)	9 - 5	Mr Dave Roberts
BRIAN TOOMEY (Kevin Ryan)	9 - 2	Mr Dave Roberts
BRIAN TREANOR (Nicky Richards)	9 - 0	c/o 01768 483392
WILLIAM TWISTON-DAVIES (Nigel Twiston-Davies)	9 - 0	Mr C. D. Broad
ALEXANDER VOY (Chris Grant)	9 - 9	Mr R. A. Hale
JOSH WALL (John O'Shea)	9 - 7	Mr L. R. James
CHARLIE WALLIS (Nicky Henderson)	9 - 10	Mr Dave Roberts
CHRISTOPHER WARD (Robin Dickin)	9 - 7	Mr Robert Stronge
ADAM WEDGE (Evan Williams)	9 - 7	Mr Dave Roberts
SAMUEL WELTON (Mrs K. Burke)	9 - 7	c/o 01969 625 088
TREVOR WHELAN (Neil King)	9 - 7	Mr L. R. James
CALLUM WHILLANS (Donald McCain)	9 - 7	Mr R. A. Hale
GARRY WHILLANS (Alan Swinbank)	8 - 7	Mr R. A. Hale
JOHN WINSTON (Ferdy Murphy)	10 - 0	Mr R. A. Hale
ROSS WISHART (David Arbuthnot)	9 - 4	Mr C. D. Broad
KIELAN WOODS (Charlie Longsdon)	9 - 12	Mr C. D. Broad

Are your contact details missing or incorrect?
If so please update us by email:
richard.lowther@racingpost.co.uk
or leave a message on 0500 007071

AMATEUR RIDERS

Riding weights and contact details

An index of agents appears on page 687

ALEXANDER, C. 10 - 0 .... 07799 191093
ALLAN, M. 9 - 2 .... 07530 633577
ALLAN, V. L. 9 - 2 .... 07703 355878
ALLWOOD, S. J. 11 - 3 .... 07738 413579
ANDERSON, A. J. 9 - 3 .... 07949 053812
ANDREWS, B. E. 8 - 2 .... 07545 288950
ANDREWS, G. 9 - 7 .... Mr C. D. Broad
BAILEY, J. 11 - 0 .... 07813 994 980
BAKER, Z. C. N. 9 - 12 .... 07769 531572
BAMONTE, D. J. 9 - 0 .... 01884 266320
BANNON, K. 8 - 0 .... 07944 415554
BARBER, J. 10 - 0 .... 07904 185720
BARBER, M. 9 - 12 .... 07974 619012
BARFOOT-SAUNT, G. C. 10 - 9 .... 01684 833227
BARNES, A. C. 8 - 0 .... 07904 144018
BARR, V. G. 9 - 4 .... 01609 780777
BARRETT, E. 9 - 7 .... 07805 683189
BARRETT, RAY 9 - 2 .... 07505 508740
BARTLEY, C. A. 9 - 0 .... 07734 303862
BELL, C. 9 - 0. .... 07775 954269
BERRY, ALAN 10 - 7 .... 07875 436963
BERRY, S. J. 10 - 0 07961038489
BETHELL, H. 9 - 8 07733424242
BEWLEY, C. D. 9 - 10 .... 07766 384822
BIDDICK, W. E. T. 11 - 0 .... 07976 556823
BIRD, A. 9 - 7 .... 07983 524849
BIRKETT, R. A. 9 - 7 .... 07855 065036
BIRKETT, S. 8 - 7 .... 07969 777694
BLAKEMORE, A. R. 8 - 2 .... 07525 812038
BOINVILLE, N. W. 9 - 7 .... 07786 331176
BOXALL, C. E. 9 - 0 .... Mr L. R. James
BREWER, F. 9 - 9 .... 01347 888208
BRIDGE, E. L. 9 - 12 .... 01980 845921
BRISBOURNE, R. M. 9 - 8 .... Mr Alan Harrison
BROCKBANK, S. 9 - 4 .... 07729 426771
BROMLEY, J. 9 - 0 .... 07792 051898
BROOKE, L. 9 - 2 .... 07786 962 911
BROTHERTON, S. 8 - 12 .... 07740 257 110
BROWN, C. L. 10 - 0 ...... 01980 626344 J. W. Mullins
BROWN, J. 9 - 7 ....
BROWN, P. 8 - 8. .... 07585 802364
BRYANT, M. P. 9 - 10 .... 07976 217542
BRYSON, K. A. 9 - 10 .... 07851 921496
BUCK, J. M. 9 - 8 .... 01984 667229
BURCHELL, D. G. 9 - 12 07824332899
BUSHBY, S. 8 - 0. .... 07938 536002
BUTTERWORTH, E. 9 - 0. .... 07917 717346
BUXTON, J. P. 9 - 3. .... 07914 455520
CAMERON, C. 9 - 7 .... 07969 818984
CAMPBELL, B. H. 8 - 10. .... 07542 403644
CARR, J. 10 - 0 .... 07706 550218
CARROLL, C. E. 9 - 8 .... 07770 472431
CARSON, G. 9 - 3. .... 07525 370078
CASEY, V. 9 - 0. .... 01740 620582
CHADWICK, A. 8 - 11 ....
CHANIN, I. 10 - 0 .... 01258 817271
CHEESMAN, T. 9 - 7 .... 07513 109598
CHENERY, M. 11 - 3 07967911360

CLARK, K. E. 8 - 0 07826827659
CLARK, R. 9 - 8. .... 07790 192789
CLARKE, S. 10 - 2 .... 07724 587530
COBB, G. 6 - 10. .... 077532 77753
COFFILL-BROWN, J. 10 - 4 .... 01372 721490
COLLINGWOOD, P. P. M. 9 - 3 .... Mr Paul Clarke
COLLINS, D. S. 11 - 3 07891882932
COLLINS, P. 11 - 7 .... 07779 794684
CONWAY, F. 9 - 7 07771922808
COOPER, K. E. 9 - 0 .... 07877 620499
COOPER, ROBERT J 10 - 7 .... 07970 948042
CORBETT, J. W. 9 - 0. .... 07507 456985
COWARD, J. M. 10 - 0 .... 07919 477619
COWLEY, J. 9 - 2 .... 07702 199317
CROSSMAN, E. 9 - 0 .... Mr A. D. Lewis
CROW, G. M. 10 - 7 .... 07748 524448
CUMANI, F. 9 - 9 .... 07810 444352
CUTHBERT, H. E. 9 - 0. .... 01228 560700
DAVID, E. 10 - 0 07989194451
DAVID, T. R. 10 - 2 .... Mr Dave Roberts
DAVIDSON, J. T. 11 - 5. .... 07789 684290
DAVIES, H. A. 10 - 0 ....
DAVIS, S. 9 - 4 .... 07960 135024
DAWSON, J. A. 10 - 0 .... 07525 984547
DAYUS, J. 9 - 7 .... 07775 687543
DEAKIN, N. 9 - 7 .... 07980 454991
DEAN, A. S. 9 - 2. .... 07528 524428
DENIEL, A. 10 - 0 .... 01302 861000
DICKIN, H. M. 10 - 0 ....
DIXON, J. 9 - 7 ....
DOOLAN, S. M. 10 - 0 .... 07902 561321
DOWSON, C. 9 - 4 .... 0784 6932708
DRAKE, S. A. 9 - 0. .... 07921 003155
DRINKWATER, S. W. 10 - 0. .... Mr Dave Roberts
DUCKWORTH, C. R. 9 - 7 .... 020 7399 0000
DUKES, H. R. 9 - 0 .... 077585 18358
DUMELOW, N. 8 - 7 07786325424
DUNN, A. 9 - 0. .... 07738 512924
DUNSDON, D. 10 - 0 .... 07885 110826
EASTERBY, W. H. 8 - 5 .... 07772 216507
EDDEN, M. L. 8 - 2 .... 07792 025352
EDDERY, J. R. 10 - 7 .... 07584 188032
EDGAR, K. 9 - 7 .... 07832 903378
EDWARDS, A. W. 9 - 7 .... 07590 683295
EDWARDS, D. M. 11 - 0 .... 07811 898002
EDWARDS, T. W. C. 11 - 0 .... 07711 361095
ELLINGHAM, C. 9 - 0. .... 0151 5260095
ELLIS, J. B. 8 - 5 .... 07827 316360
ELLIS, T. 10 - 10 .... 01926 632770
ELLWOOD, O. C. B. 10 - 7 .... 01980 618718
ENNIS, M. 10 - 0. .... S. Stronge
EVANS, C. 8 - 4 07970704456
EVANS, E. 9 - 7 .... 01873 890837
EVANS, M. L. 8 - 5 .... 07751 097359
EWART, C. A. 9 - 7. .... 020 72347834
FAIRCHILD, F. D. C. 9 - 2 07771640108
FEATHERSTONE, W. R. 9 - 10. .... 07768 279495
FEENEY, S. 8 - 0 .... 07805 703089

FERGUSON, J. 10 - 7	0782 5563773
FIZOR, S. S. 11 - 0	07514 269121
FLOOK, J. J. 9 - 7	01291 622486
FOSTER, J. E. 9 - 2	07980 301808
FOX, S. 10 - 4	Mr Paul Brierley
FOX, S. J. 8 - 12	01264 850218
FRATER, C. R. 8 - 7	01573 420615
FRENCH, A. 8 - 8	07776 306588
FURNIVAL, B. A. 10 - 0	077022 73729
GANNON, D. C. 9 - 4	0755 7685581
GARDNER, L. 9 - 12	07814 979699
GARNER, O. D. S. 9 - 7	Mr L. R. James
GARNETT, M. B. 10 - 7	01539 624314
GIBBS, B. 10 - 0	07818 407883
GIBSON, W. 8 - 7	01759 372932
GILLAM, J. 9 - 7	07847607391
GOLDIE, I. C. 10 - 0	07815 516499
GOLDSTEIN, K. A. 8 - 4	07976 516318
GORMAN, G. 8 - 8	07702 475254
GOSS, J. 10 - 0	07747 514321
GRAY, R. 8 - 6	07919 622519
GREEN, F. 9 - 5	07889 464285
GREEN, R. M. 11 - 2	07599619951
GREENALL, O. C. 10 - 0	07771 571000
GREENWOOD, T. O. M. 9 - 7	07904889779
GRISSELL, H. R. A. 9 - 7	07786 052926
GROSSETT, M. R. J. 8 - 5	01363 82370
GUEST, A. L. 9 - 7	07713 132577
HAMER, J. G. 9 - 10	Mr R. A. Hale
HAMILTON, J. 8 - 5	07766 591640
HAMPSON, B. 9 - 0	07557 056551
HAMPTON, M. L. 10 - 4	Mr Robert Stronge
HANNIG, D. A. 9 - 10	07926 914415
HARBOUR, E. 9 - 7	07814 646 230
HARDY, P. 9 - 0	07949198410
HARNEY, J. 9 - 7	
HARRISON, S. 9 - 7	01283 567971
HART, C. V. 9 - 10	07871 812251
HATCH, R. 10 - 8	07789 900222
HAWKER, R. 10 - 0	07891 960365
HAYES, N. M. 8 - 6	07794 761353
HEARD, M. R. 8 - 12	07875 189798
HENDERSON, C. P. 9 - 0	077968 44170
HENDERSON, G. 10 - 0	077659 67086
HENDERSON, R. G. 9 - 4	Mr C. D. Broad
HEPTONSTALL, R. 9 - 0	07725 185506
HERMANSSON, P. I. 9 - 0	07706 458450
HICKMAN, F. J. 8 - 10	
HICKMAN, W. H. W. 10 - 7	07851828530
HIGGINS, S. 10 - 0	077655 89362
HOBSON, C. R. W. 9 - 2	07966 734889
HODGES, R. J. 11 - 0	01885 483951
HODSON, J. E. 9 - 7	Mr Robert Stronge
HOGG, R. C. 10 - 4	07548 934272
HOLMES, C. 9 - 6	07947 774915
HOLMES, D. T. R. 12 - 0	0191 2847093
HOLT, J. 8 - 2	07805 654839
HOOPER, M. 7 - 7	07581 740089
HOOPER, R. 10 - 0	07745 316422
HORNER, L. V. 9 - 1	07581 107071
HORSFORD, D. 10 - 5	07986916251
HOWE, B. 9 - 10	01904 479295
HOWELL, T. 10 - 0	07979313335
HOWLING, A. 8 - 3	07711 542174
HUGGAN, S. 9 - 0	07807 316023
HUGHES, J. 9 - 7	07884 432672
HURLEY, C. 9 - 3	01829 760095
HUTCHINSON, A. L. 9 - 3	01638 577288

INGLIS, B. 10 - 0	07704 2424787
IRVING, D. K. 9 - 7	07739 359183
IRVING, E. 9 - 2	078703 88407
JAMES, A. M. 9 - 7	Mr L. R. James
JARRETT, R. N. 10 - 0	07527 034069
JEFFERSON, N. R. 8 - 7	07976 568152
JENKINSON, J. 10 - 4	01488 73436
JENNER, J. H. 8 - 10	07973 825149
JOHN, P. 9 - 5	07825 868211
JOHNS, A. V. 10 - 0	07919 440910
JOHNSON, M. S. 9 - 5	07816 60934
JONES, A. 9 - 5	07950 456397
JONES, A. 7 - 12	07874 808707
JONES, C. H. 8 - 7	07887 534753
JONES, C. L. 9 - 7	07795 840360
JONES, D. T. 10 - 10	07583 387576
JONES, J. 9 - 3	07775 846925
JONES, K. 9 - 12	Mr Robert Stronge
JONES, L. 9 - 7	07973 680943
KEADY, M. 9 - 7	01223 701216
KEEGAN, M. 7 - 10	07791 317483
KELLY, E. 10 - 7	07724 839047
KEMP, H. M. 10 - 2	0207 6294166
KERSWELL, S. L. 9 - 12	07799 235969
KILGARRIFF, L. 9 - 7	07851 396460
KING, R. 8 - 5	01793 815009
KINGSLEY, E. P. 10 - 0	079895 72413
KINSEY, W. R. 10 - 10	07803 753719
KOCMAN, J. 10 - 0	07950 345571
LEGG, J. 10 - 0	07825 586282
LEGG, M. D. 9 - 5	07590 690898
LENGE, D. 8 - 7	07902664443
LEWIS, S. 9 - 2	077902 70392
LILLY, Z. 9 - 2	01488 73311
LINDSAY, R. W. 9 - 6	07709 366404
LITTMODEN, E. P. 9 - 4	07714 294718
LODGE, J. 9 - 4	Mr L. R. James
LYTTLE, J. 10 - 4	07774060675
MABON, K. 8 - 10	
MADGIN, C. A. 8 - 0	07810 313537
MANN, P. R. 11 - 7	07929 535608
MANSELL, D. 10 - 9	07912974653
MARGARSON, K. L. 8 - 10	07711 898265
MARTIN, C. J. 8 - 12	Mr L. R. James
MARTIN, J. I. 10 - 0	07807 139763
MASKILL, A. P. 9 - 8	07927 023190
MASON, J. L. 8 - 13	07816 453613
MASON, P. W. 11 - 0	07921 707292
MASTERTON, L. C. 8 - 7	07747 033969
MATHIAS, J. F. 11 - 0	07791 628805
MAXWELL, D. 11 - 0	0207 5292323
MCCAFFREY, N. A. 8 - 4	07919 624024
MCCARTHY, A. J. 10 - 4	07739918053
MCCORMACK, C. 10 - 2	01287 650456
MCDOWALL, R. A. 10 - 4	07525 467712
MCGREGOR, A. L. 9 - 7	0759 6684318
MCINTYRE, M. J. 9 - 10	0755 7360664
MEEK, N. 9 - 6	0787 6505442
MELBOURN, E. 8 - 8	Mr A. D. Lewis
MICHAEL, L. 9 - 7	07584 091749
MILLER, H. G. 10 - 0	07825 750836
MILLER, M. G. 11 - 7	07977 261009
MILLER, S. 8 - 10	Mr A. D. Lewis
MILLMAN, P. B. 9 - 10	07858 091412
MILLS, A. 8 - 10	Mr L. R. James
MILLWARD, H. L. 8 - 9	07949 999338
MITCHELL, F. 9 - 4	Mr Philip Mitchell
MITCHELL, M. D. 9 - 5	07964 821380

MOORCROFT, B. 10 - 0	07971 806968	SMITH, D. J. 10 - 5	07592267929
MOORE, H. J. 9 - 0	07736 149669	SMITH, G. R. 10 - 0	07748064384
MOORE, J. D. 11 - 0	07584 077653	SMITH, M. J. J. 10 - 2	01789 772808
MORLEY, A. J. 10 - 5	01454 332216	SMITH, M. K. 10 - 0	01638 603005
MORRIS, B. M. 8 - 7	07810 837687	SMITH, R. 9 - 0	077169 19975
MORRISON, THOMAS 10 - 12	0789 6971968	SOHANTA, J. 8 - 4	07939 106358
MORSE, R. 10 - 7	07909 650442	SOLE, J. D. 10 - 0	07968 947091
MULHALL, C. A. 10 - 11	07979 527675	SPARKES, R. M. 9 - 0	07967643373
MULLINEAUX, M. 8 - 7	01829 261440	SPEKE, T. 10 - 4	07870 813256
MULRENNAN, A. C. 8 - 0	07929 349048	SPENCER, S. 10 - 5	07702 105220
MURPHY, A. L. 9 - 0	07711 992500	SQUIRES, K. M. 10 - 4	07791 507164
MURPHY, O. J. 10 - 10	07774 233222	STANLEY, M. T. 9 - 7	07967 548373
MURRAY, S. 9 - 0		STEAD, E. 9 - 2	07796 680583
NEWMAN, J. 10 - 0	07920464705	STEAD, N. A. 8 - 13	07507 161320
NICHOL, C. 9 - 0	Mr Paul Brierley	STIRLING, A. E. 10 - 0	07557 952057
NICHOL, R. 9 - 8	07898 150413	SUTCLIFFE, L. 9 - 0	07793 084446
NOLAN, M. G. 10 - 7	07521786919	SUTTON, N. R. A. 11 - 4	01189 538610
NOSWORTHY, C. C. 8 - 7	07971 106044	SWAN, G. 10 - 0	07966 801736
O'KEEFFE, S. 9 - 4	07944165177	SYDDALL, T. M. 9 - 2	07854 309600
OCKENDEN, D. D. 9 - 7	07834 360379	SYMES-MEINECK, D. 9 - 2	07541 809081
ORPWOOD, N. 10 - 12	07831 836626	TEASDALE, A. 9 - 8	07850 234133
OWEN, A. L. 9 - 0	01638 664546	TETT, F. 9 - 0	Mr Robert Stronge
OWEN, E. L. 9 - 5	07718984799	THOMAS, P. J. 9 - 0	01789 298346
OWEN, J. P. 10 - 10	07880 700559	THOROGOOD, G. 9 - 0	07958 328428
PAINTING, S. W. 10 - 0	07919 454844	TUDOR, J. E. 11 - 4	07950 381227
PARK, J. 10 - 7	07733 840203	TURNER, D. J. 9 - 6	01264 353242
PAYTER, L. R. 10 - 2	07709 671375	TURNER, H. M. 9 - 0	07717 740100
PEACOCK, S. 9 - 0		TUTTON, R. L. 9 - 0	07980 628363
PEARCE, J. 8 - 12	Mr A. D. Lewis	TUTTY, G. 8 - 3	07970 095355
PEARN, A. 9 - 7	07823 770168	TUTTY, P. L. 8 - 10	Mr R. A. Hale
PETTIS, W. 9 - 5	07930 469256	TWEMLOW, C. 10 - 0	07752487203
PHIZACKLEA, S. J. 9 - 0	01827 62901	VIDEN, Z. J. V. 8 - 7	01367 820690
PILKINGTON, J. N. 10 - 7		VORSTER, N. 8 - 1	07915 613852
PIMLOTT, O. 9 - 7	07969216409	WADLOW, O. J. 10 - 13	07904 362984
POOLES, R. L. 10 - 4	07766 244716	WALEY-COHEN, S. B. 10 - 3	07887 848425
POSTE, B. J. 9 - 7	Mr Dave Roberts	WALFORD, M. T. 11 - 0	01635 281166
POTTER, W. E. 10 - 5	07872933534	WALKER, J. 8 - 11	07969 893918
PRICE, M. R. 10 - 5	07765 490190	WALKER, S. A. 9 - 7	Mr S. T. Dodds
PRINCE, P. 9 - 0	07534 573344	WALL, M. 8 - 9	Mr A. D. Lewis
RANDELL, S. 9 - 7	07868 728440	WALL, M. J. 10 - 0	07990 995053
RAWLINSON, A. A. 9 - 0	07795 254177	WALLACE, A. 8 - 10	Mr A. D. Lewis
REYNOLDS, K. J. 8 - 8	07800 898436	WALLACE, H. A. R. 11 - 7	07974 360462
RICHARDS, J. R. 9 - 0	Mr R. A. Hale	WALTON, C. M. 9 - 7	07966 216669
RICHARDSON, J. A. 10 - 5	07979 991840	WARD-THOMAS, A. C. 12 - 0	07768 005336
RICHARDSON, R. A. 8 - 0	07891 443866	WATSON, N. 9 - 0	07974 442856
RIDLEY, J. M. 10 - 0	0755 7879646	WATSON, K. 10 - 1	07833 223701
RITCHIE, S. W. 9 - 0	07830 522160	WATSON, S. L. 9 - 0	07808 162631
ROBARTS, B. A. G. 10 - 7	07966 498559	WAUGH, A. 8 - 5	07761040963
ROBERTS, M. 9 - 0	01305 782218	WESTON, T. H. 10 - 7	07752 313698
ROBINSON, S. E. 10 - 0	07779 486778	WESTWOOD, J. J. 9 - 7	01398371414
ROBINSON, S. J. 11 - 3	07850 640067	WHEELER, G. F. 11 - 3	07778 157245
ROCHE, J. 10 - 0	07940 409709	WHITEHEAD, C. L. 9 - 0	07787 391401
ROCHFORD, M. 9 - 3	07972 908635	WILKINSON, D. S. 8 - 0	01969 640223
RODDICK, C. L. 10 - 3	07855544590	WILLEY, J. P. 9 - 4	01909 475962
ROGERSON, D. 10 - 4	07891036627	WILLIAMS, F. J. 9 - 4	07985631545
RUSSELL, S. 9 - 0	07780 657382	WILLIAMS, J. C. 9 - 0	07841 576651
RUSSELL, W. 10 - 0	01273 274733	WILLIAMS, R. J. 9 - 5	07554 886584
RYAN, S. 9 - 7	07768 373725	WILLIAMSON, C. L. 9 - 8	Mr Robert Stronge
SALMON, M. J. 10 - 0	07790226783	WILLS, C. L. 9 - 12	07791 846383
SATALIA, D. 8 - 2		WILSON, L. J. 8 - 10	07747 615037
SAYER, E. C. 9 - 4	07968320118	WILSON, R. 9 - 13	Mr J. B. Jeffrey
SAYER, N. 10 - 0	07870 192027	WILSON, R. E. 9 - 4	07770732007
SCOTT, C. M. 9 - 2	01638 722100	WINKS, R. P. 9 - 12	01226 340011
SESTON, M. 10 - 7	07738 359364	WOOD, K. 9 - 7	07429 0780666
SHARRATT, S. 10 - 3	07966 467879	WOODWARD, M. J. 10 - 10	07724 627766
SHERWOOD, J. E. 9 - 7	Mr Dave Roberts	YORK, P. 10 - 7	07774 962168
SIBBICK, E. 9 - 5	Mr A. D. Lewis	YOUNG, E. 10 - 0	07732 380 913
SLATTER, N. I. 9 - 5	Mr R. A. Hale	ZETTERHOLM, A. 9 - 0	07787 936150